OXFORD BIBLIOGRAPHICAL SOCIETY
PUBLICATIONS
THIRD SERIES VOLUME V

THE LIBRARY OF ANTHONY WOOD

Nicolas K. Kiessling

Oxford Bibliographical Society

Oxford

2002

Published by the Oxford Bibliographical Society,
care of the Bodleian Library, Oxford OX1 3BG

© Oxford Bibliographical Society and Nicolas K. Kiessling, 2002

ISBN 0 901420 56 5

Inquiries about the Society and its publications should be addressed to the
Honorary Secretary at the Bodleian Library. Proposals for publications should
be sent to the Honorary Editors at the same address.

British Library Cataloguing in Publication Data.
A catalogue record for this book is available from the British Library.

Typeset at the Department of English, Washington State University
Printed by the Alden Group, Oxford and Northampton

TABLE OF CONTENTS

Acknowledgements

Scores of people have given me help along the way. First among these is Tom Birrell who suggested the topic of the library of Anthony Wood in 1992 and who has read every word of every draft of every section that I have given him since that year. In the Bodleian Library I have asked for and received information from personnel in Duke Humfrey's Library and in Room 132 of the New Library. These include the Keeper of Western Manuscripts Mary Clapinson, the Deputy Keeper of Western Manuscripts T. D. Rogers, Colin Harris, William Hodges, Alan Coates, Geoff Groom, Steven Tomlinson, and Michael Webb. The staff at the book delivery counter in Duke Humfrey's, Jean-Pierre Mialon, Russell Edwards, and Alan Carter, were pushed to extremes when I requested and returned hundreds of volumes on each of my extended visits to the library. They provided short cuts for some of the tedious tasks, pointed out locations of reference works in Selden End, and in general made my visits very pleasant. The staff of Special Collections went beyond the call of duty more than once. Clive Hurst provided computer disks of the Wood entries and went on searches in the stacks for Wood books. Alexandra Franklin helped with ballads, Sara Shuttlesworth with STC and Wing books, and Julie Anne Lambert with ephemeral publications. John Bamborough, Giles and Lisa Barber, Jim Bell, James Hinz, Olav Lausund, the late David Lovejoy, and Paul Morgan were obliged to listen to my sorrowful complaints and offered suggestions from the very beginning. Henry Woudhuysen and James McLaverty, former editors of the *OBS*; Oliver Pickering, the editor of *The Library*; and Martin Kaufman, the editor of the *Bodleian Library Record*, applied rigorous standards to my early work related to this project. Fellow readers with whom I exchanged information were Kate Bennett, Mark Bland, Bill Clennell, Anthony Dodd, Paul Grinke, Will Hamlin, Ralph Hanna III, Theodor Harmsen, Misako Himura, Anthony Hobson, Lauren Kassel, Erica Longfellow, Giles Mandelbrote, Mark Purcell, Julian Roberts, David and Bridget Sturdy, Nicholas von Maltzahn, Michael Questier, Michael Suarez, Andrew Watson, and Gillian Wright.

At Washington State University, the Department of English generously provided financial support and research time including a year of professional leave and I thank the chairs, Susan McLeod and Victor Villanueva, for supporting my applications for funds and for professional leaves. My home base in Oxford was Linacre College where I was a Senior Visiting Member for the duration of this project. Principals J. B. Bamborough and Paul Slack have welcomed me to the college and made my stays in Oxford a pleasure. The American Philosophical Society provided a timely grant in the midst of the project. At Washington State University my colleagues Michael Hanly, Debbie Lee, Stanton Linden, and Albert von Frank discussed issues of editing and bibliography and Tom Faulkner and Rhonda Blair most generously offered their time and expertise to help with the formatting and production of this document on the typesetting program TEX. Aid came from my family as well. My mother, Esther, now in her ninety-seventh year, read the 'final' draft of the introduction, found eight errors and declared her love for Anthony 'who always spoke his mind'. My wife Karen learned to live with the same Anthony Wood and accompanied and assisted me on all my expeditions to Oxford and in searches in the libraries in the United Kingdom and in the United States. We have visited and made special requests at the British Library, Jesus College Library, Merton College Library, University of Glasgow Library, Magdalene College Library (Cambridge), National Library of Wales, Wellcome Institute Library, Newberry Library, New York Public Library, Union Theological Seminary Library, Beinecke Library, William Andrews Clark Library, Houghton Library, and Holland Library at Washington State University. The Folger Library and the Huntington Library have marvelously responsive staffs who arranged for carts of books to be wheeled to my desk when I made my visits. In the final stages, the editors of the OBS, Joad Raymond and Scott Mandelbrote, offered critical and insightful comments that have kept me on target and have made this a far better catalogue.

Time and again I have turned for answers to the publications of three great scholars of earlier ages whose contributions to the study of seventeenth-century Oxford have not yet and may never be superseded:

Andrew Clark's edition of the diaries of Anthony Wood, 1891-1900; Falconer Madan's descriptions of books published in Oxford from the beginning to 1680, 1895-1931; and Philip Bliss's edition of Wood's *Athenae Oxonienses*, 1813-1820.

It is devilishly difficult to proof-read a long bibliography. While the corrections became fewer after each review, I apologize for any errors or inconsistencies that remain and ask the readers' indulgence.

For permission to reproduce twelve photographs of Wood printed items and manuscripts, I thank the Curators of the Bodleian Library, Oxford. I also thank the anonymous readers for the periodicals *The Library* and *The Bodleian Library Record* for their close readings of my articles on the ballads in the Wood collection, the history of Wood's library from 1695 to the present, and Wood's relationship with Thomas Gore.

INTRODUCTION

In 1695 Anthony Wood bequeathed 'all my printed books, pamphlets and papers', almost 7000 printed items, to the Ashmolean Museum. In 1860 the collection, now some 6550 items, was moved to the Bodleian Library. Today most of these reside on the J-Floor of the New Bodleian Library. *The Library of Anthony Wood* is a record in alphabetical order of all the letterpress that Anthony Wood owned. The main body of this catalogue gives general bibliographical descriptions of and distinctive details about Wood's personal copies. The introduction and a series of appendices summarize and isolate information found in the entries. While I might have included Wood's manuscripts, the joint task would have made a commitment to finish far from certain. Wood himself might have made a distinction between printed items and manuscripts. In 1681 he prepared a shelf-list of his library and restricted it to printed items. The shelf-list was intended to help him in a monumental study of Oxford scholars and their publications which came to fruition in the brilliant *Athenae Oxonienses* published in two volumes in 1691 and 1692. While Wood was an accomplished archivist and depended on manuscripts for much of his information, he was also acutely aware of the limitations of manuscript materials. They were vulnerable to time, normally available at only one location, and controlled by the self-interest of the owners and archivists. Printed material on the other hand could be disseminated in a day to an audience of hundreds if not thousands. It could also, as Wood knew from personal experience, gain an author instant fame or infamy as hundreds of readers were able to scrutinize every page of a printed text within days of publication.

My major objective is to determine why, when, and how Wood acquired printed items, what he acquired, and how he organized, bound, read, annotated, and disposed of them. Hence details about the provenance, of the completeness and condition of each printed item, of the binding, and of Wood's annotations are included in each entry. The second objective is to provide an accurate catalogue of all the books that he owned. Such a catalogue does not exist at present, though there are several imperfect enumerative lists. The first, the 'Catalogus Librorum impressorum & manuscriptorum Domini Antonij a Wood', was commissioned by the Keeper of the Ashmolean Museum, John Whiteside, in 1716. It was completed shortly after the books were given permanent shelf-marks, Wood 1 to Wood 899, Wood Almanacs A to F, Wood Diaries, and [MS.] Wood B, C, D, E, and F, totaling some 1045 volumes in all. The Whiteside 'Catalogus' has an entry for each volume. For the many composite (or coupled) volumes, that is, volumes which hold more than one printed item, it often lists the short title, the city of publication and the date. But for scores of other composite volumes the cataloguer entered only a broad classification of the contents, such as 'Dialogues', 'Jests', 'A Collection of 133. Poems, Ballads, &c', or '60 pamphlets on the Civil War'. Several of these hold over 100 printed items (see Plate I and items 400-402 and 416-417 on Plate IX). The cataloguer was unaware of 700 unbound items that were later inserted in the Wood 1-899 series at 276a and 276b. A century later, in 1837, the Keeper of the Ashmolean Museum P. B. Duncan ordered an inventory of the Wood collection. This provided the Underkeeper William Kirtland with work over the next four years as he compared entries in the Whiteside Catalogus with what was on the shelves and noted both missing volumes and items removed from volumes still present. A second enumerative list was made sixty years after the transfer of the Wood collection to the Bodleian in 1860 by a staff member, R. T. Milford. His 'Hand-list of Wood Printed Books' in the major series, Wood 1 to Wood 899, excluding Wood 276a and 276b, is also a short title list. He did not record the missing books and did not make use of the Whiteside Catalogus. The Milford Hand-list is now superseded by a third enumerative list, the Bodleian compact disk catalogue. This compact disk is widely available and anyone who wishes can display on a screen the 5635 entries with 'Wood' in the shelf-mark. This list, however, does not include all of the items in the Wood collection. The list in this volume is far more accurate than any of the preceding; it is also more complete in that it includes all printed items that have escaped from Wood's own library before 1695 and from the Ashmolean Museum after 1695, or that are unrecorded in the Bodleian Library compact disk catalogue bringing the total number of items to 6760.[1] The final objective is to preserve information about each book before there is further deterioration of, for example, the bindings, the annotations, and the printed material itself. Virtually every person doing basic research in the seventeenth century has visited or will visit the Bodleian Library to use items in the Wood collection. This heavy usage attests to the relevance of the collection as a whole and at the same time takes a toll. Some heavily used volumes have been rebound more than once and with each rebinding evidence is destroyed. Even since Andrew Clark's monumental studies of Wood at the end of the nineteenth century pages have been lost, some items have been stolen from volumes, loose slips and flyleaves have disappeared, upper and lower covers have been replaced, notes on pasteboards were lost or covered over, and certain of the annotations, especially those in pencil, have become illegible. Clark himself provided an analysis of Wood's library in his edition of Wood's diary, *The Life and Times of Anthony Wood* (1891-1900), but his statements are general. He never intended to provide a comprehensive study of the books or of how Wood annotated, organized or cared for them.[2]

Anthony Wood, the Background

Nothing in Anthony Wood's background suggested that he would become a celebrated historian and diarist and the owner of one the largest collection of books and manuscripts in seventeenth-century Oxford. He was born in Oxford on 17 December 1632, the fourth of five sons to Thomas Wood and his second wife Mary Petty Wood, in 'an antient stone-house opposite to the forefront of Merton Coll.', that is, Postmaster's Hall.[3] His father died in January 1643 and his mother continued to earn the family's living by releasing leaseholds such as the Merton College indoor tennis court and the inn, Fleur de Luce, and by boarding guests. She could afford to send Anthony to a Latin school near the old church of St. Peter le Bailey on New Inn Hall Street in 1640 and in the next year to New College school. The civil war affected the family profoundly: Anthony's eldest brother joined the royalist forces, their leased house was appropriated by the royalist administration, and in the summer of 1644 when Oxford was about to be besieged by the parliamentary forces, his mother removed Anthony and his younger brother Christopher to the safer environment of the free school in Thame. In 1646 she was forced by her financial circumstances, made precarious by fires in Oxford which destroyed several of her leased buildings, to bring back her sons to parliamentarian Oxford. Anthony was tutored, unhappily for him, by his older brother Edward both at Trinity College and later at Merton where Edward became a fellow in 1648. In 1647 Anthony himself matriculated at Merton College, was elected postmaster in the same year and became Bible Clerk in 1650, all the more a sinecure when chapel services were suspended in Presbyterian Oxford. He graduated B.A. in the natural philosophy school in July 1652.[4]

Upon his graduation from college, Anthony was expected to find a profession. His mother had earlier made more than one attempt to apprentice him to a lawyer or to find a future for him in some 'mechanical trade'. A short stay from February to September 1652 in nearby Cassington and an experiment in following 'the plow' led to nothing but illness and a 'lonish and retir'd condition'. He returned to the family home on Merton Street and pursued interests in music, history, and heraldry. He became a reader in the Bodleian Library, at first restricted to 'the arts library, (for no farther could bachelaurs of arts then goe) where the books of English historie and antiquities stand'. He was admitted to his M.A. degree in 1655 but received no fellowship. His main supporter was his brother, Edward, a fellow of Merton and Junior Proctor of the university. Edward's death in May 1655 seems to have finished any hope that Anthony would become a fellow of the college. In memory of his brother Anthony prepared for publication five of his manuscript sermons and presented over forty copies to friends as gifts. In February 1660 he probably brought to an

---

[1]The series MS. Wood B-F contains manuscripts; [MS.] Wood B-F is used for letterpress in these volumes. 5635 is the number of items present in the first edition of the unrevised CD disk, still current in March 2002. This catalogue does not, by design, include almanacs, engravings, and music items. There were about 6540 printed items (plus fourteen manuscripts intermingled among printed items) in the Wood collection left to the Ashmolean Museum. Over the last three centuries, 324 items were removed and are now marked as 'missing'. Errors in Bodleian catalogue shelf-marks are noted at entries. For more details see p. xlviii; Append. II; and Index, 'Missing items'.

[2]A. Clark, *The Life and Times of Anthony Wood*, 5 vols. (Oxford Historical Society, 1891-1900) (hereafter cited as *LT*).

[3]The details from Wood's life are taken from his autobiography, Tanner MS. 102, pt. 1, the 'Secretum Antonii', and pt. 2; both are incorporated by Clark in *LT*. The 'Secretum' is quoted in full in Anthony A Wood, *Athenae Oxonienses*, ed. by P. Bliss, 4 vols. (London, 1813-20): 1.i (hereafter cited as *AO*). For Postmaster's Hall, see *An Inventory of the Historical Monuments in the City of Oxford* (London, 1939): 167 and Plate 12, item no. 81.

[4]*LT*, 1.48-129. Edward was a severe tutor, as Anthony later recalled in his 'Secretum Antonii': 'he would be somtimes so angry that he would beat him and turne him out of his chamber', *LT*, 1.162. He went to another tutor in February 1650. Wood used the third person singular perspective in his last version of the 'Secretum'.

end any hopes of his mother that he might find a profession when he remodelled his two attic rooms of the family home inserting a fire place in the east room and a window in his study, the west room. Henceforth these attic rooms were closed to friends and family and allowed him the privacy he needed for his research.[5]

Anthony Wood rambled around Oxfordshire and the neighboring counties from his early youth, but he seems never to have ventured more than 70 miles from Oxford. He went on a dozen forays from 1667 to London where he studied records in the Cottonian library at Westminster, the Tower, the Royal Library at St. James's, and the Herald's Office. After his first acquaintance with the 'great' Ralph Sheldon in July 1671, he was a regular visitor to the Sheldon residence, Weston House, near Long Compton in Warwickshire, some 30 miles from Oxford. In 1684 he arranged Sheldon's funeral at Beoley, another 30 miles northwest of Long Compton. In the later 1670s, Wood went to Bath twice for treatment of his loss of hearing. His end came quickly. In November 1695 he suffered from 'a Total Suppression of Urine' in the words of Arthur Charlett. His doctor bluntly told him that if he could not make water he must make earth. He died on 29 November just shy of his sixty-third birthday in his attic bedroom of the house in which he was born.[6] He was buried across the street in the north transept of Merton College Chapel.[7]

Wood's earliest reading in the Bodleian Library included, as he recalled later in his 'Secretum', William Burton's *Description of Leicestershire* and John Guillim's *The Display of Heraldry* (a copy of which he later owned). He recalled in the same autobiography how his life was dramatically altered upon his reading of William Dugdale's newly published *Antiquities of Warwickshire* in the summer of 1656: 'my pen cannot enough describe how A. Wood's tender affections and insatiable desire of knowledg were ravish'd and melted downe by the reading of that book. What by musick and rare books that he found in the public library, his life, at this time and after, was perfect Elysium.' Thus he found a niche and dedicated himself to do for Oxfordshire, Oxford, and the university, what Dugdale had done for Warwickshire. In time this general plan became more specifically focused on several major projects. The first, with prompting and then a commission from the Dean of Christ Church, John Fell, developed into a history of the university. Fell was so impressed by the history that he himself edited the entire work and had it translated into academic Latin for a cosmopolitan audience. The *Historia et antiquitates universitatis Oxoniensis* was published in 1674. While the *Historia* gained Wood instant fame, he was outraged at the editorial influence of Fell and immediately set about to prepare an improved version, this time to be published in English. Another project, the 'fasti', the records of persons associated with Oxford, interfered, and Wood's extensive revisions and additions to the *Historia* lay dormant for a century before John Gutch compiled them into four volumes of histories of the colleges and halls and the annals of the university. His 'fasti' led him, again with prompting by Fell, to biographies and bibliographies of Oxford persons and the first edition of the *Athenae Oxonienses*. It was the first work of its kind, a bio-bibliography in the English language. Finally, his thousands of notes on the city itself were edited and published two centuries after his death.[8] From the beginning Wood was as aware as Robert Burton of the correspondence between knowledge and print. Neither would have been satisfied without establishing himself as an author in the new world of print and publication. But each approached his objective from a different perspective. The author of the *Anatomy of Melancholy* wrote in the face of massive traditions and despaired of saying anything new in a 'scribbling age' while Wood was initially unsure about any need for printed collections of the history of the university. Burton wrote to show that he existed and to establish his credentials to his peers, 'to know a thing and not expresse it, is all one as if he knewe it not.' Wood was driven, initially, to preserve and save. He fought an uphill battle for he believed himself to be an outsider in academic Oxford and performed a task that, he later wrote, was 'more proper for a Head, or Fellow of a College, or for a Publick Professor, or Officer of the most Noble University of Oxon'. Unlike the comparatively wealthy Burton, Wood had to struggle for funds. Throughout his working life Wood averaged about 40 pounds a year which came mainly from property leases inherited from his father and mother, compiling catalogues of various libraries of acquaintances, and writing the *Historia et antiquitates* and the *Athenae*.[9]

---

[5]For attempts to apprentice Anthony, see *LT*, 1.130; for his stay at Cassington, *LT*, 1.178-181, both in his 'Secretum'. For his editions of Edward's sermons, see the notes at items 6688-9 in the bibliography.

[6]For a walk to Weston in August 1695, see below, note 29. His final days are described in letters by Charlett and Thomas Tanner, *LT*, 3.497-502. For Dr. T. Short's diagnosis, as told later by W. Huddesford, *LT*, 3.497.

[7]See A. Bott, *The Monuments in Merton College Chapel* (Oxford, 1964): 12ff., marble-slab 107, and p. 65; for the monument, p. 90-4 (and *LT*, 3, frontispiece); for the time of death and burial, p. 136.

[8]For the response to Dugdale, *LT*, 1.209. For the Gutch editions, *The History and Antiquities of the University of Oxford*, and *The History and Antiquities of the Colleges and Halls*, 4 vols. (Oxford, 1786-96); and for the city, ed. by A. Clark, *Survey of the Antiquities of the City of Oxford*, 3 vols. (Oxford, 1889-99).

[9]For Robert Burton, see *The Anatomy of Melancholy*, 6 vols. (Oxford, 1988-2001): 1.8-9. For Wood's comment on

Whatever Wood's intentions in 1656, there could have been little expectation of any outcome of distinction. He did not have the money to hire helpers, buy new or finely-bound books, and publish his findings. He was a person of average intelligence, undistinguished as a student in his studies, and not prominent enough, or sufficiently congenial or tolerant, to have gained a fellowship at his college. He accommodated himself to the political and religious regime in Cromwellian Oxford from about 1647 to 1660, and upon the restoration of Charles II, he reacted vigorously against the political and religious ferment that had led to the commonwealth. Wood shared these royalist and Anglican prejudices with hundreds of other Oxford persons. Yet he made significant historical contributions and produced the most innovative biographical and bibliographical work of his generation. What set Wood apart from his contemporaries were his persistence and physical energy which drove him to pursue objectives wherever they led, to manuscript records in colleges, wills, tombstone inscriptions, relatives and acquaintances of deceased persons, family records in private collections, ecclesiastical records in churches and cathedrals, and public records. He then stated his findings no matter how sharp, caustic or incriminating they might be. He understood what he was doing and why he was doing it, sought to be accurate in detail, to state matters truthfully as they appeared to him, to verify, and to be complete. He held to these principles and was able to maintain his focus over a period of four decades. He asked the same critical questions of persons of all faiths, parties, and persuasions. Thus he could deal with a non-conformist, if not with sympathy, at least as a contributor to the history of the city and university. He certainly judged the regicides harshly and rarely missed an opportunity to rub salt in old wounds; he was contemptuous of Presbyterian replacements and royalist time-servers who to his disgust hardly missed a beat during Cromwellian Oxford and retained their livings in the restoration. He did not agree with the misguided Quaker 'phanaticks' or Catholic 'papists', but he included them, garnered all the information that he could and wrote their biographies and compiled their bibliographies for his *Athenae*. He also judged individuals by their ability to put their ideas in print, the medium which, in his view, had totally replaced scribal tradition. Hence the bibliography, the published works, of each person was of prime importance to him.

Wood's early success as a scholar and historian depended on his making use of the vast college, university and religious resources in Oxford. He educated himself by trawling through the manuscripts of earlier antiquarians such as Thomas Allen, Roger Dodsworth, Christopher Hatton, Gerard Langbaine the Elder, John Leland, Brian Twyne, and Miles Windsor. He also read the works and became familiar with the methodology of numerous historians. He owned books by John Bale, Richard Broughton, John Caius (Keys), Thomas Caius (Keys), William Camden, Thomas Fuller, William Fulman, Gildas, Francis Godwin, William Grey, John Leland, Matthew Parker, John Pits, Brian Twyne, Polydore Vergil, and John Weever. Some of the secondary sources available to him were of little value and Wood recognized this. Many histories of the two universities, for example, concerned the precedence of one over the other. Distinguished scholars such as John Caius (see Plate IV), Thomas Caius, and Simon D'Ewes marshaled pseudo-history as fact and became bogged down in myth. Many of the reference works for his biographies, mainly dictionaries of martyrs, saints, popes or bishops by John Bale, John Foxe, Francis Godwin or John Pits, were written for very specific purposes and audiences and Wood did not fall into the most obvious traps of religious sectarianism.[10]

His education continued through personal acquaintance with an extraordinary number of Oxford writers and thinkers such as Henry Jackson, a theologian and his distant relative; Henry Foulis, his friend from Lincoln College who died in 1669; John Fell, his mentor while Dean of Christ Church, and later, Vice-Chancellor of the university; Thomas Barlow, Bodley's Librarian from 1652 to 1660 who called upon Wood to help him sort and arrange the John Selden bequest in 1659 and kindly gave Wood a pair of Selden's spectacles which they found inside one of the books; Thomas Hyde, a successor to Barlow as Bodley's Librarian, 1665 to 1701, who to Wood's discomfort, inveigled him to help in the compiling of the great 1674 catalogue of the library; Andrew Allam, a younger and brilliant fellow at St. Edmund Hall whom Wood knew only about five years before Allam died in 1685; Ralph Bathurst, President of Trinity College; John Wallis, Savilian professor of geometry and Keeper of the Archives who gave to Wood the keys to the archives and a few years later, recalled them; White Kennet, an antiquary and member of St. Edmund Hall; Arthur Charlett, Master of University College; and Jonathan Edwards, Principal of Jesus College and Vice-

---

who should have done the task, see below, p. xiv, and item 6695. R. Nochimson valued Burton's estate, excluding his library, at 1200 pounds. See N. Kiessling, *The Library of Robert Burton*, OBS, NS 22 (1988): xxviii.

[10]On Oxford versus Cambridge, J. Caius, Wood 179(1) and 480(1-2); T. Caius, Wood 480(1), and S. D'Ewes, Wood 514(8) and [MS.] Wood F. 27, ff. 233-6. Some of his reference books were J. Bale, Wood [MS.] Wood C. 44(3); Francis Godwin, Wood 344 and [MS.] Wood D. 21(1-2); and John Pits, *LT*, 1.247. The most obvious traps of sectarianism would include excision from a historical record or censorship. For how Wood dealt with a person whose religion he detested, see below, p. xxxvi at note 58.

Chancellor in 1690-1, to whom Wood dedicated volume I of the *Athenae* in 1691. The list goes on and on. His diary reveals that he spent some part of most days in taverns or coffee houses or on walks with friends who were associated in one way or another with the university: John Curtyne, a physician and a fellow of Lincoln; Matthew Hutton, an antiquarian; Nathaniel Greenwood, another antiquarian; Edward Jones, a fellow of Merton and a physician; Richard Lower, a physician who experimented with blood transfusions; Peter Nicholls, Subwarden and later Bursar at Merton College who also left Wood 40 shillings in his will upon his death in 1678; Herbert Pelham, a fellow of Magdalen and an antiquarian; John Powell and his son of the same name, fellows of Merton; Robert Plot, the first Keeper of the Ashmolean Museum; John Robinson, a fellow of Lincoln; and Robert Whitehall and Nathaniel Wight, both fellows of Merton. The topics of conversation seem to have been what one would expect in such company – university business, the problems, failures and successes of the day's archival work, current publications, current gossip, and political events.

A number of influential heads of college, in addition to Bathurst, Charlett, Edwards, Fell and Kennet, mentioned above, knew Wood's research well enough to go out of their way to help him when they wished: Thomas Crosthwayte, Principal of St. Edmund Hall; Leoline Jenkins, Principal of Jesus; John Lamphire, Principal of Hart Hall; Thomas Marshall, Rector of Lincoln; Peter Mews, President of St. John's; Nicholas Martin, Vice-Principal of Hart Hall; Obadiah Walker, Master of University; Michael Woodward, Warden of New College; and Thomas Yate, Principal of Brasenose. His network of friends extended itself through his interest in music. He had, as he wrote, a 'natural and insatiable genie' for music and began playing the violin by ear in 1651. From 1656 to 1669 he attended weekly meetings of practicing musicians led by William Ellis, the ejected organist of St. John's college. Some eighteen fellows and students of various colleges attended these sessions over the years, including Edward Lowe, organist at Christ Church, Kenelm Digby, fellow of All Souls, Nathaniel Crew, fellow of Lincoln and later Bishop of Durham, Charles Bridgeman, fellow of Queen's, Henry Lawes, and John Wilson, the public professor of music. Wood owned publications of several of these musicians. His love of music led to the acquisition of a sizable collection of scores, songs, and studies of music and was a factor is his collecting of ballads. In his personal copies of Oxford Encaenia ceremonies, he regularly commented on the musical presentations that formed part of the programmes.

Wood's views of history and documentation were developed by his acquaintance with the London antiquarians whose works he knew well: Elias Ashmole, Thomas Blount, Edward Bysshe, William Dugdale, Gilbert Sheldon, and William Prynne. With each passing year his network of informants grew until correspondence with these people occupied a portion of each day. The most important and well-known was John Aubrey who came into Wood's life in 1667 and proved an unending supplier of information, but he was only one of scores of valuable informants. Wood's relationship with the obscure antiquary, Thomas Gore, is a single example which shows how Wood made use of and was used by correspondents throughout England. In 1668 Gore was planning to revise a feeble bibliography on heraldry that he had published. His acquaintance, Aubrey, suggested he send a copy to Wood. Wood had a field day with Gore's text, making hundreds of corrections and suggestions. In addition he performed a great many time-consuming favours for Gore. The second edition, made far better with Wood's help, was published in 1674. In return, Wood asked Gore for help with parish records, at least one of which took some effort, as Gore pointed out in a letter: 'to satisfy your desire concerning the Buriall of Mr Bartholomew Parsons, I tooke a journey . . . to Ludgershale, (though almost 30 miles distant from my House)'. Wood acknowledged Gore's help in the vignette of Parsons in the *Athenae*.[11]

Some relationships with even close friends or associates were strained at times and these estrangements became more frequent in the later years of his life when his work became more intense and his fame increased. He was becoming more certain of his purpose and was determined to write what he knew to be fact. Such specificity could conflict with the standards of decorum in Oxford, where coffee house and tavern talk was one thing, but publication of these details, even if true, was quite another. A number of heads of colleges also became Wood's enemies after he achieved a measure of fame: Thomas Clayton, Warden of Wood's own college, Merton, reported that Wood was suspected 'to be Popishly affected' in

---

[11]For comments on music from the 'Secreta Antonii', see *LT*, 1.173 and 1.273-4. Wood owned books on music by Bridgeman, Digby, Lawes, Lowe and Wilson; see also Append. VII; *LT* 1.204-5; and P. M. Gouk, 'Music', in *The History of the University of Oxford*, ed. N. Tyacke, 4 (Oxford, 1997): 632f. (hereafter *HUO*). Wood's ms. biographies of musicians are at MS. Wood D. 19(4). The two editions of Gore's bibliography are in Wood's current collection, [MS.] Wood E. 3, ff. 298-331 (1668), with Wood's annotations, and the revised edition, [MS.] Wood E. 27(1) (1674). The entry of Parsons is in *AO*, 3.25. For a full discussion of Gore and Wood, see N. K. Kiessling, 'Anthony Wood and Thomas Gore and the Use of Manuscript Material,' *The Library* (London), 6th series 21 (1999): 108-123. Gore's trip to Ludgershall, Wiltshire, took place on 20 October 1671.

1679; John Hall, Master of Pembroke was 'uncivil' to Wood; Richard Bayly, President of St. John's refused to give Wood the freedom to enter college archives; Henry Aldrich, as Vice-Chancellor sided against him in a libel case; and Roger Mander, Master of Balliol, was reported to have reacted very negatively to the *Athenae*, saying that it 'deserves to be burnt' and that it was 'fit to wipe one's arse with'. His status as an outsider certainly was a factor in his relationships with the powerful. He was not a college fellow and at various times was barred from certain college archives. Both Thomas Barlow, who kept him out of Queen's College library, and John Wallis, who barred Wood from the university archives, had earlier befriended him. Though John Fell was in general his supporter, the relationship between the two was precarious when Wood discovered how much 'editing' Fell did on his manuscript of the *Historia*. Wood's feelings about being an outsider receive their clearest expression when he responded to attacks by, among others, two formidable opponents, Gilbert Burnet, the bishop of Salisbury, and Henry Hyde, second earl of Clarendon, in 1692-3. A large number of important university leaders closed ranks against him and sided with Lord Clarendon in his case of libel. Wood responded specifically to Burnet and silently to Lord Clarendon in *A Vindication of a Historiographer* (1693). He portrayed himself as being on the outside and looking in; the 'Herculean labour' of the *Athenae* would have been more proper for a fellow or public professor officer of the university, 'for one who pretends to be a *virtuoso*, and to know all men, and all things that are transacted: Or for one who frequents much society in common rooms, at public fires, in coffee-houses, assignations, clubbs, &c. . . . but the author [i.e., Wood himself], alas, is so far from frequenting such company and topicks, that he is as 'twere dead to the world, and utterly unknown in person to the generality of scholars in Oxon. He is likewise so great an admirer of a solitary and retired life, that he frequents no assemblies of the said university, hath no companion in bed or at board, in his studies, walks, or journies . . . ', etc.[12] This is nonsense. Wood described himself as everything he most certainly was not. Until his fiftieth year he was gregarious, enjoyed the friendship of scores of persons with interests similar to his, lent books to and borrowed books from numerous persons, and received valuable information from hundreds of correspondents: friends, authors, printers, and antiquarians. Many of these friends and correspondents also supplied him with printed materials. Wood seems to have been, on the whole, a convivial, if a very intense, person with scores of acquaintances. Wood's daily circuit in Oxford is revealed in a note on a single sheet (a broadside) left for a friend or family member, 'Gone to Bartlet the Bookbinder thense to West [a bookseller] - thence to M^r. Crittendum [Cruttenden at the press]'. The outgoing Wood regularly recorded in his diary the dates of the Oxford and Oxfordshire feasts and apparently attended them whenever he could until the end of his life.[13]

The final years of the 1680s mark the end of certain pleasant social engagements for Wood. His labours on the *Athenae* were all-consuming and he became more isolated from one-time companions. In the summer of 1684 his benefactor Ralph Sheldon died and in the summer of 1685 his close friend Andrew Allam died. One of those who took their places was Arthur Charlett, a pompous superior who on the one hand gave Wood over a dozen printed items and much information and on the other was always eager to give Wood bad news especially about his reputation and the reception of his *Athenae*. Wood's records of paying battels and common-room privileges end in 1686, the result of his quarreling with Merton colleagues. His loss of hearing may have ended his participation with his weekly music meetings in 1669. In that year he first noted 'great noises in his eares' and in the next year, 'a deafness' which continued to get worse in spite of numerous treatments by various doctors. Visits to Bath in 1676 and 1678 proved fruitless, costly, and must have been painful – 'I received at the drie pump in the King's bath nine thousand two hundred and odd pumps on my head in a fourtnight's time: but I found no present remedy.' By the end of the 1680s his carousings with close friends in taverns were either unrecorded in his diary or became much less frequent. He then depended even more on his numerous informants to whom he sent letters of inquiry about persons whose biographies he was composing.[14]

---

[12]For Clayton, see *LT*, 2.440; for Bayly, as opposed to his successor at St. John's, Peter Mews, *LT*, 2. 83-4; for Aldrich, *LT*, 3.438 and 4.44ff.; for Mander, *LT*, 3.369. *A Vindication of the Historiographer* (London, 1693) was signed by 'E. D.', who is generally assumed to be Anthony's nephew, Thomas Wood, but it was probably written by Anthony Wood, see notes at Wood 614(7), item 6695. Wood stated in the *Vindication* that his response was first printed in the preface to the second volume of the *Athenae* (1692), 'at the end of the Epistle to the Reader, (of which but few were Printed,)'. This response is apparently in very few copies – not in my personal copy or the half dozen that I have seen. The quotation is from *AO*, 1.clvi. In *A Vindication*, it appears in slightly different form and with some omissions, which Wood noted in his copy, i.e., Wood 614(7).

[13]For battells and common-room payments, see *LT*, 4.78-9. For Oxford feasts, see Wood Diaries 30b and Wood 276b(119); and e.g., *LT* 1.462; 2.154, 201, 255, 355; 3.109, 199, 225, 279, 312, 344, 374, 433, 471, 491. For the quotation on the single sheet, probably dating from 1663, see Wood 293(3), item 858.

[14]For Wood's relationships with Charlett, *LT*, 3.369, 395, and for a condescending letter which could not have failed

His Library, Why, When, and How He Collected

Books, and a personal library, were important to Wood from his youth and his early instincts as a collector led him to gather and save anything printed. He inherited a few schoolbooks from his older brothers, Edward and Robert Wood, and one has the signature of his youngest brother, Christopher. Four more books came to him upon Edward's death in 1655. Sixteen of his books have his mother's signature, Mary Wood: eight religious works, three political pamphlets, Lily's grammar, Bullokar's dictionary, a history book, a book of conduct for children, and a play, *A King, and No King.* Several of these had passed through his father's hands as well. Anthony Wood's instincts as a collector merged with his research interests by 1655 and from that time the two were not separable. His library of books became indispensable for the type of work he was doing. The resources in the Bodleian Library and its marvelous catalogue of 1674 could take him only so far. For current information he had to look especially to contemporary publications which the Library did not yet own, or to 'ephemera', which the Library at that time had no intention of acquiring. The latter were ballads, single-sheet publications concerning Parliament, Oxford or Cambridge proceedings such as those of Encaenia ceremonies, examination *quaestiones* and act verses, public notices, newsbooks, catalogues of sales and auctions, and pamphlets on marvels, murders and executions. To Wood, these were primary sources, for he skimmed through the prefaces and texts marking with his pen or pencil personal information about the authors, editors and compilers. It was also customary for publishers to append the two to three-page lists of books printed and sold by them (see Append. VIII). These, too, Wood went through with pen or pencil in hand.[15]

Wood often recorded purchases of printed items in thirty-nine almanacs which he used as diaries from 1657-1695, and on the title pages of the items themselves. Andrew Clark, in his edition of Wood's diaries, *The Life and Times*, often joined these two sources and where he has done so, I have added in entries references to the volume and page (though not the booksellers' names). The last acquisition on which he wrote a date, 'publish'd Nov. 8 1695' was a single-sheet notification for the reception of William III in Oxford. Wood's income of about forty pounds a year imposed a limit on how many books and what kind he could afford. He bought no finely bound books, nor does his name appear on any subscription lists for monumental folio editions. Such expensive folio books were in his collection only if they were gifts. The others he could read in the Bodleian Library. In fact the Bodleian was as much his preserve as his own study, and he noted some twenty times in his own books that the 'bib. bod.', the Bodleian Library, held certain books or earlier or later editions than his own particular copy. He wrote in Gibbons, *Concertatio* (1583), 'see 4° C. 32. Th. in bib. Bod', which is a 1594 ed.; and in *The Order and Manner of the sitting of the Lords . . . in . . . Parliament,* 'The 3ᵈ [and above: '4ᵗʰ'] edit. of this following cat. was printed in 8° 1628. printed for Tho. Walkley – 8°. K. 3. Arts BS - in bib. Bod'. He held year-long runs of the newsbook *Mercurius Aulicus* for 1642-4 but not for 1645. The run for that year could be consulted at the Bodleian Library, as he noted in the 1643 volume: 'Merc. Aul 4° M. 12 Art. BS in bib. bod 1645'. In his copy of *Bibliotheca anti-trinitariorum* by the Socinian scholar, Christophorus Sandius, he wrote 'Alia opera ch.ch. Sandii v. cat. Bib. Bod. p. 136.a.' He also referred to the 'bib. bod.' for published responses to works which he had, as in Robert Fludd's *Answer unto M. Foster,* 'v. cat bib bod pro Foster', or in Joseph Swetnam's anti-feminist treatise, 'A pamphlet called Constantia Munda written against Joseph Swetnam – 4°. L. 78. Arts in bib. Bodl.' In his catalogue of Prynne's printed books published in 1660 Wood marked those that were 'in bib. Bod'. It must have irked Wood when he noticed that the Bodleian owned the same book that

Charlett's purpose to disturb Wood, dated 1 March 1688, see MS. Wood F. 51, f. 20. For a letter of bad news that Charlett passed on to Wood, see notes at Wood 431a. For the quarrelling at Merton, *LT*, 3.197 (and Hearne, 1.32). For the first sign of deafness, 2.163f. and for Bath visits, 2.350, 407-412; Wood acquired several pamphlets and maps on these visits, Wood 276b(17-18), 467(5), 498(13), and 537(17).

[15]Schoolbooks and early ballads include Wood 34 ('Anthony Wood His booke amen' and traces of a bookplate), 43 (no signature), 46 ('Anthony Wood' and traces of a bookplate), 54 ('Anthony Wood his booke 1645'), 150 (bookplate), 272 (no signature), 308 ('Anthony Wood his booke [/] amen July: 25: 1645'), 401(67) (a ballad, 'Anthony Wood'), 401(70) (a ballad, 'Anthony Wood amen' and the year 1640 or 1641), Wood 688(1) ('Anthony Wood his book 1649'), 780 ('Liber Anthonius Wood [/] amen 1645 /'), 852 ('Anthony Wood Coll: Mert[oni] Oxon. 1649'), 882. Schoolbooks passed on via Edward Wood and Robert to Anthony are: Wood 46, 54, 70 (Robert); Wood 150, 308 (Edward and Robert); and Wood 780 (Edward and Christopher). The four he later inherited from his brother, Edward, are Wood 55, 768, 807, and 811. For Wood's marks in a list of books for sale by a publisher, see, e.g., Wood 883(2). The name of his oldest brother, Thomas Wood, does not occur in any book. Clark, *LT*, p. 22 stated that his name is in Wood 411 (a mistake for Wood 811) but that is Wood's father, Thomas, whose name also appears in [MS.] Wood C. 40(1), a volume of four items given to him by John Day. These went after his death to his wife, Mary, and then to Anthony Wood. See Append. IV.

he had, for he might have saved some money by simply using the Bodleian copy.[16]

He did not dream of creating a formal library according to any prescribed plan which was recommended by, for example, Charles Naudé. Wood owned John Evelyn's translation of Naudé's *Instructions Concerning Erecting a Library* (1661) in which Naudé stated his ideas of what should be held in a gentleman's library or the disposition, ornament and decoration of a library. Wood's choice and arrangement of books in his attic rooms was functional and for his own purposes. The library was off limits even to friends. He bought printed materials where he could afford them, in second-hand book shops or at sales of collections. He recorded in his diaries almost daily purchases in book shops, though he used the diaries more to record and keep track of the amount of money he spent than as a record of the specific items themselves. He occasionally entered the name of a book or an author, but more frequently entered unspecified purchases of 'pamphlets', 'some books' or 'severall books'. He recorded different purchases from over a score of Oxford booksellers: — Adams, John Barnes, John Barret, — Blagrave, Francis Bowman, George Chambers, Henry Clement, Amos Curteyne, Richard Davis and his wife (his favourite), William Dewey (either a bookseller or a member of Christ Church), Thomas Fichus (or Vicars), Edward Forrest senior and junior, John Forrest, Joseph Godwin, Francis Grenwaie (Grenway), Francis Haywood (Heywood, Hawood), John and Francis Oxlad, Samuel Pocock, Thomas Robinson and his widow, — Seale, [B.?] Shirley, Thomas Short, Mrs. William Webb, George West, and John Wilmot. Wood had standing orders for 'newsbooks' from various booksellers, mainly Forrest and Robinson. He was also in correspondence with or visited the shops of London booksellers Richard Chiswell, Thomas Cooper of the Pellican in Little Britain, William Cooper, Edward Millington, and Robert Scot. In 1679 and 1680 he purchased over twenty books from James Vade a bookseller on Fleet Street.[17] These persons were also sources of valuable information. Wood noted on the title page of an anonymous book, *The Perfect Politician: Or, A Full View of . . . Cromwel*, 'This book was written by Hen. Fletcher Bookseller - so Gilb. Millington Bookseller hath told me'. A conversation with Millington's nephew, Edward, led to some comments in a book on martyrs and regicides about the regicide Gilbert Millington, 'He was a drunken Fellow. . . . a Nottinghamshire man borne, & after his Tryall for being one of the Kings Judges, was committed prisoner to the isle of Jersey, where he lived divers yeares, died & was buried – so Edward Millington a Bookseller of Lond. his Nephew told me'. Wood purchased a fair number of books at sales of libraries of deceased friends, dignitaries, and Oxford scholars: twenty-three from that of his distant cousin Henry Jackson in 1662; at least seventeen from that of his friend Henry Foulis in 1669 for which he paid the large sum of 1^{li}. 3^s; and twenty-five from that of his friend Andrew Allam in 1685. The most important acquisition for his Oxford studies was the twenty items purchased on 29 Ap. 1658 'out of Dr. Langbain's study', a month after the death of the Provost of Queen's College and Keeper of the University Archives. He valued these and others for their associations. In a book owned by Nathanial Crew, once a member of his musical group, he wrote: 'This book following did belong to Mr Nath. Crew of Linc. Coll., (afterwards Bp of Durham) who exchanging it, among others, for other books, of Joseph Godwin a bookseller, living at the upper end, I afterwards bought it of him'.[18]

Wood obtained scores of printed items as gifts from a variety of acquaintants. Several older antiquarian scholars were impressed by the promising young historian and wished to help him however they could. The two most distinguished of these were William Dugdale and Elias Ashmole. Dugdale gave him copies of his folio publications *Monasticon Anglicanum* and *The Baronage of England* for both of which Wood had supplied extensive help in proofing and correcting. Dugdale later presented him with two other books, one while Wood visited Blyth Hall, Dugdale's Warwickshire manor.[19] Ashmole gave Wood a copy of his large

---

[16]Wood's last dated acquisition was Wood 266a(330). For Gibbons, see Wood 854. For *Order and Manner*, Wood 358(2). For *Mercurius Aulicus*, Wood 623-4. For Sandius, Wood 834; he entered none of these *opera* in his vignette of the heretical Sandius in the *Fasti*. For Fludd, Wood 619(13). For Swetnam, Wood 654a(3). For Prynne, '[MS.] Wood D. 22(7). Those he marked as also in 'bib. Bod.' include: Wood 26, 84(2), 160, 255(2), 325, 419, 576, 672(3), 690, 701, 784, 794(2); for a more complete list, see the Index, 'Bodleian Library'.

[17]Wood's copy of Naudé is at Wood 68(3). For more on the distinction between a collector and the 'private' library, see T. A. Birrell, 'Reading as Pastime' in R. Myers and M. Harris, *Property of a Gentleman: the Formation . . . of the Private Library, 1620-1920* (Winchester, 1991), especially pp. 128-9. For Vade, see *LT*, 2.468, 478, and note at Wood 486(4). A list of 15 'pamphlets which Mr Wood hath bought of Mr Vade - Jul. 21. 1679, & Aug. 24' and 13 Oct. and 1 Nov., is at MS. Wood F. 50, f. 11. All fifteen are present in the collection today: 1. Wood 424(25); 2. 417(15); 3. 424(29); 4. Wood 424(23) or 276a(259); 5. 424(24); 6. 660c(17); 7. 425(5); 8. 425(13); 9. 417(16); 10. 425(9); 11. 422(17); 12. 425(8); 13. 425(18); 14. 425(7); 15. 425(19).

[18]The notes on the Millingtons are at Wood 209(2) and 243(3) (in the latter, item 3059, Gilb. is probably an error for Edward). For the items purchased at estate sales, see Append. III. For the price of books of Foulis, *LT*, 2.191. The Crewe book is at Wood 334(2); he purchased it on 13 Aug. 1662 for 1^s; see also *LT*, 1.450.

[19]Dugdale's gifts are Wood 418, 420 and 367(7) and see 483(2). For Wood's visit to Blyth Hall, *LT*, 2.371; see also

folio publication, *The Institution, Laws & Ceremonies of the Most Noble Order of the Garter*, in July 1672 (Wood reciprocated with a gift of his *Historia* in 1674) and a second book, Benjamin Smithurst's, *Britain's Glory, and England's Bravery* in November 1689 shortly after it was published. Others who gave him printed items were Ralph Bathurst, President of Trinity College; Arthur Charlett, the Master of University College; Thomas Guidott [Guydot], a physician whom he met at Bath; James Harrington a younger fellow of Christ Church who wrote the preface to volume I of the *Athenae* in 1691; Francis Isaac, an antiquarian at Corpus Christi College; John Lamphire, Principal of Hart Hall; Thomas Marshall, Rector of Lincoln College; and John Wilton, an antiquarian and chaplain at Merton College.

Even before Wood had solidly established his reputation with the *Historia*, contemporary authors Clement Barksdale, Edward Benlowes, Thomas Gore, Edward Sherburne, William Sprigge, Henry Stubbe and Izaak Walton gave him copies of their own publications. Once Wood's name became associated with plans for a bio-bibliographical register of all Oxford authors, many more authors did the same, some certainly in the hope that their names, and publications, might be included: e.g., Edward Bernard, Malachi Conant, William Denton, Edmund Elys, Payne Fisher, John Gibbon, Nathaniel Johnston, Edward Joyner, William Killigrew, Samuel Leigh, John Ley, Edward Littleton, Increase Mather, John Mill, Henry Savage, Richard Sherlock, James Tyrrell, John Wagstaffe, Thomas Whorwood, Henry Wilkinson. It is striking to see the New Englander and religious Independent, Increase Mather, on this list. Mather gave three of his own publications and one of his son, Cotton, to Wood on 17 January 1691. Later, when the *Athenae* appeared, many Presbyterians and Independents were offended by what Wood wrote about them. He recorded in his diary their complaint to him: 'they were civil to me and wonder I should be false to them'. Hereafter they 'were not civil to me but were shie and denied me.' There was a single exception, 'only Increase Mather, an Independent, was civil and I acknowledge it.' It was for a different reason that Wood received publications from Catholic antiquarians and writers. He had gained their acquaintance and confidence through his long-time friendship with William Rogers, a former member of University College and later at Lincoln's Inn. In August 1669 Rogers introduced Wood to Serenus (Hugh) Cressy, one of the chaplains to Queen Catherine, and to Christopher Davenport (Franciscus à Santa Clara) another Catholic living at Lincoln's Inn, with whom Wood got on very well. He came to know Thomas Blount a short time later. All supplied him with books, pamphlets, and information during visits and by post. Cressy told the 'great' Ralph Sheldon about Wood and his forthcoming volume on the history of the university and arranged for a meeting between the two in July 1671 at the Mitre Inn in Oxford. Their common interests in antiquarian studies led to at least twenty-one visits by Wood to Weston House, several lasting over three months. At Weston House Wood catalogued and arranged Sheldon's library of books and manuscripts. For this labour he received a salary and lodging at Sheldon's magnificent estate, convivial companionship with antiquarians and especially Catholic writers, two dozen books and some manuscripts, and the promise of monetary help for the publication of the *Athenae*. The story is often told about two visits by Wood to Weston House which went on too long. Sheldon, in frustration, had to pretend to leave so that there would be no reason for Wood to stay. After Wood left for Oxford, Sheldon suddenly reappeared at Weston House, free of his guest. But Sheldon could also lean on Wood for favours. He gave Wood thirty-six copies of François Veron's *The Rule of Catholick Faith* translated into English by his uncle, Edward Sheldon, a monk at Douay, to peddle to booksellers in Oxford. Wood got rid of them all. It is most certain that Wood was highly respected by the Sheldon family and when Ralph Sheldon died in 1684, his great-nephew, heir and executor, also Ralph, of Steeple Barton, asked Wood to organize the elaborate funeral and burial service at Weston and a large cortège to convey the embalmed body to the site of a second service and burial at Beoley, Worcestershire. For this task, Wood, with his knowledge of history, heraldry, and ceremony, was the perfect choice. Wood continued a friendship with the second Ralph Sheldon and Wood's final visit to Weston was 16 August to 11 September 1695, the year of his death.[20]

2.494 and below, p. xlii and note 70.

[20]For Increase Mather and Wood's relationship with sectarians, see *LT*, 3.396. For William Rogers, *LT*, 1.168-9, 191-2. For Cressy and Sheldon and Sheldon's first visit with Wood, *LT*, 2.227-8. He seems to have first met Blount in May 1670, *LT*, 2.191. The majority of Sheldon gifts have an inscription similar to the following: 'Antonij à Wood, Oxon ex dono Radulphi Sheldon de Beolij in agro Wigorn. Arm. 8. Maij an. dom. 1676' in Wood 419. The heart and entrails of Ralph Sheldon were buried in the Long Compton church chancel. Sheldon presumably had certain rights of presentment which allowed his burial in the Long Compton and the Beoley parish churches. Wood overstayed a visit, from 4 July to 6 November 1679. Sheldon 'pretended' to leave Weston for London and Wood left shortly after. Sheldon then returned within three days. Sheldon employed the same ruse when Wood overstayed from 12 August to 27 November 1680. *LT*, 2.455, 467, 493. There was apparently a third such subterfuge. On 14 Sept. 1682 Wood went to Weston, but Sheldon disappeared to Skilts, another home to the south of Beoley, so Wood returned to Oxford the next day. Their relationship also suffered when Sheldon made the mistake of promising 100 pounds to support the publication of the *Athenae*. Wood returned to the subject of the promised money frequently and finally

Finally, Wood was on familiar terms with printers and publishers in Oxford: Henry Cruttenden, Henry Hall, John Hall, William Hall, the second Leonard Lichfield and his successor the third Leonard Lichfield, Moses Pitt, and later Obadiah Walker who had an underground Catholic press; and with the engravers Michael Burghers and David Loggan. Some gave Wood sheets and unbound copies of their productions. Notes on mainly title pages record gifts from Henry Cruttenden, Henry Hall, William Hall, Moses Pitt and the engraver David Loggan. His frequent visits to printing houses gave him a wealth of information about publications. If a book had no imprint, Wood tried to track it down. He probably learned from Lichfield himself that an ode by Nathaniel Williams was, as he noted in the text, 'Printed at Oxon. by L. Lichfeild 22. Nov. 1675'. He may have discovered from a printer, or a bookseller, that an elegy on John Fell was, as he recorded on the single sheet, 'printed at London – came downe to Oxon Dec. 9. an. 1686'. He knew printing practices and that a second edition was often a less reliable source than a first edition. He wrote on the title page of his copy of a play edited by the earl of Rochester printed in 1685: 'Note that when this Trag. as altered by Joh. E. of Roch. was published at the latter end of his poems, printed 1691, the said preface was then omitted. Therefore keep this.' He found that an earlier edition of a pamphlet by John Vicars had more woodcuts and wrote: 'Note that this pamphlet following called <u>true information</u> &c which is <u>A brief review of the most material parliamentary proceedings</u> &c is the first edition of it: And because it hath more cuts [19 vs. 8] in it, than the second edition of it, which immediatly followes after it, therefore do I preserve, & put it here'. If a book were issued in the context of a controversy, he provided relevant information such as previous editions, names, dates, published responses, and if he had used the material in his *Historia* or *Athenae*. Wood was sympathetic to the problems that the printers had with censors and made an effort to acquire books that were banned. He managed to acquire the only sheets of an aborted printing that survived and wrote in the text: 'Note that the Narrative following being privately in the press at Oxon. was stop'd from going any farther by the visitors command – with much adoe I got these two sheets following of the said narrative'. He owned a number of condemned books and noted in marginalia when a printer was jailed. He knew when a book was printed by stealth, printed beyond the seas, or pirated, that is, printed without permission. He kept track of books that were removed from the Bodleian Library and burned, such as those of John Milton and John Goodwin and found out where some of these removed books were hidden: 'Prin's [Prynne's] book against the bishops and books against archbishop Laud were taken out of the Public Library and put in the study in the gallery, quaere there'. Wood himself might have called these books 'damnable' but he was not among those who called for their removal. Neither would he have surrendered from his own library any book for such a burning. Though Wood believed Milton to be a liar and a rogue, he had some words of praise for *Areopagitica* in his *Fasti*: 'written to vindicate the freedom of the press from the tyranny of licensers, who for several reasons deprive the public of the benefit of many useful authors.'[21]

While older antiquarian scholars, authors, Catholic friends, and people at the press gave printed items to Wood, these acquaintances were far more important to him for the information he could pick from their brains. Wood asked all of them at some time or another, by letters or in personal meetings, for information about birth and death dates of various authors, of their publications, marriages, children, and anything else he needed to know for his own work as well as gossip that he wanted to know. His Catholic friends gave him some forty printed items, but Wood learned an infinite amount from them during his lengthy stays at Weston House or on his visits with them in Oxford or London. His friendship with Aubrey illustrates

came away with at least forty pounds from the second Ralph Sheldon. For Wood's peddling thirty-six copies of E. Sheldon's translation, see Wood 812 and *LT*, 2.253 (and 2.234-5). For Wood's description of his labours at Weston House, see *LT*, 2.475; Wood's salary is suggested by his comment when his visit of 4 July to 6 November 1679 was cut short: 'So there was 5^{li}. lost.' For his last visit to Weston, *LT*, 3.487f.

[21]For gifts from printers, e.g., '26 May 1662 Given to me by Hen: Hall the University Printer AWood.' Wood 276a(149). 'Given to me by Moses Pit Bookseller 4. Feb. 1681[2]. being then finished at the press.' Wood 445(11) and [MS.] Wood E. 15(5)). Wood lent a copy of Wake, *Rex Platonicus*, to W. Hall, Wood 62(2) and 62(3), 5 Aug. 1662, and may have received this new edition in return, *LT*, 1.452. Cruttenden gave him ten catalogues, e.g., [MS.] Wood E. 16(6, 7), Wood 91(5), [MS.] Wood E. 17(1, 3, 4, 6, 8); and Loggan, a map, Wood 276b(31). Burghers did Wood's portrait (Wood also did his own portraits, see Plates IV and V). For the ode by Williams, Wood 429(34). For the elegy on Fell, Wood 429(43). For John Wilmot, the earl of Rochester's revision of the tragedy, Wood 607(8). For Vicars, Wood 519(5-6); see also Wood 186, 598, 792(5), and [MS.] Wood B. 16(2-3). For Wood's notes on the context, see, e.g., Wood 200(2), 202(2), and 377(27). For the aborted narrative, Wood 514(46). For condemned books that he owned, nine of twenty-three in a list made 21 July 1683, see *LT*, 3.63-4. For a jailed printer, see Wood 422(15). For books printed to avoid censorship, see the Index, 'Printing, false, overseas, or by stealth'. Wood thought of having his volume three of the *Athenae* published in Holland, see MS. Wood F. 51, f. 18. For the removal of books by Prynne, Milton, and Goodwin from the Bodleian Library, *LT* 1.319, his 'Secretum' for June 1660, and numerous references at *LT*, 5.208 and [MS.] Wood D. 22(7) and Wood 423(58) and I. Philip, *The Bodleian Library in the Seventeenth and Eighteenth Centuries* (Oxford, 1983): 26. For Milton, *AOF*, 1.483.

the perils of a relationship between two antiquarians with strikingly different personalities. Aubrey was associated with nineteen printed items in the Wood collection. Most have inscriptions such as 'For his ever honoured Friend Mr Anthony à Wood from his affectionate servant J. Aubrey.' The printed items themselves demonstrate Aubrey's respect for Wood and his knowledge of what Wood might make use of. These gifts were, on the other hand, relatively unimportant in comparison to the huge amount of information that Aubrey communicated to Wood by word of mouth during his frequent visits to Oxford or by letter from wherever he happened to be in his rambles throughout Wiltshire and Surrey or in London or Cambridge. They helped each other, but in the end it was certainly Wood who profited more because Aubrey could neither muster the discipline and courage nor arrange the financing to get any of his numerous manuscript studies into print. In these areas Wood excelled. The break between the two, or at least on Wood's part, came when Wood inserted information, given him by Aubrey, about Edward Hyde, the first earl of Clarendon, into the *Athenae*. This information offended his son Henry Hyde, the second earl of Clarendon, who initiated a suit against Wood for defamation of his deceased father. Wood looked for a scapegoat other than himself and determined that the fault was Aubrey's. Aubrey never fully understood Wood's anger and even after the initial estrangement sent Wood the prospectus of his grand *Monumenta Britannica*. Wood remarkably ended up with six copies of this prospectus which are the only copies known to exist. Wood's final assessment of Aubrey, written after 1692 in his 'Secretum Antonii', was not generous: 'He was a shiftless person, roving and magotie-headed, and somtimes little better than crased. And being exceedingly credulous, would stuff his many letters sent to A. W. with fooleries, and misinformations, which somtimes would guid him into the paths of errour'.[22]

Purchases and gifts did not account for all of the printed items in Wood's collection. He was an opportunist and picked up any available letterpress wherever and whenever he could. The coffee houses were a prime hunting ground. He noted their first appearance in Oxford 'about the year 1650' and registered reservations about them more than once in his diary: 'The decay of study, and consequently of learning, are coffy houses, to which most scholars retire and spend much of the day in hearing and speaking of news'. Nevertheless coffee houses in Oxford were on his circuit of walks. The talk in these public spheres was certainly more wide-ranging and substantive than at taverns or inns and less in-bred than in common rooms. They were places where people read as well as discussed literary and political topics and as such provided him with information. Coffee houses were also selected by London, Oxford and Cambridge publishers and booksellers to distribute their catalogues of book and library auctions without cost, and Wood took at least ten such catalogues.[23] He also was very familiar with coffee house letters, citing them frequently in his diaries, and picked up single sheet advertisements and public notices that were set out for patrons. On an advertisement for William Docwra, he wrote, 'This paper was dispersed in every coffey-house in Oxōn. in the beg. of Sept. 1689.' At the bottom, a note in another hand is directed to the local patron: 'The Reader is desired not to take away this paper'. Wood took away the paper anyway. Public notices wherever they appeared in Oxford were collected by Wood, as he noted on many single sheets: 'stuck up in the Common Refectory of every Coll. and Hall Dec. 8. in the morn. 1670'; 'stuck up on all common places in the University' (January 1671); 'stuck up on every corner in Oxōn Apr: 15. 1671'; 'These orders were stuck up on every corner, & every Inn dore June 9, 1671'; and 'Stuck up in all public places 13. March 1680[1]'. No place was off-limits. On one single sheet, a petition by James Rossington to Parliament printed in about 1675, he wrote, 'This I found in Dr Lowers privy house 24. May 1675 in Bow Street, Lond.' Wood took it home with him, straightened it out and set it in a bundle of political pamphlets. A scrap of letterpress, the title page of *Poemation Latinum* by Francis Digby, has Wood's note, 'Tobacco wrapt up in this paper in the beginning of May 1693'. He later used this information on the title page for the second edition of his *Athenae*. He saved whatever was passed out on the streets. A catalogue of a sale of books by Rowland Reynolds has his note: 'put into my hand per ignotum, at Trin Coll. gate

---

[22]The *ex dono* inscription by Aubrey is found in Wood 431b. Aubrey may have loaned to Wood several items which were not returned, e.g., Fulman, Wood 614(1), and Norden, [MS.] Wood C. 20. Wood's assessment of Aubrey *LT*, 2.117, was not unique, for Ralph Sheldon had a similar view; see his letter to Wood, 'Yesterday came to mee honest Mr John Awbrey, whose head is so full that it will not give his tongue leave to utter one word after another. I assure you he is (to my appearance) as mad as anyone almost in the university of Bedlam', Anthony Powell, *John Aubrey and his Friends* (London, 1948): 174. For Wood's copies of Aubrey's prospectus, see items 5370-3. For more on the suit, see p. xliv, note 73.

[23]On the first appearance of coffee houses, see *LT*, 1.466, 'about the year 1650'; or 1.423, 'did not begin in Oxon till about the year 1654'. On his reservations about them, *LT*, 1.423 and 3.300 and his note in Wood 614(7). On catalogues of sales or distribution of catalogues at Sam's, Will's, Jonathan's, Richard's, or Tom's coffee houses in London, 'at the Coffee-Houses in Oxford and Cambridge', or St. Albans, e.g., [MS.] Wood E. 16(5), [MS.] Wood E. 17(2 and 8), [MS.] Wood E. 18(2), [MS.] Wood E. 20(1, 2 and 10b); see the Index, 'Coffee houses'.

Apr. 13. 1685'.[24] Occasionally he came into possession of a printed item which may have been taken from a private library, or the archives of either the university or a college. But these are rare, and in his library of 6760 items number less than a half a dozen. At Wood 276a(127) there is the following note by I. P. [Ian Philip]: 'Restored to the University Archives by decree 28 Oct. 1935'. This proclamation rightfully belongs to the University Archives for the old archive number, 530, is plainly visible along with extensive notes by a university archivist. On an account of proceedings of parliamentary visitors to the university printed in 1648 Wood wrote, 'Note that the Narrative following being privately in the press at Oxon. was stop'd from going any farther by the visitors command – with much adoe I got these two sheets following of the said narrative: – I could never see any other printed copie of it, or any of the MS copie that followed[.] This that I got, I cannot now tell justly from whence I had it, unless from Dr Langbaines papers – qu[aere]'.[25]

What Wood Collected

Wood formed his library to satisfy his own research and his personal tastes. As such it demonstrates his devotion to the history, biography, and bibliography of Oxford persons, what he turned to for amusement, and, conversely, what he was not interested in. Of most obvious importance to him were the 550 items concerning Oxford, the university, the city, and the parliament when the king's parliament moved to Oxford in 1644. Many of these items are single sheets which survive today only because Wood saved them. These include official university examination or graduation notices: twenty-six determinations or disputations by candidates for the bachelor of arts ('ordo baccalaureorum determinantium' on Egg-Saturday, the *Festum Ovorum*, before Shrove Tuesday) (none exist outside of Wood's collection); twenty-six queries to be disputed by candidates for higher degrees before inception ('quaestiones in sacra theologia discutiendae') (eighteen exist only in Wood's collection); twenty-four Encaenia items, notices either of the programme itself, 'Theatri Oxoniensis encaenia . . . celebrata', mandates for what 'doctors are to wear', or songs or poems recited at the ceremony (twenty-one exist only in Wood's collection); and six 'exercitia academica' on the manner in which programmes are to be carried out (none are listed in Wing or the ESTCR). Other rare single sheets that Wood collected were public announcements from the Vice-Chancellor about academic matters or university sponsored businesses such as the carriers (stage coaches) to London; orders for receptions; petitions to the university; celebrative ballads or verses; articles; oaths; prayers; proposals; death and plague notices; and advertisements. Cambridge documents were not high on Wood's list of priorities, but when the opportunity came to acquire seventy-nine Act Verses, he did so. Thirty-nine of these exist only in his collection.[26]

Of almost equal importance to the Oxford items were his 300 items on biography and 421 on history. The biographical items range from pamphlets on English 'champions' or on Friar Bacon or Henry Walker the ironmonger; to full treatments of the lives of Thomas Becket, Robert Devereux, Thomas Hobbes, Charles I and Charles II. There are also eighty elegies and encomia, many prepared in memory of Oxford figures such as Thomas Bodley, Robert Boyle, William Camden, Abraham Cowley, Oliver Cromwell, William Davenant, John Fell, Payne Fisher, Thomas Fuller, George Gifford, William Laud, Robert Sanders, and James Ussher. Wood wrote separate bio-bibliographies on or dealt with all of the above in detail in the *Athenae*. Most of the historical items are on English history, with about forty items concerning universal history, chronological tables or sensational events in France or Spain. Essential tools for him were the heavily used reference works such as 198 catalogues of libraries and of books for sale in bookshops or at auction and 119 newsbooks. Thirty-one of the latter contain runs of hundreds of individual issues as, for example, runs of *The Intelligencer*, Aug.-Dec. 1663, interleaved with *The Newes*, Sept.-Dec. 1663 (Wood 521(3) and 521(2)), and *The Intelligencer*, 1664-5 (Wood 391 and 392(1, 3)); *The Loyal Protestant* 1681-3

---

[24]The Docwra advertisement is Wood 276(575). For public notices see Index, 'Oxford university statues . . . distributed'. The Rossington petition is at Wood 276a(173), and the Digby slip, Wood 431c, is inserted in *AO*, Wood 431a, at 2.877 (for more on the entry at *AOF*, 2.360, see note 52 below). The Reynold's catalogue is at [MS.] Wood D. 22(15).

[25]There is a visitation document dating from 1648 which has a note, not by Wood, indicating that it was to be in the archives of Merton College with older visitation documents, Wood 514(38). The Higgs's diaries may have been taken from Merton, Wood Alm. A(1, 3). The 'Narrative' (1648), Wood 514(46), may have been one of a number of Langbaine items 'which I found among the wast papers of Dr. Thomas Barlow of the said College [Queen's]' or 'which I found among the offel papers of Dr. Thomas Barlow', *LT*, 1.249. Wood may have saved these documents in Barlow's office from destruction, as he did others. This appears to be the earliest version of a story told decades later by Wood to Tanner who told it to Thwaites who told it to Hearne, who wrote it in his diary, Hearne: 2.44.

[26]Parliament was also in Oxford in 1681. Of the 255 Oxford single sheets in the Wood collection described here, 186 exist today only in the Bodleian Library, see also Append. V. The Oxford degree ceremony programmes and statutes and the Cambridge Act Verses are in the bibliography at Oxford and at Cambridge.

(missing); *Mercurius Aulicus*, 1643-1644 (Wood 623-4); *Mercurius Politicus*, Dec. 1656-1659 (Wood 389(1) and 522-4); *Mercurius Publicus*, 1660-3, (Wood 393-4 and 520, 521(1) succeeded by *The Intelligencer*, above); and *The Publick Intelligencer*, 1657-8 (Wood 389(2) and 390). The most remarkable is a thirty-year run of the Oxford/London *Gazette* in fourteen volumes Nov. 1665-March 1694 (Wood 541-554). Most of the remaining newsbooks are single issues or runs of two to five issues. He seems never to have passed by an almanac in a bookshop and acquired 171 of them, ranging from the episcopal, meterological, protestant, Quaker, Catholic, rogues', to prophetical almanacs. These gave him information on holidays, birthdays, battle days, and any event of local or national importance. He owned thirty books on heraldry, a subject on which he was an authority and on which he made thousands of notes in his manuscripts. Happily he resisted the temptation to incorporate this material in his major works though his knowledge of heraldry gained him significant information in tracing family lines.

He held an extensive collection of publications related to political life. Most date from his lifetime, from 1632 to 1695, and include over 1200 items concerned with parliament and government; 500 on Charles I and Charles II and monarchy in general, including 19 on the subject of the eikon basilike; 280 on plots of one sort or another (including the Gunpowder, Popish and Rye House plots); 450 on the civil war; 260 on Ireland; 200 on the army, 44 on the navy; 47 on economics and commerce (from trade to usury); and 152 items dealing mainly with law. Wood's sizable number of 33 maps was necessary since he had to fix the locations of Oxford graduates and their parishes throughout the kingdom. His 15 works on architecture and surveying were evidently well used. Wood was a good amateur draftsman as is attested by his many fine drawings of Oxford buildings (see Append. VII).

Of no less importance to an antiquarian in the seventeenth century was a thorough knowledge of theological issues, and Wood acquired avidly in this area. He was far less interested in theology as an intellectual discipline than as a source of information about the authors and the controversies that might involve Oxford persons. Most of his 1000 theological items concern the constitution, government, the prayers and liturgy of the Church of England, and the clergy. The first of two impressive sub-groups includes 179 items on non-conformists, which he, and other conformists, lumped together as 'phanatiques'. These range from an important 46 items on Quakers, gathered mainly because of their importance to Oxford where they opened a meeting house in 1654, to items on Anabaptists (16), Levellers (14), Presbyterians (12), Independents (5), Ranters (3), Fifth Monarchists (3), the Family of Love (2), Libertines (2), and Brownists (2). The second subgroup includes 413 items on Catholics or anti-Catholics (including 150 items on the Popish Plot); his interest in Catholic issues was stimulated by his friendships with a number of Catholics, but the subject was important for any person writing about contemporary Oxford and its history. He owned over fifty sermons or collections of sermons and writings by Oxford graduates such as John Harmar, Peter Heylyn, William Penn, William Prynne, Gilbert Sheldon, and Henry Spelman. His thirty-four items on the American colonies run the range from curiosities and exploration to theology and include eight works by Increase and Cotton Mather and William Penn.[27]

Some 1000 items in Wood's collection can be classified as literature. Most of these, such as the 575 ballads, reflect Wood's low-brow tastes, but he, along with Samuel Pepys, did the unusual thing. They saved and protected the ephemera that they had acquired for their private entertainment. Few others did the same and 40 per cent of the ballads in the Wood collection are 'rare', that is, they are the only copies known to exist. If none of the Wood ballads had survived, we would have no copy at all. Other ephemera are equally as rare. Forty-eight of his 116 riddles, proverbs, romances, jests, garlands, and pleasant histories are known to exist only in the Bodleian Library. One volume of garlands, Wood 94, was stolen before 1837. It had contained twenty-three items, mainly garlands, and over half of these, thirteen, are not known to exist today. A list of the contents in the Whiteside Catalogus is clear evidence of their former existence.[28]

---

[27]For the Quaker meeting house, see Wood's note at Wood 515(14). Wood's friendships with Catholics and his interest in Catholic Oxford led to the rumour that he was a Catholic. In 1673 John Aubrey posed the question, 'Are you turned Roman Catholic or no?', Powell, *Aubrey*, p. 147.

[28]The figure of 575 ballads includes 107 ballads in the volumes Wood 399 and 400 that were removed from the Ashmolean Museum some time before 1837. Wood 400 was broken up into two parts with one going to the Roxburghe collection in the British Library and the other to the Euing collection in the University of Glasgow Library. Four of the twenty-three items in Wood 94 are unrecorded in the ESTCR; eight are 'rare' but unlocated today; and eight are in two locations, only one of which is determined today; two are 'rare', located in the Pepys collection or at the Huntington; one is unidentified. Another volume which contains 'rare' items is Wood 254 in which there are fourteen romances or histories, eight of which, according to Wing, exist only in the Bodleian. Wood 259, see Plate III, contains twelve items, nine of which are 'rare' and three of which are know to exist at the Bodleian and one other location.

His favourite authors were Nicholas Breton (5), Thomas Dekker (10), Thomas Deloney (12), John Dryden (10), George Gascoigne (2), Robert Greene (5), Thomas Nash (6), Martin Parker (12), John Taylor (24), Seneca (5), Terence (2), and Virgil (5). He owned thirty-eight works of plays or works related to drama: eight prologues or epilogues, nine catalogues or discussions of the genre, and twenty-one plays, usually single copies by, e.g., Beaumont/Fletcher, Aphra Behn, Pierre Corneille, John Dryden (*Secret-love, or the Maiden-queen*), Nicholas Grimald, Shackerley Marmion, Jasper Mayne, Seneca (three collections and two separate tragedies) and Shakespeare (a fourth edition of *Othello*). He held a smattering of works by standard classical, continental or English authors, usually single items: Aesop, Anacreon, Apulieus, Cervantes, Dares the Phrygian, Erasmus, Homer (trans. by Chapman), Horace, Juvenal, Lucian, Lucretius, Martial, and Ovid; and Francis Bacon, Thomas Browne, Samuel Butler, John Cleveland, Thomas Coryate, Samuel Daniel, William Davenant, John Denham, John Donne, Michael Drayton, Gabriel Harvey, George Herbert, John Heywood, Henry Howard, William Langland, Philip Sidney (two copies of *An Apologie for Poetrie* (1595), one was stolen from the Ashmolean Museum before 1837 and the other is not listed in the current Bodleian compact disk catalogue), Shakespeare (two of poetry including a 'rare' copy of *Venus and Adonis* (1630), and John Wilmot, the earl of Rochester.

Less important in general to his studies though each particular item might offer some information on authors, editors, and events that were relevant were his forty-four books under the broad classification of philosophy. This high number is misleading for Wood was no more interested in philosophy as a discipline than he was in theology. Most are standard texts by Aristotle, Boethius, Hobbes, Plato, or Cambridge act verses on philosophical studies (8), or works on physics (3), alchemy (3), and the occult (5) which were difficult to distinguish from philosophy. Others were by Oxford scholars and acquired simply for that reason. He once held sixty-six items on rhetoric and this rather high number, too, is misleading, for he got rid of thirty of these before his death (see Append. VII). Wood was neither a theologian, a philosopher nor a rhetorician; nor was he interested in printed items in these disciplines unless the authors were in some way related to Oxford. A low number of books in other disciplines such as mathematics (8) and astrology/astronomy (21) also indicates very minor interest. The number of books in his collection that were printed in German, Italian, French, Dutch, or Spanish comes to under a score. His books in French were those from his older brother, Robert, also called 'monsieur' because he spent his boyhood years, 1642-7, in France. His holdings in science and medicine were limited as well. He held twenty-four items involving the Royal Society, annually published lists of members or controversial writings in which Oxford persons were engaged, and eighty-six items on medicine. A large number of the latter were for his personal use, including thirteen cure/quack advertisements, twelve on baths, fourteen on the plague and twelve on chocolate, coffee, tea, or tobacco as medicine (or poison). Wood was a vigorous man and thought little of walking over twenty miles on a single day until a few months before his death. On the other hand his diary and 'Secretum Antonii' record from the very beginning numerous minor ailments, many visits to a half a dozen different doctors, and remedies both effective and ineffective.[29] Other items which seem to be purely for Wood's casual reading and not relevant to his studies were 139 printed items on women (including a large number of ballads on women, wives, and lovers); 79 on music reflecting his lifelong attention to various kinds of music; 54 on travel and exploration; 56 on entertainments of various kinds from fishing, hunting, swimming, card games, drinking, shovel-board, smoking to feasts, progresses, and sideshows; and 20 on horticulture. Several genres indicate his attraction to the dark and mysterious: 357 on crime, 258 on executions and murders; 102 on marvels, and 42 on witchcraft. The 105 items on conduct or etiquette (courtship, friendship, gentlemanly behaviour, instruction, mirrors, morality, self-examination, virtues) were certainly pertinent to Wood, who was not a college fellow and on occasion believed himself to be an outsider.

How Did Wood Organize and Maintain His Books?

Wood lived and worked in two attic rooms which he called his studies. He recalled in his 'Secretum Antonii' that in February 1660 he 'set up my chimney' on the east side of the east room 'as also the window in my study' on the south side of the west room overlooking Merton Street. More information about these rooms is found in a 112-page shelf-list and index of his library of printed books that he began in March 1681 and finished two months later. This shelf-list gives enough information to reconstruct the layout with the locations of books on various subjects. It begins with books, 'bundles', and 'heaps' in the west study

---

[29]On 16 August 1695, in his last year, he walked thirty miles to Weston for a month-long visit. Starting at midnight, he rested at Enstone at 5:00 a.m., a little beyond the half-way point. He slept for three hours 'and might have been at Weston by dinner time at 12', had not friends detained him. *LT*, 3.487. Arthur Charlett described Wood in a letter written shortly after Wood's death: 'He was a very strong, lusty man, Aged 65 years', *LT* 3.498 (he would have been 64 years old on 17 December 1695).

room on 'upper shelf on the E[ast] side' and continues 'In the 2^{d} shelf on the East sid[e]' and through several more shelves on the east side to the south side, to the first shelf of 'Shelves under my window', then to the west and north sides. In the west study there was a desk opposite the window facing the north wall and over the desk a shelf which held at least seventeen works on the church and theology. On the sixth shelf on the east side of the west study he recorded bundles or heaps of 'Travells', 'Travells - description of countries', 'Geography', 'Travels of various men', 'Military matters', 'Husbandry & Gardening', and then he went on to describe contents 'In the next division of the same shelf'. In a lower shelf, another division holds the categories on, and works of, 'Tobacco, drunkenness, English abuses', 'murders', 'whore-lighthuswifes', 'theeves, rogues – whores', and 'Witches'. And so on. In the east study room, also his bedroom, he began with the four shelves on the south side, then turned to the west wall, to the table, and to a shelf on the east side where there was an undisclosed number of 'Books that I bought of Mr Davys laying on that shelf. [and below] There be some books also wrapt up in a browne paper that I am pay [sic] Davys for'. His newsbooks are also on the east side of this study. Though this shelf-list is not at all a formal or an inclusive catalogue since it lists only 985 identifiable printed items, it gives an idea of how he arranged his massive collections. It served specifically as an elaborate index of authors and as a reference tool for his biographical and bibliographical work on Oxford persons. With these printed materials at his fingers' tips he could find information on virtually any political and social event emanating from the center of the kingdom, and locate and track the progress of any Oxford person in any social, political, military, or legal context. There is a single reference to a manuscript book located 'on the west side of my study upper shelf in the window'. Wood listed thirteen names and the page numbers on which they occur and, to keep straight exactly what he was doing, followed these entries with 'Note that I have made no notes from any of those manuscripts but from the 1.' (that is, from only the first manuscript book on the upper shelf).[30]

The physical layout and general organisation of books and manuscripts in his study rooms probably changed little from 1681 to the year of his death. The major difference, aside from the adding of shelves to accommodate the steady increase in the number of books, pamphlets, single sheets, and newsbooks, was in the appearance of the printed items on the shelves. During the last fifteen years of his life he engaged in a plan to enclose in sturdy bindings the hundreds of bundles and heaps of letterpress. Up to this time his shelves contained, besides unbound gatherings, a number of parchment-bound volumes and calf-bound volumes. Most of the 250 parchment-bound volumes would have been in his library in 1681. Many hold single printed items, usually printed before 1660, and were acquired in this state by Wood. A number of these were from the estate of Henry Foulis or Henry Jackson or have notes made by earlier owners on the cover or pastedowns. Some others have either strips cut from parchment manuscripts to support the spine backing, parchment manuscript pastedowns, or parchment manuscript waste paper, which Wood never would have permitted in volumes that he himself had bound, or parchment manuscript covers that were taken from discarded manuscripts, again a practice that Wood never would have allowed. Still others have obvious signs of earlier binding, such as [MS.] Wood B. 23 (item 4070) which probably was bound around 1600 since it has wastepaper and flyleaves from Sidney, *Apologie for Poetrie* (1595), and Wood 654c (item 1556) which has chain holes .[31]

Most of the calf-bound volumes in his library in 1681 were acquired in this state. These numbered 340 in 1695 and include twenty-four volumes bound in the distinctive Oxford binding with hatching on the spines. Most were bound before 1650. The 310 others can be generally described as calf with two or three fillets, sometimes with blind stamp decoration at the corners. Almost all contain items printed before

---

[30]For the 'Secretum Antonii' entry, *LT*, 1.304; see also an entry in his diary for repairing the chimney and 'dormer window' in 1667, *LT*, 2.98. The shelf-list is at MS. Wood E. 2(70). See N. Kiessling, 'The Library of Anthony Wood 1681-1999', *BLR*, 16 (1999): 470-498. See pp. 474-5 for a plate of the first page of this catalogue and for some of the details incorporated here; and pp. 492-98, for more of the items on the shelves. Wood had more than one desk, see *LT*, 1.400 and 503. For the subjects on the sixth shelf, see MS. Wood E. 2(70), pp. 17-9; and on a lower shelf, pp. 22-3. He listed bundles and heaps by subject without identifying specific items. The difference between 'bundle' and 'heap' is presumably one of organisation. Bundles were better organised and sometimes tied, e.g., 'In a bundell tyed up togeather', in MS. Wood E. 2(70), p. 51. The reference to Mr. Davys [Richard Davis] is on p. 74. The reference to manuscripts is on pp. 37-8.

[31]For items owned by Foulis or Jackson: Wood 98, 166, 184, 232(1-2), 239, 477(1-6), 579, 598, 691, 743, 776(1-3), 778, 781, and 789(1-3). For items with notes made by former owners: Wood 7, 17, 43, 55, 176, 182, 362, 381, 464, 539, 569, 695, and 819. For items with parchment waste to support, see Append. IV, note 8. For items with parchment covers: Wood 106, 335, 588, 799, [MS.] Wood C. 23, [MS.] Wood C. 35 and Jesus College 2 Arch. 2. 16(1). Wood was above all an archivist intent on preserving manuscripts and books. To have allowed a binder to cut up parchment manuscripts for binding purposes would have been sacrilege to him. He was instrumental in saving several collections from destruction. See, e.g., *LT* 1.335 and 3.202-3, and note at Dugdale, Wood 418, item 2363.

1660. Wood himself had a handful of these bound. Wood 46, 54, 150, 807 and [MS.] Wood C. 40 have his blind-stamp initials on the calf covers, but these were bound in calf before Wood acquired them; and Wood 606 he had bound on 9 July 1657 for 6ᵈ.[32]

The remaining letterpress was scattered on shelves in his two studies in gatherings of bundles and heaps. Throughout his life Wood acquired published material in sheets to save on costs. Now and then he could afford to have some important books bound and there are a handful of references in his diaries to his binding of books before 1680. In February 1657 he 'paid Beckford the bookbinder 6ˢ for binding 10 books, 6 quartoes, one folio, 3 octavos'. His regular binder from December 1661 to 1669 was Edmund Thorne, and on 2 December 1661 he paid 'to Thorne for binding of Weever and Burton Itineraryes, 10ᵈ'. The next order for Thorne in April 1662 was 'for stiching books, 10ᵈ', and more orders for stitching follow, though he hired Thorne in March and July 1663 to bind, as opposed to stitching, copies of another important book, the sermons by his brother Edward which he himself edited after Edward's death. He gave these as gifts. Wood sent out for parchment binding on 22 May 1658 a much used copy of Brian Twyne's *Antiquitatis academiae Oxoniensis apologia* which he acquired from the estate of Gerard Langbaine. Wood had blank leaves inserted for his notes (Wood 602, see Plate V). There was at least one early pasteboard binding, James Ware's *De praesulibus Hiberniae*, which Wood had Edmund Thorne bind in March 1668. Wood used this book heavily and the binding did not hold up. It was rebound shortly after 1695 by the Ashmolean Museum.[33]

Wood's rooms must have been a mess in 1681 and the inconvenience of having masses of unbound sheets and pamphlets must have irritated him. It would have been difficult to find particular printed items in bundles and piles. He knew what a well-kept and efficient library looked like because he had done inventories of a number of them for their owners. In 1681, prompted by a bequest of forty shillings from one of his Merton College friends, Peter Nicholls, Wood had two volumes of Oxford and London *Gazettes* bound. Over the next fourteen years he would find the money to have two/thirds of his unbound letterpress put in bindings. He had definite ideas about how this should be done. He was indignant when he saw the damage caused by the binding ordered by Bodley's Librarian, Thomas Lockey. In one such composite volume in the library, he wrote 'This book is spoiled in the binding by the meanes of Dr. Th. Lockey proto-bib. as very many others are.' He addressed the issue directly in a slip which he attached to his autobiography. Dr. Lockey, 'not understanding the managing of a library, did great mischeif: —'

1, by binding severall together not of a subject;
2, by binding a pamphlet with a substantiall book, as I remember a 'Philosophicall Transaction' with a substantiall book;
3, in cutting them, a margin with notes were destroyed;
4, and in placing several quartoes that had many [treatises] bound togeather and placing them below in common, some would cut out a choice book from among them and leave the rest.[34]

[32]For Oxford bindings, see Append. IV, note 7. One such binding is from 1663 or later, Wood 205. See Strickland Gibson, *Early Oxford Bindings*, OBS, vol. 10 (Oxford, 1903): 40-1, and qualifications on Gibson's dates by D. Pearson, *Oxford Bookbinding 1500-1640*, OBS, 3rd series, vol. 3 (Oxford, 2000): 38-40 The evidence for binding before Wood acquired the volumes is clearer in the thirty calf-bound exemplars containing more than one publication, e.g., Wood 134(1-3) from Langbaine was bound before Wood acquired the volume; Wood 179(1-2) from Allam was bound when Allam acquired it (see also Wood 24(1-2) from Robert Jackson, and Wood 774(1-7) and Jesus College H. 13. 23(1-2), both from Humphrey Dyson); [MS.] Wood C. 44(1-4) was bound when Wood acquired the volume; Wood 407(1-2) was bound in a fine binding when Wood acquired it; Wood 409 has parchment backing which Wood never would have permitted. For the binding of Wood 606 see *LT*, 1.220. Wood 330 seems to have been bound early, but in 1681 he listed most of the contents in a slightly different order, see MS. E. 2(70), p. 50.
[33]For binding by Beckford and another in February 1657, see *LT*, 1.213; for other binding, 1.420, 1.470, 477 (Edward's sermons), 487, and 2.180, 299. For Thorne's sewing, *LT*, 1.436, 470 ('for doing up severall books for me'), 503, and 2.75, 138, 146, 163. On the binding of Wood 602 at the cost of 8ᵈ, see also *LT* 1.249. Wood 402(1), a book of ballads, has a parchment cover and may have been sent for binding before 1680, though it contains one ballad which may have been printed after 1680. Ware's *De praesulibus*, Wood 415(1), is discussed below, p. xxxi.
[34]One of the few visitors to Wood's study rooms before the week of his death was the Vice-Chancellor John Nicholas. On 1 December 1678 at the height of the inquisition against papists in Oxford, Nicholas more or less forced Wood to admit him to his study where Nicholas gave a cursory inspection of Wood's papers to determine if Wood were involved in the popish plot. Nicholas looked in both studies, *LT*, 2.424f. For the notes on binding of the newsbooks, see below, p. xxxviii. The initial bindings of these newsbooks did not hold up, probably because of Wood's heavy use of them, and he had them rebound seven years later. For other bequests of Nicholls, see *LT*, 2.401. For Wood's annotation on binding in the Bodleian Library book, 8° C 19 Th. BS, see Philip, *The Bodleian Library*: 49f. For Wood's strictures on Lockey, written in a version of his autobiography, see *LT*, 1.335.

Before Wood sent one of his own unbound bundles to the binder, he had arranged the items in a final order. He took elaborate care in bringing together items on similar topics. His shelf-list of 1681 shows that he had arranged, in a rough fashion, all the letterpress by categories. He was to tinker with the order again and again, putting items on the same topic in heaps and then organizing them chronologically. This is indicated by his former numbers on items and earlier stitch marks, both of which are common. At times a single item has two or even three former numbers indicating its place in a preceding gathering of stitched together items or in a bundle or heap. An example is Wood 370, a volume holding ten works on tithes and church revenue. In 1681 he had recorded three of the ten items in his shelf-list of 1681, items 5, 9 and 4 in the final order in the bound volume. The first item had been in the west study among theological books listed on p. 3 of his shelf-list; the second, in a bundle of government pamphlets listed on p. 33; and the third, in the east study in a bundle 'concerning episcopacy' listed on p. 64. When he began to arrange the items for binding, he brought together items from numerous locations. He wrote on the title page of the seventh its former location, 'First heap 27'; and on the top of the title page of the tenth work its former location, number '59' in a heap, and at the bottom, he wrote in pencil a different location, '2^d heap 56'. Eventually it would be the tenth and final item in the volume. At times the classification could cause him problems. Wood inserted a parliamentary item with the exasperating title, *A Catalogue of the . . . Lords, that Have Absented Themselves from the Parliament . . . As also, a List of the Army of . . . Robert, Earle of Essex . . . A List of the Navie Royall . . . The Names of the Orthodox Divines . . . Lastly, the Field Officers Chosen for the Irish Expedition*, into a volume of parliamentary pamphlets (see item 2765, number (1) in Wood 620(1-40)). He had to qualify his choice of placement with 'This cat. hath a larg title, because it containes many things, & therefore it may be bound up in another vol. as well as this'. He reorganized the forty printed works in this volume more than once. A pamphlet by Prynne, now item number 30, was with fifteen other items in 1681 in the third of four bundles of parliamentary items. It was the only one in this third bundle, according to his shelf-list, to end up in the current volume. Some time after 1681 several more migrated to this third bundle and have on the title pages, 'Bundl. 3. Parl' (items 30-32). Eventually Wood selected the forty items for this volume, including four items from the first, second, and fourth bundles in the shelf-list of 1681.[35]

After he finished arranging the order in a bundle, he prepared a table of contents within guidelines that he made with red ink or red chalk (see Plates I and III). Some of these volumes held over one hundred printed works and the table of contents could extend over four blank flyleaves before the first item. He prepared these tables of contents before he sent the bundles to the printer. This is indicated by several versions that survive. A torn slip inserted in his *Athenae* was the earlier version of a list of contents for the current Wood 752 with portions of his entries of printed works (1), (2), (4), and (5). He had to write a new list when he added a new item, number (3) between items (2) and (4). A second list has items concerning Thomas Wolsey. Wood wrote it within guidelines made with red ink, which indicates that he intended them to be in a single volume. But he changed his mind and incorporated a number of other items into this assembly shortly before his death. It remained an unbound bundle when it went to the Ashmolean and was bound as such by the Ashmolean Museum. A third example survives on the pasted down side of a support leaf for the fragile final leaf. On the support leaf he had written a list of six titles within guidelines made with red ink beginning with *Newes from Southhampton*. The list became waste paper when he subsequently inserted *Newes from Southhampton* into a different volume. Wood often made various repairs before sending bundles off to his binder as, for example, on the title page and the final leaf in Wood 337(1), and on two single sheets in Wood 416, items (104) and (117). The repairs to the single sheets were made with slips on which there was some manuscript material, not his own, on the pasted down side. The repairs he made to a volume of ballads, now Wood 401, are complex and extensive and involve the use of blank sheets to strengthen ballads and to cover irrelevant printed and manuscript material. He repaired two mutilated title leaves in Wood 365, items (2) and (9), with slips and then wrote the item numbers in the volume on it. He made a similar repair to Wood 586(12) with a slip and on it numbered the item in red ink. This latter repair slip has on a pasted down side a Latin disputation topic not in Wood's hand. He scavenged for waste sheets of this kind, blank on both sides except for Latin topics, and used

---

[35]Former stitch marks are very common, see, e.g., notes at Wood 496(1), 586(3), and Wood Alm. A(2). For volumes with numerous items with various earlier location numbers, see Wood 373-376, 378, 398 and 501(1), 507(1), 514(1). The contents of a 'bound book of Battles', so described in MS. Wood E. 2(70), p. 37, Wood sorted and resorted and eventually put them in volumes now Wood 375, 378, and 501. For another volume in which Wood mentioned former numbers in 'heaps', see Wood 626(16-20). As with Wood 620(1-40), Wood often had problems in placing other items which covered several topics. See, e.g., notes at Wood 236(1), 519(8) and 615(24). For the bundles of parliamentary materials in the shelf-list, see MS. Wood E. 2(70), pp. 32- 35. Wood 246(1) is a made-up copy, with an illustration added from elsewhere.

them to separate items in bundles to be bound in composite volumes.[36]

Wood himself probably inserted the blank sheets after he had arranged the order. A slip at Wood 369(8) shows his arranging in progress: 'bound wit . . . [sic, mutilated] Triall of the Kings judges & speeches [Wood 369(5)] – Also cleane paper betw. them, for the entrie [Wood 369(8)?] of what [James] Heaths Cron. [Wood 145] saith of them Newsbook for that time – Characters of Cromwellians– [Wood 369(9)]'. He did not follow the instructions on the note to himself and the 'cleane paper' between items (8) and (9) has nothing of Heath's *Chronicle*. After arranging the order Wood gave the items final Arabic numbers, usually on the upper right-hand corner of title pages. It is rare to find discrepancies between Wood's numbered table of contents and what is actually in a volume. Most variations concern his dividing a publication into two parts, a practice which served his personal purposes, for it gave him the type of information he needed about items which covered more than one topic. In Wood 423(1), he neglected to add a final item, number 67. This item was apparently added at the last minute. In Wood 620 the last two, items 39 and 40, are reversed in his list, probably because the binder shuffled the two. In one volume, Wood 727(1) he wrote only the guidelines in red ink on the upper flyleaf and nothing else. In another, Wood 686(1), he forgot to complete a table of contents within his red chalk guidelines, writing only '1 B', the item number and the first letter of the title. He also omitted the Arabic numbers on the title pages. Practically all of Wood's lists of contents survive today. In two cases where they do not, at [MS.] Wood C. 32(1) and [MS.] Wood D. 31(1), the lists were probably removed to hide thefts of item (4) and items (43-44) from the volumes. After the numbering, Wood sent the tied up bundle off to his binder with specific instructions.

These specific instructions were to insure that the printed materials and his marginal annotations were not in any way damaged. He knew very well that binders would maximize profit and at the same time produce handsome volumes of calf with evenly cut side and fore-edges. They did this by cramming items of slightly different formats such as large quartos and small quartos into as small a binding as possible, saving costs on calf skin, tooling, and sewing, and then by cutting the edges evenly. Any original pastedowns or flyleaves, especially those with annotations, could be removed and replaced with clean leaves. Examples of this can be seen in almost any collection of seventeenth-century books, including those in the Bodleian Library and those formerly in the Ashmolean Museum. This practice caused horrendous damage. Some printed material on the top, bottom, inner and outer margins, as well as manuscript annotation in these areas, was routinely destroyed in every volume in the Wood collection that was later bound by the Ashmolean Museum. This type of mutilation is almost non-existent in Wood volumes where, almost certainly at Wood's instructions, the binders did not cut the fore-edges and of course retained his initial flyleaves with the tables of contents. The binders thereby preserved wide margins of space in the text, saved all the printed material and, vitally important to Wood, all marginal manuscript notes.[37]

From 1681 to 1695 Wood sent 295 bundles of letterpress to binders in batches to be bound in composite volumes. He did this whenever he had extra money and could afford the cost. At his death he had several volumes almost ready for the binder and these were bound as such by the Ashmolean Museum after 1695. He chose two distinctive quarter-parchment bindings. He had seventy-six bound in grey pasteboard covers with a strip of parchment folded over the spine, and the majority, 189, with blue paper pasted over the grey pasteboard cover and extending to the edge of the parchment covering the spine. A final twenty-six are today quarter-calf with brown paper covering the pasteboard. There is compelling evidence that they were originally quarter-parchment with grey pasteboard covers and that these were the first volumes that the Keeper at Ashmolean Museum had bound shortly after 1695.[38] Almost all of the volumes in Wood's bindings have marbled paper for the first upper and last lower flyleaves. In those that have been rebacked,

---

[36]The first list is in Wood's proof copy of *AO*, 1.28-9, Wood 431a. The second list survives at Wood 345(11). The third list is at [MS.] Wood D. 24(4), signature I4. *Newes from Southhampton* is now at Wood 376(66). For disputation topics on sheets used as waste paper, see the Index, 'Latin disputation topics'.

[37]For a book in which large quartos were crammed into a binding designed for small quartos, see Wood 631(1-63) bound by the Ashmolean Museum. Whatever the mutilation by binders hired by the Bodleian Library, even the most damaged books are preserved in a condition superior to many early modern books bound by the British Museum, where the destruction by binders is a monument to human fallibility. Such destruction by binders was common throughout the western world until very recently. For the Wood books bound by the Ashmolean Museum, see below, pp. xlvif. and note 78, and the Index, 'Ashmolean Museum, binding'.

[38]For items that were arranged in order by Wood but bound by the Ashmolean, see notes at Wood 289(1), 345(1 and 11), 608(17 and 19), and 613(1), and below, pp. xlvif. The Ashmolean Keeper apparently sent twenty-six of Wood's pasteboard volumes to the binder after shelf-marks were entered. These begin at Wood 37, 38, and 39, and end at Wood 258 and are bound in quarter-calf (the spine is calf), and brown paper over the pasteboards. They are similar to Wood's quarter-parchment, either plain pasteboard or blue paper over the pasteboard, but are more handsome with the calf spine. Most include Wood's table of contents. These quarter-calf volumes were not likely to have been

rebound or very heavily used, these flyleaves were lost or only traces survive. Wood wanted all the items in a volume to be, if possible, even. This posed a problem if he planned to include items with different formats in a specific volume. To overcome this problem, he ordered special paper templates to be cut so that items on the same subject but in smaller formats would fit evenly in volumes. Every page of a smaller item would then be pasted on to the template so that smaller octavo items would have even margins with larger quartos, or duodecimo items would have even margins with octavos or quartos. He had this done to at least 46 items. In one case, on a quarto, Charleton's *Chorea gigantum*, in the company of two other large folios on Stonehenge, he ordered his binder Sedgley: 'Past[e] paper throughout the margin of this book to make it even with Inigo Jones –'. Sometimes this was not possible and in an octavo containing items on the life of Charles I, he had to make a cross-reference: 'The said History was published by Lestrange in fol - and therefore it cannot be bound with these things.' On a flyleaf preceding a quarto item on naval battles, Wood wrote, 'Note that an account of several sea-battles were published after his majesties restauration, but they were printed in fol. papers, & therefore they cannot come in into this vol.' [sic]. The bindings that Wood ordered were sturdy, and while many have been repaired over the centuries, they have withstood the extensive use just as well as books bound in calf by the Ashmolean Museum.[39]

Wood's record of what he paid for bindings or of certain instructions on how to bind survive in only a few volumes. An example of an early binding in pasteboard is a folio on Ireland by James Ware, Wood 415(1-2), where he wrote on the upper flyleaf, '28. March 1668. for binding this book in pastborde 1^s. to M^r [Edmund] Thorne'. On an upper flyleaf of Inigo Jones's folio on Stonehenge, with blue paper pasted over the pasteboard cover, now Wood 413(1-3), he wrote, 'Binding. 1^s-4. Sedgley'. On a slip in 516(1) he reminded the binder that the volume is 'To be sewed on bords. [/] not glewed [/] parchment on the back side'. The binder followed these instructions. Beneath the upper pastedowns on the back of the boards in Wood 504(1-4), 506(1-2), he wrote his costs, '6^d for binding to . . . Chambers 8. Nov. 1692' (there is a similar note, cropped, in Wood 505(1-5)). On a flyleaf of Wood 515(1-34) he wrote, 'Binding - 5^d. Feb. 8. an. 1689[90]' and on a flyleaf of 514(1-54), a similar note with the cost 6^d. On a flyleaf in Wood 423(1-67), a large folio, the cost is higher, 'Binding [?] 1^s – 10. Mar. 1689[90]'.[40]

The manner in which Wood had his books bound shows that he was parsimonious, careful, and methodical. He arranged by subject, ordered chronologically, and bound his books so that he would have a more efficient working library. He wrote two to eight-word descriptions of the subject matter on the white parchment spines. While most of these descriptions are today very worn and difficult to read, enough of them survive to indicate that he arranged the volumes with the spines facing outwards.[41] He could tell at a glance the subject matter from his descriptions on the spines and when he opened to the first pages his table of contents would show him what specific works were present. His arrangement into chronological order would enable him to find a particular item, say a parliament document from March 1659, in seconds. The bound volumes were far superior to having piles and bundles on shelves. Though his books were attractive, especially with the blue paper pasted over the grey pasteboard, they would not have impressed his academic visitors, even if he had had them, for scholars' libraries generally presented rows of impressive, and expensive, calf-bound volumes. His books were bound for ease of use. How he made use of these books

done by Wood for several reasons. First, they occur only within the first 258 volumes which were numbered in no methodical subject order, by size mainly, by the librarians after Wood's death. If Wood had done them, he would have done so as they were arranged on his shelves and the twenty-six bindings would have ranged from Wood 1 to Wood 899. Second, some of the volume numbers, e.g., Wood 167, Wood 242, are obscured by the brown paper folded over the inside of the pasteboard. Thus they were rebound after the library was arranged in order, 1-899. Finally, many volumes show some disturbance where the calf folds on the inside of the pasteboard – there are indications that a former cover over the spine was removed. While Wood on some occasions had bound volumes rebound, this rebinding was on a grander scale. It is likely that the Keeper was not happy with the quarter-calf and stopped at Wood 258 and turned to full-calf bindings. See Append. IV, note 2.

[39]For items with templates, see Append. IV, note 9. For Charleton, see Wood 413(2). In Wood 244(1,4) the folio single sheets could not at all fit into this octavo of four items. The quarto on naval battles is at Wood 503(36). Yet the preceding 2 items, (34-35), were 'fol. papers' and had to be folded 5 times to fit into this quarto volume. At least one large single sheet was removed and is now at Wood 276a(548).

[40]Wood 216(3) has on a lower flyleaf of recycled waste paper, '1671. 1^s.3^d. stitcht' but this does not refer to the volume Wood 216, since it contains a work published in 1672. Wood 246(1) has a probable payment to Sedgley of 2^d. Wood 747(1) has the binding date, on a lower flyleaf, 'Jun 1 1687', in pencil.

[41]Wood followed the practice of Henry Foulis, who had written titles on the spines of books which Wood bought. See Wood 232(2). For examples of Wood's inscriptions, which are not generally recorded in this catalogue, see notes at Wood 862(1) and [MS.] Wood B. 31. Some libraries, including the Bodleian, shelved some books with the spines to the inside. Shelf-marks were written on the fore-edges. Wood's fore-edges were not trimmed and he could not write subjects on them. See the Index, 'Wood, A., binding' and 'Spines'.

is made clear by his annotations in them.

How Wood Read his Books

Anthony Wood created his library primarily to gain information about persons associated with the city and university of Oxford. His newsbooks, almanacs, catalogues, maps, university orders and regulations, literary works, biographies, scholarly works on history and theology, and parliamentary and government studies all served this purpose and these account for eighty-five per cent, or almost 6000, of his printed items. His ballads, books on marvels, murders, executions, and sensational events account for fifteen per cent or the remaining 1000 printed items. His annotations in the major part of his collection define his interests clearly and show what and how he read. When Wood read for pleasure and recreation, he would annotate wherever he found information about people that might be of value for his main work.

Some of his earliest acquisitions, schoolbooks, show the earliest annotations, a form of his signature, usually a simple 'Anthony Wood'. Three of the four items with his book-plate are in these early schoolbooks, but he discontinued the use of a book-plate perhaps because it was a frill. From 1648 to 1658 he often added his college to his signature, as in [MS.] Wood D. 21(2), 'Anthōy Woode Mertō Coll: 1658'. During the rest of his life he made use of a number of alternative signatures, AW (separate or as a monogram), A. Wood, Antonius Wood, Anthony Wood, or AB (for Antonius Bosco) and never maintained a consistent form. Among the more impressive and certainly one that makes a statement about himself are the Latinate forms of 'ABosco' in Wood 87(1) or '1. Aug. 1681 Bought of Tho. Vicars a stationer newlie set up on Holywell – 1ˢ-6ᵈ ABosco' in Wood 88 or the more bizarre, 'ABosco, Bellositanus', that is, of Oxford, in Wood 296. The formal and pretentious addition of à appears some time after 1660, as in Wood 19, 'Anton. à Wood 1661 è bib. B. Holydaii' (inscribed after 1661); Wood 126, 'Anthony Wood [/] 1667 [/] Ant: à Wood'; Wood 32, 'A. à Wood 26. Aprilis 1677 1ˢ - 6ᵈ'; and Wood 67, '7. Aug. 1681. Given to me by Will. Bernard M.A. fellow of Mert. coll. [/] Ant. à Bosco'. In several books he altered earlier signatures by adding the à between his Christian and surname, as in Wood 10(1): 'Ant: à [added later] Woode: Jan: 21: A.D. 1659[60]: // pret: 5ˢ-6ᵈ:'. Some of his friends were intimidated enough to adopt this latter form, as the inscriptions from John Aubrey and Thomas Blount show: 'For Mʳ Anthony à Wood.' after which Wood wrote, 'Received from Mʳ Jo. Aubrey 15 May 1682. at Oxōn' and 'Antonii à Wood ex dono Tho. Blount interioris Templi. Maij 1670.' Arthur Charlett would have none of that and wrote Wood's name only once on the thirteen that he gave or transmitted to him: 'For Mʳ Wood.'[42]

Wood was a careful reader who responded actively to the text before him. For all of his love of print, he was far from accepting the printed word as truth. He never read without a pencil, red chalk, or ink pen in his hand and the first thing he did was to note the date of publication and the name of the author or translator or editor, generally by underscoring or a mark in the margin. If either were unknown, he tried to supply information. Sometimes the identification of authors was easy. Spenser's *Shepheardes Calender* (1586) he noted, 'is set downe in Bodlies catalogue under the letters E. K, but Edm. Spen[s]er was the authour as tis generally knoune'. At other times it was more difficult. In many of his printed items he wrote tentative identifications, and his 'q' or 'qu' for *quaere* or query is the most common note. At James Harrington, *A Discourse* (1659), the author is mentioned on the last page, but Wood wanted further assurance, 'Qu[aere] whether he be the true author -'. In *The Privileges of the University of Oxford*, there were three possible authors, John Fell, Robert Waring, whom Wood first thought the author, and Richard Allestree, whom Wood settled on as the author. In the *Privileges*, he wrote, 'Written as tis said by Mʳ John Fell student of Christchurch. & Rich. Allestrie of the same, student. But qu[aere]'. He pasted a slip over this and later wrote 'Rich Allestrie', who may well have had some part in the composition. In a book signed by the pseudonymous 'Rodolphus', Wood wrote: 'Charles Croke a yonger son of Unton Croke of Merston neare Oxon (made sergeant at law by Oliver protector) was the author of the book following, entit. Fortunes uncertainty &c', and 'qu[aere] whether not judge Crokes son of Merston neare Oxon' and a brief answer, in red ink, both of which he later crossed out. On p. 7, he added more details about Croke, e.g., 'Dr. Charls Croke, I think somtimes of Ch.Ch. afterwards mini[st]er of Amers[h]am in Bucks.' Some pieces of this puzzle, never fully resolved, eventually found their way into the *Fasti*. On the title page of Alicia D'Anvers's *Academia*, he gave the author's background, 'daugh. of Sam. Clarke sometimes superior

---

[42]For his schoolbooks, see note 15, above; Append. III; and Index, 'Wood, A., schoolbooks'. For his book-plates, see Index, 'Wood, A., book-plates'. Clark believed some book-plates were mutilated and the use discontinued because they did not have an 'à' between Anthony and Wood. Clark gave a number of different forms and more examples of Wood's signature in *LT*, 1.21-23. Wood tried a blind stamp, a crude 'A W', on a single calf volumes, see p. xxiv and note 32. For more examples of 'ABosco', see Index, 'Wood, A., signatures'. For inscriptions from Aubrey, Blount, and Charlett, see Wood 204, Wood 188, and [MS.] Wood B. 36(10), items 3625, 987, 5153.

Beadle of Law in Oxon, & wife of Knightly Danvers somtimes scholar of Trin. Coll. son of Dr Dan. Danvers a physitian living neare Banbury in Oxfordshire – [/] First exposed to sale at Oxon. 14. Mar 1690[1]'.[43]

He asked friends or acquaintances such as Andrew Allam, John Aubrey, Thomas Barlow, and Arthur Charlett for information about anonymous works and he often recorded their opinions though he rarely accepted any information without further inquiry. In an anonymous *Mercurius Hibernicus* he wrote, 'Jam. Howell the author so D^r [Thomas] Barl[ow] sed qu[aere]'. In the anonymous *Alter Britanniae heros*, Wood concluded, 'Edw. Walsingham the author. qu[aere] p. 24.', because a poem on page 24 was by him. He consulted Barlow on this and was misinformed: 'written by Hen. Walsingham a Rom. Cath. & under-secretary to the Lord Georg Digby princ. secr. of State – so D^r Th. Barlow, but his name was Edw.' In one of his copies of *Tragi-comoedia Oxoniensis*, Wood wrote the correct author 'A D: 1648 [/] By Adam Littleton student of Ch.ch [/] Dr Barlow saith it was written by Joh. Carrick of the same house'. In his second copy, a gift from John Aubrey, Aubrey surmised 'This was writt (as I take it) by one . . . Cradock a (young) Student of Christ-church.' Wood had been told the name of the author of the anonymous *Of the Torments of Hell* but had to verify, 'The Torments of Hell was answer'd by Joh. Brandon. I have been informed that the Torments of Hell was written by one Sam. Richardson an Anabapt. [/] qu[aere] of Mr All[am]'.[44]

As the above examples indicate, Wood was tenacious in trying to determine authors of anonymous works. His phrase, 'Said to be writ by', is common on title pages and indicates the beginning of a search. On his first try in the anonymous anti-parliamentary work, *A Letter from a Student at Oxford* (1681) he wrote: 'This pamphlet is misliked by the house (commons) & have desired the Vicech. to make inquiry after the author, that he might be punished - But it was not writ by a scholar'. He later learned, 'This pamphlet was written by White Kennett (Cantianus) a Battler of 3 years standing of Edmund hall. Oxon.' He failed to identify the author of *The Gentlemans Companion* (1676) which he acquired in the year of its publication and his note on a flyleaf shows his initial method of search: 'The Authour A gentleman borne, & of an an[c]ient & honorable family. - v. pag. 3. Hath writ another book beside this, vide p. 100. in marg. No papist, - p. 36. 37. &c Nor no Fanatick p. 39 &c. A Cambridg man p 132' . He failed to discover the author of a satire on the university, *Sundry Things*, but dismissed the current suspect, 'Reported to be written by Joh. Wagstaff of Oriel Coll. but false.' We are no closer to identifying the author today. In a scurrilous pamphlet by some disaffected patron of a public house, Wood gave all the details on the last page, 'This pamphlett that was made one [i.e., on] Joane Fisher wife of Hen: Fisher somtimes Manciple & Butler of Queens Coll: Oxōn & who now sells Ale overaganst [sic] the said Coll: came out in February or the beginning of March A. D. 1660[1]', and later, he added in red ink, 'Tho. Hyde 2^d libr.-keeper was supposed to be the author, but false'. The author remains anonymous. Wood was wrong when he wrote on a title page that George Hickes was the author of *History of Passive Obedience*, though it was a good guess for Hickes wrote on the subject. He hedged later in his *Athenae* with 'The said History was said to be written by Dr. Geor. Hickes'.[45]

He went through the same sort of processes when trying to identify names reduced to initials in collections of poems or in ballads, or when trying to identify persons whose Christian names were not given in various kinds of lists or in political or theological items. University squabbles and city scandals in which there were generally many unidentified references to persons or the extensive use of initials were challenges to Wood. He wanted to know who did what to whom. The whys were not of as much interest to him and he made relatively few comments analyzing a particular person's stance in an argument. The internal quarrels between the President at Magdalen in 1663, Thomas Pierce and his ally John Dobson, and the expelled Henry Yerbury, for example, prompted extensive notes and identifications of persons in the publications in that year. Wood recounted the facts of the case and though his colouring of certain parties is clear enough, his comments are descriptive, not analytic. In one of the items, *Dr. Pierce his Preaching Exemplified in his*

[43]For the *Shepheardes Calender*, [MS.] Wood C. 17(1). For Harrington, Wood 626(16). For the *Privileges*, Wood 514(33) and see also Wood 514(35) where Wood assumed the author of the *Privileges* to be Waring; he later pasted a slip over this. For 'Rodolphus', Wood 155(3) and *AOF*, 2.129. For D'Anvers, Wood 517(6).

[44]For *Mercurius Hibernicus*, Wood 508(50). For *Alter Britanniae heros*, Wood 535(10). For the *Tragi-comoedia*, Wood 514(52). For Aubrey's note, Wood 615(21). For *Torments*, by Richardson, Wood 788(1).

[45]'Said to be writ by' or close variants are to be found in Wood 888(2), 893(1), and [MS.] Wood D. 26(14). For the book by Kennett, Wood 632(56). Kennett had already in 1681 supplied Wood with information about churchmen in Kent. For *Gentlemans Companion* by William Ramesey, Wood 752(4). For *Sundry Things*, Wood 515(22). For Joan Fisher, Wood 515(26). For the *History of Passive Obedience* referred to in a pamphlet by J. Parkinson, Wood 517(5), item 5135, and *AO*, 4.572. The author was Abednego Seller. For wrong guesses, see Wood 574(3), 620(17), and 818(1); and for corrections of earlier guesses, Wood 645(21) and Wood 811.

Practice, he described: 'The said Dr Yerbury saith also in his said answer (which was in ms only) that the second libell which followes was either made or approved of by Dr Pierce before mentioned, as it appeared by certaine reflections from Dobsons confession [/] Dr Yerbury also in ms. answer, doth cleer those things laid against him therein, viz his cringing to Cromwells vicechanc. when he was incorporated D^r of Phys. in Oxon. 1658 – see in the libell followinge p. 7. Also to cleer what is said of his endeavours to frustrate the letters of the king in behalf of Dr Pierce, when he was to be elected president – Also the supposed cheates & defraudating [sic], & unstatutable accompts relating to the coll.' This served as a draft for his entry on Pierce in the *Athenae* where the description is clearer, more reserved and more favourable to Yerbury. Wood's mole for all this inside information was a friend at Magdalen. He recorded in his diary on 12 October 1663 shortly after these publications appeared: 'with John Drope at the Meermaid Tavern'. City affairs could also prompt extensive identifications. A locally published ballad records the exploits of 'a notorious cheater one Robert Bullock, lately done in Oxford'. Wood owned two copies, the only ones known to exist, and made a dozen similar annotations in each, identifying names, places, and concluded with the name of the author and date of publication: 'viz Francis Shenton a drunken and broken apothecary living in the parish of S. Pet. in the Baylie .. this cheat was committed in Nov. 1663 & in the same month this ballad was published'. No one knew Oxford better than Wood.[46]

Particular kinds of documents provided him with particular kinds of information, and while the main objective of his reading is clear, to find information for his histories and bio-bibliographical entries, his annotations are varied enough to indicate that he read different types of material in different ways.

His immersion in Oxford affairs is shown by his notes on Encaenia and determination programmes. He attended these and his responses to both music and speeches in a pre-encaenia ceremony in 1672, *In laudem musices carmen Sapphicum* are typical: 'These verses were made by Dr John Fell Deane of Ch. Ch. Dispersed among the people in the Theater before the Encaenia began, 5 July 1672. Afterwards spoken from the Musick Gallery by [blank, John] Panker* a commoner of Ch. Ch. then (so much of it that is printed in Ital. character) sung by severall there present: the composition of which musick was performed by M^r [blank, i.e., Henry Aldrich] Alridge Student of Ch. Ch. It was well performed & gave great content.', and for the note reference '*or Penkhurst'. He had a second copy of this programme and copied, with some refinements, his notes into that copy. Such information did not find its way into the *Athenae*, but it provided essential background. On ten of his Encaenia programmes he recorded his personal responses to speakers and the music. On the 1674 programme, for example, he judged the speeches: at that of George Rainsford he wrote, 'Well'; at Ambrose Brown, 'Well'; at Richard Russell, 'Well, in the middle of the Theatre'; at James Parkinson, 'verie well, expelled from CCColl the Lent going before'; at Anthony Carey, viscount Falkland, 'verie well, in the middle'; at Thomas Newport 'much like a man, but his voice a little too low'; at Thomas Herbert, the earl of Pembroke, 'He spoke indifferently well but understood not what he said'; after Pembroke, 'a little crash of instrumentall musick.'; at Philip Percival, 'Well'; and then the entertainment, 'musick both vocall & instrumentall for above half an houre, of Mr. Aldriges [Henry Aldrich] compos.'; at the 'Vitae instituendae delectus', 'Lord Falkland againe verie well but his voice a little harsh because in breaking'; at Thomas Moorer, 'verie well but too fast'; and, at Robert Tracey, 'so so & too long in the middle'. In 1681 and 1695 he noted in his programme of the determinations on Egg-Saturday the number of bachelors who skipped the ceremony: '# Those names that have this marke # put after them, were not presented on Egg-Saturday 12 Feb. 1680[1]. – All these Bachelaurs were to determine from Thursday 17 Feb to 7. Mar. 1680 because the King was to come soon after, & the Parliament was to sit 21. March – The Divinity School was made use of this Lent, because the Astronomie, Geometrie & Greek Schooles, were making ready for the Lords to sit in – However their names were here put downe – 200 bach. wanting 8.' Wood kept abreast of what was going on in every facet of the university.[47]

---

[46]For other identifications, see, e.g., authors of verses and wrong information given, e.g., by A. Charlett, see Wood 108, 514(53), or 517(4); for an index, identifications of Oxford vs. non-Oxford persons, etc., see [MS.] Wood E. 27(5); for identifications in ballads, Wood 417(66 and 167); for identification of tracts by R. L'Estrange, Wood 417(20), 422(17), 428(15). Most of his catalogues are filled with scores of identifications. The two main works in the Pierce Yerbury controversy were N. G.'s *Dr. Pierce his Preaching Confuted* (by J. Dobson) and the anonymous *A True Accompt of the Proceedings* (by T. Pierce) (1663) (Wood 515(27, 28a-b) and Wood 633(5-7)). See *AO*, 4.304. See also Madan, 2644-6. For Wood's diary entry, and the 6^d he paid for drinks, *LT*, 1.501. For the Shenton ballad, Wood 401(100) and 402(23); for the latter see fig. 2 in N. Kiessling, 'The Location of Two Lost Volumes of Ballads, Wood 399 and Wood 400', *BLR*, 15 (April 1996): 267; and *LT*, 1.504-6.

[47]For the two copies of the pre-Encaenia ceremony, Wood 276a(534) and Wood 423(48). He made similar comments in the Encaenia programmes of 1675-7, 1679-84 and 1693. In 1678 there was no Encaenia scheduled and, perhaps for that reason, he took this time to go to Bath to find a cure for his loss of hearing. The Monmouth rebellion forced a cancellation of Encaenia in 1685. For the determination of 1681, Wood 276b(54) and a duplicate with his first draft

His notes on other Oxford items generally were brief, and most were simply the year of publication. When an issue might directly concern him, he would give more detail. Several of his eleven single sheets on the Oxford to London stage coach, all of which exist only in the Wood collection, were prompted by unwanted competition from a private company. A 'one day stage-coach' was started in 1671 and Wood noted on one of the single sheets, 'This coach was silenced by the Vicechanc: [Peter Mews] Order stuck up on every corner in Oxōn Apr: 15. 1671. because it was set up without his leave'. Another issue of concern was the 'Prizes of wines' which were set by the Vice-Chancellor, Ralph Bathurst. Wood wrote the year, '1673', on the single sheet and commented on the new price of Canary wines (2 shillings the quart), 'Before for severall yeares at 2^s.2^d. to the great resentment of all: who to make even money would either spend more or give the Drawer the rest. This price was raised upon pretence of carriage.' French wine was a shilling a quart, and he wrote, 'Before for severall years 1^s.1^d.' Thus many of the annotations on Oxford items were personal as well as professional.[48]

His annotations in historical and biographical publications were more related to his work on the *Historia* and later to the *Athenae*. Several of the more valuable of these are his three copies of Francis Godwin, *A Catalogue of the Bishops of England* (1601 and 1615, in English, and 1616, in Latin); James Ware, *De praesulibus Hiberniae* (1665); Brian Twyne, *Antiquitatis academiae Oxoniensis apologia* (1608), and John Weever, *Ancient Funerall Monuments* (1631). Godwin provided him with vital information about over half the bishops in England who were graduates of Oxford colleges. His favoured edition was the Latin of 1616 which came from a line of three distinguished former owners, Godwin himself, then 'Gulielmi Camdeni ex dono authoris. Martii 23. 15[i.e., 1616]', and then Brian Twyne. There are notes in half a dozen hands in this edition and Wood himself was responsible for scores of them and for an equal number of slips; on p. 593 he pasted seven slips with his notes, five of which are visible on Plate II, including one with his reference to 'Archb. Heath see in Dr Allens answer to the libell of English justice. p. 50. I have it with a black cover'. Other of Wood's notes, many lengthy, offer clarification, offer information on individuals such as their publications and epitaphs, provide references to his own *Historia*, or correct and identify Godwin's sources, e.g., 'sed haec habes e Twyno in Apol. Lib. 2. 282' (i.e., *Antiquitatis academiae Oxoniensis apologia*). The various forms of Wood's handwriting indicate that he returned to this book continuously over a long period of time.[49] He referred several times to his other edition, 'my English copie', that is, to the 1615 or 1601 edition. He made extensive use of the 1615 edition after he acquired it in 1658 from the sale of books from the estate of Gerard Langbaine, who had also made annotations. Wood was not one to accept the latest edition as the best and recorded his reservations about the accuracy of this 1615 edition in his edition of 1601: 'Another edition (with additions) of this English Cat. of Bishops came out in 1615, but being very full of faults, & not to be endured by a tolerable reader, the authour forthwith put it into Latine, & was printed the next yeare', and added later, 'This Engl. Edition I often use, when I mistrust matters related in the 2^d edit.' The 1601 edition was a gift from Ralph Sheldon and though Wood may have often used it, he wrote no other notes in it.

Ware's *De praesulibus Hiberniae* served exactly the same purpose as Godwin's history of English bishops and the annotations are similar, as his notes on an upper flyleaf reveal: 'Irish Bishops that I guess to have been Oxon men from 1501. to this present, which hereafter may be inserted in Athenae Oxōn, when I find good proofe for them', followed by dioceses, names of bishops, death dates and page references of those who had Oxford connections. He went through the book carefully, added slips with information and made customary underscorings, marks in margins, and notes, mainly biographical details such as college membership and quotations from epitaphs. He had the earlier edition and noticed an inconsistency between that and the current edition on p. 150: 'James Ware in his book de presul. Lageniae, which is but the first edition of this – saith that Jonas Wheeler was borne in Devon. – In this Edit. Oxoniensis – I have searchd matric. books for his name, & I can not find his name – nor any degree he took'. Wood was unable to clarify the issue as his entry in the *Athenae* shows: 'He was born in Oxfordshire, as 'tis said, particularly, as I suppose, within the city of Oxon'.[50]

---

of the above, Wood 276a(383); the 1695 programme is at Wood 276b(54).

[48] The single sheet on the London carrier is Wood 276a(363), and on wine, Wood 276a(372); for the latter see also *LT*, 2.281-2.

[49] Godwin is at Wood 344, and [MS.] Wood D. 21(1 and 2); Ware, Wood 415(1); Twyne, Wood 602; and Weever, Wood 414(1). William Allen's book with a black cover has since been rebound in calf, Wood 878. For Archbishop Nicholas Heath, see *AO*, 2.817-20. Wood's hand changed dramatically after 1660. For his early hand, see Plates V, VI and X; for his hand in 1665, see Plate XI.

[50] *De praesulibus* is at Wood 415(1). See also p. xxiv and note 33, above. The earlier edition is at Wood 343(1). See also *AO*, 2.890-1.

Wood acquired Brian Twyne's *Apologia* from the estate of Gerard Langbaine and Langbaine's notes are present. Shortly after he bought it, he had the volume rebound with interleaved blank leaves at the end which he used for notes. He also added seven slips, underscored, made marks in the margins, referred to Twyne manuscripts, and added entries in the index. He noted some omissions by Twyne, as 'There is alsoe another provost that Mr Twine hath omitted in his foregoing Catalouge [sic]' (see Plates IV-VI). His notes in Weever's *Ancient Funerall Monuments* are not extensive, but he owned it at least since 1661 and went through the book carefully more than once. On a slip attached to the upper flyleaf, Wood wrote what he knew about Weever. Most he gleaned from the book itself: 'Joh. Weever borne in Lancashire 1577 of Queens Coll. – Camb. p. 500. 864. Travelled p. 568 144. 150 217 647 Especially in Engl. & part of Scotland, epistl. p. 2 - p. 358. Rector of Le[o]snes p. 337. 778 - qu[aere] He dyed 1632. aged about 56 burial at Clarkenwell – Stowe Survey p. 900 [for the epitaph on tomb] of low stature p. 528'. He wrote at Weever's reference to Camden's monument in Westminster Abbey, 'Near to him lies buried Isaac Casaubon, who died Kal. Jun. 1614 t. 54', and made some corrections at Weever's copy of a verse to Camden, which he probably checked against the original in Westminster Abbey. Wood read through histories with pen in hand, marking details, writing notes to himself in the margins and inserting slips of information garnered from other sources, all to be incorporated into his own writings.

The two most marked up books in his collection were proof copies of his own publications, the *Historia* and *Athenae*. In the *Historia* he wrote well over a thousand annotations, many over 100 words in length. He read and reread and made annotations over a period of time, for notes on the same page are often in different shades of brown ink and in his different handwriting styles. They range from simple emendations and corrections, new information, especially updated information on Oxford alumni, to angry comments. What prompted most of the latter, and the preparation of a final manuscript appendix, 'Faults without comparing with the Engl. Either omitted in the transl. or in writing the orig.', were the deletions, additions and changes made by Dr. John Fell, with whom he began his quarrel in a thirty-four word manuscript response on the first page and continued on the next pages. He wrote 'Dr. Fell', or forms thereof, twenty-five times in the margins on the first thirteen pages. After that Fell's name or 'D^r F' reappears time and again, with lessening frequency, almost to the very end of the second volume. The most notorious example of Fell's editing occurs at the written portrait of Thomas Hobbes, which prompted a single sheet printed letter of rejoinder by Hobbes. Hobbes had learned of Fell's editing from John Aubrey, via Wood himself, and even though Wood was not an admirer of Hobbes, it must have been with the greatest pleasure that Wood was able to insert Hobbes' letter in most copies of the *Historia*. Wood had shown his copy of the letter to Fell and Fell did not make a fuss, but when Fell learned that Wood had inserted the letter in the *Historia*, he reacted quickly and took advantage of a printing situation which Wood described in a later account, 'the last sheet of paper being then in the presse, and one leafe thereof being left vacant, the deane supplied it with his answer'. Other corrections concerned errors by compositors some of which Wood must have himself brought to the attention of the proof-readers at the press, for he wrote in the margin, 'mended in all copies'. When he arrived at the press too late and could not correct, he wrote in the margin, 'false in 200 sheets'. He could do nothing about the errors or what he believed to be deliberate mistranslations by Richard Peers whom Fell employed to render Wood's English into Latin; nor about errors in font by a stubborn compositor who would not follow Wood's use of italics.[51]

In his copy of the *Athenae* he made thousands of minor corrections on almost every page of the text from the time of publication of the two volumes in 1691 and 1692 until his death in 1695. He also pasted in nearly as many slips, some with a few words, and some with several hundred, to indicate major changes or additions, and a few letters from friend and foe. Some of the slips with corrections or new material for the new edition are on recycled paper and contain matters of interest in their former functions. One, for example, is a slip torn from a sheet once intended as a list of contents for (currently) Wood 752. Another is a piece from the title page of *Poemation Latinum* by Francis Digby which he saved for the information to be inserted in the second edition of the *Athenae*. He knew of a Francis Digby who was a graduate of Queen's College in 1677.[52]

---

[51]The *Historia* and *Athenae* are at Wood 430-1. The portrait of Hobbes is at *Historia*, 2.376-7. Wood did not insert Fell's rebuttal of Hobbes, normally after p. [448], 'Quarundam literarum', into his own proof copy. Clark gives a detailed account of the whole matter, *LT*, 2.259-61, 290-94; see also notes at Wood 276a(18), another copy of Hobbes' letter. There were two translators, but Wood did not mention the second, Richard Reeves, in the marginalia. The convention at the time was to set quotations in italics, see Wood's note at Wood 614(21), item 1849.

[52]For the torn slip, see *AO*, 1.28-9. For the Digby slip, see pp. xix-xx and note 24. The latter is unrecorded unless it is ESTCR 31191 (publication date, '1715?'). Wood stopped short of assigning the work to the Digby of Queen's writing only that 'There is extant Poemation Latinum Authore Franc. Digby' and following that with lines of Perseus printed below the title (*AOF*, 2.360).

His annotations in other historical and biographical publications indicate that he scanned these for material on Oxford persons that could be of use to him for his own work. In Nicholas Bernard's *The Life & Death of . . . James Usher* he wrote a thirty-one line entry on the death and funeral of Ussher, 21 March - 17 April 1656, which he used almost verbatim for the *Athenae*.[53] Ireland interested him no doubt because his older brother, fighting on the royalist side, was killed there, and also because persons associated with the university had served in Ireland. James Butler, the first duke of Ormonde, was the most important of these. Ormonde had been closely involved with Irish politics since 1633. After being defeated by Cromwell's armies in 1650 he went into exile. With the restoration he received numerous honors and titles, most importantly to Wood he became Chancellor of Oxford University in 1669. Hence Wood had good reason to acquire sixteen publications by or about Ormonde. A grand reception was planned for the arrival of the Chancellor at Oxford on 4 August 1677 and he came, as Wood himself saw, with 'fourteen coaches or more'. The duke was entertained at a convocation in the Sheldonian Theatre on 6 August and Wood made notes in his programme, *Comitia philologica*: after the second of 4 speeches, 'Musick vocall & instrumentall'; at Jo. Percival (Christ Church), 'very well & much like a man.'; and, at the end, 'After these speeches were done the Orator concluded'. Butler was eventually succeeded as Chancellor by his grandson, James Butler, the second duke of Ormonde.[54]

For the best bibliographers it is essential to have a printed item in hand in order to discuss it intelligently. Wood understood this perfectly and for this reason acquired all he could by and about Oxford figures. His vignettes of two distinguished Oxford persons, William Laud and William Prynne, and of a third whom he associated with Oxford, John Milton, and his notes in books by and about them in his collection offer a perspective of how Wood read his printed items. Laud, the archbishop of Canterbury from 1633, served as Chancellor of Oxford University from 1630 to 1641 when he was forced to resign, and his statutes, begun even before his appointment as Chancellor, were an integral part of a plan to reestablish the university as a model for discipline, integrity and excellence, to reform the academic programmes, to expand the library, and to establish an academic press. For these reasons, and for his being the martyred archbishop of Canterbury, Wood held Laud in the highest regard and made the following comparison in the *Athenae*: 'Plutarch, if he were alive, would be much troubled to find a sufficient parallel wherewith to match him in all the lineaments of perfect virtue.' Between 1692 and 1695 Wood expanded his entry on Laud from three printed folio columns in the 1691-2 edition so that it came to sixteen columns in the posthumous 1721 edition.

He collected some twenty-four publications by or about Laud including one of his most prized possessions, a thirty-six page pamphlet owned by Laud himself, *Romes Master-peece* (1643). After Laud's death it had come into the hands of Richard Bayly, President of St. John's college, who died in 1667. Wood obtained it in 1675. The pamphlet is an attempt to link Laud with the papists by an anonymous author whom Laud identified on the title page as William Prynne. On the verso of the title page Wood wrote, 'All the scorings in this book, & written notes in the margin thereof, were made & done by that blessed Martyr Dr Will. Laud Archb. of Canterb. while he was a prisoner in the Tower of London'. Wood later lent this pamphlet to Henry Wharton who published it in 1695, with Laud's notes, in a volume of writings by Laud. In his entry on Laud and again in his entry on Prynne in the *Athenae* Wood told the story of Prynne obtaining a warrant in 1643 to enter Laud's cell in the Tower to confiscate any papers. 'Prynne rushing suddenly into the archbishop's chamber before he was stiring from his bed, went directly to his breeches lying by his bedside, and thrusting his hands into his pockets with very great impudence, took thence the said *Diary*.' Prynne then edited and published the diary, *A Breviate of the Life*, and Wood wrote a number of notes in his copy critical of the way Prynne edited. He commented on Prynne's additions to the manuscript text on ten different pages, e.g.: 'By which it appears that there be some envious matters of your owne put in', and 'This is of Prynns putting & not in the Diary – envious reflections'; on his attempts to sway the reader: 'Prynne put this in a larg character to make the reader believe it some scandalous matter', 'Prynne puts this in another charact. to make it envious', and 'What is the meaning that this is put in another char[acter]?'; and on his lack of precision and on misstatements. Wood cited Prynne's edition of the diary

---

[53] *AO*, 4.799-800. Wood's last manuscript sentence in the Bernard biography (Wood 307(5)) is, 'where, after the said Dr. Bernard had preached over most of this book, he was there interred', and the entry in *AO* is 'Where after the said Dr. Bernard had preached before the large auditory a sermon, it was inter'd.'

[54] Wood's notes in the *Comitia philologica* programme are at Wood 276a(406a). For Wood's description of Ormonde's arrival, see *LT*, 2.385. Other publications on the reception are: *Orders for the Reception of . . . James, Duke of Ormond*, Wood 276a(324) and *Comitia philologica, habita Aug. 6 Anno 1677. In gratulatione solenni ob adventum expectatissimum . . . Jacobi Ormondiae ducis*, Wood 423(53). For other notes on Ormonde, see Wood 202(2), Wood 235(5), Wood 426(33), Wood 552. Ormonde retired to the earl of Clarendon's home in Cornbury, near Charlbury, but moved to Kingston Hall, Dorsetshire, when Clarendon returned to his home in early 1687.

in the Laud entry in his *Athenae*, commented on the 'rascally notes and diabolical reflections thereon', and summarized his criticisms of Prynne's editing: 'neither entire, nor faithfully, . . . but altered, mangled, corrupted and glossed in a most shameful manner; accompanied with desperate untruths'. He described the same diary in the Prynne entry, 'published purposely to make him odious to the vulgar sort of people, yet the rational part, I mean those persons that were not guided by presbyterian clamours, entertained other kind of thoughts of the archbishop than they had before.'[55]

Wood's entry on William Prynne in the *Athenae*, sixteen folio columns in the 1691-2 edition and twenty columns in the 1721 edition, offers a sharp contrast to that on Laud. To Wood, Prynne represented religious non-conformity and political rebellion and Wood found him on the wrong side of most issues during the interregnum. If Wood was not sympathetic to Prynne's political or religious arguments, he nevertheless dealt thoroughly with Prynne because he was an alumnus of Oriel College, a scholar familiar with manuscript collections, and a prolific writer. Wood's exhaustive entry is an excellent example of his thoroughness, if not fairness, and illustrates common features in his vignettes: sharp and graphic characterization, basic information about birth, education, position and death, evaluations of publications by contemporaries and by the subject himself. Wood made no effort to hide his royalist and Anglican perspective. Thus we read that the 'hot-spirited' Prynne whose 'impudent' actions earned him nothing but trouble was 'fined 5000^l. to the king, to lose the remainder of his ears in the pillory, to be branded on both cheeks with the letters S. L. for a schismatical libeller, and to be perpetually imprison'd in Caernarvan castle'. Prynne's fortunes changed when the Long Parliament came into power, and the 'blessed house of commons (as by the said godly party it was called)' ordered that he be released. He was soon after elected to 'that most unhappy parliament' where he 'could scarce take quiet rest till he had fetch'd off his [Laud's] head, in requital of his ears'. Prynne's speeches in favour of the restoration of the king earned him the keepership of the records in the Tower. Wood, on his first research trip to London in 1667, described in his 'Secretum Antonii' his meeting with the older man, 'in his black taffaty-cloak, edg'd with black lace at the bottom', who 'received him [Wood] with old fashion complements, such as were used in the raigne of K. Jam. I. and told him he should see what he desir'd, and seemed to be glad that "such a yong man as he (A. W.) was" (for so he cal'd him) "should have inclinations towards venerable antiquity"'.

In the conclusion of his entry in the *Athenae*, Wood provided a frank summary of the 'right sturdy and doughty champion for the cause, a puritan beutifew' who showed 'great industry, but little judgment'. The 'generality of scholars' looked upon his work as 'rather rapsodical and confus'd, than any way polite or concise, yet for antiquaries, critics, and sometimes for divines, they are useful'. Wood was awed by the extensiveness of his writings, 'all which are in number near 200, . . . I verily believe, that if rightly computed, he wrote a sheet for every day of his life, reckoning from the time when he came to the use of reason and the state of man.' Wood then gave a series of critical appraisals of Prynne by, among others, 'M. Needham the weathercock' who also commented on Prynne's productivity, 'one of the greatest paper worms that ever crept into a closet or library', and by the 'papist', Serenus Cressy, who gave a severe evaluation of Prynne's anti-Catholicism. Prynne had throughout his career relentlessly attacked anything Catholic, and in Wood's view unfairly; hence he gave the final statement to Cressy. A bibliography of the almost 200 items authored by Prynne follows. Wood himself owned sixty-three books and pamphlets by and about him. Those by Prynne cover a host of matters: drinking of healths, stage-plays, the tyranny of bishops, taxes, William Laud, Nathaniel Fiennes, Denzil Holles, the right of visitation in the university, Quakers and papists (he linked the two in *New Discovery of Some Romish Emissaries, Quakers* (1656) and *The Quakers Unmasked, and Clearly Detected to be but the Spawn of Romish Frogs* (1664)), the barring of the Jews, Richard III, various current political controversies, the rights of secluded members of parliament, and the good old cause. Wood went through these in his usual way; he identified authors of anonymous tracts, made substantive annotations in certain items such as those involving Laud or Oxford, and wrote minor annotations such as corrections, dates, and brief identifications of persons referred to in the text. The most useful of all to Wood was his copy of *An Exact Catalogue of All Printed Books . . . by William Prynne*. In this he made scores of annotations, mainly of a bibliographic nature. He marked 33 items that he owned with either 'cat. 3' that is, his manuscript catalogue of 1681, or by 'habeo', I have it.[56]

---

[55]For Wood's portrait of Laud, *AO*, 3.125-6. For the copy of *Romes Master-peece*, Wood 533(6). For Prynne searching Laud's breeches, *AO*, 3.139, 849, and 859. For Laud's diary, Wood 657(7); see also *AO*, 3.138-140, and at Prynne, 3.874. On Laud and the university, see K. Fincham, 'Early Stuart Polity', in *HUO*, 4.200ff.

[56]For Prynne in *AO*, 3.845, 847-9, 852-4. For the meeting in the Tower with Prynne, *LT* 2.110. 'Beutifew' was a favourite word for Wood. He used 'boutefeu' and 'boutifieu' to describe other firebrands Denzil Holles, Henry Vane and Thomas Case, *AO*, 3.126, and 4.45, and below, see p. xxxvi and note 58. It is not surprising that Wood gave the last word to a Catholic critic. Wood's study of medieval theological history and his friendships with and interest

Wood kept an eye on John Milton because of his prominence both as a puritan writer and a literary figure. Though Milton was associated with Cambridge and not Oxford, Wood included him in his *Fasti*. His justification came from John Aubrey who affirmed to him that Milton was incorporated master of arts in 1635. This may be true, but Milton's name does not appear in any register. Wood relied on Aubrey for other information in his seven-column entry in the *Fasti* though it is far longer and more informative than Aubrey's own unfinished manuscript account of Milton in his 'Brief Lives'. Wood collected twelve works by Milton. One volume holds eight items, including four on divorce, *Areopagitica*, *Of Education*, *The Tenure of Kings*, and *Iconoclastes*. The single annotation by Wood in the volume is on the upper flyleaf where he wrote the titles of eight printed works and 'All written by Joh. Milton.' It was not unusual for Wood to leave an item unmarked even if he used it for his bio-bibliography. In this case he has summaries of all eight items in the *Fasti*. He was very much interested in Milton's expository prose and described Milton's general concern or argument in many of the twenty-nine different works that he listed. Milton's poetic achievements were another matter. Wood owned none of his poetry and did not go much beyond mentioning that 'he was an excellent poet' in his entry in the *Fasti*. He gave the abbreviated titles and years of publications of six poetic works, *Poemata* (1645), *A Mask* (1645) and *Poems* (1645) and *Poems*, &c. (1673-4), '*Paradise lost*: a poem in 10 books, Lond. 1669. qu. pr. in fol. with cuts, an. 1688'; and '*Paradise regain'd*: a poem in four books. Lond. 160. qu. pr. in fol. with cuts, an. 1688'.

Wood usually marked the name of Milton when he came across it in other printed items such as in his newsbooks and term catalogues. In his index to the term catalogues he recorded seventeen page and column references. He also noted the names of Milton's nephews, and pupils, John and Edward Phillips, the sons of Edward Phillips, an Oxonian who warranted an entry in the *Athenae*, and Milton's sister Anne. So in a collection of poets by Edward Phillips, *Theatrum Poetarum* (1675), which Wood acquired in 1681, he identified John Philips as 'the Maternal Nephew and Disciple of an Author most deserv'd of Fame late deceased'. He then named that 'author': 'John Milton a rogue', and added below, 'This Joh. Philips is yonger brother to the authour'. In a pamphlet, *A Letter from Major General Ludlow* (1691), Wood wrote on the title pages, 'Note that the pamphlets following which were put out under the name of Maj. Gen. Ludlow, were commonly reported to be written by Joh. Philipps nephew, by the mother, to John Milton the great Anti-monarchist–'. Wood did not write an unfavourable biography in the *Athenae* because he was impressed by 'this great scholar and frequent writer'. Yet he did not mince words when, in his view, Milton violated certain of his own basic presuppositions about the monarchy or the church, to say nothing of his 'very odd and novel positions concerning divorce'. Milton, Wood knew, gained his power by his publications and, 'being a man of parts, was therefore more capable than another of doing mischief . . . Had he been but honestly principled, he might have been highly useful to that [royalist] party'. Milton achieved infamy when he 'arrived at that monstrous and unparallel'd height of profligate impudence, as in print to justify the most execrable murder of him the best of kings'. Milton frequently appeared in other biographies in the *Athenae*. For example, in his entry of George Morley who at Breda conveyed thanks from the king to Claudius Salmasius for kinds words for his martyred father, Wood noted that the thanks were conveyed, 'not with a purse of gold as Joh. Milton the impudent lyer reported.'[57]

in Catholic writers in his studies led to an inquiry, including a search of his rooms, in December 1678 (see p. xxiv note 34, above), a prelude to criticisms that he favoured Catholics in the *Athenae*. Wood's Catholic informants and friends included Francis Davenport, Thomas Deane, William Joyner, Richard Reeves, William Rogers, and Ralph Sheldon. The bishop of Salisbury, Gilbert Burnet, is quoted by E. D. (believed to be Thomas Wood, but probably by Anthony himself, see note at Wood 614(7)), in *A Vindication of the Historiographer . . . from the Reproaches of the Lord Bishop of Salisbury* (London 1693): 18-19, 'That he [Anthony Wood] hath been visibly made a Tool by some of the Church of Rome, to Reproach all the greatest Men of our Church' and see above p. xiv and note 12. For the inquisition in 1679, see *LT*, 2. 424-5; for accusations that his *Athenae* was pro-Catholic, *LT*, 3. 368-9. His friends among the fanatics, Quakers, Puritans, Presbyterians, Levellers, Brownists, Independents, are fewer though they include William Sprigge, John Curteyne, and some members of his musical group. Some of Wood's notes in Prynne items were identifications of authors, e.g., he identified authors of unsigned items about Prynne, Wood 514(35 and 36); or true authors of items written by others and signed by 'Prynne', Wood 610(31); Prynne as the true author of a tract signed by another name, Wood [MS.] Wood D. 31(1 and 2); Prynne as author of an unsigned tract, Wood 367(18), Wood 613(17), Wood 613(58), and Wood 620(26, 29, 30 and 32); or identified signed authors of items, Wood 620(34). He made longer notes in items concerning Laud and Oxford, e.g., Wood 533(6), Wood 540, Wood 657(7), and Wood 514(34). The Prynne bibliography is now at [MS.] Wood D. 22(7) and Wood's catalogue of 1681 is at MS. Wood E. 2(70).

[57]His vignette is at *AOF*, 1.480-6. W. R. Parker, 'Wood's Life of Milton: Its Sources', *Papers of the Bibliographical Society of America* 52 (1958): 1-22, estimated that over half of Wood's vignette was taken from manuscript biographies of Milton written by Cyriack Skinner and John Aubrey. For the volume of eight items, [MS.] Wood B. 29(1-8), and the summaries, *AOF*, 1.482-3. For the term catalogues and the index, see text, p. xxxvi and note 59. The seventeen citations are: 'Milton Jo. 8.a. 58.b. 77.a. 89.a. 285.b. 294.a. 309.b. 73.b. 103b 173.a. 26.a. 599.a.

It was not Wood's custom to mark all the books that he read, and he had various other ways of keeping track of details such as making scores of lists and notes on slips and loose sheets. In a volume of ten pamphlets on regicides, a subject about which Wood felt deeply, he made almost no annotations. It contains, for example, *The Tryal of Sir Henry Vane*, unmarked, though Wood certainly perused this pamphlet. Henry Vane was a member of Brasenose College and warranted a long entry in the *Athenae* where Wood showed his religious and political disdain. He began the portrait with 'Henry Vane, or Sir Humerous Vanity as he was usually called' and has little good to say in the next six columns in the 1721 edition of this 'promoter of the rebellion, . . . an underminer, a jugling fellow, and a plotter to gain the estates of other persons that adhered to his majesty in the worst of times,' 'who from a presbyterian . . . became an independent, from that to be an anabaptist, and fifth monarchy-man, &c.' Vane was an incendiary in the house of commons against Laud and appears in the entry of Laud as 'a most notorious sectarist, an indefatigable boutefeu and promoter of discontents'. Regicides were the worst for Wood, but close behind were those who changed their colours to that of the party in power.[58]

Wood's extraordinary collection of 198 book catalogues were vital for they were his most reliable source of information about recent publications of authors unless he or the Bodleian Library owned the publication itself. The most important of all was his proof copy of the monumental Bodleian Library catalogue of 1674 edited by his friend Thomas Hyde. Wood annotated his proof copy extensively. While the Hyde catalogue served as his first recourse for information about a particular author, it had two limitations. It was far from a definitive reference work for publications, and it was a closed document in that nothing was added after its appearance in 1674. To find out about more obscure works published before 1674 and for anything published after 1674 he had to rely on other sources, including his rich collection of catalogues of various kinds. Wood acquired forty-three now very rare catalogues published before 1668 and in that year intensified his searches for book, auction and sale catalogues. He began a subscription to the term catalogues, *Mercurius Librarius, or, a Catalogue of Books Printed and Published*, a series issued during Hilary, Easter and Trinity (or Midsummer) terms. He had an almost complete run from 1668-1695 which he numbered 1-772. These were his major source for information on printed books, and he read them closely, making annotations throughout, mainly underscorings and marks, including 'q[uaere]', and lines in margins. He frequently wrote names of authors identified only by initials or added the names of authors to anonymous works, often wrote in a word or two of further explanation about persons or places, supplied some cross-references, and copied names or initials from the text to the margin. Some notes are longer. In an early issue he noted: 'All the [i.e., of] the Books in this term and all the following Terms are wanting in the [Bodleian] Libr. excepting those crossed'. Apparently he checked every item against the holdings in the Bodleian Library. Marks in both ink and red pencil show that he went over these lists more than once. In the first three issues he numbered items, and in the earlier years he marked almost every item in some way. His final issue, Trinity term 1695, with his page numbers, 765-771, has over thirty marks in the margin or minor underscoring and seven brief notes or cross-references. He also made a 113-page index of major figures and subjects for these term catalogues. He indexed, for example: Women, Womens advocate, womens vindications, women virtuous, Women Hist. of, Womens Rhetorick, Wom. History, Women parl. of, Women modish, women excellent. He made an entry for his own name: 'Wood Ant. 115.b [where he added his name, which was lacking, after the title of the *Historia*] 584.b. [an advertisement for the *Athenae*] 593. [an advertisement for the *Athenae*] 601.a [an advertisement for the *Athenae*] 635.b. [an advertisement for the second volume of the *Athenae*] 646.a. [a notice that fifty copies of volume two of the *Athenae* were yet unsubscribed] 669.b [*Vindication of the Historiographer* by E. D.]'. Wood kept close track of the reception of his books in a more specialized series, Jean Cornand de La Croze's *The Works of the Learned*, Aug.-April 1691-2, which contains three notices of his *Athenae*. Inside this volume Wood inserted a single sheet *Mercurius Eruditorum* for 12 August 1691 because it contained a dialogue about his newly issued volume one of the *Athenae*.[59]

617.b. 640.b. 623.b [not to Milton, but to John Melton] 650.b. 743.a. 747.b'. For a newsbook reference in *Mercurius Politicus*, see Wood 524. He also marked Milton's name in auction catalogues, [MS.] Wood E. 16(1) and [MS.] Wood E. 17(2). For the quotations on Milton and Phillips, see Wood 88 and Wood 363(1). For other quotations, see Wood 15(3), Wood 421(4). Wood owned a dictionary edited by Phillips, *A World of Errors*, now missing, see MS. Wood E. 2(70), p. 43 (item 1013). For the quotation from Morley's life, *AO*, 4.152.

[58]For the ten pamphlets, Wood 369. For entry on Vane, *AO*, 3.578. For the mention of Vane in the vignette of Laud, *AO*, 3.126. Also unmarked was *The Case of Mr. Hugh Peters*, Wood 369(4). Wood has no entry for Peters in his *AO*, but he mentioned him frequently as, e.g., 'that diabolical villain and pulpit-buffoon', *AOF*, 2.100.

[59]For comments on Wood's catalogues, see T. A. Birrell, *Pioneers in Bibliography*, eds. R. Myers and M. Harris (Winchester, 1988): 26f.; and his 'Books and Buyers in Seventeenth-Century English Auction Sales', *Under the Hammer*, eds. R. Myers, et al. (British Library, 2001): 51ff. For Wood's lack of participation on the Hyde catalogue (item 1523), see *LT* 2.71-2. The term catalogues are at Wood 658(1-772) (item 1562) and the index is at MS. Wood

He had acquired ninety London book auction catalogues issued by London auctioneers from 1676 to 1695. These catalogues were of libraries of deceased persons such as Robert Bruce earl of Aylesbury, Ralph Button, Richard Davis, John Maynard, Thankful Owen, Thomas Parkhurst, Lazarus Seaman, Robert Wallis, and John Warner; of subjects such as foreign books, 'Bibliotheca Gallica, Italica, Hispanica'; of 'English books', medicine or history; or of items arranged by various booksellers including John Bullord, Richard Chiswell, William Cooper, Edward Millington, and Benjamin Walford and distributed gratis by booksellers in London, Cambridge and Oxford. His book sale catalogues, if they can be distinguished from auction catalogues, were similar: of libraries of deceased persons such as William Ducie the viscount Downe, Henry Howard the duke of Norfolk, John Maitland the duke of Lauterdale, and Henry Parker; of books in general issued by London and Oxford booksellers such as William Cooper, William Crook, Richard Davis, William London, Humphrey Moseley, Henry Playford, and Philemon Stephens; of the works of specific persons such as Robert Boyle, John Gauden, Thomas Hobbes, John Ley, John Owen, or William Prynne; seven Frankfurt fair catalogues printed from 1609 to 1628, and, as with certain auction catalogues, of specialist topics such as divinity, drama, heraldry, law, the popish plot and of manuscripts.

Wood did whatever was necessary to make his searches in his catalogues easier. He removed some catalogues printed at the end of plays and inserted them in his main group of catalogues. Book and auction catalogues were generally done in haste to meet deadlines and hence numbered irregularly, wanting certain details such as complete names or dates, or poorly organized. Wood reshaped his collection of catalogues by repaginating continuously through many individual items, and he put one group of sixty-eight in a chronological order with his numbers, 1-68, and bound them in eight volumes. He read them even more closely than he read other books, making thousands of annotations, mainly marks in the margin, underscorings, additional works by, names, dates, references to other editions, cross-references such as 'v. prox. p.', 'v. supra', 'v. p. 165', 'v. infra', 'Ox' at books by Oxford authors, corrections, and an occasional 'habeo'. His testy and impatient comments are common. In *A Catalogue of Books, Printed at the Theater in Oxford* he wrote, 'Here wants the verses in fol. made by the universitie on Anne Dutchess of York, printed at the Theater an. 167[1]. [/] Tis strang that the years which these books were printed are not set downe. [/] Here wants the Oxford - book - Almanack for the year. 1673 of which 30000 were printed.' He frequently commented on the omission of Christian names of authors, a particular problem with certain surnames such as Byfield, Owen, or Smith. In one catalogue he wrote, 'Is it not a simple thing for a man to make a cat. of books, & not to set doune the Christian names of the authors? For there be severall authors that have the same S^r names–', and in another, 'No Christian names to the authours in this cat. & therefore for my use not worth a straw'.

The omission of dates of publication irked him time and again, 'In this cat are the yeares of certaine books, when printed, omitted, especially if the title cannot come within the compass of a line.' This was a more serious matter because it hindered interpretation. Time, he believed, was essential to determine the context of a work and without it, a reader could not correctly read a work. In a catalogue of dramatic plays which listed only author, title and genre and lacked dates he made his case in a draft of a letter on the verso of the title page. 'M^r { Kirkman [and] Cox { several of our Oxford scholars have read your Catalogues of plays (one at the end of Nicomede, & the other which is this by its self) and like them well, but would have lik'd them better had you set downe the yeare when they were printed, that they might have knowne when the Authors lived, and when the plays came first in use. For without time they cannot be exact judges of matters. But they hope for the future that you will not omitt those matters, . . . ' (see Plate VII). Wood's advice, if it ever reached Cox, Kirkman, or Langbaine, was ignored, and their next printed catalogue included no dates. Discrepancies bothered him. In a catalogue of law books, he noted an out of place book, Tillesley, *Animadversions* (1621), a critique of J. Selden's book on tithes, 'How comes this in here?' In a catalogue of Brian Walton's books he noted, 'Most of the books in this cat. were published after Dr Waltons death – He died 1661'. A catalogue by William Cooper was full of errors, 'This cat is very false'. His *Compleat Catalogue of . . . the Popish Plot* (1680), along with a 'continuation' and 'second continuation' show that he kept abreast of publications on the plot. He made extensive annotations in these and wrote 'habeo' beside a number of items that he himself owned, ten in the 'second continuation' alone. At the end of the first issue he added thirteen items on the popish plot published in 1679 and 1680. He himself owned eight of these (see Plate VIII). No one knew bibliography better than Wood and his collection of catalogues was the best in England. They were a primary tool for his bio-bibliographies and he used them constantly. His friends helped. John Aubrey knew that Wood was more interested in

---

F. 36, ff. 1-113. His note in an early issue is on his numbered page 177. The index entry to John Milton in the term catalogue is quoted above, p. xxxv-xxxvi note 57. Certain advertisements for the *Athenae* indicate that the publisher, T. Bennet, was remaindering the final copies in his stock. For the *Vindication*, see Wood 614(7) and above, p. xiv. *The Works of the Learned* and *Mercurius Eruditorum* are at [MS.] Wood E. 24a and b.

the bibliography at the end of Walter Charleton's lectures on anatomy than in the narrative and sent the bibliography to him with the note, 'Dr Charlton remembers him to you & tore this for you, out of his booke of Anatomical Lectures'. Charleton also knew what Wood wanted.[60]

Newsbooks served as a supplement to his catalogues in that they were also mines of biographical and bibliographical information. Wood went through them methodically and treated them carefully. Domestic newsbooks became common during and after the 1640s and Wood began a subscription to Tuesday and Friday issues of *Mercurius Politicus* and *The Publick Intelligencer* in 1656. He recorded the cost on the first page: 'Decemb: 20: 1656: I made a bargaine with Mr Forrest, to give 2^s a quarter for Newes Bookes taking them of him, the next day they come to Oxford, being every Wednesday and Saturday: whereof this is the first:'. He made further payments to Edward Forrest according to his diary entries and later made payments for the same to Thomas Robinson and still later, to Robinson's widow. Wood found it necessary to bind his newsbooks as soon as he had enough money. A bequest from Peter Nicholls allowed him to do so and his notes on the upper flyleaves of the first two volumes of his *Oxford Gazette* (1665) which became the *London Gazette* in 1666 give some details of his costs for the binding and the newsbooks themselves, '25 Jan. 1680[1] [/] Given to Roger Bartlet book-binder, for binding of this booke 2^s - 4^d, being part of the Legacie that Mr Peter Nicolls Fellow of Merton Coll. lefte to me. Ita testor [/] Antonius à Wood. [/] In this volume are contained 246 Gazetts: and Every Gazette, cost me at least 1^d - ob. so that all put togeather come to two pound 7^s & 10^d – besides binding. [and totals written in right margin] 2^s. 4$^{d\prime}$ and 2^{li} - 7^s - 10$^{d\prime}$ [and below:] Taken in peices & new bound again Dec. 21 - 2^s - 6. an. 1688'. Volume two in this series has a similar note.[61]

Wood looked at every page of an issue as his occasional elaborations, pencil lines in the margins, and underscorings indicate. He was interested primarily in publications and most of his annotations in the margins are at advertisements of books newly published. He wanted to know who was publishing what and when. He sometimes added 'q[uaere]', identifications, and dates of publication where they were wanting. He apparently kept lists of books published in each year, for in the 1664 *Intelligencer* he wrote on a slip, 'Note that some titles of book[s] for this yeare I have removed for 1663'. He sometimes marked notices that concerned biography, domestic matters, Oxford, marvelous events and of course regicides. In the 1664 volume of the *Intelligencer* he commented on a story concerning regicides in Switzerland, 'I remember this story was afterward contradicted. See p. 589'. He kept track of who was editing which newsbooks and recorded changes in editors. Just before the 31 August 1663 issue of the *Intelligencer*, he noted that 'Mr Henry Muddiman desisting from writing Merc: Publicus, Mr Roger L'strang [sic] by order succedes in writing the Intelligencer and the Newes', and at the end of the 1664 volume of the *Intelligencer* wrote 'Here endeth the newes of Mr Roger L'estrang. for the year 1664'. L'Estrange lasted one more year as the editor of the *Intelligencer*, and Wood noted on the lower flyleaf of the 1665 volume, 'Rog. L'estrange desisted from writing the Newes — Becaus the Gazets which came out twice in the week took up all.' He noted on a lower flyleaf in the 1660 volume of *Mercurius Politicus* that 'Marchiomont [sic] Needham gives of[f] writing, or rather prohibited about this time. & Merc: Publicus goes forward, who [sic] began in the beginning of the yeare 1660', and added some time later, 'Needham was prohibited v. p. 437 - ubi'. Some things he marked were of direct concern to himself. In the *London Gazette* of 1693 he made a pencil line at the advertisement for subscriptions to 'Monumenta Britannica: By Mr. Tho. [sic] Aubrey'. A few pages later he inserted a blank leaf which has a news item, dateline 'Oxford, July 31, 1693'. It reads: 'On the 29th Instant Antony A- [sic] Wood was Condemned in the Chancellors Court of the University of Oxford, for having Written and Published in the Second Volume of his Book, entituled, Athenae Oxoniensis divers infamous Libels against the right Honourable Edward late earl of Clarendon, . . . ' Some newsbooks were insignificant, as *The Universal Intelligence*, which recorded a visit by Lovelace to Oxford in 1688. Wood pointed out a number of errors in the stories and concluded with 'This is a most ridiculous & silly thing'. On another single issue, *Mercurius Academicus* (1648) he wrote, 'I could never learne that any other numbers of this

---

[60]For catalogues at the end of plays, see below, p. xxxix note 63. W. W. Greg used several of Wood's catalogues of plays for his *Bibliography of English Printed Drama* (1939-1959), see Birrell, *Pioneers*, p. 27. Wood's sixty-eight catalogues are [MS.] Wood E. 13(1) to [MS.] Wood E. 20(12). For uncertainty about the name of Byfield, see e.g., [MS.] Wood E. 14(6)). For comments on the lack of Christian names, [MS.] Wood D. 22(6)), ([MS.] Wood E. 13(3), see also [MS.] Wood E. 17(3) and E. 19(2b). For omission of dates, [MS.] Wood E. 18(11). For letters to Cox, et al. [MS.] Wood E. 28(4) and an earlier draft at [MS.] Wood C. 26(20). For Tillesley, [MS.] Wood E. 16(2). For Walton, [MS.] Wood E. 16(8). For Cooper, [MS.] Wood E. 19(5). For the popish plot catalogues, see [MS.] Wood E. 27(2-4), items 1599-1601, and Plate VIII. For Charleton's bibliography, [MS.] Wood D. 22(14).

[61]For the note of 'Decemb: 20: 1656', Wood 389(1). Edward Forrest and his son with the same name, both booksellers, cannot be easily distinguished. Wood's notes in the Oxford and London *Gazettes* are at Wood 541 and 542. See also *LT*, 2.413.

Merc. Acad. were afterwards published.'[62]

What Wood Read for Pleasure

It is clear that he collected drama and poetry mainly for biographical and bibliographical information of dramatists, poets, translators and editors. His shelf-list of 1681 indicates this as do his notes in the printed items themselves. In his shelf-list he entered plays by Terence and Seneca and the works of Sallust by the name of the translator or editor, R. Bernard, Th. Farnabie, or W. Cross. In his entry for his copy of Lucian's dialogues, he wrote in the author column 'Fr. Hicks of Oriel' and 'Th. Hicks of ch.ch.', and after his improvised titles, 'Lucian translated' and 'Lucians life', he added 'v[ide] epistle before the book'. The epistle to the reader was the crucial part for it contained details about the translator and the editor, Francis and Thomas Hickes. He described another item 'In a bundell tyed up togeather'. This was 'Seneca in English – 1581 – Tho Newton he hath put out Leylands epigrams - q[uaere; i.e., Leland] . . . In this booke are 3. playes of Jasper Heywood . . . four plays by Joh. Studley [i.e. translated by] – This booke must be perused – & the epistles before every play'. Again, he was to peruse this book for bio-bibliographical information, not for the plays of Seneca. In the margin he wrote the names of the editor and translators, not Seneca. Prefaces were more important than the plays. His note in his copy of Beaumont and Fletcher's *Valentinian: a Tragedy* suggests as much: 'Note that when this Trag. as altered by Joh. E. of Roch[ester] was published at the latter end of his poems, printed 1691, the said preface was then omitted. Therefore keep this'. Four of his catalogues were originally appended to printed plays as appendices. Wood removed these appendices and placed them in volumes of catalogues. In two cases, the plays themselves are lost, both by Thomas Goffe, but the lists of books, Wood's primary concern, were retained. He owned copies of poems of numerous English poets, though his interest was not in verse. The subject of William Winstanley's *The Lives of the Most Famous English Poets* was more to his taste and show what he was looking for: 'The book following entit. The lives . . . was usually sold in Oxon, in Octob. an 1686. [/] Tho. Elderton the poet is mention'd in the epist. ded'. He read it closely and made numerous comments.[63]

For his own pleasure Wood acquired printed items on music (66), marvels and miracles (102), executions and murders (258), a large number of ballads (575), and some prose fiction (40). He did not, however, separate his research life from his private enjoyment. He was a singer and violin player and assembled printed music with viol/violin parts for the common prayer and Christmas music, while at the same time his instinct was to annotate these works with customary information about the author or publisher. On a flyleaf before single sheet, *Hymnus eucharisticus* by Nathaniel Ingelo with the music by Benjamin Rogers, he wrote a lengthy comment on the composer who was at one time organist at Magdalen College. Most of this note he copied into his *Fasti* entry on Rogers. Two of his catalogues have sections on music. He approached these with the same intensity that he did other types of catalogues and marked practically every item in each in some way. He was always looking for connections between print and Oxford, and the quest did not stop at when he read, performed or sang for pleasure.[64]

So also executions and murders were of interest for their own sake and for his professional work. He collected pamphlets on highwaymen, murderers and executed persons such as Major Clancie, Stephen College, Thomas Dangerfield, Claude Du Vall, Richard Hainam, James Hind, and Samuel Swiftnicks, and on the executions of Catholic priests. Some of his notes in pamphlets about these persons are extensive and important for his *Athenae*. He collected six items about the protestant joyner of Oxford, Stephen College, and seems to have attended his hanging as his note in a book catalogue implies: 'Given to me by . . [Henry] Crittenden [Cruttenden] a printer, being then in the Castle Yard, Oxōn to see Steph. Golledge [sic] executed. 31. Aug. 1681'. Wood also knew others who were present and mentioned them in a note in a pamphlet: 'Tho. Chrosthwait of Qu. Coll. was with him at the gallowes. Dr. Jo. Hall of Pemb. Coll & Dr G. Reynell had severall times prayed with him.' Wood described in detail the hanging of a Catholic during the crisis of the popish plot: 'The said Ol. Plunket was hanged drawn & quarter'd at Tyburne on the first

[62]For the 1664 *Intelligencer*, Wood 391. For the 1663 volume, Wood 521(2) and for the 1665 volume, Wood 392(1, 3). For the 1660 volume of *Mercurius Politicus*, Wood 524. For the 1693 *London Gazette*, pp. 2877ᵛ and 2893, Wood 554 and *LT*, 3.429 and 4.47. For *The Universal Intelligence*, Wood 529(11) and see *LT*, 3.286-7. For *Mercurius Academicus*, Wood 514(41).

[63]For Terence and Seneca, MS. Wood E. 2(70), p. 10. For Hickes, *ibid.*, p. 50 and [MS.] Wood C. 27. For Seneca and Leland, *ibid.*, p. 51; his copy of Leland is at Wood 484(9). For Wilmot, the earl of Rochester, Wood 607(8). For Goffe and other catalogues removed from editions of plays, [MS.] Wood E. 28(1-3), Wood 896(3). For Winstanley, Wood 116(2) and see below, p. xli and note 69.

[64]For the note in Rogers, Wood 398(13-4), and a similar note in N. Ingelo, Wood 416(87), and *AOF*, 2.306-7; see also notes at J. Merbecke, Wood 314. For catalogues with music sections, see Maunsell (1595), Wood 654c(2), and Playford (1690), [MS.] Wood E. 22(9); and also J. Wilson, Wood 397(1).

of July 1681. Whereupon his quarters only (not the head) were buried in the yard belonging to St Giles ch. in the feilds neare to London, by the bodies of the Jesuits (the 5 Jesuits) Lately buried there – when continuinge till after the crop-Eard plot broke out 1683, they were taken up, & conveyed to the monastery of Ben[e]dictines . . . at Lambspring in Germany, where they were with great devotion buried'. Though Oliver Plunket was not an Oxford graduate Wood found a place for these details in the *Athenae* in the entry of his father, Patrick Plunket, who was an Oxford graduate.[65]

His notes in some of his ballads show the same sort of attention to time, context, and detail. He bought ballads, some of them salacious, just as did many other citizens of Oxford. They were to be read, passed on and reread by others until they disintegrated. Wood was an exception in that he kept his ballads and had them bound so that today they are in excellent condition. Some of his annotations reveal his obsession with identification. In one of his copies of a ballad on the tragedy involving Earl Percy of England and Earl Douglas in the battle of Chevy Chase, he searched for historical verification and wrote some notes on a slip which he pasted in, 'The battle of Chevy Chase temp. H. 4. so Mr Fulm. [William Fulman] q[uaere]'; and on the verso of the slip, 'Cheviot Chase See my Engl. Camden p. 803. v. Greys descrip. of New Castle p. 33. No mention of it in Baronii in vol. 1. Fuller Worthies in Northumb p. 306'. On the verso of the ballad he added: 'Sr Philip Sydney, in his defence of poesie saith thus of the battle of Chevy-Chase. — Certainly I must confess my owne barbarousness, I never heard the old song of Percy & Douglas, that I found not mine heart moved more than with a trumpet, & yet it is sung but by some blind crowder, with no rougher voice then rude style, which being so evill apparell'd in the dust & cobweb of that uncivil age, what would it work trimmed in the gorgeous eloquence of Pindar?' In a ballad of the 'Duchesse of Suffolks Calamity' by Thomas Deloney, Wood gave an exhaustive genealogy: 'The Duchess of Suffolk mentind [sic] in the following Ballad, was Catherine the sole daugh. & heire to William the last Lord Willoughby of Eresby, who was the fourth wife of Charles Brandon Duke of Suffolke – which Charles dying without issue by her, shee was married to Rich Bertie Esq. father to Peregrine Bertie Lord Willoughby, ancestor to the earls of Lindsey & Abendon– [Abingdon]'. His note on an anti-Catholic ballad by Walter Pope, a one-time member of Wadham and later a member of the Royal Society, 'By Walter Pope A. m. of the royal society somtimes Fellow of Wadham Coll.', made it possible to determine that this ballad was stolen from the collection of Wood.[66]

His favourite works of prose fiction were, not surprisingly, by the lively writers Thomas Deloney, Thomas Dekker, Robert Greene, Gabriel Harvey, Thomas Nash, and Laurence Price, and romances. Wood was preoccupied with historical authenticity even in the most imaginative prose. In Deloney's *Gentle Craft* he put down what he knew about the context: 'In the Beach neare Lydde in Kent, is to be seen a heape of great stones, which the neighbour Inhabitants call St Crispins, & Crispianus or Crispians Tombe, whome they report to have been cast upon this shoare (by Lydd) by shipwrack, & from hence called into the glorious company of saints. See Jacobus de Voragine in the Legend of their lives, & you may believe (perhaps) as much as is here spoken: They were here shomakers, & suffer'd Martyrdome the 10 of the calends of Nov: which day is kept Holyday, to this day, by all the Shomakers in London & elswhere.' In Deloney's *The Pleasant History of John Winchcomb* he did the same, 'The familie of the Winchcombe are & have been knights & esquires in Berks- They beare a confused coat of arms viz Azure on a chev. ingrailed or 3 cinquefo[i]les of the 1. between three close eagles of the 2. a cheif or charged with a fleur de lize betw. 2 lozenges azure.' On another page, at the printed 'Winchomb [sic] . . . was chosen sheriff', he could state emphatically, '[no] such person [oc]currs in the [cat]alogue of [m]ayors & sherriffs of London' (note is cropped). His copy of Samuel Smithson, *The Famous History of Guy Earl of Warwick*, prompted a long note of fifty-two lines, beginning: 'Of Guy Earl of Warwick from the [blank] vol. of Joh. Lelands Itineraries, ms. in bib. Bod[leian] – There is a right goodly chappal of S. Mary Magd. upon Avon river ripa dextra somu- [?] a mile above Warwick – This place of some is called Gibcliffe, of some Guycliffe, & old fame remaineth with the people there, that Guido Earl of Warwick in K. Ethelstans (or Athelstans) dayes had a great devotion to this place & made an oratorie there. . . . '[67]

---

[65]For the execution of S. College, see the catalogue, Wood 91(5), and Wood 427(31). For the note on Crosthwayte, who later became, for a short time, principal at St. Edmunds, Wood 427(31). For Plunket, see Wood 427(20-1) and *AO*, 1.506.

[66]For salacious ballads, see [MS.] Wood E. 25(1) and (51). For the ballad on Chevy Chase, Wood 401(24). Wood's copy of William Camden, *Britain* (1610) is now missing. 'Greys description' is William Gray, *Chorographia* (Newcastle, 1649), now missing; Caesar Baronius, *Life* (1639), is at Wood 432. For the Duchess of Suffolk ballad, Wood 401(29). On the stolen Pope ballad, see Kiessling, 'Ballads', *BLR*, 15 (April 1996): fig. 4, p. 271; and for a photograph of historical notes in another ballad, Wood 401(45), fig. 1, p. 265. For other ballads with Wood's historical notes, see Wood 401(37), (48) and (100), 402(23), and 416(111-2).

[67]For more on favourite authors, see pp. xxi-ii, above. For Deloney items, see [MS.] Wood C. 31(1) and [MS.] Wood

Wood's Critical Judgements

Wood's annotations show that he was a focused and aggressive reader looking for bio-bibliographical material about Oxford graduates. If his source did not include information that he deemed essential, he responded vigorously with his pen or pencil. If his source did not strictly state the 'truth' as he understood the term, or was oblivious about or tried to hide 'faults', he also responded with pen or pencil. To know the date of a publication was essential to him. He had seen the importance of this in his catalogues, and in any sort of publication, he believed, the dating set the context. Hence his most common form of annotation, after the identification of the author, was to establish the date, and even month, of the publication. If the date was not on a title page, or on a single sheet, he added it. Few things peeved him more than when he couldn't give a correct year of publication. A series of notes in Henry Fairfax's *An Impartial Relation of the Whole Proceedings against St. Mary Magdalen Colledge in Oxon* (1688) is typical. Wood added to the month of publication, 'The 2^d edit. with additions is bound up in this vol.' and 'published in Oxōn about the beginning of Feb. 1687[8]'. In the text there is some confusion about when events took place and Wood made several testy comments: 'Note that here is no date set down' and 'nor here, which breeds some confusion'; 'when was this dated?'; at 'Mr. W– P–', he wrote, 'Will Pen the Quaker' and 'qu[aere] when dat.' He owned two copies of the marvel of the whale that swallowed a Catholic priest. Neither had a printing date and Wood wrote, 'Noe date or yeare to be found in this pamphlet' and in the margin of the text at the printed '19 of October', 'qu[aere] in what yeare.' On the verso of the undated single sheet, *A Copy of Mr. Ashton's Paper*, he gave some background, 'This speech was printed by stealth & about the Middle of March 1690/1 twas scatter'd in the night time about London streets – I saw it at Oxon. in a private hand 16. Mar. 1690/1'. Similar notes are in other items: 'Noe date or yeare to be found in this pamphlet', or 'Some years since', and 'When? or in what year.' Wood wanted this basic information and if it was not there, he had to waste valuable time finding it. In his bibliographies in the *Athenae* and *Fasti* he listed items chronologically, and his methodology is clear in his entry of Milton: 'but to go on with the catal. of his books according to time'.[68]

Other critical judgements involved mainly plagiarism, accuracy, or a failure to document. He marked any form of plagiarism, sometimes in great detail as at Henry Hickman's *Justification of the Fathers*: 'This book is mostly composed & patched up from 1. Dr Pet. Heylyns Antidot. Lync. 2. From Mr Will. Morice of Werrington his book called New inclosures broken downe 3. From severall books of Joh. Goodwyn. 4. From Will. Prynnes Canterb. doome And from others without acknowledgment [/] See in Mr Tho. Pierce his letter to Dr Heylyn concerning Mr Hickman, at the end of his new discover[i]es discovered p. 280. 281. &c. where is shewed that he composed much of this book from those 4 & others.' Most of this he incorporated in his entry on Pierce in the *Athenae*. In a ballad, *John Arm-strong's Last Good Night*, he noted: 'Will. Sanderson Esquire in his Life & Death of Jam. V[I]. King of Scots takes from him the said story, p. 190. 191 without any acknowledgments, & curtailes & spoyles it –'. His less detailed comments are frequent, as in William Percey's work on swimming, 'Taken out of Sr Everard Digby de arte natandi'; William Greenwood's work on love, 'mostly taken of M[r]. Burtons Melancholy'; and a *Sixth Collection of Papers*, 'Taken from the end of J. Fox book of Acts & Mon'. In John Bales' *Brefe Chronycle*, he noted that 'These things of Sr J. Oldcastle are mostly cemilted [sic, ?] into Foxes book of martyres'. William Winstanley in his *Lives of . . . English Poets* was vague about one of his sources in the vignette of Edward Sherborne and wrote, 'saith a learned Author'. Wood identified the author as 'Edward Philipps in his Theat. poet', and at Winstanley's subsequent vignette of the same Phillips, he commented on Winstanley's sources: 'why do you not mention his Theatrum poetarum from whence you have taken all your matter in this book'. Wood remembered this theft when he wrote the entry of Phillips in the *Athenae*. He also noticed the recycling of woodcuts, dying speeches, and marvels from an earlier to a later publication. In one pamphlet of a dying speech, he wrote, 'The matters following that are scored with a pen, (besides many more) are borrowed from other dying speeches–' and 'These were Cardinall Wolseys words when he laid a dying.' Marvels, too, were reused and Wood noted several repetitions in *Mirabilis annus* 'published by certaine fanaticall people at the restauration of K. Ch. 2. purposely to amuse the Vulgar'. At a 'prodigy' of July 1660, he wrote, 'The like hapned in the last yeare of Qu. Mary'; at one of Sept. 1660, 'This hapned in the last yeare againe of Qu. Mary – This is to possess the people that the K. [Charles II] is not long lived.'; and at one of Aug.

C. 32(2). For Guy of Warwick, Wood 254(2).

[68]For concern about 'time' in his catalogues, see p. xxxvii and note 60. For the Fairfax item, Wood 517(1). For the whale item, [MS] Wood B. 35(12, and see also 13-15). For the Ashton item, Wood 367(22). For other items, Wood 186, 387(11), 428(26), 428(32) and 367(22-3). At Wood 509(29), different letters are, 'Not dated'. For the quotation from the Milton entry, *AOF*, 1.485. He arranged items 'All plac'd according to time' in a volume now Wood 426, see item (1), Oates (1680). See also Index, 'Wood, A., critical judgements'.

1660, 'This hapned the yeare before ch. 5. [sic] was put to flight & hardly escap'd his life.'[69]

Unsupported statements, discrepancies and inconsistencies irritated him, and he knew well not to rely on any one source for his own compositions. His notes to himself that he must 'find good proofe' for facts and details were endless. He demanded the same specificity from others. In John Harington's supplement to Godwin's history of English bishops he inserted a number of sceptical notes, 'q[uaere]', 'where?', and 'False'. It is not uncommon to find in histories his challenges such as 'How do yo prove that?' and 'That is onlie supposed by yo[u], yo[u] cannot prove it.' Wood did not spare his distinguished friend and superior William Dugdale and asserted his own authority more than once in his copy of Dugdale's *The Baronage of England*. At the comment that Henry Bennet, the earl of Arlington, was 'descended from worthy Ancestors' Wood wrote, 'How do you prove that? he can scarce lay claime to a coat of armes that was granted either to Gr[and]father or father. . . . The reason why he would not be called Lord Bennet was (as is conceived) because a famous Bawd called the Lady Bennet (a Bakers widow) then lived in St Margarets Lane in Westminster.' At Dugdale's reference to a record of families 'with great exactness being performed', Wood took exception to 'great exactness', underscored it and wrote, 'But with [a] great man[y] faults, as [it] appears by [the] printed copies [of] that book in bib. [Bodleian] corrected with Camdens owne hand' (Wood's note is cropped). At Dugdale's mention of John lord Crew of Stene Wood added his qualifications: 'A presbyterian, Independent & I know not what. One of the other House, or House of Lords to Oliver.'; he underscored Dugdale's printed comment of Crew's 'loyally contributing his best endeavors to the restoration' and wrote, 'When he saw to what ruin he & the restless Presbyterians had brought the nation to, then he forthsooth did endeavour &c'. Wood knew his son, Nathaniel Crew, as a student at Oxford before he became bishop of Oxford and then Durham. Crew managed to switch sides to his advantage both in politics and religion until the advent of William III. At Dugdale's mention of him, Wood could not restrain his contempt: 'One that hath sided with the times. A formall starcht nothing, another M[r] Smirk'. A later reader lined this out. Crew fared no better in the *Athenae*. Elsewhere Wood quibbled with Dugdale's dates, and at Dugdale's printed note that 'I never yet saw' Augustine Vincent's manuscripts, Wood wrote, 'You might have perused them at your pleasure, had you accepted of the invitation of Ralp [sic] Sheldon Esquire, in whose hands they were then & still are.' He himself regularly compared print against manuscript. By doing so he noted several discrepancies between an edition of George Cavendish, *The Negotiations of Thomas Woolsey* and the manuscript by Cavendish in the Bodleian Library, e.g., 'The manuscript or transcript of this book comming into the hands of a Factious person, he published it with rascally additions put in it in several places/ And at the same time when Archb. Laud was falling, whome he hooks in at the end as a parallel with Wolsey/', 'This is not in the copie written by G. Cavendish', and 'Not in the orig copie, in bib. Bod.' In a printed edition of a *Letter Sent by William Lawd* he commented twice on the translation, e.g., 'This letter was written in Latine, remaining yet to be seen in Reg[istro]: Dom[us]: Convoc[ationis]: Oxōn R. fol. 182. b. The Translatour hath mangled it & abused the authour ita testor Anth: à Woode Oxoniensis Antiquarius.'[70]

More common but less substantive were his comments on those who were for or against his party and religion. Charles II and the Church of England could do no wrong, and the writings of those on the other side were categorized hastily as 'ridiculous' and 'a piece of roguery'. I have mentioned Wood's

---

[69]For Hickman, Wood 804 and *AO*, 4.369; for the Armstrong ballad, Wood 401(48) (item 716) and for his copy of Sanderson, Wood 660e(2). For Percey, Greenwood, *Sixth Collection*, and Bale or Foxe, Wood 728(3); 741(3), [MS.] Wood D. 29(6) and 789(2). For Winstanley, see above at p. xxxix and note 63 (Wood 116(2)); for Phillips, which Wood read just as aggressively, Wood 88 and *AO*, 4.763. For his comments on repetitions of woodcuts or pictures see Index, 'Wood, A., woodcuts'; for dying speeches, Wood 422(12); and for marvels, Wood 643(4). For other plagiaries: William Fulman and Henry Savage got information from Wood himself and did not acknowledge it, see Wood 513(6) and 534(5); and [MS.] Wood C. 44(4), Wood 127(2), 251(3), and 805. In MS. Wood E. 2(70), p. 47, he wrote at David Lloyd's 'Statesmen & favorites of England – no author . . . produced therfore a plagiary' (Wood 298). See also Index, 'Wood, A., plagiarism'.

[70]For quotations demanding 'proof', Wood 251(3), Wood 605(1) and Wood 427(7). For Harington, Wood 864(1). For Dugdale, volume 1, Wood 418 and volume 2, Wood 419. Wood read the proofs of the third volume of the *Monasticon* and of the *Baronage* for Dugdale and received copies of each in thanks from him, see *LT*, 2.113 and Wood Diaries 23, f. 72[v], '3 Dec. sent to S[r] Will. Dugd. 3. stichings [sic] or bundells containing corrections on his baronagium – The 1. stitching contains 5 papers. the 2[d] – 7. papers – the 3[d]. 11. papers – with the Epitaph of Edw. [Talbot] E[arl] of Shrewsbury in the Abbey Ch. of Westm. who died 1617.' See pp. xvi-xvii and note 19, above. For Wood's uncompromising portrait of Crew in *AO*, 4.886-8 (and see also *LT*, 2.16). Wood's reference to Mr. Smirk is to Andrew Marvell's *Mr. Smirke. Or the Divine in Mode*. Even if Crew earned himself his reputation, he had more right to sue Wood than the earl of Clarendon. Hearne held the same opinion of Nathaniel Crew and ended his vignette with 'he is a digamist', Hearne, 1.305. For more on the Sheldon manuscript, Wood 414(1). For the edition of Cavendish, Wood 345(11). For the letter of Laud, Wood 514(1).

critical annotations concerning a number of these, including John Milton, Henry Vane, William Prynne, and John Crew and his son Nathaniel. In a parody of the afterlife of Thomas Wentworth, the earl of Strafford, he wrote 'Nothing but fooleries & rascallities', and of a treaty between Charles I and Prince Rupert, he wrote on the title page, 'Nothing but lyes & rascallities'. Authors of sectarian religious tracts were in general despicable and Wood's favourite word for sectaries from 1660 was 'phanatique'. He noted in a pamphlet of that year: 'This word phanatique go[es] much in fashi[on] after this'. Their publications were 'written by a cabal of phanaticks & non-conformists', 'ridiculous', 'roguery', 'ridicula'. A displeasing *Secret History* of Charles II and James II earned this judgement: 'A grand phanatick, or Presbyterian, choos you whether was author of this book'. In this context his tolerance of Catholics and Quakers is striking but not surprising. Wood was not a Catholic but had close friends of that faith to whom he was sympathetic. Because of these friendships he was under some suspicion of being a Catholic during the rabid anti-Catholicism especially from 1678 to the deposition of James II. Where he perceived inaccuracies or conjectures involving Catholics, he scribbled notes such as 'all false'. At a printed reference to the 'Principal [Robert Lister] (being popish)' he countered, 'what do you meane by that word! he was no Papist I am sure but an Orthodox Protestant. But your meaning is, he was no Puritan.' He reacted against the anti-Catholic witch hunts and in pamphlets about plots in 1641, he wrote 'A ridiculous & impertinent pamphlet' in ink over his earlier note in pencil, 'Lyes & ignorance' and 'ridiculous'. He also seems to have had some understanding of the Quaker sufferings and gathered forty-five items concerning them. He had a discussion with the Thomas Barlow about *A Tender Visitation of Love* by George Bishop and wrote on the upper flyleaf: 'This tender visitation of Love following I once communicated to Dr Tho. Barlow, who, upon his perusal of it, told me by the quotations, & various readings therein, it could not be written by a mechanical Quaker, but rather by a popish seducer, or a Jesuit.' Wood was not impressed by Barlow's conclusion and on the title page under the author's name wrote, 'Quaker'. In a second Quaker tract, *True Relation*, by an anonymous author, Wood commented on writing style and contents: 'This simple pamphlet following containing a relation of the suffering of certaine Quakers done by Oxford scholars, then under the government of Presbyterians & Independents, was published in 1654, in the raigne of Oliver. The Quakers came first to Oxon. in that yeare, & had their meetings in an old stone-house almost opposite to the common gate of New-Inne (in which house Rich. Beatrice [i.e., Betterus] Chirurgion & Quaker then lived) as they journied from the north parts of England to London – The said Rich Batrice [sic] one of the chief Quakers in Oxon. lived to the beginning of K. Jam. 2. Some but not all things in this pamphlet are true.' In two parodies of Quakers Wood wrote 'Ridicula'; he attributed one to a jealous physician and poet, Martin Llewellin of Great Wycombe, who lost business to a Quaker physician.[71]

His characterizations of those not of his persuasion or competence are as vivid as they are uncomplimentary: a Mrs. Harrison was a 'snotty covetous presbyterian'; Frances Cheynell in his pamphlet on Oxford and London: 'Y^o talk like an ignorant coxcomb'; Edward Bysshe, Garter Herald, was 'a knave to my knowledge'; Arthur Squibb, Clarencieux Herald, 'a pityfull Herald god wot'; William Cawley the regicide, 'A deformed fellow'; Philip Wharton, a 'cowardlie rebell'; the archbishop of York, John Williams, who deserted the royalists, 'This he did like a poore spirited man when he saw the kings cause decline'; the Puritan 'squint ey'd' Vice-Chancellor of the university, Daniel Greenwood, 'a morose & strict man in his office, caused the souldiers who were then garrisoned in Oxon to awe the rude schollers all the act time in St Maries church'. Payne Fisher earned his contempt by changing his allegiance from Charles I to Cromwell to Charles II, by being an ingratiating flatterer, and finally by publishing books on London monuments that were based on the work of others. He gave Wood a proof copy of one of his publications on London monuments and in another wrote a flattering inscription to Wood. A comment by Wood in the first is 'how [do] you pro[ve] yt?' In the second he corrected the pretentious Latin in Fisher's manuscript inscription. Wood elaborated upon a jibe at Fisher in the well-known satire, *Naps upon Parnassus*. Fisher had presented an elegy on the death of Archbishop Ussher to unreceptive students and was 'jeer'd in Christ-Church Hall'. Wood added in the margin of his copy: 'Payne Fisher a time serving poet got leave of Ol. Cromwell to celibrate Archb. Ushers anniversary in Christchurch hall Ox. And being a conceited Br[a]ggadocio was hummd & hist by scholars –'. He incorporated this into the vignette of Fisher in the *Athenae*.[72]

[71]For reactions to criticism of Charles II, Wood 234(3), 235(2), 240(2), 421(4). For Wentworth, Wood 366(11). For the parody on Charles I, Wood 378(38). For 'phanatique', Wood 610(63), and the Index, 'Fanatic'. For authors of religious tracts, Wood 350(2). For Charles II and James II, Wood 242(3). For 'all false', Wood 514(7) and the Index, 'Wood, A., false'. For Lister, Wood 292(6). For Catholic plots in 1641, Wood 373(6-7 and Plate I). For Barlow on the Quaker tract, Wood 515(23) and other Quaker pamphlets, Wood 515(14); 645(21)(22). The story of Llewellin is also in *AO*, 4.44. See also Index, 'Wood, A., ridiculous'; and 'Wood, A., lie'.

[72]For Mrs. Harrison, Wood 365(25). For Cheynell, Wood 514(26). For Edward Bysshe, Squibb and Cawley, Wood 209(1-2). For Wharton, Wood 419 (and the same at Wood 401(45)); for a photograph, see Kiessling, 'Ballads', *BLR*,

His Plans for his Books

Wood sold some manuscripts to the Bodleian Library in October 1690 and also sold some manuscripts and books to Jesus College probably at the same time. On 11 October 1692 he proposed a sale of more manuscripts and books to the Bodleian Library but his offer was rejected. Wood was always short of money and the urgent need for funds increased when, as a consequence of the suit brought against him by Henry Hyde the second earl of Clarendon, he had to pay a fine. In early January 1693 Wood drafted a letter to plead for more suitable terms of settlement. If this were not granted him, he argued, there would be the threat of other suits and to cover costs 'the author must be forced to sell the best part of his books'. On 21 August 1694 he was still desparate enough to engage in negotiations with the London bookseller, Mr. Bateman, 'about buying my books'. This, too, came to nothing. Wood was clearly not thinking of a bequest to the Ashmolean in 1694 and seems to have determined on this course only a week before his death, when the 'Total Suppression of Urine' made it clear to first his friends and then to himself that his end was imminent. At this critical time he sought a resolution to two issues of major concern: who should receive his materials for the second edition of the *Athenae*, and what would happen to his collections of books and manuscripts. Wood's executors, James Bisse, Arthur Charlett, and Thomas Tanner, were among visitors during the last ten days of his life and they helped him with both objectives. The first was taken care of when Charlett recommended in a letter to Wood on 21 November that Tanner would be 'carefull, true, faithfull and discreet in the disposition of them', that is, the materials for the *Athenae*. Wood then turned his attention to the second, the disposition of his books and manuscripts. He wrote his will on the following day, 22 November, and included the bequest to the Ashmolean Museum: 'I give to the said university all my printed books, pamphlets and papers, to be deposited in the Musaeum'. Wood's acquaintances seem to have learned of Wood's intention to bequeath his books to the Museum only on 23 November. He chose the Ashmolean Museum over the Bodleian Library because he expected it to be a major centre for antiquarian studies. The Ashmolean Museum was new, having been constructed to hold Elias Ashmole's great collections, and Wood had followed the progress of the construction of this building from the laying of the cornerstone on 14 April 1679 to the dedication on 21 May 1683. Another antiquarian, Robert Plot, was the first Keeper, and William Dugdale and John Aubrey, in addition to Ashmole, all antiquarians, had made bequests or gifts of books and manuscripts to the Museum. The first of Ashmole's collections arrived in 1683 just as Robert Plot was made Keeper; some of Dugdale's books and manuscripts arrived in 1686, shortly after his death, with the remainder in 1693; and Aubrey's gifts of books and manuscripts arrived at various times, some via Wood himself. Wood's respect for Dugdale and his son-in-law Ashmole was profound, and shortly after Wood's death, Charlett wrote to Archbishop Tenison that Wood wished his books and papers 'to be placed next his Freind Sr W. Dugdale's MSS'. Wood's relationship with Aubrey had begun in 1667 and had run hot and cold, but Aubrey's generosity to the Museum, and letters to him from Ashmole which urged fellow scholars to leave books and notes to the Museum, were passed on to Wood and must have had an effect on him. The new keeper of the Museum, Edward Lhwyd, a good friend of Aubrey, was a very competent naturalist, interested in antiquities, and seemed as if he would be a good administrator. Wood no doubt believed that his own collections, with those of Dugdale, Ashmole, and Aubrey, would form a very strong library for antiquarian studies.[73]

There remains a question about whether all of the books in his library at his death were indeed sent on to the Museum. Tanner and Bisse, on their visit of 23 November to Wood's attic rooms, noticed that there were, as Tanner wrote to the absent Charlett, 'MSS. not only those of his own collection, but also all others which he has in his possession'. The visitors persuaded Wood that 'some few of Dr Langbain's Miscellanea'

---

15 (April 1996): fig. 1, p. 265). For Williams, Wood 207(4). For Greenwood, Wood 514(49), 514(53), and 515(11). For Fisher's gift of a proof copy, Wood 534(7) and a second gift, Wood 372(13). For *Naps*, Wood 108; the quotation in *AO* is at 4.380-1.

[73]For Wood's plans to sell books, see *LT*, 3.343, 344, 404, 440. For the transfer of four books on rhetoric to the Bodleian, see the introduction to Append. VII. For Wood's draft of his complaint about terms, *LT*, 4.9. Conditions other than the fine were Wood's expulsion from the university and the burning of the some sheets of the *Athenae LT*, 4.44, 46. Charlett described Wood's illness in a letter to Archbishop Tenison dated 1 December, MS. Engl. Misc. d. 10, transcribed by Clark, *LT*, 3.497. Charlett's letter to Wood in now in MS. Tanner 24, transcribed in *LT*, 3.500. Wood's will is transcribed in *LT*, 3.502-4. For notes in his diaries on the construction of the new Museum, see references at *LT*, 5.157. See Wood's comment on Dugdale's gift of books to the Ashmolean Museum, *AOF*, 2.28. For Wood and the Ashmolean Museum, and Dugdale's bequest and Ashmole's encouragement to leave books to the Museum, see Arthur MacGregor, *Tradescant's Rarities* (Oxford, 1983): 46-52, 56. On the other collections, *LT*, 4.191; Stanley Gillam, 'Anthony Wood's Trustees and Their Friends', *BLR*, 15 (1994-6): 197; R. F. Ovenell, *The Ashmolean Museum 1683-1894* (Oxford, 1986): 58f. and 79. For Charlett's letter to Tenison on the disposal of books, *LT*, 3.499. For more the relationship between Aubrey and Wood, see p. xix and note 22.

should go to the Bodleian where they belonged. We also know that some manuscripts owned by Wood became part of the Bisse, Tanner, and Charlett collections. Recently Stanley Gillam has established the trail from Wood's study rooms to the three personal libraries and eventually to the Bodleian. Did Wood on his deathbed offer memento manuscripts and books to the three? Or did they, looking on the hundreds of bound volumes, bundles, and heaps, assume that no one would care if they took an interesting item or two? Fortunately most of these removed manuscripts eventually ended up where they should have gone in the first place, though some are not among the Wood bequests. The transmission of books from one owner to the next is less easy to determine, and it is not possible to tell which books, if any, his executors may have appropriated, along with the manuscripts. What can be said is that over 180 books are unaccounted for in the earliest Ashmolean shelf-list. The evidence that Wood at one time owned these is in his shelf-list of 1681, in certain books and manuscripts where he wrote 'habeo' at the mention of specific books, and in his records of purchases in his diary and manuscripts.[74]

What Happened to Wood's Books after 1695

The transit of the books from Wood's study rooms to the Museum must have taken place very soon after Wood's death. The Keeper, Edward Lhwyd, wrote about the event to another benefactor, Martin Lister, 'There is now such an other legacy of pamphlets as Mr. Ashmole's, left us by Mr. A. à Wood; but I intend to employ an other to make the catalogue'. He requested funds for shelving and binding immediately, in 1695-6 according to entries in the yearly account of the Vice-Chancellor: 'to Frogley the joyner for worke done in the Musaeum and for wainscott and shelves for Mr. Wood's books, 31^{li}. 4^s. 2^d', and 'to Thompson the bookbinder for binding of Statute Books and severall of Mr. Wood's bookes for the Musaeum of 16^{li}. 16^s. 10^d.' Shortly after, these newly bound books, mainly made up of bundles of pamphlets on the same topics, along with the books already bound, were given their permanent shelf-marks. In the next year another appeal for funds was successful: 'to Mr. Lloyd for taking a Catalogue of Mr. Wood's bookes given to the Musaeum, 6^{li}. 12^s.' For this catalogue, Lhwyd turned to a method often used by college librarians. He converted a copy of Thomas Hyde's monumental *Catalogus . . . Bibliothecae Bodleianae* (1674) into the Museum catalogue. He found a copy in Wood's own collection. This he had interleaved with blank sheets and instructed a sub-librarian, Robert Thomas, to enter the books from the Ashmole, Wood, and Lister benefactions. Thomas completed his work in 1698. He, and later at least five other persons, entered items that were not duplicated in the Bodleian Library on interleaved blank sheets opposite the relevant page of Bodleian entries. In the printed text they added some cross-references, corrected Bodleian shelf-marks, and made brief corrections. In the margins of the printed text there are some annotations by Wood, generally in the form of corrections, Bodleian shelf-marks, points of information about authors, translators or dates. These are usually easy to identify, though many in his hand and in the hands of other persons were cropped when the volume was rebound in the nineteenth century. Fortunately the collections of the major donors were catalogued separately and given shelf-marks which indicate the provenance. Thus we can identify those from the Ashmole legacy as beginning with 'A', and those from Wood legacy, with 'W'. Still, the value of this catalogue for the study of Wood's books is limited because it does not list all of them. Well over a thousand pamphlets and single sheets among the Wood printed items are also missing in this catalogue.[75]

---

[74]Tanner's letter is now among Charlett's papers, MS. Ballard 4, fol. 28, transcribed in *LT*, 3.501. It is possible that Wood bought these 'Miscellanea', as he had bought a number of Langbaine's books, upon the latter's death in 1659. These are the 'Adversaria Langbainiana', Bodleian Library MSS. Wood donat. 1-9. For Gillam, see *BLR*, 15 (1994-6): 187-210. Two manuscripts, MS. Wood E. 32 and E. 33, went to James Bisse, and, via G. P. Bisse, to the Bodleian; see *LT*, 3.428, plate IV. Some of these 180 books have been located and others may yet be discovered; see Append. II. The examination of his shelf-list, MS. Wood E. 2(70), has uncovered about 128 books that were in Wood's collection before his death but that are not today in his collection. Sources for books now lost include bibliographies of Prynne's publications and of works on heraldry listed by Thomas Gore: [MS.] Wood D. 22(7) and [MS.] Wood E. 3(fols. 298ff.) (items 1602, 1513). In both Wood marked many items that he owned, and some of these were never listed in any later catalogue. See Index, 'Missing'; and 'Wood, A., *habeo*'.

[75]For Lhwyd's letter to Lister, 5 December 1695, see R. W. Hunt, 'The Cataloguing of Ashmolean Collections of Books and Manuscripts', *BLR*, 4 (1952): 163; and for some evidence on the binding (10 February 1696), p. 164. For the Vice-Chancellor's accounts, *LT*, 4.85; see also 1.6, and Gillam, *BLR*, 15 (1994-6): 191-2. An earlier allocation, *LT*, 4.83, 1695-6, 'to Mr. Lloyd for taking a Catalogue of bookes in the Musaeum, 10^{li}. 10^s.', may have financed work on the Ashmolean books or an inventory of Wood's 127 manuscripts published by Edward Bernard in 1697. For binding by the Ashmolean Museum, see Append. IV. Wood's copy of Hyde's *Catalogus* is at Library Records b. 466, 467. On the binding of Wood's copy of the Hyde *Catalogus*, see Ovenell, *Ashmolean*, p. 91. Ovenell, 'Supplementary Notes on Ashmolean Catalogues', *BLR*, 14 (1991): 97-9, discusses the contributors to this *Catalogus*: Edward Lhwyd (1660-1709); John Whiteside (Keeper from 14 Dec. 1714 to his death in 1729); Robert (Robin) Thomas (Sublibrarian of the Museum, an undergraduate of Jesus College, made entries from May 1697 and in 1698 while Lhwyd away, May

Far more important in establishing exactly what was in the Museum from an early time is the 'Catalogus Librorum impressorum & manuscriptorum Domini Antonij a Wood'. The date of this manuscript had been a mystery until R. F. Ovenell determined that the task of compiling it was assigned by the Keeper John Whiteside in 1716-17 to his assistant, John Hausted. Ovenell identified the hands of both Whiteside and Hausted in the manuscript. There is also a revealing entry in the Museum accounts of 1716-7, 'Transcribing a Catalogue – 2-03-00', which almost certainly refers to the making of this shelf-list. Hausted normally entered a short title, and the city and year of publication. He followed the order of the books on the shelves, beginning with Wood 1-899 and then collections volumes of printed or manuscript items shelf-marked Wood F 1-42; Wood E 1-34; Wood D 1-33; Wood C 1-52; and Wood B 1-41. Because of the many composite volumes, this number of approximately 960 volumes in no way reflects the total number of printed items. For example, Wood 1-899 contain 5715 printed items, and an average of over six items per volume. In a few instances there were volume numbers alone without any titles entered after them. These volumes had been removed after the creation of the shelf-marks and before Hausted began his record in 1716-7. For volumes present, Hausted did not always record all the printed items in each volume. When he came to a volume containing perhaps scores of pamphlets, he often wrote only a general subject with no further details, as in the series Wood 498 to 519. These twenty-two entries have only headings such as 'Pamphlets 12' and 'Vol: 5 of Matters relating to Ireland 52 Pamphlets – in 1642, 43, 44'. Yet they contain over 400 printed items. Wood 401, 402, and 'Wood E 25', each with no further information than the headings of 'A Book of Ballads' or 'Ballads' are composite volumes of 103, 25 and 125 printed ballads, respectively (see Plate IX). Not surprisingly, Hausted failed to record a number of important works. His entry for Wood 79 is simply 'Reusneri Emblemata &c.' The ninth and last imprint in this volume is a 'rare' edition of Shakespeare's *Venus and Adonis* (1630).[76]

Of all the entries in the Whiteside Catalogus the most understated is that at Wood 276a-b, 'Miscellaneous Prints Papers &c a large Parchment. Fol.' and 'Another Smaller Fol. of the same'. Some time before 1840 these two volumes filled the vacancy of an item which had disappeared. The larger volume, 276a, includes a table of contents with the short titles and Roman numerals I-CCCCCLXXVI, of which 553 remain today. The hand is familiar but unidentified. The same staff member had also entered some of the lists of contents in volumes of pamphlets that the Museum had bound shortly after 1695. No equivalent list for Wood 276b has survived, but the numbering, including the Roman numerals, indicate that there were at one time 125 items present, of which 113 remain today. The two sources, the Whiteside Catalogus and the table of contents now at the beginning of Wood 276a, provide a valuable record of most of the contents in the bound volumes and 576 separate single sheets as they were shelved in the Museum in 1717. They also give us a good estimate of what has been removed since that year.[77]

1697-March 1701); William Williams (Underkeeper, who gave some support to Thomas and left in 1698; he is not listed among the hands listed by Ovenell); and David Parry (the assistant to Llwyd who became Keeper in 1709-14), see also Hunt, pp. 163-4. It is possible that the volume was bound shortly after 1695 and rebound in 1717-8. There is a second Hyde catalogue, also interleaved, now among the Wood books, an intrusion at Wood 660s. It is possible that Whiteside's entry in the museum account book, Michelmas 1717-8, refers to this second copy: 'A catalogue of the Books in the Bodleyan Library 00 15 00', and in the accounts for the following year, he wrote: 'Interleaving and binding Dr Hyde's Catalogue 02 02 06'. For a photograph of fol. 46, an interleaved sheet from the old Museum *Catalogus* with shelf-marks, see Kiessling, 'Library of Anthony Wood', *BLR*, 16 (1999): fig. 2, p. 481 and for the discussion, p. 480.

[76] The Whiteside Catalogus, now Library Records d. 1071, has the heading on fol. 1, and on fol. 4, 'Librorum Impressorum & MScriptorum Antonii a Wood Catalogus'. For Ovenell, 'Supplementary Notes' (1991), and *Ashmolean*: 121-2. Whiteside's entries in the Catalogus are, e.g., on f. 71, the entries F 1 and F 2 (Wood's manuscript copies of his 'History, or, Annals'). Whiteside also made other brief entries, e.g., a correction of the first [MS.] Wood C entry, f. 87, and the list of almanacs on p. vi. The Ashmolean Museum accounts are now in the Museum library, AMS 5(2), 1715-7 (pp. unnumbered). Ovenell refined Clark's date, 'before 1769' and '17-', *LT*, 1.6, and note 3 (Hunt followed Clark *BLR*, 4 (1952): 165). In the Whiteside Catalogus of Wood books, Wood items begin on f. vi with almanacs and end on f. 94. The B to F series also contains volumes of manuscripts and begins with F on f. 71 (the F series has mainly manuscripts). At the end, ff. 95-105, are listed manuscripts given by Dugdale, William Kingsley, John Aubrey, and Edward Morgan. The upper flyleaves, i-viii, were added in the nineteenth century, at the time of binding; some include earlier manuscript fragments pasted in, e.g., f. vi lists some 60 almanacs. Hausted had nothing to record at vacancies such as Wood 11 and [MS.] Wood E. 34. These were later filled with works published after Wood's death in 1695 (e.g., 11a, 11b, and 11c). Other places were left vacant: Wood 449, 692 and [MS.] Wood C. 50. For intrusions, see Append. IV, note 11.

[77] The entries of 276a and b in the Whiteside Catalogus are on ff. 19^v and 20. The volume removed is listed as '276 The Last Will & Testament of Cardinal Mazarini &c. Lond: 1663 [and] Some historical Remarks of the Life of Card: Mazarini Lond: 1664' (Wing H3084). Other volumes were also added, Wood 276c-e, but these do not hold Wood items. See notes at Wood 276a(1) and 276b(1). For 276b, the original Roman numerals range from I-XCIX, but there

Wood's original organisation by subjects as it existed in his shelf-list of 1681 was ignored when the volumes were arranged in the Ashmolean Museum. For example, the first thirty-three entries on his 'poeticall shelf beginning at the north end', include works by Baldwin (*Mirror for Magistrates*), Cartwright (*Royal Slave*), Coryate, Dekker, Drayton, Gascoigne, Gayton, Harvey, Lod. Lloyd, Lucian (trans. Hicks), Nash, Rainolds (*Overthrow of Stage Plays*), Sidney, Spenser, Tasso (trans., Fraunce), Vergil (trans. Twyne), Udall, and Donne. Those surviving are now scattered about at Wood 116, 328, 329, 330, 334, 482, 483, 487, 591, 616, 654, 887, [MS.] Wood B. 27, [MS.] Wood B. 30, and [MS.] Wood B. 39. If there was any principle to the organisation of these books and pamphlets in shelf-mark sequence in the Ashmolean Museum, it was by size. This was generally consistent, though different formats may occur throughout. The shelf-marks seem to have been assigned as volumes were randomly picked up from the boxes in which they arrived at the Museum. This could mean that there were sequences of volumes on similar topics, as from Wood 230 to 250, on kings and monarchy, but it could also mean that volumes on this topic could be far removed from this sequence, as some are. If individual volumes bound by the Ashmolean contain works on the same subject, it is usually because they were gathered together by Wood in bundles which the Museum then sent to binders. Often the volumes bound by the Ashmolean contain unrelated items.[78]

Volumes that were commissioned to be bound after their arrival at the Museum are also easy to identify. The first bindings were apparently twenty-six of Wood's own pasteboard bindings rebound in more handsome quarter-calf with brown paper over the pasteboard. None of these have the fore-edges cut and all retain Wood's marginalia. Most have a table of contents by Wood. Eighty-five others are bound in handsome calf, mainly smooth, but sometimes rough, with 3 fillets on the covers and blind-stamp decoration, dragons or flowers, inside corners. Unfortunately when Lhwyd sent the latter material to the binders, he gave no specific instructions to protect the manuscript marginalia or printed contents. The binders cut all the edges and in doing so cropped some manuscript or printed material in almost every volume they bound. After the return of the volume, a sub-librarian entered, in the manner of Wood, the contents on the upper flyleaves of these volumes, always with Roman numerals (as opposed to Wood's practice of using Arabic numerals), usually followed by the title, city and year. They were not always accurate and one of the compilers had difficulty with Roman numerals. Perhaps the same one seems never to have warmed up to the task and in one item wrote, 'Dabit Deus his quoque finem'.[79]

The second major survey of the Wood collection of printed items took place more than a century later. In 1837 the Underkeeper William Kirtland began an examination of each volume in the Wood collection as it was described in the Whiteside Catalogus. Over the next four years he marked fifty-two volumes that were missing and summarised his findings on an inserted page at the beginning of the Catalogus. In some cases these missing volumes contained as many as a hundred or more printed items. If these individual items within volumes were not listed in the Catalogus, we have no idea of the specific number, or the titles, of works that were stolen. Another discovery by Kirtland was that in a number of the composite volumes that remain in the library, individual works had been cut or torn out. He made desolate notes of these, such as 'deest Octr. 15. 1839 W. K.', both in the Whiteside Catalogus and in the lists on the upper flyleaves (see Plate I).[80]

---

were irregularities, e.g., current items, 44 - 68, are not numbered in Roman numerals. There is today a gap at nos. 20-24, and notes, e.g., at items 33, 39, explain that certain items are 'not here [1881]'. Item 1 was removed, another note explains, 'William Grent's World map 1641 placed in the map collection after repair EJS Parsons 16/6/59'.

[78]For the 'poeticall shelf', MS. Wood E. 2(70), pp. 49-50. The editions of Drayton, Rainolds, and Vergil are lost. For bundles arranged by Wood but bound by the Ashmolean, see p. xxvi and note 38, above, and Append. IV. For a mishmash of contents in volumes bound by the Ashmolean, see Wood 487 and 704. Some have numerous duplicates, e.g., Wood 612, indicating why Wood left the bundle or heap unbound.

[79]For the first twenty-six bindings, see above, p. xxvi and note 38, Append. IV, and Index, 'Binders and cropping'. For an omission by the Ashmolean recorder of eleven items in the table of contents, see Wood 657. For errors in Roman numerals, see Wood 610(1). The quotation, 'God will bring an end even to this', is at Wood 645(25).

[80]For the second survey, see Ovenell, *Ashmolean*: 204, 'In 1837 Kirtland and Black together surveyed and issued a written report on the condition of the Wood collection of books and manuscripts.' W. H. Black, a manuscript specialist, did the Wood manuscripts (but see an exception at item 1148). On fol. viii of Library Records d. 1071, Kirtland listed 53 volumes: 'The following Books from Wood's Lib^y now missing Novr. 25th. 1837 [/] No — 1, 50, 51, 56, 57, 58, 61, 63, 64, 66, 74, 77, 86, 94, 110b, 120, 123, 132, 161, 192, 201, 276, 282, 298, 324, 386 [lined out, found], 395, 399 (seven Sempill ballads), 400 (100 Roxburghe and Euing ballads), 440, 449, 454 [lined out, found], 490, 586 [lined out, found], 660ee [added later, not a Wood volume], 692, 729, 734, 748a, 748b, 749, 755, 758, 790, 791, 802, 827, 842, 881, 887, 887b, E 25 [since found], C 30 [probably an error for C. 50]'. With the four 'found' volumes and 660ee, which does not contain Wood books, the total comes to forty-eight missing volumes. Kirtland's continued checking for missing items until 1841 and his desolate note occurs frequently in the lists on the upper flyleaves, see the Index, 'Kirtland, William' and Append. IV, note 1, and p. 694

These volumes and printed items within volumes disappeared because the early Keepers of the Museum were often less than competent and security was often nonexistent. The Keeper Edward Lhwyd acted quickly when the Wood bequest came to the Museum, but he was absent from the library from May 1697 to March 1701, and his assistants were careless. His successor in 1709, David Parry, has been called an idle toper. His successor in 1714, John Whiteside, turned his attention to the printed books and in 1716 commissioned a catalogue to be made. The help was sometimes good, sometimes not. Ovenell gives an amusing description of one of the incompetents helpers of Lhwyd, Gilacholuim, or Giliecholum McMulen, or William MacCullum. MacCullum left his name in various places, including the flyleaves of a Bible, where the names of Lhwyd and Parry are also present. During the periods of uneven supervision in the Ashmolean Museum John Bagford, Richard Rawlinson and Humfrey Wanley were allowed free run of the library and while none of these may have been guilty of theft, all three were among the many who had access to the Museum library room. Anyone could have removed at any time bound volumes, items from bound volumes, or loose pamphlets that we know were present at one time. Only in rare instances have we been lucky enough to discover where some of these stolen items are.[81]

In a major reorganisation of the holdings in the Ashmolean Museum and the Bodleian Library in 1860, printed books including the Wood volumes were transferred to the Bodleian Library. Sixty years later, in 1922, R. T. Milford, a Bodleian staff member, prepared the third major survey, a 'Hand-list of Wood Printed Books' in Wood 1-899. Milford recorded only the short titles and years of publication and his shelf-list is more complete than that found in the Whiteside Catalogus because he usually recorded information for all the pamphlets in a composite volume. Exceptions are Wood 401 and 402, where he twice entered only 'Book of ballads', instead of listing the 103 and 25 individual ballads. He did not make lists of the contents of Wood 276a, 276b, and Wood Almanacs A-F, Wood Diaries and [MS.] Wood B-F, to which he was apparently not assigned. He gave no indication that he consulted the Whiteside Catalogus, and he listed none of the information in that volume such as the titles of volumes or works that Kirtland had marked as missing or the titles that were missing in composite volumes even if these titles were to be found on the upper flyleaves. He made a record only of the printed items that he saw in the volume before him.

Today anyone with access to the 'Bodleian Library Pre-1920 Catalogue of Printed Books on Compact Disc' can generate a list of all records with the shelf-mark 'Wood'. This exercise, in February 2002, produced a list of 5635 records. Since the library actually holds over 6500 Wood printed items, this version of the pre-1920 catalogue must be used with caution. By design, it does not contain the Wood newsbooks, music books, engravings, maps and many almanacs and lists duplicate items only once. Still, it also omits over 200 other Wood printed items which are in this bibliography. There is also a caveat for those who wish to locate a Wood item by consulting the standard Wing catalogue. The Wing record of what is held in the Bodleian Library is far from perfect, and for the Wood holdings alone 322 entries in Wing do not indicate, by 'O', that the Library holds a copy. There are also over 180 Wood publications that do not appear at all in the current Wing bibliography. The on-line ESTCR is a far superior research tool and incorporates a number of the missing items, especially ballads, that are not in Wing. It is still not a perfect record, but it changes every day as new entries are added and older entries are reedited. As of January 2001 it lacked entries for over 160 Wood items.[82]

---

[81]Ovenell, *Ashmolean*: 101-2; for Ovenell on Lhwyd away from the Museum, pp. 90-1; on Parry, p. 110. The Bible in which MacCullum left his name is at Wood 873(1). His name is also in Wood 704(1). For another scribble by MacCullum see Ashm. 825. Two significant thefts were of ballads, Wood 399 and 400, some time before 1837. The individual ballads are now in Roxburghe collection in the British Library and in the Euing collection in the University of Glasgow Library. See Kiessling, 'Ballads', *BLR*, 15 (1996): 260-291. For items that have been discovered, see Append. II, the thirty-eight shelf-marks and libraries before the final list of 'MISSING BEFORE 1717'.

[82]The Ashmolean Trustees offered to transfer several collections of printed books to the Bodleian 'to facilitate the devotion of a part of the building to the purposes of an Examination School', see W.D. Macray, *Annals of the Bodleian Library*, 2nd ed. (Oxford, 1890): 364-5. There are seventy-six music, almanac, and engraving items not in the CD catalogue. C. J. Hindle compiled a list of almanacs in 1933, see notes at Wood Alm. A(1); for A. Clark's extensive record of Wood's notes in 39 almanac diaries, see [MS.] Wood Diaries 1. About 225 duplicates in the Wood collection have only one entry in the CD catalogue. The 160 items missing from the ESTCR record (to be added soon) are truly 'rare' items. For more on the use of 'rare' and item numbers of 'rare' books, see Append. V, especially notes 1-3. While the collection has never been more carefully protected than today, occasionally volumes are mislaid. Wood 531, with thirty items, has been missing since 1994 and was not seen for this study. The volume has had a chequered history. There were over forty items present in 1717, for the Whiteside Catalogus has a partial table of contents, listing fifteen titles and references to more than thirty other items. In 1922, working with what he saw in the volume before him, Milford made thirty entries in his 'Hand-list', but two entries, items 1 and 26, were at that time 'missing'. Some items in the latest Wing compact disk catalogue (Alexandria, VA: Chadwyck-Healey,

The printed items in the collection of Anthony Wood make up one of the greatest assembled in the seventeenth century. It is today one of the jewels in the Bodleian Library and valued for a variety of reasons, certainly not only as Wood himself might have predicted, for the publications in history, antiquarian studies, and the numerous Oxford matters. The collection is also highly esteemed for its holdings in the cultural history of daily life in the seventeenth century ranging from pamphlets of trials, dying speeches, hangings, political battles, book catalogues, almanacs, travels, marvels, and the occult to the hundreds of single-sheet ballads, advertisements, and notices. Over 1000 of these publications are rare and are known to exist only in the Bodleian Library (see Append. V). We would know his world far less well without his legacy. We also marvel at his energy, rigorous standards, and thoroughness as he made unflinching observations of daily life in a seventeenth-century university in his diaries and made use of these diaries, of his library of printed books and of his rich manuscript collection to develop the new genre of biographical and bibliographical writing. This crusty fellow, average in ability, but with a driving zeal, has given us a view of life in seventeenth-century Oxford and England from his earliest memories of his schoolboy days in Oxford and Thame, to his vivid annotations in the books in his library, to his will where he recorded his dying wish that his books and manuscripts be given to the Ashmolean Museum. In this collection, now in the Bodleian Library, readers of the present and future will find a 'perfect Elysium' in reading antiquarian books.

---

ca. 1996) are not in the ESTCR.

ABBREVIATIONS AND CONVENTIONS

The entries are written in as compressed a form as possible. The order is alphabetical, with books under the same author or heading following in order of the year of publication (no attempt has been made to order according to specific day or month within a year). References to Wood's diary, *The Life and Times of Anthony Wood, Antiquary, of Oxford, 1632-1695*, ed. A. Clark; and Wood's *Athenae Oxonienses*, ed. P. Bliss, are included whenever relevant.

In the bibliographical description of printed items, the pagination of unnumbered pages begins, in double brackets, with first printed page and ends with last printed page. Blank sheets at beginning or at end are not included. Blank pages internally, enclosed by unnumbered printed pages, are included in a number enclosed in double brackets.

In the citations of signatures and folio pages, all are to the recto side unless a ^{v}, verso, is included. Hence C3 is the recto side of C3 and C3^v is the verso side.

Incorrect Bodleian Library shelf-marks in the CD catalogue have been corrected, e.g., Wood 617(7) to Wood 615(7). Inconsistent shelf-marks have been regularized, e.g., from Wood 614(17) and Wood 614(17*) to Wood 614(17a) and Wood 614(17b); or from Wood 609(20), Wood 609(20a), and Wood 609(20b) to Wood 609(20a), Wood 609(20b), and Wood 609(20c).

For notes on upper pastedown or flyleaves in a composite (coupled) volume, see the first item in the volume. For notes on lower flyleaves or pastedown, see last item in the volume.

Expansions of Wood's standard abbreviations in his notes are generally silent e.g., ā, ō, 1^d, y^e, y^o, y^r, y^t, w^n, w^t, w^{ch} (and commonly abbreviated forms for Christmas, per, pro and said) are generally written out as an or am, on or om, lord, the, you, your, that, when, what, which. I have not expanded where the abbreviated form(s) occur in Wood's signature with accompanying details, e.g., 'Oxōn' is generally retained, and where the abbreviated form is customarily used today or easy to interpret, e.g., ^{d}, for denarius, or pence; ^{s} for shilling, and C^o Oxō for county Oxon, or Oxfordshire. Non-standard abbreviations, misspellings, superscripts and punctuation, are retained. Older style use of 'j' is normally changed to modern 'i', and 'v' to 'u' in printed titles. Exceptions occur when specific older style spellings help to determine one edition from another or are manuscript transcriptions.

[/]	a line break or a paragraph break
*	following an author heading, indicates the name of the person who is the subject of the item, not the author (not used in sections of Sale and Auction Catalogues or Prospectuses and Specimen Pages)
1717 list	a manuscript list of contents of the 576 items in Wood 276a. See item 5241
a.	in the format of an entry: and
abp.	archbishop
Adams	H. M. Adams, *Catalogue of Books Printed on the Continent of Europe, 1501-1600 in Cambridge Libraries* (Cambridge, 1967)

anon.	anonymous
AO	Anthony A Wood, *Athenae Oxonienses*, ed. P. Bliss, 3rd ed., 4 vols. (London, 1813-1820)
AOF	Anthony A Wood, *Athenae Oxonienses . . . the Fasti*, ed. P. Bliss, 3rd ed. (London, 1813-1820)
ap.	*apud*
Append.	Appendix to *The Library of Anthony Wood*
ARCR	A. F. Allison and D. M. Rogers, *The Contemporary Printed Literature of the English Counter-Reformation between 1558 and 1640*, 2 vols. (Aldershot, 1989-94)
Ashm.	Ashmolean Museum
attrib.	attributed to
AW	Anthony Wood
Bib. Bod.	Bodleian Library (Wood's common abbreviation)
bibliop.	*bibliopola*
Bibl. Lyon.	J. Baudrier, *Bibliographie Lyonnaise* (Lyon and Paris, 1895-1950)
BL	British Library; when underscored, item examined at the British Library, London
BL T	British Library, Thomason collection
BLR	*Bodleian Library Record*
BN	Bibliothèque Nationale
Bodl.	Bodleian Library
bp.	bishop
books sold by	or books printed by. After formatting and page numbers, there may be a note of a list of book advertisements usually inserted by a publisher or press on unnumbered pages at the end of a book. Wood sometimes marked items in these lists
brackets, round	information printed on a page other than the title page
brackets, square	information not printed in the text, but added
bsm.	bookseller's price mark, that is, a code involving numbers and/or letters
bund.	bundle, or pile, of printed or manuscript items in Wood's rooms
ca.	*circa*
cat.	catalogue
ch.ch., Ch.Ch.	Wood's abbreviations for Christ Church Oxford

Clark	William Andrews Clark Library; when underscored, item examined at the Clark Library, Los Angeles, CA
cp.	compare
CM	Cambridge, Magdalene College, Pepys Library
d	*denarius* or pence
DNB	*Dictionary of National Biography* (London, 1882ff.)
dupl.	duplicate
ed.	edited by or edition
engr.	engraving
Engraved Portraits	F. O'Donoghue, *Catalogue of Engraved British Portraits Preserved in the British Museum*, 6 vols. (London, 1908-25)
ESTCR	English Short Title Catalog Record prepared by the Research Libraries Information Network (RLIN, www.rlg.org) (those items in Wood's library that had not been recorded in the ESTCR were sent to the ESTCR in 2001)
Euing collection	William Euing (1788-1874) bequeathed his collection to the Glasgow University Library. It includes some Wood ballads that had migrated from the Ashmolean Museum to the Roxburghe collection, and then to the possession of James Orchard Halliwell, and to Euing
excud.	*excudebat* or *excudebant*
exprim.	*exprimebat* or *exprimebant*
F	Joseph Foster, *Alumni Oxonienses*, 1500-1714 (Oxford, 1891-2)
f.	in the printer or publisher line of an entry: for
f., ff.	folio, folios
FFMadan	Francis F. Madan, *A New Bibliography of the Eikon Basilike*, *OBS*, NS vol. 3 (1949) (Oxford, 1950)
Folg	Folger Library; when underscored, item examined at the Folger Library, Washington, D.C.
Gibson	S. Gibson, *Early Oxford Bindings*, *OBS* (Oxford, 1903)
GW	*Gesamtkatalog der Wiegendrucke* (Leipzig, Stuttgart, 1925-1992)
Hearne	*Remarks and Collections*, ed. by C. E. Doble, et al., 11 vols (Oxford, 1885-1921)
Harv	Harvard University; when underscored, item examined at the Houghton Library at Harvard University
hatching	in descriptions of binding, blind lines either on the top and bottom of the spine, or on the top and bottom edges of the boards, usually within an inch of the spine. The latter hatching is an indication of Oxford binding. See Pearson, pp. 37-9

Historia	Antonius à Wood, *Historia et antiquitates universitatis Oxoniensis*, 2 vols. (Oxonii, 1674)
Hist. and Antiq.	Anthony à Wood, *The History and Antiquities of the University of Oxford and of the Colleges and Halls*, ed. J. Gutch, 3 vols. in 4 (Oxford, 1792-96 and 1786)
Holland	the more inclusive term, Netherlands, is used in the subject catalogue
Hunt	The Huntington Library; when underscored, item examined at the Huntington Library, San Marino, CA
HUO	*The History of the University of Oxford Vol. IV Seventeenth-Century Oxford*, ed. N. Tyacke (Oxford, 1997)
IA	*Index Aureliensis catalogus librorum sedecimo saeculo impressorum* (Aureliae Aquensis, 1965ff.)
illeg.	illegible
impen.	*impensis*
imp.	*imprimebat* or *impressis*
imperf.	imperfect
intro.	introduction
Intro.	Introduction to *The Library of Anthony Wood*, pp. ix-xlix
Ker	N. R. Ker, *Fragments of Medieval Manuscripts Used as Pastedowns in Oxford Bindings*, *OBS*, NS vol. 5 (1951-2) (Oxford 1954)
Keynes	G. Keynes, *John Evelyn: A Study in Bibliophily with a Bibliography of his Writings*, 2nd ed. (Oxford, 1968)
Kirtland	William Kirtland, the Underkeeper at the Ashmolian Museum. Kirtland made an inventory of Wood's books, 1837-1841
li	*libra*, that is, pound
LT	*The Life and Times of Anthony Wood*, ed. A. Clark, 5 vols. (Oxford Historical Society, 1891-1900)
Macd. & Harg.	H. Macdonald and M. Hargreaves, *Thomas Hobbes a Bibliography* (London, 1952)
Macdonald	H. Macdonald, *John Dryden; a Bibliography of Early Editions and of Drydeniana* (Oxford, 1939)
Macray	W. D. Macray, *Annals of the Bodleian Library*, 2nd ed. (Oxford, 1890)
Madan	Falconer Madan, *Oxford Books*, 3 vols. (Oxford, 1895-1931), from 1486 to 1680
marq.	marquis or marquess
Milford hand-list	'Hand-list of Wood Printed Books', a manuscript shelf-list made in 1922 by a Bodleian Library Assistant, R. T. Milford

missing in 1837	noted in 1837-41 as missing in the Whiteside cat. by the Underkeeper of the Ashmolean Museum, William Kirtland
missing in 1922	noted in 1922 in the Milford hand-list as missing in the Wood collection
Morrish	P. S. Morrish, *Dr. Higgs and Merton College Library*, in *Leeds Philosophical and Literary Society, Lit. and Hist. Section*, 21, pt. 2 (Leeds, 1988): 131-201
ms., mss.	manuscript, manuscripts
MS. Wood E. 2(70)	Wood's catalogue of printed books in his possession in 1681. Those no longer in the Wood collection are entered in this current catalogue with a reference to the page number in MS. Wood E. 2(70). See Appendix II
n.d.	no date given
N & S	*British Newspapers and Periodicals, 1641-1700: A Short-title Catalogue of Serials*, compiled by C. Nelson and M. Seccombe (New York, 1987)
no., nos.	number, numbers
n.p.	no place
n.pub.	no publisher
NUC	*National Union Catalog*
numb. numbs.	number, numbers; used in newsbook entries
NYPL	New York Public Library; when underscored, item examined at the New York Public Library, New York City
O	Oxford; when underscored, item examined at the Bodleian Library, Oxford
ob.	obolus, that is, a halfpenny
obl.	oblong printing, that is, horizontally, on a single sheet
OBS	*Oxford Bibliographical Society*
olim	formerly
o.s.	old style, here, meaning the year beginning on 25 March, which Wood normally used
p	pence
p., pp.	page, pages
Pearson	D. Pearson, *Oxford Bookbinding 1500-1640*, *OBS*, 3rd series vol. 3 (Oxford, 2000)
Pennington	R. Pennington, *A Descriptive Catalogue of the Etched Work of Wenceslaus Hollar* (Cambridge, 1982)
prob.	probably
Proctor	R. Proctor, *Index to Early Printed Books in the British Museum* (London, 1898-1901)

prox.	usually in '*v. prox. p.*', Wood's abbreviation for see nearest page
pseud.	pseudonym or fictional name
pt., pts.	part, parts
pub., publ.	published, publisher
q. or qu.	Wood's abbreviations for either '*quaere*', i.e., query; or 'quarto'
q.v.	which see
r	*recto* page, normally assumed and not noted
(rare)	a printed item for which the STC or Wing lists a single location. If there is more than one copy at the Bodleian Library, that is noted in round brackets, e.g., (rare, 2 at O); see also (two), below, and Appendix V
red chalk	Wood used red ink for underscoring and making frames to surround his list of contents in a volume. At times he used a red chalk, which has over time faded to an orange/red colour (see Plates I and III)
ref.; refs.	reference; references
resp.	*respondens,* one who defends a thesis
Rox. Ballads	*The Roxburghe Ballads*, ed. Wm. Chappell, 3 vols. (London, 1871)
rpt. of	reprint of an earlier edition published at
s	shilling
same hand in Wood 276a	a note concerning the lists of contents in the composite volumes bound by the Ashmolean Museum; many lists in these volumes are by the same librarian who recorded the list in Wood 276a (28 lists are so marked)
SC	*Summary Catalogue of Western Manuscripts in the Bodleian Library* (Oxford, 1922ff.)
sign.	signature
s.m.	shelf-mark, or a press-mark
Shirley	R. W. Shirley, *The Mapping of the World* (London, 1993)
Speed, *Prospect*	J. Speed, *A Prospect of the Most Famous Parts of the World* (London, 1627)
Speed, *Theatre*	J. Speed, *The Theatre of the Empire of Great Britaine*, (London, 1611ff.)
s.sh.	single sheet, or broadside; normally no distinction is made between quarto, folio, and large folio single sheets
s.sh. Pp. 2	the *verso* of the single sheet is numbered page 2
s.sh. (r-v)	single sheet, or broadside printed on both sides
STC	*Short-Title Catalogue of Books Printed in England*, rev. W. A. Jackson & F. S. Ferguson, completed by K. F. Pantzer, 2nd ed., 3 vols. (London, 1986-91)

Steele	R. Steele, *Bibliotheca Lindesiana* (vol. 5), *A Bibliography of Royal Proclamations*, 1 and 2 (Oxford, 1910). Citations are to part 1 unless stated otherwise. Steele references are not used passim.
t	title
Thomason	the G. Thomason tracts (1640-61) in the British Library, now available in the British Library rare book room in facsimile
t leaf	title leaf
tp, tpp	title page and title pages
trans.	translator or translated by
(two)	following the STC or Wing number; the catalogue lists only two locations; see more at Sample Entry, 10, p. lviii
typ.	*typis, typographia, typographica* or *typographum*
Union	Union Theological Seminary; when underscored, item examined at the Union Theological Seminary, New York
v	*verso* page
v.	*vide*, that is, see
var.	variant, used in line recording STC, Wing, or ESTCR entry
VD	*Verzeichnis der im deutschen Sprachbereich erschienenen Drucke des XVI. Jahrhunderts* (Stuttgart, 1983-97)
Venn	John and J. A. Venn, *Alumni Cantabrigienses ... 1751* (Cambridge, 1922-7)
visct.	viscount
vol., vols.	volume, volumes
Wing	D. Wing, *Short-Title Catalogue of Books Printed ... 1641-1700*, 2nd ed., 4 vols. (New York, 1982-1998)
Wing,	in the STC/Wing line: followed by variations in the Wing entry; these may indicate either different printings or settings if not errors in Wing
Whiteside cat.	a 'Catalogus' of Wood's printed books commissioned by the Keeper of the Ashmolean Museum, John Whiteside, in 1716 and finished a year later
Yale	Yale University; when underscored, item examined at the Beinecke Library (Yale University)

Sample Entry

A typical entry is broken down into the following ten fields.

1. Smith, John.
2. *A letter of ... John Smith [13 Jan.]*
3. London:
4. R. Royston a. N. Brooks,
5. 1665.
6. 4°. 3rd ed. Pp. [24], 166 [2]; [24], 338 (2 tpp) (misnumbering).
7. Pasteboard (blue) with parchment spine.
8. Annotations.
9. Wood 000.
10. Wing A000.

The order for headings is alphabetical. If there are multiple entries under a single heading, the order is chronological, by year of publication. No attempt has been made to arrange by date within a year. Entries published between 1 January and 25 March in the following year and given the old style date of 1641[2] are listed under 1641.

1. Heading, in **bold font**. In case of peers and churchmen, the title or position follows in normal font. If the work is edited or translated, the editor's or translator's name follows in normal font. If the author is unknown, the heading is a prominent name in the title, e.g., Jamaica, Garland, or the first word(s) in the title. Alternate names are listed in Appendix I.

2. Title, in *italic font*. Double brackets of dates indicate information present on the title page in a different form, e.g., for 'the thirteenth of January', [13 Jan.], or not present in the title. Each ellipsis is noted by an ellipsis symbol (. . .)

3. Place of publication. Single brackets indicate information found on pages other than the title page. Double brackets indicate information not present in the printed item.

4. Printer or publisher. Single brackets indicate information found on pages other than the title page. Double brackets indicate information not present in the printed item.

5. Year of publication. Single brackets indicate information found elsewhere than on the initial title page. Double brackets indicate information is not given formally on the title page.

6. Format, edition number, number of pages or of folios, or signatures in Wood's copy. Page or folio numbers begin with the first page of print and end with the last page of print; unnumbered pages are enclosed in double brackets. If Wood's copy is obviously flawed, there is a brief comment on the integrity of the item. If a list of books for sale with the publisher's name is included, usually after the end of the text, this is mentioned (see Append. VIII).

7. Binding details are incorporated in the entry of the first item in a volume immediately after and

on the same line as the format information. Wood's bindings are pasteboard (grey), i.e., with no covering; or a blue paper cover over the pasteboard (blue) and a parchment spine, and with the first upper and last lower flyleaves, marbled paper. Other bindings are described in very general terms to indicate to specialists what might be of interest.

8. A new line begins with a record of the annotations. If the entry is the first item in a composite (coupled) volume of more than one printed item, Wood or the librarian at the Ashmolean made a list of the contents which is briefly described. Wood enclosed his lists in frames mainly of red ink but some times in red chalk (see Plates I and III). Wood's annotations follow, described in as much detail, and with as many abbreviations, as possible. Wood normally wrote in dark ink. If the annotation is in pencil or red ink, that is generally noted. Annotation by other persons is recorded briefly. References to printed items are to their shelf-marks or item numbers, or to both. See Appendix II for a shelf-mark/record number concordance. For signatures of names of former owners, see Appendix III. For more information about persons or places that appear in the notes, see the Index. If Wood recorded the acquisition in his diary, as here, there is a note and a reference to LT, A. Clark's *The Life and Times of Anthony Wood*, vols. 1-3.

9. A new line begins with the Bodleian Library shelf-mark, and, if the item is not entered or is incorrectly entered in the Bodleian Library CD Catalogue, a parenthetical comment notes this, e.g., '(not in Bodl. CD cat.)'. Bodleian shelf-marks have been regularized to the sequence found in the volume itself. In certain volumes of ballads, the folio sequences, e.g., 1-4, 5-8, noting a single ballad, have been translated to 1, 2 (and the volume of twenty-five ballads, in the Bodl. CD catalogue, 1-100, is in this catalogue 1-25). The Bodl. CD catalogue numbers are present on the format line of each entry.

10. The STC or Wing reference number follows. If '(rare)' follows, the item is known to exist in only one library (i.e., the Bodleian Library; see Append. V). If '(one)' follows, the item is found only in one location, and Wing did not include the Wood copy in his list. If '(two)' follows, the item can be found at two locations only. If the item is not in the STC or Wing, or if the STC or Wing entry does not list a Bodleian copy, that is stated, e.g., 'O' not in Wing. If the item is missing from the Wood collection, copies at various libraries may have been checked. In all over 600 editions identical or similar to those missing from the Wood collection were examined in other libraries. The libraries in which copies were checked are in italics, as *O, BL, Hunt, Harv, Folg*. Variant titles, or errors, in Wing or the STC follow in single brackets, as (Wing, Smithe) or (STC, Smithe). Each variation is separated by 'and'.

THE LIBRARY OF ANTHONY WOOD

1. A., E. *News indeed: Winchester taken. Together with . . . the great victory . . . at Alsford*. London: f. L. Blaiklock, 1644. 4°. Pp. 8.
Dupl. at Wood 612(13).
Wood 377(2). Wing N1031.

2. A., E. *News indeed: Winchester taken. Together with . . . the great victory . . . at Alsford*. London: f. L. Blaiklock, 1644. 4°. Some cropping at top and bottom. Pp. 8.
AW wrote 'Dupl', in pencil. Dupl. at Wood 377(2).
Wood 612(13). Wing N1031.

3. A., E., and S. E. *A letter from his majesties quarters at Newcastle, containing the substance of the kings answer to the Scots commissioners*. London: E. G., 1646. 4°. Pp. 8 (i.e., [1-2], 3-5, 4-6).
Tp, modern notes.
Wood 501(28). Wing A4.

4. A., N. *A true and perfect account of the discovery of a . . . plot . . . by the Jesuites in Ireland, for the destroying of the duke of Ormond*. London: f. R. T., 1679. 4°. Pp. [2], 5.
Wood 510(33). Wing A20.

5. A., T. *Religio clerici*. London: f. H. Brome, 1681. 12°. No frontisp. in this issue. Pp. [12], 96. Pasteboard (blue) with parchment spine. 1st upper and last lower flyleaves, marbled paper.
Backing, fragments of a sheet with titles written by AW ('Art of simpling', at Wood 729(3) (missing), is visible). Flyleaf, upper, 3rd, AW wrote 'There is a book extant called <u>Religio Laici</u>. pen'd by John Driden the poet Laureat. But that book I have not as yet.' (there is a copy at Wood 320(1), item 2320).
Wood 773(1). Wing A32.

6. [Abbot], George. Canterbury, abp. of. *A briefe description of the whole worlde*. London: T. H[arper] sold W. Sheares, 1636. 12°. Pp. [2], 350, [5] (wanting engr. tp). Calf with 2 fillets, blind-stamped 'A W' on covers.
Cover, upper, inside, AW's book-plate, mostly torn out (see Index, 'Wood, A., bookplate'). Flyleaf, upper, signature of Edward Wood, Robert W[ood]– and other notes, washed out. Pp. 3-87, 141-150, 217, some underscoring and frequent lines in margins; 187, correction, prob. none by AW. Flyleaf, lower, 2nd^v, scribbles, not by AW.
Wood 150. STC 32.

7. Abbot, George. Canterbury, abp. of. *Cheap-side crosse censured and condemned by a letter sent from the vicechancellour and other learned men of . . . Oxford . . . As also some . . . arguments . . . by . . . John Archer*. London: A. N. f. I. R., 1641. 4°. Pp. [2], 14.
Tp, bsm.
Wood 514(6). Wing A64. Not Madan 979.

8. Abercromby, David. *Ars artium: or, the art of divine converse. A new-years-gift*. London: f. the author, sold S. Smith, 1683. 12°. Pp. [12], 55.
Tp, bsm.
Wood 792(4). Wing A79 (rare).

9. Aberdeen, University. *Augustissimo, illustrissimo, et serenissimo monarchae, Carolo secundo . . . Collegii regii universitatis Aberdonensis patrono*. [Aberdeen]: [J. Brown], [1660]. S.sh. obl.
LT 1.351.
Wood 276a(411a). Wing A90 (rare). Aldis 1624.

10. Aberdeen, University. *Dimidium plus toto. Theses logicae . . . praeside Patricio Sandilandio [12 July]*. [Aberdeen]: J. Brunus, [1660]. S.sh.
Wood 276a(411b). Wing S655 (rare). Aldis 1677.

11. Aberdeen, University. Marischal College. *Wee under-subscribers masters and professors in the colledge of New-Aberdeen, are constrained by pressing necessity to give this candid declaration*. [Oxford]: n.pub., [1660]. S.sh.
ᵛ, '1660', in pencil. LT 1.351.
Wood 423(35). Wing A92A (rare). Madan 2515.

12. Abergavenny. *The popes down-fall, at Abergaveny, or a true and perfect relation of his being carried through the fair in a solemn procession*. London: f. T. C. a. N. L., 1679. 4°. Pp. [2], 6.
[MS.] Wood B. 40(15). Wing P2931.

13. Academy of Pleasure. *Academy of pleasure*. London: f. J. Stafford & W. Gilbertson, 1656. 12°. Pp. [8], 128, [12].
Missing in 1837. 'Academy of Pleasure – Lond. 1656' in Whiteside cat.
Wood 63(1). Wing A159 (two). *O*(two), *Harv*.

14. Adam Bell.* *Adam Bell, Clim of the Clough, and William of Cloudesle*. London: E. Cotes, f. F. Grove, 1661. 4°. A-C⁴ (C4 blank).
Wood 321(6). Wing A472A (rare).

15. Adams, Richard. Οιχια . . . *The {earthly and heavenly} building, opened in a sermon . . . at the funeral of . . . Henry Hurst*. London: f. J. Weld, [1690] MDCIC. 4°. Pp. [4], 29, [1] (1 p. books printed for Weld).
Tp, author's name underscored in red ink. Pp. 22-25, vertical lines in margin, at details of Hurst's and others' lives, in red ink and pencil. AO 4.273-5.
Wood 634(8) (not in Bodl. CD cat.). Wing A490.

16. [Addison, Lancelot]. *A modest plea for the clergy*. London: f. W. Crook, 1677. 8°. Pp. [8], 164, [11] (11 pp. books printed f. Crook). Pasteboard (blue) with parchment spine. Last lower flyleaf, marbled paper; rebacked.
Flyleaf, upperᵛ, AW wrote the titles of 2 printed works in this vol., within guidelines made with red ink. Pasteboard, upper, note covered by blue paper. Tp, bsm.
Wood 885(1). Wing A524.

17. [Addison, Lancelot]. *The Moores baffled: being a discourse concerning Tanger*. London: f. W. Crooke, 1681. 4°. Pp. [5], 27, [5] (5 pp. of books sold by W. Crooke).
Tp, 'Tanger' altered to 'Tangier'.
Wood 386(15). Wing A525.

18. Adelardus. Bathoniensis. *(Questiones naturales)*. [Louvain]: [J. de Westfalia], [1475/83]. 4°. a-d⁸,e¹² (e12 blank).
a1, AW wrote the title and a cross ref. his own book, 'De isto Adelardo, vide in Histor. et Antiq. Universit. Oxon, Edit 1674 Lib. 1. p. 56. col. 1. p. 157. col. 2'.
Wood 498(12). GW 218.

19. Advertisements. *Advertisements. I shall go the round of publishing. 1. Physciansm . . .* [London]: (J. Whitlock, J. Hindmarsh, R. Clavel, A. Churchil, W. Rogers, D. Brown), [1694]. S.sh. (r-v).
Wood 276a(44) (not in Bodl. CD cat.). Not in Wing. Not in N & S (see 49.087ff.). Not in ESTCR.

20. Advice to a Painter. Manuscript. *Advice to a Painter: upon the defeat of the rebells in the west, and the execution of the late duke of Monmouth – Pictoribus atque poëtis quidlibet. –. ?: ?,* 1685. Pp. 4.
Not in AW's hand. See Savile, Wood 417(11), item 5770; and New Advice, Wood 417(21b), item 4636.
Wood 417(141).

21. Ady, Thomas. *A candle in the dark: shewing the divine cause of the distractions of the whole nation of England, and of the Christian world*. London: f. R. Ibbitson, 1655. 4°. Pp. [6], 172.
Flyleaf, upperᵛ, AW wrote, 'In 1661 was another title printed for this book, called a perfect discovery of Witches shewing &c – But no additions or cor[r]ections' (Wing A676). Tp, bsm. P. 165 (a cancel), minor underscoring.
[MS.] Wood B. 16(2). Wing A673(3).

22. Aelfric Grammaticus. Eynsham, abbott of [Parker, M. and J. Josseline, eds.]. *[A testimonie of antiquitie]*. [London]: [J. Day], [1566?]. 8°. C3-8,D-K⁸,L1-6 (wanting leaves at beginning and at end) (ff. 19(Ciii)-75(Kii), 75ᵛ blank). f. 62, i.e., H5: Here followeth the wordes of Aelfrike; K5 Lords Prayer; L5-6 summary.
Loose leaf, before the text: 'Note that this sermon following I have seen under this title A Testimonie of Antiquity shewing the auncient fayth in the church of England touching the sacrament of the body & blood &c. [/] printed at Lond. by John Day – 8° [/] Before which book is a long preface containing about 16 or 17 leaves, pen'd by some learned Antiquary & one that belonged to the church of Canterb. or Archbishop therof, for he speaketh much of that ch. & those Bishops (perhaps by J. Josselin. – q[uaere]'; followed by a fragment, on which is 'Ant: Woode: Merton Coll: Oxōn: 1658'. C3, notes by earlier owners, crossed out, and, not in AW's hand, 'published (as I take it) & first found out by Jo: Josselin. Since by Wᵐ Lisle. Lond: 1638' (possibly by Langbaine). Acquired 29 Ap. 1658 out of G. Langbaine's study, LT 1.247.
Wood 134(3). STC 159.5.

23. Aelianus, Claudius, and Heraclides Ponticus. Vulteius, Justus, ed. *De varia historia libri xi-iii. . . . Item, de politiis, sive, rerumpublicarum descriptiones, ex Heraclide*. Lugduni: ap. J. Tornaesium, 1577. 16°. Pp. 279, [22]. Calf with 2 fillets and stamp centrepiece; spine, 4 bands.
Flyleaf, upper, signatures, 2, of 'Fayrfax' and note, not in AW's hand; 2nd, ᵛ, Latin tag, not by AW. P. 249, underscoring.
Wood 197. Adams.

24. Aesop. *Aesopi Phrygis fabulae elegantissimis iconibus . . . Gabriae Graeci fabellae xxxxiiii. Batra-chomyomaxia. Galeomyomachia [Gr. and Lat]*. Parisiis: ap. H. de Marnef & vid. G. Cavellat, 1585 ('[1]585'). 16°. Pp. 448, [8]. Calf with 3 fillets.
Pp. 143, 146, 149, 312, notes; 273, 357, 369, scribbles, and some names (John Mason; 302, C–aister (?), 448, Edmund), none by AW. Lent to J. Curten, 1664, LT 2.8.
Wood 703. Not in BL, Adams, VD.

25. Aesop. Barret, William, trans. *The fables of Aesop. With his whole life*. London: R. Oulton f. F. Eglesfield, 1639. 8°. A1-5,B-Q⁸. Parchment.
Cover, upper, outside, 'H. ffoulis'; inside, 'Hen ffoulis Boke August :1: day 1651', price, and 'given by Mʳ Tho. Jacson [/] for . . . David Pary', and scribbles. Q8ᵛ and pastedown, lower, scribbles and 2 rough drawings. LT 2.179, 191. AW gave a copy, 8 Mar. 1673, to 'Tom Wood', his nephew, LT 2.258.
Wood 98. STC 189 (3).

26. Agard, [Arthur]. [Powell, Thomas, ed.]. *The repertorie of records: remaining in { the 4. treasuries on the receipt side at Westminster*. London: B. Alsop a. T. Fawcet f. B. Fisher, 1631. 4°. Pp. [6], 217. Calf with 3 fillets.
Tp, AW wrote the price, '3ˢ' and in pencil, 'nou:5:60'. LT 1.337.
Wood 489. STC 194.1.

27. Agas, Ralph. Ryther, Aug., deliniavit. *Celeberrimae Oxoniensis academiae aularum et collegiorum . . . descriptio R. Agaso autore 1578*. [London]: n.pub., [1588?]. S.sh.
Missing. Purchased 7 June 1658 from Davies, see LT 1.254. Lent to D. Loggan, 14 Oct. 1665, LT 2.49. This map eventually went to Charlett, according to Hearne, 4.261: 'the Map he [Charlett] hath of Oxford, printed and published in Q. Elizabeth's Time, formerly belong'd to Anthony à Wood'. See also 2.11, 13. But see Madan who stated that AW's copy was prob. the one 'which was in the Ashmolean Museum about 1730'. Madan also stated that Charlett's copy went to Dr. Brathwaite, warden of Winchester.
Hearne 1. STC 194.3 (one). Madan 96.

28. Age of Wonders. *The age of wonders, or miracles are not ceased. Being a true relation of a child born at Burslem, who prophesied strange things*. London: f. N. Chamberlain, 1660. 4°. Pp. 8.
Tp, AW altered the year to 16'59: March:', below, he wrote, 'To be put among miracles', in pencil.
[MS.] Wood B. 35(23). Wing A759 (two).

29. Agrippa, Henricus Cornelius. Sandford, James, trans. *Of the vanitie and uncertaintie of artes and sciences, Englished by Ja. San[ford] gent*. London: H. Bynneman, 1575. 4°. Ff. [7], 187, [1]. Parchment.
Flyleaf, upper, AW wrote, 'This book did once belong to Mʳ Joh. Day of Oriel Coll. Oxon, for those notes in the margin are of his hand writing'; he added later, in a different ink, 'Corn. Agrippa a Kᵗ, Dʳ of the lawe, judge of the prerog. court & counsellour to the emperour & a man of deep learning, an. 1530' (see LT 2.102). Tp, bsm. Text, passim, lines in margins, some underscoring, prob. none by AW; a few notes, apparently in Day's hand; pastedown, lower, a 33-line didactic poem in Latin with an equal no. of lines on

the pasted down side, in an unknown hand, and 3 annotations apparently in Day's hand.
[MS.] Wood B. 26. STC 205.

30. Agrippa, Henricus Cornelius. F., J., trans. *Three books of occult philosophy*. London: R. W. f. G. Moule, 1651. 4°. Pp. [26], 583, [13]. Calf with 3 fillets. Flyleaves, upper and lower, printer's waste paper. Flyleaf, upper, 2nd, 'Dono Noveieae [?] meae Amantissimae Jun. 18 [/] 75 [?].' Tp, bsm.
[MS.] Wood B. 22. Wing A789.

31. Agustín, Antonio. Tarragona, abp. of. *De Romanorum gentibus et familiis . . . Antonius Augustinus et Fulvius Ursinus*. Lugdunensis: ap. F. Fabrum, 1592. 4°. Pp. [8], 156. Calf with 3 fillets, stamp decoration inside corners (flowers), and roll decoration at inner, spine edge (Ashm. binding); 1 loose board. Flyleaf, upper, 2nd, titles of 7 printed works in this vol., written by an Ashm. librarian. Tp, bsm. Wood 644(1). Not in BL.

32. Airay, Henry. P[otter], C., ed. *The just and necessary apologie of Henrie Airay . . . touching his suite in law for the rectorie of Charleton*. London: [W. Jones], 1621. 8°. Pp. [6], 44. Calf with 3 fillets and stamp decoration (dragons) in corners (Ashm. binding). Flyleaf, 2nd, list of 8 printed works in this vol., by an Ashm. librarian. Tp, 'Anth: Woode: Merton Coll: Oxon'; ᵛ, 24-line note to the reader in Latin, signed Bale. P. 5, AW identified 'one Andrews & one Temple', 'Richard Andrews Nich. Temple'. Acquired 29 Ap. 1658 out of G. Langbaine's study, LT 1.247-8. Wood 112(1). STC 244.

33. Albertus Magnus, Saint. Ratisbon, bp. of. *De secretis mulierum libellus*. Lugduni: n.pub., 1615. 12°. Pp. 166. Former owner, Richard Phillips, see Wood 688(1), the next item. Wood 688(2). BL.

34. Albertus Magnus, Saint. Ratisbon, bp. of. *Speculum astronomiae:. . . Praemittuntur autem ejusdem authoris libelli, de virtutibus herbarum, lapidum, & animalium quorundam. Item de mirabilibus mundi*. Lugduni: n.pub., 1615. 12°. Pp. 166. Calf with 3 fillets; 1st and last flyleaves, printer's waste paper. Flyleaf, upper, 2nd, 'Anthony Wood his book 1649', lined out, under name of a former owner, 'Richard Phillips his book', lined out. Wood 688(1). BL.

35. Albertus Magnus, Saint. Ratisbon, bp. of. Digby, Kenelm, trans. *A treatise of adhering to God; . . . Also a conference with a lady about choyce of religion*. London: f. H. Herringman, 1654. 12°. Pp. [18], 139, [2]. Calf with 2 fillets; rebacked. Pasteboard, upper 'Birchingham' (Barthingham?). Wood 822. Wing A876.

36. Albizzi, Bartholomaeus. S., D., trans. *The alcoran of the Franciscans, or a sink of lyes and blasphemies. Collected out of . . . the book of the conformites [sic]*. London: f. L. Curtice, 1679. 12°. Pp. [24], 156 (wanting the frontispiece). Pasteboard (grey) with parchment spine. 1st upper and last lower flyleaves, marbled paper. Flyleaf, upper, 2ndᵛ, AW wrote the titles of 2 printed works in this vol., within guidelines made with red ink. Wood 874(1). Wing A881.

37. Alciati, Andrea. *Emblematum libri duo*. [Geneva]: ap. J. Tornaesium, 1614. 16°. Pp. [16], 257, [14] (misnumbering). Calf with 2 fillets, new backing. Tp, signature or words lined out. Wood 72. BL.

38. Aldeburgh, and Merlin. *A signe from heaven: or, a fearefull . . . noise heard . . . at Alborow . . . Whereunto is annexed, a prophesie of Merlins, concerning Hull*. London: T. Fawcet, 1642, 12 Aug. 4°. Pp. [2], 6. [MS.] Wood D. 28(8). Wing S3776.

39. Aleman, Matheo. *The rogue: or, the life of Guzman de Alfarache*. London: J. C. f. P. Chetwind, sold T. Johnson; 2nd-3rd tpp, H. Hills, 1656; 2nd-3rd tpp, 1655. 8°. 5th ed. Pp. [4], 1-142, 1-99, [2], 1-216 (3 tpp). Calf with 2 fillets; rebacked. Flyleaf, upper, 1st, scribbles, 2 lines of verse, not in AW's hand; 2nd, 'Rob Hungerford his booke.' Flyleaf, lower, scribble, not in AW's hand. LT 1.182. Possibly lent to O. Sedgwick, March 1660, LT 1.306.

Wood 305. Wing A904aA (rare).

40. [Aleyn, Charles]. *The historie of that wise prince, Henrie the seventh.* [London]: [T. Cotes f. W. Cooke], [1638]. 8°. Pp. 152 (wanting A⁴ and leaves at end).
B1ʳ, AW wrote, 'Ch. Aleyne the' (cropped at bottom). Other pencil notes, not in AW's hand. Text, some marks in margins and underscoring, in pencil.
Wood 90(8). STC 353.

41. Algood. Major. *A sermon preached, at the funeral of . . . Georg Ritschel, late minister of Hexham . . . with an elegie [by I. H.].* London: f. J. Hall, Newcastle upon Tyne, 1684. 4°. Pp. 24.
Passim, corrections, not in AW's hand.
Wood 634(7). Wing A925.

42. Ali Abencufian, pseud. [i.e., Miguel de Luna]. Ashley, Robert, trans. *Almansor the learned and victorious king that conquered Spaine.* London: [W. Stansby] f. J. Parker, 1627. 4°. Pp. [16], 79.
Tp, AW underscored the author's name in red chalk. Sig. A1-A2, vertical lines in margins at Ashley's reference to a library of Arabian books, and to the translator and author.
Wood 345(10). STC 354.

43. [Alleine, Richard]. *A murderer punished, and pardoned [Thomas Savage].* London: n.pub., 1671. 8°. 13th ed. Pp. 72.
Tp, AW wrote, 'This first edit. came out 1668 Oct –' (The binder had cropped most of AW's earlier note, so he rewrote it). Bsm.
Wood 173(3). Wing A997 (two).

44. [Allen, William]. Anon. *A true sincere and modest defence of English Catholiques that suffer . . . against a . . . libel [by W. Cecil] intituled; The execution of justice.* [Rouen]: [Fr. Persons' Press], [1584]. 8°. Pp. [8], 219, [1]. Calf with 3 fillets; rebacked.
Flyleaf, upper, 11 lines of bibliographical notes on this book and on the answer to it by Thomas Bilson (STC 3071), not by AW. AW marked the 3 notes with vertical lines and wrote 'vide pag 4. 5. in marg.', in red ink, over his earlier 'v p. 4, 5,', in pencil. P. [3], signature of 'Nicolas Cliffe' (cropped at top). Text, passim, some marks in margin and corrections from the ms. errata, not in AW's manner; but see pencil marks on pp. 2, 5, 11, 14. Flyleaf, lower, a ms. errata of 13 items, not by AW. AW owned the work to which this responds, W. Cecil, Wood 586(4) (item 1663); and refers to it in [MS.] D. 21(1) (item 3244) as his book 'with a black cover', see Plate II.
Wood 878. STC 373. ARCR 2.14.

45. [Allestree, Richard]. *The whole duty of man. . . . With private devotions.* London: f. M. Garthwait, 1671. 12°. Pp. [27], 474, [6]. Calf with 2 fillets and a 2nd rectangle with 2 fillets and stamp decoration at corners.
Wood 851. Wing A1176A (rare).

46. Alleyn, E. *A catalogue of the noblemen and peers of the kingdom of England . . . in the reign of Charles the second.* London: f. the author, 1662. S.sh.
AW wrote the price, '4ᵈ'.
Wood 276a(92). Wing A1199 (rare).

ALMANACS (items 47-218)

47. Andrews, William. *De rebus caelestibus, or an ephemeris, for . . . 1663.* London: T. Ratcliffe f. Co. of Stationers, 1663. 8°. A-B⁸,B⁸ (sic) (pp. unopened).
One of two almanacs acquired 16 Dec. 1662, LT 1.464.
Wood Alm. E(4). Wing A1259.

48. Atkinson, Charles. *Panterpe; id est omne delectare: or, a pleasant almanack . . . 1671.* London: f. Co. of Stationers, 1671. 8°. A¹⁶,B⁸ (ms. nos. ff. 1-40). Modern binding, half-calf, maroon; inside, paper wrapper.
This is the 15th of AW's diaries (see LT 1.3-4), with extensive interleaving from after A3 to after A15, with a blank leaf and slips, all containing diary entries or memoranda. AW's notes begin on the paper wrapper, upper, '1671 4ᵈ· Dec. 21. 70 [/] Jacob sold it at the Angell before Jobson came, he sells it now in old s. hampton buildings [/] Cirquis Jobson, a Jew borne about Mount Libanus, a Jacobit[.] The first that sold

Coffey in Oxon over against Q[ueens] Coll. circa 1655. 56 afterwards sold a[t] Tilliard'; notes continue from f. 5 to wrapper, lower[v], f. 39, and to an added blank leaf, f. 40, on which 2 slips are pasted. There are also notes on some printed almanac pp. LT 2.212-238.
[MS.] Wood Diaries 15. Wing A1306. SC 27737.

49. B[everidge], W[illiam]. *Kalendarium Julianum*. London: E. Cotes, venales prostant ap. S. Thompson, [1666]. 8°.
Missing. MS. Wood E. 2(70), p. 59, 'Kalendarium Julianum 1667 - lat. Will Beveridge'. Acquired 29 Mar. 1667, 6[d], LT 1.104.
MS. Wood E. 2(70), p. 59. Wing A1309A (3).

50. [Blount, Thomas]. *Calendarium catholicum: or an universall almanack, 1661*. N.p.: N.pub., 1661. 12°. A-B[12]. Parchment over earlier marbled paper.
B7, line in margin, at 'Thomas Morgan' and 'Mr. Pyms Son'. See note at item 1109f.
Wood 4. Wing A1321.

51. [Blount, Thomas]. *A new almanack, after the old fashion; for 1663*. London: N.pub., 1663. 12°. A[12],B[6],C[12]. Parchment, outer; marbled paper, inner.
C11[v], a correction entered. C12[v], at citation of Edmund Church, 'Note that the authour of this Alm. Th. Blount married Edm. Church his daughter.' LT 1.317.
Wood 6. Wing A1324 (rare).

52. Booker, John. *M.D.C.XLIII. Almanack et prognosticon . . . 1643*. London: F. K. f. Co. of Stationers, [1643]. 8°. A-B[8],A[8].
A5, A6, 4 numbers and 'the fast-', 'Darrell' and 'Tuesday turn', prob. not by AW.
Wood Alm. A(7). Wing A1330.

53. Booker, John. *Mercurius Coelicus, sive almanack et prognosticon . . . 1646*. London: F. K. f. Co. of Stationers, [1646]. 8°. A-B[8].
Wood Alm. A(8). Wing A1336.

54. Booker, John. *Telescopium uranicum: or in plain English, an almanack . . . M. CC. LXI*. London: f. Co. of Stationers, 1661. 8°. 31 ed. A-B[8],A[8] (ms. nos. ff. 1-44 (misnumbering)). Modern binding, half-calf, maroon; inside, brown paper wrapper.
This is the 5th of AW's diaries (see LT 1.3-4), with extensive interleaving from after A1 to after B8, Dec., with 1 or 2 blank leaves and some slips. On the brown paper wrapper, upper, AW wrote, 'Booker 1661', and '1661', in orange crayon. On the 1st blank leaf, f. 1, he wrote entries for Jan. Feb. April, June, Sept., Oct., and, [v], notes on quacks, prompted by the printed item inserted after A2, now f. 5, an advertisement by James Themut, see Wood Diaries 5b (LT 1.377). The last blank leaf, after B8, ends with entries for Jan. 1662, and [v], a brief essay on 'why learning hath decayed in these later times' (because of the imitation of the French; neglect of Fathers; discussions in coffee houses and alehouses which before were in scholar's chambers, etc. LT 1.422f.). There are also marks and notes on some printed almanac pp. LT 1.371-427.
[MS.] Wood Diaries 5. Wing A1347. SC 27727.

55. [Bretnor, Thomas]. *[A new almanack . . . 1617] [C2 begins:] Certaine physicall directions*. [London]: [f. Co. of Stationers], [1617]. 8°. C2[r-v], only (cropped at top).
Wood Alm. A(11). STC 420.10.

56. [Bretnor, Thomas]. *[A new almanack . . . 1618] [C1 begins:] Certaine physicall observations*. [London]: [f. Co. of Stationers], [1618]. C1-3, only (followed by an unidentified a leaf (1617) with former stitching marks on outer edge).
On an unidentified leaf of letterpress, notes by a former owner, illeg.
Wood Alm. A(12-13). STC 420.11.

57. Calendarium Catholicum. *Kalendarium catholicum for the year 1686*. N.p.: n.pub, 1686. 8°. A-B[8],C[4]. Calf with 3 fillets, stamp decoration (dragons) inside corners (Ashm. binding); rebacked.
Flyleaf, upper, 2nd[v], the titles of 8 printed works in this vol. Tp, AW wrote '6[d]' and 'Such an Alm. as this, was published 1661. 62. 63 – and if I am not mistaken Th. Blount of the Inner Temple had a hand in it – After it had laid dormant 20 yeares, it was againe published, when all people expected popery to be introduced'. For these early almanacs, see Wood 4 and Wood 6 (items 50f.). LT 1.13; 3.131, 176.
Wood 843(1). Wing A1854.

58. Calendarium Perpetuum. *Calendarium perpetuum*. Oxon: n.pub., 1637. Pp?

Missing in 1837. T added, inserted on the facing page, in the Whiteside cat. Not identified. Prob. an almanac.
Wood 748b. See STC 431.3. Madan 842; or, STC 419.6. Madan 848; or STC 532.111, Madan 969.

59. Coelson, Lancelot. *Speculum perspicuum Uranicum: or, an almanack for . . . 1680.* London: J. Grover f. Co. of Stationers, [1680]. 8°. A-C^8 (2 tpp) (pp. unopened).
Wood Alm. E(9). Wing A1427.

60. Coley, Henry. *Nuncius coelestis:. . . a brief description . . . 1679.* London: J. Grover f. Co. of Stationers, [1679]. 8°. A-C^8 (C5-8 unopened) (ms. nos. 1-73). Modern binding, half-calf, maroon; inside, blue paper wrapper.
This is the 23rd of AW's diaries (see LT 1.3-4), with extensive interleaving from after the upper wrapper to after B7, and again after C8, with 1 or several blank leaves and slips, all containing diary entries or memoranda. AW's notes, wrapper, upper, 'Coley 1679 [/] Spelman v[ide] June'; and '1679', in red chalk; notes continue from f. 2 to flyleaves, lower. Flyleaf, lower, f. 71, 'Done by me in Mr Sheldons Library . . . '; f. 72^v, '3 Dec. sent to Sr Will. Dugd. 3. stichings [sic] or bundells containing corrections on his baronagium – The 1. stitching contains 5 papers. the 2^d – 7. papers – the 3^d. 11. papers – with the Epitaph of Edw. [Talbot] E[arl] of Shrewsbury in the Abbey Ch. of Westm. who died 1617.', etc. There are also notes on some printed almanac pp. Not by AW, bill, 29 May 1679, with note of payment from AW, 1 July 1679, from chemist Nathaniell Wheatly. F. 22 is a printed item, an advertisement 'Wonder of Nature'; see separate entry at Wood Diaries 23b, item 6682. LT 2.430-475.
[MS.] Wood Diaries 23. Wing A1456. SC 27745.

61. Comptoir. *Comptoir almanach, oft journael, op het jaer . . . duysent ses hondert neghen-en-twintich.* Amsterdam: Broer Jansz voor C. Lodowiicksz, 1629. 4°. A-D^4 (C1 mutilated).
A diary of Griffin Higgs of Merton who was travelling to Rhenen, the court of Elizabeth, 'Winter' Queen of Bohemia. It begins on the almanac p. for January: 'Jan: 7: s.v. being Wednesday the Prince of Bohem. [Henry Frederick] drowned in a journey to Amsterdam' (and 7 more lines, mainly on purchase of mourning clothes). Entries follow for February (9 lines), beginning 'Feb: i2. s.v. I bought 2 shirts: one of 4 dutch ells:. . . ' and ending, 'Feb. i4. s.v. written to William Adkins. [/] Feb: 23. s.v. being Mondaye my man hath bin with me full 6 month: He came Aug. 23. Saturd. s.v. on Bartholomew Eve.'; and for March (14 lines, all recorded): 'Marc: 2^d. old stile. receaved a packett from M^r. Jacob. Thomas Dodd with his Accounts. Mr Jackson, and Mr Cra[w]ford. [/] March 3^d old style sent by Mr Dudley [over 'M^r. Rob. Carrs company:', lined out] to Cambs [Lambs?] to Stoke: Caver–: [?] –don: [2 words] and to Mr Jacob: to M^r. Cr- [cropped] Mr Jackson, and T: Dodde. [/] March. 4. s.v. Delivered a letter to Mr Dudley, and a watch for D^r. Mauric[e] Williams in the presence of M^r. Yelverton: Mr Crofts: M^r. C–p–er: [?] w. [a.?] the Countess of A[?]bistein. [/] March. 6. s.v. S^r. Rob. Carr and his Companie: and M^{ris} Crofts went from the Hage [/] March. 6. s.v. Barb: [/] March. 9. s.v. our Journey began towards Rhenen.' AW obtained other Higgs' diaries, most likely from Merton College library, see Wood Alm A(1) and (3), items 118, 105, recorded by Morrish, pp. 131-201, esp. [137] 1, [185] 49 n. 8, [143] 7; see also note at Wood 276a(517), item 4082, and LT 1.12.
Wood 498(14). Not in BL.

62. Crawford, Henry. *Vox Uraniae, or, astrological observations . . . for . . . 1676.* London: J. D. f. Co. of Stationers, 1676. 8°. A-C^8 (C5-6 unopened) (ms. nos. ff. 1-61). Modern binding, half-calf, maroon; inside, paper wrapper.
This is the 20th of AW's diaries (see LT 1.3-4), with extensive interleaving from after A2 to after B8, and also before and after C8, with 1 or more blank leaves and slips, all containing diary entries or memoranda. AW's notes begin on the paper wrapper, upper, 'Crawford [/] 1676 [/] Jan. 3 Monday – of Magd Coll died' (AW wrote the name, John Heather, at Jan., f. 5), etc., and notes continue to wrapper, lower^v. There are also notes on some printed almanac pp. Not by AW, epitaph of John Good, Balliol, at which AW wrote, 'vid Fasti 1661' (f. 8); and 2 addresses on an envelope (f. 32^v). LT 2.333-364.
[MS.] Wood Diaries 20. Wing A1497 (two). SC 27742.

63. [Daniel, Humphrey]. *[Daniel, 1651. For London . . . an almanack for . . . 1651].* [London]: [G. Dawson for Co. of Stationers], [1651]. 8°. B4-8,C^4, only.
Wood Alm. A(16). Wing A1580 (rare, 2 at O).

64. Digges, Leonard. Digges, Thomas, ed. *A prognostication . . . of right good effect.* London: T. Orwing, 1592. 4°.
Missing. MS. Wood E. 2(70), p. 26. AO 1.415, 'corrected and augmented by his said son Thomas . . . Lond. 1592, qu[arto]'.
MS. Wood E. 2(70), p. 26. STC 435.55 (3). *O* (severely cropped).

65. Dove, Jonathan. *Dove. Speculum anni . . . Or an almanack for . . . 1666.* [Cambridge]: J. Field, 1666. 8°. A-C⁸ (ms. nos. ff. 1-47). Modern binding, half-calf, maroon; inside, paper wrapper.
This is the 10th of AW's diaries (see LT 1.3-4), with extensive interleaving from after A1 to after B7, Dec., with 1 or 2 blank leaves, all containing diary entries or memoranda. AW's notes begin on the paper wrapper, upper, 'lent Mʳ Shippen Notitia Oxon Nov. 27 [/] Dove 1666.' (Wood 513(3), item 3110), '1666' in red chalk, and other notes, and end on the wrapper, lowerᵛ. There are also notes on some printed almanac pages. LT 2.69-97.
[MS.] Wood Diaries 10. Wing A1612 4 at O. SC 27732.

66. Dove, Jonathan. *Dove. Speculum anni . . . Or an almanack for . . . 1668.* [Cambridge]: J. Field, 1668. 8°. A-C⁸ (quire C unopened) (ms. nos. ff. 1-39). Modern binding, half-calf, maroon; inside, paper wrapper.
This is the 12th of AW's diaries (see LT 1.3-4), with extensive interleaving from after the paper wrapper to after B5, Dec., with 1 or 2 blank leaves, all containing diary entries or memoranda. AW's notes begin on the paper wrapper, upper, '1668 [/] March 10. 67[1668] lent Mʳˢ Okes 5ˢ· which my sister hath promised to pay if shee doth not', and other notes, and end on the wrapper, lowerᵛ. There are also notes on some printed almanac pp. LT 2.126-148.
[MS.] Wood Diaries 12. Wing A1614. SC 27734.

67. [Dove, Jonathan]. *Speculum anni or an almanack for . . . 1682.* Cambridge: J. Hayes, 1682. 8°. A-C⁸ (ms. nos. ff. 1-73). Modern binding, half-calf, maroon; inside, paper wrapper.
This is the 26th of AW's diaries (see LT 1.3-4), with extensive interleaving from after A1 to after C2, with 1 or more blank leaves and slips containing diary entries, memoranda, and a 'letter to Mʳ Fulman not sent' (ff. 63-4). AW's notes begin on the paper wrapper, upper, 'Nov. 23. an. 1681. 4ᵈ ob [/] Dove 1682', etc., and notes continue to wrapper, lowerᵛ. There are also a very few brief notes on some printed almanac pp. Not by AW, 4 12° leaves and a slip from the diary of Andrew Allam bound in the vol. at appropriate months (ff. 16, 21 (i.e., after 22 and before 23), 25, 29 (on which AW wrote, 'This note belongs to Mʳ A. Allum'), 48 (a slip)). LT 3.1-34.
[MS.] Wood Diaries 26. Wing A1627 (two). SC 27748.

68. [Dove, Jonathan]. *Dove. Speculum anni or an almanack for . . . 1684.* Cambridge: J. Hayes, 1684. 8°. A-C⁸ (C unopened) (ms. nos. ff. 1-67 (misnumbering)). Modern binding, half-calf, maroon; inside, paper wrapper.
This is the 28th of AW's diaries (see LT 1.3-4), with extensive interleaving from after the upper wrapper to after B7, with 1 or more blank leaves and slips containing diary entries and memoranda. AW's notes begin on the paper wrapper, upper, 'Dove 1684. 4ᵈ [/]', '1684' in red chalk, 'Will. Stane sometimes of Merton Coll. died at the beg. of the yeare 1684 . . . ' etc., and notes continue to wrapper, lower. There are also brief notes on some printed almanac pp. Not by AW, 1 slip from the diary of Andrew Allam bound in among July events (f. 32). LT 3.84-122.
[MS.] Wood Diaries 28. Wing A1629. SC 27750.

69. Dutch Almanac. *A Dutch almanack.* Amsterdam: ?, 1634. Pp?
Missing in 1837. See Wood Alm. A(3), item 105, for a 1632 'Dutch Almanack'.
Wood 1. Not in Bod. Not in BL.

70. Erra Pater. *A prognostication for ever, made by Erra Pater.* London: R. Bishop, [1649 or later]. 8°. A-B⁸,C1-7 (wanting C8).
C1ᵛ-C3, undercoring in section on 'Fayres of England'.
Wood 9(4) (not in Bodl. CD cat.). Wing E3243 (two).

71. Evelyn, John. *Kalendarium hortense: or, the gard'ners almanac.* London: J. Martyn, 1676. 8°. 6th ed. Pp. 127, [9]. Calf with 2 fillets with a vertical line, 2 fillets; rebacked.
Wood 573(1). Wing E2496.

72. Evesdropper, Adam, pseud. *Platoes cap. Cast at this yeare 1604, being leape-yeere.* London: [T. Purfoot] f. J. Chorlton, 1604. 4°. A-D⁴ (A1-2, D3-4 blank).
Tp, no. 2 in a former bundle. D1, scribble in margin, not in AW's manner.
Wood 616(2). STC 19975.

73. Faithful and True Prognostication. Coverdale, Miles, trans. *A faythfull and true pronosticatiō upō the yere M.CCCCC.xlviii. and parpetually after to the worldes ende.* (London): [J. Hereford f.] (R. Kele), [1547?]. 8°. A2-8,B⁸,D⁸,E⁴ (wanting the title leaf and sheet C).

E4, date added, 1548.
Wood 736(4). STC 20423 (two).

74. [Finé, Oronce]. Baker, Humfrey, trans. *The rules and ryghte ample documentes touchinge the use . . . of . . . almanackes . . . named ephemerides.* (London): (T. Marshe), [1558?]. A-G⁸.
Underscoring and notes on astrological matters, made before binding (some are cropped), not by AW.
Wood 9(2) (not in Bodl. CD cat.). STC 10878.5 (rare).

75. F[lorio], J[ohn]. [?]. *Perpetuall and natural prognostications of the change of weather . . . translated out of the Italian into English, by J. F.* London: [A. Islip] f. E. White, 1598. 8°. A-C⁸.
Wood 9(3) (not in Bodl. CD cat.). STC 403.9.

76. Franco, Jean. *Kalendrier ou journal, pour l'an de nostre seigneur Jesus Christ 1629.* Pariis: A. Anvers. Chez Guylliaume, 1629. 16°. A-B⁸. Parchment.
Cover, upperᵛ 'Anthony Wood'.
Wood 2(1) (not in Bodl. CD cat.). Not in BL. Not in BN. Not in NUC.

77. Franco, Jean. *Prognostication pour l'an de nostre seigneur Jesus Christ 1629.* Pariis: A. Anvers. Chez Guylliaume, 1629. 16°. A-B⁸.
Wood 2(2) (not in Bodl. CD cat.). Not in BL. Not in BN. Not in NUC.

78. Franco, Jean. *Kalendrier ou journal, pour l'an de nostre seigneur Jesus Christi 1631.* Paris: A. Anvers. Chez Guillaume, 1631. 16°. A-B⁸. Parchment.
Cover, lower, outer, AW wrote, 'French almanack 1631'.
Wood 3(1) (not in Bodl. CD cat.). Not in BL. Not in BN. Not in NUC.

79. Franco, Jean. *Prognostication pour l'an de nostre seigneur Jesu Christ, 1631.* Paris: A. Anvers. Chez Guillaume, 1631. 16°. A-B⁸.
Wood 3(2) (not in Bodl. CD cat.). Not in BL. Not in BN. Not in NUC.

80. Gadbury, John. Εφημερις: *or, a diary . . . for . . . 1660.* London: J. C. f. Co. of Stationers, [1660]. 8°. A-C⁸ (ms. nos. ff. 1-41). Modern binding, half-calf, maroon; inside, brown paper wrapper.
This is the 4th of AW's diaries (see LT 1.3-4) with extensive interleaving from after A1 to after B6, Dec., with 1 or 2 blank leaves. On the brown paper wrapper, upper, AW wrote, 'Gadbury [/] 1660', and '1660' in orange crayon. Tp, 'Anthony Woode'. On the 1st blank leaves, after A1 and A2, he wrote various entries, some for March, April, Oct. and Dec.; on the last, after B5 and B6, he wrote entres for Nov., Dec., and January 1661. There are also a few marks and notes on some printed almanac pp. Acquired 2 Jan. 1660 for 3ᵈ, LT 1.301-371.
[MS.] Wood Diaries 4. Wing A1739 (two). SC 27726.

81. Gadbury, John. Εφημερις: *or, a diary . . . for . . . 1661.* London: J. Cottrell f. Co. of Stationers, 1661. 8°. A-C⁸ (1 p. books sold). Parchment with marbled paper pasted over as center panel.
Spine and pastedown, upper, 'D: VV'; flyleaf, upper, 1st, author and year of 8 Gadbury 'Almanacks', in Whiteside's hand. AW wrote large Arabic nos. on each tp, in pencil.
Wood Alm. D(1). Wing A1740.

82. Gadbury, John. Εφημερις. *Or, a diary . . . for . . . 1668.* London: J. Cottrell f. Co. of Stationers, [1668]. 8°. A-E⁸.
Acquired 3 Dec. 1667, [7.5ᵈ, with [MS.] D. 28(16), item 3070, which was also 7.5ᵈ], LT 2.122.
Wood Alm. D(2). Wing A1747.

83. Gadbury, John. Εφημερις: *or, a diary . . . for . . . 1669.* London: f. Co. of Stationers, [1669]. 8°. A-E⁸.
Wood Alm. D(3). Wing A1748.

84. Gadbury, John. Εφημερις. *Or, a diary . . . for . . . 1670.* London: (J. C.) f. Co. of Stationers, 1670. 8°. A2-8,B⁸,C⁴,A-B⁸,C⁴ (1 p. books sold) (2 tpp).
Acquired 11 Jan. 1670, LT 2.184.
Wood Alm. D(4). Wing A1749.

85. Gadbury, John. Εφημερις: *or, a diary . . . for . . . 1673.* London: f. Co. of Stationers, [1673]. 8°. A-C⁸,B-C⁸ (A7-8 unopened) (ms. nos. ff. 1-64). Modern binding, half-calf, maroon; inside, paper wrapper.
This is the 17th of AW's diaries (see LT 1.3-4), with extensive interleaving from after wrapper, upper, to after C5, Dec., with 1 or more blank leaves and slips, all containing diary entries or memoranda. AW's

notes begin on the paper wrapper, upper, 'Gadbury 1673. 6^d [/] 27 Mar. 2. sheets to Mr Peers. 16 peices of papers pasted therin. / 5/7 peices of paper to those 2 last sheets' (for the translation of his *Historia*); and '1673 [in red chalk], . . . Nativity { Ld Bacon [/] J. Selden [/] Sr K. Digby { calculated – v[ide] ad finem', and notes continue to wrapper, lower^v. 2nd C3^v, C4^r-v, C6^v, lines, a 'q[uaere] letter at astrological matters, mainly concerning John Selden, and a correction of a date in Selden's horoscope. There are also notes on some printed almanac pp. LT 2.256-278.
[MS.] Wood Diaries 17. Wing A1752. SC 27739.

86. Gadbury, John. Εφημερις: *or, a diary . . . for . . . 1678*. London: J. D. f. Co. of Stationers, 1678. 8°.
A-C^8 (ms. nos. ff. 1-48). Modern binding, half-calf, maroon; inside, paper wrapper.
This is the 22nd of AW's diaries (see LT 1.3-4), with extensive interleaving from after the upper wrapper to after B6, with 1 or more blank leaves and slips, all containing diary entries or memoranda. Pastedown, upper, 2 notes '1677 is missing 1883' (a similar note in Diary 1676) and 'Now found. 1890'. AW's notes begin on the paper wrapper, upper, 'Gadbury 1678 [/] Memorandum that the Lib. at Lantarnam was onlie a few old writings & a an [sic] old bible' (see LT 2.381), etc., and notes continue to wrapper, lower^v. There are also notes on some printed almanac pp. LT 2.399-430.
[MS.] Wood Diaries 22. Wing A1757. SC 27744.

87. Gadbury, John. Εφημερις: *or, a diary . . . for . . . 1687*. London: J. D. f. Co. of Stationers, 1687. 8°.
A-C^8 (C unopened) (ms. nos. ff. 1-66). Modern binding, half-calf, maroon; inside, paper wrapper.
This is the 31st of AW's diaries (see LT 1.3-4), with extensive interleaving from after the upper wrapper to after B8, Dec., and after C8, with 1 or more blank leaves and slips containing diary entries, and memoranda. AW's notes begin on the paper wrapper, upper, 'Gadbury 1687 5^d 1687', '1687' in red chalk, etc., and notes continue to wrapper, lower^v. There are also brief notes on some printed almanac pp. Not by AW, copy of part of a letter, 24 June 1687, from [Thomas] Lane concerning the papist/protestant struggle at Magdalen College (f. 31); and a note of a book purchase by the Bishop of Oxford (f. 42^v). LT 3.204-51.
[MS.] Wood Diaries 31. Wing A1766. SC 27753.

88. Gadbury, John. Εφημερις: *or, a diary . . . for . . . 1688*. London: J. D. f. Co. of Stationers, 1688. 8°.
A-C^8 (C2-4 unopened) (ms. nos. 1-77). Modern binding, half-calf, maroon; inside, paper wrapper.
This is the 32nd of AW's diaries (see LT 1.3-4), with extensive interleaving from after the upper wrapper to after B8, Dec., and after C8, with 1 or more blank leaves and slips containing diary entries and memoranda. AW's notes begin on the paper wrapper, upper, 'Gadbury 1688', and '1688' in orange crayon; notes continue from f. 1^v to wrapper, lower^v. There are also brief notes on some printed almanac pp. Not by AW, a letter, 24 Jan. 1687, from John Dugdale, concerning John Davenport (f. 6). LT 3.251-294.
[MS.] Wood Diaries 32. Wing A1767. SC 27754.

89. Gadbury, John. Εφημερις. *Or, a diary . . . for . . . 1691*. London: J. R. f. Co. of Stationers, 1691. 8°. Pp. A-C^8 (ms. nos. 1-92). Modern binding, half-calf, maroon; inside, paper wrapper.
This is the 35th of AW's diaries (see LT 1.3-4), with extensive interleaving from after the upper wrapper to after B8, Dec., and after C8, with 1 or more blank leaves and slips containing diary entries and memoranda. AW's notes begin on the paper wrapper, upper, 'Gadbury 1691' '1691' in orange crayon, 'owing to Mr Basset Jan 30. 90[1] Tooth brush - half an ounce of tob[acco] Thread', and continue from f. 2 to wrapper, lower^v. There are also a few brief notes on some printed almanac pp. Not by AW, a note on collection for Scotch Episcopal clergy (f. 24); ms. waste, citation from a book (f. 60^v). LT 3.349-379.
[MS.] Wood Diaries 35. Wing A1770. SC 27757.

90. Gadbury, John. Εφημερις. *Or, a diary . . . for . . . 1692*. London: J. R. f. Co. of Stationers, 1692. 8°. A-C^8 (ms. nos. 1-92). Modern binding, half-calf, maroon; inside, paper wrapper, upper only.
This is the 36th of AW's diaries (see LT 1.3-4), with extensive interleaving from after the upper wrapper to after B8, Dec., with 1 or more 4° blank leaves and some 8° leaves and slips containing diary entries and memoranda. AW's notes begin on the paper wrapper, upper, 'Gadbury 1692 [/] Correct. 628 Ward', i.e., p. 628 of proof copy of AO, the 1st of corrections of the proof sheet which continue to f. 4; notes continue from f. 2 to C8^v. There are also a few brief notes on some printed almanac pp. Not by AW, a bill, 29 March 1692, from Edward Reade, a draper, below which AW wrote, 'making 2^s-6' and 'paid 20 May 1692' (f. 21); a note from M^r [James] Harrington, 2-line epitaph of Thomas Shadwell (f. 65); and a letter, 20 Apr. 1693 (out of place, LT 3.420-1) from James Eckersal, an 8-line epitaph of Thomas Shadwell by Thomas Browne (f. 66). LT 3.379-413. Dupl. at Wood Alm. D(5).
[MS.] Wood Diaries 36. Wing A1771. SC 27758.

91. Gadbury, John. Εφημερις. *Or, a diary . . . for . . . 1692*. London: J. R. f. Co. of Stationers, 1692. 8°. A-C^8.

Tp, 'Jo: Aubrey R[egiae] S[ocietatis] S[ocius] dedit author.' Dupl. at Wood Diaries 36. LT 1.14.
Wood Alm. D(5). Wing A1771.

92. Gadbury, John. Εφημερις. *Or, a diary . . . for . . . 1693*. London: J. R. f. Co. of Stationers, 1693.
8°. A-C⁸ (ms. nos. ff. 1-79). Modern binding, half-calf, maroon; inside, upper, brown paper wrapper and lower, paper wrapper.
This is the 37th of AW's diaries (see LT 1.3-4), with extensive interleaving from after the upper wrapper to after B8, Dec., with 1 or more blank leaves and slips containing diary entries and memoranda. AW's notes begin on the brown paper wrapper, upper, '1693' in red chalk; and on the flyleaf, upper, '1693 In the month of June were finished the shelves - the public Library - over the Div[inity] & law books set up to containe Dr Barlowes books & others that the univ[er]sitie had procured before that time'; and continue to wrapper, lower. There are also a few brief notes on some printed almanac pages. Not by AW, a receipt for legal services, 22 July 1693, from Richard Dodwell (f. 25); note of burial of Charles Conquest on 20 Sept. 1693, above which AW wrote, 'S. Peter & S. Paul's ch. in Bath (f. 51) (and see note at Wood 429(52), item 3342); a letter, 4 Oct. 1693, from Arthur Charlett concerning the Earl of Clarendon (ff. 69ᵛ-70). LT 3.413-439. Dupl. at Wood Alm. D(6).
[MS.] Wood Diaries 37. Wing A1772. SC 27759.

93. Gadbury, John. Εφημερις. *Or, a diary . . . for . . . 1693*. London: J. R. f. Co. of Stationers, 1693.
8°. A-C⁸ (with interleaved blank leaves).
Tp, signature of 'Ed. Shirburne.' [i.e., Sherburne]. Dupl. at Wood Diaries 37. LT 1.14. Sherburne gave AW 3 Wharton almanacs as well, but they are unsigned, LT 2.400.
Wood Alm. D(6). Wing A1772.

94. Gadbury, John. Εφημερις. *Or, a diary . . . for . . . 1694*. London: J. R. f. Co. of Stationers, 1694.
8°. A-C⁸.
Wood Alm. D(7). Wing A1773.

95. Gadbury, John. Εφημερις. *Or, a diary . . . for . . . 1695*. London: J. R. f. Co. of Stationers, 1695.
8°. A-C⁸.
Tp, 'W. i.' (?).
Wood Alm. D(8). Wing A1774.

96. Gallen, T[homas]. *Gallen. 1642. An almanack and prognostication*. London: R. Young f. Co. of Stationers, [1642]. 8°. A¹²,B-C⁶.
Frequent one-word entries, e.g., 'Islip'. 24 Feb. 'Jovis 24° apud Reading'.
Wood Alm. B(7). Wing A1786 (rare).

97. Gallen, Tho[mas]. *Gallen. 1683. A compleat pocket almanack*. London: M. F. f. Co. of Stationers, 1683. 12°. A⁶,B¹²,C⁶ (gold fore-edges).
On 2 inserted blank leaves, at March and at May, Allam wrote accounts, which begin 'On the 24ᵗʰ I paid Mʳ West on my own account 0ˡᵇ-15ˢ-0ᵈ after which I stood indeptd [sic] to him in all 1ˡᵇ-0ˢ-0ᵈ'.
Wood Alm. B(6). Wing A1788 (two). ESTCR 229907 (4 in O).

98. Godfridus, and Melampus. *The knowledge of things unknown: shewing the effects of the planets . . . With the husdand [sic] man's practice, . . . added, The shepheards prognostication for the weather*. London: T. B. for J. Stafford, 1649 (1652). 8°. Pp. [7], 181, [1] (2nd tp at G5; 3rd tp at I1) (misnumbering). Parchment.
Flyleaf, upperᵛ, AW wrote the titles of 4 items in this vol. (in his early hand), including, as separate items, 2 sections of 8(1). After the last, AW wrote, 'Dupl'. P. 159, at wheel of fortune: 'Stultorum plena sunt omnia.'
Wood 8(1). Wing G928 (two).

99. Gusman, pseud. *Gusmans ephemeris: or, the merry rogues calendar. . . . 1662*. London: sold at the Royal Exchange, Westminster, and in Fleet-street, [1662]. 8°. A⁴,B-C⁸,D⁴.
Tp, AW wrote the price, '2ᵈ'.
Wood 15(7) (not in Bodl. CD cat.). Wing A1801[A] (rare) (Wing CD). Not in ESTCR.

100. Halley, Edmond. *Ephemeris ad annum a nativitate Domini 1688*. London: typ. J. Heptinstall, imp. G. Cooper, 1688. 4° in 8's. C⁸ (C8 blank).
Tp, 'Jo: Aubrey, Ex dono Edmundi Halleii Autoris'.
Wood 498(15). Wing A1807 (two).

101. J[essey], [H]enry. *1648. A scripture almanack.* London: M. B. f. Co. of Stationers, [1648]. 8°. 4th ed. A-B⁸.
Tp, AW wrote, 'H. Jessey published a scripture Almanack 1657' (not recorded in Wing).
Wood Alm. A(10). Wing A1834.

102. Lilly, William. *Merlini Anglici ephemeris, or astrologicall judgments for . . . 1673.* London: J. Macock f. the Co. of Stationers, 1673. 8°. A-F⁸ (1 p. book advertisements).
Missing in 1837. LT 1.13.
Wood 748a. Wing A1906. *Folg.*

103. N., H. *1678. A yea and nay almanack for the . . . Quakers.* London: f. Co. of Stationers, 1678. 8°. A-C⁸.
Wood Alm. E(11). Wing A1947A.

104. N., H. *1679. A yea and nay almanack for the . . . Quakers.* London: (M. White) f. Co. of Stationers, 1679. 8°. A-C⁸ (pp. unopened).
Wood Alm. E(12). Wing A1947B.

105. Origanus, David. *Groote schriif almanach . . . 1632.* t'Amstelredam: voor Cornelius van der Plasse, [1632]. 8°. A-C⁸, interleaved with blanks leaves (2nd tp at C1).
This served as Griffin Higgs' diary; on the interleaved leaves, at Jan., he began 'Jan. i4. S. N[ovo]. Wednesday night betweene 9. and i0 of clocke the Queene was delivered of a young Prince: and the next day Mʳ. Hone sent to the K[in]g of England with the Newes.' and continued each month until 28 June. At October he began again and continued until 'Novemb: 29. S. V [i.e., N]. the Queene of Bohemia receaved Newes of the Kings Death at Mentz: being Thursday: upon which Day ever since she never dineth.' See Morrish, [137] 1, and note 8, and notes at Wood 498(14), item 61. LT 1.12.
Wood Alm. A(3). Not in BL.

106. Parker, George. *Mercurius Anglicanus, or the English Mercury:. . . for . . . 1691.* London: J. M. f. Co. of Stationers, 1691. 8°. A2-4,B-F⁸.
Spine and flyleaf, upperᵛ, 'F: VV'; 2nd, author and year of 12 'Almanacks', in Whiteside's hand. Most items retain AW's large arabic numbers, in pencil (cropping at side).
Wood Alm. F(1). Wing A2006.

107. Partridge, Dorothy. *The woman's almanack, for . . . 1694.* London: f. J. S., 1694. 12°. A⁴,B².
Wood Alm. F(8). Wing A2016A (rare).

108. Partridge, John. *Mr. John Partrige's [sic], new prophesie of this present year 1684.* (London): (G. Groom), (1683). 4°. Pp. 8 (unopened).
Wood 646(17). Wing P623.

109. Partridge, John. *Annus mirabilis or strange and wonderful predictions and observations gathered out of mr. J[ohn] Partridges almanack 1688.* London: printed, sold R. Taylor, 1689. 4°. Pp. [2], 32.
Tp, AW wrote, 'Bought at Oxon. 14 Jan. 1688[9] – 6ᵈ'. LT 3.296.
Wood 643(7b). Wing A2018.

110. Partridge, John. *Merlinus liberatus: being an almanack for . . . 1692.* London: R. R. for the Co. of Stationers, [1692]. 8°. A-C⁸.
Wood Alm. F(7). Wing A2034.

111. Partridge, John. *Merlinus liberatus: being an almanack for . . . 1694.* London: R. Roberts f. Co. of Stationers, [1694]. 8°. A-C⁸ (C unopened) (ms. nos. 1-70). Modern binding, half-calf, maroon; inside, brown paper wrappers.
This is the 38th of AW's diaries (see LT 1.3-4), with extensive interleaving from after the upper wrapper to after B8, Dec., and after C8, with 1 or more blank leaves and slips containing diary entries and memoranda. AW's notes begin on the paper wrapper, upper, '1694' in red chalk; flyleaf, upper, 'Jan 2 to Mʳ Long or Lang of Trin[ity] a Note to Dʳ [Dudley] Loftus', etc., and continue to flyleaf, lowerᵛ. There are also a few brief notes on some printed almanac pp. Not by AW, an apothecary's bill, 11 June 1694, from Henry Reekes (f. 32). LT 3.439-476.
[MS.] Wood Diaries 38. Wing A2036. SC 27760.

112. [Phillips, John]. *Montelion, 1660. Or, the prophetical almanack.* London: (sold H. Marsh), 1660. A-C⁸.
Tp, AW identified pseudonym as 'Joh. Philipps [sic] nephew by the mother to John Milton was author of

this Montelion, and not of the rest that follow. See in his Mercurius Verax. &c' (see Wood 15(9), item 115). LT 1.13. See G. Ungerer, 'Recovering Unrecorded Quixotic Allusions', *BLR*, 17 (April 2000): 68. Wood 15(3) (not in Bodl. CD cat.). Wing A2109 (Wing, date of pub. [1659]).

113. [Phillips, John]. *Montelion, 1661. Or, the prophetical almanack.* London: sold H. Marsh, [1661]. 8°. A-C^8 (wanting B4).
Wood 15(4) (not in Bodl. CD cat.). Wing A2110.

114. [Phillips, John]. *Montelion, 1662. Or, the prophetical almanack.* London: sold H. Marsh, [1662]. 16°. A^6,B^{8,8,2}.
Each 16° leaf is pasted on an 8° template. Acquired 24 Feb. 1662, 8^d, LT 1.431.
Wood 15(5) (not in Bodl. CD cat.). Wing A2111 (rare).

115. [Phillips, John]. *Mercurius Verax or the prisoners prognostications 1675.* London: f. R. Cutler, 1675. 8°. Pp. [4], 54.
Tp, AW identified the author, 'J. Philipps', and wrote, '4^d'.
Wood 15(9) (not in Bodl. CD cat.). Wing P2093.

116. Pigot, Francis. *Pigot. 1662. An almanack for . . . 1662.* London: f. Co. of Stationers, 1662. 8°. A-B^8,B^4 (sic).
Acquired 14 Dec. 1661, LT 1.420.
Wood Alm. E(3). Wing A2115 (rare).

117. Pond, Ben[jamin]. *A new almanack for . . . 1689.* Oxford: at the theatre for T. Guy, 1689. 8°. A-C^8.
Wood Alm. E(10). Wing A2126 (rare).

118. Pond, Edward. *Pond 1630. A new almanack for . . . MDCXXX.* [Cambridge]: printers to the Universitie of Cambridge, [1630]. 8°. A-C^8. Parchment with marbled paper pasted over as center panel.
On the spine 'A' and below 'VV'. Flyleaf, 1st^v, 'A: VV:'; 2nd, list of 13 'Almanacks.' (compressing several fragments, at (11-15), into a single entry, 'Physical Directions'), in Whiteside's hand. There are two independent lists of Wood Almanacs: in the Whiteside cat., p. vi (also in Whiteside's hand); and in a C. J. Hindle ms. catalogue (dated Apr. 1933), at Duke Humfrey's Library, Selden End R. 6. 224. 1st item, tp, top, AW wrote 'Dr Higgs'. Higgs' diary entries began in May, 'May 29. The Prince of Eng. borne [/] 30. The blazing starr seene at the sermon-tyme at Pauls Crosse [/] 31 The eclipse of the Sun.', and continue through June (9 lines), July (25 lines), August (26 lines), etc. to December (32 lines on 2 pp.), B1-8. See Morrish, [137] 1, and note 8, and notes at Wood 498(14), item 61.
Wood Alm. A(1) (11-16 are not in Bodl. CD cat.); (9) is not an almanac). STC 501.20 (two).

119. Pond, Ed[ward]. *Pond's almanack for . . . 1641.* [Cambridge]: R. Daniel, 1641. 8. A-B^8,C1-7 (wanting the final leaf). Stitch marks show that this item was bound in an earlier vol.
Tp and C5^v, scribbles.
Wood Alm. A(2). Wing A2127.

120. Pond, Edward. *Pond an almanack for . . . 1662.* Cambridge: J. Field, 1662. 8°. A-C^8 (ms. nos. ff. 1-43). Modern binding, half-calf, maroon; inside, paper wrapper.
This is the 6th of AW's diaries (see LT 1.3-4), with extensive interleaving from after A1 to after B6, Dec., with 1 or 2 blank leaves and a slip, all containing diary entries or memoranda. AW's notes begin on the paper wrapper, upper, 'Pond: 1662', and '1662' in red chalk, and 'Marmora Seldeniana set up a little before the Act time A. 1660' (LT 1.351), followed by entries for 23 Jan, 22 March, 5 Aug., 11 Oct. and, ^{v}, general notes for 1661-3. The formal diary begins after A2^v, f. 5. Wrapper, lower^r, f. 43, notes added later, on the decline of serious study, dated 1679, and a chronology of mayors, 1659-1665; ^{v}, brief notes on moral philosophers, and on an archeological find in Nov. 1662. There are also notes on some printed almanac pp. Acquired 1 Jan. 1662, 3^d, LT 1.427-466.
[MS.] Wood Diaries 6. Wing A2143. SC 27728.

121. Pond, Edward. *Pond. An almanack for . . . 1664.* Cambridge: J. Field, 1664. 8°. A-C^8 (C5-6 unopened) (ms. nos. ff. 1-46). Modern binding, half-calf, maroon; inside, paper wrapper.
This is the 8th of AW's diaries (see LT 1.3-4), with extensive interleaving from after A1 to after B8 with 1 or 2 blank leaves and slips, all containing diary entries or memoranda. AW's notes begin on the paper wrapper, upper, 'Pond 1664 [/] My mother & Brother Mounser oweth me 15^d apeice for a grace night for the Bachelors Feb. 13' and other notes, and end on the wrapper, lower^v. There are also notes on some printed almanac pp. Acquired 2 Jan. 1664, 2^d ob. LT 2.1-26.

[MS.] Wood Diaries 8. Wing A2145. SC 27730.

122. Pond, Edward. *Pond. An almanack for . . . 1669.* Cambridge: J. Field, 1669. 8°. A-C⁸ (B7-8 unopened) (ms. nos. ff. 1-45). Modern binding, half-calf, maroon; inside, paper wrapper.
This is the 13th of AW's diaries (see LT 1.3-4), with extensive interleaving from after A2 to after B8, with 1 or 2 blank leaves and slips, all containing diary entries or memoranda. AW's notes begin on the paper wrapper, upper, 'Pond. 1669. 4ᵈ [/] [John] Web[b] author of Stoneheng died as tis reported 1666. or thereabouts' (Wood 413(1 and 3), items 3904, 6488); ᵛ, 'Mū [Memorandum] in Oxō this year 1669.'; notes continue from f. 4 to wrapper, lowerᵛ. There are also notes on some printed almanac pages. Not in AW's hand, a recording of an inscription on a Roman stone brought from London to Oxford (f. 16), followed by details in AW's hand. LT 2.148-182.
[MS.] Wood Diaries 13. Wing A2149. SC 27735.

123. Pond, Edward. *Pond an almanack for . . . 1670.* Cambridge: J. Hayes, 1670. 8°. A-C⁸. (B7-8, with blank interleaf inserted, and C unopened) (ms. nos. ff. 1-43). Modern binding, half-calf, maroon; inside, paper wrapper.
This is the 14th of AW's diaries (see LT 1.3-4), with extensive interleaving from after the upper wrapper to after B5, Dec., with 1 or 2 blank leaves and slips, all containing diary entries or memoranda. AW's notes begin on the paper wrapper, upper, 'Pond 1670 { in some of my Almanacks I have put down the death of [John] Caines the Jesuit – He was borne at Compton Painsford in Com. Somers. twas W. Tillyard told me he took him to be a Jesuit'; notes continue from f. 2 to wrapper, lowerᵛ. There are also notes on some printed almanac pp. LT 2.182-212. Acquired 20 Dec. 1669, LT 2.177.
[MS.] Wood Diaries 14. Wing A2150. SC 27736.

124. [Pond, Edward]. *Pond an almanack for . . . 1677.* Cambridge: J. Hayes, 1677. 8°. A-C⁸ (ms. nos. ff. 1-54). Modern binding, half-calf, maroon; inside, paper wrapper.
This is the 21st of AW's diaries (see LT 1.3-4), with extensive interleaving from after the upper wrapper to after B6, and after C8, with 1 or more blank leaves or slips, all containing diary entries or memoranda. AW's notes begin on the paper wrapper, upper, 'Pond. 1677. [/] [Henry] Oldenburg authour of the philosophical transac[.] died 1677. So Dʳ [Robert] Plot', etc., and notes continue to wrapper, lower. Not by AW, slip with note of death, 4 Oct. 1677, of Bishop [William] Lucy (ink over pencil), after which AW wrote, 'His sons hand', and ᵛ, 'from Mʳ Lucy of Qu[eens] Coll' (f. 31b) There are also notes on some printed almanac pp. F. 25 is a printed item, an advertisement, 'The Rarity and Wonder of the World'; see separate entry at Wood Diaries 21b, item 5529. LT 2.364-399.
[MS.] Wood Diaries 21a. Wing A2157 (two). SC 27743.

125. [Pond, Edward]. *Pond an almanack for . . . 1680.* Cambridge: J. Hayes, 1680. 8°. A-C⁸ (ms. nos. ff. 1-59). Modern binding, half-calf, maroon; inside, paper wrapper.
This is the 24th of AW's diaries (see LT 1.3-4), with extensive interleaving from after the upper wrapper to after B6, and after C8, with 1 or more blank leaves and slips, all containing diary entries or memoranda. AW's notes begin on the paper wrapper, upper, 'Pound [sic] 1680. [/] Mʳ Elmy at the blew bull in the little minories by the Tower cures deafness', etc., and notes continue to wrapper, lower. There are also notes on some printed almanac pp. F. 27, not by AW, a letter, 12 Nov. 1677, from William Fulman (LT 2.392). LT 2.475-508.
[MS.] Wood Diaries 24. Wing A2160. SC 27746.

126. [Pond, Edward]. *Pond an almanack for . . . 1681.* Cambridge: J. Hayes, 1681. 8°. A-C⁸ (C2-3, 5-8 unopened) (ms. nos. 1-54, but there is gross misnumbering and rearrangement: 1, 2, 36, 3-9, 9*, 10-28, 31-35, 37-9, 42-43, 45, 26-30, 29-39, 1 unnumbered leaf, 40-41, 41-42, 1 unnumbered slip, 43-54). Modern binding, half-calf, maroon; inside, paper wrapper.
This is the 25th of AW's diaries (see LT 1.3-4), with extensive interleaving from after the upper wrapper to after B8, and after C4 and C8, with 1 or more blank leaves and slips containing diary entries or memoranda. AW's notes begin on the paper wrapper, upper, 'Pond 1681 [/] 1691. 4ᵈ', '1681', in red chalk, etc., and notes continue to wrapper, lowerᵛ. There are also notes on some printed almanac pp. Not by AW, after A7 to after B5, 10 12° leaves from the diary of Andrew Allam bound in the vol. at appropriate months; and after B5, a formal note, 21 Dec. 1681, from Raphe Sheldon, concerning the death of James Earle; to which AW added, 'fasti 1642' (mention of John Earle, AOF 2.52). Between B4-5 is inserted a printed item, an advertisement 'Money Well Bestowed'; see separate entry Wood Diaries 25b, item 4530. LT 2.509-565.
[MS.] Wood Diaries 25. Wing A2161. SC 27747.

127. Poor Robin [Winstanley, William]. *Poor Robin. 1663. An almanack after a new fashion.* London: T. Johnson, 1663. 8°. A-C⁸. Pasteboard (grey) with parchment spine.

Tp, note, AW wrote, 'Rob. Pory was a verie rich dignitary', later lined out (this pamphlet was issued with the imprimatur of Pory).
Wood 12(1) (not in Bodl. CD cat.). Wing A2182[D] (rare) (Wing CD). Not in ESTCR.

128. Poor Robin [Winstanley, William]. *Poor Robin. 1664. An almanack*. London: f. Co. of Stationers, [1664]. 8°. A-C⁸.
Wood 12(2) (not in Bodl. CD cat.). Wing A2183.

129. Poor Robin [Winstanley, William]. *Poor Robin. 1665. An almanack*. London: f. Co. of Stationers, [1665]. 8°. A-C⁸.
Wood 12(4) (not in Bodl. CD cat.). Wing A2184 (two).

130. Poor Robin [Winstanley, William]. *Poor Robin's as-tronomical [sic] predictions and observations for the year 1665*. London: f. the Authour, 1665. 8°. Pp. 48.
Prob. acquired 20 Dec. 1664, LT 1.24.
Wood 12(3) (not in Bodl. CD cat.). Wing A2184[A] (rare) (Wing CD). Not in ESTCR.

131. Poor Robin [Winstanley, William]. *Poor Robin. 1666. An almanack*. London: f. Co. of Stationers, [1666]. 8°. A-C⁸.
Wood 12(5) (not in Bodl. CD cat.). Wing A2185.

132. Poor Robin [Winstanley, William]. *Poor Robin. 1667. An almanack*. London: f. Co. of Stationers, [1667]. 8°. A-C⁸.
Wood 12(6) (not in Bodl. CD cat.). Wing A2186.

133. Poor Robin [Winstanley, William]. *Poor Robin. 1668. An almanack*. London: f. Co. of Stationers, [1668]. 8°. A-C⁸.
Acquired 18 Nov. 1667, 3ᵈ, LT 2.120.
Wood 12(7) (not in Bodl. CD cat.). Wing A2187.

134. Poor Robin [Winstanley, William]. *Poor Robin. 1669. An almanack*. London: f. Co. of Stationers, [1669]. 8°. A-C⁸.
Wood 12(8) (not in Bodl. CD cat.). Wing A2188.

135. Poor Robin [Winstanley, William]. *Poor Robin 1670. An almanack*. London: f. Co. of Stationers, [1670]. 8°. A-C⁸.
Acquired 11 Jan. 1670, LT 2.184.
Wood 12(9) (not in Bodl. CD cat.). Wing A2189.

136. Poor Robin [Winstanley, William]. *Poor Robin 1671. An almanack*. London: f. Co. of Stationers, 1671. 8°. A-C⁸ (2nd tp at C1). Pasteboard (grey) with parchment spine.
Tpᵛ, author's name entered, 'William Winstanly'.
Wood 13(1) (not in Bodl. CD cat.). Wing A2190 (two).

137. Poor Robin [Winstanley, William]. *Poor Robin 1672 An almanack*. London: f. Co. of Stationers, 1672. 8°. A-B⁸,B⁸ (2nd tp at 2nd B1).
Wood 13(2) (not in Bodl. CD cat.). Wing A2191.

138. Poor Robin [Winstanley, William]. *Poor Robin. 1673. An almanack*. London: f. Co. of Stationers, 1673. 8°. A-C⁸ (2nd tp at C1).
Wood 13(3) (not in Bodl. CD cat.). Wing A2192 (two).

139. Poor Robin [Winstanley, William]. *Poor Robin. 1674. An almanack*. London: f. Co. of Stationers, 1674. 8°. A-C⁸ (2nd tp at C1).
Wood 13(4) (not in Bodl. CD cat.). Wing A2193.

140. Poor Robin [Winstanley, William]. *Poor Robin, 1675. An almanack*. London: f. Co. of Stationers, 1675. 8°. A-C⁸ (2nd tp at C1).
Wood 13(5) (not in Bodl. CD cat.). Wing A2194.

141. Poor Robin [Winstanley, William]. *Poor Robin, 1676. An almanack*. London: f. Co. of Stationers, 1676. 8°. A-C⁸ (2nd tp at C1).
Wood 13(6) (not in Bodl. CD cat.). Wing A2195.

142. Poor Robin [Winstanley, William]. *Poor Robin, 1677. An almanack*. London: f. Co. of Stationers,

1677. 8°. A-C^8 (2nd tp at C1).
Wood 13(7) (not in Bodl. CD cat.). Wing A2196.

143. Poor Robin [Winstanley, William]. *Poor Robin, 1678. An almanack*. London: f. Co. of Stationers, 1678. 8°. A-C^8 (2nd tp at C1).
Wood 13(8) (not in Bodl. CD cat.). Wing A2197.

144. Poor Robin [Winstanley, William]. *Poor Robin 1679. An almanack*. London: f. Co. of Stationers, 1679. 8°. A-C^8 (2nd tp at C1) (A7-8, unopened).
Wood 13(9) (not in Bodl. CD cat.). Wing A2198.

145. Poor Robin [Winstanley, William]. *Poor Robin 1680. An almanack*. London: f. Co. of Stationers, 1680. 8°. A-C^8 (2nd tp at C1).
Wood 13(10) (not in Bodl. CD cat.). Wing A2199.

146. Poor Robin [Winstanley, William]. *Poor Robin 1681. An almanack*. London: f. Co. of Stationers, 1681. 8°. A-C^8 (2nd tp at C1). Pasteboard (grey) with parchment spine.
Wood 14(1) (not in Bodl. CD cat.). Wing A2200.

147. Poor Robin [Winstanley, William]. *Poor Robin 1682. An almanack*. London: f. Co. of Stationers, 1682. 8°. A-C^8 (2nd tp at C1).
Wood 14(2) (not in Bodl. CD cat.). Wing A2201.

148. Poor Robin [Winstanley, William]. *Poor Robin 1683. An almanack*. London: f. Co. of Stationers, 1683. 8°. A-C^8 (2nd tp at C1).
Wood 14(3) (not in Bodl. CD cat.). Wing A2202.

149. Poor Robin [Winstanley, William]. *Poor Robin, 1684. An almanack*. London: f. Co. of Stationers, 1684. 8°. A-C^8 (2nd tp at C1).
Wood 14(4) (not in Bodl. CD cat.). Wing A2203.

150. Poor Robin [Winstanley, William]. *Poor Robin, 1685. An almanack*. London: f. Co. of Stationers, 1685. 8°. A-C^8 (2nd tp at C1).
Wood 14(5) (not in Bodl. CD cat.). Wing A2204.

151. Poor Robin [Winstanley, William]. *Poor Robin, 1686, an almanack*. London: f. Co. of Stationers, 1686. 8°. A-C^8 (2nd tp at C1).
Wood 14(6) (not in Bodl. CD cat.). Wing A2205.

152. Poor Robin [Winstanley, William]. *Poor Robin, 1687. An almanack*. London: f. Co. of Stationers, 1687. 8°. A-C^8 (2nd tp at C1) (A6-7,C1-4, unopened).
Wood 14(7) (not in Bodl. CD cat.). Wing A2206.

153. Poor Robin [Winstanley, William]. *Poor Robin, 1688. An almanack*. London: f. Co. of Stationers, 1688. 8°. A-C^8 (2nd tp at C1) (A1-8-B1-6, etc., unopened).
Wood 14(8) (not in Bodl. CD cat.). Wing A2207.

154. Poor Robin [Winstanley, William]. *Poor Robin, 1689. An almanack*. London: f. Co. of Stationers, 1689. 8°. A-C^8 (2nd tp at C1).
Wood 14(9) (not in Bodl. CD cat.). Wing A2208.

155. Poor Robin [Winstanley, William]. *Poor Robin, 1690. An almanack*. London: f. Co. of Stationers, 1690. 8°. A-C^8 (2nd tp at C1) (C6-8, unopened).
Wood 14(10) (not in Bodl. CD cat.). Wing A2209.

156. Poor Robin [Winstanley, William]. *Poor Robin. 1691. An almanack*. London: f. Co. of Stationers, 1691. 8°. 29th ed. A-C^8 (2 tpp) (pp. unopened).
Tp, W. [i] (cropped at side).
Wood Alm. F(2). Wing A2210.

157. Poor Robin [Winstanley, William]. *Poor Robin, 1692. An almanack*. London: f. Co. of Stationers, 1692. 8°. 30th ed. A-C^8 (2 tpp).
Wood Alm. F(3). Wing A2211.

158. Poor Robin [Winstanley, William]. *Poor Robin, 1693. An almanack*. London: (J. R.) f. Co. of Stationers, 1693. 8°. 31st ed. A-C^8 (2 tpp).

Wood Alm. F(4). Wing A2212.

159. Poor Robin [Winstanley, William]. *Poor Robin, 1694. An almanack.* London: (J. R.) f. Co. of Stationers, 1694. 8°. 32nd ed. A-C⁸ (2 tpp).
Wood Alm. F(5). Wing A2213.

160. Poor Robin [Winstanley, William]. *Poor Robin, 1695. An almanack.* London: (J. R.) f. Co. of Stationers, 1695. 8°. 33rd ed. Pp. A-C⁸ (2 tpp).
Wood Alm. F(6). Wing A2214.

161. Protestant Almanac. *The Protestant almanack for . . . 1668. . . . by Philoprotest.* London: f. Co. of Stationers, 1668. 8°. A-D⁸ (2 tpp).
Acquired 11 Jan. 1668, 6ᵈ, LT 2.126.
Wood Alm. E(6). Wing A2222.

162. Protestant Almanac. *The Protestant almanack for . . . 1680. . . . By Philoprotest.* London: f. Co. of Stationers, 1680. 8°. A-C⁸ (2 tpp).
Wood Alm. E(8). Wing A2224.

163. Riders, Cardanus. *Riders (1682.) British Merlin:. . . Fitting the longitude and latitude . . . of Great Britains monarchy.* London.: T. Newcomb f. Co. of Stationers, 1682. 12°. A⁶,B¹²,C⁶, blank sheets inserted in B quire and at end. Calf, blind and roll-stamped, two clasps. Marbled pastedowns and flyleaves.
At end, 18 blank leaves were torn out, some have traces of ms. notes which may be in A. Allam's hand, see LT 3.167 and 2.509.
Wood 5. Wing A2256 (two).

164. Saunders, Richard. *1657. Apollo Anglicanus: the English Apollo.* London: f. Co. of Stationers, 1657. 8°. A-C⁸ (ms. nos. ff. 1-50). Modern binding, half-calf, maroon.
This is the 1st of AW's diaries (see LT 1.3-4) with extensive interleaving from after A1 to after B7, Dec., with 1 or 2 blank leaves. AW recorded daily events, some at the time of occurrence and others at a later time, and memoranda of various kinds. On the 1st blank leaf, f. 1, AW wrote (a good example of his early hand), 'Anno: 1656[7]: Monseur Will [Will, lined out] Jeame [James] in January [in January, lined out] taught me to lay on the violin, beginning in January and soe on till 7 months end: [/]', July: 22 1656: Mʳ [blank, i.e., Joseph] Procter departed this life in the parish of Holywell Oxō: and layeth buried in the middle of the aforesaid church: He was a rare musicion, especiall for the Lyra violl and also for the division violl, bred up to M [to M lined out] under Mʳ. J[ohn]: Jenkins the mirror of this our age / he was very good for the treble violl and also for the violin and all these comprehended in a man of three or 24 yeares of Age: [/] March: 1656: I put out my Brother Edw booke of sermons collecting of it from his owne notes all with mine owne pen: and dedicated them to Jonathan] [sic; ᵛ] Jonathan Godard. M.D. and warden of Merton: Coll:', etc. On the lower wrapperʳ⁻ᵛ, AW wrote general notes concerning the year. For the almanacs which also served as Wood's Diaries, this cat. gives only brief descriptions of what AW wrote; for full records, see LT 1.211-3.496, where A. Clark inserted records from numerous other mss. sources, mainly from the 1st version of AW's autobiography (BL MS. Harl. 5409, 1632 to March 1660) and his revised version titled 'Secretum Antonii' (Bodleian MS. Tanner 102, pt. 1, 1632 to June 1672).
[MS.] Wood Diaries 1. Wing A2327 (rare). SC 27723.

165. Saunders, Richard. *1659. Apollo Anglicanus: the English Apollo:. . . 1659.* London: E. Cotes f. Co. of Stationers, 1659. 8°. A-C⁸ (C6-7 unopened) (ms. nos. ff. 1-39). Modern binding, half-calf, maroon, inside, paper wrappers.
This is the 3rd of AW's diaries (see LT 1.3-4) with extensive interleaving from after upper wrapper to after B7, Dec., with single blank leaves. Wrapper, upper, entries for 11 March, 4 and 14 May, and an incomplete coat of arms: a shield with a talbot's head. On the 2nd interleaved leaf, after A4 (f. 7), he wrote, 'Ant: Woode: 1659' and 'the. 1. ffor this Almanack: 3ᵈ 0'; and he ended the last, after B7, '31 [Dec.] for the Kings triall – 9 ᵈ - 0 [/] the same to mounsir for new bridle: given } - 1ˢ - 0'. Wrapper, lowerᵛ, 3 entries for Nov. and Dec. There are also a few notes on some printed almanac pp. LT 1.266-289.
[MS.] Wood Diaries 3. Wing A2329 (two). SC 27725.

166. Saunders, Richard. *1663. Apollo Anglicanus: the English Apollo.* London: E. Cotes f. Co. of Stationers, 1663. 8°. A-C⁸ (ms. nos. ff. 1-44). Modern binding, half-calf, maroon; inside, paper wrapper.
This is the 7th of AW's diaries (see LT 1.3-4), with extensive interleaving from after paper wrapper to after B8, Dec., with 1 or 2 blank leaves and slips, all containing diary entries or memoranda. AW's notes begin on the paper wrapper, upper, 'AWoode 1663 [/] Saunders: Saunders', '1663' in orange crayon, and notes,

filling this, the ^v, and the following inserted blank leaf, f. 2, not all for 1663; notes end on the wrapper, lower^v. There are also notes on some printed almanac pp. LT 1.466-511. One of two almanacs acquired 16 Dec. 1662, LT 1.464 (a 3rd, Wharton, acquired 9 Jan. 1663).
[MS.] Wood Diaries 7. Wing A2333. SC 27729.

167. Saunders, Richard. *1670. Apollo Anglicanus: the English Apollo*. London: E. C. & A. C. f. Co. of Stationers, 1670. 8°. A-B⁸,A⁸ (pp. unopened).
Acquired 20 Dec. 1669, LT 2.177.
Wood Alm. F(9). Wing A2340.

168. Saunders, Richard. *1671. Apollo Anglicanus, the English Apollo*. London: A. C. f. Co. of Stationers, 1671. 8°. A-B⁸,A⁸.
Tp, AW wrote 'let the chronologie here be taken out.' 2nd A7ᵛ, A8, AW marked 2 events with pairs of vertical lines, in red ink (9 July 1669, the U. of Oxford and the New Theater; 30 Sept. 1669, death of Henry King); A8ʳ⁻ᵛ, AW corrected '1667' to '1669'.
Wood Alm. F(10). Wing A2341.

169. Saunders, Richard. *1672. Apollo Anglicanus, the English Apollo*. London: A. Clark f. Co. of Stationers, 1672. 8°. Pp. A-B⁸,A⁸ (pp. unopened).
Wood Alm. F(11). Wing A2342.

170. Saunders, Richard. *1673. Apollo Anglicanus, the English Apollo*. London: A. Clark f. Co. of Stationers, 1673. 8°. A-B⁸,A⁸ (pp. unopened).
Final leaf, A8ʳ⁻ᵛ, AW marked 3 items with a vertical line, 14, 28 June, 28 Sept. 1671 (W. Blandford, bishop of Oxford, translated to Worcester; confirmation of Dr. N. Crew; and knighting of Dr. T. Brown).
Wood Alm. F(12). Wing A2343.

171. Saunders, Richard. *1685. Apollo Anglicanus, the English Apollo*. London: M. Clark f. Co. of Stationers, 1685. 8°. A-B⁸,A⁸ (ms. nos. ff. 1-78). Modern binding, half-calf, maroon; inside, paper wrapper.
This is the 29th of AW's diaries (see LT 1.3-4), with extensive interleaving from after the upper wrapper to after B7, Dec., with 1 or more blank leaves and slips containing diary entries and memoranda. AW's notes begin on the paper wrapper, upper, 'Saunders [twice] 1685 4ᵈ.', '1685' in orange crayon, 'Arms of Dʳ Jo. Budden on his picture in W. Colliers hands are – quarterly s[able] & or, a lyon pass[ant] arg[ent] in the 1st quart', etc., and notes continue to wrapper, lowerᵛ. There are also brief notes on some printed almanac pp. Not by AW, 1 slip from the diary of Andrew Allam bound in the vol. among Feb. events (f. 15); a ms. copy of a prayer on Charles 2's recovery (f. 17); a slip on Agaphius of Cephalonia (f. 48); Latin verse, 9 lines, 'Imperat aut servit collecta pecunia cuique' (f. 59ᵛ); a letter from Richard Old (f. 65); and a ms. waste paper, 10 lines (f. 68ᵛ). Between ff. 39-40 is inserted a printed item, an advertisement, 'In Bartholomew Fair'; see separate entry at Wood Diaries 29b, item 885. LT 3.122-173.
[MS.] Wood Diaries 29. Wing A2355. SC 27751.

172. Saunders, Richard. *1690. Apollo Anglicanus . . . by Richard Saunder*. London: M. Clark f. Co. of Stationers, 1690. 8°. A-B⁸,A⁸ (2nd A5-8 unopened) (ms. nos. 1-68). Modern binding, half-calf, maroon; inside, paper wrapper.
This is the 34th of AW's diaries (see LT 1.3-4), with extensive interleaving from after the upper wrapper to after B8, Dec., and after 2nd A8, with 1 or more blank leaves and slips containing diary entries and memoranda. AW's notes begin on the paper wrapper, upper, 'Sanders Alm. 1690 [/] 6ˢ to my sister 8 Feb. . . . .', etc., and notes continue to wrapper, lowerᵛ. There are also a very few brief notes on some printed almanac pages. Not by AW, note on presentation of William Jane by George Walker (f. 17ᵛ). LT 3.319-349.
[MS.] Wood Diaries 34. Wing A2360. SC 27756.

173. [Sheppard, Samuel]. *Merlinus anonymus. An almanack . . . 1654*. London: F. Neile, 1654. 8°. A-C⁸.
Pasteboard (grey) with parchment spine.
Flyleaf, upper, 2ndᵛ, AW wrote the titles of 9 printed works in this vol., within guidelines made with red ink, and a note after a hand pointer, 'part of a cat. of play-books is in Montel. Alm. 1663 after the month of Dec/' (see Wood15(8)). A4ᵛ, identification of a reference: 'Nich. Culpeper the Almanack-maker'.
Wood 15(1) (not in Bodl. CD cat.). Wing A2381C (two) ('O' not recorded in Wing).

174. [Sheppard, Samuel]. *Merlinus anonymus. An almanack . . . 1655*. London: F. Neile, 1655. 8°. A-C⁸ (2nd tp at C2).
Wood 15(2) (not in Bodl. CD cat.). Wing A2381D (one). 'O' not recorded in Wing).

175. Shinkin ap Shone, pseud. *Shinkin ap Shone her prognostication for the ensuing yeer, 1654.* [London]: f. the author, sold at his shop at the sign of the Cows Bobby, [1653]. 4°. Pp. [2], 8 (i.e., 6). P. 8 (i.e., 6), scribbled name, Willi: Orth (?).
Wood 646(10). Wing A2385 (two).

176. Smith, John. *Smith, 1652. A new almanack.* London: f. Company of Stationers, 1652. A-C⁸. Tp, 'W. i.' (?); and in margin, 'Feb: 9: / 1652 [/] h', may be in Allam's hand. Some pp. with line in margin, e.g., at 9 Feb., at 'K. Charles buryed at Windsor. 1648'; short horizontal lines at all days of March; some pp. with 'q[uaere]' in margin, e.g., at 6 May, 'Doct. [I.] Dorislaus slain in Holland. 1649'; at July Aug. and Dec., 'q[uaere]' notes, in pencil. 3 Sept. and 4-12 Nov. (at the latter, 3 notes, in 2 hands, and at which AW wrote 'qu[aere]'), longer notes, not by Allam(?) or by AW; e.g., 3 Sept., at 'Scots routed by L. Gen. Cromwell. 1650', 'at Dunbar in Scotland. The same day 1651 K: Charle[s] beaten at Worcester. and the same day and same yeare Dundee stormed.'
Wood Alm. A(17). Wing A2394 (two).

177. Swallow, John. *[Swallow. An almanack for . . . 1643].* [London]: [A. Norton f. Co. of Stationers], [1643]. A2-A4, only (followed by an unidentified a leaf, A2).
Wood Alm. A(14-15). Wing A2411 (two).

178. Swan, John. *An ephemeris or, almanack for . . . 1667.* [Cambridge]: J. Field, 1667. 8°. A-C⁸ (ms. nos. ff. 1-41). Modern binding, half-calf, maroon; inside, paper wrapper.
This is the 11th of AW's diaries (see LT 1.3-4), with extensive interleaving from after the paper wrapper to after B7, Dec., with 1 or 2 blank leaves, all containing diary entries or memoranda. AW's notes begin on the paper wrapper, upper, '10ˢ for Dʳ Willis his fee', '1667' in red crayon, and other notes, and end on the wrapper, lowerᵛ. There are also notes on some printed almanac pp. LT 2.97-126.
[MS.] Wood Diaries 11. Wing A2475. SC 27733.

179. [Swan, John]. *Swan. A new almanack for . . . 1683.* Cambridge: J. Hayes, 1683. 8°. A-C⁸ (C5-8 unopened) (ms. nos. ff. 1-70). Modern binding, half-calf, maroon; inside, paper wrapper.
This is the 27th of AW's diaries (see LT 1.3-4), with extensive interleaving from after wrapper, upper, to after B7, with 1 or more blank leaves and slips containing diary entries and memoranda. AW's notes begin on the paper wrapper, upper, '[Swa]n 1683 4ᵈ. [/] Wildgoos rent paid July 1678 [/] Alder - v[ide] Alm 1681. 82', etc., and notes continue to wrapper, lower. There are also brief notes on some printed almanac pp. Not by AW, 2 12° leaves and a slip from the diary of Andrew Allam bound in the vol. at appropriate months (ff. 17, 37 (a slip), 42), and a few notes not by unknown persons (at ff. 14, 24, 42 (some by Allam), 50). LT 3.35-84.
[MS.] Wood Diaries 27. Wing A2490A (two). SC 27749.

180. T., J. *Endymion, 1663. Or the man-in-the-moon his northern weather-glass.* Selenopolis (aliàs Bethlehem) [London]: f. Co. of Stationers, [1663] MDCLIII (sic). 8°. A-B⁸,C⁴.
Wood 15(8) (not in Bodl. CD cat.). Wing A2492A (3).

181. Tanner, John. *Angelus Britannicus an ephemeris . . . for . . . 1661.* London: T. Mabb f. Co. of Stationers, 1661. 8°. A-C⁸. Parchment with marbled paper pasted over as center panel.
Spine and pastedown, upper, 'E: VV'; flyleaf, upper, 1st, author and year of 12 'Almanacks', in Whiteside's hand (the numbering is modern). Some items in this vol. retain AW's large Arabic numbers, in pencil (cropping at side).
Wood Alm. E(1). Wing A2498 (two) (3 at O).

182. Tanner, John. *Angelus Britannicus: an ephemeris for . . . 1672.* London: T. Rad[c]liffe a. M. Daniel f. Co. of Stationers, 1672. 8°. A-C⁸ (ms. nos. ff. 1-43). Modern binding, half-calf, maroon; inside, paper wrapper.
This is the 16th of AW's diaries (see LT 1.3-4), with extensive interleaving from after wrapper, upper, and after A4 to after B7, Dec., with 1 or more blank leaves and slips, all containing memoranda and diary entries. AW's notes begin on the paper wrapper, upper, '1672', 'Edw. Derring Coll. Christi Cant. ob[it] June 26. 1576', 'Dʳ [Thomas] Barlow put out in those things of Sʳ Hen. Saville which I have pamphlet in Oxoniensia', etc.; notes continue from f. 2 to wrapper, lowerᵛ. There are also notes on some printed almanac pp. A note not by AW dated 10 Dec. 1678 (out of place), is a military communication from G. Savage at Washam about French army movements over Grange Heath in Purbeck. At this note AW wrote 'X false', and above, 'v[ide] Gazet. nu. 1364'; on the ᵛ, AW wrote an unrelated note, 'Dʳ Fell busie in converting Lord Brudenell' (f. 9; LT 2.426-7); and an unsigned report, 11 Oct. to 22 Nov. 1672, of 6 deaths of 'a malignant Feaver' at Wadham College, at which AW wrote, 'The 6 are more somtimes then the Coll buries

in 5 year[s]' (f. 33ᵛ). F. 8, a printed advertisement, 12°, of 8 lines, 'The Tall Indian'; see Wood Diaries 16b, item 3754. LT 2.239-255.
[MS.] Wood Diaries 16. Wing A2509. SC 27738.

183. Tanner, John. *Angelus Britannicus: an ephemeris for . . . 1695.* London: W. Horton f. Co. of Stationers, 1695. 8°. 39th impr. A-C⁸ (ms. nos. 1-61). Modern binding, half-calf, maroon; inside, brown paper wrapper, upper.
This is the 39th and last of AW's diaries (see LT 1.3-4), with extensive interleaving from after the upper wrapper to after B6, Nov., with 1 or more blank leaves and slips containing diary entries and memoranda. AW's notes begin on the brown paper wrapper, upper, '1695', in red chalk, over the same in pencil, inside the folded wrapper (misbound, not enclosing the whole diary), 'Merry Drollery 1 part' (its former use was to enclose items of drollery, see Wood 326(2)-(3), items 4453f.), and continue from f. 1 to f. 48. F. 15, on a fragment of a letter addressed to Raphe Sheldon, AW stamped his wax seal, 'a talbot's head erased issuing out of a crown' (LT 3.480). F. 48, final entry, 'Let[ter] dat. Nov. 12 Dʳ [Nathaniel] Wilson Bishop of Limbrick is dead - so another letter [/] dat Nov. 14'. There are also a few brief notes on some printed almanac pp. Not by AW, a brief note concerning the spelling of David Gwynne (f. 18bᵛ); and, after AW's final entry, 'Nov. 29ᵗʰ. ob[it] ipse Antonius'. LT 3.476-496.
[MS.] Wood Diaries 39. Wing A2532. SC 27761.

184. Treasurer. *The treasurers almanacke.* London: f. M. Sparke, 1636. 8°. A-B⁸.
Wood 21(3). STC 24214.5 (rare).

185. Trigge, Thomas. *Calendarium astrologicum: or an almanack for . . . 1662.* London: D. Maxwell f. Co. of Stationers, 1662. 8°. A-B⁸,C⁴.
Acquired 14 Dec. 1661, LT 1.420.
Wood Alm. E(2). Wing A2545 (rare, 2 at O).

186. Verus Pater. [By G. Markham]. *Verus pater, or, a bundell of truths. Containing a prognostication.* London: [N. Okes] f. T. L[angley], 1622. 8°. A-C⁸.
Tp, astrological signs and A8ᵛ, note, prob. not by AW.
Wood 9(5) (not in Bodl. CD cat.). STC 24693.

187. [W., W.]. *An episcopal almanack for . . . 1674.* London: J. Macock f. Co. of Stationers, 1674. 8°. A-C⁸ (ms. nos. ff. 1-50). Modern binding, half-calf, maroon; inside, paper wrapper.
This is the 18th of AW's diaries (see LT 1.3-4), with extensive interleaving from after wrapper, upper, to after B7, Dec., and also before lower wrapper, with 1 or more blank leaves and slips, all containing diary entries or memoranda. AW's notes begin on the paper wrapper, upper, '1674 Dec. 28 / 4ᵈ [/] 1674 [/] Lord make me to know mine end & the measure of my dayes &c.' etc., and notes continue to wrapper, lowerᵛ, with records of sheets given to 'Mʳ Peers' (for translation of the *Historia*). There are also notes on some printed almanac pages. LT 2.278-304.
[MS.] Wood Diaries 18. Wing A2633. SC 27440.

188. [W., W.]. *An episcopal almanack for . . . 1675.* London: J. Macock f. Co. of Stationers, 1675. 8°. A-C⁸ (C unopened) (ms. nos. ff. 1-49). Modern binding, half-calf, maroon; inside, paper wrapper.
This is the 19th of AW's diaries (see LT 1.3-4), with extensive interleaving from after wrapper, upper, to after B7, Dec., and also before lower wrapper, with 1 or more blank leaves and slips, all containing diary entries or memoranda. AW's notes begin on the paper wrapper, upper, '1675. 3ᵈ [/] Rushworths collect v[ide] last leaf 2ᵈ edit 1675' (i.e., f. 49, the last leaf, with more information on the reprint), 'Mathematicians borne in Ox. Hen. Coley . . . ', etc., and notes continue to wrapper, lowerᵛ. There are also notes on some printed almanac pp. Not by AW, 10 Nov. 1675, portion of a note, opening with titles of Ralph Bathurst, below which AW wrote, 'This is the date of the Barbours Corporation Charter' (f. 34). LT 2.304-333.
[MS.] Wood Diaries 19. Wing A2634. SC 27741.

189. [Wharton, George]. *Naworth. 1642 a new almanack.* London: J. Dawson f. Co. of Stationers, 1642. 8°. A-B⁸,C⁴ (last 2 leaves, unopened) (2 tpp).
Tp, AW wrote 'G. W. first Alm. came out in 1637'. C4ᵛ, numbers and '69 weeks'.
Wood Alm. A(4). Wing A2671.

190. [Wharton, George]. *Naworth. 1644. A new almanack.* Oxford: H. Hall, 1644. 8°. A-C⁸ (some pp. unopened).
Wood Alm. A(5). Wing A2673. Madan 2060.

191. [Wharton, George]. *Naworth. 1645. A new almanack.* Oxford: H. Hall, [1645]. 8°. A-D⁸.

C7, C8ᵛ, D1, underscoring at description of comet of 1618 and eclipses of 1652 and 1654.
Wood Alm. A(6). Wing A2673A (rare). Madan 2060.

192. Wharton, George. *No Merline, nor Mercurie; but a new almanack . . . for . . . 1647*. [York?]: n.pub., 1647. 8°. A⁸,A-B⁸. Parchment with marbled paper pasted over as center panel.
Flyleaf, upper, 1st, 'B: VV:'; 2nd, author and year of 7 'Almanacks.', in Whiteside's hand. AW wrote large Arabic nos. on each tp.
Wood Alm. B(1). Wing A2674 (two).

193. Wharton, George. *No Merline, nor Mercurie: but a new almanack . . . for . . . 1648*. [London?]: f. the author, 1648. 12°. A¹²,B⁶,C1-5 (imperf).
Tp, 'H I' (Jackson?). Passim, underscoring and some scribbles, e.g., B3ᵛ, George Richard. C3ᵛ, signature, 'Henry Jackson'. LT 1.459-60 (see also 1.331).
Wood Alm. B(2). Wing A2675.

194. Wharton, George. *Hemeroscopeion, or a new almanack . . . for . . . 1649*. [London?]: f. the author, 1649. 12°. A¹²,B-C⁶.
Wood Alm. B(3). Wing A2664 (two).

195. Wharton, George. *Hemeroscopeion: the loyall almanack, for . . . 1650*. Londini: ex off. fidelissima, 1650. 12°. A-C⁶,D-E⁶ (leaf D1 misplaced).
Wood Alm. B(4). Wing A2665 (two).

196. Wharton, George. *Hemeroscopeion: a meteorologicall diary . . . 1651*. [London]: [J. G[rismond] f. Co. of Stationers], [1651]. 12°. A-E⁶ (tp mutilated).
Dupl. at Wood 10(1).
Wood Alm. B(5). Wing A2666 (two).

197. Wharton, George. *Hemeroscopeion: a meteorologicall diary . . . 1651*. London: J. G[rismond] f. Co. of Stationers, 1651. 12°. A-E⁶. Parchment over pasteboard (probably bound before AW acquired this vol.).
Flyleaf, upper, 1stᵛ, 'Ant: à Woode: Jan: 21: A.D. 1659[60]: // pret: 5ˢ-6ᵈ:' (à added later); 3rdᵛ, details, 'Capt. Georg Wharton borne at Kirkby-Kendall 4 Apr. 1617 Treasurer of his majesties ordinance in the tower, post restaur. Car. 2. Made a Baronet for his former service to K. Ch. 1. in Januar. (10) 1677.', and in red ink, 'The 1. Almanack that G. W. published was in 1637. So Mʳ Elias Ashmole [/] In 1640[1] - so Sʳ Edw. Sherburne' (earliest record in Wing is A2670, 1641). C1, AW underscored and entered '// q[uaere]' in margin at printed '30 *Archy* dyed 1650'. LT 1.22, 302. Dupl. at Wood Alm. B(5).
Wood 10(1). Wing A2666 (two).

198. Wharton, George. *Hemeroscopeion anni intercalaris 1652*. London: J. Grismond f. Co. of Stationers, 1652. 8°. A-G⁸ (at end, 1 p. 'Bookes worth Buying').
Wood 10(2). Wing A2667.

199. Wharton, George. *Hemeroscopeion anni aerae christianae 1653*. London: J. Grismond f. Co. of Stationers, 1653. 8°. A-F⁸ (1 p. 'Books worth buying').
B5ᵛ-C3ᵛ, some marks, prob. not by AW. F8ᵛ, AW marked 2 books in list 'Books worth buying'.
Wood 10(3) (not in Bodl. CD cat.). Wing A2668.

200. [Wharton, George]. *[Hemeroscopeion anni oerae christianae 1654]*. [London]: [J. G[rismond] f. James Crumpe], [1654]. 8°. [A]1-3,B-F⁸ (tp torn out).
Wood 10(4). Wing A2669.

201. Wharton, George. *Ephemeris: or, a diary . . . 1655*. London: f. T. Vere and N. Brook, 1655. 8°. A-L⁴ (2nd tp at G4) (at end, 2 pp. 'Books worth buying').
Wood 10(5). Wing A2661.

202. Wharton, G[eorge]. *Hemerologium: or, a register . . . 1656*. London: J. Grismond, 1656. 8°. 1,A-K⁴ (2nd tp at F4) (at end, 1 p. 'Books worth buying').
K4ᵛ, line in margin at book on cures in list, 'Books worth buying'.
Wood 10(6). Wing A2663.

203. Wharton, George. *Calendarium ecclesiasticum: or, a new almanack after the old fashion . . . 1657*. London: J. Grismond, 1657. 8°. A⁴,B-F⁸,G⁴ (2nd tp at D4) (at end, 2 pp. 'Books worth buying').
Some brief notes, e.g., at D8ʳ, at printed entry, anno 1617, 'G.W Nascitur', AW wrote 'Wharton', and

marked with 2 lines in margin entry concerning 'Haidock the sleeping Preacher'; brief marks: F2^v, F4^v-5 ('q[uaere] and '1648' in margins), G2^v, G3^v.
Wood 10(7). Wing A2657A.

204. Wharton, George. *Calendarium ecclesiasticum: or, a new almanack after the old fashion . . . 1658*.
London: J. Grismond, 1658. 8°. A^4,B-F^8 (2nd tp at D6) (at end, 3 pp. 'Books worth buying').
AW acquired a copy, 19 Nov. 1657 for 6^d, LT 1.230, but he may have bought this collection of 10 Wharton almanacs, bound together (1651-1660), on 21 Jan. 1660; see Wood 10(1), item 197. F8, one book marked in list of 'Books worth buying'.
Wood 10(8). Wing A2658.

205. Wharton, George. *Calendarium ecclesiasticum: or, a new almanack after the old fashion . . . 1659*.
London: J. Grismond, 1659. 8°. A^4,B-F^8 (2nd tp at E1) (at end, 3 pp. 'Books worth buying').
Wood 10(9). Wing A2659 (two).

206. Wharton, George. *Calendarium ecclesiasticum: or, a new almanack after the old fashion . . . 1660*.
London: J. Grismond, 1660. 8°. A^4,B-F^8 (2nd tp at E1) (at end, 3 pp. book advertisements).
Wood 10(10). Wing A2660.

207. Wharton, George. *Calendarium Carolinum: or, a new almanack . . . for . . . 1661. [With] Gesta Britannorum*. London: J. G. (J. Grismond) f. Co. of Stationers, 1661. 8°. 1-3,B-F^8 (3 pp. books sold) (2 tpp). Parchment with marbled paper pasted over as center panel.
Spine and flyleaf, upper, 1st^v, 'C: VV'; 2nd, author and year of 6 Wharton 'Almanacks', in Whiteside's hand.
Wood Alm. C(1). Wing A2652.

208. Wharton, George. *Calendarium Carolinum: or, a new almanack . . . for . . . 1662. [With] Gesta Britannorum*. London: J. G. f. Co. of Stationers, 1662. 8°. A2-4,B-F^8 (4 pp. books sold) (2 tpp).
Acquired 14 Dec. 1661, LT 1.420.
Wood Alm. C(2). Wing A2653.

209. Wharton, George. *Calendarium Carolinum: or, a new almanack . . . for . . . 1663. [With] Gesta Britannorum*. London: J. G. f. Co. of Stationers, 1663. 8°. A^4,B-F^8 (4 pp. books sold) (2 tpp).
Acquired 9 Jan. 1663, 6^d, LT 1.467.
Wood Alm. C(3). Wing A2654.

210. Wharton, George. *Calendarium Carolinum: or, a new almanack . . . for . . . 1664*. London: J. Grismond, 1664. 8°. A2-7,C-F^8 (sic; pp. unopened) (2 pp. books sold).
Wood Alm. C(4). Wing A2655.

211. Wharton, George. *Calendarium Carolinum: or, a new almanack . . . for . . . 1665*. London: J. Grismond, 1665. 8°. A-E^8 (2 pp. books sold).
Acquired 20 Dec. 1664, 6^d, LT 2.24.
Wood Alm. C(5). Wing A2656.

212. Wharton, George. *Calendarium Carolinum: or, a new almanack . . . for . . . 1666*. London: J. Grismond, 1666. 8°. A-E^8 (pp. unopened).
Wood Alm. C(6). Wing A2657.

213. Wing, John. Ολύμπια δώματα *or an almanack for . . . 1686*. Cambridge: J. Hayes, 1686. 8°. A-C^8 (C unopened) (ms. nos. 1-78). Modern binding, half-calf, maroon; inside, paper wrapper.
This is the 30th of AW's diaries (see LT 1.3-4), with extensive interleaving from after the upper wrapper to after B8, Dec., with 1 or more blank leaves and slips containing diary entries and memoranda. AW's notes begin on the paper wrapper, upper, 'Wing. 1686. 4^d [/] Lady day letter to M^r [John] Goad {Tho Willis[,] Will Laurence[,] Will How[,] G. A', etc., and notes continue to wrapper, lower^v. There are also brief notes on some printed almanac pp. Not by AW: a note on where John Durham is lodging in London (f.15); on a sheet of waste ms., ^{r}, a Latin tag, and ^{v}, Latin disputation topic (f. 29); 4 lines of verse, 'On all Religions Present & on Past . . . Rayld against all Women, & then married a Whore', after which AW wrote, 'made [by] one John Driden poet Laureat, who turn'd papist in May or June 1686.', and some time later, 'Return'd to his old opinion when the Prince of Orange came to be King' (f. 40). Between ff. 60-62 is inserted a printed item, a notice of a fund-raising Oxfordshire feast for the poor; see separate entry, Wood Diaries 30b, item 5100. LT 3.174-203.
[MS.] Wood Diaries 30. Wing A2777. SC 27752.

214. Wing, John. Ολύμπια δώματα *or an almanack for . . . 1689*. Cambridge: J. Hayes, 1689. 8°. A-C⁸ (ms. ff. unnumbered [1-65]). Modern binding, half-calf, maroon; inside, paper wrapper.
This is the 33rd of AW's diaries (see LT 1.3-4), with extensive interleaving from after the upper wrapper to after B7, Dec., and after C8, with 1 or more blank leaves and slips containing diary entries and memoranda. AW's notes begin on the paper wrapper, upper, 'Wing 1689' and '4' (price?), and '1689' in red chalk; notes continue from f. 1ᵛ to wrapper, lowerᵛ. There are also brief notes on some printed almanac pp. Not by AW, a letter about Matthew Slade, which, AW wrote, was from 'Mʳ [Edward] Hannes of chch. 6 Feb. 1689' (after B7). LT 3.294-319.
[MS.] Wood Diaries 33. Wing A2780. SC 27755.

215. Wing, Vincent. Ολύμπια δώματα *or an almanack and prognostication . . . 1658*. London: R. & W. Leybourn f. Co. of Stationers, 1658. 8°. A-C⁸ (ms. nos. ff. 1-37). Modern binding, half-calf, maroon.
This is the 2nd of AW's diaries (see LT 1.3-4) with extensive interleaving from after A4 to after B7, Dec., with single blank leaves. Acquired 1 Jan. 1658 for 4ᵈ, LT 1.235. Tp, AW wrote '1658', in red chalk. On the 1st interleaved leaf, f. 5, he wrote, 'The 1ˢᵗ day: for this Almanacke - 0 - 4ᵈ - 0' (1 Jan). On the last interleaved leaf, f. 28ᵛ, he wrote '31 [Dec.] - spent at Jeanes - 5ᵈ - 0 [/] for mending my shoes - 6ᵈ - 0', and 2 undated notes, of Bishop Juxon's death and of a man who, 45 years ago, was set in stocks with the brass that he had stolen from St. Mary's Church, hanging around his neck. There are also a few notes and marks on some printed almanac pp. LT 1.235-266.
[MS.] Wood Diaries 2. Wing A2807. SC 27724.

216. Wing, Vincent. Ολύμπια δοματα [sic]. *Or, an almanack . . . 1665*. London: W. Leybourn f. Co. of Stationers, 1665. 8°. A-C⁸ (C2-3, C5-8 unopened) (ms. nos. ff.1-43). Modern binding, half-calf, maroon; inside, paper wrapper.
This is the 9th of AW's diaries (see LT 1.3-4), with extensive interleaving from after A1 to after B8, Dec., with 1 or 2 blank leaves and slips, all containing diary entries or memoranda. AW's notes begin on the paper wrapper, upper, 'Wing 1665 [/] Qu[aere] my pamphlet when Latiduninarians [sic] came up' and other notes, and end on the wrapper, lowerᵛ. There are also notes on some printed almanac pp. Acquired 20 Dec. 1664, LT 2.24, and see 2.27-68.
[MS.] Wood Diaries 9. Wing A2814. SC 27731.

217. Wing, Vincent. Ολύμπια δώματα, *or, an almanack . . . 1667*. London: B. Wood (E. T.) f. Co. of Stationers, [1667]. 8°. A-C⁸ (2 tpp).
Acquired 23 Feb. 1667, 6ᵈ, LT 2.99.
Wood Alm. E(5). Wing A2816.

218. [Winstanley, William]. *The new Protestant almanack for . . . 1677. . . . By Philo-Protest*. London: J. Darby f. Co. of Stationers, 1677. 8°. Pp. 64.
Wood Alm. E(7). Wing A1986.

End of ALMANACS (items 47-218)

219. Almanzor. *The following maxims were found amongst the papers of the great Almanzor*. [London]: n.pub., (1693). S.sh. (r-v).
ᵛ, AW added to the date, 'Sept'.
Wood 276a(19). Wing A2896.

220. Alsted, Johann Heinrich. *Artium liberalium ac facultatum omnium systema mnemonicum*. Francofurto: in offic. Paltheniana, 1610 (2nd tp). 8°. Pp. 1-32, [1-40], 1-136 and 49-830 (A-C⁸,C⁴)(⁸,(A)-(H)⁸,(I)⁴; D-3F⁸ (F8 blank) (2nd tp at)(1). Calf with fillets and cloth clasps; spine, 4 bands.
Tp, '4' (bsm.?) and 'g.g 2 voll.', prob. not by AW. To 1st p. 135, underscoring and lines in margin. Pastedown, lower, AW wrote names of authors on the same subject: 'Henricus Bullingerus. [/] Mattheus Dresserus de moᵒ [modo?] discendi. [/] Bartho: Kek:' [Keckerman].
Wood 44. NUC.

221. Alsted, Johann Heinrich. *Lexicon theologicum*. N.p.: ap. A. Hummium, 1612. Pp. [16], 436. Parchment.
Spine, traces of earlier shelf-marks. Cover, upper, inside, 'pretium 8ᵈ', prob. not by AW.
Wood 176. Not in BL, NUC, BN.

222. Alsted, Johann Heinrich. *Thesaurus chronologiae*. Herbornae Nassoviorum: n.pub., 1628. 8°. 2nd

ed. Pp. 592, [31]. Calf with 3 fillets and edge hatching; spine, 4 bands and hatching (Oxford binding). Tp, 'Z' (?).
Wood 146. NUC.

223. Alured, Matthew. *The case of colonel Matthew Alured; or, a short account of his sufferings . . . submitted, to the consideration of the parliament and army.* London: f. L. Chapman, 1659. 4°. Pp. [2], 18 (at end, misnumbering: 16, 14, 11).
Tp, no. '18', in pencil, in a former bundle.
Wood 613(5a). Wing A2939A.

224. Ambrose, Saint. Becher, Henry, trans. *Twoo bookes . . . entytuled: Of the vocation and callyng of all nations.* (London): (R. Watkins), 1561. 8°. S⁸,T⁴. Parchment with 2 leather clasps.
Tp, 'Liber Henrici Jacksoni, Oxōn. Collegii Corporis Christi. Anno MDC. Maii. xxi°. fortiter occupa portum.' Text, notes, marks in margin, underscoring and p. nos. to 53, prob. all in the hand of Jackson. LT 1.459 (see also 1.331).
Wood 283. STC 549 (STC, [1561]).

225. [Ames, Richard]. *An elegy on the death of dr. Thomas Saffold [12 May 1691].* London: f. A. Turner, 1691. S.sh.
ᵛ, AW wrote, 'Tho. Saffold', and 'Tho. Saffold 1691'. LT 3.275.
Wood 429(48). Wing A2976B.

226. Ames, William. *Medulla ss. theologiae . . . ab authore recogn. et aucta.* Amstelodami: ap. J. Janssonium, 1634. 12°. Ed. novissima. Pp. [18], 407. Calf with 3 fillets; flyleaf, lower, printer's waste paper (Acts of the Apostles in Greek).
Flyleaf, upper, Greek, 4 words, signature of Edward Wood, lined out. Tp, bsm.
Wood 768. Not in BL.

227. Anabaptists. *A short history of the Anabaptists of high and low Germany.* London: T. Badger f. S. Brown, 1642. 4°. Pp. [4], 56.
Tp, AW wrote '6ᵈ'. Acquired 1 July 1660, 5ᵈ, LT 1.404.
Wood 647(10). Wing S3597.

228. Anabaptists. *A warning for England especially for London in the famous history of the frantick Anabaptists their wild preachings & practises in Germany.* [London]: n.pub., 1642. 4°. Pp. [2], 25.
Wood 647(11). Wing W919.

229. Anabaptists. *Arr[aignment,] tryall, [conviction, and] confession of Francis [Deane] and of John Faulkner . . . for the murther of one mr. Daniel a soliciter, . . . Also . . . an Anabaptists sermon.* London: f. R. Harper, 1643. 4°. A⁴ (tp, mutilated).
Tp, AW wrote the no. '9' on a slip used to repair the tp; 'Solicitor' in t. corrected to 'Haberdasher', not by AW.
Wood 365(9). Wing A3766.

230. Anabaptists. *A declaration of several of the people called Anabaptists.* London: H. Hills, 1659, 12 Dec. S.sh.
Wood 276a(230). Wing D619A ('O' not recorded in Wing).

231. Anabaptists. *The arraignment of the Anabaptists good old cause.* London: J. Morgan, 1660. 4°. Pp. 16.
Tp, AW altered the year to 16'59 March'.
Wood 613(28). Wing A3752.

232. Anabaptists. *The humble apology of some commonly called Anabaptists . . . Together with an apology formerly presented to the kings . . . majesty.* London: H. Hills, sold F. Smith, 1660. 4° (pp. 1-2 torn out). Pp. '3-20'.
Tp, AW wrote the price, '3ᵈ'.
Wood 608(31). Wing H3404.

233. Anabaptists. *Forgery detected, and innocency vindicated. Being a faithful account of the . . . slander raised on the Anabaptists of New-England in [by B. Baxter] mr. Baxter baptiz'd in blood.* London: J. D. f. Fr. Smith, 1673. 4°. Pp. 15, [1] (1 p. bookseller's advertisement).
Wood 619(3). Wing F1558.

234. Anacreon. B., S., trans. *Anacreon done into English*. Oxford: L. Lichfield f. A. Stephens, 1683. 8°. Pp. [20], 114.
Pp. 4, 54, 59, 65, 81, 86, 89, 'T.W.' in margins (?; most cropped).
Wood 112(7). Wing A3046.

235. Anderson, Lionel. * *The tryals and condemnation of Lionel Anderson, alias Munson [et al.]* . . . *as Romish priests*. London: f. T. Collins, a. J. Starkey, 1680. Fol. Pp. [2], 53.
Tp, AW wrote the price, '1.6', in pencil ; p. 8, at an attack by Anderson on the 'rogue' Thomas Dangerfield, 'Dangerfield memoires printed after he was imprison'd for swearing falsely in divers matters relating to the plot, do shew him to be the exactest rogue & knave in nature', i.e., Wood 372(16), item 2155. LT 3.153.
Wood 425(26). Wing T2243.

236. Anderton, William. *A true copy of the paper delivered to the sheriffs of London and Middlesex* . . . *at the place of execution, which he designed there to have spoken [15 June]*. [London]: n.pub., [1693]. S.sh.
LT 3.425.
Wood 657(30). Wing A3113.

237. Andreas, Valerius. *Fasti academici studii generalis Lovaniensis*. Lovanii: ap. H. Nempaeum, 1650. 4°. Ed. iterata. Pp. [12], 407, [1]. Calf with 2 fillets, rebacked.
See ref. to p. 130, vita of Lombard, at Wood 593, item 4213.
Wood 589. BL.

238. Andrewes, Lancelot. Winchester, bp. of. *Of the right of tithes. A divinity determination in the publike divinity schools* . . . *of the university of Cambridg*. London: f. A. Hebb, 1647. 4°. Pp. 27.
Wood 370(2). Wing A3144.

239. Andrewes, Lancelot. Winchester, bp. of. *The form of consecration of a church or chappel. And of the place of Christian buriall*. London: sold T. Garthwait, 1659. 24°. Pp. [27], 120.
Wood 733(4). Wing A3126.

240. Andrewes, Lanc[elot]. Winchester, bp. of. *Preces privatae Graecè & Latinè*. Oxonii: e theatro Sheldoniano, 1675. 12°. Pp. [5], 359, [1].
Missing. MS. Wood E. 2(70), p. 60, 'Joh. Lamphire published Bishop Andrews private prayers 1675'. AOF 2.235.
MS. Wood E. 2(70), p. 60. Wing A3149. Madan 3049. *O, Hunt, Folg, Yale*.

241. Angelos, Christopher. * *The bearer hereof [19 May 1610 to 20 March 1617] [3 testimonials of good behaviour]*. [Oxford]: [J. Lichfield a. J. Short], [1618]. S.sh.
Wood 516(3). STC 642. Madan 462.

242. Angelos, Christopher. Ἐγχειρίδιον . . . *(Enchiridion de institutis Graecorum)*. [London]: ex off. C. Legge, acad. Cantab. typog. [i.e., W. Stansby], 1619. 4°. Pp. [8], 59, [1], [6], 53, [1] (2 tpp).
Missing. MS. Wood E. 2(70), p. 16.
MS. Wood E. 2(70), p. 16. STC 636. *Folg, Hunt*.

243. Angelus a Sancto Francisco. [Mason, Richard]. *Apologia pro Scoto Anglo*. Duaci: typ. B. Belleri, 1656. 8°. Pp. [16], 133, [17]. Calf, with 2 fillets and with a vertical 2 fillets.
1st flyleaves, printer's waste paper. Flyleaf, upper, 2nd^v, AW wrote, '1294. Hoc anno nolens volens ex humanis abijt Jo. Dunsius nationi Scotus, ap minorum familia, Alexandri Alensis Britanni quondam in Gymnasio Lutetiae Auditor &c – sed qui &c. [/] Abraham Bzov[ius]. An. 1294, artic. I [/] Vide in Lib. cui tōt. De Scotorum fortitudine &c. per David Camerarium. Edit. Par. 1631. p 186' [/] 'Though Jo. Pitseus wrot almost 70 yeares after Jo. Bale, yet this authour chooses rather to defend him, because Bale in his book de scriptorib. major. Britan. doth write bitterlie against popery & papists- [/] Joh. Colganus Hibernij hath written Tractatus de vita, patria et script. Jo. Scoti Duns subtilis – Antw. 1655 - 8°- qu[aere] in this authour whether Colganus be mention'd'. Tp, bsm. P. 9, lines in margin at mention of Pitseus and Bale. I7, at Georgius Lyburnus, 'nunc episcopus Atremetum 1685'. It was not George Leyburn but his nephew John who was appointed in 1685 bp. of Adrumetum, a vague location 'in partibus infidelium', here meaning England.
Wood 59(1). BL.

244. Anglo-Saxon Chronicle. Gibson, Edmund, ed. *Chronicon Saxonicum. Ex mss codicibus . . . Latinum fecit*. Oxonii: e theatro Sheldoniano, 1692. 4°. Pp. [14], 244, [36], 64 (2 tpp). Calf with 3 fillets; 2nd rectangle

with 3 fillets and stamp decoration and stamp ornaments at corners.
Wood 384. Wing A3185.

245. Anne. Queen. *The princess Anne of Denmark's letter to the queen.* [London]: n.pub., [1688]. S.sh.
AW wrote, 'written when she left her house 26 Nov. 1688'. LT 3.285.
Wood 529(8). Wing A3224.

246. [Annesley, Arthur]. Anglesey, earl of. *Englands confusion: or a true and impartial relation of the late traverses of state in England . . . with a description of the present power ruling . . . under the mask of the good old cause.* London: n.pub., 1659 ('Printed in the Year of our Lord, 1659'). 4°. Pp. 24.
Tp, AW wrote 'Bund 1.', in pencil. P. 11, at 'Protector', 'Richard' in margin. Dupl. at Wood 613(16).
Wood 620(19). Wing A3167A.

247. [Annesley, Arthur]. Anglesey, earl of. *Englands confusion: or a true and impartial relation of the late traverses of state in England . . . with a description of the present power ruling . . . under the mask of the good old cause.* London: n.pub., 1659 ('Printed in the Year of our Lord, 1659'). 4°. Pp. 24.
Tp, AW wrote the no. in a former bundle, '10' (or 19) and 'Du[pl]', in pencil (both cropped). Dupl. at Wood 620(19).
Wood 613(16). Wing A3167A.

248. [Annesley, Arthur]. Anglesey, earl of. *A letter . . . to the earl of Castlehaven . . . concerning the wars of Ireland.* London: f. N. Ponder, 1681. 8°. Pp. [2], 75, [1].
Flyleaf, upper^v, AW wrote, 'This letter following was written by Arthur Earl of Anglesey. After it was published, James Duke of Ormonde (who was mentiond therein) wrot a letter to Anglesey to vindicate himself, dated at Dublin 12 Nov. 1681 – Replyed upon in another letter by Anglesey – Both published in two sheets in fol. in Mar. or Apr. 1682[.] See Athenae et Fasti Oxon vol. 2. p 598 [AOF 2.316-7]. [/] Anglesie spearks [sic] of himselfe and Relations in p. 4. 5. &c of the said Letter.' Tp, 'This booke came out in Oct. 1680. 6^d.' P. [76], AW commented on the printed date of the letter, 'August 1680': ''Tis said before that this letter was wrot in Aug. 1680. But in the neue account of the proceedings between the D. of Ormond & Arthur E. of Anglesy & printed in fol. 1682. p 6. tis said to be wrot 8 July –'.
Wood 202(2). Wing A3170.

249. Anonymous. Sig. A1, 'This is the day which the lord hath made, we will rejoice and be glad in it. Psal. 118.24'; D3, line 12: 'To conclude, as her excellent Maiestie with the Pro-'; D3^v, last lines: 'and glory both now and ever. Amen. [/] FINIS.'. [Oxford?]: on A1, device of [T. Creede] f. J. Chorlton (as at Wood 635(6)), n.d. 4°. A-D^4 (D4 blank) (wanting t leaf).
Some underscoring and marks in margin, e.g., A3-4, C1, C3^v, not in AW's manner. Not Wing L1021, T. Leigh, *The keeping of holy days recommended in a sermon* [on Psalm 118.24] (1684).
Wood 634(11) (not in Bodl. CD cat.). Not identified.

250. Anonymous. *An appendix to the article concerning the pope's supremacy. Pag. 90. After I finished this treatise, a learned friend sent me . . . testimony, taken out of Sir Hen. Spelman, de concil. p. 108 [Wing S4920, (1664)?; to which this anonymous author responded in these pp. 401-414].* N.p.: n.pub., [1674?]. 8°. Pp. 401-414 (i.e., 2D1-7).
P. 401, AW wrote 'Given to me by Tho. Blount esq. 25 May 1674' (Blount also gave AW Wood 833, item 306, on this date, see LT 2.286).
Wood 876(5). Not identified.

251. Anonymous, Eugenius, pseud. *A strange and true relation of the prodigious multitude of mice . . . between Rotterdam and Schedam. As also, an account how Dengy-hundred in Essex hath been formerly infested.* [London?]: n.pub., 1670. 4°. Pp. [2], 6.
[MS.] Wood B. 35(27). Wing S5841.

252. Apology. *An apology for purchases of lands late of bishops deans and chapters.* [London]: n.pub., [1660]. Fol. Pp. 4.
Tp, AW wrote '(Corn. Burgess - qu[aere])', i.e., Cornelius Burges. In AO 3.685, he wrote 'whether it was all pen'd by Burges, tho' no doubt but he had a hand in it, I know not'.
[MS.] Wood D. 31(22). Wing A3547.

253. Apostrophe. *An apostrophe from the loyal party.* (London): (n.pub.), (1681). Fol. Pp. 4.
P. 4, AW added to the year, 'Decemb.'
Wood 276a(271). Wing A3562.

254. Apprentices. *The apprentices hue-and-cry after their petition.* [London]: n.pub., [1660]. S.sh.
AW wrote, 'Decemb:1659:'.
Wood 416(18). Wing A3585 (two).

255. A[p-robert], J[ohn]. *The younger brother his apologie, or a fathers free power disputed for the disposition of his lands . . . to his sonne.* Oxford: H. Hall f. E. Forrest a. T. Gilbert, 1671. 4°. Pp. [6], 37, [1].
Wood 617(3). Wing A3593. Madan 2879.

256. Apuleius, Lucius. Adlington, W., trans. *The eleven bookes of the golden asse.* London: V. Symmes, 1596. 4°. Pp. 208 (wanting title and dedication).
AW supplied, in ms. (ff. 1-6), the title and dedication, and on his ms. tp added, 'The first edit came out in 1566. - A third edit in 1639. qu[arto].'
[MS.] Wood B. 20(5). STC 720.

257. [Arderne, James]. *A letter to mr. Henry Stubs concerning his censure upon . . . the history of the Royal Society [by T. Sprat].* London: f. O. Pullen, 1670. 4°. Pp. [2], 19.
LT 1.354.
Wood 640(3). Wing L1713B.

258. [Aristeas]. Done, John, trans. *[The auncient history of the Septuagint].* [London]: [N. Okes], [1633]. 8°. Pp. 219 (wanting A⁸).
The author and title of this work written on the spine suggest that the 2 items were in this vol. when AW acquired it. With Wood 232(1), item 4481, formerly owned by H. Foulis.
Wood 232(2). STC 750.

259. Aristotle. *In libros ethicorum Aristotelis ad Nichomachum, aliquot Conimbricensis cursus disputationes.* Coloniae: imp. haer. L. Zetzneri, 1621. 4°. 4th ed. Pp. [5] and cols. 94, [4].
Tp, scribbles and 2 signatures, Richardus Charte and ?. Col. 80, mark in margin, not by AW. Last p. [4], signature of John Vincent.
Wood 644(2). Not in BL.

260. [Armstrong, Archibald]. *Archy's dream, sometimes jester to his majestie, but exiled the court [sic] by Canterburies malice.* [London]: n.pub., 1641. 4°. A⁴.
Tp, AW wrote, 'qu[aere] a pamphlet called Lambeth Faire' (Wood 483(20), item 4017, a satire).
Wood 366(31). Wing A3708.

261. [Armstrong, Archibald]. *A choice banquet of witty jests &c.* London: T. J[ohnson], sold P. Dring, 1660. 8°.
Missing in 1837. 'Witty jests &c – London 1660' in Whiteside cat. See Madan 652.
Wood 51. Wing A3706 (possibly). *BL, Hunt.*

262. Armstrong, Thomas.* *An impartial account of all the material circumstances relating to sir Thomas Armstrong, [sic] . . . executed . . . 20th of June.* London: f. A. Banks, 1684. 4°. Pp. 8.
LT 3.97.
Wood 428(30). Wing I58.

263. Armstrong, Thomas.* *The proceedings against sir Thomas Armstrong . . . upon an outlawry for high-treason . . . his execution.* (London): (f. R. Horn, J. Baker, a. J. Redmayne), (1684). Fol. Pp. 4.
Dupl. at Wood 657(62). LT 3.97.
Wood 428(29) (not in Bodl. CD cat.). Wing P3546.

264. Armstrong, Thomas.* *The proceedings against sir Thomas Armstrong . . . upon an outlawry for high-treason . . . his execution.* (London): (f. R. Horn, J. Baker, a. J. Redmayne), (1684). Fol. Pp. 4.
Dupl. at Wood 428(29). LT 3.97.
Wood 657(62). Wing P3546.

265. Art of Courtship. *The art of courtship.* [London]: (J. Millet]) f. J. Back, 1688. 8°. A⁸,B⁴.
Wood 69(2). Wing A3789B. ESTCR 175477 (rare).

266. Arwaker, Edm[und]. The younger. *An elegy on his excellency lieutenant-general Tolmach.* London: f. F. Saunders, sold R. Taylor, 1694. Fol. Pp. 8.
LT 3.381, 455, 459.
Wood 429(53). Wing A3906.

267. Ascham, Ant[hony]. *A discourse: wherein is examined, what is particularly lawfull during the confusions and revolutions of government . . . Three parts.* London: n.pub., 1648. 8°. Pp. [24], 143. Calf with 2 fillets.
Flyleaf, upper, note by former owner A. Allam, 'Pret: 1ˢ 0ᵈ We[st]: Bibliop: Sept die 4ᵗᵒ· [16]76.', and '1ˢ - 6', lined out. LT 3.167.
Wood 567. Wing A3920.

268. Ascham, Anthony. *The bounds & bonds of publique obedience. Or, a vindication of our lawfull submission to the present government.* London: f. J. Wright, 1649. 4°. Pp. [2], 66. Pasteboard (blue) with parchment spine; rebacked. 1st upper and last lower flyleaves, marbled paper.
Flyleaf, upper, 4th, AW wrote the titles of 19 printed works in this vol., within guidelines made with red chalk (really 20, see the note at Wood 626(20), item 4112). Tp, AW wrote, below, 'Common wealth qu[aere]', in pencil. Pp. 3, 9-10, 12-3, 15, etc. to 33, some pointers, underscoring of marginalia, and of printed text, not in AW's usual style.
Wood 626(1). Wing A3198A.

269. Ascham, Roger. *A report and discourse . . . of the affaires and state of Germany.* London: J. Daye, [1570?]. 4°. Ff. [3], 33 (tp mutilated). Parchment.
Tp, AW wrote the price, '4ᵈ'. F. [3], under John Asteley, AW wrote, 'master of Jewell house/'.
Wood 360. STC 830.

270. Ascham, Roger. *Toxophilus, the schole, of partitions of shootinge conteyned in ij. bookes.* London: T. Marshe, 1571. 4° in 8's. Ff. [4], 63. Pasteboard (blue) with parchment spine. 1st upper and last lower flyleaves, marbled paper; rebacked.
Flyleaf, upper, 3rdᵛ, AW wrote the titles of 2 printed works in this vol., within guidelines made with red ink. Tp, initials of former owner, H. A. Text, some notes and on blank leaf at end, an index, not in AW's hand.
[MS.] Wood C. 36(1). STC 838.

271. Ascham, Roger. Grant, Edward, ed. *Disertissimi viri Rogeri Aschami . . . familiarium epistolarum libri tres . . . Addita est . . . oratio, de vita & obitu R. Aschami.* London: [H. Middleton] imp. F. Coldocki, [1576]. 8°. Ff. [12], 160, [38]. Parchment.
Flyleaf, upper, 2nd, religious tags, lined out, prob. written by AW. Tp, 'Ant Woode Oxon: MDCLxj', and, at top, 'G [?] Moningtoni liber ex dono domini episcopi sarisbur:'. Intro. pp. underscoring and a few marks in margins, not in AW's manner.
Wood 714. STC 826.

272. Ascham, Roger. *The schoolemaster.* London: A. Jeffes, 1589. 4°. Ff. [6], 60, [1]. Pasteboard (grey) with parchment spine. Traces of 1st and last flyleaves in marbled paper.
Flyleaf, upper, 2nd, AW wrote the titles of 2 printed works in this vol., within guidelines made with red ink. Tp, he wrote, 'In two bookes' and 'An edit. of this came out in an. 1570. at Lond. 4°.' In another hand, a shelf-mark, G.4.4. (see also Wood 255(1), item 1168); tpᵛ, AW wrote, 'Of Joh. Whitney – see p. 30' (printed text at p. 30ᵛ: Ascham's 'bedfellow' 'in Cheston'). Flyleaf waste paper, lower, 1stᵛ, a reference to an item to which this leaf was formerly attached: 'this came out in Aug. begin: 1659'.
Wood 309(1). STC 839 (Wood copy wants 'by consent of H. Marsh').

273. Ashburnham, John. *A letter written by . . . from Carisbrook castle . . . to William Lenthall [26 Nov.].* London: f. R. Royston, 1647. 4°. Pp. [2], 5.
Wood 632(60). Wing A3935.

274. Ashburnham, John. *The true copie of a letter from . . . to a friend, concerning his deportment towards the king.* [London]: n.pub., 1648. 4°. Pp. [2], 6.
Pp. 4, 5, 'q[uaere]', and a brief note, cropped.
Wood 632(24). Wing A3936.

275. Ashhurst, William. *Reasons against agreement with a late printed paper, intituled, foundations of freedome [by R. Overton].* London: n.pub., 1648. 4°. Pp. [4], 14.
Wood 609(16). Wing A3976.

276. [Ashley, Thomas]. *Prosperous proceedings in Ireland: being a remonstrance . . . of . . . Galloway, Arrowmoore, and Baltimoore, when . . . capt. Thomas Ashley . . . first arrived.* London: f. J. Hancocke, 1642, 19 Oct. 4°. Pp. 8.
Tp, former no., '28', lined out.

Wood 508(34). Wing A3980.

277. Ashmole, Elias. *The institution, laws & ceremonies of the most noble order of the garter collected and digested into one body.* London: J. Macock f. Nathanael Brooke, 1672. Fol. Pp. [12], 719 [i.e. 703], [105] p. (p. [808] blank), [47] leaves of plates.
Missing since 1695. Gift from E. Ashmole, 6 July 1672, LT 2.248.
LT 2.248. Wing A3983.

278. Ashton, John. *A copy of mr. Ashton's paper, delivered to the sheriff at the place of execution, January 28. 1690/1.* [London]: n.pub., [1691]. S.sh. (r-v).
ᵛ, AW wrote, 'This speech was printed by stealth & about the Middle of March 1690/1 twas scatter'd in the night time about London streets – I saw it at Oxon. in a private hand 16. Mar. 1690/1'; 2 words underscored. LT 3.357.
Wood 367(22). Wing A3991.

279. Ashton, John.* *A true account of all passages at the execution of John Ashton.* (London): n.pub., (1690/1). S.sh. (r-v).
P. 1, at 'January 28th.', AW added the year, 'an. 1690[1]'. LT 3.353.
Wood 367(21). Wing T2335 (3).

280. Ashton, Thomas. Chaplain in New Jersey. *Satan in Samuels mantle, or the cruelty of Germany acted in Jersey. Containing the . . . proceedings of John Mason . . . against several officers.* London: T. R., 1659. 4°. Pp. 32.
Tp, name of T. Ashton underscored. Pp. 14-5, 21, 23, 26, 28-9, correction; 25, at Fiat, AW wrote 'Peter', and in margin, 'Dʳ Fiat lately of Exceter Coll.'
Wood 613(2). Wing A3992B.

281. Assembly of Divines. *A fraction in the assembly: or the synod in armes.* London: n.pub., 1648. 4°. Pp. 16 (misnumbering).
Tp, AW wrote, 'Presbyterians', in pencil.
[MS.] Wood D. 31(46). Wing F2050.

282. Assembly of Divines. *The assembly of moderate divines.* N.p.: n.pub., [1681]. S.sh. (r-v).
AW identified 11 abbreviated references, from 'Dʳ Tho. Barlow', 'groaning board', to 'Rog. L'estrange'; another writer identified 9 references.
Wood 417(76). Wing A4018 (two).

283. Assheton, William, ed. *Evangelium armatum, a specimen; or short collection of several doctrines . . . destructive to our government . . . by . . . mr. Calamy. mr. Jenkins.* London: f. W. Garret, 1663. 4°. Pp. [10], 59.
Pp. 1, 3, 26-7, 29, 31, lines at speakers' names, mainly in pencil. On a slip now in MS. Rawl. D. 912, f. 564ʳ, AW wrote 'Jos[eph] Caryl [/] a pretender to be of a more intimate acquaintance with God than others & to be plenipotentiary commissioner & embassador from almighty God . . . [ᵛ] Another diabolical preacher [against, lined out] up of the Covenant . . . Evangelium armatum p. 26. 27 &c a preacher up of rebellion [and added later] I have this book bound in a vol. entit. Presbyterians' (AO 3.979ff.).
[MS.] Wood D. 26(4). Wing A4033.

284. Assheton, William. *A discourse against drunkenness. Published . . . to suppress debauchery and prophaneness.* London: f. R. Wilde, 1692. 24°. Pp. 44 (i.e., 48).
Each 24° leaf is pasted on a 4° template.
[MS.] Wood D. 30(11). Wing A4031A (one) ('O' not recorded in Wing) (Wing, [Assheton]).

285. Assize. *The assize of bread.* London: W. Stausby [sic], 1630. 4°. A-G⁴ (A1 blank). Parchment with 2 clasp holes.
Flyleaf, upper, 2nd, a shelf-mark, 'H.2.22.'
Wood 361. STC 881.

286. Astley, John. *The art of riding, set foorth in a breefe treatise.* London: H. Denham, 1584. 4°. Pp. [8], 79. Parchment, pastedowns and flyleaves, upper and lower, printer's waste paper (about communion).
Flyleaf, upper, AW wrote, 'AWoode 1662'. P. [7], at reference to the author, line in margin, in pencil.
[MS.] Wood C. 19(1). STC 884.

287. [Aston, Thomas]. *A collection of sundry petitions presented to the kings . . . majestie. As also to . . . parliament. . . . in behalfe of episcopacie, liturgie.* [London]: f. W. Sheares, 1642. 4°. Pp. [5], 43, [1].

1st leaf[r], AW wrote, 'Another edit. of this came out in 1660' (AW owned a copy, [MS.] Wood B. 39(7)). [MS.] Wood D. 31(17). Wing A4072.

288. Aston, Thomas. *April 2. Newes from the west of Ireland: relating what hapned to captain Weldon and captain Aston after their passage from Bristol.* London: f. F. C. a. W. W., 1642. 4°. Pp. 8.
Below, '32', may not be by AW.
Wood 507(43). Wing A4080AB (two).

289. [Aston, Thomas]. *A collection of sundry petitions presented to the kings . . . majesty. . . . As also, to . . . parliament. . . . in behalfe of episcopacie, liturgie.* London: T. Mabb f. W. Sheares, 1660. 4°. Pp. [4], 43, [1].
Tp, at t, AW wrote 'ch[arles]: i:'; below, 'July: 20: 1660:', and in different ink, 'The first edit. came out in 1642' (AW owned a copy, [MS.] Wood D. 31(17)). Bsm. '.ē' (?). P. 4, printed 'Oxford' underscored in red ink (a petition of). LT 1.321.
[MS.] Wood B. 39(7). Wing A4075A.

290. Athanasius. Hoeschelius, David, ed. *Vita s. Antonii eremitae a d. Athanasio Graece scripta.* Augustae Vindelicorum: D. Franck, 1611. 4°. Pp. [9], 163. Pasteboard with 2 clasp holes.
Flyleaf, upper[v], AW wrote, 'v[ide] vitam S Antonii scriptam per Alfons: Villegas Hispanium et in angl: linguam translatam' (Wood 351, item 6325); tp, 'Sept: xiv MDclx' and '20[d]', in pencil; and bsm.
Wood 342. BL.

291. Atkins, Thomas. *A seasonable speech, made by alderman Atkins in the rump-parliament.* [London]: n.pub., 1660. 4°. Pp. 7.
Tp, no. 50 in an earlier bundle. AW wrote 'Aprill'. P. 6, blotting of a note, illeg.
Wood 608(4). Wing S2244.

292. Atkyns, Richard. *The original and growth of printing.* London: J. Streater f. the author, 1664. 4°. Pp. [11], 24.
Frontispiece[r], 'AW.1670.' Frontispiece (Charles 2 and Scriptura, by D. Loggan), 'Ashmolean Museum', not in AW's hand.
Wood 642(2). Wing A4135.

293. [Atterbury, Francis]. Rochester, bp. of. *An answer to some considerations [in Two discourses, by A. Woodhead] on the spirit of Martin Luther and the original of the reformation.* Oxford: at the theatre, 1687. 4°. Pp. [4], 68.
LT 3.209 (see also 3.220-1).
Wood 644(5). Wing A4146.

294. [Atwood, William]. *A true account of the unreasonableness of mr. Fitton's pretences against the earl of Macclesfield.* [London]: n.pub., [1685]. Fol. Pp. 8.
Wood 276b(109). Wing A4183A (rare). 'O' not recorded in Wing).

295. A[twood], W[illiam]. *The lord chief justice Herbert's account examin'd. By W. A. . . . in sir Edward Hales his case.* London: f. J. Robinson a. M. Wotton, 1689. 4°. Pp. [2], 72, [1] (1 p. books published by Atwood).
AW wrote the author's name after initials, W. A'twood', and below, '1[s] – Jan. 10. 1688[89]'. L 3.190. AO 4.553.
Wood 629(8). Wing A4176.

296. Audiguier, V. d'. D., W., trans. *A tragi-comicall history of our times, under the borrowed names of Lisander and Calista.* London: ?, 1627-1652. Pp.?
Missing. 19 Oct. 1657, 'I exchanged these following bookes in sheets with Mr. Forrest, for . . . [sic]:. . . The History of Lysander and Calista which cost me 1[s]6[d] of Mr. Blagrave in June, A.D. 1656 – All amounting to a crowne', LT 1.230. Ed. not identified.
LT 1.230. STC 905f. Wing A4194.

297. Audley, Mervin. Castlehaven, earl of (1585-1631). See also at Touchet, item 6224. *The arraignment and conviction of Mervin lord Audley, earle of Castlehaven . . . April 25. 1631. . . . As also the beheading.* London: f. T. Thomas, 1642[3]. 4°. Pp. [2], 12.
Wood 368(2). Wing A3743.

298. August, Mr. *A treacherous plot of a confederacie in Ireland, with the rebels at Calway [sic] with . . . ammunition from France.* London: f. J. Salmon, 1641. 4°. A[4].

Tp, AW wrote after the year, '30 Nov.'
Wood 507(9). Wing T2069 ('O' not recorded in Wing).

299. Augustine, Saint. Whitford, Richard, trans. *The rule of saynt Augustyne*. London: (Wynkyn de Worde), (1525, 28 Nov.). 4°. Ff. [1], 88 and A-B⁴,C⁶.
Missing. MS. Wood E. 2(70), p. 7, 'R. Whitford - St Austins rule translated – 1525'.
MS. Wood E. 2(70), p. 7. STC 922.3. *O, BL*.

300. Augustine, Saint. *[Certaine select prayers, gathered out of st. Augustines meditations] [and] S. Augustines manuell*. [London]: [J. Daye], [1577]. 8°. Wanting 1st tp. A2-8,B-Q⁸, R1-7 (2nd tp at O4).
Pasteboard (blue) with parchment spine; rebound.
Flyleaf, upper, 1st, '4ᵈ to pay' (charge for binding?). Flyleaf, upper, a later librarian wrote bibliog. details. O4, signature of Jacomyn Steamyn (or Stermyn).
Wood 291. STC 926.

301. Augustine, Saint. *The life of s. Augustine. The first part [Confessions, 1-10]*. London: J. C. f. J. Crook, 1660. 8°. Pp. [16], [2]08 (unopened quires).
Tp, AW wrote the price, '1ˢ-8ᵈ'; bsm.
Wood 435(3). Wing A4211.

302. [Aulnoy, Marie Catherine La Mothe]. H[ickman], S[pencer], trans. *The novels of Elizabeth . . . containing the history of queen Ann of Bullen . . . rendered into English by S. H.* London: f. M. Pardoe, 1680. 12°. Pp. [1], 135, [5] (5. of books sold at the Pope's Head).
Flyleaf, upper, AW wrote, '1. Jul. 1680 10ᵈ'; and tp, '10ᵈ'. At end of books sold, lines in margin at some theological entries and at some plays.
Wood 258(4). Wing A4221.

303. Aungervyle, Richard. James, Thomas, ed. *Philobiblon Richardi Dunelmensis sive de amore librorum, et institutione bibliothecae*. Oxoniae: J. Barnesius, 1599. 4°. 2nd ed. Pp. [8], 62, [10] (leaf H4 blank) (I⁴, 8 pp. of Oxford mss.).
Dupl. at Wood 477(3).
[MS.] Wood C. 26(15). STC 959. Madan 193.

304. Aungervyle, Richard. James, Thomas, ed. *Philobiblon Richardi Dunelmensis sive de amore librorum, et institutione bibliothecae*. Oxoniae: J. Barnesius, 1599. 4°. 2nd ed. Pp. [8], 62, [8].
Tp, 'Liber Henrici Jacksoni Oxoniensis, Collegii Corporis Christi. MDCX. Maii. xxi. Qui apponit Scientia, apponit dolorem.' To p. 23, notes, not by AW. Dupl. at [MS.] Wood C. 26(15). LT 1.459 (and 1.331).
Wood 477(3). STC 959. Madan 193.

305. Austen, Ralph. *A treatise of fruit-trees . . . The spirituall use of an orchard*. Oxford: H. Hall f. T. Robinson, 1657. 4°. 2nd ed. Pp. [26], 140.
Missing. 19 Oct. 1657, 'I exchanged these following bookes in sheets with Mr. Forrest, for . . . [sic]: Austen of planting with his spirituall use . . . All amounting to a crowne', LT 1.230.
LT 1.230. Wing A4239. Madan 2327.

306. [Austin, John]. S[ergeant], J[ohn], ed. *Devotions. First part*. Roan [i.e., England]: n.pub., 1672. 8°. 2nd ed. Pp. [28], 450. Calf with 2 fillets and stamp decoration in corners; marbled edges.
Flyleaf, upper, 1st, 'Anthony à Wood Oxon. Given to me by Thom. Blount of Orleton in Herefordsh. Esq. being then at Islip neare Oxon, in his passage from Lond. to Worcester, 25 May 1674.' LT 2.286.
Wood 833. Wing A4249.

307. [Austin, Samuel]. *The character of a Quaker in his true and proper colours; or, the clownish hypocrite anatomized*. London: f. T. Egglesfield, 1671. 4°. Pp. [4], 17.
Wood 645(20). Wing A4256.

308. Awakening Word. *An awakening word in season, to the grand-jury-men of the nation [occasioned by D. Whitby's The protestant reconciler]*. London: f. Arthor [sic] Jones, 1684. 4°. 2nd ed. Pp. 16.
Tp, in imprint, 'Arthor' underscored. LT 3.64.
Wood 608(63). Wing A4277.

309. A[ylett], R[obert]. *A briefe chronologie of the holie scriptures*. London: J. Harison f. T. Man, 1600. 8°. Pp. [8], 76, [1] (wanting the t leaf).
P. 36, brief note, may not be by AW.
Wood 843(2). STC 14.

310. B., A. *A letter from a gentleman in Kent, giving satisfaction to a friend in London, of . . . the late great action [15 June]*. London: n.pub., 1648. 4°. Pp. [2], 13.
Tp, AW wrote after the year, '15. Jun.'
Wood 502(26). Wing B13.

311. B., A. *A letter of advice concerning marriage*. London: f. W. Miller, 1676. 4°. Pp. [2], 29, [1] (2 pp. books printed f. Miller).
Wood 654a(29). Wing B15.

312. B., A. *A letter from a minister to a person of quality, shewing some reasons for his non-conformity. Madam, You were pleased*. [London]: n.pub., [1679]. Fol. Pp. 4.
[MS.] Wood D. 26(12). Wing B14.

313. B., B. *The young gentlemans way to honour*. London: f. T. Parkhurst, 1678. 8°. Pp. [8], 109, [1].
Tp, AW wrote '1ˢ', in pencil. Bsm.
Wood 754(3). Wing B39.

314. B., C. *A letter sent from aboard his highnesse the prince of Wales to the royalists in Kent; . . . Also, a letter from . . . the house of peers, to his highnesse the prince of Wales*. London: f. R. W., 1648. 4°. Pp. [2], 6.
Tp, AW wrote after the year, 'Aug. 24'.
Wood 502(60). Wing B42.

315. B., Ed. *A true relation of the manner of taking of the earl of Northampton . . . by colonell Hampden, and colonell Goodwin*. London: f. F. Coules, 1642. 4°. Pp. [2], 6.
Tp, AW overwrote the former no., '13', and wrote the month, 'Aug'. P. 6, at details concerning a retreat to Oxford, '28 Aug.' and at printed 'some of them' who went to Abingdon for safety, he wrote 'Alderm. Joh. Nixon was one[,] Hen. Curtaine a bookseller another[,] [Edward?] Colledg[,] Walter a Joyner'. LT 1.56.
Wood 375(5). Wing T2999.

316. [B., H.], clericus. *A brief account of the nullity of king James's title, and of the obligation of the present oaths of allegiance*. London: f. R. Chiswell, 1689. 4°. Pp. [2], 10.
Tp, 'Lib: Steph: Hurman ex Dono Authoris.', and below, 'Mar 20 [or '90'] this given to me by Steph' (severely cropped at bottom). LT 3.439.
Wood 608(66). Wing B4512.

317. B., I. *A letter sent by I. B. . . . unto . . . Maystet [sic] R.C. esquire, . . . a large discourse of the peopling & inhabiting the cuntrie called the Ardes. . . . and taken in hand by sir Thomas Smith . . . and Thomas Smith . . . his sonne*. London: (H. Binneman f. Anthonh-son) [sic], [1572]. 8°. A-H⁴ (wanting the map; H4 blank). Pasteboard (grey) with parchment spine.
Flyleaf, upper, AW wrote the titles of 4 printed works in this vol., within guidelines made with red ink. Beneath pastedown, upper, on back of board, '6ᵈ for binding to Chamb[ers] 8. Nov. 1692' (for other notes on binding, see Index, 'Wood, A., binding'. Tp, AW wrote after Smith, 'his natural son.' and 'an. 1572'. Text, short lines in margins, in pencil.
Wood 504(1). STC 1048.

318. B., I. *The last will and testament of superstition*. London: J. Hammond, 1642. 4°. A⁴.
Tp, bsm.
[MS.] Wood D. 31(39). Wing B83B.

319. B., J., poet. *'Clarissimo nobilissimoque viro. d. Rudolpho Sheldon, me coenati suo in primis colendo'.*
N.p.: n.pub, n.d. S.sh. (engr. with 8 sacred scenes around a ms. poem by J. B.).
On each side 3 medallions containing engravings of sacred scenes, and above and below, a sacred scene with a leaf frame. LT 3.104.
Wood 276a(9) (not in Bodl. CD cat.). Not identified.

320. B., J. *A dialogue betweene a vertuous gentleman and a popish priest*. London: R. Waldegrave, 1581. 8°. A-K⁸.
Missing. MS. Wood E. 2(70), p. 10.
MS. Wood E. 2(70), p. 10. STC 1039. *O, Folg* (two), *Union*.

321. B., J. *Some reflections upon the earl of Danby [Thomas Osborne] in relation to the murther of sir Edmondbury Godfrey*. [London]: n.pub., [1679]. Fol. Pp. 4. Pasteboard (blue) with parchment spine.
Pasteboard, upperᵛ, brief note, in AW's hand, mostly covered by blue paper cover. Flyleaf, upper, 4thᵛ,

above, AW wrote 'Second Volume of tryals, narratives, dying speeches, depositions &c concerning the popish plot.'; and the titles of 30 printed works in this vol., within guidelines made with red ink; and below, 'All which are bound up togeather according to the time when they were published'. In this vol., AW added nos., in brackets, at each new printed item. P. 4, 'Memorandum that in the latter end of March 1679 Mr Ralph Sheldon of Beolie shewed me this letter in manuscript, which ended at – <u>may cry for judgment against the land</u> – as on the other side of this leafe. That which follows viz. <u>Now if you observe, the authour of this</u> etc to the end here above, was added to it when twas printed, which was in June 1679, for on the 12 of July following this printed paper was given to me as a new thing by Mr Ralph Sheldon of Steple Barton in Com. Oxon. ABosco' and 'Tho. Dangerfield in his narrative num. 27. pag. 17. saith that one Nevil a prisoner in the Kings bench, was authour of the Danby reflections/' (i.e., Wood 425(25), item 2150, p. 17, where AW made a mark in the margin). On the appearance of several of the pamphlets in this vol. in July 1679, LT 2.445, 457; on Dangerfield, LT 2.465-6.
Wood 425(1). Wing B127.

322. B., J., and Christopher Kirkby. *A compleat and true narrative of the manner of the discovery of the popish plot . . . with a full answer to . . . reflections upon the earl of Danby*. London: H. Million, 1679. Fol. Pp. [4], 4.
AW wrote the price, '2^d', and 'Latter end of July'. Purchased from Vade in July or August 1679, see his record of purchase at MS. Wood F. 50, f. 11. LT 2.457.
Wood 425(13). Wing B98.

323. B., O. F. *Tamisis triumphans, sive, panegyris Jacobo II . . . Magnae Britanniae . . . regi . . . ipso inaugurationis die [Latin verse, 23 April]*. Londini: n.pub., 1685. Fol. Pp. [2], 18.
Wood 660c(34). Wing B148.

324. B., R. *Adagia Scotica or a collection of Scotch proverbs*. London: f. N. Brooke, 1668. 12°. Pp. [2], 58. Calf with 2 fillets.
Tp, 'Dupl' in pencil by AW. Dupl. at Wood 60(1).
Wood 48. Wing B155 (two).

325. B., R. *Adagia Scotica or a collection of Scotch proverbs*. London: f. N. Brooke, 1668. 12°. Pp. [2], 58. Some leaves unopened. Pasteboard (grey) with parchment spine.
Flyleaf, upper, '8^d'; ^v, AW wrote the titles of 3 printed works in this vol., within guidelines made with red ink. Tp, '4^d'. Dupl. at Wood 48. Acquired 13 Jan. 1669, 4^d, LT 2.149.
Wood 60(1). Wing B155 (two).

326. B., R. *A caveat for sinners, or, a warning for swearers, blasphemers, and adulterers*. London: f. J. Deacon, 1683. S.sh.
Wood 417(127). Wing B161 (rare).

327. B., T. *Observations upon prince Rupert's white dog, called Boy*. [London]: n.pub., 1642[3]. 4°. A^4.
Tp, AW wrote, 'In this & other impressions are set the letters of T. B. but in the end in all, are the Letters T. P. subscribed', and '1642 Another edit of this pamphlet was printed also the same yeare, & another in 1643, but neither of them hath the picture of Boy in the title as this has'. A3^v, AW identified 'Church Minstrel with the long lock', as 'Edw Low'. Diff. ed. at 614(58).
Wood 377(27). Wing B194A.

328. B., T. *Observations upon prince Rupert's white dogge, called Boye*. [London]: n.pub., 1642[3]. 4°. Pp. [2], 10.
Tp, AW wrote 'Dupl', in pencil. Diff. ed. at Wood 377(27).
Wood 614(58). Wing B194 ('O' not recorded in Wing).

329. B., T. Λογοι απολογητικοι. *Foure apologicall tracts exhibited to the . . . authority, now erected in, . . . England*. [London]: n.pub., 1649. 4°. Pp. [4], 31.
Wood 364(23). Wing B186.

330. B., T. *The president of presidents: or, an elegie, on the death of John Bradshaw*. [London]: n.pub., [1659]. S.sh.
AW wrote, 'novemb: M DC:Lix'; ^v, 'No. 1659'.
Wood 416(17). Wing B198 (two) (Wing, presidents; elegie on).

331. B., T. *The muses congratulatory address to his excellency the lord general Monck*. [London]: n.pub., [1660]. S.sh.

AW wrote, 'March: 1660'; ^{v}, 'Mar. 1660', and '72' replaced a former no. '58' in pencil.
Wood 416(72). Wing B191.

332. B., W. *Cupid's court of salutations*. [London]: f. J. Deacon, sold R. Kell, 1687. 8°. A^8,B^4.
Wood 69(7). Wing B207 (rare).

333. Bache, Humphrey. *A few words in true love written to the old long sitting parliament, who are yet left alive and do sit there now*. (London): (f. M. W.), (1659). 4°. Pp. 11.
Tp, AW wrote, 'Not belonging to Parliment' (cropped at side), in pencil.
Wood 610(6). Wing B253.

334. Backhouse, Robert. *A true relation of a wicked plot . . . against . . . Glocester*. London: f. E. Husbands, 1644, 7 May. 4°. Pp. 31.
Wood 377(9). Wing B265.

335. Bacon, Francis. St. Albans, visct. *Essaies. Religious meditations. Places of perswasion and disswasion*. London: (J. Windet) f. H. Hooper, 1598. 12°. Ff. [3], 49. Parchment.
Pastedown, upper^r (pasted down side), Latin clause and signature of a former owner, John Stobbert. Flyleaf, upper^v, AW wrote the titles of 2 printed works in this vol., within guidelines made with red ink. Acquired 28 Apr. 1662, 6^d, LT 1.436.
Wood 769(1). STC 1138.

336. [Bacon, Francis]. St. Albans, visct. *A declaration of the practises & treasons attempted and committed by Robert late earle of Essex and his complices, . . . together with the confessions*. London: R. Barker, 1601. 4°. A-Q^4 (A1 blank).
G3, K2, lines in margin; N1, extensive notes, not in AW's hand. Acquired 29 Ap. 1658 out of G. Langbaine's study, LT 1.247.
Wood 586(10a). STC 1133.

337. Bacon, Francis. St. Albans, visct. *Sir Francis Bacon his apologie, in certaine imputations concerning the late earle of Essex*. London: [R. Field] f. F. Norton, 1604. 8°. Pp. 72. Calf with 3 fillets and stamp decoration (dragon) in corners (Ashm. binding); rebacked.
Flyleaf, upper, list of 16 printed works in this vol., by an Ashm. librarian. This vol. is made up of formerly unbound printed items (unnumbered by AW but having Ashm. Roman numerals). Some items, badly cropped. Tp, bsm.
Wood 84(1). STC 1112.

338. Bacon, Francis. St. Albans, visct. *The charge of sir Francis Bacon . . . touching duells, upon an information in the star-chamber against Priest and Wright*. London: [G. Eld] f. R. Wilson, [sold R. Wilson a. G. Potter?], 1614. 4°. Pp. 61 (1-2 blank).
Tp, 'q', twice (AW's 'quaere' or a bsm).
Wood 616(9). STC 1125.

339. Bacon, Francis. St. Albans, visct. *The historie of the raigne of king Henry the seventh*. London: W. Stansby f. M. Lownes, a. W. Barret, 1622. Fol. Pp. [5], 248. Calf, rough, with 2 fillets, spine, 6 bands. Parchment backing, ms., English and Latin.
Tp, signature of the former owner, 'Ja: Hales'. P. 108, a brief query about Richard Thomas (was he 'Ric. ap'), may not be in AW's hand.
Wood 409. STC 1159.

340. Bacon, Francis. St. Albans, visct. *Considerations touching a warre with Spaine*. [London]: n.pub., 1629. 4°. Pp. [2], 46.
P. 1, correction, prob. not by AW.
Wood 511(16). STC 1126.

341. Bacon, John. *A true relation of severall overthrows given to the rebells, by colonell Crayford . . . in two letters*. London: f. J. Hunscot, 1642, 26 Sept. 4°. Pp. 8.
Tp, former no., '20', lined out.
Wood 508(35). Wing B347.

342. Bacon, Nathaniel. *A relation of the fearful estate of Francis Spira, in . . . 1548*. London: J. B., sold A. Kemb, 1657. 12°. Pp. [14], 79. Pasteboard (blue) with parchment spine. 1st upper and last lower flyleaves, marbled paper and blue paper; rebacked.
AW wrote the titles of 3 printed works in this vol., within guidelines made with red ink. Tp, AW wrote

'6^d'.
Wood 879(1). Wing B358A.

343. B[acon], N[athaniel], collected by. *The history of the life & actions of s^t. Athanasius, together with . . . the Arian heresie.* London: f. D. Maxwell, f. C. Eccleston, 1664. 8°. Pp. [9], 227, [5].
Tp, AW wrote the price, '1.8'. Acquired 2 Jan. 1664, 1^{s}6^d, LT 2.2.
Wood 435(4). Wing B366C.

344. [Bacon, Roger]*. *The famous history of fryar Bacon.* London: T. C[otes], 1640. 8°.
Missing in 1837. 'The History of Friar Bacon – 1640' in Whiteside cat. The t is entered at the front of the vol., see 84(1). At least 8 leaves, crudely torn out (traces of letters are present on stubs).
Wood 84(14). STC 1184.5 (rare) (Folg, from Britwell, 14.6.20, EFL A5.6[Bri]).

345. Bacon, Roger. M., T., trans. *Frier Bacon his discovery of the miracles of art, nature, and magick.* London: f. S. Miller, 1659. 12°. Pp. [12], 51, [7] (7 pp. books sold by Miller). Pasteboard (blue) with parchment spine. Upper flyleaf, a remnant of marble paper; lower, slips of marbled paper pasted on a dark leaf; rebacked.
Flyleaf, upper, 5th^v, AW wrote the titles of 4 printed works in this vol., within guidelines made with red ink. At the 3rd item, *The man-mouse* (item 6301), AW cites the refutation, which he also owned (More, *Observations*, Wood 859(3), item 4548). Tp, 'Septemb: A. MDCLix: AWood'. Pp. [8-10] and p. 1, brief notes and corrections, e.g., 'De Rogero Bacono vide in commentariis Jo: Twini Bolingdunensis de rebus albionicis p: 130:' (i.e., Wood 182, item 6269).
Wood 726(1). Wing B373.

346. Bacon, Roger*. *The history of fryer Bacon: the second part: being most true and exact relation of the . . . exploits of . . . Miles Wagner.* London: f. J. Blare at the Loking glass on London Bridge (cropped at bottom), [c.1680]. 8°. A^8,B^4 (cropped).
Tp^v, AW wrote 'This book is also published under this title. [/] A most true & exact relation of the most famous & merry exploits of that worthy gent. of renowne & deep professor of Astrologye, & most expert in magick Art [/] Miles Wagner [/] Being once a servant to the famous conjurer Frier Bacon &c. in 8° in one sheet [/] It hath the picture, or y^e [?] the very same cut in the title, as this hath.'
Wood 707(3). Not in Wing. Not in ESTCR. Should be at H2120aA.

347. Bacon, Roger*. *The three famous conjurers, fryer Bacon, Bongey and Vandermast.* [London]: f. J. Clark, senior, [1680]. 8°. A2-8,B^4 (last leaf blank).
Wood 707(2). Wing T1088A (rare).

348. Bacon, Roger*. *The history of frier Bacon.* London: f. M. W., sold [D.] Newman a. B. Alsop (cropped), 1683. 8°. A^8,B^4. Parchment over boards; rebound.
Flyleaf, upper, 2nd^v, AW wrote the titles of 10 printed works in this vol., within guidelines made with red ink. At the 1st item, each small 8° leaf is pasted on an 8° template.
Wood 707(1). Wing H2120A (two).

349. Baddeley, Richard. *The boy of Bilson: or, a true discovery of the late notorious impostures of certaine Romish priests in their . . . exorcisme, . . . of . . . William Perry.* London: F.K[ingston] f. W. Barret, 1622. 4°. Pp. [6], 75.
[MS.] Wood B. 18(3). STC 1185.

350. Baes, Mart[in]. *Series summorum pontificum ordinis sancti Benedicti . . . Mart. Baes fecit.* N.p.: n.pub., n.d. S.sh. (engr.).
Possibly, acquired 30 July 1659, 1^s, LT 1.279. See also Wood 276b(15), item 941.
Wood 276a(2) (not in Bodl. CD cat.). Not identified.

351. [Bagshaw, Edward] (elder). *A short censure of the book of W. P[rynne] entituled, the university of Oxfords plea, refuted.* [London]: [f. R. Royston], 1648. 4°. Pp. [2], 12.
Tp, 'Edw. Bagshaw Esquire. the Author'. AO 3.620, 863.
Wood 514(36). Wing B398 (Wing, by R. Royston). Madan 1962.

352. Bagshaw, Edward (younger). *A true and perfect narrative of the differences between m^r Busby and m^r Bagshawe.* London: A. M., 1659. 4°. Pp. [4], 32. Calf with 3 fillets, stamp decoration (flower with 2 leaves) inside corners, and roll decoration at inner, spine edge (Ashm. binding).
Flyleaf, upper, 2nd, list of 10 printed works in this vol., by an Ashm. librarian; many in this vol. are imperfect and may have been a bundle of rejected pamphlets left by AW. Tp, top right-hand corner, 'L y^t

19' (?).
Wood 499(1). Wing B426.

353. Bagshaw, Edward (elder). *The rights of the crown of England, as it is established by law.* London:
A. M. f. S. Miller, 1660. 8°. Pp. [14], 304 (unopened). Pasteboard (grey) with parchment spine.
Tp, author's name, underscored in red ink, and price, '1ˢ'. Acquired 18 Nov. 1661, LT 1.418.
Wood 571. Wing B397.

354. Bailey, Walter. *A briefe treatise touching the preservation of the eye sight.* Oxford: H. Hall f. R.
Davis, 1654. 8°.
Missing. MS. Wood E. 2(70), p. 22.
MS. Wood E. 2(70), p. 22. Wing B450 (two) and B451. Madan 2253 and 2966.

355. Bainbridge, John; John Greaves, and Vlug Beigus. *Cl. v. Johannis Bainbrigii . . . Canicularia.
Unà cum demonstratione ortus Sirii heliaci, . . . auctore Johanne Gravio. Quibus accesserunt insigniorum
aliquot stellarum longitudines & latitudines ex astronomicis observationibus Vlug Beigi [with the Pers. text
of the last.].* Oxoniae: excud. H. Hall, impen. T. Robinson, 1648. 8°. Pp. [6], 119, [1] (misnumbering).
Tp, bsm.
Wood 704(7). Wing B472. Madan 2002.

356. [Baker, John]. *[Begin.] Advertisement to booksellers. Whereas the four Oxford cullies . . . lately
. . . pirated . . . [Advertisement of J. Blumerel's Elegantiae poeticae, here alleged to have been pirated].*
[London]: [at the Sheldonian, Oxford?], [1680]. S.sh. 4°.
AW wrote at 'Four Oxford Cullies' who were thought to have pirated a book, 'Farmours [sic] of the press in
the Theater.', and below, 'Brought downe to Oxford by a London bookseller, & dispersed there in stationers
shops about 10. March 1679/80.' LT 2.483.
Wood 516(10b). Wing B497A (rare). Madan 3252.

357. Baker, Richard. *Theatrum triumphans or a discourse of plays.* London: S. G. and B. G. f. F.
Eglesfield, 1670. 8°. Pp. [8], 141. Calf with 2 fillets.
Flyleaf, upper, 1st, A. Allam wrote, 'Pret: oˢ - 10ᵈ Ox[lad]: Sᵒʳ. Bibliop: Sextalis vicesima 1ᵐᵒ 76', i.e., Aug
21, see LT 3.167; and an entry by a later reader, 'Sum e libris Musaei Ashmoleani 1711'. Lines in margin,
pp. 29, 35, 40-2, 68-9.
Wood 95. Wing B514.

358. [Balbani, Niccolò]. C[rashaw], W[illiam], trans. *The Italian convert, newes from Italy of a second
Moses or the life of Galeacius Caracciolus.* London: A. G[riffin] f. M. S[parke], 1635. 4°. Pp. [8], 61.
Tp, AW wrote, 'I have this in 8°, among my lives in 8°. printed at London 1655. adorned with pictures.'
Diff. ed. at Wood 286.
Wood 345(7). STC 1235.6.

359. [Balbani, Niccolò]. Bèze, Théodore de, trans. C[rashaw], W[illiam], ed. *The Italian convert, newes
from Italy, of a second Moses: or, the life of Galeacius Caracciolus.* London: f. E. Archer, 1655. 8°. Pp. [17],
131. Calf with 2 fillets; rebacked.
Flyleaf, upper, 2nd, AW wrote, 'I have this booke in 4° printed at London an. 1635. but there be no pictures
in it ABosco'. Tp, bsm. Diff. ed. at Wood 345(7).
Wood 286. Wing B543.

360. Baldwin, George, et al. *The onely right rule for regulating the lawes and liberties of the people of
England. . . . By divers affectionate persons.* [London]: f. the subscribers, sold W. Larnar, 1652. 4°. Pp. [2],
15.
Wood 630(8). Wing O349aA (two) (Wing, Larner).

361. [Baldwin, William], et al. *A myrroure for magistrates.* London: in aed. T. Marshe, 1559. 4°. Ff. [6],
85 (col. p., torn out). Calf with 3 fillets, 2nd rectangle with 3 fillets and stamp decoration in corners and
in centre; 2 clasp holes; rebacked; parchment ms. backing, music notation and Latin hymn.
Flyleaves, upper, from an almanac (1560), with signatures of Elizabeth Jobson, John Brokett, and Edmund
Wernon. ¶3, signatures of John Brokett; ¶3ᵛ, signatures of Winifrid Scourfeild; ¶4, blank leaf, notes, in an
early hand. Text, notes in various hands, some by AW, see e.g., f. 4ᵛ, 'written by Ca'; f. 7, a correction;
f. 12, 'Tho. Churchyard author of this'; f. 19ᵛ, 'By Thomas Phaer.'; ff. 28ᵛ, 30ᵛ, 40; and 44, 'Will Baldwin'.
Prob. acquired 2 July 1662, LT 1.444.
Wood 328. STC 1247.

362. Bale, John. Ossory, bp. of. *A mysterye of inyquyte contayned within the heretycall genealogye of Ponce Pantolabus, is here both dysclosed & confuted.* Geneva [i.e., Antwerp]: M. Woode [i.e., A. Goinus], 1545. 8°. Ff. [4], 88. Parchment.
Pastedown, upper, AW wrote 'among Dr Barl[ow's] books'. Tp, 'A. W.' and 'ABosco'. Text, ff. 10, AW made a correction; 20^v, line in margin. F. 7, note by an earlier owner. In his catalogue, MS. Wood E. 2(70), p. 5, AW wrote, 'see in Bales mysterie of iniquity that I have fol. 42 to distinguish him [Nicolls] from another Nycolls' (a correct ref.). Lent to H. Foules, 17 Oct. 1668, LT 2.145.
Wood 779. STC 1303.

363. Bale, John. Ossory, bp. of. *A brefe chronycle concerninge the examination and death of . . . sir John Oldecastell the lorde Cobham.* London: (A. Scoloker a. W. Seres), [1548?]. 8°. A-G^8.
Flyleaf, upper^v, AW wrote 'These things of Sr J. Oldcastle are mostly cemilted [sic, ?] into Foxes book of martyres'. Passim, notes and marks, many cropped, in ink and pencil, in more than one hand, none by AW. Former owner, Henry Jackson. LT 1.459-60 (see also 1.331).
Wood 789(2). STC 1278.

364. Bale, John. Ossory, bp. of. *The first two partes of the actes . . . of the English votaryes.* (London): [S. Mierdman f.] (A. Vele); tp, pt. 2: (f. J. Bale), (1551). 8°. Ff. [8], 78, [2],120 (*^4,A-K^8; A-P^8,Q^4) (Q^4 misplaced) (2 pts.). Pasteboard (marbled paper) with calf spine (rebound).
Tp, '1552 I B'; and below, 1551, in pencil, none by AW. *4^v, 'E.K' (?). 1st K7^v, AW wrote, 'the 1. edit: of this 1. part came out: 1548' (STC 1271 (and 1546, STC 1270)). F. 120^v, scribbles and names, Richard, George, Edmunde, none by AW.
Wood 846. STC 1273.5.

365. Bale, John. Ossory, bp. of. *A declaration of Edmonde Bonners articles.* London: (J. Tysdall f. F. Coldocke), (1561). 8°. Ff. [12], 1-113, 41-70, [1] (misnumbering).
Missing. MS. Wood E. 2(70), p. 9.
MS. Wood E. 2(70), p. 9. STC 1289. O (two), Folg, Union.

366. Bale, John. Studley, John, trans. *The pageant of popes, contayninge the lyves of all the bishops of Rome, . . . to . . . 1555.* London: (T. Marshe), 1574. 4°. Ff. [20], 198, [2] (misnumbering).
Tp, AW wrote, 'Ant: Woode: Coll: Mertō 1656:'; scribbles. Text, *e1^v, signature of William Royse; passim, underscoring and notes in at least three hands, many are cropped in binding. Many uncropped notes are prob. in AW's hand, e.g., ff. 73 (last note), 76 (last), 77^v, 79^v (2nd note, in contrast to the other notes on f. 79^{r-v}); the cropped notes are not AW's, since the volume was bound, and the notes cropped, ca. 1645 (see f. 68, 'Bells crist[/]ned', a note to which AW seems to have added the cropped 'ned'; AW referred to this printed item in a ms., LT 1.184, note 6). LT 1.211.
[MS.] Wood C. 44(3). STC 1304.

BALLADS (items 367-843)

367. A., T. Perfumer to his late highnesse. *Rump rampant, or the sweet old cause in sippits.* [London]: n.pub., [1660]. S.sh.
AW wrote, 'Januar: 1659[60]'; ^v, 'Jan. 59', and '25' replaced a former no. '10' in pencil.
Wood 416(25). Wing A34 (3).

368. Alidor. *Alidor and Calista. Being an excellent new song, much in request at court.* [London]: f. J. Deacan [sic], 1684. S.sh.
Wood 417(133). Wing A926.

369. [Allibond, John]. *Rustica academiae Oxoniensis nuper reformatae descriptio [in verse].* [London?]: n.pub., [1648]. S.sh. (3 columns, 51 stanzas).
Some 20 identifications of persons or customs alluded to in this verse satire, not by AW. Also, in a later hand, 'Catalogued AH under Allibond'. Dupl. at Wood 423(28), and a 4° ed. at Wood 514(53). For a ms. version of the poem, see Wood 16. LT 1.144.
Wood 276a(520). Wing A1203 (3). Madan 1994.

370. [Allibond, John]. *Rustica academiae Oxoniensis nuper reformatae descriptio.* [London?]: n.pub., [1648]. S.sh.
19 identifications of persons or customs alluded to in this verse satire, and 2 corrections, in AW's early hand. ^v, 'Dupl', in pencil. Dupl. at Wood 276a(520), with similar notes not by AW, and a 4° edition at

514(53), with similar notes by AW (with a few additions, q.v.). Ms. version at Wood 16. See LT 1.144 and Madan 1994.
Wood 423(28). Wing A1203 (3). Madan 1994.

371. [Allibond, John]. *Rustica academiae Oxoniensis nuper reformatae descriptio*. [London?]: n.pub., [1648]. 4°. Pp. 8.
Tp, 'For my hon^d friend Mr Anthony Woode from his obedt servant, Jo. Awbrey'. AW copied the 18-9 similar annotations, but not the corrections, from both s.sh. printed versions (diff. ed. at Wood 276a(520), 18 annotations; and Wood 423(28), 19 annotations and several corrections), or from a ms. version at Wood 16 (with some 23 annotations). He added one new note and a few words at 4 others: e.g., at stanza 32, where the earlier annotators identified 'Daniel Greenwood', AW wrote, 'Dan. Greenwood with squint eyes.'; at the marginalia to stanza 33, AW added added the new note, 'Will. Collier now one of the Yeomen-Bedells'; at stanza 39, he added to previous notes the name of a college. See LT 1.144 and Madan 1994.
Wood 514(53). Wing A1202. Madan 1993.

372. Amintor. *Amintors answer to Perthenias [sic] complaint: or, the wronged shepherds vindication.* [London]: f. P. Brooksby, [1675?]. S.sh. Obl.
[MS.] Wood E. 25(136). Wing A3014 (Wing, Amintor's and Parthenia's).

373. Anabaptist. *The leacherous Anabaptist: or, the dipper dipt. A new protestant ballad.* London: f. B. Harris, 1681. S.sh.
AW wrote, 'in the beg. of Apr.'
Wood 417(56). Wing L808.

374. Ballads. *Ballads. ?: ?, ? Pp.?*
Missing in 1837. In 1837 William Kirtland first noticed (Library Records d. 1071, p. viii) that this book of ballads, Wood 400, was missing. Some time after 1837, another librarian wrote in the same vol., f. 32^v, opposite Wood 400-401 '? Have Nos. 400-401 been bound together, to form one vol., 401'. See Plate IX. That is not the case, since the early foliation in Wood 401 indicates that there were 204 fol. pages in this volume in AW's time. Wood 400, along with Wood 399, was stolen and became part of the Harleian Collection, and later part of the Roxburghe Collection in the BL and of the Euing Collection at Glasgow University Library. See 'The Location of Two Lost Volumes of Ballads, Wood 399 and Wood 400', *BLR*, 15 (April 1996): 260-291.
Wood 400. Missing.

375. Barnwel, George*. *An excellent ballad of George Barnwel an apprentice of London.* [London]: f. F. Coles, T. Vere, a. W. Gilbertson, [1658-64]. S.sh. Obl. Ff. 77-8 in this vol.
Wood 401(40). Wing E3788E (two).

376. Barton, Andrew*. *A true relation of the life and death of sir Andrew Barton, a pirate and rover on the seas.* London: f. E. W[right], [1630 ca.]. S.sh. (2 shs.). 2 pts. Pp. 36-7 in this vol.
'Another Copy 401.55', in a later hand. Diff. ed. at 401(28). Some scribbles, not in AW's hand. P. 35, extensive annotation, verse (?), illeg., and p. 38, some scribbles, both pp. pasted over with blank leaves.
Wood 402(10). STC 1539.5 (rare) (STC, sea).

377. Barton, Andrew*. *A true relation of the life and death of sir Andrew Barton, a pyrate and rover on the seas.* [London]: f. F. Coles, T. Vere, a. W. Gilbertson, [1658-64]. S.sh. Obl. Ff. 55-6 in this vol.
'Another Copy 402.37', in a later hand. Some scribbles, not in AW's hand. Diff. ed. at Wood 402(10). F. 55^v, AW wrote 25 lines, 'Hen. 8. The Kings authority over the narrow seas (studiously conserved ever by his ancestors) was about this time an. 1511. somwhat lessned by the piracies of Andrew Breton (whom our Chroncles call Barton) a Scottish man. This Breton, in revenge of his fathers death, as also other injuries, having in vaine sought redress in Flanders for a ship taken from his said father by some Portugals, obtained letters of Merc [i.e., marque] from James 4. K. of Scotl. upon condition yet, he should not exercise pyracie. Notwithstanding which he seized on divers of our lesser Barques (upon pretence of carrying Portugals goods) and pillaged them. For remedy of which inconvenience, the two sons of Tho. Howard Earl of Surrey (Lord Treasurer, & Earl Marshall of Engl) were employed. The yonger called Edward, being Lord Admirall, commanding in one ship, & Thomas the Elder brother in another. Thereupon, in severall places (though at one time) they invested Breton's two ships; which though the Scotish writers make to be farr less than ours, maintained a cruel fight. The obstinat pirat (though so greviouslie hurt that he died on the place) Encourging his men with his whistle even to his last breath – see the rest in the Lord Herbert of Cherbury his History of Hen. 8. printed 1672. p. 15. & 16. – and in severall chronicles –' [Wing H1505Af.].
Wood 401(28). Wing T2994B (rare).

378. Bath, Wife of. *The wanton wife of Bath*. London: f. F. Coles, [1641-81?]. S.sh. Obl. 2 pt.
[MS.] Wood E. 25(93). Wing W719B (two).

379. Beginning. *The beginning, progress, and end of man. [1st line] Here Adam first leads up the van.*
[London]: f. J. Deacon, [1688-9 ca.]. S.sh. (r-v). Obl. (foldout with illustrations).
ᵛ, AW wrote, 'Bought at Oxōn in Feb. 1688-9'. LT 3.299.
[MS.] Wood E. 25(10). Wing B1701B (rare).

380. Bertie, Peregrine. Willoughby, lord. *Lord Willoughby; or, a true relation of a famous and bloody battel*. London: f. F. Coles, [1650 ca.]. S.sh. Obl. Ff. 67-8 in this vol.
ᵛ, AW wrote, 'The story of the Lord Willoughby following, is to be understood as done by Peregrine Bertie Lord Willoughby of Eresby, about 29 Reg. Elizab–'.
Wood 401(35). Wing L3059 (two) (Wing, Willoughby. Or; n.d.).

381. Betty*. *The young-mans tryal: or, Betty's denial*. London: f. J. Andrews, 1655. S.sh. Obl. 2 pts.
[MS.] Wood E. 25(49). Wing Y125 (rare) (Wing, young mans and 1656).

382. [Birkenhead, John]. *The four-legg'd elder. Or, a horrible relation of a dog and an elder's maid.*
N.p.: n.pub., [1647]. 8°. Pp. [4].
Wood 899(4) (not in Bodl. CD cat.). Wing B2965A ('O' not recorded in Wing).

383. [Birkenhead, John]. *The four-legg'd Quaker, to the tune of the dog and elder's maid, or, the lady's fall*. N.p.: n.pub., [1664]. S.sh.
AW wrote, 'Joh. Birkenhead the Author – Sʳ Joh. Denham hath such another Ballad in his Poems & Translations, printed at Lond. 1668' (p. 109ff., 'News from Colchester. Or, A Proper new Ballad of certain Carnal passages betwixt a Quaker and a Colt', Wing D1005); ᵛ, 'Joh. Birkenhead'. AW stayed with the identification of the author as Birkenhead in AO 3.1205.
Wood 416(70). Wing F1661 (two).

384. [Birkenhead, John]. *A new ballad of a famous German prince and a renowned English duke, who on St. James's day one thousand 666 fought with a beast with seven heads*. [London]: n.pub., 1666. S.sh.
AW identified the German prince, and English duke, 'Prince Rupert', 'George Duke of Albemarl', and, in the ballad, at 'His Chaplain fell to his wonted work, Cry'd *Now for the King*', wrote, 'Sam. Speed M.A. of ch. ch. in Oxon, son of Dʳ Jo. Speed a physician, son of Joh. Speed the Chronologer – This Samuel Speed became afterwards vicar of Godalming in Surrey, & taking to wife a certaine person of no great fortune. did overtopp him, & lived not in good content with her [sic]. He was after that Canon of ch. ch. in Oxon'; below, 'made by Sʳ Joh: Birkenhead. ᵛ, '1666. / Sʳ Joh. Birkenhead The second part followes', and also on the ᵛ, AW gave an item no., 112, to a response to Birkenhead's ballad, which he recorded: 'Answer . . . made by one [blank] Porter': 'Oh Berkenhead how has thou troubled thy muse [/] with a Burden that noe body else would chuse [/] Of a Thump [i.e. a parody of the refrain 'With a thump'] [/] Sure Pegasus she is growne a Jade [/] Her spurs were forgot when a knight thou was made [/] And that which is worse thy wits are decay'd [/] Which hath put all thy freinds in their dump de dum dumpe' and 5 more stanzas (LT 2.285; and AO 3.1203 for Birkenhead).
Wood 416(111-2). Wing B2967AB (two).

385. [Birkenhead, John]. *The second part of the new ballad of the late and terrible fight on St. James's day one thousand 666. To the tune of the first part . . . printed at London*. N.p.: n.pub., 1666. S.sh.
Dupl. at Wood 416(113).
Wood 276a(531) (not in Bodl. CD cat.). Wing S2310A (rare, 2 at O).

386. [Birkenhead, John]. *The second part of the new ballad of the late and terrible fight on St. James's day one thousand 666. To the tune of the first part . . . printed at London*. N.p.: n.pub., 1666. S.sh.
ᵛ, AW wrote, '1666'. Dupl. at Wood 276a(531).
Wood 416(113). Wing S2310A (rare).

387. Blanket-Fair. *Blanket-fair, or the history of Temple street*. [London]: f. C. Corbet, 1684. S.sh.
ᵛ, AW wrote the year, '1684'.
Wood 417(137). Wing B3167.

388. [Blount, Charles]. *The sale of Esau's birth-right; or the new Buckingham ballad*. [London]: n.pub., [1679]. S.sh.
AW made some 10 notes on this ballad, supplying name at blanks and writing identifications in margins. At top, 'made in August an. 1679'; at 'Parliament', 'that is to meet Oct. 7'; at 'Our prating Knight . . . and

his Lady', 'Sr Rich. Temple' and 'Mary Knapp'. Blanks filled in with names of 'Lord Latimer', 'Temple', 'Danbie', 'Peter Tir' [mutilated at margin]. A note is illeg. at bottom, 'Sr R. T. –'. LT 2.461.
Wood 417(5). Wing B3315 (Wing, or,).

389. Bodnam, Clerk of. *A very godly song, intituled, the earnest petitioh [sic] of a faithfull Christian, being a clerk of Bodnam.* [London]: f. F. Coles, T. Vere, a. W. Gilbertson, [1676]. S.sh. Obl. Ff. 65-6 in this vol.
Wood 401(34). Wing V276 (rare) (Wing, 1676).

390. Bradshaw, John*. *The arraignement of the divel, for stealing away president Bradshaw.* [London]: n.pub., [1659]. S.sh.
AW wrote, 'Novemb. M DC LIX'; ^v, 'No[v]. 1659', and 'nu. 13' over former no. '4' in pencil.
Wood 416(13). Wing A3753 (3).

391. [Brome, Richard]. *The beggars chorus in the jovial crew.* [London]: f. J. Clark, [1683]. S.sh.
AW wrote '1683'.
Wood 417(117). Wing B4863 (rare).

392. Brown, Tom*, pseud. *Tom Browns delight. Or, the good fellows frolick.* [London]: f. F. Cole [sic], T. Vere, J. Wright, a. J. Clarke, [1674-9]. S.sh. Obl.
[MS.] Wood E. 25(66). Wing T1781 (rare) (Wing, London).

393. [Butler, Samuel]. *The Geneva ballad. To the tune of 48.* London: f. H. Brome, 1674. S.sh.
AW added, at 'Jack –', 'Presbitere'; at year of publ., 'Octob.'; and below, 'reprinted in 1678' ; ^v, '1674'. In AO 4.725: 'said to be written by one . . . Griffin'. Diff. ed. at Wood 276b(105) (1678). LT 2.430.
Wood 416(125). Wing B6291C (3) ('O' not recorded in Wing).

394. [Butler, Samuel]. *The Geneva ballad. To the tune of 48.* London: f. H. Brome, 1678. S.sh.
AW wrote, 'dup'. Diff. ed. at Wood 416(125) (1674). LT 2.430.
Wood 276b(105). Wing B6292 (Wing, [London]).

395. Cavalier's Complaint. *The cavaleers complaint.* London: f. R. Crofts, 1661. S.sh.
AW altered 1661 to 166'0'; ^v, '1660', and '76' over a former no. '65' in pencil.
Wood 416(76). Wing C1571.

396. Cavalier's Genius. *The cavalier's genius: being a proper new ballad.* [London]: n.pub., [1663?]. S.sh. Obl.
AW wrote, 'Tempore Ol. Cromwell protect' in red ink, lined it out in dark ink; ^v, '1660'.
Wood 416(78). Wing C1573 (two).

397. Cavalier's Litany. *The cavalier's litany.* London: f. C. Brome, 1682. S.sh.
Wood 417(108). Wing C1577.

398. Cawthorn, Lawrence*. *Misery to bee lamented: or, a doleful relation . . . which befell Lawrence Cawthorn.* London: f. F. G[rove], [1661]. S.sh. Obl. 2 pts. Ff. 185-6 in this vol.
AW wrote '1661'; 'Cawthorn' underscored in t.
Wood 401(94). Wing M2247 (rare).

399. Celia, pseud. *The happy lovers, or, Caelia won by Aminta's loyalty.* [London]: f. C. Dennisson [sic], 1688. S.sh.
Wood 417(161). Wing H670 (rare) (Wing, Dennison).

400. Charles 1*. *The manner of the kings trial at Westminster hall . . . the twentieth day of January, 1648.* [London]: f. F. Coles, [1648-80]. S.sh. Obl. Ff. 145-6 in this vol.
Wood 401(74). Wing M475bA (rare) (Wing, tryal).

401. Charles 2*. *An exit to the exit tyrannus.* [London]: n.pub., [1660]. S.sh.
AW wrote, 'March; 1659[60]'; ^v, 'Mar 59', and '61' over a former no. '42' in pencil.
Wood 416(61). Wing E3870.

402. Charles 2*. *The wonderfull and miraculous escape of our gracious king, from . . . Worster.* [London]: f. F. Coles, T. Vere, a. W. Gilbertson, [1660]. S.sh. Obl. Ff. 173-4 in this vol.
AW wrote the year, '1660'.
Wood 401(88). Wing W3361 (rare).

403. Chelmsford. *Bloody news from Chelmsford: or, a proper new ballad*. Oxford: n.pub., 1663. S.sh.
v, AW wrote, '1663'. A later librarian wrote, 'see fol. 94', i.e., ballad on the same topic at Wood 416(94).
Wood 416(103). Wing B3263. Madan 2636.

404. Chelmsford, Curate. *The careless curate and the bloudy butcher . . . from Chelmsford*. [London]:
f. W. Gilbertson, [1662]. S.sh. Obl. 2 pts. Ff. 187-8 in this vol.
AW wrote 'mense Feb: 1662[3]'; 'Chelmsford' underscored in t. Prob. acquired 17 Feb., LT 1.468.
Wood 401(95). Wing C540 (rare).

405. Chevy Chase. *A memoriable song on the unhappy hunting in Chevy Chase between earle Piercy
of England and earle Dowglas of Scotland*. [London]: 'Printed for F. Coles, T. Vere, and W[.] Gilbertson'
[mutilated], [1658-64]. S.sh. Obl. Pp. 30-1 in this vol.
'Another Copy 401.47', in a later hand. Uncorrected variant issue at Wood 401(24).
Wood 402(8). Wing M1677C (two) (Wing, does not record 2 issues at O).

406. Chevy Chase. *A memoriable song on the unhappy hunting in Chevy Chase between earle Piercy of
England and earle Dowglas of Scoland [sic]*. [London]: 'Printed for F. Coles. T. Vere. and W. Oilbertson.',
[1658-64]. S.sh. Obl. Ff. 47-8 in this vol.
'Another Copy 402.30', in a later hand. Corrected variant issue at Wood 402(8). On sheet opposite, f. 47v, a
slip pasted in, r of slip, AW wrote, 'The battle of Chevy Chase temp. H. 4. so Mr Fulm. [sic]. q[uaere]'; v of
slip, 'Cheviot Chase See my Engl. Camden p. 803 [missing, see item 1370]. v. Greys descrip. of New Castle
p. 33 [*Chorographia* (Newcastle, 1649), missing, see item 3285 below]. No mention of it in Baronii [Wood
432, item 882] in vol. 1. Fuller Worthies in Northumb p. 306'; and p. 47v, 'Sr Philip Sydney, in his defence of
poesie saith thus of the battle of Chevy-Chase. – Certainly I must confess my owne barbarousness, I never
heard the old song of Percy & Douglas, that I found not mine heart moved more than with a trumpet,
& yet it is sung but by some blind crowder, with no rougher voice then rude style, which being so evill
apparell'd in the dust & cobweb of that uncivil age, what would it work trimmed in the gorgeous eloquence
of Pindar?'.
Wood 401(24). Wing M1677C (two) (Wing, does not record 2 variant issues at O).

407. Chichester. *A most sweet song of an English merchant born in Chichester*. [London]: f. F. Coles, T.
Vere, and W. Gilbertson, [1658-64]. S.sh. Obl. 2 pts. Ff. 107-8 in this vol.
AW added after 'a rich merchant man' in line 1, 'there was'.
Wood 401(55). Wing M2923C (two).

408. Chips. *Chipps of the old block; or, Hercules cleansing the Augaean stable*. The Hague: f. S. Browne,
1659[60]. S.sh.
AW wrote, 'January:'; v, 'Jan. 59[60]', and '36' replaced a former no. '20' in pencil.
Wood 416(36). Wing C3898.

409. Christian, and Tartar. *Christians and a monster Tartar. Part 2, only, 1st line, 'The Turks and
eke the Tartars,'*. London: T. Mabb, for Charls Tyus on London Bridge, and Joshua Conyers in the Long-
Walke, n.d. S.sh. Obs. 2nd pt. only. F. 202 in this vol. (wanting f. 201).
On surviving portion, 'Deest [f.] 201 W[illiam] K[irtland] 1832'.
Wood 401(102) (not in Bodl. CD cat.). Not identified.

410. Clippers. *The clippers execution: or, treason justly rewarded [13 April 1678]*. [London]: f. F. Coles,
T. Vere, J. Wright, a. J. Clarke, [1678]. S.sh. Obl. 2 pts.
[MS.] Wood E. 25(105). Wing C4716 (rare).

411. Cloak. *The ballad of the cloak: or, the cloaks knavery*. [London]: n.pub., [1681-2]. S.sh. Revised.
AW wrote, in ink, over an earlier pencil note, 'June an. 1679'.
Wood 417(4) ([1660?] in Bodl. CD cat.). Wing B604.

412. Cock-crowing. *The cock-crowing at the approach of a free-parliament. Or good newes in a ballat*.
[London]: n.pub., [1660]. S.sh.
AW wrote, 'ffeb. 1659[60]'; v, 'Feb. 59', and '49' replaced a former no. '31 in pencil'.
Wood 416(49). Wing C4795 (rare).

413. College, Stephen. *A ra-ree show*. London: f. B. T. (or, f. A. B.), 1681. S.sh. (r-v).
Missing in 1922. See note at Wood 417(1), item 781. Aaron Smith claimed to have written this ballad, see
Wood 421(4), p. 31 (item 5940).
Wood 417(45). Wing C5226A. *O, Hunt, Harv*.

414. Comber. *The combers whistle or, the sport of the spring.* [London]: f. F. Coles, T. Vere, J. Wright, a. J. Clarke, [1674-9]. S.sh. Obl.
[MS.] Wood E. 25(133). Wing C5498.

415. Compleat. *The compleat swearing-master: a rare new Salamanca ballad.* London: f. A. Banks, 1682. S.Sh.
Wood 276a(545). Wing C5659.

416. Conceited Lover. *The conceited lover, or the enamoured young man.* [London]: f. R. Burton, [1690?]. S.sh. Obl.
[MS.] Wood E. 25(46). Wing C5695 (rare).

417. Congratulation. *A congratulation on the happy discovery of the hellish fanatick plot.* [London]: n.pub., [1682]. S.sh.
Diff. ed. at Wood 417(91).
Wood 417(121). Wing C5815A.

418. Congratulation. *A congratulation on the happy discovery of the hellish fanatick plot.* London: N. Thompson, 1682. S.sh.
Diff. ed. at Wood 417(121).
Wood 417(91). Wing C5815 (rare).

419. Conspiracy. *The conspiracy: or, the discovery of the fanatick plot.* [London]: n.pub., 1683. S.sh.
Wood 276a(546). Wing C5934 (3).

420. Coridon. *Faithful Coridon; or, coy Phillis conquer'd.* [London]: J. Deacon, [1675]. S.sh.
AW wrote the year, '(1684)', in pencil.
Wood 417(135). Wing F268B (rare).

421. Country Cousin. *The countrey cozen, or: the crafty city dame.* [London]: f. P. Brooksby, [1685?]. S.sh. Obl.
[MS.] Wood E. 25(151). Wing C6527 (two) (Wing, country).

422. Country Maid. *The country-maids delight; or; the husbandman's honour made known.* [London]: f. F. Coles, T. Vere, J. Wright, a. J. Clarke, [1674-9]. S.sh. Obl.
[MS.] Wood E. 25(18). Wing C6543 (rare) (Wing, or the).

423. Crafty Maid. *The crafty maids approbation, wherein she showes either black or brown.* [London]: f. J. Williamson, [1675 ca.]. S.sh. Obl.
[MS.] Wood E. 25(70). Wing C6778A (rare).

424. Crafty Young Man. *The crafty young-man. He kist a girle, but toucht not her maiden-head.* London: f. J. Clarke, [1680 ca.]. S.sh. Obl.
[MS.] Wood E. 25(41). Wing C6781 (rare).

425. Crosse, Robert. *'Two gospel knights / Both learned wights'.* ?: ?, [1667 ca.]. Pp.?
Missing. MS. Wood E. 2(70), p. 63, 'among Mr. Foulis papers a Ballad of Jos. Glanvill & Rob. Cross'. AW quoted 6 lines in AO 4.124. May be a ms.
MS. Wood E. 2(70), p. 63. Not identified.

426. Cuckold's Dream. *The cuckolds dream. Or, the comical vision.* London: f. F. Cole, T. Vere, J. Wright, a. J. Clark, [1674-9]. S.sh. Obl.
[MS.] Wood E. 25(82). Wing C7454 (rare).

427. Cunningham, Jasper*. *A wonderfull example of Gods justice shewed upon Jasper Conningham, a gentleman born in Scotland.* [London]: f. F. Cole, J. Wright, T. Vere, a. W. Gilbertson, [1655-8]. S.sh. Obl. 2 pts. Pp. 55-6 in this vol.
'Another Copy 401.97', in a later hand. Dupl. at 401(50).
Wood 402(16). Wing W3365B (rare, 2 at O).

428. Cunningham, Jasper*. *A wonderfull example of Gods justice shewed upon Jasper Conningham, a gentleman born in Scotland.* [London]: f. F. Cole, J. Wright, T. Vere, a. W. Gilbertson, [1655-8]. S.sh. Obl. 2pts. Ff. 97-8 in this vol.
'Another Copy 402.55', in a later hand. Dupl. at Wood 402(16).
Wood 401(50). Wing W3365B (rare, 2 at O).

429. Cupid. *Cupids golden dart, or, a dainty sonnet here is to be sold.* [London]: f. F. Coles, T. Vere, J. Wright, a. J. Clarke, [1674-9]. S.sh. Obl.
[MS.] Wood E. 25(121). Wing C7603.

430. Cupid. *Cupids victory over the virgins heart or, love in its colours.* [London]: f. J. Deacon, [1685-88]. S.sh.
AW wrote the year, '87'.
Wood 417(152). Wing C7615 (Wing, hearts).

431. Cynthia, pseud. *Fair Cynthia's sorrowful sighs.* [London]: f. P. Brooksby, [1688]. S.sh.
AW wrote the date, 'Januar', and '1688[9]'.
Wood 417(174). Wing F95 (rare) (Wing, no publ).

432. D., N. *An antidote against melancholy: made up in pills. Compounded of witty ballads, jovial songs, and merry catches.* [London]: printed by Mer. Melancholicus, sold in London a. Westminster, 1661. 4°.
Pp. [4], 76.
Tp, bsm. Pp. 11, 52, 59, three notes by a later writer, e.g. 'Ms. Ashm 36, act. 196'.
Wood 382(3). Wing D66A.

433. Dainty New Ditty. *A dainty new ditty of a saylor and his love, how one the others constancy did prove.* London: f. J. Wright, [1690?]. S.sh. Obl.
[MS.] Wood E. 25(8). Wing D122 (rare).

434. Damon and Celia. *Damon and Celia, or, the languishing lover comforted.* [London]: f. J. H., sold F. Coles, T. Vere, J. Wright, a. J. Clarke, [1674-79]. S.sh. Obl.
[MS.] Wood E. 25(152). Wing D158B (rare).

435. Dead Man's Song. *The dead mans song, whose dwelling was neer Basing-hall in London.* [London]: f. F. Coles, T. Vere, J. Wright, a. J. Clarke, [1674-9]. S.sh. Obl. Ff. 83-4 in this vol.
Earlier f. nos., cropped.
Wood 401(43). Wing D488B (two) (Wing, man's).

436. [Dean, John]. *The wine-cooper's delight.* London: f. H. L., 1681. S.sh.
Diff. ed. at Rox. 3 (244-245) (formerly in the AW collection). Dupl. at Wood 417(61).
Wood 276a(533) (not in Bodl. CD cat.). Wing D496.

437. [Dean, John]. *The wine-cooper's delight.* London: f. H. L., 1681. S.sh.
Diff. ed. at Rox. 3 (244-245) (formerly in the AW collection). Dupl. at Wood 276a(533).
Wood 417(61) (not in Bodl. CD cat.). Wing D496.

438. [Dean, John]. *The Dutch-miller, and new invented wind-miller, or, an exact description of a rare artist newly come into England.* [London]: f. F. Coles, T. Vere, J. Wright, a. J. Clarke, [1674-9]. S.sh. Obl. 2 pts.
[MS.] Wood E. 25(53) (not in Bodl. CD cat.). Wing D492aA (rare).

439. [Deloney, Thomas]. *A mournful ditty of the lady Rosamond, king Henry the seconds concubine.* [London]: f. F. Coles, T. Vere, a. W. Gilbertson, [1658 to 1664]. S.sh. Obl. 2 pts. Ff. 7-8 in this vol.
LT 1.343.
Wood 401(4). Wing M2986 (rare).

440. [Deloney, Thomas]. *A new ballad shewing how a prince of England loved the kings daughter of France, and how the prince was disastrously slain.* [London]: f. F. Coles, T. Vere, a. W. Gilbertson, [1658 to 1664]. S.sh. Obl. Pp. 26-7 in this vol.
Diff. ed. at Wood 401(61), item 443; and Wood 276b(102), item 644.
Wood 402(7). Wing N572 (two) ('O' not recorded in Wing).

441. [Deloney, Thomas]. *The Spanish ladies love, to a pleasant new tune.* [London]: f. F. Coles, T. Vere, and 'W.ilbertson' [Gilbertson], [1658 to 1664]. S.sh. Obl. 2 pts.
[MS.] Wood E. 25(11). Wing D967A (two).

442. [Deloney, Thomas]. *The most rare and excellent history, of the duchesse of Suffolks calamity.* [London]: f. F. C., J. W., T. V., W. G., [1663 to 1665]. S.sh. Obl. Ff. 57-8 in this vol.
F. 57ᵛ, AW wrote, 'The Duchess of Suffolk mentind [sic] in the following Ballad, was Catherine the sole daugh. & heire to William the last Lord Willoughby of Eresby, who was the fourth wife of Charles Brandon

Duke of Suffolke – which Charles dying without issue by her, shee was married to Rich Bertie Esq. father to Peregrine Bertie Lord Willoughby, ancestor to the Earls of Lindsey & Abendon– [Abingdon]'.
Wood 401(29). Wing D958A (rare).

443. [Deloney, Thomas]. *A new ballad, shewing how a prince of England loved the kings daughter of France*. [London]: f. F. Coles, T. Vere, a. J. Wright, [1663 to 1674]. S.sh. Obl. 2 pts. Ff.119-120 in this vol. 'Another copy 402.26' in a later hand. Diff. ed. at Wood 402(7), item 440; and at item 644.
Wood 401(61). Wing N572A (rare).

444. Devereux. Robert*. Essex, earl of. *A lamentable ditty, composed upon the death of Robert lord Devereux*. London: 'for W. Gllberson', [1649-64?]. S.sh. Obl. 2 pts. Ff. 75-6 in this vol.
Wood 401(39). Not in Wing (should be at L268A). ESTCR 234890.

445. Diseased Maiden Lover. *The diseased maiden lover. [And] The faithless lover*. [London]: f. F. Coles, T. Vere, and J. Wright, [1655-80]. S.sh. Obl. 2 pts.
[MS.] Wood E. 25(122). Wing D1668.

446. [Dobson, John]. *Dr. Pierce his preaching confuted by his practice. Sent in a letter by N. G. to a friend in London*. [London]: n.pub., [1663]. 4°. Pp. 4.
P. 2, AW's note at Joseph Brookes, a most 'couragious' and 'comical, *Terrae filius*': 'but his speech was not of his owne making, it was composed by a club of pretended wits.'; p. 4, identification of R. Busby, in his later hand, 'master of Westmister [sic] Schoole.' and, at end, in his early hand, 'Came out at Oxōn Aug: 28. 1663: the Authour of it Joh: Dobson A: m. & fellow of Magdalen Coll: was expelled the University by the Vice Cancellors Bannimus x̄ Sept: followyng: & Edm: Thorne also Bookseller, discommuned for ever for selling the said pamphlet.' See Wood 423(40), item 5250; AO 4.2, 3, 304; LT 1.473, 487-9; 2.563. Dupl. at Wood 515(28b) and Wood 633(7).
Wood 515(27). Wing D1753. Madan 2624.

447. [Dobson, John]. *Dr. Pierce his preaching confuted by his practice. Sent in a letter by N. G. to a friend in London*. [London]: n.pub., [1663]. 4°. Pp. 4.
Inserted after p. [4] and before p. 1 in Wood 515(28a), item 3123. P. 1, note by a recent librarian, 'Inserted 28* [/] For (28) see 2 leaves further on'. Dupl. at Wood 515(27) and Wood 633(7).
Wood 515(28b). Wing D1753. Madan 2624.

448. [Dobson, John]. *Dr. Pierce his preaching confuted by his practice, sent in a letter by N. G. to a friend in London*. [London]: n.pub., [1663]. 4° (wanting pp. 3-4). Pp. 2.
Dupl. at Wood 515(27) and Wood 515(28b).
Wood 633(7). Madan 2624. Wing D1753.

449. Doctor. *The doctors medicines and counsel which he gave to a maiden, or, a cloak for a gross widdow*. [London]: f. J. Clark, [1680]. S.sh. Obl.
ᵛ, notes on repair slip '16 and one quarter [/] 13 and a half', not by AW.
[MS.] Wood E. 25(43). Wing D1769 (rare).

450. Dolly and Molly. *Dolly and Molly: or, the two countrey damosels fortunes at London*. [London]: f. P. B. a. E. O., [1690-5]. S.sh. Obl.
[MS.] Wood E. 25(140) ([MS.] Wood E. 29(140) in Bodl. CD cat.). Wing D1840A (rare, 2 at O) (Wing, 1700).

451. [Duffett, Thomas]. *Amintor's lamentation for Celia's unkindness*. [London]: f. P. Brooksby, [1676]. S.sh. Obl. Pasteboard, with more recent cloth spine; recently repaired.
The 153 ballads in this volume date from 1641-1695. They are black letter (some have the refrain in Roman) and printed oblong on single sheets (chain lines are horizontal; the folio sheets are smaller than those in Wood 401-402). Most are extremely rare; 7 are not recorded in Wing; 6 of these are not recorded in the ESTCR; 103 others survive only in the Bodleian Library, according to Wing and the ESTCR; 23 survive in 2 locations; and 5 in 3 locations. Many are repaired, and there is some cropping of printed material (and perhaps of AW's notes), though in general their condition is good. The Arabic numbers, 1-153, on the items in this vol. are not by AW, in contrast to other vols. of ballads (e.g. 400 (q.v.), 401, and 402). These 153 ballads were prob. delivered to the Ashm. unbound and the ballads were then bound after 1695 and before Whiteside's death in 1729. The Whiteside cat. has the entry after Wood E. 24, '25 – [and Whiteside himself added later:] Ballads'. Some of the spreads for years of publication in Wing are desparate, based as they are on the dates of activity of the printers. AW annotated, usually only with a date, only 16 ballads in this vol. (10, 58, 60-1, 83, 94, 109-118).

[MS.] Wood E. 25(1). Wing D2442.

452. Dunsmore, Isabel of*. *The fair maid of Dunsore's [sic] lamentation. Occasioned by lord Wigmore.* [London]: f. E. Oliver, [1680 ca.]. S.sh. Obl.
[MS.] Wood E. 25(71). Wing F100A (rare) (Wing, [1700?]).

453. [D'Urfey, Thomas]. *Pretty Kate of Edenborough. Being a new Scotch song.* [London]: f. P. Brooksby, [1672 to 1685]. S.sh.
AW wrote the year, '(1682)', in ink and pencil.
Wood 417(113). Wing D2763.

454. [D'Urfey, Thomas]. *The gowlin: or, a pleasant fancy for the spring.* [London]: f. F. Coles, T. Vere, J. Wright, a. J. Clarke, [1674 to 1679]. S.sh. Obl. 2 pts.
[MS.] Wood E. 25(134). Wing D2730A (rare).

455. [D'Urfey, Thomas]. *Advice to the city, or, the Whiggs loyalty explained.* London: f. C. Tebroc [i.e., Corbet], 1682. S.sh.
Wood 417(94). Not in Wing (Wing, A651, 1994 ed. entry cancelled; see the unnumbered entry after A651, 'Engraved'. The Wood item has no engraving). Not in ESTCR (not ESTCR 374 (rare) (Hunt)).

456. [D'Urfey, Thomas]. *Advice to the city: sung to the king at Windsor, to a theorbo.* [London]: f. J. Hindmarsh, 1682. S.sh.
Wood 276a(530). Wing D2697.

457. [D'Urfey, Thomas]. *Jenneys lamentation for the loss of Jocky or, a new song in the play called the royalist.* London: f. A. Banks, [1682]. S.sh.
AW wrote twice, in ink and pencil, 'Mar. 1681/2'.
Wood 417(86). Wing J676 (rare) (Wing, 168-?).

458. [D'Urfey, Thomas]. *State & ambition a new song at the Dukes theatre.* [London]: f. P. Brooksby, [1684]. S.sh.
AW wrote the year, '(85)', in pencil.
Wood 417(147). Wing D2786A (two).

459. Dutch Fleet. *The royal victory, obtained (with the providence of almighty God) against the Dutch-fleet, June the 2d. and 3d.* London: f. F. Coles, T. Vere, R. Gilbertson, a. J. Wright, [1665]. S.sh. Obl. 2 pts. Pp. 95-6 in this vol.
Wood 402(24). Wing R2155A (two).

460. Dutch Miller. *The happy return of the old Dutch miller.* London: f. A. Banks, 1682. S.sh.
No. '90' in a former bundle. Dupl. at Wood 417(84).
Wood 276a(549). Wing H673.

461. Dutch Miller. *The happy return of the old Dutch miller.* London: f. A. Banks, 1682. S.sh.
AW wrote 'publ. in March - 1681/2'. Dupl. at Wood 276a(549).
Wood 417(84). Wing H673.

462. Dying Lovers. *The dying lovers reprieve. Or, the reward of true love.* [London]: f. F. Coles, T. Vere, J. Wright, a. J. Clarke, [1674-9]. S.sh. Obl.
[MS.] Wood E. 25(20). Wing D2953.

463. Dying Man. *The dying mans good counsel to his chidren [sic] and friends.* London: f. F. Coles, T. Veres [sic], J. Wright, a. J. Clarke, [1674-9]. S.sh. Obl.
[MS.] Wood E. 25(142). Wing D2955 (rare).

464. Edward 4*. *A pleasant new ballad of king Edward the fourth, and a tanner of Tamworth.* [London]: f. F. Coles, T. Vere, a. W. Gilbertson, [1658-64]. S.sh. Ob. 2 pts. Ff. 43-4 in this vol.
Wood 401(22). Wing P2553A (3) (Wing, between King Edward).

465. Emmerson, Christopher; George Dixon, and Richard Higgins. *A warning-peice for ingroosers of corne; being true relation how the divell met with one Goodman Inglebred of Bowton.* London: f. W. Gilbertson, [1643]. S.sh. Obl. 2 pts. Ff. 161-2 in this vol.
'Boughton', prob. not in AW's hand; and 'Norfolk', not in AW's hand.
Wood 401(82). Wing W926 (two).

466. England. *A description of old England: or, a true declaration of the times.* [London]: f. F. Coles, T. Vere, J. Wright, a. J. Clarke, [1674 to 1679]. S.sh. Obl. 2 pts.
[MS.] Wood E. 25(72). Wing D1149.

467. England, Parliament. *A proper new ballad on the old parliament. Or, the second part of knave out of doores.* [London]: n.pub., [1659]. S.sh.
AW wrote, 'octob: M DC Lix'; ᵛ, 'Oct 59', and '16' over a former no. '6' in pencil.
Wood 416(16). Wing P3671.

468. England, Parliament. *The re-resurrection of the rump: or, rebellion and tyranny revived.* [London]: n.pub., [1659]. 3rd ed. S.sh.
AW wrote, 'Decemb 1659'; ᵛ, 'Dec. 59', and '19' over a former no., '7' in pencil.
Wood 416(19). Wing R1124.

469. England, Parliament. *[Arsy] versy: or, the second martyrdom of the rump.* [London]: n.pub., [1660]. S.sh. (mutilated at edges).
ᵛ, 'Rump', not in AW's hand.
Wood 416(20) (not in Bodl. CD cat.). Wing A3782.

470. England, Parliament. *Fortunate rising, or the rump upward.* London: f. H. James, [1660]. S.sh.
AW wrote, 'Jan: 1659[60]'; ᵛ, 'Jan. 59', and '35' replaced a former no. '19' in pencil.
Wood 416(35). Wing F1618 (two).

471. England, Parliament. *A free-parliament-letany.* [London]: n.pub., [1660]. S.sh.
AW wrote, 'March: 1659[60]'; ᵛ, 'Mar. 59', and '60' over a former no. '41' in pencil.
Wood 416(60). Wing F2117.

472. England, Parliament. *The history of the second death of the rump. To the tune of, The parliament sate as snugg as a cat. I. Come buy my fine dity [/] of news from the city,.* [London]: n.pub., [1660]. S.sh.
AW wrote, 'March: 1659[60]'; ᵛ, 'Ma Feb 59', and replaced a former no. '38' with '57'.
Wood 416(57). Wing H2179.

473. England, Parliament. *A new-years-gift for the rump.* [Oxford?]: n.pub., [1660]. S.sh.
AW wrote, 'Decemb: 1659'; ᵛ, 'Dec. 59', and '21' replaced a former no. '8' in pencil.
Wood 416(21). Wing N809. See Madan 2511.

474. England, Parliament. *The parliament-complement, or the re-admission of the secluded-members.* London: f. J. Nidale, 1660. S.sh.
AW altered 1660 to 16'59: feb'; ᵛ, 'Feb. 59', and '47' replaced a former no. '29' in pencil (this is Nidale's single publication).
Wood 416(47). Wing P500 (3).

475. England, Parliament. *A proper new ballad of thf [sic] divels arse a peake, . . . or, in plain terms of the posteriors and fag-end of a long parliament.* London: f. T. James, [1660]. S.sh.
ᵛ, AW replaced '22' with 'nu. 38', in pencil.
Wood 416(38). Wing P3670.

476. England, Parliament. *The rump roughly, yet righteously handled. In a new ballad.* [London]: n.pub., [1660]. S.sh.
ᵛ, AW wrote the year, '59[1660]', and '37' replaced a former no. '21' in pencil.
Wood 416(37). Wing R2276.

477. England, Parliament. *The rump serv'd in with a grand sallet, or a new ballad.* London: n.pub., 1660. S.sh.
AW altered the date to 16'59: ffeb'. ᵛ, 'Dupl'. Dupl. at Wood 416(51).
Wood 276a(526). Wing R2277.

478. England, Parliament. *The rump serv'd in with a grand sallet. Or, a new ballad.* London: n.pub., 1660. S.sh.
AW wrote, 'ffeb 1659'; ᵛ 'Feb. 59', and '51' replaced a former no. '33' in pencil. Dupl. at Wood 276a(526).
Wood 416(51). Wing R2277.

479. England, Parliament. *The rump ululant, or penitence per force; . . . to the tune of Gerrards mistresse.* [London]: n.pub., [1660]. S.sh.

Dupl. at Wood 416(45).
Wood 276b(106). Wing R2278.

480. England, Parliament. *The rump ululant, or penitence per force; . . . to the tune of Gerrards mistresse.* [London]: n.pub., [1660]. S.sh.
AW wrote, '1659[60]: ffeb:'; ᵛ, 'Feb. 59', and '45' replaced a former no. '27' in pencil. Dupl. at 276b(106).
Wood 416(45). Wing R2278.

481. England, Parliament. *The tune to the Devonshire cant: or, an answer to the parliament dissolved at Oxford.* London: f. T. Rawe, 1681. S.sh.
3 corrections, prob. not by AW. LT 2.533.
Wood 417(48). Wing T3251.

482. England, Parliament. *A new touch of the times; or, the nation's consent, for a free parliament.* [London]: f. C. D[ennison?], [1689?]. S.sh. Obl.
AW wrote the date, 'Jan. 1688[9]'.
[MS.] Wood E. 25(111). Wing N786 (rare) (Wing, var., wants publ. and 1690?).

483. England's New Bell-man. *England [sic] new bell-man: ringing . . . judgements . . . prognosticated by the great eclipse of the sun. March 29.* London: f. F. Coles, T. Vere, a. W. Gilbertson, [1658-64]. S.sh. Obl. Ff. 159-60 in this vol. (out of order).
'Eclipse', not in AW's hand. Diff. ed. at Wood [MS.] E. 25(128).
Wood 401(81). Wing E3001A (rare).

484. England's New Bellman. *England's new bellman. Ringing into all peoples ears, Gods dreadful judgement . . . prognosticated by the . . . eclipse [29 March 1652].* [London]: f. F. Coles, T. Vere, a. J. Wright, [1663-74]. S.sh.
Diff. ed. at Wood 401(81).
[MS.] Wood E. 25(128). Wing E3001B (rare).

485. England's Object. *Englands object: or, . . . newes . . . for the taking . . . of . . . Hugh Peters.* [London]: f. F. Coles, T. Vere, a. W. Gilbertson, [1660]. S.sh. Obl. Ff. 175-6 in this vol.
AW wrote the date, 'Septemb. 1660'; 'Peters' underscored in the t. LT 1.331.
Wood 401(89). Wing E3005 (rare) (Wing, England's).

486. England's Royal Conquest. *Englands royall conquest. Truely manifested in a happy victory obtained against the Dutch fleet [25-6 July 1666]. [With, ᵛ] A pleasant new song, in praise of the leather bottell [by John Wade].* London: R. Burton, [1666]. S.sh. Obl. 2 pts. The 2nd ballad on ᵛ.
[MS.] Wood E. 25(55). Wing E3041A (two).

487. England's Warning Piece. *Englands warning-piece; or, a caviet [sic] for wicked sinners to remember their latter end.* [London]: f. R. Burton, [1641 to 1674]. S.sh. Obl.
[MS.] Wood E. 25(127). Wing E3071A (rare) (Wing, caviat).

488. English Laws. *Ignoramus-justice: or, the English-laws turn'd into a gin.* London: f. A. Banks, 1682. S.sh.
Wood 417(90). Wing I45.

489. Etna, Mount. *Mount Ætna's flames. Or, the Sicilian wonder.* [London]: f. F. Coles, T. Vere, a. J. Wright, [1669]. S.sh. Obl. 2 pts. Ff. 199-200 in this vol.
'Ætna', not in AW's hand.
Wood 401(101). Wing M2969 (rare).

490. Excellent New Hymn. *An excellent new hymne to the mobile, exhorting them to loyalty.* London: N. Thompson, 1682. S.sh.
AW wrote 'Jan 1681[2]'.
Wood 417(82). Wing E3807.

491. Excellent New Song. *An excellent new song of the unfortunate Whig's.* [London]: f. S. Maurel, 1682. S.sh.
AW wrote the year, '1682' beneath the publication date which had been altered to 1688.
Wood 417(109). Wing E3831 (two).

492. Explanation. *The explanation. To the tune of, Hey boys up go we. Our priests in holy pilgrimage.*

[London?]: n.pub., [1685]. S.sh.
AW wrote, 'published about S. Thom. day the Apost. 1688' (21 Dec.). LT 3.293.
Wood 417(164). Wing E3886B (Wing, of Hey and up we go).

493. Famous Flower. *The famous flower of serving-men; or the lady turn'd serving-man.* [London]: f. J. Hose, [1680?]. S.sh. Obl. 2 pts.
[MS.] Wood E. 25(75). Wing F370 (rare).

494. Fanatic's Barber. *The fanaticks barber or, a new cut for non-conformists. Being a true relation of the parson that was lately gelt at Chelmsford.* [London]: n.pub., [1663]. S.sh.
AW wrote, 'came out in the Beginning of Februar: 1662[3].'; ᵛ, '1662'.
Wood 416(94). Wing F401 (two) (Wing, 1655?).

495. Faustus, John*. *The judgment of God shewed upon John Faustus doctor in divinity.* [London]: 'for F. Coles, T. Vere W. Gilbertson', [1658 to 1664]. S.sh. Ob. 2 pts. Ff. 53-4 in this vol.
Wood 401(27). Wing J1177A (two).

496. Fickle Northern Lass. *The fickle northern lass, or, the wronged shepherds resolution.* [London]: f. F. Coles, T. Vere, J. Wright, a. [J.] Clarke, [1674-9]. S.sh. Obl.
[MS.] Wood E. 25(62). Wing F846.

497. Frenchman. *The French man gull'd of his gold or a warning for whore-hunters.* [London]: f. J. Clarke, [1680?]. S.sh. Obl.
[MS.] Wood E. 25(40). Wing F2187 (rare) (Wing, London).

498. Frenchmen. *The Frenchmens wonder, or, the battle of the birds [26 Feb.].* [London]: f. F. Coles, T. Vere, J. Wright, a. J. Clarke, [1674 to 1679]. S.sh. Obl. 2 pts.
Date entered at t, 1676, not by AW.
[MS.] Wood E. 25(64). Wing F2189 (rare) (Wing, London).

499. Friar. *The fryer well-fitted. [sic] Or, a pretty jest that once befell [sic].* [London]: [cropped at bottom], [1660-95]. S.sh. Obl. 2 pts.
[MS.] Wood E. 25(86). Not in Wing. Not in ESTCR (var. of Wing F2207A).

500. Gayton, Ed[mund]. *Epulae Oxonienses. Or a jocular relation of a banquet presented to the best of kings, . . . 1636, . . . at St. John Baptists colledge. The song.* [Oxford]: [W. Hall], [1661?]. Fol. With musical score. Pp. 3.
Dupl. at 416(4) and 423(17). LT 1.46, AO 3.756.
Wood 398(2). Wing G411 (rare, 3 at O). Madan 2544.

501. Gayton, Ed[mund]. *Epulae Oxonienses. Or a jocular relation of a banquet presented to the best of kings, . . . 1636, . . . at St. John Baptists colledge. The song.* [Oxford]: [W. Hall], [1661?]. Fol. With musical score. Pp. 3.
Note in blue crayon, by a later librarian. Dupl. at Wood 398(2), Wood 416(4). LT 1.46, AO 3.756.
Wood 423(17). Wing G411 (rare, 3 at O). Madan 2544.

502. Gayton, Ed[mund]. *Epulae Oxonienses. Or a jocular relation of a banquet presented to the best of kings, . . . 1636, . . . St. John Baptists colledge. The song.* [Oxford]: [W. Hall], [1661?]. Fol. With musical score. Pp. 3.
Dupl. at Wood 398(2), Wood 423(17). LT 1.46, AO 3.756.
Wood 416(4). Wing G411 (rare, 3 at O). Madan 2544.

503. [Gayton, Edmund]. *A ballad on the gyants in the physick garden in Oxford, who have been breeding feet as long as Garagantua was [sic] teeth.* [Oxford]: [W. Hall], [1662]. S.sh. (mutilated at bottom).
AW wrote the year, '1662', and below, lines that were mutilated, written in, may not be by AW. Dupl. at Wood 416(92). LT 2.164-5, AO 3.757-8.
Wood 423(38). Wing G406A (rare, 2 at O). Madan 2579.

504. [Gayton, Edmund]. *A ballad on the gyants in the physick garden in Oxford, who have been breeding feet as long as Garagantua was [sic] teeth.* [Oxford]: [W. Hall], [1662]. S.sh.
AW wrote the year, '1662'; ᵛ, 'Dupl', in pencil, and '1662'. Dupl. at Wood 423(38). LT 2.164, AO 3.757-8.
Wood 416(92). Wing G406A (rare, 2 at O). Madan 2579.

505. [Gayton, Edmund]. *Upon mr Bobard's yew-men of the guards to the physick garden.* [Oxford]:

n.pub., [1662]. S.sh.
AW wrote, 'July: 1662' and made 7 corrections; below, perhaps not by AW, 'By G. E. (IE) Edm. Geyton Esq. Bedle of Arts. Oxon.' Dupl. at Wood 416(93). LT 2.164-5, AO 3.757-8.
Wood 423(39). Wing G419 (rare, 2 at O). Madan 2580.

506. [Gayton, Edmund]. *Upon mr Bobard's yew-men of the guards to the physick garden*. [Oxford]: n.pub., [1662]. S.sh.
AW wrote, 'Edm. Gayton 1662'; ᵛ, the same. Dupl. at Wood 423(39). LT 2.164, AO 3.757-8.
Wood 416(93). Wing G419 (rare, 2 at O). Madan 2580.

507. General Sale. *A general sale of rebellious houshold-stuff*. London: f. Allen Banks, 1685. S.sh.
1685 altered to 1688, and below, AW wrote, '1687'.
Wood 417(154). Wing G510A (two).

508. George, Saint. *A most excellent ballad of s. George for England, and the kings daughter of Ægypt*. [London]: f. F. Coles, T. Vere, a. W. Gilbertson, [1658 to 1664]. S.sh. Obl. Ff. 115-6 in this vol.
AW added, at f. 116, 'The second part'. Diff. ed. at Wood 402(6).
Wood 401(59). Wing M2880A (two).

509. George, Saint. *Saint George, and the dragon, Anglice, Mercurius poeticus*. London: f. T. Scott, sold W. Leadsome, [1660]. S.sh.
Tp, AW wrote, 'Feb 1659[60]'. Diff. ed. at Wood 416(43).
Wood 276b(100). Wing S309B (3) (Wing, dragon.).

510. George, Saint. *Saint George, and the dragon, Anglice, Mercurius Poeticus*. [London]: n.pub., [1660]. S.sh.
AW wrote, 'ffeb: 1659[60]'; ᵛ, 'Feb. 59', and 'Dupl. 9', lined out. Diff. ed. at 276b(100).
Wood 416(43). Wing S309A (3).

511. George, Saint. *The second part of saint George for England*. [London]: n.pub., [1660]. S.sh.
AW wrote, 'March: .1659[60].'; ᵛ, 'Ma Feb. 59', and '54' replaced a former no. '37' in pencil.
Wood 416(54). Wing S2298 (two).

512. George, Saint. *A most excellent ballad of st. George for England, and the kings daughter of Egypt*. [London]: f. J. C., W. T., a. T. Passinger [sic], [1684-86]. S.sh. Obl. 2 pts. Pp. 22-3 in this vol.
'See another Copy 401. p. 115', in a later hand. Diff. ed. at Wood 401(59).
Wood 402(6). Wing M2881 (rare).

513. Gernutus a Jew*. *A new song: shewing the crueltie of Gernutus a Jew, who lending to a merchant*. London: E. P[urslowe] f. J. Wright, [1640 ca.]. S.sh. Obl. 2 pts. Ff. 101-2 in this vol.
'1. Judaiii 2. Shakespeare Merch of V', in pencil, not in AW's hand.
Wood 401(52). STC 11796.7 (rare) (Wing N772, [1680?], incorrect) .

514. Goddess's Glory. *The goddesses glory: or, the loyal lover wounded*. [London]: f. J. Deacon, [1685-8?]. S.sh.
AW wrote '(1688)', in pencil. Dupl. at Wood 417(145, and 176).
Wood 417(114). Wing G922A (rare, 3 at O) (Wing, [1655]).

515. Goddess's Glory. *The goddesses glory: or, the loyal lover wounded*. [London]: f. J. Deacon, [1685-8?]. S.sh.
AW wrote '1685', in pencil. Dupl. at Wood 417(114, and 176).
Wood 417(145). Wing G922A (rare, 3 at O) (Wing, [1655]).

516. Goddess's Glory. *The goddesses glory: or, the loyal lover wounded*. [London]: f. J. Deacon, [1685-8?]. S.sh.
AW wrote 'bought at Oxon. in Feb. 1688[9]', in ink. Dupl. at Wood 417(114, and 145).
Wood 417(176). Wing G922A (rare, 3 at O) (Wing, [1655]).

517. Good-Fellows. *The good-fellows counsel: or, the bad husbands recantation*. [London]: f. P. Brooksby, [1680-5]. S.sh. Obl. 2 pts.
[MS.] Wood E. 25(19). Wing G1048.

518. Gray, William*. *A noble dewel, or, an unmatchable combate betwixt sir William [Grey] and the earl of Southast*. London: f. J. Andrews, [1660]. S.sh. Obl. 2 pts. Ff. 99-100 in this vol. Mutilated at top.

Correction in t, to 'Earl of Southesk'.
Wood 401(51). Wing N1204 (rare).

519. Great Britain. *Great Bittains [sic] joy, and good news for the Netherlands.* [London]: f. F. Coles, T. Vere, and J. Wright, [1663-74]. S.sh. Obl.
[MS.] Wood E. 25(101) (not in Bodl. CD cat.). Wing G1667aA (rare).

520. Great Messenger. *The great messenger of mortality: or, a dialogue betwixt death and a beautiful lady.* [London]: f. J. Deacon, [1690 ca.]. S.sh. And a printed list of 8 'new broadsides' (only 1, Wing E3800 (1684), can be identified in Wing).
Wood 417(129). Not in Wing (should be at G1711A). Not in ESTCR.

521. Green Sickness. *The green sickness cured: or, how dee now: To the tune of, four-pence-half-penny-farthing.* [London]: f. R. Kell, [1685 ca.]. S.sh.
AW wrote, 'Bought at Oxon for a new ballet 14. Feb. 1688[9]'. LT 3.299.
Wood 417(177). Not in Wing (should be at G1814C). Not in ESTCR.

522. [Greene, George a*]. *The jolly pinder of Wakefield.* [London]: 'for F. Coles, T: Vere. a. W. Glberson' [sic], [1658-64]. S.sh. P. 42 in this vol.
'Another Copy Wood 401.61', in a later hand. Diff. ed. at Wood 401(32).
Wood 402(12) (in Bodl. CD cat.: followed by Wing D959B, incorrect). Wing J895A (rare).

523. [Greene, George a*, and Thomas Deloney]. *The jolly pinder of Wakefield: with Robin Hood, Scarlet and John. [Followed by] The noble acts newly found, of Arthur of the table round.* [London]: f. F. Coles, T. Vere, J. Wright, a. J. Clarke, [1674-9]. S.sh. Obl. 2 ballads issued together (chain lines vertical). Ff. 61-2 in this vol.
'Another Copy Wood 402.42', in a later hand. Diff. ed. of *The jolly pinder* at Wood 402(12).
Wood 401(32). Wing J896A (rare) and D959B (rare).

524. Grismond, William*. *The downfall of William Grismond, or, a lamentable murder by him.* [London]: f. F. Coles, T. Vere, a. W. Gilbertson, [1658-64]. S.sh. Obl. Ff. 155-6 in this vol.
Wood 401(79). Wing D2094A (rare).

525. Guy of Warwick. *A pleasant song of the valiant deeds of chivalry, atchieved by the noble knight sir Guy of Warwick.* London: f. J. Wright, [1640 ca.]. S.sh. obl. 2 pts. Pp. 6-7 in this vol.
Diff. ed. at Wood 401(2).
Wood 402(2). STC 12542.5 (rare).

526. Guy of Warwick. *A pleasant song of the valiant deeds of chivalry, atchieved by noble knight, sir Guy of Warwick.* [London]: f. F. Coles, T. Vere, a. W. Gilbertson, [1658-64]. S.sh. Obl. 2 pts. Ff. 3-4.
F3, AW wrote, 'Dupl'. Diff. ed. at Wood 402(2).
Wood 401(2). Wing P2560C (rare).

527. H[ammond], C[harles]. *The divils cruelty to mankind. Being a true relation of . . . George Gibbs.* Lonpuo [sic]: f. W. Gilbertson, [1663]. S.sh. Obl. Ff. 195-6 in this vol.
AW made a correction in t and below, wrote 'Mense Mar: 1662[3]. in the beg: of the said mounth. [sic]'. LT 2.11.
Wood 401(99). Wing H491C (rare).

528. Harris, Benjamin*. *The protestant cuckold: a new ballad. . . . how B. H. the protestant-newsforger, caught his beloved wife Ruth in ill circumstances.* London: f. F. Smith, 1681. S.sh.
AW wrote 'Ben. Harris', twice, at the initials of B. H.: and below, 'In the beginning of Apr. 1681'.
Wood 417(58). Wing P3829.

529. Harrison, William*. *Truth brought to light. Or, wonderful . . . news from Gloucester shire, concerning one mr. William Harrison.* London: f. C. Tyus, [1662]. S.sh. Obl. 2 pts. Ff. 191-2 in this vol.
AW wrote 'A:D: 1662'.
Wood 401(97). Wing T3153A (rare).

530. Have You Any Work. *Have you any work for a cooper? Or, a comparison betwixt a cooper's, and a joyner's trade.* London: f. R. H., 1681. S.sh. (r-v).
The next item, Wood 276a(555), recorded in the 1717 list (see note at item 5241), was moved to Wood 417(184) (item 664) where the Ashm. Roman numeral 'CCCCCLV' is still visible.
Wood 276a(553-4). Wing H1161.

531. Hen Peckt Frigate. *A general summons for those belonging to the hen-peckt-frigat [18 Oct.].* [London]: f. J. Deacon, [1679]. S.sh.
Below, AW wrote, '78-79', in pencil; and ᵛ, 'Hen peckt . . . '. Dupl. or similar ed. at Wood 61(5), missing.
Wood 417(12). Wing G511 (Wing, peckt frigat and 1688-95).

532. Hen Peckt Frigate. *A general summons for those belonging to the hen-peckt frigate, to appear at Cuckolds-Point [18 Oct.].* [London]: f. J. Deacon, [1688-95]. S.sh.
Missing in 1837. 'The Hen Peckt Frigat – Lond' in Whiteside cat. Dupl. or diff ed. at Wood 417(12) (dated by AW, 1678-9).
Wood 61(5). Wing G511 (3). *O, BL,* HH (Crawford, Rylands).

533. Hertfordshire. *The Hartford-shires murder. Or, bloody news from St. Albans.* [London]: f. F. Coles, T. Vere, J. Wright, a. J. Clarke, [1674-9]. S.sh. Obl. 2 pts.
[MS.] Wood E. 25(103). Wing H1602D (rare) (Wing, Hertford-shires).

534. Hewson, John*. *A hymne to the gentle-craft, or Hewsons lamentation.* London: f. C. Gustavus, [1660]. S.sh.
AW wrote, 'Januar: 1659[60]:'; ᵛ, 'Jan. 59', and '29' over a former no. '13' in pencil.
Wood 416(29). Wing H3884A. Wing [1661].

535. Higgs, Mary*. *A looking-glass for wanton women by the example . . . of Mary Higgs, . . . executed . . . for committing the odious sin of buggery, with her dog [18 July 1677].* [London]: f. P. Brooksby, [1677 ca.]. S.sh. Obl.
[MS.] Wood E. 25(145). Wing L3035 (rare) (Wing, London, [1680?]).

536. [Hill, Thomas]. *The dolefull dance and song of death; intituled, dance after my pipe. To a pleasant new tune.* [London]: f. F. Coles, J. Wright, T. Vere, a. W. Gilbertson, [1655-8]. S.sh. F. 60 in this vol.
'Another Copy Wood 402.48' (twice). Diff. ed. at Wood 402(14). ᵛ, AW wrote, 'This solemn Assise mentioned in the foregoing paper was kept in the court-house in the castle-yard at Oxōn 4. Jul. 1577. The judges who were infected & dyed with the Dampe, were Sʳ. Rob. Bell Baron of the Exchecquer & Sʳ Nich. Barham Serjeant at Law. – see Hist. et Antiq. Univ. Oxon. lb. 1. sub an. 1577'. AW quotes from this ballad in his discussion of the event in his Hist. & Antiq. 2.188-9 and LT 2.104.
Wood 401(31). Wing H2013A (rare).

537. [Hill, Thomas]. *The dolefull dance and song of death; intituled, dance after my pipe. To a pleasant new tune.* [London]: f. F. Coles, T. Vere, a. W. Gilbertson, [1658-64]. S.sh. P. 48 in this vol.
'Another Copy Wood 401.60'. Diff. ed. at Wood 401(31).
Wood 402(14). Wing H2013B (rare).

538. Honour of an Apprentice. *The honour of an apprentice of London.* [London]: f. F. Coles, T. Vere, a. W. Gilbertson, [1658-64]. S.sh. Obl. 2 pts. Ff. 63-4 in this vol.
Wood 401(33). Wing H2593A (rare).

539. Hood, Robin. *Robin Hood his rescuing Will Stutly from the sheriff and his men.* London: 'for F. Grove, on Snow-hill.', [1640 ca.]. S.sh. Obl. 2 pts. Ff. 35-6 in this vol.
Wood 401(18). Not in Wing (should be at R1631B). ESTCR 234834.

540. Hood, Robin. *A new song to drive away cold winter, between Robin Hood and the jovial tinker.* London: f. F. Grove, [1641 to 1660]. S.sh. Obl. 2 pts. Ff. 17-8 in this vol.
Wood 401(9). Wing N773A.

541. Hood, Robin. *The noble fisher-man: or, Robin Hoods preferment.* London: f. F. Coles, [1650?]. S.sh. Obl. 2 pts. Pp. 18-19 in this vol.
P. 17, AW wrote 'Dupl.' Diff. ed. at Wood 401(13).
Wood 402(5). Wing N1205A (rare).

542. Hood, Robin. *Robin Hood and the bishop. Shewing. How Robin Hood went to an old womans house.* London: f. F. Grove, [1650?]. S.sh. Obl. 2pts. Ff. 11-12 in this vol.
Wood 401(6). Wing R1628 (rare).

543. Hood, Robin. *Robin Hoods delight. Or, a merry combat.* London: f. J. Andrews, [1655?]. S.sh. Obl. 2 pts. Ff. 41-2 in this vol.
Wood 401(21). Wing R1635A (rare) (Wing, Hood's; [London]).

544. Hood, Robin. *Renowned Robin Hood: or, his famous archery truly related.* London: f. F. Grove, [1656?]. S.sh. obl. 2 pts. Pp. 10-11 in this vol.
Wood 402(3). Wing R1039C (3).

545. Hood, Robin. *Robin Hoods progresse to Nottingham, where hee met with fifteene forresters.* London: f. F. Grove, [1656]. S.sh. Obl. 2 pts. Pp. 14-5 in this vol.
Diff. ed. at Wood 401(19).
Wood 402(4). Wing R1641A (rare) (Wing, Hood's).

546. Hood, Robin. *Little John and the four beggers, a new merry song of Robin Hood.* [London]: f. W. Gilber[t]son, [1657]. S.sh. Obl. Ff. 33-4 in this vol.
Wood 401(17). Wing L2551A (rare) (Wing, 1657).

547. Hood, Robin. *Robin Hood and the tanner; or, Robin Hood met with his match.* [London]: f. W. Gilbertson, [1657]. S.sh. Obl. Ff. 9-10 in this vol. Conjoint with blank forms of the Excise Office printed on the both sides of the verso, i.e., of f. 9^v and f. 10^v. There are 2 forms on each verso side, 4 in all.
To have a space to annotate, AW pasted a blank sheet over the printed document, 'Excise Office, London } REceived the day and year above written, from [blank] Sub-Commissioners for Excise in the County of [blank] the sum of [blank]', on the ^{v} of f. 9 of this ballad. The blank was unpasted in 1881. On the blank AW wrote 17 lines on Robin Hood: 'There be some that prate [/] Of Robin Hood & of his bow . . . Which never shot therin I trow. [/] Robin Hood had his chief abode in Nottinghamshire in the time of K. Rich. I. who began to raigne in the yeare 1189. – [/] Joh. Major a Scotch historian [*Historia*, (Paris, 1521)], who lived in the time of K. Hen. 8. saith of him that <u>he was indeed an arch-robber–but the gentellest thief that ever was</u> – [/] Mich. Drayton the poet in his Poly-Albion in the 26. song, saith of him thus [/] From wealthy Abbots chests & churles abundant store, [/] What often times he took, he shar'd amongst the poore. [/] No Lordly Bishop came in lusty Robins way, [/] To him before he went, but for his pass must pay. [/] The widow in distress he gratiously releiv'd [/] And remedied the wrongs of many a virgin greiv'd –'.
Wood 401(5). Wing R1630D (two).

548. Hood, Robin. *The famous battle between Robin Hood and the curtall fryer.* [London]: 'Printed for F. Coles, T. Vere. W. Gilbertson', [1658 to 1664]. S.sh. Obl. 2 pts. Ff. 15-6 in this vol.
Wood 401(8). Not in Wing (should be F363A or R1629B). ESTCR 235008.

549. Hood, Robin. *The noble fisher-man. Or, Robin Hoods preferment.* [London]: f. F. Coles, T. Vere, a. W. Gilbertson, [1658 to 1664]. S.sh. Obl. Ff. 25-6 in this vol.
Diff. ed. at Wood 402(5).
Wood 401(13). Wing N1205B (rare).

550. Hood, Robin. *Renowned Robin Hood: or, his famous archery truely related.* London: f. F. Coles, T. Vere, a. J. Wright, [1663 to 1674]. S.sh. Obl. 2 pts. Ff. 31-2 in this vol.
Wood 401(16). Wing R1039D (two).

551. Hood, Robin. *Robin Hoods progresse to Nottingham, where hee met with fifteen forresters.* London: f. F. Coles, T. Vere, a. J. Wright, [1663 to 1674]. S.sh. Obl. Ff. 37-8 in this vol.
Diff. ed. at Wood 402(4).
Wood 401(19). Wing R1642 (two).

552. Hood, Robin. *Robin Hood and the shepheard: shewing, how Robin Hood, Little John.* London: f. J. Andrews, [1685]. S.sh. Obl. 2 pts. Ff. 13-14 in this vol.
Wood 401(7). Wing R1630B (rare).

553. Hood, Robin, and O. G. *Robin Hood newly reviv'd. [Conjoint with (on ^{v})] Englands joyfull holiday, or St. Georges-day . . . by me O. G.* (London): f. R. Burton (in Smithfield), [1661]. S.sh (r-v). Obl. Both, 2pts. Ff. 27-8 in this vol.
'This page and fol. 28b were covered with thick paper till 1881.' Apparently AW covered the leaf or had it done by his binder. A small part of the thick paper remains. See note at Wood 401(1), item 752.
Wood 401(14). Wing R1633 (two) (Wing, [1673?]) and G49 (rare, [1661]).

554. Houlbrook, William. Marleborough, of. *The loyal black-smith and no Jesuite; being a true relation how I . . . was betray'd.* London: f. the author, 1677. 8°. 2nd ed. Pp. [6], 72.
Wood 704(6). Wing H2940.

555. Hue and Song. *The hue-and-song after patience [sir P. Ward].* [London]: n.pub., 1683, 'Printed in the year of the Saints Tribulation'. S.sh.

Wood 276a(556) (not in Bodl. CD cat.). Wing H3297.

556. Hunting. *The hunting of the hare; with her last will and testament.* London: f. F. Coles, T. Vere, a. J. Wright, [1675]. S.sh. Obl. Pp. 79-80 in this vol.
In 1949 W. O. Hassall noted the omission of pp. 82-89 in the sequence of nos. Two, and possibly four, ballads were removed. See note at Wood 402(1), item 786.
Wood 402(22) (not in Bodl. CD cat.). Wing H3770A (rare).

557. Hutton, Luke. *Luke Huttons lamentation, which he wrote the day before his death.* London: f. F. C., J. W., T. V., W. G., [1655-8]. S.sh. Obl. 2 pts. Ff. 85-6 in this vol.
Wood 401(44). Wing H3840A (rare).

558. Ignoramus. *Ignoramus: an excellent new song.* London: f. A. Banks, 1681. S.sh.
AW wrote 'Dec.'
Wood 417(80). Wing I42A.

559. Irish Lasses Letter, pseud. *Irish lasses letter: or, her earnest request to Teague.* [London]: f. P. Brooksby, [1688]. S.sh.
AW wrote, 'Decemb. 1688. 2^d'.
Wood 417(166). Wing I1039 (rare) (Wing, no publ).

560. Isabella, Lady*. *The lady Isabellas tragedy, or, the step mothers cruelty.* [London]: f. E. A[ndrews], sold F. Coles, T. Vere, J. Wright, a. J. Clarke, [1664?]. S.sh. Obl. 2 pts.
[MS.] Wood E. 25(54). Not in Wing. ESTCR 235050.

561. J., T. *The merry mans resolution or, a London frollick.* London: f. R. Burton, [1655]. S.sh. Obl. 2 pts.
[MS.] Wood E. 25(38). Wing J40B (rare) (Wing, [London]).

562. Jack Presbyter, pseud. **Manuscript**. *Jack Presbiter, & a sonn of the pope [/] Had of late, a dispute of aright to the rope [and ^{v}] The duke of Monmouths letter to the king [1st line:] Disgrac'd undon; forlorne, made fortun's sporte [/] Bannishd the kingdome first & then ye court.* N.p.: n.pub., [1690?]. S.sh. (r-v) (14 stanzas; and 27 lines).
Not in AW's hand. The first t is possibly related to the printed Wing J61 (s.sh., at BL, unique).
Wood 417(24).

563. James 2*. *The Brimigham ballad on their royal highnesses [duke and duchess of York] return from Scotland [27 May].* London: f. N. Thompson, 1682. S.sh.
AW wrote 'May', and, at 'Hall–', '{ Hallifax'.
Wood 417(87). Wing B4694.

564. James 2*. *Englands royal renown, in the coronation of . . . king James the 2d. and . . . queen Mary, . . . the twenty third of April.* [London]: f. J. Deacon, 1685. S.sh.
Wood 417(143). Wing E3042 (two) (Wing, [1685]).

565. James 2*. *England's joyful welcome to the king, upon his return to White-hall, . . . Or, the loyal subjects delight [16 Dec.1688].* [London]: f. C. Dennisson, [1688]. S.sh. Obl.
James 2 fled shortly after this ballad was published by Dennison.
[MS.] Wood E. 25(107). Wing E2990A (two).

566. Jeffreys, George Jeffrey*. *The lord chancellors villanies discovered.* London: n.pub., 1689. S.sh.
AW wrote the name of the lord chancellor, 'Sr Georg Jeffryes', 'Feb. 1688[9]', and identified 'P–' as 'Pen'.
Wood 417(179). Wing L3043.

567. Jemmy. *Old Jemmy: an excellent new ballad.* London: N. Thompson, 1681. S.sh.
No. in a former bundle, '77' over '78'. Dupl. at Wood 417(57).
Wood 276a(557). Wing O204.

568. Jemmy. *Old Jemmy: an excellent new ballad.* London: N. Thompson, 1681. S.sh.
Dupl. at Wood 276a(557).
Wood 417(57). Wing O204.

569. Jerman of Clifton*. *A godly warning for all maidens by the example of Gods judgements shewed upon one Jermans wife of Clifton.* [London]: f. F. Coles, T. Vere, a. W. Gilbertson, [1670?]. S.sh. Obl. Ff. 105-6 in this vol.

'Clifton, Notts', in ink, not in AW's hand.
Wood 401(54). Wing G938A (rare, 2 at O) (Wing, used the imperf. Douce copy).

570. Jesuits. *The Jesuits exaltation, or, a preparation for a turn at Tyburn.* [London]: f. J. Back, 1688. S.sh.
AW wrote the date, 'January 1688/9'.
Wood 417(173). Wing J714 (rare) (Wing, no pub).

571. Jew, Saint Paul's Cathedral. *The Jewes high commondation [sic] of the metrapolitant [sic] cathedrall church of St. Paul.* [London]: f. F. Coles, T. Vere, a. W. Gilbertson, [1680]. S.sh. Obl. Ff. 125-6 in this vol.
Dupl. at Wood 401(56), item 661, where it is conjoint with *The Norfolk gentleman.*
Wood 401(64). Wing J741 (rare, 2 at O) (Wing, commendation).

572. Jew, Wandering. *The wandring Jew; or, the shoomaker of Jerusam [sic].* [London]: f. E. Wright, [1640, post]. S.sh. Obl. 2 pts. Ff. 123-4 in this vol.
Below publ., AW wrote 'An. 1620'.
Wood 401(63). Wing W696C (rare) (see STC 25015).

573. Job. *A job for a joyner or a good workman well imploy'd.* [London]: f. F. Coles, T. Vere, a. J. Wright, [1663-74]. S.sh. Obl.
[MS.] Wood E. 25(34). Wing J754 (rare) (Wing, London).

574. John and Betty. *The happy greeting of John and Betty, or, nothing better then true love.* [London]: f. F. Coles, T. Vere, J. Wright, a. J. Clarke, [1674 to 1679]. S.sh. Obl.
[MS.] Wood E. 25(138) (not in Bodl. CD cat.). Wing H668A (rare).

575. John and Betty. *The merry discourse between two lovers: or the joyful meeting betwixt John and Betty.* [London]: f. J. Clark, [1680 to 1689]. S.sh. Obl.
[MS.] Wood E. 25(77). Wing M1859 (rare) (Wing, London).

576. John and his Mistress. *An amorous dialogue between John and his mistris.* [London]: f. P. Brooksby, [1672 to 1695]. S.sh.
Missing in 1837. 'John & his Mistriss –' in Whiteside cat. Dupl. at [MS.] Wood E. 25(26). BL copy is cropped on all sides.
Wood 66(8). Wing A3020. *O, BL.*

577. John and his Mistress. *An amorous dialogue between John and his mistris.* [London]: f. P. Brooksby, [1672 to 1695]. S.sh. Obl. 2 pts.
Dupl. at Wood 66(8) (missing).
[MS.] Wood E. 25(26). Wing A3020.

578. Johnny and Jenny. *The new corant. Or the merry wooing of Jonney and Jenny.* [London]: f. F. Coles, T. Vere, J. Wright, and J. Clark, [1674-9]. S.sh. Obl.
[MS.] Wood E. 25(14). Wing N601 (rare) (Wing, London).

579. Jones, Henry. *The royal patient traveller. Or, the wonderful escapes of . . . king Charles.* [London]: f. the authour, [1660]. S.sh. Obl. Ff. 171-2 in this vol.
AW wrote the date, '1660', and 'Made by Hen. Jones an old Ballad-singer of Oxōn' (LT 1.352).
Wood 401(87). Wing J945 (two).

580. J[ordan], T[homas]. *An honest mans delight: or knavery made known.* London: f. R. Burton, [1641 to 1674]. S.sh. Obl.
[MS.] Wood E. 25(50). Wing J37A (rare) (Wing, under J., T.).

581. Jovial Tinker. *The jovial tinker; or, the willing couple.* London: f. E. Andrews, [168-?]. S.sh. Obl.
[MS.] Wood E. 25(45). Wing J1118 (rare).

582. K., W. *Newes from Hereford. Or, a wonderful and terrible earthquake.* [London]: f. F. Coles, T. Vere, a. W. Gilbertson, [1661]. S.sh. Obl. Ff. 179-80 in this vol.
At publisher, AW wrote '1661'. Above, classifications, not in AW's hand.
Wood 401(91). Wing K26A (rare).

583. Lambert, John*. *The gang or the nine worthies and champions, Lambert, &c.* London: f. C. Gustavus, [1660]. S.sh.

AW wrote, 'Januar: 1659[60]'; ᵛ, 'Jan. 59', and '34' replaced a former no. '18' in pencil.
Wood 416(34). Wing G198 (3).

584. Lambert, John*. *Roome for cuckolds: or my lord Lamberts entrance into Sodome and Gomorrah.*
London: f. L. M., [1660]. S.sh.
ᵛ, '27' over a former no. in pencil.
Wood 416(27). Wing R1924 (3).

585. Lambeth. *Five merry wives of Lambeth or, the carpenter cornuted.* [London]: f. R. Burton, [1680?].
S.sh. Obl.
[MS.] Wood E. 25(95). Wing F1113 (rare) (Wing, var., London and wants pub.).

586. Lamentable Ballad. *A lamentable ballad of the tragical end of a gallant lord, . . . performed by
a heathenish blackamore.* [London]: f. F. Coles, T. Vere, a. W. Gilbertson, [1658-64]. S.sh. Obl. 2 pts. Ff.
113-4 in this vol.
Wood 401(58). Wing L262A (one). Glasgow Univ. ('O' not recorded in Wing).

587. Lamentable List. *A lamentable list, of certaine hidious, frightfull, and prodigious signes.* London:
[J. Okes?] f. T. Lambert, [1638]. S.sh. Obl. 2 pts. Pp. 67-8 in this vol.
P. 69, scribbles, pasted over with blank leaf.
Wood 402(19). STC 15706.5 (rare).

588. Lancashire Gentleman. *An excellent ballad intituled, the unfortunate love of a Lancashire gentleman, and the hard fortune of a faire young bride.* London: f. F. Coles, T. Vere, and W. Gilbertson,
[1658-64]. S.sh. Obl. 2 pts.
[MS.] Wood E. 25(32). Wing E3784A (two) (Wing, [London]).

589. L[anfiere], T[homas]. *The wonder of wonders, or, the strange birth in Hampshire.* [London]: f. J.
Hose, a. E. Oliver, [1675?]. S.sh. Obl. 2 pts.
[MS.] Wood E. 25(104). Wing L362B (rare).

590. Law Lies. *Law lies a bleeding.* London: n.pub., 1659. S.sh. Obl. 2 pts. Ff. 167-8 in this vol.
Wood 401(85). Wing L633 (rare).

591. Leeds. *Inhumane, & cruel bloody news from Leeds in York-shire. Being a true relation of a young
man which intic't an other man's wife.* [London]: f. F. Coles, T. Vere, J. Wright, a. J. Clarke, [1674-9]. S.sh.
Obl. 2 pts.
[MS.] Wood E. 25(102). Wing I188B (rare) (Wing, Inhuman).

592. Leicestershire Frolic. *A Leicester-shire frolick; or, the valiant cook-maid.* [London]: f. R. Burton,
[1641-74]. S.sh. Obl. (cropped at top).
[MS.] Wood E. 25(28). Wing L971A (rare).

593. Litany from Geneva. *A litany from Geneva, in answer to that from St. Omers.* London: f. the use
of all true blue Brimighams, 1682. S.sh. obl.
AW wrote the month, 'May'.
Wood 417(89). Wing L2535.

594. [Llewellyn, Martin]. *Wickham wakened, or, the Quaker's madrigall in rime dogrell.* [Oxford]: [W.
Hall], 1672. 4°. Pp. [2], 8.
Flyleaf, upperᵛ, scribble, 'Elizabeth', not by AW. Tp, 'Ridicula', by AW, in pencil. P. 8, AW wrote, 'written
by Martin Lluellin. Med. Dʳ maior of Great *Wycomb [in margin, '*com. Bucks.'] or Wickham, Feb. 1671.
against a phisitian there that is a Quaker, & takes much from Lluellins practice. [/] I have heard since that
he was not the Author.' AO 4.44.
Wood 645(21). Wing L2629. Madan 2952.

595. London's Lamentation. *London's lamentation: or, an excellent new song on the loss of London's
charter.* [London]: N. T., [1683]. S.sh.
Wood 276a(544). Wing L2935.

596. Looking-Glass. *A looking-glass for drunkards: or the good-fellows folly.* London: f. R. Burton, [1641-
74]. S.sh. Obl.
[MS.] Wood E. 25(52). Wing L3016C (rare).

597. Looking-Glass for Traitors. *A looking-glass for traytors, or, high treason rewarded. . . . the exam-*

ination of . . . Edward Coleman. [London]: f. F. Coles, T. Vere, J. Wright, a. J. Clarke, [1678]. S.sh. Obl.
[MS.] Wood E. 25(33). Wing L3034A (rare).

598. Lorn, Lord of. *A pretty ballad of the lord of Lorn.* [London]: f. F. Coles, T. Vere, a. W. Gilbertson, [1658-64]. S.sh. Ob. 2 pts. Ff. 95-6 in this vol.
Wood 401(49). Wing P3320B (rare).

599. Lover's Mad Fits. *The lovers mad fits and fancies.* London: f. F. Coles, T. Vere, W. Gilbertson, a. J. Wright, [1663-5]. S.sh. Obl. 2 pts.
[MS.] Wood E. 25(39). Wing L3254E (rare) (Wing, lover's).

600. Lover's Pastime. *The lovers pastime, or an amorous encounter.* [London]: f. R. Burton, [1680?]. S.sh.
[MS.] Wood E. 25(90). Wing L3256 (rare) (Wing, London).

601. Love's Downfall. *Loves downfall. Being a sad and true relation of a young lady.* London: f. W. Thackeray, T. Passenger, a. W. Whitwood, [1678]. S.sh. Obl. 2 pts.
AW wrote the year, '(1678)'.
[MS.] Wood E. 25(61). Wing L3264cA (rare) (Wing, [London] and Passinger).

602. Love's Fancy. *Loves fancy, or, the young-mans dream.* London: f. F. Coles, T. Vere, a. J. Wright, [1675?]. S.sh.
[MS.] Wood E. 25(88). Wing L3266 (rare).

603. Love's Master Piece. *Loves master-piece: or, the coy lady over-come at last.* [London]: f. F. Coles, T. Vere, a. J. Wright, [1663 to 1674]. S.sh. Obl. 2 pts.
[MS.] Wood E. 25(87). Wing L3271 (rare) (Wing, London).

604. Love's Mistress. *Loves mistress: or, natures rarity.* [London]: f. F. Coles, T. Vere, J. Wright, a. J. Clarke, [1675]. S.sh. Obl.
[MS.] Wood E. 25(79). Wing L3272 (rare) (Wing, London).

605. Love's Wound. *Loves wound, and loves cure.* [London]: f. F. Coles, T. Vere, a. J. Wright, [1663 to 1674]. S.sh. Obl.
[MS.] Wood E. 25(137). Wing L3291 (rare, 3 at O) (Wing, London).

606. Love-Sick Shepherd. *The love-sick shepheard, or, the dying lovers reprieve.* [London]: f. R. Burton, [1641-74]. S.sh. Obl. 2 pts.
Dupl. at [MS.] Wood E. 25(74).
[MS.] Wood E. 25(12). Wing L3219 (rare, 3 at O).

607. Love-Sick Shepherd. *The love-sick shepheard, or, the dying lovers reprieve.* [London]: f. R. Burton, [1641-74]. S.sh. Obl. 2 pts.
Dupl. at [MS.] Wood E. 25(12).
[MS.] Wood E. 25(74). Wing L3219 (rare, 3 at O).

608. Loyal Health. *The loyal health. A court song.* London: f. A. Banks, 1682. S.sh.
Dupl. at Wood 417(79) and Wood 417(111).
Wood 276a(559). Wing L3347.

609. Loyal Health. *The loyal health. A court song.* London: f. A. Banks, 1682. S.sh.
Dupl. at Wood 276a(559) and Wood 417(79).
Wood 417(111). Wing L3347.

610. Loyal Health. *The loyal health. A court song.* London: f. A. Banks, 1682. S.sh.
AW wrote the date, 'published in Decemb. 1681'. Dupl. at Wood 276a(559) and Wood 417(111).
Wood 417(79). Wing L3347.

611. Loyal Litany. *The loyal letany.* [London]: n.pub., [1681]. S.sh. (r-v).
AW wrote, at beginning and at end, 'Ap. 1681'.
Wood 417(50). Wing L3348.

612. Loyal Protestants. *The loyal protestants new litany.* London: f. T. Davis, 1680. S.sh.
ᵛ, AW wrote the year, '1680'.
Wood 417(36). Wing L3359.

613. Loyal Sheriffs of London. *The loyal sherifs of London and Middlesex. Upon their election.* London: f. M. Thompson, 1682. S.sh.
Wood 417(110). Wing L3368.

614. Loyal Subject. *The loyal subjects littany.* London: n.pub., 1680. S.sh.
Wood 417(34) (349 in Bodl. CD cat.). Wing L3373.

615. Loyal Subject. *The second part of the loyal subject's litany.* London: f. B. Tooke, 1680. S.sh.
ᵛ, AW wrote the year, '1680'.
Wood 417(35). Wing S2309.

616. M., J. *Murther unparalel'd:. . . of Thomas Thin, . . . on Sunday the 12th. of February 1682.* London: for the author, J. M., 1682. S.sh.
LT 3.4.
Wood 276a(543). Wing M41 (two).

617. Mad-men's Hospital. *The mad-men's hospital: or, a present remedy to cure the Presbyterian itch. A poem.* London: N. T., 1681. S.sh. (r-v).
ᵛ, AW wrote below, 'Sept'.
Wood 417(64). Wing M241.

618. Maiden's Lamentation. *The maidens lamentation. Or, an answer to the seamen and souldiers.* [London]: f. F. Coles, T. Vere, J. Wright, a. J. Clarke, [1680?]. S.sh. Obl.
[MS.] Wood E. 25(139). Wing M270 (rare) (Wing, no publ.).

619. Maid's Complaint. *The maids complaint against the batchelors. Or, the young mens unkindness made known.* [London]: f. J. Coniers, [sic] at the Raven in Duck-Lane, [1675 ca.]. S.sh. Obl.
[MS.] Wood E. 25(9). Not in Wing. ESTCR 233336 (two) (lists Rawlinson and Douce copies only).

620. Man in Favour. *A man in favour, or, the way to preferment.* [London]: f. J. H., 1688. S.sh.
AW wrote the month, 'Jan.'
Wood 417(171). Wing M370.

621. Mansfield, Miller of. *A pleasant new ballad of the miller of Mansfield in Sherwood, and k. Henry the second.* [London]: f. F. Coles, T. Vere, W. Gilbertson, [1658-64]. S.sh. Obl. 2pts. Ff. 5-6 in this vol.
Wood 401(3). Wing P2554dA (rare).

622. Married Wife. *The married wives complaint of her unkind husband; or, a caution for maids to beware how they marry.* [London]: f. P. Brooksby, [1680?]. S.sh. Obl. 2 pts.
[MS.] Wood E. 25(148). Wing M713 (rare) (Wing, London).

623. Mattley, Dorothy*. *A most wonderful and sad judgement of God upon one Dorothy Mattley late of Ashover.* [London]: f. W. Gilbertson, [1662]. S.sh. Obl. Ff. 177-8 in this vol.
AW wrote, 'In the beg. of March 1661[2]'.
Wood 401(90). Wing M2933 (rare). (Wing, [1661]).

624. Merchant's Daughter. *The merchants daughter of Bristow [sic].* [London]: n.pub., [1635 ca.]. S.sh. Obl. Pp. 51-2 in this vol. Mutilated at top.
'Maudlin' added before t, in a later hand.
Wood 402(15). STC 3797.5 (rare).

625. Merlin. *Merlin reviv'd: or, an old prophecy lately found in a manuscript in Pontefract-castle.* [London]: n.pub., [1682]. S.sh.
Tp, AW wrote the year, '(1682)'. Listed as a ballad in Bodl. Library CD Catalogue of Ballads.
Wood 646(16) (Wood 656(16) in Bodl. CD cat.). Wing M1830.

626. Merry Country Maid. *The merry countrey maids answer to the countrey lovers conquest.* London: f. R. Burton, [168-?]. S.sh. Obl. 2 pts.
[MS.] Wood E. 25(124). Wing M1855 (two) (Wing, country maids).

627. Merry New Dialogue. *A merry new dialogue, between a courteous young knight, and a gallant milk-maid.* [London]: f. W. Thackeray, [1688-9]. S.sh. Obl. 2 pts.
[MS.] Wood E. 25(36). Wing M1871 (rare) (Wing, Thackery and London).

628. Miles, Abraham. *A sad and true relation of a great fire or two.* London: f. E. Andrews, [1662]. S.sh.

Obl. 2 pts. Ff. 189-90 in this vol.
AW wrote '1662', twice; above, 'Londinum', not in AW's hand, lined out.
Wood 401(96). Wing M2044 (rare).

629. Miles, Abraham. *A wonder of wonders; being a true relation of the . . . invisible beating of a drum, at the house of John Mompesson, . . . at Tidcomb.* [London]: f. W. Gilbertson, [1662]. S.sh. Obl. Ff. 193-4 in this vol.
AW wrote at 'Tidcomb', 'Tidworth' (later corrected to 'Tedworth') and below, 'mense Februar: 1662[3]'. Some notes in later hands, e.g., 'Tarlton the Jester is meant by this . . . wood-cut'. AW cites this ballad in Wood 467(2), item 1232. Prob. acquired 17 Feb., LT 1.468.
Wood 401(98). Wing M2045 (rare).

630. Modish London Life. *The modish London life: or, the merry meeting.* [London]: f. J. Conyers, [1688]. S.sh.
AW wrote, 'Bought at Oxon for a new Ballad 14. Feb. 1688[9]'. LT 3.299.
Wood 417(178). Wing M2380 (rare) (Wing, no publ).

631. Monck, George*. Albemarle, duke of. *Englands triumph. Or the rump routed by . . . generall George Monck.* London: f. J. Johnson, [1660?]. S.sh.
AW wrote, 'ffeb: 1659[60]'; ᵛ, 'Feb. 59', and '48' replaced a former no. '30' in pencil.
Wood 416(48). Wing E3064 (3).

632. Monck, George*. Albemarle, duke of. *The glory of the west or, the tenth renowned worthy, . . . general Monck's coming towards . . . London.* London: f. C. Gustavus, [1660]. S.sh.
AW wrote, 'Jan: 1659[60]'; ᵛ, 'Jan. 59', and replaced a former no. '23' with '39', in pencil.
Wood 416(39). Wing G881 (3).

633. Monck, George*. Albemarle, duke of. *The noble English worthies.* London: T. Milbourn, [16]59. S.sh.
ᵛ, AW wrote 'G. Monk 1659', and 'Decemb: 1659'.
Wood 416(24). Wing N1205 (3).

634. Moorfields. *News from Morefields: or, the wanton wag: or, Jone go to't.* [London]: f. J. Hose, [1690?]. S.sh. Obl. 2 pts.
[MS.] Wood E. 25(25). Wing N981 (rare) (Wing, London).

635. Much Ado. *Much a-do, about nothing: a song made of nothing.* London: f. T. Vere, [1660]. S.sh. Obl. Ff. 169-70 in this vol.
AW wrote the date, '1660'; later, round brackets added, in pencil.
Wood 401(86). Wing M3031 (rare).

636. Musgrave, Jack a*. *The lamentable ditty of the little Mousgrove, and the lady Barnet.* [London]: f. F. Coles, T. Vere a. W. Gilbertson, [1658-64]. S.sh. Obl. Ff. 91-2 in this vol.
ᵛ, AW wrote, 'Jack a Musgrave & Tho. Dacres of the north, living in an. 1543. (35. Hen. 8).'
Wood 401(47). Wing L270 (rare).

637. Musgrave, John*. *The lamentation of John Musgrave. Who was executed at Kendall.* London: f. F. Coles, J. W., T. Vere, and W. Gilbertson, [1660 ca.]. S.sh. Obl. 2 pts. Ff. 89-90 in this vol.
Wood 401(46). Not in Wing (should be before M3151). ESTCR 234986.

638. My Wife. *My wife will be my master. Or, the married-man's complaint against his unruly wife.* [London]: f. F. Coles, T. Vere, J. Wright, a. J. Clarke, [1674-9]. S.sh.
[MS.] Wood E. 25(68). Wing M3171B (rare).

639. Netherlands, News. *News form [sic] the Netherlands: being a full and true relation of a . . . battel fought betwixt the prince of Orange, and the French army [14 Aug. 1678].* [London]: f. F. Coles, T. Vere, J. Wright, a. J. Clarke, [1678-9]. S.sh. Obl.
[MS.] Wood E. 25(106) (not in Bodl. CD cat.). Wing N1009A (rare).

640. New Ballad. *A new ballade, to an old tune. Tom of Bedlam.* [London]: n.pub., [1660]. S.sh.
AW wrote, 'January: 1659[60]'; ᵛ, 'Ja. 59', and '30' over a former no. '15' in pencil.
Wood 416(31). Wing N574 (3).

641. New Ballad. *A new ballad, to the tune of, I'll tell thee, Dick.* [London]: n.pub., [1684]. S.sh.

Wood 276a(547). Wing N577.

642. New Ballad, London. *A new ballad, of Londons loyalty.* London: f. R. Sanders, 1681. S.sh.
Wood 417(60). Wing N566.

643. New Ballad, Protestant. *A new ballad, called, the protestants prophesie.* London: f. F. Coles, T.
Vere, J. Wright, a. J. Clarke, [1676]. S.sh. Obl.
AW wrote the date, 'Jan. or Feb. 1688[9].'
[MS.] Wood E. 25(117). Wing N556A (two) (Wing, called the).

644. New Ballad, Shewing. *A new ballad, shewing that a prince of England loved the kings daughter of
France, and the prince was slaine, and she after married to a forrester.* [London]: [f. F. Coles, T. Vere, a.
J. Wright, [1663-74]. S.sh. (mutilated). 2 pts.
[superscript v], verses, about Robin Hood, not legible, not in AW's hand. See similar ballads at Wood 401(61) and Wood
402(7), items 443, 440.
Wood 276b(102) (not in Bodl. CD cat.). Wing N572A (rare).

645. New Ballad, Trap. *A new balled [sic], called, trap, or, the young lass.* [London]: f. F. Coles, T. Vere,
a. J. Wright, [1675]. S.sh. Obl. 2 pts.
[MS.] Wood E. 25(30). Wing N557 (rare) (Wing, ballad and London and no publ.).

646. New Ballad, Warning. *A new ballad, intituled, a warning to youth, shewing he [sic] lewd life of a
merchants son of London.* [London]: f. F. Coles, T. Vere, a. W. Gilbertson, [1658-64?]. S.sh. Obl. 2 pts. Ff.
103-4 in this vol.
Wood 401(53). Wing N560 (two) (Wing, omits publ.; [1690?]).

647. New Courtier. *The new courtier: the tune is, Cloris, since thou art fled away.* London: P. L. f. F.
Coles, T. Vere, a. J. Wright, [1663-74]. S.sh. Obl. 2 pts.
[MS.] Wood E. 25(89). Wing N601B (rare).

648. New Game. *A new game at cards. Or, the three nimble shuffling cheaters.* N.p.: n.pub, [1680 ca.].
S.sh. Obl. 12 stanzas. Ff. 147-8 in this vol.
Wood 401(75). Wing N642 (rare) (Wing, f. F. Coles, J. Wright, T. Vere, a. W. Gilbertson; incorrect).

649. New Medley. *The new medley: or, a song composed of the rairest tunes.* London: f. F. Grove, [1652?].
S.sh. Obl. Ff. 153-4 in this vol.
Wood 401(78). Wing N668 (rare) (Wing, [1680?]).

650. New Royal March. *The new royal march.* [London]: f. J. Deacon a. J. Blare, [1686?]. S.sh.
AW wrote the year, '(1686)', in pencil.
Wood 417(149). Wing N747 (rare) (Wing, no pub).

651. New Thing. *A new-thing, of nothing: or, a song made of nothing.* London: f. T. Vere, 1664. S.sh.
[superscript v], AW wrote, '1664'.
Wood 416(106). Wing N785.

652. News from Hyde Park. *Newes from Hide-parke. Or a very merry passage.* London: E. Crowch,
f. F. Coles, T. Vere, a. J. Wright, [1663-74]. S.sh. Obl.
[MS.] Wood E. 25(92). Wing N971A (rare) (Wing, var., Crouch and wants F. Coles etc.).

653. News from the Coast. *News from the coast of Spain; or a true relation of brisk . . . encounter,
. . . betwixt the Tyger frigot, captain Harman commander; and the Schaherleas of Holland [13 Feb.].*
[London]: f. J. Clark at the Harp and Bible (? cropped at bottom), [1673-86]. S.sh. Obl. 2 pts.
[MS.] Wood E. 25(100) (not in Bodl. CD cat.). Not in Wing. Not in ESTCR (not Wing N1005A or ESTCR
43479).

654. News from the Navy. *News from the navy or a brife [sic] account of a most terrible, . . . sea fight.*
[London]: f. J. Clarke, [1672]. S.sh. obl.
Wood 276a(548). Not in Wing. Not in ESTCR.

655. News from the Stage. *News from the stage: or, a very new ballad, quite new, and not old [1st line:]
Ladies who fine as fi'pence are, [//] You men with bright rose noble hair.* London: n.pub., 1668. S.sh.
[superscript v], '1668', and, not in AW's hand, 'ffor M[r] Henry Foulis at Lincolne Colledge in Oxon.' LT 2.180. Repaired
with 2 slips; on pasted down side of one, ms. notes, not by AW.
Wood 416(117). Not in Wing. ('ghost', N1021, in 1948 ed. of Wing). Not in ESTCR.

656. Noble Gallant. *The noble gallant. Or, an answer to long days of absence.* [London]: f. J. Hose, [1675 ca.]. S.sh. Obl. 2 pts.
[MS.] Wood E. 25(80). Wing N1209A (rare).

657. Noble Riddle. *A noble riddle wisely expounded: or, the maids answer to the knights three questions.* [London]: f. F. Coles, T. Vere, J. Wright, a. J. Clarke, [1674-9]. S.sh. Obl.
[MS.] Wood E. 25(15). Not in Wing. Not in ESTCR (not Wing N1215 or N1215A, diff. pub., diff. illus.; not ESTCR 188690).

658. Noman, Dr., pseud. *A new miracle or dr. Noman's safe return from the grand Turks court at Constantinople.* London: f. J. Dean, [1684]. S.sh.
AW wrote, '1684'. Dupl. at 417(136).
Wood 276b(104). Wing N673 (Wing, Norman's).

659. Noman, Dr., pseud. and **Langley Curtis***. *A new miracle or dr. Nomans safe return from the grand Turks court at Constantinople. [conjoint with, printed inversely on ᵛ:] L–gley C–s [Langley Curtis] his lamentation in New gate.* London: f. J. Dean, [1684]. S.sh. (r-v).
AW wrote 'Dupl', in pencil. Dupl. of the 1st ballad at Wood 276b(104).
Wood 417(136). Wing N673 (3) (Wing, Norman's).

660. Norfolk Gentleman. *The Norfolke gentleman his last will and testament.* [London]: Printed [f. J. Wright], [1635 ca.]. S.sh. Obl. 2 pts. Pp. 63-4 in this vol. Mutilated at sides and bottom.
'See 2ⁿᵈ. ed. in 401.f.110', in a later hand. Diff. ed. at 401(56), which is conjoint with Wing J741.
Wood 402(18). STC 18644.5 (rare).

661. Norfolk Gentleman, and Jew. *The Norfolk gentleman his last will and testament. [Conjoint with (on ᵛ)] The Jewes high commondation [sic] of the metropolitant [sic] cathedrall church of St. Paul.* [London]: f. F. Coles, T. Vere, a. W. Gilbertson, [1658-64] and [1680]. S.sh. Obl. Ff. 109-110 in this vol.
'original edition is in N°. 402. f. 64', in a later hand. Diff. ed. of *The Norfolk Gentleman* at Wood 402(18). Dupl. of *Jewes high commondation* at Wood 401(64), item 571. ᵛ, former no., '109', visible above later 109 and a portion of the earlier '109' is beneath a trace of glue, which indicates that the number precedes the protective blank sheet which was pasted over the ballad; and, 'uncovered 1881'.
Wood 401(56). Wing N1236A (two), inner; Wing J741 [1680]) (rare, 2 at O), outer (Wing, the conjoint ballads are entered as single publications).

662. Northampton. *Strange and wonderful news from Northampton-shire, or, the discontented spirit.* [London]: f. R. Burton, sold W. Whitwood, [1675]. S.sh. Obl. 2 pts. Ff. 203-4 in this vol.
AW wrote the year, '1674'.
Wood 401(103). Wing S5867 (rare).

663. Norwich Litany. *The Norwich loyal litany.* London: f. A. Banks, 1682. S.sh.
AW wrote 'May'.
Wood 417(88) (not in Bodl. CD cat.). Wing N1341.

664. Oates, Titus*. *Oates well thresh't. Being a dialogue of country-make betwixt a farmer, and his man.* (London): (f. R. H.), (1681). S.sh. (r-v).
This item was moved here from Wood 276a(555) (it still has the Ashm. no. CCCCCLV, at the top). An Ashm. librarian entered the brief t in that vol., though not in this one, which only lists items 1-183, see Wood 417(1), item 781.
Wood 417(184). Wing O64.

665. Oates, Titus*. *Titus Tell-troth: or, the plot-founder [Titus Oates] confounded.* London: f. A. Banks, 1682. S.sh.
AW wrote the date, 'March 1681/2'.
Wood 417(85). Wing T1316.

666. Oh. *Oh! How I sigh, when I think on the man, &c. Or, the amorous virgin.* London: E. C. f. F. Coles, T. Vere, a. J. Wright, [1663-74]. S.sh. Obl.
[MS.] Wood E. 25(31). Wing O188B (rare).

667. Okey, John*. *Colonel John Okie's lamentation, or a rumper cashiered.* London: n.pub., 1660. S.sh.
AW wrote, 'March: 1659[60]:'; ᵛ, 'Mar. 59', and '63' replaced a former no. '45' in pencil.
Wood 416(63). Wing C5409A.

668. Ostend. *News from Ostend. Or the souldiers loving letter to his sweet-heart in London.* London: f. F. Coles, T. Vere, J. Wright, a. J. Clark, [1674-9]. S.sh. Obl.
[MS.] Wood E. 25(132). Wing N987B (rare).

669. Oxford. *Oxford in mourning, for the loss of the parliament. Or, London's loud laughter.* [London]: f. J. Jordan, [1681]. S.sh. Obl.
[MS.] Wood E. 25(96). Wing O856.

670. P., I. *A lecture for all sects and schismaticks to read.* London: 'Printed for F. Grove no Snow-hill', [1680?]. S.sh. Obl. 2 pts. Ff. 163-4 in this vol. (out of order).
Wood 401(83). Wing L834 (rare).

671. Pack of Hell-hounds. *A pack of hell-hounds, to hunt the devill: set forth in a new ballad.* [London]: n.pub., [1659?]. S.sh.
Wood 416(22). Wing P154 (rare) (Wing, devil and c. 1685).

672. P[arker], M[artin]. *The king and a poor northern-man.* London: 'for Francis Grove on Snow-hill', [1635 ca.]. S.sh. Obl. Pp. 45-6 in this vol.
'Another Copy Wood 401.49', in a later hand. Diff. ed. at Wood 401(25).
Wood 402(13). STC 19249.5 (rare).

673. [Parker], [Martin]. *The king and a poor northern-man.* London: 'for Grove on Snow=hill', [1635 ca.]. S.sh. No init. (M. P.). Obl. Ff. 49-50 in this vol.
'Another Copy Wood 402.45', in a later hand. Diff. ed. at Wood 402(13), (i.e., STC 19249.5).
Wood 401(25). Not in STC (should be at 19248.5). Not in ESTCR.

674. P[arker], M[artin]. *A description of a strange (and miraculous) fish, cast upon the sands . . . in Worwell.* London: f. T. Lambert, [1635?]. S.sh. Obl. 2 pts. Ff. 127-8.
Wood 401(65). STC 19226 (STC, no () in t).

675. P[arker], M[artin]. *Britaines honour. In the two valiant Welchmen.* London: E. G[riffin], sold [T. Lambert], [1640]. S.sh. Obl. 2 pts. Ff. 131-2.
AW pasted blank sheets on both verso sides. While the blank sheets are missing, the verso sides of the ballad that each had covered have the modern notes, '[This page was uncovered 1881.]'. The blank sheets had covered AW's schoolboy notes: f. 131ᵛ, 'Anthony', twice and a few scribbles, and, perhaps in AW's very early hand, though there seem to be 2 hands: To the tune of the nyghtinggall Come my lady away, lets make it holliday [/] Under neth this tree where none may see [/] Come sitt thee downe sweet heart by mee [/] and when I have gaind the fort [/] Ill show thee gallant sport [/] and soe they did agree [/] ha ha ha ha', and, 'Come my lad away lets make it [/] holliday under neth this tree [/] where none may see come sett set [sic] thee downe'; and a still shorter version, 'to the tune of the nightinggall [/] Come my lad away lets make it holliday under neth this' (for another transcription, see J. W. Ebsworth, ed., *The Bagford Ballads*, 1 (Hertford: The Ballad Society, 1876): 517). F. 132ᵛ, AW wrote his name, twice: 'Anthony Wood', and, prob. in his very early hand, 'I woult thoue god And lend me here [/] I hope thoud wout not do so my – deereest deere', and scribbles, and 3 very roughly drawn heads (see also note at Wood 401(70), item 703; and LT 1.48, Plate 1).
Wood 401(67). STC 19223 (rare).

676. P[arker], M[artin]. *An exact description of the manner how his majestie and his nobles went to the parliament, . . . the thirteenth day of Aprill.* London: sold [T. Lambert], [1640]. S.sh. Obl. Ff. 139-40 in this vol.
Wood 401(71). STC 19230 (rare).

677. P[arker], M[artin]. *Good newes from the north, truly relating how about a hundred of the Scottish rebels, . . . September, 1640.* London: E. G[riffin], sold [T. Lambert], 1640. S.sh. Obl. 2 pts. Ff. 133-4 in this vol.
A very formal 'Anthony'. ᵛ, scribbles by former owner and AW, pasted over by blank sheets.
Wood 401(68). STC 19238 (rare).

678. P[arker], M[artin]. *A true subjects wish. For the happy successe of our royall army.* London: E. G[riffin], sold [T. Lambert], [1640]. S.sh. Obl. 2 pts. Ff. 141-2 in this vol.
Wood 401(72). STC 19274 (rare).

679. P[arker], M[artin]. *The wandring Jews chronicle: or, the old historian . . . Finis. M. P.* London: f. F. Grove, [1655 to 1670]. S.sh. Obl. Ff. 121-2 in this vol.

Wood 401(62). Wing P447B (rare) (see S.T.C. 19279) (Wing, chronicle;).

680. Passing Bell. *[1st line, above emblem] A passing bell towling to call us to mind . . . to the tune of triumph and joy [1st line below emblem] Hark man what I thy God shal speak.* [London]: n.pub., [1625?]. S.sh. 2 pts. (mutilated, both at top and bottom).
H. E. Rollins, *Pepysian Garland* (1922), p. 185 (no. 2043).
Wood 276b(103) (not in Bodl. CD cat.). STC 19460 (rare).

681. Pattern. *A pattern of true love, to you I will recite, between a fair young lady, and a courteous knight.* [London]: f. F. Coles, T. Vere, a. J. Wright, [1663-74]. S.sh. Obl.
[MS.] Wood E. 25(35). Wing P872C (rare).

682. Pensive Maid. *The pensive maid, or, the virgins lamentation for the loss of her lover.* [London]: f. P. Brooksby, [1672-80]. S.sh. Obl.
[MS.] Wood E. 25(3). Wing P1434.

683. Petre, Edward*. *A new song of lulla by, or, father Peters's policy discovered.* [London]: n.pub., 1688. S.sh. Obl.
AW wrote the month, 'Jan.'
[MS.] Wood E. 25(110) (not in Bodl. CD cat.). Wing N765B (two) (Wing, Peter's).

684. Petre, Edward*. *Popery routed: or, father Petres's farewel to London.* London: n.pub., 1689. S.sh.
AW wrote the date, 'Janu. 1688[9]'.
Wood 417(170). Wing P2925 (two) (Wing, Petre's).

685. P[hillips], J[ohn]. *Jockey's farewell to Jenny or the Scottish loath to depart.* London: f. R. Burton, [1670?]. S.sh. Obl.
[MS.] Wood E. 25(91). Wing P2089 (two).

686. Pleasant Song. *A pleasant song made by a souldier, whose bringing up had been dainty: and partly by those affections of his unbridled youth.* [London]: f. F. Coles, J. Wright, T. Vere, a. W. Gilbertson, [1655-8]. S.sh. F. 59 in this vol.
Wood 401(30). Wing P2559A (rare).

687. Plow-Man. *The plow-mans prophesie. Or, the country-mans calculation.* [London]: f.J. Hose, [1680?]. S.sh. Obl.
[MS.] Wood E. 25(81). Wing P2616 (rare) (Wing, London).

688. Poor Man. *The poor man, the merchant, and the king.* London: f. C. Tyus, [1660 ca.]. S.sh. Obl. 2 pts. Ff. 51-2 in this vol.
Wood 401(26). Wing P2864 (rare).

689. Poor Robin. *Poor Robin and Betty or, sport upon sport.* [London]: f. R. Burton, [1670?]. S.sh. Obl.
[MS.] Wood E. 25(59). Wing P2874 (rare).

690. Pope. *The popes great year of jubilee. Or, the Catholicks encouragement for . . . popery.* [London]: f. F. Coles, T. Vere, a. J. Wright, [1663-74]. S.sh.
AW wrote the year, '1678'; ᵛ, '1678'.
Wood 416(128). Wing P2932A (rare) (Wing, Pope's).

691. P[ope], W[alter]. *The musical shepeherdess [sic], or, Dorinda's lamentation for the loss of Amintas.* [London]: f. J. Hose, [1660 to 1675]. S.sh. Obl.
[MS.] Wood E. 25(6) (not in Bodl. CD cat.). Wing P2913A (rare) (Wing, shepherdess).

692. [Pope, Walter]. *The Catholick ballad: or an invitation to popery.* London: f. H. Brome, 1674. S.sh.
AW wrote, 'Said to be written by Dʳ Walt. Pope M. Dʳ Fellow of the royall Societie.' (see LT 2.185; AO 4.724f.); ᵛ, '1674' and 'Dupl.' Dupl. now in the Euing Collection, no. 24. On that ballad, AW wrote, 'By Walter Pope A. m. of the royal society somtimes Fellow of Wadham Coll.'
Wood 416(126). Wing P2906.

693. [Pope, Walter]. *Room for a ballad, or, a ballad for Rome. Being a continuation of the Catholick ballad.* [London]: f. B. Harris, [1674?]. S.sh. Obl. 2 pts.
AW wrote the year, '1674', in pencil. A continuation of Wood 416(126).
Wood 416(127). Wing P2915.

694. P[ope], W[alter]. *The forc'd marriage. Or, unfortunate Celia.* [London]: f. E. Oliver, [1676 to 1685]. S.sh. Obl.
Dupl. at [MS.] Wood E. 25(143).
[MS.] Wood E. 25(24). Wing P2910.

695. P[ope], W[alter]. *The forc'd marriage. Or, unfortunate Celia.* [London]: f. E. Oliver, [1676 to 1685]. S.sh. Obl.
Dupl. at [MS.] Wood E. 25(24).
[MS.] Wood E. 25(143). Wing P2910.

696. Pope, [Walter]*. *Doctor Popes wish.* London: f. T. Horne, 1693. Fol. Pp. [2], 2.
Tp, AW wrote, 'Bought of Mʳ West 13 Oct. 1693'. LT 3.432.
Wood 417(183). Wing P2916 (3) (Wing, Pope's).

697. Pot Companions. *The pot companions: or, drinking and smoaking preferr'd before caballing and plotting.* [London]: f. R. Crumbdy, 1682. S.sh.
AW wrote the year, '1682' (the original date was overwritten by '1688').
Wood 417(93). Wing P3026 (rare).

698. Powel*. *Here is a true and perfect relation from the Faulcon at the Bank-side; . . . of one mr. Powel.* [London]: f. F. Coles, T. Vere, a. W. Gilbertson, [1661]. S.sh. Obl. Ff. 183-4 in this vol.
AW wrote '1661'; 'Powel' underscored in t.
Wood 401(93). Wing H1548 (rare).

699. Power. *The power and pleasure of love, is here describ'd an antidote of joy.* [London]: f. F. Coles, T. Vere, J. Wright, a. J. Clarke, [1674-9]. S.sh. Obl.
[MS.] Wood E. 25(144). Wing P3102.

700. Praise. *The praise of brewers: or, the brewers bravery.* [London]: f. F. Coles, T. Vere, a. J. Wright, [1663-74]. S.sh. Obl.
[MS.] Wood E. 25(63). Wing P3167 (rare).

701. Present State of England. *The present state of England: a pleasant new true ballad.* London [1st printed in Edinburgh]: n.pub., 1681. S.sh. (mutilated at bottom).
Wood 417(59). Wing P3261.

702. P[rice], L[aurence]. *A monstrous shape. Or a shapelesse monster.* [London]: M. F[lesher] f. T. Lambert, [1639]. S.sh. Obl. 2 pts. Ff. 135-6 in this vol.
AW added the year, '1640', a drawing of the monstrous head, and a scribble. ᵛ, covered by a pasted over leaf, scribbles.
Wood 401(69). STC 20317 (rare).

703. P[rice], L[aurence]. *A new Spanish tragedy. Or, more strange newes . . . September the 6, . . . 11 of October last.* London: f. S. Rand, [1639]. S.sh. Obl. 2 pts. Ff. 137-8 in this vol.
AW wrote the year, '1640 - or 41' and 'Anthony'. 'Hispania', in a later hand. F. 137ᵛ, a ballad, cropped, possibly in AW's hand: 'Good morro go- gossipe Joanne, and where have you been walking [/] I have for you at home abuch– [?] full of talking, gossepe Joanne [/] Your brinded cow and mine did goe to bull together I do[ubt?] [/] it will not hold it was shuch blustering wheather [/] gossope Joanne my d– [?] did eat asnale the gutes did bust asu[nd] [/] er the hornes hung out at tale and was not that a won[der] [/] gosspe Joanne', and scribbles; f. 138ᵛ, 'Anthony Wood amen 16 Anthony', scribbles, and a religious poem, 2 and 16 lines, similar to but more complete than that found at Wood 401(67), item 675, apparently in AW's schoolboy hand, not completely legible and with numerous misspellings and fragmented lines: 'I wolt thou god And me lend here', and 'I wolt thou god Ande lend me here I doe not so my deere of deere thy poore folk part the cloud of skie but . . . '.
Wood 401(70). STC 20318 (rare) (Wing, remove N777) .

704. P[rice], L[aurence]. *Flora's farewell: or, the shepherds love-passion song.* London: f. F. G[rove] on Snow-hill, [1641 to 1661]. S.sh. Obl. 2 pts.
[MS.] Wood E. 25(48). Wing P3364C (two).

705. P[rice], L[aurence]. *Joy after sorrow, being the sea-mans return from Jamaica: or, the lovely lasses late lamentation.* [London]: f. T. Vere, [1648]. S.sh. Obl.
AW wrote the year, '1648'.
[MS.] Wood E. 25(60). Wing P3369 (rare).

706. P[rice], L[aurence]. *The Quakers fear. Or, wonderfull . . . news from . . . Colchester . . . how one James Parnel.* [London]: f. F. Coles, J. Wright, T. Vere, a. W. Gilbertson, [1655 to 1658]. S.sh. Obl. Ff. 165-6 in this vol. (out of order).
See Joseph Smith, *Bibliotheca Anti-Quakeriana* (1873): 10, gives the date of publ., 1656.
Wood 401(84). Wing P3380A (rare).

707. [Price, Laurence]. *A new merry dialogue between John and Bessee the wo [sic] lusty brave lovers of the countrey.* [London]: f. W. Gilbertson, [1656]. S.sh. Obl. (cropped at bottom).
[MS.] Wood E. 25(85). Wing P3379 (two) (Wing, London).

708. [Price, Laurence]. *Win at first, lose at last; or, a new game at cards.* London: f. F. Grove, [1660?]. S.sh. (2 shs.). 2 pts. with heading at 2nd pt. Pp. 71-2 in this vol.
'See Another Copy Wood 401.149', in a later hand. Diff. ed., without a heading at pt. 2, at Wood 401(76).
Wood 402(20). Wing P3389A (rare).

709. [Price, Laurence]. *Win at first, lose at last; or, a new game at cards.* London: f. F. Grove, [1660?]. S.sh. Obl. 2 pts. without heading at 2nd pt. Ff. 149-50 in this vol.
'Another Copy Wood 402.71', in a later hand. Diff. ed., with heading at 2nd pt., at 402(20).
Wood 401(76). Wing P3389A (rare, 2 at O).

710. Price, Laurence, and No Fool. *Robin Hoods golden prize . . . L. P. [Conjoint with (on ᵛ)] No fool to the old fool: or, a cuckold in Querpo.* London: f. F. Grove [and] f. F. G., [1650?]. S.sh. (r-v). Obl. ᵛ, 2 pts. Ff. 39-40 in this vol.
F. 39, 'uncovered 1881'. Apparently AW covered f. 39 himself or had it done by his binder. No part of the thick paper remains. See note at Wood 401(1), item 752.
Wood 401(20). Wing P3382A (rare) (Wing, [London]). The verso ballad is not entered separately in Wing; see L1279A. ESTCR 182074 and 234836.

711. Private. *Private occurrences; or, the transactions of the four last years.* [London]: n.pub., [1688]. S.sh.
AW wrote, 'In the beginning of Dec.1688'; underscored and identified 4 allusions in this ballad: 'Fath Edm. Peters a Jesuit, one of the privie councell', 'James E. of Monmouth', 'Cuckold – Lord Ford Grey of Werk', and 'Sʳ Joh. Shorter' (and he simply repeated the printed 'Pres. Bob'); filled in name at initials P'rince' of W'ales' (James); and wrote 'qu[aere]' at an obscure reference to 'The Bricklayer'.
Wood 417(167). Wing P3531.

712. Psalm Sung. *A psalme sung by the people, before the bone-fires, made in . . . London.* [London]: n.pub., [1660]. S.sh.
AW wrote, '1659[60]'; ᵛ, '59', and '40' replaced a former no. '25' in pencil.
Wood 416(40). Wing P4148 (two).

713. Quakers' Farewell. *The Quakers farewel to England, or their voyage to New Jersey.* London: f. F. G[rove], 1675. S.sh.
ᵛ, AW wrote the year, '1675', in pencil.
Wood 416(129). Wing Q23 (two).

714. R., J., and H. C. *The taming of a shrew: or, the onely way to make a bad wife good [signed J. R. and at end, H[enry] C[rouch?]].* [London?]: f. F. Coles, in Wine [sic] street neer Hatten=Garden, [1670?]. S.sh. obl. In 3 leaves, no p. nos. or sigs. 23 stanzas and a conclusion.
Tpᵛ, AW wrote 'Before the marr[iages]'.
Wood 654a(4). Wing R32A (two) .

715. R., T. *John Arm-strongs last good night. Declaring how John Arm-strong and his eightscore men.* London: f. F. Grove, [1658?]. S.sh. (2). 2 pts. Pp. 59-60 in this vol.
'Another Copy Wood 401.93', in a later hand. Dupl. at Wood 401(48).
Wood 402(17). Wing R84C (rare, 2 at O).

716. R., T. *John Arm-strongs last good night. Declaring how John Arm-strong and his eightscore men.* London: f. F. Grove, [1658?]. S.sh. (2). 2 pts. Ff. 93-4 in this vol.
'Another Copy Wood 402.59', in a later hand. Dupl. at Wood 402(17). F. 93ᵛ, AW wrote, 'Dʳ John Spotswood Archb. of S. Andrews in Scotland in the History of the Church of Scotland [Spottiswood, Wing S5022] - Lib. VI sub an. 1596 – saith [/] That Will. Armstrong commonly called Will of Kinmouth was a notorious theif among the Scotch borders, an. 1596, (38. of Eliz) in the beginning of which yeare, he

was taken prisoner by the English & committed prisoner to Carlile [sic] castle, concerning whose escape thence he hath a larg storie worth the reading. [/] Will. Sanderson Esquire in his Life & Death of Jam. V[I]. King of Scots takes from him the said story, p. 190. 191 without any acknowledgments, & curtailes & spoyles it –' (i.e., Wood 660e(2), item 5741).
Wood 401(48). Wing R84C (rare, 2 at O).

717. Reading. *Reading fight. To the tune of Lylliburlero; or, o brother Teague, dost hear the decree?*. (London): n.pub., (1689). S.sh. (r-v).
ᵛ, AW wrote the date, 'Januar. 1688[9]'.
Wood 417(169). Wing R454 (rare).

718. Reading Skirmish. *The Reading skirmish: or, the bloody Irish routed by the victorious Dutch.* [London]: f. J. D[eacon], 1688. S.sh. Obl.
AW wrote the month, 'Decemb.'
[MS.] Wood E. 25(113). Wing R455.

719. Rebellion. *Rebellion given over house-keeping: or, a general sale of rebellious houshould [sic] stuff.* [London]: f. J. W[right], J. C[lark], W. T[hackeray], T. P[assinger], a. M. C[oles], [1688]. S.sh. Obl.
[MS.] Wood E. 25(21). Wing R593 (two) (Wing, or a . . . househould).

720. Redemptio, Scotland. *Redemptio ab aquilone, or some good out of Scotland.* [London]: n.pub., [1660]. S.sh.
AW wrote, '1659[60]: ffeb'; ᵛ, 'Feb. 59', and '46' over a former no. '28' in pencil.
Wood 416(46). Wing R660aA (rare) (Wing, 1659).

721. Religion. *Religion made a cloak for villany. Or, the loyal subjects delight, who is neither Whigg nor Tory.* [London]: f. J. W., J. C., W. T., a. T. P., [1681-4]. S.sh. Obl.
[MS.] Wood E. 25(78). Wing R901.

722. Rich and Flourishing Cuckold. *The rich and flourishing cuckold well satisfied.* [London]: f. F. Coles, T. Vere, J. Wright, a. J. Clarke, [1674-9]. S.sh. Obl.
[MS.] Wood E. 25(123). Wing R1366 (rare) (Wing, London).

723. Robbery. *Robbery rewarded, or, an account of five notorious high-way-men's exploits [17 March last past].* [London]: f. P. Brooksby, [1674]. S.sh. Obl.
[MS.] Wood E. 25(108). Wing R1570B (rare).

724. Robin and Doll. *The controversie between Robin and Dolls house-keeping.* [London]: f. R. B[urton], [1690?]. S.sh. Obl.
[MS.] Wood E. 25(135). Wing C5977 (rare) (Wing, Doll's).

725. R[obins], T[homas]. *Robin Hood and the beggar.* London: f. F. Grove, [1660 ca.]. S.sh. Obl. 2 pts. Ff. 23-4 in this vol.
Wood 401(12). Wing R1657A (rare).

726. R[obins], T[homas]. *Robin Hoods chase: or, a merry progresse between Robin Hood and king Henry.* N.p.: n.pub., [1680 ca.]. S.sh. Obl. 2 pts. Ff. 29-30 in this vol.
Wood 401(15). Not in Wing (should be at R1657F-H). Not in ESTCR.

727. R[obins], T[homas]. *Robin Hood and the butcher.* London: f. F. Grove, [1660?]. S.sh. Obl. Ff. 19-20 in this vol.
Wood 401(10). Wing R1657D (two).

728. Russell, William*. *The lord Russel's last farewel to the world.* [London]: f. J. Dean, 1683. S.sh.
Wood 417(123). Wing L3055 (3) (Wing, Russels last farewell and London).

729. S., E. *The lamenting ladies last farewel to the world. . . . Finis. ES.* London: 'Printed for Tho Vere', [1656?]. S.sh. Obl. Pp. 75-6 in this vol.
Wood 402(21) (not in Bodl. CD cat.). Wing L295 (two) ('O' not recorded in Wing).

730. S., S. *St. George for England, and st. Dennis for France, O hony soite qui maly pance.* [London]: f. W. Gilbertson, [1650 to 1659]. S.sh. Obl. Ff. 117-8 in this vol.
Wood 401(60). Wing S148C (rare).

731. S., S. *Jockies lamentation, whose seditious work was the loss of his country.* London: f. F. Grove,

[1657?]. S.sh. Obl. Ff. 151-2 in this vol.
'Scotia', not in AW's hand.
Wood 401(77). Wing J759A (rare) (Wing, Jockie's).

732. Sailor's Departure. *The saylors departure from his dearest love, wishing that still (to him) she'd constant prove.* London: f. J. Wright, [1667]. S.sh. Obl. 2 pts.
[MS.] Wood E. 25(141). Wing S289D (rare).

733. Saint Turn'd Curtezan. *The saint turn'd curtezan: or, a new plot discover'd by a precious zealot.* [London]: (f. the use of the Protestant-Cobler in Pell-Mell), [1681]. S.sh. 2 pts.
AW wrote the year, '1680 81', in pencil.
Wood 417(65). Wing S359.

734. Sanders, George. *Save a thief from the gallows, . . . The confession and repentance of George Sanders.* [London]: f. F. Coles, T. Vere, a. W. Gilbertson, [1658-64]. S.sh. Obl. 2 pts. Ff. 143-4 in this vol.
Wood 401(73). Wing S772A (rare).

735. Scott, James*. Monmouth, duke of. *The duke of Monmouth's triumph over all his misfortunes. Who is now pardoned and entertained at court.* [London]: f. J. Dean, 1683. S.sh.
Wood 660c(7). Wing D2512A (two) ('O' not recorded in Wing).

736. Scott, James*. Monmouth, duke of. *The glory of the west, or, the virgins of Taunton-dean.* London: f. J. Dean, 1685. S.sh.
Wood 417(144). Wing G882.

737. Scott, James*. Monmouth, duke of. *Monmouth degraded or James Scot, the little king in Lyme.* London: f. J. Dean, 1685. S.sh.
AW wrote, 'published in the latter end of June 1685'; ᵛ, address, not in AW's hand, 'For Mʳ Coleby [William Colby] ffellowe of Merton College in Oxford', and scribbles.
Wood 417(140). Wing M2431 (two).

738. Scott, James*. *Monmouth worsted in the west: or, his care and grief for the death of his poor souldiers.* [London]: f. G. H., 1688. S.sh. Obl.
AW wrote, 'reprinted', presumably after Wing M2432 was published.
[MS.] Wood E. 25(116 (not in Bodl. CD cat.). Wing M2433aA (two).

739. Sefautian, pseud. *Sefautian's farewel: or, fair Silvia's matchless cruelty.* [London]: f. J. Deacon, 1688. S.sh.
Wood 417(159). Wing S2412A (two) (Wing, farewel;).

740. Sefautian, and Silvia, pseud. *An answer to Sefautian's farewell: or, fair Silvia's dying complaint.* [London]: f. J. Deacon, 1688. S.sh.
Wood 417(160). Wing A3374 (Wing, Sefautians and [1685-88]).

741. [Sempill, Robert]. *'Songs, the kings Complaint', [i.e.,] The kingis complaint.* [Edinburgh]: [R. Lekpreuik], [1567]. S.sh.
Missing in 1837. This vol. contained seven Scottish ballads, all printed in 1570. They exist together only in the British Library Roxburghe Collection in III (1-7); see *The Roxburghe Ballads*, ed. Wm. Chappell (1871), 1.iii. John Bagford was familiar with this vol. while it was yet in the Ashmolean Museum, for he wrote in his commonplace book (BL MS Harl. 5910 I f. 239ᵛ), 'Anto: a Woods Collection. 399:' and the titles of the ballads in this vol. in the order in which they appeared in 399. The vol. prob. disappeared at the same time as Wood 400, and many ballads in that vol. also found their way into the Roxburghe Collection now in the BL. See 'The Location of Two Lost Volumes of Ballads, Wood 399 and Wood 400', *BLR*, 15 (April 1996): 260-291.
Wood 399(1). STC 22200 (rare, *BL* Rox. III.3; Rox. Ballads 8.371ff.).

742. [Sempill, Robert]. *The admonitioun to the lords.* Edinburgh: R. Lekpreuik, 1570. S.sh.
Missing in 1837. This is now in the Rox. collection. see *The Rox. Ballads*, ed. Wm. Chappell (1871), 1.iii.
Wood 399(3). STC 22187 (rare, *BL* Rox. III.5; Rox. Ballads 8.379ff.).

743. [Sempill, Robert]. *The cruikit liedis the blinde.* Edinburgh: R. Lekpreuik, 1570. S.sh.
Missing in 1837. This is now in the Rox. collection. see *The Rox. Ballads*, ed. Wm. Chappell (1871), 1.iii.
Wood 399(6). STC 22191 (2, *BL* Rox. III.4; Rox. Ballads 8.375ff.) & L11(PRO)).

744. [Sempill, Robert]. *Maddeis lamentation.* Edinburgh: R. Lekpreuik, 1570. S.sh.
Missing in 1837. This is now in the Rox. collection. see *The Rox. Ballads*, ed. Wm. Chappell (1871), 1.iii.
Wood 399(7). STC 22201 (rare, *BL* Rox. III.6; Rox. Ballads 8.384ff.).

745. [Sempill, Robert]. *Maddeis proclamatioun.* [Edinburgh]: [R. Lekpreuik], [1570]. S.sh.
Missing in 1837. This is now in the Rox. collection. see *The Rox. Ballads*, ed. Wm. Chappell (1871), 1.iii.
Wood 399(5). STC 22201.5 (rare, *BL* Rox. III.7; Rox. Ballads 8.388ff.) .

746. [Sempill, Robert]. *The poysonit schot.* Edinburgh: R. Lekpreuik, 1570. S.sh.
Missing in 1837. This is now in the Rox. collection. see *The Rox. Ballads*, ed. Wm. Chappell (1871), 1.iii.
Wood 399(4). STC 22204 (2, *BL* Rox. III.1; Rox. Ballads 8.366ff. & L5).

747. [Sempill, Robert]. *The regentis tragedie ending with ane exhortatioun.* Edinburgh: R. Lekpreuit, 1570. S.sh.
Missing in 1837. This is now in the Rox. collection. see *The Rox. Ballads*, ed. Wm. Chappell (1871), 1.iii.
Wood 399(2). STC 22205 (2, *BL* Rox. III.2; Rox. Ballads 8.356ff. & L5).

748. [Shadwell, Thomas]. *The delights of the bottle. Or, the town-galants declaration for women and wine.* [London]: f. P. Brooksby, a. R. Burton, [1675]. S.sh. Obl. 2 pts.
AW wrote, 'made about 1650'.
[MS.] Wood E. 25(58). Wing S2841A (two) (Wing, London).

749. She. *She is bound but won't obey; or, the married man's complaint in choosing a wife.* [London]: f. F. Coles, T. Vere, J. Wright, a. J. Clarke, [1680]. S.sh. Obl.
[MS.] Wood E. 25(67). Wing S3053 (rare) (Wing, London).

750. [Shenton, Francis]. *A true relation of a notorious cheater one Robert Bullock, lately done in Oxford.* [London]: n.pub., [1663]. S.sh. Obl. Pp. 91-2 in this vol.
'Another Copy 401.198' in a later hand. Dupl. at Wood 401(100). AW made extensive notes in the margins, identifying places and persons mentioned in the ballad, and giving dates to events, e.g., Bullock, he recorded, was '*from Reding'; at 'I took of a rich widdow', he wrote, 'Mistris [blank] Robinson widdow of Thomas Robinson Bookseller'; at Bullock's stealing from 'a rich Sadler', 'Jo: Numan' and at 'With Combes', 'Cumbes the shomaker over aganst [sic] S. Maries church'; at his stealing of brass, 'from Sherrard the Brasier', and from 'Thurstons care', 'Thurton the upholsterer'; other identifications: 'Woodfeild the Joyner.'; 'Jennings a Buttonmaker, latly under Butler of New-coll: and his sister'; Roger Frye, 'the Ale Brewer in St Ebbs parish who wa[s] to have served h[im] in with ale. Gardiner a [joy]ner in Cat street.' (in printed text, AW lined out the 'c' in 'Gardiner the Scot'; Edward Bartlet, 'The university ca[rrier]'; and at end, at 'By one of Oxford', 'viz: Francis Shenton Apothecary living in St Peters in the Baillye: this buisness [sic] was acted, & the Ballad came out, all in the mounth of November. A. D. 1663'. See LT 1.504-6 for a transcript of the ballad and AW's notes in both copies.
Wood 402(23). Wing S3101 (rare, 2 at O). Madan 2627.

751. [Shenton, Francis]. *A true relation of a notorious cheater one Robert Bullock, lately done in Oxford.* [London]: n.pub., [1663]. S.sh. Obl. Ff. 197-8 in this vol.
'Another Copy 402.91', in a later hand. Dupl. at Wood 402(23), where AW wrote similar notes. AW underscored in red ink persons mentioned or alluded to in this ballad and wrote notes of explanation; e.g., Bullock, he recorded, was 'from Reading in Berks.'; at 'I took of a rich widdow', he wrote, 'Mistris . . . Robinson widdow of Thom. Robinson bookseller, at the west end of S. Maries church.'; at Bullock's stealing from 'a rich Sadler', 'Joh. Newman' and at 'With Combes', ' . . . Combes a sho-maker living against S. Maries church'; at his theft of gloves from Thomas Bland, 'living againt S. Maries church, father to . . . . wife of Rich Witt LL. Bac.' and of brass, 'from . . . . Sherard the Brasier in S. Mich. parish.'; from 'Thurstons care', 'Edmund Thurton upholsterer, in Allsaints parish'; identifications: 'Woofield living in S. Mich. parish.'; 'Jennyngs a Button maker lately the crop-ear'd under-Butler of New-coll.'; at Roger Frye, 'an Ale-Brewer in S. Ebbs parish who was to have served him with ale.'; at 'Gardiner a sottish and drunken joyner living in Cat street' (and he lined out the 'c' in the printed 'Scot', making 'Gardiner the Sot'; at Edward Bartlet, 'The carrier of Oxon. the same who was one of the Citie Ballives an. 1669'; and at the close, 'By one of Oxford', 'viz Francis Shenton a drunken and broken apothecary living in the parish of S. Pet. in the Baylie .. this cheat was committed in Nov. 1663 & in the same month this ballad was published.' (sic). See LT 1.504-6 for a transcript of the ballad and AW's notes in both copies.
Wood 401(100). Wing S3101 (rare, 2 at O). Madan 2627.

752. Shepherd and the King. *The shepherd and the king, and of Gillian the shepherds wife.* London:

f. F. Coles, [1650?]. S.sh. Obl. 2 pts. Ff. 1-2 in this vol. Quarter-calf, about 1881.
This vol. contains 103 black-letter ballads. Most are printed oblong on large fol. sheets (chain lines are vertical). The folds are in the middle to form four-page quires. The ballads are numbered 1-103 in this catalogue. Each printed side, the inner side of the quire, is regarded as the 'recto' side; the outer side, blank, is regarded as the 'verso' side. Arabic nos., some by AW (see e.g., item 66, i.e., fol. no. 129), are on the upper right hand corner(s) each sheet, 1-204, the 1st on the verso side (the blank p. 1 of the quire) and the 2nd on the recto (the printed p. 3 of the quire). A few ballads are small fol. sheets, and a single fol. no is then on the upper right hand corner of the printed side. The Bodl. CD cat. usually follows the numbering on verso of the printed sheets. Hence most of the 103 items are numbered by increments of 2, e.g., 1, 3, 5, instead of 1, 2, 3. The Bodl. CD cat. lists four ballads twice (56, 64, 67, 99; i.e., Bodl. fol. nos., 109-110, 125, 131, 195); and omits 1 (a fragment, no. 102; i.e., Bodl. fol. nos., 201-2; the 1st part of this ballad, f. 201, was recorded as missing in 1832). The fol. nos., corresponding to the Bodl. CD cat. nos., are given after the format. Many ballads were backed with blank sheets either to give AW space for writing notes or to cover irrelevant material. On 7 of these blank sheets AW wrote notes on the particular ballads (see ballad nos. 5, 24, 31, 35, 37, 47, 66; i.e., fol. nos. 9 , 47, 60, 67, 71, 91, 129). Items 67, 68 and 69, i.e., fol. nos. 131,133 and 135, have his schoolboy notes and scribbles (uncovered in item 67 but not in items 68 and 69). For some reason, he had blank sheets pasted over conjoint printed ballads (i.e., the 2nd ballad printed on the verso) at items 14, 20, and 56; i.e., ff. 27-8, 39-40, 109-110. These three were uncovered in 1881. Some of early Arabic numbers were lost when the pages were cropped when the vol. was bound in its present form (see, e.g., items 43-4, 59, 65; i.e., ff. 83-86, 116, 128). For the entry in the Whiteside cat., see Plate IX. Ist item, ᵛ, AW wrote, 'vide Malmsburiens. de Reg. Anglorum. lib. 2. fol. 23 [i.e., at Alfred, 2.121-3]. See the 2ᵈ part of R. Parsons his conversions. Cap. 6. p 418. 419' (AW owned 3 copies, see Wood 223, 856, and 872). Text, AW corrected the 1st word, 'AN elder time there was of yore', to 'IN elder . . . '. Wood 401(1). Wing S3150B (rare).

753. S[heppard], S[amuel]. *A famous battle between Robin Hood, and Maid Marian.* N.p.: n.pub., [1653]. S.sh. Obl. 2 pts. Ff. 21-2 in this vol.
Wood 401(11). Not in Wing (lost entry, see after S144A). Not in ESTCR.

754. Sherwood, Thomas*, and Elizabeth Evans*. *Murder upon murder, committed by Thomas Sherwood . . . and Elizabeth Evans . . . the 2. of m. George Holt of Windzor.* London: f. T. Langley, sold T. Lambert, [1635]. S.sh. Obl. 2 pts. Ff. 129-30.
On blank sheet pasted to support this item, pasted to support the ballad after AW wrote the no., '129', AW wrote, 'Rowl. Holt Marchant of London ob. 1634 – Tho. Holt serj. at Law – Joh Holt recorder of Lond. 1686.' At second part of ballad, 'A W'.
Wood 401(66). STC 22431 (rare) (Wing M3089, incorrect).

755. Shoe-maker. *An excellent song, called, the shooe-makers travell.* London: E. P[urslowe?] f. E. Wright, [1648 ca.]. S.sh. Obl. 2pts. Ff. 69-70 in this vol.
Wood 401(36). Wing E3836 (rare) (Wing, n.pub.; [1690?]).

756. Shore, Jane. *The wofull lamentation of mistris Jane Shore, a goldsmiths wife.* [London]: f. F. Coles, T. Vere, a. W. Gilbertson, [1658 to 1664]. S.sh. Obl. 2 pts. Ff. 45-6 in this vol. (cropped at top).
ᵛ, AW wrote, beside woodcut, pasted on, 'This picture was taken out of another ballad of Jane Shore'.
Wood 401(23). Wing W3244B (rare).

757. Shrewsbury. *Shrowsbury for me. Being a song in praise of that most famous town.* London: f. R. Burton, [1663 to 1674]. S.sh. Obl. 2 pts.
[MS.] Wood E. 25(44). Not in Wing. ESTCR 234917.

758. Shrewsbury. *A new wonder: or, a strange and true account from Shrewsbury of a dreadful storm [4 May 1681].* [London]: f. F. Coles, T. Vere, J. Wright, J. Clarke, W. Thackeray, a. T. Passinger, 1681. S.sh. Obl.
[MS.] Wood E. 25(97). Wing N797aA (rare) (Wing, Passenger).

759. Soldier. *The soldiers delight, or the she voluntier.* [London]: f. F. Cole [sic], T. Vers [sic], J. Wright, a. J. Carlk [sic], [1674-9]. S.sh. Obl.
[MS.] Wood E. 25(69). Wing S4420B (rare) (soldier's and Coles and Vere).

760. Song upon Information. *A song upon information.* London: f. M. R., 1681. S.sh.
Wood 417(74). Wing S4684.

761. Sorrowful Assembly. *The sorrowful assembly: or, the maidens humble petition to the batchelors of*

London. [London]: f. J. Deacon, [1684-5]. S.sh.
Wood 417(134). Wing S4709B (rare).

762. Spinning Wheel. *'The spinning wheel or Innocence betrayed &c.'*. N.p.: n.pub., n.d. Pp.?
T from upper flyleaf. Missing in 1922. See note at Wood 417(1). Possibly 'The country lass, who left her spinning wheel' (Wing C6540). Not identified.
Wood 417(126). Wing C6540 (possibly) (3). BL, CM, HH (Crawford, Rylands).

763. Staffordshire. *Strange news from Stafford-shire; or, a dreadful example of divine justice*. [London]: f. F. Coles, T. Vere, J. Wright, a. J. Clark, [1677]. S.sh. Obl.
[MS.] Wood E. 25(125) (not in Bodl. CD cat.). Wing S5905A (rare).

764. Steward, James*, and George Wharton*. *A lamentable ballad, of a combate lately performed neer London, betwixt sir James Steward, and sir George Wharton*. London: f. F. Coles, T. Vere, a. W. Gilbertson, [1658-64]. S.sh. Obl. 2 pts. Ff. 87-88 in this vol.
F. 87ᵛ, AW wrote, 'The much lamented Sʳ James Stuart one of the Kings blood, & Sʳ Georg Wharton, the prime branch of that noble family, for little worthless punctilioes of honour (being intimate freinds) took the feild, & fell together by each others hand. [/] Sʳ George Wharton Eldest son of Philipp Lord Wharton was slaine in a Duel by Sʳ James Steward Kt, 8. Nov. 1609. whereupon the estate came to Sʳ Tho. Wharton father of Philip Lord Wharton the cowardlie Rebell.'
Wood 401(45). Wing L254B (rare).

765. Strange Encounter. *A strange encounter of two lovers. Or, the dying maid reviv'd*. [London]: f. F. Coles, T. Vere, J. Wright, a. J. Clarke, [1680]. S.sh. Obl.
[MS.] Wood E. 25(147). Wing S5883 (rare) (Wing, London).

766. Strephon*. *Strephon and Cloris: or, the coy shepherd and kind shepherdess*. [London]: f. J. Clarke, [1678?]. S.sh. Obl.
[MS.] Wood E. 25(22). Wing S5963.

767. Strephon*. *Loves extasie: or, Strephon and Cloas [sic] corronation [sic]*. [London]: f. J. Deacon, [1687]. S.sh.
AW wrote the year, '87'.
Wood 417(153). Wing L3265 (rare) (Wing, no pub.).

768. Strephon's Comforts. *Strephon's comforts: or, Phillis reviv'd*. [London]: f. J. Deacon, 1682. S.sh.
A correction.
Wood 417(112). Wing S5966 (rare) (Wing, wrong date, 1692).

769. Stukeley, Thomas*. *The life and death of famous Thomas Stukelie*. [London]: f. W. Gilbertson, [1643 to 1663]. S.sh. Obl. Ff. 71-2 in this vol. F. 71ᵛ, only, blank conjoint printed document, 'Be it known unto all men by these presents, That I –', concerning Office of Excise, pasted over by a blank sheet on which AW made notes on Stukeley.
F. 71ᵛ, on a blank 'Excise' document pasted on the verso of the ballad (not unpasted, nor is the document the same as that once pasted over at Wood 401(5), item 547), AW wrote 23 lines: 'Thomas Stukeley was a yonger brother, of an ancient, wealthy & worshipfull familie nigh Ilfercombe in Devonsh. being one of good parts, but valued the Less by others, because overprized by himself. [/] Stukeley with 800 men which the Pope & the Spaniard allowed him towards the conquest of Ireland, did in his passage thereto Land at Portugall, just when Sebastian K. thereof, with two Moorish Kings were undertaking a voyage into Africa – upon Sebastians sollicitations Stukely joynes with him, & landing with [sic] Africa, Stukely gave counsell, that for two or 3. dayes they should refresh their land soldiers, whereof some were sick & some were weak, by reason of their tempestuous passage – This would not be heard so furious was Don Sebastian to engage, as if he would pluck up the bayes of victorie out of the ground, before they were growne up, & so in the battle of Alcasor in Africa their army was wholly defeated, an 1578, 20. Eliz. where Stukeley lost his life [/] A fatal fight, where in one day were slaine three Kings that were, & one* that would be faine. *Stukeley'. In pencil, 'Fuller Worthies'.
Wood 401(37). Not in Wing (should be at J804AB or L1992aB). ESTCR 234889.

770. Success of the Two English Travellers. *The success of the two English travellers newly arrived in London*. [London]: f. A. Banks, [1685?]. S.sh.
AW wrote the year, '1685', in pencil.
Wood 417(146). Wing S6112B (rare).

771. Suffolk Miracle. *The Suffolk miracle. Or a relation of a young man who a month after his death appeared to his sweetheart.* London: f. W. Thackery a. T. Passenger, [1686-8]. S.sh. Obl.
AW, prob., wrote the year, '1689'.
[MS.] Wood E. 25(83). Wing S6163 (rare).

772. [Taubman, Matthew]. *The Oxford health, or, the jovial loyalist.* [London]: f. P. Brooksby, [1681]. S.sh. Obl.
[MS.] Wood E. 25(27). Wing O855.

773. Taunton. *The gossips meeting, or, the merry market-women of Taunton.* [London]: f. F. Coles, T. Vere, J. Wright, a. J. Clarke, [1674-9]. S.sh. Obl. 2 pts.
[MS.] Wood E. 25(120). Wing G1317 (rare) (Wing, London).

774. Teague and Sawney, pseud. *Teague and Sawney: or, the unfortunate success of a dear-joys devotion by St. Patrick's cross.* [London]: f. C. G., [1689]. S.sh.
ᵛ, AW wrote the date, 'beg. of Mar. 1688[9].'
Wood 417(181). Wing T604 (Wing, Sawney, or the and [1690]).

775. Thompson of Brentford*. *Terrible news from Brainford: or, a perfect . . . relation of one Thompson.* [London]: f. F. Coles, M. Wright, T. Vere, a. W. Gilbertson, 1661. S.sh. Obl. 2 pts. Ff. 181-2 in this vol.
'Brentford', not in AW's hand.
Wood 401(92). Wing T766 (two).

776. Thynne, Thomas*. *The matchless murder. Giving an account of the . . . murthering of . . . Thomas Thin [12 Feb. 1682].* [London]: f. J. Conyers, [1682]. S.sh. Obl.
LT 3.5.
[MS.] Wood E. 25(98). Wing M1078 (two).

777. Ticwhit, G. *General Monks welcome (from the citie) to Whitehall.* [London]: n.pub., [1660]. S.sh.
AW wrote, 'ffeb: 1659[60]'; ᵛ, 'Feb. 59', and '52' over a former no. '34' in pencil.
Wood 416(52) (not in Bodl. CD cat.). Wing T1159A.

778. Titus Andronicus*. *Titus Andronicus complaint.* [London]: [f. the assigns o]f T. Symcocke, [1628-9]. S.sh. P. 33 in this vol. (mutilated).
'dup', may be in AW's hand; below, lines lost in a mutilated portion written in, not in AW's hand. P. 34, 28 lines of verse, not in AW's hand and illeg., pasted over by blank sheet. The chain lines in the ballad are vertical, and the no., '33', not in AW's hand, replaced a former no. There was prob. a 2nd ballad torn from the left side of this sheet.
Wood 402(9). STC 24092.7 (rare).

779. Tobias*. *A pleasant new ballad of Tobias.* [London]: f. F. Coles, T. Vere, a. J. Wright, [1663-74]. S.sh. Obl. Ff. 73-4 in this vol.
Wood 401(38). Wing P2555B (rare).

780. Tom of All Trades. *Merry Tom of all trades. Or, a trick to get mony at every dead lift.* [London]: f. F. Coles, T. Vere, a. W. Gilbertson, [1658-64]. S.sh. Obl.
[MS.] Wood E. 25(47). Wing M1873B (rare).

781. Tom the Tory. *An excellent new ballad between Tom the Tory, and Toney the Whigg.* [London]: [f. R. H.], [1678]. S.sh. (mutilated at bottom). Cloth; rebound in early 20th century.
Flyleaf, upper, 2nd, list of 2-4 works or topics, the latter about Stephen College (see Wood 427(27-28)), in pencil, very faint: 'These Hyeroglyphick [- - illeg., Popery?] The Pope are the [– illeg.][,] Resignation of Stephen College[,] The Protestant Oxford joyner'; ᵛ, in modern hand, '*No. 19 is in place of no. 14, which is missing [/] 45 is missing [and in more recent hand] & 42, 126, 12 [12 is not missing]'. Flyleaf, 3rd-6th, AW wrote the titles of 183 printed works in this vol., within guidelines made with red ink. At item 38, 'Deest Mar. 1840. W[illiam] K[irtland]'; at items 82-3, AW drew a hand pointer at an error that he apparently made himself (he overwrote item no. '83', with '82'); at items 100-1, AW wrote, 'Dupl.' The final item, no. 184, *Oates well thresh't*, is not on the list on the upper flyleaves. It was added after 1695; removed from Wood 276a(555), and still has the Roman numeral, CCCCCLV, marking its place in that vol. The irregularities are, in sum: nos. 14b, 38, 42, 45, and 126 are missing (all 5 are identified and have entries); no. 19 was moved to 14a, leaving a gap at no. 19; AW omitted item 21b in the list on the flyleaves; there is no item 83, either in AW's list or the vol. itself; nos. 138-9, separately entered in AW's list, are a single

printed item; and no. 184, item 664, was moved here from Wood 276a(555). Item (1), above, 'Nu. 1'.
Wood 417(1). Wing E3803.

782. Tom-son. *Toms-son his repetition to his wife; . . . To the tune of, young Jemmy.* [London]: f. J.
Deacon, [1679-80]. S.sh.
AW wrote a date in pencil, '(87)' and '(87)', in ink.
Wood 417(151). Wing T1871 (two).

783. Trapaner. *The trappaner trappand or, a cunning gossip caught in a trap.* [London?]: n.pub., [1685?].
S.sh. Obl. (cropped at bottom).
Cf. Douce Ballads 2(221), no publisher.
[MS.] Wood E. 25(51). Wing T2052 (rare, 2 at O).

784. Treason Rewarded. *Treason rewarded at Tiburn: or, the traitors downfal [24 Jan. 1679].* [London]:
f. F. Coles, T. Vere, J. Wright, & J. Clarke (cropped at bottom), [1679]. S.sh. Obl. 2 pts.
[MS.] Wood E. 25(99). Wing T2080 (rare) (Wing, and J. Clarke [1678]).

785. Treason Unmasqued. *Treason unmasqued, or truth brought to light.* London: f. F. Smith, 1681.
S.sh.
Wood 417(63). Wing T2081.

786. Troy. *A proper new ballad, intituled the wandring prince of Troy. To the tune of Queene Dydo.*
London: [A. Mathewes] f. J. Wright, [1635 ca.]. S.sh. obl. 2 pts. Pp. 2-3 in the vol. Parchment; rebacked
and repaired.
Most of the 24 black-letter ballads in the vol. are in 2 parts, printed oblong on large fol. leaves (chain
lines, vertical). AW folded each ballad sheet in the middle to form four pp. and wrote p. nos. on the upper
outside corners of each fol. leaf thus making a vol. of 96 pp. plus a final sheet. The final item, an unidentified
fragment, is not a ballad and has a trace of 98 on the recto side. Most of AW's nos. on the ballads survive,
though some were lost in the initial binding or in a later repairing. A few ballads are printed in the normal
fashion (chain lines horizontal), and such ballads form a single page set of 2 pp. instead of 4 pp. (e.g.,
Wood 402(12), i.e., pp. 42-43). Some 2-part ballads, printed on an oblong sheets, seem to have been torn
in half, and only 1 of the 2 survives (see Wood 402(9), 402(11)). AW's nos., on the printed pp. only, are
given in this cat. after the format. The Bodl. CD cat. includes 22 of the ballads, omitting nos. 21, 22, and
the unidentified item, no. 25. It lists each ballad by the no. or nos. on the printed pp. Hence ballad no. 24,
the last in the Bodl. CD cat., is given the shelf-mark Wood 402(95). Pastedown, upper (a former flyleaf
now pasted down), AW wrote the date, 'Christmas 1684'; also, 'Pp. 82-89 missing 13.IV.1949 W[illiam]
O H[assall]' (i.e., 2 ballads between items 22 and 23). Since there exists no list of contents in the usual
places, on the upper flyleaves, in the Whiteside cat., or in the Milford hand-list, the titles of these 2 ballads
are unknown. P. 1, AW wrote 'dup'. This 'duplicate', a diff. ed. of the same ballad, has migrated to the
Roxburghe collection, 3.1. (43-44), where it still contains page numbers in AW's hand and style, '2' and
'3' and 1, 4, on the verso; it was the 1st ballad (i.e., pp. 1-4) in the stolen volume, Wood 400, the contents
of which AW numbered in the same way. P. 4, a note, in French, not in AW's hand, is visible, but illeg.
beneath a protective blank sheet pasted on the ᵛ side of the ballad.
Wood 402(1) (not in Bodl. CD cat.). STC 24293.7 (rare).

787. True Lovers' Knot. *The true lovers knot untyed. Being the right path to advise princely virgins how
to behave themselves.* [London]: f. F. Coles, T. Vere, J. Wright, a. J. Clarke, [1674-9]. S.sh. Obl. 2 pts.
[MS.] Wood E. 25(16). Wing T2748C (rare) (Wing, untied).

788. True Lovers' Victory. *True lovers victory or the northern couple agreed.* [London]: f. J. C[onyers],
[1671 ca.]. S.sh.
[MS.] Wood E. 25(42). Wing T2755A (rare) (Wing, [1695?]).

789. True Loyalist. *The true loyalist; or, the obedient subject.* [London]: f. J. Back, [1683-86]. S.sh.
AW lined out the written, '1686', and wrote, '1683'.
Wood 417(115). Wing T2755E (two) (Wing, 1682-1700).

790. True Protestants. *The true protestants litany.* [London]: n.pub., 1680. S.sh.
Wood 417(37). Wing T2867.

791. Two Unfortunate Lovers. *Two unfortunate lovers, or, a true relation of the lamentable end of
John True.* [London]: f. F. Coles, T. Vere, a. W. Gilbertson, [1658-64]. S.sh. Obl.
[MS.] Wood E. 25(84). Wing T3542A (rare).

792. Unconstant Phillis. *Unconstant Phillis. Or, the infortunate shepherds lamentation.* [London]: f. P. Brooksby, [1672-95]. S.sh. Obl.
[MS.] Wood E. 25(13). Wing U36 (two).

793. Unhappy Marriage. *The unhappy marriage, or, a warning to covetous parents.* [London]: f. J. Wright, J. Clark, W. Thackeray, a. T. Passinger, [1680?]. S.sh. Obl.
[MS.] Wood E. 25(76). Wing U70 (rare) (Wing, London).

794. Valiant Sea-Man. *The valiant sea-mans happy return to his love, after a long seven years absence.* [London]: f. P. B. a. E. O., [1689-95]. S.sh. Obl.
[MS.] Wood E. 25(153). Wing V39 (rare) (Wing, 1689-96).

795. Vane, Henry*. *Vanity of vanities or sir Harry Vane's picture.* London: printed f. C. Gustavus, [1660]. S.sh.
AW wrote, '1661/2 made while Sr Hen. Vane was prisoner in the Tower, or in the isle of Scilley rather'; ^{v}, '1661/2'. Some accounts, addition of 4 unnamed items, 19 total, may not be in AW's hand. Dupl. at Wood 416(32).
Wood 416(91). Wing V96 (two) (Wing vanities: or).

796. Vane, Henry*. *Vanity of vanities or sir Harry Vane's picture.* London: printed f. C. Gustavus, [1660]. S.sh.
AW wrote, 'January 1659[60]:'; ^{v}, 'Jan. 59', and '32' over a former no. 16 in pencil. Dupl. at 416(91).
Wood 416(32). Wing V96 (two) (Wing vanities: or).

797. V[icars], J[ohn]. *A letter for a Christian family.* London: f. F. Coles, T. Vere, J. Wright, a. J. Clarke, [1674-9]. S.sh. Obl.
[MS.] Wood E. 25(149). Wing V314A (rare) (Wing, [London] and F. Cole,).

798. View of the Religion. *A view of the religion of the town, or, a Sunday-mornings ramble.* [London]: n.pub., [1687]. S.sh.
AW wrote, 'published about the middle of Dec. 1688'.
Wood 417(163). Wing V368.

799. Villiers, George*. Buckingham, duke of. *A ballad. I sing the praise of a worthy wight.* [London]: n.pub., [1674?]. S.sh.
AW wrote, at t, 'On Georg Duke of Buckingham Father & son', and 2 identifications, at B and F, 'Buckingham' and 'Felton'. Below, he lined out his earlier ms. dates, 1680 and 1679, and wrote, 'published in Jan. or Feb. 1673[4]'.
Wood 417(25). Wing B599 (Wing, c. 1679).

800. Villiers, George*. Buckingham, duke of. *The litany. Of the d. of B.* [London]: n.pub., [1679 to 1680]. S.sh.
AW altered the 'B' in the t: B'ucks'; wrote the year, '(1680)' and '1679', and ^{v} '1680'.
Wood 417(39). Wing L2536.

801. Vive le Roy. *Vive le roy: or London's joy. A new song on the instalment of the present lord mayor of London.* London: f. Allen Banks, [1681]. S.sh. obl.
AW identified the mayor, 'Sr Joh. More' and Sir Pa– and Sh. Be–, 'Sr Patience Ward' and 'Sherriff Bethell', and wrote the date, 'Oct. 1681'.
Wood 417(73). Wing V665 (Wing, or,).

802. W., L. *The ill fortune of a younger brother, [/] And I wish no mans fall by such another.* [London]: f. F. Coles, T. Vere, J. Wright, a. J. Clarke, [1674 to 1679]. S.sh. Obl.
[MS.] Wood E. 25(4). Wing I47 (rare) (Wing, no pub., no date).

803. W., L. *The maidens sad complaint for want of a husband.* [London]]: f. F. Cole, T. Vere, J. Wright, a. J. Clark, [1674 to 1679]. S.sh. Obl.
[MS.] Wood E. 25(57). Wing W79aA (rare).

804. W., L. *God's great and wonderful work in Somerset-shire, the charitable farmer miraculously rewarded.* London: f. F. Coles, T. Veres, J. Wright, a. J. Clarke, [1676]. S.sh. (obl.) (mutilated). 2 pts.
AW wrote, '1676'.
Wood 276b(101). Wing W79 (rare).

805. W., L. *All things be dear but poor mens labour; or, the sad complaint of poor people*. [London]: f. J. Clark, [1680]. S.sh. Obl.
[MS.] Wood E. 25(119) (not in Bodl. CD cat.). Wing W77A (rare) (Wing, deare and but poor men's).

806. Wade, John. *A good wife is a portion every day. Or, a dialogue discoverng a good wife from a bad*. [London]: f. R. Burton, [1670 ca.]. S.sh. Obl. 2 pts.
[MS.] Wood E. 25(131). Wing W164B (rare).

807. Wade, John. *A pleasant new song, in praise of the leather bottell. Shewing how glasses and pots are laid aside [signed, John Wade]. [With, ^r] Englands royall conquest*. London: f. R. Burton, [1641 to 1674]. S.sh. Obl. 2 pts. The 2nd ballad on ^r.
[MS.] Wood E. 25(56). Wing W168C (rare).

808. Wade, J[ohn]. *The kind young man's answer to the faithful maid*. [London]: f. F. Coles, T. Veres [sic], J. Wright, a. J. Clarke, [1674 to 1679]. S.sh. Obl.
Dupl. at [MS.] Wood E. 25(129).
[MS.] Wood E. 25(5). Wing W168 (rare, 2 at O).

809. Wade, J[ohn]. *The kind young man's answer to the faithful maid*. [London]: f. F. Coles, T. Veres [sic], J. Wright, a. J. Clarke, [1674 to 1679]. S.sh. Obl.
Dupl. at [MS.] Wood E. 25(5).
[MS.] Wood E. 25(129). Wing W168 (rare, 2 at O).

810. Wade, J[ohn]. *Tis money makes a man or, the good fellows folly*. London: f. F. Coles, T. Vere, J. Wright, a. J. Clarke, [1674 to 1679]. S.sh. Obl.
[MS.] Wood E. 25(150). Wing W173 (Wing, [London]).

811. Wade, John. *A serious discourse between two lovers*. London: f. R. Hardy, [1677?]. S.sh. Obl. 2 pts.
Dupl. at [MS.] Wood E. 25(146).
[MS.] Wood E. 25(2). Wing W170AB (rare, 2 at O).

812. Wade, John. *A serious discourse between two lovers*. London: f. R. Hardy, [1677?]. S.sh. Obl. 2 pts.
Dupl. at [MS.] Wood E. 25(2).
[MS.] Wood E. 25(146). Wing W170AB (rare, 2 at O).

813. Wade, John. *The citizns [sic] joy, and the bone-lace-weavers happines [cropped], being a rare pattern for all lovers*. [London]: f. R. Burton, [1680]. S.sh. Obl.
[MS.] Wood E. 25(73). Wing W163 (rare, 2 at O) (var.).

814. Wade, John. *The west cuntrey crafty maid, or, the lusty brave miller finely trappan'd*. [London]: f. W. Thackeray, [1688-9]. S.sh. Obl. 2 pts.
[MS.] Wood E. 25(29). Wing W175B (rare) (Wing, Thackery).

815. Waller, William*, and Elizabeth Cellier*. *The Newgate salutation: or, a dialogue between sir W[illiam] W[aller] and mrs. Cellier*. London: f. the use of the students in Whittington's Colledge, [1681?]. S.sh.
AW wrote 'Waller' in the t.
Wood 426(16). Wing N918A.

816. Wapping. *The merry wives of Wapping. Or, the seaman's wives clubb*. London: f. F. Coles, T. Vere, J. Wright, a. J. Clarke, [1674-9?]. S.sh. Obl.
[MS.] Wood E. 25(126). Wing M1876 (rare).

817. Ward, John*, and Simon de Danser*. *The sea-mans song of captain Ward, the famous pyrate of the world. [Followed by] The sea-mans song of Dansekar the Dutch-man, his robberies done at sea*. [London]: 'Printed for F. Coles, J. Wright, T. Vere, a. W. Gilbertson, [1660 ca.]. S.sh. (2 shs.). 2 ballads issued together. Pp. 39-40 in this vol.
P. 39, 'Another copy Wood 401.79', in pencil; p. 40 'Another copy Wood 401.80', in pencil; and '(Part II of preceding ballad, f. 39)', all in later hands. Diff. ed. at 401(41). 2nd part has woodcut with a ship, only. Last line: 'and God will give them soon an overthrow.' See also item 6440.
Wood 402(11). Not in Wing, but cp. S2197 (Wing, 2nd half, only; sea-man's; William Gilbertson). Not in ESTCR.

818. Ward, John*, and Simon de Danser*. *The seammans [sic] song of captain Ward, the famous*

pyrate of the world. [Followed by] The seamans song of Dansekar the Dutch man, and his robberies done at sea. [London]: 'Printed for F. Coles. T. Vere. and W. Gilbertson', [1658 to 1664]. S.sh. Obl. 2 ballads issued together (chain lines vertical). Ff. 79-80 in this vol.
'Another copy Wood 402.39', 'Another copy Wood 402.40', both in a later hand. Diff. ed., Wood 402(11). 2nd part has woodcut, lion over a ship; last line: 'and God will give them soon an overthrow.'
Wood 401(41). Wing S2196 (Wing, for 1st part: seamans; William Gilbertson).

819. Warning or Lanthorn to London. *Warning or lanthorn to London, by the doleful destruction of faire Jerusalem. [Followed by] Of the horrible and woful destruction of Jerusalem.* London: f. F. Coles, J. Wright, T. Vere, a. W. Gilbertson, [1658]. S.sh. Obl. 2 ballads, 1 publ.; prob. issued together. Ff. 81-2 in this vol.
Wood 401(42). Wing W925A (rare).

820. Washington, pseud. *Away with't quoth Washington, or, the phanatick general vindicated over the left shoulder.* London: f. J. Phanatick, 1660. S.sh.
ᵛ, AW wrote the year, '1660'.
Wood 416(77). Wing A4278 (two).

821. Waterton, Justice*, pseud. *Roome for a justice. Or, the life and death of justice Waterton.* London: f. C. Gustavus, [1660]. S.sh.
AW wrote 'Jan: 1659'; ᵛ, 'Jan. 59', and '41' replaced a former no. '24' in pencil.
Wood 416(41). Wing R1923 (3).

822. West-Country Cheat. *The west-countrey [sic] cheat upon cheat; or, no jest like a true jest.* [London]: f. F. Coles, T. Vere, J. Wright, a. J. Clarke, [1674-9]. S.sh. Obl. 2 pts.
[MS.] Wood E. 25(130). Wing W1395 (two) (Wing, West-country).

823. Westminster Wedding. *A Westminster wedding, or, like unto like, quoth the devil to the collier.* [London]: f. R. Burton, [1662 ca.]. S.sh. Obl.
AW wrote the year, 'about 1662'.
[MS.] Wood E. 25(94). Not in Wing (should be at W1472aA). ESTCR 234964.

824. [Wharton, Thomas]. *A new song. Ho brother Teague.* [London?]: n.pub., [1688]. S.sh.
AW wrote the date, 'Decemb. 1688.'
Wood 417(168). Wing W1577A (Wing, Ho, and [1689?]).

825. [Wharton, Thomas]. *The second part of Lill–li burlero bullen a-la.* [London]: n.pub., 1688. S.sh.
AW wrote the month, 'Jan.'
Wood 417(172). Wing S2294B (rare) (Wing, Lilli).

826. Whigs. *The Whiggs lamentation, for the tap of sedition [i.e., anti-Shaftesbury].* N.p.: f. J. C. jun., 1683. S.sh.
Wood 417(118). Wing W1660aA (two).

827. [Wild, Robert]. *The recantation of a penitent Proteus, or the changling.* [London]: n.pub., [1663]. S.sh. Responded to by Wood 416(100), item 6592.
AW wrote, 'This Ballad was made on Rich: Lee. D. D. Chapleyne to Georg D: of Albermale & Rector of Kings hatfeild com: Hartf:'; ᵛ, '1663[4]'. Possibly acquired 12 March 1664, 2ᵈ, LT 2.6.
Wood 416(99) (not in Bodl. CD cat.). Wing W2148.

828. William 3*. *The prince of Orange welcome to London.* [London]: f. G. J., 1688. S.sh. Obl.
AW wrote the month, 'Dec.'
[MS.] Wood E. 25(118). Wing P3485A (3).

829. William 3*. *The prince of Orange's triumph, or, the downfall of the distressed Jesuits.* [London]: f. J. Back, [1688]. S.sh. Obl.
AW wrote the date, 'Dec. 1688.'
[MS.] Wood E. 25(112). Wing P3485C (two).

830. William 3*. *The civil Orange: or, the united hearts of England.* [London]: J. Back, 1689. S.sh.
AW wrote the date, 'in the beg. of Feb. 1688[9]'.
Wood 417(180). Wing C4365 (two).

831. William 3*. *A full description of these times, or the prince of Orange's march from Exeter to London.*

[London]: f. A. B., [1689]. S.sh.
AW wrote the date, 'Jan. 1688[9].'
[MS.] Wood E. 25(115). Wing F2344A (two). Wing, 1688.

832. William 3*. *A new song of an orange.* [London]: f. A. B., 1689. S.sh.
AW wrote, '2^d – Dec. 17. an. 1688'.
Wood 417(162). Wing N765AB (rare).

833. William 3*. *The protestants triumph: or, the prince of Orange joyfully entertained.* [London]: f. J. Wolrah, [1689]. S.sh. Obl.
AW wrote the date, 'Jan. 1688[9]'.
[MS.] Wood E. 25(109). Wing P3854B (two) (Wing, 1688).

834. William* and Mary*. *The subjects satisfaction, being a new song of the proclaiming king William and queen Mary [13 Feb.].* [London]: f. J. Deacon, [1689]. S.sh. Obl.
AW wrote the year, '1688[9].' LT 3.299.
[MS.] Wood E. 25(114). Wing S6106.

835. Willie and Nancy. *The loving young couple. Or, the amourous wooing between Willie and Nancie.* [London]: f. F. Coles, T. Vere, J. Wright, a. J. Clark, [1674-9]. S.sh. Obl.
[MS.] Wood E. 25(65). Wing L3296 (rare) (Wing, London).

836. Willow Green. *The willow green turned into white; or, the young man's joy and the maids delight.* [London]: f. F. Coles, T. Vere, J. Wright, a. J. Clarke, [1674-9]. S.sh. Obl.
[MS.] Wood E. 25(7). Wing W2863A (two).

837. Woman. *The young-womans complaint, or, a caveat to all maids to have care how they be married to old-men.* London: f. W. Gilbertson, [1655-65]. S.sh. Obl. 2 pts.
[MS.] Wood E. 25(37). Wing Y134 (two).

838. Women. *A description of wanton women. Wherein I briefly shall declare.* [London]: f. F. Coles, T. Vere, J. Wright, and J. Clarke, [1674-9]. S.sh. Obl.
[MS.] Wood E. 25(17). Wing D1173 (rare) (Wing, [1690?]).

839. Women. *Prides fall, or a warning for all English women.* [London]: f. F. Coles, T. Vere, a. W. Gilbertson, [1658-64]. S.sh. Obl. Ff. 157-8 in this vol.
Wood 401(80). Wing P3446A (rare) (Wing, Pride's).

840. Woodstock. *The Woodstock scuffle: or most dreadfull aparition that were lately seene in the mannor house of Woodstock.* [London]: n.pub., 1649[50]. 4°.
Missing in 1839; see note by W. Kirtland at [MS.] Wood B. 18(1), item 1148.
[MS.] Wood B. 18(10). Wing W3476 (rare, BL Thomason).

841. Worthy Example. *A worthy example of a vertuous wife, who fed her father with her own milk.* [London]: f. F. Coles, T. Vere, a. W. Gilbertson, [1663-74]. S.sh. Obl. Ff. 111-2 in this vol.
Wood 401(57). Wing W3629D (two).

842. W[ortley], F[rancis]. 1st bart. *A loyall song of the royall feast, kept by the prisoners in the Towre in August last, . . . By sir F. W.* [London]: n.pub., [1647]. S.sh.
AW wrote, 'Sr Franc. Wortley', 'published about 1647' (below 1647 and lined out, 'the latter end of 1647'), and identified 2 prisoners.
Wood 500(2). Wing W3639.

843. Young Man. *The young-mans ramble. Or the horse can trot, and the mare can amble.* London: f. T. Vere, [1680]. S.sh. Obl. 2 pts.
[MS.] Wood E. 25(23). Wing Y123 (rare) (Wing, young mans).

End of BALLADS (items 367-843)

---

844. Banbury Castle. *A letter: being a full relation of the siege of Banbury castle.* London: f. J. Wright, 1644, 4 Sept. 4°. Pp. 8.
Tp, AW wrote 'Sept' (cropped).
Wood 377(31). Wing L1347.

845. Banbury, Proceedings. *The proceedings at Banbury*. [London]: f. R. Harford, [1642]. 4°. Pp. 8.
Tp, AW lined out the former no., '18'.
Wood 374(34). Wing P3556 (Wing, omits publ.).

846. Bancroft, John. Oxford, bp. of. *Articles to be enquired of within the dioces of Oxford, in the triennial visitation*. Oxford: L. Lichfield, 1638. 4°. A⁴,B1-3.
Tp, a shelf-mark 'C: 2: B: 4 17.' (?) and 'In the name of God, Amen 1643', not in AW's hand.
Wood 516(9). STC 10313 (rare). Madan 880.

847. [Banks, Jonathan]. *The life of the right reverend . . . Edw. Rainbow [bishop of Carlisle]*. London: S. Roycroft, f. R. Clavell, 1688. 12°. Pp. [2], 29, 112.
Tp, bsm. In 2nd part, a few lines in margins, e.g., pp. 3, 9, 23, 84. LT 1.379.
Wood 307(7). Wing B669.

848. Bard, W. (spoken by). *A speech to the lord general Monck at Skinners-hall [4 Apr.]*. London: f. J. Towers, 1660. S.sh.
ᵛ, AW wrote the date, '4. Ap. 1660', and a former no., '59', in pencil.
Wood 398(6). Wing B745 (two).

849. Barebone, Praise-God*. *That wicked and blasphemous petition of Praise-God Barbone, . . . presented to that so called, the parliament . . . Feb. 9. 1659 . . . anatomized*. [London]: f. Philo-Monarchaeus, [1660]. 4°. Pp. [2], 17.
Tp, AW wrote '9 Feb', in pencil.
Wood 610(46). Wing T842.

850. Barebone, Praise-God*. *To the right honorable, the high court of parliament, . . . the . . . petition of Praise-God Barbone*. London: H. Mason, 1660. S.sh.
AW altered the date to 16'59 Feb'; scribbles 'A', 'Mh' in margin.
Wood 276a(197). Wing T1621A ('O' not recorded in Wing).

851. Barefoot, Jon. *Dr. Joⁿ Barefoot's picture*. N.p.: n.pub., n.d. S.sh. (engr.).
Missing in 1939 (a delete sign before the entry in the 1717 list).
Wood 276a(5). See *Engraved Portraits*, 1.118 (T.Q.L., to r. standing, holding hat and letter; 12 lines below. W. Crowne and M. Burghers) (may be this engraving) .

852. Bargishai, Eleazar. *A brief compendium of the vain hopes of the Jews messias. The ignorant fables of their rabbies, and the confuting of the Jewish religion*. London: n.pub., 1652. 4°. Pp. [2], 21.
Wood 637(2). Wing E332A.

853. Barker, Thomas. *Barker's delight: or, the art of angling*. London: f. H. Moseley, 1659. 8°. 2nd ed. Pp. [12], 52.
Flyleaf, upperᵛ, some additions in a later hand and 'Barkers'. Tp, AW wrote '4ᵈ'.
Wood 728(2). Wing B786.

854. B[arksdale], C[lement]. *Nympha libethris: or the Cotswold muse*. London: f. F. A. at Worcester, 1651. 8°. Pp. [13], 96. Calf with 2 fillets and with a vertical 2 fillet line.
Flyleaf, upper, AW wrote, 'Clem. Barksdale the author, gave it to me 18. May 1681/'; tp, 'Cic. pro Arch. poëta.'; p. 23, 'Idest nunc D. Tho Jamesius Custos Coll. O. A.' (i.e., Jeames, All Souls, AOF 2.291). Some corrections and underscoring, e.g., pp. 57, 65, 66 (AW corrects 'Dr. Dee' to 'Billingslie'), 79. LT 2.541.
Wood 78. Wing B804.

855. B[arksdale], C[lement]. *The disputation at Winchcombe Nov. 9. MDCLIII*. Oxford: L. L., sold E. Thorne, [1653]. 8°. Pp. [6], 39, [3]. Calf with 3 fillets, stamp decoration (dragon) inside corners, and roll decoration on spine (Ashm. binding).
Flyleaf, upper, 2nd, the titles of 6 printed works (really 7) in this vol., written by an Ashm. librarian (same hand in Wood 276a). Tp, AW wrote '18 May 1681. Donum Clem. Barksdale/' (see LT 2.541). Pp. 1, AW wrote 'Licensed by Dʳ Langbain pro vice chanc.'; 23, 28, mark in margin, in pencil; 25, a correction. AO 4.223.
Wood 835(1). Wing B793 (two). Madan 2225.

856. Barksdale, Cl[ement]. *Memorials of worthy persons: two decads*. London: I. R., 1661. 12°. Pp. [14], 204. Pasteboard (blue) with parchment spine. 1st and last flyleaves, marbled paper.
Flyleaf, upper, 3rdᵛ, AW wrote the titles of 4 printed works in this vol., within guidelines made with red ink; another writer added the short title of the 5th work, number 4 in the volume, which AW had missed.

*5, correction. P. 201, after memorial of T. Jackson, AW wrote, 'From his Life by Edw. Vaughan.' Acquired 10 May 1662, 9^d, LT 1.439.
Wood 293(1). Wing B800.

857. Barksdale, Cl[ement]. *Memorials of worthy persons. The third decad.* Oxford: A. & L. Liechfield [sic], f. the editor, 1662. 8°. Pp. [8], 104.
Flyleaf, upper^v, AW wrote, 'In these memorials following are contained the 3^d & 4th Decad - the fourth begins in p. 404 [i.e., 104?] - There are also two indexes.' (i.e., lists of persons memorialized). Acquired, with fourth decade, 18 Nov. 1663, 9^d, LT 1.503.
Wood 293(2). Wing B801. Madan 2585.

858. Barksdale, Cl[ement]. *Memorials of worthy persons. . . . The fourth decad.* Oxford: A. a. L. Lichfield, 1663. 8°. Pp. [8], 135.
P. [6], AW wrote, 'Gone to Bartlet the Bookbinder thense to West (a bookseller) - thence to M^r. Crittendum' (a note to tell where he has gone). P. 133, at A. Wheelock, AW added 'of Salop'. N.B., stitch holes show that items 2-5 in this vol. were at one time sewn together, before 1-5 were bound together. Acquired, with third decade, 18 Nov. 1663, 9^d (and 'for sewing of bookes', 5^d), LT 1.503.
Wood 293(3). Wing B802. Madan 2631.

859. B[arksdale], C[lement]. *A remembrancer of excellent men 1. Dr. John Reynolds [et al].* London: f. J. Martyn, 1670. 8°. Pp. [4], 164.
Tp, AW added, 'The 5^t Decad'. Bsm. P. 105, correction; p. 145-162, at memorial to Jeremy Taylor AW added some vertical lines in margins, underscorings, and notes (some cropped).
Wood 293(4). Wing B806.

860. B[arksdale], C[lement]. *A letter touching a colledge of maids, or, a virgin-society. Written Aug. 12. 1675.* [London]: n.pub., [1675]. 8°. A⁴.
A1, 'Clem. Barksdale the author.' A2, A4, corrections entered in text.
Wood 130(3). Wing C14 (two) (Wing does not give the author, but see A.O., 4.224).

861. [Barksdale, Clement]. *Memorials of alderman Whitmore [et al.].* London: J. Redmayne f. J. Barksdale, in Cirencester, 1681. 8°. Pp. [6], 42.
Wood 293(5). Wing B798 (3).

862. B[arksdale], C[lement]. *The old gentleman's wish, or the reformed old gentleman [and] Authors and books.* N.p.: f. J. Barksdale, in Cirencester, 1685. Fol. Pp. [4] (pp. [1], [4], blank).
P. [1], AW wrote 'dupl'. Dupl. at Wood 417(138-9). After each item, '[by Clement Barksdale?]', in blue crayon, in a modern hand.
Wood 276a(551-2) (Wood 276(551,2) in Bodl. CD cat.). Wing B804aA (two).

863. B[arksdale], C[lement]. *The old gentleman's wish, or the reformed old gentleman [and] Authors and books.* N.p.: f. J. Barksdale, in Cirencester, 1685. Fol. Pp. [4] (pp. [1], [4], blank).
Pp. [1], AW wrote 'Mar. 1684/5'; [2], 'Clem. Barksdale', and 'published in the middle of March 1684[5].'; [3], 'published in the middle of March 1684/5'; [4], 'Merton Wood with his antiquitie [/] Will live to all eternitie {Left out of this printed copie, with other matters relating to D^r [Ralph] Bathurst & Dr Will. Levinz', LT 3.135. Dupl. at Wood 276a(551-2).
Wood 417(138-9). Wing B804aA (two) (2 at O) (Wing, wish or).

864. B[arksdale], C[lement]. *A grateful mention of deceased bishops.* N.p.: n.pub., [1686?]. S.sh.
AW wrote 'Dupl', in pencil. Dupl. at Wood 417(150). Note, '[by Clement Barksdale?]' in blue crayon, in a modern hand.
Wood 276a(541). Wing B794B (rare) (2 at O).

865. 'B[arksdale], C[lement]. *A grateful mention of deceased bishops.* N.p.: n.pub., [1686?]. S.sh.
AW wrote, 'Clem. Barksdale the author 1686'. At top, note by a later librarian. Dupl. at 276a(541).
Wood 417(150). Wing B794B (rare, 2 at O).

866. Barkstead, John*. *A true narrative of the . . . late skirmish, between . . . colonell Barksteads regiment, and the petitioners of Surrey . . . at Westminster, May the 16.* London: J. Clowes, 1648. 4°. Pp. 8.
Wood 502(9). Wing T2794.

867. Barkstead, John*. *The first and second parts of invisible John made visible: or a grand pimp of tyranny portrayed, in Barksteads arraignment at the barre.* London: n.pub., 1659. 4°. Pp. [2], 6.

Wood 368(14). Wing B812.

868. Barkstead, John*. *The new lord's winding-sheet; or, an arrow shot at randome, to the Tower of London, . . . And the voting of col. Barkestead.* [London]: n.pub., 1659. 4°. Pp. 7.
Tp, no. '50', in pencil, in a former vol.
Wood 613(10). Wing B815.

869. Barkstead, John; John Okey, and Miles Corbet. *A letter from colonel Barkestead, Colonel Okey, and Miles Corbet.* London: n.pub., 1662. 4°. Pp. 7, [1].
Slip bound into this vol. has a note by AW: 'bound wit . . . [mutilated] Triall of the Kings judges & speeches [Wood 369(5)] – Also cleane paper betw. them, for the entrie [Wood 369(8)?] of what [James] Heaths Cron. [Wood 145] saith of them Newsbook for that time – Characters of Cromwellians– [Wood 369(9)]' (items 3443, 869, 3490, 6113). Tp, 'This was faign'd and written by some Royallist.'
Wood 369(8). Wing B814.

870. Barkstead, John; John Okey, and Miles Corbet. *The speeches and prayers of John Barkstead, John Okey, and Miles Corbet.* London: f. N. Brook, a. E. Thomas, 1662. 4°. Pp. [4], 22, [8], 8 (some misnumbering).
Wood 369(7). Wing B816.

871. Barlandus, Hadrianus Cornelius. Paynell, Thomas, trans. *Brief chronicle of all the earls of Holland.* London: ?, 1557. Pp.?
Missing. MS. Wood E. 2(70), p. 21. See AO 1.339.
MS. Wood E. 2(70), p. 21. Not in STC. Not in ESTCR.

872. [Barlow, Thomas, and Thomas Pierce]. *Pegasus, or, the flying horse from Oxford [2 letters, one by T. Barlow, the other signed Basilius Phllomusus (sic)].* Mongomery, heretofore called Oxford [really London]: n.pub., [1648]. 4°. [4], 1-6, 1-12 ([1] blank).
Tp, AW wrote the year, '1648'. Pp. 1-2, 4-6, 2nd 2-3, 8, 10, AW wrote brief identifications, cross-refs., and dates, e.g., p. 6, at the end, after printed 'Thine &c.', the author, 'Tho: Barlow', and 2nd p. 10, at printed 'Greenwood that well lookt Gentleman', 'squint eye'd'.
Wood 514(49). Wing B838. Madan 1988.

873. [Barlow, William]. Chichester, bp.of (died in 1568). Fry, Francis, ed. *A proper dyaloge, betwene a gentillman and an husband mā, eche complaynenge to other theyr myserable calamyte, through the ambicion of the clergye.* [Antwerp]: [J. Hoochstraten], [1529?]. 8°. A-C⁸.
Tp, signature of Hum: Dyson. Text, some scribbles, not by AW.
Wood 774(4). STC 1462.3 (rare).

874. Barlow, William. Chichester, bp. of (died in 1568). *'A dialogue describing the originall of the Lutheran factions &c.'.* London: (J. Cawood), [1553]. 8°.
Missing. In Godwin, [MS.] Wood D. 21(1), item 3244, p. 443, 'habeo'.
Not located. STC 1462.

875. Barlow, William. Lincoln, bp. of (died in 1613). *Vita et obitus . . . Richardi Cosin per Guilielmum Barlowum . . . edita [and] Carmina funebria, in ejusdem venerandi doctoris triste fatum.* Londini: deputati C. Barker, 1598. 4°. Pp. 80 (2nd tp at p. [49]).
Tp, note by former owner, A. Allam, 'Pret: 4ᵈ . . . 1678 Stev:'. LT 3.167.
Wood 345(5-6). STC 1460.

876. [Barnard, John]. *Censura cleri, or a plea against scandalous ministers, not fit to be restored.* London: f. G. Calvert, 1660. 4°. Pp. [2], 21.
Tp, AW wrote, 'Joh. Barnard lately of Linc. Coll. was the author of this -'.
[MS.] Wood D. 31(47). Wing B852.

877. Barnard, John. *Theologo-historicus, or the true life of . . . Peter Heylyn . . . an answer to mr. Baxters false accusations.* London: f. J. S., sold E. Eckelston, 1683. 8°. Pp. [15], 301 (2 tpp).
1st blank p., '1.9'. AW underscored or made marks in margins and brief notes at pp. 81, 107, 127, 152 (in pencil), 163, 176, 237, 262; and at 297-300, added 4 p. reference nos. in the 'Catalogue of such books . . . written by the Learned Doctor'.
Wood 433(4). Wing B854.

878. Barnes, Joshua. *An elegy on the death of the reverend doctor John Goad [28 Oct. 1689].* London: n.pub., 1689. S.sh.

ᵛ, AW wrote, 'Jo. Goad' and 'Jo. Goad 1689'. LT 1.151.
Wood 429(44). Wing B869 (two).

879. Barnes, Robert. *The supplicatyon made . . . unto Henrye the eyght.* [Antwerp] (London): [S. Cock]
(J. Byddell), [1531?] or (1534) or [1548]. 8°. 3 eds.
Missing. MS. Wood E. 2(70), p. 9, 'supplication of Dʳ Barnes'. Ed. not identified.
MS. Wood E. 2(70), p. 9. STC 1470 and 1471 and 1472. *Folg, Union.*

880. Barnet. *The married mens feast. Or, the banquet at Barnet.* London: P. Lillicrap f. J. Clark, 1671.
4°. Pp. [2], 6.
Wood 654a(26). Wing M712 (two).

881. [Baronius, Caesar]. B., A., i. e., Lassels, Richard, trans. *The life or the ecclesiasticall historie of s.*
Thomas archbishope of Canterbury [Trans. by A. B. of Annales eccl. by Caesar Baronius]. Colloniae [really
Paris]: [widow of J. Blageart], 1639. 8°. Pp. [6], 50, 396. Parchment.
Flyleaf, upper, 'haec historia ad verbum ex Caes. Baronii Annalium Tomo XII.° surrepta.', not in AW's
hand, and, AW wrote, 'ABosco Oxōn.' Tp, AW wrote, 'The life of Tho: Becket' and 'Becket'.
Wood 432. STC 1019. ARCR 2.488.

882. Barrow, Isaac. Tillotson, John, ed. *The works of the learned Isaac Barrow.* London: M. Flesher f. B.
Aylmer, 1687. Fol. 2nd. ed. Incomplete. Biographical introduction by A. H., a-d², only.
Wood 657(8) (not in Bodl. CD cat.). Wing B926.

883. Bartholinus, Caspar. *Anatomicae institutiones corporis humani.* Oxonii: G. Turner, 1633. 12°.
Pp. [24], 417, [47]. Calf with 2 fillets; clasp hole.
Flyleaf, upper, signature, lined out, A–de –erb . . . 1655'. Tp, 'rth 2 A' (shelf-mark?). Text, passim,
underscoring and notes, e.g., pp. 3ff. 73ff., etc. to 289-386, none in AW's hand or manner.
Wood 697(1). STC 1535. Madan 738.

884. Bartholinus, Caspar. *Enchiridion ethicum: seu epitome philosophiae moralis.* Oxonii: G. Turner,
1633. 12°. A-C¹².
Pastedown, lower, list of books on anatomy, not by AW.
Wood 697(2). STC 1535.5. Madan 739.

885. Bartholomew Fair. *'In Bartholomew Fair, at the corner of Hosier-lane, and near Mr. Parker's*
Booth; . . . a prodigious monster'. [London]: n.pub., [1685]. S.sh. 4° (10 lines).
Inserted, Wood Diaries 29 (item 171), f. 39*. AW wrote, '1685'.
[MS.] Wood Diaries 29b. Wing I109CA (one) ('O' not recorded in Wing).

886. Bartholomew Fair. *The High German artist: or, powder pimp a lim-pimp. This is to give notice.*
[London]: n.pub., [1688]. S.sh.
AW wrote, 'Barthelm. Faire 1688.' LT 3.275.
[MS.] Wood F. 50, f. 38. Not in Wing. Not in ESTCR.

887. Bartoli, Daniello. Salusbury, Thomas, trans. *The learned man defended and reform'd . . . in two*
parts. London: R. a. W. Leybourn, sold T. Dring, 1660. 8°. Pp. [24], 402, [4].
Acquired 24 Sept. 1664, LT 2.20.
Wood 130(5). Wing B988.

888. [Barwick, John]. *Querela Cantabrigiensis: or, a remonstrance . . . for the banished members . . . of*
the university of Cambridge. [London]: n.pub., 1647[8]. 8°. Pp. [12], 28, [8].
Pp. 4-5, [30-1,32-3, 35], mainly vertical lines, in pencil, most at names of persons; p. 11, AW wrote, 'q[uaere]'
at printed 'Lord Gray of Warke'. P. nos. 30-1 entered at [30-1].
Wood 207(3) (not in Bodl. CD cat.). Wing B1010.

889. Basill, William. *A letter from the atturney of Ireland concerning the taking of . . . Wexford [includes*
a letter dated 20 Oct.]. London: f. R. Ibbitson, 1649, 4 Oct. [sic]. 4°. Pp. [2], 5.
Tp, AW wrote, 'If Dupl. then to come in among battles' (no dupl. in AW's collection). P. 4, date of a letter
altered to '20' October.
Wood 510(10). Wing B1026.

890. Basing Castle. *A description of the seige [sic] of Basing castle.* Oxford: L. Lichfield, 1644[5]. 4°.
Pp. [2], 21.
P. 16, vertical line in margin, in pencil.

Wood 377(35). Wing D1170. Madan 1705.

891. Basire, Isaac. *The dead mans real speech. A funeral sermon . . . together with a brief of the life, . . . of . . . the . . . bishop of Durham [John Cosin].* London: E. T. a. R. H. f. J. Collins, 1673. 8°. Pp. [8], 128 (2nd tp at p. 29).
Flyleaf, upper, 1st, '1ˢ'. Pp. [2], AW wrote, 'Sepult. apud Aukland p. 90'; 36, '7 Death. p. 37'; 48, line in margin; 90, at a reference to the two heralds, 'Mʳ Will. Dugdale, Norroy [king of arms] & [blank]', at 'Auckland', a line in the margin; 111, at will of Cosin, 'This will concerning his religion was purposely written by him to free him from the censure of being a papist in his Exile - as [Thomas] Fuller -'.
Wood 307(6). Wing B1031.

892. Basire, Isaac, and John Barnes. Watson, Richard, trans. *The ancient liberty of the Britannick church, and the legitimate exemption thereof from the Roman patriarchate . . . by Isaac Basier . . . Three chapters concerning the priviledges of the Britannick church, . . . by f. I. Barnes.* London: f. John Mileson, sold E. Wallis, 1661. 8°. Pp. [24], 55, [19], 48, [12] (3 tpp.). Calf, speckled, with 2 fillets.
In the 1st intro., AW wrote p. nos. on rectos; A3v, 8 words of text lined out, may not be by AW; a2ᵛ, line in margin.
Wood 786. Wing B1029.

893. Basset, Ro[bert], trans. *Curiosities: or the cabinet of nature.* London: N. a. J. Okes, 1637. 12°. Pp. [23], 287. Parchment; upper and lower pastedowns and flyleaves, printer's waste paper.
Flyleaves and pastedowns, heavily annotated, not by AW. P. [1]ʳ, 'Sept 25 1645 6ᵈ', not by AW. Tp, AW wrote after the initial, B'asset'.
Wood 695. STC 1557.

894. [Bate, George]. *A compendious narrative of the late troubles in England.* [London]: n.pub., 1652. 12°. Pp. [10], 300. Pasteboard (grey) with parchment spine. Trace of upper flyleaf, marbled paper.
Flyleaf, upper, 5thᵛ, AW wrote the titles of 3 printed works in this vol., within guidelines made with red ink. In the 1st item each 12° leaf is pasted on an 8° template. Tp, AW wrote, 'W: July: 9: 1660'. Bsm. LT 1.321.
Wood 213(1). Wing B1077.

895. Bate, George. *The lives, actions, and execution of the prime actors, . . . of that horrid murder . . . of king Charles the first.* London: f. T. Vere, 1661. 12°. Pp. [9], 1-96, 49-72, 121-144 (out or order, misnumbering).
Each 12° leaf is pasted on an 8° template. Flyleaf, upperᵛ, 23 names and p. references to text. Fragment of a note on binding, on blank leaf pasted behind frontispiece for support, 'With this allowing ev . . . [/] Foot out of the snare [/] bound up[.] . . . New [/] the old snare' (Gee, Wood 648(1-2), item 3182f.). Pp. 12-3, 25, 37, 79, 51, various sorts of minor marks and annotations. Pp. 82, 89, 58, longer notes on the Scrope family, Francis Hacker, and Thomas and Robert Hammond. LT 2.507. See note at item 5993.
Wood 304(2). Wing B1084.

896. Bate, George. *Elenchi motuum nuperorum in Anglia.* Londini: J. Flesher, venalis ap. R. Royston, 1663. 8°. [11], 239, [20]. Calf, speckled, with 2 fillets, 2 vertical fillets, stamp decoration in corners, and roll decoration on edges of boards; spine, 4 bands and hatching. Flyleaves, printers' waste paper.
Flyleaf, upper, 2ndʳ⁻ᵛ, 'Ex libris Andreae Allam ex Aulā Sti Edmundi Oxon: 1675 Pret: 4ˢ-6ᵈ Oxl[ad] Sᵒʳ Bibli' and extensive notes by Allam on George Bate and this book. LT 3.167.
Wood 205. Wing B1081.

897. Bate, Henry. *Prince Charles sailing from Callice, towards the north of England . . . with prince Rupert.* London: n.pub., 1648. 4°. Pp. [2], 6.
Tp, AW wrote, 'Jul. 11'.
Wood 502(37). Wing B1091.

898. Bateman, Charles*. *An account of the tryal of Charles Bateman, chirurgeon, for high-treason [and] of John Holland and William Davis . . . and Agnes Wearing [9-11 Dec. 1685].* London: f. D. Mallet, 1685. Fol. Pp. [2], 18.
Wood 421(7). Wing A415.

899. Bateman, Stephen. *The doome warning all men to the judgemente:. . . . in maner of a generall chronicle, gathered . . . by St. Batman.* London: R. Nubery, assigned by H. Bynneman, 1581. 4°. Pp. [20], 437. Calf with 3 fillets, stamp roll decoration and 3 fillets, centrepiece; illuminated ms. backing.
Tp, 4 letters, lined out. A few hand pointers, not in AW's manner; 45, note, not by AW.

Wood 649. STC 1582.

900. Bateman, Thomas. *Sir Thomas Bateman's case upon an appeal by him . . . from a decree pronounced in chancery*. [London?]: n.pub., [1685?]. S.sh.
Wood 276b(79). Wing S3891B (rare).

901. Batten, Wil[liam]. *A declaration of . . . concerning his departure from London, to . . . the prince of Wales*. London: n.pub., 1648. 4°. Pp. [2], 5.
Wood 502(50). Wing B1152.

902. B[axter], J. *A toile for two-legged foxes: wherein their noisome properties; . . . is livelie discovered, . . . against all popish practises*. London: F. Kyngston f. T. Man, 1600. 8°. Pp. [20], 220. Parchment.
Flyleaf, upper[v], 'Libri in hoc volumine' and the titles of 3 printed works in this vol., followed by 'Liber Antonij Wood, è Musæo Johannis Spedæi M. D. C: S Johannis Oxon, emptus: A.D. 1661.' ' (24 Sept., LT 1.416). Tp, bsm.
Wood 794(1). STC 1596.

903. Baxter, Richard. *A holy commonwealth, or political aphorisms, opening the true principles of government*. London: f. T. Underhill a. F. Tyton, 1659. 8°. A[8],a-e[8],B-2L[8]; and p. nos. begin at sig. B: 517, [11] (9 pp. books printed for Underhill and Tyton). Calf with 2 fillets, and a vertical 2 fillets; rebacked.
Flyleaf, upper, 2nd, signature of 'Edw: Poole'.
Wood 459. Wing B1281.

904. Baxter, Rich[ard]. *A breviate of the life of Margaret, the daughter of Francis Charlton esq; and wife of Richard Baxter*. London: f. B. Simmons, 1681. 4°. Pp. [10], 107.
Flyleaf, upper, AW wrote, 'Given to me by Mr Moses Pit stationer Oct. 18 an. 1681.' LT 2.556.
Wood 532(15). Wing B1194.

905. Baxter, Richard. *A sermon preached at the funeral of . . . John Corbet*. London: f. T. Parkhurst, [1681]. 4°. Pp. [2], 36, [1] (1 page bibliog. of writings of Corbet).
Tp, note of purchase ('to M[r] West for this sermon'?) at bottom, all cropped except '6[d]'. Pp. 27, at Godfrey Goodman 'a *Papist* Bishop of the Protestant Church', AW wrote, 'Goodman onlie died a papist, he was not one in his life-time.'; 28, Corbet's final illness and the operation, 'of the stone'; 31, at 'a nameless Writer' who attacked Corbet's *Interest of England*, '*M[r] Sam Th[o-]mas of ch.[ch.] Ox.' (cropped at side); 2nd p. [1], at entry of *The Interest of England*, 'see p. 31' (i.e., where he had identified Thomas). AO 3.1266 (AW altered 'a nameless Writer' in Baxter's sermon (p. 31) to 'a shameless writer'). LT 1.453, 2.515.
Wood 634(3). Wing B1416.

906. Baxter, Richard. *Compassionate counsel to all young-men*. London: H. Clark f. G. Conyers, 1691. 8°. 2nd ed. Pp. [20], 180 (16 pp. books by Baxter). Calf, speckled, with 2 fillets and a vertical line of 2 fillets.
Sig. (*4), line in margin at a book by Baxter.
Wood 815. Wing B1230.

907. Bayly, Lewis. Bangor, bp. of. *The practice of piety*. [London]: n.pub., 1648. 16°. 'The last edition.' Pp. [10], 411, [4]. Calf with 3 fillets; upper and lower flyleaves, printer's waste paper.
Flyleaf, upper[r-v], minor scribbling, some by AW. Flyleaf, lower, last, the same, not by AW, and a note on the waste paper by F. Madan in 1918, Bodl. has 2 copies.
Wood 759. Wing B1478 (rare, 2 at O).

908. Bayly, Tho[mas]. *The life & death of . . . John Fisher bishop of Rochester . . . by Tho: Baily*. London: n.pub., 1655. 8°. Pp. [6], 261.
P. 2, AW made a correction.
Wood 307(3). Wing B1513.

909. Bayly, Tho[mas]. *The golden apophthegms of . . . Charles 1. and Henry marq. of Worcester*. London: J. Clowes, 1660. 4°. Pp. 8.
Tp, Bayly underlined, in red ink.
Wood 631(20). Wing G1012 ('O' not recorded in Wing).

910. Baynes, Paul. *A counterbane against earthly carefulness*. London: H. L[ownes] f. N. Newbery, 1618. 4°. Pp. 25, [2] (wanting all before B1, i.e., before p. 1).
Pp. passim, underscoring and minor notes, not by AW.
Wood 634(12) (not in Bodl. CD cat.). STC 1638.

911. Be Merry. *Be merry and wise, or, a seasonable word to the nation.* London: n.pub., 1660, 13 March. 4° (cropped). Pp. [2], 6.
Tp, AW altered date to 16'59: March'.
Wood 610(44). Wing B1555.

912. B[eale], J[ohn]. *Hereford shire orchards, a pattern for all England. Written . . . to Samuel Hartlib.* London: R. Daniel, 1657. 8°. Pp. [2], 62.
Each small 8° leaf is pasted on an 8° template. Tp, AW wrote 'Sept: 11. A. 1660'.
Wood 730(2). Wing B1558.

913. Beale, Thomas. *A true discovery of bloody plott intended to have been put in practice.* London: f. the author, sold H. Walker, 1641. 4°. Pp. [2], 6.
AW wrote, 'ridiculous', in pencil, and '18. Nov.', in ink.
Wood 373(7). Wing B1559A.

914. Beane, Richard. *A discourse concerning popish perjurers in an address to the . . . commons . . . at Oxford.* London: f. H. Brome, 1681. 4°. Pp. [4], 9, [2] (p. [1] blank).
Wood 608(54). Wing B1561.

915. Bea[u]mont, Francis, and John Fletcher. *A king, and no king.* London: A. M[athewes] f. R. Hawkins, 1631. 4°. 3rd printing. Pp. [2], 91.
Tp, signature, 'Mary Wood'.
Wood 330(8). STC 1672.

916. Beaumont, Francis, and John Fletcher. *A king and no king, as it is now acted at the Theatre Royal.* London: A. Clark, f. W. a. J. Leake, 1676. 4°. Pp. [4], 76.
Tp, 'Royal', not in AW's hand.
Wood 320(8). Wing B1591.

917. Beccadelli, Lodovico. Dudith, Andreas, trans. *Vita Reginaldi Poli.* Venetiis: D. Guerrei, & J. Baptistae fratrum, 1563. Ff. 48.
Tp, AW recorded information from the text: 'This life was written by Ludov. Becatellus Ragusionorum [sic] Archiep. in the Italian tongue, translated into Lat. as here it is, by Andr. Duditius Sbordellatus [sic] &c'. Tp[v], 'Andr Duditius was Bishop of Quinqu ecclesia [sic] in Hungrary [sic]' and 10 lines of further details about Duditius, concluding with 'De authore p. 11.b 15.b. 18.a.' Text, passim, some vertical lines in margins, a few corrections, and cross-references.
Wood 345(4). BL.

918. Beck, Margaret. *The reward of oppression, tyranny and injustice, committed by the late kings . . . by the unlawful entry, . . . of the dutchie lands of Lancaster.* London: n.pub., 1656. 4°. Pp. [6], 9.
Pp. 1, 2, 5, 7, a longer note, 'This is a most damnable lye of both the Parl . . . .', and brief notes, not by AW.
Wood 478(6). Wing B1649.

919. Becket, Saint Thomas*. Littleton, W., ed. *The prophecie of Thomas Becket, . . . concerning the wars betwixt England France, and Holland; . . . found by dr. Ailsworth.* London: f. G. Freeman, 1666. 4°. Pp. [2], 6.
Tp and p.1, AW corrected Ailsworth to Aylworth, and p. 2, at editor, W. Littleton, wrote 'Tinker alias Littleton'. See Wood 646(13), item 6240, and AO 3.1056.
Wood 646(12). Wing B1651. Madan 2725.

920. Becon, Thomas. *The reliques of Rome, contayning all such matters of religion . . . brought . . . by the pope and his adherentes.* London: J. Day, 1563 (30 Sept.). 8°. Corrected. Ff. [28], 266. Calf with 3 fillets, bronze clasps and centrepiece and corner protectors.
Board, upper, stamped 'HM'. Flyleaf, upper[v], 'Ant Woode Oxōn [lined out] of the gift of M[r] John Wilton 1665'. LT 2.38. Tp, bsm. Lent to H. Foules, 17 Oct. 1668, LT 2.145.
Wood 839. STC 1755.

921. Bede the Venerable. Stapleton, Thomas, trans. *The history of the church of Englande.* Antwerp: J. Laet, 1565. 4°. Ff. [14], 192, [4]. Calf with 3 fillets, stamp decoration (dragons) inside corners, and roll on spine ends (Ashm. binding).
Flyleaf, upper, 2nd, the titles of 13 printed works in this vol., made by an Ashm. librarian (same hand in Wood 276a). Tp, AW wrote, 'Censure of Stapletons translations of Bedes Hist. into Engl. – see Seldens

Preface to the Decem scriptores printed at London 1652. p. 9. 10' (Wing H2094). Passim, some double vertical lines in margin, a few other marks and minor underscoring, not in AW's manner.
[MS.] Wood D. 23(1). STC 1778. ARCR 2.733.

922. Bede the Venerable, and Egbertus. Ware, James, ed. *Epistolae duae, necnon vitae abbatum Wiremuthensium & Girwiensium. Accessit Egberti . . . Dialogus, de ecclesiastica institutione.* Dublinii: J. Crook, sumpt. S. Dancer & sociorum, 1664. 8°. Pp. [12], 135.
Tp, '1' [shilling]. Acquired 11 March 1665, 9^d, LT 2.31.
Wood 183(4). Wing B1660.

923. [Bedford, Samuel]. *A brief relation of the taking of Bridgewater by the parliaments forces under . . . sir Tho: Fairfax; . . . together with a letter concerning . . . Pontefract castle.* London: f. E. Husband, 1645, 25 July. 4°. Pp. 6, [1].
Tp, AW altered the former no., '12'.
Wood 378(14). Wing B1666.

924. Bedford, and T. V. *Good and true newes from Bedford:. . . Together with another letter from the Lion.* London: Printed for R. Astine. A. Coe [sic], 1643. 4°. A^4.
Tp, AW altered a former no.
Wood 376(47). Wing G1036A ('O' not recorded in Wing) (Wing, & true).

925. Bedloe, William. *Capt. William Bedloe, discoverer of the late plott.* [London]: n.pub., [1679 to 1681]. S.sh. (engr.).
Half length, facing to right; oval frame. Front. to the portrait in his *Life* (1681), engraver [R. White]. Wood 425(6), item 926, has a similar engraving (different impression). LT 2.452. There is no item at Wood 276a(7); there is a blank after VII in the list of contents at the beginning of Wood 276a.
Wood 276a(6) (not in Bodl. CD cat.). *Engraved Portraits*, 1.158.

926. Bedloe, William. *A narrative and impartial discovery of the horrid popish plot: carried on for the burning . . . cities of London and Westminster.* London: f. R. Boulter, J. Hancock, R. Smith, a. B. Harris, 1679. Fol. Pp. [13], blank leaf, 27.
Tp, AW wrote 'June 1679 beginning of July', in pencil. LT 3.452.
Wood 425(6). Wing B1677.

927. Bedloe, William*. *Tears, tears, tears: or, Rome in ashes. . . . upon . . . the death of captain Bedlow.* London: f. the edification of study Roman Catholicks, 1680, 5 Nov. S.sh.
^{v}, AW wrote the date, '5 Nov 1680', and '1680', in pencil.
Wood 417(41). Wing T610.

928. Bedloe, William, and Miles Prance. *A succinct narrative of the bloody murder of sir Edmondbury Godfrey by the papists, Oct. 12. 1678. . . . depositions given . . . by captain William Bedloe, and mr. Miles Prance.* N.p.: (for the use of M. Prance), (1683). S.sh. (r-v).
LT 2.419.
Wood 424(11). Wing S6115B (two).

929. Bee, Cornelius. *The case of Cornelius Bee and his partners [against M. Poole's proposed inclusion of critici sacri in his synopsis criticorum aliorumque s. scripturae interpretum].* [London]: n.pub., [1666?]. S.sh.
Former no., '2'.
Wood 658(784c). Wing C900 (two).

930. Bee, Cornelius. *Mr. Bee's answer to mr. Poole's second vindication of his design for printing a synopsis of criticall and other commentators [10 June].* [London]: n.pub., (1668). Fol. Pp. [4].
P. 1, former no., '6'.
Wood 658(784d). Wing B1679 (rare).

931. Bee, Cornelius. *To the considerations already printed by Cornelius Bee [an addition to Bee's case against M. Poole's proposed inclusion of critici sacri in his synopsis criticorum aliorumque s. scripturae interpretum].* [London]: n.pub., [1668?]. S.sh.
Former no., '3'.
Wood 658(784a). Not in Wing. Not in ESTCR.

932. [Beham, Hans Sebald]. *Typi in apocalypsi Joannis depicti ut clarius Vaticinia Joannis intelligi possint.* Francoforti: cum caes. majestiati privilegio, (1539). 8°. A-C^4, D1-3.

Wood 79(2) (now Arch. G. f. 2(2)). BL.

933. Behn, [Aphra]. *Prologue to Romulus*. (London): (N. Thompson), (1682). S.sh. (r-v).
Wood 417(95). Wing B1760.

934. Belfast, Presbytery. *A necessary examination of a dangerous design . . . by the presbytery at Belfast . . . in their . . . libel, by them called, a necessary presentation*. London: T. Brudenell, 1649. 4°. Pp. [2], 22.
Wood 510(13). Wing N368 ('O' not recorded in Wing).

935. Bell, Adam, pseud. *Adam Bell, Clim of the Clough, and William of Cloudesle*. London: W. Jaggard, 1610. 4°. A-B⁴,C1-3.
Tp, '23ˢ.8ᵈ', and scribble, prob. not by AW.
Wood 483(14). STC 1810 (rare).

936. Bell, Thomas. *The anatomie of popish tyrannie*. London: J. Harison f. R. Bankworth, 1603. 4°. Pp. [24], 184, [8]. Parchment.
Tp, bsm. Pp. 18, 'q[uaere]' at printed 'Weston the Jesuite', and 20, vertical line at printed 'death of . . . English priest, Cardinall Allen', both in red ink.
[MS.] Wood C. 38. STC 1814.

937. Bell, Thomas. *The tryall of the new religion*. London: W. Jaggard, 1608. 4°. A-G⁴ (A1-2 blank).
Tp, '448' and 'And', not in AW's hand.
Wood 627(2). STC 1832.

938. Bellamie, John. *A plea for the commonalty of London, or, a vindication of their rights . . . in the choice of sundry city officers . . . a speech [24 Feb. 1644]*. London: G. Miller, 1645. 8°. 2nd ed. Pp. [8], 29.
Each 8° leaf is pasted on a 4° template. Tp, '6', twice (price?).
Wood 590(4). Wing B1817.

939. Bellarmino, Saint Roberto Francesco R. *De scriptoribus ecclesiasticis liber unus. Cum . . . chronologia ab orbe conditio usque ad . . . M.DC.XXXI*. Coloniae Agrippinae: sumt. B. Gualteri, 1631. 8°. Pp. [16], 335, [1], 117. Calf with 3 fillets.
Flyleaf, upper, '2ˢ 4ᵈ', in pencil, not by AW. Tp, bsm. Pp. 34-41, some marks in margins and underscoring, not in AW's manner. Flyleaf lower, last, notes in pencil, illeg.
Wood 857. BL.

940. Benedict, Saint. *The effects and virtues of the crosse or medal of the great patriarch st. Benedict*. N.p.: n.pub., 1669. 12°. Pp. 11.
Wood 893(3). Wing E244AB (two).

941. Benedictine Order. Courbes, J[ean Baptiste] de, sculp. *Arbor Benedictina ad ill^{mu}. cardinalem Rupifucaldum ejusdem custodem ac defensorem studiosissimum*. Parisiis: cum privilegio regis A. de la Rivierre, 1625. S.sh. 426 x 572 mm (untrimmed) (engr.).
Several Benedictine items may have come to AW from Ralph Sheldon, via Dom Edward Sheldon OSB. Or, acquired 30 July 1659, 1ˢ, LT 1.279. See also Wood 276a(2), item 350.
Wood 276b(15). Not in BL. Not in BN.

942. Benedictine Order. English congregation. *Constitutiones missionis Benedictinorum congregationis Anglicanae. Editae authoritate capituli generalis anno 1661 celebrati*. Duaci: L. [sic] Kellami, 1661. 24°. Pp. 165.
Tp, signature lined out. Flyleaf, lowerᵛ, 'F. G. Mallett ad usum' not in AW's hand.
Wood 756. BL.

943. [Benlowes, Edward]. *Oxonii encomium. In florentissimam Oxonii academiam, scientiarum officinam*. (Oxonii): (H. Hall), (1672). Fol. 1,A-D² (p. nos. irregular).
D2, after the name of Benlowes's college, AW wrote, 'Cantabr.', and below, 'Antonii à Wood, Ex dono authoris /'. LT 2.361. AOF 2.358-9.
Wood 423(44). Wing B1875. Madan 2915.

944. [Benlowes, Edward]. *Magia coelestis. Invocatio . . . aenigmata evangelica*. Oxoniae: ex off. Lichfieldiana, 1673. Fol. (2 sheets, obl.).
Sheet 1 on ᵛ, AW wrote, 'Benellowes his Magia Coelestis'; sheet 2, below, an engraved anagram in an ornament, 'Benevolvs' and '1 2 3 8 6 5 4 7 9'; below the engraving, in ms., 'Cantabrigiensis.', not by AW;

and below that, AW wrote 'Edw. Benlows'. LT 2.351. AOF 2.358-9.
Wood 276a(518-9). Wing B1873 (two). Madan 2967.

945. [Benlowes, Edward]. *Oxonii elogia, academicis praecellentioribus.* [Oxford]: [at the theatre], [1673].
S.sh.
Signed by author, 'Benevolus' with his numbers, below, '1 2 3 8 6 5 4 7 9', and prob. in AW's hand, '(An. 1673)'. ᵛ, 'Will' ?? and '1673', not in AW's hand. AOF 2.358-9.
Wood 423(45). Wing B1874 (rare). Madan 2968 .

946. Benlowes, Edward, and Daniel King. Loggan, D[avid], fec[it]. *On St. Paul's cathedrall represented by mʳ Dan. King. . . . Threnodia ædis Paulinae de seipsā.* [London]: D: King. delin. et excudit, 1658. S.Sh.
424 x 530 mm (untrimmed) (engr.).
Tp, AW wrote, '1ˢ'. This particular engraving is not in the Douce copy of Daniel King, *The cathedrall and conventuall churches of England* (1656) (Bodl. Douce Prints c. 32). For Wood 276b(37-8), see note at Wood 276b(39), item 5914.
Wood 276b(36). Engraving.

947. Bennion, John. *Moses's charge to Israel's judges, opened in an assise sermon.* Oxford: sold F. Dollif, 1681. 4°. Pp. [7], 20.
Tp, AW underscored 'Bennion' and wrote, 'Edm. Hall'.
Wood 633(12). Wing B1890.

948. Bense, Petrus. *Analogo-diaphora, seu concordantia discrepans, . . . Gallicae, Italicae, & Hispanicae.* Oxoniae: G. Turner, 1637. 8°. Pp. [6], 72.
Pp. 1-4, some underscorings at grammatical matters.
Wood 42(4). STC 1885. Madan 847.

949. Berkly, Michael*. *The most sad and lamentable narration of the death of Michaell Berkly.* London: f. T. Vere a. W. Gilbertson, 1658. 8°. Pp. [2], 14.
Wood 284(9). Wing M2918 (rare) (Wing, Michael and Gilbert).

950. Berkshire, Letter. *To the right honorable Will: Lenthal speaker to the parliament.* London: f. E. Thomas, 1659[60]. S.sh.
AW added to the year, 'Jan:'.
Wood 276a(254). Wing T1716.

951. Bernard, Edward. *Edvardi Bernardi de mensuris et ponderibus antiquis libri tres. Ed. altera, purior & locupletior.* Oxoniae: e theatro Seldonio [sic], 1688. 8°. Ed. altera. Pp. [16], 261, [86]. Calf, mottled, with fillets and stamp decoration (tulips) in corners.
Flyleaf, upper, 2ndᵛ, 'Anton. à Wood [/] Ex dono Edw. Bernardi authoris – Sav. profess. Astron. Oxōn. 22. Jun. 1688'. LT 3.270.
Wood 572. Wing B1987.

952. Bernard, Edward. Burghers, M[ichael], sculp. *Orbis eruditi literaturam à charactere Samaritico.* Oxoniae: ap. Theatrum, [1689]. S.sh.
Wood 276a(24). Wing B1989.

953. Bernard, Nicholas. *A true and perfect relation of all the severall skirmishes . . . and . . . victories obtained . . . when they raised the siege of Tredagh.* London: f. J. Wright, 1641[2]. 4°. Pp. [1], 7.
Tp, under the woodcut, AW wrote, 'Newcastle'; in margin, 'In vol . . .'
Wood 507(47). Wing B2019.

954. Bernard, Nicholas. *The whole proceedings of the siege of Drogheda.* London: A. N. f. W. Bladen, 1642. 4°. Pp. [23], 90.
Wood 507(48). Wing B2020.

955. Bernard, Nicholas. *The life & death of . . . James Usher.* London: E. Tyler, sold J. Crook, 1656. 8°. Pp. [14], 119, [3] (3 pp. books sold by Crook).
Flyleaf, upper, AW wrote, 'Nicholas Bernard the author of this book – (see Canterb. dome – Nath ibid.[?]' [i.e., William Prynne, *Canterburies doome* (1646), Wood 540, item 5430]. Tp, surname of author underlined in red ink. A4ᵛ, A6, A8, brief note, underscoring, or marks in margin; A8, at Usher's family, AW wrote a reference marker, ", and '"daugh. wife of S. Tim. Tirrell of Shotover in Oxfordshire.' Text, some underscoring, lines in margins and brief notes, e.g., pp. 11, 13, 20-1 28, 34, 42-3, etc. to end. P. 108, at printed '[Usher] sitting up late in the Colledge Library of *Dublyn*', AW wrote, 'That is not allowed to be in

any library in Oxon.' Pp. 119-[120], AW wrote a 31-line entry on the death and funeral of Usher, 21 March 1655/6 - 17 Apr., which he used almost verbatim for AO 4.799-800; e.g., AW's last ms. sentence, 'where, after the said Dr. Bernard had preached over most of this book, he was there interred' varies only slightly from the entry in AO: 'Where after the said Dr. Bernard had preached before the large auditory a sermon, it was inter'd.' LT 1.203.
Wood 307(5). Wing B2012.

956. Bernard, Richard. *A guide to grand jury men . . . in cases of witchcraft.* London: F. Kingston f. E. Blackmore, 1627. 12°. Pp. [18], 267. Parchment.
Flyleaf, upper, scribble, not by AW.
Wood 575. STC 1943.

957. Bernardiston, Samuel*. *The tryal and conviction of s^r· Sam. Bernardiston, . . . for high-misdemeanor [14 Feb.].* London: f. B. Tooke, 1684. Fol. Pp. [3], 34.
1st blank, AW wrote '1^s'.
Wood 428(27). Wing T2164.

958. Beroaldus, Philippus. Salter, Thomas, trans. *A contention betwene three bretheren . . . the whore-monger, the dronkarde, and the dice-player, to approve which of them three is the worste.* London: f. T. Gosson, 1581. 8°. Ff. 25-46 only (imperf.).
Wood 736(2a). STC 1968.5 (rare, 2 at O).

959. Berrow, Jo[hn], and Jo[hn] Wade, et. al. *Certaine reasons (by way of reply to some objections . . . to a paper styled the case of John Gifford . . . why those iron-works in the forrest of Deane should be . . . demolisht.* [London?]: n.pub., [1650?]. 4°. Pp. 8.
Dupl. at Wood 609(27b).
[MS.] Wood D. 27(2). Wing C1749 (rare, 2 at O).

960. Berrow, Jo[hn], and Jo[hn] Wade, et al. *Certaine reasons (by way of reply to some objections . . . to a paper styled the case of John Gifford . . . why those iron-works in the forrest of Deane should be . . . demolisht.* [London?]: n.pub., [1650?]. 4°. Pp. 8.
Dupl. at [MS.] Wood D. 27(2).
Wood 609(27b) (not in Bodl. CD cat.). Wing C1749 (rare, 2 at O).

961. Bertius, P[etrus]. *Breviarium totius orbis terrrarum.* Francofurti: in off. Bryana. Typ. C. Rōtelii, 1627. 12°. Pp. [8], 72, [2]. Calf with 3 fillets and stamp decoration in corners (Ashm. binding).
Flyleaf, upper, 1st, name, Dr. Go–s Lopich (? illeg.) (not in AW's hand); 2nd, titles of 5 printed works in this vol., written by an Ashm. librarian (who included, as separate items, 2 sections of Wood 196(2)); and some dates, 1608 and 1757.
Wood 196(1). BL.

962. Bertius, Petrus, and Etienne de Courcelles. K., J., trans. *The life and death of James Arminius and Simon Episcopius.* London: T. Ratcliff a. N. Thompson, f. F. Smith, 1672. 8°. Pp. [5], 34, [3], 28, [2] (2 pp. books printed for Smith).
2nd p. 8, dropped line added, may not be in AW's hand.
Wood 289(2). Wing B2048.

963. Bertramus. D., S., trans. *The book of Bertram the priest, concerning the body and blood . . . To which is added, two short discourses against purgatory and invocation of saints.* London: f. W. Taylor, 1686. 12°. Pp. [36], 130.
Tp, 'Ar Charlet', cropped, over an earlier name; lines in margin. Diff. ed. at Wood 835(6).
Wood 835(5). Wing B2049A.

964. Bertramus. Lynde, Humphrey, ed. *The book of Bertram the priest, concerning the body and blood of Christ in the sacrament.* London: B. Griffin, sold S. Keble, 1687. 12°. Pp. [36], 96.
Diff. ed. at Wood 835(5).
Wood 835(6). Wing B2050.

965. [Besnier, Pierre]. Rose, Henry, trans. *A philosophicall essay for the reunion of the languages.* Oxford: H. Hall f. J. Good, 1675. 8°. Pp. [6], 79.
Tp, '6^d'. After year, AW wrote 'Oct.-74 written ['translated', crossed out] as tis reported by Hen. Rose A.M. somtimes Fellow of Lync. Coll. in Oxon.' LT 3.349; AOF 2.332.
Wood 37(4). Wing B2051A. ESTCR 11378 and 229445. Madan 3075 (Rose, H.).

966. Besongne, N[icolas]. *L'estat de la France novvellement corrigé*. Paris: la vefve Pierre David, 1661. 8°. Pp. [39], 739, [3]. Parchment over pasteboard.
Pastedown, upper, 'Hen. Foulis è Coll. Linc. Oxon. Octob[r]. 24. i660.' Tp, '1[tt] - wx' (bsm.?) and bsm. LT 2.180.
Wood 579 (not in Bodl. CD cat.). BN.

967. [Bethel, Slingsby]. *A true and impartial narrative of the . . . debates . . . in the late parliament. Together with the rise and disolution [sic] of it*. London: f. T. Brewster, 1659. 4°. Pp. 14.
Tp, AW wrote, 'This parl. began, by protector Richards call, 27. Jan. 1658[9] - Dissolved 26. Apr. 1659'.
Wood 519(11). Wing B2077 ('O' not recorded in Wing).

968. [Bethel, Slingsby]. *Ludlow no lyar, or a detection of dr. [Richard] Hollingworth's disingenuity*. Amsterdam: n.pub., 1692. 4°. Pp. xx, 63, [1].
Tp, AW wrote the price, '1[s]-0', in pencil.
Wood 363(10). Wing B2068. FFMadan 169.

969. Bevis of Hampton*. *Sir Bevis of Hampton*. London: R. Bishop, [1639?]. 4°. Newly corrected. A-H⁴,I².
Flyleaf, upper, 2nd[v], AW wrote, 'In the first time of the Normans an. 1066, Bogo or Beavose or Bevis the English man, who fought against the Normans in the battle of Cardiff in Wales, is reputed to have been Earl. of Southampton, a man for warlike prowesse much renowned; whome, while the Monks Laboured to set out with their fained fables, they have obscured his doughty Deeds in greater Darkness &c. - Camden in Britan. in Hampshire' (W. Camden, *Britannia* (London, 1594): 203, Hantshire).
Wood 321(4). STC 1996 (two).

970. Bible. *The holy bible*. Edinburgh: [R. Young], 1633. 8°. ², A-3M⁴.
Missing in 1837. Ed. not identified.
Wood 887a. STC 2311 and 2311a. *Folg, Hunt*.

971. Bible. *The holy bible*. London: Co. of Stationers, printed by the, 1650. 8°. A-2Z⁸ (last leaf blank). Calf with 2 fillets; rebacked. Flyleaf, upper, printer's waste paper.
Pastedown upper, figures and biblical references, not by AW. Backing, biblical references, not by AW, and signature, 'Anthony Wood'. Flyleaf, upper, 2nd, scribbles and 'Rob. Parry', 'Edwad [sic] Lhwyd' and 'Edward', and 'Giliecholum Macmuluen' [sic]. Last p.[v], and pastedown, lower, scribbles, bibles references, and 4 signatures by 'Giliecholum Macmulen' (for this notorious helper at the Ashm., from 22 Oct. 1703 to 1 Jan. 1707, see R. Ovenell, *Ashmolean Museum* (1986): 102-3). Text, frequent marginalia in Genesis, less and less later, none by AW. 2M7[v], signature of Robert Wyeen (prob. Robert Wynn, another Ashm. employee, 1697-1700).
Wood 873(1). Wing B2231.

972. Bible. Ailmer, John, trans. *Musae sacrae: seu Jonas, Jeremiae threni, & Daniel Graeco redditi carmine*. Oxoniae: excud. L. Lichfield, veneunt ap. J. Godwin & R. Davis, 1652. 8°. Pp. [32], 241, [6].
Tp, AW underscored the translator's surname in red ink.
Wood 817(3). Wing B2739G. Madan 2190.

973. Bible, Apocalypse. Woodhead, Abraham, ed. *The Apocalyps paraphrased [with] An extract of out Bishop Mountague's appeal . . . concerning Mahomet*. N.p.: n.pub., [1689]. 4°. No t leaf. Pp. 117, [7].
In AO 3.1163, AW stated that this work was 'not compleated', and it may never have had a t leaf. [MS.] Wood B. 36(5-6). Not in Wing (but see after W3435A). Not in ESTCR.

974. Bible, Catechism. *The doctrine of the bible: or, rules of discipline*. London: T. Radcliffe f. J. Wright, 1666. 12°. Newly corrected. Ff. [1], 210, [1] (2 ff. books printed f. E. Brewster). Calf.
Flyleaf, upper, 1st, 'Ex libris Andræ Allam Anno Domini. 1671'; 2nd, '1669 Andrew Allam his booke Amen'. Flyleaf, upper, 1st traces of accounts. F. 1[v]-27[v], a few crosses in margin, in pencil, prob. not by AW. Flyleaves, lower, accounts, mainly purchases of paper, and a date, 'March 5th 1614', and some scribbling by Allam. LT 3.167.
Wood 764. Wing D1773cA (rare).

975. Bible, New Testament. Hoole, Charles, ed. Η καινη διαθηκε. *Novum Testamentum. Huic editioni omnia difficiliorum vocabularum themata, quae in Georgii Pasoris lexico grammatice resolvuntur, in margine apposuit Carolus Hoole*. London: Excud. R. Nortonus pro J. Kyrton, 1653, 1664, 1672. 12°.
Missing. MS. Wood E. 2(70), p. 56 (ed. not identified).
MS. Wood E. 2(70), p. 56. Wing B2731-4.

976. Bible, New Testament. Hyde, Thomas, ed. *Jang ampat evangelia . . . That is, the four gospels . . . and the Acts . . . translated into the Malayan tongue. [Intro.] 'For the English Reader', by Tho. Marshall.* Oxford: H. Hall, 1677. 4°. Pp. [4], 14 (t leaf and prelims. only).
Tp, AW wrote, 'ABosco, ex dono Tho. Marshall Coll. Lync. Rectoris 20 Dec. 1677' (cropped at top), and below, 'by Th. Hyde'. AO 4.172 and 524.
[MS.] Wood B. 36(2). Wing B2796. Madan 3164.

977. Bible, Psalms. English. *The book of Psalms [extr. from a Bible].* N.p.: n.pub., [1670 ca.]. 4° in 8's. 1^v [i.e., 2G8^v],2H-2L^8. Parchment.
Wood 650. Wing B2501ff. (not identified).

978. Bible, Psalms. English. *The whole booke of Psalmes collected into English meeter by T. Sternhold, J. Hopkins [et al.].* London: J. Windet f. the assignes of R. Daye, 1598. 16°. A-Y^8,2A-2M^8.
Flyleaf, lower^v, AW wrote 'This was the Lady Grisil Pointz book given to her by her mother'.
Wood 757(2). STC 2494a.5 (two).

979. Bible, Psalms. Sternhold, Thomas and John Hopkins, eds. *The whole book of Psalms.* London: W. Bentley, 1649. 8°. Pp. [2], 77, [9].
P. [9], 'Giliecholum Macmulen' and scribbles. See note at Wood 873(1), item 971.
Wood 873(2). Wing B2438.

980. Bible, Ten Commandments. Chertsey, Andrew, trans. *Ihesus. The floure of the commaundmentes of god with many examples and auctorytees.* London: (W. de Worde), (1510, 14 Sept.). Fol. (wanting the t leaf, A1). A2-6,B-D^6 and ff. 261. Pasteboard (blue) with parchment spine.
Flyleaf, upper, 1st, 'This booke made in the 2 yeare of Henry 8 1510', not in AW's hand, and 'R[ichard] Reeve[s] Ex dono D^{ris} [Edward] Exton. M.D. Coll. Mag. Socii' (LT 2.280; AO 4.386); ^{v} AW wrote the complete t: 'The flower . . . Translated out of French'. Text, minor scribbles and notes, to colophon, f. 261^v, some cropped, none in AW's hand. D6^{r-v}, several religious platitudes or stories, e.g. 'Jesus sayde unto his dysciples' and 'Thomas one of the twelve which was callede didimus . . . ', not in AW's hand.
Wood 641. STC 23876.

981. Bibliotheca. *Bibliotheca militum: or the souldiers publick library.* London: n.pub., 1659. 4°. Pp. [2], 6.
[MS.] Wood C. 26(17). Wing B2841.

982. Biddle, John. *The apostolical and true opinion concerning the holy trinity. [With] The testimonies of Irenaeus.* London: n.pub., 1653. 8°. Pp. [18], 35, [19], 60, [2], 86 (3 tpp.). Calf with 2 fillets and a vertical line of 2 fillets.
Flyleaf, upper, 1st, A. Allam wrote 'Pret: 1^s-6^d W[est] Bibl: Sext: [August] die 18 1675'. LT 3.167. Diff. ed. at Wood 647(21).
Wood 806. Wing B2868.

983. Biddle, John. *The apostolical and true opinion concerning the holy trinity, revived and asserted: partly by twelve arguments.* [London]: n.pub., 1691. 4°. Rpt. Pp. 16, 16, [8], 24, 32 (4 pts.).
Tp, Bidle corrected to Biddle. Former no., '9', in pencil. Diff. ed. at Wood 806.
Wood 647(21). Wing B2868B.

984. Biddulph, William. Lavender, Theophilus, intro. *The travels of foure English men and a preacher into Africa, Asia.* London: F. Kyngston, f. W. Aspley, 1612. 4°. Pp. [16], 120.
Flyleaf, waste paper, a disputation topic, 'An sint quatuor genera oppositorum' and '42.', not by AW. Tp, AW wrote 'Gul. Biddulph.' and '1612'. Text, pp. 52-119, some lines, hands, and wavy lines in margins, in pencil, prob. not by AW.
Wood 387(3). STC 3052.

985. Bill of Sale. *A bill of sale. In Westminster-hall, on the 22d. of January, will be sold by inch of candle, these following goods.* [London]: n.pub., [1689?]. S.sh. (r-v).
Wood 417(175). Wing B2896B (rare).

986. B[illing], E[dward]. *A mite of affection manifested in 31. proposals.* London: f. G. Calvert, 1659. 4°. Pp. [2], 12 (misnumbering).
Tp, no. '5-', in pencil, in a former bundle (cropped at side).
Wood 613(55). Wing B2902.

987. [Biondo, Giuseppe]. M[athews], T[obie], trans. *The penitent bandito: or the history of the conversion*

& death of . . . Troilo Savelli, a baron of Rome. N.p.: n.pub., 1663. 12°. 2nd ed. Pp. 144, [5]. Calf with 2 fillets.
Flyleaf, upper, 1st, 'T.B. May 6'; 2nd^v, 'Antonii à Wood ex dono Tho. Blount interioris Templi. Maij 1670.' Tp, Wood identifies 'T.M.' as 'Tobie Mathews'. LT 2.191.
Wood 188. Wing B2936B.

988. Bird, James. *The speech of James Bird, gent. who was executed at Tyburn, . . . for the willful murther of his wife [18 Sept. 1691].* London: f. W. Humphries, 1691. S.sh.
AW wrote after the author, 'somtimes of Queens coll. Oxon.' LT 3.371-2.
Wood 422(13b). Wing B2951A (rare) (Wing, gent.,).

989. Bird, [William]. Doderidge, John, ed. *The magazine of honour; or, a treatise of the severall degrees of the nobility.* [London]: f. L. Chapman, a. W. Sheares, 1642. 8°. Pp. [4], 158. Pasteboard (grey) with parchment spine; 1st and last flyleaves, marbled paper; rebacked.
Flyleaf, upper, 2nd^v, AW wrote the titles of 2 printed works in this vol., within guidelines made with red ink. Tp, author's 1st name written in, 'Will.', prob. by AW. Acquired 29 Ap. 1658 out of G. Langbaine's study, LT 1.247.
Wood 444(1). Wing B2955A (two) ('O' not recorded in Wing).

990. [Bird, William]. *A treatise of the nobilitie of the realme.* London: A. N. f. M. Walbanke a. R. Best, 1642. 8°. Pp. [4], 157. Pasteboard (blue) with parchment spine; 1st and last upper and lower flyleaves, marbled paper.
Flyleaf, upper, 2nd^v, AW wrote the titles of 3 printed works in this vol., within guidelines made with red ink. Tp, 'ABosco/', in red ink.
Wood 442(1). Wing B2956.

991. [Birkenhead, John]. *An answer to a speech without doores: or, animadversions upon . . . mr. Challener his speech.* [London]: n.pub., [1646]. 4°. Pp. 7.
Tp, AW wrote 'Ridic', in pencil; Challener, underscored in red ink; no. 62 in a former bundle.
Wood 610(23). Wing A3351A.

992. [Birkenhead, John]. *Newes from Pembroke & Mongomery, or Oxford manchester'd by Michael Oldsworth and his lord [11 Ap.].* Mongomery [i.e., Oxford, but really London]: n.pub., 1648. 4°. Pp. [2], 5.
Tp, AW wrote 'Dup', in pencil. Diff. ed. at Wood 514(44).
Wood 614(5). Wing B2968. Madan 1982.

993. Birkenhead, John. *Newes from Pembroke and Mongomery, or Oxford manchester'd by Michael Oldsworth and his lord [11 Ap.].* Mongomery [i.e., Oxford, but really London]: n.pub., 1648 (2nd issue). 4°. Pp. [2], 5.
Tp, AW wrote, 'By Joh. Birkenhead.' (see *Hist. and Antiq.* (1796), 2.580); and corrected 11 April to 12 April. P. 3, line in margin and a correction. Diff. ed. at Wood 614(5).
Wood 514(44). Wing B2968A. Madan 1983 .

994. Birkenhead, John. *Cabala, or an impartial account of the non-conformists private designs, actings and wayes [24 Aug. to 25 Dec. 1662].* London: n.pub., 1663. 4°. Pp. [2], 37.
Pp. 3, 7, 9, AW copied, in margins, names from the text, 'Jo. Brice', 'Th. Lye', 'Will. Greenhill', 'Hen. Hibbert'; 13, underscored 'Mr. Seamor'; 22, wrote in margin, 'Edw. Bagshaw in Ireland Sept 1662'. [MS.] Wood D. 26(5). Wing B2964B.

995. Birkhead, Henry, and Henry Stubbe. *Otium literatum. Sive miscellanea quaedam poemata ab H. Birchead . . . et H. Stubbe . . . edita, nunc in unum volumen redacta; quibus accedunt deliciae poetarum Anglicanorum in Graecum translatae.* Oxoniae: H. Hall pro Ed. Forrest, [1658?]. 8°. Order of sections in this copy is: *Deliciae*: A-B^8,C1-7,D^2; *Horae subsecivae*, (Londini: Du-Gardianis, 1651) (tp is present): 1,A1-3,B-C^8,D^4; and *Poematia* (tp, cut out; imprimatur leaf, precedes *Deliciae*): A3-8,B-K^8 (AO 3.1072 and 4.574). Before the upper flyleaf, a note by F. Madan on the order in a different copy. See Madan 2377 for discussion of the order. This was originally bound in a separate vol. according to AW's note on the flyleaf, upper^v, 'In this vol. following (Otium Literatum) are contained . . . ' and the headings of the 2 sections in this printed work, within guidelines made with red ink. Tp, 'MDCLVI' and '1^s.3.', prob. by AW. *Poematia*, p. 52, at 'I. R.', AW wrote in margin, 'quis?', in red ink; p. 59, he wrote, 'These verses were published in 1654 under the name of Sam. Rowe the pupil of the Author of this book, in a book of verses made by persons of the Univ. of Oxon on the peace betw. the Engl. and the Dutch – the book is entit. Musarum Oxoniensium ΕΔΔΙΟΦΟΡΙΑ. &c. pr. at Oxon 1654 4°', i. e., Wood 484(4), item 4911 (and see item 3799).

Wood 39(2). Wing B2976. Madan 2377.

996. Bishop, George. *A tender visitation of love, to both the universities Oxford and Cambridge, and to the inns of court and chancery*. London: f. R. Wilson, sold also by R. Moon in Bristol, 1660. 4°. Pp. 19.
Flyleaf, upper[v], AW, on Barlow's judgment: 'This tender visitation of Love following I once communicated to D[r] Tho. Barlow, who, upon his perusal of it, told me by the quotations, & various readings therein, it could not be written by a mechanical Quaker, but rather by a popish seducer, or a Jesuit.' Tp, beneath author's name, AW wrote, 'Quaker.' Pp. 4-6, 10, 12, 14, 17-8, 9 minor corrections. LT 1.190.
Wood 515(23). Wing B3007. Madan 2469.

997. Bishope, George, capt. *A modest check to part of a scandalous libell intituled the case of col. Kyrle . . . concerning wood*. N.p.: n.pub., [1650 ca.]. 4°. Pp. 8.
Dupl. at Wood 533(10).
[MS.] Wood D. 27(4). Wing B3019A (rare, 2 at O).

998. Bishope, George, capt. *A modest check to part of a scandalous libell intituled the case of col. Kyrle . . . concerning wood*. N.p.: n.pub., [1650 ca.]. 4°. Pp. 8.
Dupl. at [MS.] Wood D. 27(4).
Wood 533(10). Wing B3019A (rare, 2 at O).

999. Bispham, Tho[mas]. *Iter australe, a reginensibus Oxon. Anno 1658. Expeditum*. [Oxford]: n.pub., [1660]. 4°. Pp. [6], 24.
Flyleaf, upper, 3rd, AW wrote, 'qu[aere] Masters [/] Wild { It. bor.' (Wood 465(5-6), items 4405, 6589), and 'Tho. Bispham Gent. com'; tp, 'Thomas Bispham a Gent: commoner of Queens Coll. is the authour of this poem. - The Provost & Fellowes had him with them, when they went the college progress.'
Wood 465(4). Wing B3034. Madan 2364 (Madan, London, 1658).

1000. Black Monday. *Black Munday: or, a full . . . description of that . . . eclipse of the sun which will happen on the 29. day of March 1652*. London: f. W. Ley, 1652. 4°. Pp. [2], 6.
[MS.] Wood D. 28(11). Wing B3044A.

1001. Bladen, William. *Irelands true diurnall, or a continued relation of the cheife passages that have happened there since the 11[th.] of Jan*. London: f. W. Bladen, sold R. Rayston [sic], 1641[2]. 4°. Pp. 8.
Wood 507(31). Wing B3106 (Wing, Royston).

1002. Bladen, William. *A true and exact relation of the chiefe passages in Ireland, since the first rising of the rebels . . . with a discription of an overthrow given by sir Simon Harcot [sic] [11 Jan.]*. London: T. H. f. R. Royston, 1642. 4°. A[4].
Wood 507(26). Wing B3107.

1003. [Blaise de Vigenère]. Stephens, Edward, trans. *A discourse of fire and salt, discovering many secret mysteries*. London: R. Cotes, 1649. 4°. Pp. [4], 162.
Pp. 74, 76, 84, line in margin.
Wood 316(3). Wing B3128.

1004. Blome, Richard, ed. *The fanatick history: or an exact relation and account of the old Anabaptists, and new Quakers*. London: J. Sims, 1660. 8°. Pp. [9], 224.
Tp, AW wrote 'Ian: iv: MDcLx', and a price, '1.6'. P. 1., bsm. Flyleaf, lower, 2nd[v], brief note, lined out.
Wood 888(4). Wing B3212.

1005. Bloody Bead-roll. *The bloody bed-roll: or, treason displayed*. London: n.pub., [1660]. S.sh. Rpt. of Oxford, L. Lichfield edition.
AW wrote, '1660.'; [v], '1660', and '73' replaced a former no. '52' in pencil.
Wood 416(73). Wing B3229 (rare). Madan 2482.

1006. Bloody Plot. *A bloody plot discovered to surprize the Tower, and the parliament*. London: R. Ibbitson, 1647. 4°. Pp. 8.
Tp, AW wrote the date, 'Dec. 13 1647'.
Wood 501(38). Wing B3289.

1007. Blount, Charles. *Anima mundi: or, an historical narration of the opinions of the ancients concerning man's soul after this life*. London: f. W. Cademan, 1679. 8°. Pp. [8], 109.
Tp, AW wrote '10[d]'.
Wood 859(4). Wing B3298.

1008. Blount, Charles. *A just vindication of learning: or, an humble address to . . . parliament in behalf of the liberty of the press, by Philopatris.* London: n.pub., 1679. 4°. Pp. [6], 18.
Tp, AW wrote, 'published in May 1679', and, in pencil, '3^d'.
Wood 642(4). Wing B3307.

1009. [Blount, Thomas]. *A catalogue of the lords, knights and gentlemen (of the Catholick religion) that were slain in the late warr, in defence of their king.* [London]: n.pub., [1660]. S.sh.
At 'Col. Raph Pudsey at –'; AW wrote 'Wiggan'. Col. 2, correction. Dupl. at 503(35). Repr. in Blount, *Calendarium Cath.* (1661), Wood 4, item 50. This or the dupl. was acquired 29 May 1660, LT 1.317.
Wood 276a(83). Wing C1383 (two).

1010. [Blount, Thomas]. *A catalogue of the lords, knights and gentlemen (of the Catholick religion) that were slain in the late warr, in defence of their king.* [London]: n.pub., [1660]. S.sh.
AW wrote 'May. 29', and later the year, '1660'. Dupl. at Wood 276a(83). Repr. in Blount, *Calendarium Cath.* (1661), see Wood 4, item 50. This or the dupl. was acquired 29 May 1660, LT 1.317.
Wood 503(35). Wing C1383 (two).

1011. Blount, Thomas. Νομο-λεξικον: *a law-dictionary. Interpreting such difficult and obscure works.* [London]: T. Newcomb f. J. Martin & H. Herringman, 1670. Fol. A^2,A-3Z^2.
Missing. AW received this book from Blount 12 Nov. 1670. There is no record of it having been in the Ashm. Museum. LT 2.203. See Wood 658(805), item 1016, for the tp of a later edition.
LT 2.203. Wing B3340. *BL, Hunt, Folg.*

1012. B[lount], T[homas]. *Animadversions upon s^r Richard Baker's chronicle.* Oxon.: H. H. f. R. Davis, 1672. 8°. Pp. [8], 111.
Tp, AW wrote, 'First published at Oxon Nov. 27. –71'. Text, AW made a few corrections, marks (pp. 6, 21, 25, 30 (hand pointer; see LT 2.236), 46, 80, 85-6, 88, 90, 98-9), and underscoring. LT 2.235-6 (a reference in the 'Secretum Antonii' to the 'ninth page' of Blount's ms., that is, to pp. 101-2 of Blount's text, is unmarked by AW); see also LT 2.241. AO 3.149.
Wood 225(3). Wing B3327. Madan 2920.

1013. Blount, Tho[mas]. *A world of errors discovered in the new world of words, or general English dictionary [by Edward Phillips].* [London] in the Savoy: T. N[ewcomb], f. A. Roper, J. Martin, a. H. Herringman, 1673. Fol. A-E^2,F1 (pp. [21]).
Missing. MS. Wood E. 2(70), p. 43.
MS. Wood E. 2(70), p. 43. Wing B3345. *O, Yale, Harv.*

1014. Blount, Tho[mas]. *Fragmenta antiquitatis. Antient tenures of land, and jocular customs of some mannors.* London: by assigns of R. a. E. Atkins f. A. Roper, T. Basset, a. C. Wilkinson, 1679. 8°. Pp. [7], 175, [16]. Calf with 2 fillets and a 2nd vertical line of 2 fillets.
Flyleaf, upper, AW wrote '22. Feb. 1678[9] Received from the authour this booke, by me Anth. à Wood.' P. 10, at 'Rowland le Sarcere', AW wrote, 'Baldwin le Pettour ie Farter v. Camdenum in Suffolke in Hemingston'. In the index locorum, AW corrected 'Homingston' to 'Hemingston'. LT 2.441.
Wood 675. Wing B3333.

1015. [Blount, Thomas]. *Boscobel: or the compleat history of his sacred majesties . . . preservation after . . . Worcester.* London: M. Clarke, sold H. Brome a. C. Harper, 1680 (2nd and 3rd tpp, 1681). 8°. 3rd ed. Pp. [7], 81, [7], 42, [4], 45-90 (3 tpp).
Tp, AW wrote, '1.4^d'. Text, AW made marks in margins, corrections, identifications, pp. 7, 13 (at William 'Seldon' [sic], 'Will. Sheldon natural son to - -'), 29, 35-6, etc., mainly in dark ink, but also in pencil and red ink (another ed. acquired 25 July 1660, 1^s, LT 1.327). See also LT 2.226.
Wood 235(2). Wing B3331.

1016. Blount, Thomas. Νομο-λεξικον: *A law-dictionary. Interpreting such difficult and obscure works.* London: f. H. Herringman, T. Newcomb, R. Chiswell, a. R. Bentley, sold T. Salusbury, 1691. Fol. 2nd ed. Tp only.
Name of author underscored. AW received a copy of the 1st ed. from Blount on 12 Nov. 1670, see item 1011. It was not among those bequeathed to the Ashm. LT 2.203.
Wood 658(805) (not in Bodl. CD cat.). Wing B3341.

1017. Blundell, Nicholas. *Blundel the Jesuit's letter of intelligence, to his friends the Jesuites at Cambray . . . to madam Katharine Hall [23 June].* [London]: n.pub., 1679. S.sh.
Dupl. at Wood 424(23), q.v.

Wood 276a(259). Wing B3362.

1018. Blundell, Nicholas. *Blundel the Jesuit's letter of intelligence, to his friends the Jesuites at Cambray
. . . to madame Katharine Hall [23 June].* [London]: n.pub., 1679. S.sh.
AW wrote, 'This letter was written by Peter Caryll a Benedictine monke, to M[rs] Katherine Hall of Cambray,
& was found in his pocket (being about to send it away) when he was taken (by information of a servant
maid of the house wherin he lay) at Lambeth. And being examined by a Justice of Peace Tit. Oates was
sent for to know whether he knew him, & he averring that it was Blundell the Jesuit, he was forthwith
committed to prison as Blundell'. Dupl. at Wood 276a(259). He purchased a copy from Vade, 1[d], see his
record of purchase at MS. Wood F. 50, f. 11. LT 2.453.
Wood 424(23). Wing B3362.

1019. Blundeville, [Thomas]. *The arte of logick.* London: W. Standsby, sold M. Lownes, 1617. 4°.
Pp. [16], 197.
Missing. MS. Wood E. 2(70), p. 19. BL copy, p. [6], 'he lived in Nottinghamsh. See the postscript after the
epistle to the reader', may be by AW.
MS. Wood E. 2(70), p. 19. STC 3143. BL, Folg, Yale.

1020. Boate, Arnold. *A remonstrance of divers remarkable passages and proceedings of our army in
. . . Ireland, being an extract of a letter.* London: R. Badger f. R. Lownds, 1642. 4°. A[4].
Tp, AW wrote 'May 11', in pencil; below, '<u>64</u>'.
Wood 508(19). Wing B3371.

1021. Boccalini, Traiano. Florio, Giovanni, trans. *The new-found politicke [selections from Ragguagli di
Parnaso and Pietra del paragone politico; pt. 1 tr. by G. Florio, pt. 2 by T. Scott, pt. 3 by W. Vaughan.].*
[London]: [Eliot's Court Press f. F. Williams], [1626]. 4°. Pp. 242 (wanting all before sig. B1). Calf with 3
fillets, stamp decoration (flower) inside corners, and roll decoration at inner, spine edge (Ashm. binding).
Flyleaf, upper, 2nd, the titles of 7 printed works in this vol. written by an Ashm. librarian (same hand in
Wood 276a).
[MS.] Wood B. 39(1). STC 3185.

1022. Bode, W., and W. C. *A declaration of the proceedings of the new moddel'd army in the kingdome
of Scotland [2 letters, the first signed: W. Bode, the second, W. C.].* London: n.pub., 1647. 4°. A[4].
Wood 501(41). Wing B3389A.

1023. Bodley, Thomas*. *Justa funebria Ptolemaei Oxoniensis Thomae Bodleii (Oratio funebris habita
ab oratore publico) [29 March].* Oxoniae: excud. Jos. Barnesius a. vaeneunt ap. Joh. Barnesium, London,
1613. 4°. Pp. [4], 134 (wanting at end, Oratio, pp. [14]).
Tp, 'A Woode: Mert: Coll: MDclx' (LT 1.424). P. 30, corrections; 31, at Ed. Michelborne, 'aul. Glouc.';
40-1, at L. Petrucci, lines in margins, in pencil.
Wood 484(5). STC 3194. Madan 377.

1024. Bodley, Thomas. *The life of s[r] Thomas Bodley, . . . written by himselfe.* Oxford: H. Hall, 1647.
4°. Pp. [4], 16.
Tp, scribbles, 'written' and 'Ox'. Pp. 4-5, 16, '1576' in margin, and 2 corrections.
Wood 535(4). Wing B3392. Madan 1925.

1025. Boehm, Jacob*. *The life of one Jacob Boehmen.* London: L. N. f. R. Whitaker, 1644. 4°. A[4].
Wood 532(4). Wing L2035B ('O' not recorded in Wing).

1026. Boemus, Joannes. Aston, Ed., trans. *The manners, lawes, and customes of all nations. Collected
out of the best writers.* London: G. Eld, 1611. 4°. Pp. [16], 589, [3].
Pp. 72, note, and 274ff. some marks in margin, none by AW.
[MS.] Wood B. 28(a). STC 3198.

1027. Boethius, Anicius Manlius T. S. *De consolatione philosophiae libri quinque, luculentissimis Johannis Murmellii (partim etiam Rodolphi Agricolae) commentariis illustrati.* Coloniae: ex off. E. Cervicorni,
1535. Pp. [48], 399. Calf,with 2 fillets; 2nd rectangle with 2 pairs of fillets and stamp decoration; 2 clasp
holes; rebacked.
Tp, 'Liber Antoni Wood Oxon [all lined out and:] e musæo Bartenii Holydaii S. T. D. amici sui, emptus,
A°. D[ni]. 166j' (AW's early hand; Holyday died in 1661). A3[v]-C1[v], some underscoring and numbering, prob.
not by AW.
Jesus College L. 3. 2. BL.

1028. Boethius, Anicius Manlius T. S. Colvile, George, trans. *De consolationae [sic] philosophiae.* (London): (J. Cawoode), 1556. 4°. A-2E⁴,2F1-3. Parchment.
A1, signature of Mynne Trelgon [Frelgon?]. Text, frequent underscoring and some marks in margins and corrections. 2F3, 'liber Mʳⁱ Thomae Bellone [?] generosi'. Acquired 21 Sept. 1668, LT 2.143.
Wood 331. STC 3201.

1029. [Bohun, Edmund]. *A defence of sir Robert Filmer, against the mistakes . . . of Algernon Sidney, esq; in a paper.* London: f. W. Kettilby, 1684. Fol. Pp. [2], 16.
Tp, AW wrote, '6ᵈ', and at a different time, 'Edm Bohun Esq. the author.'
Wood 428(23). Wing B3450.

1030. B[ohun], E[dmund]. *An apologie for the Church of England, against the clamours of the men of no-conscience: or the duke of Buckingham's seconds.* London: f. W. Kettilby, 1685. 4°. Pp. 12.
Wood 611(15). Wing B3447.

1031. [Bohun, Edmund]. *The history of the desertion [of the throne by James 2], or, an account of all the publick affairs in England [from Sept - 12 Feb.], . . . With an answer to a piece [by Jeremiah Collier] call'd the desertion discussed.* London: f. R. Chiswell, 1689. 4°. Pp. [8], 168.
Pp. 3, correction; 23, AW wrote, at visit of James 2 to Oxford and his return to London, 'This is a mistake – for he was called up to sit among the Bishops concerning the birth of the Pr. of Wales.'; 27, he altered the year, 1689, to 1688; 33, at printed '400 Horses', 'The exact Diary &c saith not so' and underscoring; 35, 'London', prob. not by AW; 39, AW wrote, 'This agrees not with the Diary' and at end, 'And afterwards he deserted by taking the oathes' (i.e., T. Lamplugh, the bishop of Exeter and then York); 43, short line in margin. Flyleaf lower, last, AW's note on waste paper, 'These must all be restored to my booke B.' (see LT 4.218-9). LT 3.300.
Wood 530(3). Wing B3456.

1032. Boileau-Despréaux, Nicolas. Soames, William, trans. *The art of poetry.* London: f. R. Bentley a. S. Magnes, 1683. 8°. Pp. [2], 67.
Tp, 'By Mʳ Somes', not in AW's hand, but by the same person who wrote the note in the following item, Sheffield, Wood 320(5), item 5872.
Wood 320(4). Wing B3464.

1033. Bolron, Robert. *The narrative of Robert Bolron, . . . concerning the late horrid popish plot.* London: f. T. Simmons, a. J. Sampson, 1680. Fol. Pp. [3], 36.
Tp, AW wrote the price, '1ˢ'.
Wood 425(29). Wing B3501.

1034. B[olton], E[dmund]. *The elements of armories.* London: G. Eld, 1610. 4°. Pp. [16], 201, [15]. Parchment with 2 clasp holes.
Tp, AW wrote 'Edm. Bolton' in red ink; bsm 'kp'. ² [i.e., p. [3]], AW underscored 'E. B.' and wrote 'Bolton'. On 4 leaves pasted in between lower flyleaves, AW drew some 30-40, mainly armorial, figures and wrote, 'Mʳ Burges or Berges buried at Wells at the Cath. son of Cornel[ius] Burges', 'The speare heads of Mʳ Brodricks coat must be bloody.', 'The crest of Mʳ [Thomas] Oldfeilds coat is a wheasheaf [sic] or and on it a white bird. q[uaere] buried in S. Georges ch. in Southwark', 'The crest to Mʳ Saints [i.e., Saint German's] coat is an Elephants head' (for Burgess, AO 3.681; for Oldfield, LT 1.236-7; for Brodrick, LT 2.49, where Clark quotes a description from Wood MS. F. 4, 109 (AW's 'bloody' = embrued gules); for an illustr., see J. Fairbairn, *Fairbairn's Crests* (Edinburgh, 1860); the crest of the earl of Saint German (Eliot family) includes an 'elephant's head, couped, ar. (or collard gu.)').
Wood 357. STC 3220.

1035. [Bolton, Edmund]. *The cities advocate, in this case or question of honor and armes; whether apprentiship extinguisheth gentry?.* London: [M. Flesher] f. W. Lee, [1629] (cropped). 4°. T, a cancel. Pp. [18], 61, [1].
Tp, initials, R. S. and a price, 12ᵈ.
Wood 590(2). STC 3219.

1036. Bond, John. *King Charles his welcome home, or a congratulation . . . for his . . . returne from Scotland, 1641.* London: F. L. f. T. Bates a. F. Coules, [1641]. 4°. Pp.[2], 6.
Wood 537(16). Wing B3579.

1037. Book of Pretty Conceits. *The book of pretty conceits. Or, the green forrest of youthful delights.* London: f. P. Brooksby, 1685. 8°. A⁸,B⁴.

Flyleaf, upper[v], figures, an addition, not in AW's hand.
Wood 69(8). Wing B3714 (rare).

1038. Book of Witty Riddles. *A book of witty riddles.* N.p.: ?, n.d. Pp.?
Missing in 1837. 'A Book of witty Riddles – ' in Whiteside cat. (prob. not STC 3322.5 (one) or STC 3323 (three)).
Wood 64(10). Not identified.

1039. Booker, John. *No Mercurius Aquaticus, but a cable-rope, double twisted for John Tayler.* [London]: f. G. B., 1644, 19 July. 4\spso. Pp. 8.
Missing in 1922. A note at the entry on the upper flyleaf, 'torn out'.
Wood 622(4). Wing B3729. *Hunt, Harv.*

1040. Booker, John, and [George Wharton]. *Mercurius Coelicus: or, a caveat . . . 1644 [by John Booker] [2nd p. [1]] Mercurio-Coelico Mastix. Or an anti-caveat to . . . Booker . . . by G. Naworth.* London [i.e., Oxford]: J. Raworth f. J. Partridge [i.e., H. Hall], [1644]. 4°. Pp. [2], 6, [2] 14 (misnumbering).
Tp, AW wrote 'Here is also Whartons answer.' (in the printed marginalia and after 2nd t).
Wood 622(2-3) (not in Bodl. CD cat.). Wing B3728C. Madan 1540 ('O' not recorded in Wing).

1041. [Booth, George]. [Delamere, 1st baron]. *The declaration of the lords, . . . of this once happy kingdome of England.* [London]: n.pub., [1659]. S.sh.
Dupl. at Wood 503(23).
Wood 276a(166). Wing D870. Steele 3124.

1042. Booth, George. Delamere, 1st baron. *The declaration of the lords, . . . of this once happy kingdome of England.* [London]: n.pub., [1659]. S.sh.
AW wrote the year '1659'. Dupl. at Wood 276a(166).
Wood 503(23). Wing D870.

1043. Booth, George*. Delamere, 1st baron. *An express from the knights and gentlemen now engaged with sir George Booth; to the . . . citizens of London [9 Aug.].* [London]: n.pub., [1659]. S.sh.
Wood 503(24a). Wing E3892.

1044. Booth, George. Delamere, 1st baron. *A letter from . . . in defence of his countries liberties . . . Chester Aug. 2.* [London]: n.pub., [1659]. S.sh.
AW wrote, 'Dupl', in pencil. Dupl. at Wood 503(24).
Wood 276a(167). Wing D871.

1045. Booth, George. Delamere, 1st baron. *A letter from . . . in defence of his countries liberties . . . Chester Aug. 2.* [London]: n.pub., [1659]. S.sh.
Dupl. at Wood 276a(167).
Wood 503(24). Wing D871.

1046. Booth, George. Delamere, 1st baron. *Sir George Booth's letter . . . shewing the reasons of his present engagement. Together with an answer [2 Aug.].* London: n.pub., 1659. 4°. Pp. 24.
Wood 503(25). Wing D872.

1047. Booth, Henry*. Warrington, earl of. *The tryal of Henry baron Delamere for high-treason [14 Jan. 1685].* London: f. D. Newman, 1686. Fol. Pp. [3], 87.
Tp, AW wrote, '2[s] - 6.' and '27. Mar 1686'. LT 3.177.
Wood 421(8). Wing T2189.

1048. Booth, Henry. Warrington, earl of. *The late lord Russel's case, with observations upon it.* London: f. A. Churchill, 1689. Fol. Pp. [2], 15.
Tp, AW wrote, 'Bought at Oxon 12. Mar. 1688[9]. - 6[d] -'. LT 3.294.
Wood 421(12). Wing D878.

1049. Borde, Andrew. *The fyrst boke of the introduction of knowledge.* (London): (in Lothberry, W. Copland), [1562?]. 4°. A-N[4] (wanting D4).
Tp., '1542', and signatures, 'Henricus Jackson' (see LT 1.459 and 1.331), 'R. B.', 'Sebastianus Cabotta Venetus oriu[ndus]' (cropped), and 'Ralighus[?]'. Text, scribbles, marks in margins, traces of names, and notes, most are cropped, none in AW's hand. C4[v], name, cropped; E4 'Fraunces brother God sone', H4, 'Richard Windser' and '16 of Jan: 1621'; N4[v], mainly scribbles, Christian names, and, 'Thomas Eainehill[?]' and 'Ananias Bellott'.

Wood 336(2). STC 3385.

1050. B[orde], A[ndrew]. *The merry tales of the mad-men of Gotam*. London: n.pub., 1650. 8°. Pp. [2], 22.
Missing in 1837. 'Merry Tales of the mad-men of Gotham – Lond. 1650' in Whiteside cat.
Wood 66(1). Wing B3749 (rare). BL.

1051. Border, Daniel. *A wicked plot against the person of sir William Waller*. London: f. R. Wood, 1644, 11 Jan. 4°. A⁴.
Tp, AW altered a former no., '52'.
Wood 376(58). Wing B3751 (1996). ESTCR 229595.

1052. Boreman, R[obert]. Παιδεια-θριαμβος. *The triumph of learning over ignorance, and of truth over falsehood*. London: f. R. Royston, 1653. 4°. Pp. [8], 34, [1].
Tp, bsm.
[MS.] Wood B. 24(2). Wing B3760.

1053. Boreman, R[obert]. *A mirrour of Christianity, . . . a . . . narrative of the life and death of . . . Alice dutchess Duddeley*. London: E. C. f. R. Royston a. J. Collins, 1669. 4°. Pp. [6], 48.
Tp, AW wrote, at the year of publ., the year, 1668, and price, '6ᵈ'. P. 1, at 1669, '1668'.
Wood 532(14) (not in Bodl. CD cat.). Wing B3758.

1054. [Borlase, Edmund]. *Latham spaw in Lancashire*. London: f. R. Clavel, 1670. 8°. Pp. [22], 72.
Tp, '9ᵈ', may be in AW's hand.
Wood 699(6). Wing B3769.

1055. Borlase, Ed[mund]. *The reduction of Ireland to the crown of England*. London: A. Clarke, f. R. Clavel, 1675. 8°. Pp. [50], 284. Calf with 2 fillets and stamp decoration in corners (plant with 3 pointed flowers).
Flyleaf, upper, '1ˢ.-10ᵈ.' Pp. 130-1, 137, 148, etc. marks in margins or underscoring. P. 149, also 2 notes: AW wrote, 'Th. Fuller in his Ch. Hist.' at Walter Travers and 'in what yeare qu[aere]' at Henry Alvey chosen provost Octob. 8; p. 177, 'so Camd. in his Annall. of Q. Eliz.' Title on a slip extending from the lower flyleaf (not in Wood's hand).
Wood 215. Wing B3771.

1056. B[orlase], E[dmund]. *Brief reflections on the earl of Castelhaven's memoirs*. London: G. West, 1682. 8°. Pp. [10], 67.
Tp, AW wrote, 'By Edm. Borlase 6ᵈ'. A4, line in margin at a reference to the 'Short View of the late Troubles' (by W. Dugdale, Wing D2492).
Wood 202(3). Wing B3766.

1057. Bornitius, Jacobus. *Jacobi Bornitii . . . de nummis in repub. percutiendis & conservandis libri duo*. Hanoviae: typ. Wechelianis, ap. C. Marnium & her. J. Aubrii, 1608. 4°. Pp. 102, [7]. Calf with 3 fillets, stamp decoration inside corners (2 leaves and sunflower sprouting fleur-de-lis), and roll decoration at inner, spine edge (Ashm. binding); rebacked.
Flyleaves, upper, 1st and 2nd, the titles of 19 printed works in this vol., in Whiteside's hand (correct order and the one followed in this cat. (the Bodl. CD cat. nos. are irregular)); 3rd, again the titles, 1-17 (2 entries at nos. I and VI), by an Ashm. librarian (same hand at Wood 276a). Each item was numbered by Keeper Whiteside (in Arabic nos.; some cropped) and by the 2nd librarian (in Roman numerals).
Wood 533(1). BL.

1058. Bos, Lambert van den. *The life and raigne of king Charles*. London: f. S. Miller, 1659. 8°. Pp. 229-464 and tp, only (wanting A1-Q2).
Tp, AW wrote, 'Lamb. Sylvius a Dutchman–'. Pp. 319-336, 419, a few brief notes, corrections, and 'q[uaere]' marks. Acquired 14 Sept. 1661, 1ˢ3ᵈ, LT 1.410.
Wood 244(2). Wing B3777E.

1059. [Bostock, Robert]. *The Scots constancy. Or, an answer to Cleveland's Scots apostacy*. [London]: n.pub., [1647]. 4°. Pp. 4.
Pp. 2, 4, corrections, prob. not by AW.
Wood 483(18). Wing B3796.

1060. B[ostocke], R[obert] (probable author). *The difference betwene the auncient phisicke, . . . and the latter phisicke*. London: [G. Robinson] f. R. Walley, 1585. 8°. *⁸,A-L⁸ (last 2 leaves blank).

Wood 699(5). STC 1064.

1061. Boteler, William*. *Boteler's case. Being an impartial narrative of the tryal, . . . of master William Boteler. Executed.* [London]: f. J. Clarke, a. P. Brooksby, [1678]. 8°. A-E⁴.
Tp, AW wrote, 'an . . . . ' (he did not know the year of execution). B2, AW underscored 'Battle of Seniffe', and wrote in margin, 'Seniff in Alsatia, an. 1675'.
Wood 173(4). Wing B3805 (3).

1062. Botero, Giovanni. Draudius, George, trans. *Joannis Boteri . . . tractatus duo: prior: de illustrium statu & politia, libris X. Posterior: de origine urbium, . . . libris III.* Ursellis: ap. C. Sutorium, imp. L. Zetzneri, 1602. 8°. Pp. [24], 946, [27]. Parchment, 2 clasp holes.
Cover, inside, name of Wood and 2-3 words, erased. Tp, bsms.
Wood 570. BL.

1063. Botero, Giovanni. H[awkins], T., trans. *The cause of the greatnesse of cities. . . . With certaine observations concerning the sea.* London: E. P[urslowe] f. H. Seile, 1635. 12°. Pp. [2], 236 (wanting sig. A2) (2 tpp). Parchment.
Pastedown, upper, 'Hen ffoulis Booke praetium 12d:'; flyleaf, upper, r-v, Foulis made an elaborate table.
LT 2.180.
Wood 691. STC 3396.

1064. [Bouhours, Dominique]. Sheldon, Edward, trans. *Christian thoughts for every day in the month, with a prayer [trans. of Pensées chrétiennes pour tous les jours du mois].* N.p.: n.pub., 1680. 12°.
Missing in 1837. Listed in MS. Wood E. 2(70), p. 62, 'Edw. Shelden [sic] Christian thoughts for every day in the month – 1680'.
Wood 758. Wing B3823.

1065. Bourchier, Jo[hn]. *Die lunae 6 Junii, 1642. The copy of a letter sent from sir Jo: Bourchier, to sir Thomas Barrington.* London: f. J. Hunscott, 1642, 7 June. S. sh.
ᵛ, former no., '65' in pencil; AW altered a former no., '18', to '17', both over earlier, '4. June', in pencil.
Wood 374(17). Wing B3838.

1066. Bourchier, Thomas. *Historia ecclesiastica, de martyrio fratrum ordinis minorum divi Francisci, de observantia, qui partim in Anglia . . . passi sunt. . . . d. Francisci de observantia.* Ingolstadii: Wolfgani Ederi, 1583. 12°. Ff. [10], 178, [2]. Calf with 2 fillets.
Flyleaf, upper, 2nd ᵛ, within guidelines made with red ink, 'AàBosco' (à is beneath AB), and AW wrote, 'An account of the English martyrs, from fol. 10 to fol. 46', 'With this book is bound Florentinus Leydanus his Historia . . . ' (Wood 231(2), item 4149); f. 5, underscorings and, at Bonner, 'Thomas Boner. 1. rg [?]. Edmundum', may not be by AW; passim, some underscoring, lines and marks, in ink, not in AW's usual manner; some pencil marks in margins are in his manner, e.g., ff. 27 ('q[uaere]'), 29ᵛ, 42ᵛ.
Wood 231(1). BL.

1067. Bourne, William, and Thomas Hood. *A regiment for the sea:. . . Whereunto is added an hydrographicall discourse, . . . by William Borne. Whereunto is added a new regiment, . . . by Thomas Hood.* London: W. J(ones) f. T. Weaver, 1631. 4° in 8's. Corrected. Ff. [9], 96 (2 tpp.) (pp. unopened).
Tp, AW wrote, '1ˢ 6ᵈ' and 'Septemb. xxij MDCLX:'. LT 1.332.
[MS.] Wood C. 13(3). STC 3431 (two).

1068. [Boutauld, Michel]. S[heldon], E[dward], trans. *The counsels of wisdom or, a collection of the maxims of Solomon . . . with reflexions.* London: J. Shadd f. M. Turner, 1680. 12°. Pp. [12], 276. Calf, mottled, with 2 fillets and marbled paper edges; rebound.
Flyleaf, 2ndᵛ, AW wrote 'Anthony à Wood. Given to me by Mʳⁱˢ Francis [sic] Sheldon maid of honor to Qu. Katherine, jᵒ Jan. 1680[1]. Being a translation of her Father Edward Sheldon Esq.' LT 2.510.
Wood 845. Wing B3860A.

1069. Bower, Edmund. *Doctor Lamb revived, or, witchcraft condemn'd in Anne Bodenham.* London: T. W. f. R. Best a. J. Place, 1653. 4°. Pp. [4], 44 (wanting pp. 19-22).
Tp, bsm.
[MS.] Wood B. 18(13). Wing B3869.

1070. Bowes, Jerome*. *A true report of the horrible murther, . . . in the house of sir Jerome Bowes.* London: H. L[ownes] f. M. Lownes, 1607. 4°. A-F⁴.
Tp, AW wrote the no. '2' on a slip used to repair the tp. D2, scribble, 'for God is the way', not by AW.

Wood 365(2). STC 3434.

1071. B[owles], E[dward]. *A letter from a minister in his excellence his army, to a brother of his in London . . . before Reading. April 18*. London: f. J. Rothwell, a. S. Gellibrand, 1643, 20 April. 4°. Pp. 7.
Tp, AW altered a former no.; and p. 3, corrected 'Blachgrave' to 'Blagrave'.
Wood 376(6). Wing B3872A.

1072. Boxhorn, Marcus Zuerius. *De typographicae artis inventione, & inventoribus, dissertatio*. Lugduni Batavorum: ex off. H. de Vogel (typ. W. Christiani), 1640. 4°. Pp. 51, [1]. Pasteboard (blue) with parchment spine; 1st upper and lower flyleaves, marbled paper.
Flyleaf, upper, 3rd[v], AW wrote the titles of 6 printed works in this vol., within guidelines made with red ink. P. 2, extensive notes, in Latin, on printing and books in the Bodleian Library, not in AW's hand. Text, some underscoring and marks in margin in red crayon, not in AW's manner.
Wood 642(1). BL.

1073. Boyle, Richard*. Cork, earl of. *The earle of Corkes victorie, and Tyrones overthrow. Also the driving away of the rebels out of Armagh. . . . With the copy of the letter sent from the earle of Tyrone*. London: f. J. Greensmith, 1641. 4°. A⁴.
Tp, AW wrote after the year, '13 Dec'.
Wood 507(12). Wing E72.

1074. Boyle, Richard. Cork, earl of. *A true relation of the miseralble [sic] estate that Ireland now standeth in. Manifested by a letter sent from the lord Dungarvan*. London: J. Hammond, 1642, 9 Feb. 4°. A⁴.
Tp, AW wrote below, 'Jan 30 1641', and, '1641', in pencil.
Wood 507(30). Wing C6299 ('O' not recorded in Wing).

1075. Boyle, Richard. Cork, earl of. *A letter . . . to the state at Dublin, . . . wherein is shewed the barbarous cruelty the rebels have lately used*. London: f. E. Blackmore, 1642, 9 May. 4°. Pp. 6.
Tp, former no., '13', overwritten; below, '57'.
Wood 508(15). Wing C6298.

1076. Boyle, Robert*. *On the death of . . . Robert Boyle*. London: f. S. Smith, 1692. S.sh.
AW wrote, 'Bought at Oxon 25. Jan. 1691[2]', in pencil; [v], 'Rob. Boyle 1691[2]'. LT 3.380; J. F. Fulton, *Bibliog. of R. Boyle* (Oxford, 1961), item 305, fig. 24.
Wood 429(50). Wing O310 (rare).

1077. Boyle, Roger. Orrery, 1st earl of. *A declaration of the lord Broghil, and the officers of the army of Ireland in . . . Munster*. London: J. Macock, 1659[60]. S.sh. Rpt. of Dublin: W. Bladen edition.
Dupl. at Wood 510(30).
Wood 276a(213). Wing O475.

1078. Boyle, Roger. Orrery, 1st earl of. *A declaration of the lord Broghill, and the officers of the army of Ireland in . . . Munster*. London: J. Macock, 1659[60]. S.sh. Rpt. of Dublin: W. Bladen edition.
AW wrote after the year, 'March:'. Dupl. at Wood 276a(213).
Wood 510(30). Wing O475.

1079. Boyle, Roger. Orrery, 1st earl of (presumed author). *The Irish colours displayed, in a reply of an English protestant to a late letter of an Irish Roman Catholique [P. Walsh]*. London: n.pub., 1662. 4°. Pp. [2], 17.
Wood 510(32). Wing O485.

1080. Boys, William. *The narrative of William Boys, . . . concerning the late horrid popish plot*. London: f. D. Newman, 1680. Fol. Pp. [2], 17.
Tp, bsm.
Wood 425(30). Wing B4067.

1081. Braddon, Lawrence*, and Hugh Speke*. *The tryal of Laurence Braddon and Hugh Speke, gent. upon an information of high-misdemeanor*. London: f. B. Tooke, 1684. Fol. Pp. [3], 78.
Wood 428(25). Wing T2196 (Wing, Braddon, and).

1082. Bradshaw, John*. *Reason against treason: or, a bone for [John] Bradshaw to picke*. [London]: n.pub., 1649. 4°. Pp. [2], 14.
Wood 364(19). Wing R460.

1083. Bradshaw, John*. *Bradshaw's ghost: being a dialogue between the said ghost, and an apparition of the late king Charles*. [London]: n.pub., 1659. 4°. Pp. 12.
Tp, AW wrote 'dupl' (perhaps a reference to the missing Wood 416(68), item 1086). See note at Wood 416(1), item 4435.
Wood 416(15). Wing B4164 (Wing, under William Bradshaw).

1084. Bradshaw, John*. *The last will and testament of*. London: n.pub., 1659. 4°. Pp. 7.
Tp, AW wrote 'dup'. Dupl. at Wood 610(13).
Wood 416(14). Wing B4154B.

1085. Bradshaw, John*. *The last will and testament of*. London: n.pub., 1659. 4°. Pp. 7.
Tp, AW wrote, 'dupl.' Dupl. at Wood 416(14).
Wood 610(13). Wing B4154B.

1086. Bradshaw, John*. *Bradshaws ghost; a poem: a dialogue between John Bradshaw, ferry-man Charon, Oliver Cromwel, ...* [London]: n.pub., [1660]. Fol. Pp. 4.
Missing in 1840. On the ᵛ of item 69, 'No. 68 - was missing Octʳ. 30. 1840 W[illiam] K[irtland]'. See notes at Wood 416(1), item 4435, and 416(15), item 1083 (this may be a diff. ed.; ed. not identified).
Wood 416(68). Wing B4163-5.

1087. [Brady, Robert]. *A true and exact history of the succession of the crown of England:. . . for . . . such as have been deluded . . . by the . . . brief history of the succession [by John Somers, Wing S4638]*. London: f. C. Pullen, 1681. Fol. Pp. [2], 46.
Tp, 'Brady', prob. not by AW.
Wood 660c(25). Wing B4195.

1088. [Bramhall, John] (supposed author). *An answer to a letter of enquiry into the grounds and occasions of the contempt of the clergy [by John Eachard] [signed W. S.]*. London: f. N. Ranew a. J. Robinson, 1671. 8°. Pp. [16], 91, [3] (2 pp. books sold by Ranew a. Robinson).
Flyleaf, upper, '1ˢ 4ᵈ', lined out, prob. by AW. Tp, bsm., '10.'
Wood 884(2). Wing B4211A.

1089. [Bramhall, John] (supposed author). *Fair warning, or, the burnt child dreads the fire [and] A catalogue of . . . noblemen that after sequestration compounded for their estates*. N.p.: n.pub., [1680?]. Fol. Pp. 4.
John Bramhall died in 1663 and his list may have been printed earlier than '[1680?]'. AW acquired a 'Cataloge of sequestred gent.' on 12 Dec. 1657, LT 1.231.
Wood 276a(184-185). Wing B4221.

1090. Bramstone, J. *Fifteen loyal queries for the kings most excellent majesty, . . . with a lash for . . . W. L.* London: f. G. Horton, 1660. 4°. Pp. [2], 6.
P. 1, AW wrote after W. L., 'Will. Lenthall speake[r]' (cropped at side).
Wood 608(34). Wing B4241.

1091. B[rancker], T[homas]. *Doctrinae sphaericae adumbratio; unà cum usu globorum artificialium*. Oxoniae: H. Hall, impens. J. Adams, 1662. S.sh.
AW added the author's name after initials T. B'ranker Coll: Exon:'; and underscored 'Branker', in red ink. See AO 3.1086-7.
Wood 276a(37). Wing B4244 (rare). Madan 2587.

1092. Brasbridge, Thomas. *Quaeestiones [sic] in officia M. T. Ciceronis: compendiariam totius opusculi epitomen continentes*. Oxoniae: ex off. typog. J. Barnesii, 1615. 8°.
Missing. MS. Wood E. 2(70), p. 7. AO 1.526, gives the date 1615, Oct.
MS. Wood E. 2(70), p. 7. Not in STC. See STC 3552.3 (1586) and 3552.5 (1592). Not in ESTCR. Madan 428.

1093. Brasse, John*. *In the county of Palatine in Durham, near Ferry-hill, Jan. 25th. 1682. was acted the . . . murder . . . of John Brasse, Jane Brasse*. London: f. T. M., sold R. Taylor, 1682. S.sh.
Wood 422(9). Wing I124 (Wing, omits pub. and seller).

1094. Brathwaight, James*. *A strange and wonderful example of Gods judgmenents [sic], shewed upon James Brathwaight*. London: B. A., 1645. 4°. Pp. [2], 6.
[MS.] Wood B. 35(16). Wing S5847.

1095. [**Brathwait, Richard**]. *The good wife; or, a rare one amongst women. Whereto is annexed an exquisite discourse of epitaphs. [By] Musophilus.* London: f. R. Redmer (J. Beale), 1618. 8°. A2-4,B-K⁸,L1-3 (2nd tp at C2; t leaf mutilated).
Wood 583(2-3). STC 3568.5 (two).

1096. Brathwait, Richard. *Natures embassie: or, the wilde-mans measures: danced naked by twelve satyres.* [London]: [R. Field] f. R. Whitaker, 1621. 8°. Pp. [8], 263, [1]; tpp at pp. 173, 215, 237. Calf with 2 fillets.
The annotations are not in AW's manner: curly braces in margins, passim; some corrections, underscorings, marginal brackets, '=' signs, and drawn hands; also some notes, e.g., p. 146, 'Papists' and p. 211, 'comming neare the house where thay were playing'; some printed marginal notes encircled, pp. 82, 100, 130, 132. Flyleaf, lowerᵛ, 'March: 2: 1653', may be in AW's hand.
Wood 103. STC 3571.

1097. [**Brathwait, Richard**]. *Mercurius Britanicus, or the English intelligencer. A tragic-comedy at Paris.* [London]: n.pub., 1641. 4°. Repr. with additions. A-D⁴.
Not a 'newspaper', *pace* LT 1.14.
Wood 615(20). Wing B4270A.

1098. B[rathwait], R[ichard]. *A comment upon the two tales of . . . Jeffray Chaucer.* London: W. Godbid, sold by R. Crofts, 1665. 8°. Pp. [4], 199.
Wood 112(8). Wing B4260.

1099. Bratislava. *A full and true account of the great battel fought betwixt the Turks, Hungarian rebels, and Polish army, before . . . Presburg. With two Latin letters, . . . to the king of Poland.* London: f. E. Brewster, 1683. Fol. Pp. 16.
Tp, 'AWood', in pencil. Dupl. at Wood 657(18).
Wood 559(18). Wing F2304.

1100. Bratislava. *A full and true account of the great battel fought betwixt the Turks, Hungarian rebels, and Polish army, before . . . Presburg. With two Latin letters, . . . to the king of Poland.* London: f. E. Brewster, 1683. Fol. Pp. 16.
Tp, AW wrote 'Dupl' in pencil. Dupl. at Wood 559(18).
Wood 657(18) (Wood 659(18) in Bodl. CD cat.). Wing F2304.

1101. Bravonius, Florentius. Howard, William, ed. *Chronicon ex chronicis, ab initio mundi usque ad annum Domini. 1118. deductum. Auctore Florentio Wigorniensi. Accessit etiam continuatio usq; ad annum Christi 1141.* Londini: T. Dausonus, pro R. Watkins, 1592. 4° in 8's. Pp. [8], 584. Parchment with 2 clasp holes.
Pastedown, upper, 'Liber Antho-: Woode: Coll Merton Jan: 8: A. D. 1658/9', LT 1.266. Tp, 'Ant: Woode:'; name of the former owner 'Ed. Reynolds' lined out (LT 5.67).
Wood 462. STC 3593.

1102. Bray, William. *An English-mans fundamentall appeale [29 Sept.].* N.p.: n.pub., [1659]. Fol. Pp. 4.
P. 1, no. '74' in a former bundle, in pencil.
Wood 276a(177). Wing B4301A (rare). ESTCR 231103.

1103. Brereton, William. *Shrewsbury taken. A copie of sir William Breretons letter to the parliament.* London: R. Austin, 1645. 4°. Pp. [2], 13.
Tp, AW underscored the author's name, in red ink.
Wood 377(37). Wing B4371.

1104. Brereton, William. *Sir William Breretons letter concerning . . . Chester.* London: f. E. Husband, 1645[6], 6 Feb. 4°. Pp. 8.
Tp, AW underscored, 'Brereton', in red ink, wrote the price, '1ᵈ', partially overwrote that with the former no., '44', which he later lined out.
Wood 378(47). Wing B4368.

1105. Brereton, William. *Sir William Breretons letter sent to the honoᵇˡᵉ William Lenthal . . . concerning . . . Chester.* London: f. E. Husband, 1645[6], 5 Mar. 4°. Pp. 40.
Tp, AW underscored 'Brereton' in red ink, and altered the former no., '52'.
Wood 378(55). Wing B4369.

1106. Brerewood, Edward. Brerewood, R., ed. *De ponderibus, et pretiis veterum nummorum.* London:

[W. Stansby] ap. J. Billium, 1614. 4°. Pp. [8], 56.
Missing. MS. Wood E. 2(70), p. 49.
MS. Wood E. 2(70), p. 49. STC 3612. *O, Folg, Hunt.*

1107. Brerewood, Edward. *Enquiries touching the diversity of languages, and religions.* London: J.
Norton f. J. Norton a. R. Whitaker, 1635. 4°. Pp. [24], 203.
Missing. MS. Wood E. 2(70), p. 48.
MS. Wood E. 2(70), p. 48. STC 3621. *O, Folg, Hunt.*

1108. Brerewood, Edward. *Elementa logicae. In gratiam studiosae juventutis in academiā Oxoniensi.*
Oxford: exc. H. Hall per R. Davis, 1657. 8°.
Missing. 19 Oct. 1657, 'I exchanged these following bookes in sheets with Mr. Forrest, for . . . [sic]:. . . All
amounting to a crowne', 8 items, including Brerewood, LT 1.230.
LT 1.230. Wing B4375 Madan 2329 (other eds. also printed in Ox.).

1109. Breton, N[icholas]. *The strange fortunes of two excellent princes.* London: P. Short, f. N. Ling,
1600. 4°. Pp. [6], 61. Pasteboard (blue) with parchment spine. Traces of upper and lower flyleaves in marbled
paper.
Flyleaf, upper, 2nd[v], AW wrote the titles of 6 printed works in this vol., within guidelines made with red
ink. A1, 'Guy of W' (mutilated; Guy of Warwick, the 3rd item in this vol.). P. 31, cross in margin, in pencil,
by a later reader.
Wood 321(1). STC 3702 (rare).

1110. B[reton], N[icholas]. *Fantasticks: serving for a perpetuall prognostication.* London: [M. Flesher]
f. F. Williams, 1626. 4°. A2-4,B-E[4],F1-3.
Each small 4° leaf is pasted on a 4° template. C1[v], F3[v], scribble, not by AW.
[MS.] Wood C. 17(3). STC 3650.

1111. [Breton, Nicholas]. *Crossing of proverbs &c.* London: ?, 1641. Pp.?
Missing in 1837. 'Crossing of Proverbs &c – Lond. 1641' in Whiteside cat. See STC 3643ff. and Wing
B4383b.
Wood 64(2). Not in Wing. Not in ESTCR.

1112. B[reton], N[icholas]. *Englands selected characters, describing the good and bad worthies of this
age.* London: f. T. S[later], 1643. 4°. Pp. [2], 14.
Missing in 1837.
Wood 490(3). Wing B4384 and B4384A. *Clark, Folg* (has an erasure of a no.).

1113. [Breton, Nicholas]. *Crossing of proverbs a merry book.* London: ?, 1652. Pp.?
Missing in 1837. 'Crossing of Proverbs a merry Book – Lond. 1652' in Whiteside cat. See STC 3644.5 (1632)
and Wing B4383B [1670Pp.?].
Wood 64(3). Not in Wing. Not in ESTCR.

1114. B[rett], A[rthur]. *A demonstration how the Latine tongue may be learn't.* London: f. J. S., 1669.
4°. Pp. [2], 6.
Wood 310(6). Wing B4395.

1115. Br[evint], D[aniel]. *Caroli secundi, Magnae Britannis regis, epitaphium.* [London]: excud. T. New-
combe, 1685. S.sh.
Missing in 1840. 'Epitaphium Car. regis 2[di]'. On Wood 429(38), item 5760, s.sh.[v], 'Mem[n]. No. 37. deest
Nov. 4 1840 W[illiam] K[irtland]'.
Wood 429(37). Wing B4085. *Harv, Yale.*

1116. Br[evint], D[aniel]. *Reverendissimi in Christo patris, Johannis Eboracensium archiepiscopi, 3°
Idus Aprilis 1686. Fato functi epitaphium.* [London]: T. Newcombe, 1686. S.sh.
AW wrote, in t, 'Dolben', and below initials, '<u>D. B</u>[r] Dan. Brevint q[uaere] Brevall'; [v], 'D[r] Joh. Dolben
1686', and 'Jo. Sterne Arch. of York 1686' (Dolben's predecessor at York, who died in 1680). AO 4.188f.
Wood 429(41). Wing B4086A (two) (Wing, entered under Br., D.).

1117. Brian, Thomas. *The pisse-prophet.* London: S. G. f. R. Thrale, 1655 and 1679. 12°.
Missing. MS. Wood E. 2(70), p. 22.
MS. Wood E. 2(70), p. 22. Wing B4437. *O.*

1118. Bridgeman, Carolus. *Carmen contra praecipua hujus saeculi vitia . . . Publice recitatum ipsis xiiij*

calend. Octob. Harlemo, in urbe: typog. genetrice, ex off. V. Casteleynii, 1653. S.sh.
ᵛ (pasted down side), scribbling. AO 2.261.
Wood 276a(522) (276a(384) in Bodl. CD cat.). Not in BL, NUC, BN.

1119. Bridges, Joan*. *A strange and wonderfull relation of the burying alive of Joan Bridges of Rochester.*
London: f. E. G., 1646. 4°. Pp. [2], 6.
Dupl. at Wood 612(38).
[MS.] Wood B. 35(17). Wing S5878.

1120. Bridges, Joan*. *A strange and wonderfull relation of the burying alive of Joan Bridges of Rochester.*
London: f. E. G., 1646. 4°. Corrected. Pp. [2], 6 (above the imprint a woodcut, apparently, was blocked
out).
Tp, AW wrote 'Dupl', in pencil. Dupl. at [MS.] Wood B. 35(17).
Wood 612(38). Wing S5878.

1121. Bridges, John. *A perfect narrative of the grounds & reasons moving some officers . . . to the
securing of the castle of Dublin for the parliament.* London: T. Newcomb, 1660. 4°. Pp. [2], 16.
Tp, AW wrote after t, '13 Dec. 1659, altered the year to 16'59: Jan:', and wrote below, 'sold in the beg. of
Jan. 1659[60]'. LT 1.301.
Wood 510(25). Wing B4479.

1122. Bridges, W. *The loyall convert, (according to the Oxford copy.) . . . or, some short annotations
on this book [of F. Quarles].* London: f. E. Husbands, 1644. 4°. Pp. 31.
Wood 631(16). Wing B4483B.

1123. Brief Narrative. *A brief narrative of the late treacherous and horrid designe, . . . Together with a
true copie of the commission under the great seal.* London: E. Husbands, 1643, 15 June. 4°. Pp. [2], 16.
Tp, AW wrote the subject, 'Plots', in pencil.
Wood 366(14). Wing B4614.

1124. Brinckmair, L. *The warnings of Germany.* London: J. Norton, f. J. Rothwell (J. Okes, sold H.
Overton a. J. Rothwell), 1638. 8°. Pp. [32], 69. Pasteboard (grey) with parchment spine. Traces of upper
and lower flyleaves, marbled paper. Usually issued with item 4004.
Flyleaf, upper, 1st, AW wrote, 'Many egregious lyes in this book entit The Warnings of Germany –'. 2ndᵛ,
AW wrote the titles of 3 printed works in this vol., within guidelines made with red ink. Tp, bsm.
Wood 211(1). STC 3758.

1125. Brinsley, John (elder). *Ludus literarius: or, the grammar schoole; shewing how to proceede.* London:
[H. Lownes] f. T. Man, 1612. 4°. Pp. [28], 338, [1]. Parchment with 2 clasp holes.
Pastedown, lower, signature of 'Isaacke Clarke'.
Wood 312. STC 3768.

1126. Brinsley, John (elder). *A consolation for our grammar schooles:. . . for Ireland, . . . Virginia,
. . . that all may speake one . . . language.* London: R. Field f. T. Man, 1622. 4°. Pp. [14], 84, [2].
Missing. MS. Wood E. 2(70), p. 6.
MS. Wood E. 2(70), p. 6. STC 3767. *Folg, Hunt, NYPL.*

1127. B[rinsley], J[ohn] (younger). *Calendar-reformation. Or, an humble addresse to . . . parliament,
touching dayes and moneths.* London: F. Neile, 1648. 4°. Pp. [2], 13.
Tp, AW wrote after author's initials, 'Joh. Brinsley'; a brief note by a recent librarian, 'catalogued AH'.
[MS.] Wood C. 17(5). Wing B4709.

1128. Bristol. *A copie of the articles agreed upon at the surrender of the city of Bristol . . . 26. of July.*
London: f. H. Overton, [1643]. 4°. Pp. 8.
Tp, AW altered the former no.
Wood 376(24). Wing C6203.

1129. Bristol. *The tragedy of the kings armies fidelity since their entring into Bristol.* London: n.pub.,
1643. 4°. Pp. 7.
Tp, AW lined out the former no., '25'.
Wood 376(27). Wing T2013.

1130. Bristol. *The two state martyrs, or the murther of master Robert Yeomans, and . . . George Bowcher
. . . of Bristoll.* [Oxford]: [H. Hall], 1643. 4°. Pp. [2], 34.

P. 2, correction; pp. 5, 8, 10-11, 13, lines in margin.
Wood 366(13). Wing T3535. Madan 1442.

1131. Bristol. *A letter of the apprentices of the city of Bristoll, to the apprentices of . . . London. . . . with their declaration for a free parliament.* London: I. Pridmore, 1660. 4°. Pp. 8.
Tp, AW altered the year to 16'59[60]: feb:'.
Wood 632(30). Wing L1577.

1132. Bristol. *Wonderful news from Bristol. A true . . . relation how a hen . . . brought into the world a kitling.* London: f. B. Harris, 1676. 4°. Pp. [2], 6.
[MS.] Wood B. 35(29). Wing W3368.

1133. Bristol. *The Bristol address. To . . . sir Richard Hart, kt. and Thomas Earle . . . in parliament.* London: f. H. Brome, 1681. S.sh. Pp. 2.
AW wrote, 'Given to me by Sr Hen. S. George Clar[enceux] K[ing] of Arms. 19 Mar. 1680'.
Wood 276a(174). Wing B4799.

1134. [Britaine, William de]. *Humane prudence, or, the art by which a man may raise himself and fortune to grandeur. By A. B.* London: f. R. Harford, 1680. 12°. Pp. [12], 131. Calf, mottled, with 2 fillets; rebacked.
Flyleaf, upper, 1st, 'May 13: 1680', 'Thō Everard eius Liber', and 'W^m. Itchener 1691'. Flyleaf, lower^v, scribbles, not by AW.
Wood 698. Wing B4805.

1135. Britannia Triumphalis. *Britania [sic] triumphalis; a brief history of the warres and other state-affairs of Great Britain.* London: S. Howes, 1654. 8°. Pp. [8], 207 (misnumbering). Calf, speckled, with 2 fillets and 2 vertical and horizontal fillets.
Cover, upper, inside, and flyleaf, upper, 2 signatures, 'Hen: Foulis March d 22 1653./4. p. 1^s.'; and a scribble, not by Foulis. LT 2.179. Text, notes in more than one hand, in 2 colours of ink, and underscoring in pencil. AW's hand is on p. 82, at a recounting of the story of Anne Green servant at 'Ounstu', which he corrected to 'Dunstew'.
Wood 190. Wing B4817.

1136. Brome, Alex[ander]. *A congratulatory poem, on the . . . return of . . . Charls the II.* London: f. H. Brome, 1660. 4°. Pp. [2], 18.
Tp, after the date, AW wrote, 'June: 1660'.
Wood 319(9). Wing B4849.

1137. [Brome, Alexander]. *A record in rithme, being an essay towards the reformation of the law.* [London]: n.pub., [1660?]. 4°. Pp. 8.
P. 8, AW wrote, 'Jan: 1659'. Dupl. at Wood 630(22).
Wood 483(16). Wing B4850A.

1138. [Brome, Alexander]. *A record in rithme, being an essay towards the reformation of the law.* [London]: n.pub., [1660?]. 4°. Pp. 8.
P. 8, AW wrote the date, 'Jan. 1659'. Dupl. at Wood 483(16).
Wood 630(22). Wing B4850A.

1139. Brome, Alex[ander]. *Songs and other poems.* London: f. H. Brome, 1668. 8°. 3rd ed. Pp. [30], 349 (2 pp. books printed by H. Brome) (wanting A1, a4, D5, F1). Calf with 2 fillets; vertical line, 2 fillets.
Tp, 'pr. 2-6'.
Wood 111. Wing B4854.

1140. B[romhall], T[homas]. *A treatise of specters. Or, an history of apparitions, . . . collected out of sundry authours and delivered into Engl. by T. B.* London: J. Streater, 1658. Fol. Pp. [6], 367, [25]. Pasteboard (blue) with parchment spine.
Tp, AW wrote after the initials, 'Tho. Bromhall'. Bsm.
Wood 659. Wing B4886.

1141. Brommich, Andrew*, and William Atkins*. *The trial, conviction and condemnation of Andrew Brommich and William Atkins, for beiug [sic] Romish priests, before . . . Scroggs, . . . together with the tryal of Charles Kern.* London: f. R. Pawlett, 1679. Fol. Pp. 20.
Tp, AW wrote the price, '6^d.'
Wood 425(16). Wing T2176.

1142. Brommich, Andrew*, and William Atkins*. *The tryal and condemnation of two popish priests, Andrew Brommich and William Atkyns, . . . Stephen Dugdale, . . . being there present.* London: f. J. Amery, 1679. Fol. Pp. 8.
AW wrote the price, '2ᵈ'.
Wood 425(17). Wing T2157.

1143. Bromwich, I[saac]. *The spoiles of the forrest of Deane asserted in answer to a . . . libell . . . to blast the . . . proceedings of some commissioners of parliament.* London: n.pub., 1650. 4°. Pp. [2], 14.
Dupl. at Wood 609(27a).
[MS.] Wood D. 27(3). Wing B4892.

1144. Bromwich, I[saac]. *The spoiles of the forrest of Deane asserted in answer to a . . . libell . . . to blast the . . . proceedings of some commissioners of parliament.* London: n.pub., 1650. 4°. Pp. [2], 14.
Below, right, 'Dupl' erased (?). Dupl. at [MS.] Wood D. 27(3).
Wood 609(27a). Wing B4892.

1145. B[rookes], C[hristopher]. *A new quadrant.* London: n.pub., 1649. 8°. Pp. [4], 18. Parchment over marbled pastedowns.
Tp, price, cropped. P. 3, signature, 'Jo: Aubrey. -'. Lent to N. Lloyd, 1671, LT 2.237.
Wood 124. Wing B4917A (two).

1146. [Brookes, Nathaniel]. *Englands glory, or, an exact catalogue of the lords of his majesties . . . privy councel.* London: f. N. Brooke, a. H. Eversden, 1660. 8°. Pp. 87.
Tp, AW wrote the price, '8ᵈ'. Pp. 18, 26, 65, line and correction; 72, at a list, AW wrote, 'A cat. of the Knights of the Bath is in Merc. publ. 1661. nu. 16. p. 250. 251.' (i.e., Wood 394, item 4706); 79-87, some marks at names of prelates.
Wood 445(9). Wing B4918A.

1147. [Brooksbank, Joseph]. *The organs funerall or the quiristers lamentation for the abolishment of superstition . . . discourse between a quirister and an organist.* London: f. G. Kirby, [1642]. 4°. Pp. A⁴.
[MS.] Wood D. 31(40). Wing B4975A ('O' not recorded in Wing).

1148. Brossier, Marthe*. Hartwell, Abraham, trans. *A true discourse, upon the matter of Martha Brossier . . . pretended to be possessed by a devill.* London: [F. Kingston f.] J. Wolfe, 1599. 4°. Pp. [8], 39. Pasteboard (blue) with parchment spine. 1st upper and last lower flyleaves, marbled paper; rebd. E. C. W., 1944.
Flyleaf, upper, 1st, a note by W. Kirtland and W. H. Black, 'No. 4 was not found in this volume, when examined by us, 13 June 1839; also Nos. 9, 10, and 14.'; 2nd, AW wrote the titles of 15 printed works in this vol., within guidelines made with red chalk. Tp, AW underscored the name of Hartwell, in red ink.
[MS.] Wood B. 18(1). STC 3841.

1149. Broughton, Hugh*. *An advertisement to the reader. This ensung catalogue . . . A schedule of the workes of . . . as they were preparing for the presse.* [London]: n.pub., [1650]. S.sh.
ᵛ, 'ffor the Provost of Queens Coll.', not by AW (prob. given to AW by Thomas Barlow).
Wood 658(797). Wing B4998 (two).

1150. Broughton, Richard. *The ecclesiasticall historie of Great Britaine. . . . The first tome.* Doway: widowe of M. Wyon, 1633. Fol. Pp. [32], 611, [43]. Parchment.
Cover, upper, outer, scribbles, letters of the alphabet, as on † 2, and † 4 (not in AW's hand). Flyleaf, upper, AW apparently asked Godwin to write, 'I have received for this book - 0 - 7ˢ - 0 and If it tis not perfect I am to allowe soe much for it againe. [/] Jos[eph] Godwin'. Pastedown, lower, 'Ego sum Guiliel: Alford emptus Lond: de Rich: Cartwright . . . '. AW acquired this item on 27 Apr. 1665, 7ˢ, LT 2.33 (Clark read 'Clifford' for 'Alford').
Wood 539. STC 3894. ARCR 2.77.

1151. B[roughton], R[ichard]. *Monastichon Britanicum: or, a historicall narration . . . of the antient monasteries.* London: H. Herringman, 1655. 8°. Pp. [10], 411, [5]. Calf with 3 fillets; rebacked.
Flyleaf, upper, AW wrote, '1668 vicar of Market Lavington by Ch.Ch. tarried there two years' (Edmund Beddingfield?) and 'Essay upon grammar – qu[aere]'; and some scribbles, 'b f' and 'ringing'; ᵛ, AW wrote, 'See Ath. et Fasti Oxōn vol. 1. p 854. Where besides this book youl find A true memorial of the antient, most holy & religious state of Great Britain – qu[aere] whether the same with this book –' (AOF 1.428-9).
Wood 222. Wing B5000 (Wing, historical).

1152. [**Brown, John**]. *An apologeticall relation, of the particular sufferings of the faithfull . . . of the church of Scotland, since August. 1660.* [Edinburgh?]: n.pub., 1665. 8°. Pp. [32], 424, [7]. Calf, speckled, with 3 fillets and a vertical line of 3 fillets.
Flyleaf, upper, signature of William Eyre, 1669, and in another hand, 'pret: 1ˢ-6ᵈ'.Tp, 'pʳᵗ: viˢ', not by AW.
Wood 838. Wing B5026.

1153. [**Brown, Robert**]. *The subjects sorrow:. . . upon the death of Britaines Josiah, king Charles.* London: n.pub., 1649. 4°. Pp. [3], 32.
Wood 364(35). Wing B5050.

1154. [**Browne, James**]. *The tradesmans kalendar of accounts.* Oxford: [H. Hall] f. J. B[rowne], 1647. 8°. A⁸ (last leaf blank).
Tp, AW wrote, 'James Browne'.
[MS.] Wood C. 14(7). Wing T2009 (rare). Madan 1970.

1155. **B[rowne], J[ohn]**. *The merchants avizo.* London: E. G[riffin] f. R. Whitaker, 1640. 4°. Pp. [8], 70.
[MS.] Wood C. 14(4). STC 3908.9.

1156. **Brown[e], Richard**, sergeant major general. *The lord Digbies designe to betray Abingdon.* London: f. L. Blaiklock, 1644[5]. 4°. Pp. 40.
Wood 377(36). Wing B5145. Madan 1727.

1157. [**Browne, Thomas**]. *Religio medici.* [London]: f. A. Crooke, 1642. 8°. Pp. [2], 159. Pasteboard (blue) with parchment spine. 1st upper and last lower flyleaves, marbled paper.
Flyleaf, upper, 3rdᵛ, AW wrote the titles of 4 printed works in this vol., within guidelines made with red ink. 1st item, each small 8° leaf is pasted on an 8° template. Pp. 1-25, some lines in margin and underscoring, in pencil, prob. not by AW.
Wood 870(1). Wing B5166. G. Keynes, *Browne* (1968), no. 2.

1158. **Browne, Thomas**. *A true and full coppy of . . . Religio medici.* [London]: [n.pub.], [1645]. 8°. Pp. [12], 174 (wanting A1-2,A8). Pasteboard with calf spine, modern.
P. 174, scribbles. A 1642 ed. at Wood 870(1).
Wood 115. Wing B5171. G. Keynes, *Browne* (1968), no. 5.

1159. **Browne, Thomas**, St. John's, Cambridge. *Miracles work's above and contrary to nature: or, an answer to a late translation out of Spinoza's Tractatus . . . entituled miracles no violation.* London: f. S. Smith, 1683. 4°. Pp. [2], 68.
Tp, after 'Miracles', AW wrote, 'written as tis said by Charles Blount'.
Wood 643(12). Wing B5184B.

1160. **Bruce, William**. *Ad principes populumque christianum, de bello, adversus Turcos gerendo.* Lipsiae: (imp. H. Grosii), 1595. 8°. Pp. 79, [1] (issued with Wood 139(1), item 1891).
Wood 139(2). BL.

1161. **B[ruch], R[ichard]**. *Epigrammatum hecatontades duae.* Londini: G. W[ood], impen. R. A[llott], 1627. 12°. A2-12,B-D¹². Pasteboard (grey) with parchment spine. Lower spine support, traces of marbled paper.
AW's customary table of contents was apparently removed with Owen, *Epigrammatum*, Wood 76(1), item 4854. In the Bruch item, each 12° leaf is pasted on an 8° template. Flyleaf, 1stᵛ, AW wrote, 'Rich. Bruch was Author of this book'; and on inserted slip, 'In an auction cat. tis Bruce'; ᵛ, 'Rich. Bruch The Life of religion. or, directions how to beleive, live & pray aright – Lond 1615. - 8° S. 136. Th [still the present Bodl. shelf-mark]. Treatise on the Lords Supper, with prayers before and after, on 1 Cor. 11.28. Ibid. [/] These are in the Univers. Cat. under the name of Rich. Bruce & not Bruch – quod nota.' (AW marked both entries in his copy of the T. Hyde, *Catalogus* (1674)). Tp, bsm.
Wood 76(2). STC 3926.

1162. **Brugis, T[homas]**. *The discovery of a projector. Shewing the beginning, progresse, and end of the projector and his projects.* London: B. H., sold L. Chapman a. W. Cooke, 1641. 4°. Pp. [6], 34, [2]. Pasteboard (blue) with parchment spine. 1st upper and last lower flyleaves, marbled paper.
Flyleaf, upper, 2nd, the titles of 10 printed works in this vol., written by an Ashm. librarian. Tp, 'Ridiculae qu[aere]', in pencil, prob. by AW.
[MS.] Wood D. 27(1). Wing B5222.

1163. [**Brydges, Grey**]. Chandos, 5th baron. *Horae subsecivae. Observations and discourses.* London: [Eliot's Court Press] f. E. Blount, 1620. 8°. Pp. [8], 542. Parchment.
Parchment cover, inside, upper and lower, scribbles. Text, frequent double lines in margins, and a few underscorings, not in AW's manner. Flyleaf, lower[v], 2 brief notes, not in AW's hand.
Wood 569. STC 3957.

1164. Bucelinus, Gabriel, ed. *Summorum urbis orbisque pontificum, necnon imperatorum Rom. s. r. i. septemvirorum [and] Notitia s. r. i. principum, genealogica & stemmatographica.* Ulmae: ap. J. Görlinum, 1652. 12°. a-f[12] (f12 blank) (2nd tp at c2). Calf with 2 fillets.
Some marks in margins and a note, a9[v], prob. not by AW.
Wood 274. Not in BL, NUC, BN.

1165. Bucer, Martin. Poynet, John, trans. *A treatise, how by the worde of God, Christian mens almose ought to be distributed [extr. from De regno Christi Jesu].* [published abroad?]: n.pub., [1557?]. 8°. Pp. 29.
Tp, signature of Hum: Dyson, lined out.
Wood 774(7). STC 3965.

1166. Bucer, Martin*. Golding, Arthur, trans. [from C. Hubertus]. *A briefe treatise concerning the burnynge of Bucer and Phagius, at Cambrydge, in the tyme of quene Mary.* London: T. Marshe, 1562. 8°. ¶[4],A-L[8],M[4]. Parchment.
Tp, 6[d]., may not be by AW. ¶2, note, not in AW's hand. A1[v], line in margin, in pencil.
Wood 290. STC 3966.

1167. Bucer, Martin. Milton, John, trans. *The judgement of Martin Bucer, concerning divorce. Writt'n . . . in his second book of the kingdom of Christ.* London: M. Simmons, 1644. 4°. Pp. [16], 24, [2].
Pp. 22 and 2nd p. [1], horizontal pencil lines, not in AW's manner.
[MS.] Wood B. 29(2). Wing B5270.

1168. B[uchanan], G[eorge]. [Wilson, Thomas, trans.]. *Ane detectioun of the duinges of Marie quene of Scottes, touchand the murder of hir husband.* [London]: [J. Day], [1571]. 8°. A-Y[4] (Y4 blank). Pasteboard (brown) with calf spine. 1st flyleaf, upper, marbled paper; lower, trace, marbled paper.
Flyleaf, upper, 2nd[v], 'A. Wood', may not be by AW. Tp, AW wrote 2 'corrections' in the dialectal title; after initials of author, 'George Beauchanon', '1567', and 'printed in qu[arto] 1688' (Wing B5282, publ. in 1689); signature or scribble of 'John Pinyt[?]'. A2, 'G.1.29' (a shelf-mark; see item 272).
Wood 255(1). STC 3981. See J. Durkan, *Bibliography of G. B.* (Glasgow, 1994): 220.

1169. Buchanan, George. *Rerum Scoticarum historia, libris xx. descripta, . . . Accessit de jure regni.* Francofurti: J. Wechelus, imp. S. Feyerabendii, 1584. 8°. Pp. [8], 723, [51]. Calf with 3 fillets, stamp centrepiece, and clasp holes; spine, 4 bands.
Flyleaf, upper, 'extat in folio Edenburg. 1583 [in Roman numerals]', may not be in AW's hand. Tp, AW wrote, 'Liber Ant: Wood: e Bibliotheca Bartenij Holydaij amici sui emptus. 1661'; and price ('7.2.') not in AW's hand. Text, notes, underscoring and marks in margins, not in AW's hand. Acquired 8 Apr. 1662, LT 1.436-7.
Wood 214. BL. See J. Durkan, *Bibliography of G. B.* (Glasgow, 1994): 236.

1170. Buchanan, George. *A detection of the actions of Mary queen of Scots.* [London?]: n.pub., 1651. 12°. Pp. [7], 133, [1]. Calf with 2 fillets.
Pastedowns and flyleaves, upper and lower, extensive notes, mainly in French (a few lines in English), by a previous owner. Tp[v] and *7[r-v], notes, in French, have blank leaves pasted over (by AW?).
Wood 273. Wing B5281. See J. Durkan, *Bibliography of G. B.* (Glasgow, 1994): 222.

1171. B[uck], G[eorge]. Δαφνις πολυστεφανος. *An eclog treating of crownes, and of garlandes, by G. B.* London: G. Eld f. T.Adams, 1605. 4°. A-G[4].
Tp, at G. B., AW wrote 'George Buc', in red ink.
Wood 605(2). STC 3996.

1172. Buck, George. *The history of the life and reigne of Richard the third.* London: W. Wilson, sold W. L.[,] H. M. a. D. P., 1647. Fol. Pp. [5], 150, [8].
Tp, after author's name, AW wrote, 'Of the author & his Ancestors see. Lib 2. p. 67.68.69-'; below, 'Georg Buck a man both well descended & well learned – so Camden in his Britannia, printed in Engl an. 1637. p 22 He was master of the Revells in the raigne of K. Jam. 1'. P. 26, at printed Rotheram, 'Arch-Bishop of Canterbury', AW wrote, 'York, so AW. so Godwin' (T. Rotheram was Bishop of York, 1480-1500); below, another correction. Acquired 24 Sept. 1664, LT 2.20.

Wood 660d(2). Wing B5307.

1173. Buckingham. *To the kings most excellent majestie. The petition of the inhabitants of the county of Buckingham, concerning mr. Hampden [et al.].* London: f. J. Thomas, 1641[2]. 4°. A⁴.
Wood 373(15). Wing T1554.

1174. Buckingham. *To his excellency general Monk, the congratulation and address . . . of Bucks.* [London]: n.pub., [1660]. S.sh.
AW added, 'Jan: 1659[60]'.
Wood 276a(244). Wing T1345.

1175. Budden, John. *Gulielmi Patteni, cui Waynfleti agnomen fuit . . . vita obitusq[ue].* Oxoniae: J. Barnesius, 1602. 4°. Pp. [12], 84.
Each small 4° leaf is pasted on a large 4° template. AO 2.282.
Wood 528(2). STC 4012. Madan 212.

1176. Budden, John. *Reverendissimi patris ac domini Johannis Mortoni . . . vita obitusque.* Londini: R. Field, 1607. 8°. Pp. 50.
Pp. 14-8, marks in margin, not in AW's usual style. P. 50, Wood added the burial place of Morton, 'Sepultus apud Cant'.
Wood 299(3). STC 4013.

1177. Bullinger, Heinrich. *Series et digestio temporum et rerum descriptarum à beato Luca in Actis Apostolorum.* Tiguri: ap. Froschoverum, 1548. 4°. Ff. 35.
Tp, 'Magistri Smithe', not in AW's hand; after which, 'Rich. Smythe Reg. Prof. Theol. Oxon', prob. by AW. To f. 8, marks in margin and a note, not by AW. LT 1.459 (and 1.331). In a vol. formerly owned by H. Jackson, see item 6290.
Wood 477(5). BL.

1178. Bullinger, Heinrich. *De conciliis.* Tiguri: C. Froschoverus, 1561. 8°. Ff. 183. Parchment.
Tp, note and price and signature of former owner, lined out. Former no. '57' over '55'. Pasted to a sheet at bottom edge, a slip identifying the author and work (see Index, 'Slip with title').
Wood 866. BL.

1179. B[ullokar], J[ohn]. *An English expositor.* London: J. Legatt, sold A. Crooke, 1641. 8°. 3rd. ed. A⁴,B-O⁸,P⁴. Calf with 3 fillets; rebacked. Flyleaves, printer's waste paper.
Board, upper, traces of AW's name and 'June 2' printed on a mutilated book-plate (Theatre Press Keepsake, ca. 10cm x 8.5 cm; decoration around centre blank space, 1.1 cm. wide; centre blank space, 5.7 x 6.5, with 2 lines; see Index, 'Wood, Anthony, bookplate'). Waste paper, upper, 1st, 'Anthony Wood His booke amen' (LT 1.22); flyleaf, upper, the same with '1656', lined out, and: 'Let us dance the friere of frigeing game / if you doue not you shall be shent / Shall I – Let – –'; ᵛ 'Mary Wood'. Flyleaf, lowerᵛ, song, 23 lines, written from bottom to top, 'Slaves to the world / must be tost in A Blancket / o is itt so. is it so. / hast any money boy / a litle God be thanked. / then to the Taverne / let's goe / where we will spend / & drinke to A frend / & cast away care / with A ho / with A Ho. So Ho / Her's to my mistris / the fayrest of twenty / o is itt so, is it so / come let us se / is it all empty / o is it so, is it so / Then drinke deepe / & so goe to sleepe / & cast away care / with A ho / with A ho. So Ho', probably in AW's early hand (but see LT 2.102). Waste paper, lowerᵛ, signature of AW.
Wood 34. Wing B5429.

1180. B[ulwer], J[ohn]. *Chirologia: or the naturall language of the hand. . . . whereunto is added chironomia: or, the art of manuall rhetoricke.* London: T. Harper, sold R. Whitaker, 1644. 8°. Pp. [32], 187, [23], 146, [1] (2nd tp at 2nd A1). Calf with 2 fillets; rebacked.
Wood 71. Wing B5462A (issued with B5467).

1181. Bunny, Edm[und]. *Of divorce for adulterie, and marrying againe: that there is no sufficient warrant so to do.* Oxford: Jos. Barnes, 1610. 4°. Pp. [20], a table, 171, [9].
P. 1, mark in margin.
Wood 636(5). STC 4091. Madan 330.

1182. Burgersdijck, Franco. *Idea oeconomicae et politicae doctrinae.* Lugd. Batavorum: ap. H. de Vogel, 1644. 12°. Pp. [6], 129, [2]. Calf with 2 fillets.
Flyleaf, upper, 'A M', 'Ex dono Edvardi M–' (prob. not by AW); ᵛ, '4ᵈ' and scribble, not by AW. Tp, another price, '0-3'.

Wood 894. Not in BL.

1183. [Burgess, Cornelius]. *Some of the differences and alterations in the present common-prayer-book, from the book established by law.* [London?]: n.pub., [1685 ca.]. 4°. Pp. 7.
Tp, AW wrote, 'Dr Cornel. Burges the author-'.
[MS.] Wood B. 37(4). Wing B5686.

1184. Burghers, M[ichael], sculp. *The orthography and ichnography of Trinity College chappel in Oxford, 1691.* N.p.: n.pub., 1691. S.sh. (engr.).
AW added the date, '1691'. See LT 3.449 and [MS.] Wood D. 23(6), item 6103.
Wood 276a(11) (not in Bodl. CD cat.). Not identified.

1185. Burgine, Darby, and Robert Rich. Warwick, earl of. *Victorious newes from Ireland . . . sent in letter . . . As also a letter . . . sent from . . . Robert earl of Warwick.* London: f. M. Boat, [1642], 8 July. 4°. Pp. 8.
Tp, former no., '22', overwritten.
Wood 508(28). Wing B5733.

1186. Burley, John*. *The relation of the unjust proceedings against captaine Burley at Winchester and of his magnanimous and Christian suffering.* [London]: n.pub., 1648. 8°. Pp. [32], 23. Pasteboard (blue) with parchment spine. 1st upper and last lower flyleaves, marbled paper.
Flyleaf, upper, 2nd, AW wrote the titles of 4 printed works in this vol., within guidelines made with red ink. Tp, AW wrote 'Capt. Joh. Burley was executed at Winchester 10 Feb. 1647[8]'. Bsm. A4^v, line in margin, in ink, prob. by AW; A3-A5, cross marks and, passim, short vertical lines in pencil, not in AW's manner.
Wood 670(1). Wing R884.

1187. Burley, Walter. *Tractatus perbrevis de materia et forma:. . . Walteri Burlei.* [Oxford]: (in celeberima universitate Oxoniensi per me J. Scolar), (1518, 7 June). A-B^4.
LT 3.344.
Jesus College 1. Arch. 2. 25(2). STC 4123. Madan 31.

1188. [Burnet, Gilbert]. Salisbury, bp. of. *Rome's glory; or, a collection of divers miracles wrought by popish saints.* London: printed, sold M. Pitt, 1673. 8°. Pp. [8], 136.
Wood 876(4). Wing B5868.

1189. Burnet, Gilbert*. Salisbury, bp. of. *The last words and sayings of the true-protestant elm-board, which lately suffer'd martyrdom in Smithfield . . . with a true relation of a conference between dr. B– [G. Burnet], and the said board.* (London): (f. F. Shepherd), (1682). S.sh. (r-v).
8 identifications of initialed persons in this document, not in AW's hand. LT 3.29. See item 1194.
Wood 417(97). Wing L534.

1190. Burnet, Gilbert. Salisbury, bp. of. *The life and death of sir Matthew Hale.* London: f. W. Shrowsbery, 1682. 8°. Pp. [19], 218 (cancelled leaf between pp. 140 and 141 (between K6 and K7) was torn out).
P. [19], at the list of errata, AW wrote, 'These errata are entred', in red ink. Text, in addition to the 9 corrections from the errata, AW wrote some brief notes (some cropped) and lines in margins at pp. 1, 11, 33, 46, 116, 138. LT 2.359.
Wood 433(3). Wing B5828.

1191. Burnet, Gilbert*. Salisbury, bp. of. *More last words and sayings of the true protestant elm-board: or, a full answer to a later pretended sober vindication of the dr. [G. Burnet] and the board.* [London]: f. S. Hadwel, 1682. S.sh.
5 identifications, and 'two copies see next', not by AW. Dupl. at Wood 417(101), which has similar identifications.
Wood 417(100). Wing M2706.

1192. Burnet, Gilbert*. Salisbury, bp. of. *More last words and sayings of the true protestant elm-board: or, a full answer to a later pretended sober vindication of the dr. [G. Burnet] and the board.* [London]: f. S. Hadwel, 1682. S.sh.
5 identifications, not by AW. Dupl. at Wood 417(100), which has similar identifications. LT 3.29.
Wood 417(101). Wing M2706.

1193. Burnet, Gilbert*. Salisbury, bp. of. *A real vindication of dr. B– [G. Burnet] from the base and scandalous affronts.* (London): (f. D. N.), (1682). S.sh. (r-v).

Wood 417(99). Wing R459.

1194. Burnet, Gilbert*. Salisbury, bp. of. *A sober vindication of the reverend d[r.] [Burnet] and the harmless board lately glew'd together in a profane pasquill.* (London): (f. T– Rimar), (1682). S.sh. (r-v).
6 identifications of initialed persons, not by AW. This item responds to Wood 417(97), item 1189.
Wood 417(98). Wing S4417 (Wing, dr. [Burgess]).

1195. Burnet, Gilbert*. Salisbury, bp. of. *A second letter to dr. Burnet [on S. Lowth's of the subject of church-power].* (London): (f. R. Taylor), (1684). 4°. Pp. 8.
[MS.] Wood D. 29(16). Wing S2287.

1196. Burnet, Gilbert. Salisbury, bp. of. *An answer to a letter [by S. Lowth] to dr. Burnet, occasioned by his letter to mr. Lowth [on S. Lowth's of the subject of church-power].* (London): (f. R. Baldwin), (1685). 4°. Pp. 8.
[MS.] Wood D. 29(14). Wing B5758.

1197. Burnet, Gilbert. Salisbury, bp. of. *A letter . . . to mr. Simon Lowth . . . occasioned, by his late book of the subject of church-power.* (London): (f. R. Baldwin), (1685). 4°. Pp. 8.
[MS.] Wood D. 29(15). Wing B5818.

1198. Burnet, Gilbert. Salisbury, bp. of. *Some letters containing an account of what seemed most re-markable in Switzerland, Italy, &c.* n.p.: n.pub., 1687. 12°. Pp. 225. Pasteboard (blue) with parchment spine. 1st upper and last lower flyleaves, marbled paper.
Flyleaf, upper, 3rd[v], AW wrote the titles of 4 printed works in this vol., within guidelines made with red ink. Tp, AW identified the printed 'to T.H.R.B.', 'The honorable Rob. Boyle'. Passim, AW added lines in margin and some cross marks, in pencil, at the numerous passages that were quoted in a critique of this work, A. Varillas, *Reflexions*, at Wood 724(2), item 6295. Former no. '6' over '7', in pencil.
Wood 724(1). Wing B5917.

1199. Burnet, Gilbert*. Salisbury, bp. of. *Animadversions on the reflections upon dr. B[urnet]'s travels.* [Amsterdam?]: n.pub., 1688. 12°. Pp. 57 (pp. 1-2 blank).
P. 1, former no. '4', in pencil.
Wood 724(3). Wing B5757.

1200. [Burnet, Gilbert]. Salisbury, bp. of. *The expedition of . . . the prince of Orange for England. Giving an account . . . thereof, from . . . his setting sail from Holland. In a letter [signed N. N.].* [London]: f. T. W., 1688. 4°. Pp. 8. Pasteboard (blue) with parchment spine; 1st upper and last lower flyleaves, marbled paper.
Flyleaf, upper, 3rd[v], AW wrote the titles of 5 printed works (there are really 3, with the 3rd containing 3 pts.) in this vol., within guidelines made with red chalk. Pp. 4, identification of an initial, in pencil; 7, underscoring and 3 identifications; 8, 2 identifications and '12. Dec. – 3[d] – 1688'. LT 4.292.
Wood 530(1). Wing B5790.

1201. Burnet, Gilbert. Salisbury, bp. of. *Three letters concerning the present state of Italy, . . . Being a supplement to dr. Burnets letters.* [London?]: n.pub., 1688. 8° (with an augmented errata leaf). Pp. [16], 191, [1].
Tp, former no. '2', in pencil. Below, AW wrote 'published about X[t]mas 1687'. P. 113, AW identified the ambassador of England, 'Rog. E. of Castlemayne.'
Wood 724(4). Wing B5931.

1202. [Burnet, Gilbert]. Salisbury, bp. of *An enquiry into the present state of affairs: and in particular, whether we owe allegiance to the king in these circumstances?* London: f. J. Starkey a. R. Chiswell, 1689. 4°. Pp. 16.
Tp, AW wrote, 'D[r] Gilb. Burnet' and 'Jan. 22. - 1688[9] – 3[d].' LT 4.297. Other notes, in pencil, by later librarian.
Wood 529(21). Wing B5811.

1203. [Burnet, Gilbert]. Salisbury, bp. of. *Fourteen papers, viz. I. A letter from a gentleman in Ireland, . . . II. A letter from a freeholder [S. Johnson].* London: printed, sold R. Baldwin, 1689. 4°. Pp. [3], 80.
Tp, AW wrote, 'usually sold in Oxon. in the beg. of Jan. 1688. p. 6' and at paper XI, 'Abby and other Church-lands', 'p. 60'; p. 60, in margin, 'By D[r] Joh. Willes'. LT 3.293.
[MS.] Wood D. 29(18). Wing B5794.

1204. [Burnet, Gilbert]. Salisbury, bp. of. *Reflections on a paper, intituled, his majesty's reasons for*

withdrawing himself from Rochester. London: f. J. Starkey a. R. Chiswell, 1689. 4°. Pp. 8.
Tp, AW wrote, 'Oxon. Jan. 18. 1688[9] – 2ᵈ·'. LT 3.290.
Wood 529(18). Wing B5850.

1205. Burnet, Gilbert. Salisbury, bp. of. *Six papers, . . . To which is added, I. A apology . . . II. An enquiry.* London: n.pub., 1689. 4°. Pp. 52, 8, 8.
Tp, AW wrote, '6ᵈ - 18 18 Dec. 1668'.
[MS.] Wood D. 29(19) (not in Bodl. CD cat.). Wing B5913.

1206. Burnet, Gilbert. Salisbury, bp. of. *A sermon preached at the funeral of the honourable Robert Boyle [7 Jan.; on Eccles. 2.26].* London: f. R. Chiswell a. J. Taylor, 1692. 4°. Pp. 40. Calf with 3 fillets, stamp decoration inside corners (2 leaves and sunflower sprouting fleur-de-lis), and roll decoration at inner, spine edge (Ashm. binding).
Flyleaf, upper, 2nd, the titles of 15 printed works in this vol., by an Ashm. librarian (same hand in Wood 276a), all sermons, mainly funeral sermons. Flyleaf, upper, 1st, minor scribbling. P. 24, at Boyle's weakness of sight, vertical pencil line in margin. LT 3.380, AOF 2.286.
Wood 634(1). Wing B5899.

1207. Burnet, Gilbert. Salisbury, bp. of. *A letter . . . to the lord bishop of Cov. and Litchfield [W. Lloyd], concerning a book . . . A specimen of some errors and defects . . . by Anthony Harmer [Henry Wharton].* London: f. R. Chiswell, 1693. 4°. Pp. [4], 29, [3] (3 pp. books sold by Chiswell, including those written by Burnet). Calf with 3 fillets, stamp decoration inside corners (2 leaves and sunflower sprouting fleur-de-lis), and roll decoration at inner, spine edge (Ashm. binding).
Flyleaf, upper, 2nd, the titles of 19 printed works in this vol., by an Ashm. librarian (really 18, 2 entered for item 16). Numbering of works on tpp is in Roman numerals. 1st item, p. [2], 'Donum Antonii a Woodii Acad. Oxon.' lined out. Tp, AW wrote, 'Bought at Oxon on 11. Mar. 1692. 6ᵈ'. LT 4.417; AO 4.331. AW owned a copy of the Wharton book, Wood 206(4), item 6533, and see item 6695.
Wood 611(1). Wing B5824.

1208. Burnet, Gilbert. Salisbury, bp. of. *A sermon preached at the funeral of . . . John . . . archbishop of Canterbury [30 Nov.].* London: f. R. Chiswell, 1694. 4°. Pp. [4], 36, [2] (2 pp. books printed f. Chiswell).
[MS.] Wood D. 23(5). Wing B5902.

1209. Burnet, Gilbert, and Anthony Horneck. *The last confession, prayers and meditations of lieuten. John Stern, . . . before his execution, . . . with . . . George Borosky.* London: f. R. Chiswell, 1682. Fol. Pp. [2], 28.
Flyleaf, upperᵛ, AW wrote information about the murderers, 'Capt . . . Fratz a German capt. of a Foot-company who had accompanied count Charles John Coningsmark in his Travels, & came with him into England. [/] George Borosky a polander servant to Capt. Fratz – [/] John Sterne a Sweed – somtimes a Lieutenant of Foot, in Flanders [/] Capt Fratz writes himself de Vrats alias de Vallichs see p. 24 [/] George Borodzycz p 26'; tp, 'Capt . . . [blank] Wratz [sic] then also suffered – elswhere in the Gazet he is called Capt. Fratz', bsm.; passim, some cross-hatch marks, crosses, and lines in margin, in pencil. LT 3.5.
Wood 422(8). Wing B5814.

1210. [Burrough, Edward]. *To the parliament of the common-wealth of England . . . councel and advice unto you.* [London]: n.pub., (1659). 4°. Pp. 8.
P. 8, note, not in AW's hand.
Wood 610(42). Wing B6039.

1211. Burrough, Jeremiah. *Gospel-revelation in three treatises.* London: f. N. Brook a. T. Parkhurst, 1660. 4°. Pp. [15], 662, [26] (16 pp. books sold by Parkhurst and Brook).
Missing. MS. Wood E. 2(70), p. 37.
MS. Wood E. 2(70), p. 37. Wing B6083. *Folg.*

1212. Burroughs, John. *The soveraignty of the British seas.* London: f. H. Moseley, 1651. 12°. Pp. [10], 165.
Each 12° leaf is pasted on an 8° template.
Wood 731(2). Wing B6129.

1213. Burt, William. *Concio Oxoniae habita postridie comitiorum July 13. 1658, pro gradu doctoris.* Oxoniae: excud. H. Hall, impens. T. Robinson, 1659. 12°. Pp. [6], 75.
AW underscored the name of the author, in red ink. AOF 2.217.
Wood 893(5). Wing B6146. Madan 2436.

1214. [Burton, Henry]. *A divine tragedie lately acted, or a collection of sundry memorable examples of Gods judgements upon Sabbath-breakers.* [Amsterdam]: [J. F. Stam], 1636. 4°. Pp. [10], 46, [1] (A-F⁴,G²,*,**,1).
Tp, AW wrote, 'If I am not mistaken Will. Prynne had a considerable hand in this booke – see p. 43 in another char.' (signatures end at p. 42 with G2 and begin at p. 43 with * with the text in another font and size). Brief notes or identifications, pp. 11, at example 31 of an Oxford butcher, AW wrote, 'Hawkes a Butcher somtimes Baillive of the citie of Ox (Joh. Hawkes)'; 12, 2 corrections; 13, identification; 43, 'Noy' in margin; 45, 'Noy dead' in margin (AO 2.583); 46, line in margin.
Wood 643(2b). STC 4140.7.

1215. [Burton, Henry]. *The protestation protested: or, a short remonstrance, shewing what is principally required.* [London]: n.pub., 1641. 4°. A-C⁴.
Wood 616(17). Wing B6171 ('O' not recorded in Wing).

1216. Burton, Henry*. *A narration of the life of mr. Henry Burton.* London: n.pub., 1643. 4°. Pp. [4], 51.
Pp. 2-3, 8-9, 10, 12-15, 40, lines in margin, mainly in pencil, and pp. 7, 13, 2 corrections, of spelling of Harsnet, and of year. P. 11, a mark with '234', in pencil (?).
Wood 532(3). Wing B6169.

1217. [Burton, Henry]. *A full and satisfactorie answere to the arch-bishop of Canterburies speeh [sic].* London: J. Coe, 1645. 4°. Pp. 23.
Tp, AW wrote, 'Hen. Burton put out another scandalous answer also.'
Wood 366(28). Wing B6162A.

1218. Burton, William. *Graecae linguae historia:. . . [2nd tp] Veteris linguae Persicae.* Londini, Augustae Trinobantum: T. Roycroft, venalis ap. J. Martin a. J. Allestrye, 1657. 8°. Pp. [8], 104, [5] (2nd tp, p. 61).
Tp, AW wrote '9ᵈ'.
Wood 39(3). Wing B6186.

1219. Burton, William. *A commentary on Antoninus his itinerary through Britaine.* London: T. Roycroft, sold H. Twyford, a. T. Twyford, 1658. Fol. Pp. [1], 266, [6] (wanting t leaf).
Acquired 5 Nov. 1661, 4ˢ6ᵈ, LT 1.418; bound, 2 Dec. 1661, LT 1.420.
Wood 414(2). Wing B6185.

1220. Burton, William, and George Bathurst. *In viri doctissimi . . . Thomae Alleni . . . ultimo Septembris . . . demortui, exequiarum justis . . . orationes binae [the first by W. Burton, the second by G. Bathurst.].* London: G. Stanesbeius, 1632. 4°. Pp. [4], 16.
P. 2, correction, may not be by AW. P. 3, 2 erasures of notes. P. 5, lines in margin at printed marginalia, referring to Clement Reynes, *Apostolatus Benedictinorum in Anglia* (Duaci, 1616) 'ex Biblioth . . . Rob. Cottoni'. AW noted here that an English Benedictine had access to and is quoting from a ms. in the Cottonian library (Reynes was prob. using transcripts made by a fellow Benedictine, Augustine Baker). P. 10, AW wrote, 'Gul. Burtonus'.
Wood 512(10). STC 4165. Madan 712.

1221. [Bury, Arthur]. *The account examined: or, a vindication [by himself] of dr. Arthur Bury, . . . from the calumnies of a late pamphlet [by J. Harrington], entituled, an account of the proceedings.* London: printed a. sold R. Taylor, 1690. 4°. Pp. [4], 32.
Tp, AW wrote, 'published & sold at Oxon. 25 Oct. 1690'. AW's copy of Harrington is at Wood 631(5), item 3428. LT 3.340.
Wood 631(3). Wing A171.

1222. Bury, Arthur. *To avoid the intolerable drudgery of giving full satisfaction by a several letter [Reasons for the expulsion of J. Colmer from Exeter college, Oxford, by the rector, A. Bury].* [Oxford]: n.pub., [1690]. S.sh. (r-v).
Former no. '2'. ᵛ, AW wrote, 'Feb. 1689 [/] Feb. 1689/90'. LT 3.325, 328, 360-1.
Wood 657(51). Wing B6203A (rare).

1223. Bury, Arthur. *The case of Exeter-colledge, in the university of Oxford. Related and vindicated.* London: printed, sold R. Taylor, 1691. 4°. Pp. [4], 74.
Tp, 2-word note in pencil, illeg. AW wrote, 'This came from London to Oxon. & was there publicly sold 27. Janu. 1690[1].'; and, in pencil, no. in a former bundle, '6'. LT 3.352. P. 1, a correction.
Wood 631(6). Wing B6190.

1224. Bury, John*, and William Brooks*. *A true narrative of the late design of the papists to charge their horrid plot upon the protestants. By endeavourng to corrupt captain Bury and alderman Brooks of Dublin.* London: f. D. Newman, 1679. Fol. Pp. [3], 16.
Tp, AW wrote the price, '6ᵈ'.
Wood 424(12). Wing B6215.

1225. Bury, lieutenant col. *A briefe relation of the siege at Newark, as it was delivered to the councel of state at Derby-house.* London: f. P. Cole, 1644, 26 March. 4°. Pp. 8. Pasteboard (blue) with parchment spine.
Flyleaf, 2nd-3rdᵛ, AW wrote the titles of 43 printed works in this vol., within guidelines made with red ink. Before item 26 and 39, notes by Kirtland, e.g., 'Deest Novr. 28 1839 W[illiam] K[irtland]'.
Wood 377(1). Wing B6187A.

1226. Busbequius, Augerius Gislenius. *Augerii Gislenii Busbequii d. legationis Turcicae epistolae quatuor.* Paris: ap. Æ. Beys, 1589. 8°. Ff. 186. Calf with 2 fillets and a vertical line with two fillets, stamp decoration in corners and gold-stamp centrepiece, a sheldrake.
Flyleaf, upper, 3rd, 'In Posterum' (Ralph Sheldon's motto), lined out. LT 2.281; 3.104.
Wood 715. BL.

1227. Busby, George*. *The tryal and condemnation of George Busby, for high treason.* London: f. R. Taylor, 1681. Fol. Pp. [2], 38.
Tp, AW wrote the price, '1ˢ'; bsm.
Wood 427(23). Wing T2142.

1228. [Busby, Richard], presumed author. *A short institution of grammar. For the use of Westminster-school.* Cambridge: R. Daniel, 1647. 8°. Pp. [2], 92 (misnumbering).
Tp, in t, AW underscored 'School', in red ink. A trace of a letter, cropped. MS. Wood E. 2(70), p. 16, 'Will Busbie q[uaere] M[aste]r of Westm. Schoole formerlie of ch ch. institution of grammar. qu[aere] who the author'. See note at Wise, 8° A 153(1) Art., item 6648. See also AO 3.418.
8° A 153(4) Art. Wing B6229 (rare).

1229. Bushell, Thomas. *The severall speeches and songs, at the presentment of mʳ Bushells rock to the queenes most excellent majesty [23 Aug.].* Oxford: L. Lichfield, 1636. 4°. A⁴,B².
Wood 537(13). STC 4187.5. Madan 821.

1230. Bushell, Thomas. *A just and true remonstrance of his majesties mines-royall in . . . Wales.* London: E. G., 1642. 4°. A-D⁴.
Pp. 1-29, AW wrote p. nos. on alternate pp.; A2ᵛ, C1ᵛ, C2, C3ᵛ, cross-references; B3ʳ⁻ᵛ, lines in margin and note on the author of a printed letter, 'Dʳ Joh. Thornborough æt. 94. an. 1641'.
Wood 478(4). Wing B6246.

1231. Bushell, Tho[mas]. *A brief declaration of the severall passages in the treaty concerning the surrender of . . . Lundy.* London: n.pub., 1647[8]. 4°. Pp. [2], 20.
Wood 501(31). Wing B6241.

1232. Butcher, Richard. *The survey and antiquitie of the towne of Stamford.* London: T. Forcet, 1646. 4°. Pp. [9], 47.
Tp, AW wrote, 'The said Richard Butcher died at Stanford [sic] 1661 or there abouts'. Flyleaves, lower, 1-7, AW wrote out 'The Demon or Devill of Tidworth in Wilts, in the house there of Mr . . . . [blank] Mompeston'. Final lines, 'yʳ Faithfull kinsman & real servant Jo. Mompeston [/] Tidworth in Wilts - 6. Dec. 1663', followed by a postscript, ending, 'I have a Ballad of this matter which came out in 1663' (Wood 401(98), item 629). Flyleaf, lower, 9th, AW wrote, 'Towne of Stanford', in pencil. LT 2.53, 69.
Wood 467(2). Wing B6261.

1233. Butler*, capt. *The apprehending of captayne Butler at Portchmouth [sic] . . . with bullets and ammunition for Ireland, . . . As also, a true relation of a terrible sea fight by the states of Holland.* London: f. F. C. a. T. B., 1641[2]. 4°. Pp. [2], 6.
Wood 507(25). Wing A3583.

1234. Butler, Charles, ed. *Rameae rhetoricae libri duo.* ?: ?, 1597ff. Pp.?
Missing. MS. Wood E. 2(70), p. 11. Ed. not identified.
MS. Wood E. 2(70), p. 11. STC 4196.5-4200.5.

1235. Butler, James. Ormonde, 1st duke of. *A letter sent out of Ireland . . . to . . . sʳ. Robert Poyntz,*

shewing the true estate of . . . Ireland [21 June]. London: f. T. Whitaker, [1642]. S.sh.
ᵛ, AW wrote, '10 Jun 1642'.
Wood 508(23). Wing O450.

1236. Butler, James. Ormonde, 1st duke of. *XXIX. articles of peace, concluded . . . by the marquesse of Ormond, lord lieutenant of Ireland, . . . and . . . viscount Mountgarret, . . . commissioner for the Irish at the treaty held at Dublin.* London: I. C., 1646. 4°. A⁴.
Tp, price, '1ᵈ', lined out, may not be by AW.
Wood 509(8). Wing O463 ('O' not recorded in Wing).

1237. Butler, James. Ormonde, 1st duke of. *The last articles of peace made [30 July] . . . between . . . James . . . marques of Ormond, . . . and Donogh.* London: f. E. Husband, 1646, 7 Sept. 4°. Rpt. of Dublin: W. Bladen edition. Pp. [6], 16 (i.e., 24, misnumbering).
Dupl. at Wood 612(35).
Wood 509(6). Wing L475.

1238. Butler, James. Ormonde, 1st duke of. *The last articles of peace made [30 July] . . . between . . . James . . . marques of Ormond, . . . and Donogh.* London: f. E. Husband, 1646, 7 Sept. 4°. Rpt. of Dublin: W. Bladen edition. Pp. [6], 16 (i.e., 24, misnumbering).
Tp, AW wrote 'Dupl', in pencil. Bsm. Dupl. at Wood 509(6).
Wood 612(35). Wing L475.

1239. Butler, James. Ormonde, 1st duke of. *The marquesse of Ormond's declaration, proclaiming Charles the second, king of England . . . With his summons to colonell Jones for the surrender of Dublin.* London: f. F. Tyton a. J. Playford, 1649. 4°. Pp. [2], 24.
AW wrote in margin, 'Mar. 4.'
Wood 509(35). Wing O444.

1240. Butler, James, and Richard Blake. *The marquesse of Ormonds proclamation concerning the peace concluded with the Irish rebells . . . at Kilkenney; with a speech . . . by sir Richard Blake.* London: f. F. Tyton a. J. Playford, 1649, 27 Feb. 4°. Pp. [2], 16.
Wood 509(33). Wing O458.

1241. Butler, Jo[hn], et al. *A letter [signed by J. Butler, et al.] sent to . . . William Lenthal . . . concerning the securing of Windsor castle [24, 28 Dec.].* London: J. Streater, 1659. 4°. Pp. 7 (6-7 unopened).
Wood 503(29). Wing B6267D ('O' not recorded in Wing).

1242. Butler, Nathaniel*. *A full and the [truest] narra[tive] of the . . . murde[r] . . . of John Knight . . . by the . . . bloody hand of Nathaniel Butler.* London: T. Mabb f. J. Saywell, 1657. 4°. Pp. [4], 15, [4] (tp, mutilated).
Possibly acquired 27 Sept. 1657, 6ᵈ, LT 1.226.
Wood 365(14). Wing F 2292 (3).

1243. [Butler, Samuel]. *The acts and monuments of our late parliament:. . . By J. Canne.* London: n.pub., 1659. 4°. Pp. [2], 8, [1].
Tp, AW wrote 'Ridic' and nos. in former bundles, '34' and '32' (?), in pencil.
Wood 613(33). Wood A454A.

1244. [Butler, Samuel]. *A continuation of the acts and monuments of our late parliament [9 June-7 July].* London: n.pub., 1659. 4°. Pp. [2], 9.
Tp, AW wrote 'Ridic' and 'rogue' and no. in a former bundle, '35', all in pencil.
Wood 613(34). Wing C5960aA.

1245. [Butler, Samuel]. *Mola asinaria: or, the unreasonable and insupportable burthen now press'd upon the shoulders of this groaning nation. . . . in a remonstrance, . . . by William Prynne [really by S. Butler].* London: n.pub, 1659. 4°. Pp. [2], 6.
Tp, AW wrote, at Prynne's name, 'He was not the author of it-', in red ink; below, at misprinted date, MDCLVIX, '1659'. No. 35 in a former bundle.
Wood 610(31). Wing B6325A.

1246. [Butler, Samuel]. By the author of Hudibras. *To the memory of the most renowned Du-Vall: a Pindarick ode.* London: f. H. Brome, 1671. 4°. Pp. [2], 13.
Tp, AW wrote after printed 'Author of Hudibras', 'I doubt it.'
Wood 372(11). Wing B6336.

1247. [Butler, Samuel]. *Two letters, one from John Audland . . . to William Prynne. The other, William Prynnes answer, by the author of Hudibras.* London: f. J. Edwin, 1672. Fol. Pp. 22 (misnumbering).
Dupl. at Wood 657(25).
Wood 416(122-3). Wing B6336A.

1248. [Butler, Samuel]. *Two letters, one from John Audland . . . to William Prynne. The other, William Prynnes answer, by the author of Hudibras.* London: f. J. Edwin, 1672. Fol. Pp. 22 (misnumbering).
Dupl. at Wood 416(122-3).
Wood 657(25). Wing B6336A.

1249. Buts, Joan*. *An account of the tryal . . . of Joan Buts, for being a common witch.* (London): (f. S. Gardener), (1682). S.sh. (r-v).
ʳ, mark in margin, prob. not by AW.
[MS.] Wood B. 18(15). Wing A413.

1250. [Byam, William]. *An exact relation of the most execrable attempts of John Allin . . . on . . . Francis lord Willoughby.* London: f. R. Lowndes, 1665. 4°. Pp. [2], 12, [2].
Wood 365(21). Wing B6376.

1251. Bythner, Victorinus. *Tabula directoria. In qua totum to texnikon linguae sanctae, ad amussim delineatur.* Oxoniae: G. Turner, imp. authoris, 1637. S.sh. (2.5 fol. sheets., pasted together).
A few underscorings.
Wood 276a(23). STC 4261 (two). Madan 852.

1252. C., C. *Sad and serious thoughts, or the sense and meaning of the late act concerning marriages [17 Sept. 1653].* [London]: n.pub., [1653]. 4°. Pp. 8.
Tp, in t, 'to his Reverend Friend', 'Reverend' inked out.
Wood 609(34) (not in Bodl. CD cat.). Wing C17.

1253. C., D., and D. H. *An essay towards the deciding of the . . . case of usury. . . . [by D. C.]. As also, some animadversions upon the resolution of the case [by D. H.].* London: f. J. Rothwell, 1661. 4°. Pp. [14], 18.
Prob. acquired 21 Dec. 1668, LT 2.146.
Wood 628(2). Wing C20.

1254. C., E. *The Scots remonstrance or declaration; concerning, the restoring their declared king to his just rights . . . Together, with the lord Hoptons letter.* London: f. G. H., 1650. 4°. Pp. [2], 6.
Wood 503(9). Wing C27.

1255. C., G. B. *Plots, conspiracies and attempts of . . . enemies of the Romish religion, against the princes, and kingdomes of England, Scotland and Ireland, beginning with the reformation unto . . . 1642, collected by G. B. C.* London: f. R. Rounthwait, 1642. 4°. Pp. [2], 29 (misnumbering).
Wood 586(15). Wing C34.

1256. C., H. *An extract out of a letter [by H. C.] from a gentleman [and] The addresse of the county of Northampton, to . . . Monck [25 Jan.].* [London]: n.pub., [1660]. S.sh.
Wood 276a(248). Wing C40 (3).

1257. C., N. *Diatelesma. Nu. 3. The moderne history of the world, expressing the principall passages of the Christian countries in these last six moneths.* London: T. Harper f. N. Butter a. N. Bourne, 1637. 4°. Pp. [14], 136.
Tp, signature, 'Caesar Williamson' (AOF 2.34). P. [3], at description of Apelles' picture of history and truth, line in margin, in pencil; p. 93, corrections.
Wood 485(3). STC 4293.3.

1258. C., P. *The exaltation of Christmas pye . . . a preachment at Ely house.* [London]: n.pub., 1659. 4°. Pp. 11, [1].
Wood 613(13). Wing E3706aA.

1259. C., W. *A letter from his excellencies quarters, of a discovery in sir Thomas Fairfax his army, the enemies thereof.* London: B. Alsop, 1646, 27 Aug. 4°. Pp. [2], 6.
Tp, '1ᵈ', prob. not by AW.
Wood 501(25). Wing C157.

1260. C., W. *Decimarum & oblationum tabula. A tything table.* London: J. T. f. A. Crook, 1658. 4°. Pp. [8], 39.
Tp, AW wrote, '6^d'. See note at Wood 637(1), item 6190.
Wood 370(4). Wing C148B.

1261. C., W. *A discourse for a king and parliament:. . . by a moderate and serious pen.* London: f. G. Bedell a. T. Collins, 1660. 4°. Pp. [4], 27.
Tp, AW wrote 'Aprill:', and '6^d'.
Wood 608(10). Wing C151.

1262. Cabal. *The cabal. Now the reformer.* [London]: n.pub., [1679/80]. S.sh.
AW wrote '1681 82'; and ^v, '1680 81', and '1681'.
Wood 417(43). Wing C179.

1263. Cabinet of Grief. *A cabinet of grief: or, the French midwife's miserable mean for . . . murther . . . of her husband.* [London]: [blank]. [sic, i.e., J.] Blare, 1688. 8°. Pp. [2], 14.
Tp, AW's note, ' . . . mitted in 1687', cropped at bottom.
Wood 284(10). Wing C188 (rare).

1264. [Caesar, Charles]. *Numerus infaustus. A short view of the unfortunate reigns.* London: f. R. Chiswell, 1689. 12°. Pp. [4], 89 (i.e., 125, misnumbering), [3] (3 pp. books printed for Chiswell). Pasteboard (brown) with calf spine, traces of upper and lower flyleaves of marbled paper; rebacked in 1950.
Flyleaf, upper, 3rd^v, AW wrote the titles of 4 printed works in this vol., within guidelines made with red ink. 1st item, each 12° leaf is pasted on a extension to form an 8° leaf. Tp, AW wrote, 'Bought at Ox. in the beginning of Sept. 1689'.
Wood 242(1). Wing C203.

1265. [Caius, Joannes]. *De antiquitate Cantabrigiensis academiae libri duo. Adjunximus assertionem antiquitatis Oxoniensis academiae [by Thomas Key], ab Oxoniensi quodam annis . . . conscriptam.* Londini: per H. Bynneman, 1568, Augusto. 8°. Pp. 360, [24], [39] (2nd tp at 2nd A1). Calf with 2 fillets and stamp centrepiece; spine, 4 bands, repaired. Backing, parchment ms., Latin.
Flyleaf, upper, note by A. Allam, 'Pret. 2^s-6d We[st]: Bib: April. decimo 8vo 1678 Step [?]:'; ^v, 'Antonius Weber Coloniensis meus est herus, Emptus Cantabrigiae in Regno Angliae n: – sh 1-4^d. Anno - 1573' (LT 3.167 gives 1673). Pp. 339, underscoring, 340, note, and 340b, mark in margin, not by AW. Diff ed. at Wood 480(1).
Wood 179(1). STC 4344.

1266. Caius, Joannes. *De canibus Britannicis, liber unus. De rariorum animalium et stirpium historia, liber unus. De libris propriis, liber unus.* Londini: per G. Seresium, 1570. 8°. Ff. [1], 13, [2]; [1], 30, [1]; [1], 31, [4] (3 tpp).
3rd f. 4, minor underscoring. In contemporary binding with an Allam book, Wood 179(1), item 1265.
Wood 179(2). STC 4346.

1267. Caius, Joannes. *De antiquitate Cantabrigiensis academiae libri duo. . . . Johanne Caio Anglo authore. Adjunximus assertionem antiquitatis Oxoniensis academiae [by Thomas Key].* Londini: in aed. J. Daii, 1574. 4°. Pp. 268, [18] (wanting errata leaf); [2], 27 (2 pts.) (order of the 2 pts. is reversed in this vol., i.e, *Assertio* was inserted at the beginning). Calf with 3 fillets, 2nd rectangle with 3 fillets and stamp decoration outside corners, silver-stamp centrepiece (similar to Ker, pl. XIV, no. 68), and edge hatching; spine, 4 bands and hatching (Oxford binding).
Pastedown, upper, 'oct: 19. 1664', prob. in AW's hand. Flyleaf, upper, is a letter bound with this vol., dated 27 Aug. 1570 from John Griffith to Thomas Key, Master of University College, and the author of *Assertio* (see AO 1.397-9 for how the books by the two Caii, or Keys, one of Oxford and the other of Cambridge, came to be issued together; LT 1.427, 4.199). Texts of both parts contain marks in margins, underscorings, some lined out words, cross-references (in *Assertio* to pp. in *De antiquitate*), and some notes (see esp. p. 152 and flyleaves and pastedown, lower, which AW refers to in Wood 602, item 6268, see Plate IV), not in AW's hand (one brief note, in *Assertio*, p. 20, 'De Oxon. origine', is in AW's hand). Flyleaf, after *De antiquitate*, an index, not in AW's hand. Tp of *Assertio*, 'Jo Day', which may refer to a former owner but more probably to the publisher of all 3 items in this vol. In AW's diary, 'given to Mr. Wilton 4 [for] Cay's 'Antiq.', 13 Dec. 1664, 4^s, LT 2.24 (the date on pastedown, above, may be when AW took the book; he paid John Wilton later). Diff. ed. at Wood 179(1).
Wood 480(1). STC 4345.

1268. Caius, Joannes. *Historiae Cantebrigiensis academiae ab urbe condita, liber primus (secundus)*.
Londini: in aed. J. Daii, 1574. 4°. Pp. 135, [11].
Some underscoring, lined out portions, marks in margins, and notes, not in AW's hand.
Wood 480(2) (not in Bodl. CD cat.). STC 4349.

1269. Caius, Joannes. *Johannis Caij Angli, de pronunciatione Græcae & Latinae linguae . . . libellus*.
Londini: in aed. J. Daii, 1574. 4°. Pp. 23.
Some underscoring and marks in margin, prob. not by AW. P. 23ᵛ, flyleaves, lower (2), and pastedown,
lower, notes and indices to works bound in this vol., not in AW's hand.
Wood 480(3). STC 4348.

1270. Calabria. *Dreadfull newes: or a true relation of the . . . earthquake . . . at Callabria [27 March.
Tr. from the Ital.]*. London: J. Okes f. R. Mabb, 1638. 4°. Pp. [2], 17.
[MS.] Wood D. 28(6). STC 4349.5.

1271. Calfine, Giles. *The book of common prayer confirmed by sundry acts of parliament, . . . vindicated*.
London: T. M. f. W. Potter, 1660. 4°. Pp. [2], 6.
Tp, after the year, AW wrote, 'Aprill:'.
[MS.] Wood B. 36(15). Wing C293.

1272. Calthrop, Henry. *The liberties, usages, and customes of the city of London; . . . collected by sir
Henry Colthrop*. London: B. Alsop f. N. Vavasour, 1642. 4°. Pp. [2], 25.
Wood 590(3). Wing C308.

1273. Cambridge. *'A draught of Cambridge'*. N.p.: ?, n.d. S.sh.
Missing in 1939.
Wood 276a(61). Not identified.

1274. Cambridge. *Sigillum cancellarii. Area scholaris Cantebrigiensium. Sigillum academiae*. N.p.: n.pub.,
n.d. S.sh.
Wood 423(3). Not identified.

1275. Cambridge. *Exchange ware at the second hand, viz. Band, Ruffe, and Cuffe, . . . Or, a dialogue
. . . in the famous universitie of Cambridge*. London: W. Stansby f. M. Partrich, 1615. 4°. 2nd ed. A2-
4,B⁴,C1-3.
Wood 653(3). STC 1356.

1276. Cambridge. *To the honourable the lords and commons . . . The humble petition of the university
of Cambridge*. N.p.: n.pub., [1643]. S.sh.
AW wrote, 'This came forth about the beginning of June 1643'.
Wood 423(21). Wing C358.

1277. Cambridge. *An extract of certain papers of intelligence, from Cambridge, concerning his majestie
and the armie*. [London]: n.pub., 1647. 4°. Pp. [2], 6.
Wood 612(46). Wing E3908.

1278. Cambridge. *To our reverend and deare brethren the ministers of England and Wales*. N.p.: n.pub.,
1649, 24 Oct. S.sh. (r-v).
Wood 423(30). Wing T1382B (one) ('O' not recorded in Wing).

1279. Cambridge. *Umbra comitiorum, [sic] or Cambridge commencement in types*. (Oxford, reprinted f.
the U. of Cambridge): n.pub., [1650]. 4°. Pp. 7.
P. 7, '(ie 1650', may not be by AW. Diff. ed. at Wood 614(18).
Wood 515(9). Wing U25 ('O' not recorded in Wing). Madan 2030.

1280. Cambridge. *Umbra commitiorum. [sic] Or, Cambridge commencement in types*. [London]: n.pub.,
[1650]. 4°. Pp. 8.
Tp, AW wrote 'Dup', in pencil. Diff. ed., Oxford printing, at Wood 515(9).
Wood 614(18). Not in Wing. Not Wing U25. See Madan 2030. Not in ESTCR.

1281. Cambridge. *University queries, in a gentle touch by the by*. Cambridge: n.pub., 1659. 4°. Pp. [2],
6.
Tp, no. '42', in pencil, in a former bundle.
Wood 613(47). Wing U80. Madan 2430N.

1282. Cambridge. *Selectae aliquot legum, atque ordinationum academicarum particulae . . . Novemb. 24.*
[Cambridge]: n.pub., [1663]. S.sh.
Wood 276a(321). Wing C351 (rare).

1283. Cambridge. *A poem attempting something upon the rarities of the . . . university of Cambridge.*
London: f. R. Nicolson in Cambridge, [1673]. 4°. Pp. [2], 21 (cropped at bottom).
Tp, AW wrote, 'Dup'. Bsm. Dupl. at Wood 513(5).
Wood 483(5). Wing P2669 (Wing, omits London).

1284. Cambridge. *A poem attempting something upon the rarities of the . . . university of Cambridge.*
London: f. R. Nicolson in Cambridge, 1673. 4°. Pp. [2], 21.
Tp, AW wrote the date of acquisition, '4ᵈ. May. 73.' LT 2.262. Dupl. at Wood 483(5).
Wood 513(5). Wing P2669 (Wing, omits London).

1285. Cambridge. *The fanatick rampant or an election at Cambridge.* N.p.: n.pub., [1679]. S.sh.
AW wrote 'An. 1680', half in ink and half in pencil.
Wood 417(22). Wing F400.

1286. Cambridge. *The Cambridge case, being an exact narrative of all the proceedings against the vice-chancellour . . . for refusing to admit Alban Francis, a Benedictine monk, to the degree of master of arts, without taking the oaths.* London: printed a. sold by R. Taylor, 1689. Fol. Pp. [2], 16.
Tp, AW wrote, 'Bought at Oxon in the beg. of Feb. 1688[9]. - 6ᵈ'. Pp. 1, AW wrote the year; 8, identified the Cambridge college of the lord-chancellor, 'In Trin. Coll.' LT 3.221.
Wood 421(11). Wing C331.

1287. Cambridge. *Musae Cantabrigienses, . . . Wilhelmo et Mariae . . . publicae salutis ac liberatis vindicibus, haed officii & pietatis ergo d. d.* Cantabrigiae: J. Hayes, 1689. 4°. A-M⁴,a-d⁴,e². Parchment, stabbed.
Flyleaf, upper, AW wrote 'In vigil S. Marci [24 April] 1689 Dedet mihi A. C. [Arthur Charlett] SS: T. b. e Coll. Trin' (LT 3.302); and 'Liber Musaei Ashmoleani Oxōn', not in AW's hand.
Wood 327. Wing C344.

1288. Cambridge. *1691. Prior comb. [/] Jan. 17. Mʳ Peirce. Emman. [college] [1st column; and 2nd column:] 1691 Poster. Comb. [/] Jan. 17. Mʳ Wigly Joh. [college] [bottom of p.:] Singuli suo ordine concionabuntur . . . caeterásque exercitationes ipsi per se sua in personā praestabunt . . . Gabr. Quadring, procan.* [Cambridge]: n.pub., [1691]. S.sh.
AW wrote above, 'Cambridge'; at heading, 'Prior Comb.', 'Combinatio' (may not be in AW's hand); and below, AW wrote 'Jan 27: 1691 dedit mihi J. B.' (J. A. Bernard? Or, James Bisse, LT 3.381). ᵛ (pasted down side), 'Scotchman', opposite entry on ʳ side of 'Mʳ Moore Sid.', may not be in AW's hand.
Wood 276a(516) (not in Bodl. CD cat.). Not in Wing. Not in ESTCR.

CAMBRIDGE ACT VERSES (items 1289-1367)

1289. Allison, John. Resp. in philos. M.A. Col. Regal. soc. *Existentia Dei probatur ex continuatione existentiae nostrae . . . Julii 5.* [Cambridge]: n.pub., [1670]. S.sh.
On the Cambridge theses, see LT 2.165.
Wood 276a(491). Wing A1215 (rare).

1290. Bagshaw, Edm[ond]. Resp. in Philos. Mʳᵒ in Art. Coll. Trin. soc. *Datur conceptus positivus rei immaterialis . . . Jul. 2.* [Cambridge]: n.pub., [1661]. S.sh.
Dupl. at Wood 276a(484).
Wood 276a(480). Not in Wing (should be at B392A). Not in ESTCR.

1291. Bagshaw, Edm[ond]. Resp. in Philos. Mʳᵒ in Art. Coll. Trin. soc. *Datur conceptus positivus rei immaterialis . . . Jul. 2.* [Cambridge]: n.pub., [1661]. S.sh.
Dupl. at Wood 276a(480).
Wood 276a(484). Not in Wing (should be at B392A). Not in ESTCR.

1292. Barrow, Isaac. Resp. pro gradu s. theol. doct. Coll. Trin. soc. *Spiritus sanctus est persona distincta . . . Julii 4.* [Cambridge]: n.pub., [1670]. S.sh.
Wood 276a(493). Wing B960 (3).

1293. Barton, [Francis]. [M.A. 1638, Fellow 1637] Resp. Coll. Trin. *Necessariò ponuntur orbes eccentrici.* [Cambridge]: n.pub., [1639]. S.sh.
Above, 'Quaestiones Philosophicae comitiis habitae Cantabrigiensibus Julii. 2°. 1639'. Names and colleges of 4 participants are written in (including name of responder, above), not in hand of AW.
Wood 276a(445). STC 4474.80 (rare).

1294. Billers, J[ohn]. Resp. in philos. M.A. Coll. S. Joh. Evan. soc. *Potentia irresistibilis nullum confert jus . . . Jul. 5.* [Cambridge]: n.pub., [1675]. S.sh.
AW wrote '1675', in pencil.
Wood 276a(501). Wing B2898 (rare) (Wing, n.p.).

1295. Boteler, Tho[mas]. Resp. in philos. A.M. Coll. Trin. soc. Ονειροκριται *sunt futiles . . . Julii 4.* [Cambridge]: n.pub., [1670]. S.sh.
Wood 276a(492). Wing B3804A (rare).

1296. Briggs, Thoma[s]. Resp. Coll. D. Joan. soc. *Primaeva communitas non tollit proprietatem rerum . . . Julii 2.* [Cambridge]: n.pub., [1660]. S.sh.
Wood 276a(474). Wing B4666 (two).

1297. Bright, Georg[e]. Resp. pro gradu s. theol. doct. Coll. Eman. *Pontificii non sunt ab omni cultu idolatrico penitus excusandi . . . Julii 3.* [Cambridge]: n.pub., [1671]. S.sh. (joined with Wood 276a(497)).
Wood 276a(498). Wing B4673A (rare).

1298. Brunning, Samuel. Resp. in Philos., M. spsr ° in Art. Aul. S. Kath. socio. *Non datur talis causarum concatenatio quae sit causa sufficiens, & necessaria actionis . . . Julii 1.* [Cambridge]: n.pub., [1661]. S.sh. Dupl. at Wood 276a(483).
Wood 276a(479). Wing B5232 (rare).

1299. Brunning, Samuel. Resp. in Philos., M. spsr ° in Art. Aul. S. Kath. socio. *Non datur talis causarum concatenatio quae sit causa sufficiens, & necessaria actionis . . . Julii 1.* [Cambridge]: n.pub., [1661]. S.sh. Dupl. at Wood 276a(479).
Wood 276a(483). Wing B5232 (rare).

1300. Burles, Tho[mas]. Resp. Aul. Trin. soc. L. Bac. *Ratihabitio matrimonii per procuratorem contracti, cujus mandatum eo ignorante revocatum fuit, est nullius momenti . . . Jul. 1.* [Cambridge]: n.pub., [1679?]. S.sh. (joined with Wood 276a(508)).
Wood 276a(509). Wing B5740aA (two) ('O' not recorded in Wing).

1301. Burton, [Hezekiah]. Resp. Coll. Magd. soc. *Scepticorum* Ονειροκριται *non est rationi consentanea.* [Cambridge]: n.pub., [1655]. S.sh.
Names of 2 opponents and procurator, not in AW's hand.
Wood 276a(453). Wing B6177A (rare).

1302. Cambridge, Act Verses. *Cambridge, act verses.* [Cambridge]: n.pub., n.d. S.sh.
Missing in 1939. Information is from the 1717 list.
Wood 276a(490). STC 4474.1ff. Not identified.

1303. Cambridge, Act Verses. *Dantur objectiva mentis humanae, etiam vera & realia, quae sunt planè* αφαντασα. [Cambridge]: n.pub., n.d. S.sh.
Wood 276a(438a). Not in STC or Wing. Not in ESTCR.

1304. Cambridge, Act Verses. *Omnis sensatio fit in cerebro.* [Cambridge]: n.pub., n.d. S.sh.
Wood 276a(438b). Not in STC or Wing. Not in ESTCR.

1305. Clerk, Gabriel. Resp. Coll. Petrensis. *Materia qualitercunque modificata non sufficit explicandis passionibus . . . Julii 1.* [Cambridge]: n.pub., [1662]. S.sh.
Wood 276a(487). Wing C4647A (rare).

1306. Coell, Francis. Resp. jur. civil. bac. Aul. Trin. soc. *Fides hosti data est servanda.* [Cambridge]: n.pub., [1671]. S.sh. (joined with Wood 276a(500), item 1360).
Wood 276a(499). Wing C4882 (rare).

1307. Coldwell, [William]. Resp. Coll. Regin. soc. *Regulae morum ostensivae & obligativae sunt lumine naturali cognoscibiles . . . Jul. 1.* [Cambridge]: n.pub., [1651]. S.sh.
Dupl. at Wood 276a(452).

Wood 276a(449). Wing C5019 (two).

1308. Coldwell, [William]. Resp. Coll. Regin. soc. *Regulae morum ostensivae & obligativae sunt lumine naturali cognoscibiles . . . Jul. 1.* [Cambridge]: n.pub., [1651]. S.sh.
ᵛ, AW wrote '1651'. Dupl. at Wood 276a(449).
Wood 276a(452). Wing C5019 (two).

1309. Cradock, [Samuel]. Resp. Coll Eman. soc. *Renati non possunt totaliter, aut finaliter excidere è gratia Dei . . . Jul. 1.* [Cambridge]: n.pub., [1651]. S.sh.
Wood 276a(451). Wing C6755 (two).

1310. Crouch, William. Resp. Coll. D. Joan. socio. *Status naturae non est status belli.* [Cambridge]: n.pub., [1662]. S.sh.
Wood 276a(486). Wing C7364 (rare).

1311. Cudworth, [Ralph]. Resp. Aul. Clar. praefect. *Dantur rationes boni, & mali aeternae, & indispensabiles . . . Jun. 30.* [Cambridge]: n.pub., [1651]. S.sh.
Wood 276a(450). Wing C7465 (two).

1312. Cumberland, [Richard]. [M.A. 1656; B.D. 1663]. Resp. Coll. Magd. soc. *Habitus mentis acquisiti sunt species perfectiores in memoria ordinatè repositae . . . Julii 4.* [Cambridge]: n.pub., [1659]. S.sh.
Dupl. at Wood 276a(472).
Wood 276a(466). Wing C7582aA (rare, 2 at O).

1313. Cumberland, [Richard]. [M.A. 1656; B.D. 1663]. Resp. Coll. Magd. soc. *Habitus mentis acquisiti sunt species perfectiores in memoria ordinatè repositae . . . Julii 4.* [Cambridge]: n.pub., [1659]. S.sh.
Dupl. at Wood 276a(466).
Wood 276a(472). Wing C7582aA (rare, 2 at O).

1314. Dillingham, Theoph[ilus]. Resp. pro gradu doct. in theol. Aul. Clar. praef. *Status integritatis fuit status immortalitatis . . . Julii 2.* [Cambridge]: n.pub., [1655]. S.sh.
Names of 6 opponents and procurator, not in AW's hand; ᵛ, name, again, of procurator, Dʳ. Lightfoot.
Wood 276a(455). Wing D1481 (rare).

1315. Franck, [Mark]. [M.A. 1634, B. D. 1641]. Resp. Pembroke. *Multitudo librorum est studiorum impedimentum.* [Cambridge]: n.pub., [1637]. S.sh.
Above, '1637. [/] Quaestiones Philosophicae Comitiis habitae. Octob. 2. 1637'. Names and colleges of 4 participants are written in (including name of defender, above), not in hand of AW.
Wood 276a(439a). STC 4474.75 (rare).

1316. Frost, John. Resp. Coll. Divi Joann. socio. *Fides justificat sub ratione instrumenti . . . Julii 1.* [Cambridge]: n.pub., [1656]. S.sh.
Wood 276a(457). Wing F2245 (rare).

1317. Fuller, Sam[uel]. Resp. pro gradu S.T.D. Coll. Div. Joh. *Ministerium ecclesiae Anglicanae à reformatoribus nostris nec factum est nullum nec antichristianum . . . Jun. 1.* [Cambridge]: n.pub., [1679]. S.sh. (joined with Wood 276a(505)).
Printed Jun. 1 altered to Jun. '30'.
Wood 276a(504). Wing F2397 (3) (Wing, n.p.).

1318. Fuller, Thom[as]. Resp. S.T.B. Coll. Christi socio. *Non datur externus judex infallibilis controversiarum fidei . . . Julii 5.* [Cambridge]: n.pub., [1659]. S.sh.
Dupl. at Wood 276a(471).
Wood 276a(469). Not in Wing. Not in ESTCR.

1319. Fuller, Thom[as]. Resp. S.T.B. Coll. Christi socio. *Non datur externus judex infallibilis controversiarum fidei . . . Julii 5.* [Cambridge]: n.pub., [1659]. S.sh.
Dupl. at Wood 276a(469).
Wood 276a(471). Not in Wing. Not in ESTCR.

1320. Fullwood. [Gervase, Peter or William (3 possibilities in Venn)]. Resp. Aul. Cath. soc. *Substantia immaterialis est aequè demonstrabilis ac materialis . . . Julii 5.* [Cambridge]: n.pub., [1659]. S.sh.
Dupl. at Wood 276a(473).
Wood 276a(467). Not in Wing. Not in ESTCR.

1321. Fullwood. [Gervase, Peter or William: 3 possibilities in Venn]. Resp. Aul. Cath. soc. *Substantia immaterialis est aequè demonstrabilis ac materialis . . . Julii 5*. [Cambridge]: n.pub., [1659]. S.sh.
Dupl. at Wood 276a(467).
Wood 276a(473). Not in Wing. Not in ESTCR.

1322. Gardiner, Sam[uel]. Resp. Coll. Corp. Christ. pro gradu doctorali in s. theologia. *Supremus magistratus habet summam potestatem circa sacra . . . Jul. 6*. [Cambridge]: n.pub., [1657]. S.sh.
Wood 276a(458). Wing G249 (rare).

1323. Gould, William. Resp. S.T.B. Coll. John. soc. *Religio Christiana est infallibilis certitudinis . . . Julii 4*. [Cambridge]: n.pub., [1671]. S.sh. (joined with Wood 276a(498)).
Wood 276a(497). Wing G1442 (rare) (Wing, n.p.).

1324. Grove, Robert. Resp. pro gradu S.T.D. Coll. Div. Joh. *Nullus est satisfactionum thesaurus, qui sit fundamentum indulgentiarum . . . Jul. 4*. [Cambridge]: n.pub., [1681]. S.sh.
Wood 276a(510). Wing G2151 (3) (Wing, n.p.).

1325. Hartcliffe, John. Resp. in philos. A.M. Col. Regal. soc. *In veritate rerum disquirenda errat Cartesii scepticismus . . . Jul. 1*. [Cambridge]: n.pub., [1678]. S.sh.
AW wrote '1678', in pencil.
Wood 276a(503). Wing H967 (rare) (Wing, n.p.).

1326. Hill, Joseph. Resp. S.T.B. Coll. Magd. soc. *Justitia quā coram Deo consistimus est justitia Christi mediatoris . . . Jul. 3*. [Cambridge]: n.pub., [1660]. S.sh.
Wood 276a(475). Wing H2001 (rare) (Wing, n.p.).

1327. Houl[d]sworth, [Richard]. [Holdsworth, D. D. 1637]. Resp. Dr. Eman. *Lex moralis per gratiam, quae est viatoris, non est implebilis*. [Cambridge]: n.pub., [1637]. S.sh.
Above, '1637 [/] Quaestiones pro doctoratu in Jure Civili, Comitiis habitae Octob. 2. 1637'. Names and colleges of 4 participants are written in (including name of defender, above), not in hand of AW.
Wood 276a(440). STC 4474.65 (rare).

1328. Hughes, Aud. Resp. Aul. Trin. Soc. pro gradu doctorali. *Res ab hostibus captae & ab iisdem recuperatae cedunt capientibus . . . Junii 30*. [Cambridge]: n.pub., [1662]. S.sh.
Wood 276a(488). Wing H3304 (rare) (Wing, n.p.).

1329. Ingelo, Nath[aniel]. Resp. Coll. Reginal. pro gradu doctorali in theolog. *Omnia ad salutem necessaria perspicuè traduntur in sacra scriptura . . . Julii 5*. [Cambridge]: n.pub., [1658]. S.sh.
Dupl. at Wood 276a(463).
Wood 276a(462). Wing I183 (rare) (Wing, n.p.).

1330. Ingelo, Nath[aniel]. Resp. Coll. Reginal. pro gradu doctorali in theolog. *Omnia ad salutem necessaria perspicuè traduntur in sacra scriptura . . . Julii 5*. [Cambridge]: n.pub., [1658]. S.sh.
Dupl. at Wood 276a(462).
Wood 276a(463). Wing I183 (rare) (Wing, n.p.).

1331. Lamplugh, [Josiah]. [B.D. 1657]. Resp. Coll. Corp. Christ. socio. *Novae revelationes extra scripturam sacram non sunt expectandae . . . Jul. 7*. [Cambridge]: n.pub., [1657]. S.sh.
Wood 276a(459). Not in Wing (should be at 304aA). Not in ESTCR.

1332. Lane, Erasmus. Resp. pro gradu s. theol. bac. C. C. C. soc. *Divinitas Christi probatur ab ejus cultu . . . Julii 5*. [Cambridge]: n.pub., [1670]. S.sh.
Wood 276a(494). Wing L336 (one) ('O' not recorded in Wing).

1333. Lee, Henr[y]. Resp. in philos. A.M. Coll. Eman. soc. *Idea positiva substantiae immaterialis aequè intelligibilis est ac materialis . . . Jul. 3*. [Cambridge?]: n.pub., [1671]. S.sh.
ᵛ, 'Cantab. 1671', prob. not by AW. See similar t at Wood 276a(506).
Wood 276a(496). Wing L842A ('O' not recorded in Wing).

1334. Linfeild, Ja[mes]. Resp. in philos. A.M. Coll. Trin. soc. *Idea positiva substantiae immaterialis aequè intelligibilis est ac materialis . . . Jul. 1*. [Cambridge]: n.pub., [1679]. S.sh. (joined with Wood 276a(507)).
See similar t at Wood 276a(496).
Wood 276a(506). Wing L2335 (Wing, n.p.).

1335. Low, Sam[uel]. Resp. Magd. Col. soc. *Pontifex Romanus non habet postestatem temporalem in*

ordine ad spiritualia . . . Julii 1. [Cambridge]: n.pub., [1662]. S.sh.
Wood 276a(485a). Not in Wing. Not in ESTCR.

1336. Mason, [Charles]. [D.D. 1660]. Resp. in theologia doct. Coll. Regl. *Ecclesia potestatem habet quaedam statuendi circa cultum divinum . . . Jul. 1.* [Cambridge]: n.pub., [1661]. S.sh.
Dupl. at Wood 276a(481).
Wood 276a(477). Wing M907.

1337. Mason, [Charles]. [D.D. 1660]. Resp. in theologia doct. Coll. Regl. *Ecclesia potestatem habet quaedam statuendi circa cultum divinum . . . Jul. 1.* [Cambridge]: n.pub., [1661]. S.sh.
Dupl. at Wood 276a(477).
Wood 276a(481). Wing M907.

1338. Maulyverer, John. Resp. in philos. A.M. Coll. Magd. soc. *Suppositis particularis striatis rectè solvuntur phaenomena magnetis . . . Julii 4.* [Cambridge]: n.pub., [1671]. S.sh.
Wood 276a(495). Wing M1335 (rare) (Wing, n.p.).

1339. Mildmay, [Charles]. [M.A. 1648, Fellow 1647] Resp. Coll. Pet. soc. *Lex naturae est indispensabilis . . . Jul. 1.* [Cambridge]: n.pub., [1650]. S.sh.
Wood 276a(446). Wing M2040 (rare).

1340. Natlie, [Edward]. [M.A. 1638, Fellow 1635-44] Resp. Reginalis. *Absurdum est dari orbem habitabilem in luna.* [Cambridge]: n.pub., [1639]. S.sh.
Above, 'Quaestiones Philosophicae comitiis habitae Cantabrigiensibus. Julii. 1°. 1639'. Names and colleges of 4 participants are written in (including name of responder, above), not in hand of AW.
Wood 276a(444). STC 4474.2 (rare).

1341. Obligatio. *Obligatio legum naturalium satis indicatur per poeneas annexas & praemia . . . Mart. 1.* [Cambridge]: n.pub., [1687/8]. S.sh.
Wood 276a(511). Not in Wing. Not in ESTCR.

1342. Outram, William. Resp. Christi Col. S.T.D. *Juramentum vulgò dictum solennis liga & foedus non obligat foederatos . . . Junii 30.* [Cambridge]: n.pub., [1662]. S.sh.
Wood 276a(485b). Wing O602 (rare) (Wing, London).

1343. Owen, [Andrew]. [L.L.B. 1637]. Resp. Aul. Trinit. *Capite damnati testamentum facere non possunt.* [Cambridge]: n.pub., [1637]. S.sh.
Above, ' 1637 [/] Quaestiones pro Baccalaureatu in Jure Civili comitiis habitae Octob. 3. 1637'. Names and colleges of 5 participants are written in (including name of responder, above), not in hand of AW.
Wood 276a(442b). STC 4474.16 (rare).

1344. Oxenden, George. Resp. pro gradu doctoratus in jure, Aul Trin soc. *Causa jurejurando decisa praetextu perjurii retractari non potest . . . ultimo die Junii.* [Cambridge]: n.pub., [1679]. S.sh. (joined with Wood 276a(509)).
Wood 276a(508). Wing O839 (Wing, n.p.).

1345. Peachell, John. Resp. in theol. bacc. Coll. Mag. soc. *Licet viris ecclesiasticis administrare res civiles . . . Jul. 2.* [Cambridge]: n.pub., [1661]. S.sh.
Dupl. at Wood 276a(482).
Wood 276a(478). Not in Wing. Not in ESTCR.

1346. Peachell, John. Resp. in theol. bacc. Coll. Mag. soc. *Licet viris ecclesiasticis administrare res civiles . . . Jul. 2.* [Cambridge]: n.pub., [1661]. S.sh.
Dupl. at Wood 276a(478).
Wood 276a(482). Not in Wing. Not in ESTCR.

1347. Pearson, John. Resp. Coll. Regal. pro gradu doctorali in s. theolog. *Regimen monarchicum est s. scripturae maximè conforme . . . Jul. 2.* [Cambridge]: n.pub., [1660]. S.sh.
Wood 276a(476). Wing P1006 (rare) (Wing, 'O (not found)').

1348. Penning, William. Resp. in philos. Coll. Trin. soc. *Atmosphaera causa est crepusculi . . . Jun. 30.* [Cambridge]: n.pub., [1679]. S.sh. (joined with Wood 276a(506)).
Wood 276a(507). Wing P1399.

1349. Pynfold, Tho[mas]. Resp. Aul. Trin. leg. bac. *Qui Titium interficit, Maevium interficere volens,*

tenetur lege Corneliā de sicariis . . . Julii. 1. [Cambridge]: n.pub., [1662]. S.sh.
Wood 276a(489). Not in Wing. Not in ESTCR.

1350. Roane, [William]. [LL.D.1637]. Resp. Dr. Aul. Trinitatis. *Expensae studii causā factae non privant filium legitimā.* [Cambridge]: n.pub., [1637]. S.sh.
Above, '1637 [/] Quaestiones Theologicae pro doctoratu, Comitiis habitae. Octob. 2. 1637'. Names and colleges of 9 participants are written in (including name of responder, above), not in hand of AW.
Wood 276a(441). STC 4474.36 (rare).

1351. Robotham, [Charles]. Resp. Coll. Trin. soc. *Omnium futurorum contingentium certissima est in Deo praescientia . . . Jun. 30.* [Cambridge]: n.pub., [1651]. S.sh.
Wood 276a(448). Wing R1729B (two).

1352. Rust, George. Resp. B.D. Coll. Christi socio. *Resurrectionem è mortuis scriptura docet, nec refragatur ratio.* [Cambridge]: n.pub., [1658]. S.sh.
Wood 276a(464). Not in Wing. Not in ESTCR.

1353. Sedgwick. [Obediah? B.A. 1651-2; M.A. 1655; (probably not Thomas, Reg. Prof. Div.)]. Resp. Coll. Trin. socio. *Datur internum veritatis* κριτηριον . . . *Julii 5. 1658.* [Cambridge]: n.pub., [1658]. S.sh.
Wood 276a(465). Wing S2358 (rare) (Wing, London).

1354. Spering, James. Resp. S.T.B. Coll. Reginal. *Quintum Danielis imperium non restat expectandum . . . Julii 4.* [Cambridge]: n.pub., [1659]. S.sh.
ᵛ, name of participant, not in AW's hand. Dupl. at Wood 276a(470).
Wood 276a(468). Wing S4970 (rare) (Wing, London).

1355. Spering, James. Resp. S.T.B. Coll. Reginal. *Quintum Danielis imperium non restat expectandum . . . Julii 4.* [Cambridge]: n.pub., [1659]. S.sh.
Dupl. at Wood 276a(468).
Wood 276a(470). Wing S4970 (rare) (Wing, London).

1356. Sprackling, [Robert]. Resp. Coll D. Petri socio. *Probabile est phoenomena naturae salvari posse absque occultis qualitatibus . . . Jul. 7.* [Cambridge]: n.pub., [1657]. S.sh.
Wood 276a(461). Not in Wing. Not in ESTCR.

1357. Stillingfleete, [Edward]. Resp. sen. D. Joann. Col. socio. *Homo naturā est* ζωον πολιτικον . . . *Jul. 6. 1657.* [Cambridge]: n.pub., [1657]. S.sh.
Wood 276a(460). Wing S5595 (rare) (Wing, 'O (not found)' and [London]).

1358. Templar. [Templer, John; M.A. 1648; D.D. 1666]. Resp. Coll. Trin. soc. *Animae rationalis immortalitas est demonstrabilis lumine naturali . . . Jul. 2.* [Cambridge]: n.pub., [1650]. S.sh.
Wood 276a(447). Not in Wing. Not in ESTCR.

1359. Templer, John. Resp. Coll. Trin. soc. *Dies dominicus est institutionis divinae . . . Julii 3.* [Cambridge]: n.pub., [1655]. S.sh.
Names of 3 opponents and the procurator, not in AW's hand.
Wood 276a(456). Not in Wing. Not in ESTCR.

1360. Thompson, Robert. Resp. pro gradu jur. civil. doct. Aul. Trin. commens. *Mutatio pecuniae cedit commodo & incommodo debitoris . . . Julii 3.* [Cambridge]: n.pub., [1671]. S.sh. (joined with Wood 276a(499), item 1306).
Wood 276a(500). Not in Wing. Not in ESTCR.

1361. Tudway, T[homas]. Pro gradu music. bacalaur. Coll. Regal. *Psalm the XX . . . Jul. 5.* [Cambridge]: n.pub., [1681]. S.sh.
AW wrote '1679' in pencil.
Wood 276a(512). Wing T3221 (two) (Wing, London).

1362. Watson, Tho[mas]. Resp. pro gradu S.T.D. Coll. Joh. soc. *Confirmatio episcopalis est admodum efficax, & necessaria . . . Jul. 5.* [Cambridge]: n.pub., [1675]. S.sh.
Wood 276a(502). Wing W1118 (Wing, [London]).

1363. Watson, [William]. [M.A. 1636, Fellow 1636-44]. Resp. Caio-Gonvil. *Phantasia matris dat foetui signaturam.* [Cambridge]: n.pub., [1637]. S.sh.
Above, '1637. [/] Quaestiones Philosophicae Comitiis habitae. Octob. 2. 1637'. Names and colleges of 4

participants are written in (including name of responder, above), not in hand of AW.
Wood 276a(439b). STC 4474.99 (rare).

1364. Whincop, Tho[mas]. Resp. S.T.B. Coll. Corp. Christ. soc. *Indulgentiae pontificiae nullum habent in s. scripturā fundamentum.* [Cambridge]: n.pub., [1679]. S.sh. (joined with Wood 276a(504)).
Wood 276a(505). Wing W1664A (two) ('O' not recorded in Wing).

1365. Wigmore, [Gilbert]. [B.D. 1639]. Resp. Reginalis. *Deus puniens personam conjunctam pro persona peccante, jure suo utitur.* [Cambridge]: n.pub., [1639]. S.sh.
Above, 'Quaestiones Theologicae pro Baccalaureatu in eādem facultate comitiis habitae Cantabrigiensibus. Jul. 1°. 1639'. Names and colleges of 7 participants are written in (including name of defender, above), not in hand of AW.
Wood 276a(443). STC 4474.28 (rare).

1366. Wolryche, [William]. [? M.A. 1654]. Resp. Coll. Christi soc. *Materia quomodocunque modificata non potest cogitare . . . Julii 3.* [Cambridge]: n.pub., [1655]. S.sh.
Names of opponent and procurator, not in AW's hand.
Wood 276a(454). Not in Wing. Not in ESTCR.

1367. Young, [Edward]. [D.D. 1639]. Resp. Dr. Aul. Johanensis. *Justificatio per solam fidem non est impeditiva bonorum operum chec impeditiva.* [Cambridge]: n.pub., [1639]. S.sh.
Above, 'Quaestiones Theologicae pro Doctoratu in eādem facultate comitiis habitae Cantabrigiensibus. Julii. 1°. 1639'. Names and colleges of 13 participants are written in (including name of responder, above), not in hand of AW.
Wood 276a(442a). STC 4474.63 (rare).

End of CAMBRIDGE ACT VERSES (items 1289-1367)

1368. Camden, William. *Britannia sive florentissimorum regnorum, Angliae, ...* Londini: [Eliot's Court Press] per R. Newbery, 1587. 8°. Anr. ed. Pp. [16], 648, [22] (2 tpp).
Missing. Gore, f. 308. Also listed in MS. Wood F. 51, f. 44.
Gore 308. STC 4504. *Folg, Hunt, Harv.*

1369. [Camden, William]. *Reges, reginae, nobiles, & alii in ecclesia collegiata b. Petri Westmonasterii sepulti.* Londini: E. Bollifantus, 1600. 4°. A-K⁴,L1. Parchment with 2 clasp holes.
Flyleaf, upper, on the 1st fragment, signature of 'Godfrey Clarke'. 2nd^v, AW wrote, 'Mr Will. Camden The authour.'
Wood 333. STC 4518.

1370. Camden, William. Holland, Philemon, trans. *Britain, or, a chorographicall description of the most flourishing kingdomes, England, Scotland, and Ireland.* Londini: imp. G. Bishop & J. Norton, 1610. Fol. 2 pts. Pp. [16], 208, 207-287 [i.e. 299], 302-822, [2], 233, [55].
Missing. Gift, 30 July 1675, from R. Sheldon, LT 2.319. See notes at items 406 and 6451.
LT 2.319. STC 4509.

1371. [Camden, William]. Browne, Thomas, trans. *Tomus alter, & idem: or the historie of the life . . . of that famous princesse, Elizabeth.* London: T. Harper, sold W. Web in Oxford, 1629. 4°. Pp. [34], 384, [104]. Parchment with 2 clasp holes.
Pastedown, upper, AW wrote, 'Mar. 31. 1659' (prob. bought from Ed. Forrest, see LT 1.271). ¶3^v, reference to 'Translator' underscored in red ink. 3B3, in index, a correction. 3O4^v and pastedown, lower, scribbles.
Wood 339. STC 4498.

1372. Camden, William. Philipot, John, ed. *Remaines concerning Britaine.* London: T. Harper f. J. Waterson, 1637. 4°. 5th ed. Pp. [7], 420, [2]. Calf with 2 fillets, rebacked.
Flyleaf, upper, 1st, John Skefington and William –, both surnames lined out; 2nd, John Skeffington 1628. 1651, surname, lined out. P. 6, line in margin at presentation of order of the garter to Philipot. Pp. 146, 419 line in margin, in pencil. P. 420, drawing (apple?) in margin. Flyleaf, lower, 3rd^v, scribbles by Skeffington. Acquired 24 June, 1^{s}6^d, bound 9 July 1657, 6^d; see LT 1.220.
Wood 606 (506 in Bodl. CD cat.). STC 4526.

1373. Camden, William. *Rerum Anglicarum et Hibernicarum annales, regnante Elisabetha.* Lugd. Batavorum: Elseviriorum, 1639. 8°. Pp. [16], 856, [38]. Calf with 3 fillets and edge hatching; spine, 4 bands and hatching (Oxford binding).

Tp, price, illeg., not in AW's hand. A few marks in margins, e.g. 60, 73, 96. P. 200, AW wrote, 'Powell of Sandford near to, & in the county of Oxōn. one of the band of gent[tlemen] pensioners'. Title on a slip pasted to fore-edge (not in AW's hand). Lent to H. Foules, 17 Oct. 1668, LT 2.145.
Wood 212. BL.

1374. Camden, William*. [Barksdale, Clement, comp.]. *V. cl. elogia Anglorum Cambdeniana.* Londini: T. Warren, pro E. Thorn, Oxoniensi, 1653. 8°. Pp. [2], 25. Pasteboard (grey) with parchment spine. 1st and last flyleaves, marbled paper.
Flyleaf, upper, 3rd^v, AW wrote the titles of 3 printed works in this vol., within guidelines made with red ink. Tp, AW wrote, 'By Clem. Barksdale.' P. 1, on waste paper backing of a quire, '1670' and at other fragment end of backing, p. 12, 'Penn's Tryall' (Wood 645(18-19), items 5166, 6034). P. 19, correction.
Wood 299(1). Wing C360A (two).

1375. [Camden, William]. *Institutio Graecae grammatices compendiaria, in usum regiae scholae Westmonasteriensis.* Londini: R. Nortonus, 1676. 8°. A-M^8. Calf with 2 fillets.
Flyleaf, upper, 1st, 'E Libris Ant^i. à Wood Aprilis 26to. 1677mo. Pret. 1^s6^d', twice, not in AW's hand. A1^v, AW wrote, 'A. à Wood 26. Aprilis 1677 1^s - 6^d', and on tp, 'Per Guliel. Camdenum ejusd. Scholae quondam Rectorem'. Dupl. listed in MS. Wood E. 2(70), 62.
Wood 32. Wing C370 (two).

1376. Camden, William. Smith, Thomas, ed. *V. cl. Gulielmi Camdeni, et illustrium virorum ad G. Camdenum epistolae. . . . Accesserunt annalium regni regis Jacobi I. . . . Praemittitur G. Camdeni vita. Scriptore Thoma Smitho.* London: impens. R. Chiswelli, 1691. 4°. Pp. [24], xcvi, 401, [3], 116. Calf, speckled, with 2 fillets and stamp decoration in corners (Ashm. binding?).
Pastedown, upper, 4 slips pasted with notes by AW referring to or quoting from letters in this vol. Slip 1: 'Will. Sutton Bach. of Art of ch. ch. did upon his earnest desire made to Tho. Savile became acquainted with Camden'. Slip 2^r: 5 brief notes, the 1st 3, dated 'July 23', AW copied from Thomas Short's newsletter (see LT 5.70), all lined out, 'the Deane and chapter of Lichf. having elected Dr Lloyd late B. of S. Asaph Bishop of that dioc. they this week made a return of the congedelere' [/] 'Mr Hen. Cooling one of the gent. ushers to the qu. died yesterday (son of Hen. Cooling Clerk of the counsell qu[aere]' [/] 'Tis said Dr. Will. Lancaster hath the living of S. Martins in the Fields' [/] 'Rich Carew of Antony his epist to Will. Camden –' (pp. 72-3 in text, marked with lines in pencil) [/] 'I heare that Mr Sollicitor hath compiled a treatise of our Cornish Dutchy & dedic to the prince - May 1606. qu[aere] an Davies'; slip 2^v has 3 notes: 'Matherne, in com. Monm. called by Dr Fr. Godwin of Landaff Marthern' [/] 'In Camdens epist. nu. 80. is an epist. of Georg Carlton to Camden beginning thus . . . without date' (pp. 112ff. in text) [/] and 'Edward Bolton Antiquarius to Camden - 1617. epist' (p. 188 in text). Slip 3: a quote from Usher's letter to Camden on the monument of Richard Armachanus at Dundalk (p. 86 in text, which has a line, in pencil, in margin); slip 3^v, notes on John and Edward Stradling and their epist. (pp. 54 and 51). Slip 4: 'Hen. Saviles Letter to Camden saith thus- . . . ' 20 lines on deeds and wills closing with 'Camb. epist. nu. 252' (p. 314 in text, marked by pencil); slip 4, 2nd fold: 'John Budden of Oxon intimate with Camden – two Lat. epistles to Camden' (pp. 228, 239 in text, lines in margin, in pencil), and 'Ambrose & Mich. Dormer of Ascot neare Milton made the epitaph on them in Milton church. – 1618' (p. 228 in text). Flyleaf, upper, the titles of the 2 printed works in this vol., by an Ashm. librarian. Text, some lines in margin, in pencil, see above and e.g., at T. Savile, pp. 3-4, 8, 10-11,13, 15ff.; at Tho. Allen, 315, in pencil; to 2nd p. 29 (correction), 11, 35 (correction), 77 (query).
[MS.] Wood B. 38(1). Wing C361.

1377. Campanella, Tommaso. Chilmead, Edmund, trans. *A discourse touching the Spanish monarchy.* London: f. P. Stephens, sold 'in Paul's Church-Yard', 1654. 4°. Pp. [8], 232 (pp. unopened).
Wood 511(17). Wing C401.

1378. Campania. *Strange newes from Campania . . . a true relation of one who slept at noon-time of day, how his spirit was transported . . . near unto the lake Avernus.* Attalia [really London]: n.pub., 1647. 4°. A^4.
[MS.] Wood B. 35(19). Wing S5889.

1379. Campbell, Archibald. Argyle, marq. of, et al. *Letters from the marquesse of Argyle, the earle of Lanerick, lord Warriston, and others . . . intercepted by sir R. Willys.* Oxford: H. Hall, 1645. 4°. Pp. [2], 10.
Tp, former no., '41'.
Wood 632(15). Wing A3661. Madan 1767.

1380. Campbell, Archibald*. Argyle, marq. of. *The charge of high treason, . . . exhibited to the parliament of Scotland against the marquess of Argyle [23 Jan. 1660]*. London: f. R. Lowndes, 1661. 4°. Pp. [2], 31.
Tp, AW wrote the price, '5ᵈ'.
Wood 368(16). Wing C2056.

1381. Campbell, Archibald. Argyle, marq. of. *The marquess of Argile his answer to his charge [28 Jan.]*. [London]: n.pub., 1661. 4°. Pp. [2], 16.
Tp, AW wrote the year, 'A. D. 1660[1]'.
Wood 368(17). Wing A3650.

1382. Campbell, Archibald. Argyle, marq. of. *The speech of the late marquiss of Argyll upon the scaffold May 27*. Edenburgh, repr. London: n.pub., 1661. 4°. Pp. [2], 6.
Wood 368(18). Wing A3669.

1383. Campbell, Archibald*. Argyle, earl of. *A true copy of the indictment which is preferred against Archibald earl of Argile*. (Edenbrough): (f. J. Alexander), (1681). S.sh. (r-v).
Wood 368(21). Wing T2643.

1384. Campbell, Archibald. Argyle, earl of. *The speech of the earl of Argyle at his trial on the 12th. of December 1681*. (London): (R. Janeway), (1682). S.sh. (r-v).
Wood 368(22). Wing A3678.

1385. Campion, Edmund*. *A particular declaration or testimony, of the undutifull and traiterous affection borne against her majestie by Edmond Campion Jesuit*. London: C. Barker, 1582. A-D⁴ (A¹ blank).
Item nos. 3 to 10a in this vol. were originally part of a separate vol. with ms. p. nos. 1-412 written on the top margins (prob. not by AW). A1, '1582', in pencil, prob. by AW. Tp, signature of Rych. Wryght and flourish. Acquired 29 Ap. 1658 out of G. Langbaine's study, LT 1.247. See note at item 6057.
Wood 586(3). STC 4536.

1386. [Campion, Edmund]. *Concertatio ecclesiae Anglicae Catholicae in Anglia adversus Calvinopapistas et Puritanos*. Augustae Trevirorum: ap. E. Hatotum, 1583. 8°. Ff. [6], 413, [12].
Missing. MS. Wood E. 2(70), p. 4, 'see the contents in the beg . . . . besides his martyrdome – names of other martyrs – qu[aere] whether writers'. See also AO 1.475.
MS. Wood E. 2(70), p. 4. *BL*.

1387. Campion, Edmund; Meredith Hanmer, and Edmund Spenser. Ware, James, ed. *Two histories of Ireland. (A view of the state of Ireland . . . by Edmund Spenser)*. Dublin: Soc. of Stationers [a. London: T. Harper], 1633. Fol. Pp. [12], 138, [2], 223; [8], 127, [9]. Calf, gold-stamp decoration, and gold-stamp centrepiece, a crown with 3 plumes above 'ICH DIEN' and C and P on either side of crown, i.e., Charles, Prince of Wales (see R. R. Holmes, *Specimens of royal fine and historical bindings* (London, 1893), pl. 32 (without the initials)).
Pastedown, upper, 'Ant. Woode 1661' and price '5ˢ 6ᵈ'; and, not in AW's hand, 'Daneish Invashion of Ireland Anno 31024' and '24' (?). 1st p. 138, line in margin, in red ink. P. 218-9, AW made corrections, 'Cranly' and 'Cranley' for abps. of Dublin, Thomas Crawly and Thomas Granly. 2nd p. [9], and pastedown, lower, scribbles and copied lines from text, not in AW's hand. Signatures of Mary Applebee, Elizabeth Bland and John Gregory (Gregory, AO 3.205f.). LT 1.425.
Wood 406. STC 25067.

1388. Campion, Thomas. *A relation of the late royall entertainment given by . . . the lord Knowles, . . . to . . . queene Anne, in her progresse toward Bath . . . by Thomas Campian*. London: [W. Stansby] f. J. Budge, 1613. 4°. A-D⁴.
Flyleaf, upper, '90'. Tp, AW wrote, 'Dʳ Tho. Campian – vide Musick.' and '90' (perhaps the no. in a bundle of 'music' items).
Wood 537(8). STC 4545.

1389. Camus, Jean Pierre. *Diotrephe. Or, an historie of valentines*. London: T. Harper, 1641. 12°. Pp. [12], 192. Calf with 1 fillet with decoration and also 1 vertical fillet; rebacked.
Tp, date changed to 1643.
Wood 275. Wing C412.

1390. Canne, John. *The golden rule, or, justice advanced*. London: f. P. Cole, 1649. 4°. Pp. [4], 36 (1st part ends, p. 36).

P. 36, AW wrote, 'where is the 2^{d}. – see the next.'
Wood 364(21). Wing C440.

1391. Canterbury, Tales. *The merry tales of the cobler of Canterbury*. N.p.: ?, 1655. Pp.?
Missing in 1837. 'A Discourse of the merry Cobler of Canterbury – Lon. 1655' in Whiteside cat. Several times reprinted, see STC 4579-81.
Wood 64(9). Not in Wing. Not in ESTCR.

1392. Capel, Arthur. Essex, earl of. *The earl of Essex's speech at the delivery of the petition to the king, Jan. 25*. (London): (f. F. Smith), (1681). S.sh. (r-v).
Dupl. at Wood 276a(176).
Wood 276a(154). Wing E3305A ('O' not recorded in Wing).

1393. Capel, Arthur. Essex, earl of. *The earl of Essex's speech at the delivery of the petition to the king, Jan. 25*. (London): (f. F. Smith), (1681). S.sh. (r-v).
After t, AW wrote, 'being the day after the said Count was turned out of the Kings privie councill–'. Dupl. at Wood 276a(154).
Wood 276a(176). Wing E3305A ('O' not recorded in Wing).

1394. Capel, Arthur*. Essex, earl of. *An account how the earl of Essex killed himself in the Tower of London, the 13th. of July*. London: by the assigns of J. Bill deceas'd: a. H. Hills, a. T. Newcomb, 1683. Fol. Pp. 8. Pasteboard (blue) with parchment spine; 1st upper and last lower flyleaves, marbled paper.
Flyleaf, 2nd, AW wrote the titles of 32 printed works in this vol., all on the Rye House Plot, within guidelines made with red ink (actually 34 items, AW omitted 22b and 33). On most of the earlier items (see 2-29) AW had entered preliminary nos. in pencil. When the book was in final order, he overwrote these old nos. in ink (not recorded in this cat.). See Wood 428(5), item 5614, for his note on the addition of a pamphlet. The volumes following are later intrusions and not entered in this cat., i.e., Wood 428b and 428c (J. J. Hofmann, *Lexicon*, 2 vols., 1698), signed 'Edw. Llwyd'; and Wood 429d and 429e (G. Hickes, *Antiquae literaturae septentrionales*, 2 vols., 1705). Tp, AW wrote the price, '3^{d}'. LT 3.60.
Wood 428(1). Wing A175.

1395. Capel, Arthur*. Essex, earl of. *An elegie on the earl of Essex. Who cut his own throat in the Tower [13 July]*. London: f. J. Smith, 1683. S.sh.
Wood 428(2). Wing E415.

1396. Capel, Arthur. Essex, earl of. *Excellent contemplations, divine and moral, written by lord Capel. Together with some account of his life and his letters to several persons*. London: f. N. Crouch, 1683. 12°. Pp. [2], 223, [9] (i.e., 203, misnumbering) (7 pp. books sold by Crouch) (2 tpp). Calf with 2 fillets.
Tp, 'h 1/2' (?). P. 1, at the biography, AW wrote 'mostly taken out of Dav. Lloyds memoires.' (Wing L2642).
Wood 805. Wing C469.

1397. Caradoc, Saint. Llwyd, Humphrey, trans. Collected by David Powel. *The historie of Cambria, now called Wales:. . . written in the Brytish language above two hundreth yeares past*. (London): (R. Newberie a. H. Denham), (1584). 4° in 8's. Pp. [16], 22, [2], 401, [13]. Parchment.
Cover, outside, some illeg. names, and scribbles. Tp, 'Humphrey', the remainder was lost in rebinding. ¶5, AW made a correction; ¶8, line in margin, in red ink. Pp. 1-6, some notes, not in AW's hand. 2nd p. [2], AW wrote, 'Dr Dav. Powells additions in this work are marked with a cinqu[e]-Foyle' (a printed mark, see AO 3.729, 993). Pp. 136, 142, 146, notes by Gough, e.g., 'Roger Gough his booke witnes John Lewis and Richard Jones'. Pp. 271, wavy line in margin; 316, cross-hatch mark in margin. Flyleaf, lower^{v}, 'This is Mr Roger Gough his booke wittenes Robert Amble Anno Domine 1626', and, in an older hand, 'Per [or Pos.?] me Johanem Lewis'.
Wood 464. STC 4606.

1398. Care, George. *A reply to the answer of the man of no name, to . . . the duke of Buckingham's paper [entitled A short discourse]*. London: J. Leake f. L. Meredith, 1685. 4°. Pp. [2], 36, [1] (1 p. books printed for Meredith).
Tp, no. '(6)', in pencil, in a former bundle (cropped at top). Text, marks in margins, not in AW's usual style (crosses, double lines). Responds to Wood 611(7), item 6333.
Wood 611(10). Wing C504.

1399. [Care, Henry]. *Observations on a paper intituled, the declaration of the lord Petre upon his death, . . . Being a full answer thereunto*. (London): (G. Larkin), (1684). Fol. Pp. [4].

P. [4], AW wrote, 'written by Hen. Care authour of the pacquet of advice from Rome – Jan. 1683[4]'. LT 3.86.
Wood 427(49). Wing C530.

1400. Care, Henry*. *An elegy upon the most ingenious mr. Henry Care [8 Aug. 1688].* London: G. Larkin, [1688]. S.sh.
ᵛ, AW wrote, 'Hen. Care 1688'.
Wood 429(42). Wing E483 (two).

1401. Care, Henry*, and Elizabeth Cellier*. *The triall of Henry Carr [i.e., Care], gent, at the Guildhall . . . Also the tryal of Elizabeth Cellier.* London: I. G. f. R. Taylor, 1681. Fol. Pp. [7], 26.
Tp, AW wrote 'Care' after 'Carr'. Care's trial was for publishing *The weekly pacquet*, see item 1399 and LT 2.479.
Wood 427(13a). Wing T2190.

1402. Carier, Benjamin. Strange, N., ed. *A missive to his majesty of Great Britain, king James . . . by doctor Carier, conteining the motives of his conversion to Catholike religion. . . . re-printed . . . with some marginall notes.* Paris: n.pub., 1649. 12°. Rpt. of Liege edition. Pp. [2], 28, [10], 54. Pasteboard (grey) with parchment spine. 1st upper and last lower flyleaves, marbled paper.
Flyleaf, upper, 2nd ᵛ, AW wrote the titles of 6 printed works in this vol., within guidelines made with red ink. Tp, AW wrote 'A Treatise written by M. Doctor Carier wherin he layeth downe sundrey learned & pithy considerations by which he was moved, to forsake the protestant congregation & betake himselfe to the church of Rome &c. printed at Liege 1614.' and, in pencil, 'A copie of this I gave to Dʳ [?] Jute [?]' (illeg.). At lists after p. 28, AW made 4 corrections and 2 underscorings.
Wood 869(1). Wing C572.

1403. Carion, Jean; Philip Melanchthon, and Caspar Peucer. *Chronicon Carionis.* Bernae: excud. J. le Preux, 1601. 8°. Pp. [48], 957, [48] (2nd tp, p. 393). Calf with 3 fillets. Flyleaf, upper, 2nd ᵛ, a (and line over a). Tp, name and note, mutilated, Edv. Forest. Bsms.
Wood 141.
Not in BL.

1404. Carleton, George. Chichester, bp. of. *Heroici characteres. Ad illustrissimum equitem, Henricum Nevillum.* Oxoniae: J. Barnesius, 1603. 4°. Pp. [6], 48.
Wood 460(5). STC 4636. Madan 241.

1405. Carleton, George. Chichester, bp. of. *Vita Bernardi Gilpini.* Londini: G. Jones, 1628. 4°. Pp. [4], 58.
Tp, '23.22-.', '2.4', perhaps previous shelf-marks, not in AW's hand. Pp. 2-3, 12-3, 21-3, AW made vertical lines in margin, in pencil. P. 10, correction, in ink, may not be in AW's hand.
Wood 345(3). STC 4646.

1406. Carleton, George. Chichester, bp. of. *A thankfull remembrance of Gods mercie.* London: A. Math[ewes] f. R. Mylbourne a. H. Robinson, 1630. 4°. 4th ed. Pp. [8], 292. Parchment.
Pastedown, lower, 'a - 6' and 'kx' (bsms?).
[MS.] Wood C. 43. STC 4643.

1407. Carleton, John. *The replication, or certain vindicatory depositions, occasioned by way of answer, . . . concerning the late acted cheat [of Mary Carleton].* [London]: by the authors appointment, 1663. 4°. Pp. 8.
Wood 654a(25). Wing C585A.

1408. Carleton, Mary*. *The lawyers clarke trappan'd by the crafty whore of Canterbury. Or, a true relation . . . of Mary Mauders.* London: f. J. Johnson, 1663. 4°. Pp. [2], 5.
Wood 654a(23). Wing L739F.

1409. Carleton, Mary*. *A true account of the tryal of mʳˢ· Mary Carlton [4 June].* London: f. C. Moulton, 1663. 4°. Pp. 8.
Tp, after t, AW wrote, 'commonly called by the name of the German princess–'.
Wood 654a(24). Wing T2406A (two).

1410. Carliell, Robert. *Britaines glorie: or an allegoricall dreame, with the exposition thereof.* London: G. Eld a. M. Flesher, 1619. 8°. Pp. [12], 43.
Each small 8° leaf is pasted on an 8° template. Pp. [5]-1 brief notes on contents, by Smith. P. 43, 'perlegi

totum. 5. Martii. 1619. per me Tho: Smith'.
Wood 876(2). STC 4651.

1411. Carlisle, Siege. *A true copie of the articles whereupon Carlisle was deliver'd June 8.* Oxford: H. Hall, 1645. 4°. Pp. [2], 4.
Tp, AW overwrote the former no., '3'.
Wood 378(4). Wing T2638. Madan 1802.

1412. Carman. *The car-man's poem: or, advice to a nest of scriblers.* [London]: n.pub., [1680?]. S.sh.
ᵛ, AW wrote the date, '(1680)', in pencil.
Wood 417(10). Wing C595.

1413. Carpenter, Nathanael. *Geography delineated forth in two bookes.* Oxford: J. Lichfield a. W. Turner f. H. Cripps, 1625. 4°. Pp. [14], 274, [14], 286, [2] (2 tpp). Calf with 3 fillets and edge hatching; spine, 4 bands and hatching (Oxford binding).
Waste paper, upper, 'precium - 3ˢ-8ᵈ- ob.', not in AW's hand. Flyleaf, upper, 1st, AW wrote, 'Ex dono Pet. Nicolls coll. Mert. soc.' and signature of Nicolls, lined out. Pp. 8-9, '1k,', and '2ᵒ', in margin, not by AW. 2nd part, pp. 3-80, some marks in margins, in pencil, prob. not by AW; 261, at Raleigh, Frobisher, marks; 264, 266, at W. Browne and Roger Williams, mark in margin. LT 2.45.
Wood 470. STC 4676. Madan 554.

1414. Carr, Nicholas. Hatcher, Thomas, ed. *De scriptorum britannicorū paucitate, et studiorum impedimentis, oratio.* Londini: ex off. T. Marsh, 1576. 8°. Ff. [3], 22. Pasteboard (blue) with parchment spine. 1st upper and last lower flyleaves, marbled paper.
Flyleaf, upper, 3rdᵛ, AW wrote the titles of 4 printed works (really 2) in this vol., within guidelines made with red ink.
Wood 710(1). STC 4686.

1415. Carr, William. *Remarks of the government of severall parts of Germanie, Denmark, . . . with some few directions how to travell.* Amsterdam, printed in: n.pub., 1688. 12°. Pp. [10], 210, [6]. Calf, speckled, with 2 fillets; rebacked.
Wood 169 (not in Bodl. CD cat.). Wing C636.

1416. Carranza, Bartholomé. *Summa conciliorum et pontificum a Petro . . . Accesserunt etiam statuta quaedam synodalia Parisiensis, & Senonensis ecclesiae.* Lugduni: ap. H. Cardon, 1600. 8°. Ff. [24], 655, [1]. Parchment with 2 clasp holes.
Wood 230. See IA, which cites a 1600 ed., excud. F. Helvidius / H. Cardon Lugduni.

1417. Carrol, James. *A new discovery of the sham-Presbyterian plot. Or, the substance of the information of James Carol.* (London): (f. R. Janeway), (1681). S.sh. (r-v).
Wood 276a(272). Wing C645.

1418. C[arter], M[atthew]. *A most true and exact relation of that as honourable as unfortunate expedition of Kent, Essex, and Colchester.* [London]: n.pub., 1650. 8°. Pp. [10], 214. Pasteboard (blue) with parchment spine; upper and lower flyleaves, marbled paper.
Flyleaf, upper, 3rdᵛ, AW wrote the titles of 2 printed works in this vol., within guidelines made with red ink. After the 1st, a hand pointer and 'One Matth. Carter seems to be the authour of the said Book – see page 39. 43. 78. 115'. Tp, note of former owner, 'Liber Ricard[i] Chambe[r]layne clerici Wardrop 1ᵐᵒ August 1650.' AW marked Carter's name on pp. 39, 43, and 78; 40, added a cross-ref., 'v. pag. 51' (Major Keme noted on p. 51); 68, underscored 'Hotfield'; 81, at Lord Norwich, wrote 'Goring'; 172, made a pencil line in margin; 192, made a pencil line at mention of Sir Bernard Gasquoine [sic]. LT 3.31.
Wood 581(1). Wing C662.

1419. Carter, Matt[hew]. *Honor redivivus or an analysis of honor and armory.* London: f. H. Heringman [sic], sould H. Herringman (both over earlier erased names), 1660. 8°. Pp. [11], 251.
Tp, bsm. Lent to Christopher Reynolds, 23 Oct. 1661, LT 1.417.
Wood 447(2). Wing C659.

1420. [Cartwright, William]. *The royall slave. A tragi-comedy. . . . Presented . . . by the students of Christ-church in Oxford. August 30, 1630.* Oxford: W. Turner f. T. Robinson, 1640. 4°. 2nd ed. A-H⁴.
Text, a few scribbles.
Wood 330(10). STC 4718. Madan 939. AO 3.69.

1421. [Cartwright, William]. *November. Thou sun that shed'st the dayes* [verse]. [London]: n.pub., [1647].

S.sh.
AW wrote 'Written by Will. Cartwright of ch. ch.' and the year, '1671'.
Wood 416(120). Wing C711.

1422. Cartwright, William. *An off-spring of mercy, issuing out of the womb of cruelty. Or, a passion sermon.* London: A. M., sold J. Brown, 1652. 8°. Pp. [6], 31.
Missing. MS. Wood E. 2(70), p. 56.
MS. Wood E. 2(70), p. 56. Wing C713. *Hunt.*

1423. Cartwright, William. *November: or, signal dayes . . . in relation to the crown and royal family.*
[London] in the Savoy: T. N. f. H. Herringman, 1671. 4°. Pp. [2], 5.
Tp, AW wrote, 'I have a pamphlet entit. Day-fatality, in my vol. entit. James Duke of York, nu. 16' (i.e., Wood 660c(16), item 3204, which has a cross-reference to this item).
[MS.] Wood C. 17(7). Wing C712.

1424. Carvalho, Valentino. Hay, John, trans. *Japponiensis imperii admirabilis commutatio exposita litteris.* Antverpiae: sumpt. vid. & her. J. Belleri, 1604. 8°. Pp. 92.
Wood 893(2). BL.

1425. [Carve, Thomas]. *Epitome rerum Germanicarum ab anno MDCXVII ad XLIII gestarum.* N.p: n.pub., 1644. 24°. Pp. 249.
Pastedown, upper, a former no., 355, erased. Tp, bsms.; ᵛ, 'David Parry ex dono D. Bagford'. This book migrated from the collection of Parry, the Keeper of the Ashm. Museum who died in 1714, to that of Wood before 1717 (it is in the Whiteside cat.). Not a Wood book.
Wood 700a. BL (1643).

1426. Cary, Henry. Falkland, 1st visct. *The history of . . . king Edward II.* London: A. G[odbid] a. J. P[layford], sold J. Playford, 1680. 8°. Pp. [9], 77, [3] (includes 3 pp. books sold by Playford).
Tp, AW wrote, '8ᵈ', and 'published about Christmas 1679'. Bsm. A2, AW wrote, 'see Fullers Worthies'; A2ᵛ, a qualification of a story about a gregarious intellectual Henry Cary at Oxford, 'This by some is applied to Lucius his son'; A8ᵛ, a correction and judgement, 'Why doth not the sorry scribler of this preface subscribe his name – qu[aere] whether written by – [in pencil, illeg.]'.
Wood 234(2). Wing F314.

1427. Cary, Lucius. Falkland, 2nd visct. *A draught of a speech concerning episcopacy.* Oxford: L. Lichfield, 1644. 4°. Pp. [2], 9.
Tp, 'Browne' and 'Johnson', not in AW's hand. P. 9ᵛ, signatures of John Johnson.
[MS.] Wood D. 31(5). Wing F319. Madan 1747.

1428. Cary, Lucius. Falkland, 2nd visct. *Of the infallibilitie of the church of Rome.* Oxford: H. Hall, 1645. 4°. Pp. [2], 18.
P. 10, underscoring, prob. not by AW.
[MS.] Wood C. 44(2). Wing F322. Madan 1844.

1429. [Caryll, John]. *Naboth's vinyard: or, the innocent traytor.* London: f. C. R., 1679. Fol. Pp. [2], 17.
Tp, AW wrote, 'written with relation had to the 5 Jesuits lately executed & others, for the plot.', and 'Antonii a Wood ex dono Radulphi Sheldon de Beoly Ar[miger] die Sᵗ. Simonis et Judae [28 Oct.]. 1679 published by stealth in the beginning of Oct.' LT 2.464.
Wood 424(30). Wing C745A.

1430. [Caryll, Joseph]. *Memorable dayes and workes of God, in the yeare past. 1645.* London: f. J. Bartlett, 1646. 4°. A⁴.
AW overwrote and lined out the former nos. '63' and '66'. A2ᵛ, AW made a correction, 'June' to 'July'.
Wood 378(66). Wing C780A.

1431. C[aryll], J[oseph]. *Peter's pattern, or, the perfect path to worldly happiness. . . . a funeral sermon, preached at the interment of mr. Hugh Peters.* London: n.p., 1680. 4°. Pp. 15.
Tp, in pencil, 'Dupl.' (twice; no dupl. among AW's books; but see items 2277 and 3572).
Wood 486(18). Wing C785.

1432. [Casaubon, Méric]. *[A treatise of use and custome].* [London]: [J. L[egat]], [1638]. 4°. Pp. [2], 188, [6] (wanting A1, i.e., pp. [1-2]).
'Treatise of use & custom' in MS. Wood E. 2(70), p. 49.
Wood 499(9). STC 4753 (STC, anon.).

1433. Casaubon, Méric. *De verborum usu*. London: typ. M. Flesher, sumpt. R. Mynne, 1647. 12°. Pp. [12], 173.
Missing. 'de verborum usu' in MS. Wood E. 2(70), p. 40.
MS. Wood E. 2(70), p. 40. Wing C802. *Harv, Yale.*

1434. Casaubon, Méric. *A letter . . . to Peter du Moulin . . . prebendarie of the same church:. . . concerning natural experimental philosophie*. Cambridge: f. W. Morden, 1669. 4°. Pp. [2], 36.
Tp, at 'same Church', AW wrote, 'of what.'; below, '6ᵈ'.
Wood 607(3). Wing C805.

1435. Case, John. *Summa veterum interpretum in universam dialecticam Aristotelis*. London: T. Vautrollerius, 1584. 4°. Pp. [16], 293 [i.e., 295, misnumbering].
Missing. MS. Wood E. 2(70), p. 19.
MS. Wood E. 2(70), p. 19. STC 4762. *BL, Harv* (no tp).

1436. Case, John. *Apologia musices tam vocalis quam instrumentalis et mixtae*. Oxoniae: J. Barnesius, 1588. 8°. Pp. [8], 77. Parchment with 1 fillet, gold stamped, and gold-stamp centrepiece.
Tp, price, 1ˢ-4ᵈ, prob. not by AW. Pastedown, lower, 3 lines in French, e.g., 'ie sers qui me plaist.', not in AW's hand. Acquired 19 Apr. 1662, LT 1.436.
Wood 22. STC 4755. Madan 97.

1437. Casmannus, Otho. *Marinarum quaestionum tractatio philosophica bipartita*. Francofurti: ex off. M. Z. Palthenii, 1596. 8°. Pp. [10], 444 [i.e., 244]. Parchment.
Tp, bsm. Passim, some double vertical lines in margins, not in AW's manner.
Wood 684. BL.

CATALOGUES OF SALES AND AUCTIONS (items 1438-1636) (and item 5279)

1438. Abingdon. Town hall. *At the town-hall in Abingdon on . . . May the twelfth . . . will be sold by auction these following books*. [Oxford?]: n.pub., [1693]. S.sh. 4°.
AW wrote '1692' after the date.
[MS.] Wood D. 22(16). Wing A4103 (rare).

1439. Annesley, Arthur. Anglesey, earl of. *Bibliotheca Angleseiana, sive catalogus . . . librorum . . . quos . . . sibi procuravit . . . Arthur comes d'Anglesey, . . . Quorum auctio habebitur . . . Per Thomam Philippum [25 Oct.]*. [London]: distributed at 6 d. per Catal., Mr. Nott, et al., 1686. 4°. Pp. [4], 96, [2], 78.
Tp, AW wrote cat. no. '53', in red chalk; over former no., '52'; 'at 6 d. per Catal.', lined out. From pp. 7-8, 19, etc., AW marked a few entries with horizontal or vertical lines, mainly in pencil, and occasionally underscored. These are more frequent from 2nd p. 1, among the 'English' books and include 2 'q[uaere]' letters and 1 cross reference. After p. 96, AW numbered consecutively to the end, 97-177.
[MS.] Wood E. 19(3). Wing A3166.

1440. Arthur, John. *Catalogus librorum bibliothecae . . . Joannis Arthurii. . . . Quorum auctio habebitur . . . per Edoardum Millingtonum [12 Feb.]*. [London]: distributed gratis, Mortlock, Nott, et al., [1683]. 4°. Pp. [2], 24, 20, 16, [2] (cropped).
Tp, AW wrote cat. no. '24', and, 'Given to me by Henr. Cruttenden 18. Jan. 1682[3]', LT 3.470. From p. 2, AW marked some entries with horizontal or vertical lines, mainly in pencil; in the 'English' section, from 2nd p. 1, more frequent marks, 'q[uaere]' letters, and a few notes. After 2nd p. 1, he renumbered pp., 25 to 61.
[MS.] Wood E. 16(6). Wing A3802.

1441. Atfield, Ambrose. *Catalogus variorum librorum . . . Amb. Atfield . . . nec non alterius cujusdam theologi . . . Quorum auctio habenda est . . . Per Edvardum Millingtonum [25 May]*. [London]: distributed, Nott, W. Henshman, et al., [1685]. 4°. Pp. [4], 68.
Tp, AW wrote cat. no. '41', over former no. '40', in red chalk, and 'Dupl'. From p. 20, AW marked a few entries with horizontal or vertical lines, mainly in pencil. These are more frequent among the 'English' books, from p. 30, where he underscored, wrote some notes (p. 34, identified the publisher 'A. W.' as Mʳˢ Ann Windham') and 'q[uaere]' letters. Dupl. at [MS.] Wood E. 23(4b).
[MS.] Wood E. 18(3). Wing A4105.

1442. Atfield, Ambrose. *Catalogus variorum librorum . . . Amb. Atfield . . . nec non alterius cujusdam theologi . . . Quorum auctio habenda est . . . Per Edvardum Millingtonum [25 May]*. [London]: distributed,

Nott, W. Henshman, et al., [1685]. 4°. Pp. [4], 68.
Tp, AW wrote, 'Dupl', in pencil, twice. Dupl. at [MS.] Wood E.18(3).
[MS.] Wood E. 23(4b). Wing A4105.

1443. Basset, Thomas. *An exact catalogue of the common & statute law books of this realm*. [London]: collected by T. Basset, 1673. S.sh.
AW wrote, 'This cat. stands me in little steed because the Christian names of the writers of omitted'; a note 'E. Hyde' at a work by Clarendon, lines at Fulbeck, and a 'q[uaere]' mark at Hakewel. Diff. ed. at Wood 660b(15).
Wood 660b(7). Wing B1046.

1444. Basset, Thomas. *A catalogue of the common and statute law-books of this realm*. [London]: collected by T. Basset, sold at his shop, 1682. 12°. Pp. [8], 143, [1].
Flyleaf, upper[v], AW wrote 'The titles of many Law Books you may see in the Earl of Anglesies cat. nu. 53. p 69. 70 &c [AW's cat. no. 53 is [MS.] Wood E. 19(3)] [/] There is mention made of a book entit. Declaration & pleadings in the court of the Kings Bench [Wing R436 (1684)] - in cat. 48. p. 69. 70 - which book was collected by Jo. Read - qu[aere] [AW's cat. no. 48 is [MS.] Wood E. 18(10)] [/] See [William] Londons Cat. which I have p. 122. [i.e., [MS.] Wood D. 22(6)] [/] See cat. of Books in Sion libr. 4°. C. 16. Art. Seld. [present at this location in 2000] [/] See cat., of Hen. Parkers books of Greys inn. nu. 20. 28. [AW's cat. no. 20 is [MS.] Wood E. 16(2) (1681)] [/] Joh. Statham an old Lawyer. cat. 28. p. 1 cat. 59. p. 46. [AW's cat. no. 28 is [MS.] Wood E. 17(2) (1681); on p. 1 of this cat., 'Statham's, Abridgement of the Law', titled *Liber antiquissimus, . . .* ' is marked by a line in pencil and AW wrote 'qu[aere] when printed'; it is the only one of 34 entries on p. 1 that includes no printed date of publ.] [/] . . . . [Thomas] Owen cat. 28. p. 2. [i.e., Reports in the Com. Pleas, 1659; marked by a line in pencil on p. 2] [/] . . . . [Thomas] Fanshaw ibid. p. 8. [i.e., Practice of the Exchequer-Court, 1658] [/] S[r] Georg Cary a Lawyer vid. cat. ix cat.' [AW's cat. no. 9 is [MS]. Wood E. 14(3)]. 1st item, tp, AW wrote after the year 'August –', in pencil. In the lists, pp. 2-143, AW, passim, made frequent lines in red ink, added information in red ink and in pencil (4, 7, 22-3), wrote 'q[uaere]' (7, 17-8), made cross-references to this and other catalogues (16), comments (73, 'false'), longer notes (73-4, on John Goldsborough and Thomas Hetley), etc. to the end. After p. 143, AW inserted 7 leaves and on the 1st 4, r-v, made a 'Cat. of law writers to Th. Bassets book', with over 200 main entries. Many index items are marked with lines, or underscorings, in red ink.
Wood 896(5). Wing B1044.

1445. Basset, Thomas. *An exact catalogue of the common & statute law books of this realm*. [London]: collected by T. Basset, 1684. S.sh.
Diff. ed. at Wood 660b(7).
Wood 660b(15). Wing B1047.

1446. Bear Auction House. *At the Bear, the auction-house in Ave-Mary-lane, near Ludgate-street . . . Libri Graeci & Graeco Latini [29 Nov. - 2 Dec. 1687]*. [London]: n.pub., [1687]. S.sh. 8°.
[MS.] Wood E. 20(10a) (not in Bodl. CD cat.). Not in Wing. Not in ESTCR.

1447. Bibliotheca Medica. *Bibliotheca medica, et mathematica Anglo-Latina. . . . Quorum auctio habebitur [30 Aug.]*. [London]: distributed, Wilkinson, W. Miller, et al., [1686]. 4°. Pp. [4], 24.
Tp, AW wrote cat. no. '61', in pencil, and '3[d]'. From p. 4, AW marked a few entries with horizontal lines, in pencil, and p. 7, wrote 1 'qu[aere]' letter.
[MS.] Wood E. 20(5). Wing B2840.

1448. Bibliotheca Novissima. *Bibliotheca novissima. Or a catalogue of books on divers subjects*. [London]: f. the booksellers, sold R. Taylor, 1693, June. 8°. Pp. [2], 30.
Pp. 6, 9, AW marked 5 items with red chalk.
[MS.] Wood D. 22(18). Wing B2844 (rare).

1449. Bibliotheca Parliamenti. *Bibliotheca parliamenti: libri theologici, politici, historici, . . . Classis secunda*. [London]: qui prostant venales . . . Little Britain, 1653. 8°. Pp. 12.
Wood 899(3) (not in Bodl. CD cat.). Wing B2845C ('O' not recorded in Wing).

1450. Bibliotheca Selecta. *Bibliotheca selecta: sive catalogus variorum librorum:. . . quorum auctio habebitur [21 May]*. [London]: distributed gratis, Nott, Bullord, et al, [1688]. 4°. Pp. [4], 32.
Tp, AW wrote, '6[d]'.
[MS.] Wood E. 21(5). Wing B2852 (two).

1451. Billingsley, Benjamin. *Books lately printed for Benjamin Billingsley . . . in Cornhil*. [London]:

n.pub., [1685]. S.sh. (r-v).
^r, AW wrote 'put into my hand by a Hawker when I was at London 7 Aug [Aug lined out] Sept. 1685'. LT 3.160.
Wood 896(8) (not in Bodl. CD cat.). Not in Wing. Not in ESTCR.

1452. [Birkenhead, John]. *Paul's church-yard. Libri theologici, politici, historici, nundinis Paulinis . . . prostant venales [Centuria prima, secunda].* N.p.: n.pub., [1651 or 1652]. 4°. A-B⁴.
B1, AW wrote, 'By Joh. Birkenhead'.
[MS.] Wood C. 26(16a-b). Wing B2970.

1453. [Blount, Thomas]. *The lamps of the law and lights of the gospel. Or the titles of some late spiritual, polemical, . . . new books . . . by Grass & Hay Wythers.* London: n.pub., 1658. 8°. Pp. 1-24 (1-2 blank).
Tp, AW wrote 'Tho. [Blount, cropped at side] of the inner Temple, the a[uthor]'.
Wood 899(7) (not in Bodl. CD cat.). Not in Wing. Cross referenced to Blount at L307 (wanting the entry). Not in ESTCR.

1454. [Blount, Thomas]. *[The lamps of the law and lights of the gospel. Or the titles of some late spiritual, polemical, . . . new books . . . by Grass & Hay Wythers].* [London]: n.pub., [1658]. 8°. Pp. 5-24 (wanting t leaf).
Wood 899(6) (not in Bodl. CD cat.). Not in Wing. Cross-referenced to Blount at L307 (wanting the entry). Not in ESTCR.

1455. Bowman, Thomas. *Catalogus librorum . . . in omni facultate insignium. Horum auctio . . . habebitur . . . in aedibus Thomae Bowman [28 Feb.].* [Oxford]: distributed gratis, T. Bowman, [1687]. 4°. ²,A-U²,X1,A*-L*²,a-c²,d1.
Tp, AW wrote cat. no. '54', in pencil, and former no., '56'. From A2ᵛ, AW marked a few entries with horizontal or vertical lines, mainly in pencil. These are more frequent from A*1 among the 'English' books which also includes 1 correction and 4 cross references. In this cat. without p. nos., AW numbered consecutively to the end, 1-140.
[MS.] Wood E. 19(4). Wing C1439 (one) ('O' not recorded in Wing).

1456. [Boyle, Robert]. *A catalogue of the philosophical books and tracts, written by . . . Robert Boyle.* London: f. S. Smith, 1692. 12°. Pp. [2], 17 (I3-6,K⁶).
Wood 91(6). Wing B3989, part of.

1457. Bradford, John, and William Cooper. *Catalogus . . . librorum ex bibliothecis . . . Johan. Bradford . . . Gulielmi Cooperi . . . quorum auctio habenda est [14 June].* [London]: given, Wilkinson, et al., [1686]. 4°. Pp. [4], 82.
Tp, AW wrote cat. no. '49', in red chalk. From p. 7, AW marked a few entries with horizontal or vertical lines, mainly in pencil, and occasionally underscored name of authors. These are more frequent from p. 20, among the 'English' books; after p. 30, he wrote a few identifications or 'q[uaere]' letters. Flyleaf, lower, AW observed, 'In this cat are the yeares of certaine books, when printed, omitted, especially if the title cannot come within the compass of a line.'
[MS.] Wood E. 18(11). Wing B4103.

1458. Broekhuizen, Benjamin van. *Catalogus librorum . . . Benj. Broeckhuysen . . . & aliorum: quorum auctio habenda est . . . Per Guilielmum Cooper [1 Dec.].* [London]: distributed gratis, 1684. 4°. Pp. [2], 67 (misnumbering), [1], 15.
Tp, AW wrote cat. no. '37', in red chalk; and 'published in the latter end of Oct. 1684'. From p. 5, AW marked a few entries with horizontal or vertical lines, mainly in pencil; underscored at p. 67 and 2nd p. 1, and pp. 53, 61; 2nd p. 2, wrote 'H. Elsing v[ide] infra' and below, underscored Elsing's name. After p. 64, he renumbered pp. consecutively, 66 to 89.
[MS.] Wood E. 17(11). Wing B4840.

1459. [Bruce, Robert]. Ailesbury, earl of. *Bibliotheca illustris: sive catalogus . . . librorum . . . viri cujusdam praenobilis [R. Bruce] . . . quorum auctio habebitur . . . per T. Bentley, & B. Walford [21 Nov.].* [London]: distributed at 6 d., Willis, Holford, et al., [1687]. 4°. Pp. [4], 94 (misnumbering).
Tp, AW wrote cat. no. '64', 'nobilis defuncti', 'E. of Aylesbury', and '6ᵈ', in pencil; 'Rob. Bruce E. of Ayslbury [sic]', over the similar note in pencil; and 'A cat. of manuscripts at the end'. From p. 2, AW marked a few entries with horizontal and/or vertical lines, mainly in pencil, and wrote a few brief notes (several at mss., pp. 85, 88-9); p. 18c (i.e., F*1ᵛ), at entry of his *Historia*, he wrote a longer note: 'v. pag. 17' and 'Here you see are two exemplars of the Hist. & Antiq. of Oxon - At which I wonder because that

in March 1680/1 when the parliament sate at Oxon, the E. of Aylsbury author of this library, told me in his house neare to Magd Coll. that he never saw, the said Hist. & Antiq. - whereupon I offer'd him a copie, but he was gon [sic] upon the dissolution before I could give him one'; p. 17, at a similar entry, he wrote 'pag. 18.c.', LT 3.166. AW corrected misnumbering and after p. 44 numbered consecutively, 45-100. See T. A. Birrell, 'Books and Buyers', in R. Myers, ed., *Under the Hammer* (BL, 2001): 52.
[MS.] Wood E. 20(8). Wing A801A.

1460. Bullord, John. *Bibliotheca selectissima seu catalogus . . . librorum, . . . Quos . . . sibi procuravit quidam Angliae generosus nuper defunctus. Quorum auctio habebitur . . . per Joh. Bullord [8 May].* [London]: distributed gratis, Hensman, Nott, et al., [1689]. 4°. Pp. [2], 40 (i.e., 42).
Tp, scribbles, by 'S. W.'?
[MS.] Wood E. 22(5). Wing B2856.

1461. Bullord, John. *Bibliotheca generalis ex bibliothecis duorum doctissimorum theologorum, & eximii cujusdam medici, . . . composita. Cujus auctio habebitur . . . per Jo. Bullord [8 Dec.].* [London]: distributed gratis, Will's Coffee-House, Nott, et al., [1690]. 4°. Pp. [2], 68.
[MS.] Wood E. 22(10). Wing B 2828.

1462. Button, Ralph; Thankfull Owen, and William Howell. *Catalogus librorum bibliothecis . . . Radulphi Button . . . Thankfull Owen [and] Gulielmi Hoeli. Quorum auctio habebitur . . . per E. Millingtonum [7 Nov.].* [London]: distributed gratis, Dunsmore a. Millington, 1681. 4°. Pp. [2], 24, 16, 7, [1].
Flyleaf, upper, AW wrote, 'Catal { Rad. Button [/] Gratian. Owen { SS.T.Bac. { Cat. Lib. Gul. Howell.' and 'Ex dono Mos. Pitt. Bibliop. 20. Oct. 1681.'; ᵛ, in a later hand, 'eccl. Christi Oxon. canonias'. LT 1.286.
Tp, AW wrote cat. no. '17' in red chalk. From p. 2, some items are marked with underscoring or vertical or horizontal lines, in pencil or ink; 2nd pp. 1, 12, identifications; 2nd p. 2, at an entry which has 'by the Author of the Duty of Man' (Allestree, Wing A1178ff.), AW wrote, '[h]ow doe you [k]noue yt?' (cropped). After the 1st section, he numbered pp. consecutively from 25 to 48.
[MS.] Wood E. 15(5). Wing B6341.

1463. Bysshe, Edward. *Bibliotheca Bissaeana: sive, catalogus librorum in omni arte & linguā . . . Horum auctio habetitur . . . in aedibus J. Dunmore. [With] A catalogue of sir Edward Bish's books of heraldry [15 Nov.].* [London]: distributed gratis, Tooke, [1680]. 4°. Pp. [4], 70 (without the additional cat.).
Flyleaf, upper, AW wrote, '1680'. Tp, AW wrote cat. no. '11', in orange crayon, and 'an.1680'. P. 1, a horizontal line in margin, in pencil. AW corrected the p. nos., from 2nd 18-19 to the end.
[MS.] Wood E. 14(5). Wing B6411.

1464. Castell, Edmund. *Bibliotheca Castelliana, sive catalogus variorum librorum . . . Edm. Castelli, . . . Quorum auctio habenda est . . . Per Edoardum Millingtonum [30 June].* [London]: given, place of sale, Cambridg a. W. Miller, London, 1686. 4°. Pp. [2], 26. Pasteboard (blue) with parchment spine; may have been bound or rebound later (edges uncut).
Pastedown, upper, slip attached, on which AW wrote the titles of 7 catalogues of printed books in this vol., numbered consecutively from 50 to 56 (following those bound in [MS.] Wood E. 13-18). Tp, AW wrote cat. no. '50', in red chalk; and former no., '49'. Pp. 9, 13, 15-6, 18, 24-6, AW marked a few entries with horizontal and/or vertical lines, mainly in pencil.
[MS.] Wood E. 19(1). Wing C1223.

1465. Catalogue 1680. *A catalogue of two . . . libraries of books, Latin and English, . . . exposed to sale by way of auction [22 Nov.].* [London]: distributed gratis, Bridges, S. Crouch, a. C. Wilkinson, [1680]. 4°. Pp. [4], 72 (misnumbering).
Tp, AW wrote cat. no. '12', in red chalk. From p. 2, and more among books in English, AW marked some items with vertical and horizontal lines, in pencil or ink and wrote 3 brief notes in margins, e.g., p. 65, at Byfield, *Principles* (1665), 'Byfield Nich. or Rich.' (the problem of Byfield's Christian name came up several times; here, it is Nicholas Byfield, Wing B6389; see also AW's notes at [MS.] Wood D. 31(29), [MS]. Wood E. 17(7) and [MS.] Wood E. 18(6)).
[MS.] Wood E. 14(6). Wing C1412.

1466. Catalogue 1688. *A catalogue of Latin & English books, of divinity, history, . . . &c. Will be sold by way of auction [9 Jan. 1688].* [London]: distributed gratis, Wellingtons Coffee-House, et al, 1687/1688. 4°. Pp. [2], 48.
Tp, AW wrote cat. no. '66', in pencil. From p. 3, AW marked a few entries with horizontal lines, in pencil, and wrote 4 brief notes (p. 32, at W. Cornwallyes *Essays* (1610), 'habeo' (AW owned editions of 1600 and 1616, Wood 769(2) and 498(6), items 2014f.).

[MS.] Wood E. 20(10b). Wing C1346 (rare, 2 at O).

1467. Catalogue 1688. *A catalogue of Latin, French, and English books: consisting of divinity, physick . . . Which will be sold by auction [30 Apr.]*. [London]: distributed gratis, Nott, Weld, et al., 1688. 4°. Pp. [2], 40.
[MS.] Wood E. 21(4). Wing C1353.

1468. Catalogue 1688. *A catalogue of choice English books:. . . which will be sold by auction [6 Aug.]*. [London]: distributed gratis, Nott, Weld, et al., 1688. 4°. Pp. [2], 24, 16 (last section, 9-16 and 1-8).
2nd p. 9, 'The Sale of these will begin, on Wednesday Morning Aug: 1ˢᵗ: 1688', not by AW. Note, cropped at top.
[MS.] Wood E. 21(7). Wing C1303 (two).

1469. Catalogue 1689. *A catalogue of English & Latin books, . . . [which] will be sold by auction . . . the 22d of this instant January*. [London]: destributed [sic] gratis, Manship, R. Wild, et al., 1689. 4°. Pp. 20.
Tp, '22d' in title corrected to '21st', not by AW.
[MS.] Wood E. 22(2). Wing C1312 (two).

1470. Catalogue 1689. *A catalogue of vendible and useful English and Latin books . . . will be sold by auction [18 Mar. 1689]*. [London]: distributed gratis, Nott, et al., 1688/9. 4°. Pp. [2], 22.
[MS.] Wood E. 22(3). Wing C1423 (two).

1471. Catalogue Appendix. *An appendix of some books omitted in transcribing the preceding catalogue for the press, and some few others since come to hand*. N.p.: n.pub., [1678] [includes 2 books for sale dated 1678]. 4°. Pp. 4.
Wood 658(819b) (not in Bodl. CD cat.). Wing A3571 (rare) (Wing, [1677]).

1472. Catalogus. *Catalogus librorum in regionibus transmarinis nuper editorum. Numbs.1-3, 6 [8 May, Trinity, Michaelmas, Michaelmas]*. (Londini): (ap. M. Pitt), 1676-1677. Fol. Pp. 1-14, 23-26.
Dupl. at Wood 660b(12).
Wood 658(820). N & S 034.01-034.03 and 034.06 (two).

1473. Catalogus. *Catalogus librorum in regionibus transmarinis nuper editorum. Numbs.1-10 [8 May 1676-Trinity 1679]*. London: ap. M. Pitt, 1676-1679. Fol. Pp. 42 and '39-42' (misnumbering).
P. 1, notes by a later librarian, in pencil. Dupl. at Wood 658(820).
Wood 660b(12). N & S 034.01-034.10 (two).

1474. Catalogus. *Catalogus librorum domi forísque impressorum*. Londini: veneunt S. Smith & B. Walford, 1695. 8°. Pp. [2], 94.
Wood 899(8) (not in Bodl. CD cat.). Wing C1435 ('O' not recorded in Wing).

1475. Chace, Richard; Christopher Bathurst, and George Tonstall. *Catalogus librorum . . . Rich. Chace . . . Christ. Bathurst . . . Georg. Tonstall. . . . Quorum auctio habenda est . . . per Gulielmum Cooper [24 Mar.]*. [London]: distributed, W. Cooper, 1683/4. 4°. Pp. [4], 48.
Tp, AW wrote cat. no. '31', in red chalk, and, '6ᵈ'. From p. 3, AW marked a few entries with horizontal or vertical lines, mainly in pencil; in the 'English' section, from p. 33, he added a few more marks, 'q[uaere]' letters, and notes.
[MS.] Wood E. 17(5). Wing C1785.

1476. Charleton, Walter. *Three anatomic lectures [section heading:] 'Gualteri Charletoni scripta jam in lucem emissa'*. [London]: [f. W. Kettilby], [1683]. S.sh. (r-v) (fragment). 4°.
Tp, 'A', with a vertical 'I' through the crossbar and note, by Aubrey, 'January 15. 4 [?]. Dʳ Lower died in Convent [sic] garden: the bell now rings-out for him. Dʳ Charlton remembers him to you & tore this for you, out of his booke of Anatomical Lectures.' AW corrected the date to Jan. '17'; see LT 3.351. An added entry, Inquisitio physica (1685), is not Aubrey's hand and may not be by AW (also by Charleton, see AO 4.755). AW marked most items with a vertical line in the margins.
[MS.] Wood D. 22(14). Wing C3693 (part of).

1477. Clavell, Robert, collected by. *A catalogue of all the books printed in England since . . . 1666. To the end of Michaelmas term, 1672*. London: S. Simmons f. R. Clavel, 1673. Fol. Pp. [4], 48, 32. Pasteboard (blue) with parchment spine.
Flyleaf, upper, 3rdᵛ, AW wrote the titles of 16 printed works in this vol., within guidelines made with red chalk (3, 5, and 6 are one work, and 16b and 16c, may have been added after 1695; item 17, published in

1706, was added after 1695 and is not entered in this current cat.). 1st item, pp. 1-48 and 2nd pp. 1-5 and 12-15, 17-32, AW inserted frequent lines and crosses in margins, in ink and pencil; 1st pp. 1-2, 5, 9 (at a work on communion with the Romish church, a ms. 'Mr Squire' in margin (AO 3.1114), 10, 12, 14-5, some brief notes. LT 2.176.
Wood 660b(1). Wing C4598.

1478. Clavell, Robert, collected by. *The general catalogue of books printed in England since . . . MD-CLXVI. To the end of Trinity term MDCLXXX. [Followed by] a catalogue of school books. To which is now added a catalogue of Latin . . . since MDCLXX [the latter is titled Catalogus librorum Latinorum].* London: S. Roycroft f. R. Clavell (imp. R. Clavel), 1680 and (1681). Fol. 3rd ed. Pp. [4], 1-28, [1-8], 29-100 [another work, Wood 660b(4), item 1565, intervening, and:] 101-191.
Wood 660b(3, 5-6). Wing C4601 (ESTCR 751, [4], 119, [1]).

1479. Collins, John. *A curious collection of law-books . . . of John Collins . . . and of another . . . will be exposed to sale . . . by Edward Millington [2 July].* [London]: given gratis, Richards Coffee-house, et al., [1683]. 4°. Pp. [2], 18.
Tp, AW wrote cat. no. '28'. From pp. 1-16, AW marked some entries with horizontal or vertical lines, mainly in pencil, wrote 'q[uaere]' letters, and a few notes (p. 16, at 'Miltons Doctrine', 'Jo. Milton v. infra', and below, name of Milton underscored at 'Tenures of Kings'). See references to this item in AW's notes at Wood 896(5).
[MS.] Wood E. 17(2). Wing C5370.

1480. Colomiès, Paul. *Bibliothèque choisie de m. Colomiés [sic].* La Rochelle: chez P. Savouret, 1682. 8°. Pp. [4], 208. Calf, speckled, with gold-stamps on spine.
Pastedown, upper, '259. 18^d'. Flyleaf, upper, 'C.140' (former shelf-mark?).
Wood 138. BL.

1481. Cooper, William. *A catalogue of chymicall books. . . . Collected by Will. Cooper.* London: n.pub., 1675. 8°. *,P-R^4,A-G^4 (pp. [8, 80]).
Tp, AW wrote '1^s-6^d'. In the lists, P1-E1^v, AW made frequent marks, mainly in pencil, e.g., horizonal lines, and 'q[uaere]' entries.
Wood 896(6). Wing C6061.

1482. Cooper, William. *Catalogus librorum medicorum, . . . quorum auctio habebitur . . . per Guil. Cooper [13 July].* [London]: distributed gratis, Cooper, Child's Coffee-house, et al., [1686]. 4°. Pp. [4], 12.
Tp, AW wrote cat. no. '51', in red chalk; over former no., '50'. Pp. 5, 9, 11, marked a entries with horizontal lines, in pencil.
[MS.] Wood E. 19(2a). Wing C1444.

1483. Cooper, William. *Catalogus librorum . . . viri cujusdam literati. Quorum auctio habenda est . . . Per Guilielmum Cooper [14 Feb.].* [London]: distributed gratis, Pelican, et al., 1686/7. 4°. Pp. [2], 10, 31-33, [1], 36, 8 (misnumbering).
Tp, AW wrote cat. no. '55' and former no., '54', both in pencil; 'This cat is very false', and 'Given to me by Tho. Creech the poet, Fellow of Alls. Coll. 27 Mar. 1687'. LT 3.216. From p. 3, AW marked a few entries with horizontal and/or vertical lines, mainly in pencil. These are more frequent from p. 32, among the 'English' books and include some corrections, cross references, or 'q[uaere]' letters. AW numbered consecutively after p. 10 to the end, 11-57.
[MS.] Wood E. 19(5). Wing C1434.

1484. Corneille, Pierre. Dancer, John, trans. *[Nicomede, a tragi-comedy, tr. by J. Dancer. Together with an exact catalogue of all English stage-plays printed till 1671] 'A true, perfect, and exact catalogue'.* [London]: [f. F. Kirkman], [1671]. 4°. Pp. 1-16; A-B^4 (cat. only).
Flyleaf, upper^v, AW wrote, 'This catalogue following was taken from the end of [a] Tragi=comedy called Nicomede, translated out of the French of Monsieur Corneille, by Joh. Dancer - printed at London 1671 [/] T. for Tragedy [/] M. Maske . . . . '. A1, AW wrote, '1671'; note, t for tragedy, m for masque, etc., covered by a slip. B3, AW made a correction; and B4^v, underscored names of 3 authors, in red ink. The text of the play, pp. [4], 56, is at Wood 607(6), item 2009. LT 1.20. Kirkman listed 48 plays by Shakespeare, including Arraignment of Paris, Cromwell's History, John K. of England (2d pt.), Locrine Eldest Son of K. Brutus, London Prodigal, Mucedorus, Merry Devil of Edmonton, Old-Castle's Life and Death, Puritan Widow, and Yorkshire Tragedy.
[MS.] Wood E. 28(3). Wing C6315.

1485. Coventry, William. *A catalogue of books, of the several libraries of . . . William Coventry, and . . . Henry Coventry . . . to be sold by auction [9 May]*. [London]: gratis, W. Copper, G. Wells, et al. a. at the Coffee-Houses in Oxford and Cambridge, 1687. 4°. Pp. [4], 44. Pasteboard (blue) with parchment spine; may have been bound or rebound later (edges uncut).
Pastedown, upper, slip attached, on which AW wrote the titles of 12 catalogues of printed books in this vol., numbered consecutively from 57 to 68 (following those bound in [MS.] Wood E. 13-19; this is the last of those that he himself numbered on slips and tpp). AW did not annotate the remaining catalogues now in the E series, E. 21-24). Tp, AW wrote cat. no. '57' and former no. '56', both in pencil. From p. 2, 4, 18-9, 38ff., he marked a few entries with horizontal lines, in pencil, and minor underscoring. Pp. 38-9, he supplied a Christian name, 'Obad', for 'Walker', and at a book by J. Browne, 'v[ide] prox. pag' (on the next page there is another medical book by the same J. Browne).
[MS.] Wood E. 20(1). Wing C6626.

1486. Crooke, William. *A catalogue of books newly printed for William Crook*. [London?]: n.pub., [1675]. S.sh. 4° (r-v) (fragment taken from P. B[ellon], *Mock duellist*, 1675).
[MS.] Wood D. 22(12). Wing B1854.

1487. Crooke, William. *A catalogue of such books that are printed for . . . William Crooke*. London: n.pub., 1683. 8°. Pp. [2], 14.
P. 14, addition of 10 numbers, sum total: 3425.
Wood 896(7). Wing C7234.

1488. [Crowe, William]. *The catalogue of our English writers on the Old and New Testament*. London: E. Cotes f. T. Williams, 1668. 8° 2nd ed. Pp. [8], 304. Parchment over boards.
Tp, AW wrote 'Will Crowe the author of th . . . ', cropped at bottom and side; 'N' and a price, '2.6', not by AW. P. [8], AW underscored items in errata and made the corrections in the text. Text, passim, on every page, AW made marks of some sort: dots at most items, lines in margin in red ink, dark ink, and in pencil, 'v. infra', 'v. post', 'v. supra', 'v. p. –', or 'q[uaere]', and identifications and corrections. LT 2.333.
Wood 897. Wing C7367.

1489. Crowe, William. *Elenchus scriptorum in sacram scripturam tam Graecorum quàm Latinorum*. London: typ. T. R., imp. authoris, & prostat venalis ap. M. Pitt, 1672. 8°. Pp. [15], 344, [55].
P. 136, at 'Franciscus Triggus', line in margin, in red ink. LT 2.333.
Wood 898(1). Wing C7368.

1490. Davis, Richard. *A catalogue of books printed for, and to be sold by Richard Davis at his shop near Oriel colledge*. [Oxford?]: n.pub., [1662?]. S.sh. (r-v) (fragment?).
Tp, AW wrote, '1658' (a no. of items were printed after 1660 and one is dated 1662).
[MS.] Wood D. 22(4) (not in Bodl. CD cat.). Not in Wing. Not in ESTCR (not ESTCR 213795). Madan 3.400, no. 16.

1491. Davis, Richard. *The books following, lately printed at the theater, are to be sold by Richard Davis . . . Febr. 16. 1680*. [Oxford]: [the theatre], [1680]. S.sh. (fragment?).
AW altered the year to 16'79' and wrote '1679' in margin.
[MS.] Wood D. 22(13). Not in Wing. See D425A. Not in ESTCR. See Madan, p. 400.

1492. Davis, Richard. *Catalogi variorum . . . librorum Richardi Davis . . . Pars secunda. Quorum auctio . . . Oxoniae habenda est . . . Per Guilielmum Cooper[,] Edv. Millingtonum [4 Oct.]*. London: distributed gratis, Pelican et al., 1686. 4° (with 40 pp. of addenda). Pp. [4], 191, [1], 40.
Tp, AW wrote cat. no. '52', in red chalk; over former no., '51'; and, not by AW, a note on the appendix. From pp. 10, 18-9, 23, etc., AW underscored, marked a few entries with horizontal or vertical lines, mainly in pencil, and occasionally underscored. These are more frequent from p. 105, among the 'English' books; from p. 112, he wrote a few identifications, 'q[uaere]' letters, and cross references (e.g., pp. 152-3, 'v[ide] prox. p.' and, next p., he noted an entry to the same book; or at 164, at a 1661 ed. of Glisson and Gulston, Common Law, 'v. p. 165', and at p. 165, he marked a 1679 ed. with a line in the margin). P. 191^v, he wrote, 'Appendix followes', and at p. 1 of the following 'Theologici Folio', 'Appendix to Rich Davis his Auction catalogue, which began to be sold 4 Oct. 1686 - This was published 23. Nov. 1686'. Similar annotation continues, more among books in English, from p. 18, and especially at 'bundles of stitched Sermons', pp. 35-6, where he supplied 7 Christian names of authors. LT 3.157.
[MS.] Wood E. 19(2b). Wing D427 (Wing, [Oxford 1686]).

1493. Davis, Richard. *Catalogus variorum . . . librorum Richardi Davis . . . . Quorum auctio . . . Oxoniae*

habenda est . . . per Guil. Cooper, Edv. Millingtonum [19 Apr.]. [London]: distributed gratis, the Pelican, et al., 1686. 4°. With 2 leaves of addenda. Pp. [4], 208, [4] (some cropping of nos.).
Tp, AW wrote cat. no. '48', in red chalk, over former no. '47'. From p. 3-118, AW marked a very few entries with horizontal or vertical lines, mainly in pencil. These are more frequent among the 'English' books, from p. 119, where he also wrote a few notes and 'q[uaere]' letters; at 2nd p. [1], 'Addition to Rich. Davis his cat.' and '209'. LT 3.157.
[MS.] Wood E. 18(10). Wing D426.

1494. Davis, Richard. *Catalogi variorum . . . librorum Richardi Davis . . . Pars tertia. Quorum auctio . . . Oxoniae habenda est . . . per Gulielmum Cooper [25 June].* [Oxford]: distributed gratis, the Pelican, a. in Oxford a. Cambridge, [1688]. 4°. Pp. [4], 149.
Tp, 'Ex dono B. Sherley XI. Jun. 1688'. LT 3.157. Pp. 83-122, a few horizontal lines in margin, in pencil.
[MS.] Wood E. 21(8). Wing D428.

1495. Davis, Richard. *Catalogi variorum librorum . . . Richardi Davis . . . pars quarta. Una cum libris . . . dr. Pocockii . . . Quorum auctio . . . habebitur [in Oxford] . . . per Edoardum Millingtonum [11 Apr.].* [London]: distributed gratis, West, Clements, et al., 1692. 4°. Pp. [2], 58 (some pp. unopened). LT 3.157.
[MS.] Wood E. 22(11). Wing D429.

1496. Digby, Kenelm. *Bibliotheca Digbeiana, sive catalogus librorum . . . quos post K. Digbeium . . . possedit . . . Georgius comes Bristol . . . Horum auctio habebitur [19 Apr.].* [London]: distributed, H. Brome a. B. Tooke, [1680]. 4°. Pp. [4], 135.
Tp, AW wrote cat. no. '9', in red chalk. From p. 11, some items are marked in AW's manner, with vertical and horizontal lines, in pencil or ink, 'q[uaere]' letters, and some brief notes in margins, 86, 88, 116, 124, 126, 133 (some cropped). There are also, passim, some short double vertical lines and a few cross marks, not in AW's usual manner. LT 2.371.
[MS.] Wood E. 14(3). Wing D1421.

1497. Ducie, William. Downe, visct. *Catalogus bibliothecae . . . Gulielmi Ducie. Quae prostat venalis apud Robertum Littlebury.* Londini: n.pub., 1680. 4°. Pp. [2], 40.
Tp, AW wrote cat. no. '10', in red chalk and underscored 'Duni' (i.e., Downe) and wrote, 'qu[aere]', in red ink. Pp. 2-22, some items are marked with vertical and horizontal lines, in pencil or ink, in AW's manner.
[MS.] Wood E. 14(4). Wing D2079.

1498. Frankfurt am Main. Buch-Messe. *Catalogus universalis pro nundinis Francofurtensibus vernalibus, . . . 1609.* Francofurti: imp. S. Latonis, 1609. 4°. A-D⁴. Pasteboard (grey) with parchment spine; rebacked (not bound by AW).
Flyleaf, upper, 2nd, the titles of 20 printed works (really 18), plus 2 titles (16a-b) added below, in this vol., by an Ashm. librarian. Many ms. notes in margins are cropped. 1st item, AW marked with a vertical line entries on B1ʳ⁻ᵛ (at *Hebdomada Mariana* by Stanyhurst (AW's copy is at Wood 781, item 6031) and at *Soc. Jesu* by Toletus, and wrote the p. no. '8'), D3 (at *Parthenicon Elisabethae* by G. Mart.).
[MS.] Wood C. 26(1). Not in BL.

1499. Frankfurt am Main. Buch-Messe. *Catalogus universalis pro nundinis Francofurtensibus autumnalibus . . . 1622.* Francofurti [really London]: [Eliot's Court Press], [1622] (cropped). 4°. A-D⁴,E².
Tp, AW wrote, 'Engl books paged & –', cropped at top. C2ᵛ, + in margin, prob. not by AW; C3, AW identified initials as 'Joh. Harmar'; C4ᵛ, vertical line at J. Owen, *Epigrammatum*, in pencil (AW owned 2 copies of the Lat. version, see Wood 76(1) and note, and an Engl. version, Wood 74, items 4854, 4852). In cat. of English books, D4-E2, AW numbered pp. 1-6 and marked numerous entries with vertical lines, in pencil, and wrote 'q[uaere]', twice; and made 2 identifications, in ink.
[MS.] Wood C. 26(2). STC 11329.8 (two).

1500. Frankfurt am Main. Buch-Messe. *Catalogus universalis pro nundinis Francofurtensibus vernalibus . . . 1623.* Francofurti [really London]: [Eliot's Court Press], 1623. 4°. A-D⁴,E² (last leaf blank).
A2ᵛ (3 entries marked by +, prob. not by AW), B1ᵛ (1 marked by AW). In cat. of English books, D3-E1ᵛ, AW numbered pp. from 8-13 and marked numerous entries mainly in pencil; made a cross-reference, D3ᵛ, 'v[ide] prox. p.', (on the next page there is a 2nd book by the same author (Alexander Richardson); and wrote some brief notes in ink.
[MS.] Wood C. 26(3). STC 11329.9 (two).

1501. Frankfurt am Main. Buch-Messe. *Catalogus universalis pro nundinis Francofurtensibus autum-*

nalibus . . . 1623. Francofurti [really London]: [Eliot's Court Press], 1623. 4°. A-D⁴,E² (cropped; imperf.). A3-A4, C4ᵛ-D1, a few entries marked with + (may not be by AW). In cat. of English books, D2ᵛ-E2ᵛ, AW numbered pp. from 14-22 and marked numerous entries, in pencil, made some identifications and cross-references, in ink; also some entries marked with +, in ink (may not be by AW).
[MS.] Wood C. 26(4-5). STC 11330.

1502. Frankfurt am Main. Buch-Messe. *Catalogus universalis pro nundinis Francofurtensibus vernalibus . . . 1625*. Francofurti [really London]: [G. Miller], 1625. 4°. A-E⁴.
In cat. of English books, D4-E3ᵛ, some entries are marked by a +, in ink (may not be by AW). Dupl. at [MS.] Wood C. 26(6-7).
[MS.] Wood C. 26(8). STC 11330.4.

1503. Frankfurt am Main. Buch-Messe. *Catalogus universalis pro nundinis Francofurtensibus vernalibus . . . 1625*. Francofurti. [really London]: [G. Miller], 1625. 4°. A-D⁴,E1-3 (imperf.).
In cat. of English books, D4-E3ᵛ (may have been numbered, but now these are cropped at top), AW marked numerous entries, mainly in pencil, and a cross-reference (E2, 'v[ide] prox. p.'). Dupl. at [MS.] Wood C. 26(8).
[MS.] Wood C. 26(6-7). STC 11330.4.

1504. Frankfurt am Main. Buch-Messe. *Catalogus universalis pro nundinis Francofurtensibus vernalibus . . . 1628*. Londini: [J. Bill,] prostat ap. J. Bill, 1628. 4°. A-G⁴.
A2, entry of an Oxford person, Georgii Abbatti *Explicatio*, marked by horizontal line, in pencil.
[MS.] Wood C. 26(9). STC 11331.

1505. Gauden, John. Worcester, bp. of. *Books written by dr. Gauden, and sold by Andrew Crook*. [London]: n.pub., [1660]. S.sh. 4° (fragment?).
Not identified.
[MS.] Wood D. 22(10). Not in Wing. Not in ESTCR.

1506. [Gee, Edward]. *The catalogue of all the discourses published against popery, during the reign of king James II*. London: printed, sold R. Baldwin, 1689. 4°. Pp. [3], 34.
On the blank recto of imprimatur leaf, AW wrote, 'Mʳ Will. Wake of ch. ch. the author, under R. Baldwins name' (AW does not link this item to Wake in AO 4.657ff.). Tp, he wrote '6ᵈ - 14 Mar. 1 88[9].'; pp. 2-13, he repeated the printed names, in margins, of the authors of all 76 items, and later marked many with red chalk or ink; pp. 14 to end, a few names at the remainder of the 230 entries, a few identifications, and most entries have some form of mark in red ink, crayon, or pencil, mainly vertical lines in red crayon. At end, 3 inserted blank leaves on which AW recorded an index to entries in the text: 'Names of authors alphabetically, with their books set downe according to their numbers', i.e., 73 authors, with entry nos.; some 21 include notes indicating that the person was not of a member of an Oxford college, e.g., at Altham, 'not Rog. Altham of Ch. Ch. as Mʳ Charlet sayes'; a number were later marked by lines or underscoring in red chalk, mainly, or in ink or in pencil. LT 1.19.
[MS.] Wood E. 27(5). Wing G454.

1507. Gellibrand, John. *Catalogus librorum in omni facultate & linguae, ex variis partibus Europae allatorum*. Londini: in coemeterio Paulino, 1682. A-B⁶,C².
Tpᵛ, 'Given to me by . . [Henry] Crittenden [Cruttenden] a printer, being then in the Castle Yard, Oxōn to see Steph. Golledge [sic] executed. 31. Aug. 1681' (i.e., Colledge, see, Wood 427(30); LT 2.552-3).
Wood 91(5). Wing G481 (rare).

1508. G[ibson], E[dmund], ed. *Librorum manuscriptorum in duabus insignibus bibliothecis; altera Tenisoniana, Londini; altera Dugdaliana, Oxonii; catalogus*. Oxonii: e theatro Sheldoniano, veneunt T. Bennett, Londinensis, 1692. 4°. Pp. [8], 31 (wanting pt. 2). Marbled paper wrappers; rebound with modern covers.
Tp, below year, AW wrote, '26 Dec [?]', in pencil. Dupl. at Wood 513(8), a perfect copy. LT 3.488.
[MS.] Wood C. 29 (not in Bodl. CD cat.). Wing T702A.

1509. G[ibson], E[dmund], ed. *Librorum manuscriptorum in duabus insignibus bibliothecis; altera Tenisoniana, Londini; altera Dugdaliana, Oxonii; catalogus*. Oxonii: e theatro Sheldoniano, veneunt T. Bennett, Londinensis, 1692. 4°. Pp. [8], 31, [5], 20.
2nd p. 15, note, not in AW's hand. This item may have been added after 1717 (see note at Wood 513(1), item 4024). Dupl. at [MS.] Wood C. 29.
Wood 513(8). Wing T702A.

1510. Godolphin, John, and Owen Phillips. *Catalogus . . . librorum . . . Johannis Godolphin, j.u.d.*

et d. Oweni Phillips, . . . Quorum auctio habebitur . . . per Gulielmum Cooper [11 Nov.]. [London]: gratis distribuentur, 1678. 4°. Pp. [6], 52, 59.
Flyleaf, upper, AW wrote, 'Cat. Godolphii[s] & Philipps. 1678' (cropped). Tp, AW wrote cat. no. '6', in red chalk. From p. 8, and heavily from 2nd p. 1, among books in English, AW marked items with vertical and horizontal lines, in pencil or ink, wrote some brief notes in margins, and after the 1st section, numbered pp. consecutively from 53 to 111. LT 2.415.
[MS.] Wood E. 13(6). Wing G942.

1511. G[offe], T[homas]. *[The careles shepherdess. A tragi-comedy].* 'An exact and perfect catologue [sic] of all Playes that are printed'. [London]: [R. Rogers a. W. Ley], [1656]. 4°. Pp. [6] (cat. only). Pasteboard (blue) with parchment spine. 1st upper and last lower flyleaves, marbled paper.
Flyleaf, upper, 3rd, AW wrote the titles of 5 printed works in this vol., within guidelines made with red chalk. The 1st 3 cat. items in this vol. were removed by AW from printed plays. LT 1.19-20. 1st item, p. [1], AW wrote, '1656'. Pp. [3, 5], vertical line at printed 'Friar Bacon, Green', and at 'Merc. Brittanicus, *Brathwat*'. [i.e., Rich. Brathwait].
[MS.] Wood E. 28(1). Wing G1005.

1512. Goffe, Thomas. *Three excellent tragedies [a fragment of, with heading:]* 'These books are printed for, and sold by Ga. Bedell and Tho. Collins, 1656'. [London]: [f. G. Bedell a. T. Collins], [1656]. 8°. 2nd ed. Pp. [5] (cat. only).
Flyleaf, upper ᵛ, a librarian wrote 'The catalogue opposite forms the last three leaves of Thomas Goffe's *Three excellent tragedies*, 1656' (not in AW's collection).
Wood 896(3). Wing G1006. Madan 2290.

1513. Gore, Thomas. *Catalogus alphabeticè digestus, plerorumque omnium authorum, . . . qui de re heraldica . . . scripserunt: interspersis . . . quae heraldriae facem accendit.* Oxon.: excud. H. H[all], 1668. 4°. Pp. [8], 27.
Tp, AW wrote, '4ᵈ' (which may not be the cost of the book, but rather the cost of interleaving and sewing; in his diary, 9 June, he wrote, 'to Thorne for sewing a book (Mr. Gore's book), 3ᵈ', LT 2.138. Gore sent AW a 1674 edition, now [MS.] Wood E. 27(1). AO 4.132. LT 2.138, 140, 295. AW's extensive notes and emendations to this cat. by Gore and his correspondence with Gore is discussed in, 'Anthony Wood, Thomas Gore and the Use of Manuscript Material', *The Library*, 21 (1999): 108-23.
[MS.] Wood E. 3 (fols. 298-331). Wing G1297. Madan 2802. SC 8570.

1514. Gore, Thomas. *Catalogus in certa capita, seu classes, alphabetico ordine concinnatus, plerorúmque omnium authorum, . . . qui de re heraldica . . . scripserunt.* Oxon.: typ. L. Lichfield, et prostant venales ap. R. Davis, 1674. 4°. Pp. [31], 138 (wanting the errata leaf) (misnumbering). Pasteboard (blue) with parchment spine. 1st upper and last lower flyleaves, marbled paper; rebacked.
AW wrote the titles of 5 printed works, all catalogues, in this vol., within guidelines made with red chalk. Tp, AW wrote, 'Antonii à Wood, Oxon. Ex dono Authoris j. Oct. 1674. Vice-comes Wilts. Electus an. 1680. t. 50.' (LT 1.295). a3ᵛ, AW may not have made marks in margin, in pencil, at printed acknowledgments to Dugdale and Wood ('Antonius à Woode, Oxoniensis, *A. M. in Re Antiquaria plurimum versatus, inter Principes studiorum meorum fautores memorandus.*'); 2nd p. 67, at dates of publication, 1665 and 1673, AW wrote '1675 q[uaere]'; and pp. 42, 100, 118, AW, prob., made a line in margin, in pencil. Numerous corrections prob. not by AW, e.g., a3, a4 (date of 'Praefatio' altered from 1674 to 167'3'), b1ᵛ; pp., 4-5, 11-2, 15, 46, 49-50, 2nd 67, 70-1, 73-88 (p. nos.), 78, 92, to 123, 128. Gore's entry of Wood's *Historia*, p. 137, was unmarked by AW. AW owned the 1st ed., [MS.] Wood E. 3, which he heavily annotated and sent to Gore. In MS. Wood E. 2(70), p. 37, he entered this item and added, 'T. Gore Magd. Coll' and 'Tho. Gore - de re heraldica 2ᵈ edition in which I took much paines & added several authors – High Sherriff of Wilts 1680-'. See LT 1.19, AO 4.132, and references in the preceding item.
[MS.] Wood E. 27(1). Wing G1298. Madan 3011.

1515. Greville, Robert, and Gabriel Sanger. *Catalogus librorum ex bibliotheca nobilis cujusdam Angli [R. Greville et] Gabrielis Sangar. . . . Quorum auctio habebitur . . . per Nathanielem Ranew [2 Dec. 1978 (sic)].* [London]: distributed gratis, N. Ranew, 1678. 4°. Pp. [6], 98.
Flyleaf, upper, AW wrote, 'Cat. Cujusdam n[obilis] Angli - et Gab. [Sangar] per Nath. Ranew 1678' (cropped) and 'Mʳ Walker hath Tho. Millingtons Catalogue.' Tp, correction of year from 1978 to 1678. AW wrote cat. no. '5', in red chalk. From p. 1, and slightly more from p. 35, among books in English, AW marked items with horizontal or vertical lines, in pencil or ink, and wrote some brief notes in margins. P. 80, 'habeo', in pencil, at 'The Reformed Library Keeper, by John Dury', London, 1650 (not in AW's current collection; see Dury, item 2380).

[MS.] Wood E. 13(5). Wing B4910.

1516. Gulston, William. Bristol, bp. of. *Bibliotheca Gulstoniana, sive catalogus . . . librorum . . . Gulielmi Gulstoni . . . Quorum auctio habenda est . . . per Edvardum Millingtonum [11 June].* [London]: given, Nott, Wilkinson, et al., [1688]. 4°. Pp. [4], 52.
Tp, AW wrote, '6ᵈ'; scribbles. Flyleaf, lower, 'Demy Paper', not by AW.
[MS.] Wood E. 21(6). Wing G2227.

1517. Gunter, Jaspar. *Catalogus librorum . . . ex bibliothecis G. Gunteri . . . nec non jurisconsulti cujusdam doctissimi . . . Quorum auctio habebitur . . . per Edvardum Millingtonum [20 Mar.].* [London]: given gratis, Wilkinson, et al., 1683[4]. 4°. Pp. [4], 28.
Tp, AW wrote cat. no. '30', in red chalk (over '31'), and, 'Given to me by Hen. Cruttenden X March. 1683[4].' LT 3.470. From p. 4, AW marked a few entries with horizontal or vertical lines, mainly in pencil, and wrote 2 cross-reference notes and 1 'q[uaere]' letter.
[MS.] Wood E. 17(4). Wing G2244.

1518. Hawkins, William, and Edward Reynolds. *Bibliotheca Hawkinsiana, sive catalogus variorum librorum . . . Guil. Hawkins . . . Necnon . . . Edvardo Reynoldes . . . Qui venales habentur [13 Apr.].* [London]: distributed gratis, Nott, et al., [1685]. 4°. Pp. [2], 44, [2] (misnumbering and imperf. at end).
Pasteboard (blue) with parchment spine; may have been bound or rebound later (edges uncut).
Pastedown, upper, slip attached, on which AW wrote the titles of 11 catalogues of printed books in this vol., numbered consecutively from 39 to 49 (following those bound in [MS.] Wood E. 13-17). Tp, AW wrote cat. no. '39', in red chalk, over former no. '38', and 'Given to me by Mʳ A. Allam 26. May 1685'. LT 3.167. From p. 3, AW marked a few entries with horizontal or vertical lines, mainly in pencil. These are more frequent in the 'English' section, from p. 31, where there are also 2 brief notes and several 'q[uaere]' letters. After p. 24, he renumbered pp. consecutively, 25 to 50.
[MS.] Wood E. 18(1). Wing H1182.

1519. Hobbes, Thomas. *A catalogue of the works of mr. Hobbes.* [London]: f. W. Crooke, [1675]. S.sh. (r-v).
Former no. '9'; ᵛ, AW wrote at end, '1675', and changed the date at entry of *Epistol. ad D. Wood* from 1675 to 167'4' (copies of this letter are at Wood 276a(18) and Wood 423(47), item 3616f.).
[MS.] Wood D. 22(11). Wing H2216 (rare).

1520. Howard, Henry, and George Ent. P., W., ed. *Bibliotheca Norfolciana: sive catalogus libb. manuscriptorum & impressorum . . . quos . . . Henricus dux Norfolciae, &c. Regiae Societati Londinensi . . . donavit.* Londini: Excud. R. Chiswel, 1681. 4°. Pp. [6], 175.
Tp, AW wrote cat. no. '16', in red chalk. Flyleaf, upper, AW wrote '1681', and on the tp, no. '16'. From p. 20, a very few items are marked with horizontal or vertical lines, in pencil; after pp. 154-174, including books of George Ent, more frequent marks, 3 cross-references (158, 'v[ide] prox. p'), and, at 165, at 'Ant. Woods Notitia Academ. Oxonien.', AW wrote, 'per Will. Fulman' (AW's owned 2 copies, Wood 513(3) and Wood 614(1), items 3110f.).
[MS.] Wood E. 15(4) ([MS.] Wood E. 15(16) in Bodl. CD cat.). Wing N1230.

1521. Humfrey, John. *Catalogus librorum bibliothecae Joannis Humphry. . . . Horum auctio habebitur . . . By William Cooper [4 Dec.].* London: distributed gratis, Jonathan's Coffee-House, et al., 1682. 4°. Pp. [2], 61.
Tp, AW wrote cat. no. '23', in red chalk, and '6ᵈ'. From p. 1, AW marked a few entries with underscoring or vertical or horizontal lines, mainly in pencil; in the 'English' section, from p. 25, frequent marks, 'q[uaere]' letters, and a few notes, mainly cross references, 'v. supra', 'v. infra'.
[MS.] Wood E. 16(5). Wing H3674.

1522. [Hyde, Edward, d.d., and John Ley]. *[Heading], The reverend author hath likewise published.* N.p.: n.pub., [1656]. S.sh. 4°.
ᵛ, Former no., '9'; 'Ex dono Rev[eren]di Mʳⁱ. Ley pastoris eccliae Xh Solyhul.', not in AW's hand; 2nd note, lined out. ʳ, AW wrote, 'Joh. Ley Rector of Solhull'; marked with vertical lines 11 of the 12 items; at 'A Monitor of Mortality, in two Funerall Sermons', wrote in margin, 'v. cat. N. p. 281.'; and below, wrote 'An. 1656'. AO 3.569ff. AW took this bibliog. from Hyde and Ley, [MS.] Wood B. 37(3), item 3745, and inserted it among his catalogues.
[MS.] Wood D. 22(2). Wing L1873 (part of).

1523. Hyde, Thomas, ed. *Catalogus impressorum librorum bibliothecae Bodleianae in academia Ox-*

oniensi [and, added on backing] Ms. catalogue of printed books in the Ashmolean Library. Oxford: e theatro Sheldoniano, 1674. Fol. 2 vols. Vol. 1, pp. [1-2] (Praefatio), 478 (p. 478 incorrectly numbered 480), with some late Ashmole 900-1030 ms. catalogue entries on blank leaves; vol. 2.**2-3, 272. Both vols. were interleaved with blank sheets and bound after receipt by the Ashmolean Museum. Pasteboard, half-calf.

Edward Lhwyd, Keeper of the Ashm. museum (1690-1709), chose AW's copy to serve as the main catalogue of printed books of the Ashmolean Museum. Items that were duplicated in the Bodleian Library were given Bodl. shelf-marks along with Ashm. shelf-marks (most beginning with W, for Wood, or A, for Ashmole, or L, for Lister). Items that were not duplicated in the Bodleian were entered by Ashm. librarians on interleaved blank sheets opposite the relevant page of Bodl. entries. In the printed text, they added some cross-references and some correct Bodl. shelf-marks. There are '+' signs, some editorial proofing marks, brief corrections, and short horizontal lines in margins made by unidentifiable persons (perhaps some by AW). At times a librarian added an Ashm. shelf-mark which was added again on the blank leaf inserted opposite. This was a proof copy. It was in an unbound state when in AW's possession, as a note to the binder implies, vol. 1, lower 1st flyleaf[v], in pencil, in a later hand, 'end of vol. I'. Text, passim, some comments in AW's hand, mainly in margins. These are usually easy to identify though many in his hand were cropped in rebinding (some non-Wood notes in margin are also cropped). See, e.g, vol. 1: 40 (cropped book entry and Bodl. shelf-mark), 57 ('Babington' in margin), 59 (a Bodl. shelf-mark and brief note, cropped, and 'qu[aere]'), 66 (a date, p. no., and a brief note), 78 (author, cropped, and Bodl. shelf-mark), 92-4 (correction at John Blagrave; notes at entry of Ed. Blount; at G. Boate), 99 ('Arn. Boat' in margin), 182, 196 (col. 1, bottom), 269 (right margin), 309 (at entry of Grynaeus, an addition and 'med et math'), 323 ('Tho. Har-' entry, only), 351 (cols. 1), 352 (col. 1 margins, only), 393 (in right margin, only) 450 (a note in left margin, cropped), 453 (a Bodl. shelf-mark), 476 (at Musculus, a note, cropped, but 'matric Broadgates' is visible (AO 1.367, 2.392). AW also wrote, passim, frequent 'q' or 'qu' letters (usually quaere; at times, quarto): 25, 70, 72, 76, 80, 166, 168, 173.

Vol. 2 a faint note in pencil, not by AW, on a blank leaf after p. **3, 'both library Dupl'. Notes in vol. 2 by AW are: 1, 3, 5-6 (margins, only), 68, 85 (at Pynson. 'printer – not the author the printer qu[aere]', 90, 95, 98 (in left margin, only), 152 (at Scultetus, Sermon on Psal., 'This sermon was translated from High Dutch into English by Jam. Meddus D. D. on[e] in 8° F. 54. Th. it appeares', 159, 213; he also wrote in this vol. frequent 'q' or 'qu' letters (usually quaere; at times, quarto): 1, 4, 47, 85, 90 95. AW's comments generally are corrections, Bodl. shelf-marks, or points of information about authors, or of dates, or translators. Ovenell has listed four librarians at the Ashm. whose handwriting, besides that of AW, he found in these volumes: Edward Lhwyd (1660-1709), John Whiteside (Keeper from 14 Dec. 1714 to his death in 1729), Robert (Robin) Thomas (sublibrarian of the Museum, an undergrad. of Jesus College, the predominant hand; he made entries while Lhwyd was on his grand tour, May 1697-March 1701, from May 1697 and in 1698), and David Parry (Assistant to Llwyd; he worked on a different cat., of 1692-3, along with Lhwyd and William Jones, and was Keeper, 1709-14). Also possibly present are notes by William Williams (underkeeper, who gave some support to Thomas and left in 1698). See Hunt, *BLR*, 4 (1952): 163-4; R. F. Ovenell, 'Supplementary Notes on Ashmolean Catalogues', *BLR*, 14(1991): 97-9.
Library Records b. 466, 467. Wing O864.

1524. Index Librorum Prohibitorum. *Index librorum prohibitorum cum regulis confectis per patres à Tridentina synodo delectos. . . . Nunc demum . . . Clementis papae VIII. jussu recognitus, & publicatus.* Venetiis: ap. M. de Claseris, 1597. 8°. Pp. 93. Pasteboard (blue) with parchment spine. 1st upper and last lower flyleaves, marbled paper.
Flyleaf, upper, 3rd[v], AW wrote the titles of 9 printed works in this vol. (really 10; AW missed no. 4a), within guidelines made with red chalk.
Wood 896(1). Not in BL.

1525. Index Librorum Prohibitorum. *Index expurgatorius librorum qui hoc saeculo prodierunt, . . . Philippi II. . . . jussu . . . atq; Albani ducis consilio . . . in Belgia concinnatus; anno MDLXXI.* [Strassburg]: L. Zetzneri, 1599. 12°. Pp. [76], 363. Parchment.
Cover, upper, has a slip attached, on which AW wrote 'Catalogus of Books & Books Prohibited'; slip[v], remnants of notes by AW. Tp, bsm. Flyleaf, lower[r-v], an index, not by AW.)(4[v]-)(12, a few marks in margin, not by AW.
Wood 765. BL.

1526. Jacombe, Thomas. *Bibliotheca Jacombiana, sive catalogus . . . librorum . . . Thomae Jacomb, . . . Quorum auctio habebitur . . . per Edoardum Millingtonum [31 Oct.].* [London]: distributed at 6 d., Nott, Fox, et al, 1687. 4°. Pp. [4], 108.
Tp, AW wrote cat. no. '63' and '6[d]', in pencil. From p. 2, AW marked a few entries with horizontal or

vertical lines, mainly in pencil.
[MS.] Wood E. 20(7). Wing J113.

1527. [Jaggard, William]. *A catalogue of such English bookes, as lately have bene, and now are in printing for publication [9 Oct. to Easter term]*. London: W. Jaggard, 1618. 4°. A⁴,B². Pasteboard (blue) with parchment spine; rebacked.
Flyleaf, upper, 3rd, AW wrote the titles of 18 printed works in this vol., within guidelines made with red ink. Passim, AW numbered the pp. 1-11, marked numerous entries with vertical and horizontal lines, mainly in pencil, and added some 10 brief notes, mainly cross references, with 1 'qu[aere]' entry and 1 correction.
[MS.] Wood D. 22(1). STC 14341 (rare).

1528. James, Thomas. *Ecloga Oxonio-Cantabrigiensis, tributa in libros duos [followed by] Liber secundus, in quo continetur librorum manuscriptorum dispositio secundum quatuor facultates*. London: (A. Hatfield,) imp. G. Bishop & J. Norton, 1600. 4°. Pp. [4] 144, [4], 132 (2 tpp). Parchment.
Pastedown, upper, AW wrote, 'Ant à Woode [altered from Anth Woode] Coll. Merton.' (LT 1.22-3). Flyleaf, upper, 'A.W '60' and 'Antonij à Wood. 1671.' Passim, especially in early section, marks in margin and notes in more than one hand. For notes and marks by AW, see p. 11, on a loose slip, 'R 767 divers books in this Library [Merton] omitted see there. in ecloga p. 11'; 36, note in pencil, illeg.; 39, mark in margin, in red ink; 47, correction, in red ink; 52, 'where are the manuscripts in S. Johns coll. library.'; 99, 'ex dono Rob. Grosetest.' Dupl. at Wood 513(7) which has pp. 1-52 only.
[MS.] Wood C. 28. STC 14453.

1529. James, Thomas. *Ecloga Oxonio-Cantabrigiensis, tributa in libros duos*. London: (A. Hatfield,) imp. G. Bishop & J. Norton, 1600. 4°. Pp. [4], 52 (Oxford cat. only).
Tp, AW wrote, 'That part relating to Camb. is not here.' and below, 'R. Sh.' (possibly Ralph Sheldon?). Pp. 35-7, marks in margin at mss. at Magdalen Library, may not be by AW. Dupl. at [MS.] Wood C. 28 (a complete copy).
Wood 513(7). STC 14453. Madan 195.

1530. James, Thomas. *Index generalis sanctorum patrum, ad singulos versus capitis quinti secundum Matthaeum*. Londini: in off. J. Haviland, sumpt. P. Stephens, 1624. 8°. A-D⁸,E⁴ (last leaf blank).
Wood 899(2). STC 14458.

1531. James, Thomas. *Index generalis librorum prohibitorum à pontificiis*. Oxoniae: G. Turner, 1627. 12°. *,A-L¹² (1st a. last leaves blank). Parchment over pasteboard (Ashm. binding?).
Flyleaves, upper, the titles of 7 printed works (really 8) in this vol., made by the Keeper J. Whiteside. Tp, AW wrote '10ᵈ'. This vol. is made up of bibliographical items which may have been in a bundle together when sent to the Ashm. Museum.
Wood 899(1). STC 14457. Madan 589.

1532. James, Thomas. [Verneuil, John, ed.] *Catalogus interpretum s. scripturae, juxta numerorum ordinem, quo extant in bibliotheca Bodleiana*. Oxoniae: J. Lichfield, 1635. 4° (ed. correcta). Pp. 55. Parchment over pasteboard.
Pastedown, upper, note, not by AW. Flyleaf, upper, 'Johannes Lee. 1645'. Tp, AW wrote, 'per Jo. Vernuill - q[uaere]' (i.e., Verneuil). Text, pp. 5 to p. 43, some shelf-marks, apparently to a college library (e.g., F. 1. 2; H. 3. 6) and a few entries added, not by AW. LT 1. 313.
[MS.] Wood C. 30. STC 14448. Madan 799.

1533. Jansson van Waesberge, Joannes. *Catalogi cujuscunque facultatis & linguae librorum, in Germanica, Gallia, Anglia, Belgio, &c. [Jan. to July]*. Amstelaedami: ap. Janssonio-Waesbergios, 1677. 4°. Pp. [2], 36.
Tp, bsms.
[MS.] Wood C. 26(12). Not in BL.

1534. Jansson van Waesberge, Joannes. *Catalogi cujuscunque facultatis & linguae librorum, in Germanica, Gallia, Anglia, Belgio, &c. [July 1677 to Jan.]*. Amstelaedami: ap. Janssonio-Waesbergios, 1678. 4°. Pp. [2], 27.
Tp, bsms.
[MS.] Wood C. 26(13). Not in BL.

1535. [Johnston, Nathaniel]. *The auction: or, a catalogue of some useful books, lately published*. [London]: f. R. Hardy, [1693]. 4°. Pp. 8.
Pp. 1, AW wrote, 'published about the latter end of March 1693[4]'; 3, identified printed Rev. 'Count

Palatine' as 'Nath. Crew, Bishop of Durham'; 7, identification. P. 8, 3 figures totalling 31 - 04 - 10 (prob. not be by AW), and 'Nath. Johnston M. D. the author' (prob. by AW). LT 3.447-8.
[MS.] Wood C. 26(19). Wing J873.

1536. Kidner, Thomas. *Catalogus . . . librorum . . . T. Kidner . . . quorum auctio habebitur per Guilielmum Cooper [6 Feb.].* [London]: gratis distribuentur, 1676/7. 4°. Pp. [6], 36.
Flyleaf, upper, AW wrote 'ex dono D^{ris} Thomae Marshall Coll. Linc. Oxon Rectoris, 23 Jan. 1676[7]' (LT 2.350); 'cat 1. alias secund', in pencil (cropped). Tp, AW wrote cat. no. '2', in red chalk. Pp. [5], AW wrote the year of publ., and 8-35, there are marked items in pencil or ink; after p. 19 among books 'in English', more marked items and 3 brief notes (cropped).
[MS.] Wood E. 13(2). Wing K422.

1537. La Croze, Jean Cornand de. *The works of the learned, or, an historical account and impartial judgment of books newly printed, . . . by J. de la Crose [Aug. 1691-Apr. 1692].* London: f. T. Bennet, 1691-92. 4°. 8 issues, numbered consecutively. Pp. [8], 398, [12] (and at end of several issues, advertisements of books printed f. Bennet). Pasteboard (blue) with parchment spine. 1st upper and last lower flyleaves, marbled paper.
Flyleaf, upper, 2nd, AW wrote the titles of 2 serials in this vol., within guidelines made with red ink, 'The works of the learned &c for the months of Aug. Sept. Oct. Nov. Dec. Jan. Feb. Mar. 1691. for Apr. - By Joh. de la Crose - [/] Mercurius Eruditorum &c following the month of Aug. 1691.' He inserted the 2nd into the 1st (i.e., item 1561 into this) because both contain statements about the forthcoming AO.
1st item, pp. 4-6 (Aug. 1691, quire B2-3, follows leaf B5), a review of AO: 'This Book will be of great use to all persons of any Literature, but particulaly to such as apply themselves to History or Politiques, whom it concerns every moment to know what kind of men were the Authors of those Books they read. Neither is that knowledge unnecessary to all that study; for as the writings of Authors may be said to be the Picture of their mind, so to know their Life, Religion, and most Remarkable Actions, must needs be a great help towards judging rightly their Sentiments [/] Mr. *Wood*, the Author of this History is the same that gave us, some years ago, the Antiquities of the University of *Oxford*. He seems to write impartially, and to relate whatever he knows, whether good or bad, of those whose Life he writes. The *Roman Catholicks* are not worse used by him than the Protestants of the Church of *England*; and if he seem to have less spar'd any Party, it must needs be the Dissenters. . . . [and pp. 5-6, last 2 paragraphs:] To prevent these Objections [of his favouring the Roman Catholics and of his dealing unfairly with the Dissenters], the Author observes in his Preface, that his exactness, as to what concerns the *Roman Catholicks*, proceeds only from the great number of Memoirs, which those of that Party have taken care to impart to him. It may be added, that he could not engage himself in Controversies, without deviating from his end, and laying down the Character of an Historian; that nevertheless it is plain, by his Book, that the greatest Champions of the Roman Church, at the beginning of the Reformation, as (g [marginal note to pp. '123, 304, 164, 155, 110' in this new ed. of AO]) *Bonner, Parsons, Campian, Henry Cole, Richard Smith, &c.* were no better than Hypocrites, Protestants under King *Edward* VI. and Papists under Queen *Mary*; and that those that forsook the Reformation did it by principles of Jealousie and Interest; the Author may also very well vindicate himself, by putting them in Mind of his refuting the Errours of *John (h* [marginal note to p. 345]) *Pitts* in his Ecclesiastical History of *England*; and observing a remarkable Circumstance, to wit, that Cardinal (*i* marginal note to p. 126]) *Allin* [sic] had made a Book to invite the *English* to take Arms as soon as the *Spaniards* had landed in *England*. But their invincible *Armada* being beaten, the Papists used all their endeavours to suppress it. [/] The First and Second Part of this Volume contains the Life of the Writers and Prelates, who had their Education in the University of *Oxford*, from the year 1500. to 1640, 'tis of a large extent, and treats of their Birth and Death, the Titles and Editions of their Works; and their most remarkable Actions. The Third contains the Annals of the University, a Catalogue of its Officers, of the Prelates, Monks, Martyrs, and Writers, who studied there, and the Lives of all other remarkable Persons, though not Writers, who were Members of the said University.'
P. 276 (Jan. 1692), printed advertisement for vol. 2 of AO, 'Vol. the second, Compleating that Work, is almost Finished; but by reason of the Length of the Book beyond the Proposals, and some unexpected Delays, it cannot be Published before *Easter Term* next, . . . The Subscribers will have a particular Benefit by the time taken for Printing this Volume longer than mentioned in the Proposals, by the Addition of several Lives, which otherwise must have been Omitted.'
P. 397 (March-Apr. 1692), a second notice: 'The Second Volume of the *Athenae Oxonienses*, is all Printed except *Three* or *Four* Sheets, and will be Published within *Three* Weeks, or a Month at Farthest: Tis the *First* Work of this Nature that was ever attempted in *English*, and not only Contains the Lives of those Persons who were Educated at *Oxford*, but of all the Considerable Men this Island has produced, since the Year 1480, tho they received their Education elsewhere. It gives an exact Account of their Works, &c. but

we may supersede any further Commendation of so useful a Work, when we tell the World, it was writ by that Celebrated Antiquary, the indefatigable Mr. *Wood*, who seems to have made a generous search after Truth, his particular Study; and deserves the thanks of all the Learned World, for preserving the Memory of so many Authors from Oblivion.' In the margin, AW wrote, 'This was put in by the hand of Tho. Broune the poet - as M^r – [sic, i.e., Edward] Hannes of Ch. Ch. told me' (this favourable notice by Brown (olim Ch. Ch.) was, no doubt, the much feared 'satyrical thing against me, my bile', that prompted AW to write his publisher, Thomas Bennet, on 28 March (see LT 3.385, James Bisse and Christopher Codrington were the conveyers of the false rumours of an unfavourable review by 'Thomas Browne the poet' to which AW later added, 'lies'; see also LT 3.420-1, a poem by the well-known satyrist Browne). P. 112. vertical line in margin, at title by Tim. Nurse.
[MS.] Wood E. 24a. N & S 189.2-9 (Aug. Sept. Oct. Nov. Dec. Jan. Feb. March-April).

1538. Langbaine, Gerard. Cox, Nicholas, ed. Kirkman, Franc., possible author. *An exact catalogue of all the comedies . . . that were ever yet printed*. Oxon: L. Lichfield f. N. Cox, 1680. 4°. Pp. [4], a blank leaf, 16.
Tp^v, AW wrote, 'Note that at the end of <u>Nicomede</u>, a Tragy=comedy so called, translated out of French into English by John Dancer (printed at London 1671) [[MS.] Wood E. 28(3), item 1484] is a Catalogue of all Comedies Tragedies &c that were ever printed or published, to the yeare 1671 = From which Cat. did Nich. Cox manciple of St Edmunds hall in Oxon, take this following Catalogue, adding thereunto all such that came out to this present yeare 1680 [/] The said Catalogue at the end of Nicomede was made by Franc. Kirkman stationer living in Thames=street, London. [/] M^r { Kirkman Cox { several of our Oxford scholars have read your Catalogues of playes (one at the end of Nicomede, & the other which is this by its self) and like them well, but would have lik'd them better had you set downe the yeare when they were printed, that they might have knowne when the Authors lived, and when the playes came first in use. For without time they cannot be exact judges of matters. But they hope for the future that you will not omitt those matters, and that [or, what (smudged)] are not yet extant [/ on following inserted leaf:] 1 Tragedy of Herod and Antipater - Lond 1622. qu[arto]. by Gervase Markham and Will Sampson. [/] 2 The Maske of Flowres - Lond. 1614. qu[arto] A play acted by the Gentlemen of Greys inne [/] 3 Paria Comedia - Lond. 1648 - by Thomas Vincent [/] 4 A Projector Lately dead pr. 1634 made against Will Noy lately Attorney Gen [/] 5 Tho Randolps [sic] Playes - qu[arto]. [/] 6 Joh. Skeltons Playes & Interludes'. See Plate VII. The catalogues list only author, title and genre and AW's advice, if it ever reached Cox, Kirkman, or Langbaine, was ignored, see their (Cox, Langbaine) next printed catalogue, in 1687, [MS.] Wood E. 28(5), item 1540). Pp. 3-14 vertical or horizontal lines in margins and underscoring, mainly in red ink; 13 additions or corrections. Dupl. (a fragment with some similar notes, and an earlier draft of the 'letter') at [MS.] Wood C. 26(20). LT 1.20.
[MS.] Wood E. 28(4). Wing L373A. Madan 3276.

1539. Langbaine, Gerard. Cox, Nicholas, ed. Kirkman, Franc., possible author. *An exact catalogue of all the comedies . . . that were ever yet printed*. Oxon: L. Lichfield f. N. Cox, 1680. 4°. Pp. [4], 1 and 2, 15, [1] (wanting pp. 3-14).
Pp. [1], AW wrote, 'Joh. Skelton hath not one title of a play in this booke'; [2], 'Note that at the end of Nocomede [sic], a Tragi-comedy so called, translated out of Fr. into Engl. by Joh. Dancer (printed at Lond. 1671) [AW's copy is at Wood E. 28(3), item 1484] is a catalogue of all Comedies, Tragedies &c. that were ever printed or published, to the yeare 1671 = From which cat. did Nich. Cox manciple of Edmund hall Oxon. take this following, adding therunto all such that came out to this present yeare 1680 [/] The said cat. at the end of Nicomede was made by Franc. Kirkman stationer living in Thames [S]treet, Lond.'; tp^v (i.e., p. [4]) –'M^r { [Kirkman was cropped at top] Cox [/] Severall of our Oxford scholars have read your Catalogues of playes, (one at the end of Nicomede, & the other which is this by it self) & like them well, but would have lik'd them better had you set downe the y^r, with the Edition, when they were printed, that they might have knowne when the authors liv'd, & when the playes were first used. For without time, they cannot be good judges of matters. But wee hope for the future you will not omit these matters, & other playes that are not yet set downe, as [/] 1. Tragedy of Herode & Antipater by Gerv. Markham & Will. Sampson - Lond. 1622. 4°. [/] 2. The maske of Flowers, a play by the Gentlem. of Greys inne Lond. 1614. 4°. [/] 3. Paria, Comoedia – per Tho. Vincent - Lond. 1648 [/, and added later:] 5. A projector lately dead – 1634 - against Noy lately Attorney Generall [/] 6. Thomas Randophes [sic] playes.'; 1-4, a few marks in margins, in red ink, and 2 additions: at the anonymous 'Bastard', AW wrote the name of the author, 'Th. Goffe' (AO 2.464, by Cosimo Manuche); and at '*James Shirley*, Young Admiral', AW added, 'or Example' (another play by Shirley, 1637). Dupl. (a complete copy with long notes similar to those on pp. [2] and [4], including a revised copy of the 'letter') is at [MS.] Wood E. 28(4).
[MS.] Wood C. 26(20). Wing L373A. Madan 3276.

1540. Langbaine, Gerard (younger). *A new catalogue of English plays.* London: f. N. Cox, sold by him in Oxford, 1688. 4°. Pp. [18], 32, [8].
Flyleaf, upper[v], AW wrote, 'The first edition of this book following bore this title. [/] Momus Triumphans: or, the Plagiaries of the English Stage expressed in a Catalogue of Comedies, Tragedies &c. - By Gerard Langbaine Esq. - Lond. 1688. qu[arto] published in Nov. 1687. [/] Which Title with the Book it selfe being published contrarie to the mind of the Author (as in the following Advertisement it appeares) and 500 of them sold, he forthwith caused the title following as also the Advertisement to be printed & set before the remaining part of the copies -'. For an earlier version of this note, see slip inserted in Wood 526(1), item 2028. Tp, AW wrote, '1[6]' (? over an earlier note), in pencil, and 'published in the beginning of Dec. 1687'. AW numbered pp. of preface, 1-15; A1[v]-A4[v], a cross reference and a few marks in text or margins (A4[v], correction, not by AW). Pp. 1, 2-3, 5-6, 10-12, 14-25, 27, minor annotation, mainly underscoring of authors' names in ink or red ink; 1, 18, 27, minor notes. This catalogue lists the author, title, and genre, and sometimes the format and the source. The author[s], if they received AW's advice, as written in [MS.] Wood E. 28(4) (and in [MS.] Wood C. 26(20)), to list the year in which the play was printed and performed, did not follow it. LT 1.20.
[MS.] Wood E. 28(5). Wing L377B.

1541. Lawson, George, et al. *Catalogus librorum . . . Georgii Lawsoni [and George Fawler, Owen Stockdon, Thomas Brooks]. Quorum auctio habebitur . . . per Edoardum Millingtonum [30 May].* [London]: distributed gratis, E. Millington et al., 1681. 4°. Pp. [4], 32, 64.
Tp, AW wrote cat. no. '14', over an earlier '13' (from here on, in the [MS.] E. 15-20 series of 68 catalogues, those from 14-56 were renumbered to account for the insertion of a 2nd no. 13). From p. 2, AW marked a few items with horizontal or vertical lines, in pencil or ink; and among books in English, after 2nd p. 1, made more frequent marks, wrote a number of brief notes, mainly cross references, in margins, and numbered pp. consecutively from 33 to 96.
[MS.] Wood E. 15(2). Wing M705 (Wing, 31 May).

1542. Lee, Richard. *A catalogue of the library of . . . Richard Lee . . . which will be exposed (to sale [28 Apr.].* [London?]: distributed gratis, Coffee-Houses in St. Albans, et al., 1685. 4°. Pp. [4], 28.
Tp, AW wrote cat. no. '40', in red chalk, over former no. '39', and 'Given to me by M[r] A. Allam 26. May 1685'. LT 3.167. From p. 2, which includes a short note, AW marked a few entries with horizontal or vertical lines, mainly in pencil and 1 underscoring. These are more frequent in the 'English' books, from p. 6, where there are also a few notes, mainly cross references and 1 'q[uaere]' letter.
[MS.] Wood E. 18(2). Wing L886 (two).

1543. Lloyd, John, and Thomas Raymond. *Bibliotheca Lloydiana, sive catalogus . . . bibliothecae . . . Joan. Lloydii [et] Thomae Raymondi . . . Quorum auctio habebitur . . . per Edvardum Millingtonum [3 Dec.].* [London]: given gratis, Nott, et al., 1683. 4°. Pp. [4], 28, 24, 32, 12.
Tp, AW wrote cat. no. '29', in red chalk, and, 'Given to me by Hen. Cruttenden 10 Nov. 1683' and 'Few or no Christian names of authors in this cat.' LT 3.470. From p. 2, AW marked some entries with horizontal or vertical lines, mainly in pencil; in the 'English' section, from 2nd p. 1, a few more marks, 'q[uaere]' letters, and a few notes. 4th p. 1, he wrote, 'This is an appendix to the cat. of Joh. Lloyd & S[r] Tho. Raymond', and former no., '33' (at one time this leaf was misplaced). After p. 28, he renumbered pp. consecutively, 29 to 105.
[MS.] Wood E. 17(3). Wing L2654.

1544. Lloyd, Nicholas. *Catalogus librorum . . . Nicolai Lloydii, . . . Horum auctio habebitur, . . . in aedibus Joannis Dunmore [4 July].* [London]: distributed gratis, Dunmore, 1681. 4°. Pp. [4], 55.
Tp, AW wrote cat. no. '15' and '1[s]. 6[d]'. From p. 3, and more among books in English, after p. 24, AW marked some items with underscoring or vertical and horizontal lines, in pencil or ink, with 'q[uaere]' letters, and added a few brief notes, mainly identifications of authors. LT 2.501.
[MS.] Wood E. 15(3). Wing L2664.

1545. London, William. *A catalogue of the most vendible books in England, . . . divinity, history.* London: n.pub., 1658. 4°. A-2H[4],2I[2] (last leaf blank).
Tp, AW wrote a former no, '3', and 'Is it not a simple thing for a man to make a cat. of books, & not to set doune the Christian names of the authors? For there be severall authors that have the same S[r] names-'. C2[v], hand marker at information on dates of printing. From K1 to end, AW wrote in p. nos. 1-175; he examined this more than once, making some sort of annotation on almost every p., e.g., marks in margins, corrections, cross references (e.g., N1, 'vide prox. p'), 'q[uaere]' letters, or giving further information, such as cities of publication, Christian names or colleges which authors were associated with, in pencil, red and

dark ink. LT 1.266.
[MS.] Wood D. 22(6). Wing L2850.

1546. Lye, Thomas, and T. Jennings. *Catalogus . . . librorum . . . Tho. Lye . . . cui accessit bibliotheca . . . T. Jennings . . . quorum auctio habebitur [17 Nov.].* [London]: given, W. Miller, et al., 1684. 4°. Pp. [4], 28, 48.
Tp, AW wrote cat. no. '36', in red chalk; 'This cat. was published in the latter end of Oct. 1684.'; and '6ᵈ'. P. 12, and in the 'English' section, from 2nd p. 1, AW marked a few entries with horizontal or vertical lines, mainly in pencil; wrote 2 brief notes; 1 'q[uaere]' letter; and p. 38, underscored 8 of 9 entries after J. Owen. After p. 28, he renumbered pp. consecutively, 29 to 76.
[MS.] Wood E. 17(10). Wing L3529 (two).

1547. [Maitland, John]. Lauderdale, duke of. *Bibliotheca selectissima, diversorum librorum, . . . Quorum auctio habebitur . . . Per Edvardum Millingtonum [18 Apr.].* [London]: given, Nott, Hensman, et al., 1687. 4°. Pp. [4], 38, 49.
Tp, AW wrote cat. no. '56', in pencil, and former no., '55'. From p. 4, AW marked a few entries with horizontal or vertical lines, mainly in pencil. P. 38, at a Laud fol., AW wrote 'W. Laud ms'; 2nd p. 20, a 'q[uaere]' letter; and 26, a cross reference. AW numbered consecutively after p. 38 to the end, 39-87.
[MS.] Wood E. 19(6). Wing L606.

1548. Maitland, John. Lauderdale, duke of. *Bibliotheque de feu monseigneur le duc de Lauderdale . . . Les dits livres seront vendus à l'enchére . . . à Sams coffee-house [14 May].* [London]: distributed gratis, Holford, Patridge, et al., 1690. 4°. Pp. [2], 28.
Tp, AW wrote, 'Ex dono Hen. Cruttenden 14. May 1690'. AW's 'Catalogue 7'. LT 3.26, 470. P. 9, line in margin, prob. not by AW.
[MS.] Wood E. 22(7). Wing L607.

1549. Maitland, John. Lauderdale, duke of. *The English part of the library of the late duke of Lauderdale, . . . Which will be sold by auction at Sams Coffee-house [27 May].* [London]: distributed gratis, Partridge, Hensman, et al., [1690]. 4°. Pp. [2], 16.
AW's 'Catalogue 8'. LT 3.26.
[MS.] Wood E. 22(8). Wing L611.

1550. Maitland, Richard. Lauderdale, duke of. *Catalogus librorum . . . bibliothecae nobilis cujusdam Scoto-Britanni:. . . quibus adjicitur figurarum manu-delineatarum, . . . Quorum auctio habenda est . . . per Benj. Walford [30 Oct.].* [London]: distributed, Nott a. Holford, Willis, et al., [1688]. 4°. Pp. [4], 156.
Pasteboard (blue) with parchment spine; edges uncut.
Although the 13 individual auction catalogues in this vol. follow a chronological order, AW did not number them in this vol. There is no table of contents. AW marked entries in only 1 cat. in this vol., [MS.] Wood E. 22(9)). 1st item, tp, AW wrote, 'Ric Lauder quondam Coll S. John', in pencil. AOF 2.321.
[MS.] Wood E. 22(1). Wing L615.

1551. Maitland, Richard. Lauderdale, duke of. *Catalogus librorum . . . quibus adjicitur . . . nec non tabularum aere . . . Maitland, . . . collectio secunda. Quorum auctio habebitur per Benj. Walford [28 Oct.].* [London]: distributed, Holford, Willis, et al., [1689]. 4°. Pp. [4], 128, 4.
[MS.] Wood E. 22(6). Wing L617.

1552. Manton, Thomas. *Catalogus . . . librorum . . . Thomae Manton, s.t.d. Quorum auctio habebitur . . . per Guilielmum Cooper [25 Mar.].* [London]: gratis distribuentur, 1678. 4°. Pp. [6], 70 (really 73).
Flyleaf, upper, 'Dʳ L[amphire]', and 'For Hart Hall, from the Bookseller.' (LT 3.262); AW wrote, 'Cat. Tho. M[anton] 1678' (cropped), and 'No Christian names to the authours in this cat. & therefore for my use not worth a straw'. Tp, AW wrote cat. no. '3', in red chalk. AW marked items from p. 2, and more towards the end, among books 'in English' with horizontal or vertical lines, in pencil or ink, wrote 'q[uaere]' letters, some brief notes in margins (many are cropped), and corrected p. nos. from 17-70 to 20-73.
[MS.] Wood E. 13(3). Wing M519.

1553. Massauve. *Bibliotheca Massoviana: sive catalogus . . . librorum . . . quos . . . sibi procuravit . . . Massovius, . . . Quorum auctio habebitur . . . Per Edvardum Millingtonum [1 Feb. 1688].* [London]: distributed gratis, Bentley, Mortlock, et al., 1687[8]. 4°. Pp. [4], 64.
Tp, AW wrote cat. no. '67', in pencil, and 'Cat. of manuscripts at the end'. From p. 3, AW marked a few entries with horizontal lines, mainly in pencil; 45, corrected 1 p. no.; and 49, wrote 1 'q[uaere]' letter.
[MS.] Wood E. 20(11). Wing M1029.

1554. Massinger, Philip; Thomas Middleton, and William Rowley. *[The excellent comedy, called the old law: or a new way to please you] 'An exact and perfect catalogue of all the plaies that were ever printed'*. [London]: [f. E. Archer], [1656]. 4°. a-b⁴ only.
Flyleaf, upperᵛ, AW wrote, 'This catalogue of playes following, was taken from the end of a comedy called <u>The Old Law</u> - printed at Lond 1656' (the play itself is at Wood 607(5), item 4403); a1, he wrote '1656'. In the cat. he marked a number of entries with pencil, mainly, or ink and wrote 3 brief notes: a3, at 'Extravagant shepherd [by] *Thomas Goffe*', line in margin and 'q[uaere]', in pencil; a4, at 'Humor out of breath [by] *John Doy*', corrected to 'Day', in ink; and b3, at 'Spanish Tragedie [by] Tho. Kyte', added '-q[uaere] [in pencil, and in ink:] Th. Kyte -'. LT 1.20.
[MS.] Wood E. 28(2). Wing M1048.

1555. Matthews; Vanam, and Crow. *A catalogue of the libraries of books of mr. Matthews, mr. Vanam, mr. Crow . . . exposed to sale by auction . . . by Edward Millington [28 Jan. 1689]*. [London]: given, W. Miller, 1688/9. 4°. Pp. [4], 23.
[MS.] Wood E. 22(4a). Wing M1323.

1556. Maunsell, Andrew. *The first part of the catalogue of English printed bookes: which concerneth such matters of divinitie*. London: J. Windet f. A. Maunsell, 1595. Fol. in 6's. Pp. [8], 123. Parchment over pasteboard. Chain holes.
Flyleaf, upper, mutilated (apparently a price on the ᵛ, 1s 1ᵈ (?) and perhaps a name were cut out, blottings remain on tp, opposite); also on ᵛ, AW wrote, 'All English books printed beyond sea, written by R. Catholicks are here omitted.'; a shelf-mark, BS [/] 247. Tp, signature, 'John Williames his Booke'. In this book which lists works by subject AW made some sort of annotation on pp., 1-13, 18, 21-123. These include short vertical lines in margin, 'q[uaere]' letters, corrections, repeating a date or name of an author in the margin, and underscoring of names in red and brown inks and in pencil; he sometimes expanded abbreviations in margins, e.g., p. 1 at printed 'T. C.': 'Thom Cooper'; wrote in margins cities with which authors were associated as, p. 3, at 'Rod, Gualter': 'Oxōn'; wrote in places and dates of publication; identified persons referred to, e.g., pp. 10, at 'Tho. Mathew': 'Tho. Mathews alias W. Tyndle', and 66, at 'a learned man': 'Th. Hardyng'; and added cross-references to this work, e.g., p. 106, 'v. p. 109. a', or to other sources, p. 105, 'Lond. 1594 qu[arto] v. cat. 1. ms. p. 148'. There are a few notes on authors, e.g. after Henry Smith, p. 105: 'His sermons were gathered into one vol. Lond. 1594 qu[arto] containing 35 sermons or more. vid. Cat. 1. ins. p. 301 – six more, Lond 1594. qu[arto]'. On an unbound loose leaf AW made an index of some 110 authors with page and column references (a or b) to printed entries in both part 1 and the '2ᵈ part' (see Wood 654c(2)), beginning with ʳ 'Achelly Tho. 86.a' (i.e., Achelley) and ending with ᵛ 'Worsop Edw. 2ᵈ part 27.b'.
Wood 654c(1). STC 17669 (lists Wood 654c(1 and 2) together).

1557. Maunsell, Andrew. *The seconde parte of the catalogue of English printed bookes:. . . which concerneth the sciences*. London: J. Roberts f. A. Maunsell, 1595. Fol. Pp. [6], 27.
Annotation, similar notes to those in Wood 654c(1), on every page, 1-27. In section on 'Musicke', 16-8, each of the 19 items is marked in some way, usually by a vertical line, in red ink, in the margin by an entry, by an underscoring of the author's name, in pencil, or by 3 brief notes in dark or red ink, e.g., Pp. 17a, at 'William Birde', he wrote 'v. prox. coll.' (see next column), in dark ink; 17b, at the entry of Thomas Morley he added 'Introduction to Musick' (STC 18133-4); and also 17b, at book title 'The praise of Musicke' (1586), he wrote 'habeo', in red ink (i.e., Wood 25, item 5338).
Wood 654c(2). STC 17669 (lists Wood 654c(1 and 2) together).

1558. Maynard, John. *Bibliotheca Maynardiana: sive catalogus . . . librorum . . . d. Maynard, . . . quorum auctio habebitur . . . Per Edvardum Millingtonum [13 June]*. [London]: distributed gratis, Tom's Coffee-house, et al, 1687. 4°. Pp. [2], 1-24, 49-72 (misnumbering).
Tp, AW wrote, 'Dupl.'; some numbers '13096050' and '05069031' (?). Dupl. at [MS.] Wood E. 20(2).
[MS.] Wood E. 23(3). Wing M1449.

1559. Maynard, John. *Bibliotheca Maynardiana: sive catalogus . . . librorum . . . d. Maynard, . . . quorum auctio habebitur . . . Per Edvardum Millingtonum [13 June]*. [London]: distributed gratis, Tom's Coffee-house, et al, 1687. 4°. Pp. [2], 1-24, 49-72 (misnumbering).
Tp, AW wrote cat. no. '58', in pencil and in ink (twice). From p. 4, AW marked a few entries with horizontal or vertical lines, mainly in pencil, and wrote a very few corrections, cross references (e.g., pp. 12, 18, 24, 'v[ide] prox pag' and 'v. p. 26'), or 'q[uaere]' letters (e.g., p. 5, where no city or year of publ. occurs at R. Whitintoni, *Accidentia*; AW listed a copy of this in his library in 1681, MS. Wood E. 2(70), p. 74; see at Stanbridge, John, item 6025, but it disappeared before 1695). AW numbered consecutively after p. 24 to

the end, though, in error, wrote 36, 37, 58, 59, etc. to 67. Dupl. at [MS.] Wood E. 23(3).
[MS.] Wood E. 20(2). Wing M1449.

1560. Mearne, Charles. *A catalogue of English books:. . . of mr. Charles Mearne's, . . . which will be exposed to sale by auction [17 Feb].* [London]: distributed, Nott, Gilliflower, et al., 1687. 4°. Pp. [4], 26.
Tp, AW wrote cat. no. '62', in pencil, and '3ᵈ'. From p. 4, AW marked a few entries with horizontal lines, mainly in pencil, and, pp. 10-1, wrote 2 brief notes.
[MS.] Wood E. 20(6). Wing M1580.

1561. Mercurius Eruditorum. *Mercurius eruditorum: or news from the learned world. No. 2 [12 Aug.].*
(London): (f. R. Taylor), 1691. S.sh. (r-v).
This s.sh. was inserted between the Aug. and Sept. issues of *The works of the learned* (item 1537). ᵛ, a conversation between Alex. and Theod. about various publications; that concerning AO is: '*Alex.* . . . let us say a word of it, I pray you, that I my know if I ought to insert it in my Library. *Theod.* The Stile of that Book is Plain, Clear, and Didactic; the Authors and Famous Men of whom it gives an account, are placed according to the Age they liv'd in; and there wants nothing in it but an Alphabetical Table of their Lives; which, in all likelihood, will not be forgot at the end of the Second Part: You will find in it a Catalogue of those Writers Works, and of their different Editions; as also their most remarkable actions. It quotes its Authors almost every where, and where it doth not, we may be sure it speaks upon private Memoirs. Some People, perhaps, will say, that he favours the Papists too much, and falls too hard upon the Dissenters; nevertheless he professes to tell the truth of every body, neither hath he omitted a Circumstance of the Birth of that Great Pillar of the *Roman Church*, Bishop *Bonner*, which is not very agreeable with their Celibacy, *viz.* that he was the Bastard Son of a Priest, who was himself a Bastard, and had peopled the World with half a dozen more, besides the Bishop, begotten on three sundry Women'. LT 1.15.
[MS.] Wood E. 24b. N & S 319.2 (rare).

1562. Mercurius Librarius. *Mercurius librarius, or, a catalogue of books printed and published. Numb. 1-7 [wanting no. 8] [Michaelmas-term, 1668, to Easter term 1670]. A catalogue of books printed and published at London. Numb. 1-18 [Easter term 1670 to 6 July 1674]; Numb. 1-24 [Michaelmas term 1674 (25 Nov. 1674) to Trinity term 1680]; and Numb. 1-57 [Michaelmas term 1680 to Trinity term 1695].* [London]: collected by a. printed f. J. Starkey, R. Clavel, A. Clark, et al., [from Easter term, 1675:] f. the booksellers of London, 1668 to 1695. Fol. Pp. [772] (numbered consecutively by AW). Pasteboard (blue) with parchment spine; rebacked.
This vol. holds, in addition to the almost complete run of the 'term catalogues', 58 other separate imprints. The numbering is 1-772, by AW of all pp. in the term catalogues. Thereafter each printed item is numbered 773-820 by an Ashm. librarian. AW probably had the term catalogues bound in 1695, and it seems that items 773-820 were added to the vol. after 1695. There are 59 entries for the complete vol. in this present catalogue. The term catalogues were published Michaelmas, Hilary, Easter and Trinity (or Midsummer) terms and were AW's major source of information of printed books from 1668 to 1695. He made annotations, passim, mainly underscoring and marks, including 'q[uaere]', and lines in margins, in ink and pencil and red chalk. He frequently wrote names of authors identified only by initials, or added the names of an authors to anonymous works, often added a word or two of further explanation about persons or places, supplied some cross-references, and copied names or initials from the text to the margin. In the 1st 3 issues he numbered items, and in the earlier years he marked almost every item in some way. The final issue here, Trinity term 1695, with his p. nos., 765-771, has over 30 marks in the margin or minor underscoring and 7 brief notes or cross-references. The notes are generally just names, but can be longer; on his p. 155, he wrote: 'All the [sic, i.e., of] the Books in this term and all the following Terms are wanting in the [Bodleian?] Libr. excepting those crossed'. On his p. 566, he wrote: 'This is mentioned before –qu[aere]'.
See MS. Wood F. 36, ff. 1-113, 'Index to the Mercurii Librarii or Term Catalogues of Books, printed in England', where AW made two columns and added entries in the 2nd column when the 1st became filled. He did not enter all references in order, from his pp. 1 to 771, but seems to have gone back over some earlier material, as his index entry, e.g., for John Milton shows: 'Milton Jo. 8.a. 58.b. 77.a. 89.a. 285.b. 294.a. 309.b. 73.b. 103b 173.a. 26.a. 599.a. 617.b. 640.b. 623.b [not to Milton, but to John Melton] 650.b. 743.a. 747.b'. He has number of entries under subjects, e.g., Women, Womens advocate, womens vindications, women virtuous, Women Hist. of, Womens Rhetorick, Wom. History, Women parl. of, Women modish & va[ni]ty, women excellent. His own entry is: 'Wood Ant. 115.b [where AW added his name, lacking, after the t of the *Historia*], 584.b. [advertisement for AO], 593. [advertisement for AO], 601.a [advertisement for AO], 635.b. [2nd vol. of AO], 646.a. [advertisement, 50 copies of vol. 2 are left unsubscribed for], 669.b [*Vindication of the Historiographer* by E. D. (item 6695)]. LT 1.15.
Wood 658(1-772). N & S 337.1-8; 030.101-118; 030.201.224; 030.301-357.

1563. Mercurius Librarius. *A catalogue of books continued, printed, and published in London. Numbs. 11-16 [Michaelmas Term 1672, to Hillary Term 1674].* London: collected a. sold R. Clavel, 1672-1674. Fol. P², Q, Q², Q², R,S²,T-U²,X,Y² (pp. [34]).
Passim, frequent lines and crosses in margins, in ink and pencil. These are somewhat similar to those in AW's other (these are dupl. issues) copies at Wood 658(1-772), but here there are only 2 brief notes: no. 13, Q1, at 'A true Notion', 'q[uaere] wheth. Mr Squire'; and numb. 14, S1ᵛ, at 'The Anatomy of Popery', 'qu[aere] Mr Squire' (he did not enter these at his entry of Squire in AO 3.1114).
Wood 660b(2). N & S 030.111-6.

1564. Mercurius Librarius. *Mercurius librarius, or, a faithful account of all books . . . published thee last 14 days. Numbs. 1-2 [16 to 22 April 1680].* London: f. T. Simmons a. J. Sampson, 1680. Fol. Pp. [4].
Wood 660b(14). N & S 338.1-2 (rare).

1565. Mercurius Librarius. *A catalogue of books continued, printed and published at London in Michael-mas=term, 1680. Numb. 1-2, 18 [Michaelmas 1680, Hilary 1680-1, Hillary 1684-5].* [London]: f. the book-sellers, 1680-1685. Fol. Pp. [10], [10], [4].
The last, Hillary 1684-5, has a note in a later hand, 'added June 1885'. Dupl. at Wood 658(1-772).
Wood 660b(4). N & S 030.301-2; 030.318.

1566. Miller, William. Tooker, Charles, composed by. *The famous collection of papers and pamphlets . . . from the year 1600. . . . known by the name of William Miller's collection is now to be sold.* London: n.pub., [1695?]. 8°. A-N⁴. Parchment.
Tp, 'To Harry Clement for this cat. 1ˢ – 10 May. 1695'.
Wood 99. Wing M2067A (one) ('O' not recorded in Wing; 3 copies in 'O').

1567. Millington, Edward. *Catalogus librorum (in plurimis linguis insignium) . . . per auctionem venden-dorum. Quorum auctio habebitur [29 Mar.].* [London]: gratis distribuentur, 1680. 4°. Pp. [4], 46, [2], 70.
Flyleaf, upper, AW wrote '1680', and in another hand, 'Mʳ Davis Le– of Lincoln-' (? cropped at side). Tp, AW wrote cat. no. '8', in orange crayon. From p. 3, and more among books in English, from 2nd p. 1, AW marked items with vertical and horizontal lines, in pencil or ink, wrote some 'q[uaere]' letters, 3 brief notes in margins, and after the 1st section, numbered pp. consecutively from 47 to 117. P. 5, at the entry of his *Historia* (1674) he wrote, 'v. pag. 8', and p. 8, where it is again listed, he underscored the incorrect year, (1675).
[MS.] Wood E. 14(2). Wing C1442A.

1568. Millington, Edward. *A catalogue of the libraries of two eminent persons deceased; consisting of choice English books. . . . sold by auction [16 June].* [London]: distributed gratis, Bridges, et al., 1684. 4°. Pp. [4], 26, 17-32, 31 (misnumbering).
Tp, AW wrote cat. no. '33', in red chalk, and former no., '32'. From p. 1, AW marked a few entries with horizontal or vertical lines, mainly in pencil, and wrote, mainly, some cross-reference notes and 'q[uaere]' letters (p. 17, at Bifield, N., 'qu[aere] an Rich qu[aere] an Nic'). At last p. 5, 'This leaf is printed twice' (it was). After p. 26, he renumbered pp. consecutively, 27 to 75.
[MS.] Wood E. 17(7). Wing C1379 (two) ('O' not recorded in Wing).

1569. Millington, Edward. *Bibliotheca Sturbitchiana. Sive catalogus variorum librorum . . . quorum auctio habebitur apud nundinum Sturbitchianum . . . per Edvardum Millingtonum [8 Sept.].* [London]: distributed gratis, coffee-houses in Cambridg, 1684 [September]. 4°. Pp. [4], 44.
Tp, AW wrote cat. no. '34', and, 'Given to me by Hen. Cruttenden, Sept 6. 1684'. LT 3.470. From p. 2, AW marked a few entries with horizontal or vertical lines, mainly in pencil, and, pp. 14, 25, 28, wrote 3 brief notes.
[MS.] Wood E. 17(8). Wing B2857.

1570. Millington, Edward. *Bibliotheca Gallica, Italica, Hispanica, . . . quorum auctio habebitur [10 Nov.].* [London]: [given, Nott, et al.], [1685]. 4°. Pp. [4], 16 (sheet A mutilated) (cropped at bottom).
Dupl. at [MS.] Wood E. 18(5).
[MS.] Wood E. 23(6a). Wing B2827.

1571. Millington, Edward. *Bibliotheca Gallica, Italica, Hispanica, . . . quorum auctio habebitur [10 Nov.].* [London]: given, Nott, et al., [1685]. 4°. Pp. [4], 16 (cropped at bottom).
Tp, AW wrote cat. no. '43', in red chalk, over former no. '42'. Dupl. at [MS.] Wood E. 23(6).
[MS.] Wood E. 18(5). Wing B2827.

1572. Millington, Edward. *A catalogue containing variety of . . . English books . . . Will be exposed to*

sale (by way of auction) [30 Nov.]. [London]: given, Nott, et al., 1685. 4°. Pp. [4], 52.
Tp, AW wrote cat. no. '44', in red chalk, over former no. '43', and '6^{d}'. From p. 3, AW marked some
entries with lines (mainly in pencil) and circles; underscored; and wrote some cross references (and p. 20,
at Byfield, Nic. 'qu[aere] wh. Nic. or Rich.' ('Rich' lined out)) and 'q[uaere]' letters.
[MS.] Wood E. 18(6). Wing C1255.

1573. Millington, Edward. *A catalogue containing variety of books, of the common & statute law,
. . . Will be exposed to sale [18 Feb.].* [London]: distributed, T. Goodwin, et al., 1685/1686. 4°. Pp. [4], 16.
Tp, AW wrote cat. no. '46', over former no. '45'. Pp. 2, 4, 10, 14, 15 (also underscoring), AW marked 6
entries with horizontal lines, in pencil.
[MS.] Wood E. 18(8). Wing C1256.

1574. Millington, Edward. *Bibliotheca Latino-Anglica. . . . Quorum auctio habebitur . . . Per Edvardum
Millingtonum [12 July].* [London]: distributed, Wilkinson, Henseman, et al., 1687. 4°. Pp. [2], 58.
Tp, AW wrote cat. no. '60', in pencil, and '4^{d}'. From p. 10, AW marked a few entries with horizontal and/or
vertical lines, mainly in pencil.
[MS.] Wood E. 20(4). Wing B2835.

1575. Millington, Edward. *A catalogue of books viz, [sic] divinity, history, . . . contained in the library
of a . . . citizen of London, . . . Which will be sold by auction [12 Mar. 1688].* [London]: distributed gratis,
Wilkinson, Miller, et al., [1688]. 4°. Pp. [2], 45. Pasteboard (blue) with parchment spine; edges uncut.
The individual auction catalogues in this vol. follow a chronological order and may have been stitched
together at one time by AW (there are stitch holes on all pp.) before being bound in pasteboard. There
is no table of contents. AW wrote the p. nos. 1-8 and marked entries in only 1 catalogue in this vol.,
[MS.] Wood E. 21(8), item 1494.
[MS.] Wood E. 21(1). Wing C1292.

1576. Millington, Edward. *A catalogue of . . . books English and Latin, . . . Which will be sold by
auction [30 Apr.].* [London]: given, Wilkinson, W. Miller, et al., 1688. 4°. Pp. [2], 74.
Tp, AW wrote, '6^{d}'.
[MS.] Wood E. 21(3). Wing C1295 (two).

1577. Millington, Edward. *A catalogue of ancient and modern English books:. . . Which will be sold by
auction [at Abingdon] [9 May].* [London]: given, Hawkins, Cheyney, et al., 1692. 4°. Pp. 39.
[MS.] Wood E. 22(12). Wing C1276 (two).

1578. Moore, Jonas. *Bibliotheca mathematica . . . Jonae Mori . . . quorum auctio habenda est . . . per
Edwardum Millingtonum [3 Nov.].* [London]: given gratis, Nott, et al., 1684. 4°. Pp. [2], 41.
Tp, AW wrote cat. no. '35', and 'given to me by M^{r}. A. Allam Oct. 14 - 1684'. LT 3.167. From p. 21, AW
marked a few entries with horizontal or vertical lines, mainly in pencil, underscored one author and added
one Christian name.
[MS.] Wood E. 17(9). Wing M2567.

1579. Moseley, Humphrey. *Courteous reader, these bookes following are printed for Humphrey Moseley,
and are to be sold at his shop [140 entries; nos. 118ff., 'printed this Tearm' 1653].* [London]: f. H. Moseley,
[1653]. 8°. A^{8}. Pp. [16].
A1, AW wrote '1653'.
Wood 896(2). Not in Wing. ESTCR 202996 ('O' not recorded in ESTCR).

1580. Outram, William, and Thomas Gataker. *Catalogus librorum . . . Gulielmi Outrami . . . [et]
Thomae Gatakeri . . . quorum auctio habebitur . . . per Gulielmum Cooper [12 Dec.].* [London]: distributed
gratis, W. Cooper, et al., [1681]. 4°. Pp. [2], 66.
Tp, AW wrote cat. no. '18', over former no. '17', and '6^{d} to H[enry] Clement'; from p. 2, he underscored or
marked some items with horizontal or vertical lines, more frequently after p. 43, among books in English,
mainly in pencil; pp. 57, 61, 63, 66, brief notes.
[MS.] Wood E. 15(6). Wing O600.

1581. Owen, John. *A catalogue of the other books published by dr. Owen and sold by Philemon Stephens.*
[London]: n.pub., [1656]. S.sh. (r-v). 4° (fragment).
^{r}, AW wrote, 'An. 1656'. On the r-v sides. AW marked 17 items with vertical lines and one with 'q[uaere]'.
AO 4.97ff.
[MS.] Wood D. 22(3). Not in Wing. Not in ESTCR.

1582. Owen, John. *Bibliotheca Oweniana, sive catalogus librorum . . . Joan. Oweni. Quorum auctio habebitur . . . Cum variis manuscriptis . . . Patric. Junii . . . per Edvardum Millingtonum [26 May].* [London]: distributed, Nott, et al, 1684. 4°. Pp. [4], 32, 32.
Tp, AW wrote cat. no. '32', in red chalk; over 'Oweniana' in the t, 'Audoeniana'; at manuscripts of 'Patric. Junii' in t, 'Patr. Young p. 32' (on p. 32 he wrote at author Junius, 'Pat. Yong'); and, 'Given to me by Hen. Cruttenden 1684 2. May'. LT 3.470. From p. 5, AW marked a few entries with horizontal or vertical lines, mainly in pencil, and wrote a few cross-reference notes and 'q[uaere]' letters. These are more frequent in the 'English' section, from 2nd p. 1. After p. 32, he renumbered consecutively, 33 to 63.
[MS.] Wood E. 17(6). Wing O714.

1583. Oxford Press. *A catalogue of books, printed at the theater in Oxford.* [Oxford]: [at the Sheldonian], [1677]. S.sh. (r-v).
Years of publication, in pencil, after 8 entries, and, at end '(1676, 77)'; only the last may be by AW. Dupl. at Wood 660b(8).
Wood 658(816). Wing O863I (two). Madan 3154.

1584. Oxford Press. *A catalogue of books, printed at the theater in Oxford.* [Oxford]: [at the Sheldonian], [1677]. S.sh. (r-v).
AW entered the year of publication at 5 entries, wrote 'Dr Fell' in the margin at 4 entries, and added explanations after 3, e.g., at Loggan, *Oxonia illustrata*, 'This was not printed in the Theater, but in his house in Holywell'; at the end, 'All these were printed between the yeares 1669 & the 1. of Jan. 1675[6] [/] Here wants the verses in fol. made by the universitie on Anne Dutchess of York, printed at the Theater an. 167[1]. [/] Tis strang that the years which these books were printed are not set downe. [/] Here wants the Oxford - book - Almanack for the year. 1673 of which 30000 were printed.' Dupl. at Wood 658(816).
Wood 660b(8). Wing O863I (two). Madan 3154.

1585. Oxford Press. *A catalogue of books printed at the theater in Oxford.* [Oxford]: [at the Sheldonian], [1678?]. S.sh.
Wood 660b(9). Wing O863I (two). Madan 3155.

1586. Oxford Press. *Catalogus variorum librorum apud theatrum Sheldonianum novissimis annis impressorum . . . Quorum auctio habebitur [24 Feb.].* [London]: [M. Pitt], [1679]. 4°. Pp. [2], 6.
Tp, AW wrote, 'Dupl', twice, in pencil. Dupl. at Wood 660b(13).
[MS.] Wood E. 23(4a). Wing C1457. Madan 3202*.

1587. Oxford Press. *Catalogus variorum librorum apud theatrum Sheldonianum novissimis annis impressorum . . . Quorum auctio habebitur [24 Feb.].* [London]: [M. Pitt], [1679]. 4°. Pp. [2], 6.
Dupl. at [MS.] Wood E. 23(4a).
Wood 660b(13). Wing C1457. Madan 3202*.

1588. Oxford Press. *An advertisement, concerning the printing and publishing of ancient and other usefull books.* [Oxford]: [at the theater], [1680]. S.sh. (r-v).
^v, AW wrote 'printed at the theater in Sept. 1680'. Dupl. at Wood 658(775). LT 2.497.
Wood 660b(10) (not in Bodl. CD cat.). Wing O858B (rare, 2 at O) (Wing, advertisement concerning). Madan 3273.

1589. Oxford Press. *An advertisement, concerning the printing and publishing of ancient and other usefull books.* [Oxford]: [at the theatre], [1680]. S.sh. (r-v).
AW wrote 'Dupl' in pencil. Below, by a librarian, '[Sept 1680]'. Dupl. at Wood 660b(10).
Wood 658(775). Wing O858B (rare, 2 at O). Madan 3273 (Wing, advertisement concerning).

1590. Oxford Press. *A catalogue of books printed at the theater in Oxford . . . to 1682 . . . and sold in London by Moses Pitt.* [London]: sold by M. Pitt, 1682. Fol. Pp. [4].
Dupl. at Wood 660b(11).
Wood 658(817). Wing O863K (rare, 2 at O).

1591. Oxford Press. *A catalogue of books printed at the theater in Oxford, . . . to 1682 . . . and sold in London, by Moses Pitt.* [London]: sold by M. Pitt, 1682. Fol. Pp. [4].
Pp. [2], AW made a vertical line and wrote 'Jo. Pell' in margin; [4], at end, '1682', over '1682' in pencil. Dupl. at Wood 658(817).
Wood 660b(11). Wing O863K (rare, 2 at O).

1592. Oxford Press. *Anno Domini MDCXCIV in theatro Sheldonio apud Oxoniam jam imprimuntur.*

[Oxford]: [at the Sheldonian], [1694]. S.sh.
AW wrote 'Recepi ab Albio Cunetio 10 Aug. 1694' (i.e., White Kennett). LT 3.464.
Wood 660b(16a). Wing O860B (rare).

1593. Paget, Nathan. *Bibliotheca medica . . . Nathanis Paget, M.D. Cui adjiciuntur . . . alii libri. . . . Quorum . . . auctio habebitur . . . per Gulielmum Cooper [24 Oct.].* [London]: distributed gratis, [1681]. 4°.
Pp. [4], 52. Pasteboard (blue) with parchment spine; may have been bound or rebound later (edges cut with some cropping of notes).
Pastedown, upper, slip attached, on which AW wrote the titles of 8 catalogues of printed books in this vol., numbered consecutively from 19 to 26 (following those bound in [MS.] Wood E. 13-15). Tp, AW wrote cat. no. '19', in pencil. From p. 2, some items are marked with underscoring or vertical or horizontal lines, mainly in pencil, and some notes, mainly 'q[uaere]' letters in ink or pencil and cross references, e.g., pp. 39, 'Jo. Milton v. infra' and 'v. p. 38. v infra'; or 38; 42; and 48, 'v. p[ro]x. pag.'
[MS.] Wood E. 16(1). Wing P167.

1594. Parker, Henry. *A choice collection of law-books . . . of Henry Parker . . . will be exposed to sale . . . by Edward Millingham [5 Dec.].* [London]: distributed gratis, E. Millingham et al., [1681]. 4°. Pp. [4], 12.
Tp, AW wrote cat. no. '20', in red chalk, and '6ᵈ'. AW underscored or marked some items with horizontal or vertical lines, mainly in pencil, and wrote 2 'q[uaere]' letters, 1 cross reference and, p. 11, at books on 'Law', after R. Tillesley, *Animadversions* (1621; a critique of J. Selden's book on tithes), 'How comes this in here?'.
[MS.] Wood E. 16(2). Wing P399 (two).

1595. [Parkhurst, Thomas]. *Catalogus variorum librorum . . . virorum nuperrime defunctorum quorum auctio habebitur in aedibus Johannis Bridge [19 Oct.].* [London]: given, Nott, et al., 1685. 4°. Pp. [4], 5-88 (imperfect).
Dupl. at [MS.] Wood E. 18(4).
[MS.] Wood E. 23(2). Wing P491.

1596. [Parkhurst, Thomas]. *Catalogus variorum librorum . . . virorum nuperrime defunctorum quorum auctio habebitur in aedibus Johannis Bridge [19 Oct.].* [London]: given, Nott, et al., 1685. 4°. Pp. [4], 88.
Tp, AW wrote cat. no. '42', in red chalk, over former no. '41', and '6ᵈ'. From p. 7, AW marked a few entries with horizontal or vertical lines, mainly in pencil, underscored, and wrote a few notes, mainly 'q[uaere]' letters and cross references. These are more frequent from p. 47. Dupl. at [MS.] Wood E. 23(2).
[MS.] Wood E. 18(4). Wing P491.

1597. Petreius, Theodorus, and Aubert Le Mire. *Bibliotheca Cartusiana, . . . Accesserunt origines omnium per orbem Cartusiarum, quas eruendo publicavit . . . Aubertus Miraeus.* Coloniae: ap. A. Hieratum, 1609. Pp. [32], 310, [6]; [2], 73, [2] (2nd tp at 3rd [1]). Parchment with 2 clasp holes.
Flyleaf, upper, 2ndᵛ, AW wrote, 'Gulielm. Exmewe Londinensis Carthusianus professus, hic omittitur. Scripsit varia v. notas ad Maur. Chanceium in Pitseo', AO 1.459-62. Tp, price, '1.6'. P. 212, at J. Paracevalensis, 'clar. 1500 ita Bal. et Pits.' (prob. by AW), at J. Picus, bracket in margin (may not be by AW).
Wood 224. BL.

1598. Playford, Henry. *A curious collection of musick-books, . . . with the rates, . . . to be sold by Henry Playford.* [London]: had gratis, Knight, Carr, . . . Dolliff, et al., [1690]. 4°. Pp. [4].
Tp, AW wrote, 'Donum Fr[ancisci] Dolliff XI Jun. 1690'. LT 3.332. AW marked most of the 95 entries on pp. [2-3], and 3 entries on p. [4], with mainly horizontal lines, underscored some 10 names, added 3 Christian names, 1 author's name, and 2 'q[uaere]' notes.
[MS.] Wood E. 22(9). Wing C7625.

1599. Popish Plot. *A compleat catalogue of all the stitch'd books and single sheets printed . . . of the popish plot, (September 1678.) to January 1679/80.* [London]: n.pub., 1680. 4°. Pp. 32.
Tp, AW wrote '6ᵈ', and in the cat. annotated in some way on most pp. E.g., he wrote notes on books (p. 3), identified authors (pp. 8, 11), gave authors' full names (4, 7-8, 10), supplied authors' names (7-8, 10-1, 18), or simply repeated authors' names or titles of books (7-8, 13, 15), entered vertical lines, or double lines, in margins (passim), and later, a few vertical or horizontal lines, or underscored earlier notes, in red rayon or red ink (3, 5, 7, 8, 13, etc.). On 2 blank leaves inserted after p. 32, he added, p. [1], 2 publications from 1678; after the 2nd, Montagu, *Two letters* (Wing M2468) he wrote, 'The said two Letters & the Lord Treasurers Speech were published in the latter end of Feb. 1678[9] – and the new parliament beginning to sit 6. March following, the members therof voted them scandalous about the 20 of March, as about the

same time they did a certaine pamphlet intit. A Letter from a Jesuit residing in Parys, to his freind in London, which, though penned by one Dr Nelson, yet the Lord Treasurer sent it to the stationer to have it printed.' (Wing N110). P. [1^v], he wrote 7 entries of publications in 1679 of which 4 are in his collection: 1. Wood 276a(99), 2. not identified (see no. 7 on this p.), 3. Wood 424(29), 4. Wood 276a(274) (he owned the 1st ed.; the 2nd ed. is described on this p.), 5. Wing P19A, 6. Wing J722, 7. Wood 417(18); and p. [2], 6 publications in 1680 of which 4 are in his collection: 1. Wood 426(11), 2. [MS.] Wood B. 40(3a), 3. Wing P3195B, 4. Wing 3590, 5. [MS.] Wood D. 26(6), 6. Wood 417(28). See Plate VIII and LT 1.19, 2.445. [MS.] Wood E. 27(2). N & S 51A.1.

1600. Popish Plot. *A continuation of the compleat catalogue of all the stitch'd books and single sheets, . . . of the popish plot, September 1678. From the 1$^{st.}$ of January 1679/80. to the 25$^{th.}$ of June. 1680.* London: printed, sold at the Green Dragon, 1680. 4°. Pp. 22.
Tp, AW wrote, '6^d'. Pp. 4-13, 15-20, 22, AW made some vertical lines, or double lines, in margins, and wrote 18 brief notes on books or authors; later, he made a few underscorings of earlier notes, or vertical or horizontal lines, in red rayon or red ink.
[MS.] Wood E. 27(3). N & S 51A.2.

1601. Popish Plot. *A second. [sic] continuation of the compleat catalogue of stitch'd books and single sheets . . . of the popish plot (September 1678.) From the 24th of June to Michaelmas term 1680.* London: printed by J. R., sold at the Green Dragon, 1680. 4°. Pp. 16 (1 p. of newsbooks and proclamations).
Tp, AW wrote '4' (4^d?) and, after printed 'intended to be publish'd every Term', 'but your intention was not suffered to take effect.' On all but p. 10, AW made some notes on books, or authors, wrote 'q[uaere]' letters, or vertical lines, or double lines, in margins; later, he made a few underscorings of earlier notes, or vertical or horizontal lines in margins, in pencil or red rayon. He also wrote 'habeo' at 10 entries, all of which are now in Wood 426(2, 5, 8, 9, 10, 11, 12, 17, 18, and 19); after an 11th entry on p. 13, 'The Epitaph of Captain William Bedlow', he wrote 'hab.', which is a s.sh., only at the Newberry Library (Wing E3170D). He may have been referring to *Funeral tears upon the death of Bedloe*, a s.sh. on the same topic, now at Wood 426(15), item 2369 (see also item 927).
[MS.] Wood E. 27(4). N & S 51A.3 ('O' not recorded in N & S).

1602. Prynne, William. *An exact catalogue of all printed books . . . written . . . by William Prynne . . . before, during, since, his imprisonment.* London: f. M. Spark senior, rpt. T. Childe a. L. Parry f. E. Thomas, 1660. 4°. Rept. Pp. [4], 15 (really 14, misnumbering).
Tp, AW wrote at t, 'see Pryns books that were taken out of the public lib'. Below, in another hand, at Eccles. 12.12, '& Ears'. AW wrote longer notes at many items, identifying those he owned, see, e.g., p. 1, 'I have it see my 3. cat. of books MS. p. 22' (i.e., MS. Wood E. 2(70)), or which were 'in bib. Bod'. On the 14 pp., 33 items are marked either by 'cat. 3' or by 'habeo'; 2 were removed and are no longer in the Wood collection: *Doom of cowardize* (1643) and *Levellers levelled* (1647) (see items 5423b and 5432b). Most of the notes concern bibliography: comments on the title, introduction, printing, or cross references to other citations. P. 15, AW added 5 later entries and below, there are 5 earlier references which are not in AW's hand. Flyleaf, lower, AW wrote the t of another book by Prynne, 'A short sober pacific Examination of some exuberances in, & ceremoniall appurtenances to the common prayer &c. Lond. 1661. 4° (Mr A. Allum [Allam] hath it.) With an appendix to the 4th section concerning the use of white garments in generall'; '1664 [/] 1665 [/] 1666 – cat. bod.' (relevance not clear); and a note in pencil, illeg. LT 2.173.
[MS.] Wood D. 22(7) (D. 22(3) in the Bodl. CD cat.). Wing P3950.

1603. Pulleyn, Octavian. *Catalogus librorum in omni genere insignium, quorum copia suppetit Octaviano Pulleyn.* Londini: n.pub., 1657. 4°. Pp. [2], 100.
P. 30, horizontal line in margin, in pencil. Pp. 94-7, in 'livres Francois', 8 '+' marks, may not be by AW.
[MS.] Wood C. 26(11). Wing P4201.

1604. Ravenshaw, Samuel. *Bibliotheca curiosa, sive catalogus . . . librorum, praecipue theologicorum, literatorum, & historicorum, quorum auctio habebitur [3 April].* [London]: distributed gratis, Nott, Hensman, et al., 1689. 4°. Pp. 16.
[MS.] Wood E. 22(4b). Wing B2822 (two).

1605. Rea, Walter. *Catalogus librorum bibliothecae Gualteri Rea . . . Quorum auctio habenda est, . . . per Guilielmum Cooper [19 June].* [London]: distributed gratis, [1682]. 4°. Pp. [2], 50 (misnumbering).
Tp, AW wrote cat. no. '22'; and 'Given to me by Will. Lambourne alias Paynter [Painter] Bach. of Div. & Fellow of Exeter Coll 18 May 1682'. LT 3.15. From p. 4, AW marked entries with underscoring or vertical or horizontal lines, mainly in pencil and a brief note; in the 'English' section, from p. 25, frequent marks, 'q[uaere]' letters, and some notes (p. 31, at W. Stafford, *A brief conceit* (1581), 'habeo', i.e., Wood 618(6),

item 6022). After p. 29, AW corrected p. nos., 30 to the end, 56.
[MS.] Wood E. 16(4). Wing R423.

1606. Reynolds, Rowland. *A catalogue of several books to be sold by Rowland Reynolds and by the booksellers of London and Oxford, 1685.* N.p.: [R. Reynolds], [1685]. S.sh. (r-v). 4°.
AW wrote, 'put into my hand per ignotum, at Trin Coll. gate Apr. 13. 1685'. LT 3.138.
[MS.] Wood D. 22(15). Not in Wing. Not in ESTCR.

1607. Rogers, Daniel. *Catalogus variorum librorum bibliothecae . . . Danielis Rogers. Una cum bibliotheca . . . anonymi, . . . Horum auctio habebitur . . . By William Cooper, Edward Millington [21 June].* [London]: given gratis, Ponder, Nott, et al., 1683. 4°. Pp. [4], 34 (really 44), 27. Pasteboard (blue) with parchment spine; may have been bound or rebound later (edges are uncut; rebound).
This volume contains catalogues numbered 27-37 (in the series of 68 catalogues in [MS.] Wood E. 13-20).
Tp, AW wrote cat. no. '27', in orange crayon, and, 'Donum Hen. Cruttendon [sic] 13 June 1683'. LT 3.470.
From p. 2, AW marked some entries with horizontal or vertical lines, mainly in pencil; in the 'English' section, from p. 18, more frequent marks, 'q[uaere]' letters, and a few notes. After misnumbering at p. 29, he renumbered pp. 29 to the end, 70.
[MS.] Wood E. 17(1). Wing R1794.

1608. [Rothwell, John]. *A catalogue of the most approved divinitie-books.* [London]: [J. Rothwell], [1655]. 8°. Pp. 1-36, 49-50 (A-B⁸,C²,D1). Pasteboard (brown) with calf spine; flyleaves, 1st and 2nd, marbled paper and blue paper.
Flyleaf, 2nd, upperᵛ, AW wrote the titles of 6 printed works in this vol., within guidelines made with red chalk. On every p. (except p. 3), AW marked, in pencil, authors and/or works.
Wood 91(1). Wing R2002 (rare).

1609. [Rothwell, John]. *A catalogue of approved divinity books, . . . reprinted . . . to this present year, 1657.* London: f. J. Rothwell, 1657. ⁶,A-D⁸,E²,H²,E3-8,F⁸,G⁴ (pagination, irregular; 1st tp, 'Mensis Junii 18. Much inlarged') (2nd tp at sign. 3, 'Mensis Junii 12.').
Passim, i.e., almost every p., 'Ox' entered at books by Oxford authors; after some, also 'q[uaere]'; a few corrections, cross-references, and identifications, in ink and pencil.
Wood 91(3). Wing R2003.

1610. Rutgers, Joannes. *Catalogus bibliothecae . . . Jani Rutgersii . . . Quorum auctio habebitur in aedibus Elzevirianis [7 Mar.].* Lugduni Batavorum: ex off. Elzeviriana, 1633. 4°. Pp. [4], 126 (after 124, nos. cropped).
Tp, after year, 'stylo novo.' may not by AW. Passim, + marks, may not be by AW.
[MS.] Wood C. 26(10). Not in BL.

1611. Sandius, Christophorus. *Bibliotheca anti-trinitariorum, sive catalogus scriptorum, & succincta narratio de vita eorum auctorum.* Freistadii: ap. J. Aconium, 1684. 8°. Pp. [16], 296. Calf with 2 fillets and stamp decoration in corners.
Flyleaf, upper, 1st, AW wrote '2ˢ-8ᵈ.'; 2ndᵛ, 'Alia opera . . . Sandii v. cat. Bib. Bod. p. 136.a.' See AOF 2.280.
Wood 834. BL.

1612. Scott, Robert. *Catalogus librorum ex variis Europae partibus advectorum.* Londini: venales prostant ap. dictum R. Scott, 1674. 4°. Pp. [4], 206. Parchment over pasteboard.
7 of the 8 items in this vol. are duplicates; most were cropped in binding. They were not numbered by AW.
1st item, Tp, printed 'Little Britane' altered to 'Little Britaine'. Pp. 4-202, a number of entries are marked with horizontal or vertical lines, in pencil or ink, not all are in AW's manner. P. 140, AW corrected the printed 'Thom. Withe', 'Th. de Albiis'. P. 204, last printed line, lined out.
[MS.] Wood E. 23(1). Wing S2078.

1613. Scott, Robert. *Catalogus librorum Roberti Scott, . . . quorum auctio habenda est . . . per Benjaminum Walford [13 Feb.].* [London]: distributed, W. Nott, Holford, et al., [1688]. 4°. Pp. [4], 175, [1].
Tp, AW wrote cat. no. '68', in pencil. From p. 4, AW marked a few entries with mainly horizontal lines, in pencil, and wrote 1 cross reference (p. 4, 'v[ide] pag. 20', entries of Lud. Capelli).
[MS.] Wood E. 20(12). Wing S2080.

1614. Seaman, Lazarus. *Catalogus . . . librorum . . . Lazari Seaman, S.T.D. Quorum auctio habebitur . . . cura Gulielmi Cooper [31 Oct.].* Londini: ap. E. Brewster a. G. Cooper, 1676. 4°. Pp. [6], 137 (misnumbering and H⁴ is followed by h⁴). Pasteboard (blue) with parchment spine; may have been bound or rebound later (edges cut with some cropping of notes).

Pastedown, upper, slip attached, on which AW wrote the titles of 6 catalogues of printed items in this vol. Flyleaf, upper, 'Ex dono Rad. Sheldon [/] Dec. 1677' (LT 3.105), and, in pencil, 'Cat 2^d al[iu]s 1.' (he referred to it by both nos. see LT 1.19, note 2). Tp, AW wrote cat. no. '1', and, in red chalk, no. '2'. All 68 catalogues in this series, [MS.] Wood E. 13 to E. 20, are numbered consecutively. AW frequently marked items from p. 4, with vertical and horizontal lines, in pencil or ink, and sporadically wrote in margins identifications, 'q[uaere]' letters, corrections, and cross-references (p. 16, at 2 works on law, 'see cat of law books', i.e. Wood 896(5), item 1444; p. 82, '[vid]e prox. p'); some are cropped. He corrected the printed p. nos. 57-137, to 65 to 148.

[MS.] Wood E. 13(1). Wing S2173.

1615. Sill, William, and Cornelius Callow. *Catalogus variorum librorum . . . Sill . . . Cornel. Callow. . . . Quorum auctio habebitur . . . per Edoardum Millingtonum [21 Nov.].* [London]: given, Fox, Wilkinson, et al., 1687. 4°. Pp. [4], 23.

Tp, AW wrote cat. no. '65', in pencil. From p. 3, AW marked a few entries with mainly horizontal lines, in pencil.

[MS.] Wood E. 20(9). Wing S3786.

1616. Smith, Richard. *Bibliotheca Smithiana: sive catalogus librorum, . . . Horum auctio habebitur . . . per Richardum Chiswel [15 May].* [London]: distributed gratis, R. Chiswel, et al., [1682]. 4°. Pp. [4], 374 (misnumbering).

Pp. 4-371 (i.e., to 2nd 371) some lines in margin, in ink. Dupl. at [MS.] Wood E. 16(3).

[MS.] Wood E. 23(6b). Wing S4161A.

1617. Smith, Richard. *Bibliotheca Smithiana: sive catalogus librorum, . . . Horum auctio habebitur . . . per Richardum Chiswel [15 May].* [London]: distributed gratis, R. Chiswel, et al., [1682]. 4°. Pp. [4], 374 (gap between 196 and 273).

Tp, AW wrote cat. no. '21', in red chalk; after R. Smith in title, 'Secondarie of the compter.'; and below, '1^s to H[enry] Clement-'. He marked entries with underscoring or vertical or horizontal lines, mainly in pencil, and wrote some notes, more in the 'English' section, after p. 273 (misnumbering), and extensively from 362 to 374 (cropping): 'q[uaere]' letters in pencil or ink, some corrections (316, at Barnes, his praise of musick, 'He was not the author only publisher'), and mainly repetition of authors' names. At p. 372, at a section of pamphlets intended to be sold, AW marked those already published and at the end wrote 'most of these thing are published'. Dupl. at [MS.] Wood E. 23(6b). AO 3.1031-4 (see also 3.251 and note). AW attempted to correct p. nos. from 281 to end.

[MS.] Wood E. 16(3). Wing S4161A.

1618. Soleysel, Franciscus de. Clappier, Duc du. *Catalogus librorum bibliothecae . . . Francisci de Soleysel d. du Clappier, qui venales reperiuntur apud Joann. Baptistam Gimeaux.* Lugduni: sold J. B. Gimeaux, 1668. 8°. Pp. 56.

Tp, 'R. S.' (Ralph Sheldon), LT 3.105. Some horizontal lines at items and corrections, e.g., pp. 8, 10-1, 38, 40, 43-6.

Wood 896(4b). Not in BL. Not in BN. Not in NUC.

1619. Starkey, John. *Books printed for John Starkey at the sign of the Miter . . . in Fleetstreet.* [London]: f. J. Starkey, [1660]. 8°. Pp. [8].

Tp, AW wrote '1660.'

Wood 896(4a). Not in Wing. Not in ESTCR (2 at O; Malone 264(5) is imperf.).

1620. Stephens, Philemon. *These books are to be sold by Philemon Stephens.* N.p.: n.pub., [1657?]. S.sh. (r-v) (fragment).

AW wrote 'An. 1657'.

[MS.] Wood D. 22(5) (not in Bodl. CD cat.). Not in Wing. Not in ESTCR (not ESTCR 214466).

1621. Stephens, Philemon. *These books following are to bee sold by Philemon Stephens at the Gilded Lion in St. Pauls Churchyard.* [London]: [f. P. Stephens], [1659 or later]. 8°. A^4.

A1^v, at works by Tho. Bedford and Joh. Udall, lines in margin.

Wood 91(2). Not in Wing. ESTCR 214466.

1622. Stokes, [David]. *Catalogus librorum . . . d$^{ris.}$ Stokes & aliorum. Quorum auctio habenda est . . . per Gulielmum Cooper [1 Dec.].* [London]: distributed gratis, Pellican and T. Basset, 1685. 4°. Pp. [2], 66.

Tp, AW wrote cat. no. '45', in red chalk. From p. 1, AW marked a few entries with horizontal or vertical

lines, mainly in pencil, underscored, and wrote 1 identification (p. 64, at printed 'Mother Hubberds Tale', he wrote 'Jo. Skelton' and 'q[uaere]').
[MS.] Wood E. 18(7). Wing S5717A.

1623. Stubbe, H[enry], et al. *Catalogus variorum librorum . . . viz. d. Hen. Stubb [and Dillingham of Oundle, Thomas Vincent, Cawton Westmonastery, John Dunton]. Quorum auctio habebitur [29 Nov.].* [London]: distributed gratis, T. Parkhurst, [1680]. 4°. Pp. [4], 44, 52, 150 (misnumbering). Pasteboard (blue) with parchment spine; may have been bound or rebound later (edges cut with some cropping of notes).
Pastedown, upper, slip attached on which AW wrote the titles of 6 catalogues of printed books in this vol., numbered consecutively from 13 to 18 (following those bound in [MS.] Wood E. 13(1-6) and [MS.] E. 14(7-12)). Tp, AW wrote cat. no. '13', in red chalk, and 'few or no Christian names in this cat.' From p. 19, and more among books in English, from 3rd p. 1, a few items are marked with vertical and horizontal lines, in pencil or ink; 3rd pp. 8, 45, 77, 101, AW wrote a 4 brief notes in margins (e.g., p. 77, at printed 'Chetwinds watch charged', 'The same with that mentioned the next pag' (Wing C3798)), and after the 1st section he numbered pp. consecutively from 2nd p. 1 to the end, 45 to 154 (i.e., 254).
[MS.] Wood E. 15(1). Wing S6031.

1624. Terne, Christopher, and Thomas Allen. *Bibliothecae medicae, sive, catalogus variorum librorum . . . Christ. Terne [and] Thomae Allen . . . cum appendice . . . Roberti Talbor . . . Quorum auctio habenda est . . . per Eduardum Millingtonum [12 Apr.].* [London]: given, Nott, et al., 1686. 4°. Pp. [4], 24.
Tp, AW wrote cat. no. '47', in red chalk, over former no. '46', and underscored names of owners. Pp. 1-15, AW marked a few entries with horizontal or vertical lines, in pencil.
[MS.] Wood E. 18(9). Wing T759.

1625. Tokefield, George. *A catalogue of such books as have been entered in the register of the company of stationers: and printed [25 Dec. 1662 - 25 Dec. 1663].* London: publ. by G. T. f. S. Speed, 1664. 4°. Pp. 8.
AW made 2 identifications, a correction and underscored names of 5 authors.
[MS.] Wood D. 22(8). Wing T1759 (two).

1626. Universal Historical Bibliotheque. *The universal historical bibliotheque: or an account of most of the considerable books printed in all languages [Jan., Feb., Mar. 1686[7]].* London: f. G. Wells, 1687. 4°. Pp. [7], 203 (3 pts.). Pasteboard (blue) with parchment spine. 1st upper and last lower flyleaves, marbled paper.
[MS.] Wood E. 26. N & S 643.1-3.

1627. Verneuil, John. *A nomenclator of such tracts and sermons as have beene printed, or translated into English.* Oxford: H. Hall, 1642. 12°. 2nd ed. Pp. [8], 211. Calf, speckled, with 2 fillets. Flyleaves, upper and lower, printer's waste paper.
Pastedown, upper, AW wrote 'Vernevill'. P. 92, marks in margin, not in AW's manner.
Wood 891 (not in Bodl. CD cat.). Wing V242. Madan 1289.

1628. Voet, Gijsbert. *Catalogus variorum librorum . . . viri in Angli defuncti: [et] . . . ex bibliotheca . . . Gisberti Voetii . . . Quorum auctio habebitur [by M. Pitt] [Nov. 25].* [London]: distributed gratis, M. Pitt, et al., [1678]. 4°. Pp. [6], 106, 28, 20, 89-96, 44, 251-270 (apparently a composite work with an unidentified section with the heading 'Volumes of Tracts 4to.', and including 161 lots in all, after 2nd p. 44). Pasteboard (blue) with parchment spine; may have been bound or rebound later (edges cut with some cropping of notes).
Pastedown, upper, slip attached, on which AW wrote the titles catalogues numbered 7-12 of printed books in this vol. (following nos. 1-6 bound in [MS.] Wood E. 13). Each tp is numbered in red chalk. Flyleaf, upper, AW wrote, 'Cat. Voetii per M. Pitt 1678' and '7' in pencil. Tp, AW wrote cat. no. '7', in red chalk. From p. 5, and more among books in English, from 2nd p. 89, some items are marked with vertical and horizontal lines, in pencil or ink; 2nd p. 89 to 258, AW wrote a number of brief notes in margins, and after the 1st section, numbered pp. consecutively from 107 to 228 (228 is p. 269 of last section; he did not renumber the final p. 270).
[MS.] Wood E. 14(1). Wing V675.

1629. Wallis, Robert. *A catalogue of the library of . . . Robert Wallis . . . Which will be sold by auction [2 Apr.].* [London]: distributed gratis, Nott, Weld, et al., 1688. 4°. Pp. [2], 26.
[MS.] Wood E. 21(2). Wing W621 (two) (Wing, Richard Wallis).

1630. Walton, Brian. Chester, bp. of. *Bibliotheca Waltoniana, sive catalogus librorum . . . Briani Waltoni . . . Horum auctio habebitur 30 Apr.* [London]: distributed gratis, S. Carr, 1683. 4°. Pp. [2], 34, 12.
Tp, AW wrote cat. no. '26', in red chalk, and, 'Most of the books in this cat. were published after D' Waltons death – He died 1661'; former nos., '25' and '6'. From p. 4, AW marked some entries with horizontal or vertical lines, mainly in pencil; in the 'English' section, from p. 24, frequent marks, 'q[uaere]' letters, and some notes, mainly cross-references, but see p. 27, at J. Paybody's Apology (1629), 'Perhaps Tho. Paybody - q[uaere]. This cat. is very false' (AW was correct; it was Thomas Paybody). After p. 34, he renumbered consecutively, pp., 34 to 45.
[MS.] Wood E. 16(8). Wing W656.

1631. Warner, John. Rochester, bp. of. *Bibliotheca Warneriana, sive catalogus librorum . . . Joan. Warneri . . . Quorum auctio habenda est . . . Per Edvardum Millingtonum [16 Feb.].* [London]: given gratis, Nott, Wilkinson, et al., 1685. 4°. Pp. [4], 24, 28.
Tp, AW wrote cat. no. '38', in red chalk. Pp. 3-4, 20-1, 24, and slightly more in the 'English' section, from 2nd p. 1, AW marked a few entries with horizontal or vertical lines, mainly in pencil, and wrote a few brief notes and 'q[uaere]' letters. After p. 24, he renumbered pp. consecutively, 25 to 51. Dupl. at [MS.] Wood E. 23(5).
[MS.] Wood E. 17(12). Wing W899.

1632. Warner, John. Rochester, bp. of. *Bibliotheca Warneriana, sive catalogus librorum . . . Joan. Warneri . . . Quorum auctio habenda est . . . Per Edvardum Millingtonum [16 Feb.].* [London]: given gratis, Nott, Wilkinson, et al., 1685. 4°. Pp. [4], 24, 28.
Tp, AW wrote, 'Dup[l]', in pencil (cropped). Dupl. at [MS.] Wood E. 17(12).
[MS.] Wood E. 23(5). Wing W899.

1633. Whately, William, and Simon Rutland. *Bibliotheca Whateliana: sive catalogus . . . bibliothecae . . . d. Whately. . . . [et] Simonis Ruland. Quorum auctio habebitur . . . per Edvardum Millingtonum [23 April].* [London]: distributed gratis, Bridges-Coffee House, et al., 1683. 4°. Pp. [4], 43, [1], 20, 16.
Tp, AW wrote cat. no. '25', and, 'Donum Hen. Cruttenden in vigi. paschalis' (7 Apr.). LT 3.470. From p. 2, AW marked some entries with horizontal or vertical lines, mainly in pencil; in the 'English' sections, from 2nd p. 1, more frequent marks, 'q[uaere]' letters, and a few notes. From 2nd p. 1, he renumbered pp., 13 to 92.
[MS.] Wood E. 16(7). Wing W1558.

1634. Wilkinson, Henry. *Catalogus librorum in bibliotheca aulae Magdalenae.* Oxoniae: H. Hall, 1661. 8°. A-C⁸.
Passim, i.e., on almost every p., 'Ox' entered at books by Oxford authors, also 'q[uaere]', and line marks. Wood 91(4). Wing W2228. Madan 2545.

1635. Worsley, Benjamin. *Catalogus librorum . . . Benjaminis Worsley, . . . quorum auctio habebitur . . . Per Joan. Dunmore & Ric. Chiswell [13 May].* [London]: gratis distribuentur, 1678. 4°. Pp. [5], 26, 51, [1], 58, 27-32, 40 (misnumbering).
Tp, AW wrote cat. no. '4', in red chalk. P. [1], AW wrote, 'Cat. Wors[ley]' (cropped at side); below, printed words lined out and '[to] gentlemen of your Colledge.' substituted, not by AW. From p. 3, and slightly more among books in English, after 2nd p. 1, AW marked items with horizontal or vertical lines, in pencil or ink, wrote some brief notes in margins, and after the 1st section, numbered pp. consecutively from 27 to 180.
[MS.] Wood E. 13(4). Wing W3612.

1636. Wray, Edward. *Catalogus librorum . . . Eduardi Wray . . . Quorum auctio habenda est . . . Per Guilielmum Cooper [20 June].* [London]: distributed gratis, Pelican, S. Carr, et al., [1687]. 4°. Pp. [2], 50.
Tp, AW wrote cat. no. '59', in pencil, and '3ᵈ'. From p. 4, AW marked a few entries with horizontal or vertical lines, mainly in pencil, and wrote 3 brief notes.
[MS.] Wood E. 20(3). Wing W3666.

End of CATALOGUES OF SALES AND AUCTIONS (items 1438-1636)

1637. Caterpillars of this Nation. *The catterpillers of this nation anatomized.* London: f. M. H., 1659. 4°. Pp. [2], 4, 38.
Flyleaf, upper, 'let me dye' (?), prob. not in AW's hand. Tp, bsm. (or the price, '6.').

Wood 371(9). Wing C1490.

1638. Catherine, Queen*. *To the queen, on her birth-day.* [London]: n.pub., 1663, 5 Dec. S.sh.
Wood 416(105). Wing T1598 (rare) (Wing, queen on her birthday).

1639. Catholic Church. Cassandrum, Georgius, ed. *Ordo Romanus de officio missae.* Coloniae: ap. haer.
A. Birckmanni, 1561. 8°. Ff. [16], 69.
Tp, AW wrote '6^{d}'. Text, a note, some underscoring and marks in margin, none by AW.
Wood 835(4). BL.

1640. Catholic Church. *Contra aemulos & detractores juris pontificii seu canonici.* Parisiis: e typog. S.
Prevosteau, 1605. 8°. Pp. 96 (errata pasted on to p. 96). Paper, brown.
Tp, no. '28' over '27'.
Wood 877. Not in BL.

1641. Catholic Church. *A manuall of prayers gathered out of many famous, and godly authours; augmented with divers points of the princesse manuall.* Paris: [English Secret Press, no. 21], 1630. 8° (wanting
sigs. M1, 4, 5 ,8; pp. 177-8, etc.). Pp. [40], 432. Parchment.
Wood 763. STC 17277 (two). ARCR 2.223.

1642. Catholic Church. *The arch-confraternity of the holy rosary of our blessed lady.* London: [English
Secret Press], 1636. 24° (in twelves). a^{12},b^{4} (last leaf blank). Marbled paper cover, vellum and cardboard
cover over marbled paper.
Missing in 1837. In the Whiteside cat. it replaced Wood 755, 'Gazaphylacii naturae & artis &c Lond:
1702' (the latter is the original entry). The single surviving copy of the *Arch-confraternity* is BL C.iii.a.14
(3455.a.7, lined out); it has, on B4, the signature, 'Maregeret Weddsmith Her Book 1750' (no annotation
by AW).
Wood 755. STC 17548 (one). ARCR 2.907.

1643. Catholic Church. *Clemens papa IX. ad futuram rei memoriam.* Romae: Ex typ. rev. Camerae
Apostolicae, 1668. S.sh.
A condemnation of *Rituel Romain du Pape Paul V* (Paris, 1668). LT 2.181.
Wood 276a(120) (not in Bodl. CD cat.). BL.

1644. Catholic Church. *Formula indulgentiarum cum quibus s. d. n. Clemens papa IX. Coronas, . . . ben-
edicit per occasionem canonizationis ss. Petri de Alcantara, & Mariae Magdalene de Pazzis.* Romae: Ex
typ. rev. Camerae Apost., 1669. S.sh.
AW added, '1669', in pencil. LT 2.181.
Wood 276a(121). Not in BL, BN, NUC.

1645. Cato. Penkethman, J[ohn], trans. *A handful of honesty. Or, Cato in English verse.* London: A.
Matthewes, f. R. Hawkins, 1623. 8°. A-C^{8}.
A1, 'Hen: Foulis. Novemb: 6. 1652. P. -' (cropped at top and side). Tp, bsm.
Wood 84(4). STC 4861 (rare).

1646. Causa. *Causae veteris epitaphium, in antecessum, ab anonymo autore scriptum.* (Paganopoli) [Lon-
don]: (excud. utis Homericus redivivus, prostant venales in off. G. Abington), [1682]. Fol. Pp. 4.
P. 1, AW wrote '1682', in pencil; p. 4, 'published in the middle of Nov. 1682'.
Wood 417(107). Wing C1532.

1647. Cavalieri, Giovanni Battista. *Effigies pontificarum Romanorum.* Romae: (typ. B. Bonfadini),
1595. Ff. [7], 236, [10]. Calf, 4 fillets and edge hatching; spine, 4 bands and hatching (Oxford binding).
Tp., bsm.
Wood 252. BN.

1648. Cavaliers, Prayer. *The cavaliers new common-prayer booke unclasp't.* York: S. Buckley, 1644. 4°.
Rpt. of London: G. B. edition. Pp. 16.
Wood 377(42). Wing C1578. Madan 1678.

1649. Cavalli, Stefano. A., P., trans. *A short account of the life and death of pope Alexander the IX
. . . and coronation of . . . Clement the IX.* London: f. M. Pitt, 1667. 4°. Pp. [5], 28.
[MS.] Wood C. 39(3) (Wood 39c(3) in Bodl. CD cat.). Wing C1579.

1650. Cave, John. *Daphnis. A pastoral elegy on the death of . . . Francis Wollaston.* Oxford: L. Lichfield,

f. the author, 1685. S.sh.
ᵛ, AW wrote, 'Fr. Wollaston' and 'Fr. Wollaston 1685'.
Wood 429(40). Wing C1586aA (rare).

1651. Cave, William. *Tabulae ecclesiasticae . . . a Christo nato ad annum usque MDXVII.* (Londini):
(J. D. imp. R. Chiswell), (1674). Fol. Pp. [3].
Wood 276a(51-52). Wing C1608 (3).

1652. Cavendish, Christiana*. Devonshire, countess of. *An elegy on the truly honourable, . . . countesse
of Devonshire.* [London]: n.pub., [1675]. S.sh.
AW wrote, 'Her life is printed', in pencil; ᵛ, 'Countess of Devon– Her life is extant' (by Thomas Pomfret,
London, 1685; Wing P2799).
Wood 429(45). Wing E442.

1653. [Cavendish, George]. *The negotiations of Thomas Woolsey, . . . containing his life and death.*
London: n.pub., [1650?]. 4°. Pp. [1-7], 102, [103-4].
Flyleaf, upper, AW wrote, 'The author puts Cambridge before Oxford, p. 52' and 'The manuscript or
transcript of this book comming into the hands of a Factious person, he published it with rascally additions
put in it in several places/ And at the same time when Archb. Laud was falling, whome he hooks in at
the end as a parallel with Wolsey/'. ᵛ, AW wrote the titles of 2 printed works following, within guidelines
made with red ink, which indicates that these three were together before AW collected and put together
most of the items in this vol. (see note at Wood 345(1)). After the 2 works, AW added details about
George Cavendish and his sources, and concluded, 'This book was written in the time of qu. Mary, who
began to raign 1553, see p. 6. 13'. Frontispiece, from the mouth of Wolsey, 'Ego Meus et Rex', which AW,
apparently, changed to 'Ego & Rex'. Tp, bsm. Text, AW made a number of annotations, line in margins,
underscorings, corrections, identifications, and comments about the Cavendish transcript, e.g., pp. 2, 6-7,
9-10, 13, 15, etc. P. 93, he underscored '(at which time it was apparant that he had poisoned himselfe)'
and wrote in the margin, 'This is not in the copie written by G. Cavendish'. Pp. 100, 103, similar notes,
e.g., 'Not in the orig copie, in bib. Bod.' Possibly lent to John Beby, 4 Mar. 1663, LT 1.470.
Wood 345(11). Wing C1619A ('O' not recorded in Wing).

1654. Cavendish, William. Newcastle, duke of. *Being commanded by his excellency the ˡᵈ marquis of
New-Castle to publish the following articles . . . Jo. Rolleston.* [Oxford]: n.pub., [1662]. S.sh.
'26 May 1662 Given to me by Hen: Hall the University Printer AWood.' LT 1.441.
Wood 276a(149). Wing N876 (rare). Madan 2587.

1655. [Cawley, John]. *The case of founders kinsmen: with relation to the statutes of – [All Souls] college,
in the university of – [Oxford].* London: f. J. Whitlock, [1694]. 4°. Pp. [4], 23.
Tp, AW wrote, 'This pamphlet came to Oxon from London, as a new thing 9 Octob. 1694 – 6ᵈ·'. See LT
3.469.
Wood 631(10). Wing C1649 (Wing, [1695?]).

1656. Cawthorn, Lawrence*. *A sad and sorrowfull relation of Laurence Cauthorn, butcher; who was
buried whilest he was alive.* London: f. A. Rice, 1661. S.sh.
Wood 365(18). Wing S244E (rare).

1657. [Cawton, Thomas]. *The life and death of that holy . . . mʳ Thomas Cawton . . . to which is
annexed, a sermon.* London: f. T. Basset and R. Hall, 1662. 8°. Pp. [8], 120 (2nd tp at p. 89). Calf with 2
fillets.
Slip, pasted to lower flyleaf, with author and short title. Flyleaf, upper, 1st, '6ᵈ'. A2, in dark ink, AW
wrote, 'Tho. Cawton fil. was not the authour of this life, but another - see p. 69 [last 5 words crossed
out, in pencil]. See also the ep. to the reader before the serm[on] at the end –'. P. [8]ᵛ, underscoring and
line in margin, in pencil at reference to an author. Some marks or brief notes, e.g., pp. 22-3, 66, 68, 69
(underscoring and hand pointer in margin), 83, 89, 91.
Wood 297. Wing C1653.

1658. C[ecil], E[dward]. Wimbledon, visct. *The government of Ireland under . . . John Perrot . . . beginning 1584. and ending 1588 [signed E. C. S., i.e. Sir Edward Cecil].* London: [A. Mathewes] f. T. Walkley,
1626. 4° (wanting sigs. a2-d2). Pp. [10], 136, [3].
Tp, AW wrote, 'by Sʳ Edw. Cecil'. A former owner wrote, ' . . . Mr. Curtin this author I . . . [cropped at
top] gave me this book that he hath continued the History of Ireland downwards if pray you procure me
the part or parts of it . . . '. A2ᵛ, 'Sʳ Ed: Cecil', not in AW's hand. A3, a correction.

Wood 504(2). STC 21490.

1659. Cecil, Edward. Wimbledon, visct. *A journall, and relation of the action which . . . Edward lord Cecyl . . . did undertake upon the coast of Spaine, 1625.* [London]: [Eliot's Court Press?], 1626. 4°. Pp. [2], 30.
Flyleaf, upper, scrap sheet, scribbles, not in AW's hand.
Wood 511(14). STC 4892.5.

1660. C[ecil], R[obert]. Salisbury, earl of. *The copie of a letter [signed R. C. (not R. Crompton)] to the . . . earle of Leycester, . . . With a report of certeine petitions . . . made to the queenes majestie . . . from . . . parliament, and her majesties answeres.* London: C. Barker, 1586. 4°. Pp. [4], 32, [1].
Flyleaf, upper[v], addition of at least 2 lines (cropped), totaling 30. 6. P. [1], in lower left corner, opposite addition, '6'. Tp to end, pp. numbered 197-234 (in a former collection, not by AW; see also 615(10), item 2423, where the nos. begin). Dupl. at Wood 616(15).
Wood 616(3). STC 6052.

1661. C[ecil], R[obert]. Salisbury, earl of. *The copie of a letter [signed R. C. (not R. Crompton)] to the . . . earle of Leycester, . . . With a report of certeine petitions . . . made to the queenes majestie . . . from . . . parliament, and her majesties answeres.* London: C. Barker, 1586. 4°. Pp. [4], 32, [1].
Dupl. at Wood 616(3).
Wood 616(15). STC 6052.

1662. [Cecil, William]. Burghley, 1st baron. Norton, T., probably by. *A declaration of the favorable dealing of her majesties commissioners appointed for the examination of certaine traitours, and of tortures unjustly reported to be done.* [London]: [C. Barker], 1583. 4°. A[4].
Prob. acquired 29 Ap. 1658 out of G. Langbaine's study, LT 1.247, see note at Wood 586(1), item 6057.
Wood 586(5). STC 4901.

1663. [Cecil, William]. Burghley, 1st baron. *The execution of justice in England for maintenaunce of publique and Christian peace, against certeine stirrers of sedition.* London: [C. Barker], 1583[4]. 4°. 2ndly impr. A-E[4].
Tp, 'S[r] Will Cecill', in pencil, prob. in AW's hand. B1[r-v], B3, B4, C1[v], D3, some lines in margins, in pencil, and cross-ref., at 'Priest Nicolas Morton', in ink; E3[v], 'q[uaere]' in margin, in pencil. Prob. acquired 29 Ap. 1658 out of G. Langbaine's study, LT 1.247, see note at Wood 586(1), item 6057.
Wood 586(4). STC 4903.

1664. Cecil, William. Burghley, 1st baron. *The copie of a letter sent out of England to don Bernardin Mendoza . . . declaring the state of England . . . found in the chamber of one Richard Leigh a seminarie priest, . . . lately executed . . . Whereunto are adjoyned certaine late advertisements [by W. Cecil].* London: J. Vautrollier f. R. Field, 1588. 4°. Pp. [2], 38, [3], and A[4],B[6] (2 pts., with pt. 2 reset).
Wood 511(2-3). STC 15412.

1665. [Cecil, William]. Burghley, 1st baron. *A true report of sundry horrible conspiracies . . . detected to have (by barbarous murders) taken away the life of the queenes . . . majestie.* London: C. Yetsweirt, 1594, Nouember. 4°. Pp. 31.
Tp, 'Lopez. Conspiracie', prob. not in AW's hand. Acquired 29 Ap. 1658 out of G. Langbaine's study, LT 1.247.
Wood 586(8). STC 7603.

1666. Cedrus Britannica. *Cedrus Britanica [sic], et laurus regia sive rex & corona. A poetical hexameron.* [London]: n.pub., 1660. 4°. Pp. 12.
AW numbered this item '5'.
Wood 605(4) (not in Bodl. CD cat.). Wing C1654 (one) ('O' not recorded in Wing).

1667. Cellier, Elizabeth. *Malice defeated: or a brief relation of the accusation and deliverance of Elizabeth Cellier.* London: f. E. Cellier, 1680. Fol. Pp. [2], 48.
Tp, bsm.
Wood 426(5). Wing C1661.

1668. Cellier, Elizabeth. *The matchless rogue; or, a brief account of the life of don Thomazo [T. Dangerfield] the unfortunate son.* London: f. E. Cellier, 1680. Fol. Pp. [2], 6.
Wood 426(9). Wing C1662.

1669. Cellier, Elizabeth*. *Modesty triumphing over impudence. Or, some notes upon a late romance*

[Malice defeated] published by *Elizabeth Cellier.* London: f. J. Wilkins, 1680. Fol. Pp. 19.
Responds to Wood 426(5), item 1667.
Wood 426(14) (Wood 427(13) in Bodl. CD cat.). Wing M2379.

1670. Cellier, Elizabeth*. *The scarlet beast stripped naked, being the mistery of the meal-tub the second time unravelled; or a brief answer to the popish-midwives scandalous narrative [by E. Celliers] intituled mallice defeated.* London: D. Mallet, [1680]. Fol. Pp. 8 (1-4, 1-4).
Responds to Wood 426(5), item 1667.
Wood 426(6). Wing S826.

1671. Cellier, Elizabeth*. *The triall of Elizabeth Cellier, at the kings-bench barr [11 June].* London: f. R. Taylor, 1680. Fol. Pp. 17.
Wood 427(13b) (not in Bodl. CD cat.). Wing T2187.

1672. Cellier, Elizabeth*. *The tryal and sentence of Elizabeth Cellier; for writing, printing, and publishing, . . . malice defeated.* London: f. T. Collins, 1680. Fol. Pp. [3], 9-39 (a 2nd Bodl. copy, Ashm. 1677(14), has the same pagination).
Tp, AW wrote the price, '1^s', and, in another hand, 'D. N'.
Wood 426(17). Wing T2171.

1673. Censorinus. Carrio, Lud., ed. *Censorini ad Q. Caerellium de die natali.* Lutetiae: ap. A. Beysium, 1583. 8°. Pp. [16], 55, [21], 27, [9] (a^8,A-G^8,H^4). Parchment.
Tp, signatures of other owners, Isaacus Casaubonus, 1611, and Barton Holyday, 1620, and 'Anton. à Wood 1661 è bib. B. Holydaii' (Holyday died in 1661; AW added this inscription later). Passim, notes and corrections in hand of Casaubon. Acquired 8 Apr. 1662, LT 1.436-7.
Wood 19. BL.

1674. Century of Sacred Distichs. *A century of sacred distichs or, religion in verse.* Oxford: L. Lichfield f. J. Barksdale, 1685. 8°. Pp. [2], 14.
Wood 90(6). Wing C1672 (rare).

1675. Ceremonies. *The ceremonies for the healing of them that be diseased with the kings evil, used in the time of king Henry VII.* London: H. Hills, 1686. 12°. Pp. [2], 20.
Wood 893(4). Wing C1675.

1676. Ceriziers, René de. Lowre, William, trans. *The innocent lord; or, the divine providence. Being the incomparable history of Joseph.* London: S. G. f. C. Adams, 1655. 8°. Pp. [17], 143.
Missing. MS. Wood E. 2(70), p. 56.
MS. Wood E. 2(70), p. 56. Wing C1681. O, Hunt, Harv.

1677. Certain Considerations Touching. *Certaine considerations touching the present factions in the kings dominions.* London: n.pub., 1648. 4°. Pp. [2], 12.
Wood 502(75) (not in Bodl. CD cat.). Wing C1697.

1678. Certain Considerations Wherein. *Certaine considerations wherein the prelates doe acknowledge that they stand by the meer mercy of the king and parliament.* [London?]: n.pub., [1642?]. 4°. *^{4}.
[MS.] Wood D. 31(6). Wing C1698.

1679. [Cervantes, Miguel de]. *The famous history of don Quixote de la Mancha.* London: f. G. Conyers, 1686. 8°. Pp. [2], 20, [2].
P. [21], 'Don Quixot', may be by AW, and scribble.
Wood 259(12). Wing C1772 (two).

1680. Chaloner, [Richard]. *M^r· Challenor his confession and speech . . . before his execution [5 July].* London: P. Cole, 1643. 4°. Pp. [2], 6.
Wood 366(16). Wing C1800 ('O' not recorded in Wing).

1681. Chaloner, Thomas*. *Lex talionis. Or, a declamation against m^r. Challener, the crimes of the times, and the manners of you know whom.* [London]: n.pub., 1647. 4°. Pp. [2], 10.
Tp, 'Challener' underscored in red ink. P. 10, 'T: Shirley Med', and AW added, 'me tenet.' (Shirley was apparently the previous owner).
Wood 612(60). Wing L1861.

1682. [Chaloner, Thomas]. *A true and exact relation of the strange finding out of Moses his tombe.*

London: J. G. f. R. Lowndes, 1657. 8°. Pp. [4], 39.
Flyleaf, upper[v], AW wrote, 'The true and exact relation following, did when it first came out, seem a great wonder to the Presbyterian Divines, & puzled many of them, till the roguery was discovered//'; tp, 'This is a meere lye, it was writt by Thomas Chaloner: esquire and invented at a tavern: London'. P. 39[v], 3 monetary entries, e.g. '0 12 0'. LT 1.234.
Wood 246(3). Wing C1805.

1683. [Chamberlain, Robert]. *Conceits, clinches, flashes, and whimzies.* London: R. Hodgkinsonne f. D. Frere, 1639. 12°. A[4],B-F[12],G[6].
Missing in 1837. 'Conceits, Clinches &c – London 1639' in Whiteside cat. The BL copy has scribbles which may be by AW.
Wood 50. STC 4942 (one). *BL.*

1684. [Chamberlayne, Edward]. *The present warre parallel'd. Or a briefe relation of the five yeares civil warres of Henry the third.* [London]: n.pub., 1647. 4°. Pp. [2], 33.
Tp, AW wrote 'Edw Chamberlayne', in pencil. P. 33[v], signature of John Gerish [?].
Wood 608(71). Wing C1845.

1685. [Chamberlayne, Edward]. *Englands wants: or several proposals probably beneficial for England, . . . by a true lover of his country.* London: f. J. Martyn, 1667. 4°. Pp. 43.
Tp, AW wrote after t, 'D[r] Edw. Chamberlaine.' and '6[d]'; below, 'Another edition after this' (Wing C1840ff.). Also, 'Entered A H' (i.e., catalogued in the Bodleian Library). Acquired 4 Nov. 1667, LT 2.120.
[MS.] Wood D. 27(7). Wing C1839.

1686. Chamberlayne, Edward. *Angliae notitia; or, the present state of England.* [London], in the Savoy: T. N. f. J. Martyn, 1669. 12°. 3rd ed. Pp. [12], 480. Pasteboard (blue) with parchment spine.
Flyleaves, upper and lower, printer's waste (schoolbook, mathematics). Flyleaf, upper, 3rd, AW wrote, '1. Edit. came out 1669 [Wing C1819]. 8°. the authors name concealed. [/] 2. Edit. 1669. the authors name on it [Wing C1820]. [/] 4. Edit. 1670 [Wing C1822]. LT 1.351.
Wood 566(1). Wing C1821.

1687. Chamberlayne, Edward. *Angliae notitia: or, the present state of England . . . The second part.* [London], in the Savoy: T. N. f. J. Martyn, 1671. 12°. Pp. [22], 527.
Wood 566(2). Wing C1836A.

1688. Chamberlen, Peter*. *Publique bathes purged. Or, a reply to d[r] Chamberlain his vindication of publique artificial bathes.* [London]: n.pub., 1648. 4°. Pp. [2], 14.
P. 4-5, lines in margin, in pencil, at a question and answer about Dr. Grent's baths.
Wood 615(17). Wing P4149A (rare).

1689. Chambers, David. Morin, Jean, ed. *Davidis Camerarii Scoti de Scotorum fortitudine, doctrina, & pietate, libri quatuor [The dedication is to Charles 1].* Parisiis: P. Baillet, 1631. 4°. Pp. [22], 288. Parchment, with clasp holes.
Flyleaf, upper, '107' (?) and '3[s]'. Dedication, 3 cross marks, not in AW's manner.
Wood 652. *BL.*

1690. Chapman, Geo[rge]. *The funerals of . . . prince Henry [and] An epicede or funerall song.* London: T. S[nodham] f. J. Budgde (J. Budge), 1613 (1612). 4°. A2-4, B[4],C1; A[2],B-D[4],E[2] (2nd tp, at A1). Pasteboard (blue) with parchment spine. Trace of upper flyleaf in marbled paper.
Flyleaf, 2nd[v], AW wrote the titles of 14 printed works in this vol., within guidelines made with red ink and 'Memorandum that I have a larg fol. endorsed Epitaphs, Elegies. The first of which is entituled Threnodia Henricianarum Exequiarum [Wood 429(1), item 3850] &c and the last An Elegy on his Excellency Lieu. Gen. Tho. Tolmach [Wood 429(53), item 266]. But these, in number, 51 or more, being in fol. papers, could not be boud [sic] with the former, wh[ich] are in qu[arto]'. 1st item, each 8° leaf is pasted on a 4° template. E2[v], scribbles.
Wood 319(1). STC 4974.

1691. Chapman, Henry. *Thermae redivivae: the city of Bath described.* London: f. the author, sold J. Edwin, 1673. 4°. Pp. [6], 17.
Tp, AW wrote after author, 'Keeper of the Sun taverne in Bathe ///'.
Wood 467(5). Wing C1953.

1692. Chapman, John. *A most true report of the myraculous moving and sinking of a plot of ground,*

. . . *at Westram in Kent [18-29 Dec.].* [London]: T. Creede, 1596. 4°. A⁴,B1-3 (imprint cropped). Pasteboard (blue) with parchment spine. 1st upper and last lower flyleaves, purple paper.
Flyleaf, upper, 3rd-4th, AW wrote the titles of 31 printed works in this vol., within guidelines made with red ink. No. 28, *Wonderful blazing star*, item 6683, is missing.
[MS.] Wood D. 28(1). STC 4997 (two).

1693. Chappell, Richard. *A true and good relation, of the valliant exploits, . . . of sir Simon Harcourt, and sir Charles Coote.* London: f. F. Coules a. W. Ley, 1641[2]. 4°. Pp. [1], 7 (misnumbering).
Wood 507(28). Wing T2486 ('O' not recorded in Wing).

1694. [Chappuzeau, Samuel]. *The history of jewels [tr. from the French].* London: T. N. f. H. Kemp, 1671. 8°. Pp. [16], 128.
Tp, bsm. ('1.' ?).
Wood 700b(3). Wing C1959.

1695. Character. *The character of a pilfering taylor, or a true anatomy of monsieur Stich.* London: n.pub., 1675. 4°. Pp. [2], 6.
Tp, AW wrote 'May 24'.
Wood 500(12). Wing C1983.

1696. Character. *The character of a town-gallant.* London: f. W. L., 1675. 4°. Pp. 8.
Wood 500(10). Wing C1992.

1697. Charles 1*. Almansa y Mendoza, A. de, by. *The joyfull returne, of the most illustrious prince, Charles, . . . from the court of Spaine . . . Translated out of the Spanish.* London: E. All-de f. N. Butter a. H. Seile, 1623. 4°. Pp. [2], 46.
P. 14, a correction.
Wood 537(12). STC 5025.

1698. Charles 1*. *A true relation and journall, of the . . . entertainment given to . . . prince Charles by the king of Spaine . . . at Madrid.* London: J. Haviland f. W. Barret, 1623. 4°. Pp. [2], 35.
P. 1, note with details of Charles's journey, not by AW. P. 6, at 'disguised', AW wrote, 'incognito'.
Wood 537(11). STC 5032.

1699. Charles 1. *His majesties commission, and further declaration: concerning the reparation of Saint Pauls church.* London: R. Barker, by the assignes of J. Bill, 1633. 4°. Pp. [2], 23.
Flyleaf, upper, 'December. 20. 1633. The second [second, lined out] Commission about Sᵗ Paules Church. &c. A little varyed and issued the .2ᵈ. tyme.', not in AW's hand.
Wood 467(8). STC 9256.

1700. Charles 1. *His majesties answer to a message sent to him by the house of commons, concerning licences . . . to go into Ireland [19 Mar.].* London: R. Barker, assignes of J. Bill, 1641[2]. S.sh.
Dupl. at Wood 507(46).
Wood 276a(125). Wing C2100. Steele 2055.

1701. Charles 1. *His majesties answer to a message sent to him by the house of commons, concerning licences . . . to go into Ireland [19 Mar.].* London: R. Barker, assignes of J. Bill, 1641[2]. S.sh.
Dupl. at Wood 276a(125).
Wood 507(46). Wing C2100.

1702. Charles 1. *His majesties declaration to both houses of parliament . . . in answer to that presented to him at New-market [9 March].* London: R. Barker, assignes of J. Bill, 1641[2]. 4°. Pp. [2], 6.
Tp, AW rubbed out a former no.; below, a 2nd no., '25'. Dupl. at Wood 609(28).
Wood 373(33). Wing C2269.

1703. Charles 1. *His majesties declaration to both houses of parliament . . . in answer to that presented to him at New-market [9 March].* London: R. Barker, by the assignes of J. Bill, 1641[2]. 4°. Pp. [2], 6.
Tp, AW wrote 'Dupl', in pencil. Dupl. at Wood 373(33).
Wood 609(28). Wing C2269.

1704. Charles 1. *His majesties declaration, . . . published with the advice of his privie councell [in answer to the remonstrance of the commons, 1 Dec.].* London: R. Barker, assignes of J. Bill, 1641[2]. 4°. Pp. [2], 25.
Tp, AW wrote 'Aug or Sept' and 'qu[aere] date', in pencil, and later, 'This Declaration is in answer chiefly

to the Remonstrance of the state of the Kingdome presented by the appointment of the Parl. to his Maj. at Hampton Court 15 Dec. 1641 which Remonstrance was printed & made publick without the consent of his Maj.' Diff. ed. at Wood 614(35).
Wood 373(8). Wing C2251.

1705. Charles 1. *His majesties declaration, . . . published with the advice of his privie councell [in answer to the remonstrance of the commons, 1 Dec.]*. London: n.pub., 1641[2]. 4°. Pp. [2], 6.
Tp, AW wrote, 'Against the Remonstrance of the state of the kingdome – The Remonstr. was draune up in [Aug., lined out] Dec. 1641'; and in pencil, 'presented to his Majestie in Dec 1641'; and 'Dupl', in pencil. Diff. ed. at Wood 373(8).
Wood 614(35). Wing C2249AB.

1706. Charles 1*. *Five matters of state, which hath lately hapned between his majesty, and his high court of parliament*. London: f. F. Coules, a. T. Bates, 1642. 4°. A⁴.
Tp, AW rubbed out former nos.; below, '58'.
Wood 373(61). Wing F1112.

1707. Charles 1*. *Five remarkable passages, which have very lately happened betweene his majestie and the high court of parliament*. London: f. F. Cowles, a. T. Bates, [1642]. 4°. Pp. 5, [3].
Tp, AW lined out former nos. '38' and '43' and wrote the dates cited in the t, '22 24 26 Ap. 1642'. Below, former no., '45'. Also, 'Hull', prob. not by AW, in pencil. Dupl. at Wood 614(44).
Wood 373(54). Wing F1120.

1708. Charles 1*. *Five remarkable passages, which have very lately happened betweene his majestie, and the high court of parliament*. London: f. F. Cowles a. T. Bates, [1642]. 4°. Pp. 5, [3].
Tp, AW wrote 'Dupl', in pencil. Dupl. at Wood 373(54).
Wood 614(44). Wing F1120.

1709. Charles 1. *His majesties answer, by way of declaration to a printed paper, entituled, a declaration*. London: R. Barker, by the assignes of J. Bill, 1642. 4°. Pp. [2], 11, [1].
Tp, AW lined out a former no., '48', and altered a 2nd; below, '65' and 'Begin of May', in pencil. P. 6, date in margin, '26. Mar 1642'.
Wood 373(65). Wing C2090.

1710. Charles 1. *His majesties answer, to a printed book, intituled, a remonstrance . . . May 26*. Oxford: L. Lichfield, 1642. 4°. Pp. [2], 45.
Tp, AW lined out 2 former nos.
Wood 374(8). Wing C2108. Madan 1006.

1711. Charles 1. *His majesties answer to the XIX propositions of both houses*. Oxford (rpt.): L. Lichfield, 1642. 4°. Pp. [2], 38.
Tp, AW lined out former nos. '67' and '70', and altered '29' to '19'; below, to establish dates, he recorded 3 that he found in the text, e.g., '26 Jan p. 1 [/] 9 Sept p. 35 [/] 26 May p [38]', in pencil. Bsm.
Wood 374(19). Wing C2121. Madan 1007.

1712. Charles 1. *His majesties declaration . . . occasioned by a false . . . imputation laid upon his majestie, of an intention of . . . leavying war against his parliament*. London: R. Barker, by assignes of J. Bill, 1642. 4°. Pp. [2], 13.
Tp, AW wrote 'dupl', in pencil. P. 13ᵛ, signature of 'Mary W'. Diff. ed. at Wood 374(20) (item 1718).
Wood 614(57). Wing C2237A.

1713. Charles 1. *His majesties declaration to all his loving subjects, upon occasion of his late messages*. Oxford: L. Lichfield, 1642. 4°. Pp. [2], 22.
Tp, AW lined out '19' and altered '86' to '36'; and wrote '25 Aug', in pencil.
Wood 374(36) (not in Bodl. CD cat.). Wing C2257. Madan 1045.

1714. Charles 1. *His majesties demands to the gentry of York-shire, concerning the towne of Hull*. London: f. R. Lowndes, 1642. S.sh.
Tp, AW wrote, 'These things are in another pamphlet following' (items 1721f., 2629). A correction from 'his' to 'your' Majesties person, may be by AW. ᵛ, he lined out a former no., and wrote a date, 'Apr. –[?]'.
Wood 373(60). Wing C2295.

1715. Charles 1. *His majesties message sent to the parliament, April 8. 1642. Concerning his resolution to goe into Ireland*. London: f. D. I, 1642. 4°. Pp. [2], 6.

Tp, below, '35'.
Wood 508(5). Wing C2448A.

1716. Charles 1. *His majesties message to . . . parliament, April 28. 1642. Concerning his refusall to passe the bill for the militia.* London: R. Barker, by the assignes of J. Bill, 1642. 4°. Pp. [2], 5.
Tp, AW wrote 'Dup', in pencil. Diff. ed. at Wood 373(58), item 1726.
Wood 614(46). Wing C2453.

1717. Charles 1. *His majesties message to the house of peeres April 22.* London: n.pub., 1642. S.sh.
On ᵛ, blank, AW wrote an extensive index, some 75 entries and p. numbers, beginning with 'Fleetstreet - 9. White Friers 9 . . . Long Parliament 25 . . . Society of Jesus p 130 216 . . . prerogative court of Canterbury 176, 199 . . . Sorbon -Th. Bouchier 292 6 . . . Ely rents 299 . . . Temple barr 357 . . . College of Arms. 541. 542 Quaere Court of Arches 2 part. p. 362 Court of Audience of Canterbury ibid. p. 364' etc. to 'Assembly of Divines in Joh. White 1644 . . . '.
Wood 276a(131). Wing C2482 (two). Steele 2083.

1718. Charles 1. *His majesties proclamation and declaration . . . occasioned by a false . . . imputation [16 June].* Oxford (rpt.): L. Lichfield, 1642. 4°. Pp. [2], 30.
Tp, AW lined out former no., '66', and altered '21' to '20'; bsm. Diff. ed. at Wood 614(57) (item 1712).
Wood 374(20). Wing C2548. Madan 1008.

1719. Charles 1. *His majesties proclamation, declaring his expresse command, that no popish recusant, . . . shall serve him in his army [10 Aug.].* Oxford: L. Lichfield, 1642. 4°. Rpt. of York ed. Pp. [2], 6.
Wood 375(2). Wing C2574. Madan 1023.

1720. Charles 1. *His majesties proclamation, for the suppressing of the present rebellion, under the command of Robert earle of Essex.* Oxford (rpt.): L. Lichfield, 1642. 4°. Pp. [2], 10. Pasteboard (blue) with parchment spine; rebacked.
Flyleaf, upper, 3rd-4th, AW wrote the titles of 47 printed works in this vol. (really 48, AW omitted 23a), within guidelines made with red ink. At 3 items, 8, 15 and and 39, 'deest Octr. 15. 1839 W[illiam] K[irtland]'. A second librarian noted, at item 47, 'Removed. Found missing Aug. 20, 1918'. When AW reordered the pamphlets for binding, he lined out, rubbed out, or overwrote old numbers. Tp, AW lined out the former no., '16', and rubbed out another.
Wood 375(1). Wing C2637. Madan 1020.

1721. Charles 1. *His majesties second message to the parliament, concerning sir John Hothams refusall to give his majestie entrance into . . . Hull.* London: R. Barker, assignes of J. Bill, 1642. S.sh.
Dupl. at Wood 373(56).
Wood 276a(132). Wing C2769.

1722. Charles 1. *His majesties second message to the parliament, concerning sir John Hothams refusall to give his majestie entrance into . . . Hull.* London: R. Barker, assignes of J. Bill, 1642. S.sh.
ᵛ, AW overwrote a former no. Dupl. at Wood 276a(132).
Wood 373(56). Wing C2769.

1723. Charles 1. *The kings majesties answer to the petition of the house of commons, . . . the nine and twentieth of this instant Jan.* London: f. F. C[oles] I. W[right], 1642. S.sh.
Wood 375(31). Wing C2135 (two).

1724. Charles 1. *May the 18. 1642. His majesties last proclamation, May the fourteenth, 1642. Also . . . resolution concerning the establishment of religion.* N.p.: f. J. Tomson, a. A. Coe, 1642. 4°. A⁴.
Tp, AW lined out a former no., and overwrote a pencilled note, illeg.; below, '62'.
Wood 373(67). Wing C2375A (rare).

1725. Charles 1*. *A relation of divers remarkable proceedings betwixt the kings majesty and his loyall subjects [17 May].* London: f. F. Coules, a. T. Bates, 1642. 4°. A⁴.
Tp, AW lined out a former no., '47'; below, '61'.
Wood 373(64). Wing R803.

1726. Charles 1. *His majesties message to . . . parliament, April 28. 1642. Concerning his refusall to passe the bill for the militia.* London: n.pub., 1642 'Printed in the yeare,'. 4°. Pp. [2], 5, [1].
AW lined out the former no. '27' and altered a 2nd to '58'. Diff. ed. at Wood 614(46), item 1716.
Wood 373(58). Wing C2453B (3).

1727. Charles 1. *His majesties answer to the petition; concerning the disbanding of his gaurd [sic]*. London: f. W. Gaye, 1642, 1 June. 4°. Pp. 8 (misnumbering).
Tp, AW lined out 2 former nos., '58', '65'.
Wood 374(10). Wing C2130.

1728. Charles 1. *His majesties declaration to the ministers, free-holders [3 June]*. London: T. P. a. M. S. f. W. Gay, 1642, 7 June. 4°. Pp. 8.
Tp, AW lined out 1 former no., '64' and altered '17' to '16'. Dupl. at Wood 614(50). See item 6734.
Wood 374(16). Wing C2286.

1729. Charles 1. *His majesties declaration to the ministers, free-holders [3 June]*. London: [T. P. a. M. S. f. W. Gay] (cropped at bottom), [1642, 7 June] (cropped). 4°. Pp. 8.
AW wrote 'Dupl', in pencil. Dupl. at Wood 374(16).
Wood 614(50). Wing C2286.

1730. Charles 1. *A proclamation forbidding all his majesties subjects belonging to the trained bands . . . to rise, march*. London: n.pub., 1642, 9 June. S.sh. Rpt. of York edition.
ᵛ, former no., cropped, and AW wrote '29. May see after'.
Wood 374(9). Wing C2649.

1731. Charles 1. *His majesties message to the house of commons: concerning an order . . . for the borrowing of one hundered thousand pounds . . . for Ireland*. London: L. Norton a. J. Field f. E. Husband a. J. Franck, 1642, 5 Sept. 4°. Pp. 15.
Tp, former no., '26', lined out.
Wood 508(32). Wing C2478.

1732. Charles 1. *An agreement betwixt his majesty and the inhabitants of the county of Oxford, for provisions for . . . horses*. Oxford: L. Lichfield, 1642, 21 Dec. 4°. Pp. [2], 5.
P. 5ᵛ, 'Agreement wᵗʰ the Countie of Oxford. Dec. [1]642', prob. not by AW.
Wood 516(6a). Wing C2079. Madan 1134.

1733. Charles 1*. *The requests of the gentlemen of the grandjury of this county of Oxford . . . read, and considered of: and thereupon the . . . kings commissioners have . . . ordered as followeth. [The requests are not included]*. Oxford: L. Lichfield, 1642, 19 Dec. 4°. Pp. [2], 5.
P. 5ᵛ, 'Requests of the grand Jury of Oxfordsh. 21 Dec. [1]642', prob. not by AW.
Wood 516(6b). Wing R1121A ('O' not recorded in Wing). Madan 1132.

1734. Charles 1. *The collection of all the particular papers that passed between his majesty, both houses, . . . concerning the late treaty*. Oxford: L. Lichfield, 1643. 4°. Pp. [2], 42, [2] (2 tpp; wanting pp.43-8).
Wood 612(9). Wing C2157. Madan 1336.

1735. Charles 1. *The collection of all the particular papers that passed between his majesty, both houses, . . . concerning the cessation*. Oxford: L. Lichfield, 1643. 4°. Pp. [4], 12, [2], 13, [1], '14'-'16', [3], 21, [1] (4 tpp.).
Wood 612(6-8). Wing C2156A ('O' not recorded in Wing). Madan 1329.

1736. Charles 1. *His majesties declaration . . . in answer to a declaration of the lords and commons upon the . . . the late treaty of peace and severall intercepted letters . . . to the queene [3 June]*. Oxford: L. Lichfield, 1643. 4°. [2], 48, [2] (last [2] blank). Calf with 3 fillets, stamp decoration inside corners (2 leaves and sunflower sprouting fleur-de-lis), and roll decoration at inner, spine edge (Ashm. binding).
Flyleaf, upper, 2nd, and lower, 1st, the titles of 72 printed works in this vol. (1-55 (with misnumbering, and correction, of Roman numerals XL-XLIX), and 56-72). Many items are cropped. Numbering of works on tpp is in Roman numerals. There are really 76 items: items (6)-(8) are a single item; there are 3 at item (10); 3 at item (52); 2 at item (56); and 2 at item (59). This vol. includes 32 duplicate pamphlets (28 so marked by AW). The unbound pamphlets were bound after 1695.
Wood 612(1). Wing C2232. Madan 1374.

1737. Charles 1. *His majesties gratious message and summons to the city of Glocester [10 Aug.]*. Oxford: L. Lichfield, 1643. S.sh.
Wood 376(30). Wing C2324 (rare). Madan 1439.

1738. Charles 1. *His majesties message to both houses, concerning disbanding of both armies, and his majesties returne to . . . parliament [12 Apr.]*. Oxford: L. Lichfield, 1643. 4°. Pp. [2], 5.
Tp, no. 32 in a former bundle.

Wood 612(14). Wing C2458. Madan 1318.

1739. Charles 1. *His majesty taking in his princely consideration the present condition of divers . . . subjects [wounded soldiers].* Oxford: L. Lichfield, 1643. S.sh.
Note, 'This was red publikely in the aforesaide places & at the time appoynted, Sunday. 7. of May. 1643.', not by AW. LT 1.105.
Wood 276a(126). Wing C2822 (rare). Madan 1345. Steele 2418.

1740. Charles 1. *Two speeches . . . to . . . parliament assembled at Oxford [22 Jan, 7 Feb.].* Oxford: L. Lichfield, 1643[4]. 4°. Pp. [2], 6.
Wood 612(5). Wing C2862. Madan 1534.

1741. Charles 1*. *The grounds and motives inducing his majesty to agree to a cessation of armes for one whole yeare, with the Roman Catholiques of Ireland.* Oxford: L. Lichfield, 1643, 19 Oct. 4°. Pp. [2], 22 (wanting the device on p. 6).
Tp, former no., '39', lined out.
Wood 508(46). Wing G2134. Madan 1475.

1742. Charles 1. *His majesties most earnest . . . desire for peace, expressed in two . . . messages to . . . parliament [4 July, 8 Sept.].* Oxford: L. Lichfield, 1644. 4°. Pp. [2], 5.
Missing. AW wrote 'Dupl' on the tp of Wood 612(19). No dupl. in AW's collection.
Not located. Wing C2498. Madan 1680.

1743. Charles 1. *His majesties most earnest . . . desire for peace, expressed in two . . . messages to . . . parliament [4 July, 8 Sept.].* Oxford: L. Lichfield, 1644. 4°. Pp. [2], 5.
Tp, AW wrote 'Dupl', in pencil. No dupl. in AW's collection.
Wood 612(19). Wing C2498. Madan 1680.

1744. Charles 1. *His majesties speech to . . . parliament assembled at Oxford [16 April].* [Oxford]: L. Lichfield, 1644. 4°. Pp. [2], 5.
Tp, no. 37 in a former bundle.
Wood 612(16). Wing C2812. Madan 1612.

1745. Charles 1. *An order for publishing declarations and books set forth by his majesties command [24 Mar.].* Oxford: L. Lichfield, 1644. 4°. Pp. [2], 6.
Tp, no. 39 in a former bundle.
Wood 612(15). Wing O373. Madan 1585.

1746. Charles 1. *A proclamation for the better defence of the kings royal person, and of the university and city of Oxford [28 April].* Oxford: L. Lichfield, 1644. S.sh.
In a note I. P[hilip] explains that this s.sh., formerly at Wood 276a(127), is now at University Archives 530: 'Restored to the University Archives by decree 28 Oct. 1935'. This proclamation rightfully belongs to the University Archives. The old archive number, 530, is plainly visible, and there are extensive notes in the hand of an archivist. For a transcription of the notes, see LT 1.106-7.
University Archives 530 (formerly Wood 276a(127)). Wing C2602 (3) (Wing, incorrect date). Madan 1617.

1747. Charles 1*. *The great eclipse of the sun, or, Charles his waine over-clouded, by the evill influences of the moon . . . by . . . his queen.* [London]: G. B., 1644, 30 Aug. 4°. Pp. 8.
Wood 533(8). Wing G1688.

1748. Charles 1. *A proclamation for preventing of disorders in the night-time, in the garrison of Oxford [3 Feb.].* Oxford: L. Lichfield, 1645[6]. S.sh.
Wood 276a(128). Wing C2589 (rare). Madan 1838. Steele 2641.

1749. Charles 1*. *The Irish cabinet: or his majesties secret papers, for establishing the papall clergy in Ireland, together with two . . . relations of the . . . victories.* London: f. E. Husband, 1645[6], 20 Jan. 4°. Pp. 24 (p. unopened).
Wood 509(3). Wing C2353.

1750. Charles 1. *His majesties declaration to the marquesse of Ormond, . . . Dec. 1646. With . . . Ormonds proceedings against this kingdome.* London: W. Orton, 1646. 4°. A⁴.
Wood 509(13). Wing C2279.

1751. Charles 1. *His majesties last . . . message [20 Dec.] . . . to . . . parliament . . . and to the com-*

missioners of . . . Scotland . . . for a personall treaty. [London]: n.pub., 1646. 4°. Pp. [2], 5.
Wood 612(39). Wing C2373.

1752. Charles 1*. *The manner of the discovering the king at Southwell, on Tuesday the 5. of April [sic for May] 1646 [and 4 other pieces].* London: B. Alsop a. J. Coe, 1646. 4°. Pp. [2], 6.
Tp, '1^d', prob. not by AW.
Wood 501(8). Wing M466.

1753. Charles 1. *His majesties grievances sent by a message . . . to col. Hammond, governor of the Isle of Wight, with a letter from col. Hammond, concerning his treaty [13 Nov.].* London: R. Ibbitson, 1647. 4°. Pp. 8.
Pp. 6-7, line in margin.
Wood 612(53). Wing C2346.

1754. Charles 1. *His majesties message to . . . parliament, from the Isle of Wight, Novemb. 17. 1647. desiring a personall treaty at London.* London: R. Austin, 1647. 4°. Pp. [2], 6.
Wood 612(54). Wing C2465.

1755. Charles 1. *His majesties most gracious declaration, . . . Hampton-court [11 Nov.].* London [Oxford]: f. R. Royston (L. Lichfield), 1647. 4°. Pp. [2], 5.
Tp, no. 43 in a former bundle; ornament drawn, at bottom. Pp. 2, 4, 5^v, scribbles, notes, and some lines in Greek (cropping at bottom).
Wood 612(51). Wing C2507. Madan 1959.

1756. Charles 1*. *Treasons anatomie or the duty of a loyall subject in vindicating his gracious soveraigne, in . . . answer to a declaration, published by the house of commons, Feb. 15.* [London]: n.pub., 1647[8]. 4°. Pp. 15.
Tp, AW underscored 'Ireland' and wrote 'Ireland' in the margin, and overwrote former '16' with '18'.
Wood 509(18). Wing T2083.

1757. Charles 1*. *Collections of notes taken at the kings tryall, . . . Janua. 23.* N.p.: n.pub., [1648[9]]. 4°. Pp. 8.
Wood 364(13). Wing C5219 (Wing, By Robert Ibbitson).

1758. Charles 1*. *The fatall blow: or, the most impious and treasonable fact of Hammond, in . . . hurting his sacred majestie.* London: n.pub., 1648. 4°. Pp. [2], 6.
Wood 533(9). Wing F541.

1759. Charles 1. *His majesties declaration . . . concerning the remonstrance of the army. Together with his majesties letter to generall Fairfax; and his protestation and proposals to . . . the army [23 Nov.].* London: f. R. Brysons, 1648. 4°. Pp. [2], 6.
Wood 609(8). Wing C2230.

1760. Charles 1. *His majesties finall answer concerning episcopacie [1 Nov.].* London: f. R. Best, 1648. 4°. Pp. [3], 29.
Tp, bsm.
[MS.] Wood D. 31(21). Wing C2306.

1761. Charles 1. *His majesties reasons against the pretended jurisdiction . . . January 22.* [London]: n.pub., 1648[9]. S.sh.
AW wrote, 'This paper was translated into Lat. by Dr Tho. Pierce – printed 1674. 75 qu[arto] with other things of that D^r.' (see AO 4.306).
Wood 364(11). Wing C2740.

1762. Charles 1. *His majesties ultimate answers to the . . . commissioners, concerning Ireland & episcopacie [16, 18 Nov.].* London: f. R. Lowndes, 1648. 4°. A^4.
Tp, AW wrote after t, 'Ireland', and after year, '16 Nov.'
Wood 509(32). Wing C2873.

1763. Charles 1. *The kings majesties answer to the paper . . . concerning church-government [6 Oct.].* London: E. Griffin f. T. Hewer, 1648, 12 Oct. 4°. Pp. [2], 14.
Tp, former no., '44'.
[MS.] Wood D. 31(20). Wing C2125.

1764. Charles 1*. *The charge against the king discharged.* [London?]: n.pub., [1649]. 4°. Pp. [2], 34.
Wood 364(20). Wing C2046 ('O' not recorded in Wing).

1765. Charles 1*. Θρηνωδια. *Sive elegia in injustissimam trucidationem . . . Caroli primi.* N.p.: n.pub., 1649. 4°. Pp. [2], 6.
Wood 364(28) (not in Bodl. CD cat.). Wing T1128aA (rare).

1766. Charles 1. *King Charls his speech made upon the scaffold . . . 30 of Jan. 1648.* London: P. Cole, 1649. 4°. Pp. 8.
Wood 364(15). Wing C2792aA.

1767. Charles 1*. *A list of the names of the judges of the high court . . . for triall of the king.* N.p.: 'printed from R. J.', 1649. S.sh.
AW wrote in the numbers of the judges, '20', '40', etc., to the last, 126; and made a correction.
Wood 364(7). Wing L2471 (Wing, printed at London for R. J. The 2 Bodl. copies have: printed from R. J.).

1768. Charles 1*. *M. s. sanctissimi regis, & martyris, Caroli. Siste viator. Luge, obmutesce, mirare!.* N.p.: n.pub., [1649?]. S.sh.
Wood 364(26). Not in Wing. Not in ESTCR.

1769. Charles 1. *The princely pellican. Royall resolves . . . from his majesties divine meditations.* [London]: n.pub., 1649. 4°. Pp. [8], 48 (p. 1 blank). Calf with 3 fillets, stamp decoration, dragonesque interlace, inside corners, and roll decoration at inner, spine edge (Ashm. binding).
P. [1], list of 4 printed works in this vol., by an Ashm. librarian. Tp, bsm.
Wood 492(1). Wing P3491.

1770. Charles 1*. *The none-such Charles his character.* London: R. I. sold J. Collins, 1651. 8°. Pp. [7], 196, [18]. Pasteboard (grey) with parchment spine. 1st and last flyleaves, marbled paper rebacked.
Flyleaf, upper, 2nd^v, AW wrote the titles of 4 printed works in this vol., within guidelines made with red ink, and added after the last, 'The said History was published by Lestrange in fol - and therefore it cannot be bound with these things.' (fol. is at Wood 407(2); see note at Wood 244(4), items 4104, 3553).
Wood 244(1). Wing N1226A.

1771. Charles 1*. C., J., trans. *The full proceedings of the high court of justice against king Charles [20 Jan. 1648] . . . Hereunto is added, a parallel of the late wars [by E. Chamberlayne].* London: f. W. Shears, 1655. 8°. Pp. [2], 189 (misnumbering).
Tp, price, '10^d'. AW made some corrections, pp. 16-7, 24, 29 (also a 'q[uaere]', in pencil), and marks, pp. 99-100.
Wood 670(2). Wing F2354 ('O' not recorded in Wing).

1772. Charles 1*. *The great memorial: or, a list of . . . those pretended judges who . . . sentenced our late . . . king Charles.* London: f. E. Thomas, 1660. S.sh.
Missing in 1939. Short t, 'The great memoriall' in 1717 list. Dupl. at Wood 364(16).
Wood 276a(85). Wing G1709 (4). *Hunt.*

1773. Charles 1*. *The great memorial: or, a list of . . . those pretended judges who . . . sentenced our late . . . king Charles.* London: f. E. Thomas, 1660. S.sh.
Tp, AW wrote the month, 'May:', and underscored 2 forenames. Dupl. at Wood 276a(85), lost.
Wood 364(16). Wing G1709 ('O' not recorded in Wing).

1774. Charles 1*. *Majesty in misery, or an imploration to the king of kings; written . . . at Carisbrook castle, 1648.* (London): n.pub., (1681). S.sh. (r-v).
AW wrote '1681' in pencil.
Wood 657(3). Wing C2422.

1775. Charles 1*. *On the martyrdom of king Charles the first. January the 30th. 1648[9].* London: f. J. Norris, 1683. S.sh. (r-v).
Wood 364(27). Wing O316 ('O' not recorded in Wing).

1776. Charles 1, and James Harrington. *Certaine queries, proposed by the king, to the . . . commissioners . . . of parliament, . . . touching . . . Easter. With an answer . . . by sir James Harrington.* London: f. J. Giles, 1647, 27 Apr. 4°. Pp. [2], 6.
Wood 612(66). Wing C2155.

1777. Charles 1, and Prince Rupert. *The bloody treatie: or, proceedings between the king and prince Rupert*. London: f. J. C., 1645, 13 Dec. 4°. Pp. 8.
Tp, AW wrote, 'Nothing but lyes & rascallities', and altered the former no., '35'.
Wood 378(38). Wing B3294.

1778. Charles 1, and William Strode. *The kings majesties speech . . . before the university and city of Oxford [2 Nov.]. Together with a gratulatory replication . . . by . . . William Strode*. London: n.pub., 1642. 4°. Rpt. of Oxford edition. Pp. 7, [1].
Wood 514(10). Wing C2778A. Madan 1056.

1779. Charles 1, and Thomas Wriothesley. *The treaty with the earle of Southampton . . . and other commissioners from Oxford . . . And the kings going out of Oxford. . . . Also how the Irish rebells fell on Bunracy*. London: f. P. L., 1646, 30 Apr. 4°. Pp. 8.
Tp, 2 subject headings, prob. not by AW.
Wood 501(6). Wing T2101. Madan 1857.

1780. Charles 2*. *The copie of a letter from a commander in the fleet with his highness the prince of Wales . . . September the 7*. [London]: n.pub., 1648. 4°. Pp. [2], 4.
Tp, AW wrote after the year, 'Sept. 7.'
Wood 502(67) (not in Bodl. CD cat.). Wing C6114.

1781. Charles 2. *The declaration of his highnesse prince Charles, . . . concerning . . . his present engagement upon the fleet in the Downes, with his . . . letter to the lord major . . . of London [29 July]*. London: n.pub., 1648. 4°. Pp. [2], 6.
Tp, AW wrote after the year, 'Jul. 29.'
Wood 502(39). Wing C2972.

1782. Charles 2. *Prince Charles his declaration, . . . With his letter to sir Marmaduke Langdale, and sir Thomas Glemham [18 June]*. [London?]: n.pub., 1648. 4°. A⁴.
Tp, AW wrote after the year, 'Jun. 18.'
Wood 502(29). Wing C2961.

1783. Charles 2. *The resolution of the prince of Wales, concerning . . . Cromwel, and the routing of the Scottish army. . . . Likewise, his majesties declaration concerning all those who have taken up arms against him [23 Aug.]*. London: n.pub., 1648. 4°. Pp. [2], 6 (unopened).
Tp, AW wrote after the year, 'Aug. 23'.
Wood 502(59). Wing C3601A.

1784. Charles 2*. *A great victory obtained by prince Charles his ships; upon the north coast . . . . Also, a new rising in Lancashire. . . . Likewise, the declaration of the Coruish-men, [sic] concerning prince Charles*. London: f. R. Williamson, 1649. 4°. Pp. [2], 6.
Wood 503(3). Wing G1779.

1785. Charles 2. *His maiesties declaration to all his subiects of the kingdome of England [23 Oct.]*. [London]: n.pub., [1649]. S.sh., fol.
ᵛ, AW wrote, '23. Oct. 1649'.
Wood 503(7). Wing C3003A.

1786. Charles 2. *Three intercepted letters. The one from Charles Stuart, . . . The other two from the lord Digby and Daniel Monro*. London: M. Simmons, 1649. 4°. Pp. 8.
AW wrote below, 'July 1649', in pencil.
Wood 510(3). Wing C3610.

1787. Charles 2. *A declaration of the proceedings of the prince of Wales and his coming to . . . Jersey. . . . with a proclamation of the states of Holland, . . . And a list of the parliaments navy [26 Mar.]*. London: f. R. W., 1649, 30 Mar. 4°. Pp. [2], 6 (misnumbering). Pasteboard (blue) with parchment spine. Flyleaves, upper, 2nd and 3rd, AW wrote the titles of 37 printed works in this vol., within guidelines made with red ink. At no. 18, 'Deest Novʳ. 1840 W. K[irtland]'. The Milford hand-list (1922) records also nos. 14 and 15 as 'missing'. Before binding, AW rearranged the pamphlets and many show earlier nos. The vol. was bound after 11 June 1692 when he purchased no. 37 (possibly in Nov. 1692; the 3 following vols., were bound at the same time, see notes at Wood 504(1), 505(1) and 506(1), items 317, 5562, 6186). 1st item, tp, AW wrote after the year, 'Mar. 26'.
Wood 503(1). Wing D753.

1788. Charles 2. *C R [/] A declaration of the king, proclaimed at Dover and Sandwitch [sic] and other market towns in Kent*. [London]: n.pub., [1659]. S.sh.
AW added, 'March: 1659[60]'.
Wood 276a(216). Wing D690B (3) (Wing, [London? 1648?]) ('O' not recorded in Wing).

1789. Charles 2. *C. R. His majestys gracious message to general Monck . . . in Scotland*. Paris: cum priviledgio, 1659. S.sh.
AW wrote, 'This was lookd upon as a forgerie/', in red ink.
Wood 276a(110). Wing C3035A (two). Steele 3136.

1790. Charles 2*. *Certamen Brittanicum, Gallico Hispanicum. A true relation of a conference . . . between Charles Stuart . . . Don Lewis de Haro, and the cardinall Mazarine*. London: n.pub., 1659. 4°. Pp. [2], 10.
Tp, no. '13', in pencil, in a former bundle.
Wood 613(3). Wing C1765.

1791. Charles 2. *C R[.] King Charles his speech to the six eminent persons who lately arrived at Brussells, . . . touching his restoration [18 March]*. Anwerp [sic]: cum privilegio, 1660. S.sh.
AW added '1659' after date of the speech, March 18, and, 'supposed to be fictious:'.
Wood 276a(133). Wing C3608 (two). Steele 3164.

1792. Charles 2*. *Englands genius pleading for king Charles to the . . . lords and commons in parliament*. London: f. J. Jones, 1660. S.sh.
AW wrote 'Aprill:'.
Wood 416(80). Wing E2965 (two).

1793. Charles 2*. *Englands joy for the coming in of our gratious soveraign king Charles the II*. London: f. H. Brome, 1660. S.sh.
AW wrote, 'May:'; ᵛ, 'May 1660'.
Wood 416(84). Wing E2988.

1794. Charles 2*. *Englands triumph. A more exact history of his majesties escape after the battle of Worcester*. London: J. G. f. N. Brook, 1660. 8°. Pp. [8], 128.
Flyleaf, upper, AW wrote, 'Kemet the picture', lined out, and 'Rich Pendrell preserver and conductor of his sacred Maj. K. Ch. 2 after his escape from Worcester, died 8. Feb. 1671 & was buried in the north side of the yard of S. Giles's ch. in the Fields neare to London – over his grave is a fair Altar - monument & about 10 English verses engraven thereon.' (LT 2.241). P. 41, vertical line in margin. Acquired 13 Nov. 1660, 9ᵈ, LT 1.338.
Wood 235(3) (not in Bodl. CD cat.). Wing E3060.

1795. Charles 2*. *A great and bloody plot discovered against his royal majesty, Charles*. London: f. S. Chamberlain, 1660. 4°. Pp. 8.
Tp, AW wrote 'Aprill:'.
Wood 608(9). Wing G1649.

1796. Charles 2. *His majesties gracious letter and declaration, sent to the house of peers, by sir J. Greenvill, from Breda [14 Apr.]*. London: J. Macock a. F. Tyton, 1660. 4°. Pp. 14 (p. 1 blank).
Wood 608(14). Wing C3015.

1797. Charles 2. *His majesties gracious message to the house of commons [18 June]*. London: J. Bill a. C. Barker, 1660. Fol. Pp. 7.
Wood 657(37). Wing C3038.

1798. Charles 2. *His majesties gracious speech to . . . parliament, . . . At the passing of the act of free pardon, indempnity and oblivion [29 Aug.]*. London: J. Bill a. C. Barker, 1660. 4°. Pp. 8.
Wood 608(25). Wing C3042.

1799. Charles 2. *His majesties letter. To the generals of the navy at sea. Together with his majesties . . . declaration . . . with the answer [14 Apr., 3 May]*. London: S. Griffin f. J. Playford, 1660. 4°. Pp. 8.
Wood 608(11). Wing C3114.

1800. Charles 2. *King Charls II. His declaration to all his loving subjects . . . Dated . . . 4/14 of Aprill 1660. And read in parliament, May 1 . . . with his . . . letter . . . to . . . gen. Monck*. [London]: [W. Godbid f. J. Playford], [1660]. 4°. Pp. 8 (imprint cropped).
Wood 608(12). Wing C2984.

1801. Charles 2. *A letter from k. Charls the second, . . . to mr Cawton . . . in defence of himselfe in matters of religion.* London: W. Wilson f. R. Lownds, 1660. 4°. Pp. 7.
Tp, AW added after the year, 'Aprill:'.
Wood 632(45). Wing C3097A.

1802. Charles 2. *A letter from the king to F. M. . . . Bruxels 10. April.* [London]: n.pub., [1660]. S.sh.
Wood 276a(161). Wing C3099.

1803. Charles 2*. *News from the royall exchange: or gold turn'd into mourning.* London: f. C. King, 1660. S.sh.
AW altered 1660 to 16'59: March'; ᵛ, 'Mar. 1659', and for note on ᵛ, see Wood 416(68), item 1086.
Wood 416(69). Wing N1014.

1804. Charles 2. *A proclamation touching the election of fit persons to serve in parliament.* London: f. M. B., 1660. S.sh.
AW altered the year to 16'59', and later added, 'Fictions', and underscored the month, November, in the proclamation.
Wood 276a(129). Wing C3590.

1805. Charles 2*. *To the kings most excellent majesty. The humble and grateful acknowledgement of many ministers . . . concerning ecclesiastical affairs [25 Oct.].* London: f. J. Rothwell, 1660. S.sh.
[MS.] Wood D. 26(3). Wing T1517.

1806. Charles 2*. *A true relation of the reception of his majestie and conducting him through the city of London [29 May].* London: f. J. Clarke, 1660. 4°. Pp. 8.
Wood 398(12). Wing T3033A.

1807. Charles 2. *Two letters from his majesty. The one to the speaker of the commons . . . The other to . . . generall Monck. . . . Together with the resolve of the house thereupon [14 Apr.].* London: E. Husband a. T. Newcomb, 1660. Fol. Pp. 7.
Wood 657(23). Wing C3624.

1808. Charles 2*. *Upon the kings most excellent majestie an anagram & acrostick.* [London]: for Theodorus Microcosmus, 1660. S.sh.
AW altered 1660 to 16'59: feb:'; ᵛ, 'Feb. 1659'.
Wood 416(55). Wing U113 (rare).

1809. Charles 2*. *Vox populi suprema rex Carolus. Or, the voice of the people for king Charles.* London: f. Theodorus Microcosmus, 1660. S.sh.
AW wrote, 'Aprill'; ᵛ, 'Apr 1660', in pencil.
Wood 416(75). Wing V734 (3).

1810. Charles 2*. *The form of his majesties coronation-feast which was solemnized and kept at Westminster-hall [23 Apr.].* London: f. R. Crofts, 1661. S.sh.
Perhaps one of several items acquired 27 Apr. 1661, LT 1.389.
Wood 398(19). Wing F1568 ('O' not recorded in Wing).

1811. Charles 2. *His majestie's gracious speech to . . . parlament [20 Nov.].* London: R. Norton, 1661. 4°. Pp. [2], 6.
Wood 608(40). Wing C3046.

1812. Charles 2. *His majestie's gracious speech to . . . parlament, . . . The day of their adjournment [30 July].* London: J. Bill a. C. Barker, 1661. Fol. Pp. [2], 6, [1].
Wood 657(38). Wing C3044.

1813. Charles 2*. *A true copie of the list, or roll, of the kings majesties most royall proceeding from the Tower through London to White-hall.* London: f. R. Williams, 1661. S.sh.
AW wrote, 'Coronation of Ch: 2'.
Wood 398(16). Wing T2648 (two).

1814. Charles 2*. *Several useful queries, . . . propounded for the safety of the king.* London: n.pub., 1662. 4°. Pp. 8.
Wood 608(43). Wing S2814A (Wing, safety . . . of the King).

1815. Charles 2*. *At the court at Oxford, the sixt of October 1665 . . . preventing . . . the infection.*

Oxford: L. Lichfield, 1665. S.sh.
LT 2.48.
Wood 276a(306). Wing E808A (two). Madan 2685. Steele 3441.

1816. Charles 2. *His majesties gracious letter to his parliament of Scotland, May 23. 1672. With their answer. As also the speech of . . . the duke of Lauderdaile [12 June].* [London], in the Savoy: T. Newcomb, 1672. Fol. Pp. 12.
Wood 657(31). Wing C3022.

1817. Charles 2*. *The oaths of allegiance & supremacy.* London: assigns of J. Bill a. C. Barker, 1672. S.sh.
At bottom, 'London', not in AW's hand.
Wood 276a(144) (not in Bodl. CD cat.). Wing O83 (two).

1818. Charles 2. *An abstract of the patent granted by his majesty, for erecting a corporation for relief of the poor widows and children of clergy-men [1 July].* London: f. H. Brome, [1678]. S.sh.
Wood 276a(38). Wing C2886.

1819. Charles 2*. *Conjuratio Jesuitica in Carolum II. [Parricidium Edmundburii Godfredi, Otii & Bedloi elogia].* [London]: n.pub., 1680. Fol. Pp. [2], 10.
Wood 424(7). Wing C5880A.

1820. Charles 2. *His majesties . . . speech to . . . parliament . . . at Oxford [21 Mar.].* Oxford: at the theater, [1681]. Fol. Pp. 7.
Tp, former no. '7'. LT 2.531.
Wood 657(41). Wing C3163.

1821. Charles 2. *His majesties letters to the bishop of London and the lord mayor . . . 22th day of July.* (London): (S. Roycroft), (1681). S.sh. (r-v).
Wood 276a(168-169). Wing C3120.

1822. Charles 2. *Charles the second by the grace of God of England, Scotland, . . . [A recommendation of William Morgan's lately published survey of London and Westminster, 15 Feb. 1681/2].* [London]: n.pub., [1682]. S.sh. 4°.
Wood 658(776). Not in Wing. See Wing C3611Aff. Not in ESTCR.

1823. Charles 2. *By the king. A proclamation for the apprehending of James duke of Monmouth, Ford lord Gray [28 June].* London: by the assigns of J. Bill deceas'd, and by H. Hills a. T. Newcombe, 1683. S.sh.
Wood 660c(6). Wing C3440.

1824. Charles 2. *His majesties declaration to all his loving subjects, concerning the treasonable conspiracy against his sacred person.* London: by the assigns of J. Bill deceas'd, H. Hills, a. T. Newcomb, 1683. 4°. Pp. 20, [1].
Tp, AW wrote the price, '4ᵈ'.
Wood 428(17). Wing C2998.

1825. Charles 2*. *A list of all the conspirators that have been seiz'd, (and where committed) since the discovery of the . . . plot.* [London]: n.pub., [1683?]. S.sh. (r-v).
AW made footnotes in red ink and identified 5 persons associated with Oxford colleges, Fran. Charlton, '(a) somtimes gent. com. of ch. ch.'; Mr. Trenchard, '(b) somtimes fellow of New Coll'; Mr. Robert West, '(c) of Magd. Coll'; John Ayloff (Ayliffe), 'somtimes gent. com. of Edm. hall'; and William Rumbold, 'Will. Rombold [sic] before mention'd was committed prisoner to the Tower for high treason against Oliv. Cromwell about 28. May 1655, being one of the plot then lately discovered, different from that at Salisbury in March going before[.] He was then a marchant.' LT 3.19, 58, 168.
Wood 428(18). Wing L2378.

1826. Charles 2*. *A true relation of the late kings death. On Monday, being the 2d. of February.* [London]: n.pub., [1685]. S.sh.
AW added glosses, a-f, in the margins for the abbreviations of persons or rites, e.g., '(b)' at printed 'D.' and '(b) Duke of York' in the margin. At the bottom, 'This paper came first to Oxōn in the begin. of March 1685/6 [sic]'. AW owned a diff. ed., Wood 236(4), on which he wrote similar notes, but dated it 1684/5. LT 3.134.
Wood 242(4). Wing T2986 (diff. setting; see following entry).

1827. Charles 2*. *A true relation of the late king's death. On Munday, being the 2d. of February.* [London]: n.pub., [1685]. S.sh.
AW added glosses, a-h, in the margins for the abbreviations of persons or rites, e.g., '(b)' at printed 'C.F.' and '(b) Capuchin Fryer' in the margin. At printed 'Mr. H.', 'Huddleston a Benedictin monke one of the preservers of the King in his flight from Worcester batt. 1651' At the bottom of the s.sh., 'This paper came to Oxon. in the beginning of March 1684/5 being about [blank] weeks after the Kings death, but few believed it.' (that the King, before his death, was received into the Catholic church by Huddleston). Flyleaf, lower, AW recorded another account of Charles's death and of a written commitment to the Catholic faith 'found in his strong box' (see Wing, C2942ff.) taken from 'The great Historical, Geographical & Poetical Dictionary &c. vol. in Car. 2.', 15 lines in all. AW owned diff. ed., Wood 242(4), with similar notes. LT 3.134.
Wood 236(4). Wing T2986 (diff. setting; see previous entry).

1828. Charles 2. *Murder will out: or, the king's letter, justifying the marquess of Antrim [10 July 1663].* London: n.pub., 1689. 4°. Pp. 8.
AW wrote, 'Jan. 27. an. 1688[89] – 2ᵈ'. In a later hand, 'Carolus II.'
Wood 510(35). Wing M3095.

1829. Charles 2*. *State tracts: being a collection of several treatises relating to the government. Privately printed in the reign of k. Charles II [including reprints of: a list of the lords, the benefit of the ballot, the political catechism, reasons for the indictment of the duke of York, and 3 other treatises, and works by Charles Blount, François di Aix de la Chaise, Charles II, Anthony Ashley Cooper (5), William Coventry, Denzel Holles, John Lucas, Andrew Marvell, Slingsby Bethel, and James Stewart].* London: n.pub., 1689. Fol. Pp. [4], 1-240, 367-468 (wanting 3Q-5A²). Calf with 2 fillets, 2nd rectangle formed by roll decoration and stamp decoration (leaves below and blossoms at tops) outside corners, and roll decoration at inner, spine edge (Ashm. binding); rebacked.
Wood 560(1). Wing S5329.

1830. Charles 2, and Edward Hyde. *His majesties gracious speech to the lords & commons, together with the lord chancellor's, at the opening of the parliament [8 May].* London: J. Bill a. C. Barker, 1661. Fol. Pp. [2], 26.
Wood 657(40). Wing C3071.

1831. Charles 2*, and James 2*. Phillips, John (possible author). *The secret history of the reigns of k. Charles II. and k. James II.* [London?] (Printed at Cologn): n.pub., 1690. 12°. Pp. [4], 214.
Tpᵛ, AW wrote, 'A grand phanatick, or Presbyterian, choos you whether was author of this book'. Some scattered brief notes or marks, e.g., pp. 50; 83; 84-5, 'q[uaere]' and 'q[uaere] when', in pencil; 113, AW identified 'W–P' as 'Edm. Warcup'; 144-5, wrote 'Anne Hyde'; 170-1; 195, wrote 'Will. Brent', in pencil; 200; 203.
Wood 242(3). Wing S2347 ('O' not recorded in Wing).

1832. Charles Emmanuel 1. Savoy, duke of. *A relation of the now present warres, betweene . . . Charles Emanuel, . . . and the l. cardinal of Mantua, . . . Translated out of the Latin copie.* London: W. Stansby f. N. Butter, 1615. 4°. A-C⁴,D² (A1-2 blank).
Wood 615(6). STC 5045.

1833. Charles the Tenth. Sweden, king of. *The most heavenly and Christian speech of . . . Carolus Gustavus Adolphus on his death-bed . . . translated out of High-Dutch.* London: f. T. Vere, 1660. 4°. Pp. 8.
Tp, AW altered 1660 to '59: March'.
Wood 610(19). Wing C3655.

1834. [Charleton, Walter]. *The Ephesian matron.* London: f. H. Herringman, 1659. 12°. Pp. [18], 124.
Pasteboard (blue) with parchment spine. 1st upper and last lower flyleaves, purple dyed paper.
Flyleaf, upper, 2ndᵛ, AW wrote the titles of 3 printed works in this vol., within guidelines made with red ink. AW attributed item (1) to Jer. Taylor (so also in AO 3.790, but see a similar work attributed to Charleton at AO 4.752). Above, a note by a later writer, 'E Lib. Clar: viri A Wood'. Tp, bsm. (?), '7'.
Wood 818(1). Wing C3671.

1835. Charleton, Walter. *Chorea gigantum, or, the most famous antiquity of Great-Britan, vulgarly called Stone-heng.* London: f. H. Herringman, 1663. 4°. Pp. [16], 64.
Each 4° leaf is pasted on a fol. template. Tp, '1ˢ', bsm., and on blank leaf, 'Stonehenge'. Blank leaf, 3rd, (p. [4]), AW wrote binding instructions, 'Past paper throughout the margin of this book to make it even

with Inigo Jones –' (i.e., Wood 413(1), item 3904), and 'Charlton'. Acquired 18 Nov. 1662, 1ˢ, LT 1.461, and AO 4.753-4.
Wood 413(2). Wing C3666 (Wing, gigantum;).

1836. [Charpentier, François]. *A treatise touching the East-Indian trade, or, a discourse . . . concerning the establishment of a French company for the commerce of the East-Indies.* London: T. Mabb f. H. Brome, 1664. 4°. Pp. [6], 62.
Tp, AW wrote, '8ᵈ'. Acquired 22 Nov. 1664, LT 2.23.
[MS.] Wood C. 14(12). Wing C3714.

1837. [Chartier, Alain]. [Painter, William, trans. (not by Chartier)]. *Delectable demaundes, and pleasaunt questions, . . . in matters of love, . . . with morall and politique devises. Newly translated out of the Frenche.* London: J. Cawood for N. Englande, [1566]. 4°. Ff. 100. Parchment. Flyleaf, upper, printer's waste paper, 'Secundum usus Sarum', fol. vi.
Tp, signature of Peter Fearne (?). Some brief notes, not in AW's hand, e.g., fol. 3ᵛ, 8, 12, 34ᵛ.
Wood 525. STC 5059.

1838. Chasteigner, Henri Louis. Poitiers, bp. of. *Celebriorum distinctionum tum philosophicarum, tum theologicarum synopsis.* Londini: [R. Field] ex off. typogr. Soc. Stat., 1617. 4°. Pp. [4], 133.
Tp, 'Thomas Ellis hunc librum possidet.' (lined out) and a second autograph (illeg. blotted out, and cropped at side); below, prob. by AW, '12ᵈ'. Pp. 117, 133ᵛ, note in Latin, not in AW's hand.
Wood 607(2a). STC 5064.

1839. Chaucer. *Canterbury tales.* N.p.: ?, n.d. Pp.?
Missing in 1837. 'Canterbury Tales –' in Whiteside cat.
Wood 66(4). Not identified.

1840. Chaucer, Geoffrey. Kinaston, Francis, trans. *Amorum Troili et Creseidae libri duo priores Anglico-Latini.* Oxoniae: J. Lichfield, 1635. 4°. Pp. [22], 105, [8], 159 (books 1-2, only; wanting A2-3).
Acquired 24 Dec. 1661, 6ᵈ, LT 1.421. See also AO 3.38-9.
Wood 482(2). STC 5097. Madan 804.

1841. Chauncie, William. *The rooting out of the Romishe supremacie.* London: H. Middleton f. J. Perin, 1580. 8°. Pp. 141, [1].
Tp, signature of Hum: Dyson. Dupl. at Wood 794(2).
Wood 774(3a). STC 5103.

1842. Chauncie, William. *The rooting out of the Romishe supremacie.* London: H. Middleton f. J. Perin, 1580. 8°. Pp. 141, [1].
At entry on upper flyleaf, AW added 'in bib. Bod'. Former owner, John Speed. Acquired 24 Sept. 1661, see Wood 794(1), item 902, and LT 1.416. Dupl. at Wood 774(3a).
Wood 794(2). STC 5103.

1843. Chauncy, Maurice. *Historia aliquot nostri saeculi martyrum.* Moguntiae: (ap. S. Victorem excud. F. Behem), 1550. Ff. [8], 65, [3]. Parchment with 2 clasp holes.
Tp, 'Henrici Jacksoni Oxoniensis, Collegii Corpori Christi MDC', 'pretium 2ˢ-6ᵈ', and 1 note on the author by Jackson; also, 'Antonii à Uuood, Oxon. Ex bib. Hen. Jacksoni consanguinij sui. 1662' (20 Oct., LT 1.459; also LT 1.23) and 2 notes about the author, e.g. 'Camney vel Chauney vel Chancaeus, vide in bib. Carthusiana per Theod. Petreium edit Col. 1609.' Text, notes and marks in margins, in 3 hands, in Jackson's, an earlier hand, and some in pencil. The marks in pencil, to f. 12, often over earlier marks, may be by AW.
Wood 341. BL.

1844. Cheapside Cross. ? ?. ?: ?, ? 4°.
Missing. The list of titles prepared by AW is also missing from this vol. The entry in the Whiteside list indicates that this was prob. a theological work concerning the Cheapside Cross (see note at [MS.] Wood D. 31(18)).
[MS.] Wood D. 31(44). Not identified.

1845. Cheapside Cross. ? ?. ?: ?, ? 4°.
Missing. The list of titles prepared by AW is also missing from this vol. The entry in the Whiteside list indicates that this was prob. a theological work concerning the Cheapside Cross (see note at [MS.] Wood D. 31(18)).

[MS.] Wood D. 31(43). Not identified.

1846. Cheats. *Several new cheats brought to publique view; or, the good old cause turn'd to a new cheat.* London: n.pub., 1659. 4°. Pp. [2], 5.
Wood 613(26). Wing S2783.

1847. Cheeke, William. *Anagrammata, et chron-anagrammata regia.* Londini: W. Stansby, 1613. 8°. A-E⁸.
Flyleaf, upperᵛ, AW wrote, 'Gul Cheeke quondam e Coll. B. Mar. Magd. Oxon. (Austro-brittannus) fuit author istius libri [/] Gul. Cheek A. Magd. adm. erat. B.A. 14 Feb. 1595'. Tp, translation of a Greek phrase to Latin 'difficilia quae pulchra', not by AW.
Wood 105(2). STC 5107.

1848. Cheke, John. *De pronuntiatione Graecae potissimum linguae disputationes cum Stephano Wintoniensi Episcopo, septem contrarijs epistolis comprehensae.* Basileae: per N. Episcopium iuniorem, 1555, Oct. 8°. Pp. 349.
Missing. Listed in MS. Wood E. 2(70), p. 16. See AO 1.243.
MS. Wood E. 2(70), p. 16. O̲ (two), BL.

1849. Cheke, John. *The true subject to the rebell, or the hurt of sedition, . . . with the authors life [by G. Langbaine].* Oxford: L. Lichfield, 1641. 4°. Pp. [24], 64.
Tp, 'By Gerard Langbaine D.D.' lined out, and, in AW's early hand, 'The preface was writt by Gerard Langbaine Mʳ of Arts & fellow of Quens Coll Oxon, since Dʳ of D: & provost of the same'. Pp. [5], [10], AW noted words and sections that should be 'In Ital[ics]'; [11], note at a printed anecdote of Tavernour: 'Mʳ Ric: Taverner of Wood-eaton:' (AW reproduced the anecdote about Taverner preaching 'at the mount of St. Mary's', i.e., the stone pulpit at the university church, with his sword at his side and a chain of gold hanging around his neck, in AO 1.421 and in *Hist. and Antiq.*, 2.152; Hearne also used the story, see LT 1.387); [16], [19-22] some underscoring and lines in margin, in ink and pencil.
Wood 614(21-22). Wing C3778. Madan 995.

1850. Chepstow. *(2) Great news from Chepstow-castle in Monmouth-shire. Being a true account of several strange apparitions in the air.* London: f. Edmoud [sic] Jones in the Strand, 1690. S.sh. (r-v).
[MS.] Wood D. 28(30). Not in Wing. Not in ESTCR.

1851. Cheshire. *One and twenty Chester queries, . . . reflecting upon the late memorable affairs . . . in Cheshire, by several . . . under the conduct of the lord Lambert.* London: n.pub., 1659. 4°. Pp. 7.
Wood 503(27). Wing O332.

1852. Cheshire. *An address intended to his majesty by the ministery of Cheshire . . . July 24.* London: n.pub., 1660. S.sh.
Wood 276a(206). Not in Wing (should be at A542A). Not in ESTCR.

1853. Chester, Robert*. *Memoriae sacrum. Resiste viator, paucis te volo: Robertus Chester . . . sero partu [2 July 1659].* N.p.: n.pub., [1659]. S.sh.
Dupl. at Wood 429(16).
Wood 276a(30). Wing M1683 (rare, 2 at O).

1854. Chester, Robert*. *Memoriae sacrum. Resiste viator, paucis te volo: Robertus Chester . . . sero partu [2 July 1659].* N.p.: n.pub., [1659]. S.sh.
ᵛ, AW wrote, 'Rob. Chester 1659'. Dupl. at Wood 276a(30).
Wood 429(16). Wing M1683 (rare, 2 at O).

1855. [Chestlin, Robert]. *Persecutio undecima. The churches eleventh persecution. Or, a briefe of the puritan persecution of the protestant clergy.* [London]: n.pub., 1648. 4°. Pp. [4], 74.
Pp. 11-2, 16-22, 26-7, 29, 33-4, etc., to 66, some comma marks and pointers in margin, not in AW's usual style; also frequent underscoring and cross marks in margin which may be by AW, e.g., pp. 18, at Pym and John White; 22 at Dr. Fell; 64, at Pym, Captaine Ven and Richard Wiseman.
Wood 619(12). Wing C3785.

1856. Chetwind, Charles, collected by. *A narrative of the depositions of Robert Jenison . . . proving that mr. William Ireland . . . was in London.* London: f. H. Hills, T. Parkhurst, J. Starkey, D. Newman, T. Cockeril, T. Simmons, a. J. Tonson, 1679. Fol. Pp. [5], 13.
Tp, AW wrote the price, '6ᵈ.' Purchased from Vade in Oct. 1679, see his record of purchase at MS. Wood F. 50, f. 11.

Wood 425(7). Wing C3792.

1857. Chevreau, Urbain. H., I., trans. *A relation of the life of Christina queen of Sweden [tr. from Brieve relation de la vie de Christine reyne de Suede]. Whereunto is added, her genius [tr. from Le genie de la reyne Christine, by Saint-Maurice].* London: J. C. f. H. Fletcher a. N. Heathcoate, 1656. 4°. Pp. [4], 42.
Tp, bsm. Flyleaf, lower, scribble, 'morey house'.
Wood 532(13). Wing C3803.

1858. Cheynell, Francis. *Chillingworthi novissima. Or, the sickness, heresy, death, and buriall of William Chillingworth.* London: f. S. Gellibrand, 1644. 4°. 1,A-G⁴,H1-3.
A4, a correction; C1, C2, C3 (in red ink), C4ʳ⁻ᵛ, etc., to E4ᵛ, line in margin, mainly in pencil; E2ᵛ, date of Chillingworth's funeral, in margin, '24. Jan. 1643-4', may be in AW's hand (though he normally wrote dates in o.s.; he recorded the date as 1643 in AO 3.94).
Wood 619(7). Wing C3810.

1859. [Cheynell, Francis]. *Aulicus his hue and cry sent forth after Britanicus, who is generally reported to be a lost man.* London: n.pub., 1645. 4°. Pp. [2], 6.
Wood 622(8). Wing C3808.

1860. [Cheynell, Francis]. *An account given to the parliament by the ministers sent by them to Oxford.* London: M. F. f. S. Gellibrand, 1647. 4°. Pp. [2], 53.
Tp, AW wrote, 'The authour Fr: Cheynell', and after the year, '1646. mense Februarii'. Pp. 3-6, 13, 16 marks in margin and a brief note, mainly in pencil; p. 12, at scholars who accepted the parliamentary 'ministers', AW wrote 'cheifly of New inne & Magdalen Hall'; 30, date and cross-refs. LT 1.130.
Wood 514(25). Wing C3806. Madan 1917.

1861. [Cheynell, Francis]. *The sworne confederacy between the convocation at Oxford and the Tower of London.* London: n.pub., 1647, 5 June. 4°. Pp. [2], 10.
Tp, AW wrote, 'semel insanivimus omnes'. Pp. 1-3, 5, 10, underscorings, identifications, and comments in margins. E.g., p. 1, ''Yᵒ talk like an ignorant coxcomb. Can yo[u] or any one think that the D. & Canons of Ch.ch. have power within themselves to call a Deligacy for University business?'; 2, 'Nothing more false. The Acts of Convocation will tell yo[u] otherwise', and at printed name, Mr. [M.] Unit, 'a puritanical & busie [?] person'; 3, at the laws of decimation which may 'behead' some colleges, 'Who taught yo[u] that doctrine? the Devill sure.'; 5, at enemies of God raging in Oxford, 'certainly yo[u] meane by these, Presbyterians, Independents &c.'; 10, at end, '& so much for this impertinent discourse, without sense, truth, reason or honesty – '.
Wood 514(26). Wing C3817. Madan 1924.

1862. [Cheynell, Francis]. *The beacon flameing [sic] with a non obstante: or a justification of the firing of the beacon, by way of animadversion upon . . . the beacon's quenched, subscribed by col. Pride [pref. signed by L. Fawne et al.].* London: A. Miller, 1652. 4°. Pp. [4], 22.
Tp, bsm and a scribble. P. 22, a correction, may not be by AW.
Wood 609(47). Wing C3804.

1863. Cheynell, Francis, and William Erbery. *Truth triumphing over errour and heresie. Or, a relation of a publike disputation at Oxford . . . between master Cheynell . . . and master Erbury [14 Jan.].* London: f. E. B. a. S. G., 1646[7]. 4°. Pp. 7.
Tp, AW wrote, 'Fr. Cheynell - author - q[uaere]' in red ink. LT 1.130.
Wood 514(23). Wing C3818. Madan 1909.

1864. [Cheyney, John]. *A supplement to a late book intituled, the non-conforming conformist.* [London]: [J. M. f. J. Robinson], [1680]. 8°. Pp. 145-160 only (i.e., L⁸). Calf with 3 fillets, stamp decoration inside corners (dragons), and roll decoration at spine edge (Ashm. binding).
Flyleaf, upper, 2ndᵛ, the titles of 7 printed works in this vol.
Wood 883(1). Wing C3820.

1865. Childe, William. *The first set of Psalmes of .III. voyces fitt for private chappells or other private meetings with a continuall base either for the organ or theorbo newly composed after the Italian way.* London: James Reave, 1639. 22 leaves. Obl. Parchment.
Leaf 22ᵛ, signatures, John Aldridge and 'Samuell Aldridge His booke 1657'.
Wood 119. STC 5137 (cantus secundus only).

1866. Childrens' Petition. *The childrens petition: or, a modest remonstrance of . . . the accustomed severities of the school-discipline*. London: f. R. Chiswell, 1669. 12°. Pp. 70.
Wood 792(3). Wing C3869A.

1867. Childrey, J[oshua]. *Britannia Baconica: or, the natural rarities of England, Scotland, & Wales . . . historically related*. London: f. the author, sold H. D., 1661. 8°. [2nd ed.]. Pp. [30], 184. Pasteboard (blue) with parchment spine. 1st upper and last lower flyleaves, marbled paper.
Flyleaf, upper, 3rd, AW wrote 'AW: 1663'; ᵛ, he barely began his list, '1 B', within guidelines made with red chalk (and did not write Arabic nos. on either tp in this vol.). Tp, AW wrote '1ˢ 5' and 'Joshuah Childrey'. P. 73, at 'No snakes . . . about Badminton', AW made an X mark and 'q[uaere]'.
Wood 686(1). Wing C3871.

1868. Chillenden, Edmund. *The inhumanity of the kings prison-keeper at Oxford. Or a true relation of the . . . cruelties . . . of William Smith*. London: G. D. f. J. Bull, 1643. 4°. Pp. [2], 28, [1] (misnumbering).
Wood 514(13). Wing C3876. Madan 1431.

1869. [Chillenden, Edmund]. *A true relation of the state of the case between the . . . parliament and the officers of the army [11-12 Oct.]*. London: J. C., 1659. 4°. Pp. 14.
Tp, AW wrote 'Bund. 2 num. 2', in pencil.
Wood 620(24). Wing C3879A.

1870. Choice Collection. *A choice collection of wonderful miracles, ghosts, and visions*. (London): (f. B. Harris, sold L. Curtis), (1681). Fol. Pp. 4.
Missing in 1939. T is from the 1717 list. Dupl. at Wood 417(51).
Wood 276a(573). Wing C3915. *Clark, Harv, Folg*.

1871. Choice Collection. *A choice collection of wonderful miracles, ghosts, and visions*. (London): (f. B. Harris, sold L. Curtis), (1681). Fol. Pp. 4.
P. 4, AW wrote at end, 'In the beginning of Apr.' Dupl. at Wood 276a(573), missing. LT 2.531.
Wood 417(51). Wing C3915.

1872. Cholmley, Hugh. *Two letters the one being intercepted by the parliaments forces*. [London]: f. E. Husbands, 1643, 12 July. 4°. Pp. 8.
Tp, AW altered the former no., '10', and lined out no. '12'.
Wood 376(16). Wing C3924.

1873. Cholmley, Hugh. *An exact relation of the surrender of Scarborough castle by sir Hugh Cholmely . . . to coll. sir Matthew Boynton*. London: f. J. Field, [1645]. 4°. Pp. 8.
Tp, AW made a correction in the t, wrote the date, 'July 1645', in pencil; and altered the former no. '14'.
Wood 378(16). Wing E3698 (two).

1874. Chrestiens. *A, B, C, des Chrestiens. Mon enfant appren doctrine dés ta ieunesse*. N.p.: pour Jacques Caillove, n.d. 8°. A-C⁸.
Tp, signature of 'Edward Southcot'.
Wood 836(12). Not in BL. Not in BN (though same t and Caen, chez Jacque le Bourgeois, 1669-85).

1875. Christian Man. *A necessary doctrine and erudition for any Christen man, set furthe by the kynges maiestie of Englande &c. TB [cropped at bottom]*. (London): (T. Barthelet), (1543, 29 May). A-Z⁴,a-d⁴,e⁶.
Calf, speckled, with 3 fillets, 1 additional vertical fillet, stamp decoration inside 4 corners; rebacked.
A1ᵛ, signature of Laurence Waltham; A2ᵛ-B, e5ᵛ-e6 marks and a note, not in AW's hand. e6ᵛ, 'ABosco'.
Jesus College 1. Arch. 2. 25(1). STC 5170.3 (as in 5170, but n4ᵛ catchword is 'welthe' and line 1 ends 'wysdome').

1876. Christmas Carols. *Good and true, fresh and new Christmas carols*. London: E. P. f. F. Coles, 1642. 8°. A⁸,B⁴.
Wood 110(3). Wing G1036 (rare).

1877. Christmas Carols. *New carolls for this merry time of Christmas*. London: H. B. f. A. Kemb, 1661. 8°. A⁸,B⁴.
Wood 110(4). Wing N589 (rare).

1878. Christmas Carols. *New Christmas carrols; being fit also to be sung at Easter, Whitsontide*. [London]: J. M. sold by W. Thackeray a. T. Passinger, [1662?]. 8°. Newly reprinted. A⁸,B⁴.
See Wing C3965aA.

Wood 110(5). Wing N595 (rare).

1879. Christmas Carols. *A cabinet of choice jewels: or, the Christians joy and gladness. . . . Christmas carrols.* [London]: J. M. f. J. Deacon, 1688. 8°. Pp. [4], 20.
Wood 110(6). Wing C187 (rare).

1880. Christmas, Father. *Travels of old father Christmas.* N.p.: ?, n.d. Pp.?
Missing in 1837. 'Travels of old Father Christmas' in Whiteside cat. If 'Tryall of Father Christmas', then it may be Wing K510A-511A and similar to J. King, Wood 110(1), item 3973.
Wood 110b. Not identified.

1881. Christopherson, John. *Exhortation to all menn to take hede and beware of rebellion.* London: J. Cawood, 1554. 8°. A⁸-2F⁸,2G⁴. Parchment.
Flyleaf, upper, notes, 9 lines in Latin, not by AW. Tp, 'Anthony Wood Coll: Merton Oxon A. D. MDCLX1', lined out. See C. J. Fordyce and T. M. Knox, 'The Library of Jesus College', *OBS Proceedings and Papers*, 5 (1936-39), (Oxford, 1940): 66.
Jesus College N. 3. 24 Gall. STC 5207.

1882. Christ's Hospital. *A psalm of thanksgiving to be sung by the children of Christs-hospital, . . . 1676.* London: W. Godbid, 1676. S.sh.
2 notes, neither by AW: above, 'This is the First Mʳ [blank] Curtis their Organist made', and, after musical score, 'Dʳ Chr. Gibbons'. LT 2.341.
Wood 416(131). Wing P4140 (two).

1883. Chudleigh, James. *Serjeant major James Chudleigh his declaration.* [Oxford]: [L. Lichfield], 1643. 4°. Pp. [2], 5.
Flyleaf, upper ᵛ, AW wrote, 'James Chudleigh of Devonsh. son of Sʳ Georg. Chudl. Bᵗ, was matriculated as a member of Ch. Ch. in Oxōn on the first of Sept. 1634, aged 16 yeares'; tp, at t, 'qu[aere] whether here' in pencil; below, 'James Chudley or Chudleigh'.
Wood 376(8). Wing C3983. Madan 1398.

1884. Chudleigh, James. *A most miraculous . . . victory obtained by James Chidleigh . . . against sir Ralph Hopton.* [London]: f. R. D., 1643, 29 Apr. 4°. Pp. 5 (i.e., 8, misnumbering).
Tp, AW altered a former no. to '9'. Dupl. at Wood 612(10c).
Wood 376(9). Wing M2908 (Wing, Chudlegh).

1885. Chudleigh, James*. *A most miraculous . . . victory obtained by James Chidleigh . . . against sir Ralph Hopton.* [London]: f. R. D., 1643, 29 Apr. 4°. Pp. 5 (i.e., 8, misnumbering: 3,4,5,5,4,5).
Tp, AW wrote 'Dupl', in pencil. Dupl. at Wood 376(9).
Wood 612(10c). Wing M2908 (Wing, Chudlegh).

1886. Churchyard, Thomas. *A light bondell of livly discourses called Churchyardes charge.* London: J. Kyngston, 1580. 4°. Ff. [5], 16.
Passim, notes, mainly in red ink (some cropped by the binding), not in AW's hand (similar hand in Wood 482(6)); but three in dark ink, F2, F3ᵛ, prob. in AW's hand; some underscoring, in green ink; and marks in margins, in pencil.
Wood 482(7). STC 5240.

1887. Chute, [Chaloner]. *Mr. Chute's case upon the decree obtained against his late father (by the lady Dacres) for 5000 l. and interest.* [London: n.pub., [1685]. S.sh. Pp. 2.
Wood 276b(94) (not in Bodl. CD cat.). Wing C4278 (rare).

1888. Chute, [Chaloner]. *Mr. Chutes case upon the lady Dacres appeal in, 1685.* [London]: n.pub., [1685]. S.sh.
Wood 276b(92) (not in Bodl. CD cat.). Wing C4277 (rare).

1889. Chute, [Chaloner]. *Mr. Chutes petition of appeal consists of these nine points.* [London]: n.pub., [1685]. S.sh.
Wood 276b(93) (not in Bodl. CD cat.). Wing C4279 (rare).

1890. Chylinski, Samuel Boguslaus*. *An account of the translation of the Bible into the Lithuanian tongue, . . . with a copy of the testimoniall . . . by several doctors of divinity [15 Nov.].* Oxford: H. Hall, 1659. 4°. Pp. [2], 8.
Pp. 3-4, lines in margin, in pencil, may not be by AW.

[MS.] Wood B. 37(2). Wing C4280. Madan 2423.

1891. Chytraeus, David. *Chronicon anni M.D.XCIII. M.D.XCIIII. et initii M.D.XCV*. Lipsiae: imp. H. Grosii, 1595. 8°. Pp. [2], 150 (issued with Wood 139(2), item 1160). Parchment.
Wood 139(1). BL.

1892. Chytraeus, Nathan. *[Variorum in Europa itinerum deliciae; seu, ex variis manu-scriptis selectiora tantum inscriptionum maxime recentium monumenta]*. [Herbornae Nassouiorum]: n.pub., [1594]. 8°. Pp. [18], 842 (wanting tp and G4). Parchment.
Cover, upper, inside, names, or signatures, of John Dod, Henry Herbert and John Vaughan. Scribbles, pp. 225 and, p. 769, AW corrected 'Cantabrigiae' in text to 'Cantuariae'.
Wood 109. BL.

1893. Cicero, Marcus Tullius. Grimald, Nicholas, trans. *Marcus Tullius Ciceroes thre bookes of duties, . . . turned . . . into English, . . . Wherunto the Latine is adjoyned*. (London): (R.Tottil), 1558 (14 Ap.). 8°. Ff. [16], 168. Calf, mottled; flyleaves upper and lower, printer's waste.
Name scripted on lower board, Ja (?) Brystowe (LT 2.122-3). Tp, William Taylor and W T blotted out. Bsm. Some scattered notes and scribbles in various hands, none by AW.
Wood 742. STC 5281.8.

1894. Cicero, Marcus Tullius. Webbe, Joseph, trans. *The familiar epistles of M.T. Cicero Englished*. London: E. Griffin, [1620]. 12°. Pp. [24], 916 (imperf., ends at 2R2). Parchment; rebound.
Pasted to a sheet at fore-edge, a slip identifying the author and work (see Index, 'Slip with title'). P. [1], '576', prob. not by AW. Acquired from Thomas Hallum, 18 Feb. 1667, 1ˢ6ᵈ, LT 2.99.
Wood 713. STC 5305.

1895. Cillard. Dublin, alderman of. *A continuation of the Irish rebels proceedings, with our victories over them, . . . a letter by alderman Cillard [but signed S. Sullian]*. London: f. G. Lindsey, 1642. 4°. Pp. [2], 6.
Tp, below, '11', may not be by AW.
Wood 507(39). Wing C4324.

1896. Cirencester. *A particular relation of the action before Cyrencester (or Cycester)*. [Oxford]: [L. Lichfield], 1642[3]. 4°. Pp. [2], 16.
Tp, AW overwrote the former no., '29', with '33'.
Wood 375(33). Wing P597. Madan 1229.

1897. Cirencester. *A relation of the taking of Cicester*. London: n.pub., 1642[3]. 4°. A⁴.
Tp, AW lined out a former item no., '39'.
Wood 375(34). Wing R875.

1898. Cirencester. *A warning-peice [sic] to all his majesties subjects of England: being the lamentable complaint of . . . prisoners from Cyrencester*. [Oxford]: n.pub., 1642[3]. 4°. Pp. [2], 6.
Wood 375(35). Wing W932. Madan 1238 (Wing, piece).

1899. City Dames. *The city-dames petition, in the behalfe of the long afflicted, but well-affected cavaliers*. [London]: n.pub., 1647. 4°. Pp. [2], 6.
Wood 654a(12). Wing C4350.

1900. [Clarges, Thomas]. *Hyporites [sic] unmasked, or, the hypocrisie of the new usurpers discovered, . . . propounded by . . . a sufferer for the good old cause*. London: f. Goodman Constant, 1659. 4°. Pp. [2], 6.
Tp, nos. 31 and 29 in former bundles.
Wood 610(4a). Wing C4429A.

1901. Clark, Margaret*. *Warning for servants: and a caution to protestants. Or, the case of Margret Clark, lately executed for firing her masters house in Southwark*. London: f. T. Parkhurst, sold J. Collier, 1680. 8°. Pp. [8], 32.
Tp, bsm. P. 32, at printed 'Nathaniel Gardiner present Curate of Kingston', last 4 words lined out.
Wood 654a(31). Wing C4483.

1902. Clarke, Francis. *Praxis curiae admiralitatis Angliae*. Londini: imp. G. Crooke, 1667. 8°. Pp. [7], 48, [15]. Pasteboard (blue) with parchment spine. 1st upper and last lower flyleaves, marbled paper.
Tp, AW wrote '9ᵈ', and underscored the author's surname in red ink. Acquired 28 Jan. 1669, LT 2.149.
Wood 731(1) (not in Bodl. CD cat.). Wing C4441.

1903. [**Clarke, Samuel**]. *The life of Tamerlane the great.* London: T. R. a. E. M. f. T. Underhill, 1653. 4°. Pp. [2], 61.
Tp, AW wrote the price, '6^{d}'.
Wood 345(9). Wing C4535.

1904. Clarke, Samuel. *The life & death of . . . sir Francis Drake.* London: f. S. Miller, 1671. 4°. Pp. [2], 71, [4] (4 pp. books printed and sold by S. Miller).
Pp. 23-6, 28-32, 43-4, etc., to 61, lines in margin and some underscoring, in pencil. P. [4]^{v}, 2 numbers (?).
Wood 535(3). Wing C4533.

1905. Clarkson, David. *The case of protestants in England under a popish prince, if any shall happen to wear the imperial crown.* London: f. R. Janeway, 1681. 4°. Pp. 35.
Tp, note, in pencil, cropped at top.
[MS.] Wood B. 40(10). Wing C4569.

1906. Clavell, John. *A recantation of an ill led life.* London: A. M[athewes] f. R. Meighen, 1634. 4°. 3rd ed. Pp. [22], 47.
Wood 371(6). STC 5371.

1907. Clay, Thomas. *Briefe, easie, and necessary tables.* London: G. Eld and M. Flesher, sold by L. Becket, 1622. 8°. 2nd impression. Pp. [10], 84.
Tp, bsm.
Wood 21(5). STC 5372.

1908. [**Cleaver, Robert**]. *A godlie forme of householde government: for the ordering of private families, according to the direction of Gods word.* London: F. Kingston f. T. Man, 1600. 8°. Pp. 384. Parchment.
Cover, upper^{v}, signature or name of Rob. Cawdrey. Flyleaf, upper, 'John Pinson is my name and [3-4 words illeg.]', a multiplication, name (illeg.), and 'AWood 1660'; ^{v}, scribble. Tp, AW wrote '6^{d}'; at top, '64' (?). Text, pp. 94, 128, 'William Smith'; 290, 384, scribbles, not by AW.
Wood 819 (891 in Bodl. CD cat.). STC 5384.

1909. Cleombrotus, pseud. *The most strange and wonderful predictions of Cleombrotus an heathen Jew.* London: f. L. Curtis, 1679. 4°. Pp. 8.
Wood 646(15). Wing M2922.

1910. Cleveland, John. *The character of a London diurnall.* [Oxford]: [L. Lichfield], 1644[5]. 4°. [2nd ed.]. Pp. [2], 6.
Wood 622(6). Wing C4660. Madan 1709.

1911. Cleveland, John*. *A full answer to a scandalous pamphlet, . . . [by J. Cleveland] a character of a London diurnall.* London: E. P. f. F. Coles a. L. Blaikeloke, 1645. 4°. Pp. [2], 14.
Wood 622(7). Wing F2340. Madan 1765.

1912. C[leveland], J[ohn]. *The character of a moderate intelligencer with some select poems.* [London]: n.pub., [1647]. 4°. Pp. 12.
Wood 622(13). Wing C4668.

1913. [**Cleveland, John**]. *The hue and cry after s^{ir} John Presbyter.* [London]: n.pub., [1649]. S.sh.
6 brief notes identifying allusions, in 2 hands, prob. none in AW's hand.
Wood 416(8). Wing C4671A (3).

1914. C[leveland], [John]. *Poems. By J. C. With additions.* N.p.: N.pub., 1651 ('Printed in the Year 1651.'). 8°. 6th ed. Pp. [2], 56. ¶2-8,A-E^{8},D^{4} (imperf., cropped, and ends with catchword 'THE', and a blank leaf followed by traces of at least 7 leaves that were cut out).
Wood 84(12). Wing C4683A-4686 (not identified).

1915. C[leveland], J[ohn]. *A character of a diurnal-maker by J. C.* London: n.pub., 1654. 4°. Pp. [2], 6.
Tp, before printed year, a date (or a word), lined out, and '1654'.
Wood 622(18). Wing C4657.

1916. [**Cleveland, John**]. *The idol of the clownes, or, insurrection of Wat the tyler, with his priests Baal and Straw.* London: n.pub., 1654. 8°. Pp. [12], 154. Pasteboard (grey) with parchment spine; thick yellow paper flyleaves, upper and lower.
Flyleaf, upper, 3rd^{v}, AW wrote the titles of 3 printed works in this vol., within guidelines made with red

ink. Tp, bsm. Acquired 1 Jan. 1659, 10^d, LT 1.266.
Wood 453(1). Wing C4673.

1917. [Cleveland, Philip]. *Upon the most ingenious and incomparable musophilist of his time, m^r. John Cleaveland [28 April 1658]*. London: f. W. Shears, 1658. S.sh.
After a printed reference to the author, 'Phil. Cleaveland', not by AW.
Wood 429(12). Wing C4699C (rare) (Wing, Cleveland).

1918. Clifford, Henry. Cumberland, earl of. *The declaration of the right honourable Henry earle of Cumberland . . . in York-shire*. York: S. Bukley, 1642. 4°. A^4.
Wood 375(4). Wing C7577.

1919. Clifford, James. *The divine services and anthems usually sung in the cathedrals and collegiate choires in the Church of England*. London: W. G., sold H. Brome, 1663. 8°. Pp. [23], 240. Modern paper, brown over contemporary paper.
Flyleaf, upper (former cover), AW wrote 'Jam. Clifford of Magd. Coll. somtime chorister or clerk [/] Clerke [/] living 1684 q[uaere] Mr West [Robert? also of Magd., who is mentioned in a note at Wood 428(18), item 1825] [/] Adr[rian] Batten hath more services in this book than any body besides [/] Will[iam] for John Mundy' (in the index AW wrote the entry, 'Will. Mundy p. 13 Joh Mundy was D^r of mus.' Tp, signature of Maur. Holding and note cropped at bottom. Text, AW underscored surnames of all authors of prayers, and on 2 flyleaves, lower, an index, 23 author entries.
Wood 814. Wing C4703.

1920. [Clifford, Martin]. *A treatise of humane reason*. London: f. H. Broome, 1675. 12°. Pp. [3], 91. Pasteboard (blue) with parchment spine. 1st upper and last lower flyleaves, blue paper.
Flyleaf, upper, 2nd, AW wrote the titles of 4 printed works in this vol., within guidelines made with red ink; 3rd-4th, 50 lines from 'Roger L'estrange in his Observator, num. 290 14. Feb. 1682': AW quoted L'Estrange's response to the demand by 'Trimmer' as to why he, in 1674, licensed *Humane Reason* which should have been burned (as it was). L'Estrange admitted that he failed to read the item, which was perused by 2 reliable persons (whom AW identified in the margin as 'Dr Sprat I think & Dr South') and made a mild counter attack. Sig. A1, 'Humane Reason'. Tp, AW wrote 'published in Aug. 1674' (i.e., Wing C4707) and '6^d'; below imprint at the printed 1675, '74. Aug.', and AW continued with 'said to be written by Matthew [sic] Clifford Master of Suttons Hospital', over which a slip was later pasted. LT 2.297. Responded to by E. Stephens, M., A., and A. Warren, Wood 841(2-4), items 6041, 4318, 6469.
Wood 841(1). Wing C4708A (rare).

1921. Cobbet, [Ralph]. *A letter sent by col. Cobbet from the general council of officers to gen. Monk. With his answer [27 Oct.]*. London: n.pub., 1659. 4°. Pp. [2], 5, [1].
Tp, former no., '16', in pencil.
Wood 632(66). Wing C4774.

1922. [Cock, Charles George]. *Englands compleat law-judge, and lawyer [signed Theophilus Philopatros]*. London: f. E. Paxton, 1656. 4°. Pp. [14], 26.
Wood 630(15). Wing C4788 ('O' not recorded in Wing).

1923. Cock, Thomas, and Roger Dixon. *Advice for the poor by way of cure & caution. [Followed by] A directory for the poore, against the plague and infectious diseases [16 June] [signed R. Dixon.]*. N.p.: n.pub., [1665]. 4°. Pp. 8.
Wood 534(3d). Wing C4790 (two).

1924. Cockeram, Henry. *The English dictionarie*. London: [Eliot's Court Press] f. N. Butter, 1623. 8°. A2-8,B-K^8,L^4; 2nd A-I^8,K1-2 (wanting 2nd K3-8,L1-2). Parchment.
Tp, scribbles, cropped. Parchment cover, lower, inside, some multiplications.
Wood 31. STC 5461.

1925. Codomannus, Laurentius. *Chronographia. A description of time, from the beginning of the world . . . out of Laurentius Codomannus his annales sacrae scripturae*. London: R. Field f. R. Dexter, 1596. 8°. 3rd ed. Pp. 98, [18].
Tp, AW wrote, 'Sept: 11: A.D. 1660' (see LT 1.331).
Wood 142(2). STC 5472.

1926. Codrington, Robert. *The life and death, of the illustrious Robert earle of Essex*. London: F. Leach f. L Chapman, 1646. 4°. Pp. [5], 50.

Missing since 1994. In Whiteside cat.
Wood 531(4). Wing C4877.

1927. Coffee. *The vertue of the coffee drink.* [Oxford]: it is to be sold [W. Hall], [1660]. S.sh.
T.p., AW wrote, in his early hand, where this coffee is to be sold: 'by James Gough at M^r [blank] Sury'es [sic] a taylor by Queens Coll Corner Oxon: December: A: 1660'. See note at Wood 679(1), item 2866.
Wood 679(9). Wing V646 (two). Madan 2488.

1928. Coffee House. *The character of a coffee-house [in verse] . . . by an eye and ear witness.* [London]: n.pub., 1665. 4°. Pp. [2], 10.
LT 1.169.
[MS.] Wood D. 30(5). Wing C1967.

1929. Coffee, and Chocolate. *The vertues of chocolate East-India drink. The properties of cavee Egipt drink.* [Oxford]: [W. Hall], [1660]. S.sh. 4°.
AW dated this advertisement of the drink after the printed '*sold by* James Gough *at* M. Sury's *neare East gate*': 'Decemb: 1660'. See note at Wood 679(1), item 2866. LT 1.201.
Wood 679(10). Wing V648 (rare). Madan 2487.

1930. Coins, True Portraiture of. *A true purtraiture of sundrie coynes the 8 of Aprill 1611 in the Harkirke [Sefton, Lancs.].* [London]: n.pub., [1611]. S.sh.
Missing in 1939.
Wood 276a(28). STC 20126.3 (rare). HH (Crawford, Rylands).

1931. Cokayne, William. *The foundations of freedome, vindicated: or, the reasons of William Ashurst . . . against . . . The peoples agreement, examined.* London: f. J. Harris, 1649. 4°. Pp. [2], 13.
Wood 609(23). Wing C4904.

1932. Coke, [Thomas]. *A true narrative of the great solemnity of the circumcision of Mustapha prince of Turkie.* London: J. C. f. W. Crook, 1676. Fol. Pp. [2], 6.
Wood 559(9). Wing C4905.

1933. Colchester. *An elegie, on the most . . . murder, committed at Colchester, upon . . . sir Charles Lucas, and sir George Lisle.* London: n.pub., 1648. 4°. Pp. [2], 6.
Tp. AW wrote, '28. Aug 1648'.
Wood 502(64). Wing E424.

1934. Colchester. *The remonstrance and declaration of the knights, esquires, . . . in Colchester, now in armes for the king.* [London]: n.pub., 1648. 4°. Pp. 8.
Wood 502(11). Wing R962.

1935. Colchester. *A true and perfect relation of the condition of those . . . in Colchester . . . in yeilding up . . . to lord Fairfax.* [London]: n.pub., 1648. 4°. Pp. [2], 6.
Tp, AW wrote after the year, 'Aug 28'. Dupl. at Wood 609(14).
Wood 502(63). Wing T2553.

1936. Colchester. *A true and perfect relation of the condition of those . . . in Colchester . . . in yeilding up . . . to lord Fairfax.* [London]: n.pub., 1648. 4°. Pp. [2], 6.
Tp, nos. 33 and 45 (cropped at side) in former bundles. Formerly at Wood 502(45); see notes at Packet, Wood 502(1), item 4718, and Scarborough, Wood 502(46a), item 5777. Dupl. at Wood 502(63).
Wood 609(14). Wing T2553.

1937. Colchester. *To the parliament of the common-wealth of England, &c. A . . . testimony of Colchester.* [London]: n.pub., [1659[60]]. S.sh.
A minor correction in text, and below, not by AW, 'The originall Coppie is the the Hands of the Speaker . . . & all for to be read in the House'.
Wood 276a(225). Wing T1581A (one) ('O' not recorded in Wing) (Wing, [1659]).

1938. C[ole], J[ohn]. *Quercus regia in agro Staffordiensi, non, ut olim, Jovi, sed jam Jehovae.* [London]: n.pub., [1660?]. S.sh.
AW wrote, 'June 1660' (line over 1660).
Wood 416(85). Wing C5022A (two) (Wing, Staffordiensis).

1939. Cole, Robert. *The last true intelligence from Ireland [16 Mar.].* London: f. H. Blunden, 1642. 4°.

Pp. 8.
Wood 507(45). Wing C5024.

1940. Cole, Robert. *True intelligence from Ireland. Dated from Dublin [2 Ap.].* London: f. H. Blunden, 1642. 4°. Pp. 7.
Tp, former no., '6', lined out.
Wood 508(7). Wing C5028.

1941. Cole, William. *A rod for the lawyers:. . . To which is added, a word to the parliament.* London: n.pub., 1659. 4°. Pp. 20.
Wood 630(18). Wing C5039.

1942. Coleman, Edward*. *The tryal of Edward Coleman, gent. for conspiring the death of the king.* London: f. R. Pawlet, 1678. Fol. Pp. [3], 104.
1st sheet, AW wrote, 'Edw. Coleman was a ministers son. Bred in Cambridge, reconciled to the Ch. of Rome by a R. C. priest – Jan. 20. an. 1678[9] twas commonly reported that Edw. Colemans writings between him & Le Chese [printed 'the French Kings present Confessor', p. 7] from 1675 to the time of his apprehension were found in the house of Dan. Arthur a merchant'. LT 2.419. Tp, AW wrote the price, '3ˢ'. P. 53, lines in margin.
Wood 424(4). Wing T2185.

1943. Coleman, Edward*. *The answer of Coleman's ghost, to H. N's poetick offering.* [London]: n.pub., [1679]. Fol. Pp. 3.
Tp, AW wrote the name in the t, 'Hen. Nevill'. P. 3, 'December. 1678'.
Wood 424(5). Wing A3285 ('O' not recorded in Wing).

1944. Coles, W[illiam]. *The art of simpling An introduction to the knowledge and gathering of plants.* London: J. G. f. N. Brook, 1656. 12°. Pp. [24], 175 (2 pts.).
Missing in 1837. 2nd pt. at Wood 729(5). See LT 1.467.
Wood 729(3). Wing C5089 and C5089A. O, Hunt, Clark, Folg.

1945. Coles, William. *'Perspicillum microcosmologicum' [i.e., heading at 2nd tp: of The art of simpling].* London: J. G. f. N. Brook, 1656. 12°. Pp. 125-175 (pt. 2, only).
Missing in 1837. 2nd tp in Whiteside cat. In binding, separated from Coles, Wood 729(3).
Wood 729(5). Wing C5089 or C5089A.

1946. College, Stephen*. *The arraignment, tryal and condemnation of Stephen Colledge for high-treason.* London: f. T. Basset, a. J. Fish, 1681. Fol. Pp. [4], 102.
Tp, AW wrote the price, '2.6'; and pp. 18, marks and note at Combes Coffee-House in Oxford, 'A stranger that set up for a time'; 20, at Bishops changing their hats, 'I have this' (Wood 417(38), item 1967?, missing); 39; 48- 54; 70-1; 88-9 at testimonies, lines in margin, in pencil; 58 and 96, at mention of Charlett's testimony in text, 'Arth. Charlet'; 85, 'He. Finch' and 'Heneage Finch son Heneage E. of Nottingh.'; 100, at mention of a disrupter at court, 'An inhabitant of Bristow'. LT 2.551.
Wood 427(28). Wing A3761.

1947. College, Stephen* (spurious). *A letter from mr. Stephen Colledge to a person of quality, upon his removal to Oxford, to be try'd . . . Tower, 15 Aug. 1681.* [London]: (f. F. Smith), (1681). S.sh.
Wood 427(26). Wing C5224.

1948. [College, Stephen*]. *A letter from the grand-jury of Oxford to the London-grand-jury, relating to the case of the protestant-joyner.* (London): (f. Al. Banks), (1681). S.sh. Pp. 2.
Wood 427(24) (26 in Bodl. CD cat.). Wing L1522.

1949. College, Stephen* (spurious). *A letter written from the Tower by mr. Stephen Colledge (the protestant-joyner) to Dick Janeways wife.* (London): (f. R. J.), 1681. S.sh. (r-v).
Wood 427(25). Wing C5226.

1950. College, Stephen. *The speech and carriage of Stephen Colledge at Oxford, before the castle, on Wednesday August 31.* London: f. T. Basset, a. J. Fish, 1681. Fol. Pp. [2], 6.
Tp, AW wrote the price, '3ᵈ', in red ink. Pp. 2-3, 6, notes on the participants and locations, e.g., p. 2, at printed 'in the Barbers shop' where S. Dugdale spoke treason with College, 'In the shop of – Prince a barber under the Angell Inn in Oxon.'; at printed 'I lodged at Colonel Vernon's', 'Edw. Vernon who married the widdow of . . . . Brook of North-Aston in Com Oxōn', LT 3.106; p. 3, 'E. of Rochester, living at Adderbury'; p. 6, explanations at mention of names, e.g., 'Tho. Chrosthwait of Qu. Coll. was with him

at the gallowes. [/] Dr. Jo. Hall of Pemb. Coll & Dr G. Reynell had severall times prayed with him.' LT 2.553.
Wood 427(31). Wing C5229.

1951. College, Stephen. *A true copy of the dying words of mr. Stephen Colledge, . . . August 31. 1681 at Oxford*. (London): (f. E. Colledge), (1681). S.sh. Pp. 2.
P. 2, AW identified 4 persons mentioned, Dr. Thomas Marshall, Dr. Joh. Hall, Laur. Hyde and Lord Howard of Escrick. At the end, he wrote, at blessings, 'Where is a blessing for the King'. LT 2.553.
Wood 427(30). Wing C5231.

1952. Collins, John. *Salt and fishery*. London: A. Godbid a. J. Playford, 1682. 4°. Pp. [8], 164, [4].
Tp, AW wrote, '15 July 1682 given to me (AW) by the authour at Oxōn'. LT 3.24.
[MS.] Wood C. 14(11). Wing C5380A.

1953. Colman, Morgan. *Alpin son of k. Achaii [genealogies of king James I and queen Anne]*. [London?]: n.pub., [1608]. Fol. Pp. [9] (sizes vary, pp. are out of sequence, 2 half-sheets).
Wood 276a(73-79). STC 5568.

1954. Colminero De Ledesma, Antonio. Wadsworth, James, tr. *Chocolate: or, an Indian drinke. . . . rendred in the English*. London: J. G. f. J. Dakins, 1652. 8°. Pp. [14], 40, [3].
Tp, name of Wadsworth underscored in red ink. Possibly acquired 12 Jan. 1661, 4^d, LT 1.201, 378.
Wood 679(3). Wing C5400.

1955. Colynet, Anthony. *The true history of the civill warres of France, betweene the French king Henry the 4. and the leaguers*. London: (T. Orwin) f. T. Woodcock, 1591. 4° in 8's. Pp. [8], 549, [1].
Cover, upper and lower, writing, illeg., not in AW's hand. Flyleaf, upper, mutilated, some scribbles remain, and 'Andrew Bordman', lined out and overwritten. Tp, scribbles. Text, some marks, hands, and scribbles in margins, prob. not by AW, and pp. 81, 83, 88, 148, 219, names of former owners and witnesses: Andrew Boreman (Boorman, i.e, Bowerman) of Tilehurst, Berks., 1620 and 1623, William Wickins, William Hamlett, Thomas Looker, John Chau (cropped).
Wood 475. STC 5590.

1956. Combat. *Combate between a Roman capon & and French cock*. N.p.: n.pub., n.d. Pp.?
Missing in 1922. T from AW's list on upper flyleaf, see Wood 416(1), item 4435.
Wood 416(102). Not in Wing. Not in ESTCR.

1957. [Comber, Thomas]. *Friendly and seasonable advice to the Roman Catholicks of England. . . . By a charitable hand*. London: f. H. Brome, 1677. 8°. 3rd ed. Pp. [23], 152, [4] (4 pp. books sold by Brome).
Wood 869(6). Wing C5468.

1958. [Comenius, Johann Amos]. *The history of the Bohemian persecution*. London: B. A. f. J. Walker, 1650. 8°. [8], 376.
Flyleaf, upper^v, Joh. Amos Comenius, not by AW. Tp, '1^s', prob. not by AW.
Wood 211(3). Wing C5508.

1959. Comines, Philippe de. Sleidanus, Johannes, trans. *De rebus gestis Ludovici, ejus nominis undecimi, Galliarum regis, & Caroli, Burgundiae ducis*. Parisiis: ap. A. Wechelum (excud. Parisiis Andreas Wechelus) [has no imprint of J. Dupuys], 1569. 8°. Pp. [16], 649, [24]. Calf with 2 fillets, stamp centrepiece and 4 bands on spine.
Tp, '1 50' and '49' (crossed out), prob. an earlier shelf number. Text, some notes, numbers, and marks in margins, prob. not by AW.
Wood 199. IA.

1960. [Compton, Henry]. London, bp. of. *The bishop of London his letter to the clergy of his diocess [25 Apr.]*. London: f. H. Brome, [1679]. S.sh.
Wood 276a(288). Wing C5669.

1961. [Compton, Henry]. London, bp. of. *The bishop of London's second letter to the clergy of his diocess [6 July]*. London: f. H. Brome, [1680]. S.sh.
Wood 276a(289). Wing C5672.

1962. Compton, Henry*. London, bp. of. *A true narrative of all the proceedings against the lord bishop of London*. London: printed, a. sold by R. Taylor, 1689. Fol. Pp. [3], 12.
Tp, AW wrote, 'Commonly sold at Oxon on S. Tho. day Dec. 21. 1688'. LT 3.195-6.

Wood 421(9). Wing T2774.

1963. Conant, Malachi. *Urim and Thummim; or the clergies dignity and duty recommended in a visitation sermon [27 April]*. Oxford [London]: H. Hall f. J. Collins, 1669. 4°. Pp. [4], 26.
Tp, 1st 3 words lined out: 'Liber Ant. Woode. Ex dono authoris, quondam socii Coll. Magd. Oxon. Sept. 6. 1669'. LT 2.124. AOF 2.282.
Wood 633(4). Wing C5690 (two). Madan 2824.

1964. [Concini, Concino]. *[The last will and testament of the marquis d'Ancre. Together with his arraignment. His obsequies. His wifes teares. . . . The rousing of the soldat François]*. [London]: F. Kyngston f. W. Arondell, 1617. 4°. A2-4,B-G⁴ (wanting general title leaf and last leaf) (tpp at B2, C3, E1, F1, G1).
Wood 345(15-20). STC 5621.

1965. Coninck. *Coninck. Den Coninck der Coningen wilt loven*. N.p.: n.pub, n.d. S.sh. P. 98 in this vol.
16 figures representing professions, colored, and 4 verses on each.
Wood 402(25) (not in Bodl. CD cat.). Not in BL.

1966. Considerations Divine. *Considerations divine, rational and political, calculated for the present state of affairs in England*. [London]: n.pub., [1660]. S.sh.
AW added the date, 'Feb 1659[60]'.
Wood 276a(279). Wing C5908C (rare).

1967. Contents. *The contents (hats for caps) contented*. [London]: n.pub., 1680. S.sh.
Missing in 1840. T from upper flyleaf; see note at Wood 417(1), item 781. BL copy has stitch marks and erasures.
Wood 417(38). Wing C5955A (one). *BL*.

1968. Conventicula. *Upon the suppression of conventicles. A translation from the Latine copy [i.e., Conventicula fanaticorum dissipata]*. (London): n.pub., (1685). S.sh. (r-v).
A date (?), in pencil, cropped at top.
Wood 417(142). Wing U118.

1969. Cooke, Alexander. *Pope Joane. A dialogue betweene a protestant and a papist. Manifestly proving, that a woman called Joane was pope of Rome*. London: [R. Field] f. E. Blunt a. W. Barret, 1610. 4°. Pp. [8], 128. Pasteboard (blue) with parchment spine. 1st upper and last lower flyleaves, marbled paper.
Flyleaf, upper, 3rdᵛ, AW wrote the titles of 3 printed works in this vol., within guidelines made with red ink. Pp. 2, 3, 103, 106, 127, 128, notes and underscoring, not by AW.
[MS.] Wood C. 39(1). STC 5659.

1970. Cooke, Edward, tactician. *The character of warre, or the image of martiall discipline*. London: T. Purfoot, 1626. 4°. Pp. A⁴,¶²,B-K⁴ (K4 blank).
I3, correction; K1, 2 printed lines lined out.
Wood 635(4). STC 5668.

1971. [Cooke, Edward]. Middle Temple, of. *Argumentum anti-Normannicum:. . . that William, duke of Normandy, made no absolute conquest of England*. London: J. Darby, 1682. 8°. Pp. [11], clxiv. Pasteboard (grey) with parchment spine. Traces of 1st and last flyleaves, marbled paper.
Flyleaf, upperᵛ, AW wrote the titles of 4 printed works in this vol., within guidelines made with red ink. Tp, 'A. Ch .' (Arthur Charlett?) and scribble. Bsm. P. i, 'Dupl', in pencil (possibly a duplicate in Charlett's library; there is no duplicate in the Wood collection).
Wood 234(1). Wing C5998B.

1972. Cooke, Edward, colonel. *Certain passages which happened at Newport, in the Isle of Wight, Novemb. 29. 1648. relating to king Charles I*. London: f. R. Chiswell, 1690. 4°. Pp. [8], 26, [2] (2 pp. books printed f. R. Chiswell).
Tp, author's name underscored in pencil. P. 3, AW supplied the Christian name for Rolph, 'Edm.' Pp. 5, 7, 21, 23, underscoring, a correction, and identifications (some were cropped in binding).
Wood 609(9). Wing C5997.

1973. Cooke, John. *King Charls his case: or, an appeal . . . concerning his tryal*. London: P. Cole, f. G. Calvert, 1649. 4°. Pp. 43.
Wood 364(18). Wing C6025.

1974. Coombes, John. *The case of John Coombes, Valentine Houseman, and Edward Pearce*. [London]:

n.pub., [1682 ca.]. S.sh.
Corrections (lines) made in text, prob. not by AW.
Wood 276b(72). Wing C927 (two).

1975. [**Cooper, Anthony Ashley**]. Shaftesbury, earl of. *A seasonable speech, made by a worthy member . . . in the house of commons, concerning the other house. March.* [London]: n.pub., [1659]. 4°. Pp. 8.
P. 1, AW wrote 'said to be written by capt. Silas Titus'. P. 4, 4 identifications, in AW's early hand, and p. 8, AW wrote 'This came out ye beginning of Aprill: 1659', also in his early hand.
Wood 620(17). Wing S2898.

1976. Cooper, Anthony Ashley*. Shaftesbury, earl of. *A time-serving speech, . . . By a worthy member of parliament.* London: n.pub., 1680. Fol. Pp. 8.
Wood 657(43). Wing T1279.

1977. Cooper, Anthony Ashley*. Shaftesbury, earl of. *An answer to a paper, entituled, a brief account of the designs of the papists against the earl of Shaftsbury.* (London): (f. T. Davies), (1681). Fol. Pp. 4.
Wood 427(36). Wing A3328.

1978. Cooper, Anthony Ashley*. Shaftesbury, earl of. *A brief account of the commitment of the earl of Sh. and the crimes laid to his charge.* (London): (f. H. R.), (1681). S.sh. Pp. 2.
P. 2, AW wrote, 'In the beginnning of Jul. 1681'.
Wood 427(32). Wing B4503B.

1979. Cooper, Anthony Ashley*. Shaftesbury, earl of. *A civil correction of a sawcy impudent pamphlet, . . . A brief account of the designs which the papists have had against the earl of Shaftsbury.* (London): (f. A. B.), (1681). Fol. Pp. 4.
Wood 427(35). Wing C4364.

1980. Cooper, Anthony Ashley*. Shaftesbury, earl of. *A diaologue [sic] between the e. of Sh– and l. Bell– in the Tower, concerning the plot.* London: f. A. T., 1681. S.sh. (r-v).
AW wrote the year, '1681', in pencil, and identified Sh– and Bell–, Sh'aftsbury', Bell'asis'.
Wood 417(66). Wing D1330 (Wing, Bellhaven).

1981. Cooper, Anthony Ashley. Shaftesbury, earl of. *The e. of Shaftsbury's expedient for setling the nation. Discoursed with his majesty in the house of peers [24 March].* London: printed, sold L. Curtis, 1681. 4°. Pp. 7.
Tp, author's name underscored in red ink.
Wood 608(58). Wing E80C.

1982. Cooper, Anthony Ashley*. Shaftesbury, earl of. *A modest vindication of the earl of S[haftesbur]y: in a letter to a friend concerning his being elected king of Poland.* (London): (f. [blank] Smith Bookseller in Chief to His Majesty Elect of Poland), (1681). Fol. Pp. 4.
Wood 427(37). Wing M2375.

1983. Cooper, Anthony Ashley*. Shaftesbury, earl of. *A particular account of the proceedings at the Old-Bayly, the 17 & 18 of this instant October, with relation to the earl of Shaftsbury.* [London]: (T. Newcomb), (1681). S.sh. Pp. 2.
Wood 427(34). Wing P586.

1984. Cooper, Anthony Ashley*. Shaftesbury, earl of. *The proceedings at the sessions house in the Old-Baily, London, . . . upon the bill of indictment for high-treason against Anthony earl of Shaftsbury [24 Nov.].* London: f. S. Mearne, a. J. Baker, 1681. Fol. Pp. [2], 48.
Tp, AW wrote the price '1 6^d' in ink, over pencil inscription, and 'He was committed to prison 2d. Jul. 1681'. Pp. 11, 17-18, 24, 29-32, etc. to 41, mainly lines and underscoring, in red ink; p. 21, at Wilkinson's testimony that Shaftesbury said the scholars, among others, would help the crown if Parliament were held at Oxford: 'How could this be, when the major part of s[c]holars (viz. the juniors, who are the fighting men) were sent home to make roome for the court & parliament.'
Wood 427(39). Wing P3564.

1985. Cooper, Anthony Ashley*. Shaftesbury, earl of. *Some memoirs: or, a sober essay for a just vindication of the right honourable the earl of Shaftsbury.* London: f. S. Lee, 1681. Fol. Pp. [2], 18.
Tp, AW wrote the price, '6^d' and 'This was published in Novemb. 1681. or in Octob –'. P. 11, correction of date; p. 13, identification of 'Young Tonge' as, 'Simpson Tongue'.
Wood 427(40). Wing S4518.

1986. Cooper, Anthony Ashley. Shaftesbury, earl of. *A speech lately made by a noble peer of the realm.* (London): (f. F. S.), (1681). S.sh. (r-v).
Underscoring of '*that we cannot trust the King*'; ˅, lines in margin and undercoring.
Wood 276a(103a) (84 in Bodl. CD cat.). Wing S2902.

1987. Cooper, Anthony Ashley*. Shaftesbury, earl of. *Some modest reflections upon the commitment of the earl of Shaftsbury, arising from the late indictment against mr. Stephen Colledge.* (London): (f. R. Baldwin), 1681, 12 July. Fol. Pp. 4.
Wood 427(33). Wing S4524.

1988. Cooper, Anthony Ashley*. Shaftesbury, earl of. *The last will and testament of Anthony king of Poland.* [London]: (f. S. Ward), (1682). S.sh. (r-v).
AW wrote the year, '1682'; and after Anthony in t, 'Earl of Shaftsbury'.
Wood 417(106). Wing L514aA (3) ('O' not recorded in Wing).

1989. Cooper, Anthony Ashley*. Shaftesbury, earl of. *Memoires of the life of Anthony late earl of Shaftsbury.* London: f. W. Davis, 1682, 1683. Fol. Pp. [2], 10.
Tp, AW wrote 'published about the middle of Feb. 1682'. P. 3, identification.
Wood 427(41). Wing M1671.

1990. Cooper, Anthony Ashley*. Shaftesbury, earl of. *An elegy on the right honourable Anthony earl of Shaftsbury.* London: f. L. Curtis, 1683. S.sh.
Wood 427(42). Wing E434A.

1991. Cooper, Anthony Ashley*. Shaftesbury, earl of. *An elegy on the right honourable Anthony earl of Shaftsbury [and] An elegy on the death (the much to be lamented) Anthony k. of Poland.* London: n.pub., 1683. S.sh.
At the 1st poem, AW wrote, 'This written by a Whigg came out first by it self'; at the 2nd, 'This written by a Tory was in opposition to that of Whigge – & were both printed togeather'; in 1st t, he changed the date in the t from 1683 to 1682/3.
Wood 427(43). Wing E435.

1992. Cooper, Anthony Ashley*. Shaftesbury, earl of. *Sh– ghost to doctor Oats. In a vision, concerning the Jesuits and lords in the Tower.* (London): (f. J. Knight), (1683). Fol. Pp. 4.
AW wrote in t, Sh'aftsburies'.
Wood 417(122). Wing S2832.

1993. Cooper, Anthony Ashley*. Shaftesbury, earl of. *A supplement to the last will and testament of Anthony earl of Shaftesbury.* (London): (f. J. Smith), (1683). Fol. Pp. 4.
Tp, AW, probably, underscored 'Will', in red ink.
Wood 427(44). Wing S6187.

1994. C[ooper], T[homas]. *Vox & votum populi Anglicani. Shewing how deeply the nation resents the thought of capitulating, now, with his majestie, . . . a letter to the earle of Manchester.* London: f. H. Seile, 1660. 4°. Pp. [2], 14.
Wood 608(16). Wing C6060.

1995. Coote, Charles*. Mountrath, 1st earl of. *A true relation of the transactions between sir Charls [sic] Coot . . . and Owen-Roe-O-Neal; as it was reported to the parliament from the councel of state.* London: f. E. Husband, 1649, 28 Aug. 4°. Pp. 19.
Wood 510(6). Wing T3061 (Wing, Charles).

1996. Coote, Charles. Mountrath, 1st earl of. *The declaration of sir Charls Coot . . . and the rest of the council of officers of the army in Ireland . . . concerning the re-admission of the secluded members.* London: J. Macock, 1659[60]. 4°. Rpt. of Dublin: W. Bladen edition. Pp. 8.
AW wrote in the margin, '16 Feb.'
Wood 510(28). Wing M2980.

1997. Coote, Charles. Mountrath, 1st earl of, et al. *The declaration of the army in Ireland, . . . for a free parliament, and the re-admitting of all the members secluded in 1648. Together with a letter [signed W. G.] [18 Feb.].* London: S. Griffin f. J. Playford, 1659[60]. 4°. Rpt. of Dublin edition. Pp. [2], 4.
Wood 510(29). Wing D634.

1998. Coote, Charles. Mountrath, 1st earl of. *The declaration of sir Charls Coot . . . and the officers and*

souldiers under his command. London: f. T. Vere a. W. Gilbertson, 1660. 4°. Pp. [2], 5 (misnumbering). Tp, AW altered the year to 16'59: Januar:'.
Wood 510(27). Wing M2981.

1999. Coote, Edmond. *The English schoole-master . . . by Edward [sic] Coote.* London: B. A. a. T. F. f. Co. of Stationers, 1641. 4°. 19th ed. Pp. [4], 85, [1]. Parchment.
Wood 313. Wing C6067 (rare).

2000. Coppe, Abiezer. *Copp's return to the wayes of truth:. . . or, truth asserted . . . Also a letter of m*ʳ *Durie's.* London: T. Newcomb, 1651. 4°. Pp. [12], 28.
Wood 647(19). Wing C6090.

2001. Corbet, John. *An historicall relation of the military government of Gloucester: from the beginning of the civill warre.* London: M. B. f. R. Bostock, 1645. 4°. Pp. [6], 140. Pasteboard (blue) with parchment spine.
Flyleaf, upper, 2nd\ʸ, 3rd-4th, AW wrote the titles of 66 printed works in this vol., within guidelines made with red ink. At item 2, 'deest Janʸ. 1840 W[illiam] K[irtland]'; at item 25, 'missing June [19]54' (missing also in 1922). Tp, the price, '1.6'. P. 33, AW wrote in margin 'Sʳ Matth. Carew of Glocestershire–'.
Wood 378(1). Wing C6252B.

2002. Corbet, John. *The epistle congratulatory of Lysimachus Nicanor of the society of Jesu, to the covenanters in Scotland, wherin is parallelled our sweet harmony.* Oxford: L. Lichfield, sold T. Fickus, 1684. 4°. Pp. [6], 9, [1], 81.
Wood 617(9). Wing C6247.

2003. Corddel, Lawrence*. *An exact relation of the barbarous murder committed on Lawrence Corddel.* London: f. J. Jones, 1661. 4°. Pp. [2], 5.
Wood 365(17). Wing E3682.

2004. [Cordemoy, Louis Géraud de]. *A philosophicall discourse concerning speech, . . . Englished out of French.* [London]: f. John Martin, 1668. 12°. Pp. [22], 125, [5] (5 pp. books sold by J. Martin).
Tp, '10ᵈ'. Acquired 13 Jan. 1669, 9ᵈ, LT 2.149.
Wood 37(2). Wing C6282.

2005. [Corker, James]. *Roman-Catholick principles, in reference to God and the king, explained in a letter, . . . by a well-wisher [signed M. B.].* London: n.pub., 1680. 4°. Pp. [2], 12, [1] (cropped).
Tp, AW wrote, 'Antony à Wood, ex dono Radulphi Sheldon de Beoly Aug. 14. 168[0]' (cropped at side; AW was at Weston in Aug.; see also [MS.] Wood B. 40(3b), acquired in 1680). P. 12, AW wrote, 'James Corker, O.S.B. a condemned prisoner in Newgate, the authour.' LT 3.105. See Plate VIII.
[MS.] Wood B. 40(3a). Wing C6302.

2006. [Corker, James]. *Roman-Catholick principles, in reference to God and the king, a letter [signed M.B.].* [London]: n.pub., 1680. 4°. 3rd ed. Pp. [2], 20, [1].
Tp, AW wrote, 'Donum AWood 1680', and p. 20, 'James Corker (Ord. S. Ben. mon[k]) a condemned prisoner in Newgate relating to the plot, wrot this book. Ita testor AWood. an. 1680.' A gift, with [MS.] Wood B. 40(3a), from Ralph Sheldon. LT 3.105.
[MS.] Wood B. 40(3b). Wing C6303.

2007. [Corker, James]. *Stafford's memoires: or, a brief and impartial account of the birth and quality . . . of William, late lord viscount Stafford.* [London]: n.pub., 1681. Fol. Pp. [2], 76.
Tp, AW wrote, 'James Corker a Benedictine Monke, & condemned prisoner in Newgate relating to the p. plott, wrot this book & caused it to be published – [/] AWood. ex dono R. S[heldon] Dec. 18. an. 1681 [/] Rob. Hancock Fellow of Clare hall, in Cambridge and Rector of Northill [sic] in Bedfordsh. answer'd this book in another entit. The Loyaltie of popish principles examined &c' (Wing H643). P. 76, 'printed in 8°', in pencil. LT 2.562; 3.105.
Wood 427(11). Wing C6306.

2008. C[orker], J[ames]. *A remonstrance of piety and innocence; containing the last devotions . . . of several Roman-Catholicks, . . . executed on account of the plot.* London: n.pub., 1683. 12°. Pp. [4], 190. Calf with 2 fillets and a vertical line of 2 fillets.
Flyleaf, upper, 2nd\ʸ, AW wrote 'These things were gathered togeather by James Corker O. S. B. a condemned prisoner in Newgate, & by him caused to be published, in Nov. 1682' and 'Given to me by R[alph] S[heldon] 13 Dec. 1682'. LT 3.34.

Wood 830. Wing C6301A.

2009. Corneille, Pierre. Dancer, John, trans. *Nicomede. A tragi-comedy . . . Together with an exact catalogue of all the English stage-plays printed [by F. Kirkman]*. London: f. F. Kirkman, 1671. 4° (wanting the catalogue; some cropping). Pp. [4], 56.
AW himself removed the cat. and placed it at [MS.] Wood E. 28(3). See also note on Dancer at Wood 235(5), item 2168, where AW conflated Dancer and Dauncey.
Wood 607(6). Wing C6315.

2010. Cornish, Henry*. *The tryals of Henry Cornish, esq; for conspiring the death of the king, . . . and John Fernley, William Ring, and Elizabeth Gaunt [19 Oct. 1685]*. London: printed a. sold by G. Croom, 1685. Fol. Pp. [2], 42.
Tp, AW wrote the price, '1ˢ'; p. 42, identified the recorder, 'Sʳ Thom. Jennour', and below, 'By letters dat. 25 Mar. 1686 tis said that his Ma. Jam. 2 hath granted & confirmed to the widdow & son of the late Alderman Cornish all the estate he died possessed of –'.
Wood 421(5). Wing T2250A ('O' not recorded in Wing).

2011. Cornwall. *To the right worshipful our worthy patriots of . . . Cornwall, assembled at Truroe . . . The humble remonstrance of us gentlemen [27 Dec. 1659]*. [London]: N. Thomas, 1659[60]. S.sh.
Wood 276a(118). Wing T1718 (two).

2012. Cornwall. *To the right worshipful the high sheriffs . . . of Cornwall, . . . The . . . petition [27 Dec. 1659]*. [London]: n.pub., [1660]. S.sh.
Wood 276a(114). Wing T1722 (two).

2013. Cornwall, and Devon. *The association, agreement and protestation, of the counties of Cornwall, and Devon. January 5*. Oxford: L. Lichfield, 1643[4], 18 Jan. 4°. Pp. [2], 9.
Wood 376(55). Wing A4052. Madan 1515.

2014. Cornwallis, William. Olney, Henry, ed. *Essayes. By sir William Corne-Waleys*. (London): [S. Stafford a. (R. Read)] f. E. Mattes, 1600 (1601). 8°. A⁴,B-N⁸,O⁴ (last 2 leaves blank).
H⁴ᵛ, a facetious response to the text, 'And: I He[nry] Leighe have done wᵗʰ tobacco - H. L.'; K7ᵛ-K8, lines in margin. Prob. acquired with Bacon's *Essays* (formerly owned by John Stobbert), Wood 769(1), item 335, 28 Apr. 1662, 6ᵈ, LT 1.436.
Wood 769(2). STC 5775.

2015. [Cornwallis, William]. *Essayes of certaine paradoxes*. London: [G. Purslowe] f. T. Thorp, 1616. 4°. A²,B-G⁴,H².
Wood 498(6). STC 5779.

2016. Corraro, Angelo. Bulted, J., trans.; Torriano, G., trans. *Rome exactly describ'd, as to the present state of it, under pope Alexandre . . . In two curious discourses [A relation of the state of the court of Rome, by A. Corraro, tr. by J. Bulted. And a new relation of Rome. As to the government of the city, Engl. by G. Torriano]*. London: T. Mabb f. M Young, J. Starkey a. J. Playfere, 1664. 8°. Pp. [18], 109, [15], 64 (wanting the frontisp.; 3 tpp).
P. 3, 2nd tp, price '1.6'.
Wood 666(3). Wing C6345.

2017. [Corrozet, Gilles]. *[Memorable conceits of divers noble and famous personages of Christen dome]*. [London]: [[R. Field] f. J. Shaw], [1602]. 12°. Pp. [6], 396 (t and pp. 217-238 supplied in MS copy; ends at p. 396). Calf with 2 fillets, a vertical line and stamp decoration in corners.
Pastedown, upper, 'Hen: Foulis. 1653' (also lower pastedown, 'Henry Foulis'); ms. t and pp. 217-238, not in AW's hand; text, some marks in margins, not in AW's manner. LT 2.180.
Wood 732. STC 5795.

2018. Corte, Claudio. Bedringfield, Thomas, trans. *The art of riding, conteining diverse necessarie instructions*. London: H. Denham, 1584. 4°. Pp. [12], 112.
[MS.] Wood C. 19(2). STC 5797.

2019. Coryate, Thomas. *The Odcombian banquet: dished foorth by Thomas the Coriat . . . in prayse of his crudities and crambe too*. [London]: [G. Eld] f. T. Thorp., 1611. 4°. A-P⁴ (A1 blank).
A1, AW wrote, 'These verses are printed before Coryats Crudities, which caused the book to sell– But here they are printed by themselves without the Crudities'. Tp, bsm. G4ᵛ, at contribution of Christopher Brooke, line in margin.

Wood 483(4). STC 5810.

2020. Coryate, Thomas. *Thomas Coriate traveller for the English wits: greeting. From the court of the great mogul.* [London]: W. Jaggard a. H. Fetherston, 1616. 4°. Pp. [8], 56 ([1] blank).
Sig. A1, AW wrote, 'Th. Coryate [/] A letter to his mother ult [pp. 49-52] Oct 1616 from Agra [i.e., Asmere] in East India, containing a speech that he spoke to the Great Mogul in the Persian tongue, for which he received from him 10£ of our English money. [/] Purchas Travells part. 1 lib. 4. cap 17 [/] certaine observations from the Moguls Court & East India – Ibid.' Pp. 9, at printed 'M. *Equinoctiall Pasiecrust* of the middle Temple', AW wrote 'Joh Hoskyns' (who was a source for Aubrey and his *Brief Lives*); 10, an identification; 10, 31, 37, notes that the passage also appeared in 'Purchas his pilgrimages'; 44-5, lines, in pencil, in margin.
Wood 498(2). STC 5811.

2021. Cosin, Richard. *An answer to the two first and principall treatises of a . . . libell, . . . an abstract of certeine acts of parlement.* London: H. Denham f. T. Chard, 1584. 4°. Pp. [12], 350 (wanting the abstract). Calf with 2 fillets, stamp decoration, dragonesque interlace, inside corners (Ashm. binding?).
Flyleaf, upper, 2nd, portion with annotation torn out. Tp, note and numbers, in 2 hands, neither in AW's. A2, annotation, not in AW's hand. Text, some underscoring, passim. P. 274, signature, 'Robert Bate' (?). Flyleaf, lower[r-v], an index, not in AW's hand.
Wood 491. STC 5819.5.

2022. Cosin, Richard. *An apologie for sundrie proceedings by jurisdiction ecclesiasticall.* London: deputies of C. Barker, 1593. 4°. Pp. [30], 130, [10], 140, [4], 256 (3 tpp). Calf with 2 fillets, 2nd rectangle with 3 fillets and stamp decoration outside corners.
Flyleaf, upper, price, 1[s] 6[d], not in AW's hand. Tp, and text, a few scribbles and notes, not in AW's hand. Names of Thomas Rob[b]ins, e.g., A2 and p. 45, and Mary Kembele p. 45.
Wood 493. STC 5821.

2023. Cosin, Richard. *Ecclesiae Anglicanae politeia in tabula digesta.* Oxonii: excud. L. Lichfield, imp. T. Fickus & J. Howel, 1684. Fol. Ed. ult. a-b[2], and, obl., A-G[2].
a2[v], 'This Dedication was written by Christopher Wase', may not be by AW.
Wood 657(9). Wing C6365.

2024. Cotta, John. *The triall of witch-craft.* London: G. Purslowe f. S. Rand, 1616. 4°. Pp. [8], 128.
Tp, AW wrote, 'The 2[d] Edition came out A° 1624' (STC 5837).
[MS.] Wood B. 21(2). STC 5836.

2025. [Cotton, Robert Bruce]. *A short view of the long life and raigne of Henry the third, king of England.* [London]: [J. Okes, a. B. Alsop a. T. Fawcet f. B. Fisher], 1627. 4°. Pp. 49 (misnumbering).
Wood 486(2). STC 5864.

2026. C[otton], R[obert Bruce]. *Serious considerations for repressing of the increase of Jesuites, priests, and papists, without shedding of blood.* [London]: n.pub., 1641. 4°. Pp. [2], 52.
Tp, at initials, R. C'otton', in pencil, may not be by AW. '8' and Bsm.
[MS.] Wood D. 24(8). Wing C6497.

2027. Cotton, Robert Bruce. *A treatise, shewing that the soveraignes person is required in the great councells or assemblies of the state.* [London]: n.pub., 1641. 4°. Pp. [2], 14.
Tp, AW wrote, 'This was published when K. Ch. 1. was forced to leave his Parl. by Tumults an. 1641'.
Wood 518(3b). Wing C6503.

2028. Cotton, Robert Bruce. *An abstract out of the records of the Tower, touching the kings revenue: and how they have supported themselves.* London: f. G. Tomlinson, T. A. a. A. C., [1642]. 4°. Pp. [2], 27. Pasteboard (blue) with parchment spine.
Flyleaf, upper, 1st[v], AW pasted a slip over his note to item 10 in this vol.: 'said to be writt by D[r] W. Petty somtime fellow of Brasenose Coll: in Oxon published in June: 1662. pr: 1[s] after the fire again [and in red ink:] 1667'; on the pasted down side of the waste paper slip, he wrote concerning G. Langbaine, *A new catalogue of English plays* (London, 1687) now at [MS.] Wood E. 28(5), item 1540, 'The first edition of this book bore this tit. Momus triumphans or the plagiaries of the English stage' (Wing L377); 2nd[v], AW wrote the titles of 10 printed works in this vol., within guidelines made with red chalk. 1st item, a former no., '3'; and bsm.
Wood 526(1). Wing C6476.

2029. Cotton, Robert Bruce. *The forme of governement of the kingdome of England collected out of the fundamental lawes and statutes of this kingdome.* London: f. T. Bankes, 1642. 4°. Pp. 19.
Tp, publ. date altered to 1643.
Wood 518(4). Wing C6492.

2030. Cotton, Robert Bruce. *The troublesome life and raigne of king Henry the third.* London: f. G. Lindsey, 1642. 4°. Pp. [2], 14.
P. 10, marks in margin.
Wood 486(3). Wing C6504.

2031. [Cotton, Robert Bruce]. *A brief survey (historical and political) of the life and reign of Henry the III.* London: 'Printed in the year' and, overpasted and cropped at bottom, 'Printed for James Vade', 1680. 4°. Pp. 32.
P. 1 (blank leaf), 'H.3. 80', not in AW's hand (a former shelf-mark). For more on the publisher Vade, see W. H. Hart, *Index Expurgatorius* (London, 1872) and Hugh Bowler, *London Sessions Records*, Catholic Record Society, 34 (London, 1934). MS. Wood F. 50, fols. 9-11 contain receipts of 15 purchases from James Vade (and others from J. Wilmot, an Oxford bookseller) in 1679. For other purchases from Vade in 1679, see LT 4.468, 478.
Wood 486(4). Wing C6482C. ESTCR 189954.

2032. Cotton, Robert, and John Hayward. *The histories of the lives and raignes of Henry the third, and Henry the fourth.* London: f. W. Sheares, 1642. 12°. Pp. [2], 318.
Tp, bsm. Acquired 2 Nov. 1661, LT 1.418.
Wood 240(5). Wing C6494.

2033. Cotton, Rowland*. Heigham, Edward, ed. *Parentalia. Spectatissimo Rolando Cottono . . . memoriae & pietatis ergo.* Londini: A. M[athewes], 1635. 4°. A-D⁴,d¹,E-G⁴,H².
Wood 484(8). STC 5870 .

2034. Court of Curiosities. *The court of curiosities, and the cabinet of rarities with the new way of wooing.* [London]: f. P. Brooksby, [1685]. 8°. A⁸,B⁴.
B2ᵛ, name, in pencil, 'John Dovaston Esq.', in a late hand.
Wood 69(10). Wing C6588 (rare).

2035. [Courtin, Antoine de]. *The rules of civility; or, certain ways of deportment observed in France . . . . Translated out of French.* London: f. J. Martyn a. J. Strakey, 1671. 12°. Pp. [11], 154. Pasteboard (grey) with parchment spine. 1st upper and last lower flyleaves, marbled paper. Several pamphlets show stitch holes from former binding.
Flyleaf, upper, 2ndᵛ, AW wrote the titles of 5 printed works in this vol., within guidelines made with red ink. Tp, AW wrote '9ᵈ'.
Wood 752(1). Wing C6602.

2036. Cousin, Gilbert. Chaloner, Thomas, trans. *Of the office of servauntes, . . . newely Englyshed.* (Londini): (in off. T. Berthe[leti]), (1543). 8°. A-C⁸.
Tp, AW wrote 'This translation was made by Sʳ Tho. Chaloner somtimes Embass. to Ferdinando the Emperour'.
Wood 824(2). STC 5879.

2037. Covell, William. *A declaration unto the parliament, council of state, and army, shewing . . . the causes of the peoples tumults.* London: n.pub., 1659. 4°. Pp. 23.
Tp, AW wrote, 'first heap 73', in pencil.
Wood 626(19). Wing C6612.

2038. C[oventry], W[illiam]. *A letter written to dr. Burnet, giving an account of cardinal Pool's secret powers.* London: f. R. Baldwin, 1685. 4°. Pp. 40.
Tp, line in margin at portion added to t, in red ink. Dupl. at Wood 617(5).
Wood 611(2). Wing C6631.

2039. C[oventry], W[illiam]. *A letter written to dr. Burnet, giving an account of cardinal Pool's secret powers.* London: f. R. Baldwin, 1685. 4°. Pp. 40.
Tp, 'Dupl', cropped at top. Dupl. at Wood 611(2).
Wood 617(5) (not in Bodl. CD cat.). Wing C6631.

2040. Coverte, Robert. *A true and almost incredible report of an Englishman, that (being cast away*

. . . *in Cambaya.* London: J. N[orton] f. H. Perry, 1631. 4°. Pp. [6], 68, [1].
Flyleaf, upper, waste paper[v], a disputation topic, not by AW, lined out.
Wood 387(5). STC 5897.

2041. Cowell, John. *The interpreter: or booke, containing the signification of words.* London: [R. Hodgkin-son] f. W. Sheares, 1637. 4°. †[4],A-4C[4]. Calf with 3 fillets and 4 bands on spine.
Flyleaf, upper, 1st, 'AW .1658.' and several multiplications of numbers, which may be in AW's hand. Also, scribbles of former owners. Tp[v], extensive notes, a few extending to † , in 2 hands, on plants, and some law matters, neither in AW's hand.
Wood 311. STC 5902.

2042. [Cowley, Abraham]. *A satyre. The puritan and the papist. By a scholler in Oxford.* [Oxford]: [H. Hall], 1643. 4°. Pp. [2], 9.
Wood 483(15). Wing C6688. Madan 1569.

2043. Cowley, A[braham]. *A proposition for the advancement of experimental philosophy.* London: J. M. f. H. Herringman, 1661. 8°. Pp. [2], 53, [8].
Tp, AW wrote '6[d]' and after the imprint, 'q[uaere]' and 'B' (?).
Wood 730(4). Wing C6684.

2044. [Cowley, Abraham]. *The visions and prophecies concerning England, Scotland, and Ireland, of Ezekiel Grebner.* London: f. H. Herringman, 1661. 12°. Pp. [10], 82. Pasteboard (blue) with parchment spine. 1st upper and last lower flyleaves, marbled paper.
Flyleaf, upper, 3rd[r-v], AW wrote the titles of 17 printed works in this vol., within guidelines made with red ink. 1st item, each 12° leaf is pasted on a 4° template. Tp, AW wrote '8[d]' and 'This came out in Jan. or Feb: A: 1660[1]'. Bsm.
Wood 646(1). Wing C6696.

2045. Cradock, Francis. *An expedient for taking away all impositions, and for raising a revenue without taxes.* London: f. H. Seile, 1660. 4°. Pp. [4], 12.
Wood 526(9). Wing C6742.

2046. Crakanthorpe, Richard. *Justinian the emperor defended, against cardinal Baronius.* London: G. Eld, sold N. Newbery, 1616. 4°. Pp. [10], 50, [1].
Missing. MS. Wood E. 2(70), p. 49. AO 2.362.
MS. Wood E. 2(70), p. 49. STC 5977. *O, Folg, Hunt, Harv.*

2047. Crane, Tho[mas]. *Job's assurance of the resurrection. A sermon . . . at the funeral of . . . Richard Sherlock.* London: f. P. Burton in Warrington, 1690. 4°. Pp. [4], 32 ('Errata' pasted on p. 32).
Pp. 22, 26 corrections (from 'Errata'), not by AW.
Wood 634(9). Wing C6819.

2048. Cranford, J[ames]. *The teares of Ireland.* London: A. N. f. J. Rothwell, 1642. 8°. Pp. [18], 80.
A4, correction in text; A6[v], AW wrote, 'James Cranford author of the Ep. but whether of the work it self is uncertaine'.
Wood 211(4). Wing C6824 (entry in Wing wants author).

2049. Cranmer, Thomas. P., E., trans. *A confutatiō of unwritté verities.* [Wesel?]: [J. Lambrecht?], [1556?]. 8°. A-O[8] (last leaf blank). Parchment over pasteboard.
Tp, 'Liber Henrici Jacksoni Oxoniensis, Coll. Corp. Cī. MDC Maii. xxi. liberati.' and 'pretium - 3[s].' Passim, some notes, including emendations from the errata, in Jackson's hand, and frequent underscoring and lines in margin. LT 1.459-60 (see also 1.331).
Wood 789(1). STC 5997.

2050. Craven, Anthony*. *A true . . . narrative of the several proceedings in the case concerning the lord Craven . . . and upon the indictment of perjury, . . . against major Richard Faulconer.* London: R. White, 1653. Fol. Pp. [4], 47.
Tp, AW wrote, 'The same yeare came out an answer to this intit. The Lord Cravens case answered in behalf of the common wealth – fol.'
Wood 657(57). Wing T2536.

2051. Craven, William. *The lord Craven's case. Considerations humbly offered [in respect to the confis-cation of his estate].* [London]: n.pub., [1659?]. Fol. Pp. 3, [1].
Wood 657(56). Wing L3045B ('O' not recorded in Wing).

2052. Crawford, Lawrence. *Irelands ingratitude to the parliament of England. Or, a remonstrance of . . . shewing the Jeuiticall [sic] plots against the parliament*. London: E. Griffin, 1643[4]. 4°. Pp. [2], 13. Tp, former no. overwritten. P. 13ᵛ, notes, not by AW: 'February 20ᵗʰ. 1693' and 3 loans of 2ˢ.6. Wood 508(48). Wing C6864.

2053. Creamer, Thomas*. *A gun-powder-plot in Ireland for the blowing up of the chiefest church in Dublin . . . by the information of T. Creamer . . . With a relation of a battell fought by the lord Moore*. London: f. J. Thomas, 1641. 4°. A⁴. Wood 507(6). Wing C6868.

2054. [Crespin, Jean]. *Acta martyrum, eorum videlicet, qui hoc seculo in Gallia, Germania, Anglia, . . . ab Wicleffo & Husso ad hunc usque diem*. Genevae: ap. J. Crispinum, 1556 (cal. Martii). Pp. [16], 291, [9]. Parchment with 2 clasp holes. Tp, 'ABosco e musæo Jacksoni'; and in Jackson's hand, 'Liber Henrici Jacksoni Oxoniensis, Collegii Corporis Christi, A°. MDC. Maii. xxi. liberati. pretium 4ˢ.' Pp. 4-70, at lives of Wycliff and Hus, frequent lines in margin, in pencil, in AW's manner. P. 150-1, marks in margin, not in AW's manner. Pp. 383, 395, 397, line in margins. Final printed p., 5 brief notes, in Jackson's hand. Jesus College E. 4. 7. BL.

2055. Cressy, Serenus. *Exomologesis or a faithfull narration of the occasion and motives of the conversion unto Catholique unity*. Paris: n.pub., 1647. 8°. Pp. [24], 655. Parchment. Flyleaf, upperᵛ, a price, 3ˢ-6ᵈ; p. 176, a reference, and pastedown, lower, 2 brief references, none by AW. Wood 828. BL.

2056. [Cressy, Serenus]. *Q. Why are you a Catholick? This question answered as followeth*. N.p.: n.pub., 1672. 8°. Pp. [6], 87. Each small 8° leaf is pasted on an 8° template. Flyleaf, upper, '32' (?). Tp, AW wrote 'By Serenus Cressy'. Pp. 17, 20, corrections. Wood 869(4). Wing C6901aA (two). ESTCR 232724.

2057. C[ressy], S[erenus]. *An epistle apologetical of S[erenus] C[ressy], to a person of honour [E. Hyde]: touching his vindication of dr. Stillingfleet*. N.p.: n.pub., 1674. 8°. Pp. [2], 138. Calf, dark, with gold-stamp fillets, 2 inner rectangles and elaborate gold-stamp decoration; gold fore-edges. Flyleaf, upper, 3rdᵛ, 'Ant. à Wood ex dono Radulphi Sheldoni de Beoly Armigeri. An. 1674.' LT 2.294. Wood 722. Wing C6893.

2058. Crimsal, Richard. *Cupid's soliciter of love*. London: T. Haly f. F. Coles, 1680. 8°. A⁸,B⁴. Wood 69(6). Wing C6913 (rare).

2059. Crispe, Samuel*, pseud. *Don Samuel Crispe: or, the pleasant history of the knight of fond love*. London: [f. H. Marsh?], 1660. 4°. A-C⁴,A². 2nd A1, at printed 'Mr. S. C's Character.', AW wrote, 'One Joh. Crispe was D.D. before 1641'. [MS.] Wood C. 31(5). Wing D1846 (two).

2060. Croce, Giovanni. H., R., trans. *Sextus. Musica sacra: to sixe voyces. . . . Newly Englished [by R. H.] (set to sonnets by Francesco Bembo)*. London: T. Este, the assigne of W. Barley, 1608. 4°. A-C⁴ (1 of 6 part-books, only). Wood 481(6). STC 6040.

2061. Crocus, Richardus. Ducherius, G., ed. *Orationes . . . duae, altera a cura, qua utilitatem laudemque Graecae linguae tractat, altera a tempore, qua hortatus est Cantabrigienses, ne desertores essent ejusdem*. [Lutetiae Parisiorum]: [cura S. Colinaei, sumpt. D. Ichman.], [1520]. 4° in 8's. a-c⁸,d1-2 (imperf.). Tp, AW wrote '(edit. circa 1526)'; note, not in AW's hand, lined out, and 2 modern notes in pencil. Text, some p. nos. written in at top, cropped. Pencil line in margins, b2ᵛ, c3ᵛ, and c4. Notes, possibly by B. Twyne, on c3ᵛ: 'episcopi omnes Angliae pene erant Oxonienses.' with a drawn hand pointer. Notes by AW on c4 at mention of Grocyn and Linacre, 'docti Oxonienses'; and on d1, 'V[ide] Caium de antiqu: Cant lib. 1. p 152' (he marked this passage in his copy, Wood 480(1)). Wood 498(3). BL.

2062. Croft, Herbert. Hereford, bp. of. *A short narrative of the discovery of a college of Jesuits at a place called the Come, in the county of Hereford. To which is added a true relation of . . . father Lewis*. London: T. N. f. C. Harper, 1679. 4°. Pp. [3], 18. P. 18, note on the outcome of the trial of Lewis, not by AW. Flyleaf, lower, 3rdᵛ, Latin tag, not by AW;

4th (marbled paper), 'for Mr Charlot', sic, not by AW. This prob. came to AW via Charlett.
[MS.] Wood D. 24(10). Wing C6977.

2063. Crofts, Robert. *The lover: or, nuptiall love*. London: B. Alsop a. T.F[awcet] f. R. Meighen, 1638.
8°. ², A-E⁸, F1-5.
Flyleaf, upper, 2nd^v, at item 2, AW added 'Rob. Craft Art. bac. 20 March 1590 – not the same'. P. [1],
signature, Humphry Barcoll (Barcott?). E3, scribble.
Wood 741(2). STC 6042.

2064. [Croke, Charles]. Rodolphus (pseud.). *Fortune's uncertainty, or youth's unconstancy*. London:
f. T. Dring, 1667. 8°. Pp. 99.
Flyleaf, upper, 1st, AW wrote, 'Charles Croke a yonger son of Unton Croke of Merston neare Oxon (made
sergeant at law by Oliver protector) was the author of the book following, entit. <u>Fortunes uncertainty</u> &c';
2nd, a similar note, preceded by 'qu[aere] whether not judge Crokes son of Merston neare Oxon' and a
brief answer 'so the report goes', in red ink, both crossed out. P. 7, details about Croke, e.g., 'Dr. Charls
Croke, I think somtimes of Ch.Ch. afterwards min[iste]r of Amers[h]am in Bucks.', see AOF 2.129. Passim,
underscorings or marks in margins; identifications to p. 55, of, e.g., Thom. Johnson, Thom. Goodwin, Rich.
Croke, Col. Unton Croke. Acquired 6 July 1667, 8^d, LT 2.112 (and see 3.108).
Wood 155(3). Wing C7008 (3).

2065. Crompton, Hugh. *The distressed Welshman, born in Trinity-lane . . . By Hugh Crumpton*. [Lon-
don]: f. W. Thackeray, 1688. 8°. A⁸, B⁴.
Wood 259(13). Wing C7027C (rare).

2066. Crompton, Richard. *Star-chamber cases. Shewing what causes properly belong to the cognizance
of that court*. London: [M. Flesher] f. J. Grove, 1630. 4°. Pp. [2], 57.
Tp, AW wrote, 'Crompton Burgess for the Univer. of Ox. v[ide] orig. jurid.' (AO 1.634). P. 57, line in
margin, in pencil.
[MS.] Wood B. 39(5). STC 6056.

2067. Cromwell, Henry. *The lord Henry Cromwells speech in the house*. [London]: n.pub., 1659. 4°.
Missing in 1837, when W. Kirtland wrote on the upper flyleaf of this vol., 'deest W. K.' The Folger Library
copy, C7037, has a note with an illegible month and '13, 1659' on the tp.
Wood 610(17). Wing L3047A. *Folg*.

2068. Cromwell, Oliver. *The copy of a letter written by colonel Cromwel, to the committee at Cam-
bridge. . . . Concerning the . . . siege at Gainsborough [31 July]*. London: E. Blackmore, 1643, 3 Aug. 4°.
Pp. [2], 6.
Missing in 1839; see note at Wood 376(1), item 3001.
Wood 376(23). Wing C7051. O (Pamph. 976(40) has a former no. rubbed out), *Hunt, Harv, Folg*.

2069. Cromwell, Oliver. *An abstract of a letter . . . April 26. 1645. Of a great victory obtained . . . against
a party of the earle of Northamptons regiment . . . neere Oxford*. London: f. F. Coles, 1645. 4°. Pp. [2], 7.
Missing in 1839; see note at 378(1). Dupl. at Wood 632(57). The Folger copy is the 1st in a vol. of 3 tracts
(Wing C7039, S3892, and B2969) once owned by 'Dr. [P.] Bliss'; on the tp, top centre, '2'.
Wood 378(2). Wing C7039. Madan 1772. *Folg*.

2070. Cromwell, Oliver. *An abstract of a letter . . . April 26, 1645. Of a great victory obtained . . . against
a party of the earle of Northamptons regiment . . . neere Oxford*. London: f. F. Coles, 1645. 4°. Pp. [2], 7.
Dupl. at Wood 378(2) missing.
Wood 632(57). Wing C7039. Madan 1772.

2071. Cromwell, Oliver. *Good newes out of the west, . . . in a letter sent from lieueenant [sic] generall
Cromwel, to a worthy member of the house of commons*. London: M. Simmons, 1645. 4°. A⁴.
Wood 378(9). Wing C7089.

2072. Cromwell, Oliver. *Lieut: generall Cromwells letter [of Sept. 14] to the house of commons, . . . of
taking the city of Bristoll; and . . . of p: Ruperts marching to Oxford*. London: f. E. Husband, 1645, 18
Sept. 4°. Pp. 8.
Missing in 1922. See note at Wood 378(1). Dupl. or diff. ed. at Wood 612(31) (not identified).
Wood 378(25). Wing C7114 or C7114A. *NYPL, Folg*.

2073. Cromwell, Oliver. *Lieut: generall Cromwells letter [of Sept. 14] to the house of commons, . . . of
taking the city of Bristoll; and . . . of p: Ruperts marching to Oxford*. London: f. E. Husband, 1645, 18

Sept. 4°. Pp. 8.
Tp, AW wrote 'Dup', in pencil. Dupl. or diff. ed. at Wood 378(25) missing.
Wood 612(31). Wing C7114.

2074. Cromwell, Oliver. *Lieut: generall Cromwells letter [of 17 Oct.] to . . . William Lenthall . . . of the surrender of Langford-house neer Salisbury.* London: f. E. Husband, 1645, 24 Oct. 4°. Pp. 7.
Tp, AW underscored, 'Cromwells', in red ink, and overwrote a former no. '33'. Diff. ed. at Wood 632(59).
Wood 378(36). Wing C7110.

2075. Cromwell, Oliver. *Lieut: generall Cromwells letter [of 17 Oct.] to . . . William Lenthall . . . of the surrender of Langford-house neer Salisbury.* London: f. E. Husband, 1645, 20 Oct. 4°. Pp. 7.
Tp, AW underscored 'Cromwells', in red ink; and wrote 'Dupl'. Diff. ed. at Wood 378(36).
Wood 632(59). Wing C7109.

2076. Cromwell, Oliver. *Livetenant [sic] generall Cromwels letter sent to . . . William Lenthall . . . concerning the storming and taking of Basing house.* [London]: T. W. f. E. Husband, 1645, 16 Oct. 4°. Pp. [2], 4, [1].
Tp, AW underscored 'Cromwels' in the t, in red ink, and lined out the former no., '29'.
Wood 378(32). Wing C7108.

2077. Cromwell, Oliver. *A full relation of the great victory . . . against the . . . Scots [23 Aug.].* London: f. J. Wright, 1648. 4°. Pp. [1], 8.
Dupl. at Wood 609(5).
Wood 502(58). Wing F2362.

2078. Cromwell, Oliver. *A full relation of the great victory . . . against the . . . Scots [23 Aug.].* London: f. J. Wright, 1648. 4°. Pp. [1], 8.
Tp, AW wrote 'Dupl', in pencil. Dupl. at Wood 502(58).
Wood 609(5). Wing F2362.

2079. Cromwell, Oliver. *A letter sent from . . . to the marquis of Argyle, and generall Lesley, and his protestation concerning the Scottish forces.* [London]: f. C. W., 1648. 4°. Pp. [2], 6.
Missing in 1922. See note at Wood 502(1). AW wrote the t on the upper flyleaf as: 'Cromwell's letter to the Marq. of Argyle & Gen. Lesley, & his protestation concerning the Scotch forces under the command of Gen. Munro &c & other things'.
Wood 502(69). Wing C7106. *Harv.*

2080. Cromwell, Oliver*. *A true copy of divers intercepted letters sent from the committee at Derby-house to lieut. gen: Cromwell [9-13 June].* [London]: n.pub., [1648]. S.sh.
On slip inserted after the s.sh., AW wrote 'Jun. 13. 1648.'
Wood 502(22). Wing T2634.

2081. Cromwell, Oliver. *A letter written by . . . of the total routing of the Scoth [sic] army, neer Preston [18 Aug.].* London: I. M., 1648, 21 Aug. 4°. Pp. 8 (2-3 unopened).
Tp, AW wrote after the year, 'Aug. 18'.
Wood 502(47). Wing C7116.

2082. Cromwell, Oliver. *A letter written by . . . of the total routing of the Scoth [sic] army, neer Preston [18 Aug.].* London: I. M., 1648, 21 Aug. 4°. Pp. 8.
Missing in 1922. See Wood 502(1). AW wrote the t on the upper flyleaf as: 'Cromwells letter to the H. of Com. concerning the fight neare Preston – The Scots army totally defeated &c.' This was apparently a dupl. of Wood 502(47) and perhaps for that reason removed.
Wood 502(53). Wing C7116.

2083. Cromwell, Oliver. *Lieut: general Cromwel's letter to . . . William Lenthal . . . of the several great victories obtained against the Scots and sir Marmaduke Langdales forces.* London: f. E. Husband, 1648, 23 Aug. 4°. Pp.14, [1].
Wood 502(55). Wing C7111.

2084. Cromwell, Oliver. *Lieut: general Cromwels letter . . . containing a narrative of his proceedings in the managing the affairs . . . in Scotland [2 Oct.].* London: f. E. Husband, 1648, 10 Oct. 4°. Pp. 8.
Wood 502(71). Wing C7108B.

2085. Cromwell, Oliver. *Lieut: general Cromwels letter . . . concerning his last proceedings in Scotland*

. . . with another letter . . . to the committee of estates, representing the great damage . . . England hath received [5, 9 Oct.]. London: f. E. Husband, 1648, 19 Oct. 4°. Pp. 16.
Wood 502(72). Wing C7108A.

2086. Cromwell, Oliver*. *The transactions of several matters between lieut: gen: Cromwel and the Scots, for surrendring the towns of Berwick, Carlisle and all other garrisons [20 Sept.].* London: f. E. Husband, 1648, 2 Oct. 4°. Pp. 24.
Wood 502(68). Wing C7176D.

2087. Cromwell, Oliver. *A letter [of Nov. 25?] from the . . . lord lieutenant of Ireland . . . concerning the . . . surrendring of Enistery, . . . Kingsale, and the fort there.* London: J. Field f. E. Husband, 1649. 4°. Pp. 8.
Wood 510(12). Wing C7101.

2088. Cromwell, Oliver. *A letter from . . . from Dunbar [3 Sept.].* London: E. Husband a. J. Field, 1650. 4°. Pp. 16.
Missing in 1922. AW wrote the t on the upper flyleaf as: 'Letter from Gen. Cromwell containing a relation of the said victory &c.'
Wood 503(15). Wing C7097. *O, Hunt, Folg.*

2089. Cromwell, Oliver. *A letter from the lord lieutenant of Ireland . . . relating the several successes it hath pleased God lately to give the parliaments forces there. Together with the . . . surrender of Kilkenny.* London: E. Husband a. J. Field, 1650. 4°. Pp. 22.
Wood 510(15). Wing C7103.

2090. Cromwell, Oliver. *Several letters and passages between . . . Cromwell and the governor of Edinburgh castle.* London: J Field f. F. Tyton, 1650, 25 Sept. 4°. Pp. 15.
Wood 503(16). Wing C7166.

2091. Cromwell, Oliver*. *A perfect list of all the victories obtained by the lord general Cromwell, from the time that his excellency was made captain general . . . to the present time.* London: R. Ibbitson, 1652. S.sh.
Missing. Flyleaf to this item, 'Mem^d - No. 18 Deest Novr. 1840 W[illiam] K[irtland]'. AW wrote the t on the upper flyleaf of this vol. as: 'List of all the victories obtained by Cromwell since he was made Capt. General to 1652 &c.'
Wood 503(18). Wing P1491 (rare). BL T.

2092. Cromwell, Oliver. *The last speech of . . . the lord protector to the parliament [12 Sept.].* London: R. Wood, 1654. 4°. Pp. 8.
Tp, no. 53 in a former bundle.
Wood 609(37). Wing C7091.

2093. Cromwell, Oliver*. *A true account of the late bloody and inhumane conspiracy against his highness the lord protector.* London: T. Newcomb, 1654. 4°. Pp. 94.
Tp, bsm. P. 9, AW added detail, 'Tho. Henshaw kinsman to Tho. Henshaw of Kensington Esq.'
Wood 367(9). Wing T2381.

2094. Cromwell, Oliver*. *The articles of the perpetual peace, concluded between . . . Oliver, lord protector . . . and . . . the Netherlands [trans. out of the Dutch copie].* [London]: n.pub., 1654, 2 May. 4°. 'Reprinted at London'. Pp. [2], 17.
Wood 503(20). Wing C7040E.

2095. Cromwell, Oliver*. *A copie of quaeries, or, a comment upon the life . . . of the grand tyrant . . . Oliver.* [London] Utopia: n.pub., 1659. 4°. Pp. 11, [1].
Missing since 1994.
Wood 531(24) (not in Bodl. CD cat.). Wing C6197 ('O' not recorded in Wing).

2096. Cromwell, Oliver*. *The world in a maize, or, Oliver's ghost.* London: n.pub., 1659. 4°. Pp. 8.
Missing since 1917. 'Not here 1917' (this note was recorded by T.A. Birrell before the vol. was missing in 1994).
Wood 531(26). Wing W3587.

2097. Cromwell, Oliver*. *A conference held between the old lord protector and the new lord general, truly reported by Hugh Peters [a satire].* London: n.pub., 1660. 4°. Pp. [2], 6.

Missing since 1994.
Wood 531(28). Wing C5731 ('O' not recorded in Wing).

2098. Cromwell, Oliver*. *A parly between the ghosts of the late lord protector, and the king of Sweden, at their meeting in hell.* London: f. L. Whimbleton, 1660. 4°. Pp. 19.
Missing since 1994.
Wood 531(27). Wing P497.

2099. Cromwell, Oliver; Henry Ireton, and John Bradshaw. *The speeches of Oliver Cromwell, Henry Ireton, and John Bradshaw. Intended to have been spoken at their execution, . . . publish't by Marchiamont [sic] Needham and Pagan Fisher.* London: n.pub., 1660[1]. 4°. Pp. 12.
Wood 608(37). Wing S4876 (two).

2100. Cromwell, Oliver, and Robert Venables. *Letters from Ireland, relating the several great successes . . . unto the parliaments forces there. [Two, dated September 17, signed O. Cromwell, the 3rd, R. Venables].* London: J. Field f. E. Husband, 1649. 4°. Pp. 20.
Pp. 6, 8, AW wrote in a date and corrected a name, Aston for Ashton.
Wood 510(8). Wing L1778.

2101. Cromwell, Oliver, and W. L. *Lieutenant general Cromwel's letter concerning the total routing of the Scots army. With another letter written from Manchester [signed W. L.].* London: f. E. Husband, 1648, 22 Aug. 4°. Pp. 8.
Tp, AW wrote after the year, 'Aug. 17'.
Wood 502(48). Wing C7092.

2102. Cromwell, Richard*. *Fourty four queries to the life of queen Dick. By one who will at any time work a job of journey-work, to serve his countery.* [London]: n.pub., 1659. 4°. Pp. 7.
Tp, no. '49', in pencil, in a former bundle.
Wood 613(53). Wing F1622.

2103. Cromwell, Richard*. *A true catalogue, or, an account of the several places and most eminent persons in the three nations, . . . by whom Richard Cromwell was proclaimed lord protector.* [London]: n.pub., [1659]. 4°. Pp. 76.
Missing since 1994.
Wood 531(30). Wing T2593.

2104. Crouch, H[umphrey]. *The compleat bell-man. Being a pattern for all sorts of people to take notice of the most remarkable times and dayes in the year.* [London]: f. F. Coles, [1650 ca.]. A⁸ (all leaves printed on 1 side and pasted back to back).
Wood 110(8). Wing C7277bA (rare).

2105. C[rouch], H[umphrey]. Sometimes attrib. to. *Londons lord have mercy upon us. A true relation of five modern plagues.* London: f. R. Harper, [1637]. S.sh. (last burial entry, 11 May 1637).
ᵛ, AW wrote '1636', in pencil.
Wood 416(3). STC 4273 (3).

2106. Crouch, H[umphrey]. *A new and pleasant history of unfortunate Hodg of the south.* London: f. T. Locke, 1655. 8°. Pp. [2], 13.
Wood 259(6). Wing C7286 (rare).

2107. Crouch, Humphrey. *The Welch traveller.* London: W. Gilbertson or W. Whitwood, 1657 or 1671. 12°. Pp. 23 or 24.
Missing in 1837. 'The Welch Traveller –' in Whiteside cat. Dupl. or diff. ed. at Wood 84(13) (1657).
Wood 66(14). Wing C7288B (rare) or C7289 (3). *O*, and *BL*.

2108. Crouch, Humphrey. *The Welsh traveller. Or the unfortunate Welshman.* London: f. W. Gilbertson, 1657. 8°. Pp. 24 (all pp. cropped at top).
Dupl. or diff. ed. at Wood 66(14) (missing).
Wood 84(13). Wing C7288B (rare).

2109. Crouch, Jo[hn]. *An elegie upon the much lamented death of . . . the earl of Tiveot, governour of Tangiers.* London: f. T. Palmer, 1664. S.sh.
After t, 'about May day – 64', not in AW's hand. ᵛ, AW wrote, 'Earl of Tiveot 1664'.
Wood 429(21). Wing C7297.

2110. Crouch, Jo[hn]. *An elegy upon the marquess of Dorchester. And earl of Kingston.* London: printed a. sold by W. Davis, [1680]. S.sh.
AW wrote the year, '1681'; ᵛ, 'Marq. of Dorc. 1681'.
Wood 429(35). Wing C7296.

2111. [Crouch, Nathaniel]. *A journey to Jerusalem:. . . travels of fourteen English-men, in the year, 1669 . . . in a letter from T. B. in Aleppo.* London: T. M. f. N. Crouch, 1672. 12°. Pp. [36], 87, [6].
Tp, AW wrote, 'AW. 1673. 6ᵈ'. Bsm.
Wood 158(3). Wing C7341.

2112. [Crouch, Nathaniel]. *A view of the English acquisitions in Guinea, and the East-Indies . . . by R. B.* London: f. N. Crouch, 1686. 12°. Pp. [5], 182, [6] (6 pp. books sold by Crouch).
Missing in 1837.
Wood 802. Wing C7356. *Hunt, NYPL, Folg.*

2113. Crowne, William. *A true relation of all the remarkable places and passages observed in the travels of . . . Thomas lord Howard.* London: [F. Kingston] f. H. Seile, 1637. 4°. Pp. [4], 70.
Flyleaf, upper, waste paper, a disputation topic and '35', not by AW. Tp, 'K.3.13', shelf-mark of an owner or library.
Wood 387(7). STC 6097.

2114. Cuffe, Henry. M., R., ed. *The differences of the ages of mans life.* London: B. A[lsop] a. T.F[awcet] f. L. Chapman, 1633. 8°. Pp. [14], 135. Pasteboard (blue) with parchment spine. 1st upper and last lower flyleaves, marbled paper; rebacked.
AW wrote the titles of 3 printed works in this vol., within guidelines made with red ink. Lower flyleaf, 1stᵛ, has the date of binding, 'Jun 1 1687', in pencil. Tp, bsm. Pp. 2ff. some short horizontal pencil lines in margin, not in AW's manner.
Wood 747(1). STC 6104.

2115. Cuffe, Maurice. *True newes from Munster in Ireland, being a copy of a letter sent to the countesse of Thomond in Northamptonshire sent to the countesse of Thomond in Northamptonshire [28 May].* London: f. H. Seale [sic], 1642, 15 June. 4°. Pp. [2], 5.
Wood 508(21). Wing C7473 (Wing, f. H. Seyle and 16 June).

2116. Culmer, Richard*. *Antidotum Culmerianum: or, animadversions upon a late pamphlet, entitled Cathedrall newes from Canterbury.* Oxford: H. Hall, 1644. 4°. Pp. [4], 35.
Pp. 11, underscoring, prob. not by AW; 13, hand pointer at 'Dicke Culmer' and his residence, may not be by AW.
[MS.] Wood D. 31(51). Wing A3500. Madan 1770.

2117. Culmer, Richard*. *The razing of the record. Or, an order to forbid any thanksgiving for the Canterbury newes publisht by Richard Culmer.* Oxford: n.pub., 1644. 4°. Pp. [4], 15.
Tp, AW underscored the name of Culmer, in red ink. Bsm. AOF 1.447.
[MS.] Wood D. 31(50). Wing R420. Madan 1676.

2118. Culmer, Richard, ed. *[Dean and chapter newes from Canterbury].* [London]: [R. Cotes], [1649]. 4°. 2nd ed. Pp. 24 (wanting the t leaf and all after p. 24).
[MS.] Wood D. 31(49). Wing C7479.

2119. Culmer, Richard. *The ministers hue and cry, or, a true discovery of the insufferable injuries . . . now acted against ministers and impropriators.* London: A. Miller, 1651. 4°. Pp. [2], 21, [1].
Tp, AW underscored the name of the author, in red ink.
[MS.] Wood D. 31(52). Wing C7481.

2120. Culpeper, C. *A message sent from the king of Scots, and the duke of York's court in Flanders, to the lord Douglas, and collonel Brown.* Aberdeen: D. Straugham, [1659]. 4°. Pp. 7.
Tp, former nos. '29' and '27', in pencil.
Wood 632(35). Wing C7483A.

2121. Culpeper, Tho[mas]. *A discourse, shewing the many advantages which will accrue . . . by the abatement of usury.* London: T. Leach f. C. Wilkinson, 1668. 4°. Pp. [12], 34.
Tp, AW wrote the price, '6ᵈ'. Bsm.
Wood 628(3a). Wing C7555.

2122. [Culpeper, Thomas]. *A short appendix to a late treatise concerning the abatement of usury*. London: T. Leach f. C. Wilkinson, 1668. 4°. Pp. 7.
Wood 628(3b) (not in Bodl. CD cat.). Wing C7563 ('O' not recorded in Wing).

2123. Cupid's Master-piece. *Cupids master-piece[,] or, the free-school of witty and delightful comple-ments*. London: f. J. Andrews, [1656]. 8°. A[8],B[4] (cropped).
Wood 79(4) (now Arch. G. f. 2(4)). Wing C7605 (rare) (Wing,16[5]6).

2124. Curfet, Colonel. *A true relation of the Scots taking of Cocket Iland . . . And of their proceedings at the siege of Newcastle [12 Feb.]*. London: f. A. Coe, 1644. 4°. A[4].
Tp, AW wrote, '1643 qu[aere]' and overwrote that with the former no., '59', which he later lined out. At the date, '1644', he underscored '44' and wrote '43'. Dupl. at Wood 612(25).
Wood 376(65). Wing C7622.

2125. Curfet, Colonel. *A true relation of the Scots taking of Cocket Iland . . . And of their proceedings at the siege of Newcastle [12 Feb.]*. London: f. A. Coe, 1644. 4°. A[4].
Tp, AW wrote 'Dupl', in pencil; and entered the year, '1643'. Dupl. at Wood 376(65).
Wood 612(25). Wing C7622.

2126. C[urtis], W. (probable author). *A more full relation of the continued successes of his excellency sir Thomas Fairfax*. London: f. F. Coles, 1645[6]. 4°. Pp. [2], 6.
Tp, AW overwrote the price, '1[d]', with the former no., '47', and lined out that no.
Wood 378(50). Wing C159 (Wing, C., W.).

2127. C[urtis], W., and J[ohn] R[ushworth] (probable authors). *Sir Thomas Fairfax his victorious proceedings in the taking of Launceston*. London: f. M. Walbancke, 1645[6], 4 Mar. 4°. Pp. 8.
AW wrote and later lined out the price, '1[d]', and altered the former no., '51'.
Wood 378(54). Wing S3894.

2128. Curtius Rufus, Quintus. Brende, John, trans. *The historie of Quintus Curtius, conteining the actes of the great Alexander*. [London]: in aed. R. Warde, 1584. 8°. Ff. [3], 259. Calf with 6 fillets, 2 gold-stamped; gold-stamp decoration and oval centrepiece; 2 clasp holes; spine, 5 bands and gold-stamp decoration.
Tp, signature, 'Ja: Cuningham' and 'precium - 1[s] - 4[d]'; a brief note in pencil, illeg. and 'Hist. la Fere', not in AW's hand.
Wood 180. STC 6145.

2129. Curtius Rufus, Quintus. *Q. Curtii Rufi historiarum libri, accuratissime editi*. Amstelodami: ap. J. Janssonium, 1663. 16°. Pp. 284, [22] (first leaf blank). Calf, speckled, with 2 and 4 fillets and stamp decoration inside corners.
Wood 775. Not in BL.

2130. Cusack, George*. *The grand pyrate: or, the life and death of capt. George Cusack*. London: f. J. Edwin, 1676 (1675). 4°. Pp. 31 (2nd tp at p. 25).
Wood 372(14). Wing G1505 ('O' not recorded in Wing).

2131. Cynosura Grammaticae Latinae. *Cynosura grammaticae [Latinae] id est tabula grammaticalis, etymologicam pariter & syntacticam Latini sermonis rationem . . . .* N.p.: n.pub., n.d. S.sh. (cropped at side).
Wood 276a(21) (not in Bodl. CD cat.). Not identified.

2132. Cyrano de Bergerac, Savinien. S[t]Serf, Tho[mas] [sic], trans. Σεληναρχια. *Or, the government of the world in the moon*. London: J. Cottrel, sold H. Robinson, 1659. 8°. A-M[8],N[4] (A1 torn).
Each small 8° leaf is pasted on an 8° template. 1st leaf, A1, with traces of annotation not by AW, cut out; last leaf, N4[v], signature 'S[r] John Huband Gllast. [?] prenobilis', pasted over with a slip (see LT 2.197).
Wood 682(2). Wing C7719.

2133. D., E. *Complaints and queries upon Englands misery: acted Octob. 13, 1659 by some officers of the army against the parliament*. London: J. C., 1659. 4°. Pp. [1], 6 (i.e., 7, misnumbering).
Tp, no. '3', in pencil, in a former bundle.
Wood 533(12). Wing D14.

2134. D., E. *The declaration of the officers of the army opened, examined & condemned, and the parliament vindicated*. London: n.pub., 1659. 4°. Pp. [2], 50, [1].

Tp, no. 20 in a former bundle.
Wood 610(39). Wing D15.

2135. D., F.*. *A sermon taken out of an Oxford scholar's [F. D.'s] pocket, who was found dead in Bishop's Wood, near High-gate on . . . Feb. 15. 1685/6.* London: f. T. Fabian, 1688. 4°. Pp. [6], 33.
[MS.] Wood D. 23(8). Wing D20.

2136. D., L. *An exact relation of the proceedings and transactions of the late parliament:. . . dissolved the 12 Decemb. 1653.* London: f. L. Chapman, 1654. 4°. Pp. [4], 27 (see note at item 2703).
Wood 519(10). Wing D52.

2137. Daffy, Anthony. *Directions given by mee . . . For taking my safe, innocent, and successful cordial drink; called elixir salutis.* [London]: n.pub., [1670?]. 4°. Pp. 8.
Wood 534(3b). Wing D105 (rare).

2138. Daffy, Anthony. *Elixir salutis: the choise drink of health.* London: f. the Author, by W. G., 1674. 4°. Pp. 8.
Tp, wax seal, mutilated.
Wood 534(3a). Wing D106 (rare).

2139. Daffy, Anthony. *Daffy's original elixir salutis, vindicated against all counterfeits.* [London]: n.pub., [1679?]. 4°. Pp. 8.
Wood 534(3c). Wing D107 (rare).

2140. Dagget, George. *The estate of the poor in Sion college London, truly stated [4 May].* (London): (f. R. Chiswell), (1688). S.sh. (r-v).
Tp, scribble altering printed Sion: 'S.tion'.
Wood 657(29). Wing D108.

2141. Daillé, Jean. *The plots of the Jesuites, . . . of Robert Parsons . . . Adam Contzen . . . Tho. Campanella . . . how to bring England to the Romane religion without tumult [tr. from the preface of J. Daill's An apologie for the Reformed churches.].* London: f. M. Spark, 1653. 4°. Pp. [2], 12 (wanting the frontisp.).
Pp. 10-1, at Rob. Parsons, 2 lines in margin and a 'q[uaere]'.
Wood 586(17). Wing P2603.

2142. Dale, John. *The analysis of all the epistles of the New Testament.* Oxford: L. Lichfield, 1652. 12°. Pp. [10], 216.
Missing. Purchased 24 Dec. 1656, 1ˢ1ᵈ, LT 1.210. AO 4.161.
LT 1.210. Wing D123. Madan 2192.

2143. Dalgarno, Geo[rge]. *Tables of the universal character. [2nd section] To . . . doctors, d. Wilkins, . . . and d. Ward . . . Grammatical observations.* [Oxford]: [L. Lichfield], [1657]. Fol. Pp. [4].
Ms. letters of the alphabet were written as mnemonic references. These may not be in AW's hand.
Wood 276a(20). Wing D130 (two). Madan 2335.

2144. Dalton, Andrew*. Commissioners for Irish Affairs. *To all justices of the peace, mayors, sheriffes . . . These are to certefie [a brief on behalf of Andrew Dalton and his family] [23 Feb. 1653].* N.p.: n.pub., [1653]. S.sh. 4°.
Dupl. at Wood 510(20).
Wood 276a(145) (Wood 276a(f.112) in Bodl. CD cat.). Wing T1323A (rare, 2 at O) (Wing, certifie).

2145. Dalton, Andrew*. Commissioners for Irish Affairs. *To all justices of the peace, mayors, sheriffes . . . These are to certefie [a brief on behalf of Andrew Dalton and his family] [23 Feb. 1653].* N.p.: n.pub., [1653]. S.sh. 4°.
Above, 'a Brief', in pencil. Dupl. at Wood 276a(145).
Wood 510(20). Wing T1323A (rare, 2 at O) (Wing, certifie).

2146. Dalton, James. *A strange and true relation of a young woman [Joyce Dovey] possest with the devill . . . Also a letter from Cambridge wherein is related the late conference between the devil . . . and one Ashbourner . . . of S. Johns Colledge.* London: E. P. f. T. Vere, 1647. 4°. Pp. [2], 6.
MS. Wood E. 2(70), p. 24, 'In this book [at one time made up of 2 items, [MS.] Wood B. 19(1 and 2)] I have put a little pamphlet concerning the Devills taking away one Ashburnes a scholler of St. Johns Coll Camb. – an. 1646'.

[MS.] Wood B. 18(6). Wing D142 (two).

2147. Damon, William. *Welcome newes from Ireland, or a victorious battell of the protestant armie.* London: f. J. Greensmith, 1642. 4°. A⁴.
Tp, AW wrote below the year, 'Dec.', in pencil. Bsm.
Wood 507(22). Wing D158A.

2148. Dance of Death, and Desiderius Erasmus. Aemilius, Georgius, trans. *Imagines mortis. His accesserunt epigrammata, . . . Ad haec, medicina animae [et al.].* Coloniae: ap. haer. A. Birckmanni, 1566. 8°. A-M⁸ (last leaf blank). Parchment; flyleaf, upper and backing, printer's waste paper.
Tp, signature of W. Cowbye. Text and M7ᵛ-8ᵛ, a few notes and scribbles and surnames, Halford, Holmes, Dobson; none by AW.
Wood 844. Not in BL.

2149. Danger. *The danger and unreasonableness of a toleration: in reference to some late papers . . . concerning liberty of conscience.* London: f. W. Davis, 1685. 4°. Pp. [2], 6.
Wood 611(14). Wing D177.

2150. Dangerfield, Tho[mas]. *Mr. Tho. Dangerfeilds particular narrative, of the late popish design.* London: f. H. Hills, J. Starkey, T. Basset, J. Wright, R. Chiswell, a. S. Heyrick, 1679. Fol. Pp. [7], 75.
P. [1]ᵛ, AW wrote, 'Nov'; and tp, the price, '2.6.' P. 1, in margin, '1679'; some marks, corrections, and underscoring, e.g., A1 and pp. 5, 12, 13, 17 (see notes at items 321, 2291). LT 2.465-6; 3.153.
Wood 425(25). Wing D192.

2151. Dangerfield, Thomas. *The case of Tho. Dangerfield: with some remarkable passages . . . at the tryals of Elizabeth Cellier . . . and the earl of Castlemain.* London: f. the author, 1680. Fol. Pp. [2], 38.
Tp, AW wrote the price, '1ˢ 4ᵈ'; and bsms.
Wood 426(19). Wing D184A.

2152. Dangerfield, Thomas. *The information of Thomas Dangerfield, gent. delivered at the bar of the house of commons [26 Oct.].* London: by the assigns of J. Bill, T. Newcomb, and H. Hills, 1680. Fol. Pp. 15 (p. 1 blank).
Wood 426(20). Wing D188A.

2153. Dangerfield, Tho[mas]. *Mr. Tho. Dangerfeild's second narrative:. . . relating to the murder of sir Edmundbury Godfrey.* London: f. T. Cockerill, 1680. Fol. Pp. [5], 29.
Tp, AW wrote the price, '1ˢ', in red chalk.
Wood 425(27). Wing D193.

2154. Dangerfield, Thomas. *Tho. Dangerfield's answer to a certain scandalous lying pamphlet. Entituled, malice defeated, or, the deliverance of Elizabeth Cellier.* London: f. the author, sold at R. Taylor's, 1680. Fol. Pp. 20.
Wood 426(8). Wing D183.

2155. Dangerfield, [Thomas]. *Dangerfield's memoires, digested into adventures, receits, and expenses.* London: J. Bennet, f. C. Brome, 1685. 4°. Pp. [4], 37.
Tp, AW wrote the author's forename, the price, '6ᵈ', and 'published in the latter end of Apr.'; above, in pencil, an earlier no., '34'. P. [4], 'All the summs of money which he received (as they followe in this book) Dangerfie[l]d borrowed under the guise of a decayed gent. or a Kt that had been rob'd on the high way &c', see also LT 3.153-4. Pp. 2, 8, 9, 11, AW wrote identifications or a correction, e.g., p. 2, at 'Capt. S–s at H–', he wrote, 'Capt. Saunders of Hadnam'. See note at item 235
Wood 372(16). Wing D194B.

2156. Daniel, Samuel. *[The civile wares betweene the howses of Lancaster and Yorke corrected and continued].* [London]: [H. Lownes f. S. Watersonne], [1609]. 4° in 8's. Pp. [6], 231, [1] (wanting engraved tp). Calf with 3 fillets, stamp decoration inside corners, and roll decoration at inner, spine edge (Ashm. binding).
Flyleaf, upper, 2ndᵛ, list of 7 printed works in this vol., by an Ashm. librarian.
Wood 482(1). STC 6245.

2157. D'Anvers, Alicia. *Academia: or, the humours of the university of Oxford. In burlesque verse.* London: printed a. sold R. Taylor, 1691. 4°. Pp. [4], 67, [1] (2nd p. [1] books sold by R. Taylor).
Tp, AW wrote, 'daugh. of Sam. Clarke sometimes superior Beadle of Law in Oxon, & wife of Knightly ['Knightly', added later] Danvers somtimes scholar of Trin. Coll. son of Dʳ Dan. Danvers a physitian living

neare Banbury in Oxfordshire – [/] First exposed to sale at Oxon. 14. Mar 1690[1]'. LT 3.356.
Wood 517(6). Wing D220.

2158. Darda. *A perfect relation of the most glorious and entire victory obtain'd by the Christian army . . . over the whole Turkish forces near Darba [sic]*. (London): (N. T.), (1687). S.sh. (r-v).
ᵛ, AW wrote, 'published in London 20 Aug. 1687'.
Wood 559(22). Wing P1513.

2159. Darell, John. *Strange news from th' Indies: or, East-India passages further discovered*. London: f. S. Bowtel, 1652. 4°. Pp. [8], 39.
Wood 387(8). Wing D251.

2160. Darell, John. *A true and compendious narration; or (second part of Amboyna) . . . and acts of hostility which the Hollanders have exercised*. London: T. Mabb, f. N. Brooke, 1665. 4°. Pp. [5], 39.
Tp, AW wrote out, after initials, 'Jo. Darell' (whose name appears at the end of the preface).
Wood 387(15). Wing D252 (Wing, Amboyney).

2161. Dares, the Phrygian. Paynell, Thomas, trans. *The faythfull and true storye of the destruction of Troye*. (London): (J. Cawood), 1553. 16°. A-J⁸.
Each 16° leaf is pasted on an 8° template. Passim, commentary in margins, e.g., f5ʳ, f7ᵛ, f8ʳ⁻ᵛ, not in AW's hand. Pagination and some dating continue from preceding items, Wood 87(1-2)).
Wood 87(3). STC 6274.5.

2162. Darrell, John*. Co., G., ed. *A breife narration of the possession, dispossession, and, repossession of William Sommers: and of some proceedings against mr John Dorrell*. [Amsterdam?]: n.pub, 1598. 4°. A-E⁴ (last leaf blank). Pasteboard (blue) with parchment spine. 1st upper and last lower flyleaves, marbled paper; rebacked.
Flyleaf, upper, 2ndᵛ, AW wrote the titles of 4 printed works in this vol., within guidelines made with red ink. Tp, 'William Chadley [? cropped] oweth the booke'. AW numbered odd pp. and, B1, marked 2 biographical details about Dorrell with vertical lines.
[MS.] Wood B. 19(1). STC 6281.

2163. Darrell, John. *A detection of that sinnful, shamful, lying, and ridiculous discours, of Samuel Harshnet, entituled: a discoverie of the frawdulent practises of John Darrell*. N.p.: [English Secret Press?], 1600. 4°. Pp. [8], 208, [3].
P. 208, identification, prob. not by AW. Responds to Harshnet, [MS.] Wood B. 19(2).
[MS.] Wood B. 19(4). STC 6283.

2164. Darrell, John. *A true narration of the strange and grevous vexation by the devil, of 7. persons in Lancashire, and William Somers*. N.p.: [English Secret Press?], 1600. 4°. Pp. [8], 106, [1].
AW wrote, '6ᵈ'. Acquired 21 Mar. 1662, LT 1.434.
[MS.] Wood B. 19(3). STC 6288.

2165. Darton, [Nicholas]. *Ecclesia Anglicana, or Dartons cleare & protestant manifesto*. [Oxford]: [H. Hall], 1649. 4°. Pp. [2], 13.
Tp, AW wrote, 'Dup', in pencil. Dupl. at Wood 515(8).
[MS.] Wood B. 36(16). Wing D272 (two). Madan 2022.

2166. Darton, [Nicholas]. *Ecclesia Anglicana, or Dartons cleare & protestant manifesto*. [Oxford]: [H. Hall], 1649. 4°. Pp. [2], 13.
Tp, AW wrote, 'Nich. Darton'. Dupl. at [MS.] Wood B. 36(16).
Wood 515(8). Wing D272 (two). Madan 2022.

2167. Darye, –. *'of schools and library'*. ?: ?, ? Pp.?
Missing. Acquired 18 July 1662, 1ˢ minus 5ᵖ, which was the cost of a 2nd item in this purchase ([MS.] Wood C. 14(9)); see LT 1.444.
LT 1.444. Not identified.

2168. D[auncey], J[ohn]. *The history of his sacred majesty Charles the II*. London: f. J. Davies, 1660. 12°. Pp. [23], 136.
Each 12° leaf is pasted on an 8° template. Tp, AW wrote, 'The author. Joh. Dancey. Aet. 21', 'J. D.', and, on blank leaf portion, 'Hen. Foulis of Linc. Coll use to tell me that John Dauncy of Putney neare London, aged 21 was the author of this book'; ᵛ, 'one Joh. Dancer wrot several things & translated from French into English (1) Nocomede, Trag. com. - Lond. 1671. [i.e., Corneille, *Nicomède*, Wood 607(6), item 2009] (2)

The comparison of Plato & Aristot. with the opinions of the Fathers on their Doctrine. &c. Lond. 1673 Oct. ded. to Jam. D. of Ormond chanc. of the Univ. of Ox.' (by Rene Rapin, Wood 288) and 'John Dancer alias Dauncy'. A7, after 'I. D.', again, the author's name, but crossed out, and 'James Davies the publisher', in red ink, identifying the author of the dedication. Text, a few marks in margins and corrections. Flyleaf, lower, 3rd, date, '1659' on marbled paper. LT 1.327.
Wood 235(5). Wing D291.

2169. Dauncey, John. *The history of . . . Henrietta Maria de Bourbon, queen of England*. London: E. C. f. P. Chetwind, 1660. 12°. Pp. [11], 132. Pasteboard (brown) with calf spine. 1st upper and last lower flyleaves, light blue paper on one side.
Flyleaf, upper, 2nd^v, AW wrote the titles of 4 printed works in this vol., within guidelines made with red ink; and tp, '8^d'. Bsm.
Wood 245(1). Wing D293.

2170. [Davenant, Charles]. *The songs in Circe*. London: f. R. Tonson, 1677. 4°. Pp. [2], 13.
Each small 4° leaf is pasted on a 4° template. Tp, AW wrote, 'Ch. Davenant, author of Circe. q[uaere]', and '20 May 1677'.
Wood 382(2). Wing D313.

2171. D[avenant], W[illiam]. *The triumphs of the prince d'Amour. A masque [24 Feb.]*. London: [A. Mathewes] f. R. Meighen, 1635. 4°. Pp. [6], 16, [1].
Tp, AW wrote, 'Will. Davenant the author'.
Wood 615(25). STC 6308.

2172. [Davenant, William]. *London, king Charles his Augusta, or, city royal. Of the founders, the names, and oldest honours of that city*. London: f. W. Leybourn, 1648. 4°. Pp. [8], 12.
Tp, item no. '3' in a former bundle.
Wood 590(5). Wing D328.

2173. Davenant, William. *A panegyrick to his excellency, the lord generall Monck*. London: f. H. Herringman, 1659[60]. S.sh.
AW wrote, 'March:'; ^{v}, 'Mar. 59[60]', 'Sr Will. Davena[nt]', and '66', in ink, replaced a former no. '55' in pencil.
Wood 416(66). Wing D332.

2174. Davenant, William*. *An elegy upon the death of s^r· William Davenant*. [London]: n.pub., [1668]. S.sh.
^{v}, AW wrote, 'Will. Davenant 1668'.
Wood 429(27). Wing E469A (two).

2175. [Davenport, Christopher]. *An explanation of the Roman Catholikes belief*. N.p.: n.pub., [1656]. S.sh.
AW wrote, 'Given to me by Mr Tho. Blount 26. Oct. 1673'. See note on this s.sh. at Davenport, Wood 876(6), item 2180. LT 2.273.
Wood 276a(103b) (not on 1717 list). Wing D354 (two) (Wing, 1676?).

2176. [Davenport, Christopher]. *A cleare vindication of Roman Catholicks from a fowle aspersion: to wit, that they . . . promote a bloody . . . designe [signed L. P.]*. N.p.: n.pub., 1659. 4°. Pp. 7.
Tp, former no., '22' (twice).
[MS.] Wood B. 40(6). Wing D 351 (rare).

2177. Davenport, Christopher. *Religio philosophi peripati discutienda*. Duaci: typ. B. Belleri, 1662. 8°. Pp. [10], 162, [13].
Flyleaf, upper, 1st, AW wrote 'AWood. [lined out and:] This book was given to me by the authour, 1667'; and 2nd^v, 'Note that most of the works of Fr. à S. Clara were printed at Doway in 2. vol. in fol. an. 1665 – But this book is not printed among them.–'. In MS. Wood E. 2(70), 74, AW wrote the entry of Davenport's works, now missing: '– his works – but his supplement before mentioned is not there' (i.e., Wood 657(15-16), now present, and see the following item). Tp, AW underscored the name of the author, in red ink.
Wood 883(6). BL.

2178. Davenport, Christopher. *Opera omnia scholasticorum et historicorum*. Duaci: B. Belleri, 1665, 1667. Fol. 2 vols.
Missing. LT 2.192, 223. MS. Wood E. 2(70), 74, '– his works – but his supplement before mentioned is not

there' (i.e., Wood 657(15-16), now present). The entry in AW's catalogue probably refers to Davenport's *Opera*.
LT 2.192. BL.

2179. [Davenport, Christopher]. *An explanation of the Roman Catholick's belief: concerning the principal points controverted.* N.p.: n.pub., 1670. 8°. 4th ed. Pp. [2], 10 (wanting the last leaf).
Tp, 'For Mr Ant: à [à added later by AW] Wood. F. à S. Clara'. LT 2.203. Dupl. at Wood 876(6).
Wood 836(2). Wing D353 (rare, 3 at O).

2180. [Davenport, Christopher]. *An explanation of the Roman Catholick's belief: concerning the principal points controverted.* N.p.: n.pub., 1670. 8°. 4th ed. Pp. [2], 11.
Flyleaf^v, AW wrote, 'The author of this explanation following (which is indeed χρύψις μᾶλλον ἤ ανάπλυξις was Fran[c]is Davenport an English man somtimes of Mert. Coll. in Oxon, afterwards a Rom. Catholick & publick professor of Div. at Doway, confessor to Henrietta Maria Queen of England, & provincial of the Franciscans in Engl. – In several of his books he stiles himself Franciscus à Sancta Clara – He presented one of these explanations to Oliver Cromwell, & some eminent Parliament, of Cromwells persuasion, an. 1656' (possibly the s.sh., Wood 276a(103b), item 2175; an 8° version also was published in 1656). Tp, 'ex dono Authoris'. P. 11. underscoring and mark in margin. LT 2.203. Dupl. at Wood 836(2).
Wood 876(6) (not in Bodl. CD cat.). Wing D353 (rare, 3 at O).

2181. Davenport, Christopher. *Praecedentia Angliae humiliter exponitur, & fortissime demonstratur.* [Duaci?]: n.pub., [1670?]. 4°. Plates 1-4, and pp. 15 (^{4},A-B^4). Calf with 3 fillets, stamp decoration inside corners (2 leaves and sunflower sprouting fleur-de-lis), and roll decoration at inner, spine edge (Ashm. binding); rebacked.
Flyleaf, upper, 1st^r, 'Hic Liber datur', not in AW's hand; 2nd^v, list of 10 printed works in this vol., by an Ashm. librarian. After the flyleaves, 4 plates: of Thomas Pickering; of a serpent around the neck of a man, A. Brouwer pinxit, K. O. fecit; of Ralph Sheldon's coat of arms, a fesse between 3 sheldrakes (W. Rogers, who gave this pamphlet to AW, knew R. Sheldon – for similar plates, see Wood 276b(40-1) and LT 3.104 and the facing plate I); and of a king, 'per me reges regnant', M. Burghers sculp. Tp, 'Antonii à Wood, Ex dono Gulielm. Rogers de Hospitio Lincoln.' and 'per Franc. à Sta Clara vulgo Davenport [/] Extat hic liber, in Supplemento Historiae provinciae Angliae, &c. script. per eundem F. a S. Clara. edit. Duaci 1670'.
Signature, 'Gu: Rogers e d[ono] Fr. de S' (cropped at side) (see LT 2.169, 192, 203, 223 and AO 1.lxviii, 3.1221ff., and J. B. Dockery, *Christopher Davenport* (London, 1960): 134-5.
Wood 487(1). Not identified (BL, a 1671 ed.).

2182. Davenport, Christopher. *Supplementum historiae provinciae Angliae, in quo est chronosticon, continens catalogum . . . Angliae. Annectitur, disputatio de antiqua provincia praecedentia.* Duaci: typ. B. Belleri, 1671. Fol. Pp. [2], 15.
Tp, AW wrote, 'Antonii à Wood Oxōn. Ex dono Authoris scil[icet] Franc. à Sta Clara vulgo Davenport, an. 1672. Extat hoc supplimentum [sic] in primo vol. operum ejusdem F. a Sta Clara, edit. Duaci 1665'. P. 8 an underscoring. See LT 2.192, 203, 223.
Wood 657(15-16). BL.

2183. D[avenport], J[ohn]. *The profession of the faith of . . . J. D. . . . made publiquely . . . at his admission into one of the churches of God in New-England.* London: f. J. Handcock [sic], 1642. 4°. Pp. 8.
Tp, AW underscored the author's initials in the t, in red ink, and wrote, 'John Davenport'. Bsm.
[MS.] Wood B. 36(14). Wing D364.

2184. David Antiochenus. [Pococke, Edward, trans.]. *The nature of the drink kauhi, or coffe, and the berry of which it is made, described by an Arabian phisitian.* Oxford: H.Hall, 1659. 8°. Pp. [7].
Wood 679(2). Wing D374. Madan 2438.

2185. Davies, John. *A discoverie of the true causes why Ireland was never entirely subdued . . . untill the beginning of his majesties happie raigne.* (London): [W. Jaggard] f. J. Jaggard, 1612. 4°. Pp. [4], 287.
Flyleaf insert, AW wrote, 'Joh. Davis [scribble, lined out, and:] the Author, a Judge in Ireland'. Tp, 2 notes, lined out, and 'by Sir John Davies' in pencil, may not be in AW's hand.
Wood 504(3). STC 6348.

2186. D[avies], J[ohn]. *The ancient rites, and monuments of the . . . cathedral church of Durham.* London: f. W. Hensman, 1672. 8°. Pp. [8], 164.
Tp, AW wrote, 'Jo. Davis, was not the Author', 'The author of this book was living 1639 v. pag. 47. v. life of S. Cuthb.' (but see Wing entry). Tp^v, AW copied Thomas Barlow's note from the upper flyleaf of

Barlow's copy, 8° B 288 Linc. in the Bodleian Library; the substantive variations in the original are in double brackets: 'The private note of D[r] Tho. Barlow of Qu. Coll. concerning this book runs thus [/] Liber hic omnino Apochryphus, μυσᾶρας et legendae putidae plurimum, verae historiae (praxi et cultu monachorum superstitioso exceptis) parum habet, adeo ut mirari subit inscitiam ejus qui [condidit, imprudentia ejus qui] edidit, [et ἀβλεψίαν]] et negligentiam (veritati et Ecclesiae Anglicanae damnosam) qui praelo permisit.' The passage was marked by a vertical line in red ink in the Barlow copy (by AW?).
Wood 216(2). Wing D392.

2187. Davis, Mr. *Mr. Davis his case, upon the appal [sic] of mr. Thomas Skinner.* N.p.: n.pub., [1671]. S.sh.
Wood 276b(88). Wing M2261 (3).

2188. Davy, Hen[ry]. *The true copie of a letter sent from an inhabitant of Bridgewater.* London: f. R. Lownes, 1643. 4°. Pp. [2], 6.
Tp, AW altered a former no.
Wood 376(49). Wing D442.

2189. [Dawbeny, Henry]. *The pourtraiture of his royal highness, Oliver late lord protector.* London: T. N. f. E. Thomas, 1659. 12°. Pp. 69. Pasteboard (grey) with parchment spine. 1st and last flyleaves, marbled paper.
Flyleaf, upper, 2nd[v], AW wrote the titles of 4 printed works in this vol., within guidelines made with red ink. 1st item, each 12° leaf is pasted on an 8° template. Text, some vertical lines in margins, e.g., pp. 13, 48, 57.
Wood 243(1). Wing D448A.

2190. Day, John. *Day's dyall or, his twelve howres that is, twelve severall lectures.* Oxford: J. Barnes, 1614. 4°. Pp. [8], 329, [2].
See note in MS. Wood E. 2(70), f. 1, 'Examen judicii Cantabrigiensis cuiusdam qui se &c. see the rest of the title in the preface to the reader to Days Diall – I have the book & I have put in a paper at the place – [i.e. ¶3[v], the paper is no longer there] Joh. Day his works I have [i.e., this volume, [MS.] C. 40(1-4)] - great reading shewed in that book – well skilld in the fathers, schoolmen[,] councills &c. a plaine man & a primitive Christian, wholy composed to good in his function'.
[MS.] Wood C. 40(3). STC 6425. Madan 410.

2191. Day, John. *Concio ad clerum [on 2 Kings 6.1-4] . . . habita in templo B. Mariae Oxon.* Oxoniae: J. Barnesius, 1615. 4°. 2nd ed. Pp. [4], 26, [2].
Tp, after 'Editio secunda', AW wrote, 'prima edit. an. 1612. 4°. Oxon.' (STC 6420).
[MS.] Wood C. 40(4). STC 6421. Madan 429.

2192. Day, John. *Davids desire to goe to church:. . . two sermons in S[t] Maries in Oxford.* Oxford: J. Barnes, 1615. 4°. Pp. [8], 48. Calf with 3 fillets, stamp centrepiece, edge hatching, and gold stamp roll decoration on edges; spine, 4 bands and hatching (Oxford binding). Flyleaf, upper and lower, printer's waste paper.
Cover, upper and lower, stamped 'A W'. Flyleaf, upper[v], AW wrote, 'Davids desire to go to ch. in two sermons, was first published at Ox. 1612 Oct'. Tp[v], signature of 'Mary Wood' and AW wrote, 'This book I found in the closet of my mother Mary Wood anno 1666[7] after her decease, having been given formerlie to my father by the author' (pasted over by a leaf of support, later removed). LT 1.22; 2.101-2. Pp. 2-3, 5, 8, etc. to 20, some underscoring, esp. at repetition of words.
[MS.] Wood C. 40(1). STC 6423. Madan 430.

2193. Day, John. *Day's festivals or, twelve of his sermons.* Oxford: J. Barnes, 1615. 4°. Pp. [8], 352.
P. 161, printed 'M. T. H.' (i.e., Theo. Higgons, part of a title by Edward Hoby), underscored.
[MS.] Wood C. 40(2). STC 6426. Madan 431.

2194. Daye, Lionel. *Concio ad clerum habita Oxonii . . . 1609 [on Luke 22.31].* Oxoniae: L. Lichfield, 1632. 4°. Pp. [4], 33.
Tp, 'Lib. Ant a Wood [lined out ('a' added later), and:] Ex dono Johannis Wilton Coll: Mertonensis S.T.B: Aug: iij A.D. MDCLXIIV' (may be by AW). LT 2.38.
Wood 634(13). STC 6435. Madan 717.

2195. Deacon, John. *The grand impostor examined: or, the life, tryal, . . . of James Nayler.* London: f. H. Brome, 1656. 4°. Pp. [6], 50 (misnumbering).
Tp, brief note, not in AW's hand. P. 50, scribbles. Diff. ed. at Wood 645(8).

Wood 619(2). Wing D484.

2196. Deacon, John. *The grand impostor examined: or, the life, tryal, and examination of James Nayler.* London: f. H. Brome, 1657. 4°. Pp. [6], 47 (misnumbering).
Diff. ed. at Wood 619(2).
Wood 645(8). Wing D485 (two).

2197. Deacon, John. *Nayler's blasphemies discovered. Or, several queries to him proposed. With his owne answers thereunto.* London: S. Waterson, 1657. 4°. Pp. [2], 60.
Wood 645(7). Wing D486 (rare).

2198. Decoy Duck. [Taylor, John by?]. *The decoy duck: together with the discovery of the knot in the dragons tayle.* London: f. F. Couls, T. Bates, I. Wright, a. T. Banks, 1642. 4°. A⁴.
Missing in 1922. Removed from the vol. after 1841 and before 1922.
Wood 614(54). Wing D804. *O, Hunt, Harv* (2, 2nd cropped), *Folg*.

2199. Dedekind, Friedrich. *Grobianus et Grobiana, de morum simplicitate, libri tres.* Franc(oforti ad Moenum): ap. haer. C. Egen., (imp. A. Loniceri, J. Cnipii Andronici secundi, P. Steinmeyers), 1584. 8°. Ff. 96.
Wood 92(2) (not in Bodl. CD cat.). BL.

2200. Dedicus, Joannes. *Questiones moralissime super libros ethicorum.* (in celeberima universitate Oxoniensis): (J. Scolar), (1518, 15 May). Ff. 75, [1]. Parchment wrapper, ms. Latin, with illuminated capitals (currently in conservation).
Tp, 'ABosco'. 'Duplicate', not in AW's hand, lined out, and a former Jesus College shelf-mark. LT 3.344.
Jesus College 1. Arch. 2. 25(1). STC 6458. Madan 29.

2201. Dee, Arthur. Hasolle, James, trans. *Fasciculus chemicus: or chymical collections. . . . Whereunto is added, the arcanum or grand secret of hermetick philosophy.* London: J. Flesher f. R. Mynne, 1650. 8°. Pp. [50], 268 (2 tpp). Pasteboard (grey) with parchment spine. 1st 2 upper and last 2 lower flyleaves, thick dark grey paper.
AW wrote the titles of 3 printed works in this vol. (really 2), within guidelines made with red ink. Tp, AW wrote the name of the author 'By Arth. Dee Dʳ of phys.' a2, a3, mark at biographical information and note at a bishop with fame in 'chymistry', 'perhaps Thornborough Bishop of Worcester'.
Wood 680(1-2). Wing D810.

2202. [Dekker, Thomas]. *The wonderfull yeare. 1603. Wherein is shewed the picture of London, lying sicke of the plague.* London: T. Creede, solde [N. Ling, J. Smethwick, a. J. Browne], [1603?]. 4°. A-F⁴.
[MS.] Wood B. 35(2). STC 6536.3.

2203. [Dekker, Thomas]. *1603. The wonderfull yeare. Wherein is shewed the picture of London, lying sicke of the plague.* London: T. Creede, sold [by N. Ling, J. Smethwick, a J. Brown], 1603 (date shaved). 4°. A-F⁴. Calf with 3 fillets, stamp decoration inside corners, and roll decoration at inner, spine edge (Ashm. binding).
Flyleaf, upper, 2nd, the titles of 25 printed works in this vol., by an Ashm. librarian. There are 7 duplicates in this vol.
Wood 616(1). STC 6535 (rare).

2204. [Dekker, Thomas], attrib. to. *The meeting of gallants at an ordinarie: or the walkes in Powles.* London: T. C[reede], sold M. Lawe, 1604. 4°. A-D⁴ (D3-4 blank).
Wood 616(5). STC 17781.

2205. [Dekker, Thomas]. *Newes from Graves-end: sent to nobody.* London: T.C[reede] f. T. Archer, 1604. 8°. A-F⁴ (A1 blank).
Wood 112(6). STC 12199.

2206. Dekker, Tho[mas]. *Newes from hell; brought by the divells carrier.* London: R. B[lower, S. Stafford, a. V. Simmes] f. W. Ferebrand, 1606. 4°. A-H⁴ (A1 blank).
Tp, AW wrote 'Or the devills answer to Pierce Pennyless' (the running title) and the price, '6ᵈ'.
Wood 487(6). STC 6514.

2207. Dekker, Thomas. *Troia-nova triumphans. London triumphing, or, the . . . receiving of sir John Swinerton into . . . London, after his taking the oath of maioralty [29 Oct.].* London: N. Okes, sold J. Wright, 1612. 4°. A-C⁴,D² (D2 blank).

Wood 537(7). STC 6530.

2208. [Dekker, Thomas]. *The belman of London. Bringing to light the most notorious villanies.* London: [T. Purfoot] f. N. Butter, 1616. 4°. 4th impress. A-I⁴.
Tp, bsm., 'd'.
Wood 371(3). STC 6483.

2209. Dekker, T[homas]. *English villanies seven severall times prest to death by the printers.* London: M. Parsons, sold J. Becket, 1638. 4°. A-O⁴. Pasteboard (blue) with parchment spine. 1st upper and last lower flyleaves, marbled paper.
Flyleaf, upper, 3rd^r-v, AW wrote the titles of 11 printed works in this vol., within guidelines made with red ink. Tp, bsm.
Wood 371(1). STC 6492.

2210. Dekker, Thomas. *English villanies, eight severall times prest to death by the printers; . . . now the ninth time . . . discovered by lanthorne and candlelight.* London: E. P. f. N. Gamage, 1648. 4°. A-M⁴.
Tp, AW wrote, 'By Thomas Dekker'. Bsm.
Wood 609(11). Wing D862.

2211. Dekker, Thomas, and Samuel Vincent. Vincent, Samuel, ed. *The young gallant's academy. Or, directions how he should behave himself . . . To which is added, the character of a town-huff [A republ. of The gull's hornbook] . . . by Sam. Vincent.* London: J. C. f. R. Mills, 1674. 8°. Pp. [20], 100 (4 pp. of intro. misplaced after p. 98).
Tp, AW wrote '8^d'. Bsm.
Wood 754(2). Wing V426.

2212. Deliquium. *The deliquium: or, the grievances of the nation discovered in a dream.* [London]: n.pub., [1681]. S.sh. (r-v).
AW wrote the date at the beginning, '1681', in pencil, and '81', in ink; at end, '1681. December', in ink. Dupl. at Wood 417(55).
Wood 276a(550). Wing D908 (Wing, 1680?).

2213. Deliquium. *The deliquium: or, the grievances of the nation discovered in a dream.* [London]: n.pub., [1681]. S.sh. (r-v).
AW wrote below, 'Published in the beginning of Aprill an. 1681.' Dupl. at Wood 276a(550).
Wood 417(55). Wing D908 (Wing, 1680?).

2214. Dell, William. *The tryal of spirits both in teachers & hearers. . . . Whereunto is added a . . . confutation of . . . Sydrach Simpson . . . With a brief testimony against divinity-degrees in the universities.* London: (R. White) f. G. Calvert, 1653 (1654). 4°. Pp. [8], 68; [12], 49; [1], 30 (2 tpp).
LT 1.295.
[MS.] Wood B. 24(3). Wing D931. Madan 2215.

2215. [Deloney, Thomas] . *The garland of good will.* [London]: [f. R. Bird], [1631]. 8°. A2-8,B-H⁸ (wanting tp) (A2, A Table. [/] In the Second Part).
Wood 79(5) (now Arch. G. f. 2(5)). STC 6554 (rare).

2216. D[eloney], T[homas]. *The gentle craft. A discoverie containing many matters of delight.* London: f. J. Stafford, 1652. 4°. Pp. [5], 66. Pasteboard (blue) with parchment spine. 1st upper and last lower flyleaves, marbled paper.
Flyleaf, upper, 2nd, AW wrote, 'In the Beach neare Lydde in Kent, is to be seen a heape of great stones, which the neighbour Inhabitants call St Crispins, & Crispianus or Crispians Tombe, whome they report to have been cast upon this shoare (by Lydd) by shipwrack, & from hence called into the glorious company of saints. See Jacobus de Voragine in the Legend of their lives, & you may believe (perhaps) as much as is here spoken: They were here shomakers, & suffer'd Martyrdome the 10 of the calends of Nov: which day is kept Holyday, to this day, by all the Shomakers in London & elswhere.' (LT 2.367-8, i.e., 8 Kal. Nov., or 25 Oct.); ^v, AW wrote the titles of 5 printed works in this vol., within guidelines made with red chalk. 1st item, acquired 6 March 1660, 6^d, LT 1.306.
[MS.] Wood C. 31(1). Wing D954 (rare).

2217. D[eloney], T[homas]. *The pleasant history of John Winchcomb, in his yonger years called, Jack of Newbery.* London: E. Crouch f. T. Passenger, 1672. 4°. 13th time impr. A-K⁴.
Tp, AW wrote, '6^d - Feb. 1676/7'; ^v, 'The familie of the Winchcombe are & have been knights & esquires

in Berks- They beare a confused coat of arms viz Azure on a chev. ingrailed or 3 cinquefo[i]les of the 1. between three close eagles of the 2. a cheif or charged with a fleur de lize betw. 2 lozenges azure.' (in his diary, AW wrote about this pamphlet, 'I bought it of a pedler in Warwickshire', LT 2.367). D4, at battle of Flodden, AW wrote '1513' in the margin; E1, at meeting with the king, whose messenger is 'Garret King at Arms', underscored in red chalk, AW wrote, 'I have seen the catalogue of all the officers at arms & I find no such person, but I beleive he means Garter.' E3^v, at 'Will Summers', AW wrote over an earlier note in red chalk, 'the Kings foole'; I3^v, at printed 'Winchomb [sic] . . . was chosen sheriff', AW wrote, '[no] such person [oc]currs in the [cat]alogue of [m]ayors & sherriffs of London' (cropped at side); I4^v, underscoring of 'Nan Winchcomb', in red chalk.
[MS.] Wood C. 32(2). Wing D963 (two).

2218. D[eloney], T[homas]. *The pleasant history of Thomas of Reading, or, the six worthy yeoman [sic] of the west.* London: f. W. Thackeray, 1672. 4°. (corrected). A-H^4.
Tp, scribble, in pencil.
[MS.] Wood C. 32(3). Wing D966 (two).

2219. [Deloney, Thomas]. *A most delightful history of the famous clothier . . . Jack of Newbery . . . Written by W. S. F. C.* London: f. W. Thackeray, 1684. 8°. Pp. [1], 20, [2] (2 pp. books sold by Thackeray).
Wood 254(8). Wing D957C (rare).

2220. D[eloney], T[homas]. *The garland of good-will.* London: J. Millet f. T. Passenger a. J. Deacon, 1685. 8°. A-H^8.
Missing in 1837. 'The Garland of Goodwill – Lond. 1685' in Whiteside cat.
Wood 94(2) (not in Bodl. CD cat.). Wing D947 (two). O, *Hunt.*

2221. Democritus, pseud. *Democritus turned statesman: or twenty quaeries between jest and earnest.* London: n.pub., 1659. 4°. Pp. 8.
Wood 613(44). Wing D978.

2222. [Denham, John]. *Coopers hill. A poëme.* [Oxford]: [H. Hall], 1643. 4°. Pp. [2], 10.
Wood 330(2). Wing D994. Madan 1570.

2223. [Denham, John]. *A panegyrick on . . . the lord general George Monck.* London: f. R. Marriot, 1659. 4°. Pp. [2], 5.
Tp, after year of pub., AW wrote, 'March: said to be made by Jo. Denham: [added later:] see whether it be in his works –' and '3 heap next before the politick'. LT 2.152.
Wood 319(8). Wing D1004.

2224. [Denham, John]. *The prologue to his majesty at the first play presented at the cock-pit in Whitehall, . . . Novemb. 19.* London: f. G. Bedell a. T. Collins, 1660. S.sh.
Notes on the author, not by AW: 'John Denham esq; at his Maties. first comeinge into England. By S^r Jo: Denham K^t of the Bath.'
Wood 398(17). Wing D1007A.

2225. Denham, John. *On mr. Abraham Cowley his death, and burial.* (London): (f. H. Herringman), (1667). Fol. Pp. 4.
Wood 429(26). Wing D1003.

2226. [Denham, John]. Pengry, Moses, trans. *Coopers Hill Latine redditum.* Oxonii: e theatro Sheldoniano, 1676. 4°. Pp. [2], 21.
See note at Wood 383(4). Tp, 'Anthony à Wood Oxon, given to me by <u>Moses Pengry</u> Bac. Div. & Fellow of Brasenose Coll. who translated this poem from Engl. into Latine, June 15. 1676.', and in different inks: '{ v. Alm[anacks] Sept. Oct. 78', and 'Chapl. to the Earl of Devon.' AOF 2.332; LT 2.349, 419.
Wood 383(5). Wing D997. Madan 3101.

2227. Denham, John. *The true Presbyterian without disguise.* (London): (f. J. B.), (1680). S.sh. (r-v).
AW underscored the name of the author, in red ink.
Wood 417(27). Wing D1013.

2228. Denton, William. *Jus Caesaris et ecclesiae vere dictae. Or a treatise wherein Independency, Presbytery . . . [Followed by] An apology for the liberty of the press.* London: f. the author, sold J. Kersey a. H. Faythorn, 1681. Fol. Pp. [8], 248, 9.
In last section, 'Liberty of the Press', pp. 4, 6, marks in margin, in pencil, prob. not by AW. AW received a number of items from the author, see AO 4.307f. (see LT 3.361).

Wood 660f(2) (600f(2) in Bodl. CD cat.). Wing D1066 (Wing, Fathorn).

2229. Denton, William. *Jus regiminis: being a justification of defensive arms in general, and consequently of our late revolutions.* London: n.pub., 1689. Fol. Pp. [8], 91.
AW received a number of items from the author, see AO 4.307f. (see LT 3.361).
Wood 660f(3). Wing D1067.

2230. Denton, William. *Some remarks recommended unto ecclesiasticks of all perswasions.* [London]: n.pub., [1690?]. Fol. Pp. 46, [1].
AW received a number of items from the author, see AO 4.307f. (see LT 3.361).
Wood 660f(4). Wing D1068.

2231. Derbyshire. *To the honourable, the knights, citizens, and burgesses of the house of common [sic] . . . the humble petition . . . of Darby [14 March].* London: n.pub., 1642. S.sh.
ᵛ, AW overwrote the former no., '26'.
Wood 373(38). Wing T1454.

2232. Dering, Edward. *A lecture or exposition upon a part of the v. chapter of the epistle to the Hebrues.* London: J. Awdely, [1573]. 8°. A-H⁴,I².
Wood 736(7). STC 6691.

2233. Dering, Edward. *Three speeches of . . . the first concerning the freedome of mʳ. Wilson.* London: f. J. Stafford, 1641. 4°. Pp. 14.
Tp, former no., '9'. Bsm.
[MS.] Wood D. 31(25). Wing D1118.

2234. Descartes, René. *Renatus Des-cartes excellent compendium of musick: with necessary . . . animadversions thereupon [by William Brouncker].* London: T. Harper, f. H. Moseley, sold at his shop, a. by T. Heath, 1653. 4°. Pp. [16], 94, [1] (2nd tp at p. 59).
Tp, Bsm.
Wood 481(5). Wing D1132.

2235. Devereux, Robert. Essex, earl of. *Victorious news from the earle of Essex . . . 19 Sept. 1642.* London: f. W. Cooke, [1642], 23 Sept. 4°. Pp. [2], 4.
Tp, AW overwrote the former no., '17'.
Wood 375(11). Wing V346A (rare).

2236. Devereux, Robert. Essex, earl of. *Good and true newes from Redding . . . proceedings of . . . the earl of Essex.* London: f. J. G., 1643. 4°. A⁴ (p. nos. incorrect).
Wood 376(5). Wing G1037.

2237. Devereux, Robert. Essex, earl of. *Most hapy [sic] and wellcome newes; from his excellencie the earle of Essex.* London: f. T. Rider, 1643. 4°. A⁴.
Tp, AW wrote '1642 qu[aere]' in pencil, and overwrote that with the item no.; at a date of a battle, 'Jan. 16', AW wrote, 'an 1642', and below imprint date, '1642/3'. A2, A4, corrections.
Wood 375(29). Wing E3324 (3).

2238. Devereux, Robert*. Essex, earl of. *An apologie and vindication (from all false . . . aspersions) for . . . Robert D'Evreux, earle of Essex, . . . With a true and briefe chronologie of successefull things done.* London: T. Harper, 1644. 4°. Pp. [2], 23.
Missing since 1994. In Whiteside cat. Dupl. at Wood 612(24).
Wood 531(6). Wing A3541.

2239. Devereux, Robert*. Essex, earl of. *An apologie and vindication (from all false . . . aspersions) for . . . Robert D'Evreux, earle of Essex, . . . With a true and briefe chronologie of successefull things done.* London: T. Harper, 1644. 4°. Pp. [2], 23.
Tp, AW wrote 'Dupl' twice (cropped at side and at bottom); bsm. Dupl. at Wood 531(6) missing.
Wood 612(24). Wing A3541.

2240. Devereux, Robert*. Essex, earl of. *A briefe and compendious narrative of . . . Robert, earle of Essex, . . . and in what manner his buriall is to be solemnized.* London: J. Coe, 1646. 4°. Pp. [2], 14.
Missing since 1994. Dupl. at Wood 612(43). In Whiteside cat.
Wood 531(8). Wing B4525.

2241. Devereux, Robert*. Essex, earl of. *A briefe and compendious narrative of . . . Robert, earle of Essex, . . . and in what manner his buriall is to be solemnized.* London: J. Coe, 1646. 4°. Pp. [2], 14.
Tp, AW wrote 'dup', in pencil. Dupl. at Wood 531(8).
Wood 612(43). Wing B4525.

2242. Devereux, Robert, and Jo. Bridges. *Two letters: the one from . . . Robert, earl of Essex, . . . The other [by J. Bridges] from Warwick-castle, . . . concerning . . . Gloucester.* [London]: f. E. Husbands, 1 Sept., 1643. 4°. Pp. 7.
Tp, AW wrote 'Dupl.', in pencil. Dupl. at Wood 376(32).
Wood 632(4). Wing E3337.

2243. Devereux, Robert, and Jo. Bridges. *Two letters: the one from . . . Robert, earl of Essex, . . . The other [by J. Bridges] from Warwick-castle, . . . concerning . . . Gloucester.* [London]: f. E. Husbands, 1643, 1 Sept. 4°. Pp. 7.
Tp, AW lined out the former no., '29', and underscored the name of Essex in red ink. P.7, he wrote the year, '1643'.
Wood 376(32). Wing E3337.

2244. Devil's Cabinet. *The devils cabinet broke open: or a new discovery of the high-way thieves, . . . advice of a gentleman lately converted from them.* London: f. H. Marsh, 1658. 4°. Pp. [8], 40 (some misnumbering).
Dupl. at Wood 609(45).
Wood 371(8). Wing D1224.

2245. Devil's Cabinet. *The devils cabinet broke open: or a new discovery of the high-way thieves, . . . advice of a gentleman lately converted from them.* London: f. H. Marsh, 1658. 4°. Pp. [8], 40 (some misnumbering).
Tp, AW wrote 'Dupl.' Dupl. at Wood 371(8).
Wood 609(45). Wing D1224.

2246. Devil's Delusions. *The divels delusions or a faithfull relation of John Palmer and Elizabeth Knott two . . . witches lately condemned . . . in St. Albans [signed] B. Misodaimon.* London: f. R. Williams, at St. Albans, 1649. 4°. Pp. [2], 6.
[MS.] Wood B. 18(7). Wing D1227.

2247. Devon. *A declaration of the gentry of the county of Devon . . . with a letter from Exeter . . . to . . . William Lenthall [14 Jan.].* [London]: n.pub., [1660]. S.sh.
ᵛ, AW wrote the title and date.
Wood 276a(256). Wing D678A.

2248. Devon. *Devon ss. Ad general quarterial. session. . . . We think it our duty [6 Oct. Declaration concerning the late rebellion].* London: F. Collins, sold R. Taylor, 1685. S.sh.
Wood 660c(13). Wing A466.

2249. D'Ewes, Simonds. *The severall votes and resolutions agreed upon by both houses . . . Concerning the securing of . . . England and . . . Wales [15 Mar.]. . . . and . . . sir Symon Dewes. who speake as followeth [9 Mar.].* London: f. J. Thomas, 1641[2]. 4°. A⁴.
This letterpress is in a section of Twyne mss. on the precedence of Oxford over Cambridge (cf. at f. 238, AW's note at end of a citation, by Twyne, from the 'Monume[n]tensis lib. 9° Historiae Rerum Britan. c. 12', 'Whence it appears that Oxōn was a noble city at that time. (ie) A.D. 516.').
[MS.] Wood F. 27 (ff. 233-6). Wing E2301B.

2250. D'Ewes, Simonds. *Two speeches spoken by . . . The first touching the antiquity of Cambridge, lately published by John Thomas, . . . The other concerning the priviledge of parliament, in causes civill and criminall.* London: f. T. Payboby, 1642. 4°. Pp. (2), 6.
Tp, AW wrote beside the 1st speech, 'Utinam.' and below, 'The first of these speeches is answer'd in Hist. et Antiq. Univ. Oxon. lib 1'. P. 2, extensive note in Latin, by Brian Twyne (see preceding item and note at 514(14), item 2373; Twyne did research in D'Ewes' sources, see MS. Wood F. 27, items 228ff.; and for AW's comments on Twyne, f. 238), and 2 corrections, on the inside margin, prob. by AW. P. 3, notes in ink and pencil, in AW's hand, in a general argument that Cambridge is more ancient than Oxford, e.g., 'answ.' and 'Ans:', in pencil. At a reference to the Saxon *Anonymus* in a 'Library', AW identified the location, 'viz the Library of Sʳ Rob: Cotton neare the parliament house.' See Madan 967. LT 1.77.
Wood 514(8). Wing D1256.

2251. Dey, Rich[ard]. *Two looks over Lincolne [John Williams], . . . discovering his erronious and popish tenets . . . a petition.* London: n.pub., 1641. 4°. Pp. [2], 32.
Tp, bsm.
[MS.] Wood B. 40(2). Wing D1288.

2252. Dialogue. *Dialogue between a butcher and a fishmonger.* ?: ?, ? 4°.
Missing. In a list of 'Mr. Woods Duplicats', MS. Wood F. 51, f. 44, item 15.
MS. Wood F. 51(15). Not identified.

2253. Dialogue. *A dialogue. Wherin is plainly layd open the tyrannicall dealing of lord bishops against Gods children [a reply to J. Bridges' Defence, STC 3734]. . . . Published, by . . . Martin Mar-prelat.* [Amsterdam]: [Cloppenberg Press?], 1640. 4°. Rpt. A-C⁴,D².
B3, vertical line in margin, at list of dictionaries.
[MS.] Wood D. 31(3). STC 6805.3.

2254. Dialogue at Oxford. *A dialogue at Oxford between a tutor and a gentleman, . . . concerning government.* London: f. R. Janeway, 1681. 4°. Pp. [2], 21.
Wood 614(16). Wing D1290.

2255. Dialogues. *The dialoges of creatures moralysed.* [Antwerp]: be to sell, upo[n] Powlys churchyarde, [1530?]. 4°. A-2R⁴,S2-3 (wanting tp). Pasteboard (blue) with parchment spine; pastedowns and flyleaves, printer's waste paper.
Spine, 'Fables in Black Letter / With Cuts', prob. by AW, in pencil. Flyleaf, upperᵛ, AW wrote: 'AWoode 1661' and 'Dialogues & fables translated out of Latine by Anon.' Text, e.g., A1, 'AWood.'; 2N1, 2R1, 2S3ᵛ, note or scribble, not in AW's hand.
Wood 638. STC 6815.

2256. Dick, William. *Breviate of the lamentable case of the late sir William Dick in Scotland his estate.* N.p.: n.pub., [1657?]. S.sh.
Wood 276b(90). Wing B4413A (rare) (Wing, 1667?).

2257. Dickenson, Henry. *The last true newes from Yorke, Nottingham, Coventry and Warwicke:. . . 24 of August, to the 4 of September.* London: f. J. Wright, 1642, 7 Sept. 4°. A⁴.
Wood 375(6). Wing D1383.

2258. Dickensonus, Joannes. *Miscellanea ex historiis Anglicanis concinnata, autore I. D.* Lugduni Batavorum: ex off. T. Basson, sumpt. L. Elsevirii, 1606. 4°. Pp. 70, [1]. Parchment.
Parchment coverᵛ, a note by the former owner, Edwin Sandys, concerning his *Speculum Europae*: 'I have understoode by sondry letters of Samuel Calvert, that my Speculum is translated into French, and printed in France: but because the Printer hearing an inckling that it shoulde be called in (as it was shortly after) had dispersed the same into the partes moste remote from Paris; Samuel hath not bene able to get any copy thereof.' (first published in 1605, and then 1629; a French version, translated from an Italian edition, was printed in 1626, see DNB; for AW's summary of the above, see AO 2.473; see also, LT 2.42 and J. H. van Dorsten, *Thomas Basson* (Leiden, 1961) p. 90).
Wood 332. BL.

2259. Dickinson, Edmund. *Delphi Phoenicizantes.* Oxoniae: H. Hall, imp. R. Davis, 1655. 8°. 1,*⁴,A⁸,a3,B-O⁸,P⁴ (p. nos. erratic). Pasteboard (brown) with parchment spine; upper and lower backing, traces of marbled paper.
Flyleaf, upper, 2ndᵛ, AW wrote the titles of 5 printed works (really 3) in this vol., within guidelines made with red chalk. Tp, he wrote '1.2ᵈ.' Acquired 23 Nov. 1663, LT 1.503.
Wood 39(1). Wing D1385. Madan 2274.

2260. Digby, Francis. *Poemation Latinum.* [London]: n.pub., 1695. S.sh. (imperf.).
A torn slip, a tp, now in Wood 431a, *Athenae Oxonienses*, 2 vols. (1691-2), at ii, col. 877, with Wood's note, 'Tobacco wrapt up in this paper in the beginning of May 1693'.
Wood 431c. Not in Wing. ESTCR 31191 (one) (ESCTR, [1715?]).

2261. [Digby, George]. Bristol, earl of. *A true and impartiall relation of the battaile betwixt, his majesties army and that of the rebells, neare Newbury in Berk-shire, Sept. 20.* [Oxford]: [L. Lichfield], 1643. 4°. Pp. [2], 9.
Tp, AW altered the former no. P. 7, a brief note for emphasis, 'visc-Falkl'.
Wood 376(38) (not in Bodl. CD cat.). Wing B4777. Madan 1453.

2262. Digby, George. Bristol, earl of. *The earle of Bristoll his speech in the house of lords . . . upon the bill of indemnity [20 July].* London: n.pub, 1660. 4°. Pp. [2], 5.
Tp, AW wrote, 'July:', and underscored Bristoll, in red ink.
Wood 608(24). Wing B4773.

2263. Digby, George, and Thomas Eliot. *August. 6. Two letters the one from.* London: A. N. f. R. Lownds, 1642. 4°. Pp. 7.
Tp, AW lined out the former no., underscored the surnames of the authors, and after 'August. 6.', wrote, 'Aug. 1'.
Wood 374(30). Wing B4781.

2264. Digby, George, and Murrough O'Brien. Inchiquin, earl of. *The Irish papers, containing the lord Digbyes letter, and the lord Inchiquins answer.* London: F. Leech, 1646. 4°. Pp. 8 (misnumbering).
Wood 509(10). Wing B4766.

2265. Digby, John. Bristol, earl of. *A speech made by the right honourable . . . May 20 . . . Together with the votes of both houses.* London: f. J. Smith, a. A. Coe, 1642. 4°. A⁴.
Tp, AW lined out 2 former nos., '52', '55'. A4ᵛ, 'These votes are mentiond in the following pamphlet nu.' (Wood 374(3)).
Wood 374(2). Wing B4797.

2266. Digby, John. Bristol, earl of. *An apologie of John earl of Bristol.* Caen [i.e., London?]: n.pub., 1656. 4°. Repr. Pp. [6], 72, [2], 24 (2 tpp.).
Pp. 1st 23, 25, 27, line in margin.
Wood 609(40)(41). Wing B4788.

2267. Digby, Kenelm. *Observations upon Religio medici.* London: F. L. f. L. Chapman a. D. Frere, 1644. 8°. 2nd ed. T leaf is a cancel. Pp. [2], 124.
Acquired 6 Nov. 1666, 6ᵈ, LT 2.92.
Wood 870(2). Wing D1443.

2268. [Digges, Dudley]. *Of the circumference of the earth: or, a treatise of the North-east [sic] passage.* London: W. W[hite] f. J. Barnes, 1612. 8°. Pp. [4], 26.
Tp, 'North-east' corrected to 'North-weast'.
Wood 158(2). STC 6847.

2269. Digges, Leonard, ed. *An arithmetical warlike treatise named Stratioticos compendiously teaching the science of nombers [sic].* London: R. Field, 1590. 4° (corrected edition). Pp. [14], 380 with a foldout. Parchment.
Pastedown, upper, and tp, scribbles, not by AW. Text, a few scribbles, not by AW. Pastedown, lower, notes by Johannes Chamden, Poughdon and Ploudon.
[MS.] Wood C. 24. STC 6849.

2270. Digges, Leonard. *A booke named tectonicon. Briefly shewing the exact measuring, and speedie reckoning all manner of land.* London: F. Kingston, 1647. 4°. Ff. [2], 26 + 2 unnumbered illus.
Tp, AW wrote, 'septemb: xxij AD MDclx:', and '1ˢ 4ᵈ'. Bsm. LT 1.332.
Wood 481(4). Wing D1468.

2271. Dillon, Thomas*. Dillon, 4th visct. *The coppy of a letter sent by the rebells in Ireland to the lord Dillon, to declare . . . the cause of their taking up of armes.* London: f. J. Thomas, 1641. 4°. Pp. [1], 6.
Tp, AW wrote after the year, 'Dec. 18'.
Wood 507(16). Wing C6137.

2272. [Dillon, Wentworth]. [Roscommon, earl of]. *A letter from Scotland: written . . . upon the speech made by a noble peer [Anthony Ashley Cooper].* [London]: n.pub., [1681]. S.sh. Pp. 2.
Wood 276a(150). Wing R1931B.

2273. Dillon, Wentworth. Roscommon, earl of. *An essay on translated verse.* London: f. J. Tonson, 1684. 4°. Pp. [16], 24.
Wood 320(6). Wing R1930.

2274. Dio Cassius. *The emperor Augustus his two speeches, . . . the first . . . to the married Romans, the other to the unmarried.* London: f. J. B., 1675. 4°. Pp. [2], 6.
Trace of a note at bottom, cropped.

Wood 608(48). Wing D1503A.

2275. Diodorus, Siculus. Stocker, Thomas, trans. *A righte noble and pleasant history of the successors of Alexander . . . taken out of Diodorus Siculus: and some of their lives [from the Vita Demetrii] written by . . . Plutarch [trans. out of Fr. of C. of Seissell]*. London: H. Bynneman f. H. Toy, 1569. 4°. Ff. [4], 259, [7]. Parchment with 2 leather clasps.
Parchment, upper, outer, scribbles, 'Stonehouse'.
Wood 597. STC 689.

2276. Dionysius Carthusianus. *The lyfe of prestes. . . . tr. into the Englyshe tonge.* (London): (R. Redman), [1533?]. A-L⁸. Calf with 3 fillets; rebacked.
Tp, 'ABosco', and Hum[phrey] Dyson.
Jesus College H. 13. 23(1). STC 6894.

2277. Discourse. *Discourse of true happyness.* ?: ?, ? 4°.
Missing. In a list of 'Mr. Woods Duplicats', MS. Wood F. 51, f. 44, item 12 (possibly Thomas Tryon, Wing T3200, or item 1431 above).
MS. Wood F. 51(12). Not identified.

2278. Discourse. *A discourse of the married and single life.* London: [F. Kingston] f. J. Man, 1621. 8°. Pp. [14], 115.
Wood 750(3). STC 6908.

2279. Dispersed United. *The dispersed united; or, twelve healing questions propounded to persons of ingenious principles.* [London]: n.pub., 1659. 4°. Pp. 8.
Tp, no. in former bundle cropped at side.
Wood 613(50). Wing D1674.

2280. Docwra, William*. *An advertisement on the behalf of William Dockwra, . . . concerning the penny-post.* N.p.: n.pub., [1689]. S.sh.
At top, AW wrote, 'This paper was dispersed in every coffey-house in Oxōn. in the beg. of Sept. 1689.' At the bottom, in another hand, 'The Reader is desired not to take away this paper' (and a scribbled repetition of the same). AW took away the paper. LT 3.310.
Wood 276a(575). Wing D1782 (two).

2281. Dod, [John]. *Old mʳ Dod's sayings.* London: A. Maxwell, 1667. S.sh.
Wood 276a(286). Wing D1783 (rare).

2282. Doddridge, John. *The history of the ancient and moderne estate of the principality of Wales, dutchy of Cornewall, and earldome of Chester.* London: T. Harper, f. G. Emondson a. T. Alchorne, 1630. 4°. Pp. [16], 142. Pasteboard (blue) with parchment spine; upper and lower flyleaves, traces of marbled paper.
Flyleaf, upper, 2ndᵛ, AW wrote the titles of 6 printed works in this vol., within guidelines made with red ink. Tp, bsm.
Wood 478(1). STC 6982.

2283. Dominium Maris. *Dominium maris: or, the dominion of the sea. Expressing the title, . . . of the Adriatick sea [To the Reader signed Clareamontos; trans. from Italian].* London: W. Du Gard, 1652. 4°. Pp. [10], 22.
Tp, bsm.
[MS.] Wood C. 13(5). Wing D1843.

2284. Don Tomazo. *Don Tomazo, or the juvenile rambles of Thomas Dangerfield.* London: f. W. Rumbald, 1680. 8°. Pp. [xvi], 222.
Tp, 'mn', bsm.(?), and on sheet pasted behind tp, 'given to me by Perit being then finished at the Press 4 Feb. 1681' (Charles Perrot? see LT 2.515f., AO 3.1185).
Wood 155(5). Wing D1848.

2285. Donne, John. *Poems, by J. D. With elegies on the authors death.* London: M. F[lesher] f. J. Marriot, 1635. 8°. Pp. [14], 388, [31].
Missing. MS. Wood E. 2(70), p. 50, 'Poems 1635 – elegies on his death at the latter end – by Arch. Wilson – Sr Lucius Cary Sydney Godolphin - Edw. Hyde'.
MS. Wood E. 2(70), p. 50. STC 7046. Keynes 79. *O, Folg, Hunt.*

2286. [Donne, John] (younger). *To the right honorable, the lord chancellor, the humble petition of Covent-garden.* [London]: n.pub., [1661]. S.sh.
'Authore D. D^ne Donne [mutilated at end] Jun. 1661', not in AW's hand.
Wood 416(89). Wing D1877A (rare) (Wing, honorable the).

2287. Donne, John (younger). *Dr. Donne's last will and testament. July 21. 1657.* [London]: n.pub., 1662, 23 Feb. S.sh.
AW added after the date, 'in which yeare the said J: Donne dyed. qu[aere]' (AOF 1.503). Dupl. at Wood 416(95).
Wood 276a(284). Wing D1875.

2288. Donne, John (younger). *Dr. Donne's last will and testament. July 21. 1657.* [London]: n.pub., 1662, 23 Feb. S.sh.
^v, AW wrote, '1662', in pencil, and over it, '95'. Dupl. at Wood 276a(284). See note there.
Wood 416(95). Wing D1875.

2289. Donzellinus Brixianus, Cornelius. *Methodus linguae Graecae, libris IIII. comprehensa: unà cum brevissimo totius grammaticae compendio.* Basileae: per J. Oporinum, (1551). Pp. [10], 404. Calf, speckled, 18th century.
Tp, 'ABosco'. Bequeathed to Jesus College Library in 1712 by Jonathan Edwards, Principal.
Jesus College N. 1. 8. BN (BN, 454 pp.).

2290. Dordevic, Bartolomej. *The rarities of Turkey, gathered by one that was sold seven times a slave.* London: f. the author, 1661. 8°. Pp. [18], 125, [3].
Tp, AW wrote, '8^d'; B1, B2, marks in margin (B1, 't^x', bsm?).
Wood 156(2). Wing D1921A (rare).

2291. [Dormer, John]. *The new plot of the papists. To transform traitors. Into martyrs.* London: n.pub., 1679. 4°. Pp. [1-2], 5-6, 9-16, 7-8 (no. (and sigs.) out of order, but not narrative).
Tp, AW wrote, '6^d'; 'came out the latter end of July 1679. but soon after suppressed/'; and 'Tho. Dangerfield in his narrative (in the <u>first</u> 2^d vol. of popish pamphlets nu. 27) pag. 17. saith that one Dormer a reputed priest wrot this pamphlet', i.e., Wood 425(25), item 2150. LT 2.457. At [MS.] Wood E. 27(2) (item 1599, see Plate VIII) AW wrote of this pamphlet, 'It doth not answer the title, but mostly against Oates, Bedlow, Prance, Dugdale – prohibited to be sold'. Purchased from Vade in July or August 1689, see his record of purchase at MS. Wood F. 50, f. 11.
Wood 424(29). Wing D1924.

2292. Dorney, John. *A briefe and exact relation of the most materiall and remarkeable [sic] passages . . . in the . . . seige . . . of Glocester.* London: f. T. Underhill, 1643. 4°. Pp. [2], 17.
Tp, AW lined out the former no., '35'.
Wood 376(36). Wing D1931.

2293. Dorset. *A declaration of the knights . . . in the county of Dorset.* London: n.pub, 1660. S.sh.
AW added to the date, 'Aprill:'.
Wood 276a(219). Wing D696.

2294. Dorset. *To the kings most excellent majestie. The humble address of . . . the county of Dorset [12 June].* London: f. R. Clavel, 1660. S.sh.
Wood 276a(204). Wing T1511 (3).

2295. [Doubleth, George Rataller]. *Mare belli Anglicani injustissimè Belgis illati Helena [signed S. de Burmania].* N.p.: n.pub., 1652. 4°. Pp. 42 (pp. unopened).
Tp, bsm. Dupl. at Wood 533(2).
[MS.] Wood C. 13(7). BL.

2296. [Doubleth, George Rataller]. *Mare belli Anglicani injustissimè Belgis illati Helena [signed S. de Burmania].* [Hagae]: n.pub., 1652. 4°. Pp. 42.
Tp, bsm. and scribbles. Dupl. at [MS.] Wood C. 13(7).
Wood 533(2). NUC.

2297. [Doughty, John]. *The kings cause rationally, briefly, and plainly debated, as it stands de facto.* [Oxford]: [H. Hall], 1644. 4°. Pp. [2], 47. Parchment, hair-side outside.
Cover, upper, 'Woods brothers . . . ' illeg., not by AW. Doughty was Wood's brother's sponsor. Flyleaf, upper, signature 'Mary Wood'; AW wrote, 'This book was given to my mother (by the authour) at Oxon,

– unknowne as yet to me /' and, later, in red ink, 'Dr John Doughtie was the Authour'. LT 1.21, 2.101. [MS.] Wood B. 34. Wing D1962. Madan 1558.

2298. Douglas, Robert. *The forme and order of the coronation of Charles the second, . . . at Scoone, the first day of January, 1651. [Followed by] Sermon . . . by master Robert Dowglas*. Aberdene: James Brown, 1651. 4°. Pp. 24.
Tp, AW wrote after '1651' in t, '50'.
Wood 633(9). Wing D2027.

2299. Dousa, Georgius. *De itinere suo Constantinopolitano, epistola*. [Leiden]: ex off. Plantiniana, ap. C. Raphelengium, 1599. 8°. Pp. 141, [1]. Parchment, rough.
Flyleaf, upper, 2nd, scribble, ανθρωπος. Tp, bsm. Passim, underscoring and marks in margins and, esp. 9-17, notes, not in AW's hand.
Wood 152(1). BL.

2300. Downame, John. Payne, Jo., sculp. *The Christian warfare against the devill world and flesh*. London: W. Stansby, [1634]. S.sh., frontispiece only (engr.).
A later comment on removed item (32): 'xxxii not here [1881]'. There is no record of what was at this location.
Wood 276b(33). STC 7137.

2301. Downame, John. *A briefe concordance, or table to the Bible*. London: f. N. Bourne a. R. Young, 1642. 8°. A-G^8.
Tp, name cropped at bottom. G8^v, scribbles, a note of a bill, 'Thomas Hodgkins' (?), and a 2nd name, blotted out, none by AW.
Wood 875(2). Wing D2065.

2302. Drake, Francis. *The voyages and travels of the renouned captain, sir Francis Drake, into the West-Indies, and round about the world*. London: M. H. a. I. M. f. P. Brooksby, 1683. 4°. Pp. [2], 22. Pasteboard (blue) with parchment spine. 1st upper and last lower flyleaves, marbled paper. Rebacked, R. H[arvey] 9.12.51.
Flyleaf, upper, 2nd^v-3rd, AW wrote the titles of 14 printed works in this vol. (really 15, he omitted no. 14), within guidelines made with red ink.
Wood 387(1) (nos. differ in Bodl. CD cat.). Wing D2122aA (two).

2303. Drake, William. *The long parliament revived: or, an act for continuation, . . . Also m^r. Will. Prynne his five arguments fully answered . . . By Tho. Phillips*. London: for the author, sold at the Castle and Lion, 1661. 4°. Pp. [2], 22.
Tp, AW wrote 'Of the author of this book, see at the end of it.'; '10^d' (twice, once lined out); 'Apr 1660', in pencil; and altered the year to 1660. Flyleaf, lower, AW wrote 35 lines, apparently copied from some publication of 15 Nov. and 20 Nov. 1660, on the apprehension and examination of the author, William Drake, with the result that 'the book to be burnt by the hand of the common Hangman'. The last 14 lines are: 'Resolved that the said book entit. The Long parl. revived, is a seditious pamphlet, & it was referred to a Committee to draw up an impeachment against Will. Drake of Lond. Merchant: which being reported & agreed upon, is as followeth, viz. [/] The Knights, Citizens & Burgesses in parl. assembled, do in the name of themselves & all the Commons assembled in parl. do impeach Will. Drake of Lond Merchant of sedition, for writing, printing & publishing a seditious pamphlet, entit. The Long Parliament revived – Resolved that he remaine in custody'. On the author, see K. Sharpe, *Reading Revolutions* (New Haven and London, 2000): 253-4.
Wood 620(34). Wing D2137A.

2304. Drayton, Michael. Selden, John, ed. *Poly-Olbion*. London: [H. Lownes] f. M. Lownes, J. Browne, J. Helme, J. Busbie, [1612]. Fol. Pp. [13], 303 (plus maps) (wanting portrait). Calf with 3 fillets, an extra line with 3 fillets and stamp decoration (6) in corners.
Tp, 'Antonii à Bosco' and signatures of former owners, Caroli Hickmot (LT 2.105), and an earlier owner, lined out. P. [13] (A4^v), AW wrote the name of the editor, 'John Selden' and made a mark at a reference to an Oxford author, John Malverne. Pp. 14-22, 49-54, 66-73, 83, 85, extensive underscoring at OE and ME (Arthurian) lore, may not be in AW's hand, and p. 49, a note, 'meaning Stone-henge', not in AW's hand. Acquired 15 Apr. 1669, 7^s, LT 2.153.
Wood 403. STC 7226.

2305. Drewrey, H. *The vindication of the seperate brethren of the spirit, against a libel, called, the*

resolution of the round-heads [to pull down Cheap-side cross]. London: Published by H. Drewrey, 1641[2]. 4°. No sigs. 4 leaves.
Wood 614(37). Wing D2167A (two).

2306. D[ring], T[homas]. *A catalogue of the lords, knights, . . . that have compounded for their estates.* London: f. T. Dring, 1655. 8°. Pp. A-L⁸ (last 2 leaves blank).
Tp, AW wrote, 'In this book are the generality of mens & townes names false printed –'. Bsm. A7ᵛ, correction, in red ink; C1ᵛ, D5, corrections.
Wood 445(6). Wing D2187.

2307. D[rope] J[ohn]. *An hymenaean essay, or an epithalamy . . . of . . . Charles the second with . . . Katharine, infanta of Portugall. 1662.* [Oxford?]: n.pub., 1662. 4°. Pp. 12.
Tp, AW entered the author's name after initials, D'rope. M: of A: and fellow of Magd: Coll: Oxon.' and before printed date, not by AW, 'Donum autoris anno domini', and below, AW wrote, 'AWoode: donum Authoris Maii xxj A.d. MDcLxii.' (LT 1.440; Drope was godfather to John, son of Robert and Mary Wood, 15 Aug 1664, see LT 5.14; AOF 2.228).
Wood 319(14). Wing D2189 (3). Not in Madan.

2308. [Drope, John]. *Upon the most hopefull and ever-flourishing sprouts of valour, the indefatigable centrys of the physick-garden.* [Oxford]: [W. Hall], 1664. S.sh.
AW wrote, 'John Drope M. of A. fellow of Magd. Coll. the author'. In the text, several faintly printed words are filled in. Dupl. at Wood 416(107). LT 2.165, AOF 2.228.
Wood 423(41). Wing D2190 (rare, 2 at O) (Wing, 166[4]). Madan 2658.

2309. [Drope, John]. *Upon the most hopefull and ever-flourishing sprouts of valour, the indefatigable centrys of the physick-garden.* [Oxford]: [W. Hall], 1664. S.sh.
AW wrote, 'The author John Drope. A. m. & fellow of Magd: Coll: Oxōn.'; ᵛ, 'Dupl', in pencil. Dupl. at Wood 423(41). LT 2.165, AOF 2.228. Also, a note by a later librarian of another copy in the Ashm. collection, f. 285.
Wood 416(107). Wing D2190 (rare, 2 at O) (Wing, 166[4]). Madan 2658.

2310. Drummond, William, and James 5 of Scotland. Gibson, Edm., ed. *Polemo-middinia. Carmen macaronicum. Autore Gulielmo Drummundo . . . Accedit . . . Cantilena rustica . . . Christs kirk on the green.* Oxonii: e theatro Sheldoniano, 1691. 4°. Pp. [12], 22.
Tp, AW wrote the editor's name after initials, 'Edm. Gibson Art. Bac. Coll. Regin. Oxōn'.
Wood 318(3). Wing D2204.

2311. Drusius, Joannes. Curiander, Abel, ed. *[J. Drusii ad voces Ebriacas Novi Testamenti commentarius duplex. . . . Nec non vitae operumque J. Drusii] [2nd tp:] Vitae operumque Joh. Drusii.* Franekerae: F. Heynsius, 1616. 4°. (:)⁴,Aa⁴,B-E⁴,F⁶; pp. [1-8], 185-192, 9-52 (pt. 2, only, with pp. 185-192 of pt. 1).
Pp. [8], 185-192, 9, 16-19, 28-9, Vertical lines in margins, in pencil.
Wood 345(2) (not in Bodl. CD cat.). BL.

2312. Dryden, John. *Secret-love, or the maiden-queen.* London: H. Herringman, 1668. 4°. Pp. [12], 66, [2].
Wood 607(7). Wing D2353. Macdonald, 70 a.

2313. Dryden, John. *Absalom and Achitophel. A poem.* London: f. J. T., sold W. Davis, 1681. Fol. 2nd ed. Pp. [6], 27.
P. 2, signature of 'Robert Bryne'.
Wood 320(2). Wing D2215. Macdonald, 12 d.

2314. D[ryden], J[ohn]. *An elegy on the usurper O[liver] C[romwell].* (London): (f. J. Smith), (1681). S.sh. (r-v) (mutilated at edges).
AW identified the author, 'John Dr[y]den po[et] Laure[ate] to K. C.' (cropped at side) and, ᵛ, at printed 'A Rogue like Hodge', AW wrote, 'Roger Lestrange'.
Wood 416(12). Wing D2268. Macdonald, 3 b.

2315. Dryden, John. *His majesties declaration defended: in a letter to a friend. Being an answer to . . . a letter . . . concerning . . . the reasons which moved him to dissolve the two last parliaments.* London: f. T. Davies, 1681. Fol. Pp. 20.
Tp, AW wrote 'v. Decl of the K in the last vol. of popish papers', in pencil (prob. a ref. to the next item by G. Savile, Wood 657(22), item 5766). Bsm.

Wood 657(21). Wing D2286. Macdonald, 129.

2316. [Dryden, John]. Atterbury, Francis and Francis Hickman, trans. *Absalon et Achitophel. Poema Latino carmine donatum.* Oxon: typ. Lichfieldianis, prostant ap. J. Crosley, 1682. 4°. Pp. [2], 29 (i.e., 39). Tp, AW wrote, 'By Franc. Atterbury & Franc Hickman of ch. ch.' P. 39ᵛ, the name, 'Ed Wells', may not be by AW (perhaps the student of Christ Church in 1694, see LT 3.460).
Wood 483(21). Wing D2222. Macdonald, 12 k.

2317. Dryden, [John]. *Prologue to his royal highness, upon his first appearance at the Duke's Theatre since his return from Scotland.* London: f. J. Tonson, 1682. S.sh.
Wood 276a(560). Wing D2335. Macdonald, 98 a.

2318. Dryden, [John]. *Prologue to the dutchess, on her return from Scotland.* [London]: (f. J. Tonson), (1682). S.sh. (r-v).
Wood 276a(561). Wing D2337. Macdonald, 99.

2319. Dryden, John. *A prologue written by mr. dryden, to . . . the loyal brother [by T. Southern].* (London): (f. J. Tonson), [1682]. S.sh. (r-v).
AW wrote, 'The Loyal Brother was written by Tho. Southern 1682'.
Wood 417(102). Wing D2341. Macdonald, 97.

2320. Dryden, [John]. *Religio laici or a laymans faith. A poem.* London: f. J. Tonson, [1682]. 4°. Pp. [16], 28. Pasteboard (blue) with parchment spine.
Flyleaf, upper, 2nd , 'E Libris in Musaeo Ash', not by AW (a similar note on flyleaf, lower, 1st); 2ndᵛ, list of 9 printed works in this vol., not by AW. This is a problematic vol. in that it may not have been bequeathed to the Ashm. Museum as part of the Wood collection in 1695. The evidence for is that the 9 items were bound in a typical Wood binding and the vol. was at its present location, Wood 320, in 1717. On the other hand, this vol. lacks a list of contents in AW's hand and the normal sequence of Arabic numbers on tpp of items in the vol. Nor are there annotations anywhere in this vol. in AW's hand. Tp, 'Ex dono Author-' (cropped), not in AW's hand. There is no evidence in Wood's diary that he knew Dryden (see LT 3.191, 355, and 2.473), though he referred to this work in a note at Wood 773(1), item 5.
Wood 320(1). Wing D2343 (rare). Macdonald, 16 a iii.

2321. Dryden, John. *Threnodia augustalis: a funeral-Pindarique poem.* London: f. J. Tonson, 1685. 4°. Pp. [2], 25.
Wood 320(3). Wing D2383. Macdonald, 20 a.

2322. Du Chastelet de Luzancy, Hippolyte*. *An account of the barbarous attempt of the Jesuites upon mr. de Luzancy, upon his conversion to the protestant religion.* [London]: n.pub., [1675]. S.sh. (r-v).
Wood 657(13). Wing A239.

2323. Du Jon, François (younger). *The painting of the ancients . . . Englished, with some additions.* London: R. Hodgkinsonne, sold D. Frere, 1638. 4°. Pp. [8], 355. Parchment.
Flyleaf, upperᵛ, 'n/w' (?). Tp, AW wrote, '1ˢ-4ᵈ'. Bsm. Text, passim, short pairs of vertical lines and some '*' marks, not in AW's manner. Acquired 1 Oct. 1662, 1ˢ2ᵈ, LT 1.457.
[MS.] Wood C. 22. STC 7302.

2324. Du Moulin, Louis. *Oratio auspicalis, cui subjuncta est laudatio . . . Guil. Cambdeni.* Oxoniae: L. Lichfield, 1652. 4°. Pp. [16], 27.
Dupl. at Wood 498(4). AOF 2.125-8.
Wood 512(13). Wing D2546. Madan 2186.

2325. Du Moulin, Louis. *Oratio auspicalis, cui subjuncta est laudatio . . . Guil. Cambdeni.* Oxoniae: L. Lichfield, 1652. 4°. Pp. [16], 27.
Tp, presentation copy 'For Dʳ Langbaine Prov. of Qu: Coll'. P. 8, 16-7 corrections (2 of Greek spellings), prob. not by AW; 21, on the maternal lineage of Camden, AW wrote 'viz. Curwen . . . de Workington in Com: Cumbria'. AOF 2.125-8. Prob. acquired 3 May 1658 from G. Langbaine's study, LT 1.248. Dupl. at Wood 512(13).
Wood 498(4). (Ashm. 498(4) in Bodl. CD cat.). Wing D2546. Madan 2186.

2326. Du Moulin, Louis. *Amplissimo senatui academico [petition to the university, not to be deprived of the professorship of ancient history].* [Oxford]: n.pub., [1660]. S.sh.
'Dupl', in pencil. Dupl. at 515(2). Year, not in AW's hand. 1 correction. AOF 2.125f.
Wood 423(31). Wing D2528 (rare, 2 at O). Madan 2491.

2327. Du Moulin, Louis. *Amplissimo senatui academico [petition to the university, not to be deprived of the professorship of ancient history]*. [Oxford]: n.pub., [1660]. S.sh.
Year, not in AW's hand. Dupl. at Wood 423(31). AOF 2.125f.
Wood 515(2). Wing D2528 (rare, 2 at O). Madan 2491.

2328. Du Moulin, Louis. *The last words of . . . being his retraction of all . . . reflections he had made on the divines of the Church of England*. London: f. R. Royston, 1680. 4°. Pp. 19.
Pp. 15-7, line in margin. LT 2.499.
Wood 532(10). Wing D2542.

2329. Du Moulin, Pierre (elder). S[tafford], R[obert], trans. *Heraclitus: or meditations upon the vanity & misery of humane life*. Oxford: J. Barnes, 1609. 12°. Pp. [12], 121.
Each 12° leaf is pasted on an 8° template. Tp, initials T. J. Text, some short horizontal pencil lines in margin, not in AW's manner.
Wood 747(3). STC 7325.5. Madan 322.

2330. Du Moulin, Pierre (elder), and François Clouet. Philanax Orthodoxus, trans. *The monk's hood pull'd off; or, the Capucin fryar described [trans. from du Moulin's Le Capucin and by another from Clouet's Journal des Capucins]*. London: f. J. Collins, 1671. 8°. Pp. [17], 141, [3], 51, [2].
Tp, AW wrote '1. 3^{d}'.
Wood 874(2). Wing D2592.

2331. Du Moulin, Pierre (elder), and Lancelot Andrewes. *Of episcopacy. Three epistles . . . answered by . . . Lancelot Andrews*. [London]: n.pub., 1647. 4°. Pp. [2], 63, [1].
Tp, 'entered A. H.' (i.e., in Bodleian Library cat.). Bsm.
[MS.] Wood D. 25(11). Wing A3143.

2332. [Du Moulin, Pierre] (younger). *A true relation of the late expedition of . . . Robert earle of Essex, for the relief of Gloucester*. London: f. R. Rounthwait, 1643. 4°. Pp. [2], 21, [1].
Tp, AW lined out the former no., '38'. Dupl. at Wood 612(3).
Wood 376(41). Wing T2979.

2333. [Du Moulin, Pierre] (younger). *A true relation of the late expedition of . . . Robert earle of Essex, for the relief of Gloucester*. London: f. R. Rounthwaite, 1643. 4°. Pp. [2], 21, [1].
Tp, AW wrote 'Dupl - q[uaere]' and 'Dupl', in pencil. Dupl. at Wood 376(41).
Wood 612(3). Wing T2979.

2334. [Du Moulin, Pierre]. Basire, Isaac, also attrib. to; Bramhall, John, also attrib. to; Playford, Matthew(?), trans. *The history of the English & Scotch presbytery. . . . Written in French, by an eminent divine of the Reformed Church, and now Englished*. Villa Franca [really London]: n.pub., 1659. 8°. Pp. [59], 324.
Tp, AW wrote 'said to be written by D^{r} Jo. Bramhall Bishop of Derry in Ireland.' P. 1, a correction.
Wood 888(2). Wing D2558A.

2335. [Du Refuge, Eustache]. *The art of complaisance or the means to oblige in conversation*. London: f. J. Starkey, 1673. 12°. Title leaf is cancelled by a bifolium. Pp. [13], 180, [11] (11 pp. books sold by Starkey).
Tp, AW wrote '9^{d}/' and 'Another edit. 1677' (Wing D2686B); tp and A2^{v}, brief notes by another person.
Wood 752(2). Wing D2686A.

2336. Du Tillet, Jean. Meaux, bp. of. *La chronique des roys de France . . . jusques au roy Henry, troisiesme*. Paris: par Jean d'Ongoys, 1575. 8°. Ff. [8], 180. Parchment.
Tp, 8-9 word note, illegible, by Th. James, 1597; and author's name, 'J. Tilius. latine . . . '.
Wood 140. BN.

2337. Du Vair, Guillaume. Cotton, Charles, trans. *The morall philosophy of the stoicks*. London: f. H. Mortlock, 1667. 8°. Pp. [7], 118.
Wood 870(4) (not in Bodl. CD cat.). Wing D2916.

2338. Du Val, Pierre, trans. *A geographical dictionary*. London: J. C., sold H. Brome, 1662. 8°. Pp. [4], map, 138, [2] (misnumbering; 2 pp. books sold by Brome).
Tp, AW wrote '8^{d}'. Bsm. Acquired 7 Jan. 1662, LT 1.428.
Wood 702(2). Wing D2920A.

2339. Dublin. *A faithfull remonstrance, of all the chiefe matters . . . in and about Dublin, and other parts of Ireland [26 Jan. to 1 Mar.]*. London: f. J. Wright, 1642. 4°. Pp. [2], 6.
Wood 508(40). Wing F283.

2340. Dublin. *A declaration of the protestant clergie of the city of Dublin, . . . why they cannot consent to the taking away of the book of common prayer [9 July]*. [London]: n.pub., 1647. 4°. Pp. [2], 6.
Wood 509(21). Wing D756.

2341. Dublin, and P. T. *The distressed estate of the city of Dublin . . . With the copie of a . . . letter [signed P.T.] . . . sent from one of the chiefe of the rebels*. London: f. J. Thomas, 1641. 4°. A⁴.
Tp, AW wrote below, 'Dec. 17'.
Wood 507(15). Wing D1702.

2342. Dubrovnik. *A true relation of the terrible earthquake which happened at Ragusa [6 Apr.] [transl.]*. [London] in the Savoy: T. Newcomb, 1667. 4°. Pp. 8.
[MS.] Wood D. 28(14). Wing T3059.

2343. Ducci, Lorenzo. Blount, Edward, trans. *Ars aulica or the courtiers arte*. London: M. Bradwood f. E. Blount, 1607. 12°. Pp. [20], 288. Parchment with 2 clasp holes.
P. [4], after name of Blount, AW wrote, 'Bookseller', in red ink; p. 13 to end, some parallel short vertical lines in margins, not in AW's usual manner.
Wood 451. STC 7274.

2344. [Duchesne, André]. *Les antiquitez et recherches des villes*. Paris: N. a. J. de la Coste, 1631. 8°.
6th ed.
Missing. Gore, f. 302ᵛ.
Gore 302. BN.

2345. Duck, Arthur. *Vita Henrici Chichele archiepiscopi Cantuariensis*. Oxoniae: J. Barnesius, 1617. 4°.
Pp. [2], 108, [1].
Each small 4° leaf is pasted on a large 4° template. AO 3.257-8. 1st item, tp, A. Allam wrote, 'pret 1ˢ-4ᵈ We[st]: B[ibliopola (cropped at side)] April: decimo 8ᵛᵒ 16[cropped] Steph:'. LT 3.167.
Wood 528(3). STC 7278. Madan 451.

2346. Duck, Arthur. *De usu et authoritate juris civilis Romanorum, in dominiis principum christianorum, libri duo*. London: typ. R. Hodgkinsonne, 1653. 8°. Ff. [7], 181, [16]. Calf, mottled, with 3 fillets and a 2nd vertical line of 3 fillets.
Tp, bsms. Flyleaf, upper, note by a later librarian. Pasted to a sheet at bottom edge, a slip identifying the author and work (see Wood 208 for a list of similar slips by a former owner). Acquired 23 Nov. 1666, 3ˢ4ᵈ, LT 2.93.
Wood 674. Wing D2427.

2347. [Duckworth, Richard]. *Tintinnalogia: or, the art of ringing*. London: W. G. f. F. Stedman or f. F. S., sold T. Archer, 1668 or 1671. 8°. Pp. [8], 136.
Missing in 1837. Prob. a gift of John Aubrey, see MS. Wood F. 39, f. 131, Aubrey gave a 'ringing book' to AW.
Wood 729(4). Wing 1304B (two) or T1304C (rare, *O*).

2348. Dudley, Gamaliel. *A true copie of colonel sʳ Gamaliel Dudley's letter to . . . prince Rupert, from Newark, 4. March. 1644. . . . of sʳ Marm. Langdales march northward*. Oxford: L. Lichfield, 1644[5]. 4°.
Pp. [2], 6.
Dupl. at Wood 632(14).
Wood 377(38). Wing D2439. Madan 1736.

2349. Dudley, Gamaliel. *A true copie of colonel sʳ Gamaliel Dudley's letter to . . . prince Rupert, from Newark, 4. March. 1644. . . . of sʳ Marm. Langdales march northward*. Oxford: L. Lichfield, 1644[5]. 4°.
Pp. [2], 6.
Tp, AW wrote in pencil, 'Dupl'. Dupl. at Wood 377(38).
Wood 632(14). Wing D2439. Madan 1736.

2350. Dudley, Jane, lady. *The life, death and actions of . . . lady Jane Gray, . . . Containing foure . . . discourses written with her owne hands*. London: G. Eld f. J. Wright, 1615. 4°. A-C⁴.
Wood 532(11). STC 7281.

2351. Dudley, Robert*. Leicester, earl of. *In adventum illustrissimi Lecestrensis comitis ad collegium Lincolniense. Carmen gratulatorium.* Oxoniae: J. Barnes, 1585, tertio Idus Jan. [11 Jan.]. S.sh. 4°.
Wood 516(2). STC 7286 (rare). Madan 58.

2352. Dudly, Richard. *A narrative of the life, . . . of Richard Dudly . . . with his speeches . . . at his execution.* London: n.pub., 1669. 4°. Pp. [2], 6.
Tp, AW wrote, 'Richard Dudly was executed at Tyborne 28. Aprill A°. d. 1669.' LT 2.155.
Wood 372(9). Wing N198 (two) ('O' not recorded in Wing).

2353. [Dugard, Samuel]. *The marriages of cousin germans, vindicated from the censures of unlawfull-nesse and inexpediency.* Oxford: H. Hall f. T. Bowman, 1673. 8°. Pp. [16], 116.
Dupl. at Wood 718.
Wood 843(8). Wing D2459. Madan 2973.

2354. [Dugard, Samuel]. *The marriages of cousin germans, vindicated from the censures of unlawfulnesse and inexpediency.* Oxford: H. Hall f. T. Bowman, 1673. 8°. Pp. [16], 116. Calf, mottled, with 2 fillets.
Flyleaf, upper, AW wrote '. . . Dugard of Trin. Coll. Ox. the author.', and later, 'Sam. Dugard A.m. coll. Trin. 1667', 'Hen. Dugard A.B. Coll. Trin 1667'. Dupl. at Wood 843(8).
Wood 718. Wing D2459. Madan 2973.

2355. Dugard, William. *Rhetorices elementa.* ?: ?, 1648ff. 8°. 9 eds. before 1680.
Missing. MS. Wood E. 2(70), p. 16. Ed. not identified.
MS. Wood E. 2(70), p. 16. Wing 2468-2470C.

2356. Dugdale, Gilbert. *The time triumphant, declaring in briefe, the ariual of . . . king James into England.* London: R. B[lower], 1604. 4°. A-B⁴.
Wood 537(4). STC 7292.

2357. Dugdale, Gilbert. *A true discourse of the practices of Elizabeth Caldwell . . . on the parson of ma: [sic] Thomas Caldwell.* London: J. Roberts f. J. Busbie, 1604. 4°. A2-4,B-D⁴ (dedication of R. Armin, at D4). Pasteboard (blue) with parchment spine (rebound E.E.W. 7.5.45).
Flyleaf, 2nd^{r-v}, AW wrote the titles of 35 printed works in this vol., within guidelines made with red ink. Tp, AW made a correction in the t, 'parson' to 'person'. All items in this vol. are numbered in Arabic nos. by AW and in Roman numerals by an Ashm. librarian. Repairs to several tpp were done when they were bound (e.g., Wood 365(2), 365(9)).
Wood 365(1). STC 7293.

2358. Dugdale, John. *A catalogue of the nobility of England, according to their respective precedencies . . . 1684.* London: f. R. Clavell, 1685. S.sh.
Col. 1, a line in margin at Charles Beauclair. LT 3.107.
Wood 276a(81) (now at (92b)). Wing D2471.

2359. Dugdale, Stephen. *The further information of Stephen Dugdale, gent. delivered at the bar of the house of commons [30 Oct.].* London: f. T. Parkhurst, a. T. Simmons, 1680. Fol. Pp. [2], 20, [1].
P. 19, at 'Names in the Plot', AW wrote, 'These are in his former narration'; p. [21], lines in margin at explanation of misplaced time sequence in the testimony.
Wood 426(27). Wing D2474.

2360. Dugdale, Stephen. *The information of Stephen Dugdale, gent. delivered at the bar of the house of commons [1 Nov.].* London: by the assigns of J. Bill, T. Newcomb, and H. Hills, 1680. Fol. Pp. [3], 11.
Wood 426(21) (not in Bodl. CD cat.). Wing D2475.

2361. [Dugdale, William]. *His majesties answers to certain papers, delivered . . . at Uxbridge, upon the close of the treaty: one concerning the militia, and two concerning Ireland [ca. 15 Apr. Pp.197ff. of A full relation of the late treaty for a peace at Uxbridge].* Oxford: L. Lichfield, 1645. 4°. Pp. [2], 199-200, 193-6.
Pasteboard (grey) with parchment backing.
An upper flyleaf, on which AW wrote the titles of item nos. 1-10, is missing. On the remaining 2 flyleaves, upper, AW wrote the titles of printed works in this vol., nos. 11-35, within guidelines made with red ink. Item no. 5, except for what is apparently sig. 1, is missing (see the entry, Ireland, Wood 509(5)); the Whiteside cat. does not record the t and has only: 'Vol: 6 of Matt^{es} relating to Ireland 35 Pamphlets 1645, 46, 47, 48'. At no. 26, 'Deest Jun^{ij} 1841 W. K[irtland]', but AW recorded the t on the upper flyleaf. Tp, AW wrote in margin, '1645'.
Wood 509(1). Wing D2480A. Madan 1766.

2362. Dugdale, William. *Monastici anglicani, volumen tertium et ultimum: additamenta quaedam in volumen primum, ac volumen secundum, jampridem edita: necnon fundationes, . . . diversarum ecclesiarum cathedralium ac collegiarum*. [London]: excud. T. Newcomb, prostant venales A. Roper, J. Martin, & H. Herringman, 1673. Fol. Pp. [6], 392, [2], 218. Calf with 3 fillets, 2nd rectangle with stamp decoration inside fillets and outside at corners (Ashm. binding).
Pp. 13, note and correction; 63, brief note, may not be in AW's hand; some pencil marks, in a later hand (e.g., 9 (and a slip with notes not in AW's hand), 89, 257); 96, note in Latin, prob. in AW's hand; 277, cross-reference; 280, lines in margin; 2nd 189, cross-reference. Received from Dugdale, 1 May 1673, LT 2.262.
Wood 420 (not in Bodl. CD cat.). Wing D2486B.

2363. Dugdale, William. *The baronage of England, or an historical account of the lives and most memorable actions of our English nobility*. London: T. Newcomb, f. A. Roper, J. Martin, a. H. Herringman, 1675. Fol. Vol. 1, pp. [12], 790, [2] (plus unnumbered leaves of genealogies inserted after pp. 268, 324, 334, 348, 372). Calf with 3 fillets, 2nd rectangle with stamp decoration inside fillets and outside at corners; rebacked (Ashm. binding with some cropping of AW's notes).
Flyleaf, upper^v, AW wrote, 'Antonij à Wood Oxōn. Ex dono authoris 3° Junij an. 1675'. Notes by a later librarian, 'MS. notes at p. 523 paper [/] 666 paper [/] 733' (the 1st 2 notes on 'paper' survive, in AW's hand, see below; there is no 'paper' or note at 733, which may be a mistake for 773, see below). Preface, p. [5], AW wrote at top, 'A preface is never printed in columes [sic], as this.'; at R. Glover's ms. record of families, 'with great exactness being performed', AW underscored great exactness and wrote, 'But with [a] great man[y] faults, as [it] appears by [the] printed copies [of] that book in bib. [Bodleian] corrected with Camdens owne hand' (cropped at margin); at printed 'Augustine Vincent, at that time Windsore Herald', AW underscored 'at that time' and wrote 'He was not Windsore Herald till 6. June 1621'; and at what progress Vincent made, AW underscored the printed 'I never yet saw' and wrote, 'You might have perused them at your pleasure, had you accepted of the invitation of Ralp [sic] Sheldon Esquire, in whose hands they were then & still are.' P. [6], notes on collections of mss. of Lord Hatton and of pipe-rolls made by Roger Dodsworth: Hatton, 'After his death Mr Dudgale got all the historicall MSS, larger books & others of worth for S^r Jo. Cottons Library. The rest wee bought of a Bookseller for the Bodleian.', and Dodsworth: 'Most, if not all wee have in the Bodleian libr.'
P. [12], AW, apparently, pasted a more recent errata list, 'A Review of the Errata' over an earlier errata list , 'The Most Material Mistakes . . . ', and over early notes he had made. In the text itself, AW entered most of the corrections (over 100) that are listed in the errata list (at least one, p. 666, seems to come from the earlier list), and below the pasted over errata list he wrote, 'Mistakes which the author hath made in the Errata.', some 14, many with forceful comments (where he has not found the error, he wrote 'qu[aere]'), and below these, 'The author needed not to have troubled the Reader to count 73 lines from the top of the page for a fault, but. 5. or 6. sometimes less from the bottome' (a good suggestion). There are few marks in margins and a few notes in the text. Between pp. 2-3, a loose slip with notes, not in AW's hand. Corrections or lines in margins, not made from the errata list, are on, e.g., pp. 171, 188-9, 257, 268 (foldout, with notes, e.g., 'Will Percy buried in ch. church cath[edral] Oxon. 28. May 1648. he died without issue'). Between pp. 442-3, a bound slip with notes not in AW's hand. P. 460, a correction. Between pp. 522-3, blank leaf, with extensive notes^{r-v} by AW, from 'Mr Sheldon's book nu. 51. p. 20.', on the Balliol family (or Baylol). P. 657, AW wrote a long note about a servant of Emanuel, Earl of Sunderland, Martha Jeanes, who had, by him, a child who became a gent. commoner of Trinity College (see LT 1.146-7; 2.498, AO 3.1000). She was sister to Nathaniel Jeanes, butler of Merton College to whom AW paid his battels, see LT 5.322. Between pp. 666-7, blank leaf, with AW's notes on 'John Lord Strange[,] Hillyngdon church in Middlesex[.] In the Chancell[.] A faire raised antient monument' etc. with the epitaph. P. 715, a reference mark at Richard, son of Edmund Grey of Wilton, and AW's note, 'In Eaton Coll. Chap. by Wyndsore I find this Epitaph. Here Lyeth buryed Richard Grey Lord Grey of Cotenore, Wylton & Ruthyn . . . ' (and 53 more words). Between or on pp. 732-3, there is no note (see above). P. 773, note, cropped, 'Hugh de Samford of Samford or Sa[nd]ford in Oxfordsh. about 2 miles S from Oxon.' (cropped). P. [792], AW added in the index, 'Walerie omitted v. p. 454'. LT 2.316.
Wood 418 (not in Bodl. CD cat.). Wing D2480.

2364. Dugdale, William. *The baronage of England, . . . Tome the Second*. London: T. Newcomb, f. A. Roper, J. Martin, a. H. Herringman, 1676. Fol. Vol. 2, pp. [8], 488, [3].
Missing. AW's note in Wood 419, the volume received from R. Sheldon, mentioned a 2nd copy: 'June 10, following I received another copie from the Authour, Corrected & amended in many places with his owne hand, for which I return'd him thanks June 11' (this 2nd copy is not among AW's books. See LT 2.345).
LT 2.345. Wing D2480.

2365. Dugdale, William. *The baronage of England, . . . Tome the Second*. London: T. Newcomb, f. A. Roper, J. Martin, a. H. Herringman, 1676. Fol. Vol. 2, pp. [8], 488, [3]. Calf with 3 fillets, 2nd rectangle with stamp decoration inside fillets and outside at corners; rebacked (Ashm. binding, and some cropping of AW's notes).

Flyleaf, upper, 2nd[v], 'Pret 13[s] - 6[d]–', prob. not in AW's hand; 'Antonij à Wood, Oxon ex dono Radulphi Sheldon de Beolij in agro Wigorn. Arm. 8. Maij an. dom. 1676.'; 'June 10, following I received another copie from the Authour, Corrected & amended in many places with his owne hand, for which I return'd him thanks June 11' (Dugdale send this latter copy, now missing, in appreciation of AW's earlier assistance, which was substantial; AW stated in AOF 2.26 that he send Dugdale '16 sheets of corrections, but more of additions. . . . He [Dugdale] remitted a good part of them into the margin of a copy of large paper of his three tomes of *Baronagium*.'); and, in a later hand, 'MS. notes p. 482-3 [/] 478-9 [/] 459 [/] 59 [/] 80 paper (wrong place) [/] 462 with paper'. Actually AW made scores of notes, e.g., he corrected all errors in the 'Errata', listed on p. [8] (76 in all), and added below, 'Faults in the Errata' (he wrote 3). Notes, beyond the correction of errata, are more and more frequent after p. 363. See, e.g. (not an exhaustive list), pp. 80 (identification, whatever paper was here has been removed), 182 (on Leycester, cropped), 225 (a 16-line note on Robert Dudley and on Dugdale's source: 'hist. et Antiq. Univers. Oxon. lib. 2. p. 275. but tis not well translated'), 279 (on Arabella Smith, cropped), 363 (correction to Will. Peter), 367, 369, 390 (Philip Wharton: 'cowardlie rebell' and corrections), 391-4, 399, 407, 414-6 (Edward Wotton and a reference to a source with more detail, Lewis Owens ([MS.] Wood D. 24(6)); and a slip with a brief note on John Lord Harrington and his son, John), 418-9, 422-3, 425 (3 loose slips, 2 with notes on different Robert Carrs and 1 on Edmund Waller), 426 (loose slip with notes on Lewis Lord Aubigny), 428-9, 431 (slip with notes on *Foot out of the Snare* by J. Gee (Wood 648(1)) and a 'Scottish-man' debater Dr. Eggleston), 432 (on S[r] John Danvers et. al. with 2 slips with notes on the Purbeck family), 433-5, (433, on Denzil Holles at the printed 'instrumental in the happy Restauration', AW wrote, 'After he and the restless Presbyterians had brought all things into confusion', and on the Chesterfield and Campden families), 437-8, 451-3, 460 (a pasted slip with notes on Richard Weston), 462 (on Campden, and a pasted-in sheet with notes on the family and Campden church in Glouc.), 463-70, etc. to end.

See esp. 482-3, on Lord Crew of Stene, 'A presbyterian, Independent & I know not what. One of the other House, or House of Lords to Oliver.'; he underscored the comment of Crew's 'loyally contributing his best endeavors to the restoration' and wrote, 'When he saw to what ruin he & the restless Presbyterians had brought the nation to, then he forthsooth did endeavour &c', and at Nathaniel, Bishop of Durham, AW wrote a frank evaluation, which someone later lined out, 'One that hath sided with the times. A formall starcht nothing, another M[r] Smirk', and notes on Benet, Earl of Arlington, e.g., at 'descended from worthy Ancestors' he wrote, 'How do you prove that? he can scarce lay claime to a coat of armes that was granted either to Gr.father or father. . . . The reason why he would not be called Lord Bennet was (as is conceived) because a famous Bawd called the Lady Bennet (a Bakers widow) then lived in St Margarets Lane in Westminster.', and a slip with a brief note; 484 at Barbara, Duchess of Cleveland, concerning her 'personal virtures', AW underscored this phrase and wrote, 'For making her husband (Roger E of Castlemain) a cuckold'; 486 at Lovisa Dutchess of Portsmouth, at printed, 'Of such Honourable Women, whom His Majesty hath deservedly raised . . . ', AW underscored 'Honourable' and 'deserved' and wrote, 'Qu[aere] what was in her that deserved this honor', and made a correction, 'died about the last of May 1646 at the Bath. false'; and, 486 at Lee Earl of Litchfield, who was advanced as an 'encouragement' to others in virtuous endeavors, AW underscored 'encouragement' and wrote, 'Made an Earle because he has newly married a daug. [Charlotte Villiers] of Barbara Duchess of Cleveland by . . . [blank]'. See LT 2.7, 2.345, and AW's suggestions for a 2nd ed., now MS. Wood D. 20 (LT 2.434).
Wood 419 (not in Bodl. CD cat.). Wing D2480.

2366. Dugdale, William. *The antient usage in bearing of such ensigns of honour as are commonly call'd arms. With a catalogue of the present nobility*. Oxford: at the theater, f. M. Pitt, London, 1682. 8°. Pp. [9], 210 (pp. 194-210 books printed at the theater).
1st blank, 'Given to me by Moses Pit Bookseller 4. Feb. 1681[2]. being then finished at the press.' (for Pitt, see LT 5.161). P. 162, AW made a correction from errata list. Blank leaf before p. 149, 'The collection following was made by Charls Hatton Esq' (list of shires, knights, and members of Parliament).
Wood 445(11). Wing D2477A.

2367. Dugres, Gabriel. *Jean Arman du Plessis, duke of Richelieu, . . . his life*. London: T. Fawcet, f. the author, 1643. 8°. Pp. [2], 70.
Tp, after author, AW wrote, 'vide p. 5' (for biographical information about the author). Bsm.
Wood 307(2). Wing D2495 (3).

2368. [**Duke, Richard**]. *A panegyrick upon Oates.* [London]: n.pub., [1679]. S.sh. (r-v).
^v, AW wrote the date, 'August 1679'. LT 2.457.
Wood 425(21). Wing D2505C.

2369. [**Duke, Richard**]. *Funeral tears upon the death of captain William Bedloe.* [London]: n.pub., [1680].
S.sh.
AW wrote the date, 'Aug. 1680'.
Wood 426(15). Wing D2505A.

2370. [**Duncon, John**]. *The returnes of spiritual comfort and grief in a devout soul. Represented (by
entercourse of letters) to . . . Lady Letice, vicountess Falkland.* London: f. R. Royston, 1648. 12°. Pp. [23],
202, [1].
Missing in 1837. MS. Wood E. 2(70), p. 56, 'Lettice Morison vic. Falkland her works which may be brought
in Lucius Ld. Falkland - v. pedigree Falkland Cary'. See also AO 2.570, LT 3.205.
Wood 790. Wing D2605. *O, Hunt, Clark, Folg.*

2371. Dunton, John. *A true journall of the Sally fleet.* London: J. Dawson f. T. Nicholes, 1637. 4°. Pp.
[map], [4], 26, [17].
Flyleaf, upper, Latin tag, not by AW, but by some later scribbler (blotting on opposite leaf). Tp, 'November
3, 1637. pr. 6^d.', not by AW.
Wood 387(6) (not in Bodl. CD cat.). STC 7357.

2372. [**Dunton, John**]. Kainophilus, pseud. *A voyage round the world.* London: f. R. Newcome, [1691].
8°. Pp. [28], 158.
Tp, '1^s-' in pencil (cropped).
Wood 155(6). Wing D2634A.

2373. [**Duppa, Brian**]. *Two prayers; one for the safety of his majesties person; the other for the preservation of this university and city of Oxford.* Oxford: L. Lichfield, 1644. 4°. Pp. [2], 6.
Tp, note, in Brian Twyne's hand (though Clark, LT 1.107, suggests G. Langbaine's, Ian Philip inserted a
note in the Duke Humfrey's copy of Madan (in Selden End), at no. 1648, in which he identified the hand
as Twyne's): 'This was when the Army of the Earle of Essex and the parlament forces came marching
to Oxford over Sanford ferry, & so to Cowley, & Cowley greene & Bullington greene on the East side of
Oxford. Wednesdaye, May 29. 1644'. For Twyne's hand, see also Wood 514(8), item 2250.
Wood 514(14). Wing D2667. Madan 1648.

2374. [**Duppa, Brian**]. *Private formes of prayer fit for these sad times.* Oxford: L. Lichfield, 1645. 4°.
Pp. [2], 69.
Flyleaf, upper^v, 'By Duppa', not in AW's hand.
Wood 377(43). Wing D2665. Madan 1818.

2375. Duppa, Brian. *The soules soliloquie: and, a conference with conscience. . . . a sermon.* [London]:
f. R. Royston, 1648. 4°. Pp. [2], 21.
Tp, AW underscored the name of the author, in red ink.
Wood 633(11). Wing D2666aA.

2376. D'Urfey, Thomas. *Several new songs. . . . Set to as many new tunes, by the best masters in music.*
London: J. Playford f. J. Hindmarsh, 1684. Fol. Pp. [2], 20.
Wood 657(1c). Wing D2776.

2377. D'Urfey, Thomas. *A third collection of new songs, . . . set to music by the best masters.* London:
J. P. f. J. Hindmarsh, 1685. Fol. Pp. [2], 28.
Wood 657(1b). Wing D2788.

2378. Durham, Letter. *The humble advice, and tender declaration . . . in . . . Durham, Northumberland
. . . to the lord general Monk.* London: H. Hills, [1659]. S.sh.
AW added the date, 'Octob: M DC Lix'.
Wood 276a(332-3). Wing H3393.

2379. D[urham], W[illiam]. *The life and death of . . . Robert Harris.* London: f. S. B., sold J. Bartlet,
1660. 8°. Pp. [7], 119.
P. [1], 'Ant: Woode: A: D: MDCLX' (Acquired 14 Apr., LT 1.310). Tp, AW wrote 'Writt by Will: Durham
minister of Tredington com̄: Wigorn:', bsm. A3^v, 'E. Reyn' expanded to 'Ed: Reynolds'. P. 1, at place of
Harris's birth, 'When? qu[aere] whether not an 1578.' P. 3, at matriculation at Magdalen Hall, 'when?

qu[aere] whether not 1592 or therabouts'. P. 4, at the Puritan Mr. Goffe not appointed as Harris's tutor because 'the Principal [Robert Lister] (being Popish)' didn't want Goffe, AW wrote: 'what do you meane by that word! he was no Papist I am sure but an Orthodox Protestant. But your meaning is, he was no Puritan.'; to end, explanatory or corrective notes and dates, e.g. p. 8, Wood gives 'an. 1604' as the year of a fearful plague in Oxford; p. 37, 'Pegasus' in margin as a source for an exposé of Harris's revenues (AW owned three printed works on the subject, Wood 514(49-51); p. 62, at another vague reference, AW added the specific time, 'At night'. LT 1.265; AO 1.lxvi and 3.458-60.
Wood 292(6). Wing D2831.

2380. Dury, John. *The reformed librarie-keeper*. London: W. Du-Gard, 1650. 12°.
Missing. In a cat., [MS.] Wood E. 13(5), at an entry of 'The Reformed Library Keeper' AW wrote 'habeo'.
[MS.] Wood E. 13(5). Wing D2882.

2381. Dury, John. Hartlib, Samuel, ed. *The unchanged, constant and single-hearted peace-maker drawn forth into the world. Or, a vindication of mr. John Dury from . . . The time-serving Proteus [by W. Prynne]*.
London: J. Clowes f. R. Wodenothe, 1650. 4°. Pp. [6], 18.
Pp. 3-4, line in margin; 9, 'White' in margin, prob. by AW.
Wood 619(10). Wing D2894.

2382. Dying Speeches. *The dying speeches of several . . . who suffered for their zeal against popery*.
London: n.pub., 1689. 4°. Pp. [4], 35.
Tp, AW wrote, 'bought at Oxon 9. Jan. 1688[9]. 6ᵈ'. LT 3.294.
Wood 368(29). Wing D2957.

2383. Dyve, Lewis. *A letter . . . giveing . . . an account of the whole conduct of the kings affaires in Irland, . . . Septem. 1648. Until . . . June 1650. Together with . . . letters*. Hague: S. Broun, 1650. 4°. Pp. 56, 23.
Tp, bsm.
Wood 510(16). Wing D2979.

2384. E., C. *A letter to the lord general Monck in answer to his excellencies letter unto . . . Devon*.
[London]: n.pub., [1660]. S.sh.
AW added 'Jan: 1659:'.
Wood 276a(242). Wing E6 (3).

2385. E., C. *Strange and wonderful news from Durham. Or the virgins caveat against infant-murther, . . . sent by C. E. to his friend in London*. London: n.pub, 1679. 4°. Pp. [2], 5.
Wood 365(30). Wing E6A (rare) (Wing, Durham, or,).

2386. E., J. *A letter from a souldier of good place in Ireland, . . . touching the notable victorie . . . against the Spaniards, . . . and of the yeelding up of Kynsale*. London: [T. Creede?] f. S. Waterson, 1602. 4°. Pp. [2], 25.
Dupl. at Wood 616(16).
Wood 504(4). STC 7434.

2387. E., J. *A letter from a souldier of good place in Ireland, . . . touching the notable victorie . . . against the Spaniards, . . . and of the yeelding up of Kynsale*. London: [T. Creede?] f. S. Waterson, 1602. 4°. Pp. [2], 25.
Tp, AW wrote 'dupl', in pencil. Dupl. at Wood 504(4).
Wood 616(16). STC 7434.

2388. [Eachard, John]. *The grounds & occasions of the contempt of the clergy and religion enquired into, in a letter . . . to R. L. [signed T. B.]*. London: W. Godbid f. N. Brooke, 1670. 8°. Pp. [6], 131, [5] (5 pp. books sold by Brooke). Pasteboard (blue) with parchment spine. 1st upper (now pasted down under the cover) and last lower flyleaves, marbled paper; rebacked.
AW wrote the titles of 6 printed works in this vol., within guidelines made with red ink. 1st item: flyleaf, upper, AW wrote 'Tho. Hobbes of Malmsbury wrot two letters to John Echard concerning the contempt of the clergy which are printed with some other works of his that were published in 8°'; ᵛ, name of Wood, not in his hand. Tp, AW wrote 'Joh. Echard of Catherine in Cambridge, the author.' and '10ᵈ'. LT 2.240, 242.
Wood 884(1). Wing E50.

2389. [Eachard, John]. *Some observations upon the answer [signed W. S.] to . . . grounds . . . of the*

contempt of the clergy:. . . in a second letter [signed T. B.]. London: f. N. Brooke, 1671. 8°. Pp. [12], 200.
Tp, AW wrote '1^s-4^d'; bsm, 1.4.
Wood 884(3). Wing E60.

2390. Eachard, John. *A vindication of the clergy, from the contempt imposed upon them by the author [J. Eachard] of the grounds . . . of the contempt.* London: A. Clark f. H. Brome, 1672. 8°. Pp. [16], 135.
Tp, AW wrote '10^d.' On a small slip, unattached, AW wrote, on both sides, '3 bookes concerning the contempt of the clergy' (Wood 884(1-6) all concern this topic). Diff. ed. at Wood 884(4).
Wood 843(5). Wing E65.

2391. Eachard, John*. Bramhall, John, not by. *An answer to two letters of T. B. [The grounds . . . of the contempt of the clergy, and some observations upon the answer to it] by the author of the vindication of the clergy.* London: f. H. Brome, 1673. 8°. Pp. [8], 63, [1].
Tp, at T. B., 'i e John Eachard', in pencil, not by AW.
Wood 884(5). Wing A3457aA.

2392. [Eachard, John]. *A free and impartial inquiry into the causes of that . . . esteem . . . that the nonconforming preachers are generally in with their followers.* London: J. M. f. R. Royston, 1673. 12°. Pp. 204. Calf with 2 fillets.
P. 1, signature of owner, Rich. Banckes and price 0-1^s-0. Flyleaf, lower, 1st, 'Luke warmnes. p. 163', in pencil, may not be by AW.
Wood 816. Wing E49B.

2393. Eachard, John. *A vindication of the clergy, from the contempt imposed upon them by the author [J. Eachard] of the grounds . . . of the contempt.* London: f. C. Brome, 1686. 8°. T leaf is a cancel. Pp. [16], 135.
Tp, AW wrote 'First edit. of this came out in 1672. Oct. at Lond.', i.e., Wood 843(5).
Wood 884(4). Wing E66 (rare).

2394. [Earle, John]. Salisbury, bp. of. Blount, Edward, ed. *Micro-cosmographie. Or, a piece of the world characteriz'd; in essayes and characters.* London: W. Bentley f. W. Shears, 1650. 12°. Pp. [10], 105. Pasteboard (blue) with parchment spine. 1st upper and last lower flyleaves, blue paper.
Flyleaf, upper, 3rd^v, AW wrote the titles of 5 printed works in this vol., within guidelines made with red ink. Tp, AW wrote 'Jo. Earle the author afterwards Bishop of Sarum' (1663-5).
Wood 739(1). Wing E89.

2395. East India Company. *A true relation of the unjust, cruell, and barbarous proceedings against the English at Amboyna.* London: G. Purslowe [a. T. Cotes] f. N. Newberry, 1632 (2nd tp.,1624). 4°. 3rd impress. Pp. [11], 38, [2], 20, [2], 34, [1].
Wood 387(13). STC 7453.

2396. East India Company. *A remonstrance of the directors of the Netherlands East India company . . . With the acts of the processe, against the sayd English.* London: J. Dawson, f. the East India Co., 1632. 4°. 3 pts. Pp. [8], 29, [2], 38, 6, 47 (some pp. out of order).
Wood 387(14). STC 7450a.

2397. Edinburgh, Letter. *A letter from a person of quality in Edenburgh . . . a true accompt of generall Moncke [25 Oct.].* London: S. Griffin, f. T. Hewer, [1659]. S.sh.
Wood 276a(331). Wing L1423 (3) ('O' not recorded in Wing).

2398. Edinburgh, Letter. *A letter from several ministers in and about Edinburgh, to the ministers of London, concerning the re-establishing of the covenant [11 March].* London: f. R. Hills, 1659[60]. 4°. Rpt. of Edinburgh: f. C. Higgins edition. Pp. 8.
Tp, AW added to the year 'March:'.
Wood 632(31). Wing L1505.

2399. Edward 2*, and Richard 2*. *A true relation of the manner of the deposing of king Edward II. . . . As also, an exact account of the proceedings . . . against king Richard II.* London: R. Baldwin, 1689. 4°. Pp. [2], 36.
Tp, AW wrote, 'Jan. 27 - an.1688[9] - 6^d - published after . . . ' (cropped at bottom). P. 17, pencil line in margin.
Wood 486(5). Wing T3002 ('O' not recorded in Wing).

2400. Edwards, George. *Reverendis et eruditis viris in theologia, medicina, et jure civili doctoribus,* *academiae Oxoniensis.* [Oxford, probably]: [George Edwards], [1674]. S.sh., 12 of various fol. sizes (engr.). P. 1, AW wrote the year, '1674', and '2ˢ.6ᵈ.' LT 2.301-2. Wood 276b(19). Wing E196. Madan 2997.

2401. Edwards, [Richard]. *The paradyse of daynty devises.* London: [R. Jones f.?] H. Disle, 1578. 4°. F. [3], 50 (really 41. After f. 25, nos. erratic); A-I⁴,K²,L⁴,M² (wanting K3-4).
Flyleaf, upper, AW wrote 'Rich Edwards In his paradise of dainty devises, are these authours following that have verses' and 24 authors with f. references, in red and brown ink. Tp, 'published by H. D. ie Hen. Disle (de insula) the printer –', in red ink. Bsm. Passim, notes, mainly in red ink (some cropped by the binding), not in AW's hand; some underscoring in yellow and green ink; and poem numbers corrected, after no. 34, in pencil, not in AW's hand (similar hand in Wood 482(7)).
Wood 482(6). STC 7517 (3).

2402. Edwards, Thomas. *Gangraena: or a catalogue and discovery of many of the errours, . . . of the sectaries of this time.* London: f. R. Smith, 1646. 4°. 2nd ed. Pp. [24], 124 (i.e., 224, misnumbering; wanting pp. 77-80). Pasteboard (grey) with parchment spine; flyleaf, lower, traces of marbled paper; rebacked.
Flyleaf, upperᵛ, AW wrote the titles of 4 printed works in this vol., within guidelines made with red ink. Tp, bsm. Pp. 72, 75, vertical lines in margin, at places and names, in pencil and ink.
Wood 655(1). Wing E229.

2403. Edwards, Thomas. *The second part of gangraena: or a fresh and further discovery of the errors, . . . of the sectaries of this time.* London: T. R. a. E. M. f. R. Smith, 1646. 4°. Pp. [4], 212.
Tp, scribble or bsm. P. 21, line in margin, in pencil, at Master Erbury. See LT 1.130; 3.36; AO 3.360ff.; see reference to Edwards in notes at T. Oates, Wood 424(13), item 4788.
Wood 655(3). Wing E235.

2404. Edwards, Thomas. *The third part of gangraena. Or, a new and higher discovery of the errors, heresies, . . . of the sectaries of these times.* London: f. R. Smith, 1646. 4°. Pp. [35], 295, [1] (some misnumbering).
Tp, bsm.
Wood 655(4). Wing E237.

2405. Egerton, Thomas. Brackley, visct. *The speech of the lord chancellor of England, . . . touching the post-nati.* London: [A. Islip] f. Soc. of Stationers, 1609. 4°. Pp. [12], 118, [2].
Tp, AW wrote 'Tho. Egerton Baron of Ellensmere L. Chanc'. Bsm.
[MS.] Wood B. 39(6). STC 7540.5.

2406. Eglisham, George. *The fore-runner of revenge being two petitions: the one to the kings . . . majesty: the other, to . . . parliament, wherein is expressed divers actions of the late earle of Buckingham. [Tr. of Prodromus vindictae].* London: n.pub., 1642. 4°. Pp. [2], 23.
Tp, 'D51', shelf-mark in another collection; 'No: 2ᵈ', and '1642', prob. none by AW.
Wood 614(51). Wing E256bA.

2407. Ehrensten, Edvard, and D. Mevius. *An answer to two Danish papers: the one called jus feciale armatae Daniae [of Frederick 3]; the other, a manifest, . . . translated out of the Latine [variously attr. to E. Ehrensten and D. Mevius].* London: f. D. Pakeman, 1658. 4°. Pp. [2], 60.
Tp, no. '4' in a former bundle.
Wood 615(13). Wing A3456A ('O' not recorded in Wing).

2408. Eighteen New Court-Queries. *Eighteen new court-quaeries, by several well-wishers to our settlement.* London: n.pub., 1659. 4°. Pp. [2], 6.
Tp, no. '38', in pencil, in a former bundle.
Wood 613(45). Wing E263.

2409. Eikon. Εικων η πιστη. *Or, The faithfull pourtraicture of a loyall subject, in vindication of* Εικων Βασιλικη *[by J. Gauden] . . . in answer to an insolent book, intituled* Εικων Αληθινη. [London]: n.pub., 1649. 4°. Pp. [6], 96.
Tp, brief note, cropped at top and side, not in AW's hand.
Wood 492(2). Wing E314 ('O' not recorded in Wing). FFMadan 158.

2410. Eikon Basilike. *The pourtracture of his sacred majestie in his solitudes.* [London]: reprinted in R. M., 1648[49]. 12°. Rprt. Pp. [6], 187. Calf with 2 fillets.
Wood 270. Wing E276. FFMadan 13.

2411. Eikon Basilike. Εικων βασιλικη δευτερα. *The pourtraicture of his sacred majesty king Charles II. Found in the strong box.* [London]: published by King James, 1694. 8°. Pp. [1], xvi, 320. Pasteboard (brown) with calf spine.
Wood 237. Wing E312 ('O' not recorded in Wing). FFMadan 132.

2412. El., M. *A list of the names of the members of the house of commons:. . . together with . . . money, . . . as they have given to themselves [1st century].* [London]: n.pub., 1648. 4°. Pp. 8.
Tp, AW wrote 'Mostly if not all taken from the History of Independency – by G. Wharton.' (AW owned the *History* by C. Walker, Wood 617(18), item 6392), and '2ᵈ'. Pp. 2, 6, mark in margin at Edmond Prideaux and Richard Ingoldsby. P. 8, note, not by AW, 'The author of this was sayd to be Wharton the figure-flinger. The 2ᵈ Century came out in a sheet on one side.' (i.e., Wood 620(10); see also AO 4.7-8).
Wood 620(8). Wing E317B.

2413. El., M. *The second centurie [A list of the names of the members of the house of commons . . .].* [London]: n.pub., [1648?]. S.Sh.
Short lines at 3 names. ᵛ, not by AW, 'The 2ᵈ. Centurie of Parliament men with the number and names of the places of trust, and profitt the[y] have gott into by this rebellion'. See 1st century at Wood 620(8).
Wood 620(10). Wing E317C.

2414. Elder, John. *The copie of a letter sent in to Scotlande, of the arivall and . . . marryage of . . . Philippe, . . . to Marye.* (London): (J. Waylande), [1555]. 8°. A-F⁸.
Missing. MS. Wood E. 2(70), p. 41.
MS. Wood E. 2(70), p. 41. STC 7552. *O, Folg, Hunt.*

2415. Elderton, William. *A new merry newes, as merry as can bee, from Italy, Barbary, Turkie and Candee.* London: ?, 1631. 8°.
Missing in 1837. 'News from Italy Barbary &c. – Lond. 1631' in Whiteside cat. The identification of the Whiteside entry as the Elderton book is only a guess. It would have been reprinted from the edition of 1606 (STC 7558 (rare)).
Wood 66(2). Not identified.

2416. Elford, Walter*. *Committee navie, July 2. 1649 . . . Tuesday the 27. of January, 1658.* [London]: n.pub., [1658]. S.sh. (r-v).
Wood 276a(180-181) (not in Bodl. CD cat.). Not in Wing. Not in ESTCR.

2417. Elford, Walter. *To the supreme authority of the nation, the parliament . . . the humble petition of Walter Elford [24 Aug. 1648].* [London]: n.pub., [1659]. S.sh. (r-v).
P. 1, at top, 'V[ide] Cases', at bottom, no. '19' in a former bundle; text, at 'Parliament', AW added 'pretended'.
Wood 276a(178-179). Wing E498B. ESTCR 174937 (rare).

2418. Eliot, John. *Sir John Eliot his grave and learned speech . . . in . . . parliament. Desiring an orderlie proceeding in matters of religion.* London: f. V. V., 1641. 4°. A⁴.
Tp, no. 10 in a former bundle and below, AW wrote, 'Sʳ Joh. Eliot a parl. man died about 1629'. Bsm.
Wood 614(24). Wing E501.

2419. Eliot, Robert*. *A strange and wonderfull discovery of a . . . murther . . . of Robert Eliot of London.* [London]: n.pub, 1662. 4°. Pp. 7.
P. 7ᵛ, subtraction, 99 minus 74 6 4 = 24 13:8, may not be by AW.
Wood 365(20). Wing S5845 (3) ('O' not recorded in Wing).

2420. Elizabeth 1. *By the quene. The quenes majestie understandynge [2 Nov. 1560].* London: R. [Jugge a. J. Cawood], [1560]. S.sh. (mutilated).
Wood 276a(122). STC 7920. Steele 533.

2421. Elizabeth 1. *Declaratio causarum, quibus adducta Angliae regina, Belgis . . . oppressis, copias quasdam auxiliares miserit.* Londini: C. Barkerus, 1585. 8°. Pp. [4], 33, [1].
Wood 580(3). STC 9190.

2422. Elizabeth 1. *Declaration des causes, qui ont esmeu la royne d'Angleterre, a donner secours pour la defence du peuple . . . es païs bas.* Londres: C. Barquer, 1585. 8°. Pp. [2], 28, 7, [1].
Wood 580(2). STC 9192 (STC, causes qui).

2423. Elizabeth 1. *A declaration of the causes mooving the queene of England to give aide to the defence*

of the . . . lowe countries. [Followed by] An addition. London: C. Barker, (1585). 4° (1st p. [1] mutilated). Pp. [4], 20, 5, [1].
Tp, '1585', may not be by AW; tp to end, pp. numbered, 167-194 (by a former owner; see also Wood 616(3), item 1660, where the nos. continue). Pp. 1, 8-9, 2nd 4-5, notes and/or underscoring, not by AW.
Wood 615(10). STC 9189.5.

2424. Elizabeth 1. *Dichiaratione delle caggioni che hanno mosso la . . . reina d'Inghilterra a dar'aiuto alla difesa del populo . . . negli paesi bassi.* Londra: C. Barcher, 1585. 8°. [2], 38. Parchment.
Tp, '6.$^{d.}$', and shelf-mark, '2 [/] R 22 C', and a Greek phrase, 'μακρα και μακρα', none by AW.
Wood 580(1). STC 9193.

2425. Elizabeth 1. *Een verclaringhe der oorsaken beweghende de coninghinne van Enghelandt, hulpe te gheven tot bescherminghe des . . . volckes der Nederlanden.* Londen: C. Barker, 1585. 8°. Pp. 30, 7, [1].
Wood 580(4). STC 9191.

2426. Elizabeth 1*. *The royall passage of her majesty from the Tower of London to her palace of White-hall.* London: S. S[tafford] for J. Millington, 1604. 4°. A-D⁴. Pasteboard (blue) with parchment spine; rebacked.
Flyleaf, upper, 2nd, AW wrote the titles of 20 printed works in this vol. (really 21 items; 2 at 14), within guidelines made with red ink. Tp, signature of Edw. Hoby and cipher (AO 2.194-5), and a motto, 'Uni soli & semper.'
Wood 537(1). STC 7592.

2427. Elizabeth 1*. *The life and death of queene Elizabeth.* London: J. Okes, 1639. 8°. A-C⁸. Pasteboard (brown) with calf spine. 1st upper and last lower flyleaves, marbled paper.
Flyleaf, upper, 2nd^v, AW wrote the titles of 5 printed works in this vol., within guidelines made with red ink.
Wood 258(1). STC 7587 (two).

2428. Elizabeth 1. *The golden speech of queen Elizabeth to her last parliament [30 Nov]1601.* London: T. Milbourn, [1659]. S.sh.
AW wrote below, 'Decemb: 1659'.
Wood 276a(112). Wing E528 (two).

2429. [Ellis, Clement]. *Piae juventuti sacrum. An elegie on the death of . . . George Pitt.* [Oxford]: [H. Hall], 1658. 4°. Pp. [8], 21.
Tp, AW wrote, 'Clem. Ellis [underlined in red ink] of Qu. Coll. author of this booke'.
Wood 319(6). Wing E567. Madan 2382.

2430. Ellis, Humphry. *Pseudochristus: or, a true and faithful relation of the grand impostures, . . . acted . . . by William Frankelin and Mary Gadbury.* London: J. Macock f. L. Fawn, 1650. 4°. Pp. 62, [1].
Wood 647(17a). Wing E579.

2431. Ellis, Tho[mas]. *An exact and full relation of the last fight, between the kings forces and sir William Waller.* London: f. B. Allen, 1644, 5 July. 4°. Pp. 8.
Dupl. at Wood 612(20).
Wood 377(15). Wing E605.

2432. Ellis, Tho[mas]. *An exact and full relation of the last fight, between the kings forces and sir William Waller.* London: f. B. Allen, 1644, 5 July. 4°. Pp. 8.
Tp, AW wrote 'Dup', in pencil. Dupl. at Wood 377(15).
Wood 612(20). Wing E605.

2433. Elphinstone, John. Balmerino, baron. *The lord Balmerino's speech in the high court of parliament in Scotland, . . . Concerning the levying of an army against the papists in Ireland [4 Nov.].* London: f. T. B., 1641. 4°. A⁴ (p. unopened).
Tp, AW wrote in margin, 'Scotland'.
Wood 507(7). Wing B607('O' not recorded in Wing).

2434. Ely, Isle of. *A letter from a gentleman of the isle of Ely . . . to colonel Roderick Mansel, containing . . . the first discovery of the pretended presbyterian plot [28 Nov.].* [London]: n.pub., [1679]. Fol. Pp. 4.
Wood 276a(163) (not in Bodl. CD cat.). Wing L1398.

2435. Elyot, Thomas. *The boke named the gouernour.* London: [T. Marsh], 1557. 8°. Ff. [8], 216. Calf with

2nd rectangle with 3 fillets and stamp centrepiece and decoration outside corners; ms. backing, rebacked. Pastedowns and flyleaves, printer's waste paper. Flyleaf, upper^v, signature of Thomas Tyron (?), twice, and Latin tags. Tp, Latin tag, scribbles, and signature, lined out; ^v, 20 lines of verse, in English, 'But as an olde booke sayeth whoso will assay . . . Blood will have blood, eyther first or last', by a former owner. Text, some brief marks and notes, in more than one hand, none in AW's hand; f. 216^v, 17 lines of verse, 'O god that guydes this golden globe'. Pastedown, lower, 6 lines of verse, 'Whoso in pompe of proud estate'. Wood 661. STC 7640.

2436. Elys, Edmund. *Dominus est Deus. Gloria aeterna . . . Jesu Christi vindicata, contra egregiam errorum farraginem, quae inscribitur catechesis ecclesiarum Polonicarum.* [Oxford?]: n.pub., 1690. 8°. Pp. [2], 13.
Tp, AW wrote 'Oxon.'
Wood 843(4). Wing E670 (rare) (Wing, vindicate).

2437. [Elys, Edmund]. *Ecclesiae Anglicanae filii collatio cum . . . J. S. de fidei Christianae certitudine; cui accesserunt epistola ad scholasticos Oxonienses.* Oxonii: typ. Lichfieldianis, 1690. 8°. Pp. [2], 30.
Wood 843(3). Wing E671A (rare).

2438. [Elys, Edmund]. *A vindication of the honour of king Charles I. against . . . Ludlow.* [London]: n.pub., 1691. 8°. Pp. [2], 14.
Flyleaf, upper, AW wrote 'Edm. Elys' and on tp, 'Edmund Elys the author'.
Wood 363(7). Wing E699 (rare).

2439. [Elys, Edmund]. *An earnest call . . . to beware of . . . the regicide Ludlow.* [London]: n.pub., 1692. 8°. Pp. [2], 20.
Tp, AW wrote, 'Edm. Elys the author'; p. no., '20 ll.', not in AW's hand.
Wood 363(12). Wing E671 (rare).

2440. [Elys, Edmund]. *The letter torn in pieces: or a full confutation of Ludlow's suggestions.* London: T. J., sold N. Hooper, 1692. 4°. Pp. 8.
Tp, AW wrote, 'Edm. Elys the author.' P. nos., '8 ll.', not in AW's hand.
Wood 363(13). Wing E679.

2441. [Elys, Edmund]. *Dei incarnati vindiciae. Contra varias . . . Fausti Socini blasphemias.* London: impen. S. Smith, 1693. 4°. Pp. [4], 26.
Tp, AW wrote, 'From Edm. Elys the author 24 Feb. 1692[3]'. LT 3.417.
[MS.] Wood D. 23(2). Wing E666.

2442. Elys, Edm[und]. *A letter to the author [S. Nye] of . . . Considerations on the explications of the . . . trinity [26 June].* [London]: n.pub., [1694]. 4°. Pp. 3.
P. 1, AW wrote, 'Apr. 1695'. P. 3^v, epitaph of Zachariah Mayne, Magd. (cropped), not in AW's hand. Dupl. at Wood 617(8).
[MS.] Wood D. 23(10). Wing E678 (rare, 2 at O).

2443. Elys, Edmund. *A letter to the author [S. Nye] of . . . Considerations on the explications of the . . . trinity [26 June].* [London]: n.pub., [1694]. 4°. Pp. 3.
Dupl. at [MS.] Wood D. 23(10).
Wood 617(8). Wing E678 (rare, 2 at O).

2444. Elys, Edmund. *Animadversions upon a late discourse concerning the divinity, and death of Christ.* [London]: n.pub., [1695]. 4°. Pp. 4, 8.
P. 1, AW wrote, 'Apr. 1695'.
[MS.] Wood D. 23(11). Wing E662.

2445. England 1688A. *A collection of papers relating to the present juncture of affairs in England [15 papers].* [London]: n.pub., 1688. 4°. Pp. [2], 34. Pasteboard (blue) with parchment spine. 1st upper and last lower flyleaves, marbled paper.
Flyleaf, upper, 3rd^v, AW wrote the titles of 7 printed works in this vol., within guidelines made with red ink (really 19 in all, for as he noted in his 1st entry, there are '12 of these collections'; he omitted the last item, no. 19). 1st item: tp, a printed list of 15 papers, after 2 of these, no. 13, 'Princes Ann's Letter to the Queen' and no. 15, 'Prince of Orange his Declaration of Novem. 28. 1688. from Sherborn-Castle', he wrote 'I have it by its self' (at Wood 529(8), item 245; Wood 529(5), item 5992, has annotation similar to that found below in this item, at p. 34); below, AW wrote, 'usually sold in Ox. 16 Dec. 1688 - 6^d'. Pp.

15, a note erased; 18, AW wrote, 'qu[aere] when was this written'; 23, fills about name of Del'amere' and added 'Bothe' (G. Booth); 34, after paper 15 (see above), 'usually reported soon after the publication of this, that this was none of the princes declaration, nor done by his command, but pen'd by Samu. Johnson commonly called Julian Johnson'. LT 3.292.
[MS.] Wood D. 29(1). Wing C5169A.

2446. England 1688B. *A second collection of papers relating to the present juncture of affairs in England [7 papers]*. [London]: n.pub., 1688. 4°. Pp. [2], 34.
Tp, at paper II of a list of VII, 'An Answer to a Paper, Reflections on the Prince of Orange's Declaration', AW wrote, 'I have it by it self' (Wood 529(4), item 6610); below, '6[^d]'.
[MS.] Wood D. 29(2). Wing S2264.

2447. England 1688C. *A third collection of papers relating to the present juncture of affairs in England [4 papers]*. London: printed, sold R. Janeway, 1688. 4°. Pp. [2], 38.
Tp, AW wrote, 'sold in Ox. 20. Dec. 1688[.] 6^d'; at the 3rd paper, 'Three Letters', which begins on p. 11, he wrote at a story of the king and Father Clare who kissed the king's hand, 'This is mention'd in the Addit. to Dr Burnets Travells' (see Wood 724(1-4), items 1198ff. and 6295) and 2 shorter notes, including the identification of the Bishop of Oxford as 'Dr Sam. Parker' (bp. 1686-8); pp. 12-27, a few short identifications, dates (o.s. 1687 for 1688), and underscorings. LT 3.292.
[MS.] Wood D. 29(3). Wing T900.

2448. England 1688D. *A fourth collection of papers relating to the present juncture of affairs in England [12 papers]*. London: printed, sold R. Janeway, 1688. 4°. Pp. [2], 34.
Tp, AW wrote, 'published in he latter end of Dec. 1688[.] 5^d'. LT 3.292.
[MS.] Wood D. 29(4). Wing F1686.

2449. England 1688E. *A fifth collection of papers relating to the present juncture of affairs in England. [8 papers; a letter to the king, signed Philanax Verax, was also issued with this work, see pagination]*. London: printed, sold R. Janeway, 1688. 4°. Pp. [1-2], 1-24, 1-8 (A letter), 33-4.
Tp, AW wrote, 'Jan. 10 - 1688 - 6^d'. LT 3.187, 292.
[MS.] Wood D. 29(5). Wing F889.

2450. England 1688F. *A sixth collection of papers relating to the present juncture of affairs [6 papers]*. London: printed, sold R. Baldwin, 1689. 4°. Pp. 1-8, 1-16, 1-15.
Tp, AW wrote, 'Jan. 18. - 1688 - 6^d'; 1st p. 15, '1688'; 3rd p. 1, at printed 'An Oration of John Hales', AW wrote, 'Taken from the end of J. Fox book of Acts & Mon'; 3rd p. 13, at printed 'Letter frem [sic] the Jesuits', 'This seems all to be faigned.'
[MS.] Wood D. 29(6). Wing S3929 ('O' not recorded in Wing).

2451. England 1688G. *A seventh collection of papers relating to the present juncture of affairs in England [6 papers]*. London: printed, sold R. Janeway, 1689. 4°. Pp. [2], 34.
Tp, AW wrote 'bought at Ox. 8. Jan. 1688 - 6^d'. Above, in pencil, '2^d part', may be by AW. This item would, chronologically, be the 1st part, with [MS.] Wood D. 29(7a) (purchased 25 Jan.), following. P. 8, AW wrote, '1688'. LT 3.292.
[MS.] Wood D. 29(7b). Wing S2744 ('O' not recorded in Wing; 5 at O).

2452. England 1688G. *A seventh collection of papers relating to parliaments, and the penal laws and tests. I. A letter from a freeholder . . . II. A word in season [7 papers]*. [London]: n.pub., 1689. 4°. Pp. [2], 36, [1].
Tp, AW wrote, '25 Jan. 1688 - 6^d'.
[MS.] Wood D. 29(7a). Wing S2743.

2453. England 1688H. *An eighth collection of papers relating to the present juncture of affairs in England [6 papers]*. London: n.pub., 1689. 4°. Pp. [2], 34.
Tp, AW wrote, '29. Jan. 1688 - 6[^d]'.
[MS.] Wood D. 29(8). Wing E265B.

2454. England 1688I. *A ninth collection of papers relating to the present juncture of affairs in England [7 papers]*. London: printed, sold R. Janeway, 1689. 4°. Pp. [2], 34.
Tp, AW wrote, 'Bought at Oxon. 12. Mar. 1688 - 6^d'. P. 1, at the 1st paper, 'Dialogue between two Friends', he wrote, 'This seems to have been written by an Oxford scholar – it was written by Thom. Armsted [Armstead] M. A. ch. ch.' (AO 4.661f.; AOF 2.399); pp. 6-7, 3 identifications, Thomas Sprat, Jo. Massy [Massey], and Henry Aldridge [Aldrich].

[MS.] Wood D. 29(9). Wing N1164 ('O' not recorded in Wing; 5 at O).

2455. England 1688J. *A tenth collection of papers relating to the present juncture of affairs in England [5 papers]*. London: printed, sold R. Janeway, 1689. 4°. Pp. [2], 34.
Tp, AW wrote, '22. Mar. 1688-9'.
[MS.] Wood D. 29(10). Wing T727 ('O' not recorded in Wing; 5 at O).

2456. England 1688K. *Eleventh collection of papers relating to the present juncture of affairs in England and Scotland [7 papers]*. London: printed, sold R. Janeway, 1689. 4°. Pp. [2], 34.
[MS.] Wood D. 29(11). Wing E498.

2457. England 1688L. *The twelfth and last collection of papers (vol. I.) relating to the present juncture of affairs in England and Scotland [13 papers]*. London: printed, sold R. Janeway, 1689. 4°. Pp. [2], ii, 40.
Tp, AW wrote, 'published in the beginning of June 1689', in ink, over the same, in pencil. LT 3.293.
[MS.] Wood D. 29(12). Wing T3392.

2458. England 1689. *Seven Papers, viz. I. The grounds and reasons of the laws against popery [8 papers]*. London: printed, sold R. Baldwin, 1689. 4°. Pp. [2], 42.
Tp, AW wrote, 'Jan. 29. - an. 1688[9] - 6ᵈ'.
[MS.] Wood D. 29(17) (not in Bodl. CD cat.). Wing S2738 ('O' not recorded in Wing).

2459. England and Scotland's Covenant. *England and Scotlands covenant with their God*. [London]: f. E. Husband, 1645. 12°. Pp. 58.
Dupl. at Wood 888(1).
Wood Alm. A(9). Wing E2931.

2460. England and Scotland's Covenant. *England and Scotlands covenant with their God*. [London]: f. E. Husband, 1645. 12°. Pp. 58. Pasteboard (blue) with parchment spine. 1st upper and last lower flyleaves, marbled paper.
AW wrote the titles of 4 printed works in this vol., within guidelines made with red ink. 1st item, each 12° leaf is pasted on an 8° template. P. 31, AW identified the author of an 'Exhortation', 'written by Philip Nye.' Dupl. at Wood Alm. A(9).
Wood 888(1). Wing E2931.

2461. England, Army. *Directions for musters [heading at 1st B1:] The exercise of the English, in the militia of the kingdome of England [heading at 2nd B1:] The English military discipline exactly described, in 48 postures of the musquet, . . . 36. of the pike*. Cambridge: T. Buck a. R. Daniel, 1638. 4°. Pp. 8, 8, [42] (i.e., B², C3-4; B⁴; and 48 and 36 figures on 21 copper plates. Wanting all before B1) (bibliog. data is from STC 6903). Calf with 3 fillets, stamp decoration inside corners, and roll decoration at inner, spine edge (Ashm. binding).
Flyleaf, upper, 2nd, the titles of 6 printed works in this vol., by an Ashm. librarian.
Wood 635(1) (not in Bodl. CD cat.). STC 6903 (two) (prob. part of).

2462. England, Army. *Dublin the 24 of May, 1642. A perfect relation of the proceedings of the English army against the rebels [12-23 May]*. London: f. R. Rounthwait, 1642. S.sh.
Wood 508(20). Wing P1516.

2463. England, Army. *The list of the army raised under the command of . . . Robert, earle of Essex*. London: f. J. Partridge, 1642. 4°. A-C⁴.
Missing since 1994. In Whiteside cat.
Wood 531(5). Wing L2413.

2464. England, Army. *Sundry observations of severall passages and proceedings in the north*. London: f. F. C., 1642, 29 July. 4°. Pp. 8.
Tp, AW altered the former no., '20'.
Wood 376(22). Wing S6179.

2465. England, Army. *The resolution of the valiant Danes*. [London]: f. H. Watson a. W. Cook, [1642], 24 Nov. 4°. A⁴.
Tp, AW overwrote the former no., and wrote the year, '1642'.
Wood 375(24). Wing R1158.

2466. England, Army. *The round-heads remembrancer: May 16*. [Oxford?]: n.pub., 1643. 4°. Pp. [2], 6.
Tp, AW altered the former no., '12'.

Wood 376(13). Wing R2009. Madan 1366.

2467. England, Army. *An exact relation of foure notable victories obtained by the parliament forces.* London: B. Alsop, 1644. 4°.
Missing in 1922. See also note at Wood 376(1), item 3001 (whence the t).
Wood 376(67). Wing E3676 (rare). BL T.

2468. England, Army. *A true relation of the happy successe of his majesties forces in Scotland . . . Also, causes of a solemne fast [by Andrew Ker].* [Oxford]: [L. Lichfield], 1644[5]. 4°. Pp. [2], 17.
Wood 377(32). Wing T2965. Madan 1707.

2469. England, Army. *Three great victories obtained by the parliament forces against the cavaliers: the first by lord Fairfax in Yorkshire.* [London]: A. Coe, 1644, 26 Feb. 4°. Pp. [8].
Missing in 1922. See also note at Wood 376(1) (whence the t).
Wood 376(66). Wing T1092 (two). BL T, Dublin-Trinity.

2470. England, Army. *God appearing for the parliament, in sundry late victories [4 March].* London: f. E. Husbands, 1644[5], 10 Mar. 4°. Pp. [2], 22.
Missing in 1839; see note at Wood 377(1). Between items 38 and 40, p. stubs are visible.
Wood 377(39). Wing G906. *O, Hunt, Folg.*

2471. England, Army. *Three great victories: I. obtained by collonel Jones . . . Chester. II. . . . Devizes, by . . . Cromwell. III. The copie of a letter from . . . Leshley . . . of the glorious victory . . . against Montrosse.* London: J. Coe, 1645. 4°. A⁴.
Tp, AW wrote the month, 'Sept', in pencil, and altered the former no., '25'. Dupl. at Wood 612(30).
Wood 378(28). Wing T1093.

2472. England, Army. *Three great victories: I. obtained by collonel Jones . . . Chester. II. . . . Devizes, by . . . Cromwell. III. The copie of a letter from . . . Leshley . . . of the glorious victory . . . against Montrosse.* London: J. Coe, 1645. 4°. A⁴.
Tp, AW wrote 'Dupl', twice in pencil. Dupl. at Wood 378(28).
Wood 612(30). Wing T1093.

2473. England, Army. *A true relation of the expedition made into . . . Conaugh, by the British army of Ulster.* London: f. R. W., 1645. 4°. Pp. [2], 6 (p. unopened).
Tp, AW wrote, 'June 45', in pencil.
Wood 509(2). Wing T2950A (two) ('O' not recorded in Wing).

2474. England, Army. *Englands remembrancer: in two parts. Or, a catalogue of . . . victories, . . . obtained . . . by the parliaments forces.* London: f. T. Underhill, 1645[6], 4 Feb. 4°. Pp.8.
Tp, 'Dupl', cropped at top. P. 4, printed 'Oxford' is underscored. P. 8, a 31st victory was added, not by AW. Dupl. at Wood 378(45).
[MS.] Wood B. 39(8). Wing E3032.

2475. England Army. *Englands remembrancer: in two parts. Or, a catalogue of . . . victories, . . . obtained . . . by the parliaments forces.* London: f. T. Underhill, 1645[6], 4 Feb. 4°. Pp. 8.
Tp, AW altered the former no., '42', and at the date, altered 'Febr. 4' to 'Febr. 14'. P. 8, AW added a final victory, '31 The surrender of Chester – Thanksgiving day [/] For it Feb. 5', abridged from a note by another person who wrote it in the dupl. at [MS.] Wood B. 39(8).
Wood 378(45). Wing E3032.

2476. England, Army, et al. *A great overthrow given to the kings forces in Wales.* London: f. M. Walbancke, 1645[6], 26 Feb. 4°. Pp. 8.
Tp, AW wrote '1ᵈ' and the former no. '48', both later lined out.
Wood 378(52). Wing G1742.

2477. England, Army. *A coppie of a letter, sent from one of the agitators in the army, to an agitator in the citie.* London: n.pub., 1647. 4°. Pp. [2], 6.
Wood 632(17). Wing C6144.

2478. England, Army. *Englands appeale to its own army. Or the loud cry of an oppressed kingdome.* [Oxford]: [J. Harris a. H. Hills], [1647]. 4°. A⁴.
Tp, AW wrote the year, '1647'; 'Ent[ered in catalogue]', in a later hand.
Wood 612(61). Wing E2944. Madan 1934.

2479. England, Army. *A letter really written by a moderate cavallier to an intelligent and moderate independent . . . in the now marching army.* London: n.pub., 1647. 4°. Pp. 7.
Wood 632(16). Wing L1587.

2480. England, Army. *The resolution of the armie concerning the city of London, after their ending of the work at Colchester. Also two great fights at Colchester [14 Aug.].* London: n.pub., 1648. 4°. Pp. [2], 6.
Tp, AW wrote after the year, 'Aug. 15'.
Wood 502(42). Wing R1144.

2481. England, Army. *A true narrative of the late mutiny made by several troopers.* London: f. J. Field, 1649, 1 May. 4°. Pp. 14.
Wood 368(6). Wing T2799.

2482. England, Army. *A brief narrative of the great victorie . . . near Dunbar.* London: W. Du-Gard, 1650. 4°. Pp. [4], 3.
Missing in 1922. AW wrote the t on the upper flyleaf as: 'Another Relation of the same matter &c.' (i.e, Wood 503(13)).
Wood 503(14). Wing B4613. *O, Hunt* (former nos. in ink, 19 and 17), *Folg.*

2483. England, Army. *A true relation of the proceedings of the English army now in Scotland, . . . Contained in . . . letters read in parliament [6 Aug.].* London: E. Husband a. J. Field, [1650]. 4°. Pp. 16.
Wood 503(12). Wing T3023.

2484. England, Army. *Edinb. 22 Julii, 1650. Sess. 17. A short reply unto a declaration, entituled, the declaration of the army of England, upon their march into Scotland.* London: J. Field f. F. Tyton, 1650, 16 Aug. 4°. Pp. 40.
Bsm.
Wood 503(11). Wing S3626.

2485. England, Army. *A true relation of the routing the Scotish army near Dunbar, Sept. 3. . . . Also the lord generals proclamation concerning the prisoners.* London: J. Field, 1650, 9 Sept. 4°. Pp. 15.
Wood 503(13). Wing T3040.

2486. England, Army. *To the supreame authoritie the parliament . . . The humble petition of the officers of the army.* London: M. Simmons f. L. Chapman, 1652. S.sh.
Wood 276a(192). Wing T1748B. Steele 2972.

2487. England, Army. *An account of the affairs in Ireland, in reference to the late change in England: with a declaration of several officers of the army in Ireland [14 Dec.].* London: f. N. Brook, 1659. S.sh. Rpt. of Dublin edition.
ᵛ, AW wrote '14 Dec 1657' (wrong year).
Wood 510(24). Wing A229.

2488. England, Army. *The answer of the officers at Whitehall to the letter from the officers of the parliaments army in Scotland . . . Oct. 22.* Edinburgh: C. Higgins, 1659. 4°. Pp. 8.
Tp, former nos., 'nu 7' and '5', in pencil.
Wood 632(34). Wing A3298.

2489. England, Army. *The armies declaration [of 27 Oct. 1659] examined and compared, with their declaration May 6. their petition and addresse May 12. and their petition and representation.* London: n.pub., 1659. 4°. Pp. [2], 28, [1].
Tp, nos. 21 and 19 in former bundles.
Wood 610(41). Wing A3713.

2490. England, Army. *The armies vindication of this last change. Wherein, is plainly demonstrated, the . . . right of the army to settle these nations upon . . . righteousnesse and freedome.* London: T. M., 1659. 4°. Pp. [2], 22.
Tp, nos. 56 and 53 in former bundles.
Wood 610(25). Wing A3719.

2491. England, Army. *The army's plea for their present practice: tendered to the consideration of all . . . men.* London: H. Hills, 1659. 4°. Pp. [2], 30.
Tp, nos. 11 and 14 in former bundles.
Wood 616(7). Wing A3716.

2492. England, Army. *A declaration of the faithfull souldiers of the army:. . . to stand by the good old cause and maintain the liberties.* London: n.pub., 1659. 4°. Pp. [2], 5 (tp mutilated).
Wood 613(23). Wing D667.

2493. England, Army. *A declaration of the general council of the officers of the army: agreed upon at Wallingford-house [27 Oct.].* London: H. Hills, 1659. 4°. Pp. [2], 19.
Flyleaf, upper, no. 18 in a former bundle. Tp, no. 15 in a former bundle.
Wood 610(34). Wing D673.

2494. England, Army. *The humble petition and address of the officers of the army, to the parliament of the commonwealth of England [12 May].* London: H. Hills, f. him a. F. Tyton, 1659. 4° (cropped). Pp. [2], 13.
Tp, no. 8 in former bundle. Dupl. at 610(50).
Wood 610(47). Wing H3428.

2495. England, Army. *The humble petition and address of the officers of the army, to the parliament of the commonwealth of England [12 May].* London: H. Hills, f. him a. F. Tyton, 1659. 4° (cropped). Pp. [2], 13.
Tp, AW wrote 'Dupl'. Pp. 5, 7, 13^v scribbles by 'John –' and 'William Spring'. Dupl. at 610(47).
Wood 610(50) (not in Bodl. CD cat.). Wing H3428.

2496. England, Army. *The humble representation of some officers of the army, to . . . lieutenant-general Fleetwood [1 Nov. 1659].* [London]: n.pub., [1659]. 4°. Pp. 11.
Nos. 8 and 6 in former bundles. Pp. 6, 10, correction.
Wood 610(43). Wing H3639.

2497. England, Army. *Let me speake too? Or, eleven queries, humbly proposed to the officers of the army.* London: n.pub., 1659. 4°. Pp. [2], 6.
Tp, no. '51', in pencil, in a former bundle.
Wood 613(54). Wing L1329.

2498. England, Army. *A letter from a captain of the army, to an honourable member of parliament [2 Jan.].* London: J. Streater a. J. Macock, 1659[60]. 4°. Pp. 8.
Wood 632(25). Wing L1366.

2499. England, Army. *A letter of the officers of the army in Scotland . . . to the officers of the army in England [22 Oct.].* (London): n.pub., (1659). 4°. Rpt. of Edinburgh: C. Higgins edition. Pp. 8.
P. 1, 'Bund 2 nu 6' (cropped) and former no., '4', in pencil.
Wood 632(33). Wing L1580.

2500. England, Army. *A seasonable enquiry after the sure way to peace, in England: directed principally to the army.* [London]: n.pub., 1659. 4° (sigs. A2-A4 cropped). Pp. [2], 17.
Wood 610(2). Wing S2230.

2501. England, Army. *A timely warning, and friendly admonition to the forces in Scotland under general Monck. . . . By some . . . under . . . major general Lambert.* London: n.pub., 1659. 4°. Pp. [2], 6.
Tp, nos. 43 and 30 (or 39?) in former bundles.
Wood 610(3). Wing T1283.

2502. England, Army. *A true copy of a message sent to general Monck from severall officers . . . October twenty nine.* [London]: n.pub., [1659]. S.sh.
Wood 276a(334). Wing T2626.

2503. England, Army. *Truth seeks no corners: or, seven cases of conscience humbly presented to the army and parliament.* [London]: n.pub., 1659. 4°. Pp. [4], 7.
Tp, no. '61', in pencil, in a former bundle (cropped at bottom).
Wood 613(57). Wing T3159.

2504. England, Army. *An alarum to the officers and souldiers of the armies of England, Scotland, and Ireland.* [London]: n.pub., [1660]. 4°. Pp. 12.
P. 12, AW wrote 'March: 1660[61]'. See note at Wood 632(42), item 4619.
Wood 608(72). Wing A835.

2505. England, Army. *A copy of a letter; written to one of the members of parliament now sitting:. . . upon*

the fallacies . . . of the army, in their seven unalterable fundamentals, lately published. [London?]: n.pub., [1660]. 4°. Pp. 8.
P. 8, AW wrote, 'ffeb: 1659[60]'.
Wood 632(29). Wing C6176 (rare) (Wing, 1659/60?).

2506. England, Army. *The remonstrance & address of the armies of England, Scotland, and Ireland, to . . . Monck [9 Apr.].* London: J. Macock, 1660. 4°. Pp. 15 (1-2 blank).
Wood 632(78) (not in Bodl. CD cat.). Wing R959.

2507. England, Army. *To his excellency the lord general Monck, . . . the humble address of the officers [2 May].* London: W. Godbid f. J. Playford, 1660. S.sh.
Wood 276a(226). Wing T1357.

2508. England, Baronets. *A catalogue of the baronets of this kingdom of English; from the first erection of that dignity until this time.* London: E. Cotes f. A. Seile, 1667. 4°. Pp. [7], 60.
Tp, a crude '1ˢ' (?).
Wood 445(10). Wing C1368 ('O' not recorded in Wing).

2509. England, Chronicle. *[St. Albans Chronicle]. Descrypyion of Englonde [out of R. Higden, Poly-chronicon].* (London): (Julyan Notary), (1515). Fol. +2-4,a-z⁶,st⁴ (wanting t leaf). Calf with 2 fillets, stamp centrepiece, and 2 clasps; spine, 4 bands (probably Oxford c. 1600).
Pastedown, upper, filled with scribbles, in more than one hand, none in AW's hand, e.g., 'Oliver Snell', 'a great hed & a littell witt [/] a fitt man to turne a spitt', and year, 1627 and 1628. Flyleaf, upper, signature of 'Mʳ Olliver Snell this booke is mine', ᵛ, signatures of Nicholas Snell, and, AW wrote, 'Will: Caxton qui claruit A° 1483, Hunc librum scripsit:/ Ant: Woode: 1660 vid Pitseo: p. 670 ad an. 1483.', and a few rough drawings of heads and a man, a partially drawn coat of arms, and an addition of sums, which may be by AW. Text, a number of readers have made annotations on almost every p. in this book, though little if any can be assigned to AW; some notes were cropped in earlier binding. Pastedown, lower, scribbles, some by Snell.
Wood 408. STC 10000.

2510. England, Chronicle. *This is the cronycle of all the kyngs names that have ben in Englande.* [London]: (imprinted by R. Pynson), [1518?]. 4°. A-B⁴. Parchment with 2 clasp holes.
Pasteboard, upper, bibliog. details of items (2-3) in this vol. added by a later librarian. Text, some scribbles and underscoring, not in AW's style.
Wood 336(1). STC 9983.3 (rare).

2511. England, Chronicle. *A briefe cronicle contaynyng the accoumpte [of] the raygnes of all kynges in this realme, from the entring of Brutus, to this present yeare.* London: T. Marshe, [1561]. 8°. A-B⁸ (B8 blank),2nd A⁸,a-o⁸ (tp mutilated). Parchment.
Cover, upper, inside, 'From Fabian see Diij', in pencil (on sig. Diii, a pencil mark at 'as Fabyan writeth', prob. by AW (AO 1.256-7)). Tp, AW wrote the year, 'A:D: M:D:Lxi.' From 2nd A1ᵛ (563 years of Brut's reign, and, 511, of his descendants) to g7ᵛ, notes, marks, and dates in margins and underscoring, from creation to British history to, at g7ᵛ, '1457.', in more than one hand. Flyleaf and cover, lower, 2 names, John Cop– and illeg.
Wood 137. STC 9976.

2512. England, Church of. *An homilie a-gainst disobedience and wyl-full rebellion. [Followed by] A thanksgeving for the suppression of the last rebellion.* (London): (R. Jugge a. J. Cawood), [1570?]. 4°. A-K⁴. Calf with 3 fillets, stamp decoration inside corners, and roll decoration at inner, spine edge (Ashm. binding).
Flyleaf, upper, 2nd, the titles of 19 printed works in this vol., written by an Ashm. librarian. A1, '4ᵈ', prob. not by AW.
Wood 633(1). STC 13680.

2513. England, Church of. *King's primer. Preces privatae in studiosorum gratiam collectae, & regia authoritate approbatae.* Londini: G. Seres, 1573. 16° in 8's. Noviter impressae. A-B⁸,B-2H⁸. Calf with 2 fillets, and inner rectangle with stamp decoration outside corners, a centrepiece, and the initials 'T R'; rebacked.
Tp, scribbles, and initials 'T R', in purple ink. 2H7ᵛ, drawing of a horse. 2H8,ᵛ, scribbles, not by AW.
Wood 762. STC 20380.

2514. England, Church of. *Articuli per archiepiscopum, episcopos & reliquum clerum Cantuariensis*

provinciae in synodo inchoata Londini [24 Nov. 1584]. Londini: A. J[effes], [1585?]. 4°. A⁴. Pasteboard (blue) with parchment spine. 1st upper and last lower flyleaves, marbled paper.
Flyleaf, upper, 2nd^v, AW wrote the titles of 11 printed works in this vol., within guidelines made with red ink. Tp, he wrote, 'A: Woode Aug: 16: 1660: 2^d'. LT 1.327.
[MS.] Wood D. 25(1). STC 4584.

2515. England, Church of. *The booke of common prayer.* London: deputies of C. Barker, (1592). 16°. A-2S⁸ (wanting 4 leaves between Z8 and 2A1). Calf with 2 gold-stamp fillets, gold-stamp decoration and gold and gold-stamp fore-edges; clasp holes.
Tp, AW wrote 'A. Woode: 1661.' (former owner, Grisil Poyntz; see Wood 757(2)).
Wood 757(1). STC 16317 (rare).

2516. England, Church of. *A forme of common prayer, together with an order of fasting:. . . To be read every Wednesday during this visitation.* London: B. Norton a. J. Bill, 1625. 4°. A2-4,B-N⁴,O1-3.
B2, I2, O2^v, O3^v, note or scribble, not by AW.
[MS.] Wood B. 37(5). STC 16540.

2517. England, Church of. *Articles agreed upon by the arch-bishops and bishops . . . and the whole clergie; in . . . 1562. . . . Re-printed.* London: B. Norton a. J. Bill, 1630 [1660?]. 4°. A-D⁴.
Tp, AW wrote, 'Ant Woode Aug: 16: 1660. 4^d'. LT 1.327.
[MS.] Wood D. 25(3). STC 10055. STC [1662?].

2518. England, Church of. *Constitutions, and canons ecclesiasticall. . . . agreed upon . . . 1603.* London: J. Norton f. J. Norton a. R. Whitaker, 1633 [1640?]. 4°. A-P⁴.
Tp, AW wrote, 'Ant Woode: Aug: 16: A D: 1660: 9^d'. LT 1.327.
[MS.] Wood D. 25(4). STC 10077.

2519. England, Church of. *A forme of common prayer, together with an order of fasting:. . . To be read every Wednesday during this visitation.* London: R. Barker a. assignes of J. Bill, 1636. 4°. A-N⁴ (last leaf is blank).
A1, signature, 'Mary Wood'. LT 1.21.
[MS.] Wood B. 37(6). STC 16553a.

2520. England, Church of. *Constitutions and canons ecclesiasticall; . . . agreed upon . . . at London and York. 1640.* London: R. Barker a. the assignes of J. Bill, 1640. 4°. A-G⁴ (1st leaf blank).
Tp, former nos., '14' and '13', both lined out. E1^v, note, 'Constitutions agreed upon A° 1603 . . . ', 19 lines, not by AW.
[MS.] Wood D. 25(6). STC 10080.

2521. England, Church of. *Englands complaint to Jesus Christ, against the bishops canons [STC 10080].* [Amsterdam]: [Cloppenberg Press?], 1640. 4°. A-F⁴,G².
[MS.] Wood D. 25(7). STC 10008.

2522. England, Church of. *The bishops manifest: or, a comparative relation of conformitie of the English prelates to those . . . in the reign of king Hen. the eighth.* London: f. W. R., 1641. 4°. Pp. [2], 6.
Tp, bsm.
[MS.] Wood D. 31(7). Wing B3029.

2523. England, Church of. *A christal for the clergie, especially those that are corrupt in doctrine.* London: f. R. P., 1641[2]. 4°. A⁴.
Tp, bsm. A4^v, scribbles, not by AW.
[MS.] Wood D. 31(32). Wing C3932.

2524. England, Church of. *A discourse of sacriledge. Wherein is briefly shewn, 1. the just collation, 2. the unjust ablation . . . of the clergie.* London: f. R. Lowndes, 1641[2]. 4°. Pp. [2], 26.
Tp, bsm. Dupl. at Wood 619(8).
Wood 370(3). Wing D1601.

2525. England, Church of. *A discourse of sacriledge. Wherein is briefly shewn, 1. the just collation, 2. the unjust ablation . . . of the clergie.* London: f. R. Lowndes, 1641[2]. 4°. Pp. [2], 26 (mutilated).
Tp, AW wrote 'Dupl.' Dupl. at Wood 370(3).
Wood 619(8). Wing D1601.

2526. England, Church of. *Englands rejoycing at the prelats downfall [signed, an ill willer to the Romish*

brood]. England [sic]: n.pub., 1641. 4°. A-B⁴.
[MS.] Wood D. 31(8). Wing E3023.

2527. England, Church of. *A collection of prayers and thanksgivings, used in his majesties chappell and in his armies.* Oxford: L. Lichfield, 1643. 4°. Pp. [2], 17.
[MS.] Wood B. 37(8). Wing C4094A. Madan 1450.

2528. England, Church of. *A forme of common-prayer, to be used upon the solemn fast appointed . . . upon the second Friday in every moneth, beginning on the tenth day of November next.* Oxford: L. Lichfield, 1643. 4°. Pp. 76.
P. 2, signature, 'Mary Wood'.
[MS.] Wood B. 37(7). Wing C4111. Madan 1469.

2529. England, Church of. *A forme of common-prayer, to be used upon the solemne fast, appoynted . . . upon the fifth of February.* Oxford: L. Lichfield, 1644[5]. 4°. Pp. 16.
[MS.] Wood B. 37(9). Wing C4112. Madan 1703.

2530. England, Church of. *The form and manner of making & consecrating bishops, priests and deacons.* London: R. Barker a. J. Bill, [1660]. 4°. Pp. [2], 29.
Tp, AW wrote, 'Aug: 21: A.D. 1660. 4ᵈ'. LT 1.327.
[MS.] Wood D. 25(2). Wing C4105.

2531. England, Church of. *A form of prayer, with thanksgiving, to be used . . . the 28ᵗʰ· of June, 1660, for his majesties happy return to his kingdoms.* London: J. Bill a. C. Barker, 1660. 4°. A-E⁴,F².
Acquired 29 June 1660, 6ᵈ, LT 1.318.
[MS.] Wood B. 37(10). Wing C4170.

2532. England, Church of. *Instructions to the ministers and church-wardens concerning the making of terriers.* N.p.: n.pub., [1660?]. S.sh.
Wood 276a(278). Not in Wing. Not in ESTCR.

2533. England, Church of. *A perfect catalogue of all the arch-bishops & bishops.* London: f. R. Pawley, 1660[1]. S.sh.
Col. 1, in lists, AW added names and dates of 7 who died, were transferred or were newly appointed, all from 1661-3. Dupl. at Wood 445(8).
Wood 276a(86). Wing P1473.

2534. England, Church of. *A perfect catalogue of all the arch-bishops & bishops.* London: f. R. Pawley, 1660[1]. S.sh.
Dupl. at Wood 276a(86).
Wood 445(8). Wing P1473.

2535. England, Church of. *A catalogue of the prelates and clergie of the province of Canterbury.* London: f. N. Brooke, 1661. S.sh.
Wood 276a(88). Wing C1409.

2536. England, Church of. *A form of common prayer, to be used upon the thirtieth of January, being . . . appointed for fasting and humiliation.* London: J. Bill, 1661. 4° (cropped). A-H⁴.
Acquired 28 June 1661, LT 1.401.
[MS.] Wood B. 37(13). Wing C4113.

2537. England, Church of. *A form of prayer, to be used upon the twelfth of June . . . being the several days appointed for a general fast.* London: J. Bill a. C. Barker, 1661. 4°. A-G⁴,H².
Acquired 8 Feb. 1661, 1ˢ, LT 1.380.
[MS.] Wood B. 37(11). Wing C4143.

2538. England, Church of. *A form of prayer, with thanksgiving, to be used . . . the 29ᵗʰ of May yearly, for his majestie's happy return to his kingdoms.* London: J. Bill a. C. Barker, 1661. 4°. A-E⁴,F².
Acquired 28 June 1661, LT 1.401.
[MS.] Wood B. 37(12). Wing C4171.

2539. England, Church of. *A book of the valuations of all the ecclesiasticall preferments in England and Wales; entituled nomina & valores omnium.* [London]: n.pub, 1680. 12°. Pp. [4], 383. Pasteboard (grey) with parchment spine. 1st upper and last lower flyleaves, marbled paper.

A clear example of AW's heading written on the spine, 'Valuation of ch. Livings [/] Graduats of Oxon'. Tp, AW wrote '2ˢ 4ᵈ' and 'published about Christmas day 1679'. P. 60, at printed 'Lifton', AW wrote 'Lyfton', in red chalk.
Wood 862(1) (Wood 682 in Bodl. CD cat.). Wing B3720.

2540. England, Church of. *The ceremonies, form of prayer, and services used in Westminster-abby at the coronation of king James the first . . . With the coronation of king Charles the first in Scotland*. London: R. Taylor, 1685. Fol. Pp. 16. Pasteboard (blue) with parchment spine. 1st upper and last lower flyleaves, marbled paper.
Flyleaf, upper, 3rdʳ⁻ᵛ, AW wrote the titles of 22 printed works in this vol., within guidelines made with red chalk.
Wood 398(1). Wing C1676.

2541. England, Church of. *A collection of cases and other discourses lately written to recover dissenters*. London: f. T. Basset a. B. Tooke, 1685. 4°. Pp. [4] (tp and table of contents of vol. 1 only).
Tp for 2nd vol. is at Wood 658(777-8), item 2542.
[MS.] Wood D. 22(17). Wing C5114.

2542. England, Church of. *A collection of cases and other discourses lately written to recover dissenters*. London: f. T. Basset a. B. Tooke, 1685. 4°. Pp. [4] (tp and table of contents only).
Table of contents, 'A Catalogue of all the Cases and Discourses', AW wrote 'Dup' in pencil. Tp for 1st vol. is at [MS.] Wood D. 22(17), item 2541.
Wood 658(777-8) (not in Bodl. CD cat.). Wing C5115.

2543. England, Church of. *The private office for every day, before dinner and supper*. N.p.: n.pub., [1685?]. 8°. Pp. 8 (i.e., *⁴).
Wood 883(4). Not in Wing. Not in ESTCR.

2544. England, Church of. *A form of prayer with thanksgiving for the safe delivery of the queen, and happy birth of the young prince [17 June]*. London: C. Bill, H. Hills, a. T. Newcomb, 1688. 4°. A⁴.
See LT 3.255, 268.
Wood 883(3). Wing C4168.

2545. England, Church of. *A list of the members return'd to serve in this present convocation, summon'd to meet on the sixth of November at St. Paul's*. London: J. Tonson, 1689. S.sh.
Numerous lines in margins, some underscorings, and AW wrote 3 brief notes: e.g., at Oxford graduates, Mr. Oatley and Mr. Lloyd: 'Adam Oteley of Trin. Coll. in Camb incorp. M.A Oxon. 1692 Vide in Lichfield' and 'Franc. Lloyd M.A. Oriel Coll'.
Wood 276a(96). Wing L2458.

2546. England, Committee of Safety. *A brief account of the meeting, proceedings, and exit of the committee of safety*. London: f. T. Williamson, 1659[60]. 4°. Pp. 24.
Wood 613(8). Wing B4510.

2547. England, Earl Marshall. *By the right honorable the lords, commissioners for the office of earle marshall of England [10 Nov.]*. [London]: [W. Stansby], [1618]. S.sh.
Wood 276a(147). STC 8581. Steele 1225.

2548. England, Education. *London, anno Dom. 1647. A brief declaration of those that have accepted the trust of receiving and distributing . . . money . . . at both the universities*. [London]: n.pub., [1647]. S.sh.
Wood 276a(305). Wing B4565. Madan 1919.

2549. England, Exchequer. *To the right ho:ᵇˡᵉ the lords com:ᵉˢ of his ma:ᵗⁱᵉˢ treasury May it please yo:ᵉ lor:ᵖˢ [blank]*. N.p.: n.pub., n.d. S.sh. (engr.).
A form with blanks to be filled in. Not identified. See also excise form at item 547.
Wood 276a(59). Not in STC. Not in Wing. Not in ESTCR.

2550. England, Flood. *More strange newes: of wonderfull accidents hapning by the late overflowings of waters, in Summerset-shire, Gloucestershire*. London: W. J[aggard] f. E. White, [1607]. 4°. A-D⁴ (1st leaf blank).
Tp, date, '1607', may not be in AW's hand.
[MS.] Wood D. 28(3). STC22916.

2551. England, Headlands. *[A note] of the head-lands of England, as they [beare] one from another . . . 4 March 1604*. London: R. Barker, [1605]. S.sh. (mutilated, wanting map).
Wood 276a(56). STC 10019.5.

2552. England, Law. *The lawes against witches, and conjuration. . . . Also, the confession of mother Lakeland*. London: f. R. W., 1645. 4°. Pp. 8.
[MS.] Wood B. 18(5). Wing L694aA (rare).

2553. England, Law. *Certain quaeres for the publike good, concerning the avoiding of . . . unnecessary orders, delayes, . . . in . . . English courts*. London: f. F. Leach, 1647. 4°. Pp. [2], 6.
Wood 630(3). Wing C1737.

2554. England, Law. *A list of the names of the judges of the high court of justice, for the tryall of James earl of Cambridge [et al.]*. N.p.: f. W. Wright, 1648[9]. S.sh.
ᵛ, AW wrote '1648'.
Wood 366(32). Wing L2470 (Wing, James,).

2555. England, Law. *To the law, and to the testimonie:. . . cases of conscience*. London: f. G. Whittington, 1648. 8°. Pp. [14], 98, [4]. Calf, rough, with 3 fillets and stamp decoration (flower) in corners (Ashm. binding).
Flyleaf, upper, 2nd, the titles of 5 printed works in this vol. by an Ashm. librarian (same hand in Wood 276a); 3rd, '6ᵈ' and numbers; ᵛ, AW wrote 'said to be written by one – Borhell one of the (stationers of Lond) q[uaere]'. Tp, 'sayd to be writ by [above line, prob. by AW: 'Borhel'] one of the', may not be by AW, cropped at side. Acquired 29 Ap. 1658 out of G. Langbaine's study, LT 1.247-8.
Wood 893(1) (not in Bodl. CD cat.). Wing T1652.

2556. England, Law. *Certaine proposals of divers attorneys of the court of common pleas, for the regulating the proceedings at law*. London: f. W. Lee a. D. Pateman, 1650. 4°. Pp. [6], 16.
Tp, 'a' in margin after title.
Wood 630(6). Wing C1728.

2557. England, Law. *The names of the justices of peace, in England and Wales*. London: f. T. Walkley, 1650. 8°. Pp. 78.
Pp. 44-5, at Oxon., AW made 4 corrections in the lists; 51, underscoring of John Whorwood, of Stourton, Staff.
Wood 445(3). Wing N133.

2558. England, Law. *Proposalls concerning the chancery*. London: W. Ellis, sold G. Badger, 1650. 4°. Pp. [2], 27 (plus 1 fold-out p.).
Tp, a short note, not in AW's hand, 'Approved by the Committee for regulating proceedings in the Cʳᵗᵉ of Justice'.
Wood 630(7). Wing P3718.

2559. England, Law. *A list of all the prisoners in the upper bench prison, remaining in custody the third of May, 1653*. London: f. L. Chapman, 1653. 4°. Pp. [2], 24, [1].
Wood 500(4). Wing L2381.

2560. England, Law. *Rules and orders for the court of common pleas*. London: f. R. Marriot, 1654. 4°. Pp. [2], 55.
Wood 630(13). Wing R2249A.

2561. England, Law. *Rules and orders for the court of the upper bench . . . made . . . 1654*. London: f. A. Roper, 1655. 4°. Pp. [2], 39.
P. 39, an 'Index' of 22 items, not in AW's hand.
Wood 630(14). Wing R2250.

2562. England, Law. *A declaration of the Christian-free-born subjects of the . . . once flourishing kingdom of England. To which is adjoyned the petition of right*. [London]: n.pub., 1659. 4°. Pp. [2], 28.
Tp, nos. 4 and 60 in former bundles.
Wood 610(40). Wing D645.

2563. England, Law. *Englands safety in the laws supremacy*. London: n.pub., 1659. 4°. Pp. 22.
Tp, no. 21 (?) in a former bundle (cropped at bottom); bsm.
Wood 610(58). Wing E3044.

2564. England, Law. *Englands settlement, upon the two solid foundations of the peoples civil and religious liberties*. London: n.pub., 1659. 4°. Pp. [2], 33.
Tp, no. in a former bundle (?), cropped at bottom.
Wood 613(56). Wing E3051.

2565. England, Law. *A vindication of the laws of England, . . . Together with some proposals to the parliament*. London: f. J. Starkey, 1659. 4°. Pp. [2], 14.
Wood 630(19). Wood V512.

2566. England, Law. *Divers serious cautions, plainly shewing the unlawfulness of the oath of abjuration*. London: f. J. Johnson, [1660]. S.sh.
AW added the date, 'ffeb: 1659[60]'.
Wood 276a(270). Wing D1714 (two).

2567. England, Law. *To the king's most excellent majesty, and to the lords spiritual and temporal in this present parliament assembled. The humble petition of . . . prisoners for debt, in the kings-bench-prison, and elsewhere*. [London]: n.pub., [1661?]. S.sh.
Wood 500(7). Not in Wing (apparently a variant of a part of T1496eA-fA). Not in ESTCR.

2568. England, Law. *Law unknown, or, judgement unjust. . . . With a brief relation of the killing of John Townesend, by major Crosby at St. Albones*. [London]: n.pub., 1662. 4°. Pp. 11.
Tp, AW wrote 'Conventicles', in pencil.
Wood 647(23). Wing L636.

2569. England, Law. *A letter from a justice of peace to a counsellor at law concerning conventicles, with the counsellors reply*. [London?]: n.pub., [1680]. 4°. Pp. 8 (cropped).
P. 8, AW wrote, 'About 1679'.
Wood 632(53). Wing L1405.

2570. England, Law. Cooke, Edward, trans. *Magna charta, made in the ninth year of k. Henry the third, . . . with . . . observations from the l. chief just. Coke's comments upon it [in his Institutes]*. London: assignes of R. a. E. Atkins f. T. Simmons, 1680. 4°. Pp. [8], 68, [2]. Pasteboard (blue) with parchment spine. 1st upper and last lower flyleaves, marbled paper (last lower, only traces remain).
Flyleaf, upper, 3rdᵛ, AW wrote the titles of 8 printed works in this vol., within guidelines made with red ink. He wrote Arabic nos. on tpp. (nos. 3-7 corrected, overwritten, to 4-8).
Wood 629(1). Wing M253.

2571. England, Law. *Another new-years-gift for arbitrary judges: or some sober reflections on injustice*. (London): n.pub., (1681). S.sh. (r-v).
Dupl. at Wood 426(35).
Wood 276a(277). Wing A3271.

2572. England, Law. *Another new-years-gift for arbitrary judges: or some sober reflections on injustice*. (London): n.pub., (1681). S.sh. (r-v).
Dupl. at Wood 276a(277).
Wood 426(35). Wing A3271.

2573. England, Law. *[Begin.] Fides aboriginū Britā. s. juris naturalis. . . . Cook, Calvin's case [The oath to be taken at the court leet. Engraved]*. N.p.: n.pub., [1683?]. S.sh. Engraving. 4°.
AW wrote, 'Ant. à Bosco ex dono Jos[eph] Crowther S.T.P. et principalis A. B. Mariae Virginae. 5. Aug. 1683'.
[MS.] Wood B. 36(4). Not in Wing. Not in ESTCR.

2574. England, Lords Commissioners. *Oxon: 12.Octobris 1644. This boord being informed, that in the city of London, the farthing tokens are decryed*. [Oxford]: [H. Hall], 1644. S.sh.
AW wrote the year, '1644', in pencil.
Wood 423(20). Wing T923 (rare). Madan 1685*.

2575. England, Lords Commissioners. *By the lords and other his majesties commissioners. An order for the observance . . . of the statute made for the reliefe . . . of persons infected with the plague*. Oxford: L. Lichfield, 1645. S.sh.
Wood 276a(148) (not in Bodl. CD cat.). Wing E929 (rare). Madan 1775. Steele 2615.

2576. England, Lords Commissioners. *Oxford, 12. die Maii. . . . An order of the lords, for the better

direction of the overseers . . . against the spreading of the . . . plague. Oxford: L. Lichfield, 1645. S.sh.
Wood 276a(311). Wing E930B (rare). Madan 1776.

2577. England, Lords Commissioners. *Oxford, 4. die Junii. . . . An order of the lords and governour, for the better direction of the overseers . . . against the spreading of . . . the plague.* Oxford: L. Lichfield, 1646. S.sh.
Wood 276a(312). Wing E930 (rare). Madan 1870. Steele 2657.

2578. England, Lords Treasurers. *A perfect catalogue of all the lords treasurers . . . to . . . 1679.* [London]: n.pub., [1679]. Fol. Pp. 4.
Wood 276a(102) (not in Bodl. CD cat.). Wing P1474.

2579. England, Map. Manuscript. *England.* N.p.: n.pub., n.d. S.sh. MS.
Drawne, or traced, with cities entered in hand, not by AW.
Wood 276a(57) (not in Bodl. CD cat.). Not identified.

2580. England, Navy. *A declaration of the causes moving the queenes majestie . . . to . . . send a navy . . . against the king of Spaines forces.* London: deputies of C. Barker, 1596. A2-4.
Tp, note, 'This published before the voiadge to Calets./ [Calais]', not in AW's hand. P. nos. entered, 269-274 (part of an earlier collection), prob. not in AW's hand.
Wood 511(5b). STC 9203.

2581. England, Navy. *Newes from Sally: of a strange delivery of foure English captives from the . . . Turkes.* [London]: n.pub., 1642. 4°. A2-4 (wanting the t leaf).
A2, AW wrote at 'October', 'In what yeare. qu[aere]'.
[MS.] Wood B. 35(14). Wing N997.

2582. England, Navy. *True newes from our navie, now at sea.* London: f. F. Wright, 1642. 4°. Pp. 8.
Tp, AW lined out the former no., '24', and wrote the month, 'Nov.'
Wood 375(23a). Wing T2844A.

2583. England, Navy. *A declaration of the officers and company of sea-men abord his majesties ships.* London (printed in Holland and re-printed at): n.pub., 1648. S.sh.
Wood 502(51) (not in Bodl. CD cat.). Wing D727.

2584. England, Navy. *A bloudy fight at sea, between the parliament of England's fleet, . . . and prince Ruperts navie, neer Carthaginia Road.* London: f. G. W., 1650. 4°. Pp. [2], 6.
Wood 503(17). Wing B3239.

2585. England, Navy. *Bloudy newes from sea: being a perfect narrative, . . . of the . . . engaging, between two hundred sail of English and Dutch-men of war, upon the coast of Scilley.* London: f. G. Horton, 1652. 4°. Pp. 8.
Wood 503(19). Wing B3278 (two).

2586. England, Navy. *A description & plat of the sea-coasts of England, from London, . . . to Edinburgh . . . as also: all those parts over against us, as Norway.* London: M. S. f. T. Jenner, 1653. 4°. Pp. [6], 41 (i.e., 45), and 2 maps.
[MS.] Wood C. 13(6). Wing D1139.

2587. England, Navy. *A letter from the commanders and officers of the fleet . . . unto general Monck in Scotland [4 Nov.].* London: S. Griffin f. T. Hewer, 1659. 4°. Pp. [2], 5.
Tp, former nos., '30' and '28', in pencil.
Wood 632(67). Wing L1516.

2588. England, Navy. *An exact relation of the several engagements and actions of his majesties fleet, under . . . prince Rupert.* London: f. J. B., 1673. 4°. Pp. [2], 21.
Flyleaf preceding, AW wrote, 'Note that an account of several sea-battles were published after his majesties restauration, but they were printed in fol. papers, & therefore they cannot come in into this vol.' (e.g., Wood 276a(548); but the preceding 2 items in this vol., nos. 34 and 35, were 'fol. papers' and had to be folded 5 times to fit into this quarto vol.).
Wood 503(36). Wing E3696.

2589. England, Navy. *An account of the late great victory, obtained at sea, against the French . . . near the Cape of Barfleur in May.* London: f. J. Rawlins, 1692. 4°. Pp. [4], 27.

Tp, AW wrote, 'Jun. 11. an 1692 6^{d}'. A second note, cropped at bottom. LT 3.390.
Wood 503(37) (not in Bodl. CD cat.). Wing A310.

2590. England, Parishes. *A book of the names of all parishes, market towns, . . . in England and Wales.*
London: M. S. f. T. Jenner, 1657. 4°. Pp. 197. Pasteboard (blue) with parchment spine.
Tp, initials, 'R. S.' and 'J. V.' Pp. 16ff. and 98-106, at Cheshire, Cornwall and Lincoln, numerous additions,
none in AW's hand. P. 133, 'where is Rutlandshire?', in AW's hand (it is out of alphabetical order, at pp.
96-7). Pp. 181-8, at Yorkshire, marks in margins, in dark and red ink, and underscoring, may not be by
AW.
Wood 468. Wing B3717 ('O' not recorded in Wing).

2591. England, Parliament. *A record of some worthy proceedings: in the . . . howse of commons in the
late parliament.* [Amsterdam?]: [G. Thorp?], 1611. 8°. Pp. 48.
Wood 519(2). STC 7751.

2592. England, Parliament. *Articles exhibited in parliament against William archbishop of Canterbury.*
[London]: n.pub., 1640, Printed in the yeare. 4°. Pp. [2], 5.
Tp, scribbles, not in AW's hand, mostly covered by a repair over which AW wrote the no. of the item, '18'.
P. 3, brief comment, 'indeed Fulsome stuff.', not in AW's hand.
Wood 366(18). Wing A3822B.

2593. England, Parliament. *Anno regni Caroli regis . . . decimo septimo . . . An act for the speedie and
effectuall reducing the rebells in . . . Ireland [3 Nov. 1640].* London: R. Barker, assignes of J. Bill, 1641.
Fol. A-B^{4}.
Tp, bsm.
Wood 507(11). Wing E1127.

2594. England, Parliament. *Another declaration from both houses of parliament: sent to his majesty,
March 23.* London: R. Oulton & G. Dexter, 1641[2]. 4°. Pp. [2], 5.
Tp, AW rubbed out 2 former nos.; below, a no., '23'.
Wood 373(42). Wing E1213.

2595. England, Parliament. *Articles of accusation, exhibited . . . against s^{r}. John Bramston, . . . s^{r}. R.
Berkley [et al.].* [London]: f. I. H., 1641. 4°. Pp. [2], 48.
Tp, no. 2 in a former bundle; AW wrote 'Dec 164-' and 'Jul 16–', in pencil, faint, both cropped at side.
Bsm.
Wood 614(32). Wing E2521.

2596. England, Parliament. *The articles or charge exhibited in parliament against sir Francis Winde-
banck . . . whereunto is annexed the letter that he sent [11 Jan.].* [London]: n.pub., 1641. 4°. Pp. [2], 6.
Tp, no. 3 in a former bundle.
Wood 614(25). Wing A3882A.

2597. England, Parliament. *Certaine queries of some tender conscienced Christians. About the late
protestation commended to them.* [London]: n.pub., 1641. 4°. Pp. [2], 10.
Wood 614(36). Wing C1741.

2598. England, Parliament. *A conspiracie discovered: or the report of a committee to the house of commons [17 June].* [London]: n.pub., 1641. 4°. Pp. [2], 4. Pasteboard (blue) with parchment spine; rebacked.
Flyleaf, upper, 2nd, 'Item 12 wanting – but not in Catal. Item 66 wanting – prob. removed long ago as a
duplicate. R. H[ill?] 1.xii.1921.' And a note by C. J. H[indle], stating that 15 items were found at Hope
adds. 1127-8, and restored to this vol. in January 1932 (diurnals). Flyleaves, 3rd-5th, AW wrote the titles
of 67 printed works in this vol., within guidelines made with red ink; his heading, 'Vol. 1 Pamphlets containing matters making for, and against, the rebellion that broke forth an. 1642 [and a hand sign] Note that
the pamphlets relating to the most noble Thomas Earle of Strafford are in a volume entit. [blank space,
not given, but see Wood 366(1-11), e.g., items 6505ff.]'. At item 5 in the list, 'deest Octr 1839 W[illiam]
K[irtland]'; see Plate I. There is also a note in a later hand, 'Diurnals taken out' (later restored). Item 1,
p. 1, at 'Mr. Fynes', AW wrote, 'Nath. Fiennes'.
Wood 373(1). Wing C5932.

2599. England, Parliament. *The declaration agreed upon by the committee of the house of commons to
sit in the Guildhall [6. Jan. 1641] [and a 2nd declaration: 3 Jan. 1641].* [London]: [f. J. Hunscott], [1641[2]].
S.sh.

A correction, 'Stode' to 'Strode'. ^v, '3/6 } Jan', and '1641'.
Wood 373(9). Wing E2548A. Steele, 1922.

2600. England, Parliament. *A declaration of the lords and commons in parliament: with the additionall reasons, last presented to his majestie [12 Mar.] . . . Whereunto is annexed, his majesties speech [9 Mar.].* London: n.pub., 1641[2]. 4°. Pp. 8.
Tp, AW overwrote a former no. Diff. ed. at Wood 614(30).
Wood 373(32). Wing E1484A.

2601. England, Parliament. *A declaration of the lords and commons in parliament. With the additionall reasons, last presented to his majestie [12 Mar.] . . . Whereunto is annexed, his majesties speech [9 Mar.].* [London]: ('P.i. . .d f. . J') [i.e., Printed for John Thomas, [1641[2]]. 4°. Pp. 8 (imprint cropped).
Tp, AW wrote 'Dupl', in pencil. Diff. ed. at Wood 373(32).
Wood 614(30). Wing E1485A.

2602. England, Parliament. *The diurnall occurrences of every dayes proceeding in parliament since the beginning thereof [20 Jan - 10 March 1628[9]].* London: R. H., sold W. Cooke, 1641. 4°. Pp. [2], 77.
Tp, AW wrote, 'Most of these occurrences are, if I mistake not remitted into the body of J. Rushworths collections'.
Wood 519(3a). Wing E1526.

2603. England, Parliament. *The diurnall occurrences, or dayly proceedings of . . . parliament [3 Nov. 1640 - 3 Nov. 1641]. With a continuation of all the speeches [June -3 Nov. 1641]. [2nd tp] The heads of a conference delivered by mr. [John] Pymm. . . . Junii 24, 1641.* London: f. W. Cook, 1641. 4°. Pp. [8], 1-6 (Pym), 1-276, [8], 277-429 (some further misnumbering) (¶⁴,A-I⁴ (¶1 blank)). Calf with 2 fillets.
Flyleaf, upper, AW wrote, 'Taken from y^t – to the – [illeg.]', and, by a later librarian, in pencil, 'One pamphlet after the list of contents [Pym is sometimes issued separately, Wing P4268, but here the signatures are continuous] & another at the end [here listed separately, signatures begin anew at A, Warmestry, Wood 494(2), item 6459]'. 1st item, tp, signature of Rob. Warner. ¶3, underscoring of W. Thomas and H. Percie; line in margin at Sergeant Wild. Pp. 2nd 1-2, 7, 16, 29, 38, 128, 181, 237, AW wrote corrections, cross-refs., or identifications, e.g., pp. 29, at printed Rich. Farmer of 'Kiddington', correction to 'Somerton', and at 'Will. Stone', identification, 'Stones [sic] of Steeple-Barton.'; 128, at a speech by William Thomas, 'June 1641' and 'This speech is concerning Deanes, & their office, what it was originally & what it is at this present – He endeavours in this speech to prove the office to be of little use, & therefore to be utterly abolished' (a summary of adjacent paragraph); and, 237 at Hyde's speech, 'Edw. Hyde'. Some lines in margins (p. 277, 'q[uaere]'), mainly in pencil.
Wood 494(1). Wing E1527.

2604. England, Parliament. *Foure matters of high concernment.* London: R. Oulton & G. Dexter, f. F. Coules, & T. Banks, 1641. 4°. Pp. [2], 5, [1].
Tp, AW overwrote a former no., below, a 2nd no., '2', and AW wrote the date, 'March 1641[2]' and 'Mar 2', in pencil.
Wood 373(28). Wing F1662.

2605. England, Parliament. *An humble petition and remonstrance presented unto . . . parliament, concerning . . . the transportation of leather.* [London]: n.pub., 1641. 4°. Pp. [4], 12.
Tp, bsm.
[MS.] Wood C. 14(6). Wing H3439.

2606. England, Parliament. *The Irish petition to this parliament in England. Shewing in what distresse . . . they are in, and how bloudily the rebels daily proceed against them.* London: for for [sic] D. Williams, 1641. 4°. Rpt. of Dublin edition. A⁴.
Tp, AW wrote below, 'Dec 1' in pencil and in ink.
Wood 507(10). Wing I1043.

2607. England, Parliament. *March 2. Matters of great note and consequence. 1. Diverse questions . . . 2 a true relation of the strange and untimely deathes . . . of Shirborne castle.* London: f. G. Thompson, 1641[2]. 4°. Pp. [2], 5.
[MS.] Wood B. 35(9) (not in Bodl. CD cat.). Wing M1306.

2608. England, Parliament. *An ordinance of the lords and commons in parliament. For the safety and defence [5 Mar.].* London: f. J. Hunscott, 1641[2]. 4°. Pp. 15.
Flyleaf, upper^v, disputation topic, lined out. Tp, below, AW wrote the date, 'Mar. 5'; and a 2nd no., '9'.

Wood 373(29). Wing E2033.

2609. England, Parliament. *The priviledges and practice of parliaments in England. Collected out of the common lawes.* [London]: n.pub., 1641. 4°. Pp. [4], 46.
Wood 518(3a). Wing P3534 ('O' not recorded in Wing).

2610. England, Parliament. *A relation touching the present state and condition of Ireland . . . And also the examination of Hubert Petit.* London: E. G. f. R. Best, 1641[2]. 4°. Pp. 8.
Tp, AW wrote, '11 Mar. 1641'. Dupl. at Wood 614(29).
Wood 507(40). Wing E2699A.

2611. England, Parliament. *A relation touching the present state and condition of Ireland . . . And also the examination of Hubert Petit.* London: E. G. f. R. Best, [1641[2]] (cropped). 4°. Pp. 8.
Tp, AW wrote 'Dup', in pencil. Dupl. at Wood 507(40).
Wood 614(29). Wing E2699A.

2612. England, Parliament. *A report of the committee of the charge against Matthew Wren [5 July].*
[London]: n.pub., 1641. 4°. Pp. [2], 2.
Tp, former no. '12'.
[MS.] Wood D. 31(9). Wing E2704B.

2613. England, Parliament. *Severall votes resolved upon by both houses of parliament, concerning the securing of . . . of England and . . . Wales . . . March 16.* London: f. J. Hunscott, 1641[2]. S.sh.
Wood 276a(134). Wing E2306. Steele 2036.

2614. England, Parliament. *To the right honourable the house of peeres . . . The humble petition of the knights, gentlemen, . . . of the county of Oxford.* London: f. F. L. a. W. W., 1641[2]. S.sh.
Tp, 'came forth Thurs[d]ay 10th Aprill', not in AW's hand.
Wood 516(5). Wing T1635.

2615. England, Parliament. *A true relation of the unparalleld breach of parliament by his majesty, on Tuesday the 4th. of January.* London: n.pub., 1641[2], 21 Jan. 4°. Pp. [2], 6.
Wood 373(10). Wing T3068B.

2616. England, Parliament. *Severall votes resolved upon by both houses of parliament, concerning the securing of the kingdome.* London: f. J. Hunscout [sic], 1641[2], 26 March. S.sh.
Wood 373(39). Wing E2307.

2617. England, Parliament. *An abstract of the proceedings in parliament, in the time of Edward the 3.*
London: f. F. Coles, 1642. 4°. A⁴. Pasteboard (blue) with parchment spine.
Flyleaf, upper, 3rd, AW wrote 'Parl', in pencil, and the titles of 12 printed works in this vol., within guidelines made with red ink (he omitted 3a).
Wood 519(1). Wing E962.

2618. England, Parliament. *The answer of both houses of parliament, presented to his majestie at York the ninth of May.* London: R. Barker, by the assignes of J. Bill, 1642. 4°. Pp. [2], 5.
Tp, AW lined out a former no., '46', and altered a 2nd; below, '59'.
Wood 373(63). Wing E1219.

2619. England, Parliament. *A complaint to the house of commons, and resolution taken up by the free protestant subjects of the citties of London . . . and the counties adjacent.* Oxford: L. Lichfield, 1642[3]. 4°.
Pp. [2], 18.
Tp, AW wrote 'Dup', in pencil (cropped at side). Bsm. Diff. ed. at Wood 614(56).
Wood 614(62). Wing C5622. Madan 1152.

2620. England, Parliament. *A complaint to the house of commons, and resolution taken up by the free protestant subjects of the cities of London . . . and the counties adjacent.* Oxford: L. Lichfield, 1642[3]. 4°.
Pp. [2], 18.
Tp, no. 22 in a former bundle; AW wrote 'Here be many good truths in this little pamphlet'. P. 3, 'W. Laud' written in margin and underscored in red ink. Diff. ed. at Wood 614(62).
Wood 614(56). Wing C5623A. Madan 1153.

2621. England, Parliament. *The declaration and votes of both houses of parliament, concerning the magazine at Hull [26 Apr.].* London: Fr. Leach, 1642. 4°. Pp. [2], 6.

Tp, AW lined out former nos. and wrote 'see another pamphlet following' (e.g. Wood 373(58, 59)). Below, '42'.
Wood 373(57). Wing E1325 (two) (Wing, O impf.[?]).

2622. England, Parliament. *A declaration of the lords and commons . . . upon the statute of 5 H. 4. whereby the commission of array is supposed to be warranted*. London: f. E. Husbands a. J. Frank, 1642. 4°. A2-4,B⁴,D⁴,D⁴; Pp. 1-14, 25-32, 23-30 (wanting t leaf).
Tp, AW altered the former no. '72' to '26' and wrote 'concerning the Array Jun. 1642', 'see another thing p. 27' (AW here noted, on 2nd p. 27, the printed item, 'The Copy of the Kings Letter sent with the Commission of Array to Leicestershire'), and 'See Whitlocks memorialls, p. 57. a.' (i.e., Wing W1986). P. 27 (1st), AW wrote a date in the margin.
Wood 374(26). Wing E1475.

2623. England, Parliament. *A declaration of the lords and commons assembled in parliament. For the raising of all power . . . Together with his majesties . . . answer*. Oxford (rpt.): L. Lichfield, 1642. 4°. Pp. [2], 6, [2], 9 (2 tpp).
Tp, AW lined out the former no., '79'; and wrote 'This Declaration was made 8 Aug 1642', in pencil.
Wood 374(35). Wing E1428 and C2207. Madan 1021-2.

2624. England, Parliament. *A declaration or remonstrance of the state of the kingdome, . . . 19 of May*. [London]: f. T. P., 1642. 4°. Pp. [2], 48. Pasteboard (blue) with parchment spine; rebacked.
Flyleaf, upper, 1st, note by modern librarians concerning the restoration, in 1910 and 1932, of 4 items (5, 12, 18, 27) at an earlier time removed to Hope adds. shelf-marks. Flyleaves, upper, 3rd-5th, AW wrote the heading, 'Vol. 2 Pamphlet containing matters making for, & against, the rebellion that broke forth in 1642', and the titles of 36 printed works in this vol., within guidelines made with red ink. Tp, AW lined out the former no. '6'; below, price, 6ᵈ, prob. not by AW, cropped. There is a closely related item at Wood 614(48), item 2625.
Wood 374(1). Wing E1518.

2625. England, Parliament. *The declaration or remonstrance of the lords and commons . . . with divers depositions and letters [19 May]*. London: f. J. Hunscott a. J. Wright, 1642. 4°. Pp. [2], 59 (i.e., 51, misnumbering).
Flyleaf, upper, addition of 4 figures, and total of '1-2-6', upside down, may not be in AW's hand; ᵛ, AW's instructions for another bound vol., partially lined out: 'A larger [? and 3 words illeg.] then this is the 1. Vol. of Battles'. Tp, AW wrote 'Dupl', twice, in pencil; ᵛ, signature of 'Mary W[ood]'. There is a closely related item at Wood 374(1), item 2624.
Wood 614(48). Wing E1517.

2626. England, Parliament. *The declaration, votes, and order of assistance of both houses of parliament, concerning the magazine at Hull*. London: R. Barker, by the assignes of J. Bill, 1642. 4°. Pp. [2], 14.
Tp, AW overwrote a former no. to make '59'; below, '56' and '4 May'.
Wood 373(59). Wing E1520 (Wing, assistance,).

2627. England, Parliament. *The humble petition and advice of both houses of parliament, with XIX propositions [2 June]*. [London]: f. J. Hunscott, a. J. Wright, 1642. 4°. Pp. [2], 6.
On a slip inserted before the item, AW wrote, 'letters after 26. May 1642'. Tp, he lined out 1 former no., '68', and altered a 2nd from '74' to '75'.
Wood 374(13). Wing E1565.

2628. England, Parliament. *The humble petition of the lords and commons . . . Presented to his majestie at York, the seventeenth of June*. Oxford (rpt.): L. Lichfield, 1642. 4°. Pp. 22.
Tp, AW lined out 3 former nos. '23', '67', '22'.
Wood 374(21). Wing E1578. Madan 1009.

2629. England, Parliament. *The humble petition of the lords and commons to the king, for leave to remove the magazine at Hull*. London: T. P. f. T. B., [1642]. 4°. Pp. 8.
On slip before tp, 'Mugleswick in county pal[atine] of Durham' (i.e., Wood 373(49), item 4574). Tp, AW rubbed out former nos.; date, '8. Apr. 1642', and, wrote in pencil, 'Apr 1642'; below, a no., '38'.
Wood 373(51) (not in Bodl. CD cat.). Wing E1583A ('O' not recorded in Wing).

2630. England, Parliament. *The late letters from both houses of parliament . . . to his majesty*. Oxford: L. Lichfield, 1642. 4°. Pp. [2], [6].
Tp, AW lined out the former no., '22'.

Wood 375(19). Wing E1623. Madan 1070.

2631. England, Parliament. *The manner of the impeachment of the XII. bishops accused of high treason,* . . . *Whereunto is added the said petition . . . of the said bishops*. London: f. J. Hunscott, 1642. 4°. A⁴.
Tp, AW wrote, '4 Dec. 1641', in pencil.
[MS.] Wood D. 31(15). Wing M474.

2632. England, Parliament. *A message from both houses of parliament sent to Yorke to the kings most excellent majestie [28 March]*. London: f. A. Coe, 1642. 4°. A⁴.
AW rubbed out a former no., '35'; below, a no., '27'.
Wood 373(46). Wing E1653A.

2633. England, Parliament. *An order made in parliament concerning the suppressing of those men* . . . *in the countie of Durham [18 Mar.]*. London: f. F. Leach a. F. Coles, 1642. 4°. Pp. [7].
Tp, AW wrote the date, '18. Mar. 1641[2]'; and rubbed out a former no. Dupl. at Wood 614(53).
Wood 373(40). Wing E1687.

2634. England, Parliament. *An order made in parliament concerning the suppressing of those men* . . . *in the countie of Durham [18 Mar.]*. London: f. F. Leach a. F. Coles, 1642. 4°. Pp. [7].
Tp, no. 20 in a former bundle. AW wrote 'Dupl', in pencil. Dupl. at Wood 373(40).
Wood 614(53). Wing E1687.

2635. England, Parliament. *The parliaments resolution concerning the kings determination for the removall of the terme to Yorke [12 May]*. London: T. F. f. T. Bankes, 1642. 4°. Pp. [8].
Missing in 1922; see t written at Wood 373(1): 'The parliaments resolution concerning the kings determination for the removal of the terme to York – And other things'.
Wood 373(66). Wing E2144 (rare). O.

2636. England, Parliament. *The petition of both houses of parliament, presented to his majestie at Yorke, March 26*. London: f. A. C., 1642. 4°. A⁴.
Tp, AW rubbed out a former no.
Wood 373(45). Wing E2160.

2637. England, Parliament. *The petition of the lords and commons, presented to his majestie by the earle of Stamford [18 April] . . . with his majesties answer*. London: R. Barker, by the assignes of J. Bill, 1642. 4°. Pp. [2], 14.
Tp, AW lined out former no., '37' and altered a 2nd. Dupl. at Wood 614(42).
Wood 373(53). Wing E2179.

2638. England, Parliament. *The petition of the lords and commons, presented to his majestie by the earle of Stamford [18 April] . . . with his majesties answer*. London: R. Barker, by the assignes of J. Bill, 1642. 4°. Pp. [2], 14.
Tp, AW wrote 'Dupl', in pencil. Dupl. at Wood 373(53). The Bod. CD cat. also lists a second work at this location, Wing E1586. Both it and the true Wood 614(42) are parliament documents dated 18 April.
Wood 614(42). Wing E2179.

2639. England, Parliament. *A remonstrance or the declaration of the lords and commons, . . . 26 of May, 1641*. London: f. E. Paxton, and T. P., 1642. 4°. Pp. [1], 16.
Tp, AW lined out 2 former nos., '55', '62'; and wrote at '1641', twice, '1642'.
Wood 374(7). Wing E2226A.

2640. England, Parliament. *Several letters from the committees in severall counties. To . . . William Lenthall . . . speaker of the house of commons, . . . June 27*. London: f. J. Hunscott, a. J. Wright, 1642. 4°. Pp. 14 (i.e., 16, misnumbering).
Tp, AW lined out former nos. '20', '64', '69', and altered '22' to '23'; bsm.
Wood 374(23). Wing S2775.

2641. England, Parliament. *That great expedition for Ireland by way of underwriting proposed, by . . . parliament, . . . is heere vindicated*. London: f. J. Hunscott, 1642. 4°. Pp. [2], 14.
Tp, former no., '9', lined out.
Wood 508(11). Wing T839.

2642. England, Parliament. *Three petitions presented, to . . . parliament. 1. The humble petition . . . of Cornwall. 2. The Cheshire petition*. London: f. R. Robinson, 1642. 4°. A⁴.

[MS.] Wood D. 31(33). Wing T1108.

2643. England, Parliament. *To the kings most excellent majesty, and the lords and peeres . . . The humble petition . . . of all the bishops and prelates now called . . . to . . . parliament.* London: f. J. Hunscutt, 1642. S.sh.
AW added 9 surnames to prelate petitioners, e.g., to J. Eborac: 'Williams'; 2 others added by another. [MS.] Wood D. 31(14). Wing T1496C.

2644. England, Parliament. *The humble desires and propositions of the lords and commons in parliament assembled: tendered to his majesty 1. February, 1642 with . . . answer thereunto.* Oxford: L. Lichfield, 1642[3], 4 Feb. 4°. Pp. [2], 14.
Wood 375(32). Wing E1562. Madan 1219.

2645. England, Parliament. *The votes agreed on by the lords and commons concerning a treaty.* Oxford: L. Lichfield, 1642[3], 7 March. 4°. Pp. [2], 18.
Tp, AW overwrote a former no.
Wood 375(38). Wing E2435. Madan 1264.

2646. England, Parliament. *Articles of impeachment by the commons . . . against sir Thomas Gardiner, . . . for severall great crimes.* [London]: n.pub., 1642, 23 May. 4°. Pp. [2], 6.
Tp, no. 68 in a former bundle.
Wood 614(49). Wing E2524A.

2647. England, Parliament. *New votes of both houses of parliament, the 20*[th.] *of May.* [London]: n.pub., 1642, 24 May. 4°. Pp. 8.
Tp, AW lined out the former no., '58', and at 'His Majesties Resolution to take up Arms', wrote, 'see in the next pamphlet' (York (1642), Wood 374(4), item 6736).
Wood 374(3). Wing E1671.

2648. England, Parliament. *A declaration and resolution of the lords and commons in parliament. Concerning his majesties late proclamation for suppressing the present rebellion.* London: f. E. Husband and J. Franke, 1642, 15 August. 4°. A[4].
Wood 375(3). Wing E1313A.

2649. England, Parliament. *An ordinance and declaration of the lord and commons assembled in parliament. For the assessing.* London: f. R. D., 1642, 17 Dec. 4°. A[4].
Wood 375(25). Wing E1770A.

2650. England, Parliament. *Anno regni Caroli . . . decimo septimo. At the parliament begun . . . the third day of November, An. D. 1640. . . . An act for the confirmation of the treaty . . . between the two kingdoms.* Oxford: L. Lichfield, 1643. 4°. A-D[4],E[2].
Tp, no. 3- (cropped at side) in a former bundle.
Wood 612(11) (not in Bodl. CD cat.). Wing E1101. Madan 1576.

2651. England, Parliament. *The declaration of the lords and commons . . . assembled at Oxford . . . concerning . . . peace . . . and the reasons enforcing their absence from Westminster [19 Mar.].* Oxford: L. Lichfield, 1643[4]. 4°. Pp. [2], 38.
Tp, no. 33 in a former bundle.
Wood 612(10b). Wing E1356A. Madan 1563.

2652. England, Parliament. *A declaration of the lords and commons . . . of their proceedings touching a treaty for peace, . . . with the several letters and answers [19 Mar.].* Oxford: L. Lichfield, 1643[4]. 4°. Pp. [2], 23.
Tp, no. 34 in a former bundle. P. 18, at signatures, notes on signers, prob. not in AW's hand (cropped at side).
Wood 612(10a). Wing E1356D. Madan 1560.

2653. England, Parliament. *A letter from a grave gentleman once a member of this house of commons, . . . concerning . . . why he left the house, and concerning the late treaty.* [Oxford]: [L. Lichfield], 1643. 4°. Pp. [2], 22.
Tp, former no., '30'.
Wood 632(9). Wing L1403. Madan 1349.

2654. England, Parliament. *The plotts revealed, and the parliament vindicated.* London: f. F. Coles a.

F. Leach, 1643. 4°. Pp. [2], 22.
Wood 376(73). Wing P2604 (Wing, revealed;).

2655. England, Parliament. *A copy of a letter from the members of both houses assembled at Oxford, to the earle of Essex, . . . desiring a treaty of peace [27 Jan.].* Oxford: L. Lichfield, 1643[4], 30 Jan. 4°. Pp. [2], 6.
Tp, former no., '25'.
Wood 632(5). Wing E1285A (two). Madan 1525.

2656. England, Parliament. *A letter from the lords at Oxford and other lords . . . to the . . . privy-councell . . . of Scotland.* Oxford: L. Lichfield, 1643[4], 1 March. 4°. Pp. [2], 5.
Tp, former no., '26'.
Wood 632(6). Wing E2814. Madan 1542.

2657. England, Parliament. *An ordinance or declaration of the lords and commons . . . for the encouragement of adventurers to make new subscriptions for townes, cities, and lands in Ireland.* London: f. J. Wright, 1643, 15 July. 4°. Pp. [2], 10.
Tp, former no. lined out.
Wood 508(44). Wing E2114.

2658. England, Parliament. *An ordinance . . . for the utter demolishing . . . of all monuments of superstition or idolatry, out of all the churches and chappells [28 Aug.].* [London]: f. E. Husbands, [1643] 29 Aug. 4°. Pp. 8.
[MS.] Wood D. 31(45). Wing E2069.

2659. England, Parliament. *An ordinance of the lords and commons . . . to prevent the coming over of the Irish rebells.* London: f. E. Husbands, 1643, 12 Sept. 4°. Pp. 8.
Tp, former no., '38', lined out.
Wood 508(45). Wing E2097.

2660. England, Parliament. *A copy of a letter from the speakers of both houses of parliament . . . dated July 4. 1643. To the lords, justices, and councell, of . . . Ireland. . . . with the answer.* Oxford: L. Lichfield, 1643, 18 Nov. 4°. Pp. [2], 26.
Tp, former no., '34', lined out.
Wood 508(42). Wing C6129. Madan 1490.

2661. England, Parliament. *A declaration and ordinance . . . touching the great seale of England. And his majesties declaration . . . upon occasion thereof.* Oxford: L. Lichfield, 1643, 21 Nov. 4°. Pp. [2], 18.
Tp, no. 36 in a former bundle.
Wood 612(4). Wing E1307. Madan 1491.

2662. England, Parliament. *An orderly and plaine narration of the beginnings and causes of this warre. Also a . . . resolution against the warre on the parliaments side.* [Oxford]: [L. Lichfield], 1644. 4°. Pp. 24.
Tp, AW wrote 'Dupl', in pencil. Dupl. at 612(28).
Wood 377(40). Wing O391. Madan 1620.

2663. England, Parliament. *An orderly and plaine narration of the beginnings and causes of this warre. Also a . . . resolution against the warre on the parliaments side.* [Oxford]: [L. Lichfield], 1644. 4°. Pp. 24.
Tp, AW's note, in pencil, cropped at top, followed by '44 Dupl Dupl q[uaere]', in pencil at top, and 'dupl', in ink below. P. 24, note, not in AW's hand. Dupl. at Wood 377(40).
Wood 612(28). Wing O391. Madan 1620.

2664. England, Parliament. *Orders presented to his majesty by advice of . . . parliament . . . at Oxford, . . . for . . . rating and levying of monies.* [Oxford]: L. Lichfield, 1644. 4°. Pp. [2], 9.
Tp, former no. in a bundle, '38'.
Wood 526(2) (not in Bodl. CD cat.). Wing E1760 (Wing, Printed, at Oxford, by). Madan 1622.

2665. England, Parliament. *The schedule. In this schedule is contained the excise, set and to be set upon severall commodities [20 May?].* [Oxford]: L. Lichfield, 1644. 4°. Pp. [2], 17.
Wood 526(3). Not in Wing. ESTCR 203516 ('O' not recorded in ESTCR). Madan 1639.

2666. England, Parliament. *The parliaments kalender of black saints.* London: f. G. Bishop, 1644, 24 Aug. 4°. Pp. 8.
Wood 377(28). Wing P512.

2667. England, Parliament. *An ordinance . . . for regulating the university of Cambridge [14 Feb.].*
London: f. J. Wright, 1645[6]. 4°. Pp. [2], 5.
Wood 514(16). Wing E1915.

2668. England, Parliament. *Directions of the lords and commons . . . for the electing and choosing of*
ruling-elders . . . For the . . . presbyteriall-government [19 Aug.]. London: f. J. Wright, 1645, 20 Aug. 4°.
Pp. [2], 10. Pasteboard (blue) with parchment spine. 1st upper and last lower flyleaves, marbled paper.
Flyleaf, upper, 2nd, AW wrote the titles of 16 printed works in this vol., within guidelines made with red
ink.
[MS.] Wood D. 26(1). Wing E1523A.

2669. England, Parliament. *An ordinance . . . Together with rules and directions concerning suspention*
from the sacrament of the Lords supper. London: f. J. Wright, 1645, 21 Oct. 4°. Pp. [2], 14.
Pp. 9-10, 13, in lists, AW wrote 'q[uaere]' at William Thomas, Humphery Chambers and Henry Cornish.
[MS.] Wood D. 26(2). Wing E2099.

2670. England, Parliament. *An ordinance of the lords and commons . . . for raising of twenty thousand*
pounds a moneth for the relief of Ireland [16 Feb. 1647]. London: f. E. Husband, 1646[7], 24 Feb. 4°. Pp.
47.
Wood 509(14). Wing E1914.

2671. England, Parliament. *The propositions of the lords and commons . . . for a safe and well grounded*
peace. Sent to his majesty at Newcastle [15 July]. London: f. J. Wright, 1646, 17 July. 4°. Pp. [2], 29.
Wood 612(36). Wing E2209.

2672. England, Parliament. *Comparatis comparandis: the second part. Or, a parallell of the former, and*
later force, upon the two houses of parliament. [London]: n.pub., 1647. 4°. Pp. 32.
Wood 631(18). Wing C5603. Madan 1938 and 1958.

2673. England, Parliament. *A declaration of the lords and commons . . . die Martis, 30. Martii 1647.*
That the two houses having received information of a dangerous petition [tending to create mutiny in the
army and obstruct the relief of Ireland]. London: f. J. Wright, 1647. S.sh.
AW underscored 'Ireland' and wrote 'Ireland' in the margin.
Wood 509(16). Wing E1351.

2674. England, Parliament. *Die Martis 15. Junii 1647. Ordered by the lords and commons . . . that the*
generall be required to deliver the . . . king . . . at Richmond. London: f. J. Wright, 1647. S.sh.
Wood 657(33). Wing E1733O.

2675. England, Parliament. *The grand account. Or, a remonstrance, wherein is plainly discovered the*
vast summes of money levyed upon the kingdome by ordinance of parliament. . . . Also vox populi, or, the
cry of the commons against committee-men. Oxford: [J. Harris a. H. Hills], 1647. 4°. Pp. [2], 9.
Wood 501(42). Wing G1486. Madan 1947 (Wing, conflates Oxford and London eds.).

2676. England, Parliament. *An ordinance . . . for the putting out of . . . London and Westminster*
. . . for six moneths, all delinquents, papists, and others that have been in arms against the parliament [17
Dec.]. London: f. J. Wright, 1647. 4°. Pp. [2], 6.
Wood 612(55). Wing E2009.

2677. England, Parliament. *An ordinance . . . for the raising of moneys to be imployed towards the*
maintenance of forces . . . under . . . sir T. Fairfax [7 July]. London: f. E. Husband, 1647. 4°. Pp. 40.
Tp, AW wrote 'Dupl', in pencil. No dupl. in AW's collection, but see Wood 501(33), item 2681.
Wood 612(47). Wing E2020A.

2678. England, Parliament. *An ordinance . . . for the visitation and reformation of the universitie of*
Oxford [1 May]. London: f. J. Wright, 1647. 4°. Pp. [2], 6.
Dupl. at Wood 612(52a) and Wood 612(52c).
Wood 514(27). Wing E2071. Madan 1920.

2679. England, Parliament. *An ordinance . . . for the visitation and reformation of the universitie of*
Oxford [1 May]. London: f. J. Wright, 1647. 4°. Pp. [2], 6.
Dupl. at Wood 514(27) and Wood 612(52c).
Wood 612(52a). Wing E2071. Madan 1920.

2680. England, Parliament. *An ordinance . . . for the visitation and reformation of the universitie of Oxford [1 May]*. London: f. J. Wright, 1647. 4°. Pp. [2], 6.
Dupl. at Wood 514(27) and Wood 612(52).
Wood 612(52c). Wing E2071. Madan 1920.

2681. England, Parliament. *An ordinance of the lords and commons . . . for the raising of monies to be imployed towards the maintenance of forces [23 June]*. London: f. J. Wright, 1647. 4°. Pp. [2], 34.
Passim, some underscoring, and, p. 34, flower marker in margin, may not be by AW.
Wood 501(33). Wing E2020.

2682. England, Parliament. *An ordinance . . . against unlicensed or scandalous pamphlets, and for the better regulating of printing [28 Sept.]*. London: f. E. Husband, 1647, 30 Sept. 4°. Pp. 8.
Wood 612(50). Wing E1802.

2683. England, Parliament. *The charge of the commons . . . against Charls Stuart . . . Jan. 20*. London: R. Harford, 1648[9]. 4°. Pp. 8.
Wood 364(9). Wing E2537.

2684. England, Parliament. *Die Veneris, 21 April, 1648. Ordered by the lords and commons . . . that the boursers and treasurers for the colledges in Oxforde*. [London]: n.pub., [1648]. S.sh.
AW wrote they year, '1648'. Dupl. at 514(37).
Wood 423(27). Wing E1733L (rare, 2 at O). Madan 1980.

2685. England, Parliament. *Die Veneris, 21 April, 1648. Ordered by the lords and commons . . . that the boursers and treasurers for the colledges in Oxforde*. [London]: n.pub., [1648]. S.sh.
Tp, note 'I appoint M^r. Prestwich & M^r. Zanchy [/] M^r. Prestwich alone', not in AW's hand, and below, 'John Palmer Custos'. Acquired from Palmer's study, 22 March 1660, LT 1.307. Dupl. at Wood 423(27).
Wood 514(37). Wing E1733L (rare, 2 at O). Madan 1980.

2686. England, Parliament. *Lex parlamentorum: or, an abstract of the antiquity and jurisdiction of . . . parliament, according to the lawes and constitutions*. London: n.pub., 1648. 4°. Pp. [2], 6.
Pp. 2-6, minor underscoring.
Wood 518(5). Wing L1859 ('O' not recorded in Wing).

2687. England, Parliament. *An ordinance . . . for repaying of ten thousand pounds borrowed for the . . . treaty [21 Sept.]*. London: R. Cotes, 1648. 4°. Pp. [1], 5.
Wood 609(5a). Wing E1920A (two).

2688. England, Parliament. *A proclamation for tryall of the king*. London: R. Ibbitson, 1648[9]. 4°. Pp. [2], 6.
Wood 364(8). Wing E2195.

2689. England, Parliament. *Die Martis, 16 Januarii, 1648. An act of the commons of England assembled in parliament, for the adjourning*. London: f. E. Husband, 1648[9], 16 Jan. S.sh.
'This was the first Act made by the House of Commons after they had voted down the King and lords, and assumed the Supremacy', not by AW.
Wood 276a(235). Wing E2504. Steele 2819.

2690. England, Parliament. *Die Veneris, 21 April. 1648. An order of the commons . . . enabling the visitors of Oxford to displace such fellows, . . . as shall contemn the authority of parliament*. London: f. E. Husband, 1648, 24 Apr. S.sh.
Dupl. at Wood 514(39).
Wood 276a(135). Wing E2647. Madan 1979. Steele 2753.

2691. England, Parliament. *Die Veneris, 21 April. 1648. An order of the commons . . . enabling the visitors of Oxford to displace such fellows, . . . as shall contemn the authority of parliament*. London: f. E. Husband, 1648, 24 Apr. S.sh.
Dupl. at Wood 276a(135).
Wood 514(39). Wing E2647. Madan 1979. Steele 2753.

2692. England, Parliament. *Die Veneris 21. April. 1648. Ordered by the lords and commons . . . that in regard of the late contempt of the fellows, . . . if they do not appeare, or . . . submit to the authority of the parliament in the visitation*. [London]: n.pub., [1648, 21 Apr.]. S.sh.
^{v}, note indicating that this was to be in the archives of Merton College with older visitation documents,

not in AW's hand.
Wood 514(38). Wing E1733E (two). Madan 1986.

2693. England, Parliament. *A declaration of the several proceedings of both houses . . . with those in . . . Kent now in arms*. London: f. E. Husband, 1648, 5 June. 4°. Pp. 15.
AW wrote after the date, '29. May. 1648'.
Wood 502(15). Wing E1512.

2694. England, Parliament. *A particular of the several victories and the occasions of . . . thanksgiving appointed by both houses of parliament to be kept . . . the 7. of September*. London: f. E. Husband, 1648, 28 Aug. 4°. Pp. 8.
Wood 502(61). Wing E2153.

2695. England, Parliament. *Die Sabbathi; 20 Januarii. 1649[50] . . . Henr: Scobel, cler. parl. dom. com. [An answer to a petition presented by lieut-gen. Hammond, col. Okey and other officers]*. [London]: n.pub., [1649 (or 1650?)]. 4°. S.sh.
Wood 610(52). Wing L1979A (two).

2696. England, Parliament. *Severall votes and orders of the house of parliament [23-25 Oct. 1649]*. London: R. Cotes, 1649. S.sh.
Wood 445(5). Wing E2298.

2697. England, Parliament. *A declaration of the parliament of England, of their just resentment of the horrid murther . . . of Isaac Dorislaus, . . . at the Hague, on the 12*[th] *of May*. London: f. E. Husband, 1649, 21 May. Fol. Pp. numbered 237, 246, and 247. Tt^2.
Wood 365(10). Wing E1504. ESTCR 208594 (two) ('O' not recorded in ESTCR).

2698. England, Parliament. *The true state of the transactions of colonel George Monk with Owen-Roe-mac-Art-O-Neal; as it was reported to the parliament*. London: f. E. Husband, 1649, 15 Aug. 4°. Pp. 15.
AW wrote at top, '9 May 25', and no. '25', in pencil.
Wood 510(4). Wing T3119 ('O' not recorded in Wing).

2699. England, Parliament. *An act for a day of publique thanksgiving [1 Nov.]*. London: J. Field f. E. Husband, 1649, 11 Oct. S.sh.
[v], 'To the Constable of Woollvercott. By Vertue of a Warrant from the high Shreife of this County you are to cause this act and Declaration, herewith sent to you, to be published on Sunday Next by the Minister in your Parish Church, and that you make returne of the doing theireof to the Said Shreiffe, and if it be hindered or Neglected by any you are to return their Names – Likewise to him, hereof you are not to fayle [/] Dated, 24 October: 1649: John Wood:' LT 1.158-9.
Wood 510(9). Wing E993.

2700. England, Parliament. *Die Jovis, 18 Julii, 1650. Resolves . . . for . . . making void of all licences . . . to any persons comprised within the late act for remaining delinquents from London*. London: E. Husband a. J. Field, 1650. S.sh.
Wood 503(10). Wing E2277.

2701. England, Parliament. *An answer to a paper entitled a true narrative of the . . . dissolution of the late parliament . . . by a member of the house*. London: T. N. f. G. Calvert, 1653[4]. 4°. Pp. [2], 10.
Wood 519(9). Wing A3329.

2702. England, Parliament. *Discourses political and moral, of the conveniency and justice of reserving some lands in Ireland, towards satisfying the arrears and publique faith of England [10 June]*. N.p.: n.pub., [1653]. 4° (large). Pp. 3.
Tp, AW wrote below, 'Jun 10. 53'. LT 1.181.
Wood 510(19). Not in Wing (not E793C). Not in ESTCR.

2703. England, Parliament. *A true narrative of the cause and manner of the dissolution of the late parliament . . . 12 of Decemb. 1653. By a member of the house*. N.p.: n.pub., 1653 (Printed in the Year). 4°. Pp. 8.
Tp, AW wrote below, 'To be bound up with the proceedings of that parl. which I have elsw', in pencil (i.e., Wood 519(10), item 2136).
Wood 519(8). Wing T2777aA ('O' not recorded in Wing).

2704. England, Parliament. *Ordinances for ejecting scandalous ministers and schoolmasters*. London:

?, 1654. Pp.?
Missing. In a list of 'Mr. Woods Duplicats', MS. Wood F. 51, f. 44, item 47.
MS. Wood F. 51(47). Not identified.

2705. England, Parliament. *A narrative of the late parliament, (so called) their election and appearing, the seclusion of a great part of them*. [London]: n.pub., 1657[8]. 4°. Pp. 32.
Tp, AW wrote the price, '8ᵈ'. Bsm. Pp. 4, 9-13, 15-17, 22-3, a correction, 6 brief identifications or corrections after names, and lines in margin, in ink and pencil. See also items 5993 and 6532.
Wood 620(14). Wing N194.

2706. England, Parliament. *An apologie and vindication of the major part of the members of parliament excluded . . . January 24. 1659*. London: T. Radcliffe, 1659[60]. 4°. Pp. 16.
Tp, AW wrote, above, 'Parl' and below, 'Jan 24', in pencil.
Wood 610(26). Wing A3542.

2707. England, Parliament. *A declaration of the parliament assembled at Westminster [23 Jan.]*. London: J. Streater a. J. Macock, 1659[60]. 4°. Pp. 16.
Wood 610(38). Wing E1491.

2708. England, Parliament. *A declaration of the proceedings of the parliament & army; and the resolution of the souldiery*. London: f. E. Richardson, 1659. 4°. Pp. 7.
Tp, AW wrote 'Bund. 2 nu. 3', in pencil.
Wood 620(25). Wing D752 (4) ('O' not recorded in Wing).

2709. England, Parliament. *England anatomized: her disease discovered, and the remedy prescribed, in a speech by a member of the (so called) parliament*. [London]: n.pub., [1659]. 4°. Pp. 8. Calf with 3 fillets, stamp decoration inside corners (2 leaves and sunflower sprouting fleur-de-lis), and roll decoration at inner, spine edge (Ashm. binding); rebacked.
Flyleaf, upper, 2nd, and lower, 1st, the titles of 64 printed works in this vol., by an Ashm. librarian. On the upper flyleaf, 1-41 (40-41 were written as LX and LXI) and on the lower flyleaf, 42-64 (also incorrect Roman numerals, see note at Wood 610(64)). Item 4b is not in the list and item 53 has 2 entries, 53 and 54. Item no. 17 was removed before 1837. The same errors in Roman numeration occur on the tpp of works in this vol.; all were later corrected. Most of AW's brief entries of the dates in the items in this vol. are in his early hand. Many have up to 2 nos. which designated their places in earlier bundles.
Wood 610(1). Wing E2927.

2710. England, Parliament. *The humble petition of divers . . . delivered . . . to . . . parliament [6 July] . . . With the parliaments answer there-unto*. London: f. T. Brewster, 1659. 4°. Pp. 14.
Tp, no. 59 in a former bundle.
Wood 610(51). Wing H3463.

2711. England, Parliament. *Long parliament-work, (if they wil please to do't) for the good of the common-weath*. London: T. L. f. G. Calvert, 1659. 4°. Pp. [2], 16.
Tp, no. '26', in pencil, in a former bundle (cropped at bottom).
Wood 613(43). Wing L2992.

2712. England, Parliament. *Loyal queries, humbly tendred to the serious consideration of the parliament, and army*. London: n.pub., 1659. 4°. Pp. 8.
Tp, no. '47', in pencil, in a former bundle.
Wood 613(52). Wing L3361.

2713. England, Parliament. *The moderate man's proposall to the parliament about tithes*. London: A. W. f. G. Calvert, 1659. 4°. Pp. 7.
Tp, AW wrote, at top, 'Tithes', and at bottom the no. in a former bundle, '48', in pencil.
Wood 370(8). Wing M2326.

2714. England, Parliament. *No return to monarchy; and liberty of conscience secured, without a senate, . . . over the peoples representatives, . . . tendered to . . . parliament*. London: f. T. Brewster, 1659. 4°. Pp. 8.
Tp, no. 52, in pencil, in a former bundle.
Wood 613(11). Wing N1191.

2715. England, Parliament. *The parliaments plea: or XX. reasons for the union of the parliament & army*. [London]: n.pub., 1659. 4°. Pp. 23.

P. 1, no. 15 in a former bundle.
Wood 616(8). Wing P521.

2716. England, Parliament. *Several resolves prepared by the commanding junto to pass the house.* [London]: n.pub., 1659. 4°. Pp. 8.
Tp, no. 33 in a former bundle.
Wood 610(7). Wing S2810.

2717. England, Parliament. *To the supreme authority, the parliament . . . The humble address . . . of watermen.* London: J. Streater, a. J. Macock, 1659[60]. S.sh.
Wood 276a(194). Wing T1744 (3). Steele 3149.

2718. England, Parliament. *A true narrative of the proceedings in parliament . . . from 22 Sep. untill this present [16 Nov.].* London: J. Redmayne, 1659. 4°. Pp. [4], 72 (pp. unopened).
Tp, at 'this present', AW wrote, 'Nov. 16. an. 1659', and below, 'dupl.', in pencil. Dupl. at Wood 613(1).
Wood 519(12). Wing E2382.

2719. England, Parliament. *A true narrative of the proceedings in parliament, . . . from 22 Sep. untill this present [16 Nov.].* London: J. Redmayne, 1659. 4°. Pp. [4], 72. Calf with 3 fillets, stamp decoration inside corners, and roll decoration at inner, spine edge (Ashm. binding).
Flyleaf upper, 1st, 'Museum'; 1st^v and 2nd^{r-v}, the titles of 63 printed works in this vol. (really 65, including 5b and 10b), by an Ashm. librarian (same hand in Wood 276a). Numbering of items on tpp is in Roman numerals. AW's Arabic nos., in pencil, survive on 33 pamphlets in this vol. and indicate how he arranged, and rearranged, them in earlier bundles. Most of the items, including those with annotations in margins, were trimmed to small quarto size in the binding. Tp, no. '45' in a former bundle. Dupl. at Wood 519(12).
Wood 613(1). Wing E2382.

2720. England, Parliament. *Certain considerations: being the legitimate issue of a true English heart:. . . to regulate their elections of members [25 Apr.].* London: n.pub., 1660. 4°. Pp. [2], 6.
Tp, AW wrote 'Parl and 3 bund', in pencil; and altered the year to 16'59 March'.
Wood 620(40). Wing C1691.

2721. England, Parliament. *A declaration of the people of England for a free-parliament.* [London]: n.pub., [1660]. S.sh.
AW wrote 'Januar: 1659[60] [/] 200: 90 & 5 hands' (really 285 signers). LT 1.301.
Wood 276a(214). Wing D737.

2722. England, Parliament. *Die Veneris, 18 Maii, 1660. Upon complaint this day made by the commons in parliament, it is ordered by the lords.* London: J. Macock a. F. Tyton, 1660. S.sh. Pasteboard (blue) with parchment spine. 1st upper and last lower flyleaves, marbled paper.
Flyleaf, upper, 2nd^{r-v}, AW wrote 'K. Ch 1.', in pencil, and the titles of 10 printed works in this vol., within guidelines made with red ink.
Wood 369(1). Wing E2858.

2723. England, Parliament. *Englands directions for members elections.* [London]: n.pub., [1660]. S.sh.
AW wrote, 'March: 1659[60]'; ^v, 'Mar 59', and '62' replaced a former no. '44' in pencil.
Wood 416(62). Wing E2959.

2724. England, Parliament. *The form of writs to be issued forth under the great seal of England, for the election . . . in the parliament [25 April].* London: J. Redmayne, 1660. S.sh.
AW altered the year to 16'59 March'. LT 1.304.
Wood 620(37). Wing F1583 ('O' not recorded in Wing).

2725. England, Parliament. *The humble answer of the house of peers to his majesties . . . letter and declaration [23 May].* London: J. Macock a. F. Tyton, 1660. 4°. Pp. [4], 4 (p. [1] blank).
Wood 608(15). Wing E2806.

2726. England, Parliament. *Instructions lately agreed on . . . for the commissioners sent . . . to the Hague, unto the kings . . . majesty. Together with the speech made . . . by . . . Denzell Holles [16 May].* London: f. R. Clavel, 1660. 4°. Pp. [4], 3 (p. [1] blank).
P. [1], AW wrote, 'To come in betw. Sr Harb. Grimstons speech and the E. of Manchester' (see notes at Wood 608(1a) and 608(19), items 5161, 4538).
Wood 608(17). Wing E1595 ('O' not recorded in Wing).

2727. England, Parliament. *A letter to general Monk, expressing the sense of many . . . old parliamenters, and old Puritanes [22 Jan. 1659]*. [London]: n.pub., [1660]. S.sh.
AW wrote 'dupl.', in ink. Dupl. at Wood 276a(246).
Wood 276a(245). Wing L1704 (3) ('O' not recorded in Wing).

2728. England, Parliament. *A letter to general Monk, expressing the sense of many . . . old parliamenters, and old Puritanes [22 Jan. 1659]*. [London]: n.pub., [1660]. S.sh.
Dupl. at Wood 276a(245).
Wood 276a(246). Wing L1704 (3) ('O' not recorded in Wing).

2729. England, Parliament. *A letter to the kings . . . majesty from the commons . . . in answer of his . . . letter [2, 14 May]*. London: E. Husbands a. T. Newcomb, [1660]. Fol. Pp. [2], 6.
Wood 657(24). Wing E2622.

2730. England, Parliament. *No droll, but a rational account, making out the probable fall of the present, with the rise . . . of a free parliament*. London: f. Y. E. (f. H. Brome), [1660]. 4°. Pp. 16.
Tp, AW wrote 'Parl' and 'Jan 30', in pencil and in ink, and below, '1659'. P. 16 , 1660 altered to '59'.
Wood 610(62). Wing N1175.

2731. England, Parliament. *No new parliament: or, some queries . . . humbly offered to the present parlament-members [12 Mar. 1659[60]]*. London: n.pub., 1660. 4°. Pp. [2], 5 (misnumbering).
Tp, AW wrote 'parl', in pencil; altered the year to 16'59: March' and later, wrote 'Mar. 12. an. 1659'.
Wood 613(62). Wing N1183.

2732. England, Parliament. *The oath of allegiance, enacted 13. Jacobi, cap. 4*. [London]: n.pub., 1660. S.sh.
AW altered the date to 16 '59: March' (LT 1.363).
Wood 276a(143) (not in Bodl. CD cat.). Wing O71 (one) ('O' not recorded in Wing).

2733. England, Parliament. *A pertinent speech made by an honourable member of the house of commons, tending to the establishment of kingly government*. London: n.pub., 1660. 4°. Pp. [2], 6.
Tp, AW altered the year to 16'59: March:'.
Wood 610(20). Wing P1674.

2734. England, Parliament. *A proclamation of both houses of parliament, for proclaiming of his majesty king of England*. London: J. Macock, a. F. Tyton, 1660. S.sh.
Wood 276a(130). Wing E2196. Steele 3188.

2735. England, Parliament. *The qualifications of the succeeding parliament*. [London]: n.pub., [1660]. S.sh.
AW wrote 'fictions March: 1659[60]'.
Wood 620(38). Wing Q38 (4).

2736. England, Parliament. *To his excellency the lord general Monck. The humble address of the members of parliament . . . February 4, 1659*. London: f. T. P., [1660]. S.sh.
ᵛ, AW wrote 'Feb. 4: 59'.
Wood 276a(241). Wing T1356B ('O' not recorded in Wing).

2737. England, Parliament. *The funeral of the good old cause: or, a covenant of . . . parliament against the solemn league and covenant*. London: R. Royston, 1661. 4°. Pp. 8.
Wood 613(31). Wing F2538.

2738. England, Parliament. *A reply to the funeral of the good old cause, or covenant*. [London]: n.pub., 1661. 4°. Pp. [2], 5.
Wood 613(32). Wing R1073.

2739. England, Parliament. *The poll-bill, as to be given in charge [orders respecting]*. [London], in the Savoy: (by the assigns of J. Bill a. C. Barker), (1666). Fol. Pp. 4.
Wood 657(32). Wing P2772 ('O' not recorded in Wing).

2740. England, Parliament. *Articles of treason, exhibited in parliament, against Edward earl of Clarendon [14 Nov. 1667]*. [London]: n.pub., [1667]. S.sh.
At 'Mr. Seymor's Speech', AW wrote, 'Edw. Seymore afterwards a Kt. & speaker of Parl.' At 'he has corruptly sold several Offices': 'see the 15 head' (i.e., printed item XV. 'That he [Clarendon] procured the

Bills of Settlement for *Ireland,* and received great sums of Money for the same, in a most corrupt and unlawful manner.'). LT 2.122.
Wood 276b(108). Wing A3878 (Wing, exhibitted).

2741. England, Parliament. *The grand concern of England explained; in several proposals offered to . . . parliament, . . . by a lover of his countrey.* London: n.pub., 1673. 4°. Pp. [2], 62 (misnumbering).
Tp, AW wrote, 'q[uaere] wh[o?] in cat.'; 'R. S.' (Ralph Sheldon), LT 3.105.
[MS.] Wood D. 27(8). Wing G1491.

2742. England, Parliament. *Votes and addresses . . . 1673, concerning popery and other grievances [29 March].* [London]: n.pub., [1673]. 4°. Pp. 7.
Wood 608(47). Wing E2257.

2743. England, Parliament. *The voice of the nation, or, an humble address to . . . parliament, for their just severity to repress . . . atheism and prophaneness.* London: f. H. Brome, 1675. S.sh.
[MS.] Wood D. 30(10). Wing V680.

2744. England, Parliament. *An impartial account of divers remarkable proceedings the last sessions of parliament relating to the horrid popish plot.* London: n.pub., 1679. Fol. Pp. [2], 26 (misnumbering).
Tp, AW wrote 'pret. 1ˢ-0' and 'This booke is onlie a collection made from Coffey-Letters, & in the said letters I have seen all the particulars except the Latine pardon of Tho. E. of Danby = A cheat & written on purpose to get money –'; '16' over former no. '8' in pencil, and '17'. LT 2.475.
Wood 424(17). Wing I62.

2745. England, Parliament. *To the nobility of England (Exemplar literarum quas comites & barones Angliae miserunt papae super negotio Scotorum, anno regni regis, Edwardi primi, 29. [/ and translation on p. 2] The coppy of a letter sent by the earls and barons of England to the Pope.* Oxford: L. Lichfield, through M. Pitt & H. Mortlock, of London, [1679, 8 Feb.]. Fol. Pp. 2 (or large s.sh.).
Missing in 1939. 'A pamphlett dedicated to the nobility England [sic], containing a letter from the barons of England to the pope' (Innocent XI).
Wood 276a(67). Wing T1577 (two). Madan 3210. O, BL.

2746. England, Parliament. *An authentical account of the formalities, and judicial proceedings, upon arraigning, at Westminster, a peer . . . before a lord high-steward.* London: f. Y. H., [1680]. 4°. Pp. 36.
Tp, AW wrote the year, '1680-81', in pencil.
Wood 629(5). Wing A4264.

2747. England, Parliament. *A coppy of the journal-book . . . for the sessions of parliament begun [21 Oct. to 30 Dec. 1678].* London: n.pub., 1680. 8°. Pp. [4], 215. Pasteboard (blue) with parchment spine; 1st and last flyleaf, upper and lower, marbled paper.
Flyleaf, upper, 2ndᵛ, AW wrote a brief description of the 1st printed work and a long t of the 2nd in this vol., within guidelines made with red ink.
Wood 621(1). Wing E2544.

2748. England, Parliament. *A true and perfect collection of all messages, addresses, &c. from the house of commons [1660-79].* London: n.pub., 1680. Fol. Pp. [2], 50.
Tp, AW wrote the price, '1ˢ-6', and 'In the latter end of this book are many things relating to the popish plot – And therefore tis bound up here – published in the latter end of 1679'. Bsm.
Wood 424(31). Wing E2746.

2749. England, Parliament. *A collection of the substance of several speeches and debates . . . upon occasion of the bill for disabling James duke of York from inheriting the imperial crown.* London: f. F. Smith, 1681. Fol. Pp. 20.
Tp, AW wrote, 'published in the latter end of the yeare 1680'; at a bill 'disabling James D. of York', 'v. p. 14. 15'; and '6ᵈ'. Pp. 3-9, AW identified the speakers; p. 3, at a motion to punish R. L'Estrange, 'The house addressed to his Maj. to put him out of the commission & all other employments for ever which was granted, & the Lord Chanc. gave order to strike him out of the Roll–'. Dupl at Wood 660c(20).
Wood 427(10). Wing E2538.

2750. England, Parliament. *A collection of the substance of several speeches and debates . . . upon occasion of the bill for disabling James duke of York from inheriting the imperial crown.* London: f. F. Smith, 1681. Fol. Pp. 20.
Tp, at L–, AW wrote, 'Lovelace'; and below, 'dupl', in pencil. P. 17, 'At the end of the B of Carlile [sic; E.

Rainbowe] speech – qu[illegible] Duke of York', in pencil. Dupl. at Wood 427(10).
Wood 660c(20). Wing E2538.

2751. England, Parliament. *The debates in the house of commons assembled at Oxford the twenty first of March, 1680[1]*. (London): (f. R. Baldwin), (1681). Fol. (cropped). Sheets A and B only are re-set. Pp. 20.
Pp. 1-19, speakers identified, not in AW's hand.
Wood 657(64). Wing E2546.

2752. England, Parliament. *The debates in the . . . house of commons, assembled at Oxford, March 21. 1680[1]. Printed from R. Baldwin's printed copy. To which is added the whole proceeding*. London: f. J. Peacock, 1681. Fol. Pp. 10 (i.e., 12: 1-8, 7-10, misnumbering).
Tp, above, right, former no. '20' (?) in pencil.
Wood 657(65-66). Wing E2545.

2753. England, Parliament. *Englands appeal to the parliament at Oxford, March 21st. 1680/1*. (London): (R. Janeway), (1681). S.sh. (r-v).
Former no. '6'. LT 2.521.
Wood 657(52) (not in Bodl. CD cat.). Wing E2945.

2754. England, Parliament. Jones, W., ed. *An exact collection of the most considerable debates . . . at the parliament held [21 Oct. 1680 to 18 Jan. 1681]*. London: f. R. Baldwin, 1681. 8°. Pp. [8], 295.
Flyleaf, upper, 1st and 2nd, AW wrote an index of persons whose initials he identified: 'Mr Arth. [Charl]et [? mutilated] his observation, of the names of those who spoke in the debate followinge. [/] p. 47. 57. 69. 239. Booth or Buscawen', etc., some 50 names with p. nos. of their speeches. AW wrote many names beside the initials where they occur in the text, and identified others not in this index, mainly in ink (see pp. 17, 20, 25, where he wrote 1st in pencil and later overwrote the names in ink). On p. 32, AW wrote 'q[uaere]', in pencil, at 'H. made a Speech . . . ', and on a loose slip, 'Tis said in Joh. Hamdens triall for high misdemeanors, 6. Feb 1683 that he did not sit in the last Westm. Parliament, which was in Oct 1680, he being then in France – see p. 32 . . . . [/] So then this J. H. must be either be [sic] John Hunt of Milborne Port in Somersetsh. or Joh. Hales of New Shoreham in Sussex. q[uaere]'. On a second slip, pasted on p. 61, AW wrote 'J. B. either Joh. Birch or Joh. Booth both for Webley – Heref.'
Wood 621(2). Wing E2575.

2755. England, Parliament. *Heads of the expedient proposed in the parliament at Oxford, in lieu of the former bill for excluding the duke of York*. (London): (F. Collins), (1681). S.sh. (r-v).
LT 2.504-5.
Wood 660c(24). Wing H1294.

2756. England, Parliament. *Vox patriae: or the resentments & indignation of the free-born subjects of England, against popery, . . . to . . . parliament held at Oxford [21 March 1681]. With a perfect list*. London: f. F. Peters, 1681. Fol. Pp. [2], 26.
Tp, former no. '4' in pencil.
Wood 657(48). Wing V725.

2757. England, Parliament. *Vox populi, vox dei: or, Englands general lamentation for the dissolution of the parliament*. [London]: (f. T. B.), (1681). S.sh. (r-v).
P. 1, AW wrote, 'See in Oxford parl.', in pencil.
Wood 657(50). Wing V737.

2758. England, Parliament. *A short state of the case between the physicians & surgeons, relating to the surgeons bill, now before the . . . house of commons*. [London]: n.pub., [1690?]. S.sh. (r-v).
v, AW wrote, 'Walt. Charlton presid. of the coll. of physitians in the place of Dr Dan. Whistler 1684. qu[aere]', cropped at side. AO 4.133 and 4.752 (where AW corrected: Charleton became president in 1689, though Whistler died in 1684).
Wood 657(70). Wing S3630B (Wing, [169-]).

2759. England, Parliament. *Anno regni Gulielmi III. regis Angliae, . . . sexto & septimo. At the parliament begun at Westminster the twentieth day of March, Anno Dom. 1689 [to 20 Nov. 1694]. An act for the kings most gracious, general and free pardon*. London: C. Bill a. executrix of T. Newcomb, 1695. Fol. Pp. [2], 483-515.
Wood 657(36). Wing E1065aA (two) ('O' not in Wing). ESTCR 228757.

2760. England, Parliament List. *The order and manner of the sitting of the lords . . . in the higher house of parliament* (signed E. G[rimstone]). London: n.pub., 1624. 4°. A-C⁴. Pasteboard (blue) with parchment spine; 1st upper and last lower flyleaves, marbled paper.
Flyleaf, upper, 2nd^v, AW wrote the titles of 8 printed works in this vol. (listed by year of sessions), within guidelines made with red ink: 'Catalogues of Parliament men for the yeares 1624 . . . 1658', and 'Catalogues of Parl. men for Scotland and Ireland for the yeares 1653 . . . 1658'. Tp, underscoring, in pencil. A2, 'School', may not be in AW's hand. Some minor annotation by AW, e.g., A4, correction and line in margin. Flyleaf, lower, similar notes about the contents of the vol., pasted over with marbled paper.
Wood 358(1). STC 7743 (two).

2761. England, Parliament List. *The order and manner of the sitting of the lords . . . of parliament.*
London: E. Allde f. T. Walkley, 1626. 4°. A-C⁴ (C4 blank).
Flyleaf, upper^v, AW wrote, 'The 3^d [and above: '4th'] edit. of this following cat. was printed in 8° 1628. printed for Tho. Walkley – 8°.K.3.Arts BS - in bib. Bod' (no longer at this location). Some corrections and additions, A3, A4^v, B, to end, not in AW's hand, though some lines in margin may be by AW, e.g., A4^v.
Wood 358(2). STC 7744.

2762. England, Parliament List. *A catalogue of the dukes, . . . in this parliament . . . 3. November, 1640.* London: [J. Dawson] f. T. Walkley, 1640. 8°. Pp. [2], 11.
Tp, AW wrote the price, '2^d'. P. 10, at Charles Wilmot, horizontal line in margin.
Wood 358(4). STC 7746.9.

2763. England, Parliament List. *A catalogue of the names of the knights . . . for this parliament . . . 13. of Aprill, 1640.* London: [J. Dawson] f. T. Walkley, 1640. 8°. A⁸.
Tp, signature of 'John Blayne' and 'Tendit in ardua virtus' in his hand. A2^v, A4^v, A5, A6^v, A8, a vertical line by a name.
Wood 358(3). STC 7746.7.

2764. England, Parliament List. *A catalogue of the names of the knights . . . for this parliament [3 Nov.].* London: [J. Dawson] f. T. Walkley, 1640. 8°. A⁸.
A5, line in margin and correction of John Shelden to John Selden.
Wood 358(5). STC 7746.13.

2765. England, Parliament List. *A catalogue of the names of the dukes, marquesses, earles and lords, that have absented themselves from the parliament . . . As also, a list of the army of . . . Robert, earle of Essex . . . A list of the navie royall . . . The names of the orthodox divines . . . Lastly, the field officers chosen for the Irish expedition.* [London]: n.pub., 1642. 4°. Pp. [2], 21. Pasteboard (blue) with parchment spine.
Flyleaves, upper, 1st^v-3rd^v. AW wrote the titles of 40 printed works in this vol., within guidelines made with red ink (really 39, one item at (15-16)); the last 2, nos. 39, 40, are reversed in the bound vol. After the 1st entry, AW wrote, 'Note that in this pamphlet, which consists of three sheets, are the lists of the Army of Rob. Earl of Essex . . . ', 9 lines, much the same as the t, above. This vol. contains pamphlets concerning the parliament during the interregnum period, with many lists of participants on the royalist and commonwealth sides. AW several times reorganized these items and made frequent annotations. He wrote Arabic nos. on tpp. 1st item, tp, 'This cat. hath a larg title, because it containes many things, & therefore it may be bound up in another vol. as well as this.' In t, 'from the Parliament' is underscored. There are a few marks in ink and pencil on various pp., e.g., 7-12, AW numbered twenty different regiments with lists of names, and marked 4 names; 14, 'v. p. 13' at Tho. Hamond (John Hamond is on p. 13); 19-21, extensive underscoring and 2 corrections.
Wood 620(1). Wing C1393.

2766. England, Parliament List. *The names of such members of the commons house . . . as have already subscribed . . . for the speedy reducing of the rebels, . . . Also a speciall order . . . concerning the free offer of the county of Buckingham.* Lo[ndon]: [A. N. for J.] Franck, 1642. S.sh. (mutilated at bottom).
^{v}, no. '39', may not be in AW's hand.
Wood 508(9). Wing N129 ('O' not recorded in Wing).

2767. England, Parliament List. *A catalogue of sundrie knights, aldermen, . . . who denying to contribute money . . . are in custody in Gresham colledge.* [London]: f. J. Jackson, G. Green, a. F. Smith, 1642, 7 Nov. S.sh.
^{v}, AW wrote the date, '2 Nov. 1642'.
Wood 375(20). Wing C1367.

2768. England, Parliament List. *A more exact and necessary catalogue of pensioners in the long parliament*. [London]: n.pub., 1648. S.sh.
2nd col., identification of J. B., 'Birch', and a mark in margin at Algernoon Sidney. ᵛ, AW wrote 'Pensioners 1648'.
Wood 620(9). Wing M2697A (rare).

2769. England, Parliament List. *The names of the knights, . . . of the parliament . . . Novem. 3. 1640*. London: f. T. Walkley, 1652. 8°. Pp. 26.
A few minor corrections and notes, e.g., p. 26, at printed 'Philip Earl of Pembroke', AW wrote, 'son of Philip'.
Wood 358(7). Wing N135 (two).

2770. England, Parliament List. *A list of the names of all the members of this present parliament, . . . With the names of the members . . . for regulating the abuses*. London: R. Ibbitson, 1653. S.sh.
Tp, AW wrote 'This Parl. called the Little or Praise-God Barebones parl. met at Westminster . . . July 1653'; below, note in pencil, cropped; ᵛ, Ju[ly], cropped at side.
Wood 620(13). Wing E2463.

2771. England, Parliament List. *The names of the members of parliament. . . . Which began . . . Fourth of June, 1653 . . . With the severall transactions since that time*. London: M. Simmons f. T. Jenner, 1654. 4°. Pp. [2], 70.
Wood 519(7). Wing N142.

2772. England, Parliament List. *A catalogue of the names of this present parliament, interrupted April 19. 1653. Whereof those that do not yet sit, are marked*. London: D. Maxwell, 1659. S.sh.
In t, at 'not yet sit', AW wrote '1659'; ᵛ, 'Parl. interupted 1653'.
Wood 620(23). Wing C1403.

2773. England, Parliament List. *A list of the names of the long parliament, anno 1640*. London: n.pub., 1659. 8°. Pp. 70.
Tp, AW wrote the year, '1643', in red ink, above a reference to the parliament at Oxford. Pp. 8, 22-3, 27-8, 31-2, etc. a few marks in margins and corrections. Between pp. 38-9, a slip was bound into the vol. On this AW wrote, after Coke's book appeared in 1694, 'It doth appear in Roger Cokes 2ᵈ vol. of Detection - p. 77 that [t]he Scottish & Irish citizens & Burgesses met which which [sic] were chose to sit in parl. 1654 . 56 . 58. did sit at Westminster among the English Kᵗˢ and Burgesses, & not at Edenburgh or Dublin' (i.e., *A detection of the court and state of England* (1694), Wing C4973).
Wood 358(8). Wing L2475 ('O' not recorded in Wing). Madan 2427.

2774. England, Parliament List. *The grand memorandum: or, a true and perfect catalogue of the secluded members . . . sitting 16. March, 1659. . . . Also . . . of the rumpers*. London: f. E. Husbands, 1660. S.sh.
AW altered the year to 16'59'. Underscoring of one Christian name, John Corbet. ᵛ, 'To be taken o[ut?]', cropped, in red ink.
Wood 620(33). Wing G1503 ('O' not recorded in Wing).

2775. England, Parliament List. *A list of the names of the knights citizens . . . of the cinque ports . . . for the parliament [25 Apr.]*. London: f. R. Pawley, 1660. S.sh.
2 corrections; 1 addition. At bottom, 'I have another cat. of these names in qu[arto]'. Diff. ed. at Wood 620(39).
Wood 276a(87). Wing L2472 (rare).

2776. England, Parliament List. *A perfect list of the names of the knights, citizens, burgesses, and barons of the cinque ports . . . for the parliament begun [25 Apr.]*. London: printed for Robert Pawley, 1660. 4°. Pp. 7, [1] (misnumbering).
AW wrote '25 Apr'. P. 4, 6, a few pen and pencil marks in margins and an underscoring; 8, an underscoring and mark in margin. Diff. ed. at Wood 276a(87). LT 1.304.
Wood 620(39). Wing P1498 ('O' not recorded in Wing) (Wing, for for Robert Pawley [sic]).

2777. England, Parliament List. *A list of the knights, citizens, and burgesses . . . in the parliament [8 May]*. London: f. N. Books [i.e., Brooks], 1661. S.sh.
Col. 1, line in margin, col. 4, brief addition at Sir Antony Cope, 'Bart'.
Wood 276a(89). Wing L2450 (rare).

2778. England, Parliament List. *A list of the members elected for the parliament . . . at Westminster the 8th of May*. London: f. T. Poole, 1661. S.sh.
Col. 5, name of Sir William Portman is marked in pencil.
Wood 276a(91). Wing L2454 (rare).

2779. England, Parliament List. *A most exact list of the names of the knights, citizens, . . . of the cinque-ports . . . for the parliament [8 May]*. [London]: [T. Walkley], [1661]. 4°. Pp. 8 (obl.) (all cut at bottom; 2 cut fragments, loose, survive).
See Wood 276a(89-90) and LT 1.400.
Wood 487(4). Wing M2876A (rare).

2780. England, Parliament List. *A perfect list of the knights, citizens, burgesses of the cinque ports . . . for the parliament ensuing [8 May]*. N.p.: n.pub., [1661]. S.sh.
At 'Richard Ingoldsby', AW wrote, 'Kt of the Bat[h]:'; he added some corrections and marks after entries; and at 'Published to prevent false Copies', he wrote, 'This Coppy is false - I have a truer among my pamphlets for 1661' (see Wood 276a(89), Wood 487(4), and Wood 620(39)). LT 1.400.
Wood 276a(90). Not in Wing (should be at P1498C). Not in ESTCR.

2781. England, Parliament List. *A list of one unanimous club of voters in his majesties long parliament, dissolved in 78*. [London]: n.pub., [1679]. Fol. Pp. 4. See Plate VIII.
Wood 276a(99). Wing L2403.

2782. England, Parliament List. *A list of the names of the knights, citizens, . . . that were returned to serve . . . at Oxford, March 21*. [London]: n.pub., [1681]. Fol. Pp. [4].
Wood 657(67). Wing L2474 ('O' not recorded in Wing).

2783. England, Parliament List. *The Oxford list of the names of the knights, citizens, . . . in the parliament [21 March]*. Oxford: L. Lichfield, f. J. Starkey, sold, at London, 1681. S.sh.
AW wrote, col. 6, a cross-reference, and at bottom, 'This is the truest cat. – the false came out on 19. Mar. The true which is this came out 23 March'. LT 2.531.
Wood 276a(94). Wing O857.

2784. England, Parliament List. *A true and compleat list of the lords spiritual and temporal, . . . of the present parliament [19 May]*. London: T. Newcomb, sold T. Basset, 1685. S.sh.
Col. 3, an underscoring of William Wrenn; col. 7, a line at entry of Heneage Finch.
Wood 276a(95). Wing T2423A.

2785. England, Parliament List. *A true list of the lords spiritual and temporal, summoned by the letter of . . . the prince of Orange, . . . 22th [sic] day of January*. [London]: f. J. Starkey, A. a. W. Churchil, 1689. S.sh.
Wood 276a(104). Wing T2730.

2786. England, Parliament List. *A true list of the knights, citizens, and burgesses of the parliament [20 March]*. [London]: E. Jones, sold R. Baldwin, 1690. S.sh.
At bottom, in pencil, faint, AW wrote in pencil, 'qu[aere] Notitia Anglicae' (by E. Chamberlayne, Wood 566(1-2)).
Wood 276a(97). Wing T2727.

2787. England, Parliament Satire. *Certaine propositions offered to the consideration of . . . parliament*. London [Oxford?]: n.pub., 1642. 4°. Pp. 8.
Wood 614(59). Wing C1731. Madan 1125*.

2788. England, Parliament Satire. *The parliaments knell*. [London]: n.pub., [1647]. S.sh.
AW wrote the year, '(1653)'.
Wood 416(7). Wing P513.

2789. England, Parliament Satire. *The plague at Westminster. Or, an order for the visitation of a sick parliament*. [London]: f. V. V., 1647. 4°. A⁴.
Wood 612(59a). Wing P2335.

2790. England, Parliament Satire, by Mercurius Melancholicus, pseud. *The cuckoo's-nest at Westminster, or the parlement between the two lady-birds, quean Fairfax & lady Cromwell*. [London]: in Cuckoo-time, in a Hollow-tree, 1648. 4°. Pp. 8.
Wood 654a(13). Wing C7459.

2791. England, Parliament Satire. *[The cryes] of Westminster. Or a whole pack of parliametary [sic] knavery opened, and set to sale*. [London]: Printed in a Hollow-tree, for the good of the State, [1648]. S.sh. Obl. Mutilated at top.
Wood 416(6). Wing C6911 (Wing, Parliamentary).

2792. England, Parliament Satire. *An excellent receipt to make a compleat parliament*. [London]: n.pub., [1659]. S.sh.
AW added the date, 'October: MDCLix:'.
Wood 276a(234). Wing E3834 (two).

2793. England, Parliament Satire. *The good old cause explained, revived, & asserted. And the long-parliament vindicated. In remonstrance to . . . lord Fleetwood*. [London]: n.pub., [1659]. 4°. Pp. 8.
Wood 613(22). Wing G1078.

2794. England, Parliament Satire. *One and thirty new orders of parliament, and the parliaments declaration, published for the satisfaction of the people of the three nations*. [London]: n.pub., 1659. 4°. Pp. 8 (sigs. A⁴; without a ballad).
Diff. ed. at Wood 610(35).
Wood 610(36). Not in Wing. Not in ESTCR (not Wing O331).

2795. England, Parliament Satire. *One and thirty new orders of parliament, and the parliaments declaration: published for the satisfaction of the people off [sic] the three nations . . . Together with the parliaments ghost, to the tune of Mad Tom*. [London]: n.pub, 1659. 4°. Pp. [2], 8 (i.e., 6, misnumbering; no. sigs. with a ballad on pp. 5, 8).
Tp, AW wrote, 'ridic.', in pencil. No. 70 in a former bundle. Diff. ed. at Wood 610(36).
Wood 610(35). Wing O331.

2796. England, Parliament Satire. *Resolves of the committee of safety. Whereunto is added the saints dictionary*. London: n.pub., 1659. 8°. Pp. 15.
Wood 899(5) (not in Bodl. CD cat.). Wing R1171 (two) ('O' not recorded in Wing).

2797. England, Parliament Satire. *Twelve queries humbly proposed to the consideration of the parliament & army, for the better security of, . . . the present government*. London: n.pub., 1659. 4°. Pp.7.
Tp, no. '7', in pencil, in a former bundle; see note at Wood 620(21), item 6706.
Wood 613(41). Wing T3402.

2798. England, Parliament Satire. *White-halls petition to the parliament*. London: n.pub., 1659. S.sh.
Wood 416(26). Wing W1881.

2799. England, Parliament Satire. *The acts and monuments of the late rump, from . . . their last sessions, untill the coming in of the secluded members*. London: n.pub., 1660. 4°. Pp. [2], 6.
Tp, AW altered the year to 16'59 feb' and wrote, in pencil, no. in a former bundle, '36'.
Wood 613(35). Wing A455.

2800. England, Parliament Satire. *The breech wash'd by a friend to the rump*. Oxford: f. C. Gustavus, [1660]. S.sh.
AW wrote, 'January: 1659[60]'; below, a note by a librarian, 'Thomason received this Jan. 19. 1659/60'; ᵛ, 'Jan. 59', and '33' replaced a former no. '17' in pencil.
Wood 416(33). Wing B4340 (3). Madan 2434.

2801. England, Parliament Satire. *A coffin for the good old cause; or, a sober word by way of caution to the parliament and army*. (London): (f. the author), (1660). 4°. Pp. 8.
P. 8, AW wrote the year, 'Jan: 1659'. Responded to by Wood 613(30), item 5106.
Wood 613(29). Wing C4889.

2802. England, Parliament Satire. *The life and death of m^ris Rump*. London: f. Theodorus Microcosmus, 1660. S.sh.
AW wrote, 'March'; ᵛ, 'Ma. 1660 59', and '65', which replaced a former no. '49' in pencil.
Wood 416(65). Wing L2006 (two).

2803. England, Parliament Satire. *The petition of the rump to the honourable city of London. Sheweth, that having a wrinkle more in their arse since they knew of general Monk's fidelity*. [London]: n.pub., [1660]. S.sh.
Dupl. at Wood 416(53).

Wood 276b(107). Wing P1835.

2804. England, Parliament Satire. *The petition of the rump to the honourable city of London. Sheweth, that having a wrinkle more in their arse since they knew of general Monk's fidelity.* [London]: n.pub., [1660]. S.sh.
AW wrote, 'ffeb: 1659[60]'; ᵛ, 'Feb. 59', and '53' over a former no. '35' in pencil. Dupl. at 276b(107).
Wood 416(53). Wing P1835.

2805. England, Parliament Satire. *The private debates, conferences and resolutions, of the late rump imparted to publick view.* London: n.pub., 1660. 4°. Pp. 30.
Tp, AW wrote '6ᵈ' and 'March', and, in pencil, the no. in a former bundle, '47'.
Wood 613(38). Wing P3529.

2806. England, Parliament Satire. *The proceedings, votes, resolves, and acts of the late half-quarter parliament, called the rump.* London: f. J. Thomason, 1660. Fol. Pp. 11.
AW altered 1660 to 16 '59: Mar:'; and, '58' written over a former no. '39' in pencil.
Wood 416(58). Wing P3628B.

2807. England, Parliament Satire. *Ratts rhimed to death. Or, the rump-parliament hang'd up in the shambles.* London: n.pub., 1660. 8°. Pp. [6], 89 (wanting A4). Pasteboard (blue) with parchment spine; rebacked.
Wanting AW's table of contents. Each of the 7 printed works in this vol. has AW's Arabic no. (1-7) and an Ashm. Roman numeral (I-VI, the 2nd and 3rd items are joined) on the tp. Tp, '9' (pence), and 'July: 14: 1660 A W' (LT 1.18, 321).
Wood 326(1). Wing R307.

2808. England, Parliament Satire. *The red-coats catechisme or instructions to be learned by everyone that desires to be admitted to be one of the parliaments janizaries.* London: n.pub., 1660. 4°. Pp. 8.
Tp, AW altered the year to 16'59: feb'.
Wood 613(63). Wing R657 (rare).

2809. England, Parliament Satire. *Vae vae . . . The rump desparing [sic], or the rumps proverbs, and lamentations.* London: n.pub., 1660. 4°. Pp. [1], 7.
Tp, AW altered the year to 16'59: March', and wrote, in pencil, the number in a former bundle, '45' (cropped).
Wood 613(37). Wing V17.

2810. England, Parliament Satire. *A dialogue between the ghosts of the two last parliaments.* London: f. A. Banks, 1681. S.sh.
AW identified, col. 1, 'M–D' as M'aynar'd, in red ink; col. 3, 'M– J– and W–', as 'Sʳ Jo. Maynard [/] Sʳ Will. Jones [/] Sʳ Fr. Winnington'. Below, 'This part was published in the middle of March 1680/1 the rest following in the beginning of Apr. 1681'. Dupl. at Wood 417(53) with some similar annotation. LT 2.534.
Wood 276a(525). Wing D1332.

2811. England, Parliament Satire. *A dialogue between the ghosts of the two last parliaments.* London: f. A. Banks, 1681. S.sh.
AW wrote, 'This side was published in Mar. 1680/1' (i.e., the left column), and 'The two other sides were published in the begin. of Apr. 1681' (the other 2 columns). ᵛ, '1680-1681'. Dupl. at Wood 276a(525), with some similar annotation. LT 2.534.
Wood 417(53). Wing D1332.

2812. England, Parliament Satire. *The ghost of the late house of commons, to the new one appointed to meet at Oxford.* [London]: f. B. Harris, sold L. Curtis, 1681. S.sh.
AW wrote, 'have another', in pencil. Dupl. at Wood 657(4). LT 2.521.
Wood 417(46). Wing G640.

2813. England, Parliament Satire. *The ghost of the late house of commons, to the new one appointed to meet at Oxford.* [London]: f. B. Harris, sold L. Curtis, 1681. S.sh. (imperf., 1st 8 words of t cropped at top).
AW wrote, '21 Mar. 1680[1]', in ink, over pencil; below, 'This was published about the middle of March 1680[1], but did not come to Oxon till 21. of the said mounth'. Text, 3 identifications at blanks, M'aynar'd, B'axter' and O'wen'. Dupl. at Wood 417(46). LT 2.521.
Wood 657(4). Wing G640.

2814. England, Parliament Satire. *The parliament dissolv'd at Oxford, March 28. 1681. From Devonshire.* [London]: n.pub., [1681]. S.sh.
No. 15 in a former bundle. AW wrote '1681', in pencil. LT 2.533. Dupl. at Wood 417(47).
Wood 276a(523). Wing P501.

2815. England, Parliament Satire. *The parliament dissolv'd at Oxford, March 28. 1681. From Devonshire.* [London]: n.pub., [1681]. S.sh.
Dupl. at Wood 276a(523). LT 2.533.
Wood 417(47). Wing P501.

2816. England, Parliament Satire. *Plain dealing: or, a dialogue between Humphrey and Roger, about chusing the next parliament.* (London): (f. F. Smith), (1681). S.sh. (r-v).
Wood 276a(567). Wing P2353.

2817. England, Privy Council. *At the court at Hampton-court the 28th day of July 1681 [order for the protection of protestant refugees].* (London): (assigns of J. Bill, T. Newcomb a. H. Hills), (1681). Fol. Pp. 4.
Wood 657(34). Wing E805A.

2818. England, Privy Council. *A true account of the whole proceedings betwixt . . . James duke of Ormond, and . . . Arthur earl of Anglesey . . . before the king and council.* London: f. T. Fox, 1682. Fol. Pp. [6], 28.
Tp, AW wrote the price, '1ˢ' and 'published in latter end of Nov. 1682'. Pp. 1, 4-7, vertical lines in margin, in ink and pencil; 6, underscoring of 2 dates, 'about October 1680' and 7 Oct.; 8, at 7 Oct., a cross-reference, 'v. p. 6'; 19, horizontal line in margin; 21, correction; 23, vertical line and underscoring.
Wood 657(61). Wing T2408.

2819. England, Proclamation. *At the court of Whitehall. . . . Whereas by the late act of uniformity [16 Feb., a proclamation ordering the necessary changes of names in the liturgy].* London: assigns of J. Bill deceas'd, H. Hills, a. T. Newcomb, 1684[5]. S.sh.
Wood 660c(33). Wing E832.

2820. England, Public Documents. *A commission with instructions and directions, . . . for compounding for wards, ideots, and lunaticks [11 Dec.].* London: B. Norton a. J. Bill, 1618. 4°. Pp. [4], 30.
Wood 616(10). STC 9239.

2821. England, Star Chamber. *A decree of starre-chamber, concerning printing [11 July].* London: R. Barker, by assignes of J. Bill, 1637. 4°. A-H⁴.
Tp, a shelf-mark, 'K.3.37.'
Wood 642(3). STC 7757.

2822. England, Star Chamber. *The sea-gull, or the new apparition in the star-chamber at Westminster.* [London]: n.pub., 1644. 4°. Pp. [2], 6.
Wood 612(22). Wing S2170.

2823. England, Star Chamber. *The Sussex picture, or, an answer to the sea-gull [see Wood 612(22)].* London: F. N., 1644, 29 July. 4°. A⁴.
Wood 612(23). Wing S6205.

2824. England, Trade. *Considerations touching trade, with the advance of the kings revenue, and present reparation of his majestie.* [London]: n.pub., 1641[2]. 4°. Pp. 16.
Tp, bsm.
[MS.] Wood C. 14(5). Wing C5921.

2825. England's Delightful. *Englands delightful new songs.* London: f. J. Back, [1685]. 8°.
Missing in 1837. 'Englands delightful new Songs' in Whiteside cat.
Wood 94(8) (not in Bodl. CD cat.). Wing E2957 (rare). O.

2826. England's Present Case. *Englands present case stated in a further remonstrance of many thousands.* [London]: n.pub., 1659. 4°. Pp. 15.
Tp, AW underscored 'late proclamation' in t and wrote in margin 15- and 16-, both cropped at side; after imprint date, 'December'; and, in pencil, no. in a former vol., '6-' (cropped at side);.
Wood 613(59) (not in Bodl. CD cat.). Wing E3018.

2827. England's Redemption. *Englands redemption: or, a path way to peace.* London: f. C. King, 1660. 4°. Pp. 8.
Tp, AW altered the date to 16'59: March'.
Wood 613(6). Wing E3022.

2828. England's Remarques. *England's remarques: or, a view of all the counties of England and Wales.* (London): (f. W. Jacob a. L. Curtis), (1676). Fol. Pp. [2] (p. [2] located between items (52) and (53) in this vol.).
Wood 276a(58). Wing E3025 (two).

2829. English Loyalty. H., W., trans. *English loyalty vindicated by the French divines; or, a declaration . . . of threescore doctors of Sorbonne, for the oath of allegiance . . . in English, by W. H.* London: f. N. Thompson, 1681. 4°. Pp. [8], 15.
Tp, AW entered the translator's name after initials 'Wibur-' [?], in pencil (cropped at side), and below, wrote 'published in the latter end of Oct. or beginning of November' (cropped at bottom). Dupl. at Wood 617(20).
Wood 608(57). Wing E3096.

2830. English Loyalty. H., W., trans. *English loyalty vindicated by the French divines; or, a declaration . . . of threescore doctors of Sorbonne, for the oath of allegiance . . . in English, by W. H.* London: f. N. Thompson, 1681. 4°. Pp. [8], 15.
Tp, AW wrote 'Dupl', in pencil. Dupl. at Wood 608(57).
Wood 617(20). Wing E3096.

2831. English Presbyterian. *The English Presbyterian and Independent reconciled.* London: f. E. Brewster, 1656. 4°. Pp. [2], 140.
Tp, bsm.
[MS.] Wood D. 26(8). Wing E3113A (rare).

2832. English Rogue. *The English rogue . . . To which is added a canting dictionary.* [London]: f. J. Blare, 1688. 8°. Pp. [2], 22. At one time probably pasteboard with parchment spine; rebound, parchment over boards by 'E. E. W. 30.4.45' (some texts and marginal notes, cropped).
Flyleaf, 2nd^v, AW wrote the titles of 10 printed works (numbered in Arabic nos.) in this vol., within guidelines made with red ink. Printed items numbered in Roman numerals (AW's Arabic nos. were possibly cropped in rebinding).
Wood 284(1). Wing E 3115A (rare).

2833. English Traveller. [Van Langeren, J., sculp.]. *[A direction for the English traviller].* [London]: [sold M. Simmons], [1636]. 8°. Obl. P. nos.: 3, an unnum. map of England in circle, and 4 to 39; plates (wanting t leaf, p. 2, and pp. 40-41). Parchment.
P. 39^v, AW wrote, 'bought of Jos: Godwin: praet: 1^s A: 1662. [30] Sept.' LT 1.454.
[MS.] Wood C. 49 (not in Bodl. CD cat.). STC 10421.

2834. Eniautos. Ενιαυτος τεραστιος *Mirabilis annus, or the year of prodigies and wonders.* [London]: n.pub., 1661. 4°. Pp. [10], 88.
On the recto of 1st series of copper cuts, AW wrote, 'This book came forth the beginning of Aug: 1661. [and at a later time] and this copie seems to be a second impression, most of the first being seised on.' After the copper cuts, on an inserted leaf^{r-v}, AW quoted some 65 lines from R. L'Estrange, *Modest plea*, which deals with printing, subversion, and pseudo-prodigies: 'A modest plea both for the *caveat [in margin, *The Caveat to the Cavaliers], & the authour of it &c. Lond. 1662 3^d edit. in Oct. [/] P. 9. - Nor is the press less active, or less dangerous than the pulpit. They have their private instruments & combinations to disperse their libells; . . . [etc. to the last paragraph copied by AW:] Let what I have observed, suffice, for persecutions: and now the people are startled, see what encouragement the wretch gives them to rebell, & cast off the yoke – [/] Then followes animadversions on severall of the pretended prodigies –'. Tp, '2^s' and 'These prodigies were published by certaine fanaticall people at the restauration of K. Ch. 2. purposely to amuse the Vulgar'. Text, some notes or vertical lines in margins, pp. 39, at a 'prodigy' of July 1660, 'The like hapned in the last yeare of Qu. Mary'; 40, at a 'prodigy' of Sept. 1660, 'This hapned in the last yeare againe of Qu. Mary – This is to possess the people that the K. is not long lived.'; 41, at a 'prodigy' of Aug. 1660, 'This hapned the yeare before ch. 5. [sic] was put to flight & hardly escap'd his life.'; etc., 44, 46, line at devil in the likeness of a bishop appearing to a Magdalen scholar; 47; 49; 52, 73 lines in pencil; 84, lines in pencil at 2 accidents at Christ Church; 85, identification of one who swooned at an ordination at Christ Church, 'Savill Beadley of New Coll. afterw. Fell[ow] of Magd. Coll.' LT 1.308, 347, 378, 387, 410

(acquired 20 Sept. 1661, 2ˢ).
Wood 643(4). Wing E3127A.

2835. Eniautos. *Mirabilis annus secundus: or, the second part of the second years prodigies.* [London]: n.pub., 1662. 4°. Pp. [6], 53, [1] (A1 and H4 are blank).
Pp. 33-4, underscoring; 46, underscoring of 'Lover of clean linnen' (describing the Arch-Bishop of Armagh, Dr. Brommell) and a cross ref. to p. 49 (where the Bishop of London is described by the same phrase), and underscoring of 'foolish Phannatick' people. Dupl. at Wood 643(7a) which has some similar annotation.
Wood 608(42). Wing M2204.

2836. Eniautos. *Mirabilis annus secundus: or, the second part of the second years prodigies.* [London]: n.pub., 1662. 4°. Pp. [6], 53, [1] (wanting A1 (a blank leaf), H4 blank).
Tp, AW wrote, 'Dupl'. Dupl. at Wood 608(42) which has some similar annotation. Pp. 32-5, a brief note at date of sermon by Mr. South of Christ Church, in ink, and lines in margin, in pencil and ink; 36, line in margin at execution of Col. Barkstead; 46, underscoring of Arch-Bishop Brommel, a 'Lover of clean Linnen' and a cross ref. to p. 49; 47, identification of Mr. Bowde: 'Somtimes of Wadham. Coll:' 48, line in margin, in pencil; 49, at the 'Bishop of *London*, (another lover of clean linnen)': 'Dʳ Gilb. Sheldon, who, as report went, had a Bastard in Olivers dayes q[uaere]'LT 1.437.
Wood 643(7a). Wing M2204.

2837. Eniautos. *Mirabilis annus secundus; . . . the second year of prodigies.* [London]: n.pub., 1662. 4°. Pp. [8], 89 (misnumbering, 1-25, 40-89).
Pp. 45, AW identified 'one *Rauson*, Parson of *Tatnal*': 'Ralph Rauson [Rawson] of Bras. Coll. in Oxon.'; 70, vertical line in margin at a double tide, in red ink; 82, at 'Mr. Venning': 'Ralph Venning'; 86, identification of a 'railing prelate', 'Dʳ Joh. Gauden of Worcest.' and vertical line at his book, *A Pillar of Gratitude*, in red ink. LT 1.431, 433, 466.
Wood 643(6). Wing M2205.

2838. Epictetus; Cebes, and Theophrastus. Healey, J., trans. *Epictetus manuall. Cebes table. Theophratus characters.* London: G. Purslowe f. E. Blount, 1616. 12°. Pp. [12], 167, [23], 96 (2 pts.). Pasteboard (blue) with parchment spine. 1st upper and last lower flyleaves and pastedowns, marbled paper.
Flyleaf, upper, 2ndᵛ, AW wrote the titles of 3 printed works in this vol., within guidelines made with red ink. Tp, scribble.
Wood 735(1). STC 10426.

2839. Erasmus, Desiderius. *[Responsio ad annotationes Eduardi Lei] [heading: 'Epistolae aliquot illustrium virorum'].* Basil: ex aedibus J. Frobenii, 1520. 4°. Pp. [2], 27-175, [1] (pt. 3 only).
Tpᵛ, 20 lines, index, not in AW's hand. Flyleaf, lower, 7 titles, followed by a 6-line poem in Latin, 'Epitaphium Lucretiae'; ᵛ, several lines in Latin and some scribbles; and pastedown, lower, notes in Latin, none by AW. For former owners, see More, Wood 639(1).
Wood 639(2). BL.

2840. Erasmus, Desiderius. Chaloner, Thomas, trans. *The praise of folie. Moriae encomium.* (London): (in the house of T. Berthelet), 1549 (1569). 4°. A-T⁴.
Missing. MS. Wood E. 2(70), p. 41, 'Sʳ Tho. Chaloner, translation of Moriae Encomium 1549'. A 1644 ed. is listed in MS. Wood F. 51, f. 44: 'The prayse of folly. 12mo. Lond. 1644' (ed. not identified).
MS. Wood E. 2(70), p. 41. STC 10500. *O, Hunt, Harv* (erasures on tp).

2841. Erasmus, Desiderius. Wilson, John, trans. *Moriae encomium; or, the praise of folly.* London: f. W. Leak, 1668. 8°. Pp. [8], 160. Calf with 2 fillets.
Flyleaf, upper, 1st, sigil of circle on top of a cross (inverted, possibly a reference to Twyne ms. no. 24) and 6. Tp, initials 'E Ha=' (Elizabeth Hales? AW owned 2 other items with her signature).
Wood 746. Wing E3208.

2842. Erbery, William. *Nor truth, nor error, nor day, nor night; . . . Being the relation of a publike discourse . . . between mr. Cheynel, and mr. Erbery [response to Truth triumphing, by F. Cheynell, Wood 514(23)].* [London]: n.pub., 1647. 4°. Pp. [6], 22.
Tp, AW wrote 'Erbury', in red ink; below, 'published either by Erbury or one of his party. rather by Cheynell –'; and, after the year, '1646'. AO 3.360ff. LT 1.130.
Wood 514(24). Wing E3234 ('O' not recorded in Wing). Madan 1953.

2843. Erswicke, John. *A briefe note of the benefits that grow to this realm by the observation of fish-dayes. . . . Collected out of severall statutes . . . of . . . Elizabeth.* London: f. T. Bankes, 1642. 4°. Pp. 8.

[MS.] Wood C. 14(10). Wing E3250.

2844. Espagne, Jean d'. *Popular errors, in generall poynts concerning the knowledge of religion*. London: f. T. Whittaker, 1648. 8°. Pp. [6], 222. Calf, speckled, with 2 fillets; lower flyleaves, printer's waste paper. Pasted to a sheet at bottom edge, a slip identifying the author and work (see Index, 'Slip with title'). Wood 785. Wing E3267 (Wing, 12°).

2845. Essex. *A new found stratagem framed in the old forge of Machivilisme, and put upon the inhabitants of the county of Essex*. [London?]: n.pub., 1647. 4°. Pp. 14, [1] (pp. unopened). Tp, AW wrote the month, 'Apr'. Wood 501(29). Wing N641.

2846. Essex. *Divers remarkable passages concerning the originall and progresse of the . . . action in Essex: and the reason of seizing on the lord Capel's sonne*. [London]: n.pub., 1648. 4°. Pp. [2], 17. P. 5, at Earl of Norwich, double lines in margin. Wood 502(30). Wing D1712.

2847. Essex. *The ingagement and declaration of the grand-jury, freeholders, and other inhabitants of . . . Essex [4 May]*. [London]: n.pub., 1648. 4°. Pp. [2], 6. Tp, AW wrote after the year, 'May 4'. Wood 502(4). Wing E732.

2848. Essex. *The Essex watchmen's watchword to the inhabitants*. London: f. R. Smith, 1649. 4°. Tp, AW wrote after the year, '(Feb. 15. 1648)'. Wood 502(74). Wing E3342A.

2849. Essex. *The declaration and address of the gentry of . . . Essex, who have adhered to the king [17 Apr.]*. London: f. G. Bedell, a. T. Collins, [1660]. S.sh. Wood 276a(223). Wing D523 ('O' not recorded in Wing). Steele 3181.

2850. Estienne, Charles. *Dictionarium historicum. Geographicum. Poeticum*. [Geneva]: ap. S. Crispinum, 1621 (pridie Cal. Mart.). Pp. [8], cols. 1132. Calf with 3 fillets and 2 metal clasps; spine, 5 bands. Cover, upper, initials 'R B'. Flyleaf, upper, signature of 'Robert Blithe' and 'Pretium: - 0 - 4ˢ', prob. by R. Blithe. Wood 379. NUC.

2851. [Estienne, Henri]. *A mervaylous discourse upon the lyfe, . . . of Katherine de Medicis*. Heydelberge [i.e. London]: [H. Middleton?], 1575. 8°. Pp. 196. Pasteboard (grey) with parchment spine. Traces of 1st and last flyleaves in marbled paper. Flyleaf, upper, 2ndᵛ, AW wrote the titles of 3 printed works in this vol., within guidelines made with red ink. Tp, signature of – (erased) Caverlay. Wood 260(1) (not in Bodl. CD cat.). STC 10550.

2852. Estienne, Henri. Blount, Thomas, trans. *The art of making devises: Whereunto is added, a catalogue of coronet-devises both on the kings, and the parliaments side, in the late warres*. London: f. J. Holden, 1650. 4°. Pp. [17], 87. Flyleaf, upper, 'Blount of Devises', not in AW's hand. Tp, AW wrote 'Sept: 11: A.D. 1660', and later, in red ink, 'Tho. Blount the translator, his armes in the picture title -'. P. 81, line in margin at Capt. Sidenham. LT 1.331. Wood 605(3). Wing E3352.

2853. [Eunapius. Hornanus, Hadrianus, trans. *The lyves, of philosophers and oratours]*. [London]: [[J. Charlewood? f.] R. Johnes], [1579]. 4°. Ff. [8], 43, [4] (wanting t leaf and last leaf). Wood 345(14). STC 10566.

2854. Eusebius. Caesarea, bp. of. *Historiae ecclesiasticae. Eusebij . . . libri IX. Ruffino interprete. Ruffini presbyteri Aquileiensis, libri duo. Recogn. per Beat. Rhenanum. Item ex Theodorito episcopo Cyrensi, Sozomeno, & Socrate Constantinopolitano libri xii*. Basileae: Froben, 1528. Fol. Pp. [12], 636, [60]. Calf with 3 fillets, inner rectangle with roll decoration and stamp decoration outside corners, and roll decoration at inner, spine edge. Tp, names of a former owner, 15 August 1576, lined out; scribbles and Latin Christian tags, not by AW. Text, some annotation, in more than 1 hand, none by AW. Wood 660a. BL.

2855. Evan, Enoch ap*. *A true relation of a barbarous and most cruell murther, committed by one Enoch ap Evan.* London: N. Okes, 1633. 4°. Pp. [2], 17.
Tp, some colouring of red for blood on the picture; ᵛ, 'This story is mentioned by James Howell in his fourth vol. of familiar letters p. 103 – but much different from what is here related – I have the booke – see there –' i.e., Wood 723.
Wood 365(7). STC 10582 (two).

2856. Evance, Daniel. *Justa honoraria : or, funeral rites in honor to the great memorial of . . . Robert earl of Essex.* London: f. E. Husband, [1646]. 4°. Pp. 27.
Missing since 1994. In Whiteside cat. LT 1.131, 'satyrical notes written by Wood in the margin, but I doubt whether they are his own.'
Wood 531(10). Wing E3442.

2857. Evans, Philip*, and John Lloyd*. *Short memorandum's [sic] upon the deaths of m. Philip Evans and m. John Lloyd, both priests . . . 22. day of July.* [London]: n.pub., [1679]. S.sh. (r-v).
AW wrote the price, '1ᵈ'.
Wood 425(12). Wing S3604.

2858. [Evans, Rhys]. *King Charls his starre.* [London]: n.pub, 1654. 8°. Pp. [2], 46.
Tp, AW wrote, 'Arise Evans.' after cryptogram.
Wood 235(4). Wing E3460 (two).

2859. [Evelyn, John]. *An apology for the royal party: written in a letter . . . by a lover of peace . . . With a touch at the pretended plea for the army [27 Oct.].* [London]: n.pub., 1659. 4°. 2nd ed. Pp. [2], 14.
Wood 632(32). Wing E3483 (two). Keynes, no. 19.

2860. [Evelyn, John]. *A character of England. As it was lately present-ted [sic] in a letter, to a noble man of France.* London: f. J. Crooke, 1659. 12°. Pp. [6], 66.
Lent to Arthur Crew, 14 May 1659, LT 1.278.
Wood 582(3). Wing E3486. Keynes, no. 15.

2861. Evelyn, John. *The late news or message from Bruxels unmasked, and his majesty vindicated, from the base calumny.* London: f. R. Lowndes, 1660. 4°. Pp. [2], 6.
Tp, AW wrote 'March'. Responds to M. Nedham, Wood 632(42), item 4619.
Wood 608(3). Wing E3503. Keynes, no. 21.

2862. Evelyn, J[ohn]. *Fumifugium: or the inconveniencie of the aer and smoak of London dissipated. Together with some remedies.* London: W. Godbid f. G. Bedel a. T. Collins, 1661. 4°. Pp. [12], 26.
Acquired 12 Dec. 1663, 6ᵈ, LT 1.508.
[MS.] Wood D. 27(5). Wing E3488. Keynes, no. 23.

2863. Evelyn, J[ohn]. *Publick employment and an active life with all its appanages, . . . prefer'd to solitude.* London: J. M. f. H. Herringman, 1667. 8°. With cancel t leaf. Pp. [13], 120 (wanting sig. A7 and the errata slip).
Tp, AW wrote '1ˢ 2ᵈ' and underscored the initials of the author, in red ink. Acquired 29 Mar. 1667, LT 2.104.
Wood 730(5). Wing E3511. Keynes, no. 86.

2864. Evelyn, John. *A philosophical discourse of earth, relating to the culture . . . of it for vegetation and the propagation of plants.* London: f. J. Martyn, 1676. 8°. Pp. 182.
Wood 573(2). Wing E3507. Keynes, no. 93.

2865. Everard, Edmund*. *The depositions and examinations of mr. Edmund Everard . . . concerning the popish plot.* London: f. D. Newman, 1679. Fol. Pp. [3], 16.
Tp, AW wrote the price, '6ᵈ'.
Wood 424(18). Wing E3527.

2866. Everard, Giles. R[owland], J[ohn], ed. *Panacea; or the universal medicine, being a discovery of the wonderfull vertues of tobacco taken in a pipe.* London: f. S. Miller, 1659. 8°. Pp. [16], 79, [1], 55, [8] (8 pp. books sold by Miller). Pasteboard (blue) with parchment spine. 1st upper and last lower flyleaves, marbled paper; rebound.
AW wrote the titles of 8 printed works in this vol. and below, added another, 'coffey-' (really 10 in all: nos. 1-8 and there are 2, 9 and 10, on 'coffey'), within guidelines made with red ink. Throughout there are pencil marks of the Ashm. shelf-mark, Wood 679, apparently put in to assure that these items, during

rebinding, would be replaced in the correct vol. (the 2 last s.shs. have specific directions, i.e., to be placed at the end). On tpp, the Ashm. librarian overwrote AW's Arabic numerals with Roman numerals. Tp, AW wrote '9ᵈ'. Acquired 14 Feb. 1662, LT 1.430.
Wood 679(1). Wing E3530.

2867. Ewich, Johann. *De officio fidelis et prudentis magistratus tempore pestilentiae rempub. a contagio preservandi liberandique libri duo.* Neapoli Nemetum [Neustadt a. d. Haardt]: M. Harnisch, 1582. 8°. Pp. 191. Parchment.
Tp, AW wrote, 'in bib. B[odleian]', and numbers, 59 and 60; ᵛ, signature of 'Wil [?] Thomas 1636 p 4'.
Wood 454. BL.

2868. Exeter. *A true copy of the articles agreed on at the surrender of Exeter.* London: f. F. Coles, 1646. 4°. Pp. [2], 14.
Tp, '2ᵈ', prob. not by AW.
Wood 501(3). Wing T2636.

2869. Exeter. *A letter from Exeter, . . . also, a letter to . . . William Lenthall.* London: f. T. Creake, [1660]. S.sh.
Wood 276a(255). Wing L1464.

2870. Exoneratorium. *Exoneratorium curatorum.* [London]: (R. Wyer), [1552 ca.]. A-F⁴.
Tp, 'Hum[phrey] Dyson'.
Jesus College H. 13. 23(2). STC 10634.3 (rare).

2871. Expedient. *An expedient or a sure & easy way of reducing all dissenters . . . to an exact . . . obedience.* [London]: n.pub., (1672). 4°. Pp. 16.
P. 1, AW wrote 'Given to me by Will. Rogers of the Inner Temple 26. May 1675'. LT 2.314.
Wood 617(11). Wing E3875.

2872. Expedients. *Expedients for publique peace.* [London]: n.pub., 1660. 4°. Pp. 20.
Tp, AW wrote 'Aprill'.
Wood 608(5). Wing E3877.

2873. Eyre, Thomas. Hassop, of. *The case of Thomas Eyre esq; respondent to the petition of Thomas Eyre, William Ing, Henry Balgay.* [London]: n.pub., [1684?]. S.sh.
A correction, not in AW's hand.
Wood 276b(81) (not in Bodl. CD cat.). Wing C1185A (rare) (Wing, Eyre, esq.).

2874. Eyre, Thomas. Hassop, of. *The case of Thomas Eyre of Hassop in the county of Derby, esq; William Inge esq; and divers other . . . appelants from a degree [forest of High Peak].* [London]: n.pub., [1684]. S.sh.
A year, '1682.' supplied in margin, prob. not in AW's hand.
Wood 276b(77) (not in Bodl. CD cat.). Wing C1186 (rare, 2 at O).

2875. Eyre, Thomas. Hassop, of. *The case of the king and queen dowager, by their atturnies the lord privy seal, the earl of Chesterfield.* [London?]: n.pub., [1685?]. S.sh.
Wood 276b(73). Wing C1098 (rare).

2876. Eytzinger, Michael. *Thesaurus principum hac aetate in Europa viventium.* Coloniae Agrippinae: ap. G. Kempensem, 1591. 8°. Pp. [14], 263. Parchment with 2 clasp holes.
Tp, price, '1ˢ', may not be in AW's hand.
Wood 439. BL.

2877. F., D. *The equallity of the ministery plainly described, both by scriptures, fathers, and councels.* [London]: n.pub., 1641. 4°. Pp. [2], 14.
[MS.] Wood D. 31(31). Wing F7.

2878. F., H. *A true and exact relation of the severall informations, examinations, and confessions of the late witches, . . . executed in . . . Essex.* London: M. S. f. H. Overton a. B. Allen, 1645. 4°. Pp. [8], 36.
Tp, scribble, 'D P' (?).
[MS.] Wood B. 18(8). Wing F23.

2879. F., J. *The laws discovery: or a brief detection of . . . errors and abuses contained in our English laws.* London: R. I. f. G. B., 1653. 4°. Pp. 8.

Wood 630(9). Wing F40.

2880. F., J. *A friendly letter of advice to the souldiers from a quondam-member of the army.* [London]: n.pub., 1659. 4°. Pp. 8.
Tp, former no., '70', in pencil.
Wood 632(37). Wing F36.

2881. F., N. *The fruiterers secrets.* London: R B[radock], solde by R. Jackson, 1604. 4°. Pp. [4], 28.
Wood 618(4). STC 10650.

2882. F., R. *The army's martyr: or a faithful relation of the barbarous . . . proceedings . . . upon mr. Robert Lockier.* London: n.pub., 1649. 4°. Pp. 8.
Tp[v], note by a royalist against Lockier, 'a Leveller', not in AW's hand.
Wood 368(7). Wing F50.

2883. Fairebrother, William. *An essay of a loyal brest; in four copies of verses.* London: J. Field, 1660. 4°. Pp. [2], 12.
Tp, AW wrote, 'June: 1660'.
Wood 319(11). Wing F110.

2884. Fairfax, Ferdinando. *A letter from the right honourable Ferdinando lord Fairfax, to . . . Robert earle of Essex.* London: f. J. Wright, 1643, Oct. 18. 4°. Pp. [2], 6.
Tp, AW overwrote a former no. with '43'.
Wood 376(43). Wing F119.

2885. Fairfax, Ferdinando*. *A true relation of the great victory . . . the lord Fairfax, and sir Thomas Fairfax his son, . . . in Yorkshire, . . . 11. of April.* London: f. R. White, a. T. Underhill, 1644. 4°. A[4].
Wood 377(6). Wing T2962.

2886. Fairfax, Fer[dinando]. *A letter sent from the right honorable, the lord Fairfax . . . concerning the great victory, . . . at Selby.* [London]: f. E. Husbands, 1644, 19 April. 4°. Pp. 8.
Wood 377(6a). Wing F121.

2887. Fairfax, Ferdinando. *A copy of a letter . . . to the major of Hull; . . . concerning the great victory . . . at York.* London: f. E. Husbands, 1644, 6 July. 4°. Pp. 8.
Dupl. at Wood 632(13).
Wood 377(17). Wing F112.

2888. Fairfax, Ferdinando. *A copy of a letter . . . to the major of Hull; . . . concerning the great victory . . . at York.* London: f. E. Husbands, 1644, 6 July. 4°. Pp. 8.
Tp, AW wrote in pencil, 'Dupl'. Dupl. at Wood 377(17).
Wood 632(13). Wing F112.

2889. Fairfax, Henry. *An impartial relation of the whole proceedings against St. Mary Magdalen colledge in Oxon.* [London]: n.pub., 1688. 4°. Pp. [4], 36. Pasteboard (blue) with parchment spine; rebacked.
Flyleaf, upper, 2nd[v], AW wrote 'Oxon', in pencil, and the titles of 6 printed works in this vol., within guidelines made with red ink. Tp, AW wrote 'The 2[d] edit. with additions is bound up in this vol.' and 'published in Oxōn about the beginning of Feb. 1687[8]'. Also, brief identifications, queries, underscorings, and corrections, e.g., pp. 1, 'Franc. Bagshaw a Capt. of a Foot-company of scholars, in Monmouths rebellion 1685'; 3, 'Note that here is no date set down' and 'nor here, which breeds some confusion'; 5, 'when was this dated?'; 7-9; 14, at 'Mr. W– P–', 'Will Pen the Quaker' and 'qu[aere] when dat.'; 18, 20, 23-4, 28-9, 31. LT 3.246.
Wood 517(1). Wing F125.

2890. [Fairfax, Henry]. *An impartial relation of the illegal proceedings against St. Mary Magdalen colledge in Oxon, . . . 1687. Collected by a fellow of the said colledge.* London: printed a. sold, R. Baldwin, 1689. 4°. Pp. [2], 66, [2] (pp. [67-8] books printed f. R. Baldwin).
Flyleaf, upper, 'M[r] Tho Collins school Master of Magd: Coll hath several times told mee M[r] Hen Fairfax was author of this following narrative', cursive, prob. not by AW (though Collins was an informant of AW, see AO 3.540). Below, note in pencil, illeg. Tp, at 'Collected by a Fellow', AW wrote, 'I have enquired, but cannot learne by whome' and '1[s]– 22. Mar. 1688'. Pp. 49, 64, [68]. LT 3.246.
Wood 517(3). Wing F126 ('O' not recorded in Wing).

2891. Fairfax, Thomas*. *A fuller relation of the taking of Bath by sir Thomas Fairfax.* London: f. T.

Bates, 1645. 4°. Pp. [2], 5, [1].
Tp, AW altered the former no., '15'.
Wood 378(17). Wing F2492.

2892. Fairfax, Thomas*. *A glorious victory obtained by s*ʳ*. Thomas Fairfax, June, the 14.* London: f. R. Wood, 1645. 4°. A⁴.
Tp, AW overwrote former no., '5'.
Wood 378(6). Wing G870 (two).

2893. Fairfax, Thomas*. *The parliaments severall late victories in the west.* London: f. E. Husbands, 1645[6], 21 Jan. 4°. Pp. 8.
Tp, AW wrote the price, '1ᵈ', and overwrote the former no., '37'.
Wood 378(40). Wing P524.

2894. Fairfax, Thomas. *Sir Thomas Fairfax letter to both houses . . . taking of Dartmouth.* London: f. J. Wright, 1645[6], 24 Jan. 4°. Pp. 8.
Tp, AW overwrote the former no., '40'.
Wood 378(43). Wing F191.

2895. Fairfax, Thomas*. *A fuller relation of sir Thomas Fairfax's routing all the kings armies in the west.* London: f. M. Walbanck, 1645[6], 21 Feb. 4°. Pp. 14.
Tp, AW underscored 'Fairfax's' in red ink, wrote the price, '1ᵈ1/2', and altered the former no., '45'.
Wood 378(48). Wing F2491 (Wing, 1645).

2896. Fairfax, Thomas. *Sir Thomas Fairfax letter to the hono*ᵇˡᵉ *William Lenthall . . . since his advance from Exeter, and . . . at Torrington.* London: f. E. Husband, 1645[6], 24 Feb. 4°. A⁴.
Tp, AW lined out the former no., '48'.
Wood 378(51). Wing F195.

2897. Fairfax, Thomas*. *Sir Thomas Fairfax's proceedings about the storming of Exeter.* London: f. M. Walbank, 1645[6], 9 Feb. 4°. Pp. 7.
Tp, AW wrote, and lined out, the price, '1ᵈ', and altered the former no., '43'.
Wood 378(46). Wing S3897.

2898. Fairfax, Thomas*. *His majesties whole army in the west conquered.* London: f. M. Walbancke, 1645[6], 16 Mar. 4°. Pp. [2], 15 (misnumbering).
Tp, AW wrote and later lined out the price, '1ᵈ 1/2', and overwrote the former no., '57'.
Wood 378(60). Wing F163.

2899. Fairfax, Thomas. *Sir Thomas Fairfax's letter from Cornwall.* London: f. J. Wright, 1645[6], 24 Mar. 4°. Pp. [2], 10.
Tp, AW wrote and later lined out the price, '1ᵈ', and lined out the former no., '59'.
Wood 378(62). Wing F171.

2900. Fairfax, Thomas. *A summons from his excellency sir Thomas Fairfax to sir Ralph Hopton . . . in Cornwall.* London: f. E. Husband, 1645[6], 11 Mar. 4°. Pp. 8.
Tp, AW wrote the price, '1ᵈ' (cropped), and altered the former no., '55'.
Wood 378(58). Wing F238.

2901. Fairfax, Thomas*. *The proceedings of the army under the command of sir Thomas Fairfax [July 1-6].* London: f. S. Gellibrand, 1645, 9 July. 4°. Pp. 8.
Flyleaf, upperᵛ, multiplication, 20 x 25 = 2250. Tp, AW altered the former no., '7'.
Wood 378(8). Wing P3573.

2902. Fairfax, Thomas. *Sir Thomas Fairfax's letter to . . . William Lenthall . . . concerning the taking of Bridgewater.* London: f. E. Husband, 1645, 28 July. 4°. Pp. 7.
Tp, AW wrote the price, '1ᵈ', and altered the former no., '13'.
Wood 378(15). Wing F193.

2903. Fairfax, Thomas. *Sir Thomas Fairfax's letter to . . . William Lenthall . . . concerning the taking of Sherborn castle.* London: f. E. Husband, 1645, 19 Aug. 4°. Pp. 8.
Tp, AW altered the former no., '17'.
Wood 378(19). Wing F194.

2904. Fairfax, Thomas*. *The great champions of England: being a perfect list of the lords and commons . . . and the general officers . . . under . . . Thomas Fairfax.* London: f. F. Leach, 1646. S.sh. (with a large engraving of Fairfax on horseback).
Some underscoring, some marks in columns, and a correction. At name of Devonshire members of the house of commons, Samuel Browne is underscored, see note at Wood 358(6), item 6405.
Wood 620(3). Wing G1676.

2905. Fairfax, Thomas. *Sir Thomas Fairfax knight generall of the forces raised by the parliament. Suffer the bearer hereof [passport granted to G. Tryme under the articles of surrender of Oxford] [26 June].* [Oxford]: [L. Lichfield], 1646. S.sh. 4°.
The name of the letter bearer, George Tryme, the signature of Fairfax, the date, etc., are entered in ms. with a seal.
Wood 514(19b). Wing F236 (two). Madan 1881.

2906. Fairfax, Thomas*. *Several letters to . . . William Lenthall . . . concerning the gallant proceedings of sir Tho. Fairfax army in the west.* London: f. E. Husband, 1646, 13 Apr. 4°. Pp. 8.
Tp, '1ᵈ', prob. not by AW.
Wood 501(4). Wing S2781.

2907. Fairfax, Thomas*. *Sir Thomas Fairfax's further proceedings in the west.* London: f. M. Walbank, 1646, 22 Apr. 4°. Pp. [2], 6.
Wood 501(5). Wing S3896. (Wing, Walbanck).

2908. Fairfax, Thomas. *Sir Thomas Fairfax his summons into Oxford, and the governours answer.* London: E. Purslow, 1646, 14 May. 4°. Pp. [2], 6.
Tp, '1ᵈ', prob. not by AW.
Wood 501(11). Wing F239. Madan 1864.

2909. Fairfax, Thomas*. *An exact and true relation of the many severall messages, that have passed between . . . Tho. Fairfax, and the . . . governour of Ragland-castle, touching surrender thereof [18 Aug.].* London: f. F. Coles, 1646, 19 Aug. 4°. Pp. 8.
Wood 501(24). Wing E3622.

2910. Fairfax, Thomas. *A declaration of . . . and his councell of warre, . . . shewing the grounds of their present advance towards . . . London [3 Aug.].* Oxford: J. Harris a. H. Hills, 1647. 4°. Pp. [2], 10.
Dupl. at Wood 612(48).
Wood 501(36). Wing F141A. Madan 1951.

2911. Fairfax, Thomas. *A declaration of . . . and his councell of warre, . . . shewing the grounds of their present advance towards . . . London [3 Aug.].* Oxford: J. Harrris a. H. Hills, 1647. 4°. Pp. [2], 10.
Tp, no. 48 in a former bundle. Dupl. at Wood 501(36).
Wood 612(48). Wing F141A. Madan 1951.

2912. Fairfax, Thomas. *A declaration of . . . and his councell of warre, . . . shewing the grounds of their present advance towards . . . London.* London: f. G. Whittington, 1647. 4°. Pp. [2], 10.
Tp, no. 4 in a former bundle; AW wrote 'Aug' at the imprint date, in pencil; '2ᵈ', in ink, may not be in AW's hand.
Wood 612(63). Wing F141.

2913. Fairfax, Thomas*. *The grand informer. Or the prerogative of princes . . . a . . . vindication of . . . the army.* Oxford: I. H[arris] a. H. H[ills], 1647. 4°. Pp. 15.
Wood 612(65) (not in Bodl. CD cat.). Wing G1499 (Wing, informer, or). Madan 1940.

2914. Fairfax, Thomas. *A particular charge or impeachment, in the name of . . . sir Thomas Fairfax . . . against Denzill Hollis [et al.].* London: f. G. Whittington, 1647. 4°. Pp. '1-8, 7-13, [1]' (there is some misnumbering).
Tp, AW wrote at top, 'qu[aere] the answer', in pencil (which is the next item, Wood 620(5)), and below, '16 June 1647' and 'qu[aere] wh[ich] among articles'.
Wood 620(4). Wing E741dA ('O' not recorded in Wing).

2915. Fairfax, Thomas. *A remonstrance from . . . and the army under his command. Concerning their . . . proceedings hitherto.* London: M. S. f. G. Whittington, 1647. 4°. Pp. 21.
Wood 501(37). Wing F227.

2916. Fairfax, Thomas. *A representation, from his excellencie sir Thomas Fairfax, and the army under his command. Humbly tendered to the parliament, concerning the just and fundamentall rights and liberties ['St. Albons June 14. 1647'].* N.p.: n.pub., [1647]. A⁴.
Wood 501(30). Not in Wing. Not in ESTCR. Not Wing F230-1.

2917. Fairfax, Thomas. *Two letters from . . . sir Thomas Fairfax, one to both houses of parliament; . . . the other to the lord major, aldermen and common-councel of London [8 July].* London: f. L. Chapman, 1647, 10 July. 4°. Pp. 11.
Wood 501(35). Wing F245.

2918. Fairfax, Thomas. *The articles of agreement between the lord generall, and the Kentish men, at the delivering up of the city of Canterburie: A letter from York; and the storming of Pembroke.* London: B. A., 1648. 4°. Pp. [2], 1[-6].
Tp, AW wrote after the year, 'Jun. 9'.
Wood 502(20) (not in Bodl. CD cat.). Wing F138.

2919. Fairfax, Thomas. *A copy of some papers lately passed betwixt the lord Fairfax . . . and the earle of Norwich, lord Capel, and sir Charles Lucas [19 June].* N.p.: n.pub., 1648. 4°. Pp. [2], 5.
Tp, AW wrote after the year, '21. Jun'.
Wood 502(31). Wing C6198A (Wing, London).

2920. Fairfax, Thomas*. *The displaying of the life-guards colours, or a true narrative of the late actings of his excellencies [Lord Fairfax's] life-guard.* London: n.pub., 1648. 4°. Pp. [2], 14.
Tp, AW wrote after the printed date, '47', and in pencil, '1647'. Bsm.
Wood 501(40). Wing D1675.

2921. Fairfax, Thomas. *The lord generals letter in answer to the message of the Kentish-men, May 31.* London: f. L. Chapman, 1648, 2 June. 4°. Pp. 8.
Wood 502(16). Wing F182.

2922. Fairfax, Thomas. *A petition from . . . lord Fairfax and the general councell . . . to . . . the commons of England, . . . concerning . . . peace. Together with the said agreement [20 Jan.].* London: f. J. Partridge, R. Harford, G. Calvert, a. G. Whittington, 1649. 4°. Pp. 29 (misnumbering).
Wood 610(53-54). Wing F213.

2923. Fairfax, Tho[mas]. *A proclamation of . . . Requiring all persons who have engaged for the king . . . to depart the city.* London: f. T. Turner, 1649. 4°. Pp. [2], 6.
Flyleaf, after p. 6, waste paper with a Latin disputation topic, 'Et accidentii' (cropped), not by AW.
Wood 503(8) (not in Bodl. CD cat.). Wing F220.

2924. Fairfax, Thomas. *A declaration of . . . Thomas lord Fairfax and the knights and gentry in the north of England.* London: f. G. Horton, 1659. 4°. Pp. 7.
Tp, AW added to year, 'Januar:'.
Wood 610(32). Wing D777B (two) (Wing, of the North).

2925. Fairfax, Thomas. *A letter sent from the lord Fairfax, &c. [also signed by H. Cholmley and H. Arthington] dated at Popleton, January 1, 1659.* London: J. Streater a. J. Macock, 1659[60]. 4°. Pp. 7.
Wood 632(62). Wing F188.

2926. Fairfax, Thomas. *The declaration of Thomas lord Fairfax . . . and city of York . . . Leeds [13 Feb. 1659].* London: f. J. Williamson, [1660]. S.sh.
Wood 276a(212). Wing F154.

2927. Fairfax, Thomas, and Thomas Blagge. *Articles concerning the surrender of Wallingford [by sir Thomas Fairfax and Thomas Blagge, 22 July].* Oxford: H. Hall, 1646. 4°. Pp. [2], 5.
Dupl. at Wood 612(41).
Wood 501(23). Wing A3815A (two). Madan 1897.

2928. Fairfax, Thomas, and Thomas Blagge. *Articles concerning the surrender of Wallingford [by sir Thomas Fairfax and Thomas Blagge, 22 July].* Oxford: H. Hall, 1646. 4°. Pp. [2], 5.
Tp, AW wrote 'Dupl', in pencil. Dupl. at Wood 501(23).
Wood 612(41). Wing A3815A (two). Madan 1897.

2929. Fairfax, Thomas, and Thomas Blagge. *Articles of agreement concluded . . . by . . . sir Tho.*

Fairfax . . . and . . . Thomas Blagge . . . concerning the rendring of . . . Wallingford. London: f. J. Wright, 1646, 25 July. 4°. Pp. [2], 6.
Tp, '1ᵈ', prob. not by AW.
Wood 501(22). Wing F138.

2930. Fairfax, Thomas, and Oliver Cromwell. *Three letters, from the right honourable sir Thomas Fairfax, lieut. gen. Crumwell [sic] . . . of the great victory . . . 14 of June.* London: f. J. Wright, 1645. 4°. Pp. [2], 10.
Tp, AW wrote the price, '1ᵈ1/2', and lined out a former no., '6'.
Wood 378(7). Wing F240.

2931. Fairfax, Thomas*, and W. Curtis*. *The late victorious proceedings of sir Thomas Fairfax against the enemy in the west.* London: f. M. Walbancke, 1645[6], 9 Mar. 4°. Pp. [2], 13.
Tp, AW wrote and later lined out the price, '2ᵈ', and altered the former no., '53'.
Wood 378(56). Wing L560.

2932. Faldo, Thomas. *Reformation of proceedings at law.* [London]: H. Hils, in Southwarke, 1649. 4°. Pp. [2], 25, [1].
AW altered former no. '4' to '5'.
Wood 630(5). Wing F308.

2933. Family of Love. *A description of the sect called the Familie of Love: with their common place of residence. Being discovered by* mʳˢ *Susanna Snow.* London: n.pub., 1641. 4°. Pp. [2], 6.
Wood 647(3). Wing D1168.

2934. Fanatic Character. *The character of a phanatique.* London: f. H. Marsh, 1660. S.sh.
AW altered the date to 16 '59: March'. LT 1.303.
Wood 276a(260). Wing C1971.

2935. Fanatic Creed. *The phanatiques creed, or, a door of safety; in answer to a bloody pamphlet intituled A door of hope [15 Jan.].* London: f. H. Brome, 1661. 4°. Pp. [2], 14.
Tp, AW altered the year to 166'0'.
Wood 608(36). Wing F402.

2936. Fanatic League. *A phanatique league and covenant . . . by the assertors of the good old cause.* [London?]: f. G. H. the Rumps Pamphleteer-General, [1660]. S.sh.
AW added the date, 'March: 1659[60]'.
Wood 276a(261). Wing F395.

2937. Fanatic Library. *Bibliotheca fanatica: or, the phanatique library.* [London]: n.pub., 1660. 4°. Pp. [2], 7 (i.e., 6).
Tp, AW altered the year, 16'59: March'.
[MS.] Wood C. 26(18). Wing B2826.

2938. Fanatic Play. *A phanatique play. The first part.* London: n.pub., 1660. 4°. Pp. [2], 6.
Tp, AW altered the date to 16'59' and 'March'.
Wood 615(23). Wing F397.

2939. Fanatic Prayer. *A phanatique prayer, by sir H. V. divinity-professor of Raby castle.* [London]: n.pub., [1660]. S.sh.
AW added the date, 'ffeb: 1659'.
Wood 276a(268). Wing F398A.

2940. Fanatic Queries. *Fanatique queries, propos'd to the present assertors of the good old cause.* London: f. Praise-God-Barebones, [1660]. 4°. Pp. [2], 5, [1].
Tp, AW wrote '1659[60]: ffeb:'. LT 1.303.
Wood 613(25). Wing F399.

2941. Fancy. *Fancies ague-fittes, or beauties nettle-bed.* London: G. Simson f. W. Jones, 1599. 8°. A⁴,B-I⁸,K⁴ (last leaf blank).
Tp and p. [3], signature of Phillip Woolfe. K4, coat of arms, drawne, with a helmet and bird crest.
Wood 736(2b). STC 10684.

2942. Fannant, Thomas. *An historicall narration of the manner and forme of . . . parliament, . . . begun*

at Westminster 1386. [London]: n.pub., 1641. 4°. Pp. [4], 36.
Wood 518(2). Wing F415 (Wing, historical).

2943. Fanshaw, Thomas. *A declaration of the knights and gentry of the county of Hertford [signed by Thomas Fanshaw and 13 others].* London: D. Pakeman, 1660. S.sh.
AW added to the year, 'Aprill'.
Wood 276a(217). Wing F419 (two) ('O' not recorded in Wing).

2944. Faria, Francisco de. *The information of Francisco de Faria, delivered at the bar of the house of commons [1 Nov.].* London: by the assigns of J. Bill, T. Newcomb, and H. Hills, 1680. Fol. Pp. [3], 12.
Wood 426(22). Wing F425.

2945. Faria, Francisco de. *The narrative of segnior Francisco de Faria, . . . Wherein is contained the several informations . . . touching the horrid popish plot.* London: J. Gain, f. R. Taylor, 1680. Fol. Pp. [2], 3, 38.
Tp, AW wrote the price, '1ˢ'; pp. 2nd 1-2, 4, 11, line in margin and brief notes, e.g., 'Franc. de Faria æt. 27. an 1680', and 'This is in the former narrative of Faria.' (Wood 426(22)).
Wood 426(28). Wing F426.

2946. Farissol, Abraham ben Mordecai, and Albertus Bobovius. Hyde, Thomas, trans. *[Hebrew: Igereth orhoth 'olam] id est, itinera mundi. Lat. versione donavit & notas adjecit T. Hyde. Calce exponitur Turcarum liturgia, peregrinatio Meccana, . . . [by A. Bobovius]. Accedit castigatio in Angelum à Sancto Joseph].* [Oxoniae] (Oxonii): (e theatro Sheldoniano) [impen. H. Bonwick], 1691. 4°. Pp. [8], 196, [4], 31 (2 tpp) (wanting sheet a, and 2nd t leaf misplaced).
[MS.] Wood B. 38(2). Wing F438.

2947. Farmer, Jacob. *A letter sent out of Ireland. To one mr. Bell . . . Being a true relation of the present estate of Ireland.* London: f. J. Smith, 1642. 4°. A⁴.
Tp, AW wrote after the year, 'Jan. 9. 1641'.
Wood 507(24). Wing F440 (Wing, Ireland, to).

2948. Farmer, John. *[Divers & sundry waies of two parts in one, . . . uppon one playnsong].* [London]: [T. Este, the assigne of W. Byrd], [1591]. 8°. A2-4,B-C⁸,D1-3 (wanting tp). Calf with 3 fillets, stamp decoration (dragons) in corners (Ashm. binding); rebacked.
Flyleaf, upper, 2nd, list of 8 printed works, by an Ashm. librarian. A3, at top, AW wrote, in pencil, 'Plaine Song', etc.; most is cropped and illeg. B4, 'John Rogers his boo[k]', cropped at side.
Wood 90(1). STC 10698 (two).

2949. Farnaby, Thomas. *Index rhetoricus.* ?: ?, 1625ff. Pp.?
Missing. MS. Wood E. 2(70), p. 46. Ed. not identified.
MS. Wood E. 2(70), p. 46. STC 10703ff. Wing F454.

2950. [Farnaby, Thomas]. *Phrases oratoriae elegantiores.* Londini: F. Kyngstonius, 1631. 6th ed. A-E⁸,F1-7 (imp.; interleaved with blanks). Parchment with 2 clasp holes.
A much-used schoolbook. Passim, numerous definitions, exercises, and translations, in various hands, added on blank leaves, by several persons. Cover and pastedown (mutilated), upper, inside, and tp, names, including Johannes –?, Ingoldesby and 'Christopher Stace his Booke'. The name of the author of this book is also identified, 'Tho. Farnibie' (prob. in AW's hand). AW listed an apparent dupl. in MS. Wood E. 2(70), p. 16: 'Thom. Farnabie - 1 phrases dup. [and] 2 sistema grammaticum'.
Wood 43. STC 10707 (two).

2951. Farnaby, Thomas. *Systema grammaticum.* Londini: excud. T. & R. C., imp. A. Crooke, 1641. 4°. Pp. [12], 104.
Missing. MS. Wood E. 2(70), p. 16, 'Thom. Farnabie - 1 phrases dup. [and] 2 sistema grammaticum'.
MS. Wood E. 2(70), p. 16. Wing F464. *O, Hunt, Folg.*

2952. Farr, Richard*. *The cheating solliciter cheated:. . . the life and death of Richard Farr.* London: f. T. J[ohnson], 1665. 4°. Pp. [3], 58.
Wood 372(8). Wing C3766 ('O' not recorded in Wing).

2953. Fast and Loose. *Fast and loose. Or, the armies figgaries: being some animadversions upon their late declaration.* [London]: n.pub., 1659. 4°. Pp. 11.
Tp, nos. 49 and 46 in former bundles.
Wood 610(61). Wing F539.

2954. Fauchet, Claude. *Origines des chevaliers, armoiries, et héraux.* Paris: J. Périer, 1600. 8°. Pt. 2.
Missing. Gore, f. 313.
Gore 313. Not identified.

2955. Fauchet, Claude. *Origines des dignitez et magistrats de France.* Paris: J. Périer, 1600. 8°. Pt. 1.
Missing. Gore, f. 313.
Gore 313. Not identified.

2956. Fauchet, Claude. *Les antiquitez gauloises et françoises.* Paris: ?, 1609. Pp.?
Missing. Gore, f. 313.
Gore 313. BN, 1599 and 1611 eds.

2957. Faustus, John*, pseud. *The second report of doctor John Faustus. Containing his apparances, and the deedes of Wagner.* London: A. Jeffes f. C. Burby, 1594. 4°. A-I⁴ (sig. F2 imperf.).
Tp, 'F' (? cropped at bottom).
[MS.] Wood B. 20(4). STC 10715.3 (two).

2958. Faustus, John*. *The history of the wicked life and damnable death of dr. John Faustus.* [London]: f. T. Passinger, [1600]. 8°. A⁸,B⁴.
Tp, AW made clear the print in 'Mephostophiles'.
Wood 707(5) (not in Bodl. CD cat.). Not in Wing. Not in ESTCR. Not H2151ff. Should be at H2191aA.

2959. Faustus, John*. *The first part of doctor Faustus.* [London]: J. M. f. J. Deacon, 1688. 8°. A⁸,B⁴.
Wood 707(4) (not in Bodl. CD cat.). Not in Wing (not F977A (one)). Not in ESTCR.

2960. Fawne, Luke. *A beacon set on fire: or the humble information of certain stationers, citizens of London [L. Fawne et al.], to the parliament . . . concerning the vigilancy of Jesuits.* London: f. the subscribers hereof, 1652. 4°. Pp. 16.
Tp, bsms. P. 10, AW added a name, 'de Cressy', and a Christian name, 'Will' Joyner, to a list of converts to 'Popery', in red ink.
Wood 609(33). Wing F564.

2961. Fawne, Luke. *A second beacon fired. Humbly presented to the lord protector [signed by Fawne et al.].* London: f. the subscribers hereof, 1654. 4°. Pp. [2], 12.
Wood 609(48) (not in Bodl. CD cat.). Wing L565.

2962. Fearful apparitions. *Fearefull apparitions or the strangest visions that ever hath been heard of.* London: f. J. Hammond, 1647. 4°. Pp. [2], 5.
Flyleaf, upperᵛ, 'Fearfull Apparitions', not by AW. P. 5ᵛ, scribbles.
[MS.] Wood B. 35(18). Wing F576.

2963. Featley, Daniel. *Ancilla pietatis: or, the hand-maid to private devotion. [Followed by] The summe of saving knowledge: delivered in a catechisme.* London: (G. Miller) f. N. Bourne, 1626. 12°. 2nd ed. Pp. [36], 764, [18], 56 (3 tpp.) (C12, final leaf, torn out). Parchment.
Pastedown, upper, AW wrote 'Anthony Wood His Booke/', name lined out; and, in another hand, 'I cannot tell wose [sic] Booke it is'. Tpᵛ, 'Mary Wood'. Flyleaf, lower, mostly torn out, but scribbles are on the fragment.
Wood 787. STC 10726 (pt. 2 sometimes issued separately, STC 10739).

2964. Featley, Daniel. Καταβαπτισται καταπτυστοι. *The dippers dipt, or, the Anabaptists duck'd.* London: f. N. B. a. R. Royston, 1647. 5th ed. C1 (only) (engr.).
Wood 276b(27). Wing F588.

2965. Featley, Daniel*. *Featlaei* παλιγζενεσια: *or, doctor Daniel Featley revived: proving, that the protestant church . . . is the onely Catholick and true church.* London: f. N. Brook, 1660. 12°. Pp. [12], 114, [2], 86 (2 tpp.). Calf, speckled, with 2 fillets.
Flyleaf, upper, AW wrote '9ᵈ'. Pasted to a sheet at bottom edge, a slip identifying the author and work (see note at Wood 208). Tp, bsm. In biography section, 2nd pp. 9 and 14 (corrections), 39 (line in margin), 41 ('q[uaere]' in margin), 57 (information added), 75 (a correction).
Wood 782. Wing F581.

2966. Feilding, Basil*. Denbigh, 2nd earl of. *Two great victories: on[e] obtained by the earle of Denbigh at Oswestrey.* London: J. Coe, 1644. 4°. A⁴.
Wood 377(14). Wing T3450.

2967. [**Fell, John**], et. al. *The privileges of the university of Oxford, in point of visitation: cleerly evidenced by letter to an honourable personage. Together with the universities answer.* [London]: f. R. Royston, 1647. 4°. Pp. [2], 9.
P. 9ᵛ, '(Sheld)', not by AW (prob. not a Sheldon item). Diff. ed. at Wood 514(33). LT 1.143. AO 3.1271. On the authorship, see the next item and Wood 514(35), item 6455.
[MS.] Wood C. 47(2). Wing F619A. Madan 1956.

2968. [**Fell, John**], et. al. *The privileges of the university of Oxford, in point of visitation: cleerly evidenced by letter to an honourable personage. Together with the universities answer.* [London]: n.pub., 1647. 4°. Pp. [2], 9.
Tp, AW wrote, 'Rich Allestrie'; on slip pasted over a note, 'An. 1647'; beneath the slip, pasted over, 'Written as tis said by Mʳ John Fell student of Christchurch. & Rich. Allestrie of the same, student. But qu[aere]'. Diff. ed. at [MS.] Wood C. 47(2). LT 1.143. AO 3.1271. On authorship, see Wood 514(35), item 6455. Wood 514(33). Wing F619A. Madan 1956.

2969. [**Fell, John**]. *The interest of England stated: or a . . . just account of the aims of all parties now pretending.* [London]: n.pub., 1659. 4°. Pp. 16.
Tp, AW wrote, 'Dʳ Jo Fell' and a former no. in a bundle '64', both in pencil.
Wood 533(13). Wing F613.

2970. [**Fell, John**]. *The life of that reverend . . . dr. Thomas Fuller.* London: f. J. W.[,] H. B. a. H. M., 1661. 8°. Pp. [6], 106, [5]. Rough calf with 3 fillets and stamp decoration in corners (flower with point) (Ashm. binding).
Flyleaf, upper, 4th, list of 9 printed works in this vol., written by Ashm. librarian (same hand in Wood 276a). P. 1, at 'born at All Wincle', AW wrote 'Dav. Lloyd in his memories printed 1668. p. 523. saith he was borne at Oundle.' Pp. 22-5, 44-5, some marks in pencil. P. 63, underscoring. LT 1.408.
Wood 292(1). Wing F616.

2971. Fell, John. *The life of the most learned, . . . dr. H. Hammond.* London: J. Flesher f. J. Martin, J. Allestry a. T. Dicas, 1661. 8°. Pp. [2], 245.
Tp, AW underscored 'Fell' and wrote, '1ˢ3ᵈ'. Bsm. Pp. 1, 4, 81, mark or note in margin. Acquired 20 July 1661, 1ˢ3ᵈ, LT 1.405. See also AO 3.494.
Wood 251(4) ((8) in Bodl. CD cat.). Wing F617.

2972. Fell, John*. *To the memory of the right reverend father in God, John, lord bishop of Oxford.* [London]: n.pub., [1686/7]. S.sh.
AW wrote, 'printed at London – came downe to Oxon Dec. 9. an. 1686'; ᵛ, 'Dʳ Joh. Fell 1686' and 'Bishop Fell 1686'. LT 3.191-2; AO 4.193ff., 869f.
Wood 429(43). Wing T1571 (two).

2973. [**Fell, Margaret**]. *To the general council of officers. The representation of divers citizens of London.* London: J. Clowes, 1659. S.sh.
Wood 276a(108). Wing F638B.

2974. Fell, Margaret. *A declaration and an information from us the people of God called Quakers, to . . . the king and . . . parliament [5 April].* London: f. T. Simmons a. R. Wilson, 1660. 4°. Pp. [2], 8.
Tp, AW wrote, 'July: 21:'.
Wood 608(21). Wing F628.

2975. Feltham, Owen. *Resolves a duple century.* London: (E. Purslow) f. H. Seile, 1634 (1633). 4°. 5th ed. Pp. [7], 448, [21] (2 tpp). Calf, rough, with 2 fillets; rebacked.
Flyleaf, upper, 1st, 'Antonius Wood sive [?] . . . '(lined out and blotted out and illeg.); 2nd, 'Antonius Wood . . . Oxon 1656' (lined out and several words are illeg.). LT 1.22.
[MS.] Wood B. 25. STC 10760.

2976. [**Feltham, Owen**]. *A true and exact character of the Low-countreyes.* London: f. W. Ley, 1652. 12°. Pp. 24.
'Dupl'. Diff. ed. at Wood 582(1).
Wood 8(2) (not in Bodl. CD cat.). Wing F659B.

2977. [**Feltham, Owen**]. *A brief character of the Low-countries under the States.* London: f. H. S., sold R. Lowndes, 1659. 12°. Pp. [6], 100. Pasteboard (blue) with parchment spine.
Flyleaf, upper, AW wrote 'The times anatomized &c. <u>Lond</u> 1647. Oct. written by Tho. Fuller . . . quaere';

^v, AW wrote the titles of 7 printed works (really 6; 2 entries for item no. 4) in this vol., within guidelines made with red ink.
Wood 582(1). Wing F649.

2978. Felton, [William]. *The examination and confession of captain Lilbourne and captaine Viviers . . . being sent in a letter from mr. Daniel Felton, a scholer of Trinity colledge*. London: f. T. Wright, 1642. 4°. A⁴.
Flyleaf, upper^v, AW wrote, 'I cannot find Dan. Felton to be scholar or student of Trin Coll.–' (there is no record of Trinity scholar, Daniel or William, in Foster or Venn, see Madan). Tp, AW wrote the date, '14 Dec'.
Wood 375(27). Wing F665. Madan 1127.

2979. Fenner, Dudley. *An answere unto the confutation of John Nichols his recantation*. London: J. Wolfe f. J. Harrison a. T. Manne, 1583. 4°. Ff. [5], 100.
Missing. MS. Wood E. 2(70), p. 2, 'Somthing of – [?] bound with it'. Ed. not identified.
MS. Wood E. 2(70), p. 2. STC 10764 and 10764.3. *Union*, and *Folg*, *Hunt*.

2980. Fenton, Geoffrey, trans. *Golden epistles, . . . gathered, as wel out of the remaynder of Guevaraes [sic] woorkes, as other authours*. London: [H. Bynneman f.] R. Newberie, 1582 (15 Oct.). 4°. Corrected. Pp. [4], 347, [3].
A few notes, underscoring and marks in margin (some cropped); last p., scribbles, none by AW.
[MS.] Wood C. 34(2). STC 10796.

2981. Fenton, Roger. *[A treatise of usurie]*. [London]: [F. Kyngston f. W. Aspley], [1612]. 4°. Pp. [12], 155 (wanting A1-2, i.e. pp. [1-2]).
Wood 499(8). STC 10807.

2982. [Ferguson, Robert]. *A letter to a person of honour, concerning the kings disavowing the having been married to the d[uke] of M[onmouth]'s mother [10 June 1610 [that is, 1680]]*. [London]: n.pub., [1680]. 4°. Pp. 23. Pasteboard (blue) with parchment spine; traces of marbled paper, upper and lower flyleaves; rebacked.
Flyleaf, upper, AW wrote the titles of 37 printed works in this vol. (really 38, 2 at no. 4), within guidelines made with red ink; traces of lower flyleaf, marbled paper, remain. One is missing, no. 35. 1st item, tp, AW wrote '1680' after the heading and on p. 23 below the incorrectly printed '1610'. Text, pp. 6-20, some lines and crosses in pencil, not in AW's manner. LT 2.493.
Wood 660c(1). Wing F750.

2983. [Ferguson, Robert]. *A just and modest vindication of the proceedings of the two last parliaments*. [London]: n.pub., [1681]. 4°. Pp. 48.
P. 1, note on dates of the sessions, not in AW's hand. LT 2.531-3.
Wood 608(60). Wing F741.

2984. [Ferguson, Robert]. *An enquiry into, and, detection of the barbarous murther of the late earl of Essex*. [London]: n.pub., 1689. 4°. Pp. [4], 75.
Tp, AW wrote, 'some copies are dated 1684', and 'commonly sold in Oxon, in the latter end of Dec. 1688 – 1ˢ –'; ^v, 'This book being commonly sold in London in Dec. 1688, was called in about Christmas Eve. [/] This came to nothing for the countess of Essex his widow confessed before certaine nobility & the B. of Sarum Dʳ Burnet, that her husband had murderd himself, in the beginning of May 1689' (i.e., the date of her 'confession'). LT 3.60, 294.
Wood 428(26). Wing F739 ('O' not recorded in Wing).

2985. [Ferguson, Robert]. *A representation of the threatning dangers, impending over protestants in Great Brittain, before the coming of . . . the prince of Orange*. [London]: n.pub., 1689. 4°. Pp. [2], 54 (pp. unopened).
Tp, AW wrote, 'Jan. 18 - 1ˢ - 0 - 1688[9]. Dʳ Gil. Burnet author. [and below] some say – Ferguson.' LT 4.297.
Wood 529(19). Wing F757.

2986. [Ferne, Henry]. Chester, bp. of. *Episcopacy and presbytery considered*. Oxford: L. Lichfield, 1644. 4°. Pp. [2], 30.
Tp, 'by Dʳ. . . . Ferne, afterwards Bishop of Chester', not in AW's hand. Notes cut out on pp. 5-6, 25-6. Dupl. at Wood 617(14). LT 1.435.
[MS.] Wood D. 25(10). Wing F793. Madan 1715.

2987. [**Ferne, Henry**]. Chester, bp. of. *Episcopacy and presbytery considered.* Oxford: L. Lichfield, 1644. 4°. Pp. [2], 30.
Dupl. at [MS.] Wood D. 25(10).
Wood 617(14). Wing F793. Madan 1715.

2988. Ferrand, Jacques. [Chilmead, Edmund, trans.]. Ερωτομανια *or a treatise discoursing of the essence, causes, symptomes, prognosticks, and cure of love or erotique melancholy.* Oxford: L. Lichfield, sold E. Forrest, 1640. 8°. Pp. [40], 363. Pasteboard (grey) with parchment spine. 1st upper and last lower flyleaves, marbled paper.
Flyleaf, upper, 2nd[v], AW wrote the titles of 3 printed works in this vol., within guidelines made with red ink. After item 1, 'It was printed at Paris in the French Language in 1623.' Tp, name (lined out, Peter L–on) and note by another former owner. P. 363, again, lined out, Peter L–on. In MS. Wood E. 2(70), p. 38, at 'James Ferrand M.D.', AW noted, 'seems to be of ch.ch.' AO 3.350 (N.B., Chilmead was at Ch.Ch. as were the 8 writers of prefatory poems in this vol.). See LT 1.288.
Wood 741(1). STC 10829. Madan 942.

2989. Ferrandus, Fulgentius. *Ferrandi . . . ad reginum comitem paraeneticus, qualis esse debeat dux religiosus in actibus militaribus.* [(Argent.)]: [(ap. J. Hervagium)], [(1526, Aug.)]. 8°. Ff. 25, [2] (wanting all after sig. D3; bibliog. data from VD).
Wood 835(3). VD F776.

2990. F[errar], R[ichard]. *Epitaph upon the honourable and truly noble sir Kenelm Digby [11 June].* London: f. H. Herringman, 1665. S.sh.
[v], AW wrote, 'S[r] Ken. Digby 1665'.
Wood 429(22). Wing F51 (rare) (Wing, under F., R.).

2991. Ferrarius, Joannes. Bavande, William, trans. *A woorke of . . . touchynge the good orderynge of a common weale.* London: J. Kingston f. J. Wight, 1559. 4°. Ff. [4], 212, [3].
Missing. MS. Wood E. 2(70), p. 25.
MS. Wood E. 2(70), p. 25. STC 10831. *O, Folg, Hunt, Harv.*

2992. Fiat Justitia. *Fiat justitia, & ruat coelum. Or, somewhat offer'd in defence of the imperial crown of England, and its successor. In answer to a speech . . . against the d. [of York] by a true Englishman* [London]: n.pub., [1679?]. Fol. Pp. 4.
Pp. 1, AW wrote the price, '1[d]'; and 4, 'July latter end. 1679'. Purchased from Vade in July or August 1679, see his record of purchase in MS. Wood F. 50, f. 11.
Wood 660c(17). Wing F845.

2993. Fidge, George. *The English Gusman; or the history of that unparallel'd thief James Hind.* London: T. N. f. G. Latham, junior, 1652. 4°. Pp. [6], 46 (H[2], pp. [47-50], are inserted in S., E., Wood 372(2) after A4).
Tp, AW added to initials, G. F'idge', in pencil, and p. 46, wrote a note concerning the end of Hind, 'carried afterwards to Worcester & was hanged there', and below, 'Twentie horse of Hinds Company the great robber, committed 40 robberies about Barnet (not far from Lond) in the space of two houres. – about 22. Sept. 1649'. Flyleaf, lower, 1st[r-v]: 'An abstract of James Hind his Examination of what he confessed of his perambulations', 67 lines in all, telling of his adventures in 1649 until his imprisonment at Newgate, and then recounting his early life and Oxford connections, line 41ff.: 'This James Hind (borne at Chipping-Norton) was a little dapper desperat fellow; & his life here written by one who calls himself Georg. Fidge is very weakly performed – many things are true in it, but most are false, & many material things are omitted. I remember one James Dewy son of M[r] Will. Dewy of S. Ebbs parish in Oxon, who long before my acquaintance with him, was one of his desperate companions; a little man, but verie metalsome & daring. Also I remember one – Haywood of Einsham neare Oxon . . . [and] Arthur Roe a tanner of Oxōn . . . '. All of the above is quoted in LT 1.155-7. Possibly lent to O. Sedgwick, March 1660, LT 1.306.
Wood 372(2). Wing F852 (one) ('O' not recorded in Wing).

2994. F[idge], G[eorge]. *The great eater of Grayes-inne, or the life of m[r.] Marriot the cormorant.* London: f. the author, sold W. Reybould, 1652. 4°. Pp. [4], 41.
P. 41[v], expenses, 7 figures, totalling 6-1-0, pasted over with a blank leaf of support.
[MS.] Wood B. 35(20). Wing F853.

2995. Fiennes, Nathaniel. *Master Fynes his speech in parliament: touching the proffer of the citie of London . . . to disburse 60000[l]. towards the suppressing the rebellion in Ireland.* London: f. F. C. a. T. B.,

1641. 4°. Pp. [2], 5.
Tp, AW wrote, 'Nath.' Below, '6', may not be by AW.
Wood 507(35). Wing F879.

2996. Fiennes, Nathaniel. *A most true and exact relation of both the battels . . . neer Keynton below Edge-hill . . . Worcester.* London: f. J. Hunscott, 1642, 9 Nov. 4°. Pp. 13.
Tp, AW lined out the former no., '22', and underscored the name of the author. For note on p. 13ᵛ, see Wood 375(18).
Wood 375(17). Wing F875.

2997. Fiennes, Nathaniel. *Colonell Fiennes his reply to a pamphlet entituled, An answer.* London: f. T. Underhill, 1643. 4°. Pp. 16.
Tp, AW altered a former no. and underscored the author's surname in red ink.
Wood 376(29). Wing F877.

2998. Fiennes, Nathaniel. *Colonell Fiennes letter to my lord general [Fairfax] concerning Bristol.* London: T. P. a. M. S. f. T. Underhill, 1643. 4°. Pp. [2], 6.
Tp, AW altered the former no. and underscored the author's surname in red ink. Dupl. at Wood 632(3).
Wood 376(25). Wing F874.

2999. Fiennes, Nathaniel. *Colonell Fiennes letter to my lord general [Fairfax] concerning Bristol.* London: T. P. a. M. S. f. T. Underhill, 1643. 4°. Pp. [2], 6.
Tp, AW wrote 'dupl' (cropped at top), in pencil. Dupl. at Wood 376(25).
Wood 632(3) (not in Bodl. CD cat.). Wing F874.

3000. Fiennes, Nathaniel. *A relation made in the house of commons, by . . . concerning the surrender of . . . Bristoll, August 5.* London: f. R. D., [1643]. 4°. Pp. 28.
Tp, AW altered the former no., '23'; underscored the author's surname in red ink; and wrote below, 'This book was answered by Clem. Walker'.
Wood 376(26). Wing F876.

3001. Fiennes, Nathaniel*. *A full declaration of all particulers concerning the march of forces under collonel Fiennes to Bristol.* London: f. R. D., 1643, 18 April. 4°. Pp. [2], 18. Pasteboard (blue) with parchment spine; rebacked.
Flyleaf, upper, 1st, AW wrote, 'Serjeant Maj. Kirle – nu. 17. p. 37' (i.e., Wood 376(17), item 3609); 2ndᵛ, 3rd-5th, the titles of 73 printed works in this vol., within guidelines made with red ink. Before items 2 and 23, 'Deest Octr 1839 W[illiam] K[irtland]'; before items 66, 67, 71, 'missing 29.7.[19]75' (the latter 3 were also missing in 1922).
Wood 376(1). Wing F2343A ('O' not recorded in Wing).

3002. [Fiennes, William]. Saye and Sele, 1st visct. *Folly and madnesse made manifest. Or, some things written to show how contrary . . . practises of the Quakers . . . are [Followed by] The Quakers reply manifested to be railing.* [Oxford]: [H. Hall], 1659[60]. 4°. Pp. [2], 140 (2nd tp at p. 59).
Flyleaf, upper, AW wrote, 'Said to have been written by William Lord Say. [/] written by Will. Fiennes Lord Say. printed at Oxon. [/] Two books in this vol.' Tp, AW wrote, 'Oxon.', and, in pencil, 'Will. Lord Say the author'. AO 3.549.
Wood 645(13-14). Wing S788 (two) ('O' not recorded in Wing). Madan 2441.

3003. Fife, Letter. *A letter from the noblemen, gentlemen, . . . of Fife, . . . to the lord general Monck. With his lordships answer [14 Dec.].* [London]: n.pub., [1659]. S.sh.
Wood 276a(113). Wing L1534A (3).

3004. Fifteen Comforts. *The XV. comforts of rash and inconsiderate marriage, or select animadversions upon the miscarriage of a wedded state. Done out of French.* London: f. W. Davis, 1682. 12°. Pp. [16], 104.
Pp. [4], identification; 2, note; 35, 37, pencil mark, none by AW.
Wood 750(4). Wing F885AB.

3005. Fifth of November. *The fifth of November, or the popish and schismaticall rebells.* Oxford: f. H. Hall a. W. Webb, 1644. 4°. Pp. [8], 18.
Wood 377(41). Wing F891. Madan 1605.

3006. Figulus, Wolfgangus, and Guido Aretinus. *De musica practica liber primus. Guidonis Aretini dialogus de dimensione monochordi,. . . adiectis primi libri brevissimis, rudimentis. [and] Wolfgangi Figuli . . . libri primi musicae practicae elementa brevissima in usum puerorum conscripta. Georgius Fabricius.*

Noribergae: (In off. U. Neuberi, haer. J. Montanus), 1565. 8°. a-f^8,g^4 [i.e., ff. 52];A-C^8,D1-7 [i.e., ff. 31] (2nd tp at A1).
Tp, AW wrote, 'Wolf[g]angi Figuli musica practica'. Many words on tp are marred by over-writing. Text, some underscoring in red and black pencil. P. nos. added, prob. not by AW.
Wood 90(2). VD T1460.

3007. Figure of Six. *The figure of six*. London: ?, 1659. Pp.?
Missing in 1837. 'The Figure of Six – Lond. 1659' in Whiteside cat. See Wing N7 (1652), and N7A (1654).
Wood 64(5). Not in Wing. Not in ESTCR.

3008. Figure of Three. *The figure of three &c*. London: ?, 1619. Pp.?
Missing in 1837. 'The Figure of Three &c. – Lond. 1619' in Whiteside cat. See STC 10865.5 (1636).
Wood 64(4). Not in STC. Not in ESTCR.

3009. Filmer, Robert. *Observations upon Aristotles politiques, touching forms of government*. London: R. Royston, 1652. 4°. Pp. [8], 51.
Missing in 1837. See Wood 490(1), item 5517.
Wood 490(2). Wing F921. *Hunt, Harv, Yale*.

3010. [Filmer, Robert]. *An advertisement to the jury-men of England, touching witches. Together with a difference between an English and Hebrew witch*. London: I. G. f. R. Royston, 1653. 4°. Pp. [8], 24.
Pasteboard (blue) with parchment spine. 1st upper and last lower flyleaves, marbled paper.
Flyleaf, upper, 2nd^v, AW wrote the titles of 3 printed works in this vol., within guidelines made with red ink.
[MS.] Wood B. 16(1). Wing F909.

3011. Filmer, Robert. *A discourse whether it may be lawful to take use for money, . . . published by sir Robert Twisden*. London: f. W. Crook, 1678. 12°. Pp. [38], 119, [9] (8 pp. books printed for Crook).
Pasteboard (blue) with parchment spine. 1st upper and last lower flyleaves, marbled paper.
Flyleaf, upper, 3rd^v, AW wrote the titles of 6 printed works in this vol., within guidelines made with red ink (really 8, AW listed a single work for (3a) and (3b), and omitted the last item, (7). He wrote Arabic nos. on tpp. 1st item, each 12° leaf is pasted on a 4° template.
Wood 628(1). Wing F911.

3012. Finch, Edward*. *An answer to the articles preferred against Edward Finch, vicar of Christ-Church, by some the parishioners*. [London]: n.pub., 1641. 4°. Pp. [3], 14 (pp. unopened).
Tp, the year was altered to '1643'.
[MS.] Wood D. 31(35). Wing F930.

3013. Finch, Edward*. *[The petition and articles or severall charge [sic] exhibited in parliament against Edward Finch, vicar of Christs church in London]*. [London]: [Sould R. Harford], [1641]. 4°. Pp. 14 (wanting the t leaf).
[MS.] Wood D. 31(34). Wing E2157.

3014. [Finch, Heneage (elder)]. Nottingham, earl of. *An exact and most impartial accompt of the indictment, . . . of twenty nine regicides*. London: f. A. Crook a. E. Powel, 1660. 4°. Pp. [2], 283.
Flyleaf, upper, 1st^r, AW wrote 'In this following book are the Tryalls of' 29 regicides and p. refs., e.g. 'Sr Hardr Waller p. 17. 22. 272'; ^{v}, 'Sr Will Brereton p. 248. 249'. Tp, AW wrote 'November: xxiij: A: MDClx:' and '3^s'. Text, an identification, underscorings, corrections, and cross-references, e.g., pp. 9, 168, 179, 180, 248-9, 251. Acquired 24 Nov., 1^{s}6^d, LT 1.338; see also LT 2.507.
Wood 369(3). Wing N1403A.

3015. Finch, Heneage (elder)*. Nottingham, earl of. *On his majesties most gracious and prudent delivery of the great seal of England to . . . sir Heneage Finch*. [London]: n.pub., 1673. S.sh.
^{v}, '1673'.
Wood 416(124). Wing O296 (two).

3016. [Finch, Heneage (elder)]. Nottingham, earl of. *The speech of the lord high steward, . . . against the lord viscount Stafford [7 Dec.]*. London: by the assigns of J. Bill, T. Newcomb, a. H. Hills, 1680. Fol. Pp. 12 (p. 1 blank).
Wood 427(2). Wing N1409.

3017. Finch, Heneage (younger), Winchilsea, 2nd earl of. *A true and exact relation of the late prodigious earthquake and eruption of mount Ætna*. [London] in the Savoy: T. Newcomb, 1669. 4°. Foldout map and

pp. 30.
Tp, AW wrote, '6ᵈ' and 'Heneage Finch E. of Winchelsea, author of this relation.'
[MS.] Wood D. 28(19). Wing W2967.

3018. Finch, Henry. *A true relation of the twenty weeks siege of London derry [sic], by the Scotch, Irish, and dis-affected English*. London: R. I. f. S. G. a. A. W., 1649. 4°. Pp. [2], 14.
Wood 510(2). Wing F935 (Wing, twenty-weeks and Londonderry).

3019. Fisher, James. *The wise virgin: or, a wonderfull narration of the various dispensations of God towards a childe*. London: f. J. Rothwel, 1658. 8°. 4th ed. Pp. [26], 170.
Flyleaf, upperᵛ, '5ᵗʰ. Id: 1664.'
Wood 246(4). Wing F1007.

3020. [Fisher, Joan]*. *The deviil [sic] incarnate, or a satyr upon a satyr; being a display of the hairy devill, countess of Bedlam*. [Oxford?]: n.pub., [1660[1]]. 4°. Pp. 8.
P. 8, AW wrote, 'This pamphlett that was made one [i.e., on] Joane Fisher wife of Hen: Fisher somtimes Manciple & Butler of Queens Coll: Oxōn & who now sells Ale overaganst [sic] the said Coll: came out in February or the beginning of March A. D. 1660[1]', and later, in red ink, 'Tho. Hyde 2ᵈ libr.-keeper was supposed to be the author, but false'. LT 1.382.
Wood 515(26). Wing D1219 (rare). Madan 2551.

3021. Fisher, Payne. *Integerrimo vere viro, cognatoque sibi plurimis nominibus honorando, . . . Rhodolpho, vel Raufio Freke . . . P. Piscator. Aeternitatem sub hoc pulvere praestolatur Gulielmus Freke*. N.p.: n.pub., 1657. S.sh.
Wood 429(9). Wing F1026 (rare).

3022. [Fisher, Payne]. *Epitaphium Roberti Blakii . . . P. P.* N.p.: n.pub., 1658. S.sh. Ed. altera.
AW wrote the name of the author, 'Payne Fisher', and another person added scribbles, ᵛ, AW wrote, twice, 'Rob. Blake 1658'.
Wood 429(14). Wing F1018 (rare).

3023. Fisher, P[ayne]. *Heic jacet bellicosissimus ille Robertus Bartu*. N.p.: n.pub., 1668, 1 Jan. S.sh.
ᵛ, AW wrote, '1666', and 'Rob. Bertie Earl of Lindsay 1668'. Also, a Latin heading, not by AW.
Wood 429(23). Wing F1019 (two).

3024. Fisher, Payne. *Elogium sepulchrale pro victoriosissimo Georgio Monacho*. [London]: n.pub., [1670].
S.sh. Impressio postrema.
Monumental enclosure for this elegy, drawn in ink, with inscriptions, not by AW. Also, a dedication to Thomas Barlow, not in AW's hand. ᵛ, AW wrote, 'Georg Monk 1669'. This is prob. one of the items AW referred to in comments on Barlow, 'He gave me Fisher's poems and broke my head', see 19 Apr. 1675, LT 2.312.
Wood 429(28). Wing F1016 (rare).

3025. Fisher, Payne. *A catalogue of the most memorable tombes*. London: n.pub., 1674. 4°.
Missing. In a list of 'Mr. Woods Duplicats', MS. Wood F. 51, f. 44, item 13.
MS. Wood F. 51(13). Wing F1014 (Wing, publ. date, 1668).

3026. Fisher, P[ayne]. *Deus, et rex, rex, & episcopus. Carmen ad clerum. Cui carmini sua superaddidit elogia sepulchralia P. F.* London: (impensis authoris), (1675). 4°. Pp. [2], 1-98, [18], 99-104, 11 (2nd tp at p. 15). Calf, speckled, with 2 and 4 fillets and a vertical line of 4 fillets.
Flyleaf, lower, an index of 36 items, not in AW's hand.
Wood 317. Wing F1015 and 1015B. See ESTCR 226586.

3027. F[isher], P[ayne]. *Impressio secunda carminis heroici in honorem (nuperiùs) excellentiae suae. Jampridem ter honorabilis Josephi Williamson*. [London]: Typ. T. B., 1675. 'MDCXXLV'. 4°. Pp. [7], 22.
Flyleaf, upper, misplaced, a note on author and translator of item 5 in this volume, not in AW's hand. Tp, a correction of one date, and at date of publication, AW lined out a handwritten, '35', and wrote '1675'.
P. 22, at a list of works by Payne Fisher, AW marked all 25 entries and added a final one, 'Hist. of the tombes & mon. in London' (Wood 534(7)). AO 4.377-82.
Wood 383(4). Wing F1021.

3028. Fisher, Payne. *The tombes, monuments, and sepulchral inscriptions, lately visible in St. Pauls cathedral, compleatly rendred in Latin and English*. London: f. the author, [1684]. 4°. Pp. [12], 5-168, [4] (proof copy; up to p. 5, unnumbered double brackets).

Tp (A1), AW wrote, 'Donavit mi[hi] Author P. Pis[cator] – an[.] 1685', LT 3.160; below, note cropped. Tp (A1) and A2, notes, presumably by Fisher, 'This title is to be reprinted' and 'this leaf is to be reprinted'. Pp. [7], 7, 14, 69, 71 etc. underscoring or a few lines in margin; 72 to 164, some notes, corrections, and a cross-ref.; e.g., 72, at 'Lately', AW wrote, 'when Pauls church was rebuilding 168 [and in pencil] 0'; 77, a correction; 79, at an assertion, 'Tomkyns appears to be', 'how [do] you pro[ve] yt?'.
Wood 534(7). Wing F1041.

3029. [**Fisher, Payne**]. *Juxta suorum cineres repulverescit, . . . coll. Henricus Norwood.* [London]: typ. G. Downing, 1690. S.sh. (mutilated at top and bottom).
AW wrote '[donum] authoris Pagani Piscatoris Nov. 22. an 1690'. LT 3.160.
Wood 429(46). Wing F1028 (rare).

3030. Fisher, Tho[mas]. *Warlike directions: or the souldiers practice.* London: T. Harper, 1644. 8°. 3rd ed. Pp. [4], 86, [6]. Calf with 3 fillets, stamp decoration inside corners, roll decoration on spine (Ashm. binding).
Flyleaf, 2nd, the titles of 5 printed works in this vol., made by an Ashm. librarian (same hand in Wood 276a). Tp, bsms.
Wood 672(1). Wing F1061 (rare).

3031. Fitzer, William. *Caracters and diversitie of letters used by divers nations in the world . . . Curiously cut in brasse by John Theod: de Bry deceased.* Franckfort on the Mayne: J. N. Stolzenberger f. W. Fitzer, 1628. 4°. Pp. 12 and A-I⁴ (I4 blank),M4,N2-4, followed by 24 unnumbered plates, the letters of the alphabet. Calf, speckled, with 2 fillets, and edge hatching (Oxford binding).
Cover, upper, inside, 'Anthony Woode: Merton Coll: Bought out of Dʳ Gerard Langbaine's studie May: 5: 1658:' (AW's early hand) (LT 1.248). Flyleaves, upper and lower, notes, not in AW's hand. Text, a few scribbles. N3, note, not in AW's hand. Waste paper, lower, 'preti 3ˢ-0-0', may be in AW's hand.
Wood 129. STC 10933.

3032. Fitz-Geffrey, Charles. *Affaniae: sive epigrammatum libri tres: ejusdem cenotaphia.* Oxoniae: Jos. Barnesius, 1601. 8°. A1,A8,B-M⁸,N⁴ (2nd tp at M2) (wanting A2-7). Pasteboard (brown) with calf spine; 1st upper and last lower flyleaves, marbled paper.
Flyleaf, upper, 3rdᵛ, AW wrote the titles of 3 printed works in this vol., within guidelines made with red chalk; 4th, 'Edw. Michelborne often in this book. [/] Hilarius Verus v. lib 2.' (i.e., C5ᵛ, Ad Hilarium Verum); H6ᵛ, at Ad Richardum Caraeum, 'v. post.' Other notes, e.g., sig. C3, C8ᵛ, H8ᵛ, and flyleaf, lower, not in AW's hand. AW wrote at the top of pp., from where the text begins in this copy, the odd p. nos., 13 to 197, in pencil (pp. 1-12 (i.e., A2-7) were present when he entered the numbers). AO 2.607.
Wood 82(1). STC 10934. Madan 206.

3033. Fitzgerald, David. *A narrative of the Irish popish plot, for the betraying that kingdom into the hands of the French.* London: f. T. Cockerill, 1680. Fol. Pp. [3], 35.
1st blank p., AW wrote the date, 'Nov. 1680'. P. 3, John Mullowny, underscored.
Wood 422(19). Wing F1072.

3034. Fitz-Harris, Edward*. *An account of the proceedings and arguments of the counsel on both sides concerning the plea of mʳ· Fitz-Harris [7 May].* (London): (f. T. Davies), (1681). S.sh.
Wood 427(16). Wing A354.

3035. Fitz-Harris, Edward*. *An answer to the protestation of the nineteen lords aganst [sic] the rejecting of the impeachment of mr. Fitz-Harris.* (London): (f. C. Pulleyn), (1681). Fol. Pp. 7.
Wood 427(18). Wing A3438.

3036. Fitz-Harris Edward*. *The arraignment and plea of Edw. Fitz-Harris esq; with all the arguments in law.* London: f. F. Tyton, a. T. Basset, 1681. Fol. Pp. [3], 66 [1].
Tp, bsm.
Wood 427(19). Wing A3746.

3037. Fitz-Harris, Edward. *The confession of Edward Fitz-Harys esq; . . . Together with his last speech.* London: f. S. Carr, 1681. S.sh. (r-v).
Wood 427(22). Wing F1091.

3038. Fitz-Harris, Edward*. *The examination [sic] of Edw. Fitzharris, relating to the popish plot [10 March].* London: f. T. Fox, 1681. Fol. Pp. 18 (p. 1 blank).
Tp, AW wrote, 'son of Sʳ Edw. Fitzharris a papist'.

Wood 427(14). Wing E3717.

3039. Fitz-Harris, Edward*. *The proceedings in relation to the tryal of Edward Fitz-Harris.* [London]: (f. J. Millet), (1681). Fol. Pp. 4.
Wood 427(17). Wing P3570.

3040. Fitz-Harris, Edward*, and Oliver Plunket*. *The tryal and condemnation of Edw. Fitz-Harris, esq; for high-treason, . . . As also the tryal and condemnation of dʳ Oliver Plunket.* London: f. F. Tyton, a. T. Basset, 1681. Fol. Pp. [3], 103, [1].
1st blank, AW wrote, '2ˈ6ᵈ'; tp, the same; pp. 103-103ᵛ, 'The said Ol. Plunket was hanged drawn & quarter'd at Tyburne on the first of July 1681. Whereupon his quarters only (not the head) were buried in the yard belonging to Sᵗ Giles ch. in the feilds neare to London, by the bodies of the Jesuits (the 5 Jesuits) Lately buried there – when continuinge till after the crop-Eard plot broke out 1683, they were taken up, & conveyed to the monastery of Ben[e]dictines [ᵛ] they were taken up & conveyed to the monastery of Benedicttins [sic] at Lambspring in Germany, where they were with great devotion buried/'. LT 2.545 and AO 1.506. Lent to West, bookseller, 12 Nov. 1682, LT 3.29.
Wood 427(20-1). Wing T2140.

3041. Fitzherbert, Nicolas. *Nicolai Fierberti, Oxoniensis in Anglia academiae descriptio.* Romae: ap. G. Facciottum, 1602. 12°, in 8's. Pp. 55.
AO 2.120f.
Wood 183(3). BL. Madan 211. ARCR 1.475.

3042. Fitzherbert, Nicolas. *Nicolai Fizerberti antiquitate & continuatione Catholicae religionis in Anglia, & de Alani cardinalis vita.* Romae: ap. G. Facciottum, 1608. 8°. Pp. [8], 100, [1].
Some underscoring, lines in margin (pp. 58-67 in pencil), and notes (55, and 74, cropped), may be in AW's hand. AO 2.120f.
Wood 183(2). BL. ARCR 1.476.

3043. Fitzwalter*. Barony of. *Robert baron Fitzwalter [genealogy].* N.p.: n.pub., [1668]. S.sh. and fragment of the same, but a different setting, with ms. additions.
Some ms. additions in more than one hand; none by AW. Last printed entry: 'Henry Mildemay son and heir now living'. Ends with ms. entry, 'Benjamin Mildemay now livinge 1668'.
Wood 276a(72). Not in Wing. Not in ESTCR. Diff. ed., ESTCR 233428 (ends with 'Benjamin Mildemay now living, anno 1667').

3044. Flacius, Matthias. *Historia certaminum inter Romanos episcopos & sextā Carthaginensem synodum, Africanesque ecclesias, de primatu seu potestate papae.* Basileae: n.pub., [1554]. 8°. Pp. 5-214, [28] (wanting the 1st 2 leaves). Calf with 3 fillets, stamp decoration (dragons) inside corners (Ashm. binding); rebacked.
Flyleaf, upper, 2nd, the titles of 6 printed works in this vol., written by an Ashm. librarian (same hand in Wood 276a).
Wood 824(1). BL.

3045. Flagellum Dei. *Flagellum Dei: or, a collection of the several fires, plagues and pestilential diseases that have hapned . . . from the Norman conquest.* London: f. C. W., 1668. 4°. Pp. 11.
P. 9, 'A great fire in Oxford - A°. 1644', not in AW's hand.
[MS.] Wood D. 28(18). Wing F1127.

3046. Flamsteed, J[ohn]. *A correct tide table, shewing the true times of high-waters at London-bridg, . . . 1683.* London: f. J. Baker, [1683]. S.sh.
Wood 276a(42). Wing F1134 (rare).

3047. [Flatman, Thomas]. *Naps upon Parnassus. A sleepy muse nipt and pincht.* London: f. N. Brook, 1658. 8°. A-G⁸,H⁴. H4 blank (G to end books sold by N. Brook). Calf with 2 fillets; rebacked by C. P. 1.10.69.
Flyleaf, upper, 3rdᵛ, AW wrote, 'by Sam. Austen of Wadham coll', in pencil (AO 3.675). Tp, at top, scribble, 'Bellin 2' (Bullin 2?). AW identified authors of liminary verses, signed in text only by initials, e.g., A4ᵛ, 'Walter Pope Fellow of Wadham Coll. in Oxford'; A5ᵛ, 'Silvanus Taylour Mʳ of A. of Wadham Coll.'; A7ᵛ, 'Georg Castle Mʳ of A. and Fellow of Allsoules Coll. in Oxford' and at Alexandro Amidei Firorentino, 'A Jew living in Oxon. a teacher of Hebrew.'; B1, B1ᵛ, B2ᵛ, etc.; and some names entered in pencil, e.g., C1ᵛ, C2ᵛ. Some authors or persons cited in text are given lengthier entries, e.g. B5, at 'Pagan Fisher . . . jeer'd in Christ-Church Hall', AW wrote: 'when he made the anniversary speech of Archb. Usher. March 21.'

and 'Payne Fisher a time serving poet got leave of Ol. Cromwell to celibrate Archb. Ushers anniversary in Christchurch hall Ox. And being a conceited Br[a]ggadocio was hummd & hist by scholars –'. G6, H2ᵛ, lines in margins at 2 books sold by N. Brooks.
Wood 108. Wing F1140.

3048. F[latman], T[homas]. *A panegyrick to his renowed [sic] majestie, Charles the second.* London: f. H. Marsh, 1660. S.sh.
After initials of author, AW wrote, 'Flatman qu[aere]', in pencil, and after year, 'May:'; ᵛ, 'May 1660'.
Wood 416(83). Wing F1149.

3049. Flatman, Thomas. *A Pindarique ode on the death of . . . Thomas earl of Ossory.* London: J. G. f. B. Tooke, 1681. Fol. Pp. [2], 5.
P. 5ᵛ, AW wrote 'Th. E. of Ossory 1680'.
Wood 429(36). Wing F1150.

3050. Flavel, John. Huishe, Alexander, ed. *Tractatus de demonstratione methodicus & polemicus.* Oxoniae: J. Lichfield & J. Short, 1619. 8°. Pp. [10], 144, [12].
Missing. MS. Wood E. 2(70), p. 19. AW mentioned only the 1619 ed. in AO 2.207.
MS. Wood E. 2(70), p. 19. STC 11031. Madan 478. *O, BL, Harv.*

3051. Flayderus, Fridericus Hermannus. *De arte volandi.* [Tübingen]: Typ. T. Werlini, 1628. 12°. Pp. [2], 45 (2 leaves unopened).
Wood 36(3). NUC.

3052. Flecknoe, Richard. *Fifty five enigmatical characters, all very exactly drawn to the life.* London: f. W. Crook, 1665. 8°. Pp. [6], 125 (i.e., 135, misnumbering), [3].
Tp, AW wrote '8ᵈ'. Bsm. Acquired 5 Dec. 1667, LT 2.122.
Wood 868(6). Wing F1480.

3053. Fleetwood, Charles*. *The form of the new commissions by which the forces act, that are under the command of Charles Fleetwood.* Loydon [sic]: at the sign of the impudent rebell, 1659. S.sh.
Wood 276a(337). Wing F1577.

3054. Fleetwood, Charles. *To the supream authority, the parliament . . . The humble petition of Charles Fleetwood.* [London]: n.pub., [1659]. S.sh.
AW wrote 'Januar: 1659'.
Wood 276a(201). Wing F1241.

3055. Fleetwood, Charles. *The lord general Fleetwoods answer to the humble representation of collonel Morley, . . . wherein he declares . . . for a free parliament.* [London]: n.pub., 1659, 8 Nov. 4°. Pp. 24.
Tp, nos. '9' and '7', in pencil, in former bundles.
Wood 613(15). Wing F1239.

3056. Fleming, Abraham, trans. [or rather written by?]. *A bright burning beacon, forewarning all wise virgins to trim their lampes against the comming of the bridegroome.* (London): (H. Denham), (1580). 8°. A-Q⁴.
Tp, bsm.
Wood 699(4). STC 11037.

3057. Fletcher, G[iles]. *Of the Russe common wealth. Or maner of governement by the Russe emperour.* London: T. D[awson] f. T Charde, 1591. 8°. Ff. [3], 116. Parchment, with 2 clasp holes.
Tp, 'P. 83', not in AW's hand. Acquired 6 Nov. 1666, 1ˢ8ᵈ, LT 2.92. Diff. ed. at Wood 167(2).
Wood 455. STC 11056.

3058. Fletcher, G[iles]. *The history of Russia, or the government of the emperour of Muscovia.* London: R. Daniel f. W. Hope a. E. Farnham, 1657. 8°. Pp. [8], 1-144, 169-280 (imperf.).
Flyleaf, upperᵛ, AW wrote, 'The first edit. of this book came out at Lond. 1591. in 8°, with this title - [/] Of the Russe commonwealth. Or manner of government by the Russe emperour (commonly called the emperour of Moskovia) withe the manners & fashions of the people of that country &c. [/] The author was employed by Qu. Elizabeth to the Emperour of Russia concerning various matters' and, after 1695 in a later hand, 'Vide W. 455' (i.e., Wood 455, AW's copy of the 1st ed.). Tp, AW wrote, 'The first edit of this book came out 1591 in 8°.'; and he copied from elsewhere the lost printed pages, 144-168, on 21 leaves bound in the book after p. 144.
Wood 167(2). Wing F1332.

3059. [**Fletcher, Henry**]. *The perfect politician: or, a full view of . . . Cromwel.* London: J. Cottrel, f. W. Roybould a. H. Fletcher, 1660. 8°. Pp. [6], 359.
Tp, AW wrote, 'This book was written by Hen. Fletcher Bookseller - so Gilb. Millington Bookseller hath told me'. The bookseller was Edward Millington, not Gilbert, see item 6636. A4, vertical line in pencil at errata list. Some marks in margin or brief notes, e.g., pp. 337, brief note; 339-40; 344, AW identified 'Garter Principal King of Armes' as 'Edw. Bysshe'; 349; 353-4.
Wood 243(3). Wing F1334.

3060. Fletcher, Robert. *The nine English worthies:. . . beginning with king Henrie the first, and concluding with prince Henry.* London: H. L[ownes] f. J. Harrison, 1606. 4°. Pp. [20], 52.
Wood 483(22). STC 11087.

3061. Fletcher, William. *An answer to malice defeated: or, some reflections upon madam Cellier's case.* London: f. the author W. Fletcher, 1680. S.sh.
Wood 426(7). Wing A3360 (3).

3062. Floddan Field. *Floddan Field in nine fits being an exact history of that . . . battle . . . between English and Scots.* London: by P. L. f. H. B., W. P., a. S. H., 1664. 8°. Pp. [3], 87.
Acquired 30 June 1664, 4^d, LT 2.15.
Wood 84(8). Wing F1365.

3063. Florio, John. *A worlde of wordes, or a most copious, and exact dictionarie in Italian and English.* London: A. Hatfield f. E. Blount, 1598. Fol. Pp. [18], 462.
Missing in 1837. In the Whiteside cat., 'An Italian Dictionary d. London 1598'.
Wood 395. STC 11098. *O, Folg, Hunt, NYPL.*

3064. Florus, Lucius Annaeus. Stadius, Joannes, ed. *J. Stadii in L. Julii Flori historiarum libr. IV. commentarii.* Coloniae Agrippinae: ap. A. Hiert, 1612. 8°. Pp. 228.
Text, reference entries on each leaf, a few hand pointers, not by AW. Flyleaf, lower, errata list; ^{v}, maxims, not by AW, and after, in AW's hand, 'rogues'; also some scribbles.
Wood 185(2). BL.

3065. Florus, Lucius Annaeus. Stadius, Joannes, ed. *L. Julii Flori rerum à Romanis gestarum libri IV.* Coloniae Agrippinae: ex off. A. Hierat, 1612. 8°. Pp. 152, [19]. Calf with 4 fillets, 2 clasps (cloth), and edge hatching; spine, 4 bands and hatching (Oxford binding).
Flyleaf, upper, notes, not by AW; ^{v}, signature of Anthony à Wood, lined out, and a second signature, illeg. Tp, bsm. Text, some corrections and, p. 143, a note, not in AW's hand.
Wood 185(1). Not in BL, NUC, BN.

3066. Florus, Lucius Annaeus. B[olton], E. M., trans. *The Roman histories of Lucius Julius Florus.* London: W. Stansby f. T. Dewe, [1621?]. 12°. Pp. [24], 503. Parchment.
Wood 191. STC 11104.

3067. Fludd, Robert. *Doctor Fludds answer unto m. Foster, or, the squeesing of parson Fosters sponge, ordained by him for the wiping away of the weapon-salve.* London: [J. Beale a. G. Purslow?] f. N. Butter, 1631. 4° (wanting A2). Pp. [6], 144, 68. 2 pts.
Flyleaf, upper, 'HI', a shelf-mark in a former collection; and a no. in a former bundle (cropped at top); ^{v}, AW wrote 'v. cat bib bod pro Foster' (AW found W. Foster's book at 4° C 81 Th.; his own copy is at Wood 498(10); see also AO 2.573). Tp, correction of location of ref. to Psal. 92.7, prob. by AW; underscoring, and 'x138' (?). In the text, the annotation, marks in margins, and underscoring, in 2 hands, was not by AW.
Wood 619(13). STC 11120.

3068. Ford, Philip. *A vindication of William Penn . . . from the late aspersions spread abroad on purpose to defame him.* (London): (f. B. Clark), (1683). S.sh. (r-v).
Wood 559(5). Wing F1470.

3069. [**Ford, Simon**]. *The conflagration of London: poetically delineated. And directed to . . . J. L.* London: f. S. Gellibrand, 1667. 4°. Pp. 27.
Tp, at J. L., AW wrote, 'Langham', and '6^d'.
[MS.] Wood D. 28(17). Wing F1480.

3070. Ford, Simon. *Londini quod reliquum. Or, Londons remains [with] Actio in Londini incendiarios.* London: f. S. Gellibrand, 1667. 4°. Pp. [3], 16 (r-v pp. have same no., hence pp. [1-32]); followed by [1], 16.
Tp, '7$^{d.ob}$'; bsm. Acquired 3 Dec. 1667, LT 2.122, and note at item 82.

[MS.] Wood D. 28(16). Wing F1488.

3071. Fortescue, John, and Ralph de Hengham. Selden, John, ed. *De laudibus legum Angliae. . . . Hereto are added the two sums of sir Ralph de Hengham. . . . With notes . . . by . . . John Selden.* London: printed J. Streater [et al.], sold G. Sawbridge [et al.], 1672. 8°. Ff. [1-7], 3-132 [imperf.]; pp. [6], 51, [13], 140.
Flyleaf, upper, A. Allam wrote, 'Pret: 2ˢ 6ᵈ Ellis Bibliop: Maii quinto 1677', LT 3.167. Pasted to a sheet at bottom edge, a slip identifying the author and work (see also Index, 'Slip with title').
Wood 671. Wing F1613.

3072. Foster, Henry. *A true and exact relation of the marchings of the two regiments . . . of London.* London: f. Benjamin Allen, 1643, 2 Oct. 4°. A-B⁴.
Tp, AW lined out the former no.
Wood 376(40). Wing F1625 ('O' not recorded in Wing).

3073. [Foster, T.]. *A winding-sheet for England's ministry . . . sent to John Owen, . . . late vice-chancellor of Oxford.* [London]: n.pub., [1658?]. 4°. Pp. 8.
Tp, AW wrote at top, '59', and at bottom, '2ᵈ heap 56', in pencil.
Wood 370(10). Wing F1637.

3074. Foster, William. *Hoplocrisma-spongus: or, a sponge to wipe away the weapon-salve.* London: T. Cotes f. J. Grove, 1631. 4°. Pp. [16], 56.
Tp, 'Lib: Thomae ffortescue Coll. Exoniae Socii'; bsm, and scribble; ᵛ, note by Fortescue. Pp. 8-56, X marks in margins, prob. not by AW. LT 1.425.
Wood 498(10). STC 11203.

3075. Foulkes, Robert*. *A true and perfect relation of the tryal and . . . execution . . . of . . . mʳ. Robert Foulks.* [London]: f. L. White, 1679. 4°. Pp. 8.
LT 2.435-6.
Wood 365(29). Wing T2570 (one) ('O' not recorded in Wing) (Wing, [1679]).

3076. Fowler, Edward*. Gloucester, bp. of. *Reflections upon that act of the Gloucester common-council: which occasioned dr. Fowler's printing his discourse of offences.* London: f. H. Mortlock, 1683. 4°. Pp. [2], 13.
Wood 631(12). Wing R724.

3077. [Fowler, Edward]. Gloucester, bp. of. *An answer to the paper delivered by mʳ Ashton at his execution.* London: f. R. Clavell, 1690. 4°. Pp. 31, [1] (1 p. books printed f. R. Clavell).
P. 1, AW wrote, 'After this following pamphlet was published, came out another by stealth in behalf of Mʳ [John] Ashton, called The Loyal Martyr &c but I could never see it' (Wing L3353A), and an earlier note, much the same, in pencil. Tp, 'Edw [Fowler] B. of Gloc. the author', in pencil. LT 3.357.
Wood 367(23). Wing F1695 ('O' not recorded in Wing).

3078. [Fox, George]. *Saul's errand to Damascus:. . . Or, a faithful transcript of a petition contrived by some persons in Lancashire, . . . against . . . Quakers. Together with the defence of the persons thereby traduced [G. Fox, J. Nayler, J. Lawson].* London: f. G. Calvert, 1653. 4°. Pp. [10], 38. Pasteboard (blue) with parchment spine. 1st upper and last lower flyleaves, marbled paper with traces of print on non-marbled side (see note at Wood 645(26), item 5171). Waste paper backing inside spine, advertisement for Sᵗ. Aldates Academy Oxford M[-] Hewlett of Magdalen Hall Terms for Boarding and Tuition Twenty-four Guineas Per Annum [/] Jo Bucklersbury, London (rebound in 19th century).
Flyleaves, 2nd-3rd, AW wrote the titles of 26 printed works in this vol. (really 25; 2 entries for no. 13), within guidelines made with red ink. Following the titles, AW drew a pointer and wrote, 'Note that in my book entit. Oxoniensia Vol. 4. are these pamphlets relating to Quakers [/] A relation of some of the sufferings inflicted upon the servants of the Lord called Quakers, &c. by certaine scholers of Oxford – printed 1654. [/] A true Testimony of the zeale of Oxford professors who persecute the servants of that living God (the Quakers) &c. by Rich Hubberthorne – printed 1654' (i.e., Wood 515(14) and 515(15), items 5488, 3712). Tp, former no., '3'.
Wood 645(1). Wing F1894 ('O' not recorded in Wing).

3079. F[ox], G[eorge], and John Rous. *To the parliament of the commonwealth of England. A declaration of the sufferings of several of the people of God . . . in New England [signed G. F. and John Rous].* N.p.: n.pub., 1659. 4°. Pp. 18.
Pp. 1, AW wrote '1659 or 60'; a correction, may not be by AW; 2, 6-7, 14, corrections, may not be by AW;

18, at end, AW wrote '1659'.
Wood 645(12). Wing F1957A (two) ('O' not recorded in Wing).

3080. France. *Execution remarquable d'un jeune homme, qui a esté pendu & brusté pour avoir rollé dans l'eglise Sainte Margueritte, au Fauxbourg Sainct Anthoine [and several chansons, e.g., p. 3] Chanson nouvell sur le chant, des canaries [and, p. 5] Roquantin nouveau*. N.p.: n.pub., n.d. S.sh. (3 shs., r-v) (all sheets are related).
Wood 276b(123-25). Not in BL, BN, NUC.

3081. France. Parliament. *A newe order for banqueroupts [a decree of the parliament of Paris against W. Buhigue, 26 June 1582]*. London: T. Dawson f. T. Charde, 1582. 8°. A⁸,B⁴ (last leaf blank).
Wood 824(5). STC 19200 (rare).

3082. France. *A declaration exhibited to the French king . . . concerning the holy league. Whereunto is adjoyned: An advertisement to the three estates*. London: (A. Jeffes f. T. Cadman), 1587. 8°. Pp. 54. Calf with 3 fillets, a second vertical line and decoration in corners (dragons) (Ashm. binding).
Flyleaf, upper, the titles of 6 printed works in this vol. by an Ashm. librarian (same hand in Wood 276a).
Wood 699(1). STC 13100.

3083. France. B[asset?], R., trans. *An epitome of all the lives of the kings of France*. London: J. Okes, sold J. Becket, 1639. 8°. Pp. [13], 344, [7]. Calf with 2 fillets; rebacked.
Flyleaf, upper, 1st, 'Hen ffoulis Booke December 1: 1651 Pre: In [?]', scribbles, and 'Phillip Comines authoris huius libri', lined out; 2nd, three purchases by Foulis, 'For Pots [?] 8 0 For the horse 2 0 For good ale 0 2' (smeared); 3rdᵛ 'S. J. pr. 1ˢ.6ᵈ'. Text, some underscoring and a few marks in margin, in unidentifiable hand(s); p. 305, a note on the 3rd use of the same woodcut, in AW's hand; Z8, note, prob. in Foulis's hand.
LT 2.179.
Wood 268. STC 11273.

3084. France. *A character of France. To which is added, Gallus castratus. Or an answer to a late slanderous pamphlet called the character of England [i.e., Evelyn, Wood 582(3)]*. London: f. N. Brooke, 1659. 12°. Pp. [8], 45, [3], 38 (2 tpp).
Tp, bsm.
Wood 582(4). Wing C2016.

3085. France. *A true relation of the prodigious battle of birds, fought . . . between . . . Dole and Salines [26 Feb.]*. [Oxford]: [f. J. Colley]. (Printed in French at Lisle, March 17th. 1676), 1676. 4°. Pp. [2], 4.
[MS.] Wood D. 28(22). Not in Wing. Not in ESTCR. Not Wing T3027. Madan 3103.

3086. France, Spain. *An account from Paris of the articles of peace concluded betwixt . . . France and Spaine*. [London]: n.pub., [1659]. S.sh.
Wood 276a(142). Wing A174.

3087. Frances, Robert. *The dying speech of Robert Frances of Grays-inn, esq; July 24*. (London): (G. Croom), (1685). Fol. Pp. 4.
Flyleaf, upperᵛ, AW wrote notes on the murder of Thomas Dangerfield by Robert Frances: 'Thomas Dangerfield having been found guilty of perjury relating to the popish plot, he was sentenced to walk about Westminster hall with a paper upon his head – Afterwards to stand in the pillory in the old pallace yard before Wesminster hall dore – next at the Old Exchange – then to be whipped at the Carts tayl from Aldgate to Newgate – and thence at another time from Newgate to Tyburne – After which last had been performed, & in his returne to Newgate, Mʳ Rob. Frances of Greys Inn being accidentally in Holburne when the coach (containing Dangerfield) passed by, he drew up to it, & said [underscored in red chalk:] How now friend, have yo[u] had your heat this morning? Whereupon Dangerfield being alwaies ready with ill Language in his mouth, answered, [underscored in red chalk:] Go, & be hang'd yo[u] son of a whore – whereupon Frances having a little cane in his hand, thrust it toward his face, which hitting exactly upon his eye, broke the ball thereof, so that all the cristalline part thereof falling out, Dangerfield dyed within few dayes after, viz. about the beginninge of July 1685. Frances thereupon being seized on (before the coroner had brought it in wilful murder) he was committed to Newgate, & being tryed at the Old Bayly in the next sessions following, the Jury brought him in guilty of murder, wherepon [sic] he was hang'd at Tyburn 24 of the said month. [/] Had this had hapned to a man that had not suffer'd the law, twould have been scarce brought in manslaughter'; and 'Detection of the court & state of England &c. by Roger Coke Esq. vol. 2. lib. 5. p. 447' followed by and 7 lines, 'When Dangerfield was returning from Tyburn (after he had been whipped to that place from Newgate) he was run into the eye with a tack at the end of a cane,

by one Rob. Francis (a fierce papist) of which, with the agony of his whipping, he soon after died; but his body was so swoln & near tyr'd with the whipping, that it was a question whether he died of the whipping, or woud [sic] in his eye.' Tp (p. 1), AW wrote a former no., '35', and 'The matters following that are scored with a pen, (besides many more) are borrowed from other dying speeches–'; pp. 1-2, underscoring, and at an underscored passage on p. 2, 'And if I had been as zealous in the Service of God, as my Prince' etc., he wrote 'These were Cardinall Wolseys words when he laid a dying.' LT 3.153.
Wood 422(12). Wing F2054.

3088. Francisco de Los Santos. *The Escurial; or, a description of that wonder of the world . . . [tr. and abridged] by a servant of the earl of Sandwich*. London: f. T. Collins a. J. Ford, 1671. 4°. Pp. [8], 23.
Tp, 'published about the beginning of Aug. 1671. and the fier hapned about two months before', prob. by AW.
[MS.] Wood D. 28(20). Wing F2061.

3089. Frank, John*. *The birth, life and death of John Frank. [2nd tp] The birth, life and death of John Frank, and of the pranks and jests*. [London]: J. M. f. J. Deacon, n.d. 12°. A⁸,B⁴ (2 tpp).
Pastedown, lower, numbers (scribbles).
Wood 259(15). Wing B2978C (rare).

3090. [Franzini, Girolamo], and Andrea Palladio. *Le cose meravigliose dell'alma città di Roma [and] L'antichità di Roma, di m. Andrea Palladio*. Roma: Appresso V. Accolti, 1589. 8°. Pp. 128 (2nd tp at p. 81). Calf with 3 fillets and stamp decoration in corners (dragon) (Ashm. binding).
Flyleaf, upper, 1st, note by an Ashm. librarian; 2nd, titles of 3 printed works in this vol., written by an Ashm. librarian. Text, some marks in margin and underscoring, e.g., pp. 47-8, 88, 90, 93, 97.
Wood 218(1). Not in BL, NUC, BN.

3091. [Franzini, Girolamo], and Andrea Palladio. *Mirabilia Romae. A donde se trata delas yglesias, reliquias, estationes. [2nd tp] Las antiguedades de Roma, . . . por Andres Palladio*. Roma: por Iosepe delos Angeles, 1575. Pp. 160 (2nd tp at p. 105). Parchment over pasteboard.
Tp, signature, 'Tho. Bodley.' LT 1.425.
Wood 162. Not in BL, NUC, BN, Adams.

3092. Frarinus, Petrus. Fowler, John, trans. *An oration against the unlawfull insurrections of the protestantes of our time, under pretence to refourme religion*. Antverpiae: ex off. J. Fouleri, 1566. 8°. A-L⁸ (L⁸ without signature).
On B4ᵛ-B5 and B8ᵛ-C1, AW wrote p. nos. in a manner of cross-referencing woodcuts at K4-5; K6ᵛ, line in margin at Christopher Goodman's 'blast' of the trumpet (Geneva, 1558), in red ink (also underscoring of Goodman's book, F2; AW refers to these in MS. Wood E. 2(70), p. 10, 'see at a leaf layd downe in the middle – & at the latter end –'; and for more on the 'first blast', see AO 1.722f., where AW attributes the anonymous 'blast', really by J. Knox, to Goodman); L8ᵛ, 'AW'.
Wood 800(3). STC 11333. ARCR 2.309.

3093. Fraunce, Abraham. *The countesse of Pembrokes Emanuel. Conteining the nativity . . . of Christ: . . . with certaine psalmes of David*. London: T. Orwyn f. W. Ponsonby, 1591. 4°. A-E⁴ (E4 blank).
Wood 482(5). STC 11338.5 (two) ('O' not recorded in STC).

3094. Fraunce, Abraham. Tasso, Torquato, adapted from, and Watson, Thomas, trans. from. *The countesse of Pembrokes Yuychurch. Conteining the affectionate life, and unfortunate death of Phillis and Amyntas*. London: T. Orwyn f. W. Ponsonby, 1591. 4°. A-M⁴.
Tp, bsm.
Wood 482(4). STC 11340.

3095. Frederick 1*. Bohemia, king of. *The magnificent, . . . entertainments given to . . . Frederick, count Palatine . . . and Elizabeth, . . . Together with a true relation . . . after their landing upon the coasts of Germany*. London: [T. Snodham] f. N. Butter, 1613. 4°. A-C⁴.
Wood 537(10). STC 11357.

3096. Frederick 1*. Bohemia, king of. *The mariage of prince Fredericke, and . . . the lady Elizabeth. With the showes . . . before, and after the wedding*. London: [T.C[reede] for W. Barley, sold W. Wright], [1613]. 4°. A-B⁴ (2nd time imprinted) (t leaf mutilated).
Wood 537(9). STC 11359 (STC, Fridericke).

3097. Frederick 3. Palatine, Elector. *A Christian confession of . . . Friderich . . . the third, count Palatine*

. . . Whereunto is added the lantgrave his answere to the French king. London: C. Barkar, 1577. 8°. A-E⁸,F1-7.
Wood 795(7). STC 11348.

3098. Freeman, Lyon. *The common-wealths catechism.* London: J. Clowes, 1659. 8°. Pp. [6], 26.
Tp, AW wrote after the year, 'Jan:'.
Wood 836(3). Wing F2135.

3099. French Lady. *The cruel French lady: or, a true . . . relation of the most execrable murthers.* London: f. R. Vaughan, 1673. 4°. Pp. 8.
P. 5, drawing and scribble.
Wood 365(23). Wing C7418 (two).

3100. Frith, John. *A boke made by John Frith.* ?: ?, 1533ff. Pp.?
Missing. MS. Wood E. 2(70), p. 5. Ed. not identified.
MS. Wood E. 2(70), p. 5. STC 11381-11386.

3101. Frith, Mary*. *The womans champion; or the strange wonder being a true relation of the mad pranks . . . of mrs. Mary Frith.* London: G. Horton, 1662. 4°. Pp. [2], 6.
Wood 654a(22). Wing W3323B (rare).

3102. Fry, John. *The clergy in their colours; or a brief character of them.* London: f. G. Calvert, 1650. 8°. Pp. [2], 60.
Tp, at t, AW wrote 'Presbyterian', and below, 'Answered by Dʳ Francis Cheynell in 4ᵗᵒ. vide p. 7. i[.] e[.] Jo. Fryes Bellows'. P. 7, 'Bellows' underscored.
Wood 836(5). Wing F2255.

3103. Fulbecke, William. *A direction or preparative to the study of the lawe.* London: [A. Islip? f.] T. Wight, 1600. Ff. [8], 95. Calf, speckled.
Tp, 'ABosco'. Ff. 29ᵛ, 62ᵛ to 89, some brief notes, in 2 hands, neither AW's; 44, underscoring.
Jesus College R. 8. 16. STC 11410.

3104. Fulbecke, William. *[An abridgement, or rather, a bridge of Roman histories, . . . from Titus Livius to Cornelius Tacitus].* [London]: [T. E[ast] f. R. More], [1608]. 4°. Pp. [8], 209, [7] (wanting the tp).
P. 15, note on usurers, not in AW's hand. Last p., scribble.
Wood 592. STC 11413.

3105. Fulke, William. *A most pleasant prospect in the garden of naturall contemplation.* London: E. G[riffin] f. W. Leake, 1640. 8°. 3rd ed. Ff. [3], 71.
Missing. In a list of 'Mr. Woods Duplicats', MS. Wood F. 51, f. 44, item 35.
MS. Wood F. 51(35). STC 11441. *O*.

3106. F[uller], R[obert]. *Missale Romanum vindicatum. Or, the mass vindicated from d. Daniel Brevents . . . tract.* [London]: n.pub., 1674. 12°. Pp. [24], 176.
Missing in 1837. Listed in MS. Wood E. 2(70), p. 62, 'R. F. an answer to Dr Brevints book of the mass'.
Wood 827. Wing F2395. *O, Hunt, Clark, Union, Folg.*

3107. Fuller, Tho[mas]. *Abel redivivus: The dead yet speaking. The lives and deaths of the moderne divines.* London: T. Brudenell f. J. Stafford, 1651. 4°. Pp. [14], 599. Calf with 2 fillets and 2 vertical fillets; rebacked.
Flyleaf, upper, 'AW', and scribbles '5ˢ', '3ˢ' (?). Flyleaf, lower, 2ndᵛ, 'AWood', '5ˢ-6ᵈ', in ink, and a note, in pencil, '5ˢ 6ᵈ The mony I had from my brother' (Robert). See note at Wood 196(4), item 6379.
Wood 352. Wing F2400.

3108. [Fuller, Thomas]. *An alarum to the counties of England and Wales, with the oath, of abjuration, for ever to be abjur'd.* [London]: n.pub., 1660. 4°. Pp. 14.
Tp, AW altered the year to '59 feb:'.
Wood 610(10). Wing F2402.

3109. Fullonius, Gulielmus. Palsgrave, John, interp. *Ecphrasis Anglica in comoediam Acolasti. The comedye of Acolastus translated . . . after suche maner as chylderne are taught in the grammer schole.* [(London)]: [(in aed. T. Berthel[eti]], 1540. 4°. A-2A⁴,2B² (wanting 2B3-4). Parchment, stabbed.
Tp, 'in dupl. Bod', in pencil, notes by a former owner, illeg., and '23. e', inside a rectangle (an earlier shelf-mark?).

Wood 325. STC 11470.

3110. [**Fulman, William**]. *Academiae Oxoniensis notitia.* Oxoniae: typ. W. H[all], impen. R. Davis, 1665. 4°. Pp. [6], 56.
In the list on the upper flyleaf to this vol., AW wrote after the t, '1665 the first edit.' Tp, 'Gul. Fulman CCC. Author', in red ink. Minor underscoring, e.g., pp. 45, underscoring of Joannes Selden and of the death year of W. Chillingworth, in pencil; see also 47, 50, 52, 55. Dupl. at Wood 614(1); later ed. at Wood 513(6). LT 3.139. Lent to [W.] Shippen, 27 Nov. 1666, LT 2.93.
Wood 513(3). Wing F2523. Madan 2690 (exc. . . . per).

3111. [**Fulman, William**]. *Academiae Oxoniensis notitia.* Oxoniae: typ. W. H[all], impen. R. Davis, 1665. 4°. Pp. [6], 56. Rough calf with 3 fillets and stamp decoration inside corners (flower with point), and roll decoration at inner, spine edge (Ashm. binding).
Flyleaf, upper, 3rd^{r-v}, titles of 62 items in this vol. by an Ashm. librarian (same hand in Wood 276a). Really only 60 items, for there are some discrepancies, e.g., 21-22, 27-28 and 40-41 are single works, and 2 are at 17 (17a and 17b); 2 are missing (39, marked as missing by W. Kirtland in 1841, and 54, removed after 1841); 27 are dupl. or variants of other items in the Wood collection. The numbering here and on tpp is in Roman numerals. This 3rd flyleaf was originally part of the 1st item for it has above the list of titles 'p$^{rt.}$ 6^{d}. Jan: 1665, Oxōn. [a 5-pointed star and] Jo: Awbrey'. 1st item, tp, 'Liber Antonii a Wood', by an Ashm. librarian. From p. 21 on, notes, some times extensive, mainly by Aubrey; none that are obviously in AW's hand (see p. 45, 2nd ms. entry from top; and 51, 2nd ms. entry from bottom, for brief notes that may be in his hand). Many notes were cropped by Ashm. binders. LT 3.139; AO 4.240-1. Dupl. at Wood 513(3); diff. ed. at Wood 513(6).
Wood 614(1). Wing F2523. Madan 2690 (exc.. . . per).

3112. [**Fulman, William**]. *A short appendix to the life of Edmund Stanton.* London: n.pub., 1673. 12°. Pp. [2], 14.
Missing. Listed as a dupl. in MS. Wood E. 2(70), 62. Dupl. at Wood 292(9).
MS. Wood E. 2(70), p. 62. Wing F2526 (rare, 2 at O). *O.*

3113. [**Fulman, William**]. *A short appendix to the life of Edmund Stanton.* London: n.pub., 1673. 12°. Pp. [2], 14.
Dupl. listed in MS. Wood E. 2(70), 62.
Wood 292(9). Wing F2526 (rare, 2 at O).

3114. [**Fulman, William**]. *Notitia Oxoniensis academiae.* London: typ. T. R., impen. R. Davis (Oxford), 1675. 4°. Pp. [4], 112. 2nd ed.
In the list on upper flyleaf to this vol. AW wrote after the t, 'last & best edition.' Tp, AW wrote, 'Per Gulielm. Fulman A.m. CCC. Oxōn' and 'The additions in this 2^{d} edition were all taken from Hist. et Antiq. Univ. Oxon. Edit. 1674. fol. – which Mr Fulman saw & perused by parcells as it came from the press, which made him so quick as to come out the yeare after.' (LT 3.139; AO 4.240f.; and MS. Wood D. 9, Fulman's critique of the *Historia*). P. 3, AW underscored the reference to himself and his 1674 *Historia*. Pp. 17, 27, 29-30, 33, 35, 51, 53, 55, etc. to 112, underscorings, lines in margins, corrections, and 'q[uaere]' entries. P. 57, in margin at his own entry, the printed 'Antonius Wood, Antiquarius', AW added an 'à' and later wrote in the margin, in red ink, 'Anton. à Wood'. P. 97, at Johannes Donne, Decanus Londinensis, AW wrote, 'ie. Ecclīae S. Pauli.' Earlier ed. at Wood 513(3) and Wood 614(1).
Wood 513(6). Wing F2524. Madan 3036.

3115. [**Fulman, William**], [ed.]. *Rerum Anglicarum scriptorum veterum tom. I. Quorum Ingulfus nun primum.* Oxoniae: e theatro Sheldoniano, 1684. Fol. Pp. [6], 598, [24] (part of a 3 vol. set, see Gale, Wood 411-2). Calf, with 3 fillets; 2nd rectangle with 3 fillets and stamp decoration on inside of fillets and floral decoration at 4 corners (Ashm. binding).
P. [2], page nos. of the 4 later sections given, prob. by AW.
Wood 410. Wing F2525.

3116. Fumblers Hall. *Lawes and decrees of Fumblers hall.* London: ?, 1658. Pp.?
Missing in 1837. 'The Laws & Decrees of Fumblers Hall Lond. 1658' in Whiteside cat.
Wood 61(1). Not in Wing. Not in ESTCR.

3117. Fumblers Hall. *Fumblers hall kept & holden in feeble court at the sign of the labour in vain in do little lane.* London: ?, 1660. Pp.?
Missing in 1837. 'Fumblers Hall Kept & holden in Feeble Court &c. – Lond.1660' in Whiteside cat.

Wood 61(2). Not in Wing. See Wing F2527A ([1675]). Not in ESTCR.

3118. Further Account, Rebels. *A further account, of the proceedings against the rebels in the west of England; who . . . received sentence of death, at Dorchester [10 Sept.].* (London): (E. Mallet), [1685]. Fol. Pp. 4.
P. 1, former no. '38' in pencil.
Wood 660c(11). Wing F2545.

3119. G., C. *The minte of deformities [in verse. Signed C.G.].* London: [G. Simson] f. W. Jones, 1600. 4°. A-C⁴.
Tp, initials, J. L. C3ᵛ, scribble, not by AW.
Wood 653(2). STC 11491.

3120. G., D. *A letter from Sᵗ. Omars [sic], in farther confirmation of . . . the popish plot, . . . a letter from mr. Jennison, proving mr. [William] Ireland to have been in London.* London: n.pub., 1679. Fol. Pp. [2], 22.
Tp, AW wrote '20 July 1679', and 'Ex dono Mʳⁱ [Richard] Watkyns', LT 2.456.
Wood 425(11). Wing G8.

3121. G., E., serjeant at arms. *A description of the island and city of Candia.* [London]: sold J. Overton, 1668. S.sh.
Wood 276a(53). Wing G10 (rare).

3122. G., L. *The court's apology. Containing a short vindication of the courtiers . . . by L. G. [Followed by] The presbyter's plea, containing a reply to the customary impeachments wherewith the Presbyterians are scandal'd.* London: n.pub., 1663. 8°. Pp. 64 (2 tpp).
Tp, Bsm.
Wood 664(3). Wing G43.

3123. G., N. *Dr. Pierce his preaching exemplified in his practice. Or, an antidote to [or rather, a confirmation of] . . . a surrilous [sic] . . . pamphlet [entitled dr. Pierce his preaching confuted by his practice] . . . by N. G. In a letter from a friend of truth [T. Pierce, signing himself J. F.].* [London]: n.pub., 1663. 4°. Pp. [4], 1-4, 1-9 (pp. [1-2] blank; pp. 1st 1-4 extraneous and belong to Wood 515(28b), item 447).
Flyleaf, upperᵛ, AW wrote, 'Note that Francis Drope M. A & Fellow of Magd Coll. shew'd me Dʳ Hen. Yerbury's answer to this libell following, & the very next going before. In which answer, he saith that Dʳ Tho. Pierce President of Magd. Coll. was the author, or at least the approver, of the first libell, or that going before – Also that Mr. Jo. Dobson who repeated several verses thereof at the coffey-house, for which he was conveen'd before the vicechancellour, did confess before him the said vicech that he did first of all heare them repeated by Dʳ Pierce, who had them in manuscript when he was last in Lond. – But the next day when he was conveen'd againe, he retracted what he had said before, choosing rather to take the blame on himself, than put it on his President Dʳ Pierce. [/] The said Dʳ Yerbury saith also in his said answer (which was in ms only) that the second libell which followes was either made or approved of by Dʳ Pierce before mentioned, as it appeared by certaine reflections from Dobsons confession [/] Dʳ Yerbury also in ms. answer, doth cleer those things laid against him therein, viz his cringing to Cromwells vicechanc. when he was incorporated Dʳ of Phys. in Oxon. 1658 – see in the libell followinge p. 7. Also to cleer what is said of his endeavours to frustrate the letters of the king in behalf of Dʳ Pierce, when he was to be elected president – Also the supposed cheates & defraudating [?], & unstatutable accompts relating to the coll.'
Tp, AW wrote, 'This pamphlet came from London to Oxon. 8. Sept. 1663[.] It includes the former [i.e., Wood 515(28b)]'. Pp. 2nd 1-3, 5, 7-9, 13 identifications of persons or references in this libellous attack against H. Yerbury, e.g., p. 1, at printed '*Terrae Filii*', 'Joseph Brooke of Ch. ch. & John Edwards of Sᵗ Joh. coll. lately of Trin. Coll.'; 5, at printed 'Busby's *followers*', 'Jam. Carkess M. of A. of ch. ch. & Tho. Brattle B. of A. of the same, the one Master, the other Usher of the Free-Schoole joyning to Magd. Coll. both bred under Dʳ Ric. Busby Master of Westminst.'; 8, identified printed '*Italianized Doctor*' as 'Dʳ Yerbury took his Doct. of Phys. degree at Padoua'; and 9, identified a reference to 'Dʳ Tho. Janes [or Jeanes] Fellow of Magd. Coll - who wrot a pamphlet, or at least had a hand in it (when he was a junior in Cambridge) in vindication of the murder of K. Ch. 1. upon pretence of which Dʳ Pierce turn'd him out of his fellowship 1662, when then most of the fellowes were against his expulsion.' The final 3-word correction on p. 9 is prob. not in the hand of AW. LT 1.473, 487-9, 500. Dupl. at Wood 633(8).
Wood 515(28a). Wing G48 (two). Madan 2625.

3124. G., N. *Dr. Pierce his preaching exemplified in his practice. Or, an antidote to [or rather, a confirmation of] . . . a . . . pamphlet.* [London]: n.pub., 1663. 4°. Pp. [2], 9 (wanting 1st pp. 1-4).

Tp, 'This came . . . Oxon beg . . . ' (lined out, prob. by AW); and AW wrote, 'This came from London to Oxōn Sept.: 8. 1663'. Pp. 1-3, 5-9, notes, some extensive, not by AW. P. 5, AW provided a title, 'The primitive rule of reformation' for an earlier note by another person, '*by his sermon intituled.' (i.e., Wood 633(5), item 5249). LT 1.473, 487-9, 500. Dupl. at Wood 515(28a).
Wood 633(8). Wing G48 (two). Madan 2625.

3125. G., T. *The friers chronicle: or, the true legend of priests and monkes lives*. London: [G. Purslowe] f. R. Mylbourne, 1623. 4°. A-I⁴.
Final leaf, I4, is supported by an leaf on the pasted down side of which AW had written a preliminary list of 6 titles, within guidelines made with red ink, beginning with Newes from Southhampton (Wood 376(66)); he later altered the order of the pamphlets and the sheet with the original list became waste paper.
[MS.] Wood D. 24(4). STC 11510.

3126. G[adbury], J[ohn]. Ψευδο-αστρολογος. *Or, the spurious prognosticator unmasked. . . . the manifold errors published by mr. W. Lilly, in his Merlin 1659, by G. J.* London: n.pub., 1660. 4°. Pp. [2], 14.
Tp, AW wrote, 'This came out in Decemb: 1659'.
Wood 622(20). Wing G97B.

3127. Gadbury, J[ohn]. *A brief relation of the life and death of . . . mr. Vincent Wing*. London: T. M[ilburn], 1670. 4°. Pp. [4], 36.
Wood 532(6). Wing G76.

3128. G[adbury], J[ohn]. *The scurrilous scribler dissected: or, a word in William Lilly's ear, concerning his reputation*. [London]: n.pub., [1675 to 1681?]. S.sh.
Dupl. at Wood 622(25).
Wood 276b(122). Wing G97C (rare, 2 at O)) (Wing, 1693 (Lilly died in 1681)).

3129. G[adbury], J[ohn]. *The scurrilous scribler dissected: or, a word in William Lilly's ear, concerning his reputation*. [London]: n.pub., [1675 to 1681?]. S.sh.
AW wrote at initials of J. G., 'Joh. Gadbury'. AO 1.36. Dupl. at Wood 276b(122).
Wood 622(25). Wing G97C (rare, 2 at O) (Wing, 1693 (Lilly died in 1681)).

3130. [Gadbury, John]. *A new narrative of the popish plot*. [London]: n.pub., [1680?]. 4°. Pp. 8.
AW wrote, '1679 80', in pencil. See Plate VIII.
Wood 417(18). Wing G93A.

3131. [Gaetani, Enrico]. *Instructions for young gentlemen; or the instructions of cardinall Sermonetta to his cozen Petro Caetano*. Oxford: [L. Lichfield] f. F. Bowman, 1644. 16°. Pp. [8], 122, [1].
Tp, AW wrote '6ᵈ'. A reissue of STC 11514.
Wood 792(2). Not in Wing. Not in ESTCR. Madan 1757.

3132. Gaffarel, Jacques. Chilmead, Edward, trans. *Unheard-of curiosities concerning the talismanical sculpture of the Persians*. London: G. D. f. H. Moseley, 1650. 8°. Pp. [39], 433, [1] and illus.
Missing. MS. Wood E. 2(70), p. 40. Also listed in MS. Wood F. 51, f. 44.
MS. Wood E. 2(70), p. 40. Wing G105. *O, Folg*.

3133. Gage, Thomas. *A duell between a Jesuite and a Dominican, begun at Paris, gallantly fought at Madrid, and victoriously ended at London, . . . 16 day of May*. (London): (f. T. Williams), (1651). 4°. Pp. 8.
[MS.] Wood D. 24(9). Wing G108.

3134. [Gainsford, Thomas]. *The true and wonderfull history of Perkin Warbeck*. London: E. G[riffin] f. N. Butter, 1618. 4°. Pp. [10], 112 (wanting dedication). Parchment.
Tp, bsm. Pastedown, lower, '/k/' (shelf-mark?).
Wood 354. STC 11525.

3135. [Gale, Theophilus]. *The life and death of Thomas Tregosse*. London: n.pub., 1671. 8°. Pp. [2], 66, [1].
Tp, name of Tregosse underlined in red ink (Tregosse matriculated at Exeter College). Pp. 10-11, 2 corrections, in dark ink; 20-1, vertical lines in margin, in pencil.
Wood 289(4). Wing G147.

3136. Gale, Thomas, ed. *Historiae Britannicae, Saxonicae, Anglo-Danicae, scriptores XV. ex vetustis codd. [and vol. 2] Historiae Anglicanae scriptores quinque*. Oxoniae: e theatro Sheldoniano, 1691. Fol. Vol.

1 (Wood 412), pp. [22], 796, [44]. Vol. 2 (Wood 411) e theatro Sheldoniano: 1687 [sic], pp. [12], 594, (29). Calf, with 3 fillets; 2nd rectangle with 3 fillets and stamp decoration on inside of fillets and floral decoration at 4 corners; both rebacked (Ashm. bindings).
Vol. 1, Flyleaf, lower^v, 'Hecuba ye Daughter', prob. not in AW's hand.
Wood 411-2. Wing G154. ESTCR MNULASN7347-B (1687) and MAHGBBI44240-B (1691).

3137. Galenus, Claudius. Linacre, Thomas, trans. *[Caleni [sic] Pergamensis de temperamentis, et de inaequali intemperie libri tres, T. Linacro interprete.* (ap. Cantabrigiam): (J. Siberch), (1521). 4°. ⁴,A-R⁴,S⁶ (wanting the first four leaves). Parchment with 2 leather bands visible. Ms. backing, Latin.
Passim, at top pp., headings, f. nos. until printed nos. appear at f. lxv, and a few brief notes, none in AW's hand. F. lxxiiii^v, scribbles and 'D^r [John] Dowlands'.
Wood 497. STC 11536.

3138. Gand, Louis de. *Sol Britannicus regi consecratus.* Londini: J. Beale & S. Buckley, 1641. 8°. Pp. [8], 160. Parchment.
Pastedown, upper, name lined out. Tp, 'Pretium -i^s' by a former owner.
Wood 256. Wing G194.

3139. [Garbrand, John]. *The grand inquest, or a full and perfect answer . . . by which it is pretended . . . the duke of York may be proved to be a Roman-Catholick.* London: f. J. Vade, 1680. 4°. Pp. 3-26 (pp. 1-2 torn out).
Wood 608(55). Wing G203.

3140. [Garcie, Pierre]. Copland, Robert, trans. *The rutter of the sea with the havens [a tr. of Le grand routier].* (London): (W. Copland), [1567?]. 8°. A-E⁸,F⁴ (last leaf blank). Pasteboard (grey) with parchment spine. 1st upper and last lower flyleaves, marbled paper.
Flyleaf, upper, 3rd^v, AW wrote the titles of 9 printed works in this vol., within guidelines made with red chalk. The 2nd author in the 3rd item was added, in pencil, not by AW. 1st item, tp, AW wrote, 'Translated by Rob. Copland'. D4-E5, sections are numbered, 1-26, not by AW, and some underscoring, prob. not by AW.
[MS.] Wood C. 13(1). STC 11553.3.

3141. Gardiner, Richard. *Specimen oratorium.* Londini: H. Moseley, 1653. 8°. Pp. [2], 21.
Pp. 7, AW wrote, at funeral of Dr. J. Budden, a cross-ref., 'In Reg. S. Aldati. 14.'; 13, a correction.
Wood 113(4). Wing G232A (one) ('O' not recorded in Wing).

3142. Gardiner, Stephen. Bale, John, trans. Bonner, Edmund, preface. *De vera obediencia, an oration . . . with the preface of E. Bonner.* Roane [really London?]: M. Wood [J. Day], 1553 (26 Oct.). 8° (wanting sigs. A1-B4,I7-K4). Ff. 1-58.
Flyleaf, upper, signature of 'Frauncis Coffyns' and 'Ant. à Wood'.
Wood 761. STC 11586.

3143. Garland. *Beautiful garland.* ?: ?, ? Pp.?
Missing in 1837. 'Beautiful Garland' in Whiteside cat.
Wood 94(13). Not in STC. Not in Wing. Not in ESTCR.

3144. Garland. *Springs delightful garland.* N.p.: ?, n.d. Pp.?
Missing in 1837. 'Springs delightful Garland' in Whiteside cat.
Wood 94(11). Not in STC. Not in Wing. Not in ESTCR.

3145. Garland. *Robin Hoods garland; or delightful songs, shewing the noble exploits of Robin Hood.* London: f. W. Gilbertson, 1663. 8°. *⁴,A-E⁸,F⁴.
Wood 79(6) (now Arch. G. f. 2(6)). Wing R1637 (rare).

3146. Garland. *Neptunes fair garland.* London: I. M[illet?] f. I. Deacon, 1676. 8°.
Missing in 1837. 'Neptunes Fair Garland' in Whiteside cat.
Wood 94(14). Wing N435 (one). CM.

3147. Garland. *The true-lovers garland.* [London]: f. J. Back, 1687. 8°.
Missing in 1837. 'True Lovers Garland – 1687' in Whiteside cat.
Wood 94(5) (not in Bodl. CD cat.). Wing T2742 (two). O (olim Christie-Miller), CM.

3148. Garland. *The country garland.* [London]: f. P. Brooksby, 1688. 8°.
Missing in 1837. 'Country Garland – 1688' in Whiteside cat.

Wood 94(10) (not in Bodl. CD cat.). Wing C6530B (rare). O.

3149. Garland. *Englands fair garland*. [London]: f. R. Kell, 1688. 8°.
Missing in 1837. 'Englands Fair Garland – 1688' in Whiteside cat.
Wood 94(6) (not in Bodl. CD cat.). Wing E2963 (rare). O (olim Christie-Miller).

3150. Garland. *Floras fair garland*. London: J. M[illet] f. P. Brooksby, 1688. 8°.
Missing in 1837. 'Flora's Fair Garland – 1688' in Whiteside cat.
Wood 94(16) (not in Bodl. CD cat.). Wing F1366A (two). O, NNM.

3151. Garland. *New jovial garland*. London: f. J. Conyers, 1688. 8°.
Missing in 1837. 'New Jovial Garland' in Whiteside cat.
Wood 94(15) (not in Bodl. CD cat.). Wing N651aA (rare). O.

3152. Garland. *The Irish garland or, the undaunted courage of the protestant arms*. London: f. P. Brooksby, [1689?]. 8°. Pp. [3], 13.
Missing in 1837. 'Irish Garland' in Whiteside cat.
Wood 94(21). Wing I1038B (rare). O.

3153. Garland. *New crown garland*. London: f. J. Back, 1689. 8°.
Missing in 1837. 'New Crown Garland – 1689' in Whiteside cat.
Wood 94(19) (not in Bodl. CD cat.). Wing N604A (rare). O.

3154. Garland. *Princely orange garland*. N.p.: ?, 1689. Pp.?
Missing in 1837. 'Princely Orange Garland – 1689' in Whiteside cat.
Wood 94(20). Not in Wing. Not in ESTCR.

3155. Garland. *Protestant garland of joy*. London: f. M. C., 1689. 8°. A^8,B^4.
Missing in 1837. 'Protestant garland – 1689' in Whiteside cat. Dupl. (or a diff. ed.) at Wood 84(6), q.v.
Wood 94(17). Wing P3834A (rare). ESTCR 188727.

3156. Garland. *The protestant garland of joy and delight*. [London?]: f. M. C. (A2, 'Printed f. M. C–C[?]', cropped), 1689. 8°. A^8,B^4.
Dupl. (or diff. ed.) at Wood 94(17) (missing).
Wood 84(6). Wing P3834A (rare). ESTCR 188727 and 219592 (latter is incorrect).

3157. Garland. *Protestant orange garland*. N.p.: ?, 1689. Pp.?
Missing in 1837. 'Protestant Orange Garland – 1689' in Whiteside cat.
Wood 94(18). Not in Wing. Not in ESTCR.

3158. Garland. *Robin Hood's garland*. [London]: f. W. Thackeray, 1689. 8°. A-E^8.
Missing in 1837. 'Robin Hoods Garland – 1689' in Whiteside cat. (LT 1.18).
Wood 94(1). Wing R1639 (rare). *Hunt*.

3159. Garland. *The royal garland of protestant delight*. London-bridge: f. J. Blare, 1689. 8. A^8,B^4.
Missing in 1837. 'Royal Garland – 1689' in Whiteside cat.
Wood 94(22) (not in Bodl. CD cat.). Wing R2131 (two). O, *BL*.

3160. Garland. *The west-country garland*. [London]: f. P. Brooksby, 1689. 8°.
Missing in 1837. 'West Country Garland – 1689' in Whiteside cat.
Wood 94(23) (not in Bodl. CD cat.). Wing W1401 (rare). O (olim Christie-Miller).

3161. Garland. *The city and country garland*. [London]: f. P. Brooksby, J. Deacon, J. Blare, J. Back, [1690?]. 8°.
Missing in 1837. 'City & Country Garland –' in Whiteside cat.
Wood 94(4). Wing C4348 (rare) (dispersed, Britwell collection, Christie-Miller, 1921).

3162. Garland. *Golden garland [or] [R. Johnson], Golden garland of princely delight*. [London]: f. J. Blare or f. J. Deacon, [1690]. 8°. A-G^8 (1 p. books sold by Deacon).
Missing in 1837. 'Golden Garland' in Whiteside cat. (ed. not determined).
Wood 94(12) (not in Bodl. CD cat.). Wing G1017 (two). O (olim Christie-Miller), CMPepys, or J804A (3) BL, *Harv*, *Folg*.

3163. Garland. *New garland of delight compo,'d [sic] of wit*. [London]: f. J. Deacon, [1690?]. 8°.
Missing in 1837. 'New Garland of Delight –' in Whiteside cat.

Wood 94(9). Wing N643 (rare) (olim Christie-Miller; now in a private collection).

3164. Garnet, Henry*. *A true and perfect relation of the whole proceedings against the late most barbarous traitors, Garnet a Jesuite, and his confederats:. . . And lastly . . . Garnets execution.* London: R. Barker, 1606. 4°. With cancel tp. A-3F⁴ (3F4 blank). Calf with 3 fillets and edge hatching; spine, 4 bands and hatching (Oxford binding); waste paper sheet, upper and lower, letterpress, biblical and rhetorical topic. Wastepaper, upper, 1st^r, 'Liber Antonii Wood Oxon ex dono Francisci Isaac. nuper CCC A[rt]: m^i qui obiit apud . . . anno D[omi]no 1663.', all lined out. 2nd^v, titles of 4 printed works in this vol. of 5, not in AW's hand. Tp, bsm. LT 1.508. All items in this vol. came from Francis Isaac.
Wood 587(1). STC 11619a.5.

3165. Garrard, Edm[und]. *The countrie gentleman moderator. Collections of such intermarriages, as have beene betweene the two royall lines of England and Spaine.* London: E. All-de, 1624. 4°. Pp. [6], 67. P. 28, AW wrote, 'All this is out of Holinsheds Chron.'
Wood 486(9). STC 11624.

3166. G[arret], W[illiam]. Ανθολογια. *The life & death of m^r Samuel Crook.* London: J. Flesher, f. P. Stephens, 1651. 8°. Pp. [4], 61.
Tp, bsm.
Wood 292(8). Wing G272.

3167. G[arter], B[ernard]. *The joyfull receyving of the queenes . . . majestie into . . . Norwich:. . . wherein are set downe divers orations in Latine [16 Aug.].* London: H. Bynneman, [1578]. 4°. A-G⁴.
Wood 537(2). STC 11628.

3168. Garway, Thomas. *An exact description of the growth, . . . of the leaf tee, alias tay.* [London]: n.pub., [1664?]. S.sh.
AW wrote, 'published an 1664', in ink, over '1664', in pencil.
Wood 276a(36). Wing G282 (two) (Wing, '1660?').

3169. [Gascoigne, George]. *A hundreth sundrie flowres bounde up in one small poesie.* London: (H. Bynneman) [a. H. Middleton?] f. R. Smith, [1573]. 4°. Pp. [8], 445. Parchment with 2 clasp holes.
Pastedown, upper, diary entries, mainly about purchases of sack and claret, may be in Thomas Wood's hand. Tp, signatures of an early owner, illeg., and price, 'iiis', lined out; signatures of Tho. Wood, and another price, 'x^siiii^d'. A3, 'Mary Wood'. P. 201, at 'Master F. I.', AW wrote in the margin, 'Freeman Jones vid. pref[ace]' (presumed F. J.), where, A3, the name is underscored. Other notes, at pp. 293, [446-7], not in AW's hand. LT 1.21, 78.
Wood 329(1). STC 11635.

3170. Gascoigne, George. *The steele glas. . . . Togither with the complainte of Phylomene.* (London): (H. Binneman) f. R. Smith, (1576). 4°. A⁶,B-P⁸,Q1-5 (2nd tp. at I3).
A1^v, AW wrote the name 'Georg Gascoign' beneath the engraving; A5, signature and notes of Thomas Walmesley. Q3^v, note, not in AW's hand. Q5, line in margin.
Wood 329(2). STC 11645.

3171. Gascoyne, Thomas*. *The tryal of s^r Tho. Gascoyne bar. for high-treason, . . . 11th of February 1679.* London: f. T. Basset, a. S. Heyrick, 1680. Fol. Pp. 67.
Tp, the price, '2^s', in pencil. Bsm. Pp. 34-5, lines in margin, in pencil.
Wood 426(2). Wing T2219.

3172. Gasser, Achilles P., and Jan de Ruucx. *Historiarum et chronicorum totius mundi epitome . . . Accessit genealogia d. Caroli V [by] Joanne Guilielmo Ruchio Gandavo.* Antverpiae: in aed. J. Steelsii (typ. J. Graphei), 1536. 8°. Ff. [1], 108, [14]. Parchment.
Tp, note, not in AW's hand, illeg. Passim, underscorings, some marks in margins, and a few notes, not by AW.
Wood 133. BL.

3173. Gates, Geffrey. *The defence of militarie profession.* London: H. Middleton f. J. Harison, 1579. 4°. Pp. 63. Parchment, ms., Latin, 14th century civil law text with gloss.
Tp, bsm.
[MS.] Wood C. 35. STC 11683.

3174. Gauden, John. Worcester, bp. of. *The religious & loyal protestation, of John Gauden . . . fift of January.* London: f. R. Royston, 1648[9]. 4°. Pp. [4], 12.

Tp, AW underscored 'John Gauden' in red ink.
Wood 364(3). Wing G367.

3175. Gauden, John. Worcester, bp. of. *Antisacrilegus: or, a defensative against the plausible pest, . . . of that nameless paper, (supposed to be the plot of dr. C. Burges, and his partners;)*. London: J. B. f. A. Crook, 1660. 4°. Pp. 18, [1] (1 p. books written by Gauden).
Tp, AW underscored the name of the author, in red ink, and wrote in margin, 'C. Burges'.
[MS.] Wood D. 31(23). Wing G343.

3176. Gaya, Louis de. *The art of war*. London: f. R. Harford, 1678. 8°.
Missing. In a list of 'Mr. Woods Duplicats', MS. Wood F. 51, f. 44, item 9.
MS. Wood F. 51(9). Wing G398. L, C, OM; 5.

3177. Gayton, E[dmund]. *Wil: Bagnal's ghost. Or the merry devil of Gadmunton*. London: W. Wilson f. T. Johnson, 1655. 4°. Pp. [4], 48.
Wood 500(6). Wing G422.

3178. [Gayton, Edmund]. *Walk knaves, walk. A discourse intended to have been spoken at court . . . By Hodg Turbervil*. London: n.pub., 1659. 4°. Pp. [2], 18.
Tp, AW wrote 'Edm. Gayton the author', and, in pencil, the no. in a former bundle, '62'.
Wood 613(12) (not in Bodl. CD cat.). Wing G421.

3179. [Gayton, Edmund]. *Wit revived or, a new and excellent way. As dry as dust toss off a can*. London: ?, 1660. Pp.?
Missing in 1837. 'Wit reviv'd &c – Lond: 1660' in Whiteside cat. See Wing G423 (1655) and Wing G424 (1674).
Wood 64(1). Not in Wing. Not in ESTCR.

3180. G[ayton], E[dmund]. *Diegerticon ad Britanniam*. [Oxford?]: [H. Hall?], [1666]. S.sh.
After initials, AW wrote 'Edm. Gayton', in red ink, and '1666', twice. AO 3.757.
Wood 416(115). Wing G410 (rare). Madan 2743.

3181. G[ayton], E[dmund]. *To m^r Robert Whitehall at the wels at Astrop*. [Oxford?]: [H. Hall?], [1666]. S.sh. (r-v).
AW wrote '1666' and ^v 'Edm: Geyton [sic] Esquire Bedle of Physicke a° 1666.' and added later 'In the time of Long Vacation./'. See response, in ms., at Wood 416(116), item 6570. LT 2.94; AO 3.757.
Wood 416(114). Wing G417 (rare, 2 at O). Madan 2745.

3182. Gee, John. *The foot out of the snare: with a detection of sundry late practices . . . of the priests and Jesuits in England. Whereunto is added a catalogue of popish bookes lately dispersed in our kingdome*. London: H. L(ownes) f. R. Milbourne, 1624. 4°. 4th ed. Pp. [10], 116, and [28, i.e., 117-146]. Pasteboard (blue) with parchment spine. 1st upper and last lower flyleaves, marbled paper.
Flyleaf, upper, 4th^v, AW wrote the titles of 3 printed works (really 4) in this vol., within guidelines made with red ink. Tp, signature of John Newton and below, 10^d, and bsm. See LT 2.9. Some vertical lines in margins, e.g., pp. 17, line in margin at a catalogue by Master Ley (see a reference to this, AO 3.576); 28 and 45, lines in margin, in red ink, at Fitz-Simons (noted in MS. Wood E. 2, f. 70, 'Hen. Fitzimmons a Jesuit & his book p. 28. 45', see also numerous other references on MS. Wood E. 2, f. 70, last 11 lines, to persons and publications cited in this book by Gee); 39, 43, 58, 63, 85 lines in margins, in pencil; 81, at Lord Gerard, AW wrote, 'Gilbert Lord Gerard died 1622'. After p. 116, 'A Catalogue of Popish Priests names', pp. are supplied by AW on rectos, 117 to 143; over a period of time, he made some sort of annotation on most pp.: vertical lines in pencil and/or ink, 'q[uaere]' notes to himself, identifications, underscoring, cross-references (e.g., p. [120], 'v. p. 122', p. [135], at F. Davenport, 'now living called by the nam of Fr. a S. Clara' (he died in 1680). See note at Wood 304(2), item 895.
Wood 648(1). STC 11704.

3183. Gee, John. *New shreds of the old snare. . . . A catalogue of English nunnes [gone abroad]*. London: [J. Dawson] f. R. Mylbourne, 1624. 4°. Pp. [4], 121.
Wood 648(2). STC 11706.

3184. Genealogiae Caesarum. *'Genealogiae caesarum a Julio usque ad Neronem delineatio'*. N.p.: n.pub., n.d. S.sh.
Missing in 1939. Not Goad, Genealogion Latinum (1676), Wing G900A.
Wood 276a(68). Not identified.

3185. Geoffrey of Monmouth. Alanus de Insulis, ed. *Prophetia Anglicana. Merlini Ambrosii Britanni, ex incubo olim . . . vaticinia & praedictiones:. . . cum septem libris explanationum.* Francofurti: typ. J. Bratheringii, 1603. 8°. Pp. [16], 269, [2]. Calf with 3 fillets, stamp decoration inside corners, and roll decoration at inner, spine edge (Ashm. binding).
Flyleaf, upper, 2nd, the titles of 9 printed works in this vol., written by an Ashm. librarian (same hand in Wood 276a) and below, 'Mc mulin', which indicates that these entries were made before 1707, at the very latest, see Ashmolean Museum Library Manuscripts 5(1) and R. Ovenell, *Ashmolean Museum* (1986): 102-3; ᵛ, 'For Mʳ George [Joye?] Psalams [sic] of David The R R', not in AW's hand.
Wood 704(1). BL.

3186. George, Saint*. *The history of . . . sᵗ· George of Cappadocia . . . The institution of that . . . order . . . commonly called the garter: with the names of the knights.* London: n.pub., 1661. 4°. Pp. [4], 48.
AW noted in AO 3.559 that this pamphlet was 'taken and stoln' from Heylyn's larger work, Wood 536(1).
Wood 536(3). Wing H2142.

3187. George, Saint*. *Sᵗ. George for England: or, a relation of the manner of the election . . . of the knights of . . . the garter, which is to be solemnized on the 15. 16. and 17. of April next.* London: f. J. Thrale, 1661. 4°. Pp. [2], 12 (pp. unopened).
Wood 536(2). Wing S310.

3188. George, Saint*. *The life and death of the famous champion of England, st. George.* [London]: f. W. Thackeray, [1688-89]. 8°. A2-8,B⁴. Parchment over boards, modern.
Flyleaf, upper, 2ndᵛ, a librarian wrote, 'There ['can be little', lined out] is no [added, above] doubt that the damage done to this volume was done before it came into the Bodleian Library in 1858. 1882'; 4thᵛ, 5th, AW wrote the titles of 14 printed works in this vol., within guidelines made with red ink.
Wood 254(1). Wing L2016A (rare).

3189. [Georgirenes, Joseph]. Samos, abp. of. *From the arch-bishop of the isle of Samos in Greece. An account of his building the Grecian church in So-hoe feilds.* London: f. A. F., [1682]. S.sh. (mutilated at bottom).
Last line, mutilated, written in, not by AW. LT 2.379.
Wood 417(103). Wing G537 (3).

3190. Gerard, Charles. Macclesfield, earl of. *The answer of Charles earl of Macclesfield, to the petition . . . of Alexander Fytton.* N.p.: n.pub., [1685]. Fol. Pp. 4.
Wood 276b(113). Wing M116A (rare).

3191. Gerard, John*, et al. *The triall of mr. John Gerhard, mr. Peter Vowell, and Sommerset Fox, . . . With their charge, . . . to have murthered . . . the lord protector [30 June].* London: R. Ibbitson, 1654. 4°. Pp. 12.
Dupl. at Wood 609(36).
Wood 367(10). Wing T2200.

3192. Gerard, John*, et al. *The triall of mr. John Gerhard, mr. Peter Vowell, and Sommerset Fox, . . . With their charge, . . . to have murthered . . . the lord protector [30 June].* London: R. Ibbitson, 1654. 4°. Pp. 12 (cropped at top).
Dupl. at Wood 367(10).
Wood 609(36). Wing G2200.

3193. Gerard, John*. *A true and impartial relation of the death of m. John Gerhard, . . . beheaded on Tower-hill, July 10 [and his speech].* (London): n.pub., (1654). 4°. Pp. 8.
Wood 367(11). Wing T2501.

3194. Gerbier, Balthazar. Ouvilly, baron. *The interpreter of the academie for forrain languages, and all noble sciences, and exercises, concerning military architecture, or fortifications.* [London]: n.pub., 1648. 4°. Pp. [2], 3, [1], 91 (plus numerous illustrations, unnumbered).
Wood 607(9). Wing G563 (Wing, London).

3195. Gerbier, Balthazar. Ouvilly, baron. *The first lecture of an introduction to cosmographie:. . . read publiquely at sʳ· Balthazar Gerbiers academy.* London: f. R. Ibbitson, 1649. 4°. Pp. [4], 16.
Tp, a price, '6-'.
Wood 386(2). Wing G558.

3196. Gerbier, Balthazar. Ouvilly, baron. *Subsidium peregrinantibus. Or an assistance to a traveller.*

Oxford: f. R. Gascoigne, 1665. 8°. Pp.[18], 120. Pasteboard (grey) with parchment spine. 1st and last flyleaves, marbled paper.
Flyleaf, upper, 3rd^v, AW wrote the titles of 4 printed works in this vol., within guidelines made with red ink.
Wood 158(1). Wing G572. Madan 2700.

3197. [Geree, John]. *The character of an old English protestant; formerly called a puritan, now a nonconformist.* [London]: n.pub., [1670?]. S.sh.
AW wrote the date, 'St Peters day 1670' (29 June); ^v, '1670'. LT 2.196.
Wood 416(119). Wing C2013 (3) (Wing, also at G588A (rare)).

3198. German Giant. *The true effigies of the German giant, now to be seen . . . near Charing-Cross, whose stature is nine foot and a half in height [engraving and verse].* London: f. M. Collins, 1664. S.sh.
AW wrote beside the engraving, 'An irish man as larg as this, was to be seen at the blew bore, Oxon an. 1681 at the Act time.' The year was 1st altered, in dark ink, from 1664 to 1668, after which AW wrote, '1660', in red ink. Acquired 3 Aug. 1668, LT 2.140; 2.549.
[MS.] Wood B. 35(24) (placed after (31)). Wing T2692 (rare) (Wing, 1660).

3199. Gery, William. *Proposals for reformation of abuses and subtilties in practice against the law.* London: f. W. Shears, 1659. 4°. Pp. [2], 6.
Wood 630(20). Wing G622.

3200. Gesner, Salomon. *Libri quatuor de conciliis, quorum unus generalem tractationem, alter historicam narrationem.* Witebergae: imp. C. Bergeri, excud. J. Schmidt, 1607. 8°. Pp. [24], 552, [51] (books 1 and 2 only). Calf with 3 fillets.
Praefatio, some underscoring and numbers in margin, prob. not by AW.
Wood 865. BL. BL, (1601).

3201. Gesta Romanorum. *Ex gestis Romanorum. Cum applicationibus moralisatis ac misticis.* (Roth-om[agum]): Thomas Laisné, (1521, 20 Nov.). Ff. 197, [13] (wanting [14], tp cropped). Calf over wood boards, 5 fillets and stamp centrepiece; 2 clasps; rebacked.
Tp, signatures, '–icardi S-ypp precium x^d – (?)' and '–vinson (?)'.
Wood 193. BL.

3202. Ghibbesius, Jacobus Albanus. *Carminum . . . pars lyrica: ad exemplum Q. Horatii Flacci.* Romae: ex off. Fabii de Falco, 1668. 8°. Pp. [20], 221, [1]. Calf with 2 fillets; stamp decoration in corners.
Flyleaf, upper, AW wrote, '1^s - West' (bookseller), and in pencil, 'e musaeo Phil Fell' (died in Feb. 1683; the younger brother of John) (LT 3.37; see also 2.401). P. 221, line in margin at an announcement by Ghibbes of a 2nd book of lyrics (AW described the 1668 edition, and a preliminary plate (by A. Clower), in AOF 2.339, though the plate, or 'the author's picture', is absent from his copy).
Wood 104. BL.

3203. Gib, Wil[liam]. *The last votes from the armie: June 26. 1647. . . . concerning their marching towards the suburbs of London [signed 'Wil. GIB'].* London: f. T. Watson, 1647, 28 June. 4°. A^4.
Wood 501(34). Wing L511.

3204. Gibbon, J[ohn]. *Day-fatality: or, some observation of days lucky and unlucky, concluding with some remarques upon the . . . birth-day of . . . James duke of York [14 Oct.].* [London]: n.pub., [1679]. Fol. Pp. 8.
On initial blank flyleaf^v, AW wrote a cross-reference, 'November or signal Dayes observed in that month &c. written by Will. Cartwright – I have it in vol. . . . nu. 7' (i.e., [MS.] Wood C. 17(7), item 1423; see also AO 3.70); p. 1, 'written by Joh. Gibbon Blew-Mantle Officer of Armes'. LT 3.23.
Wood 660c(16). Wing G647.

3205. G[ibbon], J[ohn]. *Unio dissidentium heir apparent and presumptive made one.* [London?]: n.pub., [1680]. Fol. Pp. 4.
P. 4, beneath initials of I. G., 'J Gibbons Herald' not in AW's hand; below that, AW wrote, '1679 Joh. Gibbon Blew-Mantle, officer of Armes, an. 1679'. LT 3.23.
Wood 660c(18). Wing G653A.

3206. Gibbon, John. *Introductio ad Latinam blasoniam. An essay to a more correct blason.* London: J. M. for the author, sold J. Crump, B. Billingsley, a. A. Churchill, 1682. 8°. Pp. [15], 165, [3]. Calf, speckled, with 2 fillets; rebacked.

Flyleaf, upper, 2nd, note by author, 'Dominum Antonium a Silvā Historiæ Academiæ Oxoniensis Authorem [et multis aliis nominibus memorandum] [sic] Hoc Libro Donat Author Indignus', below which AW wrote, '17. June 1682 Hunc librum recepi ab authore, de quo vide p 135. 161. 38 [prob. 138, where Gibbon also cites AW's *Historia*] et de gente sua p. 159. 160'. Pp. 31, 35, 55, 63, 111, 113, 135, 164, some brief notes, mainly corrections, or marks in margin. LT 3.23.
Wood 446. Wing G650.

3207. [Gibbon, Nicholas]. Goddard, [Jonathon], sculpsit. *A summe or body of divinite real.* N.p.: n.pub., [1653]. S.sh. (engr.).
AW wrote, at top, 'Published in the beginning of the yeare 1653.' This large s.sh. has nail holes (rust visible) and was at one time hung. It may be the copy, once in possession of the city of Oxford, that AW described in AO 4.788. See also note by E. Cannan, 1887, attached to this engraving.
Wood 276b(29). Wing G657 (rare).

3208. Gibbon, Nich[olas]. *Theology real, and truly scientificall; in overture for the conciliation of all Christians.* [London]: n.pub., [1663?]. Fol. Pp. 8.
P. 1, AW wrote '1662-3'. AO 4.788.
Wood 657(26). Wing G658 (Wing, real and [1687?]).

3209. Gibbons, John. *The perfect speech of m[r]. John Gibbons . . . at Tower-hill . . . 22 of August.* London: f. T. Cook, 1651. 4°. Pp. [2], 13.
Wood 367(4) (not in Bodl. CD cat.). Wing G660.

3210. Gibbons, John, and John Fenn, eds. *Concertatio ecclesiae Catholicae in Anglia, adversus Calvinopapistas & Puritanos, . . . [With] Duo edicta Elizabethae reginae Angliae contra sacerdotes societatis Jesu.* Augustae Trevirorum: ap. E. Hatotum, 1583. 8°. Pp. 369, [1], 175. Pasteboard (grey) with parchment spine. 1st upper and last lower flyleaves, marbled paper.
Flyleaf, upper, 2nd[v]-3rd[r-v], AW wrote the title of 1 printed work in this vol., and the headings of the 9 sections in the 1st part, and the headings of 2 sections in the 2nd part, within guidelines made with red ink; at end, 'see 4° C. 32. Th. in bib. Bod' (i.e., *Concertatio*, 1594 ed.). Tp, 'Liber Henrici Jacksoni, Oxon. Colleg. Corp. Chrī MDC Maii xxi. pretium 4[s] [over 4[d]]' (LT 1.459-60 (see also 1.331)), a 2nd signature, 'Ægid: [Ma? Tha? Tra?]son' (illeg.). Text, to p. 14, marks in margin and underscoring, not by AW; 79-80, 211-5, 222, 224, 255, 303, brief marks or notes by AW. 2nd p. 23ff. underscoring and marks in margin, not in AW's manner.
Wood 854. BL. ARCR 1.524.

3211. Gifford, George. *A discourse of the subtill practises of devilles by witches and sorcerers.* London: [T. Orwin] f. T. Cooke, 1587. 4°. A[2],B-I[4].
Tp, below, 'B' (?).
[MS.] Wood B. 20(2). STC 11852.

3212. Gifford, George. *A dialogue concerning witches and witchcrafts . . . by George Giffard.* London: R. F[ield] a. F. K[ingston], sold A. Johnson, 1603. 4°. A-M[4].
Tp, below, 'C' (?).
[MS.] Wood B. 20(6). STC11851.

3213. Gifford, George*. *An elegy upon . . . George Gyfford, . . . rector of St. Dunstan in the East, London.* London: f. T. Parkhurst, 1686. S.sh.
Wood 276a(538). Wing E488A (rare).

3214. G[il], A[lexander]. *A treatise concerning the trinitie of persons in unitie of the deitie. Written to Thomas Mannering an Anabaptist.* London: S. Stafford, 1601. 8°. Pp. [6], 74.
Someone altered the date of pub. to 1603; AW has the correct date in AO 2.598. A3, lines in margin, prob. not by AW. Former owner, Henry Jackson. LT 1.459-60 (see also 1.331).
Wood 776(3). STC 11879 (two).

3215. Gil, Alexander. *Logonomia Anglica. Qua gentis sermo facilius addiscitur.* Londini: J. Beale, 1619 and 2nd ed. 1621. 4°. Pp. 152 or 150.
Missing. MS. Wood E. 2(70), p. 6, 'Alex Gill – Logonomia Anglica'. Ed. not identified.
MS. Wood E. 2(70), p. 6. STC 11873 and 11874. *Folg* and *O, Folg.*

3216. Gil, Alexander. Παρεργα, *sive poetici conatus Alexandri ab Alexandro Gil.* Londini: imprim. A. Matth[ewes,] sumpt. R. Milbourne, 1632. 12°. Pp. [20], 91, [3] (A2-12,B-E[12]; E12 blank).

Tp, 'Ant. à Wood. 1681' and '5. sh[eets] in tw[elve]'.
Wood 76(3). STC 11879.9.

3217. Gilby, Anthony. *A commentarye upon the prophet Mycha.* [London]: [J. Day], 1551. 8°. A-O⁸.
Parchment.
Flyleaf, upper, signature and Latin clause by Henry Jackson; ᵛ, 'In hoc volum.' the titles of 3 printed works
and the price, 2ˢ 4ᵈ, by Jackson. LT 1.459-60 (see also 1.331). Tp, name of a former owner, cropped at top.
Text, notes and marks in margin in more than one hand, none by AW.
Wood 776(1). STC 11886.

3218. Gildas. Vergil, Polydore, ed. *De calamitate excidio, & conquestu Britanniae.* [Antwerp?]: [C. Rure-
mund?], [1525?]. 8°. A-E⁸,F⁴. Parchment, rough.
Flyleaf, upper, brief note in a later hand. Text, some underscoring and notes, not in AW's hand.
Wood 164(1). STC 11892 (not printed in England. See D. Rhodes, *Library*, 6 (1979): 355-60).

3219. Gildas. Joscelyn, John, ed. *Gildae . . . de excidio & conquestu Britanniae.* London: excud. J. Daius,
1567. 8°. Ff. [8], 99. Parchment.
Tp, AW wrote on a slip pasted over a note 'Obijt Gildas circa An. d. 583. æt. 90.' and 'ABosco', in red
ink; at imprint, 'Extat etiam Parisijs 1576'. Below, name of a former owner, rubbed out. Text, AW wrote a
few notes, in Latin, and made a number of corrections, passim. The lines in margins are not in his manner
and a few notes are not by him (ff. [5ᵛ], 16, 48ᵛ).
Wood 777. STC 11893 (two).

3220. Gildas. [Habington, Thomas, trans.]. *The epistle of Gildas.* London: T. Cotes, f. W. Cooke, 1638.
12°. Pp. [132], 327 (some pages unopened).
Tp, '1 . 8', and AW wrote name of translator: 'by Tho Abington'. Acquired 2 Nov. 1661, LT 1.418.
Wood 183(5). STC 11895.

3221. Gillingham, Dorset. *To the right honourable, the knights, citizens, and burgesses of the parliament
of England . . . the humble petition of the tenants.* [London]: n.pub., [1641]. S.sh. Pp. 3, [1] (last blank).
Wood 276b(96) (old no., (74), in Bodl. CD cat.). Wing T1647 (rare).

3222. Giovio, Paolo. Daniel, Samuel, ed. *The worthy tract of Paulus Jovius, contayning a discourse of
rare inventions, both militarie and amorous called imprese.* London: [G. Robinson] f. S. Waterson, 1585. 8°.
A-I⁸,H1-7 (wanting sig. H8).
Tp, AW wrote the Bodl. shelf-mark, 'v. 8°. G. 27. Art' (an Italian copy is currently at this location).
Wood 672(2). STC 11900.

3223. Giraffi, Alessandro. Howell, James, trans. *An exact historie of the late revolutions in Naples.*
London: f. R. Lowndes, 1650. 8°. Pp. [7], 146 (frontispiece, a hand-coloured figure).
Tp, bsm.
Wood 246(2). Wing G785A ('O' not recorded in Wing).

3224. Glanius, W. *A relation of an unfortunate voyage to . . . Bengala.* London: f. H. Bonwick, 1682. 8°.
Pp. [4], 184.
Tp, AW wrote, 'Bought at Oxon 20. Feb. 1681[2]. 1ˢ-2ᵈ'. LT 3.6.
Wood 153(2). Wing G794.

3225. Glanvill, Jos[eph]. *The vanity of dogmatizing: or confidence in opinions.* London: E. C. f. H.
Eversden, 1661. 8°. Pp. [32], 250, [6].
Flyleaf, upperᵛ, AW wrote, 'All, or most of this book is contained in Scepsis Scientifica, written by the said
Jos. Glanvill' (Wing G827). Tp, '1ˢ8ᵈ'. P. 27, correction.
Wood 127(2). Wing G834.

3226. G[lanvill], J[oseph]. *Some philosophical considerations touching the being of witches and witchcraft
. . . . in a letter to . . . Robert Hunt.* London: E. C. f. J. Collins, 1667. 4°. Pp. [2], 62, [1] (1 p. books sold
by Collins).
Flyleaf, upperᵛ, AW wrote (1st line, cropped at top), 'The whole impression was burnt. it was printed
again in octob. 1666. [/] Joseph Glanvill the authour. [/ and in diff. ink:] 1. Edit. 1666 2. Edit. 1667' (acc.
to Wing, the 1st and 2nd eds. have the same imprint year 1667: G832, G832A). LT 2.87.
[MS.] Wood B. 16(3). Wing G832.

3227. Glanvill, Joseph. *A blow at modern sadducism [or, Saducismus triumphatus].* London: [?], 1668
or 1682, 1888, 1689. 8°.

'The demon or devil of Tidworth', missing in 1839; see note by Kirtland at [MS.] Wood B. 18(1), item 1148. This possibly a section of the Glanvill book, e.g., pp. 159-183 in the 1668 ed. Ed. not identified. [MS.] Wood B. 18(14). Wing G799f. or G822ff.

3228. Glanvill, Jos[eph]. *Plus ultra: or, the progress and advancement of knowledge since the days of Aristotle.* London: f. J. Collins, 1668. 8°. Pp. [35], 149, [6] (1 p. books printed for Collins). Calf with 2 fillets; rebacked by B[rian] E. T[aylor], 9.11.[19]59.
Flyleaf, upper, 1st, AW wrote '2^s-6. of Mr West 17. Mar. 1680[1].' Below, a Latin clause and scribble, not by AW. Tp, author's name underscored in red ink; lower right corner, O with a horizontal line, underscored twice (?). Pp. 2, AW identified an anonymous friend of Glanvill, 'Rob. Crosse Rector of Bishope Chue neare Bathe' (AO 4.122ff.); 14, 118 (red ink), 124 (pencil), lines in margin. AW referred to this work in Wood 640(5-6), item 6078.
Wood 681. Wing G820.

3229. [Glanvill, Joseph]. Λογου θρησκεια: *or, a seasonable recommendation, and defence of reason, in the affairs of religion; against . . . fanaticisms.* London: E. C[otes] a. A. C[larke] f. J. Collins, 1670. 4°. Pp. [2], 36.
Tp, AW wrote, 'by Jos. Glanvill'.
[MS.] Wood B. 36(11). Wing G812.

3230. Glanvill, Joseph. *A praefatory answer to mr. Henry Stubbe . . . wherein . . . the impertinency of his arguings . . . in his animadversions on plus ultra, are discovered.* London: A. Clark f. J. Collins, 1671. 8°. Pp. [16], 212, [4] (2 pp. books printed for Collins). Calf with 2 fillets, stamp decoration inside corners.
Flyleaf, upper, AW wrote, '1.6^d. Jan. 28. - 1680[1]'. Tp, Glanvill underscored in red ink. AW numbered some pp. in the introduction. LT 1.354.
Wood 667. Wing G821.

3231. [Glanvill, Joseph]. *An essay concerning preaching.* London: A. C. f. H. Brome, 1678. 12°. Pp. [3], 112.
Missing in 1837 (the original cataloguer omitted no. 842 in the Whiteside cat., and the same cataloguer inserted it later. The Glanvill item is not an intrusion).
Wood 842. Wing G808. *O, Hunt, Union, Folg.*

3232. Glanvilla, Ranulphus de. *Tractatus de legibus & consuetudinibus regni Angliae, tempore regis Henrici secundi compositus.* [London]: [A. Islip] in aed. T. Wight, 1604. 8°. Ff. [9], 116, [17]. Calf with 3 fillets; parchment ms. backing, inventory list in English.
Flyleaf, upper, A. Allam (?) wrote 'Pret: 1^s-0^d. Lock:'. Text, minor underscoring and a few marks in margins, not in AW's manner.
Wood 668. STC 11906.

3233. Gloucester. *Good newes from all quarters of the kingdome; particularly from Gloucester.* London: T. Paine a. M. Simmons, 1643, 13 Sept. 4°. Pp. [6], 10.
AW altered the former no., '34'.
Wood 376(37). Wing G1054.

3234. Glynne, William. *The case of sir William Glynne baronet, in opposition to a bill intended for an act of parliament to restore the earl of Derby to the manner of Hawarden.* [London]: n.pub., [1685]. S.sh.
Wood 276b(76). Wing C1003 (two).

3235. [Goad, Thomas]. *Cithara octochorda pectine pulsata Horatiano cantionem concinens novam, triumphum Britannicum [5 Nov.].* Londini: excud. E. A[llde], imp. N. Fosbroke, 1605. 4°. A-E^4 (A1 blank). Tp, bsm.
Wood 483(9). STC 11923.5 (3).

3236. G[oad], T[homas]. *The dolefull even-song, or a true, . . . narration of that . . . calamity, which befell . . . m^r. drury a Jesuite, . . . in the Black-friers [26 Oct.].* London: J. Haviland f. W. Barret a. R. Whitaker, 1623. 4°. A-K^4 (A1-2 blank). Pasteboard (blue); rebacked with leather spine.
Flyleaf, upper, 2nd^{r-v}, AW wrote the titles of 12 printed works (really 13, with addition of 2b) in this vol., within guidelines made with red ink. Tp, bsm. See note at item 4240.
Wood 643(1). STC 11923.

3237. Godfrey, Edmond Berry*. *The proclamation promoted, or an hue-and-cry and inquisition . . . upon the . . . murder of . . . sir Edmondberry Godfry . . . An hasty poem.* London: f. J. L., 1678. S.sh.

Diff. setting at Wood 417(3).
Wood 424(10). Wing P3639.

3238. Godfrey, Edmond Berry*. *The proclamation promoted, or an hue-and-cry and inquisition . . . upon the . . . murder of . . . sir Edmondberr,y [sic] Godfry . . . An hasty poem.* London: f. J. L., 1678. S.sh.
ᵛ, AW wrote, '1 Nov. 1678.' Diff. setting at Wood 424(10). LT 2.419.
Wood 417(3). Wing P3639.

3239. [Godinho, Nicolao]. *Vita patris Gonzali Sylveriae . . . in urbe Monomotapa martyrium passi.*
Lugduni: sumpt. H. Cardon, 1612. 8°. Pp. [8], 200.
Passim, underscoring, marks in margins, and notes, none by AW.
Wood 152(2). BL.

3240. Godolphin, John. Συνηγορος θαλασσιος. *A view of the admiral jurisdiction. Whereunto is added . . . an extract of the ancient laws of Oleron.* London: W. Godbid f. E. Paxton a. J. Sherley, 1661. 8°. Pp. [52], 207, [16] (2 tpp).
Tp, AW wrote '1ˢ 9ᵈ'.
Wood 731(3). Wing G952.

3241. God's Judgement. *Gods judgement from heaven; or . . . a monster in Flanders.* London: f. T. Vere and W. Gilbertson, 1658. 8°. Pp. [2], 14 (14 misnumbered as 8).
Wood 246(6). Not in Wing. Not in ESTCR (cp. Wing M2467).

3242. Godwin, Francis. Hereford, bp. of. *A catalogue of the bishops of England.* Londini: [Eliot's Court Press] G. Bishop, 1601. 4° in 8's. Pp. [8], 547. Parchment, with gold-stamp sheldrake at center.
The sheldrake stamp is of the former owner, Ralph Sheldon. Cover, upper, inside, '3ˢ xᵈ', may not be in AW's hand. Flyleaf, upper, 'ABosco' in red ink, and, in dark ink, 'Another edition (with additions) of this English Cat. of Bishops came out in 1615 [[MS.] Wood D. 21(2). STC 11938], but being very full of faults, & not to be endured by a tolerable reader, the authour forthwith put it into Latine, & was printed the next yeare [[MS.] Wood D. 21(1); STC 11941].' and 'This Engl. Edition I often use, when I mistrust matters related in the 2ᵈ edit.' P. 286, correction of death date of E. Gheast, '76' for '1578'. LT 1.247.
Wood 344. STC 11937.

3243. Godwin, Francis. Hereford, bp. of. *A catalogue of the bishops of England, since the first planting of Christian religion in this island, together with a briefe history of their lives.* London: [Eliot's Court Press] f. T. Adams, 1615. 4°. Pp. [12], 699, [1] (misnumbering). Calf with 3 fillets, gold-stamp centrepiece, and edge hatching (backing, printer's waste, Bible; Oxford binding?).
Flyleaf, upper, 1st, 7-line note, by Langbaine. Notes by AW cover a 30-year span, with some in his very early and some in his very late hand. This, and the variety of persons who made the numerous annotations, make some attributions difficult. Clark, LT 4.238, understated when he wrote: 'In this Wood has a few notes.' Flyleaf, upper, 2ndᵛ, 25-line note which may be by AW (this writing style is frequent in this vol.), followed below with a note clearly written by AW, 'Of several Bishops v. Seld. Baronagium p. 148. 149 &c' (AW owned a copy, Wood 457(2), and cites it several times in notes in this item). Tp, signature of 'Ger. Langbaine', and Εκιας οναρ ανος' (for Langbaine's notes, see also pp. 119, 457, 492 (1st only), 493-4, 664 (central note)), and AW wrote, 'Anthōy Woode Mertō Coll: 1658'. His annotations are found on pp. 95 (correction, 'Rogerus perhaps – q[uaere]'), 120 (AW's early hand; on John Peckham in register at Merton College), 131-2 (notes about inclusion in *Historia*, 1.151-4, anno 1314 and anno 1312, or *Hist. and Antiq.* 1.380ff.), 138 (T. Bradwardine at Merton College and a reference to MS. Twyne XXI), 145 (reference to Leland), 178 (a reference to a bequest to Queen's College by E. Gryndall also included in his *Historia*, 2.115, or *Hist. and Antiq. of the Colleges* (1786): 144), 180 (last note is by AW and some of the others may be by AW; the note on Sancroft was added by another person), 203 (AW noted the omission in text of Fitz-James's connection to Merton College), 211-3 (loose slip with a reference to MS. Twyne XXI and St. Swithinus), 232 ('See Selden's Baronagium p 146'), 235 ('see in 3. part of Parsons his conversions p. 192' (Wood 856)), 247 (last note is by AW), 291 ('A. W.' and notes in AW's early hand), 382 ('see in Lelands Encomia p 41' (Wood 484(9)), 396 (a note on Seth Ward as Bishop of Exeter, who sat Bishop from 1662; the 2nd note is not by AW), 404 ('A. W.' and notes on W. Stapleton in his early hand), 409 (a note on Edmund Stafford), 421 (reference to Ware's *de script. Hib.*; AW owned 2 copies, Wood 343(3) and [MS.] Wood C. 26(14)), 480 (?), 488, 496 (reference to Heylyn's *Ecclesia restaurata* p. 90 (Wing H1701ff.), 502 (AW added 2 names to a list made by an earlier annotator), 509 (i.e., 511, last note), 553 (last line), 664 (1st note, 'custos privati segelli v. Seld. of Baronage p. 83'). Flyleaf, lower, 1st, slip with 11 lines of notes by AW on 'Episcopatus Sodrensis' and its value (Isle of Man). Acquired 29 Ap. 1658 out of G. Langbaine's study, 3ˢ, LT 1.247; 4.238; A. Wood, *Survey of the Antiquities in the City of Oxford*, ed. A. Clark (1890):

2.5. See AW's reservations about this ed. at Wood 344, item 3242.
[MS.] Wood D. 21(2). STC 11938.

3244. Godwin, Francis. Hereford, bp. of. *De praesulibus Angliae commentarius: omnium episcoporum necnon et cardinalium ejusdem gentis [followed by] Ad commentarium de praesulibus Angliae . . . appendix.* London: [W. Stansby a. Eliot's Court Press] ex off. Nortoniana, ap. J. Billium, 1616. 4°. Pp. [16], 664, 180, 16 (2 pts.). Parchment with 1 gold-stamp fillet, a 2nd rectangle with 1 gold-stamp fillet and decoration outside corners, gold-stamp centrepiece; probably bound (by Twyne?) some time after 1622 since there is a note by Camden(?), in an appended section, dated Octobr[is] 1622. This note was cropped (3rd p. 13)). Pastedown, upper, note, 'an. 1733. these notes were all transcribed by W Morland subkeeper & librarian' (transcription not found). Tp, 'Gulielmi Camdeni ex dono authoris. Martii 23. 15 [i.e., 1616]'. AW transcribed a great deal of material to here from other sources: 'I collected various matters thence which I entered into my Godwin 'de praesulibus in margine' (note in MS. Wood E. 4, see LT 2.175). While it is difficult to ascribe certain annotations to AW, it is clear that he wrote extensively in the vol. Clark, LT 4.238, understated AW's annotations: 'In this Wood has several notes, both marginal and on inserted slips.' Those one might with confidence state are AW's include the following. Flyleaf, upper, 2nd, AW wrote, from about 1660 (the 1st is in his early hand, the last are references to books published in 1673) 16 separate notes on sources for the study of bishops (including details of copies owned by Dr Oldsworth, Seth Ward, as reported by Dr Bathurst, W. Dugdale, and W. Barlow). Scores of similar notes by AW occur passim, in the margins from pp. 95 (correction of Robertus to Ro'gerus'), 102 ('sed haec habes e Twyno in Apol. Lib. 2. 282'), 129 (where he twice refers to his own printed copy of the *Historia*, which he does 16 times up to p. 300 and with no less frequency after p. 300 (at times to 'my English copie' (eventually the English *Hist. and Antiq.*) e.g., p. 465), 133, 150 (last line), 151-2, 160 (1st note), 161 (1st note), etc., often mixed with notes by others (see p. 184, where at least 3 of the 5 notes are by AW), to the last printed p., 3rd p. 16, of 'Ad commentarium de praesulibus Angliae'. AW also included scores of slips pasted in, passim. Very few slips have notes in another hand, see 404-5, 472-3 (though the 7 lines below are by AW), and 2nd 180-1 at ^r side of note on 'Mariae. Owen Oglethorpe'. For leaves, as opposed to slips, with notes in AW's hand, see, e.g., 230-1, 234-5, 318-9, 330-1, 436-7 (a large slip), 470-1 (a large slip with references to a book he owned by Lassels, Wood 159, item 4043), and 478-9.
AW wrote the notes in this book over a long period of time, as is indicated by the various forms of his writing: cp. notes on inserted leaf after p. 318 and slip preceding the inserted leaf; or p. 437 and slip; p. 443 (a note on a book by W. Barlow, 'habeo' (see item 874, missing) and slip pasted to p. 443; or the 7 ms. items on slips before or pasted to p. 593 (see Plate II; on one he cited W. Allen's 'answer to the libell', 'I have it with a black cover' (Wood 878, item 44); on another he outlined materials for an entry of Godfrey Goodman, AO 2.863ff.); or compare entries on 2nd p. 133, where AW wrote an 18-line note on Walter Skirlaw, taken from R. Dodsworth, to which he added at a later time, 'I have entred this in coll. univ.' (see *Hist. and Antiq. of the Colleges* (1786): 46-7) and his note on the slip pasted to the preceding page, 131. He cited several times works of Dugdale (151, 184, 244, 231, 253, etc.) and has numerous 'quaere' notes to himself (247, 292, 297, etc.). Notes in red ink are by AW. There is a neat hand, similar to that of AW at his most formal, but that I cannot ascribe to him, see pp. 12, 34, 59 (last note), 71 and 73 (both citing 'Ramesay', 'in bib. Cotton'), 83 (1st note), 90, 118 (1st and last 2 notes), 122, 123 (last note, with pencil guidelines), 137-8, 147 (note below text), 150 (4 and a half-line note in contrast to clear examples of AW's hands in the last note (5 words) and on the slip), 184 (3rd from top), 185, etc.
In addition to the above, notes in the hands of at least 7 persons are present in margins or on inserted leaves. For hand no. 1: see flyleaf, upper, 3rd^v, and similar hand at e.g., pp. 254, 335, 362 (last note), 381, 412, 447, 546, 2nd p. 141, and 3rd p. 13 (1st note): Camden's? For hand no. 2: tp, Godwin's (ex dono only). For hand no. 3, Brian Twyne: see, e.g., the leaf or leaves inserted between: pp. 76-7, 98-9 (heading (?) and f. no. 2^v, line 10 from bottom to 3^r-v); 150-1, 182-3, 184-5, 266-7, 302-3 (^r of insert only), 346-7, 606-7 (AW commented in a ms. on Twyne's notes on S. Giraldus, on leaves inserted between pp. 606-7, see LT 2.174-5 and 4.241), 644-5, 2nd pp. 32-3, 2nd pp. 60-1, 2nd pp. 108-9 (heading only?, remainder by hand no. 4). For hand no. 4, apparently a colleague of Twyne: leaves inserted between pp. 98-99 (insert f. no. 1 (prob. not the heading), 2^r and 2^v, to line 10 from bottom, 4^r and 4^v, to line 6 from bottom), and leaves inserted between 2nd 108-9. For hand no. 5, perhaps another colleague of Twyne, also very familiar with archives: marginalia (always uses = as hyphen), e.g., 9 (in English), 57-9, 60, 67, 78, 97-8, 101, 103, 111-8 (118, not the 2nd note; the last two notes are by AW), 123-4, 126, (not 129, AW), 131, (133, also AW), 139, 148, 150 (where the 4-line note on the slip and the last line are by AW), 154, etc., (p. 298 in English). For hand no. 6: pp. 84, 87, 96-7, 98, 101, etc. to 590, a very distinctive hand, all on heraldry, by an unidentified person, but antedating writer no. 5. For hand no. 7, a professional scribe: leaf inserted between pp. 222-3. See LT 1.247 (AW acquired an English version of this Latin ed. from Langbaine in 1658, [MS.] Wood D 21(2); see also Wood 344, another English ed., a gift from R. Sheldon, which has a note on this Latin ed.); and LT

4.238. He wrote a separate index to this book, see LT 4.241, 'Notae ad Godwinum'.
[MS.] Wood D. 21(1). STC 11942. SC 8569.

3245. G[odwin], F[rancis]. Smith, Thomas, trans. *The man in the moone: or, a discourse of a voyage thither: by F. G. B[ishop] of H[ereford]. To which is added nuncius inanimatus*. London: J. Kirton, 1657. 8°. 2nd ed. Pp. [7], 126, [4], 13, [3], 21, [1] (1 p. books sold at Kings Arms) (3 tpp). Pasteboard (blue) with parchment spine. 1st upper flyleaf, remnants of, and last lower flyleaf, marbled paper.
Upper waste paper backing, AW wrote a t, 'Nationall Excellencies of Engl' (i.e., Wood 686(2)). Flyleaf, upper, 3rd^v, AW wrote the titles of 2 printed works in this vol., within guidelines made with red ink. 1st item, tp, AW wrote after initials, 'Franc. Godwyn Bishop of Heref.'; and '1^s-3^d'. Below, crossed out and pasted over with a slip, a note by AW, 'Domingo Gonzales the author translated by E. M. the 1 edit. came out in Lond. 1638' (STC 11943). A later scribble, illeg., partly over the slip, not in AW's hand.
Wood 682(1). Wing G970.

3246. Godwin, Master. *July 18. 1642. A perfect diurnall of all the proccedings [sic] of the English and Scotch armies in Ireland, from the 14 of June*. London: f. J. Raworth, 1642. 4°. Pp. 7.
Tp, former no., '29', lined out.
Wood 508(31). Wing G967 (Wing, proceedings).

3247. Godwin, Thomas. *Synopsis antiquitatum Hebraicarum*. Oxoniae: excud. Jos. Barnesius, 1616. 4°. Pp. [8], 190, [9].
Missing. MS. Wood E. 2(70), p. 47, 'his antiq'.
MS. Wood E. 2(70), p. 47. STC 11965. Madan 445. *O, Folg, Hunt*.

3248. Goffe, Thomas. *Oratio funebris habita in ecclesia cathedrali Christi Oxon in obitum . . . Gulielmi Goodwin*. Oxoniae: J. Lichfield & J. Short, 1620. 4°. A^4,B^2.
Wood 512(5). STC 11979. Madan 488.

3249. Golding, Arthur, trans. *The warfare of Christians: concerning the conflict against the fleshe*. London: (H. Binneman) f. J. Shepparde, 1576. 8°. Pp. [8], 75.
Missing. MS. Wood E. 2(70), p. 9.
MS. Wood E. 2(70), p. 9. STC 5201 (4). *BL, Folg*.

3250. Gondi, Jean François Paul. Retz, cardinal de. *France no friend to England. Or, the resentments of the French upon the success of the English. . . . in a . . . remonstrance [Trés humble et trés importante remontrance au roi, by J. F. P. de Gondi]*. London: n.pub., 1659. 4°. Pp. [2], 25.
Tp, no. 30 in a former bundle.
Wood 610(59). Wing R1186.

3251. Gonzalo, pseud. *The divine dreamer: or, a short treatise discovering the true effect . . . of dreames; . . . The dreame . . . before the death of the late earle of Stafford*. [London]: n.pub., 1641. 4°. Pp. [1-14], '15-20'.
P. [7], [13], 16, 19, scribbles.
Wood 614(12). Wing D1720.

3252. Good, Tho[mas]. *To the right honorable, the right worshipful, and the reverend, . . . of the diocess and county of Worcester, . . . proposal . . . in behalf of ingenious young scholars*. [Oxford]: [L. Lichfield], [1675]. S.sh.
AW wrote, 'Oxōn Febr. (16) 1674[5]'. LT 2.308.
Wood 423(49). Wing G1031 (rare). Madan 3059.

3253. [Good, Thomas]. *A brief English tract of logick*. [Oxford]: [L. Lichfield], 1677. 8°. Pp. [2], 40.
Tp, AW wrote, 'Dr Tho. Good the Master of Balliol Coll. in Oxōn the authour-'. LT 2.247; AO 3.1154-5.
Wood 42(5). Wing G1028 (rare). Madan 3142.

3254. Good Wives Complaint. *The good wives complaint against the fudling schools*. London: ?, n.d. Pp.?
Missing in 1837. 'The good wives Complaint against the Fudling Schools – Lond' in Whiteside cat.
Wood 61(8). Not in STC. Not in Wing. Not in ESTCR.

3255. Goodall, Charles. *The colledge of physicians vindicated, and the true state of physick in this nation faithfully represented: in answer to . . . The corner stone [by A. Huyberts; Wing H3858]*. London: R. N. f. W. Kettilby, 1676. 8°. Pp. [13], 191, [7]. Calf, mottled, with 2 fillets, stamp decoration in corners; clasp holes.

Wood 685. Wing G1090.

3256. Goodenough, Mary*. *Fair warning to murderers of infants: being an account of the . . . execution of Mary Goodenough*. London: f. J. Robinson, 1692. 4°. Pp. [6], 14.
Wood 365(34). Wing F105 (3) ('O' not recorded in Wing).

3257. G[oodgroom], R[ichard]. *A copy of a letter written to an officer of the army . . . concerning the right and settlement of our present government*. London: T. Newcomb, 1656. 4°. Pp. [2], '1-6', '3-38', [2] (wanting '7-23', [1], '1-2').
Each small 4° leaf is pasted on a 4° template. Tp, bsm. Pp. 1-2, 5 minor underscoring, in pencil, prob. not by AW.
Wood 626(3). Wing C6173A.

3258. Goodman, Nicholas. *Hollands leaguer: or, an historical discourse of the life and actions of dona Britanica Hollandia*. London: A. M[athewes] f. R. Barnes, 1632. 4°. A2-4,B-G⁴ (wanting the frontisp.) (last leaf blank).
Flyleaf, upperᵛ, AW wrote, 'The same title following (Hollands leaguer &c) is the title of a comedy – pen'd by Shakerlie Marmion–' (i.e., STC 17443f.); tp, 'Nich. Goodman – see at the end' (i.e., signed on G3), and below, 'A Woode Sept: 1: MDCLX.'
Wood 654a(2). STC 12027.

3259. Goodwin, John. *Cretensis: or a briefe answer to an ulcerous treatise . . . by mʳ Thomas Edwards, intituled, Gangraena*. London: M. S. f. H. Overton, 1646. 4°. Pp. [2], 50.
Wood 655(2). Wing G1161.

3260. Gookin, Vincent. *The great case of transplantation in Ireland discussed; or, certain considerations, wherein the . . . inconveniences in the transplanting the natives of Ireland . . . are shewn*. London: f. J. Crook, 1655. 4°. Pp. [4], 32 (and a variant tp). See note at item 6696.
Wood 510(22a). Wing G1274.

3261. Gordon, J[ohn]. Salisbury, dean of. *England and Scotlands happinesse: in being reduced to unitie of religion, under . . . king James*. London: V. S[immons] f. W. Aspley, 1604. 4°. Pp. [2], 47.
Wood 594(2). STC 12062.3.

3262. Gore, Tho[mas]. *Nomenclator geographicus Latino-Anglicus & Anglico-Latinus. [Followed by] The second part. [Followed by] Series alphabetica, Latino-Anglica, nominum gentilitorum sive cognominum*. Oxoniae: typ. G. Hall, 1667. 8°. Pp. [14], 314 (tpp also at pp. 161 and 287) (passim unopened to p. 285).
Flyleaf, upper, 2nd, '1ˢ9ᵈ in sh[eets]', in pencil, may be by AW.
Wood 149(2). Wing G1299. Madan 2768.

3263. Goring, George. Norwich, earl of. *The declaration of colonel Goring to the house of commons*. [London]: n.pub., 1641. 4°. Pp. [2], 5.
Tp, above, 'June 1641' and below, 'qu[aere] the date' and an illegible phrase, all in pencil; later, 'Col. George Goring afterwards Earl of Norwich son of George Lord Goring of Hurst-Pierpont in com. Sussex', in ink.
Wood 373(2). Wing G1303B.

3264. Goring, George*. Norwich, earl of. *A fight the lord Goring beaten at Coulchester [sic] in Essex. . . . With the particulars . . . Also a declaration from the gentlemen of South-Wales*. London: f. R. Smithurst, 1648. 4°. Pp. [2], 6.
Tp, AW wrote after the year, 'Jun. 13.' P. 6, 'Culpepper' underscored.
Wood 502(21). Wing F903 (Wing, fight:).

3265. Goring, George. Norwich, earl of. *A declaration of his excellency, George lord Goring . . . with the gentry . . . of . . . Essex, in armes for the . . . defence of their generall petition*. [London]: n.pub., 1648, 12 July. S.sh.
ᵛ, AW wrote, 'Jul. 12 1648'.
Wood 502(38). Wing N1330 (Wing, [1648]).

3266. Goring, George; Arthur Capel, and Charles Lucas. *The earl of Norwich, lord Capel, & sir Charls Lucas, their peremptory answer, in refusing to surrender Colchester, . . . With his excellencies summons, and articles offered them*. London: f. R. White, 1648. 4°. Pp. [2], 14.
Wood 502(32). Wing N1337 ('O' not recorded in Wing).

3267. Goring, George; Arthur Capel, and Charles Lucas. *A letter from the earl of Norwich, the lord Capel. and sir Charles Lucas, to . . . generall Fairfax.* London: B. A., 1648. 4°. Pp. [2], 6.
Tp, AW wrote after the year, 'Aug. 14'.
Wood 502(41). Wing L1519.

3268. Goring, George*, and Charles Lucas*. *The demands and proposals of the earle of Norwich, and sr. Charles Lucas . . . Also, the proceedings of the Scots royalists . . . Likewise, the discovery of a great designe in . . . London.* London: n.pub., 1648. 4°. Pp. [2], 6.
Tp, AW wrote after the year, '19. Aug'.
Wood 502(49). Wing N1331 ('O' not recorded in Wing).

3269. G[osnold], J[ohn]. *Holy and profitable sayings of mr. J. G. who departed this life [3 Oct. 1678].* London: f. D. M., 1678. S.sh.
Wood 532(7). Wing G1311A (two).

3270. Gotham College. *The fooles complaint to Gotham colledge.* London: printed by Ridibundus, 1643. 4°. A⁴.
Wood 533(5). Wing F1419.

3271. Goughagun, John*. *Whereas it appears to unto us, whose names are subscribed [an appeal for charity on behalf of J. Goughagun, deprived of his estate in Ireland. Signed by clergy of the parishes of London] [4 Oct. 1657].* (London): n.pub., [1657]. S.sh.
AW wrote '1657' in the margin, underscored 3 names, marked 7 names with short horizontal lines in margins, and wrote 'q[uaere]' at Thomas Henchman; ᵛ, he wrote, '4 Oct. 1657'.
Wood 510(23). Wing W1623 (rare).

3272. Goulart, Simon. Grimeston, Edward, trans. *Admirable and memorable histories containing the wonders of our time . . . Vol. 1.* London: G. Eld, 1607. 4° in 8's. Pp. [8], 646. Parchment.
Flyleaf, upperᵛ, 'John Anderedon [?] his booke' and notes, not in AW's hand. Tp, signature of John –, blotted out. P. 636, scribble.
Wood 604. STC 12135.

3273. Grafton, Richard. *An abridgement of the chronicles of England.* [London]: in aed. R. Tottyll, 1564. 8°. Ff. [11], 181, [14] (wanting 1st B1). Calf with 9 fillets, stamp decoration; rebacked.
Tp, 'Johannis Sleddi liber prec. – xiiᵈ' (prob. not '2 xiiᵈ). Text, some notes, not in AW's hand (see LT 2.56). Acquired 24 Mar. 1662, 9ᵈ, LT 1.434.
Wood 144 (not in Bodl. CD cat.). STC 12150.

3274. [Grafton, Richard]. W. W., corr. *A briefe treatise, contayning many proper tables and easie rules.* London: widdowe Charlewood f. T. Adams, 1593. 8°. Pp. 127. Pasteboard (grey) with parchment spine.
Flyleaf, upper, 3rdᵛ, AW wrote the titles of 5 printed works in this vol., within guidelines made with red ink. Tp, 'pretium: 0ᵈ' [sic], by former owner (Foulis?); ᵛ, 'Hen ffoulis: booke. praetium: 0ᵈ:'. Diff. ed. at Wood 142(3).
Wood 9(1) (not in Bodl. CD cat.). STC 12160 (rare).

3275. Grafton, Richard. *A briefe treatise containing many proper tables and easie rules.* London: [G. Eld] f. T. Adams, 1611. 8°. Pp. 135, [1].
Tp, AW wrote 'Dup' in pencil. Bsms. P. 96, a correction, at Browne, AW wrote 'Broome'. Diff. ed. at Wood 9(1).
Wood 142(3). STC 12166.

3276. Graham, Richard. Preston, visct. *An account of the araignment, . . . of James lord Preston. For high treason.* (London): (f. T. Collins), (1691). 4°. Pp. 4.
Tp, AW wrote, 'Rich' above printed 'James', and added the date, 'Jan. 1690[1]'. LT 3.350.
Wood 367(20). Wing A237 (two).

3277. Graham, Richard*, and John Ashton*. *The arraignment, trials, conviction and condemnation of sir Rich. Grahme, . . . and John Ashton, . . . for high-treason [and] Two letters . . . One from the late king James to the pope.* London: f. S. Heyrick a. T. Cockerill, 1691. Fol. Pp. [3], 138 (2nd tp at p. 77, and 'Letters', at p. 133).
Tp, AW wrote, 'Ox. 2 Mar. 1690[1]. 9ˢ-6.' LT 3.353.
Wood 421(14-16). Wing A3766A.

3278. Grand Cheat Cried Up . *The grand cheat cryed up under-hand by many in the factious . . . part*

of the army. [London]: n.pub., [1659]. S.sh.
AW wrote the date, 'Decemb: 1659'.
Wood 276a(340). Wing G1489.

3279. Grand Rebels. *The grand rebels detected, or, the presbyter unmasked, . . . by a lover of his countrey.*
London: n.pub., 1660. 4°. Pp. 12.
Tp, AW wrote 'March'.
Wood 608(2). Wing G1511.

3280. Grant, William. *The vindication of the vicar of Istleworth . . . from a scandalous pamphlet,*
. . . *Whereunto are likewise added . . . impieties . . . of G. Barrell.* [London]: n.pub., 1641. 4°. Pp. 20.
Pp. 4, at printed 'Mr. Bifeld', AW wrote, 'Rich Byfield q[uaere]'; 5, line in margin at 'Bifield'.
[MS.] Wood D. 31(29). Wing G1525.

3281. Graswinkel, Dirk. *Theod. J. F. Gkaswinkelii [sic]: I. C. Maris liberi vindiciae: adversus Gulielmum*
Welwodum Britannici [de dominio maris]. Hagae-Comitem: ex typog. A. Vlac, 1653. 4°. Pp. [8], 30 (pp.
unopened).
Tp, bsm. P. 30, a correction, prob. not by AW.
[MS.] Wood C. 13(9). BL.

3282. Gratarolus, Gulielmus. *De vini natura, artificio, et usu, deque re omni potabili. . . . Huic addita*
quędam opuscula ejusdem authoris. (Argentorati): (excud. T. Rihelius), (1565). 8°. Pp. [8], 400, [24] (wanting
the opuscula). Calf with 3 fillets, inner rectangle with 3 fillets and stamp decoration outside corners, and
silver-stamp centrepiece.
Tp, former no. '9', in ink; and a reference, not by AW, to a book on a similar topic by Jacobus Praefectus
(Venice, 1559).
Wood 678. BL.

3283. Gratianus. *Decretum aureum divi Gratiani.* Parisius: venund. in edibus J. Parvi, [1526]. 8°. Ff. 422,
[44]. Calf with elaborate stamp decoration, including 2 heads in medallions on upper cover and 6 on lower,
and bronze clasps, pastedown, lower, parchment ms., Latin; rebacked.
Pastedown, upper, and tp, 4 signatures, 3 lined out or illeg., 'liber Gulielmi Lowedalli', price 'iiii^s iiii^d', and
a brief note. Tp^v, 13 lines in 2 early hands and 'Anthony Wood Coll: Mert[oni] Oxon. 1649', lined out. F.
[44]^v, 'Anthony Wood', lined out. Text, a few notes and some underscoring, not by AW.
Wood 852. Not in BL.

3284. Graunt, John. *Natural and political observations . . . made upon the bills of mortality.* London: T.
Roycroft f. J. Martin, J. Allestry, a. T. Dicas, 1662. 4°. Pp. [16], 85, [1], plus tables (misnumbering).
Flyleaf, upper, the name of the title and author, prob. by AW; ^v, AW wrote, 'This book came out the latter
end of Feb. 1661[2] [/] The 2 edition came out the beginning of Apr. 1662 but with noe additions at all.'
[and some time later:] 'Againe I think in 8°.' (Wing G1599a and G1600; and 2 other eds., 1665 and 1676).
Tp, AW wrote, '1^s 2^d' and 'This book was published in the latter end of Feb. 1661[2]'. Acquired 1 March
1662, 9^d (?), LT 1.433.
[MS.] Wood D. 27(6). Wing G1599.

3285. G[ray], W[illiam]. *Chorographia, or, a survey of Newcastle upon Tine.* London: by S. B. [or by J.
B.], 1649. 4°. Pp. [8], 34.
Missing. Gore, f. 314^v.
Gore 314. Wing G1975 and 1975A. *Hunt, Folg.*

3286. Great Conspiracy. *A great conspiracy of the papists . . . discovered [10-11 Jan.].* London: f. J.
Thomas, 1641. 4°. A^4.
Tp, AW wrote, 'Plots', in pencil; and A4, at a letter to the Catholic, 'Mr. Napper', he wrote, 'Edm. Napier
of Halywell' (i.e., Holywell, LT 1.191ff.).
Wood 373(14). Wing G1681.

3287. Greatrakes, Valentine. *A brief account of m^r Valentine Greatrak's, and divers of the strange cures*
by him lately performed. London: f. J. Starkey, 1666. 4°. Pp. [1], 96.
Frontispiece^r, 'Ashmolean Museum A. Woods Coll.' Tp, AW wrote, 'Val. Gratricks birth p 15.' Pp. 5, in
margin, AW identified a man who was imprisoned for writing a pamphlet: 'David Lloyd'; 18-9, 22, 25-6,
35-38 vertical lines in margins; 26, also the date, 'Apr. 1665' of a healing; 81, correction. Responds to
Wonders no miracles by D. Lloyd (Wood 643(9), item 4192). Acquired 3 June 1666, 1^s, LT 2.79.
Wood 643(10). Wing G1789.

3288. [**Greaves, Edward**]. *Morbus epidemius anni 1643. Or, the new disease.* Oxford: L. Lichfield, 1643. 4°. Pp. [2], 25.
Tp, AW printed neatly, 'written by Edw; Greaves: M. D. & Fellow of Alls: coll: Oxon.', and later added, 'written upon occasion of a new desease raging in Oxford 1643, the K & court being then there.'
Wood 498(11). Wing G1792. Madan 1502.

3289. Greaves, Edward. *Oratio habita in aedibus collegii medicorum Londinensium, 25 Jul. 1661, die Harvaei memoriae dicato.* London: J. Cotterel pro S. Speed, 1667. 4°. Pp. [4], 25.
Tp, AW wrote 2 notes, on the rank of the author, cropped at side: 'He ass[umed] the title B^t. but [was] none. S[o] W. Dug[dale] Mar. 16[76-85]', and 'Julii primo 1676, Antonii à Wood, ex dono Thomae Guidotti M. B. dum Bathonis' cropped at bottom. AW was in Bath 23 June-14 July. LT 2.350.
Wood 498(5). Wing G1794.

3290. Greaves, John. *A discourse of the Romane foot, and denarius.* London: M. F. f. W. Lee, 1647. 8°. Pp. [8], 134.
Tp, AW underscored 'Greaves' in red ink. Bsm. Acquired 5 Nov. 1661, 1^{s}3^d, LT 1.418.
Wood 218(3). Wing G1800.

3291. Greaves, Thomas. *De linguae Arabicae utilitate et praestantia oratio.* Oxonii: L. Lichfield, 1639. 4°. T leaf is a cancel. Pp. [4], 21.
Wood 512(12). STC 12209.5. Madan 904.

3292. Grebner, Paul. *A brief description of the future history of Europe, from anno 1650 to an. 1710. . . . With principal passages . . . out of . . . Paul Grebner.* [London]: n.pub., 1650. 4°. Pp. [12], 38.
Tp, AW wrote 'prophecies', in pencil; a scribble, 'Hen'.
Wood 646(7). Wing B4570.

3293. Green, Robert*; Henry Berry*, and Lawrence Hill*. *The tryals of Robert Green, Henry Berry, & Lawrence Hill, for the murder of s$^{r.}$ Edmond-bury Godfrey.* London: f. R. Pawlet, 1679. Fol. Pp. [3], 92.
1st blank p., AW wrote the price, '2^s-6'; tp, the same; pp. 18, at testimony by Mr. Praunce [sic], 'This contradits [sic] what is said p. 27', and 'see pag. 34–'; 27, 34, cross-references. Flyleaf, lower, AW wrote 'News-Letter dat. 15. May 1686 [/] Yesterday Miles Prance was by Habeas corpus brought up from Newgate to the court of the Kings bench, & charged with an information setting forth that at the triall of Green, Berry & Hill some yeares since in the Old Bayly, he being produced as witness for the King & sworne to speak the truth, did falsely & corruptly say & sweare that Sr Edm. Bury Godfrey was by them strangled with a linnen handkerchief, wherein in truth he was not so by them strangled, & that thereby Miles Prance did committ wilful & corrupt perjury – [/] News Letter dat. 15. Jun. 1686 [/] The Attorney General renewing his motion against Miles Prance, the court gave this sentence - that he pay a fine of 100^{li}, that he stand in the pillory on Munday next in the pallace yard at Westm. – On the Wednesday after at the Exchange, & on Munday following at charing cross – that he be whipt from Newgate to Tyburne & be committed till al these things were done –'; on a slip pasted on this p., 'The same letter tells us that the Q. Dowager hath begd of the K. the remission of the last punishment viz. whipping – letter dat. Jul. 1. saith that Miles Prance hath obtained that part of his sentence of whipping to be taken of[f] & is return'd to the ch. of Rome', ^{v}, fragment of religious writing, not in AW's hand; and, on a small loose slip, 'see News letter 15. May 86' and an unused heading, 'Apr.' LT 3.185, 189.
Wood 424(8). Wing T2256.

3294. Green, Robert*, and Laurence Hill*. *The behaviour and execution of Robert Green and Laurence Hill . . . at Tyburn [21 Feb.].* London: f. L. C., 1678[9]. 4°. Pp. 8.
Missing in 1837. Traces of 4 leaves remain in the vol. AW's title on the upper flyleaf: 'Of the execution of Robert Green & Laur Hill – 1678'.
Wood 586(20). Wing B1704. *Hunt, Folg.*

3295. Greene, Robert. *The royal exchange. Contayning sundry aphorismes of phylosophie . . . Fyrst written in Italian.* London: J. Charlewood f. W. Wright, 1590. 4°. ¶⁴,A-I⁴.
Wood 499(4). STC 12307.

3296. Greene, R[obert]. *A notable discovery of coosenage.* [London]: [J. Wolfe f. R. Nelson], [1591]. 4°. Ff. [5], 16 [tp mutilated; wanting all after f. 16].
Tp, AW wrote, 'R. Greene'. F. 16^v, scribbles, prob. not by AW.

Wood 371(2). STC 12279 (rare).

3297. Greene, Robert. *Greenes mourning garment*. London: G. Purslowe, 1616. 4°. A2-4,B-I⁴,K1-3 (sig. K3 mutilated).
Tp, AW underscored the author's name in red ink. B1, B2ʳ-B3, B4ᵛ, C2ᵛ, E4, etc., a few lines in margins, in pencil.
Wood 614(10). STC 12252.

3298. Greene, Robert. H[ind?], I., ed. *Greens, groats-worth of wit*. London: B. Alsop f. H. Bell, 1617. 4°. Newly corrected. A-G⁴ (tp mutilated).
Tp, AW wrote 'Rob. Green.'; above, 'E64', a shelf-mark in another collection (see Wood 616(4), item 4476, for a similar shelf-mark, 'E65'); below, signature of William Chester.
Wood 614(9). STC 12247.

3299. Greene, Robert. *Theeves falling out, true men come by their goods*. London: B. Alsop f. H. Bell, 1621. 4°. A-F⁴.
Tp, AW underscored 'Greene', in red ink.
Wood 371(5). STC 12237.

3300. Greenway, Margret. *A lamentation against the professing priest and people of Oxford; and to all in the cages of unclean birds, called colleges*. [London]: n.pub., [1657?]. S.sh.
AW wrote, 'An. 1657 or therabouts'.
Wood 515(17). Wing G1861 (rare). Madan 2322.

3301. Greenwood, William. Απογραφη στοργης. *Or, a description of the passion of love*. London: f. W. Place, 1657. 12°. Pp. [16], 127, [9].
Tp, AW wrote, 'mostly taken of M. Burtons Melancholy.' Bsm. Lent to O. Sedgwick, March 1660. LT 1.306. See also AO 2.653.
Wood 741(3). Wing G1869.

3302. Gregorius, Monk. Crosfield, Thomas, ed. *A letter, relating the martyrdome of Ketaban, . . . done in Engl.* Oxford: J. Lichfield, 1633. 4°. Pp. [6], 23.
Tp, AW wrote, 'by Th. Crosfeild M. A. fellow of Qu. Coll. Ox.' AOF 1.479.
[MS.] Wood D. 24(7). STC 12344. Madan 752.

3303. Gregory 15. Pope. *The popes letter to the prince [of Wales]: in Latine, Spanish, and English. [With] A Jesuites oration to the prince.* London: [E. Allde a. Eliot's Court Press] f. N. Butter, 1623. 4°. Pp. [2], 34.
P. 9, mark in margin, prob. not by AW.
[MS.] Wood D. 23(13). STC 12357.

3304. Gregory 15. Pope. **Manuscript**. *Greg: Pap: 15. Venerabili fratri episcopo Conchen in Hispaniarum regnis inquisitori generali.* N.p.: n.pub., 1623, 19 April. S.sh.
Not in AW's hand.
Wood 276b(112).

3305. Gregory, John. *The works of . . . John Gregory. The first containing notes and observations . . . the second his posthuma.* London: R. Royston a. N. Brooks, 1665. 4°. Pp. [24], 166 [2]; [24], 338 (7 tpp). Pasteboard (blue) with parchment spine; waste paper, newsbook letterpress dated 1660.
Waste paper, upper, AW wrote 'This booke came out 1671. 4°' (does not refer to this item), and '1663 qu[aere]'; 2nd p. [3], at the dedication by 'Ed. Bysh', AW wrote 'Byshe' in red ink. 2nd p. 112, line in margin at a reference to Osney Abbey, in red ink. Acquired 22 Apr. 1665, 4ˢ6ᵈ, LT 2.33.
Wood 338. Wing G1913.

3306. Grent, William. *A new and accurate map of the world drawne according to the truest descriptions . . . with briefe . . . notes upon . . . cosmographie.* [London]: sold by T. Jenner, 1641. S.sh. (3rd state) 720 x 910 mm.
The vol. now Wood 276b has 113 entries. The contents in this vol. were gathered together in 1717 and, along with the vol. now Wood 276a, replaced a former vol. at Wood 276 (Mazzarini, *Will*), which had been lost or removed. An Ashm. librarian, perhaps in 1837, described the replacement as 'Another Smaller Fol. of the same', i.e., the same as the newly inserted vol. Wood 276a (in Library Records d. 1071, ff. 19ᵛ and 71; see also note at Wood 276a(1)). It was rebound in ca. 1881 (calf, quarter, with green cloth, 320 x 455 mm; a number of items show stitch holes from the earlier binding, e.g. 19(ff. 1-12), 30). There is no

list of contents as in Wood 276a. The description in the 1922 Milford hand-list is, 'Maps & Miscellaneous Papers'. The printed works in this volume are numbered in older Arabic nos. to no. 18, and a few of these may be by AW (e.g., 2, 5 and 1st no. 13). After no. 18, only one other item, 100, retains an older Arabic number. All items are numbered in Roman numerals in the characteristic Ashm. manner, to XCIX. In 1881, a Bodleian librarian renumbered all items after XLIII to account for the insertion of 24 *Ordo baccalaureorum determinantium*, determinations by candidates for the degree. The librarian added new Arabic nos., the order of which is followed here, from items 44 to 125 (N.B., the Bod. CD cat. follows an irregular pattern, mixing old and new styles of numeration, see note at Wood 276a(1)). 8 items (excluding maps and engravings) are not in the Bod. CD catalogue. 8 items are missing: on item XXV, there is a note, 'XX-XXV not here [1881]'; on item XXXIII, 'XXXII not here [1881]'; on item XXXIX, 'XXXVII-XXXVIII not here [1881]'. There are 4 mss. items in this vol.: 16, 43, 112, 114 (the last has 4 nos., 114-117). On the pastedown, upper, there is a reference to the preparation of a catalogue of engravings: 'Contents (not already in formal Catalogue) catalogued in slip catalogue cf. prints &c. G R Scott 1920.' Flyleaf, upper, note, 'William Grent's World map 1641 placed in Map collection after repair. E J S P[arsons] 16/6/59' (i.e., Wood 276b(1)). The map is currently in the Map Collection and the no. '1.' is visible on the ᵛ side. Wood 276b(1); now Maps (E) B1 (420). R. W. Shirley, *The Mapping of the World* (1993), item 313.

3307. [**Grenville, Denis**]. *Counsel and directions divine and moral: in . . . letters of advice.* London: f. R. Clavell, 1685. 8°. Pp. [20], 210, [1] (1 p. books printed for Clavell).
Tp, AW wrote '1ˢ-6'. 2nd p. [1], line in margin at a book printed for Clavell.
Wood 883(5) (not in Bodl. CD cat.). Wing G1938A.

3308. **Greville, Fulke**. Brooke, baron. *The life of the renowned Sᵗ Philip Sidney.* London: f. H. Seile, 1652. 8°. Pp. [8], 247.
Missing. MS. Wood E. 2(70), p. 31. Acquired 12 Dec. 1663, 8ᵈ, LT 1.508. Also listed in MS. Wood F. 51, f. 44.
MS. Wood E. 2(70), p. 31. Wing B4899. *O, Hunt, Folg.*

3309. **Greville, Robert**. Brooke, baron. S., J., ed. *The nature of truth its union and unity with the soule, in a letter.* London: R. Bishop f. S. Cartwright, 1640. 12°. Pp. [20], 189. Calf with one gold-stamp fillet; redone.
Wood 837. STC 12363.

3310. **Greville, Robert***. Brooke, baron. *England's losse and lamentation, occasioned by the death of . . . Robert lord Brooke.* London: f. L. Chapman, 1642[3]. 4°. A⁴.
Tp, AW lined out the former no., '36'.
Wood 375(42). Wing E2992.

3311. **Greville, Robert***. Brooke, baron. *The last weeks proceedings of the lord Brooke.* London: R. O. a. G. D., 1642[3], 1 March. 4°. Pp. [2], 6.
Tp, AW overwrote a former no. P. 6, under escutcheon, 'These are the Armes of Howard'.
Wood 375(40). Wing L513.

3312. **Greville, Robert***. Brooke, baron. *A true relation of the death of the lord Brooks.* London: f. T. Bates, 1643. 4°. A⁴.
Tp, AW lined out a former no., and corrected 'taking' to 'marching'.
Wood 375(41). Wing T2942.

3313. **Greville, Robert**. Brooke, baron. *A worthy speech made by . . . lord Brooke, at the election of his captaines and commanders at Warwick castle.* London: f. J. Underwood, 1643, 26 Feb. 4°. Pp. 8.
Missing in 1839; see note at Wood 375(1), item 1720. Found. Huntington copy, 441550, which has stitch holes, as the preceding item in Wood 375, and 2 notes in AW's hand (both mutilated). Tp, after title, '[1 or 2 illegible words] to fight [against?] the King' (all scratched out), and after the printed 'February the 26.', '1642' (also scratched out).
Wood 375(39). Wing B4915. *Hunt.*

3314. **Grey, Henry**. Stamford, earl of; et al. *A true relation of the transaction of the commands of both houses of parliament in the execution of the militia in . . . Leicester.* London: f. G. Lindesay, 1642, 5 July. 4°. A-B⁴.
Tp, AW lined out the former no., '18'.
Wood 374(22). Wing T3060A.

3315. **Grey, Henry**. Stamford, earl of. *[A] most true relation of divers notable passages of divine provi-*

dence . . . obtained by the parliaments forces under the command of the earle of Stamford, in . . . Devon [25 April]. London: f. L. Blaikelocke, 1643. 4°. Pp. [2], 6 (tp, cropped at top).
Wood 376(7). Wing M2928.

3316. Grey, Henry. Stamford, earl of. *A letter to the lord Grey of Grooby.* [London]: f. A. Coe, 1644. 4°. A⁴.
Tp, AW altered former no., '61'; and wrote 'Mar 1643', in pencil, and above the date, '1644', '3'.
Wood 376(68). Wing G1969 ('O' not recorded in Wing).

3317. Griffin, William. *Newes from London-Derry in Ireland: or, a true and sad relation of the . . . estate of London-Derry [20 Feb.].* London: f. W. Ley, 1642. 4°. Pp. [2], 5.
Tp, AW wrote after the year, '20 Feb'. The same, on the blank p. [6].
Wood 507(36). Wing G1985 ('O' not recorded in Wing).

3318. [Griffith, Alexander]. Cambro-Britannicus, Mercurius, pseud. *Mercurius Cambro-Britannicus. Or, news from Wales, touching the . . . propagation of the gospel.* London: n.pub., 1652. 4°. Pp. [6], 23.
At the beginning of the vol., AW noted that this item was 'against Vav. Powell'.
Wood 476(10). Wing G1987 (Wing, ; or,).

3319. [Griffith, Alexander]. *Strena Vavasoriensis, a new-years-gift for the Welch itinerants, or a hue and cry after mr. Vavasor Powell.* London: F. L., 1654. 4°. Pp. [4], 24 (wanting final sheet).
Tp, AW wrote, 'Alex. Griffith the author', and 'Mʳ Griffiths Letters, see Merc. Cambro-Britan- p. 12. in margin' (i.e., Wood 476(10)). Bsm. Pp. 3, 5, 8, AW added notes, e.g., 'He went to Lond. in Aug. 1642'.
Wood 476(11). Wing G1988.

3320. G[riffith], G[eorge]. St. Asaph, bp. of. *A bold challenge of an itinerant preacher [V. Powell] modestly answered by a local minister.* [London]: n.pub., 1652. 4°. A⁴.
Tp, AW wrote, 'published by George Griffith Ch.Ch. or Alex Griffith' (last 3 words lines out).
Wood 647(20). Wing G1996.

3321. [Griffith, Matthew]. London. { *A generall bill of mortality, of the clergie of London . . . 1641 . . . 1647.* [London]: n.pub., [1647]. S.sh.
Some lines in margin or underscoring. AW wrote some notes: col. 4, a correction; col. 2, at Leonard Fosterlane, M. Ward identified as 'Will. Ward'; below, 'Mʳ Georg Smith put into the place of Mʳ Will Ward who resigned S. Leonards Foster Lane – A puritan'.
Wood 276a(84). Wing G2013 (Wing, 1646). ESTCR 226488.

3322. Grigg, William. *The Quaker's Jesus: or, the unswadling of . . . James Nailor.* London: M. Simmons, sold J. Cranford, 1658. 4°. Pp. [16], 69.
Tp, bsm.
Wood 645(9). Wing G2023.

3323. Grimald, Nicholas. *Archipropheta, tragoedia.* Coloniae: M. Gymnicus excud., 1548. 8°. A-E⁸,F⁴.
Missing. MS. Wood E. 2(70), p. 53.
MS. Wood E. 2(70), p. 53. *BL.*

3324. Grimston, Harbottle. *The speech of sʳ. Harbottle Grimston . . . Speaker of the . . . house of . . . commons, to the kings . . . majesty. Delivered . . . at Whitehal, 29 May.* London: E. Husbands a. T. Newcomb, 1660. 4°. Pp. 8.
Wood 608(18). Wing G2040.

3325. [Grimston, Harbottle]. *The speech which the speaker of the house of commons made unto the king . . . at his passing of the bills [29 Aug.].* London: E. Husband a. T. Newcomb, 1660. 4°. Pp. 6 (i.e., 8, misnumbering).
Wood 608(26). Wing G2044.

3326. Grimston, Harbottle, and John Selden. *Master Grimstons argument concerning bishops: with mr. Seldens answer. Also severall orders . . . concerning church-government.* [London]: n.pub., 1641. 4°. Pp. [2], 5.
Tp, bsm.
[MS.] Wood D. 31(13). Wing G2028.

3327. Griselda*, trans. out of Italian. *The pleasant and sweet history of patient Grissel.* [London]: f. J. Clarke, W. Thackeray, a. T. P[assinger], 1686. 8°. A⁸,B⁴ (A8, B1, mutilated) (2 tpp).

Wood 254(12). Wing P2532 (rare).

3328. Groitzch, Gregor. *Libellus continens Salae fluvii descriptionem*. Lipsiae: typ. haeredum I. Bervaldi, 1584. 8°. Pp. 50.
Missing. Gore, f. 315.
Gore 315. VD G3383.

3329. Groot, Hugo de. *Silva, ad Franciscum Augustum Thuanum, Jac. Augusti f.* Lutetiae Parisiorum (really Amst.): N.pub., 1622 (? or 1621; date, a Roman numeral, is mutilated). 12°. Pp. 12 (A⁶). Pasteboard (brown) with calf spine; lower spine backing, trace of marbled paper.
Backing, upper, trace of waste paper on which AW wrote 'Cowley Proposition' (i.e., Wood 730(4)). Flyleaf, upper, 2nd^v, AW wrote the titles of 7 printed works in this vol. (really 6; item 62(20 has 2 entries), within guidelines made with red chalk. Each item has Ashm. Roman numerals in addition to AW's Arabic numbers. Tp, printed name of author at top, rubbed out; signature of 'Joannis Barclaij.' Text, some marks in margins, not by AW.
Wood 62(1). BL.

3330. Grove, John*, and William Ireland*. *A true relation of the execution of mr. John Groves, and mr. William Ireland [16 Dec.]*. London: f. D. M., 1679. 4°. Pp. 8.
Wood 586(19). Wing T2948 (one) ('O' not recorded in Wing).

3331. Groves, Robert. *Gleanings or, a collection of diverse remarkable passages, . . . many of them relating to our late troublesome times*. London: R. Ibbitson, sold A. Williamson, 1651. 8°. 2nd ed. Pp. [6], 163, [12] (Bodl. note: 'title-leaf is a cancel', see note).
Flyleaf, upper^v, AW wrote 'A new title was put to these gleanings, which makes the second edit. 1651 [Wing G2162A] [/] The collector hath endeavoured to glean all things against K. Ch. 1, Bishops & orthodox clergy.' Pp. 35, 153, 2 references to other works, e.g., 'vid: Howels Epist: vol: 1: sect: 5. 147', not in AW's hand.
Wood 864(2). Wing G2162B (one) ('O' not recorded in Wing).

3332. Grunaeus, Simon. *Basiliensium monumentorum antigrapha*. Lignicii: typ. Sartorianis (N. Sartorius), 1602. 8°. Pp. 93, [3]. Parchment.
Tp, bsm.
Wood 107. BL.

3333. Grundall, William, ed. *Hawking, hunting, fouling, and fishing, with the true measures of blowing. . . . collected by W. G.* London: A. Islip, sold R. Olive, 1596. 4°. A-L⁴ (F⁴ blank).
Flyleaf, upper^v, Latin tag, not by AW. Tp, bsm. C2, a pointer, not in AW's manner.
[MS.] Wood C. 36(2). STC 12412.

3334. [Guarna, Andreas]. *Bellum grammaticale, sive, nominum verborumque discordia civilis tragico-comoedia*. Londini: B. A[lsop] & T. F[awcet], imp. J. Spenceri, 1635. 8°. Pp. [12], 66.
Tp, 'Dr Gardiner Can. of Christch. hath often told me that Dr Leonard Hutten was the author of this play. A. W.', and below, 'A. Wood'. A4^v at name of Johannes Spencerus, 'Bibliopola'; A7^v, errata entries underlined.
Wood 76(4). STC 12417.

3335. Guazzo, Stefano. Pettie, George, and Barth. Young, trans. *The civile conversation of m. Stephen Guazzo, . . . foure bookes, the first three translated . . . by G. Pettie . . . the fourth . . . by Barth. Young*. London: T. East, 1586. 4°. Ff. [7], 229, [1]. Parchment.
Flyleaf, upper, a Bod. shelf-mark, 'Jur. 4° F. 37', with a note in pencil, 'This leaf, with the first signature inserted from a copy turned out of the Bodl Libr as being a quadruplicate. WDM [W. D. Macray] 1865' (this is a made-up copy; the library now has 3 rather than 4 copies since the one listed at 4°. F 37 Jur. in the 1843 Bodl. Libr. Cat. was removed in 1865). Text, passim, underscoring and marks and notes in margin, in early hands; none by AW. AO 1.553.
[MS.] Wood B. 27. STC 12423.

3336. Guerdon, Aaron, pseud. *A most learned, conscientious, and devout exercise, or sermon, . . . at sir P. T.'s [Peter Temple's] house . . . by lieutenant-general O. Cromwel, as . . . taken in characters by Aaron Guerdon*. London: n.pub., 1680. 4°. Pp. [2], 17.
Wood 633(2). Wing C7118.

3337. Guevara, Antonio de. Briant, Fraunces, trans. *A dispraise of the life of a courtier*. (Londini): (in aed. R. Graftoni), (1548, August). 8°. A-O⁸. Pasteboard (grey) with parchment spine; 1st upper and last lower flyleaves, marbled paper.

Flyleaf, upper, 3rd^v, AW wrote the titles of 3 printed works in this vol., within guidelines made with red ink. Tp, 'Carolus Griseus. 1552. 10°. Martii', a Greek phrase, an astrological symbol of mercury, scribbles or initials, and by a later owner, '1617. Februa.' Text, passim, some notes in two hands; none by AW. Wood 664(1). STC 12431.

3338. Guevara, Antonio de. Hellowes, Edward, trans. *[The familiar epistles of sir Anthonie of Gueuara . . . with other epistles of the same authour]*. [London]: [[H. Middleton] f. R. Newberrie], [1577]. 4°. Newly impr. Pp. [4], 402, [5] (wanting the t leaf and sig. A4). Calf, speckled, with 2 fillets, stamp decoration (dragon) inside corners, and roll decoration on spine (Ashm. binding).

Flyleaf, upper^v, the titles of 2 printed works in this vol., by an Ashm. librarian (same hand in Wood 276a). Passim, a few notes, some underscoring and marks in margin, not by AW. [MS.] Wood C. 34(1). STC 12434.

3339. Guido de Monte Rocherii. *Manipulus curatorum*. (London): R. Pynson, (1500, 28 Apr.). 8°. Ff. 141, [3]. Parchment.

Tp, 'Liber Henrici Jacksoni Oxoniensis, Collegii Corp. Christi. M DC Maii. xxi. liberati.' and bibliog. data of a Paris ed., 1556. LT 1.460. F. [33^v], scribble, 'YONGE', not by AW. Wood 778. STC 12471. Proctor 9798.

3340. [Guidott, Thomas]. *The names of subscribers and friends*. N.p.: n.pub., [1686 to 1691]. Fol. Pp. [3].

P. [1], AW wrote after heading, 'to M^r . . . Guidotts book', see Wood 658(808), a prospectus, and (809), items 5386 and 3341. LT 3.439. Wood 658(783). Not in Wing (see G2197). Not in ESTCR.

3341. Guidott, Thomas. *Thomae Guidotti Anglo-Britanni, de thermis Britannicis*. Londini: sold B. Aylmer, M. Bently [sic], a. W. Nott, 1691. S.sh. 4°. Tp only, cancel.

Below, 'Dr Guidot remembers him kindly to you: the Printers have made him almost weary of his Life: but now all is over', in J. Aubrey's hand; M. Bently corrected to R. Bently. LT 3.439. Wood 658(809) (not in Bodl. CD cat.). Wing G2191.

3342. [Guidott, Thomas]. *An epitaph on don Quicksot; by a Quaker . . . [F. 2] On don Quicksilver*. [Bath]: n.pub., [1694]. 4°. Ff. 2.

F. 1, at t, AW wrote Quicksot's alternate name, 'alias Dr Char. Conquest who died at Bathe in Septemb. an. 1693', and below, 'By Tho. Guidot a phisition of Bath'. F. 2, at t, he notes Quicksilver's alternate name, 'alias. Will. Gold or Gould M. D. a physitian of Bathe.'; in margin, identification of 'Men of W–', 'Wadham' (Guidott's and Gold's college); and below, 'By Tho. Guidot a phisition of Bath 1694'. LT 3.431 and Wood Diaries 37, item 92; on Guidott, AO 4.733-5. Wood 429(52). Wing G2193 (rare) (Wing, brs.).

3343. [Guillemeau, Jacques]. Banister, Richard, additions by. *A treatise of one hundred and thirteene diseases of the eyes*. London: F. Kyngston f. T. Man, 1622. 12°. (a)-(e)^12,f^6,A-O^12, P1-5. Missing. MS. Wood E. 2(70), p. 22. MS. Wood E. 2(70), p. 22. STC 12499.5. *Folg, Hunt*.

3344. Guillim, John. *A display of heraldry*. London: ?, 1610, 1632, 1638. Pp.? Missing. Lent to Obadiah Sedgwick, March 1660, see LT 1.182, 306. Ed. not identified. LT 1.182. STC 12500-12503.

3345. Guillim, Joseph. Ακαματον πυρ. *Or, the dreadful burning of London:. . . a poem*. London: f. H. Herringman, 1667. 4°. Pp. [6], 14. Tp, after author's initials, AW wrote, 'Joseph Guillim of Brasenose Coll: 4^d'. Acquired 9 Oct., LT 2.119. [MS.] Wood D. 28(15). Wing G31 (Wing, G., J.).

3346. Guinea. *The golden coast, or a description of Guinney*. London: f. S. Speed, 1665. 4°. Pp. [6], 88. Flyleaf, upper, AW wrote 'Description of Guynney'. Wood 386(10). Wing G1014 ('O' not recorded in Wing).

3347. Guinea. *A true relation of the inhumane . . . actions, . . . murders of Negroes or Moors: Committed on three English-men in old Calabar in Guinny*. London: f. T. Passinger and B. Hurlock, 1672. 4°. Pp. 19. Wood 365(22). Wing T2970 ('O' not recorded in Wing).

3348. Guise, House of. *The contre-Guyse: wherein is deciphered the pretended title of the Guyses, and*

the first entrie of the saide family into Fraunce. London: J. Woolfe, 1589. 4°. A-M⁴. Calf with 3 fillets, stamp decoration inside corners (2 leaves and a sunflower sprouting a fleur-de-lis), and roll decoration at inner, spine edge (Ashm. binding); rebacked.
Flyleaf, upper, 2nd, the titles of 26 printed works in this vol. by an Ashm. librarian (same hand in Wood 276a) (really 28 items, 2 are at nos. 9 and 22). No. 26 was stolen.
Wood 615(1). STC 12506.

3349. Gulter, Giles. *The archbishops crueltie, made knowne in a true story of one mr. Edward Rood, who was minister at Saint Helens in Abingdon*. [London]: n.pub., 1641. 4°. A⁴.
[MS.] Wood D. 31(11). Wing G2229.

3350. Gusman, pseud. *The Dutch rogue or, Gusman of Amsterdam . . . the life . . . of d. de Lebechea*. London: A. M. f. G. Hill, 1683. 12°. Pp. [12], 275.
Missing in 1837. 'The Dutch Rogue or Gusman of Amsterdam – Lond. 1683' in Whiteside cat.
Wood 282. Wing D2905. *O, Hunt, Clark*.

3351. G[winne], M[atthew], and Henry Price. *Epicedium in obitum illustrissimi herois Henrici comitis Derbeiensis*. Oxoniae: J. Barnesius, 1593. 4°. A-B⁴.
Red lines made as borders, and underscoring, on several pp., may be by Sadleir, who had written his poems in this vol. (Wood 460(1, 3)) within similar borders. A2ᵛ, AW wrote the surnames of M. G. and H. P., 'Gwynn' and 'Price'.
Wood 460(6). STC 11500. Madan 143.

3352. H., E. *Straffords plot discovered, and the parliament vindicated*. London: R. Raworth f. J. Dallam, 1646. 4°. Pp. [6], 16.
Wood 366(12). Wing H24.

3353. H., F. *An elogie [sic], and epitaph, consecrated to . . . Charles*. [London?]: n.pub., 1649. 4°. Pp. [3], 10.
Wood 364(31). Wing H25 ('O' not recorded in Wing).

3354. H., I. *The petition and articles exhibited in parliament against John Pocklington*. London: n.pub., 1641. 4°. Pp. [2], 5.
[MS.] Wood D. 31(36). Wing E2158 ('O' not recorded in Wing).

3355. H., I. *The antipodes, or, reformation with the heeles upward. Being a compendious narrative . . . of the great hypocrisie of our pretending reformers*. Oxford: [J. Harris a. H. Hills], 1647. 4°. Pp. 11 (misnumbering).
Wood 612(62). Wing H42. Madan 1944.

3356. H., J. *Work for chimny-sweepers: or a warning for tabacconists*. London: T. Este [a. T. Creede] f. T. Bushell, 1602. 4°. A-F⁴,G². Pasteboard (blue) with parchment spine. 1st upper and last lower flyleaves, marbled paper; rebacked.
Flyleaf, upper, 2ndᵛ, AW wrote the titles of 11 printed works in this vol., within guidelines made with red ink. Response at R. Marbecke, [MS.] Wood D. 30(2), item 4365.
[MS.] Wood D. 30(1). STC 12571.

3357. H., J. *A true and perfect relation of that most horrid & hellish conspiracy of the gunpowder treason [5 Nov. 1605]*. London: f. Fr. Coles, 1662. 4°. Pp. 16.
Wood 608(41). Wing H82C (two).

3358. H., J., and A. B., et al. B., H., ed. *Two essays of love and marriage. . . . to disswade him from love [signed J. H.]. And an answer thereunto by another gentleman [signed A. B.]*. London: f. H. Brome, 1657. 12°. Pp. [2], 123. Pasteboard (blue) with parchment spine. 1st upper and last lower flyleaves, marbled paper and a remnant of marbled paper.
AW wrote the titles of 6 printed works in this vol., within guidelines made with red ink. The 6th, in different ink, is an enigmatic 'The Conclusion: A. a Wood'; it is not present, nor is it listed in the Whiteside cat. 1st item, each 12° leaf is pasted on an 8° template. Tp, bsm. Flyleaf, lower, an index, not by AW.
Wood 750(1). Wing H84.

3359. H., J., and D. H. *The princes first fruits: or, a full and perfect relation of two victories obtained by col. Rich . . . neer Sandown castle . . . August 10. & 14*. [London]: n.pub., 1648. 4°. Pp. [2], 6.
Tp, AW wrote after the year, 'Aug. 15'.
Wood 502(43). Wing H77 ('O' not recorded in Wing).

3360. H., M. *Epicedia: or funeral verses upon the . . . death of . . . Hmphrey [sic] Colles of Cates-lade [15 Nov. 1661; signed M. H.].* [London?]: n.pub., [1661]. S.sh.
Repaired after AW acquired this s.sh. Scribbles and a joggerel, not in AW's hand. ᵛ, AW wrote, 'Hump. Colles 1661', partially covered by support slip.
Wood 429(18). Wing E3141A (rare) (Wing, Humphrey).

3361. H., R. *Remarks on the life and death of the fam'd mr. [Thomas] Blood.* London: f. R. Janeway, 1680. Fol. 2nd ed. Pp. [2], 14, 4.
P. 5, AW wrote, 'Tho. Allen alias Allyn alias Ayliff a chirurgion or Dʳ of physick at Rumford – so in the hue and crye after him, when he, with others, had assasianated [sic] James D. of Orm. – see my 3ᵈ vol. of Gazets. nu. 529'; p. 8, 'Aug. 8. 1667 his maj. by consent of the privy counsell ordered a proclamation to be issued out to apprehend Jo. Lockier, Timot. Butler[,] Thom. Blood & other persons who rescued Joh. Mason a prisoner for treason, at Darringon neare Wentbridge in Yorksh. &c. 100ˡⁱ to be given to him that shall [turn] in either of them – see first vol. of Gazets. nu. 181'. LT 2.222.
Wood 426(33). Wing H113 (two).

3362. H., W. *The reformed travailer.* London: W. White, 1606. 4°. A-K⁴ (K4 blank).
Tp, date of publ., faint, altered first to '1626', then to '1616'.
Wood 386(4). STC 12580.

3363. H., W., and Robert Balsame. *A more perfect and particular relation of the late great victorie in Scotland . . . to which is . . . added a letter written from master [Robert] Balsame .* London: M. B. f. R. Bostock, 1645, 25 Sept. 4°. Pp. [2], 10.
Tp, AW altered the former no., '23'.
Wood 378(26). Wing H157.

3364. Habin, Richard*. *A true account from Chichester, concerning the death of Habin the informer.* London: f. J. Pool, 1682. 4°. Pp. [8], 8.
Wood 365(32). Wing T2325.

3365. Habington, William. *The historie of Edward the fourth, king of England.* London: T. Cotes f. W. Cooke, 1640. Fol. Pp. [4], 232. Pasteboard (blue) with parchment spine, traces of marbled upper and lower flyleaves.
Upper flyleaf opposite tp has a portrait of Edward 4 pasted on it, R. Elstracke sculpsit. Tp, bsm.
Wood 660d(1). STC 12586.

3366. Haddon, Walter. Hartwell, Abraham, trans. *A sight of the Portugall pearle, that is, the aunswere of . . . against the epistle of Hieronimus Osorius.* (London): (W. Seres), [1565?]. 8°. A1-7,B⁸,C⁴,A-F⁸ (1st leaf and last 2, blank).
Tp 'W: Mownti [?] ex dono magistri Sereli Augusti 18. 1565.'
Wood 800(2). STC 12598.

3367. Haines, Richard. *England's weal & prosperity proposed: or, reasons for erecting publick work-houses . . . To which is added a model of government for such works houses . . . printed in . . . (79).* London: f. L. Curtis, 1681 (1679). 4°. Pp. 8, 16 (2 pts.; sections are in reversed order).
Tp, lower case 'w' (bsm?).
[MS.] Wood D. 27(9, 10). Wing H201, H201A.

3368. Hakewell, William. *The libertie of the subject: against the pretended power of impositions.* London: R. H., 1641. 4°. Pp. [8], 142, [1]. Pasteboard (blue) with parchment spine; traces of upper and lower marbled flyleaves.
Flyleaf, upper, 2ndᵛ, AW wrote the titles of 4 printed works in this vol., within guidelines made with red chalk. 1st item: each small 4° leaf is pasted on a 4° template. Tp, AW wrote after the author, 'Kinsman to Sʳ Th. Bodley. – Counsellour of Lync. Inn. an. 1611 – somtimes of Exeter Coll. – created A.m. 1613. v. pref.' P. [5, the preface], unscoring of 'smal Treatise' which was lately 'false printed' and 'stoln without my [Hakewell's] consent'.
Wood 527(1). Wing H210.

3369. Hakewill, W[illiam]. *Modus tenendi parliamentum: or, the old manner of holding parliaments in England. . . . together with, the priviledges of parliament: and the manner how lawes are . . . enacted . . . By W. Hakewel.* London: J. G., sold A. Roper (and a torn cancelled tp, f. J. Benson), 1659. 12°. Pp. [8, including cancel], 220. Pasteboard (blue) with parchment spine.
Flyleaf, upper, 2ndᵛ, AW wrote the titles of 4 printed works in this vol., within guidelines made with red

ink (really 3; AW made 2 entries for the 1st item). Tp, AW wrote the price, '1.2'.
Wood 457(1). Wing H215.

3370. Halberstadt. *A full relation concerning the wonderfull and wholsome fountain. At first discovered in Germany, two miles from . . . Halberstadt.* London: T. W. f. J. Kirton, 1646. 4°. Pp. [2], 21.
Wood 615(16). Wing F2355.

3371. H[ale], T[homas], and William Petty. *An account of several inventions and improvements . . . relating to building of our English shipping, . . . the proceedings relation to the mill'd-lead-sheathing, . . . a treatise of naval philosophy, written by sir Will. Petty.* London: f. J. Astwood, sold R. Simpson, 1691. 12°. Pp. [3], cxxv, [37], 132 (2nd tp, f4).
1ᵛ, AW wrote the first of several notes in the 1st part providing background on the quarrell between Peter Pett and the earl of Clarendon: 'Tho. Hale a great ingenioso of Lond. was Author of this book; being instigated to write it by Sʳ Peter Pett that he might vex Henry Earl of Clarendon, who put him to great trouble to get his patent revok'd'; pp. lvi, lvii, lxix, lxxii, where AW explained at 'patent' and 'Cessit Processus': 'The said patent was obtained by Hen. E. of Clar. [/] This was done by the endeavour of Sʳ peter pett', and pp. lxxviii, lxxxix; xcvii, at mayors of London and conservacy of the river, 'These Lord Mayors did by the instigation of Sʳ Peter Pett apply themselves to the government against the Earl of Clarendon patent'; cxii, cxv; cxvi, at names of patentees, 'These things reflect upon the E. of Clarendon patent, who knew when he took it out that there were prior patents in being' ; cxxii, at Petitioning Seamen, 'petitioning against patents particularly that of the E. of Clar. was by the instigation of Sʳ Peter Pett, who drew their petitions'.
Wood 68(4). Wing H265.

3372. Hales, [Edward]. *A speech, spoken by mr. Hayles, a student of University-colledge . . . with his majesties gracious acceptance.* (London): (f. A. M.), (1687). S.sh. Pp. 2.
P. 1, AW wrote the year, '1687', in pencil; p. 2, 'published at Lond. 14. Sept'. LT 3.233. Dupl. at Wood 515(33b), missing.
Wood 423(63). Wing H266B.

3373. Hales, [Edward]. *A speech, spoken by mr. Hayles, a student of University-colledge . . . with his majesties gracious acceptance.* (London): (f. A. M.), (1687). S.sh. Pp. 2.
Missing in 1922. AW's entry on the upper flyleaf of the vol., 'Speech spoken by Mʳ Edw. Hales before his Majestie in University Coll – in Sept. 1687'. Dupl. at Wood 423(63).
Wood 515(33b). Wing H266B.

3374. Halesiados*. *Halesiados. A message from the Normans, to the generall of the Kentish forces, with the generalls answer . . . Also two state-pasquils.* [London]: n.pub., 1648. 4°. Pp. [2], 10.
Wood 502(44). Wing H282.

3375. [Hall, George]. Chester, bp. of. *The triumphs of Rome over despised protestancie.* London: n.pub., 1655. 4°. Pp. [4], 148.
Tp, 'Ant Woode', lined out; 'october xxii M DC Lix', and, at a later date, 'George Hall Bish. of Chester, the author', LT 1.284-6; below, price, 'i6ᵈ' may not be in AW's hand. Bsm. P. 32, at fornication 'in their Streets', AW wrote, 'stews'.
Wood 627(3). Wing H337.

3376. Hall, John. *Poems. [2nd tp] The second book of divine poems.* Cambridge (2nd tp, London): R. Daniel f. J. Rothwell [London]. 2nd tp, E. G. for J. Rothwell., 1646, 1647. 8°. Pp. [16], 104.
Tp, AW wrote at 'John Hall', 'of Durham.'; bsm. Notes by other persons: p. [7] (A4), 'John Crooke' in margin; p. [16] (A8ᵛ), poem about Hall, 'To the memory of the forgetful John Hall: [/] The Author of this nonauthentick poeme' and 6 more lines (last line cropped at bottom).
Wood 84(10). Wing H355.

3377. H[all], J[ohn]. *An humble motion to the parliament of England concerning the advancement of learning: and reformation of the universities.* London: f. J. Walker, 1649. 4°. Pp. [2], 45.
Tp, AW wrote, 'Joh. Hall of Durham', and beneath the year, '1649'.
Wood 515(10). Wing H350. Madan 2023.

3378. Hall, John. Davies, John, ed. *Paradoxes, by J. De la Salle.* London: f. F. Eaglesfield, 1653. 12°. Pp. [20], 165, [1].
A1, printed 'Fear-God Full-Flesh' smudged out.
Wood 735(2). Wing H354 ('O' not recorded in Wing).

3379. [Hall, Joseph]. *Virgidemiarum, sixe books.* N.p.: n.pub., [1597]. 8°. Pp. 3-101 [1] (B-G⁸,H1-3) (imperf. Pt. 2 only; begins with stubs of 8 leaves).
Wood 79(3) (now Arch. G. f. 2(3)). STC 12716.

3380. [Hall, Joseph]. *[Virgidemiarum, or biting satyrs, lib. 6].* [London]: [J. Harison f. R. Dexter], [1602]. 8°. Pp. [14], 64, 105, [1] (wanting tp (A1), and 2nd A1-2). Parchment.
Pastedown, upper, 'I. Ward' (? prob.), a 2nd scribble, and 'Cantabr. 1603. – xiᵈ'.
Wood 75. STC 12718.

3381. [Hall, Joseph]. Knight, William, ed. *Mundus alter et idem, sive, terra australis ante hac semper incognita longis itineribus peregrini academici [author, Mercurius Britannicus].* [London a. Hanau, sold] Francof.: ap. haer. Ascanij de Rinialme, [1607?]. 8°. Pp. [16], 224 (bibliog. data supplied; t leaf and p. 54 are blank, having received no impression from the engraving and the 5 maps are wanting).
¶1, AW wrote 'Mundus alter et idem sive terra australis' and, in pencil, the Bodl. shelf-mark, '8° B 41 Art. Seld. vide Jos. Hall' (still at this location today); ¶2 at Dom. Henrico, 'ob. 1643'.
Wood 824(3). STC 12685.3.

3382. Hall, Joseph. Healey, John, trans. *The discovery of a new world, or, a description of the south Indies, . . . by an English Mercury.* [London]: [G. Eld] f. E. Blount a. W. Barrett, [1613-4]. 8°. Pp. [34], 241 (leaf ¶4 cancelled) (wanting the t leaf and the translator's letter to the author). Parchment.
Flyleaf, upper, 2nd, AW wrote 'J. Hall his description of Tenterbelly/'. A former shelf-mark, G.3.1.
Wood 751. STC 12686.3.

3383. Hall, Thomas. *Comarum ἀκοσμία. The loathsomnesse of long haire.* London: J. G. f. N. Webb a. W. Grantham, 1654. 8°. Pp. [6], 125.
Each 8° leaf is pasted on a 4° template. Tp, after author, underscored in red chalk, AW wrote, 'Vicar of Kingsnorton in Com. Wigorn.' and '8ᵈ'.
Wood 653(6). Wing H429.

3384. Hallowes, John, et al. *Aprill the 22ᵗʰ· New and true newes from Ireland [two letters, the 2nd signed J. Hallowes].* London: f. F. Coules, 1642. 4°. Pp. [2], 6 (misnumbering).
Tp, AW wrote, above, 'Mar 20' in pencil and after the year, 'Ap. 6'.
Wood 508(4). Wing H456B.

3385. Hamilton, James. 1st duke. *The copy of a letter from duke Hamilton, to the ministers at Lancaster.* London: f. E. Husband, 1648, 25 Aug. 4°. Pp. 7.
Tp, AW wrote after the year, 'Aug. 10'.
Wood 502(40). Wing H479.

3386. Hamilton, James; Henry [Rich] Earl of Holland, and Arthur Capel. *The several speeches of duke Hamilton earl of Cambridg, Henry earl of Holland, and Arthur lord Capel, upon the scaffold [9 March].* London: f. P. Cole, F. Tyton, a. J. Playford, 1649. 4°. Pp. 43.
Wood 366(34). Wing H482.

3387. Hammond, Henry. *A copy of some papers past at Oxford, betwixt the author of The practicall catechisme, and mr. Ch.* London: R. Cotes f. R. Royston, 1647. 4°. Pp. [2], 131.
Tp, in t, after catechisme, 'H. Hamm.' (H. Hammond), and the author's name altered to Ch'eynell', prob. by AW. Bsm.
Wood 617(7). Wing H530. Madan 1921.

3388. Hammond, Henry. *To the right honourable, the lord Fairfax, . . . the humble address of Henry Hammond.* London: f. R. Royston, 1649. 4°. Pp. [2], 19.
Tp, AW wrote, 'Jan. 15. 1648[9]'.
Wood 364(4). Wing H606.

3389. Hammond, Henry. *Of the daily practice of piety; also devotions & praiers in time of captivity.* London: J. F. f. R. Royston, 1660. 12°. Pp. [8], 67, [1].
Missing. MS. Wood E. 2(70), p. 35, 'The daily practice of piety'. See AO 3.498.
MS. Wood E. 2(70), p. 35. Wing O142 (rare, *BL*).

3390. Hamond, Tho., and E. R. *The late commotion of certaine papists in Herefordshire. Occasioned by the death of one Alice Wellington.* London: S. S[tafford] f. I. Chorlton a. F. Burton, 1605. 4°. A-F⁴.
Wood 586(13). STC 25232.

3391. Hampden, John. *A discreet and learned speech:. . . concerning the accusation of high treason . . . against himselfe, the lord Kimbolton.* London: f. I. W. or f. F. Coules a. T. B., 1641. 4°. Pp. [2], 6.
Missing in 1922. See note at Wood 373(1). T on upper flyleaf: 'M^r Jo. Hādens speech concerning the accusation of hig [sic] treason against himself, the Lord Kymbolton &c.' Prob. the same as MS. Wood E. 2(70), p. 68, 'Mr Joh. Hampden his speech' (ed. not identified).
Wood 373(12). Wing H628 and 630. *Folg,* and *Folg, Hunt, Clark.*

3392. Hampden, John*. *The tryal and conviction of John Hambden, esq; upon an indictment of high-misdemeanour.* London: f. B. Tooke, 1684. Fol. Pp. [3], 56.
1st blank p., AW wrote, '1 6', in pencil.
Wood 428(24). Wing T2160.

3393. Hampden, John*. *The tryal of John Hambden, gent. for conspiring the death of the king [30 Dec.].* London: E. Mallet f. D. Mallet, 1685. Fol. Pp. [2], 4.
Tp, AW wrote the price, '3^d'.
Wood 421(6). Wing T2193.

3394. Hampshire. *England's standard:. . . Or, a remonstrance of the lovers of the commonwealth, inhabitants of Hampshire, delivered to the council of the officers of the army [21 Nov.].* London: f. L. Chapman, 1659. 4°. Pp. 8.
Tp, nos. 44 and 38 in former bundles.
Wood 610(30). Wing E3054.

3395. Hampton Court. *Hampton-court conspiracy, with the downfall of the agitators and levellers.* [London]: n.pub., 1647. 4°. Pp. [2], 6.
Wood 612(59b). Wing H636.

3396. Hanam, Richard*. *The English villain: or the grand thief. . . . Richard Hanam.* London: f. J. Andrews, [1656]. 8°. Pp. [2], 14.
Wood 284(7). Wing E3123 (two).

3397. Hanger, Philip. *A true relation how eighteen men were casta way [sic] at sea.* London: f. C. Harper, 1675. 4°. Pp. [3], 11.
Flyleaf, upper, scribbles. P. 1, AW made some marks and wrote, at printed 'Some years since', 'When? or in what year.'
Wood 387(11). Wing H648.

3398. Harchius, Jodocus. *Pro instauratione reipublicae Angl. proque reditu . . . Reginaldi Poli.* Londini: J. Cawodi, 1554. 8°. A-C^8,D^4 (D4 blank).
Tp, AW wrote, 'B Bod', lined out (8° C. 154(3) Th., still at this location today). Some marks and lines in margins, not in AW usual manner.
Wood 84(2). STC 12753.

3399. Harcourt, Daniel. *A new remonstrance from Ireland, containing an exact declaration of the cruelties, . . . by the . . . popish rebells in . . . Ulster [and] 'The Levites Lamentation' [23 Oct. 1641].* London: f. H. Shephard, [1643]. 4°. Pp. [2], 1-6, 1-23 (misnumbering).
Tp, AW wrote 'Oct. 41' and 'May 42', in pencil. Flyleaf, upper, scribbles, not in AW's hand. 2nd p. 1, 'This Levites Lamentation was printed & sold with the Remonstrance–' (see Wing L1827). P. 15 [i.e. 24]^v, signatures of Richard Bovett, some Greek (John 1.1), and scribbles. Dupl. at Wood 614(27-28).
Wood 508(27). Wing H692 (Wing, gives a separate entry for the 2nd item, L1827).

3400. Harcourt, Daniel. *A new remonstrance from Ireland, containing an exact declaration of the cruelties, . . . by the . . . popish rebells in . . . Ulster [and] 'The Levites Lamentation' [23 Oct. 1641].* London: f. H. Shephard, [1643]. 4°. Pp. [2], 1-6, 1-23 (misnumbering, 21, 23, 15).
Tp, AW wrote 'Dupl.' Dupl. at Wood 508(27).
Wood 614(27-28). Wing H692 (Wing, gives a separate entry for the 2nd item, L1827).

3401. H[arcourt], W[illiam]. *The papists new-fashion'd allegiance: a letter lately seiz'd . . . April the 12th. 1679.* [London]: n.pub., [1679]. Fol. Pp. 4.
P. 3, AW wrote, 'This was printed in August 1679'.
Wood 276a(165). Wing H696.

3402. [Harding, Samuel]. *Sicily and Naples, or, the fatall union. A tragoedy.* [Oxford]: [W. Turner], [1640]. 4°. Pp. [4], 96 (imperf., wanting all before A1).

On 3 blank leaves before A1: 1st[v], the title and 'M: H: 1755'; 3rd[v], the dramatis personae, not in AW's hand. A1, at dedicatory verses to S. H., AW wrote, 'Coll. Exon. q[uaere]' (see AO 3.31-2); A3 at Joh. Hall, AW crossed out and answered a 'qu[aere]' note with 'epī fil' (i.e., son of Bishop Hall of Exeter). Wood 330(7). STC 12757. Madan 945.

3403. Hardyng, John. *The chronicle of Jhon Hardyng in metre*. London: in off. R. Graftoni, 1643 (Jan.). 8°.
Missing. In a list of 'Mr. Woods Duplicats', MS. Wood F. 51, f. 44, item 7.
MS. Wood F. 51(7). STC 12766.7 or 12767.

3404. Hare, John. *The marine Mercury. Or, a true relation of the strange appearance of a man-fish . . . Whereunto is added . . . how sir Simon Heartley . . . gave battell*. [London]: n.pub., 1642. 4°. A⁴.
[MS.] Wood B. 35(10). Wing H763.

3405. Harflete, Henry. *A banquet of essayes, fetcht out of famous Owens confectionary [Epigrammatum libri tres]*. London: T. R. & E. M., sold J. Barber, 1653. 8°. Pp. [6], 86.
Wood 868(3). Wing H766.

3406. Harington, John. Chetwind, John, ed. *A briefe view of the state of the Church of England, as it stood . . . to . . . 1608. . . . And may serve as an additional supply to doctor [F.] Goodwins catalogue of bishops*. London: f. J. Kirton, 1653. 12°. Pp. [10], 211, [3]. Pasteboard (blue) with parchment spine. 1st upper and last lower flyleaves, remnants of marbled paper.
Flyleaf, upper, 2nd[v], AW wrote the titles of 3 printed works in this vol., within guidelines made with red ink. Mainly vertical lines in red ink, or pen or pencil, and underscoring on pp. [3], 59-60 (in vignette of Dr. John White), 62, 64, 71-3 (in vignette of Dr. Thomas Bilson), 76-7 ('q[uaere]' at reference to a 'Distick written to B. Cox'), 79 (correction), 89 (identification, 'S[r] Wal. Ralegh'), 96 (line at reference to Dr. H. Cotton's 19 children), 114 (in vignette of Bishop T. Godwin, at a reference to his son who writes 'no lesse learnedly', AW wrote 'where?'), 152, 192 (in vignette of M. Hutton, at story of his son Luke Hutton and death for a robbery, AW wrote 'False', see AO 3:51-2), 193, 198. Acquired 9 July 1657, 10[d], LT 1.220. See also note at item 3884.
Wood 864(1). Wing H770.

3407. Harmar, John. *Ad . . . Lambertum Osbalstonum epistola: cui intexitur apologia pro . . . Joanne Williams archiepiscopo Eboracensi*. Londini: (venund. ap. O. Pullenum), 1649. 8°. Pp. [2], 90, [1].
Dupl. at Wood 817(2).
Wood 62(5). Wing H781.

3408. Harmar, John. *Ad . . . Lambertum Osbalstonum epistola: cui intexitur apologia pro . . . Joanne Williams archiepiscopo Eboracensi*. Londini: (venund. ap. O. Pullenum), 1649. 8°. Pp. [2], 90, [1].
Dupl. at Wood 62(5).
Wood 817(2). Wing H781.

3409. Harmar, John. *Oratio Oxoniae habita, in schola publica linguae Graecae assignatā*. London: Typ. G. Du Gardi, 1650. 8°. Pp. [16], 61. Calf, speckled, with 2 fillets and a vertical line of 2 fillets; flyleaf, lower printer's waste paper.
Tp, former no. 30 (? smudged).
Wood 817(1). Wing H792.

3410. Harmar, John. *Oratio . . . protectoris elogium complectens, Oxoniae habita . . . Cui accesserunt ejusdem ad protectorem carmina de pace cum Belgis sancita*. Oxoniae: H. Hall, 1654. 4°. Pp. [4], 9, [2].
Wood 512(15). Wing H794. Madan 2244.

3411. Harmar, John. *Oratio gratulatoria . . . Richardi Cromwelli*. Oxoniae: A. Lichfield, 1657. 8°. A⁸,B1 (imperf.).
Wood 62(6). Wing H791. Madan 2323.

3412. Harmar, John. *Aeternitati sacrum. Serenissimus, potentissimus, auspicatissimus princeps, Olivarus, ejus nominis primus, ex nobili Cromwellorum familia oriundus*. Londini: J. Macock, 1658. S.sh.
Wood 429(15). Wing H782 (rare).

3413. Harmar, John. *Oratio steliteutica. . . . sive stricturae in hujus aevi delatores & pasquillos, & in terrae filios . . . eorumque similes, elisae*. Londini: excud. R. Daniel, 1658. 8°. Pp. 30, [1].
A copy acquired 9 Feb. 1667, 6[d], LT 2.98. Dupl. at Wood 898(3). AO 3.920.
Wood 62(4). Wing H795. Madan 2365.

3414. Harmar, John. *Oratio steliteutica. . . . sive stricturae in hujus aevi delatores & pasquillos, & in terrae filios . . . eorumque similes, elisae.* London: excud. R. Daniel, 1658. 8°. Pp. 30, [1].
Tp, scribbles. Flyleaf, lower[v], 'Ant: Wood', may not be by AW. A copy acquired 9 Feb. 1667, 6[d], LT 2.98.
Dupl. at Wood 62(4). AO 3.920.
Wood 898(3). Wing H795. Madan 2365.

3415. Harmar, John. *Vindiciae academiae Oxoniensis, sive oratio apologetica, quā exercitiorum academicorum in trimestre vacatio a crimine vindicatur.* Oxoniae: typis A. & L. Lichfield. Impens. J. Nixon, 1662. 8°. Pp. [6], 58.
Wood 62(7). Wing H798 (rare). Madan 2581 (Wing, (and Madan) 'excud.' and 'per').

3416. Harmar, John. *Oratio panegyrica in honorem Caroli secundi.* Oxoniae: typ. W. H[all], imp. authoris, 1663. 8°. Pp. [6], 24.
Pp. 12-3, 17-8, marks in pencil, may not be by AW (AO 3.919-20).
Wood 113(6). Wing H793. Madan 2639 (has 'honoram' in t and different publ. info.).

3417. Haro, Lewis de. *A translate of a letter from don Lewis de Harro . . . sent unto the king of Scots at Brussels.* [London]: n.pub., 1659[60]. S.sh.
AW added 'Jan:' before printed year, 1659.
Wood 276a(196). Wing H803.

3418. Harpford. Manuscript. *Out of a letter dated at Harpford neare to Honiton in Devon. 30 Sept. 1685.* N.p.: n.pub., [1685]. S.sh.
Former no. '40' in pencil; 7 extracts from 'Letter' and 'News Letter' sources, Oct. to Dec. 1685. LT 3.168, 170.
Wood 660c(12b).

3419. Harpur, Jo[hn]. *The jewell of arithmetick.* London: F. Kyngston, sold J. Browne, 1617. 4°. Pp. [10], 180 (many leaves unopened).
Wood 316(2). STC 12796.

3420. Harrington, James*. 1611-77. *Decrees and orders of the committee of safety of the commonwealth of Oceana. [A satire on the commonwealth of Oceana of J. Harrington].* London: n.pub., 1659. 4°. Pp. 8.
Tp, AW underscored Oceana in the t; wrote 'a peice of Roguery', in red ink; and the no. in a former bundle, '24', in pencil.
Wood 626(5). Wing D806.

3421. Harrington, James. 1611-77. *A discourse upon this saying: the spirit of the nation is not yet to be trusted with liberty; lest it introduce monarchy.* London: J. C. f. H. Fletcher, [1659]. 4°. Pp. [2], 14.
Tp, AW wrote 'first heape 25', in pencil; p. 14, after name of author, 'Qu[aere] whether he be the true author -', in red ink.
Wood 626(16). Wing H813.

3422. Harrington, J[ames]. 1611-77. *Pour enclouer le canon. [A tract in favour of a commonwealth.].* (London): (f. H. Fletcher), (1659). 4°. Pp. 8.
Tp, AW wrote, 'Jam. Harrington'; below, in pencil, 'May 2'.
Wood 626(4). Wing H819.

3423. Harrington, James. 1611-77. *The censure of the rota upon m[r] Miltons book, entituled, The ready and easie way to establish a free common-wealth.* London: P. Giddy, 1660. 4°. Pp. 16.
Tp, a classification, in pencil, illeg., faded.
Wood 626(11). Wing H808.

3424. [Harrington, James]. 1611-77. *The rota: or, a model of a free-state, or equall common-wealth.* London: f. J. Starkey, 1660. 4°. Pp. [2], 29.
Tp, AW wrote, 'This goes under the name of Ja. Harrington.'; and altered the year to 16'59[60]: ffeb'.
Wood 626(10). Wing H821.

3425. Harrington, James. 1611-77. *The use and manner of the ballot.* N.p.: n.pub., [1660]. S.sh.
Under t, AW wrote, 'James Harrington' and then folded this single sheet for binding in this vol. (blotting on [v]). [v], 'p. 12.2 & 12.3', a later addition.
Wood 626(13). Wing H823.

3426. Harrington, James. 1611-77. *The wayes and meanes whereby an equal & lasting commonweath*

[sic] may be suddenly introduced. London: f. J. S., 1660. 4°. Pp. [2], 5.
Wood 626(9). Wing H825.

3427. [Harrington, James]. 1611-77. *The benefit of the ballot: with the nature and use thereof: particularly in . . . Venice.* [London?]: n.pub., [1680]. Fol. Pp. 4.
Wood 626(12). Wing H806A.

3428. [Harrington, James]. 1664-93. *An account of the proceedings of . . . Jonathan [Trelawney] lord bishop of Exeter in his late visitation of Exeter college.* Oxford: at the theatre, 1690. 4°. Pp. [2], 58.
Tp, AW wrote, 'First published at Oxon. 23. Sept. 1690 Jam. Harrington of ch. ch. M. A. the author.'; and, in pencil, no. in a former bundle, '4-' (cropped). Response is at Wood 631(3). LT 3.340.
Wood 631(5). Wing H826.

3429. [Harrington, James]. 1664-93. *The case of the university of Oxford. This university enjoy'd at the first institution.* N.p.: n.pub., [1690]. S.sh. (t also printed on ᵛ).
Below, AW wrote, 'James Harrington of Ch. Ch. drew up this -'.
Wood 276a(304). Not in Wing (not C1174-5). Not in ESTCR.

3430. Harrington, James. 1664-93. *A defence of the proceedings of . . . the visitor and fellows of Exeter college in Oxford. With an answer to 1. The case . . . 2. The account examin'd [by A. Bury followed by a copy of the proceedings of dr. [Edward] Master upon . . . appeal].* London: f. T. Bennet, 1691. 4°. Pp. [4], 48, 8.
Tp, AW wrote, 'James Harrington the aut[hour]' (cropped at side). LT 3.360-1.
Wood 631(8 and 09). Wing H830.

3431. [Harrington, James]. 1664-93. *A vindication of mr. James Colmar . . . from the calumnies of three late pamphlets.* London: f. T. Bennet, 1691. 4°. Pp. [7], 43, [1] (1 p. books printed for Bennet).
Tp, AW wrote 'First exposed to sale in Oxf. 5. 6. May 1691', and, in pencil, the name of the author, 'Ja Har' (cropped at side). LT 3.360-1.
Wood 631(7). Wing H835.

3432. [Harrington, James]. 1664-93. *Reasons for reviving and continuing the act for the regulation of printing.* [London]: n.pub., [1693]. S.sh.
AW wrote, at end, 'printed in (January) 1692[3] written by James Harrington of Ch. Ch'; repeated by another writer, above. Dupl. at Wood 642(6).
Wood 276a(291). Wing R511 (Wing, [1693?]).

3433. [Harrington, James]. 1664-93. *Reasons for reviving and continuing the act for the regulation of printing.* [London]: n.pub., [1693]. S.sh.
AW wrote, '1692 (Nov) [lined out and] Jan.' (i.e., 1693); and 'written by Jam. Harrington'. Dupl. at Wood 276a(291).
Wood 642(6). Wing R511 (Wing, [1693?]).

3434. [Harrington, James], 1664-93, and **Gerard Langbaine** *The case of the university of Oxford; shewing, that the city is not concern'd to oppose the confirmation of their charters by parliament.* [Oxford]: n.pub., [1690?]. Fol. Pp. 7.
P. 1, AW wrote, 'I have this in quarto, in' [sic] (i.e., Langbaine and Harrington, Wood 631(2)); p. 7, 'This case of the Univ. of Oxon. was drawn up on Tuesday 21. Jan. 1689[90] by Jam. Harrington B. of A. of ch. ch. whome the Vicech. had appointed, with a Bedle to wait on him, to attend at London – in opposition to the Towne party – But soon after, viz. 22. Jan. Dʳ Wallis arrived in London, in order to oppose the Towne party when the hearing was to be on the 24. Jan. (Friday) an. 1689[90]'. LT 3.322-4.
Wood 423(66). Wing C1175.

3435. [Harrington, James], 1664-93, and **Gerard Langbaine**. *A defence of the rights and priviledges of the university of Oxford: containing, 1. an answer [by G. Langbaine] to the petition of the city of Oxford. 1649. 2. The case of the university of Oxford [by J. Harrington]; presented to the honourable house of commons [24 Jan. 1690].* Oxford: at the theatre, 1690. 4°. 2 tpp. Pp. [8], 54.
Tp, AW wrote, 'Given to me by A. C. [Arthur Charlett] 23 Ap. 1690 Jam. Harrington author'. LT 3.322.
Wood 631(2). Wing L366.

3436. Harris, John. *The Puritanes impuritie: or the anatomie of a Puritane or seperatist.* London: T. Fawcet, 1641. 4°. Pp. [2], 6.
Wood 647(5). Wing H860.

3437. Harris, R[obert]. *Two letters written . . . in vindication of himselfe from the known slanders of an unknown author [T. Pierce in Pegasus].* [Oxford]: [L. Lichfield], 1648. 4°. Pp. 8.
Tp, AW wrote at t, 'Mr Rob: Harris President of Trinity Coll: in Oxford', 'Pegasus', and at a quote from a letter by W. T. who wished to publish this pamphlet, 'This was done by Mr Harris himselfe.' Response to Wood 514(49). LT 1.265.
Wood 514(51). Wing H879. Madan 1990.

3438. H[arris], W[alter]. *A farewel to popery: in a letter to dr. Nicholas.* London: f. W. Kettilby, 1679. 4°. Pp. [2], 41.
Tp, AW wrote after author's initials, 'Walter Harrys D^r of Physick.', and below, '6^d', and altered the year to 1679/8. Pp. 5, 6, 9, 10, 27, AW wrote notes, most were cropped at side, e.g., p. 5, at W. H.'s leaving his college to follow the example of Mr. R., 'he resigned h[is] Fellowship of New. Coll. Aug[ust] 1673.' and identified Mr. R., 'Mr Rich. Reeves schoolmaster of Magd. Coll.'; p. 6, at printed 'I [Harris] spent at Paris', AW wrote in the margin, '[wh]ere I thinke he [too]k his Doctors [de]gree of Physick.'; p. 10, at printed 'The *Author* of the guide in *Cantroversies* [sic] is no doubt an *Oxonian*', AW wrote 'he writes himself R. H. [/] I think not R. H.' (it is really Abr. Woodhead, Wing W3447A). LT 2.269-70.
[MS.] Wood B. 40(16). Wing H884.

3439. Harrison, Hen[ry]. *The last words of a dying penitent.* London: R. Taylor, 1692. 4°. Pp. [2], 31. LT 3.387.
Wood 365(35). Wing H892.

3440. Harrison, Henry*, and John Cole*. *The arraignment, tryal, conviction and condemnation of Henry Harrison, gent. for the barbarous murther of Andrew Clenche [and] the tryal of John Cole.* London: T. Braddyll, sold W. Battersby a. R. Baldwin, 1692. Fol. Pp. [3], 46 (2nd tp at p. 35).
P. 1, AW added a date, '4 Jan. 1691'. LT 3.381.
Wood 422(14). Wing A3765 ('O' not recorded in Wing).

3441. [Harrison, Robert]. *A strange relation of the suddain and violent tempest, which happened at Oxford May 31.* [Oxford?]: f. R. Sherlock in Oxford, 1682. 4°. Pp. [2], 12.
Flyleaf, upper, AW wrote, 'Harrison a poore child of Qu[eens] C. the authour. in June 1682'. LT 3.13, 17.
Wood 515(33a). Wing H908.

3442. Harrison, Thomas*. *Observations upon the last actions . . . of maj. gen. Harrison.* London: H. Lloyd a. R. Vaughan, 1660. 4°. Pp. [2], 18.
Wood 369(6). Wing O122 (Wing, Major General).

3443. Harrison, Thomas. *The speeches and prayers of some of the late king's judges, viz. major general [Thomas] Harison.* [London?]: n.pub., 1660. 4°. Pp. [4], 96.
Tp, AW wrote, 'Januar: v. MDCLX' [i.e., 1661]; ^v, slip, pasted in, 'D^r [Ralph] Bath[urst] hath told me that many of the things in this book were fathered [?] upon those that suffered' (LT 1.378). Pp. 62, 75, identifications, 'Col. James Turner, a steward hanged for a burghlory', 'Major Gen. Rich. Browne'.
Wood 369(5). Wing S4875.

3444. Harry, George Owen. *The genealogy of . . . James . . . king of Great Brittayne, &c. with his lineall descent from Noah.* London: S. Stafford f. T. Salisbury, 1604. 4°. Pp. [2], 1-40, 7 plates, pp. 49-67, and 2 plates.
AW numbered the first 4 [folio] plates, 41-47. Slip at pp. 60-1, 'Shrewsbury Castle Feb. 1659'. Listed as 'dup.' in MS. Wood E. 2(70), p. 42.
Wood 594(5). STC 12872.

3445. Harsnet, Samuel. York, abp. of. *A disco[very] of the fr[audu]lent practises of John [Darrel] . . . in his proceedings concerning the pretended possession and dispossession of William Somers.* London: [J. Windet f.] J. Wolfe, 1599. 4°. Pp. [8], 324, [4] (tp mutilated).
Tp, AW wrote, 'Sam. Harsnet the Author, afterwards Archb. of York.'
[MS.] Wood B. 19(2). STC 12883.

3446. H[arsnet], S[amuel]. York, abp. of. *A declaration of egregious popish impostures . . . practised by Edmunds, alias Weston a Jesuit, and divers Romish priests.* London: J. Roberts, 1603. 4°. Pp. [8], 283. Parchment.
Tp, AW underscored the name Edmunds in red ink; below, he wrote, 'The Author Sam. Harsnet, afterwards Archb. of Yorke'. Flyleaf^v and pastedown, lower, scribbles, not by AW.
[MS.] Wood C. 46. STC 12880.

3447. Harst, de. W., L., trans. *A panegyrick of . . . princess Christina, . . . queene of Swedland, Goths and Vandals*. London: f. T. Dring, 1656. 12°. Pp. [16], 75, 5.
Wood 260(2). Wing H923.

3448. Hartlib, Samuel. *The true and readie way to learne the Latine tongue*. London: R. a. W. Leybourn, 1654. 4°. Pp. [8], 52.
P. 52, scribble, not in AW's hand.
Wood 310(7). Wing H1002.

3449. Hartlib, Samuel. *The compleat husband-man: or, a discourse of the whole art of husbandry*. London: printed a. sold E. Brewster (f. R. Wodenothe), 1659. 4°. Pp. [8], 80 (i.e., 88), [6], '103-118', [26] (misnumbering) (3 tpp.).
Tp, bsm. Pp. 74ff., correction of p. nos., prob. not by AW.
Wood 618(7). Wing H980 ('O' not recorded in Wing).

3450. Harvey, Gabriel. *A new letter of notable contents. With a straunge sonet, intituled Gorgon, or the wonderfull yeare*. London: J. Wolfe, 1593. 4°. A-D⁴. Parchment.
Pastedown, upper, AW wrote, 'Liber AWood 1669'. Tp, bsm., 'i'. D2, vertical line in margin at reference to Greene and Marlow, in pencil, may be by AW.
[MS.] Wood B. 30(1). STC 12902.

3451. Harvey, Gabriel. *Pierces supererogation or a new prayse of the old asse, a preparative to . . . Nashes s. fame*. London: J. Wolfe, 1593. 4°. Pp. [22], 120 [i.e., 220], [14] (2 tpp).
*2, ***1ᵛ-***2, a mark and 2 vertical lines in pencil, one at reference to Oxford, may be by AW.
[MS.] Wood B. 30(2). STC 12903.

3452. Harvey, Richard. *An astrological discourse upon the great and notable conjunction of . . . Saturne & Jupiter, . . . the 28. day of April, 1583*. London: H. Bynneman (with the assent of R. W[atkins]), 1583. 8°. 2nd ed. ¶⁸,A-E⁸,F² (p. nos. cropped).
Wood 583(4). STC 12911 (two).

3453. Harward, Simon. *A discourse of the severall kinds and causes of lightnings*. London: J. Windet, sold J. Chorlton, 1607. 4°. A-C⁴.
Tp, AW underscored the name of the author in red ink; above, 'C 47' (a former shelf-mark?); ᵛ, A2, B4, scribbles, not by AW.
[MS.] Wood D. 28(2). STC 12918.

3454. Haslerig, Arthur. *A letter from sir Arthur Haselrigge . . . to an honourable member of the late parliament*. London: n.pub., 1659. 4° (cropped). Pp. 7.
Wood 632(38). Wing H1123.

3455. Haslerig, Arthur*. *Sir Arthur Hasilrig's meditations or, the devil looking over Durham*. [London]: n.pub., [1660]. S.sh.
AW added the date, 'ffeb: 1659[60]'.
Wood 276a(269). Wing S3874.

3456. Haslerig, Arthur*. *Sir Arthur Hesilrigs lamentation and confession. Upon his being voted from sitting in th[i]s long-expected parliament, Feb. 21. 1660*. London: E. Mason, 1660. 4° (inner and outer forms reset). Pp. 7.
Tp, AW altered 1660 in the t to 16'59', and in the imprint, to 16'59: ffeb:'. Diff. ed. at Wood 608(35).
Wood 610(27). Not in Wing. Not in ESTCR (not Wing S3872 , i.e., ESTCR 203734).

3457. Haslerig, Arthur*. *Sir Arthur Hesilrigs lamentation, and confession. Upon his being voted from sitting in this long expected parliament [21 Feb.]*. London: E. Mason, 1660. 4° (inner and outer forms reset). Pp. 7.
Tp, AW wrote 'Dupl.' Diff. ed. at Wood 610(27).
Wood 608(35). Wing S3872.

3458. Haslerig, Arthur*. *To the right honourable the parliament . . . The humble petition of Arthur Haslerig*. [London]: f. Any Body, [1660]. S.sh.
Dupl. at Wood 276a(199).
Wood 276a(190). Wing T1706D (3).

3459. Haslerig, Arthur*. *To the right honourable the parliament . . . The humble petition of Arthur*

Haslerig. [London]: f. Any Body, [1660]. S.sh.
AW wrote 'March: 1659[60]'. Dupl. at 276a(190).
Wood 276a(199). Wing T1706D (3).

3460. Haslerig, Arthur; Herbert Morley, and Valentine Walton. *The true copys of several letters from Portsmouth . . . by { col. sir Arthur Haslerig, col. Herbert Morley, col. Valentine Walton . . . to the lord Fleetwood.* London: J. Clowes, 1659. 4°. Pp. [2], 12, [1].
Tp, former no., '66', in pencil.
Wood 632(65). Wing T2609.

3461. Haslerig, Arthur, and Robert Lilburne. *A letter from . . . to . . . William Lenthal . . . of a great victory obtained by the parliaments forces in Northumberland. Together with colonel Lilburn's letter.* London: f. E. Husband, 1648, 7 July. 4°. Pp. 8.
Tp, AW wrote after the year, 'Jul. 1.'
Wood 502(34). Wing H1121.

3462. Haslock, John. *A true and perfect relation of the surrender of the . . . island of Scillie, to captain Batten.* London: B. I., 1646. 4°. A⁴.
Dupl. at Wood 612(42).
Wood 501(27). Wing H1120 (Wing, Hasclock).

3463. Haslock, John. *A true and perfect relation of the surrender of the . . . island of Scillie, to captain Batten.* London: B. I., 1646. 4°. A⁴.
Tp, AW wrote 'Dupl', above, and below, 'Aug', in pencil. Dupl. at Wood 501(27).
Wood 612(42). Wing H1120 (Wing, Hasclock).

3464. Hastings, Theophilus. Huntington, earl of. *Reasons for the indictment of the d. of York, presented to the grand-jury of Middlesex [26 June].* [London]: n.pub., [1680]. S.sh.
Wood 660c(22). Wing H3776.

3465. Haunce, Everard*. *A true report, of the araignement and execution of the last popishe traitour, Everard Haunce.* London: H. Bynneman, 1581. 8°. A-C⁴.
Tp and text, to C4ᵛ, some notes in Latin and English, cropped, in an earlier hand than AW's.
Wood 284(3). STC 12934.

3466. Haward, Lazarus. *A continuation of the diurnal occurrences and proceedings of the English army against the rebels in Ireland [1 Apr. to the present, 15 Apr.; 2 letters, the 1st by Lazarus Haward].* London: f. J. T[homas?], 1642. 4°. Pp. [2], 5, [1].
Dupl. at Wood 614(40).
Wood 508(8). Wing C5964.

3467. Haward, Lazarus. *A continuation of the diurnal occurrences and proceedings of the English army against the rebels in Ireland [1 Apr. to the present, 15 Apr.; 2 letters, the 1st by Lazarus Haward].* London: f. J. T[homas?], 1642. 4°. Pp. [2], 5, [1].
Tp, AW wrote 'Dupl', in pencil. Dupl. at Wood 508(8).
Wood 614(40-41). Wing C5964.

3468. Haward, Lazarus. *The charges issuing forth of the crown revenue of England, and dominion of Wales. With the severall officers of his majesties courts, customes, . . . with their severall fees.* London: f. M. Wright, 1660. 4°. Pp. [8], 55.
Tp, notes by former owners lined out: 'To Mʳ. H–', 'To Mʳ. Talbot', and below, 'Eliza Hales' (LT 3.99).
Wood 526(7). Wing H1164.

3469. Hawes, Stephen. *The historie of graund amoure and la bel pucell, called the pastime of pleasure.* (London): [W. Copeland f.] (R. Tottell), 1555. 4°. A-2D⁴ (wanting Q3-4 and 2 leaves of quire P).
Wood 336(3). STC 12951.

3470. Hawke, Michael. *Killing is murder, and no murder: or an exercitation concerning a scurrilous pamphlet, of one William Allen [i.e., S. Titus].* London: f. the author, sold at the Stationers shops, 1657. 4°. Pp. [8], 56.
Tp, a completion, and then a correction, of a ref. to Horace, '5', and over that, '8', may not be in AW's hand. Responds to S. Titus, Wood 631(14), item 6204.
Wood 631(15). Wing H1171A.

3471. Hawkins, John. *Discursus de melancholia hypochondriaca potissimum.* Heidelbergae: typ. W. Fitzeri, per D. Fuchs, 1633. 4°. Pp. 24.
Tp, bsm.
Wood 534(4). BL.

3472. Hawkins, John. *Particulae Latinae orationis, collectae.* London: ap. T. Harperum, 1635. 8°. Pp. [8], 199, [1].
Missing. MS. Wood E. 2(70), p. 16.
MS. Wood E. 2(70), p. 16. STC 12959. *BL.*

3473. H[awkins], R[ichard]. *A discourse of the nationall excellencies of England.* London: T. Newcomb f. H. Fletcher, 1658. 8°. Pp. [14], 248.
Flyleaves, upper, scribbles, not by AW. A6ᵛ, AW wrote out the name, H'awkins'. Text, some marks, corrections and brief notes, most apparently not by AW; e.g., pp. 6, 11 ('The End' prob. not by AW), 13, 14 ('British' for printed 'English'), 15-6, 82, 162 (not by AW), 168, 172, 185 (not by AW), 211, 240, 249. Acquired 6 Nov. 1661, 6ᵈ, LT 1.418.
Wood 686(2). Wing H1177.

3474. [Hawkins, William]. *Ecloga cui nomen pestifugium.* Londini: excud. A. M[athewes], imp. R. Milbourn, 1630. 4°. A⁴.
Wood 483(10). STC 12965 (two). Madan 653.

3475. [Hawles, John]. *The English-mans right. A dialogue between a barrister at law, and a jury-man.* London: f. R. Janeway, 1680. 4°. Pp. [2], 40.
Wood 629(6). Wing H1185.

3476. Hawles, John. *Remarks upon the tryals of Edward Fitzharris, Stephen Colledge, count Coningsmark, the lord Russel, collonel Sidney, Henry Cornish, and Charles Bateman. . . . on the earl of Shaftsbury's grand jury, . . . and the award of execution against sir Thomas Armstrong.* London: f. J. Tonson, 1689. Fol. Pp. [4], 104.
Tp, AW wrote, 'published about the middle of March 1688/9 – 2ˢ-6'. LT 3.294.
Wood 421(13). Wing H1188.

3477. Hawling. *The most true and wonderfull relation of a starre of a great magnitude, . . . that was seene at Haulin [2-4 Dec.].* London: f. F. Coles, 1658. 4°. Pp. [2], 6.
[MS.] Wood D. 28(10). Wing M2927 (two).

3478. H[ayes], J. *The compleat trades-man, or a guide for the true stating of any question touching interest or rebate . . . Or, certain numbers contracted.* London: f. J. Starkey, 1656. 12°. A⁶,B-D¹²,E⁶ (some leaves unopened). Pasteboard (grey) with parchment spine.
Flyleaf, upperᵛ, AW wrote the titles of 6 printed works in this volume, within guidelines made with red ink, and added the author's name to the 1st, 'J Hayes'. Tp, bsm.
Wood 21(1). Wing H1208A. ESTCR 188203 (rare).

3479. Hayne, Thomas. *A briefe discourse of the scriptures: declaring the . . . lives, . . . of the fathers, from the creation of Adam, unto the death of Joseph [not by T. Hayne].* London: W. White, 1614. 4°. Pp. [4], 121, [3].
Tp, signature of James Wither. Bsm.
[MS.] Wood B. 36(8). STC 12975.

3480. Hayne, Thomas. *Grammatices Latinae compendium, anno 1637.* London: E. Griffin f. A. Hebb, 1640. 8°. Pp. [16], 144.
Pp. [7-9], some underscoring and, at a brief history of Latin grammar books in England, AW marked with short vertical lines in margins, in red ink, some 25 printed lines which were later borrowed by J. Twells, see AW's note at 8° A 153(3) Art., item 6264, and see item 6648
Wood 42(2). STC 12978a.

3481. H[ayward], J[ohn]. *A treatise of union of . . . England and Scotland.* London: F. [Kingston] f. C. B[urby], 1604. 4°. Pp. [4], 58.
P. [4], underscoring of 7 lines on the reputation and kingship of James 1.
Wood 594(4). STC 13011.

3482. Hayward, J[ohn]. *The first part of the life and raigne of king Henrie the IIII.* London: J. Wolfe [i.e., J. Windet?], 1599 [i.e., 1610?]. 4°. Pp. [8], 149.

A3ᵛ, text mutilated and note in margin, cropped. Pp. 18, 113, 140, 146, short pencil line in margin, may not be by AW.
Wood 486(6). STC 12996.

3483. Hayward, John. *The life, and raigne of king Edward the sixt*. London: [Eliot's Court Press a. Oxford, J. Lichfield?] f. J. Partridge, 1630. 4°. Pp. [4], 179, [1]. Calf with 3 fillets, stamp decoration inside corners, and roll decoration at inner, spine edge (Ashm. binding).
Flyleaf, 2ndᵛ, list of 3 printed works in this vol., by an Ashm. librarian. 1st item, note cropped at bottom; bsm. Pp. 4, 6, 9, 18, 33, 46, 53, 86, 105, 129 short line in margin, in pencil, at, e.g., Sir Anthony Browne, Cardinall [R.] Poole, Doctor [R.] Pates, Doctor [R.] Coxe, Doctor [E.] Bonner, Sir Francis Bryan, Sir Peter Mewcas, [C.] Tonstall, and Mr. Body a commissioner in Cornwall.
Wood 485(1). STC 12998.

3484. Head, Richard. *The canting academy, or, the devils cabinet opened*. London: F. Leach f. M Drew, 1673. 12°. Pp. [7], 192, [16]. Calf with 2 fillets and a vertical line; rebacked.
K7, line in margin at a reference to Johannes à Casa in praise of sodomitry, in pencil.
Wood 745. Wing H1243.

3485. [Head, Richard]. *Jackson's recantation, or, the life and death of the notorius high-way-man*. London: f. T. B., 1674. 4°. 1,A-E⁴.
Flyleaf, upper, AW wrote, 'XI Septemb. 1685 Dedit mihi Paganus Piscator in cubiculo suo juxta le Fleet, London.', LT 3.160; ᵛ, a formal inscription by Payne Fisher within an engraved design: 'viro Multis nominibus Colendo Eruditiss. Humaniss. Dom. Antonio Wood Nup. Coll. Merton. OX. Socio Et istius Acad. Antiquitatum Scolasticarum Thesaurario, Recordatorique Fidissimo &c.', which AW corrected, twice: at 'Socio', he added 'nunquam fui socius. AW.', and at 'scolasticarum', he inserted an 'h', sc'h'olasticarum; below, a note by AW, cropped. Tp, he wrote, 'This book was written by Rich. Head a Bookseller in London'. E4ᵛ, after the printed postscript by Samuel Swiftnicks, AW wrote, 'Sam. Swiftnicks an Irish man & a great robber on the high way', and marked this note with red chalk.
Wood 372(13). Wing H1256.

3486. H[ead], R[ichard]. *Proteus redevivus: or, the art of wheedling, or insinuation, . . . by the author of the first part of the English rogue*. London: W. D., 1675. 8°. Pp. [16], 352. Calf, mottled, with 2 fillets; rebound [R.] H[arvey] 30 May 1952.
Tp, AW wrote 'Rich. Head'. Also '3.' (?).
Wood 753. Wing H1272.

3487. [Hearne, Robert]. *Obsequium & veritas: or a dialogue between London and Southwark, concerning . . . the last parliament, at Oxford, March 21st. 1681. In a dialogue betwixt a shoo-maker, and a taylor*. (London): (f. the author), (1681). S.sh. (r-v).
Former no. '18'.
Wood 657(53). Wing H1308.

3488. Heath, James. *An elegie upon dʳ Tho. Fuller [15 Aug. 1661]*. London: n.pub., 1661. S.sh.
ᵛ, AW wrote, 'Tho. Fuller 1661'.
Wood 429(17). Wing H1323 (two) (Wing, Dr.).

3489. Heath, James. *The glories and magnificent triumphs of . . . k. Charles II*. London: N. G., R. H., a. O. T., 1662. 8°. Pp. [22], 272 (2 pp. books printed for H. Brome). Calf with 2 fillets.
Flyleaf, upper, 'Pret: 1ˢ-4ᵈ', prob. in Allam's hand. Tp, bsm. Slip, pasted to lower flyleaf, to show author and short title while the book lies on its upper cover (see Index, 'Slip with title').
Wood 248. Wing H1335.

3490. H[eath], J[ames]. *A brief chronicle of the late intestine war in the three kingdoms*. London: J. Best f. W. Lee, 1663. 8°. 2nd impression. Pp. [19], 864, [32]. Calf with 2 fillets and also 2 vertical fillets (marbled edges).
Tpᵛ, signature of George Sheldon.
Wood 145. Wing H1320 ('O' not recorded in Wing).

3491. H[eath, Ja[mes]. *An elegy on the much lamented death of dʳ· Sanderson, late lord bishop of Lincolne [Jan. 1662]*. London: f. W. Gilbertson, 1663. S.sh.
ᵛ, AW wrote, 'Dʳ Sanderson Bishop of Linc.', and 'Dʳ Sanderson 1662'.
Wood 429(19). Wing H60 (rare) (Wing, Dr. and under H., J.).

3492. [Heath, James]. *Flagellum: or the life and death, . . . of O. Cromwell*. London: W. G. f. R. Taylor, 1665. 8°. 3rd ed. Pp. [8], 200.
Tp, bsms. A few lines in margin or underscoring, e.g., pp. 39, 44, 51, 55, 61-2, 69, 71, 73, 85, 88, 107, 115, 117.
Wood 243(4). Wing H1330.

3493. [Heath, Robert]. *A Machavillian plot, or, a caution for England [an information by sir R. Heath, 16 Nov. 1629, concerning the increasing of the king's revenue] presented in a time when princes were so pious*. London: n.pub., 1642. 4°. Pp. [2], 11.
Tp, no. 15 in a former bundle, lined out and replaced with no. 14 (or 18).
Wood 614(60). Wing H1339.

3494. Heers, Henry. *The most true and wonderfull narration of two women bewitched in Yorkshire . . . as it is attested uuder [sic] the hand of . . . Heers [in Observationes medicae oppido rarae]*. [London]: f. T. Vere a. W. Gilbertson, 1658. 8°. Pp. [2], 13.
Wood 707(7). Wing H1368 (rare).

3495. Hegg, Robert. Hall, John, ed. *In aliquot sacrae paginae loca lectiones. Ex autoris autographo manu-scripto fideliter transcriptae*. Londini: prostant vaenales ap. N. Webb a. G. Grantham, 1647. 4°. Pp. [4], 32.
Tp, AW wrote, '6ᵈ' and 'A: Wood' (latter is lined out).
[MS.] Wood B. 36(3). Wing H1369.

3496. [Hegg, Robert]. *The legend of st. Cuthbert with the antiquities of the church of Durham. By B. R.* London: f. C. Eccleston, 1663. 8°. Pp. [9], 93. Pasteboard (grey) with parchment spine; repaired. 1st flyleaf, trace of marbled paper; last flyleaf, marbled paper.
Flyleaf, 2ndᵛ, AW wrote the titles of 3 printed works in this vol., within guidelines made with red ink. Pp. 6, 8, 17, 19, 21-2, 31, 33, 34, etc. to 79, mainly brief corrections; p. 37, AW wrote on the death of Bede: 'translating in the time of his sickness Sᵗ Johns Gospell into English. &c. ms'. Acquired 8 Apr. 1664, 6ᵈ, LT 2.8.
Wood 216(1). Wing H1370.

3497. [Heinsius, Daniel]. *Emblemata amatoria: jam demum emendata*. [Amsterdam]: [D. Pietersz], [1612]. 4°. A-H⁴ (wanting F2; obl.). Parchment with 2 clasp holes.
Tp, 2 coats of arms, drawn.
Wood 114. NUC.

3498. Heinsius, Daniel. *Cras credo hodie nihil. Sive, modus tandem sit ineptiarum. Satyra Menippea*. Lugd. Batavorum: ex offic. Elzeviriana, 1621. 12°. Pp. [16], 101, [1]. Calf with 2 fillets; rebacked.
Flyleaf upper, AW wrote '18'.
Wood 767. BL.

3499. Heliodorus. Underdowne, Thomas, trans. *An Aethiopian historie*. London: H. Middleton f. F. Coldocke, 1577. 4°. Corrected. Ff. [4], 152. Parchment, rebound E.E.W. 31.1.45.
Ff. 12, 14, 16ʳ⁻ᵛ, 24ᵛ, 34ᵛ, 49, 54ᵛ, 66ᵛ, 67ᵛ, 81, 84ᵛ, etc., mark in margin, none may be by AW.
Wood 599. STC 13042 (two).

3500. Heliodorus. Crusius, Martin, ed. *Martinii Crusii Aethiopicae Heliodori historiae epitome*. Francofurti: J. Wechelus, imp. B. Jobini [Strasbourg], 1584. 8°. Pp. 388, [7], 67. Parchment with clasp holes.
Tp, '28 Julii 1637', not in AW's hand.
Wood 217. BL.

3501. Hell. *Hell broke loose: or, a catalogue of many of the spreading errors, heresies and blasphemies of these times*. London: f. T. Underhil, 1646[7], 9 March. 4°. Pp. 7.
Wood 647(15). Wing H1377.

3502. Hell. *Hell broke loose: or, an answer to the late . . . declaration of the phanatiques entituled, A door of hope, &c.* London: n.pub., 1661. 4°. Pp. [2], 21.
Tp, AW altered the year to 166'0'.
Wood 608(32). Wing H1378.

3503. Hell Broke. *Hell broke loose*. London: various publishers, 1646, 1651, or 1661. 4°.
Missing in 1841. At the short t, *Hell broke loose*, on the upper flyleaf, 'deest 1841 W. K[irtland]'. This may be *Hell broke loose: or, an answer*; or *Hell broke loose: or, a catalogue*; or *Hell broke loose: or the notorious*

design. AW had copies of the 1st two, at Wood 608(32) and Wood 647(15). Not identified. Wood 617(15). Wing H1377-H1379.

3504. Helwich, Christopher. Schuppius, Johann Balthasar, rev. [Lee, Samuel, ed.]. *Christophori Helvici, v.c. theatrum historicum et chronologicum. Accessit etiam tractatulus ad periodum Julianam.* Oxoniae: Excud. H. Hall, imp. J. Godwin, J. Adams, & E. Forrest, 1651. Fol. 5th ed. Pp. [22], 185, [19]. Calf with 2 fillets, a vertical line with 2 fillets and edge hatching; spine, 4 bands and hatching (Oxford binding). Pasteboard cover, upper, 'Antonius Woode, A.D. 16–', rubbed out. See AO 4.347. Wood 405. Wing H1412. Madan 2170.

3505. Henrietta, Queen. *A true relation of the queenes majesties returne out of Holland . . . written by one in the same storme.* Oxford: [H. Hall], 1643. 4°. Rpt. of York edition. Pp. [2], 13. Wood 375(43). Wing T3032. Madan 1335 (Wing, queene's).

3506. [Henripetri, Adam]. Stocker, Thomas, trans. *[A tragicall historie of the troubles and civile warres of the lowe countries, otherwise called Flanders [from Fr. of C. Ryckewaert (?) who signed the dedication Theophile]].* [London]: [J. Kyngston [a. T. Dawson] f. T. Smith], [1583]. 4°. a2-5,A-2H⁸. Ff. [4], 139, [1], 64 (wanting the tp and the final leaf). Parchment. Flyleaf, upperʳ, 4 signatures of 'Anthony Wood'; ᵛ, 'Mary Wood'. a2ʳ, '1ˢ'. Wood 595. STC 17450.3.

3507. Henry 3. France, king of. Aggas, E[dward], trans. *Directions from the king, to the governors of the provinces, concerning the death of the duke of Guyse [24 Dec. 1588].* London: J. Woolfe, 1589. 4°. A⁴. Wood 615(2). STC 13096.

3508. Henry 3. France, king of. *The French kinges declaration upon the riot, felonie, and rebellion of the duke of Mayenne, & the duke . . . of Aumalle.* London: [R. Ward] f. T. Cadman, 1589. 4°. Pp. [2], 18. Tp, 'H1' (cropped at top), a former shelf-mark(?). Wood 615(3). STC 13098.5.

3509. Henry 4. France, king of. *An answer to the reflections on the five Jesuits speeches. . . . Together with the speech of Henry IV. king of France in behalf of the Jesuits.* [London]: n.pub., [1679?]. Fol. Pp. 4. P. 4, AW wrote the date, 'Aug. 1679'. Wood 424(26). Wing A3441 ('O' not recorded in Wing).

3510. Henry 8. *A famous speech . . . made in the parliament house [24 Dec. 1545].* London: n.pub., 1642. 4°. A⁴. Tp, bsm. Wood 614(17a). Wing H1471.

3511. Henry 8*. *The pleasant and delightful history of king Henry 8th. and a cobler.* [London]: f. C. Dennisson, [1670?]. 12°. A⁸,B⁴ (2 tpp). Wood 254(11). Wing P2530 (two).

3512. Henry 8*. *The pleasant and delightful history of king Henry VIII. and the abbot of Reading.* London: J. M[illet] f. C. Dennisson, [1680?]. 8°. Pp. (4), 17, (3) (1 p. books sold by Dennisson) (2 tpp). Wood 254(10). Wing P2530A (two).

3513. Henshaw, Joseph. *Horae succisivae, or spare-houres of meditations.* London: G. D., sold J. Sweeting, 1650. 12°. 6th ed. Pp. [7], 268. Missing. MS. Wood E. 2(70), p. 5, 'J. H. Meditations Holy & humane in 12° 1650 – bound with a discourse of eternity Hawkins qu[aere] cat.' (see below, item 5479, Puget de la Serre, ed. H. Hawkins). MS. Wood E. 2(70), p. 5. Wing H1477C (rare). *BL*.

3514. Hentzner, Paulus, and Daniel Gruber. *Itinerarium Germaniae, Galliae, Angliae, Italiae:. . . Hic libro accessere . . . monita peregrinatoria duorum doctissimorum virorum [by D. Gruber]:. . . epitome praecognitorum historicorum.* Noribergae (Norimbergae): typ. A. Wagenmanni, sumpt. sui ipsius a. J. Güntzelii, 1629. 8°. Pp. [16], 614, 2Q-3B⁸,3C² and fold out table. Parchment. Pastedown, upper, 'AW'. Text, underscoring and marks in margin, not in AW's usual manner. Wood 157. *BL*.

3515. Herbert, Edw[ard]. *A short account of the authorities in law, upon which judgement was given in sir Edw. Hales his case.* London: f. M. Clark, 1688. 4°. Pp. 39. Tp, AW wrote, '8ᵈ – Dec. 12. an. 1688'. Pp. 3, correction (noted in the errata on p. 39), and 11, 2 corrections.

LT 3.190.
Wood 629(7). Wing H1496.

3516. Herbert, George. *The temple*. Cambridge: T. Buck a. R. Daniel, 1635. 12°. Pp. [8], 192, [3]. 4th ed. Calf with 4 fillets, one gold stamped; gold-stamped centrepiece.
Wood 93. STC 13187.

3517. Herbert, Philip*. Pembroke, 4th earl of. *The earle of Pembroke's speech in the house of peeres when the seven lords were accused of high-treason.* [London]: n.pub., 1648. 4°. Pp. [2], 6.
Missing since 1994.
Wood 531(16). Wing E79AB.

3518. Herbert, Philip*. Pembroke, 4th earl of. *Pembrokes passe from Oxford to his grave. [Followed by] The epitaph.* [London]: n.pub., [1648]. S.sh.
Missing since 1994.
Wood 531(21). Wing P1130 (two). Madan 1996.

3519. Herbert, Philip*. Pembroke, 4th earl of. *The manner of the election of Philip Herbert . . . for knight of the shire for Bark-shire. Together with two speeches, the one spoken by a wel-affected tanner : the other, a godly speech of his lordships, as it was heard with much content without an oath.* [London]: n.pub., 1649. 4°. Pp. [2], 6.
Missing since 1994.
Wood 531(17). Wing M467 ('O' not recorded in Wing).

3520. Herbert, Philip*. Pembroke, 4th earl of. *The earle of Pembrokes last speech.* London: n.pub., 1650. 4°. Pp. [2], 5, [1].
Missing since 1994.
Wood 531(18). Wing E79 ('O' not recorded in Wing).

3521. Herbert, Philip*. Pembroke, 4th earl of. *The life and death of Philip Herbert. Likewise a discourse with Charon in his voyage to Hell.* [London]: n.pub., [1650]. 4°. Pp. [8].
Missing since 1994. In Whiteside cat., 'Life & death of Philip Herbert E of Pembroke. wth other things relating to him'.
Wood 531(14). Wing L2007 ('O' not recorded in Wing).

3522. Herbert, Philip*. Pembroke, 4th earl of. *The last will and testament of the earl of Pembroke.* [London?]: n.pub., [1679]. Fol. Pp. 4.
Missing since 1994.
Wood 531(20). Wing L531A.

3523. Herbert, Philip. Pembroke, 4th earl of. *The earl of Pembrokes speech in the house of peers, when the seven lords were accused of high-treason.* N.p.: n.pub., [1680?]. Fol. Pp. 4.
P. 1, AW wrote 'Dupl', in pencil. Diff. ed. at Wood 531(16).
Wood 276a(153). Wing E79B.

3524. Herbert, Tho[mas]. *An answer to the most envious, scandalous, . . . pamphlet, . . . Mercuries message.* London: n.pub., 1641. 4°. Pp. [2], 6.
Tp, AW wrote, 'in verse'. Bsm.
Wood 366(24). Wing H1527.

3525. Herdson, Henry. *Ars mnemonica, . . . [2nd tp] Ars memoriae.* Londini: G. Dawson, 1651. 8°. Pp. [6], 92 (2nd tp, p. 65).
Wood 36(2). Wing H1546.

3526. Heresbach, Conrad. Googe, Barnaby, trans. *The whole art and trade of husbandry.* London: T. S[nodham] f. R. More, 1614. 4°. Ff. [11], 183. Parchment.
Flyleaf, upper, scribble, not by AW; [v], bsm. Flyleaf, lower[v], 'a/y' and 'g[?]/k' (?).
[MS.] Wood B. 41. STC 13201.

3527. Hermes. *Hermes Anglo-latinus: or, directions for young Latinists.* London: R. Hodgkinsonne f. T. Slater. (Imprim. T. Wykes), 1639. 12°. A2-12,B-F[12],G1-5 (wanting A1 (blank leaf?)). Pasteboard (brown) with calf spine.
Pasteboard, upper, AW wrote 'Dupl. in bib. [Arthur] Charlet', penciled out. Flyleaf, upper[v], AW wrote the titles of 4 printed works in this vol., within guidelines made with red chalk. Tp, bsm.

Wood 37(1). STC 13216.

3528. Herodian. [Maxwell?, James, trans.]. *Herodian of Alexandria his history of twenty Roman caesars and emperors.* London: [Eliot's Court Press a. M. Flesher] f. H. Perry, 1629. 4°. Pp. [24], 262, [2], 110. Parchment.
P. 127, scribbles in margin.
Wood 600. STC 13222.

3529. Heth, Thomas. *A manifest and apparent confutation of an astrological discourse [by R. Harvey] lately published . . . With a briefe prognostication, . . . of the conjunction of Saturn and Jupiter . . . the 29. of Aprill.* [London]: R. Walde-graue by the assignment of R. Watkins, [1583]. 8°. A1-7,B-E⁸,F1-3.
Wood 583(5). STC 13255.

3530. Hewes, John. *A perfect survey of the English tongue, taken according to the use and analogie of Latine.* London: E. All-de, f. W. Garret, (solde M. Lawes), 1624. 4°. A-Y⁴,Z².
At sig. D, on waste paper around quire, 'Dupl' (no duplicate in AW's collection). A few corrections in text, E2ᵛ, H3ᵛ, H4ᵛ.
Wood 310(10). STC 13260.

3531. Hewett, John. Canterbury. *A declaration from the Isle of Wyght, and county of Hampshire concerning the king: and the triall of captain Burley.* London: R. I., 1648. 4°. Pp. 6 (pp. 1-2 unopened).
AW wrote after the printed date, '47'.
Wood 501(39). Wing H1628 (Wing, Hewat).

3532. Hewit, John. *The speech and deportment of John Hewit . . . at the place of execution on Tower-hill, June 8 . . . with an elegie.* London: n.pub., 1658. 4°. Pp. 14, [2].
Wood 367(16). Wing H1638 (two).

3533. Hewit, John. *The true and exact speech and prayer of doctor John Hewytt. Upon the scaffold on Tower-hill, . . . June 8.* N.p.: n.pub., 1658. 4°. Pp. 8.
Wood 367(17). Wing H1639.

3534. H[ewlett], J[ohn]. *The description and use of a quadrant.* London: f. the author, 1665. 8°. Pp. [4], 54.
P. 1, 'Hewlet' in pencil; ᵛ, 'Hewlett of Oxon the author. A. m'. LT 1.508. Acquired 8 Mar. 1670, 6ᵈ, LT 2.189.
Wood 583(7). Wing H1643A (rare).

3535. Hewson, John*. *Colonel Huson's (or the cobler's) confession, in a fit of despair.* [London]: n.pub., [1659-60?]. 4°. Pp. 8.
Tp, AW wrote 'Januar: 1659:'.
Wood 610(28). Wing C5409.

3536. Hewson, John*. *The out-cry of the London prentices for justice to be executed upon John lord Hewson.* London: f. G. Adolphus, 1659. 4°. Pp. 7 (i.e., 8).
Tp, brief note, illeg.
Wood 608(53). Wing O598.

3537. Hewson, John*. *The coblers last will and testament: or, the lord Hewson's translation.* [London]: n.pub., [1660?]. S.sh.
AW wrote, 'January: 1659[60]:'; ᵛ, 'Jan. 59.', and '30' over a former no. '14' in pencil.
Wood 416(30). Wing C4785 (3).

3538. Hewson, John*. *Hewson reduc'd : or, the shoomaker return'd to his trade.* London: f. A. Rice, 1661. 4°. Pp. 8.
[MS.] Wood C. 31(2). Wing H1647 (rare, 2 at O).

3539. Hewson, M[ichael]. *A letter out of Ireland, from an eminent divine of the Church of England [M. Hewson] giving a full and true account of the sickness, death and funeral, of the late bishop of Chester [T. Cartwright].* (London): (f. R. Taylor), (1689). S.sh. (r-v).
AW wrote after t, 'Dʳ Tho. Cartwright'. In text, he underscored March 12 and Palm-Sunday and wrote in margins, '11' (later lined out) and 'Palm Sunday was on the 13 of Apr - 1689'. ᵛ, after 'Hewson', 'Hewetson' (may not be by AW).
Wood 510(36). Wing H1646 ('O' not recorded in Wing).

3540. Hexham, Henry. *A true and briefe relation of the famous seige of Breda.* Delft: J. Moxon, sould H. Hondius, 1637. 4°. Pp. [8], map foldout, 46, 16, [4].
Pp. 1, date, cropped; 12-3, underscoring.
Wood 635(7). STC 13265.

3541. [Heylyn, Peter]. *Augustus. Or, an essay of those meanes and counsels, whereby the commonwealth of Rome was . . . reduced unto a monarchy.* London: B. A[lsop] a. T. F[awcet] f. H. Seile, 1632. 12°. Pp. [10], 227, [1].
P. 1, signature, lined out.
Wood 735(3). STC 13268.

3542. Heylyn, Peter. *The historie of that most famous saint and souldier . . . s^t· George of Cappadocia; . . . [With] The institution of the . . . order of . . . the garter.* London: T. Harper f. H. Seyle, 1633. 4°. Pp. [18], 429, [2]. (2nd ed.) (pp. unopened). Pasteboard (blue) with parchment spine; rebacked.
Flyleaf, upper, 2nd^v, AW wrote the titles of 5 printed works in this vol., within guidelines made with red ink. Tp, at year, 'P. H.' LT 1.440.
Wood 536(1). STC 13273.

3543. Heylyn, Peter. Μικροκοσμος: *A little description of the great world.* Oxford: W. Turner, sold [M. Allot, London], 1636. 4°. 7th ed. Pp. [20], 808, [1]. Calf with 3 fillets and edge hatching; and spine, 4 bands (Oxford binding).
Flyleaf, mutilated, some figures in addition remain. P. [9], a correction in the index. P. 77-80, marks in margin and 2 notes, in pencil, may not be by AW.
Wood 469. STC 13282. Madan 830.

3544. [Heylyn, Peter]. Hall, Robert, pseud. ΗΡѠΟΛΟΓΙΑ [sic] *Anglorum. Or, an help to English history . . . By Robert Hall.* London: T. a. R. Cotes, f. H. Seile, 1641 [altered to 1651]. 12°. Pp. [6], 379. Tpp at pp. 9, 49, 161, 181. Calf with 2 fillets and also 2 vertical fillets; rebacked.
Flyleaf, upper^v, AW wrote, 'This edit. is to be kept, because in those following which came out after the authors death are many mistakes as to time –', in red ink; below, '1641', in black ink, may not be by AW. Tp, after author, AW wrote 'alias Peter Heylyn.', in red ink. Pp. 13, 16, underscoring; 30, 70, 108, 168, 182, 204, AW added to lists or corrected, e.g., to arch-bishops of York, '1641. Jo. Williams'.
Wood 186. Wing H1713.

3545. [Heylyn, Peter]. *A briefe relation of the remarkeable occurrences in the northerne parts: viz. the landing of the queenes majestie.* [Oxford]: H. Hall, 1642[3]. 4°. Pp. [2], 12.
Tp, AW lined out a former no. and wrote 'written by Dr Pet. Heylyn.'
Wood 375(44). Wing H1686. Madan 1265.

3546. [Heylyn, Peter]. *A letter from an officer in his majesties army, to a gentleman in Glocester-shire, upon occasion of certain querees.* [Oxford]: [L. Lichfield], 1643. 4°. Pp. [2], 15.
Tp, '10 Apr.', prob. not by AW; margin, 2-lines of verse, smudged, 'A loyall hart fixed in a subjects brast [/] is like the gold of Opher lockt in a silver chest', not in AW's hand. Bsm.
Wood 632(8). Wing H1724. Madan 1350.

3547. [Heylyn, Peter]. *A letter to a gentleman of Leicester-shire, shewing, out of the publicke writings which have passed betwixt his majestie and . . . parliament.* [Oxford]: [H. Hall], 1643. 4°. Pp. [2], 29.
Tp, AW wrote a former no., '28', in ink; and 'Beg. of 1643', in pencil.
Wood 375(46). Wing H1725. Madan 1348.

3548. [Heylyn, Peter]. *Lord have mercie upon us: or, a plaine discourse declaring that the plague of warre, . . . tooke its beginning in . . . London.* [Oxford]: [H. Hall], 1643. 4°. Pp. [2], 49.
Wood 376(72). Wing H1726. Madan 1486.

3549. Heylyn, Peter. *The rebells catechism.* [Oxford]: [L. Lichfield], 1643[44]. 4°. Pp. [2], 29 (misnumbering). Rough calf with 3 fillets, stamp decoration inside corners (2 leaves, flower and point), and roll decoration at inner, spine edge (Ashm. binding).
Flyleaf, upper, 2nd, the titles of 21 printed works in this vol., by an Ashm. librarian. No. 15 was removed before 1841. Tp, AW wrote 'By Peter Heylyn D. D.' and below, 'Septemb: xxij A.D. MDclx'. P. 5-6, 2 corrections. LT 1.332.
Wood 617(1). Wing H17131. Madan 1543.

3550. [Heylyn, Peter]. *A briefe relation of the death and sufferings of the . . . archbishop of Canterbury.*

Oxford: [H. Hall], 1644[5]. 4°. Pp. [2], 30.
Tp, AW wrote, 'By Pet. Heylyn D.D.'; pp. 8-10, added some brief reference notes; and 23, identified Hinde: 'Joh. Hinde'. P. 28, scribbles. Dupl. at Wood 486(13).
Wood 366(29). Wing H1685. Madan 1722.

3551. [Heylyn, Peter]. *A briefe relation of the death and sufferings of the . . . archbishop of Canterbury.*
Oxford: [H. Hall], 1644[5]. 4°. Pp. [2], 30.
Dupl. at Wood 366(29).
Wood 486(13). Wing H1685. Madan 1722.

3552. Heylyn, Peter. *Extraneus vapulans: or the observator rescued from the violent . . . assaults of Hamon L'Estrange [in his Observator observed] and . . . dr. Bernard.* London: J. G. f. R. Lowndes, 1656. 8°. Pp. [14], 351, [1]. Calf with 2 fillets; rebacked.
Flyleaf, upper, A. Allam wrote 'pret. 1ˢ-2ᵈ.' Tp, bsm. LT 3.167.
Wood 663. Wing H1708.

3553. [Heylyn, Peter]. *Observations on the historie of the reign of king Charles: published by H. L.*
London: f. J. Clarke, 1656. 8°. Pp. [10], 249, [14].
Flyleaf, upperᵛ, AW listed the work Heylyn responded to, 'The history of the raigne of K. Charles was published by Hammon L'estrange in fol – which I have elsewhere' (at Wood 407(2); see note at Wood 244(1), items 4104, 1770). P. 216, AW wrote 'Jenny Rider' at printed Ginne Rider. Dupl. at Wood 269.
Wood 244(4). Wing H1727.

3554. [Heylyn, Peter]. *Observations on the historie of the reign of king Charles: published by H. L.*
London: f. J. Clarke, 1656. 8°. Pp. [8], 249, [16]. Calf with 2 fillets and also 2 vertical fillets.
Waste paper fragment, upper, 'Mʳ Allum hath this sticht'. Tp, bsm. Pp. 119-21, 132, 219, 227, lines in margin in ink and pencil; pp. 36, identification of Bishop of Lincolne, 'Jo. Williams', and 224, at a reference to a ms., 'De jure Paritatis Episcoporum', AW wrote, 'pend by the authour of this booke'. Dupl. at Wood 244(4).
Wood 269 (not in Bodl. CD cat.). Wing H1727.

3555. [Heylyn, Peter]. *A short view of the life and reign of king Charles.* London: f. R. Royston, 1658. 12°. Pp. [3], 96.
Tp, AW wrote, 'By Pet. Heylyn D D.'
Wood 244(3). Wing H1735.

3556. Heylyn, Peter. *Certamen epistolare, or, the letter-combate. Managed by Peter Heylyn, d.d. with 1. mʳ· Baxter [in reference to the Grotian religion discovered] 2. Dʳ· Barnard [&c.].* London: J. M. f. H. Twyford, T. Dring, a. J. Place, 1659. 8°. Pp. [16], 397, [2]. Calf with 2 fillets.
Wood 719. Wing H1687.

3557. Heylyn, Peter. *Historia quinqu-articularis: or, a declaration of the judgement of the western churches . . . reproched in these last times by the name of Arminianism.* London: E. C. f. T. Johnson, 1660. 4°. Pp. [32], 80, 112, [2], 110, [15] (3 pts.). Calf, speckled, with 2 fillets and a vertical line of 2 fillets.
Flyleaf, upper, 2nd, signature of 'Edw: Poole:'. P. 26, a cross-reference, prob. not by AW.
[MS.] Wood C. 45. Wing H1721.

3558. Heywood, John. *A dialogue conteinyng the nomber in effect of all the proverbes in the Englishe tongue.* Londini: (T. Berthelet), 1546. 4°. A-K⁴,L1-5.
Missing. MS. Wood E. 2(70), p. 41. AW also owned a 1598 ed., in Wood 335.
MS. Wood E. 2(70), p. 41. STC 13291 (two). *Hunt.*

3559. Heywood, John. *The workes of John Heiwood newlie imprinted.* London: F. Kingston, 1598. 4°. A-2C⁴ (2nd tp at L1; 3rd, at R1; 4th, at X2; 5th at 2A1ᵛ). Parchment cover, a ms. text of law French.
Tp, bsm. Cover, lower, inside, signatures of John Upton.
Wood 335. STC 13289.

3560. H[eywood], T[homas]. *[Philocothonista, or, the drunkard, opened, . . . and anatomized [signed Tho. Faenilignam]].* [London]: [R. Raworth], [1635]. 4°. Pp. [4], 91 (defective, wanting all before sig. ¶3). ¶3, AW wrote, '1604 qu[aere]' (the copy was defective when he acquired it). P. 1, note or scribble, in Latin, in red ink, illeg.
[MS.] Wood D. 30(6). STC 13356.

3561. Heywood, Thomas. *Porta pietatis, or, the port or harbour of piety. Exprest in sundry triumphes,*

. . . at the initiation of . . . sir Maurice Abbot . . . into the majoralty of . . . London. London: J. Okes, 1638. 4°. A-B⁴,C².
Wood 537(14a). STC 13359.

3562. Heywood, Thomas. *A true discription of his majesties royall and most stately ship called the Soveraign of the Seas.* London: J. Okes, 1638. 4°. Pp. [2], 50 (wanting the frontisp. and sigs. A3,4).
[MS.] Wood C. 13(4). STC 13368.

3563. [Heywood, Thomas]. *A true relation, of the lives and deaths of . . . English pyrats, Purser, and Clinton.* London: J. Okes, 1639. 8°. A2-8,B⁸,C1-7 (2nd tp at B5).
Wood 284(4). STC 20512 (rare).

3564. Heywood, Th[omas]. *Englands Elisabeth: her life and troubles.* Cambridge: R. Daniel, sold J. Sweeting, 1641. 12°. Pp. [12], 201.
Wood 258(2). Wing H1779.

3565. H[eywood], T[homas]. *The life of Merlin, sirnamed Ambrosius. His prophecies.* London: J. Okes, sold J. Emery, 1641. 4°. Pp. [63], 376. Calf with 3 fillets; rebacked.
Flyleaf, upper, first, torn out, traces of notes remain. Tp, 'A:Woode. 1655.'
Wood 348. Wing H1786.

3566. [Heywood, Thomas]. *A preparative to studie: or the vertue of sack.* London: n.pub., 1641. 4°. Pp. [2], 5.
Tp, bsm.
[MS.] Wood D. 30(9) (not in Bodl. CD cat.). Wing H1790 ('O' not recorded in Wing).

3567. H[eywood], T[homas]. *The famous and remarkable history of sir Richard Whittington.* London: f. W. Thackeray a. T. Passinger, [1686-88]. 4°. A⁸,B⁴, only (pp.15-24), wanting pp. 1-14.
Wood 254(5). Wing H1782 (3).

3568. Hickathrift, Thomas*. *The pleasant history of Thomas Hickathrift.* [London]: f. W. Thackeray, a. T. Passinger, [1687-8]. 8°. Pp. [4], 18, [2].
Wood 259(11). Wing P2551E (rare).

3569. Hickeringill, Edm[und]. *Jamaica viewed.* London: f. J. Williams, 1661. 8°. 2nd ed. Pp. [16], 87.
Tp, AW wrote, '7ᵈ'; bsm. A6, AW wrote, 'The island Jamaica belongeth properly to the Earl of Veraguo, who is lineally descended from Christoph. Columbus the discoverer of the Indies, and not to the Duke of Modina, as was by some conceiv'd. The length of the island is computed to be from Pinea Morante East, to Punta Negrillo West, to be 50 leagues, and the breadth from Laguaya south, or S. Iago to the port of Sᵗ Anna Sevill towards the north about 20 leagues.'
Wood 156(4). Wing H1817.

3570. Hickeringill, Edmund. *Curse ye Meroz, or the fatal doom. In a sermon [9 May].* London: J. R. f. J. Williams, 1680. 4°. Pp. [8], 38.
Wood 633(17). Wing H1803.

3571. Hickeringill, Edmund*. *Observations on a late famous sermon [by E. Hickeringill], intituled, Curse ye Meroz.* London: n.pub., 1680. 4°. Pp. 8.
Wood 633(18). Wing O100.

3572. [Hickeringill, Edmund]. *Reflections on a late libel, intituled, Observations on a late famous sermon. [Together with, p. 39:] Hugh Peters's sermon [in verse; signed A. B. on p. 45].* London: f. J. Williams, 1680. 4°. Pp. [2], 45.
Wood 633(19). Wing H1824.

3573. [Hickes, George]. *Ravillac redivivus, being a narrative of the late tryal of mʳ· James Mitchel a conventicle-preacher, who was executed the 18th of January.* London: H. Hills, 1678. 4°. Pp. 78.
Tp, bsms.
Wood 365(26) (not in Bodl. CD cat.). Wing H1860.

3574. [Hickes, George]. *The spirit of popery speaking out of the mouths of phanatical-protestants, or the last speeches of mr. John Kid and mr. John King, . . . executed . . . With . . . the history of the archbishop of St. Andrews [James Sharp] his murder.* London: H. Hills, sold W. Kittleby, 1680. Fol. Pp. [12], 73, [6].
Tp, bsm. Dupl. at Wood 560(3).

Wood 422(6-7). Wing H1874.

3575. [Hickes, George]. *The spirit of popery speaking out of the mouths of phanatical-protestants, or the last speeches of mr. John Kid and mr. John King, . . . executed . . . With . . . the history of the archbishop of St. Andrews [James Sharp] his murder.* London: H. Hills, sold W. Kittleby, 1680. Fol. Pp. [12], 73, [6]. Tp, bsm. P. 11, ms. extract from the London *Gazette*, not in AW's hand. Dupl. at Wood 422(6). Wood 560(3). Wing H1874.

3576. [Hickes, George]. *A word to the wavering: or an answer to the enquiry . . . Whether we owe allegiance to the king in these circumstances?* London: n.pub., 1689. 4°. Pp. [2], 10 (pp. unopened). Tp, AW wrote, '6. Feb. 1688 - 3 [d.]'. Responds to G. Burnet Wood 529(21), item 1202. Wood 529(22). Wing H1878A.

3577. Hickes, William. *Oxford jests.* London: ?, 1675. 12°. Missing in 1837. 'Oxford Jests – Lond. 1675' in Whiteside cat. In his Diary, LT 2.176, AW wrote that this work came out in a 2nd ed. in 8° in Nov. 1669. Wood 56. Not in Wing. See Wing H1891-2; and Madan 3037 (and 2815, 2873). Not in ESTCR.

3578. Hickman, Hen[ry]. Πατρο-σχολαστικο-δικαιωσις, *or a justification of the fathers . . . an answer to . . . Tho. Pierce's . . .* Αυτοκατακρισις. *[Followed by] An advertisement . . . concerning a clause in ď Heylins examen historicum.* Oxford: H. Hall. f. J. Adams a. E. Forrest, 1659. 8°. 2nd ed. Pp. [68], 110, [14]. Calf with 3 fillets; flyleaf, upper and lower, printer's waste paper.
Flyleaf, upper, 2nd, AW wrote 'This book is mostly composed & patched up from 1. Dr Pet. Heylyns Antidot. Lync. 2. From Mr Will. Morice of Werrington his book called New inclosures broken downe 3. From severall- books of Joh. Goodwyn. 4. From Will. Prynnes Canterb. doome [Wood 540, item 5430] And from others without acknowledgment [/] See in Mr Tho. Pierce his letter to Dr Heylyn concerning Mr Hickman, at the end of his new discover[i]es discovered p. 280. 281. &c. where is shewed that he composed much of this book from those 4 & others.' (most of this is in AO 4.369); ^v, note in a modern hand. I6^v, underscoring, in pencil, may not be by AW. Pastedown, lower, scribble, not by AW.
Wood 804. Wing H1912. Madan 2443.

3579. H[ickman], H[enry]. *Plus ultra: or Englands reformation, needing to be reformed. Being an examination of doctor Heylins history . . . by H. N., O. I. Oxon.* London: f. the authors, 1661. 4°. Pp. [4], 52 (misnumbering).
Tp, AW underscored the initials of the author, in red ink.
[MS.] Wood D. 23(9). Wing H1913.

3580. [Hickman, Henry]. *Apologia pro ministris in Angliā (vulgo) non-conformistis, ann: 1662. Aug. 24 . . . ejectis adversus argutiolas . . . Durelli, Ellisii, aliorumque. Per Irenaeum Eleutherium.* Eleutheropoli: n.pub., 1664. 8°. Pp. [12], 144.
Tp, price, not by AW.
Wood 795(5). Wing H1904.

3581. Hide, Thomas. *A consolatorie epistle to the afflicted catholikes.* Lovaine [really East Ham]: J. Lyon [Greenstreet House], 1580. 8°. 1,A-G^8 (last leaf blank).
Some underscoring and marks in margin, not in the manner of AW.
Wood 800(4). STC 13377. ARCR 2.431.

3582. Hierocles of Alexandria. Hall, John, trans. *Hierocles upon the golden verses of Pythagoras.* London: J. Streater f. F. Eaglesfield, 1657. 8°. Pp. [48] (i.e., a^8,B^8,A^8), 177. Calf with 2 fillets.
AW numbered odd pp., 1-21, in the biographical introduction of Hall; wrote 1 identification, 'T. White'; and made numerous vertical lines in margins at bibliographical items, as on A1 (his p. 19), at a printed comment on E. Benlowes's 'debauches & intemperance which diverted' him from scholarship. LT 2.361. AO 2.457ff.
Wood 744. Wing H1938.

3583. [Hierro, Augustin de]. Howell, James, trans. *The process, and pleadings in the court of Spain upon the death of Anthonie Ascham.* London: W. Du-Gard, 1651. 4°. Pp. [4], 15.
Tp, 'Jam. Howell hath a thin fol. extant concerning this matter'. P. 11, line in margin at name of William Sparks.
Wood 365(11). Wing H1944 ('O' not recorded in Wing).

3584. Higford, William. *Institutions or advice to his grandson.* London: T. Warren f. E. Thorn of Oxford,

1658. 8°. Pp. [12], 97 (3 pts.). Calf with 2 fillets and a vertical line; flyleaves, 1st upper and last lower, printer's waste paper.
Flyleaf, upper, 2nd, scribble; ᵛ, AW wrote 'published by Clem. Barksdale', in red ink (smudged, see AO 3.429; 4.225) and 'reprinted 1675 vd [vide]' in pencil (not in Wing). Pp. [4], AW wrote 'Cl. Barksdale'; 86, correction, not by AW. Acquired 9 Feb. 1667, 8ᵈ, LT 2.98.
Wood 737. Wing H1947 (Wing, institutions; or,).

3585. Higgens, John*. *A sad, but a true relation of a person who . . . was found dead in a wood near Highgate [15 Feb.].* (London): (G. Croom), (1685/6). Fol. Pp. 3.
P. 1, AW wrote, '1685'.
[MS.] Wood D. 23(7). Wing S249 (two).

3586. H[igginson], F[rancis]. *A brief relation of the irreligion of the northern Quakers.* London: T. R. f. H. R., 1653. 4°. Pp. [10], 36.
Tp, former no. '4'.
Wood 645(2). Wing H1953.

3587. Higgs, Griffin, resp. *Miscellaneae theses theologicae.* Lugduni Batavorum: ex offic. B. & A. Elzevir, 1630. 4°. A⁴.
For Higgs, see notes and references at Almanacs, Comptoir, Wood 498(14).
[MS.] Wood B. 36(12). Not in BL. Not in NUC.

3588. Hilary, Saint*. *Sᵗ. Hillaries teares shed upon all professions, . . . written by one of his secretaries that had nothing else to do.* London: n.pub., 1642. 4°. Pp. 8.
Wood 654a(6). Wing T508.

3589. Hildebrandt, Andreas. L., S., trans. *The genealogie and pedigree of the . . . kings in Sueden . . . from the yeare 1250.* London: [J. Beale] f. J. Boler, 1632. 4°. 1,A-E⁴ (E4 blank).
Tp, bsm.
Wood 487(3). STC 13458.

3590. Hilgard. Nun. *A strange prophecie, against bishops, prelates, . . . written by Hilgard a nunne, 1558.* London: J. Thomas, 1641. 4°. A⁴.
[MS.] Wood D. 31(12). Wing H1983.

3591. Hill, Lawrence*. *An account of, (together with) the writing it self that was found in the pocket of Lawrence Hill, at the time he and Green were executed.* (London): (f. R. Pawlet), (1679). Fol. Pp. 3.
P. 2, AW wrote, 'The notes following were written by Will. Scroggs Lord Ch. Justice of the Kings bench'.
Wood 424(9). Wing A425 ('O' not recorded in Wing).

3592. Hill, Miles. *A true and impartiall account of the plunderings, losses, and sufferings of . . . Hereford by the Scottish army . . . during their siege . . . 1645.* London: E. G. f. L. C., 1650. 4°. Pp. [2], 14.
Tp, AW lined out the former no., '19'. Bsm.
Wood 378(22). Wing H2004.

3593. [Hill, Thomas], Londoner. Dethick, Henry, ed. *The gardeners labyrinth:. . . gathered out of the best approved writers . . . by Dydymus Mountaine [pseud.].* London: J. Wolfe, 1586. 4°. Pp. [6], 80, [8], 180, [12]. Parchment.
Flyleaves, upper, 7 signatures of Edward Withington, and a 'Thomas'.
[MS.] Wood C. 16. STC 13487.

3594. Hill, Thomas. *Naturall and artificiall conclusions. Compiled first in Latine, by . . . authors, . . . of the . . . university of Padua . . . and divers other places.* London: J. Bell, 1650. 8°. A2-8,B-G⁸.
Wood 727(2). Wing H2018 (two).

3595. Hill, William. *A brief narrative of that stupendious tragedie late intended to be acted by the satanical saints.* London: n.pub., 1663. 4°. Pp. [8], 48.
Tp, 'Anthony à Wood E Coll. Mert. Oxon. 23. Jan. 1662/3'. P. [1], AW wrote 2 notes, e.g., about Hill's father, 'an excise or committee man in Herefordsh.'; p. [8], notes on the author, William Hill: 'somtimes bible Clerk of Merton Coll. in Oxon. a notorious informer against the Cavaliers while in that College, & alwaies readie to bring that College into division & Combustion. from an. 1640 to 1651'. AO 3.801; LT 1.467.
Wood 368(19). Wing B4612.

3596. Hilliard, John. *Fire from heaven. Burning the body of one John Hittchell of Holne-hurst . . . With the fearefull burning . . . of Dorchester [6 Aug.].* London: [E. Allde] f. J. Trundle, 1613. 4°. A-C⁴. [MS.] Wood D. 28(4). STC 13507.3 (two).

3597. Hilton, John. *Catch that catch can, or a choice collection of catches, rounds, & cannons.* London: f. J. Benson a. J. Playford, 1652. Sixes. Pp. [10], 123. With a number of interleaved blanks. Calf with 3 fillets, 1 metal clasp; rebacked.
Cover, upper, inside, 'Anthony Wood [/] 1667 [/] Ant: à Wood', and scribbling. After certain quires, blank leaves with ms. scoring for tunes. Before tp, 3 blank leaves on which AW wrote music scores, with titles of songs at top: 'In a season: [/] From that fair lane: [/] our sweet mall: [/] Boat a boat: [/] Why so pale [/] Har- [?] now Bell, [/] Sʳ Eglam[ore]'; A5-6, index, some songs marked. After A5, 3 ms. pages, with words and score for 'drink to night of the moone shine bright . . . (see the printed version on p. 35), and score, 'The Ground.' After p. 36, score only, 1 p. After p. 60, score only, 1 p. After p. 96, scores and words, 4 pp.: 'Mark how these knavish rests good earnest makes of jests . . . Mʳ Cranford.', 'Boy come back & let the wine alone for wee have drunk the captaines health . . . ', and 'Kisse mine arse was a marchants man & dwelt in Lumbard street Licke my hole was his owne kinsman Tis merry tis merry when mault men meet Turd upon thy face sow smothe pop thy nose in mine arse pop in mine arse for sooth'. Final inserted leaf, some brief notes on scores (LT 1.18).
Wood 126 (not in Bodl. CD cat.). Wing H2036.

3598. Hinckley, John. *Two sermons.* Oxford: H. Hall f. R. Davis, 1657. 12°.
Missing. 19 Oct. 1657, 'I exchanged these following bookes in sheets with Mr. Forrest, for . . . [sic]: . . . Hinclye's 'Sermons', 8° . . . All amounting to a crowne'. LT 1.230.
LT 1.230. Wing H2049. Madan 2338.

3599. Hind, James. *The humble petition of James Hind . . . together with the speech and confession of the bishop of Clonwel [sic, i.e., Clonmel].* London: f. G. Horton, 1651. 4°. Pp. [2], 6. Pasteboard (blue) with parchment spine. 1st upper and last lower flyleaves, marbled paper. Rebound by E.E.W. 7.5.45.
Flyleaf, upper, 3rdʳ⁻ᵛ, AW wrote the titles of 18 printed works in this vol., within guidelines made with red ink. LT 1.155.
Wood 372(1). Wing H2052.

3600. Hind, James*. *No jest like a true jest: . . . mad exploits of capt James Hind.* London: f. J. Deacon, [1657]. 8°. A⁸, B⁴.
Tp, AW wrote, '1657'. LT 1.155.
Wood 284(8). Wing N1177 (Wing, [1672]). (ESTCR 26880, [1657]).

3601. [Hinde, Thomas](?). *Directions for the use of this famous, . . . cordial drink.* N.p.: n.pub., [1673 ca.]. S.sh.
AW wrote, 'This water was first brought into Oxford 1673. 3ˢ half pint.' LT 2.277.
Wood 276a(34) (not in Bodl. CD cat.). Wing D1536 (rare).

3602. Hinde, Thomas. *Under God. Humbly desiring his blessing to this famous . . . cordial drink.* [N.p.]: n.pub., [1673]. S.sh.
AW added the date, '1673'.
Wood 276a(33) (not in Bodl. CD cat.). Wing H2062 (rare).

3603. Hinde, William. *A faithfull remonstrance of the holy life . . . of John Bruen.* London: R. B. f. P. Stephens, a. C. Meredith, 1641. 8°. Pp. [14], 227, [9]. Calf with 2 fillets; rebacked. Flyleaves, printer's waste paper.
Flyleaf, upper, 2ndᵛ, AW wrote, 'Johannes Bruen Cestreus. Generosi filius annorum 18, matriculatus fuit in Univers. Oxon. Decemb. 20 a° 1577. Ex aula Albana.' Tp, bsm. P. 174, cross mark in margin, in pencil, prob. not by AW. Flyleaf, lower, 1stᵛ, note in French, not by AW.
Wood 303. Wing H2063.

3604. Hippolytus, Saint. Scaliger, Joseph Juste, ed. *Hippolyti episcopi canon paschalis: cum Josephi Scaligeri commentario. . . . Josephi Scaligeri elenchus & castigatio anni Gregoriani.* Lugduni Batavorum: ex off. Plantiniana, ap. F. Raphelengium, 1595. 4°. Pp. [12], 78. Calf, rough, with 3 fillets, stamp decoration inside corners. and roll decoration at inner, spine edge (Ashm. binding).
Flyleaf, upper, 2ndᵛ, list of 6 printed works in this vol., by an Ashm. librarian.
Wood 481(1). BL.

3605. Histoire. *Histoire contenant en bref toutes les choses plus memorables, que sont passees depuis l'an*

de grace 1500. jusques à l'an present 1629. Paris: En Anvers. Chez Guillaume, 1629. 16°. A-D^{8,4} (the quire of ^{4}, which is a table giving sunrises and sunsets, may not belong to this book).
Wood 2(3) (not in Bodl. CD cat.). Not in BL. Not in BN. Not in NUC.

3606. Histoire. *Histoire: contenant en bref toutes les choses plus memorables, qui sont passée depuis l'an de grace 1500. jusques à l'an present 1631.* Paris: En Anvers. Chez Guillaume, 1631. 16°. A-D^8.
Wood 3(3) (not in Bodl. CD cat.). Not in BL. Not in BN. Not in NUC.

3607. Historians Guide. *The historians guide: or, Englands remembrancer . . . from the year 1600. until the year 1679.* London: f. W. Crook, 1679. 12°. 2nd ed. Pp. [4], 120, [8] (8 pp. books sold by Crook).
After p. 59, AW added some corrections and vertical marks in margins, e.g., p. 59, 'false', at note, May 15, 1665, of an ancient monument found 3 miles from Bath. Pp. 99 and 117 'q[uaere]' in margins. Pp. [121-8], 6 catalogue entries marked by vertical lines in red ink or underscoring. LT 2.25, 37, 423-4, 450 (AW may have had an earlier ed. of *Englands remembrancer*).
Wood 207(5). Wing H2094B.

3608. Historica Britannica. H[unt], M., ed. *Historica Britannica hoc est, de rebus gestis Britanniae.* Oxoniae: L. Lichfield, imp. M. Hunt, 1640. 12°. Pp. [8], 220, [44]. Parchment.
Flyleaf, upper^v, 'Math. Hunt Author', prob. not in AW's hand.
Wood 198. STC 10013. Madan 940.

3609. Historical Passages. *The historicall passages, of England . . . from October 1642. to this present July, 1643.* [Oxford]: [L. Lichfield, prob.], 1643. 4°. Pp. [2], 43.
Tp, 'Ant: Woode Merton: Coll: Oxōn: M: DC LIX:'. Pp. 22-3, 30, 31, 33, 37-8, some lines, 'q[uaere]' entries, and identifications, e.g., p. 38, at 'Master Sedgwicke' AW wrote 'Jo[hn] Sedgwick. q[uaere]' (see AO 3.65 and esp. Bliss's note, 3.66).
Wood 376(17). Wing H2107 (two) ('O' not recorded in Wing). Madan 1422.

3610. History. *The history of the two children in the wood, revived: or, murther reveng'd.* [London]: I. M. f. J. Blare, 1687. 8°. A^8,B^4 (2 tpp; cropped).
Wood 704(5). Wing H2188D (rare).

3611. Hobbes, Thomas. *Humane nature.* ?: ?, 1650 or 1651. 12°. Pp. 170 or 168.
Missing. MS. Wood E. 2(70), p. 38. Ed not identified.
MS. Wood E. 2(70), p. 38. Wing H2242 and 2243 (and 2243A). Macd. & Harg. 15 or 16. *Folg* and *Folg.*

3612. Hobbes, Thomas*. *Mr Hobbes considered in his loyalty, religion, reputation, and manners. By way of letter to Dr Wallis [in reply to Wallis's Hobbius Heauton-timorumenos].* London: f. A. Crooke, 1662. 8°. Pp. 63.
Missing. Acquired 30 June 1664, 6^d, LT 2.15. Also listed in MS. Wood F. 51, f. 44.
LT 2.15. Wing H2217. Macd. & Harg. 63*BL.*

3613. Hobbes, Thomas. *Ad nobilissimum dominum Gulielmum comitem Devoniae, &c. De mirabilibus *pecci, carmen.* [London]: n.pub., [1666?]. 4°. A-C^4 (A1 blank).
A2, AW wrote the year, '1666'. C4^v, 'Londini 1666 edit: 2$^{a..}$' (?).
Wood 467(4). Wing H2222. Macd. & Harg. 8.

3614. Hobbes, Thomas. *To the right honorable and others, the learned members of the Royal Society, . . . two propositions . . . one is lately published by dr. [John] Wallis.* N.p.: n.pub., [1671]. S.sh.
AW added the dates, '1673.', '1671.'
Wood 276a(15). Wing H2263 (part of). Macd. & Harg. 70.

3615. Hobbes, Thomas. *To the right honourable and others, the learned members of the Royal Society, . . . a confutation of a theoreme [which John Wallis uses].* N.p.: n.pub., [1671]. S.sh.
AW added the date, '1673.'; also '1671.', prob. in a later hand.
Wood 276a(16). Wing H2263 (part of). Macd. & Harg. 69.

3616. Hobbes, Thomas. *Epistola . . . ad . . . Antonium à Wood authorem historiae & antiquitatum universitatis Oxoniensis; inserenda ad pag. 344, 345 [20 Apr. 1674].* [London?]: n.pub., [1674]. S.sh.
In t, '344, 345' altered to '444, 445', after which, 'in lib. 2', not in AW's hand (the biography of Hobbes is at *Historia,* 2.376-7; 2.444-5 refers to the place where this leaf was inserted in all printed copies; a copy once owned by E. Ashmole, now Ashm. 1818(59), has the same emendations, including the following:) in the letter, 4 minor corrections, not by AW. See LT 2.285 ('April, about the last, received an epistle from Hobbs dated 20 Apr.'; 2.286, 2.288 ('July 11 . . . Hobbs' epistle to A. W. published in all coffey-houses

in Oxford. [John] Fell stormes'), 2.293ff. Dupl. at Wood 423(47). See further comments and references at Wood 430, item 6685.
Wood 276a(18) (17 in Bodl. CD cat.). Wing H2235. Madan 2998. Macd. & Harg. 82.

3617. Hobbes, Thomas. *Epistola . . . ad . . . Antonium à Wood authorem historiae & antiquitatum universitatis Oxoniensis; inserenda ad pag. 344, 345 [20 Apr. 1674].* [London?]: n.pub., [1674]. S.sh.
In t, '344, 345' altered to '444, 445 in lib. 2', not by AW; in the letter, identification of J. A. as 'Johannes Aubrey' and 5 minor corrections. See more complete notes at dupl. at 276a(18).
Wood 423(47). Wing H2235. Madan 2998. Macd. & Harg. 82.

3618. Hobbes, Thomas. *Thomae Hobbesii Malmesburiensis vita.* Londini: typis, 1679. 4°. Pp. [2], 14 (cropped in binding). Calf with 3 fillets and stamp decoration in corners (flower with point); rebacked (Ashm. binding).
Flyleaf, upper, 2nd[v], list of 21 printed works in this vol., written by an Ashm. librarian. AW's numbering also survives in most books, 1-18, which indicates that these 18 items were together in Wood's personal library (perhaps bound together; there are inconsistencies in order from items 15-20). For the 1st item, see AW's note at Wood 657(6) and LT 2.500.
Wood 345(1). Wing H2267. Macd. & Harg. 91.

3619. H[obbes], T[homas]. *Behemoth. The history of the civil wars of England.* [London]: n.pub., 1680. 8°. Pp. [2], 286.
Flyleaf, upper, 1st, AW wrote subjects and specific p. nos. in Hobbes' text (he went only to p. 79): 'Concerning Aristotle and his tenets p. 54. 55. 56 [/] Ethnicks & morall philosophy p. 58 [/] School divinity, against it p. 22. 54 [/] Universities p. 21. 22. 30. 31. 52 53 - 74. 77. [/] Religion p. 60. 61 [/] Heresie p. 11. 12 [/] Presbyterians p. 29. 30. 31. 32 . . . [etc. /] Luther p. 24. 25. 26 [/] The Scots p. 36. to 42. 43. 44. - 47.' Loose slip of ms. paper (formerly part of a letter addressed to AW) attached by clip; [r], similar subject and p. references to this book (AW apparently copied from this slip on to the flyleaf), but with additional subjects, e.g., 'pop[e] [and] against papists . . . pope & bishops . . . clergy'; at bottom, upside down, the portion of Wood's draft of a letter: 'therefore I beg your pardon for putting [torn] trouble to tell me the names if you be pleased to rub [?] up your memory & tell me the names at length that those letters concern I shall take it for' (ends abruptly); [v], the address of a letter: 'For M[r]. Anthony Wood [liv]ing over against the great Gate Merton Colledge Oxōn at Oxford'. Text, to p. 65, vertical lines in margins, in red ink; p. 53, at Hobbes' account of the origins of the university, AW wrote 'false', 'false', and 'veri false again', in red ink. LT 2.472.
Wood 213(2). Wing H2214. Macd. & Harg. 89.

3620. Hobbes, Thomas*. *Considerations upon the {* reputation, loyalty, manner, & religion, of Thomas Hobbes. London: f. W. Crooke, 1680. 8°. Pp. [6], 63, [10] (9 pp. books sold by W. Crook). Calf, speckled; rebacked.
Flyleaf, upper[v], 'For his ever honoured Friend Mr Anthony à Wood from his affectionate servant J. Aubrey.'; and AW wrote, 'Received 25. Ap. 1680. AW'. Tp, Aubrey wrote, 'It was first printed 1662', and, [v], 'These Considerations were first printed 1662. [about 300] [sic] of which I had 2. or 3. the Impression all sold long since and this was reprinted from mine. it was printed first ανονυμως. I spake to W. Crooke to mention the first Impression, but he forgot it.' Pp. 5, Aubrey added a gloss on Hobbes' view of regal power and sovereignty, 'B[p] Manwaring [of S[t] Davids] preach't this Doctrine, for which he was committed Prisoner to the Tower. then thought M[r] H[s] tis time for me to shift for my selfe.'; 40, Aubrey identified the author of a sermon, 'S. Ward at S[t] Laurence church - Lond.' LT 2.472, 485, 508.
Wood 431b. Wing H2218. Macd. & Harg. 64.

3621. Hobbes, Thomas. *The last sayings, or dying legacy of.* London: f. the author's executors, 1680. S.sh.
Missing in 1939 (a delete sign before the entry, xiv, 'The dying legacy of mr. Thom. Hobbes', in the 1717 list).
Wood 276a(17). Wing H2245. Macd. & Harg. 96. *O, Folg.*

3622. Hobbes, Thomas. *The life of mr. Thomas Hobbes . . . written by himself in a Latine poem. And now translated into English.* London: f. A. C., 1680. Fol. Pp. [2], 18.
Tp, AW wrote, 'came out about 10. Jan. a fortnight after the Lat. copie in vers. was published in 4° – an. 1679[80]'. For the Latin, Hobbes, Wood 345(1). LT 2.480, 500.
Wood 657(6). Wing H2251. Macd. & Harg. 92.

3623. Hobbes, Thomas. *Memorable sayings of mr. Hobbes in his books and at the table.* [London]:

[n.pub.], [1680]. S.sh. (engr.).
Missing in 1939. A delete sign is before the entry in the 1717 list, 'Thom. Hobbes's memorable sayings and picture'. There is a Bodl. copy at Firth b.16(54)).
Wood 276a(14) (not in Bodl. CD cat.). Wing H2251A. Macd. & Harg. 97.

3624. Hobbes, Thomas. *The art of rhetoric, with a discourse of the laws of England.* London: f. W. Crooke, 1681. 8°. Pp. [7], 168, 208 (2nd tp at 1st p. 135). Calf with 2 fillets.
Wood 128. Wing H2212. Macd. & Harg. 13.

3625. Hobbes, Thomas. *Tracts of mr. Thomas Hobbs.* London: f. W. Crooke, 1682. 8°. Pp. [7], 339, [5], [4], 160, [8], 85, [2]. Includes 7 pp. of Hobbes' books printed by Crooke. Calf, speckled, with 2 fillets and 2 vertical fillets.
Cover, upper, inside, 'For Mr Anthony à Wood.' and AW wrote, 'Received from M^r Jo. Aubrey 15 May 1682. at Oxōn'. LT 3.14.
Wood 204. Wing H2265. Macd. & Harg. 100.

3626. [Hobbes, Thomas], and [Richard Blackburne]. *Thomae Hobbes Angli Malmesburiensis philosophi vita. [Followed by] Vitae Hobbianae auctarium [by R. Blackburne].* Carolopoli (Londini): ap. Eleutherium Anglicum (ap. G. Crooke), 1681. 8°. Pp. [25], 241, [2]. Calf, speckled, with 2 fillets and a vertical line of 2 fillets.
'For my very worthy Friend Mr Anthony à Wood, Antiquarie of Oxford. from his affectionate friend, and humble Servant Jo: Aubrey.'; and AW wrote, 'I received this book at Weston 6. Nov. 1680 – AWood.' LT 2.500. A8^v, below a printed poem and its implied author, John Aubrey, AW wrote, 'Ista carmina composit erant per Rob. [underscored in red ink and in margin, 'Rich.', in red ink] Blackborne Editorem, contra voluntatem Attici [i.e., Aubrey], et hic sub ejusd. nomine posita-'. B4^v, lines in margin, at a reference to J. A. (Aubrey). P. 2, AW corrected an incorrect p. ref. to his *Historia*, from 'pag. 444' to '376' (the entry of Hobbes is on p. 2.376 and the Hobbes' *Epistola* was inserted after p. 2.444; see notes at Wood's *Historia*, Wood 430); p. 199, at entry to Tho. Tenison, 'vide transac. philosophic. Num. 64', in red ink, and lines in margin, in pencil. See M. Hunter, *John Aubrey and the Realm of Learning* (New York, 1975): 79 and the reference there to MS. Wood F. 39, fol. 350.
Wood 434. Wing H2268. Macd. & Harg. 93.

3627. Hobry, Marie*. *A hellish murder committed by a French midwife [M. Hobry].* London: f. R. Sare, published by R. Taylor, 1688. 4°. Pp. [4], 39.
Tp, AW wrote, 'This pamphlet was published before, or about the time she was burnt/'. P. 39, 'March 2. an. 1687[8] the said Mary Hobrey [sic] a popish French midwife, was burnt in Leycester Feilds neare London for murthering her drunken husband a protestant/'. LT 3.258.
Wood 365(33). Wing H1384.

3628. H[oddesdon], J[ohn]. *The history of the life and death of s^r. Thomas More.* London: f. G. Eversden, a. H. Eversden, 1662. 12°. Pp. [12], 178.
Tp, AW wrote, 'Joh. Roper son in law to S^r Th. More wrot the life first of all.' A4, author identified, 'J. Hoddesdon', not in AW's hand. Pp. 5, 31, 33, 125, underscoring or line in margin; p. 49, correction. Acquired 29 Aug. 1662, LT 1.454.
Wood 289(6). Wing H2293.

3629. Hodges, Thomas. *A cordiall against the feare of death.* Oxford: H. H. f. T. Robinson, 1659. 4°. Pp. [10], 30.
Tp, 'Hodges' underscored. AOF 2.53.
Wood 634(10). Wing H2318. Madan 2446.

3630. Hodnet, William. Manuscript. Cantabr. *A panegyricke. . . . to . . . Humphry Clarke, in honour of his . . . nuptialls.* N.p.: n.pub., n.d. Fol. Pp. [4] (pp.[2-3] blank).
A letter, with the ms. 'panegyricke' on p. 1, addressed to Clarke on p. 4.
Wood 276a(537) (not in Bodl. CD cat.).

3631. Hofheimerus, Paulus. *Harmoniae poeticae.* Norimbergae: ap. J. Petreium, 1539. 8°. a-b^8,c^4 (c4 blank). Parchment.
Wood 23(1). See Wood 23(2). BL.

3632. Hofheimerus, Paulus, and Ludovicus Senflius. *Harmoniae poeticae.* Norimbergae: ap. J. Petreium, n.d. [1539]. 8°. a-d^8.
Wood 23(2). See Wood 23(1). BL.

3633. Holder, William. *A discourse concerning time . . . for the better understanding of the Julian year and calendar. The first column also in our church-calendar explained.* London: J. Heptinstall, f. L. Meredith, 1694. 8°. Pp. [7], 120. Calf, speckled; rebacked.
Cover, upper, inside, 'For Mʳ Anthony à Wood. from Dʳ Holder/' and AW wrote, '18 June 1694' (he entered this several months after he received it, see MS Aubrey 13.267, where he told Aubrey that he received the Holder book, 1 Feb. 1694, and LT 1.309).
Wood 147. Wing H2385.

3634. Holder, William. *A treatise of natural grounds, . . . of harmony.* London: J. Heptinstall f. the author, sold J. Carr, 1694. 8°.
Missing. In Wood 431a, AW wrote 'I have the book & the title runs thus A Treatise of the natural Grounds & Principles of Harmony. Lond. 1694. oct. He hath also written Discourse concerning Time . . . 1694' (Wood 147). Ed. not identified.
Not located. Wing H2389, H2389A-B.

3635. Holland, Henry. *A treatise against witchcraft: or a dialogue, wherein the greatest doubts concerning that sinne, are briefly answered.* Cambridge: J. Legatt, 1590. 4°. Pp. [64], 24.
Flyleaf, upper, 'HI' (?). Tp, bsm, '3.10 [?]' (?). C3ᵛ, mark in margin at the 'devil's name', and E2ᵛ-E3, underscoring, not in AW's manner.
[MS.] Wood B. 20(3). STC 13590.

3636. H[olland], H[enry], bookseller. *Ecclesia Sancti Pauli illustrata. The monuments, inscriptions, and epitaphs.* London: J. Norton, sold H. Seyle, 1633. 4°. A⁴,a²,blank leaf,B2-4,C-H⁴,I1 (wanting all after sig. I1).
AW numbered the pp. from A4 to I1ᵛ, 1-61. On a blank leaf inserted after a2, AW wrote, r-v, the locations of, and inscriptions on, the monuments of Sebba, King of the East Saxons, Etheldred, Fulk Lovel, Roger Niger, Thomas de Eures [Evers], and John of Gaunt (cp. Stow, pp. 624-7, Wood 472, item 6060).
Wood 467(7). STC 13584.

3637. Holland, Richard. *Notes shewing how to get the angle of parallax of a comet.* Oxford: L. Lichfield f. R. Davis, 1668. 8°. Pp. [4], 20.
Tp, AW wrote 'By R [blank] Holland, Teacher of the Mathematicks, Oxon. Æt: 70' LT 2.33. Acquired 21 Dec. 1668, LT 2.146.
Wood 704(8). Wing H2433. Madan 2804.

3638. Holland, T[homas]. *Oratio Sarisburiae habita VIII. Id. Jun. Cum . . . Henricus . . . episcopus Sarisburiensis gradum doctoratus in theologiae susciperet, ex decreto convocationis Oxoniensis.* Oxoniae: J. Barnesius, 1599. 4°. A⁴,B².
Tp, AW wrote below, 'De insigniis Doctoris q[uaere] hic.'
Wood 512(3). STC 13596. Madan 190.

3639. Hollanders. *The Hollanders embassage to England. Concerning the good will which they bear to the protestants in Ireland . . . With the humble petition of the inhabitants of the countie of Essex.* London: f. J. Smith, 1642. 4°. A⁴.
Tp, former no., '32', overwritten.
Wood 508(38). Wing H2446.

3640. Hollar, W[enceslaus], sculp.; Gage, D., delin. *Oxforde. [with] Prospect of Oxforde from the east.* N.p.: n.pub., [1643?]. S.sh. Pasteboard (green, over blue) (upper board missing).
Flyleaf, upper, 1st, AW wrote, 'Binding [?] 1ˢ – 10. Mar. 1689[90]'. ᵛ, a few scribbles, 'Hugo' and 'gᵇʳⁱˢ' (? twice), prob. not in AW's hand; 2ndᵛ, note by later librarian concerning the plates in items Wood 423(6-11) (q.v.); 3rd, heading, 'Oxoniensia Vol. 1 Pol', in pencil, and AW wrote the titles of 66 printed works in this vol., within guidelines made with red ink. The t of item 67 was added in another hand. He acquired item no. 67 on 8 March 1690 and it may have been inserted at the last second (while no titles were listed in the Whiteside cat., the number was: '67, Pamphlets on Several Occasions'; see also Wood 423(65-66)). The final item, 68, dated 5 March 1690 in the t, was prob. inserted after 1922, see note at Wood 423(68). Item 13 was stolen before 1922.
On the upper flyleaf, at item 1, AW wrote that this map 'was made in the time of K. Jam. 1', but it was done by Hollar, prob. in 1643 (Wadham is there, as is Pembroke). AW loaned to Loggan in 1665 a map by Agas, item 27. There may be a 2nd 'old map', that is, the Hollar, in addition to the Agas, see note at Loggan, Wood 276b(31), item 4211). See also H. Hurst, *Oxford Topography* (OHS, 1899): 9; and LT 1.254 (and 2.49), where Clark cites Macray, p. 474-5. Prob. acquired 10 June 1664, 6ᵈ, LT 2.14.

Wood 423(1). Pennington 1054 (includes 'sould by John Overton').

3641. Hollar, W[enceslaus], sculp. *Cambridge. The prospect of Cambridge from the London Road [and] The armes of such princes and noble men . . . of the earldome of Cambridge.* N.p.: [J. Overton], [1650]. S.sh., 254 x 282, 334 x 420.
Pennington copy has the seller, J. Overton, and is trimmed to 254 x 282, 261 x 290.
Wood 423(2). Pennington 960.

3642. Hollar, W[enceslaus], fecit. *A true & exact groundplatt [sic] . . . of Candia.* [London]: sold J. Overton, [1668]. S.sh.
On blank side of sh., 'Museo Ashmoleano dedit V. Cl. Jo. Aubrey Armiger S. R. S.' and signature, 'Ludovicus Rex', who apparently gave this to Aubrey. It was integrated into the Wood Collection after 1695.
Wood 276a(54). Wing T2435B (rare, but see Pennington 1128).

3643. Hollar, W[enceslaus], fecit. *The kingdome of England, & principality of Wales, . . . in six mappes, portable for every mans pocket.* [London]: sold T. Jenner, 1671. Fol. Tp and 6 fold-out maps. Calf, speckled, with 2 fillets and 2 metal clasps; rebacked.
Flyleaf, upper, 1st, '3ˢ.–6 1674. came out about 1650' (really 1644).
Wood 466. Wing H2448. Pennington 652A; Quartermaster's map.

3644. Holles, Denzel. *A true relation of the unjust accusation of certain French gentlemen.* London: J. Darby f. R. Chiswel, 1671. 4°. Pp. [2], 44.
Tp, AW wrote the date, '1671', in ink over pencil, and made a correction in the t. Pp. 4, a note at printed 'Murrel a Chirurgion', 'Will Morrell alias Bowyer the notorious Impostor & cheat'; 10, identified the chief justice as, 'Sʳ John Keeling, of a poore false spirit, apt to domineer where he had power.'
Wood 372(12). Wing H2480.

3645. Holles, Denzil. *'Denzell Holles his speech - 1660'.* ?: ?, 1660. Pp.?
Missing. MS. Wood E. 2(70), p. 33.
MS. Wood E. 2(70), p. 33. Not identified.

3646. [Holles, Denzil]. *The case stated concerning the judicature of the house of peers in the point of appeals.* [London?]: n.pub., 1675. 8°. Pp. [2], 84, [4].
Flyleaf, upper, AW wrote, 'Dupl'. Tp, 'said to be written by Denzill Lord Hollis'. P. [3], a correction. Dupl. at Wood 629(3).
Wood 457(3). Wing H2452.

3647. [Holles, Denzil]. *The case stated concerning the judicature of the house of peers in the point of appeals.* [London?]: n.pub., 1675. 8°. Pp. [1], 84, [4].
Each 8° leaf is pasted on a 4° template. P. [3], correction. Dupl. at Wood 457(4).
Wood 629(3). Wing H2452.

3648. [Holles, Denzil]. *A letter of a gentleman to his friend, shewing that bishops are not to be judges in parliament in cases capital.* [London]: n.pub., 1679. 8°. Pp. [2], 119. Pasteboard (blue) with parchment spine; rebacked.
Flyleaf, upper, 1st, AW wrote, 'An argument for Bishops rights in judging in capital causes in parl. [/] by Tho. Hunt – qu[aere]' (his copy is at Wood 574(3)); 2nd, A. Allam wrote, 'This Letter was wrot by my Lᵈ Hollis. pret: 9ˢ.'; 2ndᵛ, AW wrote the titles of 3 printed works in this vol., within guidelines made with red ink. Tp, AW wrote, 'written by Denzill Lᵈ Holles'; and a recent note, 'Catalogued AH [A. Hackman]'. LT 2.434.
Wood 574(1). Wing H2461aA.

3649. Hollingworth, Richard. *A modest plea for the Church of England.* London: f. R. Royston, 1676. 8°. Pp. [54], 126, [1] (1 p. books printed f. R. Royston).
Sig. A1 (apparently), flyleaf, upper, 'Pret: 0ˢ-10ᵈ We[st]: Bibliop Octo: vicesimo 4ᵗᵒ 1676.', in hand of A. Allam (see LT 3.167).
Wood 885(2). Wing H2503A.

3650. Hollingworth, Richard. *The character of king Charles I.* London: R. Tayler, 1692. 4°. Pp. [12], 28.
Wood 363(11). Wing H2500. FFMadan 170.

3651. Hollingworth, Richard. *A defence of king Charles I: occasion'd by the lyes and scandals.* London: f. S. Eddowes, 1692. 4°. Pp. [4], 40.

Tp, AW wrote 'Bought of M[r] [George] West 2. Dec. 1691' (LT 3.377). Pp. 1, AW identified a sympathetic jailer of Charles 1, 'Col. Rich. Browne'; 3, identified the author of a 'late lewd Pamphlet . . . Ludlow' (i.e., Wood 363(1), item 4305), as 'Jo. Philipps the author'.
Wood 363(3). Wing H2502. FFMadan 165.

3652. Hollingworth, Richard. *Dr. Hollingworth's defence of k. Charles the first's . . . Εικων Βασιλικη; against . . . dr. [Anthony] Walker, . . . proving . . . the aforesaid book . . . not dr. [J.] Gauden's.* London: f. S. Eddowes, 1692. 4°. Pp. [4], 27.
Tp, below, numbers, '(4), 27 ll.', in a later hand (similar p. no. entries at nos. (12), (13), (15) in this vol.).
Wood 363(8). Wing H2503. FFMadan 168.

3653. Hollingworth, Richard. *A second defence of king Charles I. By way of reply to . . . Ludlow's letter to dr. Hollingworth.* London: f. S. Eddowes, sold R. Taylor, 1692. 4°. Pp. [8], 53, [2].
Tp, AW wrote the price, '1[sh]'.
Wood 363(5). Wing H2504. See FFMadan 163.

3654. Hollingworth, Richard. *The death of king Charles I. proved a down-right murder.* London: R. Norton f. W. Kettilby, 1693. 4°. Pp. [18], 24.
Tp, p. nos., '(16), 24 ll.', not in AW's hand. a3[v], a correction, may not be by AW.
Wood 363(15). Wing H2501 (Wing, Charles 1,). FFMadan 174.

3655. Holloway, James. *The free and voluntary confession and narrative of James Holloway.* (London): (f. R. Horn, J. Baker, a. J. Redmayne), (1684). Fol. Pp. 16.
Wood 428(28). Wing H2509.

3656. Holy Roman Empire. *The acts of the diet of Regenspurgh: held in the yeeres 1622 and 1623.* London: [Eliot's Court Press] f. N. Butter, 1623. 4°. Pp. [2], 38.
Wood 615(8). STC 13613.

3657. Holyday, Barten. *A survey of the world.* Oxford: W. Hall f. the authour, 1661. 8°. Pp. [8], 118, [1].
Missing in 1837. 'A Survey of the World by B. Holyday – Oxon. 1661' in Whiteside cat.
Wood 86. Wing H2533. Madan 2558. *Hunt.*

3658. Homer. Chapman, George, trans. *The whole works of Homer.* ?: ?, [1616] or [1634]. Pp.?
Missing. MS. Wood E. 2(70), p. 11. Ed. not identified. Acquired 14 Nov. 1667, 1[s]4[d], LT 2.120.
MS. Wood E. 2(70), p. 11. STC 13624-13624.5.

3659. Hood, Robin*. *The noble birth and gallant atchievements [sic] of . . . Robin Hood.* London: J. M., sold J. Deacon, [1690 ca.]. 4°. A-C⁴.
Wood 321(5). Wing N1203A (two).

3660. Hooker, Richard. [Jackson, Henry, ed.]. *A learned and comfortable sermon. A learned discourse of justification. A learned sermon of the nature of pride. A remedie against sorrow. Two sermons upon . . . s. Judes epistle [ed. H. Jackson]. [And probably] The answere of mr. Richard Hooker to a supplication preferred.* Oxford: J. Barnes, 1612, 1614. 4°.
Missing. MS. Wood E. 2(70), p. 1, 'Rich. Hooker His smaller works, published by H. Jackson – who also published Wickliffs wicket'. See AO 1.697-8, where AW lists five pamphlets of Hooker's sermons, ed., acc. to AW, by H. Jackson; published in Oxford, 1612, 1614 (see also AO 3.577). Ed. not identified.
MS. Wood E. 2(70), p. 1. STC 13706ff. Madan 352-6, 413. *Hunt.*

3661. Hoole, Charles. *The common rudiments of Latine grammar, usually taught in all schools:. . . 1. The common accidents examined. 2. The termination.. . . 3. Propria quae maribus, ...* [London]: W. Godbid, f. John Saywel, 1657. 8°. Pp. [10], 154 (last p. blank), [20] (1 p. books sold by 'Saywel'), [2], 18, [2], 128. 4 tpp.
Tp, AW underscored the name of the author, Hoole, in red ink (similar underscoring on the 2nd tp). 'W[anting]', cropped at side, prob. not by AW. In MS. Wood E. 2(70), p. 16, 'Common rudiments of grammar – with other things bound with it'. See note at Wise, 8° A 153(1) Art., item 6648.
8° A 153(5) Art. Wing H2678B.

3662. Hoole, Charles. *Childrens talke, English and Latine [and] Pueriles confabulatiunculae Anglo-Latinae in varias clausulas distributae.* London: ?, 1659 or 1673. 8°. Pp. [7], 95, [1].
Missing. MS. Wood E. 2(70), p. 7, 'Ch. Hoole Pueriles confabulatiunculae'. AW lists 1633, 1653 eds. in AO 3.759. Ed. not identified.

MS. Wood E. 2(70), p. 7. Wing H2671 and H2672. *Yale.*

3663. Hooper, John. *'His smaller works in 8°'*. ?: ?, ? Pp.?
Missing. MS. Wood E. 2(70), p. 9. Not identified.
MS. Wood E. 2(70), p. 9. STC 13741-13765.

3664. Hooper, Margaret*. *Most fearefull and strange newes from the bishoppricke of Durham, being a true relation of one Margret Hooper.* London: f. J. Thomas, 1641. 4°. Pp. [2], 6.
[MS.] Wood B. 35(8). Wing M2889.

3665. Hopkins, William. *A message sent from . . . Ireland to a member of the army, under . . . lord . . . Fairfax, concerning their proceedings.* London: B. A., 1649. 4°. Pp. [2], 6.
Tp, AW wrote, 'Little or nothing concerning Ireland' and after year, 'ult Febr 1648[9]', i.e., the date of the message.
Wood 509(34). Wing H2755.

3666. Hopton, Arthur. *A concordancy of yeares.* (London): [N. Okes] f. Co. of Stationers, 1616. 8°. Pp. [14], 252, [1], with interleaved blank leaves. Parchment over pasteboard.
Flyleaf, upper, first, 'Anthony Woode: Mert Coll: Oxō May: i: 1658.' (AW's early hand), a 2nd 'Anthony Wood' is prob. not by him; 3rd-6th, ms. poem, possibly AW's early hand (but see LT 1.249): 'Rustica Academiae Oxoniensii nuper reformatae descriptio:. . . 1648', with 23 annotations in margins, e.g., identifications of some unnamed persons and ending with 'ffinis: These verses as it is reported were made by Dr John Allibond, somtimes fellow of Magd: Coll: Oxō: and now Rector of Bradwell Cō: Glocest:' (Allibond died in 1658); printed copies, with similar annotations, are at Wood 276a(520), Wood 423(28) and a quarto ed. at Wood 514(53); see AOF 2.70, LT 1.144, 249. Flyleaf, lower, last^v, more certainly by AW, death dates and/or burial places of Oriel College persons, Tho. Gammond 1653, Thom. Dove 1656-7, and Fletcher 1657, all 'buried in Oriell Coll Chappell'; 'Joh. Rous sen: fellow: obiit 1652 et sep:. . . '; '[John] Sanders provost ob: 20: Mar: 1652[3]'; Yong, [John] Fricker 1660, Brotherick [John Broderwick], 'Loyd. [Owen Lloyd] A.b. ob. Mar. 21. 1672', and [John?] Mathews. LT 1.210, 249 (on date of acquisition, see note at dupl. at Wood 18(1)).
Wood 16. STC 13780.

3667. Hopton, Arthur. *A concordancy of yeares.* (London): [N. Okes] f. Co. of Stationers, 1616. 8°. Pp. [14], 252, [1]. Pasteboard (grey) with parchment spine; 1st upper and last lower flyleaves, grey paper.
Flyleaf, upper, 1st^r, 'Will. Rastell q[uaere]' (Rastall, author of 3rd work in this vol.), lined out; ^v, AW wrote the titles of 3 printed works in this vol., within guidelines made with red chalk. Tp, 'Ant: Wood: 1658:', lined out (acquired 14 May 1658, 1^s5^d, LT 1.249, but Clark read '1653'). Bsm. Dupl. at Wood 16, which is interleaved with blank leaves.
Wood 18(1). STC 13780.

3668. Hopton-Heath. *The battaile on Hopton-heath in Staffordshire.* [Oxford]: H. Hall, 1643. 4°. Pp. [2], 8.
Tp, AW lined out the former no., '37', and wrote, 'Mar. 1642/3'; p. 7, at 'Northampton', 'Jam. E. of Nhampt.'
Wood 375(45). Wing B1162. Madan 1294.

3669. Horace. Bond, John, ed. *Quinti Horatii Flacci poemata, scholiis . . . a J. Bond.* London: [R. Field], imp. G. Bishop, 1606. 8°.
Missing. MS. Wood E. 2(70), p. 11, 'Joh. Bonds notes on horace'. Ed. not identified.
MS. Wood E. 2(70), p. 11. STC 13790aff. and Wing H2777ff.

3670. Horace. H[awkins], T[homas], trans. *Odes of Horace the best of lyrick poets.* London: A. M[athewes] f. W. Lee, [1625]. 4°. Pp. [12], 99.
Missing. MS. Wood E. 2(70), p. 53, 'Odes of Horace made Engl – Sr Tho. Hawkins'. Ed. not identified.
MS. Wood E. 2(70), p. 53. STC 13800. *Yale.*

3671. Horace. Rider, Henry, trans. *All the odes and epodes of Horace.* London: R. Cotes, 1644. 12°. Pp. [10], 140. Calf with 2 fillets.
Wood 81. Wing H2767 (rare).

3672. Horace. Dillon, Wentworth, trans. *Horace's art of poetry.* London: f. H. Herringman, 1680. 4°. Pp. [8], 32.
Tp, AW underlined Roscommon in red ink and wrote, 'q[uaere] Wentwo. Dillon', and 'Nov.' LT 3.124.

Wood 482(3). Wing H2768.

3673. Horn Fair. *Hey for horn fair &c*. London: ?, 1672. Pp.?
Missing in 1837. 'Hey For Horn Fair &c – Lond.1672' in Whiteside cat. See Wing H1658A (1674), and H1658AB (c. 1687).
Wood 61(3). Not in Wing. Not in ESTCR.

3674. Horne, Robert. *A caveat to prevent future judgements*. London: G. M[iller] f. P. Stephens a. C. Meredith, 1626. 4°. Pp. [4], 34.
Missing. MS. Wood E. 2(70), p. 69.
MS. Wood E. 2(70), p. 69. STC 13820 (rare, *O*, owned by Th. Paine; some marks, not by AW).

3675. Host, Matthaeus. *Historiae rei nummariae veteris libri quinque*. Francoford. ad Oderam: ap. J. Eichorn, 1580. 8°. Pp. [104], 811. Calf with 3 fillets; 2nd rectangle with 1 fillet and stamp decoration outside corners with Bohemian and Saxon associations: oval centrepiece upper, figure with Joh:Geo[rge]: D:G: P:EL:B:E:D:P (Elector of Brandenburg); oval centrepiece lower, arms with surrounding inscription, 'AUGUSTUS. 1578. RUDOLPHUS. II. D.G. EL. ROM. IMPERA. SEMPER'.
Flyleaf, upper, presentation copy to Jerome Tobing, Luneberg, with an elaborate note in Latin (see LT 1.426; Macray, p. 455); and some marks in margin and underscoring, not by AW.
Wood 561. BL.

3676. Hotham, John. *Letter to a worthy member of the house of commons, concerning the late discovery at Hull*. London: f. E. Husbands, 1642. S.sh.
ᵛ, AW lined out 2 former nos., and wrote, 'Sʳ Jo. Hotham'.
Wood 374(11). Wing H2907.

3677. Hotham, John. *A true and exact relation of all the proceedings of sir Hugh Cholmleys revolt*. London: f. R. Best, 1643, 7 Apr. 4°. Pp. [2], 9.
Missing in 1839; see note at Wood 376(1).
Wood 376(2). Wing H2909A. *O, Hunt, Folg*.

3678. [Hotman, François]. Varamundus, Ernestus, trans. *De furoribus Gallicis, horrenda & indigna Amirallii Castillionei, . . . caede*. Londini: ex off. H. Bynneman, 1573. 8°. Pp. 212. Parchment.
Tp, signatures: 'Thomas Collinson', 'Hen: Foulis March d: 2. 1653/4 p: 3ˢ'. LT 2.179. Text, passim, notes, to p. 85, and p. 129, not in AW's hand.
Wood 184. STC 13846.

3679. How, Samuel. *The sufficiency of the spirits teaching, without humane-learning:. . . To which is added a postscript . . . by William Kiffen*. London: G. L. f. T. Malthus, 1683. 4°. T leaf is a cancel. Pp. [6], 42.
Tp, after name of author, AW wrote, 'Cobler'. Bsm.
[MS.] Wood B. 24(8). Wing H2953.

3680. Howard*. Genealogy. *'The genealogy of the Howards'*. N.p.: ?, n.d. S.sh.
Missing in 1939. See item 3311 for a reference to the 'armes' of Howard.
Wood 276a(69). Not identified.

3681. Howard, Charles*. Nottingham, earl of. *The royal entertainement of . . . the earle of Nottingham, sent ambassador . . . to . . . Spaine*. London: V. Sims f. W. Ferbrand, 1605. 4°. Pp. [4], 21 (p. [1] blank).
Wood 537(5). STC 13857.

3682. Howard, Edward, and Bernard Howard. *A memorial delivered to his majesty by the honourable Edward Howard and Bernard Howard of Norfolk . . . of what they demand from their brother . . . Henry*. [London]: n.pub., [1677]. Fol. Pp. 8.
P. 8, AW wrote, 'This was printed either in Febr. or beginning of March an. 1676/7'.
Wood 276b(87) (old no., (65) in Bodl. CD cat.). Wing H2970 (rare).

3683. Howard, Henry. Surrey, earl of. *Songes and sonnettes*. London: ap. R. Tottell, 1565. 8°. Ff. 117, [3].
Missing. MS. Wood E. 2(70), p. 54.
MS. Wood E. 2(70), p. 54. STC 13864. *Hunt*.

3684. Howard, Henry. Norfolk, duke of (1655-1701). *The case of the duke of Norfolk represented to the supreme judicature*. [London]: n.pub., [1685?]. S.sh.

Wood 276b(82) (old no., (60), in Bodl. CD cat.). Wing C1065 (two) (Wing, entry not in alpha order).

3685. Howard, Henry*. Norfolk, duke of (1655-1701). *The heads of the judges arguments for the deceased duke of Norfolk, in the case between him and his brother mr. Charles Howard.* [London?]: n.pub., [1685]. S.sh.
Wood 276b(84) (old no., (62), in Bodl. CD cat.). Wing H1296 (two).

3686. [Howard, Robert]. *The life and reign of king Richard the second.* London: f. M. L. a. L. C. sold L. Curtis, 1681. 8°. Pp. [8], 240.
Flyleaf, upper[v], AW wrote, 'The life of K. Rich. 2 following was published for example for the fanatical crew of the times (1680[1]) to Imitate – and it seems the author would have K. Ch. 2 deposed, because he & his brethren could not obtaine their ends by aggravating the popish, or Oates his, plot, nor by lyes & slanders that followed &c.' Tp, he wrote, 'published in Jan. 1680[1]', and in different ink, '1[s]-6'. Bsm. LT 2.514-5.
Wood 234(3). Wing H3001.

3687. [Howard, Robert]. *Historical observations upon the reigns of Edward I. II. III. and Richard II.* London: f. J. Partridge a. M. Gillyflower, 1689. 8°. Pp. [3], 192.
A1[v], at advertisement for *The Ladies New-Years-gift,* AW wrote 'By the Marq. of Halyfax'. Tp, AW identified the author, 'Geo. Savile Marq. of Halyfax the author' and 'published about the beginning of Feb. 1688' (Wing H304ff.). Flyleaf, lower, upside down, 'Marq. of Halyfax'.
Wood 240(4). Wing H2997 ('O' not recorded in Wing).

3688. Howard, Robert. *The history of the reigns of Edward and Richard II.* London: F. Collins, f. T. Fox, 1690. 8°. Pp. [6], xli, 183 (pp. unopened).
Flyleaf, lower, Latin tag, cropped.
Wood 234(4). Wing H2999.

3689. Howard, Robert. *A letter to mr. Samuel Johnson, occasioned by a scurrilous pamphlet entituled, Animadversions on mr. Johnson's answer to Jovian.* London: f. T. Fox, 1692. 8°. Pp. [2], 72.
Wood 112(3). Wing H3000.

3690. Howard, Thomas. *The pourtraiture of . . . sir Thomas Howard knight, . . . earle of Arundell and Surrey.* London: f. T. Walkley, 1639. S.sh.
Col. 1, lines in margin, in pencil; col. 4, AW wrote at Henry Wilmot, 'Afterwards Lord Wilmot', in ink. Date, '1639', entered in ink over a faint imprint date.
Wood 276a(82). STC 13870.7 (rare).

3691. Howard, William*. Stafford, visct. *The late viscount Stafford found more guilty by his pretended innocency.* London: f. B. Harris, 1680. S.sh. (r-v).
[v], AW wrote the date, 'Jan. 2' (i.e., 1681).
Wood 427(5). Wing L561.

3692. Howard, William. Stafford, visct. *The speech of William Howard, . . . upon the scaffold [29 Dec. 1680].* [London]: n.pub., [1680]. Fol. Pp. 4.
P. 2, underscored: 'as wicked as any of those that so falsly have accused me'.
Wood 427(3). Wing S5157.

3693. Howard, William*. Stafford, visct. *Animadversions upon the speech of William (late) viscount Stafford, on the scaffold.* London: f. R. Baldwin, 1681. Fol. 2nd ed. Pp. [4], 8.
Wood 427(6). Wing A3208A.

3694. Howard, William*. Stafford, visct. *The tryal of William viscount Stafford for high treason.* London: by the assigns of J. Bill, T. Newcomb, a. H. Hills, 1680/1681. Fol. Pp. [2], 218. Pasteboard (blue) with parchment spine.
Flyleaf, upper, 4th[v], list of 50 printed works in this vol., written within guidelines made with red ink. All are present, plus two unrecorded items, 427(13b) and (51). Above: 'Volum. Fourth Of Tryalls, dying speeches, memoires[,] Informations, arraignements[,] Letters'. AW brought together items from different bundles which is indicated by former nos., as many as 3, on numerous tpp in this vol. (not recorded in items in this vol.) Tp, AW wrote the price, '5[s]'. LT 2.506.
Wood 427(1) (not in Bodl. CD cat.). Wing T2238.

3695. Howard, William*. Stafford, visct. *The two last prayers . . . at his execution [29 Dec. 1680].* London: n.pub., 1681. 8°. Pp. [12].

Wood 427(4). Wing S5159 (rare).

3696. Howard, William*. Escrick, baron of. *A vision in the Tower, to the L. H. in his contemplation.* (London): (f. T. N.), (1681). S.sh. (r-v).
AW identified L. H., H'oward'.
Wood 417(67). Wing V658C.

3697. Howell, Ja[mes]. *Instructions for forreine travell.* London: T. B. f. H. Mosley, 1642. 12°. Pp. [9], 236. Calf with 2 fillets; rebacked.
Flyleaf, upper, book purchase entries, not in AW's hand. Flyleaf, lower[v], p. numbers, 30, 31, 37, 51, etc.
Wood 168. Wing H3082.

3698. H[owell], J[ames]. Δενδρολογια. *Dodona's grove, or, the vocall forrest. . . . With parables, reflecting upon the times. And England's teares for the present warres.* [Oxford]: [H. Hall], 1644. 4°. 2nd ed. Pp. [16], 172. 3 pts.
Wood 487(5). Wing H3059. Madan 1692.

3699. [Howell, James]. *Mercurius Hibernicus: or, a discourse of the late insurrection in Ireland.* Bristoll: n.pub., 1644. 4°. Pp. [4], 14.
Tp, AW wrote, 'Jam. Howell the author so D[r] [Thomas] Barl[ow] sed qu[aere]'. LT 1.50; and former no., '43', lined out.
Wood 508(50). Wing H3093.

3700. Howell, James. *A letter to the earle of Pembrooke concerning the times, and the sad condition both of prince and people.* [London]: n.pub., 1647. 4°. Pp. [2], 12.
Missing since 1994. In Whiteside cat., this item and the following were described as: 'Passages concerning Oliver Cromwel &c – 30 Pamphlets'. This number, 30, apparently includes the 15 listed in the Whiteside cat. and 15 grouped together under Philip Herbert (see note at Wood 531(14) and Cromwell to make a total of 30.
Wood 531(15). Wing H3085.

3701. [Howell, James]. *A winter dreame.* [London]: n.pub., 1649. 4°. Pp. [2], 20.
Tp, '6' no. in a former bundle (?).
Wood 609(22). Wing H3129.

3702. Howell, James. *Epistolae Ho-Elianae. Familiar letters domestic and forren, by J. H. (A new volume of letters, by J. Howell. [Followed by] The vote). [2 vols. in 6 pt.]. With a fourth volume of new letters.* London: f. H. Moseley, 1655. 8°. 3rd ed. Pp. frontis., [24], 309, [5], 115, [21], 38, [14], 126, [10] (2 pp. works by Howell) (4 vols.). Calf, speckled, with 2 fillets and a vertical fillet; rebacked. 1st upper and last lower flyleaves, printer's waste; rebound R. H[arvey] 4.2.61.
Pastedown, upper, signature of Jn°. [?] Jones 1641. Tp, alteration of 'forren' in the t. 1st p. [4], a wax sigillum attached, with an explanation, by a later Ashm. librarian. Text, AW made a few lines and marks, e.g., 1st pp. 119, 251, 261, etc. until 3rd p. 31 At end, in a catalogue of works by Howell, AW marked all with short vertical lines, in red ink. Flyleaf, lower, 1st, AW elaborated on a printed entry, 'Parthenopoeia, or the Hist of the most renowned Kingdome of Naples &c. The 1. part of it was written by Scipio Mazzela – Englished by Samson Lennard herald of armes The 2d part compiled by James Howell esq. who besides some supplements to the 1. part, draws on the thred of the story to these present times 1654' (Wing M1542). Printer's waste, lower, notes at text, not by AW. AW's diary entry, 8 Apr. 1658, has: 'for borrowing Howell's 'Letters,' 6[d]', LT 1.242. Though the next item, Mainwaring, Wood 723b, was listed in the Whiteside cat., it is not a Wood book as the annotation shows: flyleaf, upper, ex dono T. Mainwaring to an unknown person, and Randole Holme to Josiah Rock in 1683; [v], 'Bibliothecae bodianae [sic] dono dedit Browne Willis Arm. Æd X[ti]. Socio commmensalis.' LT 1.9; 2.188. AW owned a copy, Wood 673(2), item 4352.
Wood 723a. Wing H3073.

3703. H[owell], J[ames]. *A brief account of the royal matches . . . from . . . 800. to . . . 1662.* London: J. G. f. H. Brome, 1662. 4°. Pp. [2], 6.
Wood 486(11). Wing H3057.

3704. Howell, James. *The pre-eminence and pedigree of parliament.* London: f. D. Newman a. T Cockeril, 1677. 4°. Pp. 23 (1-2 blank).
Wood 518(7). Wing H3108.

3705. [Howell, William]. *Medulla historiae Anglicanae . . . the monarchs.* London: f. A. Swalle, 1687.

8°. 3rd ed. Pp. [16], 483 (2 tpp, cancellandum and cancellans). Calf with 2 fillets and stamp decoration in corners.
Flyleaf, upper, 1st, AW wrote, 'Reported to be written by Dr Will. Howell of Cambridge'. Pp. 286, 384, 386, 435, 446-7, line in margin, in ink or pencil, prob. by AW. Flyleaf, lower^v, scribble. Acquired 19 Jan. 1663, 3^d, LT 1.467; 3.58. See note at item 5940.
Wood 601. Wing H3142.

3706. [**Howell, William**]. *Prayers in the closet: for the use of all devout Christians. . . . Collected out of the best companion, by the author of the same.* Oxford: at the theater f. J. Howell, 1689. 8°. *⁴.
Wood 836(4). Wing H3133C (two).

3707. [**Howell, William**]. *The word of God the best guide to all persons, . . . or, a collection of scripture texts.* Oxford: at the theater f. J. Howell, 1689. 8°. Pp. [12], 213, [3].
Wood 843(7). Wing H3132.

3708. Howson, John. Durham, bp. of. *Uxore dimissa propter fornicationem aliam non licet superinducere. Tertia thesis . . . proposita & disputata in vesperiis Oxonii. 1602. Accessit ejusdem theseos defensio [R. Burhill] contra reprehensiones T. Pyi* (i.e., Wood 636(4), item 5244). Oxoniae: J. Barnesius & veneunt Londini ap. S. Watersonum, 1606. 4°. Pp. [2], 36; [12], 206, [20]. 2 tpp. Calf, rough, with 3 fillets, stamp decoration (dragon) inside corners, and 4 bands on spine (Ashm. binding).
Flyleaf, upper, 3rd, the titles of 5 (really 4, 2 are listed for Wood 636(1)) printed works in this vol., written by an Ashm. librarian. Tp, A. Allam wrote 'Pret: 0 . . . W[est]: Bi[b] . . . decimo 8vo . . . Step' (cropped). 2nd tp, AW wrote 'Rob. Burhill c.c.c. author'. 2nd p. [9], a correction.
Wood 636(1-2). STC 13887. Madan 282, 280.

3709. Howson, John. Durham, bp. of. *To the minister churchwardens and parishioners of [blank] in the diocese of Oxon. [31 Aug.].* [Oxford]: [J. Barnes], [1622]. 4°. *⁴.
Wood 516(8). STC 13880 (two). Madan 506.

3710. Hoyerus, Michael. *Oratio encomiastica, de sanctitate vitae, . . . Joannis Duns Scoti.* Duaci: typ. B. Belleri, 1656. 8°. Pp. 46 (A-C⁸; C8 blank).
Tp, note by A. H., 'Entered Catalogue'.
Wood 59(2). BN.

3711. Huarte, Juan. Camilli, Camillo, trans.; C[arew], R[ichard], trans. *Examen de ingenios. The examination of mens wits.* London: A. Islip, f. R. Watkins, 1594. 4°. Pp. [16], 333, [2]. Parchment with 2 clasp holes.
Flyleaf, upper, notes lined out. Tp, AW entered the translator's name after initials, 'Ric. Carew'. A4^v, a word, not in AW's hand; to p. 84, some underscoring.
Wood 315. STC 13890.

3712. Hubberthorn, Richard. *A true testimony of the zeal of Oxford-professors and university-men who for zeal persecute the servants of the living God.* London: f. G. Calvert, 1654. 4°. Pp. [2], 14.
LT 1.190-1.
Wood 515(15). Wing H3240. Madan 2245.

3713. H[ubberthorn], R[ichard]. *Something that lately passed in discourse between the king and R. H. Published to prevent the mistakes . . . R. H.* London: P. L. f. G. C., 1660. 4°. Pp. [2], 6.
Tp, AW wrote, 'July: 21:' and entered the author's name after initials, R. H'ubberthorne'.
Wood 608(23). Wing H3234.

3714. [**Hubert, Francis**] . *The deplorable life and death of Edward the second, king of England.* London: [N. Okes] f. R. Michell, 1628. 8°. Pp. [3], 150. Parchment.
Between pp. 80 and 81, a loose slip of paper with 'Ed. 2' and ^{v}, notes, all in AW's hand, cropped.
Wood 83. STC 13900.

3715. Hubert, Robert. *A catalogue of many natural rarities, . . . Collected by Robert Hubert, . . . daily to be seen, . . . at the . . . musick house.* London: T. Radcliffe f. the author, 1665. 8°. Pp. [2], 76.
Flyleaf, upper, scribbles, numbers, '8' . P. 67, at printed 'A good load-stone', AW wrote, 'largest in the world Mus. Oxon.' Pp. 1, 5-7, 11, 29, etc. to 76, 'a' letters in margins, prob. not by AW.
Wood 700b(2). Wing H3244.

3716. Hudson, Michael. *The royall, and the royallist's plea, shewing, that the kings majesty hath the chiefe power in this realme.* [London]: n.pub., 1647. 4°. Pp. [8], 22.

P. [1], bsm.
Wood 612(58). Wing H3262 (Wing, royalists).

3717. Hue and Cry. *A hue & crie after the good old cause.* [London]: n.pub., [1659]. 4°. Pp. 8.
Tp, AW wrote the no. in a former bundle, '23', in pencil, and p. 8, 'Octob: 1659'.
Wood 613(24). Wing H3291.

3718. H[ughes], W[illiam], trans. *Munster and Abingdon or the open rebellion there, and unhappy tumult here. . . . That from Sleidan comm. l. 10. this from . . . witnesses.* Oxford: H. Hall f. R. Blagrave, 1657.
8°. Pp. [14], 110.
Tp, under Abingdon in t, AW wrote, 'Berks', in red ink. P. 1, corrections of Muncer and Munster. AO 4.543.
Wood 453(2). Wing H3344. Madan 2340.

3719. Hugo, Hermannus. *De prima scribendi origine.* Antverpiae: Ex offic. Plantiniana, ap. B. & J. Moretos, 1617. 8°. Pp. 227, [3]. Calf with three fillets; rebacked.
Pastedown, upper, signature of W(?) Creed (twice). Flyleaf, upper, 1st, '10^d'; 2nd, 'Philolaus Systema', not in AW's hand. Tp, bsm. Possibly acquired 10 Dec. 1663, LT 1.507.
Wood 40. BL.

3720. Hugo, Hermannus. *De vera fide capessenda ad neoevangelicam synodum Dordracenam apologetici libri tres.* Antverpiae: ex off. Plantiniana ap. B. Moretum, & viduam J. Moreti, & J. Meursium, 1620. Pp. [32], 401, [19]. Parchment.
Cover, upper, inside, '1^s-8^d', 'pr 8^d' and bsm. Flyleaf, upper^v, bsm.
Wood 170. BN.

3721. Hull. *More newes from Hull.* London: f. R. Cooper, 1642. 4°. A^4.
Tp, AW overwrote former nos.; below, '55'.
Wood 373(55). Wing M2711 (two).

3722. Hull. *More plots found out, and plotters apprehended. A true relation . . . being sent in a letter from Hull . . . the first . . . of July.* London: f. H. Overton, 1643. 4°. Pp. 8.
Tp, AW altered the former no., and former no., '2'.
Wood 376(18). Wing M2714.

3723. Hull, Kingston upon. *To his most excellent majesty Charles the second . . . The humble address of the maior, . . . of Kingston upon Hull.* London: R. W. f. F. Tyton, 1660. S.sh.
At name of Henry Hibbert, vertical line in margin.
Wood 276a(203). Not in Wing (should be at T1372aA). Not in ESTCR.

3724. Humbie, A. *A letter from Newcastle, to the right honourable the lord high chancellour of Scotland.* London: f. R. Bostock a. S. Gellibrand, 1644, 26 Oct. 4°. Pp. 5.
Wood 377(34). Wing H3366.

3725. Humble Wishes. *The humble wishes of a loyal subject.* London: f. A. Banks, 1681. S.sh.
AW wrote 'Dec'.
Wood 417(78). Wing H3651.

3726. [Humfrey, John]. *Materials for union, proposed to publick consideration, . . . By – m.a. Pem. col. Oxon.* Oxford: n.pub., 1681. 4°. Pp. 7.
Tp, AW wrote, 'supposed to be written by Joh. Humphred [sic] sometimes of Pemb. Coll. M. A.', in red ink, and, 'published in the latter end of March 1681'.
[MS.] Wood D. 26(14). Wing H3685.

3727. Humours, Table of. *A table of the humo[urs in a] mans body.* N.p.: n.pub., n.d. S.sh. (mutilated; part of a larger work, cf. the printed: 'Place this Table in page 39').
Wood 276a(31). Not identified.

3728. Humphrey, Lawrence. *Optimates, sive de nobilitate, ejusque antiqua origine, natura, officiis . . . libri tres. . . . Adjunctus est . . . Philo Judaeus de nobilitate.* Basileae: per J. Oporinum, (1560, Martio). 8°. Pp. 381, [1]. Calf with 3 fillets, stamp centrepiece (Ker, pl. VII, no. 7), and spine, 6 bands; rebacked (Oxford binding).
Pastedowns, 2 Latin ms. fragments, 12th century, theology (Ker, no. 1602), with some notes, not in AW's hand. Tp, an owner's symbol (superimposed letters CIS?); and some annotation, presumably by a former

owner, rubbed out. Text, passim, some notes in 4 hands, none by AW.
Wood 443. BL.

3729. Humphrey, Lawrence. *Ad illustrissimam R. Elizabetham, L. H. vice-can. Oxon. oratio Wood-stochiae habita [31 Aug.].* Londini: apud J. Dayum, 1572. 4°. A-C⁴,D².
Tp, at L. H., AW wrote, 'Laurentius Humfrey.'
Wood 512(2). STC 13959.5.

3730. Humphrey, Lawrence. *Joannis Juelli . . . episcopi Sarisburiensis vita & mors, eiusq; verae doc-trinae defensio.* London: ap. J. Dayum, 1573. 4°. Pp. [36], 269, [31]. Parchment.
Flyleaf, upper, scribbles and Latin material; signature 'Georgii Hockinni' (or Heckini). Flyleaf, lower, names, 'Richard', 'George Marke', 'John Sparke'. Tp, 'Henrici Jacksoni Oxoniensis . . . [erased word] pretium. 3ˢ.'; and 'Jo. Argallus, 1573. Decembr. primo' with a price, erased (AO 1.760). *1 (errata p.), 'Liber Henrici Jacksoni, Collegii Corp. Christi, Oxon: Maii 21°˙ 1600. Cui magis de deo quam deo credam?' with his peculiar mark, a 3-pedalled flower on a curly stem. In the text, annotations in several hands. For Jackson's notes, passim, e.g., pp. 1-4, 269; for Argall's, pp. 153, 155, 177-181. AW's notes, often names of persons or places in margins, are indexed on a slip bound as the flyleaf, upper, 2nd. Other notes by AW are on pp. 19, in margin, 'non credo' and 'vix credo'; 21, 'in com. Oxon'; 27; 29; 31, 'Obiit Jac. Curtoppus 19 Jul. an. 1557. et sepultus jacet in Ecclesia Cath. Christi Oxoniae. Vide Histor. et Antiq. Univer. Oxon lib. 2. p. 286. 2 et p. 260'; 44, at 'ex Smithina officina', 'out of the [Richard] Smithes forge.'; 80, 'vulgo Thomam [Christ Church bell]'; 88, at Pet. Caraeus, 'Carew' and at Rich. Bartaeo, 'Bertey'; 105, 'Weston' (Hugh?); 130, 'Quatervois'; and 253. LT 1.459 (and 1.331).
Wood 538. STC 13963.

3731. Hungerford, Edward. *Sir Edward Hungerfords vindication, for the surrendring of Malmsbury.* London: f. F. Leach, 1643, 6 May. 4°. A⁴.
Tp, AW wrote 'Thomas' over 'Edward' (the letter is authored, A4, by 'Thomas Hungerford').
Wood 376(11). Wing H3727.

3732. Hunt, Nicholas. *Newe recreations . . . Judiciary exercises.* London: A. Math[ewes] f. L. Faune, 1631. 12°. Pp. [22], 286. Parchment.
1st tp, 'praetium 8ᵈ Decem. 17ᵗʰ 1634 Henry: Daniell'.
Wood 20. STC 13992.

3733. [Hunt, Thomas]. *The great and weighty considerations, relating to the duke of York.* London: n.pub., 1680. Fol. Pp. [1-2], 1-8, 13-35.
Tp, bsm. P. 8, marks in margin, not in AW's manner.
Wood 660c(23) (not in Bodl. CD cat.). Wing H3751.

3734. [Hunt, Thomas]. *The rights of the bishops to judge in capital cases in parliament, cleared. Being a full answer to two books [by D. Holles and T. Barlow].* London: T. Braddyll f. R. Clavel, 1680. 8°. Pp. [8], 166.
Flyleaf, upperᵛ, AW wrote, 'When this following book first came [out], it was the common report that it was written by Dʳ Tho. Barlow Bishop of Linc. & Sʳ Joh. Birkenhead [/] pret. 1 - 3ᵈ - Oxon. [/] Tho. Turner a com[mon] Lawyer seems to be the author.' Tp, below, AW wrote, 'Dʳ Tho. Barlow'. LT 2.435.
Wood 574(3). Wing H3759.

3735. Huntingdon, Robert*. *Sundry reasons inducing major Robert Huntingdon to lay down his com-mission [2 Aug., 12 Aug.].* London: n.pub., 1648 ('Printed in the Yeare. 1648'). 4°. Pp. [2], 14.
Wood 609(4). Wing H3774 ('O' not recorded in Wing).

3736. Hursey, Roger. *Brave newes from Ireland: of a remarkable battle fought . . . against six regiments of the rebels, captain Hursey being chief commander.* London: f. [I. G] (cropped), 1641[2]. 4°. A⁴.
Wood 507(32). Wing H3789 (two) ('O' not recorded in Wing).

3737. Hurst, Henry. Αγνοια . . . *Or, the inability of the highest improved natural man to attaine . . . three sermons.* Oxford: H. Hall. f. R. Davis, 1659. 8°. Pp. [12], 203, [8] (7 pp. books sold by Davis).
Missing in 1837. T in the Whitehead cat. is 'Sermons by Henry – Oxon 1659'.
Wood 881(2). Wing H3790. Madan 2447. *Harv.*

3738. Hurst, Henry. *The faithful and diligent servant of the lord, blessed . . . a funeral discourse on the death of mr. Thomas Cawton.* London: f. T. Parkhurst, 1677. 4°. Pp. [4], 31.
Tp, 'Hurst' underscored in red ink.

Wood 634(6). Wood H3793.

3739. Huserus, Conradus, trans. from German. *Tractatus de imposturis et ceremoniis Judaeorum nostri temporis [trans. from Marcus Lombardus?].* Basileae: per P. Pernam, [1575?]. 4°. Pp. 66, [1].
Text, notes in more than one hand, none in AW's hand. LT 1.459 (and 1.331).
Wood 477(4). BL.

3740. Huttichius, Joannes. *Collectanea antiquitatum in urbe atque agro Moguntino repertarum.* Mogunt.: Ex aedibus J. Schoeffer, 1520 or 1525. Fol.
Missing. Acquired 11 Nov. 1659, 8^d, LT 1.287. Ed. not identified.
LT 1.287. BL.

3741. Hyde, Edward. Clarendon, earl of. *Two speeches made in the house of peers . . . for, and against accommodation, . . . by the earl of Pembroke [Philip Herbert], . . . by the lord Brooke [Robert Greville; both are by E. Hyde] [19 Dec.].* [London]: n.pub., 1642[3]. 4°. Pp. 7.
Tp, no. 24 in a former bundle.
Wood 614(52). Wing P1125A.

3742. [Hyde, Edward]. Clarendon, earl of. *Second thoughts; or the case of a limited toleration, stated.* [London]: n.pub., [1671]. 4°. Pp. 10.
Tp, AW wrote 'Dupl', in pencil. Dupl. at Wood 614(15).
Wood 611(18). Wing C4425 (Wing, before 1685).

3743. [Hyde, Edward]. Clarendon, earl of. *Second thoughts; or the case of a limited toleration, stated.* [London]: n.pub., [1671]. 4°. Pp. 10.
P. 10, AW wrote at different times, 'Published 1671.', 'Donum AWood.', and 'Penned as tis said by Ed. E. of Clarendon.' Dupl. at Wood 611(18).
Wood 614(15). Wing C4425 (Wing, before 1685).

3744. Hyde, Edward. Clarendon, earl of. *Two letters . . . one to . . . the duke of York: the other to the dutchess, occasioned by her embracing the Roman Catholick religion.* [London]: n.pub., [1680?]. Fol. Pp. 4.
P. 1, AW wrote '167-' in pencil. LT 2.219.
Wood 276a(155). Wing C4429.

3745. Hyde, Edward, d.d., and John Ley. *A debate concerning the English liturgy, . . . drawn out in two English & two Latin epistles.* London: A. M. f. E. Brewster, 1656. 4°. Pp. [14], 62, [1] (wanting the preliminary list of Ley's works).
Tp, former no. (?), '8', and bsm. AW removed the bibliography of Ley and inserted it among his catalogues, see Catalogues, Hyde and Ley, [MS.] Wood D. 22(2), item 1522.
[MS.] Wood B. 37(3). Wing L1873.

3746. Hyde, Henry. *A true copy of sir Henry Hide's speech on the scaffold, . . . taken in short-hand . . . by John Hinde [4 March].* London: P. Cole, 1650. 4°. Pp. 15.
Flyleaf, upper^{r-v}, AW wrote notes of 21 and 17 lines about Hyde: 'Sr Hen. Hyde Brother to Dr Alex. Hide, afterwards Bishop of Salisbury – beheaded 4. Mar. 1650 – His crime was the receiving and acting by vertue of a commission from Charles Stuart as K. of Gr. Britaine, France & Ireland, being qualified by him as his agent, to the court of the great <u>Mogul</u> Turk, with intent to destroy the trade of the Turky company & the Parliaments interest, not only in Constantinople, but also in Mytylene, Anatolia & Smyrna; in which places he had a commission to be Consul. His aime being likewise to seize upon the English Merchants goods, for the use of the said Charles Stuart. For the effecting of which designe, he presum'd to discharg Sr Tho. Bendish of his Embassie, being Leeger [i.e., ledger] there for the state of England: he procured audience of the grand visier, & raised great feares & uproars among the Merchants &c [and] Merc. polit. nu. 53 June 22 an. 1651. [/] Smyrna March 26. 1651 [/] Some of Sr Hen. Hydes abettors, who gave in their names of him, & against the present government, have met with vengeance here; for one was stab'd to death by a servant, & no justice. Another wounded almost to death, but recovered; two are mad, one Mr Pixley, in whose house I am, was the first man for Hyde; he had shut himself in his chamber, & would have hanged himself, but wee of the house broke in upon him & prevented him – In my opinion the management of such an important trade, should not be confin'd in a disposal of a company &c' (apparently a quote from *Merc. polit.*). Dupl. at Wood 609(24).
Wood 367(6). Wing H3871.

3747. Hyde, Henry. *A true copy of sir Henry Hide's speech on the scaffold, . . . taken in short-hand . . . by John Hinde [4 March].* London: P. Cole, 1650. 4°. Pp. 15.

Tp, AW wrote 'Dupl.' Dupl at Wood 367(5).
Wood 609(24). Wing H3871.

3748. Hyde, R. *Ten short notes humbly tendred to the right honourable the lords and commons . . . wherein his majesties revenue and the interest of trade are under consideration [21 June 1661]*. N.p.: n.pub., [1661]. S.sh.
Wood 276a(275). Not in Wing. Not in ESTCR.

3749. I., C. *The copy of a letter sent from a person of much honour . . . present at that hot encounter betwixt . . . lord Goring . . . and . . . lord Fairfax . . . on the 13. of June, in the suburbs of Colchester.* [London]: n.pub., 1648. 4°. Pp. [2], 6.
Tp, AW wrote after the year, '15 Jun'.
Wood 502(25). Wing I2.

3750. I., T. *A perfect narrative of the proceedings of the army under . . . col. Michael Jones . . . in their last advance from Dublin.* London: f. J. Wright, 1648, 17 Oct. 4°. Pp. [2], 10.
Wood 509(31). Wing I14.

3751. I., W. *A confutation of a late paper, entituled, an answer to the lords protestation [respecting the impeachment of E. Fitzharris]. In a letter.* (London): (f. T. D.), (1681). Fol. Pp. 7.
Wood 657(28). Wing I17.

3752. Ichthuothera. Ἰχθυοθηρα, *or, the royal trade of fishing. Discovering the profit the Hollanders have made thereof. [Preceded by letters patent, 22 Aug. 1661, Charles the second . . . To all whom (appointing a council of the royal fishing)].* London: J. F. f. R. Royston (J. Bill a. C. Barker), 1662 (1661). 4°. Pp. [2], 8, 30 (2 pts.).
Tp, AW wrote, '5ᵈ'. Acquired 18 July 1662, LT 1.444.
[MS.] Wood C. 14(9). Wing I31 (with a reissue of Wing C3611A).

3753. Impropriations Purchased. *Impropriations purchased by the commissioners sitting at Goldsmiths-hall for compositions with delinquents.* London: R. Cotes, 1648. 4°. Pp. [3], 24.
Wood 370(6). Wing I107.

3754. Indian. *'The Tall Indian-KING, who was betrayed on Board of an English Interloper, and Barbarously abused on Board . . . Now to be seen at mr. Cartors at the Sign of the Black Bull near Carfax in Oxon, for 3d. a peece'.* N.p.: n.pub., [1678]. S.sh. 12°. 8 lines.
Inserted out of place at Wood Diaries 16, item 182, January 1672, f. 8. Above, AW wrote, 'A tall man, under 30, taller by the head than I, gentile clothes, & rings & pendants in his eares, & rings on his fingers-'; in the text, over the printed 'Indian', 'African'; and below, 'Dec. 2. 1678 [/] His name Escelin K. of Neumon in Guinny in Africa – Christned at Christ Ch. Lond. by the name of Joseph circa 25. Jan.' LT 2.425.
[MS.] Wood Diaries 16b (not in Bodl. CD cat.). Not in Wing. Not in ESTCR.

3755. Indies, Elephant. *A true and perfect description of the strange and wonderful she-elephant, sent from the Indies, . . . at London, August 1. 1683.* London: f. R. Taylor, 1683. S.sh.
[MS.] Wood B. 35(32). Wing T2527 (two).

3756. [Ingelo, Nathaniel, and Benjamin Rogers]. *Hymnus eucharisticus.* [London]: n.pub., [1660]. S.sh.
Flyleaf, upper, AW wrote a 28-line introduction: 'Hymnus Eucharisticus. Made by Dʳ Nathan. Ingelo Fellow of Eaton Coll. neare Windsore, somtimes of Qu. Coll. in Cambridge: – an. 1660. [/] It was then put into English by the author: [/] To this Hymnus Eucharisticus Ben. Rogers of Windsore, Bach. of Musick, did at the request of the Lord Mayor of Lond. & Aldermen compose a song of four parts [/] This song was admirably well performed by about 12. voices, 12 Instruments & an Organ, by mostly his Majesties servants, in the Guild hall of the citie of London, on the "12 [in margin: "5] of July (Thursday) 1660, on which day his Maj. K Ch. 2. James Duke of York Hen. Duke of Gloc. & both Houses of Parliament were entertained with a most sumptuous dinner & banquet. [/] Copies of these papers were printed in Lat. & English: one was delivered to the K. & the two Dukes, & others to the Nobility &c purposely that they might look on them, while it was performed [above: sung] by the said servants belonging to his Majestie. [/] It gave very great content, & Benj. Rogers who composed the song, being then present, gained great credit for what he had done, & a good reward. [/] It was sunge in the Lat. tongue'. AW was not in London for this event, 5 July. For an account by another person, see Wood 416(87). See LT 1.321 and also AOF 2.306-7, which includes much of the above. On the item itself, AW wrote the year, '1660'. Dupl. at Wood 416(86).
Wood 398(13-4). Wing H3886 (rare, 2 at O).

3757. [Ingelo, Nathaniel, and Benjamin Rogers]. *Hymnus eucharisticus.* [London]: n.pub., [1660]. S.sh.
ᵛ, address, 'Mʳ Colson', not in AW's hand. Dupl. at Wood 398(13-4); see notes there.
Wood 416(86) (not in Bodl. CD cat.). Wing H3886 (rare, 2 at O).

3758. [Ingelo, Nathaniel], and Benjamin Rogers. *A song of thanksgiving.* [London]: n.pub., [1660]. S.sh.
AW wrote the year, '1660'. Dupl. at 416(87). This is a translation of Wood 398(13-4); see notes there.
Wood 398(15). Wing R1793A (rare, 2 at O).

3759. [Ingelo, Nathaniel], and Benjamin Rogers. *A song of thanksgiving.* [London]: n.pub., [1660]. S.sh.
AW wrote the year, '1660'. ᵛ, 'Dupl.', in pencil. Dupl. at Wood 398(15). Not in AW's hand: 'This musique was performd at Guild Hall London in the year 1660 at the great ffeast, for king Charles the Second, by [lined out] with about 20 of his majesties servants, and the 2 Houses of Parliament at Dinner in the said Hall: Composed by Ben: Rogers then of Windsor by order of Sʳ Tho: Allen Lord Mayor; and the Court of Aldermen performed to his Majesties Great Sattisfaction being Instrumentall, and vocale musique in Lattine, about the year 1653 was severall Sets of Airs of the said B. R. for the violins, and organ, of 4 parts, sent into Germany to the Arch Duke Leopolds Court (who is now Emperour) and plaid there by his own Musitiones to his great content[,] He himselfe, being a composer'. This is a translation of Wood 398(13-4); see notes there. LT 1.321.
Wood 416(87) (not in Bodl. CD cat.). Wing R1793A (rare, 2 at O).

3760. Ingoldsby's Regiment*. *The representation of colonell [Richard] Inglesby's regiment in . . . Oxford [7 Sept.].* [London?]: n.pub., [1649]. 4°. A².
Tp, AW wrote 'Dup', in pencil. Waste paper after A2, Latin disputation topic, 'sit analoge', not by AW. Dupl. at Wood 515(6); Wood 609(20b and 20c).
Wood 503(6). Wing R1100 (rare, 4 at O). Madan 2017.

3761. Ingoldsby's Regiment*. *The representation of colonell [Richard] Inglesby's regiment in . . . Oxford [7 Sept.].* [London?]: n.pub., [1649]. 4°. A².
Dupl. at Wood 503(6), Wood 609(20b), Wood 609(20c).
Wood 515(6). Wing R1100 (rare, 4 at O). Madan 2017.

3762. Ingoldsby's Regiment*. *The representation of colonell [Richard] Inglesby's regiment in . . . Oxford [7 Sept.].* [London?]: n.pub., [1649]. 4°. A².
A1, AW wrote 'dup', in pencil. Interleaved with a dupl. at Wood 609(20c). Dupl. at Wood 503(6); Wood 515(6); Wood 609(20c).
Wood 609(20b). Wing R1100 (rare, 4 at O). Madan 2017.

3763. Ingoldsby's Regiment*. *The representation of colonell [Richard] Inglesby's regiment in . . . Oxford [7 Sept.].* [London?]: n.pub., [1649]. 4°. A².
Interleaved with a dupl. at Wood 609(20b). Dupl. at Wood 503(6); Wood 515(6); Wood 609(20b).
Wood 609(20c). Wing R1100 (rare, 4 at O). Madan 2017.

3764. Ingpen, William. *The secrets of numbers.* London: H. Lowns f. J. Parker, 1624. 4°. Pp. [16], 100, [3]. Pasteboard (grey) with parchment spine. Traces of upper and lower flyleaves in marbled paper.
Flyleaf, upper, 2ndᵛ, AW wrote the titles of 4 printed works in this vol., within guidelines made with red ink. All 4 items in this volume have stitch holes which indicate that they were together before the current binding.
Wood 316(1). STC 14089.

3765. Innocent 9*. Pope. *A passionate satyr upon a devillish great he-whore . . . at Rome.* [London]: n.pub., [1679]. S.sh. (r-v).
ᵛ, AW wrote the year, '(1680)'.
Wood 417(23). Wing P662.

3766. Innocent 9*. Pope. *A second consultation between the pope and the Turk, concerning the propagation of the Catholick faith.* London: f. N. M., 1679. S.sh.
ᵛ, AW wrote 'Jan 167-[?]'.
Wood 417(17). Wing S2268 (two).

3767. Inquisition. *The cruell proceeding of the inquisition against them which deny the errors of the*

Roman church [Jacobus Salgado]. N.p.: n.pub., n.d. S.sh. (engr.).
Portions of this engraving exist in an more complex engraving in Salgado, *Slaughter-house* (1680); Madan 3.380.
Wood 276a(13) (not in Bodl. CD cat.). Not identified.

3768. Interest. *Interest of money mistaken. Or a treatise, proving, that the abatement of interest is the effect and not the cause of the riches of a nation, and that six per cent. is a proportionable interest.* London: n.pub., 1668. 4°. Pp. 24.
Acquired 21 Dec. 1668, LT 2.146.
Wood 628(4). Wing I266A.

3769. Ireland. *An exact and true relation of the late plots which were contrived and hatched in Ireland.* London: f. F. Coules, 1641. 4°. Pp. 1-5, [6-8].
Tp, AW wrote the year, '1641', and a correction. Scribble, washed out.
Wood 507(5). Wing E3621.

3770. Ireland. *The happiest newes from Ireland that ever came to England . . . Being a true and ekact [sic] relation of a great overthrow given by the earle of Clanrickards company [20 Dec.].* London: f. J. Greensmith, 1641. 4°. A⁴.
Tp, AW wrote below, '20 Dec'.
Wood 507(17). Wing H665.

3771. Ireland. *The humble petition of the protestant inhabitants of the counties of Antrim, Downe, Tyrone, &c. . . . concerning bishops.* London: n.pub., 1641. 4°. Pp. [2], 12.
Wood 507(4). Wing H3573.

3772. Ireland. *A proclamation of the lords justices for the apprehension of the chiefe rebels . . . With the true and last newes from Ireland.* London: f. H. Shepheard, 1641. 4°. Pp. [2], 14.
Tp, AW wrote, '8 Feb', in pencil. Below, '4', may not be by AW.
Wood 507(33). Wing I626A ('O' not recorded in Wing).

3773. Ireland. *The true and last newes from Ireland . . . Containing a true relation of the brave atchievements of . . . Francis Moore . . . A true copy of the election of . . . generall Plumquet [sic].* London: f. J. Wright, 1641[2]. 4°. Pp. [2], 6.
Tp, after Plumquet, AW wrote 'R[ichard] Plunket'; after the year, '1 Jan.'
Wood 507(23). Wing T2511.

3774. Ireland. *A true coppie of divers letters, sent from the governors of Ireland, to the parliament in England [or rather, a report of the proceedings in parliament 11 Nov. 1641 thereon] With a prophecie of the earle of Essex [in verse, by J. Crag].* [London]: f. S. Horten, 1641. 4°. A⁴.
Tp, in the woodcut, AW wrote, 'Dʳ Joh. Bastwicks picture' (see, e.g. AO 3.855-6, note 8).
Wood 507(21). Wing T2635.

3775. Ireland. C., R., trans. *A declaration sent to the king of France and Spayne, from the Catholiques or rebells in Ireland . . . translated out of French by R. C.* London: f. I. T., 1642. 4°. Pp. 8.
Tp, former no., '12', overwritten; below, '53'.
Wood 508(14). Wing D791.

3776. Ireland. *The particular relation of the present estate and condition of Ireland.* London: f. J. Hunscott, 1642. 4°. Pp. 20.
Tp, AW wrote, 'Feb. 14. 1641'. P. 20, upside down, scribbled jobs for 'Morn. 1. Mʳ. Harris Watch.', 2-4, illeg.
Wood 507(34). Wing P602.

3777. Ireland. *The protestation of the rebels in Ireland, and how they were beaten at the castle of Baltimore, . . . With, a relation of a great battell . . . betweene captaine Nuse, . . . and Tead-Rast . . . January 15.* London: f. I. H., 1642. 4°. A⁴.
Tp, former no. overwritten.
Wood 508(39). Wing P3870.

3778. Ireland. *Timely advice, or, motives to incite all men . . . . to subscribe to the propositions for Ireland.* London: f. E. D., 1642. 4°. A⁴.
Dupl. at Wood 614(61).
Wood 508(36). Wing T1282.

3779. Ireland. *Timely advice, or, motives to incite all men . . . to subscribe to the propositions for Ireland.* London: f. E. D., 1642. 4°. A⁴.
Tp, no. 5 in a former bundle; AW wrote 'Dupl', in pencil. Dupl. at Wood 508(36).
Wood 614(61). Wing T1282.

3780. Ireland. *The last newes from Ireland . . . Together with a list of the field officers chosen . . . for the Irish expedition.* London: f. I. Green a. A. Coe, 1642, 13 June. 4°. A⁴.
Tp, AW wrote, 'Jun 13', in pencil.
Wood 508(24). Wing L494.

3781. Ireland. *New intelligence from Ireland, received the 17. of June, 1642.* London: f. E. Blackmore, 1642, 22 June. 4°. Pp. [2], 5.
Wood 508(25). Wing N649.

3782. Ireland. *True intelligence from Ireland, relating how the rebels stole away 300. horse . . . and have taken the earle of Kildares chiefe house.* London: f. J. Sweeting, 1642, 30 June. 4°. Pp. [2], 4.
Wood 508(26). Wing T2709.

3783. Ireland. *Good and bad newes from Ireland.* London: f. F. Coles, 1642, 13 July. 4°. A⁴.
Tp, former no. '23', overwritten.
Wood 508(29). Wing G1034.

3784. Ireland. *A proclamation concerning a cessation of armes. Agreed and concluded on at Siggingstowne [15 Sept.].* London: f. E. Husbands, 1643, 21 Oct. 4°. Rpt. of Dublin: W. Bladen edition. Pp. 10.
Tp, former no., lined out.
Wood 508(47). Wing I605.

3785. Ireland. *A polt [sic] discovered in Ireland and prevented without the shedding of blood.* London: J. Coe, 1644. 4°. A⁴.
Tp, AW wrote, 'Sep. 44', in pencil.
Wood 508(52). Wing P2594.

3786. Ireland. *Good news from Ireland, being an exact relation of the late good successe at Sliggo against the Irish rebels.* London: f. J. Wright, 1645[6], 15 Jan. 4°. Pp. [2], 5.
Tp, former no., '37' (?), lined out.
Wood 509(4). Wing G1060 ('O' not recorded in Wing) (Wing, 1645).

3787. Ireland. *?.* N.p.: n.pub., [1646?]. 4°.
Missing in 1922. A leaf, A1?, is all that survives, ʳ, AW's no. '5'; ᵛ, printed, 'The Explanation of the *Frontispeece.*', with 22 lines of verse, beginning, '*Marke and behold yee bloudy* Irish *Nation*'.
Wood 509(5). Not identified.

3788. Ireland. *Exceeding good newes from Ireland: being a perfect relation of the late great overthrow given to the rebels . . . certified by . . . letters [13 Nov.].* London: f. R. Woodnoth, 1646. 4°. Pp. [2], 6.
Tp, price, '1ᵈ', lined out, may not be by AW.
Wood 509(12). Wing B208 ('O' not recorded in Wing) (Wing, B., W.).

3789. Ireland. *Victorious newes from Ireland. Being an exact relation of the routing a great army of the rebels under . . . general Roe-O-Neal.* London: f. W. Smith, 1646. 4°. A⁴.
Tp, price, '1ᵈ', lined out, may not be by AW.
Wood 509(9). Wing V345 (two) ('O' not recorded in Wing).

3790. Ireland. *The bloody diurnall from Ireland . . . propositions, orders, . . . of the confederate Catholiques assembled at Kilkenny.* London: n.pub., 1647. 4°. Rpt. of Kilkenny edition. Pp. 8.
Tp, AW wrote, '46-47 q[uaere]', in pencil.
Wood 509(15). Wing B3232.

3791. Ireland. *Two letters from Corke in Ireland.* [London]: n.pub., 1648. 4°. Pp. [2], 6.
Tp, AW wrote, 'Not dated' (i.e., the letters are not dated).
Wood 509(29). Wing L3459 ('O' not recorded in Wing).

3792. Ireland. *A perfect and particuler [sic] relation of the severall marches and proceedings of the armie . . . from the taking of Drogheda.* London: f. F. Leach, 1649. 4°. Pp. 8.
Dupl. at Wood 609(21).

Wood 510(11). Wing P1471.

3793. Ireland. *A perfect and particuler [sic] relation of the severall marches and proceedings of the armie . . . from the taking of Drogheda.* London: f. F. Leach, 1649. 4°. Pp. 8.
Tp, AW wrote, 'Dupl', in pencil. Dupl. at Wood 510(11).
Wood 609(21). Wing P1471.

3794. Ireland. *Ireland's declaration: being a remonstrance of the generality of the good people of Ireland [Dublin, 13 Mar. 1649].* [London]: n.pub., [1660]. S.sh.
AW wrote below, 'fictions'; ᵛ, '31 Mar 16–' (cropped). Thomason recorded 'March. 19. 1659'.
Wood 510(14). Wing I1022.

3795. Ireland. *A true and perfect account of the miraculous sea-monster. Or, wonderful fish lately taken in Ireland.* [London]: f. P. Brooksby a. W. Whitwood, 1674. 4°. Pp. 8.
Tp, AW wrote, 'published about Christmas 1673', and below, 'Hawt. Mar. Morg.', perhaps a gift from Hawtaine [Houghton] Maria Morgan, LT 2.280.
[MS.] Wood B. 35(28). Wing T2520.

3796. Ireland. *A collection of certain horrid murthers in several counties of Ireland. Committed since the 23. of Octob. 1641.* London: f. H. Brome, 1679. 4°. Pp. [10], 22, [1].
P. 10, AW wrote, at the murder of bishop of Killala, 'No such thing appears in Wareus de praesulibus Hibern' (his copy is heavily annotated, Wood 415(1), item 6451). Passim, AW, in pencil, underscored and entered lines in margins and Arabic numbers totaling the numbers of murders in the various cities.
Wood 506(2). Wing C5118.

3797. Ireland. *A true relation of the extraordinary thunder & lightning, . . . in the north of Ireland.* London: n.pub., 1680. Fol. Pp. [4].
[MS.] Wood D. 28(27). Wing T2951.

3798. Ireland. *The journal of the proceedings of the parliament in Ireland, with the establishment of their forces there.* London: f. R. Clavell, 1689. 4°. Pp. 20.
Wood 510(37). Wing I422A.

3799. [Ireland, Thomas] (?). *Momus elencticus, or a light come-off upon that serious piece of drollerie presented by the vice chancellor of Oxon. . . . at Whitehall, to expell the melancholy of the court.* [London]: n.pub., [1654]. 4°. Pp. 7.
Flyleaf, upperᵛ, AW wrote, 'This Momus Elenctitus following was made on several persons of the Univ. of Oxon, who had written verses on the peace made between Oliver Lord Protector of Engl & the common wealth thereof, & the states of Holland. which verses were put into a Book entit. Musarum Oxoniensium ΕΛΔΙΟΦΟΡΙΑ. sive ob faedera auspiciis sereniss. Oliveri Reipub. Angl. Scot. . . . Oxon 1654. in 4°' (i.e., Wood 484(4), item 4911; and see item 995), and a brief note, not in AW's hand. Tp, AW wrote the year, '1654', in pencil; pp. 2-5, 14 identifications. LT 1.189; AOF 2.200
Wood 515(13). Wing I294. Madan 2246.

3800. [Ireland, Thomas]. *Speeches spoken to the king and queen, . . . in Christ-Church hall, Oxford [29 Sept.].* London: [J. Grismond] f. R. Royston, 1663. 4°. Pp. 8.
Wood 515(30). Wing I295. Madan 2621.

3801. Ireland, Thomas. *Verses spoken at the appearance of the king and queene . . . in Christ-Church hall [29 Sept.].* Oxford: H. Hall f. R. Davis, 1663. 4°. Pp. 7 (p. [8] blank).
Wood 515(29). Wing I296. Madan 2622.

3802. Ireland, William*; Thomas Pickering*, and John Grove*. *The tryals of William Ireland, Thomas Pickering, and John Grove; for conspiring to murder the king.* London: f. R. Pawlet, 1678. Fol. Pp. [3], 84.
P. [1], engraving of Pickering (age 53) pasted on. Tp, AW wrote the price, '2ˢ-6'. LT 2.434.
Wood 424(6). Wing T2268.

3803. Ireton, Henry*. *Independency stript & whipt. Or, Iretons petition, . . . examined and confuted, together with the character of an Independent, by a lover of his country.* [London]: n.pub., 1648. 4°. Pp. [2], 14.
Wood 617(13). Wing I145.

3804. Ireton, Henry. *A declaration and prolcamation [sic] of the deputy-general of Ireland, concerning*

the . . . plague; and for . . . fasting and prayer [30 July]. London: J. Field, [1650]. 4°. Rpt. of Cork edition. Pp. 15.
Tp, AW wrote 'Hen. Ireton'.
Wood 510(17). Wing I1030.

3805. Ireton, John. *Mr. John Iretons oration at the choosing of the new lord mayor.* [London]: n.pub., [1659]. 4°. Pp. 8.
P. 8, AW wrote 'M: Dc: Lix'.
Wood 616(14). Wing I1035.

3806. Isack, I. *A famous victory obtained, by* { *Sir William Brewerton [sic, et al.].* London: B. Alsop, 1644, 2 Feb. 4°. A⁴.
Tp, AW lined out a former no., '54'; and wrote the dates, 'Jan. 1643', in pencil, and '1643'.
Wood 376(60). Wing I1062 (one) ('O' not recorded in Wing).

3807. Italy. *The character of Italy: or, the Italian anatomiz'd, by an English chyrurgion.* London: f. N. Brooke, 1660. 12°. Pp. [11], 93, [3] (3 pp. books sold by N. Brook).
AW wrote the date, 'July: 21. 1660:' (purchased from Davis, see LT 1.321 and note 3).
Wood 582(6). Wing C2018.

3808. Iter Boreale. *Iter Boreale his country clown: or, the country scourg'd for their barbarisme to the citizens.* [London]: f. the authour, 1665. S.sh.
AW wrote, 'written in time of the great plague, when the Londoners were forced to fly into the Country'; ᵛ, '1665'. LT 2.40.
Wood 416(108) (by R. Wild in Bodl. CD cat.). Wing I1091 (Wing, for the author).

3809. Ivie, Thomas. *Alimony arraign'd: or the remonstrance and humble appeal . . . from . . . chancery . . . wherein are set forth the unheard-of practices . . . of lewd . . . women.* London: n.pub., 1654. 4°. Pp. [2], 52, [1].
Tp, 'ABosco'. Bsm.
Wood 654a(16) (not in Bodl. CD cat.). Wing I1108.

3810. Izacke, Richard. *Antiquities of the city of Exeter.* London: E. Tyler a. R. Holt, f. R. Marriott, sold G. Marriott, 1677. 8°. Pp. [8], 64, 191, [62]. Calf, speckled, with 2 fillets and 2 vertical fillets; rebacked.
Flyleaf, upper, 1st, AW wrote, 'I bought this book out of Dʳ Lockyes studie - of Mr. Crossley Dec. 4. 1679. pret. 2ˢ-6ᵈ' (LT 2.471; Thomas Lockey died 29 June 1679, AOF 2.242). Flyleaf, 2ndᵛ, subject heading, not by AW. Tp, after author, AW wrote 'town clerk an. 1682'. P. [43], AW commented at the entry of James Turbervill: 'You say on p. 127 that he lived a privat life'. Some marks in margins and underscoring in text, e.g., pp. 127, 133, 148 (brief note), 151, 157, 171, in ink and pencil.
Wood 203. Wing I1110.

3811. J., G. *A letter sent into France to the lord duke of Buckingham . . . of a miracle.* [London]: n.pub., 1649. 4°. Pp. [2], 5.
Tp, '4ᵈ', 'pret: 6', and '9. Roy–' (a shelf-mark?, lined out), prob. not by AW.
Wood 364(25). Wing J9 (3).

3812. J., H. *The history of the life and death of pope Joane: who was elected to the papacy, an. 855. under the name of Johannes Anglus.* London: f. F. Coles, 1663. 4°. Pp. [2], 16.
[MS.] Wood C. 39(2). Wing J14 (rare, 2 at O).

3813. J., P. *An addition to the relation of some passages about the English-Irish army, before they came to the siege at Namptwich.* London: f. R. Bostocke, 1643[4]. 4°. Pp. [4], 12.
Tp, AW altered a former no., '56'.
Wood 376(62). Wing J24.

3814. J., T. *A discourse, betweene Upright the shoomaker and master Pattent, the smith. . . . in Smithfield [20 Aprill 1639].* London: B. Alsop a. T. F[awcet] f. F. Groves, 1640. 8°. A⁸.
Wood 704(4). STC 14066 (two).

3815. J., T. *A letter of advice to . . . Monck, tending to the peace and welfare of this nation.* [London]: n.pub., 1659[60]. 4°. Pp. 8.
Tp, AW wrote after the year, 'Jan:'.
Wood 632(69). Wing J38.

3816. Jacob, Henry. Birkhead, Henry, ed. *Philologiae* ανακαλυπτηριον *oratione celebratum inaugurali, . . . publicavit à quindecennis H. B.* Oxoniae: H. Hall, 1652. 4°. Pp. [12], 98.
Tp, AW wrote the price, '8ᵈ'. Acquired 29 Aug. 1662, LT 1.454.
Wood 512(11). Wing J97. Madan 2184.

3817. Jamaica. *The present state of Jamaica. . . . To which is added . . . Hen. Morgan's voyage.* London: F. Clark f. T. Malthus, 1683. 12°. Pp. [10], 117 (4 pp. books sold by Malthus).
Flyleaf, lower, 2ndᵛ, random notes concerning anti-royalist books on waste paper now the flyleaf; after a line cropped at top, AW wrote, 'Mr [Robert] West [/] Published as an example for these times, & perhaps the author would have the K deposed/ K. Ed. 2. K- Ch- } bound with it' (AW may have been referring to the volume Wood 234(1-4) which concerns kingship. See esp. the note at Wood 234(3), item 3686).
Wood 156(5). Wing P3268.

3818. Jamaica. *A sad and terrible relation of the dreadful earth-quake that happened at Jamaco [7 July].* [London]: f. P. Brooksby, J. Deacon, J. Blare, a. J. Back, 1692. 8°. Pp. [2], 14.
Tp, 'Jamaco' corrected to 'Jamaca', perhaps by AW. LT 3.391.
[MS.] Wood D. 28(31). Wing S244F (one) ('O' not recorded in Wing).

3819. James*. Wales, prince of. *An account of the pretended prince of Wales, and other grievanses, that occasioned the . . . prince of Orange's coming . . . To which is added, a short account of the murther of the earl of Essex.* [London]: n.pub., 1688. 4°. Pp. [2], 37.
Tp, AW wrote, '6ᵈ – Jan. 10. 1688[9]'. Pp. 5, 7-8, line in margin; p. 10, at judgment of Dr. Willis, 'q[uaere]'. LT 3.297.
Wood 529(15). Wing A340.

3820. James 1. *Daemonologie, in forme of a dialogue, divided into three bookes.* Edinburgh: R. Waldegraue, 1597. 4°. Pp. [10], 81. Pasteboard (blue) with parchment spine. 1st upper and last lower flyleaves, marbled paper.
Flyleaf, upper, 2ndᵛ, AW wrote the titles of 3 printed works in this vol., within guidelines made with red ink. Tp, AW wrote, 'written by James K. of Scotl. afterward of England. v[ide] [John] Spotswood Ch. hist. of Scotland.' (Wing S5022ff.). Pp. 47, 57, 72-3, minor underscoring and marks in margin, not in AW's normal manner.
[MS.] Wood B. 21(1). STC 14364.

3821. James 1. Βασιλικον δωρον. *Or his maiesties instructions to his dearest sonne, Henrie the prince.* London: R. Field f. J. Norton, 1603. 8° (a variant, some sheets being of a different setting). Pp. [36], 154. Calf with 3 fillets, stamp decoration inside corners (dragons), roll decoration on spine (Ashm. binding).
Flyleaf, 2nd, the titles of 5 printed works in this vol. written by an Ashm. librarian (same hand in Wood 276a). Tp, '4ᵈ' over an earlier price and scribbles. P. 154, scribbles.
Wood 673(1). STC 14353.

3822. [James 1]. *A counter-blaste to tobacco.* London: R. B[arker], 1604. 4° (wanting all after sig. C1). A2-4,B⁴,C1.
Tp, 'By Kᵍ. James', not in AW's hand. B1ᵛ, B2ᵛ, scribbles by George Cole; and C1ᵛ, by Nicholas Crosse (?).
[MS.] Wood D. 30(3). STC 14363.

3823. James 1. *His majesties commission to all the lords, and others of the privie counsell, touching the creation of baronets.* London: R. Barker, 1611. 4°. Pp. [2], 44. Pasteboard (blue) with parchment spine.
Flyleaf, upper, 3rd, AW wrote the titles of 11 printed works in this vol., within guidelines made with red ink.
Wood 445(1). STC 9225.

3824. James 1. *A publication of his ma*ᵗⁱᵉˢ *edict, and severe censure against private combats and combatants.* London: R. Barker, 1613[4]. 4° (wanting Q1 and Q2). Pp. [2], 116.
P. 3, 'R', a scribble, in margin.
Wood 616(6). STC 8498.

3825. James 1. *James by the grace of God, king of England, . . . To all . . . the humble supplication and petition of one religious Philotheos [13 Oct. 1621].* [London]: [W. Stansby], [1621]. S.sh.
Notes, not in AW's hand. At bottom, 'Gabriel Gonzaga', not in AW's hand. On blankᵛ, accounts, and 'King James his Brefe for Philotheos about Sᵗ. Helens Temple at Jerusalem' not in AW's hand.
Wood 276a(124). STC 8673 (two). Steele 1320.

3826. James 1*. *The connexion: being choice collections of . . . matters in king James his reign.* London: f. W. Crook, 1681. 8°. Pp. [8], 176 (1 p. books printed f. Crooke).
Tp, AW wrote '1.3ᵈ' and 'Nov. 1680'. Bsm.
Wood 251(2). Wing C5882 ('O' not recorded in Wing).

3827. James 1*. *A just vindication of the honour of king James . . . against the . . . pamphlet, printed by B. Took.* (London): (f. R. Oswell), [1683]. Fol. Pp. 4.
Wood 276a(182). Wing J1243.

3828. James 1, and Charles 1. Bayly, Thomas, ed. *Witty apophthegms delivered at severall times, and upon severall occasions, by king James, king Charls [et al.].* London: f. E. Farnham, 1658. 12°. Pp. [8], 168, [2].
Missing in 1837. 'Witty Apothegms – Lond. 1658' in Whiteside cat.
Wood 58. Wing W3236. *Hunt, Clark.*

3829. James 1, and George Abbott. *King James his letter . . . to the lord archbishop of Canterbury; concerning preaching and preachers; with the bishop of Canterburies letter.* [London]: f. T. Walkeley, 1642. 4°. Pp. [2], 9. Calf with 3 fillets, stamp decoration inside corners (2 leaves, sunflower spouting fleur-de-lis]), and roll decoration at inner, spine edge (Ashm. binding); rebacked.
Flyleaf, upper, 2nd, the titles of 78 printed works in this vol., by an Ashm. librarian (same hand in Wood 276a). There are 10 duplicates in this vol. Tp, AW identified the archbp., 'Dʳ George Abbot'. Bsm.
Wood 632(1). Wing J139.

3830. James 2*. *To his royal highnes the duke [of York], upon his arrival [at Windsor, 2 Sept.].* [London]: n.pub., [1679]. S.sh. (r-v).
ᵛ, AW wrote '1681'.
Wood 660c(27). Wing T1377.

3831. James 2*. *A letter from a gentleman in the city . . . concerning the bill for disabling the duke of York to inherit the imperial crown [8 Nov. 1678].* London: n.pub., 1680. 4°. Pp. [2], 21.
Wood 632(54). Wing L1390.

3832. James 2*. *On the arrival of his royal highness. The duke [of York] into England.* London: f. G. K., 1680. S.sh.
Year in Roman numerals altered to MDCLXX'I'X, and '79'.
Wood 276a(529). Wing O300.

3833. James 2*. *A prospect of a popish successor.* [London]: n.pub., [1680[1]]. S.sh.
Missing in 1922. AW entered the t on the upper flyleaf at the beginnning of Wood 417(1). BL has stitch marks and 3 folds; no discernable AW marks.
Wood 417(42). Wing P3804 (one). *BL.*

3834. James 2*. *A letter from a person of quality in Scotland, to a person of honour in London: concerning . . . James, duke of York.* [London]: (f. J. Heath-coat), (1681). S.sh. (r-v).
Wood 660c(28). Wing L1424.

3835. James 2*. *Memoirs of the most remarkable enterprises and actions of James duke of York.* London: f. R. Janeway, 1681. Fol. Pp. [2], 12.
Tp, bsm. P. 6, at printed 'Gough', AW wrote 'Goffe'.
Wood 660c(29). Wing M1672.

3836. James 2*. *An anniversary poem on the sixth of May, his royal highness miraculous deliverance, . . . from the shipwreck.* London: f. J. Hindmarsh, [1683]. S.sh.
Wood 660c(31). Wing A3243.

3837. James 2*. *The proceedings at the kings-bench-bar upon the execution of the writ of enquiry of damages at the suit of . . . the duke of York against Titus (formerly stil'd doctor) Oates.* [London]: sold at the entrance into the Old-Spring Garden, 1684. S.sh.
Wood 660c(32). Wing P3561.

3838. James 2. *To . . . William, lord archbishop of Canterbury . . . and John lord archbishop of York [directions concerning preachers] [5 March].* (London): (C. Bill, H. Hills, a. T. Newcomb), (1685[6]). 4°. Pp. 14 (p. 1 blank).
Wood 608(64). Wing J389.

3839. James 2. *'King James 2. his letter to the lords of the privie councill, after he had left England'*. N.p.: n.pub., [1687 or 1692]. Fol. or 4°.
Missing in 1922. AW wrote the t on upper flyleaf of this vol. (not identified).
Wood 660c(35). Wing J200 or J202 (prob. not L549A).

3840. James 2. *The commissioners proposals to . . . the prince of Orange. With his highnes's answer [8 Dec.]*. (London): (f. R. Bentley), (1688). S.sh. (r-v).
Wood 529(10). Wing C5561.

3841. James 2. *His majesties reasons for withdrawing himself from Rochester [22 Dec.]*. [Rochester]: n.pub., [1688]. S.sh.
LT 3.290.
Wood 529(16). Wing J376.

3842. James 2. *His most sacred majesties, and his . . . privy councils letters [dated 3 July and 16 July 1687], relating to the college of physicians*. London: f. R. Taylor, 1688. 4°. Pp. [2], 6, 7. Parchment.
[MS.] Wood C. 48. Wing H2088.

3843. James 2. Manuscript. *A declaration of his most sacred majesty, king James the second [8 May]*. [London]: n.pub., [1689]. S.sh. Pp. 3.
AW copied this declaration (no° printed version in the Bodl. Library) and inserted it before 2 pamphlets which respond to it.
Wood 608(67). Wing J165.

3844. James 2. *His majesties letter to the lords and others of his privy councel [4/14 Jan. 1688/9]*. London: n.pub., [1689]. S.sh.
Wood 529(20). Wing J208 (Wing, majesty's).

3845. James 2. *The king's reasons (with some reflections upon them) for withdrawing himself from Rochester [22 Dec.]*. [London]: n.pub., [1689]. S.sh.
AW wrote, 'sold at Oxon in the beginning of Janu. 1688-9'. LT 3.290.
Wood 529(17). Wing K607A ('O' not recorded in Wing).

3846. James 2*. *Quadriennium Jacobi: or, the history of the reign of king James II*. London: f. J. Knapton, sold R. Taylor, 1689. 12°. 2nd ed. Pp. [7], 258, 5 (5 pp. books sold by Knapton).
Tp, AW wrote, 'Bought at Oxon in the beg. of Oct. 1689'; p. 120, at year 1687, 'Ther might be a great deal more said for that yeare'; brief marks, corrections or notes on pp. 121, 124, 128, 131, 148, 152, 155, 161.
Wood 242(2). Wing Q6 (Wing, punctuation incorrect).

3847. James 2*. *The true and genuine explanation of one k. James's declaration*. [London]: n.pub., 1692. 4°. Pp. 4.
Wood 483(6). Wing T2483 (rare) (Wing, King James's).

3848. James 2, and Louis de Duras. Feversham, earl of. *The king's letter to the general of his army, with the general's letter to the prince of Orange [11 Dec.]*. [London]: n.pub., 1688. S.sh.
A correction of printed 'Passion' to 'Nation', may not be by AW; below, AW identified the author of the 2nd letter, 'Feversham'.
Wood 529(14). Wing J205.

3849. James 5. Scotland, of (really James 1 of Scotland). *Christs kirk on the green, composed (as is supposed) by king James the fifth*. [London]: R. Royston, 1663. S.sh. Obl.
AW mistakenly entered the item no. '105' and lined it out; ᵛ, '1663'. Repaired with 3 slips; on pasted down sides, ms. notes, not by AW.
Wood 416(104). Wing J413 (Wing, Christ's).

3850. James, F[rancis] (born in 1608). *Threnodia Henricianarum exequiarum sive panolethria Anglicana. Et apotheosis Henrici duci Glocestrensis maximae spei*. N.p.: n.pub., [1660]. S.sh. Pasteboard (blue) with parchment spine.
Flyleaf, upper, 2nd-3rd, AW wrote the titles of 51 epitaphs and elegies in this vol., within guidelines made with red ink (today, 50 items are present, with the addition of current nos. 51 and 52 (neither on AW's list) and the theft of 4, 20 and 37). At item 20, 'deest Novʳ. 5. 1840 W[illiam] K[irtland]'; at item 37, 'deest W. K.' On the 1st item, an elegy for the duke of Gloucester who died in 1660, AW wrote the date of '1612' under the author, F. James, because he noted 2 citations to Henry, Prince of Wales (who died in 1612);

AW also wrote this date at his entry, in AOF 1.359, of an earlier F. James for the time of composition of this poem, again in error. Both records prompted later ms. marginalia: in this item, 'Strangely wrong!' and '1660'; and in AOF 1.359 (Bodl. Lib., R. Ref. 131), '1660! Upon the death of Henry, Duke of Gloucester'. Also, on the s.sh. a note by a later librarian, 'not printed at Oxford. The Q is unknown there'. ᵛ, AW wrote, 'Prince Hen 1612'.
Wood 429(1). Not in Wing. Not in ESTCR.

3851. James, John, lessee. *The case of John James, the lessee of George Durdant, plaintiff, against William Richardson, defendant; in a writ of error in parliament.* [London?]: n.pub., [1680]. S.sh.
Wood 276b(75) (old no., (52), in Bodl. CD cat.). Wing C932A (two).

3852. James, Thomas. *An apologie for John Wickliffe, shewing his conformitie with the now Church of England; with answere to . . . father Parsons.* Oxford: J. Barnes, 1608. 4°. Pp. [8], 75, [5].
AO 2.467. All items in this vol. came from Francis Isaac, see Wood 587(1).
Wood 587(3). STC 14445. Madan 308.

3853. James, Thomas. *The Jesuits downefall, threatned against them by the secular priests for their wicked lives, . . . Together with the life of father Parsons.* Oxford: Jos. Barnes, sold John Barnes [in London], 1612. 4°. [12], 72. Pp. [12], 72 (pp. unopened).
Tp, a slip pasted over the note, 'Ant. Woode Merton Coll: Oxōn MDC_VIII [sic]'. P. 54, AW wrote at printed 'to resigne' (i.e., R. Persons), 'He resigned 13. Feb. 1573'; 56, at books of Persons, 'vide p. 55. 58. 59' (cp. MS. Wood E. 2(70), p. 1, where this book appears with 'v. p. 56'). AO 2.65f., 467.
[MS.] Wood D. 24(2). STC 14459. Madan 357.

3854. James, Thomas. *The humble . . . request of Thomas James . . . to the Church of England; for, and in the behalfe of bookes touching religion.* [Oxford?]: n.pub., [1625?]. 12°. Pp. 15, [1].
Pp. 7, at printed 'Cooke', AW wrote 'Rob Cocus author Censura Patrum' (STC 5469); 15, after initial of author, 'Th. James S. T. Professor'. AO 2.467.
Wood 795(3). STC 14455. Madan 560.

3855. James, Tho[mas]. *A manuduction, or introduction unto divinitie: containing a confutation of papists by papists.* [London]: [J. Jaggard] f. H. Cripps a. H. Curteyne, 1625. 4°. Pp. [8], 136, [8]. Calf with fillets and roll decoration at edges, and a vertical line of the same, stamp decoration (2 leaves and sunflower sprouting fleur-de-lis) inside corners (Ashm. binding).
Flyleaf, upper, 2nd, the titles of 17 printed works in this vol. written by an Ashm. librarian (really 18, 2 at item 3 (3a and 3b). 1st item, after p. 136, AW added p. nos. 137-139, and in unnumbered indices of mss., pp. 138ff., identified the son of John Fox, 'Sam. Fox', and made a vertical line at printed 'Ric. Smiths book of the visibilitie of the Church'.
[MS.] Wood B. 40(1). STC 14460. Madan 561.

3856. [Jane, Joseph]. Εικων ακλαστος. *The image unbroaken. . . . impudence, . . . in a libell [by J. Milton].* [London]: n.pub., 1651. 4°. Pp. 268.
Tp, signature of former owner, William Rawlins of Abingdon.
Wood 492(4). Wing J451('O' not recorded in Wing).

3857. Jeffreys, George Jeffrey*. *An account of the flight, discovery and apprehending George lord Geffries [12 Dec.].* [London]: n.pub., [1688]. S.sh.
Wood 368(26). Wing A290.

3858. Jeffreys, George Jeffrey. *The chancellor's address & confession to both houses.* (London): n.pub., (1689). 4°. Pp. 4.
P. 4, AW wrote the date, '20. March. 1688[9]'. LT 3.300.
Wood 368(25). Wing J525 (3).

3859. [Jeffreys, George Jeffrey]. *The lord chancellours discovery and confession: made . . . in the Tower.* (London): (f. R. Lee), (1689). S.sh. (r-v).
ᵛ, AW wrote the date, 'Begin. of Feb. 1688[9]'. LT 3.298.
Wood 368(27). Wing L3042.

3860. Jenison, Robert. *The narrative of Robert Jenison.* London: f. F. Smith, T. Basset, J. Wright, R. Chiswel, a. S. Heyrick, 1679. Fol. Pp. 51.
AW wrote the price, '1ˢ.6ᵈ.' Purchased from Vade in Oct. 1679, see his record of purchase in MS. Wood F. 50, f. 11.

Wood 425(18). Wing J561.

3861. Jenison, Robert. *The informations of Robert Jenison of Grayes inn, esquire. Relating the horrid popish plot [9 Nov.].* London: f. T. Basset, a. R. Tonson, 1680. Fol. Pp. [3], 8.
Tp, AW wrote the price, '3^{d}'.
Wood 426(25). Wing J560.

3862. Jenkins, David*. *The cordiall of judge Jenkins, for the good people of London; in reply to a thing, called, an answer to the . . . paper of mr David Jenkins; by H[enry] P[arker].* [London]: n.pub., 1647. 4°.
Pp. 24.
Tp, 2 prices, '4$^{\text{d.}}$' and '6^{d}'. Diff ed. at Wood 612(68).
Wood 476(7). Wing J586.

3863. Jenkins, David*. *The cordiall of judge Jenkins, for the good people of London; in reply to a thing called, an answer to the . . . paper of mr David Jenkins; by H[enry] P[arker].* London: n.pub., 1647. 4°. Pp.
[2], 14.
Tp, AW wrote 'Dup', in pencil. Diff. ed. at Wood 476(7).
Wood 612(68). Wing J585.

3864. Jenkins, David. *A discourse touching the inconveniences of a long continued parliament.* [London]:
n.pub., 1647. 4°. Pp. [2], 10.
Tp, AW wrote the price, '2^{d}'.
Wood 476(8). Wing J590.

3865. Jenkins, David. *Judge Jenkins remonstrance to the lords and commons [21 Feb.].* [London]: n.pub.,
1647[8]. 4°. Pp. 8.
Dupl. at Wood 612(57).
Wood 476(4). Wing J604.

3866. Jenkins, David. *Judge Jenkins remonstrance to the lords and commons [21 Feb.].* [London]: n.pub.,
1647[8]. 4°. Pp. 8.
AW wrote 'Dupl', in pencil. Dupl. at Wood 476(4).
Wood 612(57). Wing J604.

3867. Jenkins, David. *Judge Jenkin's [sic] plea delivered in to the earle of Manchester [14 Feb.].* [London]:
n.pub., 1647[8]. 4°. Pp. 7.
Wood 476(6). Wing J598.

3868. Jenkins, David. *A recantation of judge Jenkins, . . . delivered at Westminster the 10 of April 1647.*
[London]: n.pub., [1647]. S.sh. Pasteboard (blue) with parchment spine; upper and lower flyleaves, traces
of marbled paper.
Flyleaf, upper, 2nd, AW wrote the titles of 18 printed works in this vol., within guidelines made with red
ink. Tp, after 'Recantation' in t, AW wrote, 'rather protestation'; ^{v}, 'Justice Jenkins his Recantation.' AW's
vignette of Jenkins in AO was one of the items cited in the Clarendon libel case. LT 1.337; AO 3.643-4.
Wood 476(1). Wing J 603.

3869. Jenkins, David. *The vindication of judge Jenkins prisoner in the Tower [29 Apr.].* [London]: n.pub.,
[1647]. 4°. Pp. 8.
Wood 476(2). Wing J613.

3870. Jenkins, David. *The answer of judge Jenkins, to the imputation put upon his plea [14 Feb.].*
[London]: n.pub., 1648. 4°. Pp. [2], 6.
Wood 476(5). Wing J581.

3871. Jenkins, David*. *Verses in honour of the reverend and learned judge . . . Jenkin.* [London]: n.pub.,
1648. 4°. Pp. 8.
Tp, AW wrote, 'Yet not promoted according to his sufferings at the restaurat. of Ch. II.' AO 3.643-8, and
LT 1.337, 3.5.
Wood 476(9). Wing V258.

3872. Jenkins, David*. *The triall of judge Jengins [sic] at the house of commons Barre [21 Feb.].* London:
R. Ibbitson, 1648, 21 Feb. 4°. Pp. [2], 6 (p. nos. erratic).
Wood 476(3). Wing T2194.

3873. J[enner], T[homas]. *Divine mysteries that cannot be seene, made plaine . . . collected from the sermons of several divines of London.* London: sold by T. Jenner, 1651. A-C⁸,D1-3.
Tp, below, note in pencil, illeg. Rpt. of STC 14493.
Wood 90(5). Wing J664A. ESTCR 188913.

3874. Jenner, Thomas. *Londons blame, if not its shame: manifested by the great neglect of the fishery.* [London]: f. T. J., 1651. 4°. Pp. [2], 12.
Tp, scribble, not by AW.
[MS.] Wood C. 14(8). Wing J667.

3875. Jessey, Henry. *A narrative of the late proceeds at White-hall, concerning the Jews: who had desired by r. Manasses . . . that they might return into England.* London: f. L. Chapman, 1656. 4°. Pp. [2], 14.
Tp, 3 lines of shorthand, not by AW. Between pp. 6-7, backing (part of flyleaf, lower, with a Latin disputation tag, not by AW).
Wood 637(3). Wing J696 (Wing, proceed's [sic]).

3876. J[essey], H[enry]. *The lords loud call to England: being a true relation of some late . . . judgments . . . also of the odious sin of drinking healths.* London: f. L. Chapman a. Fr. Smith, 1660. 4°. Pp. [4], 35 (misnumbering).
Tp, AW wrote, 'This pamphlett cam out in the middle of Aug: 1660:', and wrote the author's name, Jessey, after the initials. Text, pp. 2, identification of a scholar who suddenly died at Pembroke, 'Will: Grosvenur'; 13, 28, vertical lines in margin. See LT 1.322, 331. Prob. MS. Wood E. 2(70), p. 19, 'News from Oxōn', for the heading on p. 1 is: 'Of the Lords strange hand at Oxford'.
Wood 643(3). Wing J694. Madan 2472.

3877. Jesuits. *Le pater noster des Jesuites, dedié à Philippes III. roy d'Espagne pour ses estreines en la presente année M. DC. XXVII.* N.p.: n.pub., [1627?]. S.sh. (r-v).
A slip pasted on verso has a brief note on pasted down side, illeg. Flyleaf, last lower, has a note, upside down and obscured by a slip pasted over: 'Anthony à Wood [/] given to me by Dʳ Thomas Marshall Rector of Lync. Coll. the publisher, 5 May 1679'. It is not clear to what item this refers, though it is not to this *Le pater noster* (AW had 4 books formerly owned by Marshall).
Wood 876(7) (not in Bodl. CD cat.; not similar to any of the Arch. B. e. 14 variants). Not in BL. Not in BN.

3878. Jesuit's Catechism. *'The Jesuits catechisme'.* ?: ?, ? Pp.?
Missing. Acquired 16 Oct. 1662, LT 1.458. There are books with similar titles, e.g., by Ignatius Loyola. It is prob. not the preceding item, 3877.
LT 1.458. Not identified.

3879. Jewel, John. Salisbury, bp. of.; Garbrand, John, ed. *A viewe of a seditious bul sent into Englande, from Pius quintus bishop of Rome, anno. 1569. . . . Whereunto is added a short treatise of the holie scriptures.* London: R. Newberie & H. Bynneman, 1582. 8°. Pp. [6], 175 (A1-3,B-M⁸).
Wood 836(10-11). STC 14613.5.

3880. Jewel, John. Salisbury, bp. of. *An apology for the Church of England.* ?: ?, 1562-1685. Pp.?
Missing. MS. Wood E. 2(70), p. 56, 'Jo. Juell Apol. for the English church'. Ed. not identified.
MS. Wood E. 2(70), p. 56. STC 14581ff.

3881. John and Kate. *A pleasant dialogue betwixt honest John and loving Kate.* London: f. J. Clarke, W. Thackeray a. T. Passinger, 1685. 12°. Pp. 24.
Missing in 1837. 'Dialogue betwixt honest John & loving Kate – ' in Whiteside cat. BL copy has stitch marks, edges repaired, some notes, not by AW.
Wood 66(9). Wing P2543 (two) *BL*, CMPepys.

3882. John of Salisbury. B., H. L., ed. *Policraticus: sive de nugis curialium, & vestigiis philosophorum, libri octo.* Lugduni Batavorum: ex off. Plantiniana ap. F. Raphelengium, 1595. 8°. Pp. [16], 597, [18]. Parchment.
Flyleaf, upper, 1stᵛ, 2 references, not by AW. Tp, bsm. Text, some underscoring and notes; flyleaf, lower, 1st, index, none by AW.
Wood 867. BL.

3883. John of Salisbury. *Metalogicus.* Parisiis: ap. H. Beys, 1610. 8°. Pp. [16], 242. Parchment.
Tp, bsm. P. 87, underscoring of 'Robertus Pullus'.

Wood 47. BL.

3884. Johnson, Christopher. *Gulielmi Wiccammi Winton. Episcopi ortus atquè vita [14 Dec.]*. [London?]: n.pub., [1564]. S.sh.
AW wrote 'These verses are printed in a book intit. A breif View of the state of the Church of England as it stood in Q. Eliz. & K. James his raigne to the yeare 1608, being a character & history of the Bishops – & may serve as an additionall supply to Dr Godwins Cat. of Bishops [[MS.] Wood D. 21(1, 2), item 3243f.] written by Sr Joh. Harrington K^t – Lond. 1653. 8° – p. 37. 38 –' (i.e., Harington, Wood 864(1), item 3406). Lines in the poem counted by 20s, in pencil, prob. not by AW.
Wood 276b(99). STC 14656.5 (rare).

3885. Johnson, E. *A short answer to a book . . . called, considerations touching the dissolving, or taking away the court of chancery*. London: n.pub., 1654. 4°. Pp. [4], 12.
Wood 630(12). Wing J770cA (two) ('O' not recorded in Wing).

3886. Johnson, Edward, gent. *An examination of the essay [toward settlement upon a sure foundation]: or, an answer to the fifth monarchy*. London: f. W. Thomas, 1659. 4°. Pp. 8.
Tp, no. '77', in pencil, in a former bundle.
Wood 613(61). Wing J770A.

3887. Johnson, Francis. *A true copy of the speech of mr. Francis Johnstons, alias Dormore, alias Webb, alias Wall [22 Aug.]*. [London]: n.pub., [1679]. Fol. Pp. 4.
P. 4, AW wrote 'Tis commonlie reported that this speech was not spoken by the sufferer – but another which more affected the people'. LT 2.461, and see note at item 6383.
Wood 425(15). Wing J775.

3888. Johnson, John*. *An account of the behaviour, confession, and last dying speeche of sir John Johnson [23 Dec. 1690]*. (London): (f. L. Curtiss), (1690). S.sh. (r-v).
LT 3.348.
Wood 422(13a). Wing A242.

3889. [Johnson, Richard]. *The pilgrimage of man. Wandering in a wildernes of woe*. London: R. B(lower), 1612. 4°. A2-4,B-E^4 (E4 blank).
Tp, AW wrote, 'Miseries, Abuses', and below, 'Abuses'.
Wood 653(7). STC 14691.5 (rare). STC, Blower.

3890. [Johnson, Richard]. *The most pleasant history of Tom a Lincoln . . . the red-rose knight*. [London]: H. Brugis f. W. Thackery, 1682. 4°. 12th imp. A-I^4.
Wood 321(2). Wing J808 (two).

3891. [Johnson, Samuel]. *Julian the Apostate: a short account of his life*. London: f. L. Curtis, 1682. 12°. Pp. xx, [4], 94 (i.e., 118, misnumbering).
LT 3.18-9, 64, 178, 187.
Wood 835(7). Wing J831.

3892. Johnson, Thomas, delineavit; Oliver, John, fec[it]. *The hott and cross baths*. Aqua Forti: n.pub., 1676. S.sh. 315 x 440 mm (untrimmed) (engr.).
In Bath. With the hot bath and the 'Lepers Bath' and lodgings, and the cross bath and 'Lord Brookes Gallery'.
Wood 276b(17). Not in Wing. Not in ESTCR.

3893. Johnson, Tho[mas], delineavit, 1675; Oliver, John, fecit, 1676. *The kings and queens baths*. N.p.: n.pub., 1676. S.sh. 315 x 441 mm (untrimmed) (engr.).
In Bath. LT 2.350.
Wood 276b(18). Not in Wing. Not in ESTCR. For Johnson, see Laurence Binyon, *Cat. of Drawings by Br. Artists* (1902), 3.9.

3894. Johnston, Archibald. Warriston, lord. *A letter to the house, from the laird Wareston*. London: E. Mason, 1659[60]. S.sh.
AW added to date, 'Jan:'.
Wood 276a(202). Wing L1737A ('O' not recorded in Wing).

3895. Johnston, Nathaniel. *The king's visitatorial power asserted. . . . an impartial relation of the late visitation of St. Mary Magdalen college in Oxford*. London: H. Hills, 1688. 4°. Pp. [36], 352.

P. [1], 'Memorandum that on Tuesday Sept. 4, an[.] 1688 I dined with Dr Nath. Johnston author of the following book, in his house in Leicester Street in Westminster, at which time he gave me the said book, & told me it was mostly compiled from mine entit. <u>Hist. et Antiquit. Univ. Oxon.</u>, & told me farther it was published at London & in Westm. about the 10 of Aug the same yeare. [/] Two dayes after I returned to Oxōn, & on the 7 of Sept. int. hor. 7. et 8 post merid. I met near C.C. Coll. gate D^r Jo. Beale & Dr Phineas Elwood: The last of which, told me of the said Dr Johnstons book, & asked me with great concernment what need was there for me to compile & publish <u>Hist. et Antiq. Oxon</u>? which hath given advantage to the enimies of the Universitie of Oxon to write against it &c. ridiculous!', LT 3.276-7; below, in pencil, 'Washington a Barister hath written against this book' (Robert Washington (1689), Wing W1029). Pp. 129-143, AW lined in margins portions of the text and wrote, e.g., (p. 129), 'Hist. et Antiq. Univ. Oxon. p. 13' and a few 'qu[aere]' reminders. P. 143, underlined in text, reference to 'the Laborious Mr. Wood'. So also, pp. 161-222, most pp. marked with p. refs. to his *Historia*.
Wood 517(2). Wing J879.

3896. Johnston, Robert. M[ay], T[homas], trans. *The historie of Scotland*. London: W. Wilson, f. A. Roper, 1646. 12°. Pp. [12], 164, [1]. Pasteboard (grey) with parchment spine. 1st and last flyleaves, marbled paper.
Flyleaf, upper, 3rd^v, AW wrote the titles of 3 printed works in this vol., within guidelines made with red ink. Tp, AW wrote after T. M., 'Tho. May. qu[aere]'. Bsm. P. 1, bsm. or scribble.
Wood 172(1). Wing J880.

3897. Jones, George. *[Part of an advertisement of Jones's friendly pills]*. (London): n.pub., (1675?). S.sh. (r-v) (pp. 3-4, only).
Wood 276a(35). Wing J941ABff. (unidentified fragment).

3898. [Jones, Henry], Kilmore, dean of. *A perfect relation of the beginning and continuation of the Irish-rebellion [May-12 Jan.]*. London: J. R., 1641[2]. 4°. Pp. 16 (misnumbering).
Wood 507(27). Wing J942A.

3899. Jones, Henry, Kilmore, dean of. *A remonstrance of divers remarkeable passages concerning the church and kingdome of Ireland, . . . presented . . . to the . . . commons*. London: f. G. Emerson a. W. Bladen, 1642. 4°. Pp. [7], 80 (misnumbering).
Dupl. at Wood 616(23).
Wood 507(42). Wing J943.

3900. Jones, Henry, Kilmore, dean of. *A remonstrance of divers remarkeable passages concerning the church and kingdome of Ireland, . . . presented . . . to the . . . commons*. London: f. G. Emerson a. W. Bladen, 1642. 4°. Pp. [8], 80 (misnumbering).
P. [1], '8^d'. Tp, AW wrote 'Dupl', in pencil. Dupl. at Wood 507(42).
Wood 616(23). Wing J943.

3901. Jones, Henry, Kilmore, dean of. *A remonstrance of the beginnings and proceedings of the rebellion in . . . Cavan. Whereunto is added, the acts . . . of the Romish clergy*. London: f. G. Emerson, 1642, 11 Aug. 4°. Pp. 48 (misnumbering; A², B-F⁴).
Tp, AW wrote a correction, '1642'. Former no., 24, lined out. Dupl. at Wood 614(47).
Wood 508(30). Wing J944.

3902. Jones, Henry, Kilmore, dean of. *A remonstrance of the beginnings and proceedings of the rebellion in . . . Cavan. Whereunto is added, the acts . . . of the Romish clergy*. London: f. G. Emerson, 1642, 11 Aug. 4°. Pp. 48 (misnumbering; A², B-F⁴).
Tp, AW wrote 'dupl.' Dupl. at Wood 508(30).
Wood 614(47). Wing J944.

3903. Jones, Henry*. *The bloody murtherer, . . . his just condemnation*. London: H. Lloyd f. J. Edwin, 1672. 8°. Pp. [4], 62.
Tp, 'Colled [mutilated] Trinity'.
Wood 173(2). Wing B3261bA (3).

3904. Jones, Inigo. Webb, John, ed. *The most notable antiquity of Great Britain vulgarly called Stone-heng on Salisbury plain. Restored by Inigo Jones*. London: J. Flesher, f. D. Pakeman and L. Chapman, 1655. Fol. Pp. [7], 109, [1]. Pasteboard (blue) with parchment spine.
Flyleaf, upper, 1st, 'Binding. 1^s-4. Sedgley' (1665 or later; see also Hearne, 1719, 7.58, for a ref. to Sedgley; and Wood 413(2), item 1835). Tp, bsm. P. 2, at discussion of druids, red chalk line in margin. Acquired 24

Oct. 1662, LT 1.461, and AO 4.753-4.
Wood 413(1). Wing J954.

3905. Jones, John. *The bathes of Bathes ayde*. London: (T. East) f. W. Jones, (1572). 4°. Ff. [8], 35, [4] (tp mutilated; tables, 2 s.shs. after f. 23, removed to MS. Ashm. 1457, ff. 1,2).
Tp, bsm. a4, AW identified printed Joannis Ludi as 'Lowthe, A.mʳ'. F. 32 and K4ᵛ, notes, not in AW's hand.
Wood 498(13). STC 14724a.3.

3906. Jones, John. *The peace of justice, or, the authoritie of a justice of peace*. London: W. Bentley f. W. Shears, 1650. 12°. Pp. [8], 23, [2].
P. [1], t and year, not by AW.
Wood 733(3). Wing J973 ('O' not recorded in Wing).

3907. Jones, Jo[hn]. St. Alban's. *Fanum sᵗⁱ· Albani poema carmine heroico*. Londini: impens. authoris, 1683. 4°. Pp. [4], 23.
Wood 467(6). Wing J982.

3908. Jones, Michael*. *The late succesful [sic] proceedings of the army, commanded by collonel Michael Jones, . . . against the rebels in Ireland*. London: f. J. M., 1647. 4°. Pp. 8.
Tp, AW lined out a former no., '26'.
Wood 509(27). Wing L559A (Wing, successful).

3909. Jones, Michael. *Lieut: general Jones's letter to the councel of state, of a great victory . . . in . . . Dublin . . . Together with the list of all the prisoners and ammunition taken*. London: E. Husband, 1649, 11 Aug. 4°. Pp. 11.
Wood 510(5). Wing J983.

3910. Jones, Philip*. *Articles of impeachment of transcendent crimes, . . . committed by col. Philip Jones [18 May]*. London: n.pub., 1659. 4°. Pp. 16.
Wood 368(15). Wing A3860.

3911. Jones, Theophilus, et al. *A letter sent from Ireland, dated at Dublin Decemb. 15. 1659. Super-scribed, for the . . . speaker to the parliament [signed by T. Jones and ten others]*. London: J. Streater a. J. Macock, 1659[60]. 4°. A⁴.
Wood 510(26). Wing L1601.

3912. Jones, Thomas. *Prolusiones academicae, in duas partes distributae*. Oxoniae: typ. H. Hall, imp. R. Davis, 1660. 12°. 2 pts., with engr. title. Pp. [26], 303, [1], [8], 52, [2], 52, [14] (2 tpp).
AO 3.708.
Wood 672(5). Wing J991A. Madan 2502.

3913. Jones, Tho[mas]. *Elymas the sorcerer: or, a memorial towards the discovery of the bottom of this popish-plot*. London: f. H. Jones, 1682. Fol. Pp. 39, [1]. Response at Wood 427(50f.), items 6485f.)
Tp, AW wrote the price, '1ˢ·', and 'in summer time'. P. 3, after a passage in French, 'The English followes.', in red ink. P. 31, a correction; 32, identification of A. A, 'Sʳ Allen Apsley'; 39, identification of C. P. Miles Veteranus, 'Capt. Rob. Pugh somtimes Jesuit, afterwards a secular priest'. LT 2.13, 81; 3.295.
Wood 427(47). Wing J992.

3914. Jonston, Joh[n]. *Inscriptiones historicae regum Scotorum*. Amsteldami: Excud. C. Claessonius[,] A. Hartio, bibliop. Edemburgensi, 1602. 4°. Pp. [14], 60 and 10 engravings, H3-K4. Pasteboard (grey) with parchment spine. 1st upper and last lower flyleaves, marbled paper.
Flyleaf, upper, 3rdᵛ, AW wrote the titles of 5 printed works in this vol., within guidelines made with red ink. Tp, '272' at top of page. P. 60, uncoding of the year of an inscription from the upper-case letters, 1566, prob. by AW.
Wood 318(1). STC 14787.

3915. Jordan, Tho[mas]. *Poeticall varieties: or, varietie of fancies*. London: T. C[otes] f. H. Blunden, 1637. 4°. Pp. [10], 52.
Wood 330(5). STC 14788.

3916. [Jordan, Thomas]. *A speech made to the lord general Monck, at Clotheworkers hall in London [13 March]*. [London]: n.pub., [1659 to 1660]. S.sh.
ᵛ, AW wrote the date, '13 Mar. 59[60]', and a former no., '54', in pencil.

Wood 398(3). Wing J1065.

3917. [**Jordan, Thomas**]. *A letany for the new-year, with a description of the new state.* [London]: n.pub., [1660]. S.sh.
AW wrote, 'January: 1659[60]'; ᵛ, 'Jan. 59', and '28' over former no. '12' in pencil.
Wood 416(28). Wing J1033B (two).

3918. [**Jordan, Thomas**]. *A speech made to his excellency the lord general Monck, and the councell of state, at Drapers-hall . . . the reader may take notice that the other speech is a forged cheat [28 March].* London: f. H. Broome, 1660. S.sh.
ᵛ, AW wrote the date, '28. Mar. 1660', and a former no., '56', in pencil. Responds to Wood 398(4).
Wood 398(5). Wing J1061C (3) ('O' not recorded in Wing).

3919. Jordan, Tho[mas]. *A speech made to his excellency the lord general Monck, and the council of state, at Goldsmiths hall [10 Apr.].* London: f. H. B., 1660. S.sh.
ᵛ, AW wrote the date, '10 Ap. 1660', and a former no., '60', in pencil.
Wood 398(7). Wing J1062.

3920. Jordan, Tho[mas]. *A speech made to his excellency George Monck . . . at Vinteners-hal [12 Apr.].* [London]: n.pub., [1660]. S.sh.
ᵛ, AW wrote the date, '12 Ap. 60', and the current item no., '8', in ink, over a former no., '61', in pencil.
Wood 398(8). Wing J1063.

3921. Jordan, Tho[mas]. *A speech made to his excellency the lord general Monck and the council of state, at Fishmongers-hall . . . Spoken by Walter Youkcny [i.e., Yeokney] [13 Apr.].* London: W. Godbid, 1660. S.sh.
Wood 398(9). Wing J1064 ('O' not recorded in Wing).

3922. Jordan, Tho[mas]. *London's resurrection to joy and triumph, expressed in sundry shews . . . celebrious to the . . . lord mayor.* London: f. H. Brome, 1671. 4°. Pp. [2], 22.
Tp, AW wrote the price, '3ᵈ', and '1671'.
Wood 537(20). Wing J1040.

3923. Joseph, ben Gorion, pseud. Morwyng, Peter, trans. *A compendious . . . history of the latter times of the Jewes commune weale.* (London): (R. Jugge), 1561. 8°. Ff. [7], 259. Calf with 2 fillets, inner rectangle, 3 fillets, and some blind and gold-stamp decoration; 2 clasp holes.
Wood 227. STC 14796.

3924. Joyce, George*. *A true narrative of the occasions and causes of the late lord gen. Cromwell's anger . . . against lieut. col. George Joyce.* [London]: n.pub., [1659]. Fol. Pp. 4.
P. 1, at top, AW wrote, 'Case 1659'; at bottom, no. '58' in a former bundle; p. 4, '1659', all in pencil.
Wood 276a(187) (not in Bodl. CD cat.). Wing J1124.

3925. Joye, George. *The refutation of the byshop of Winchesters derke declaration of his false articles.* [London]: [J. Herford], 1546. 8°. Ff. [8], 192.
Missing. MS. Wood E. 2(70), p. 8.
MS. Wood E. 2(70), p. 8. STC 14828.5. *Folg, Hunt.*

3926. [**Joyner, Edward**]. *Armante Gulielmo anno salutis 1692.* [Oxford]: n.pub., [1692]. S.sh. (r-v).
AW wrote, 'Ex dono Edv. Joyner authoris 3. Jan. 1692[3]'. LT 3.413.
Wood 417(182). Wing J1156 (rare).

3927. [**Joyner, Edward**]. *In obitum Mariae Mag. Brit. &c. reginae.* [Oxford]: [e theatro Sheldoniano], [1694]. S.sh. and fol. pp. 2 (one s.sh. and one ms. letter).
Wood 276a(539) is a 20-line ms. poem, possibly in the hand of Joyner, addressed, 'For the much honour'd Mʳ Tho. Collins of Mag. Col.' At the end of the poem (p. 1) is 'Antonius a Wood è Col Mert:', not by AW, and, in AW's hand, 'Convers. S. Pauli an. 1694 [25 Jan. 1695]'. Wood 276a(540) is a 23-line printed version of the poem. Below, AW wrote, 'Edw. Joyner alias Lyde Author – printed at the Theater in the later end of Feb. 1694[5].' For notes concerning Joyner, see Wood 307(4). LT 3.477.
Wood 276a(539 and 540). Wing J1157 (rare).

3928. [**Joyner, William**]. Lyde, William, pseud. *Some observations upon the life of Reginaldus Polus . . . by G. L.* London: f. M. Turner, 1686. 8°. Pp. 142.
Flyleaf, upper, AW's 5-part outline of Joyner's book, with the comment, 'Where are the observations/'.

Tp, he wrote, 'Will. Lyde alias Joyner. the author', and '9$^{\rm d}$'. Tp$^{\rm v}$, not by AW: 'Wilhelmi liber est rudis, indigestaque moles, Quam Chaos affirmes esse, vel esse nihil', 'Haec fecit dum scripsit Edvardus frater Wilhelmi Praedicti, authoris hujusce libr. [and in another hand, possibly AW's:] 21 Apr. 1695' (Apparently Edward had access to his brother's book and wrote these playful verses in it, see LT 3.481 and 2.427; see also AW's note at Wood 276a(539-40) written in Feb. 1695). P. 15, Wood added the location of Pole's ashes: 'His altar tombe against a wall is remaining at Canterb.' P. 95, correction of a date. Pp. 112-4, 116, line in margins, in ink and pencil.
Wood 307(4). Wing J1160.

3929. Junius, Franciscus. *Francisci Junii academia. Libellus . . . in quo . . . ortus academiarum . . . exponuntur. Ad calcem adjectus est academiarum totius Europae, . . . catalogus.* Heidelbergae: n.pub., 1587. 4°. Pp. [12], 68, [8]. Parchment, ms., recto and verso, Latin.
Tp, year corrected to, in Roman numerals, 1588. P. 12, note, not in AW's hand.
Wood 588. BL.

3930. Junius, Hadrianus. *Nomenclator, omnium rerum propria nomina variis linguis explicata indicans.* Antverpiae: C. Plantini, 1577. (1576. Decimo Kalend. Septembris). 8°. Pp. [8], 432, [70] (interleaved with blank pp. after p. 368). Calf with 2 fillets, blind-stamp oval centrepiece, and 2 clasp holes; rebacked.
Pastedown, upper, name lined out. Tp, signature 'Henrici Goffe [Cuffe] sum . . . liber pretium [? all lined out] – 3$^{\rm s}$', and above, '2$^{\rm s}$-10$^{\rm d}$'; and 'Thomae Savili. Kal. Apr.' Text, a few underscorings and definitions added, and flyleaf, lower, 2nd, two notes, in Greek and Latin, not in AW's hand. Possibly acquired 27 Dec. 1656, 1$^{\rm s}$, LT 1.210.
Wood 45. BL.

3931. Juvenal. [Wood, Thomas, trans.]. *Juvenalis redivivus. Or the first satyr of Juvenal.* [London]: to be sold by most booksellers, 1683. 4°. Pp. [8], 30, [5] (some nos. cropped). A-E^4,F^2 (F2$^{\rm v}$ blank).
Wood 484(11). Wing W3410.

3932. Juvenal, and Persius. Farnaby, Thomas, ed. *Junii Juvenalis et Auli Persii Flacci satyrae.* London: excud. J. Legat, imp. P. Stephani & C. Meredith, 1633. 8°. 4th ed. Pp. [8], 190.
Missing. MS. Wood E. 2(70), p. 11, 'Tho. Farnabie notes on Juvenall – 1633'.
MS. Wood E. 2(70), p. 11. STC 14892. *Hunt.*

3933. Juxon, William*. Canterbury, abp. of. *Justa Juxonia.* N.p.: n.pub., n.d. Pp.?
Missing in 1840. On Wood 429(21), $^{\rm v}$, 'Deest. No. 20. Justa Juxonia 1840 W[illiam] K[irtland]'.
Wood 429(20). Not identified.

3934. K., F. *The present great interest both of king and people [16 Sept.].* [London?]: n.pub., [1679]. Fol. Pp. 4.
Wood 276a(156). Wing K8.

3935. K., T. *Terrible newes from York sent in a letter to London.* [London]: f. J. Coe, 1642. 4°. A^4.
Tp, AW rubbed out former nos., and wrote, 'A silly pamphlet made & published by a Ballad-maker'; after the year, he added, 'Ap. 8'; A2$^{\rm v}$, the year, '1642'; A4$^{\rm v}$, at a woodcut of 'Mr. Holk chief Agent in the Uprore', he wrote, 'This is a picture set to every common Ballad; and now it must serve for the picture of M$^{\rm r}$ Holke' (see note at Wood 373(44), item 4219), and '8. Ap. 1642'.
Wood 373(52). Wing K23 (Wing, f. Iohn Gee).

3936. [Keall, Robert]. *The trades increase.* London: N. Okes, sold W. Burre, 1615. 4°. Pp. [6], 56.
Pasteboard (blue) with parchment spine. Traces of 1st upper and last lower flyleaves, marbled paper; rebacked.
Flyleaf, upper, 2nd, AW wrote the titles of 14 printed works in this vol., within guidelines made with red ink. P. 6, at errata, 'Errata.', may not be by AW.
[MS.] Wood C. 14(1). STC 14894.7.

3937. [Keble, Samuel]. *Restitution to the royal author or vindication of king Charls . . . book; intituled* 'Εικων βασιλικη'. London: f. S. Keble, 1691. Fol. Pp. 8.
Tp, AW wrote the name of the author of a letter printed on pp. 6-7 in this item, 'Will. Levett'. LT 3.384.
Wood 363(2). Wing K121B (Wing, authour). FFMadan 163.

3938. K[eepe], H[enry]. *Monumenta Westmonasteriensia: or an historical account of . . . the abby church of Westminster.* London: f. C. Wilkinson a. T. Dring, 1682. 8°. Pp. [16], 368.
Tp, AW underscored the author's initials and wrote, 'published in May 1682. 3$^{\rm s}$'. Text, corrections, e.g., p.

126, vertical lines in margins in pencil, red and dark ink, underscoring, e.g., pp. 45, 48, 74, 116, 126, 188, 108, 207, 214-5, etc., to 368 (underscoring of 'John Wilson').
Wood 210(2). Wing K126.

3939. Keepe, Henry. *The genealogies of the high-born prince & princess, George and Anne, of Denmark.* [London]: N. Thompson, 1684. 8°. Pp. [16], 106, [4] (4 pp. books printed and sold by Thompson). Calf with 2 fillets and a narrow rectangle with 2 fillets.
Wood 441. Wing K124A.

3940. [Keepe, Henry]. *A true and perfect narrative of the strange . . . finding the crucifix & gold-chain of . . . Edward the . . . Confessor, . . . by Charles Taylour.* London: J. B., sold R. Taylor, 1688. 4°. Pp. [5], 34.
[MS.] Wood D. 23(3). Wing K128.

3941. Kelsey, Thomas. *Articles of high crimes . . . exhibited against lt. col. Tho. Kelsey.* London: f. L. Chapman, 1659. 4°. Pp. [2], 6.
Tp, no. '69', in pencil, in a former bundle.
Wood 613(60) (613(6) in Bodl. CD cat.). Wing K3842.

3942. Kelton, Arthur. *A chronycle with a genealogie declaring that the Brittons and Welshemen are lineallye dyscended from Brute.* (London): (R. Grafton), (1547). 8°. a⁴,b-d⁸,e¹² (e12 blank).
Tp, 'Ant: Woode Merton Coll: Oxōn 1658' and 'One Arth. Kelton was living in Shrewsbury temp. Hen. 8'. Acquired 29 Ap. 1658 out of G. Langbaine's study, see LT 1.247 and Wood 134(1).
Wood 134(2). STC 14918 (two).

3943. K[emp], A[nne]. *A contemplation on Bassets Down-hill by the most sacred adorer of the muses.* [Oxford]: [H. Hall], [1658?]. S.sh.
AW identified the location, 'neare Meysey-Hampton or Down-Ampney in Gloucestershire' and the initials, 'Anne Kemp', and wrote the date, 'printed 1658 or thereabouts'. LT 1.323.
Wood 416(11). Wing K257 (rare). Madan 2392.

3944. Kendall, George. *Fur pro tribunali. Examen dialogismi cui inscribitur fur praedestinatus.* Oxoniae: exc. H. Hall per T. Robinson, 1657. 8°.
Missing. 19 Oct. 1657, 'I exchanged these following bookes in sheets with Mr. Forrest, for . . . [sic]: . . . Fur praedestinatus . . . All amounting to a crowne', LT 1.230.
LT 1.230. Wing K284. Madan 2344 (prob.).

3945. [Kennett, White]. Peterborough, bp. of. *A letter from a student at Oxford to a friend in the country. Concerning the approaching parliament.* London: f. J. Seeres, 1681. 4°. Pp. [2], 22.
Tp, AW wrote, 'published in the middle of March an. 1681/0 [/] (160/1) [sic]'; ᵛ, '22. March 1680[1] [/] 'This pamphlet is misliked by the house (commons) & [over 'who'] have desired the Vicech. to make inquiry after the author, that he might be punished - But it was not writ by a scholar – [/] This pamphlet was written by White Kennett (Cantianus) a Battler of 3 years standing of Edmund hall. Oxon. It came downe to Oxon about the 15 Martii 1680.' Pp. 2, a correction; 3, some marks and 3 notes (all cropped) on Brome, on Will. Wright ('a g[–] cocker'), and a corrective note at 'Chancellour' in the text: 'Steward this shews i[t] not to be wr[itten] by a schola[r]'); 5, at Deputyship in the text, 'Deputy – this shews again [that] it is not wri[tten] by a scholar.'; 12, vertical line in margin. LT 2.439, 521, 523, 530-1. AO 4.792-3.
Wood 632(56). Wing K301.

3946. [Kennett, White]. Peterborough, bp. of. *To mr. E. L. on his majesties dissolving the late parliament at Oxford, March 28 [in verse].* [London?]: n.pub., 1681. S.sh.
After date of publication, AW wrote, 'in the beg. of Apr.' and, later, 'White Kennet a Batler of S. Edm. hall, of 3 yeares standing, the authour'. See Wood's note in Wood 632(56), and LT 2.521, 534. Dupl. at Wood 417(44).
Wood 276a(524). Wing K305.

3947. Kennett, White. Peterborough, bp. of. *To mr. E. L. on his majesties dissolving the late parliament at Oxford, March 28 [in verse].* [London?]: n.pub., 1681. S.sh.
Dupl. at Wood 276a(524). LT 2.534.
Wood 417(44). Wing K305.

3948. Kennett, White. Peterborough, bp. of. *The righteous taken away from the evil to come, applied to the death of the queen, in a sermon preach'd at St. Martin's church.* Oxford: L. Lichfield f. G. West, 1695.

4°. Pp. [4], 31.
P. [1], 'For my worthy Friend Mr Anth. a Wood. Feb 7. 1694[5]'. LT 3.479.
[MS.] Wood D. 23(4). Wing K303.

3949. Kent. *Strange newes from Kent*. [London]: f. R. Cooper, 1642. 4°. A^4.
Tp, AW wrote, 'A simple pamphlet', and altered a former no.; below, '54'.
Wood 373(62). Wing S5894.

3950. Kent. *Bloudy newes from Kent being a relation of the great fight at Rochester and Maidstone*.
London: f. R. W., 1648. 4°. Pp. 6.
Wood 502(17). Wing B3273.

3951. Kent. *The declaration and resolution of the knights . . . of Kent, now in armes for . . . the kings
. . . person*. London: f. R. W., 1648. 4°. Pp. [2], 6.
Wood 502(13). Wing D556.

3952. Kent. *An impartiall narration of the management of the late Kentish petition*. London: n.pub., 1648.
4°. Pp. [2], 6.
Tp, AW wrote after the year, 'May p. 2'. Pp. 2-3, 'May 13.', 'May 15', and '16'.
Wood 502(12). Wing I87.

3953. Kent. *Newes from Kent a true . . . relation of the particular commotions . . . of the Kentish designe*.
London: R. I. f. G. Hutton, 1648. 4°. Pp. [2], 6.
AW wrote after the year, 'May 27'.
Wood 502(14). Wing N977 ('O' not recorded in Wing) (Wing, Kent. A).

3954. Kent. *The declaration of the gentry of the county of Kent [signed by Richard Spencer and 29 others]*.
London: f. G. Bedell, 1660. S.sh.
AW added to the year, 'Aprill'; and at the signer William Somner, 'Antiquarius'.
Wood 276a(218). Wing D679 (Wing, A declaration) ('O' not recorded in Wing).

3955. Kent. *The declaration of the nobility, . . . of Kent*. [London]: n.pub., [1660]. S.sh.
AW wrote 'Jan: 1659[60]'.
Wood 276a(209). Wing D720.

3956. Kent, and Essex. *Kentish long-tayles and Essex calves; or, the copie of a letter . . . containing a
relation of the late insurrections [14 June]*. London: f. R. M., 1648. 4°. Pp. 8.
AW wrote after the year, '14. Jun'.
Wood 502(23). Wing K325.

3957. Kent, and Surrey. *Praemonitus, praemunitus. Or, a wholesome admonition to the worthy partriots
[sic] . . . of Kent, Surrey*. London: n.pub., 1648. 4°. Pp. 8.
Wood 502(19). Wing P3166.

3958. Ker, George, and David Grahame. *A discoverie of the unnaturall and traiterous conspiracie
of Scottisch papists, . . . as it was confessed by m. George Ker, . . . and David Grahame*. London: T.
Snodham, sould T. Este, 1603. 4°. A-D^4.
T leaf mutilated and repaired before AW numbered it, in red ink. Repair slip, below, on pasted down side,
has a Latin disputation topic, not by AW. D4, scribbles, prob. not by AW.
Wood 586(12). STC 14939.

3959. K[eynes], J[ohn]. *A rational compendious way to convince, . . . all persons . . . dissenting from
the true religion*. [London]: n.pub., 1674. 12°. Pp. [30], 124.
Tp, nos. '2' above '3'.
Wood 869(5). Wing K393.

3960. Kiffen, William, et al. *A letter sent to . . . the lord mayor of . . . London*. London: H. Hills,
1659[60]. S.sh.
Wood 276a(193). Wing L1623 (two) ('O' not recorded in Wing).

3961. Kilburne, Richard. *A topographie, or survey of the county of Kent*. London: T. Mabb f. H.
Atkinson, 1659. 4°. Pp. [8], 422, [12] (wanting the portrait). Calf with 2 fillets, and a vertical 2 fillets.
Tp, 'v̂ K', prob. a cataloguer's note.
Wood 471. Wing K434.

3962. Kilburne, William. *A new-years-gift for Mercurius Politicus*. London: T. Milbourn, [1659]. S.sh.
AW wrote 'Decemb: 1659'.
Wood 622(19). Wing K436 (two).

3963. Killigrew, Anne. *Poems*. London: f. S. Lowndes, 1686. 4°. Pp. [21], 100, [2].
Frontispiece[r], 'Ashmolean Museum Woods Lib[y].', and slip, pasted on: 'M[rs] Ann Killegrew was borne in S[t]
Martins Lane in London the latter end of th[e] Troubl, and christened in a privat Chamber, the Offices in
the Common Prayer Book being not Publikly th[e]n allowed.', not in AW's hand.
Wood 644(6). Wing K442.

3964. Killigrew, William. *The artless midnight thoughts of a gentleman at court*. London: f. T. Howkins,
1684. 12°. 2nd ed. Pp. [5], 262. [4] (2 pp. books printed for Howkins). Calf, speckled, with 2 fillets.
Flyleaf, upper, 1st, AW wrote 'Nov. 18. 1691 Given to me by the author'. LT 3.375.
Wood 832. Wing K455 ('O' not recorded in Wing).

3965. Kinder, Phil[ip]. *Pietati sacrum. H. S. E. quod mortale fuit I. N. R. I. praestolans epiphaniam,
depositum Henrici baronis Hastings [1649, 9 Kal. Julii]*. [London]: n.pub., [1650]. S.sh.
At top, note by a librarian, 'Confer MS. Ashm. 788, f. 147'. [v], AW wrote, 'Hen. Ld Hasting 1649'.
Wood 429(6). Wing K483 (two).

3966. Kineton, and Edgehill. *A relation of the battaile lately fought between Keynton and Edghill*.
Oxford: L. Lichfield, 1642. 4°. Pp. [2], 6.
Wood 375(16). Wing R815. Madan 1063.

3967. K[ing], D[aniel]. *The cathedrall and conventuall churches of England and Wales. Orthographically
delineated [W. Hollar]*. [London]: printed, sold, J. Overton, [1656]. Fol. or 4°.
Missing in 1939 (ed. not determined).
Wood 276a(66). Wing K484-486.

3968. [King, Gregory]. *The order of the installation of prince George of Denmark, Charles duke of
Somerset, . . . Knights . . . of the most noble order of the garter [8 Apr.]*. London: f. B. Tooke, 1684. Fol.
Pp. [2], 14.
Tp, 2 notes, 'The Author and publisher of the Order was one M[r]. King of [the] Heralds Offices' and 'See
M[r]. Ashmole of the Garter, pag. 357', both cropped and not by AW; below, AW wrote, 'Gregory King the
author.' Pp. 2, 'usually' underscored; 3-4, 6, notes or underscoring, not by AW; 9, underscoring in pencil.
Wood 657(10). Wing K495.

3969. [King, Gregory]. *The order of the installation of Henry duke of Norfolk, Henry earl of Peterborow,
. . . Knights . . . of the most noble order of the garter [22 July]*. London: f. R. Clavel, 1685. Fol. Pp. [3],
12.
1st blank, AW wrote, 'Jo Dugdale', in pencil (prob. a reference to a cat. of the nobility of England by J.
Dugdale, Wood 276a(81)). Tp, 'See M[r] Ashmoles book of the Garter, p. 337' a note he copied from the
previous item Wood 657(10) (AW had received a copy of Ashmole's book, a gift from the author, in 1672
(Wing A3983), but it was not among the books bequeathed to the Ashm.); 'The author Gregory King
one of the pursevants of Armes –'; and 'This order of the installation &c being complained of to Will. L-d
Archbishop of Canterb. as containing several peices of popery, the <u>following Advertisement</u> was made by
the author, tho his name be not set to it –'.
Wood 657(11). Wing K494.

3970. K[ing], H[enry], Chichester, bp. of. *A deepe groane, fetch'd at the funerall of . . . Charles the first*.
[London]: n.pub., 1649. 4°. Pp. [2], 6.
Tp, AW wrote, 'D[r] Hen. King Bishop of Chich.' Diff. ed. at Wood 364(30).
Wood 364(29). Wing K498.

3971. [King, Henry], Chichester, bp. of. B., I., written by. *A groane at the funerall of . . . Charles the
first*. [London]: n.pub., 1649. 4°. Pp. [2], 6.
Tp, 'The same with the former.', i.e. Wood 364(29) (a diff. ed.).
Wood 364(30). Wing K500 (two).

3972. King, Josiah. *The afternoon tryall of old father Christmas*. London: E. C. f. J. Ratcliff, 1658. 8°.
Pp. [6], 20, [1].
Wood 110(2). Wing K510A (rare).

3973. King, Josiah. *The examination and tryall of old father Christmas*. London: f. T. Johnson, 1658.

8°. Pp. 32 (p. 1 blank). Pasteboard (brown) with calf spine; rebound by H, 22 June 1950. Flyleaf, upper, 2nd[v], AW wrote the titles of 7 (really 8) printed works in this vol. (he omitted item (2)), within guidelines made with red ink.
Wood 110(1). Wing K510B (rare).

3974. K[ing], Philip. *The surfeit. To ABC*. London: f. Ewd. Dod, 1656. 12°. Pp. [2], 82. Tp, bsm. Pp. 13, at printed initials, P. K., AW wrote 'Philipp - see pag. 70'; 22, AW supplied '(2)', in red ink, in a blank after printed 'Henry'; 55, AW made 2 corrections. See note at item 5562.
Wood 739(3). Wing K515 (two).

3975. King, William. *Poems of m[r] Cowley and others*. Oxford: W. Hall for the Author, 1668. 4°. Pp. [4], 55.
LT 2.499.
Wood 644(7) (not in Bodl. CD cat.). Wing K543. Madan 2805.

3976. [Kirk, Thomas]. *A modern account of Scotland*. [London]: n.pub., 1679. 4°. Pp. [2], 17.
Wood 386(13). Wing K629.

3977. K[irkman], F[rancis]. *The counterfeit lady unveiled. . . . Mary Carleton*. London: f. P. Parker, 1673. 8°. Pp. [10], 220. Calf with 2 fillets.
Pp. 197, 214, correction, and, in margin, AW added the year of her execution, 'an. 1672.'
Wood 267. Wing K630A.

3978. K[irkman], F[rancis]. *The unlucky citizen experimentally described . . . advice to all*. London: A. Johnson, f. F. Kirkman, 1673. 8°. Pp. [22], 296. Calf, speckled, with 2 fillets and stamp decoration in corners.
Flyleaf, upper, '2[s]-6 1679. Dec', prob. by AW. Tp, '2.6'.
Wood 302. Wing K638.

3979. Knewstub, John. *An aunsware unto certaine assertions tending to maintaine the churche of Rome, to be the true . . . church*. London: T. Dawson f. R. Sergier, 1579. 4°. *[4],A-N[8],O[4], or ff. [3], 61, [1]. Missing. MS. Wood E. 2(70), p. 9, 'against Roome to be the true church bound with other things'. Ed. not identified.
MS. Wood E. 2(70), p. 9. STC 15037.5 or 15038 or 15039. *Folg, Union*, and *Folg*.

3980. Knight, Arthur. *The speech of m[r] Arthur Knight of Grays-inne, . . . executed in the Covent-garden the second day of March, 1652*. London: f. T. Heath, [1653]. 4°. Pp. 8.
Wood 367(8). Wing K685.

3981. Knights, List of. *A list of knights made since his majestie came to London, May 29. 1660*. London: S. Griffin, 1660. S.sh.
AW added 9 forenames or other bits of information.
Wood 445(7). Wing L2400.

3982. Knights of the Blade. *A notable and pleasant history of the famous renowned knights of the blade, commonly called hectors or st. Nicholas clerkes*. London: f. R. Harper, 1652. 4°. Pp. [2], 14.
Wood 371(7). Wing N1389 (two).

3983. Knights of the Round Table, and Arthur. *La devise des armes des chevaliers de las table ronde / qui estoient du temps du tresrenōme . . . Artus roy de la grant Bretaigne avec la description de leurs armoiries*. [Paris]: on les vend a Paris en la rue Sainct Jaques, [1520?]. 8°. a-m[8] (wanting all after m8) (most coats of arms, coloured by hand). Parchment.
Flyleaf, upper[v], '180 coats of Armes in this booke.', not in AW's hand. Tp, 'Ant à Woode Merton: Coll Oxōn: 1658:' (Clark questions the genuiness of the signature, LT 1.23; it is in AW's early hand though he inserted the à after 1658; see also LT 1.182).
Wood 436. BL, NUC, BN.

3984. Knollys, Charles. Banbury, earl of. *The case of Charles earl of Banbury*. [London]: n.pub., [1692?]. S.sh.
Wood 276b(74). Wing C891 (Wing, 1698).

3985. [Komenský, Jan Amos]. Anchoran, John, ed. *Porta linguarum, . . . [2nd tp] The gate of tongues unlocked*. Londini: T. Cotes, sumpt. M. Sparkes (T. Cotes f. M. Sparkes), 1633. 8°. 2nd ed. Pp. [32], 282, [4].

Flyleaf, lower, printer's waste paper. See note at Wood 35(1), item 5722. Wood 35(2). STC 15079.

3986. Kossuma, Albert*. Prince. *A true and exact relation of the horrid and cruel murther lately committed upon prince Cossuma Albertus.* London: R. Vaughan, 1661. 4°. Pp. 6.
P. 3, AW wrote, ''twas commonly reported that he was a cheat, & no prince./'; and p. 6, 'This Cossuma Albertus a prince of Transylvania, was buried in Rochester Cathedrall with great solemnity 23 Oct. 1661. See my vol. of News books (Merc. public) for an. 1661. numb. 44.' Flyleaf, lower^v, OT and NT passages on tree of Jesse: 'Esay 11.1.10. Rom.15.12' (with lines over 10, 15, and 12), may not be by AW. LT 1.417. Wood 365(19). Wing T2447B (one) ('O' not recorded in Wing).

3987. [Kynaston, Francis]. *The constitutions of the musaeum Minervae.* London: T. P[urfoot] f. T. Spencer, 1636. 4°. Pp. [12], 20.
Missing. MS. Wood E. 2(70), p. 6.
MS. Wood E. 2(70), p. 6. STC 15099. *Folg, Hunt.*

3988. L., J. *Good news from Scotland: being a true relation of the present condition of the army under . . . Crumwell.* London: f. G. Calvert, 1648. 4°. Pp. 7.
Wood 502(70). Wing L29.

3989. L. L. *A letter written to a member sitting at Westminster.* London: n.pub, 1660. 4°. Pp. 8.
Tp, AW altered the year to 16'59[60]: Januar:', and below t, wrote 'not dated'.
Wood 632(27). Wing L42.

3990. L., N. *A letter sent from Portsmouth, from a very worthy person there, to a friend . . . in London. . . . N. L. [20 Dec.].* [London]: n.pub., [1659]. S.sh.
Wood 276a(339). Wing L47.

3991. L., S. *A letter to . . . lord Lambert, from a lover of peace and truth. Also, a declaration from the king of Scots, how the army shall be fully satisfied all their arrears.* [London]: n.pub., 1659. 4°. Pp. [2], 8.
Tp, former nos. '16' and '13', in pencil. Also, 'S. L.' in margin, in a modern hand.
Wood 632(40). Wing L62.

3992. L., S. *A letter from a gentleman of the lord ambassador Howard's retinue, . . . dated at Fez.* London: W. G. f. M. Pitt, 1670. 4°. Pp. [2], 36.
Tp, AW wrote 'Hen. Howard afterwards Duke of Norfolke', and '6^d'.
Wood 387(10). Wing L61.

3993. [L., T.]. *A prophesie that hath lyen hid, above these 2000. yeares.* London: [E. Allde] f. N. Fosbrooke, 1610. 4°. Pp. [8], 50 (misnumbering).
Wood 646(2). STC 15111.3.

3994. L., T. *True newes from Norwich: being a certaine relation how that the cathedrall blades of Norwich . . . did put themselves into a posture of defence.* London: f. B. Allen a. I. B., 1641. 4°. Pp. 8.
[MS.] Wood D. 31(48). Wing L81.

3995. L., W. *King Charles vindicated, or the grand cheats of the nation discovered.* [London]: f. Theodorus Microcosmus (pseud.), 1660. 4°. Pp. 15.
Tp, AW altered the year to 16'59' and added 'March:'.
Wood 526(6). Wing L89.

3996. L., W., and R. E. *A letter from one of the persons under censure of parliament, written upon the publishing of his majesties late speech in the upper-house, with an answer thereunto [signed R. E.].* London: f. W. Shears, 1660. 4°. Pp. [2], 6.
Wood 632(49). Wing L91.

3997. La Fin, Charles de. Umfrevile, William, trans. *A letter written upon occasion from the Low-countries, concerning a difference, betwixt the prince of Orange, and the states.* London: f. N. Butter, 1641[2], 22 March. 4°. Pp. [2], 6.
Wood 616(22). Wing L176.

3998. La Noue, François de. Aggas, Edward, trans. *The politicke and militarie discourses of the lord de la Novve.* London: f. T. C(adman) a. E. A(ggas) by T. Orwin, 1587. 4°. Pp. [16], 458. Parchment.
Possibly acquired 8 Jan. 1661, LT 1.380.

[MS.] Wood C. 15. STC 15215.

3999. [La Peyrère, Isaac de]. *Men before Adam . . . Romans [5.12-14] . . . By which are prov'd, that the first men were created before Adam. [Followed by] A theological systeme.* London: n.pub., 1656 (1655). 8°. Pp. [16], 61, [19], 351 (2 tpp.).
Tp, bsm. P. 346, marks in margin, in pencil, prob. not by AW, and other notes deliberately cropped. Acquired 8 Apr. 1664, 2^{s}4^d, LT 2.8.
Wood 889(3). Wing L427.

4000. La Ramée, Pierre de. Wotton, S., trans. *The art of logick. Gathered out of Aristotle.* London: J. D[awson] f. N. Bourne, 1626. 8°. Pp. [16], 189.
Missing. MS. Wood E. 2(70), p. 19. Wotton 'fuit Cantab. so Mr Fulman'.
MS. Wood E. 2(70), p. 19. STC 15248. *O*.

4001. Labbé, Philippe. *Tableaux genealogiques de la maison royale de France: et le blazon royal des armoiries des roys, reynes, dauphins, fils & filles.* La Haye: A. Vlacq, 1654. 12°. Pp. [8], 279. Calf, rough, with 3 fillets and stamp decoration (dragons) in corners (Ashm. binding).
Flyleaf, upper^v, a list of 7 printed works in this vol., made by an Ashm. librarian. Tp, AW wrote the price, '1^s.'. Bsm.
Wood 583(1). BL.

4002. Lackner, Christoph. *Aphorismi politici pro principe, republica, pace, bello, oeconomia, et bonis moribus, ex horologio principum [of A. de Guevara], in decadas distributi.* Tubingae: typ. E. Wildii, 1625. 8°. Pp. 122.
Pp. 63-72, underscoring, prob. not by by AW.
Wood 672(4). Not in BL.

4003. Lackner, Christoph. *Galea martis, hoc est, bona militia pro publica saluta epitomicè . . . conscripta.* Tubingae: typ. E. Wildii, 1625. 8°. Pp. [32], 192.
Tp, AW wrote, 'in b[ibl]. bod[leian].'
Wood 672(3). Not in BL.

4004. Lacrimae Germaniae. *Lacrymae Germaniae: or, the teares of Germany.* London: J. Okes, sold H. Overton a. J. Rothwell, 1638. 8°. Pp. [8], 72.
Wood 211(2). STC 11792 (usually issued with Wood 211(1) (item 1124), as here).

4005. Ladle, Tom*. *The pleasant history of Tom Ladle.* [London]: f. J. Blare, [1683-1695]. 4°. Pp. 23, [1] (2 tpp.).
Wood 259(9). Wing P2551F (two) (Wing, 1683-1700).

4006. Lake, John. Chichester, bp. of. Στεφανος πιστου: *or the true Christians character . . . a sermon . . . at the funeral of mr. William Cade.* London: W. Godbid f. N. Brooke, 1671. 4°. Pp. [18], 28.
Tp, 'Lake' underscored.
Wood 634(5). Wing L198.

4007. Lamb, Doctor. *Doctor Lamb's darling: or, strange and terrible news from Salisbury, . . . of the . . . contract . . . made between the devil, and mistris Anne Bodenham.* London: f. G. Horton, 1653. 4°. Pp. 8.
[MS.] Wood B. 18(12). Wing D1763.

4008. Lambard, William, ed. *Archeion, or, a discourse upon the high courts of justice in England.* London: E.P[urslowe] f. H. Seile, 1635. 8°. Newly corrected. Pp. [14], 276. Calf, speckled, with 3 fillets; backing, printer's waste.
Flyleaf, upper, 3rd^v, note copied from S. Daniel concerning the life of William the Conqueror, not by AW.
Wood 669. STC 15144.

4009. Lambert, John*. *The lord Lambert's letter to the speaker.* London: n.pub., 1659[60]. 4°. Pp. 7.
P. 7, AW wrote, 'Januar: 1659[60]'.
Wood 632(39). Wing L3048.

4010. Lambert, John*, pseud. *The recantation and confession of John Lambert, esq. Taken from his mouth by C. Prince.* London: f. C. Gustavus, 1659[60]. 4°. Pp. 7.
Wood 610(29). Wing R610.

4011. Lambert, John*. *A curtain-conference, being a discourse betwixt . . . John Lambert esq; and his lady.* London: f. W. L., [1660]. S.sh.
AW added the date, 'Jan: 1659'.
Wood 276a(266). Wing C7688 (3).

4012. Lambert, John*. *A hue and cry after Lambert.* [London]: n.pub., [1660]. S.sh.
AW added the date, 'Aprill: 1660'.
Wood 276a(264). Wing H3281 (two).

4013. Lambert, John*. *The message of John Lambert esq, in answer to the proclamation.* London: f. J. Dukeson, 1660. S.sh.
Wood 276a(267). Wing M1902.

4014. Lambert, John*. *A packet of severall letters being intercepted . . . which were sent from John Lambert esq. to many of the phanaticks.* London: f. J. Morgan, 1660. 4°. Pp. [2], 5.
Tp, AW added after the year, 'Aprill'.
Wood 632(46). Wing P159.

4015. Lambert, John*. *Poor John: or, a lenten dish. Being the soliloquies of John Lambert.* [London]: f. the benefit . . . of afflicted brethren, [1660]. S.sh.
AW added the date, 'March: 1659'.
Wood 276a(265). Wing P2863 ('O' not recorded in Wing).

4016. Lambert, John, and Edmund Waring. *A second, and a third letter from the lord Lambert, . . . with a letter from major Edm: Waring, . . . of the surrender of Chester.* London: T. Newcomb, 1659. 4°. Pp. 8.
Wood 503(26). Wing L242.

4017. Lambeth Fair. *Lambeth faire, wherein you have all the bishops trinkets set to sale.* [London]: n.pub., 1641. 4°. A⁴,B². See note at item 260.
Wood 483(20). Wing L246.

4018. Lampadius Luneburgensis. *Compendium musices.* Bernae in Helvetiis: per Samuelem Apiarium, 1554. 8°. A-G⁸. Parchment.
Tp, AW wrote, 'in bib. B[odleiana]', to record another copy; signature of owner, E. Banyster. Pastedown, lower, torn out, with remainder showing traces of annotation.
Wood 26. BL.

4019. Lampoons. *Lampoons.* [London?]: n.pub., [1687]. S.sh.
AW wrote the year, '1688', and identified two initialed persons, Lord 'Dover' and Lord 'Salisburies'.
Wood 417(155). Wing L306A.

4020. Landen, Flanders. *Remarks upon the London Gazette, relating to the streights-fleet and the battle of Landen in Flanders [Aug.].* [London]: n.pub., [1693]. 4°. Pp. 8. Inserted after London *Gazette*, numb. 2893, Wood 554(1).
P. 1, 'Caf: dug: 3ᵈ' (?); 8, AW wrote, 'Bought of Mʳ G. West, 2 Sept. 1693'. See LT 3.448.
Wood 554(2). Wing R948.

4021. Langbaine, Gerard (elder). *Episcopall inheritance. Or a reply to the examination of a printed abstract of the answers [by C. Burges].* Oxford: L. Lichfield, 1641. 4°. Pp. [8], 52 (misnumbering).
Tp, former nos., '14' and '13'.
[MS.] Wood D. 25(8). Wing L367. Madan 999.

4022. [Langbaine, Gerard] (elder). *The answer of the chancellor, masters and scholars . . . to the petition, . . . of the city of Oxon [24 July].* Oxford: H. Hall, 1649. 4°. Pp. 46, [2 blank].
P. [47], AW wrote, 'Q[uaere] how this controversie was concluded, in Dr. GL' [Dr. G. Langbaine]. Diff. ed. at Wood 515(5).
Wood 614(6). Wing L363. Madan 2019.

4023. [Langbaine, Gerard] (elder). *The foundation of the universitie of Cambridge, with a catalogue of the principall founders . . . and total number of students, magistrates and officers.* London: M. S[immons] f. T. Jenner, 1651. 4°. Pp. [2], 17.
Wood 513(2). Wing L368.

4024. [Langbaine, Gerard] (elder). *The foundation of the universitie of Oxford, with a catalogue of the principall founders and speciall benefactors . . . students, magistrates and officers.* London: M. S[immons] f. T. Jenner, 1651. 4°. Pp. [2], 17. Pasteboard (blue) with parchment spine; rebacked in 20th century.
Flyleaf, upper, 4th, above, AW wrote a heading, 'Oxoniensia', in pencil, and then the titles of 7 printed works in this vol., within guidelines made with red ink. An 8th t, not in AW's hand and added after 1695, records the final work in this vol. (and refers to another copy in the Lister collection). 1st item, acquired 25 Jan. 1658, 6ᵈ, LT 1.235. Pp. 14, AW made a correction, 'Creke' for 'Greek'; and 15, lines in margin at gift, by P. Bisse, of 1849 books to Wadham College. AO 3.447f.
Wood 513(1). Wing L370. Madan 2150.

4025. [Langbaine, Gerard] (elder). Ivory, John, ed. *The foundation of the university of Cambridge, with a catalogue of the principal founders and special benefactours of all the colledges, and totall number of students, magistrates and officers therein being, anno 1672.* [Cambridge]: [J. Hayes f. J. Ivory], [1672]. S.sh. Obl.
Wood 423(4-5). Wing L369 ('O' not recorded in Wing; ESTCR 223648 has place of publication and publisher).

4026. [Langbaine, Gerard] (elder). *The answer of the chancellor, masters and scholars . . . to the petition . . . of the city of Oxon.* Oxford: H. Hall, sold R. Davis, 1678. 4°. 2nd ed. Pp. 46.
Tp, AW wrote, 'By Dʳ Gerard Langbaine of Qu. Coll. an. 1649'; 'The 1ˢᵗ edit. came out 1649. qᵗᵒ'; and 'This edition was published at Oxon. 7 Feb. 1677[8] upon certaine differences then on foot between the University & Towne.' Diff. ed. at Wood 614(6).
Wood 515(5). Wing L364. Madan 3184.

4027. Langbaine, Gerard (younger). *An account of the English dramatick poets.* Oxford: L. L[ichfield] f. G. West a. H. Clements, 1691. 8°. Pp. [16], 556, [33].
Passim, a few marks in margins, underscoring, corrections, cross references, e.g., pp. 17, 43, 57, 59-66, etc. to 514-5, 519, 541, 546 to Oo3, where, at entry of Sackvile and Norton: AW wrote, 'From the first vol. of Ath. et Fasti Oxon'. Dupl. (missing) at Wood 887b(3).
Wood 116(3). Wing L373.

4028. Langbaine, Gerard (younger). *An account of the English dramatick poets.* Oxford: L. L[ichfield] f. G. West a. H. Clements, 1691. 8°. Pp. [16], 556, [33].
Missing in 1837. Dupl. at Wood 116(3).
Wood 887b(3). Wing L373. *Folg.*

4029. Langdale, Marmaduke. 1st baron. *The declaration of . . . and other loyall subjects now in action for his majesties service in the northern parts.* London: n.pub., 1648. 4°. Pp. [2], 6.
P. 6, AW wrote 2 footnotes, 'Barwick was surprizd by Sʳ Marmaduke Langdale in the latter end of Apr. 1648', and 'Sʳ Tho. Glemham & Sʳ Philip Musgrave took in Carlile [sic] for the use of the pr. of Wales in the beginning of May 1648'.
Wood 502(3). Wing L379 ('O' not recorded in Wing).

4030. Langdale, Marmaduke. 1st baron. *An impartiall relation of the late fight at Preston.* [London]: n.pub., 1648. 4°. Pp. [2], 5.
Wood 502(57). Wing L381.

4031. Langford, John. *A just and cleere refutation of a false and scandalous pamphlet, entituled Babylons fall in Maryland [by Leonard Strong].* London: f. the author, 1655. 4°. Pp. 35.
Wood 386(8). Wing L387.

4032. Langhorne, Richard. *Mr. Langhorn's memoires, with some meditations and devotions . . . and his speech at his execution.* [London]: n.pub., 1679. Fol. Pp. [2], 22.
Tp, Wood wrote the price, '6ᵈ'. Purchased from Vade in July or August 1679, see his record of purchase in MS. Wood F. 50, f. 11.
Wood 425(5). Wing L397.

4033. Langhorne, Richard. *The petition and declaration of Richard Langhorne [10 July].* [London]: n.pub., [1679]. Fol. Pp. 4.
Wood 425(3). Wing L398.

4034. Langhorne, Richard. *The speech of Richard Langhorn esq; at his execution July 14.* [London]: n.pub., [1679]. Fol. Pp. 4.

Wood 425(4). Wing L399.

4035. Langhorne, Richard*. *The tryall of Richard Langhorn . . . for conspiring the death of the king.* London: f. H. Hills, T. Parkhurst, J. Starkey, D. Newman, T. Cockeril, a. T. Simmons, 1679. Fol. Pp. 68, [1].
Tp, AW wrote the price, '2s-4'. P. 19, an identification, not by AW.
Wood 425(2). Wing T2212.

4036. Langhorne, Rowland. *Major generall Laughorn's [sic] letter to the honourable William Lenthall . . . the taking of Carmarthen.* London: f. E. Husband, 1645, 28 Oct. 4°. A⁴.
Tp, AW overwrote the former no., '30'.
Wood 378(33). Wing L402.

4037. Langhorne, Rowland. *A declaration by major general Laughorn [sic], and the rest of the forces . . . in Wales, of the grounds of their engagement . . . in relation to the king, parliament and kingdom.* London: f. L. Chapman, 1648, 15 May. 4°. Pp. 15 (misnumbering).
Wood 502(5). Wing L401.

4038. Langhorne, Rowland, and Joh[n] Rushworth. *Two letters sent to the hono*ble *William Lenthal . . . concerning the great victory . . . at Cardiffe.* London: f. E. Husband, 1645[6], 2 March. 4°. Pp. 8.
Tp, AW wrote and later lined out the price, '1d', and overwrote the former no., '50'.
Wood 378(53). Wing L402A ('O' not recorded in Wing).

4039. [Langland, William]. *The vision of Pierce Plowman.* London: O. Rogers, 1561, 21 Feb. 4°. *²,A-2H⁴,I².
Missing in 1837. 'The Vision of Pierce Plowman – Lond. 1561' in Whiteside cat.
Wood 324. STC 19908. *O* (two), *Folg, Hunt* (two).

4040. Lanquet, Thomas. *Coopers chronicle, . . . newly enlarged and augmented, . . . unto the late death of queene Marie, by me Thomas Cooper.* Londini: [T. Powell] [(in the house late T. Berthelettes)], 1560. 4°. Ff. [30], 376, [8] (wanting colophon leaf). Parchment with 2 clasp holes.
Acquired 6 Nov. 1661, 6d, LT 1.418.
Wood 463. STC 15218.

4041. Larkin, Edward. *Speculum patrum: a looking-glasse of the fathers, . . . to which are added, the characters of some of the chief philosophers.* London: f. H. Everden, 1659. 8°. Pp. [4], 99 (issued with Wood 435(2)). Pasteboard (grey) with parchment spine; 1st upper and last lower flyleaves, marbled paper.
Flyleaf, upper, AW wrote the titles of 3 printed works in this vol., within guidelines made with red ink (4, if items 1 and 2 are separate). Tp, he wrote the price, '2s'. Acquired, with Wood 435(2), 29 Aug. 1662, in sheets, LT 1.454.
Wood 435(1). Wing L444.

4042. Larkin, Ed[ward]. *The true effigies, or portraicture of the chief philosophers, historians, poets.* London: E. Cotes, f. H. Eversden, 1659. 8°. Pp. 223, [1] (issued with Wood 435(1)).
Acquired, with Wood 435(1), 29 Aug. 1662, in sheets, LT 1.454.
Wood 435(2). Wing L445.

4043. Lassels, Richard. *The voyage of Italy, . . . in two parts.* Paris: (V. du Moutier) sold in London, by J. Starkey, 1670. 12°. Pp. [46], 1-251, [2], 1-447, [4] (2nd tp at 2nd p. 1). Calf, speckled, gold-stamp decoration on spine (French?).
Flyleaf, upper, price, '5 - 6'; Sheldon's motto 'In Posterum', inscribed directly over 'Erskin' (LT 2.455, 3.104-5); and AW wrote, 'Antonii à Wood, ex dono Radulphi Sheldon de Beolie in agro Wigorn. 5 July 1679.'
Wood 159. Wing L465.

4044. Last and Best Edition. *The last and best edition of new songs: such as are of the most general esteem either in town or court.* London: n.pub., 1677. 8°. A⁴,B-D⁸.
Tp, the price, '6d'.
Wood 326(7). Wing L469 (3).

4045. Laud, William*. Canterbury, abp. of. *The bishops potion or a dialogue between the bishop of Canterbury, and his phisitian.* [London]: n.pub., 1641. 4°. Pp. [2], 4.
Wood 366(22). Wing B3032 (Wing, potion, or,).

4046. Laud, William*. Canterbury, abp. of. *Canterburies amazement: or the ghost of the yong fellow Thomas Bensted.* [London]: f. F. Coules, 1641. 4°. Pp. 8.
Wood 366(21). Wing C456.

4047. Laud, William. Canterbury, abp. of. *The copie of a letter sent . . . unto the universitie of Oxford: specifying, his willingnesse to resigne his chancellor-ship [28 June].* [London]: n.pub., 1641. 4°. Pp. [2], 5.
P. 5, catchword lined out in this made-up forgery of Wood 616(20) (see items 4052-3 and Madan).
Wood 616(19). Wing L581. Madan 971.

4048. Laud, William. Canterbury, abp. of. *A letter sent by William Lawd . . . With divers manuscripts to the university of Oxford. Together with the answer.* [London]: n.pub., 1641. 4°. Pp. [2], 5. Pasteboard (blue) with parchment spine; rebacked.
Flyleaf, upper, 1st, AW wrote, 'Binding. 6^{d}. Feb. 8. 1689[90]'; 3rd, above, AW wrote a heading, 'Oxoniensia Vol. – –', in pencil; and then the titles of 54 printed works in this vol., within guidelines made with red ink (he omitted 15b). Many of the items in the vol. have 2 numbers (or more) to record an earlier order which is almost parallel (1-51 vs. 1-54). Some printed before July 1644 may have come from the collection of Brian Twyne; two, items 8 and 14, have notes by Twyne. Tp, bsm.; over the year, 1641, an alteration, prob. by AW, to read 1640; and note, 'v[ide] Cat Canc', in pencil, may not be in AW's hand. P. 1, he wrote, 'This letter was written in Latine, remaining yet to be seen in Reg[istro]: Dom[us]: Convoc[ationis]: Oxōn R. fol. 182. b. The Translatour hath mangled it & abused the authour ita testor Anth: à Woode Oxoniensis Antiquarius.' and p. 3 at a later time, he wrote a similar note concerning the answer: 'This epistle was written in Latine, as tis to this day remaining in Reg: Dom: Conv: R. fol. 183. a. but the Translator hath much erred, & abused the University in it.' P. 2, AW, apparently(?), added at printed name of the author, 'W[illiam]. Canterbury', 'Dat: ex Ædibus meis Lambethanis 6. Nov: 1640'; p. 5, AW wrote at printed 'From, Oxford 1640', 'E Domo nostrae convocationis Nov: 10 1640' and at orator's name, Strode, 'Sanctitatis Vestrae devotiss^{a} Cultrix Oxōn Academia.' LT 1.51.
Wood 514(1). Wing L590. Madan 969.

4049. Laud, William*. Canterbury, abp. of. *Mercuries message, or the coppy of a letter sent to William Laud, . . . now prisoner in the Tower.* [London]: n.pub., 1641. 4°. A^{4}.
Tp, AW wrote, 'in verse'.
Wood 366(23). Wing M1748.

4050. Laud, William. Canterbury, abp. of. *The recantation of the prelate of Canterbury.* London: n.pub., 1641. 4°. Pp. [2], 41.
Wood 366(26). Wing R613.

4051. Laud, William*. Canterbury, abp. of. *Rome for Canterbury: Or a true relation of . . . William Laud.* [London]: n.pub., 1641. 4°. Pp. 8.
Tp, bsm.
Wood 366(25). Wing R1895.

4052. Laud, William. Canterbury, abp. of. *The true copie of a letter sent from . . . to the university of Oxford, when he resign'd his office of chancellour.* Oxford: L. Lichfield, 1641. 4°. Pp. [2], 5, [1], '6-8'.
P. 1, AW wrote, 'This letter is not in Reg[istro]: R. nor the next that followes, the reason is because twas sent when the Regesters were in the hands of a Committee at London. AWoode.'; p. 6, at the answer, 'This letter is not in the Reg: for the reason before expressed.' LT 1.51. Dupl. at Wood 616(20).
Wood 514(5). Wing L601. Madan 970.

4053. Laud, William. Canterbury, abp. of. *The true copie of a letter sent from . . . to the university of Oxford, when he resign'd his office of chancellour.* Oxford: L. Lichfield, 1641. 4°. Pp. [2], 5, [1], '6-8'.
Tp, AW wrote 'D[upl]', in pencil (cropped). Dupl. at Wood 514(5).
Wood 616(20). Wing L601. Madan 970.

4054. Laud, William. Canterbury, abp. of. *The archbishop of Canterbury's speech: or his funerall sermon.* London: P. Cole, 1644[5]. 4°. Pp. [1-2], 5-19.
Wood 366(27). Wing L599.

4055. Laud, William*. Canterbury, abp. of. *An elegie on the most reverend father in God William lord arch-bishop of Canterbury.* [Oxford]: [L. Lichfield], 1644[5]. 4°. Pp. [2], 9.
Wood 366(30). Wing E426. Madan 1731.

4056. Laud, William*. Canterbury, abp. of. *Four queries resolved for the satisfaction of all men,*

. . . touching the late arch-bishop. London: f. J. Hancock, 1645. 4°. Pp. 16.
[MS.] Wood D. 31(19) (not in Bodl. CD cat.). Wing F1666.

4057. Launoy, Jean de. *De varia Aristotelis in academia Parisiensi fortuna*. Hagae-Comitum: n.pub., 1656. 4°. 2nd ed. Pp. [8], 94. Calf with 3 fillets, stamp decoration inside corners, and roll decoration at inner, spine edge (Ashm. binding); rebacked in 1951.
Flyleaf, upper, 2nd^v, the titles of 9 printed works in this vol. and 1 added later, by an Ashm. librarian. There is some cropping. 1st item, tp, 'ABosco. Oxōn. 1670'. Pp. 4, 25, 28, and 61, have: a date, double lines in margin, 'Abaelard', and underscoring; prob. none by AW. Bsm.
Wood 607(1). BL.

4058. Lavater, Ludwig. Harrison, Robert, trans. *Of ghostes and spirites walking by nyght*. London: H. Benneyman f. R. Watkyns, 1572. 4°. Pp. [16], 220. Pasteboard (blue) with parchment spine. 1st upper and last lower flyleaves, marbled paper.
Flyleaf, upper, 3rd^v, AW wrote the titles of 6 printed works in this vol., within guidelines made with red ink. Item 1, tp, below,'E' (?); p. 220, name, 'ma: styward [?]'.
[MS.] Wood B. 20(1). STC 15320.

4059. Lawcey, William. *Sir Phillip Stapleton dead of the sicknesse at Callice:. . . a letter*. London: R. Ibbitson, 1647. 4°. Pp. [2], 6.
P. 3-4, AW wrote the name of 'Will. Batten' and 'Major Kem' in the margins.
Wood 620(7). Wing L637.

4060. Lawes, Henry. *Ayres and dialogues*. [London]: T. H. f. J. Playford, 1653. Fol. Pp. [10], 36, 28 (wanting tp; photocopy supplied, B. M. (BL) copy).
Sig. a2, 'Jan: 13: 1656/6' overwritten (?) by '1666/7' (LT 2.98). Pp. [2-3], some marks in margin. P. [10] underscoring of authors in the table; at Francis Finch, 'q[uaere] [and in pencil:] C. Bull [?]'. P. 36, at music books printed and sold by Playford, 6 are marked, including the one currently at Wood 397(1). LT 2.398.
Wood 397(2) (not in Bodl. CD cat.). Wing L638.

4061. Lawrence, George. *Laurentius Lutherizans. Or the protestation of George Laurence*. London: f. R. Harford, 1642. 4°. A⁴.
Tp, AW wrote, 'protestation–' in margin.
Wood 476(16). Wing L658.

4062. L[awrence], G[eorge], and C[hristopher] L[ove]. *The debauched cavalleer: or the English Midianite*. London: L. N. f. H. Overton, 1642. 4°. Pp. 8.
Tp, completion of initials with names; a marginal note, in ink, possibly in AW's early hand; and below AW wrote in red ink 'Christop. Love – George Lawrence - both of New Inne – the authours'. AO 3.278-81.
Wood 476(15). Wing L656.

4063. [Lawrence, Thomas]. *Verses spoken to the king, queen, and dutchesse of Yorke in St John's library in Oxford*. [Oxford]: [H. Hall f. R. Davis], [1663]. 4°. Pp. [2], 2, and a duplicate leaf, of pp. 1-2.
2nd p. 2, at end, AW wrote, in red ink, 'These verses were spoken by Thom Laurence a gent-com. of St Johns coll – [/] Afterwards Fellow of Univ. coll.' The 2nd tp, apparently belonging to one of the duplicate pp. 1-2, is to be found at Library Records d. 1071, f. 95, pasted in as waste paper on which to write the notice of Dugdall mss. in the Ashm. Museum. LT 1.498.
Wood 515(31). Wing L623B. Madan 2623.

4064. Lawrence, Tho[mas]. *Mercurius centralis: or, a discourse of subterraneal cockle, muscle, and oyster-shels, found in . . . Norfolk*. London: J. G. f. R. Royston, 1664. 12°. Pp. [9], 94. Pasteboard (blue) with parchment spine. 1st upper and last lower flyleaves, 1 side of leaf, dyed purple.
Flyleaf, upper, 3rd^v, AW wrote the titles of 3 printed works in this vol., within guidelines made with red ink. Acquired 16 Aug. 1664, 4^d, LT 2.19.
Wood 700b(1). Wing L689C.

4065. Lawson, John. *Two letters from vice-admiral John Lawson . . . the one, to . . . the lord mayor . . . of London; . . . The other, to . . . the commissioners for the militia [28 Dec. 1659]*. [London]: n.pub., [1659]. S.sh.
Wood 276a(117). Wing L721.

4066. Lawson, John. *Two letters from vice-admiral John Lawson, . . . to the lord mayor . . . 13th of December, 1659 . . . 21, December*. London: J. Streater, 1659. S.sh.

Wood 276a(336). Wing L720.

4067. Lawson, William; Gervase Markham, and S. Harward. *A new orchard and garden:. . . With the country housewife's garden [by G. Markham] . . . Whereunto is newly added the art of propagating plants [by S. Harward]*. London: W. Wilson f. J. Harison, 1648. 4° 2nd ed. Pp. [8], 134 (2 tpp).
[MS.] Wood C. 25(6). Wing L730.

4068. Lazarillo, de Tormes. Rouland, David, trans. *The plesant historie of Lazarillo de Tormes a Spaniarde, . . . drawne out of Spanish*. London: A. Jeffes, 1596. 4°. A-H⁴.
Tp, below, 'G'.
Wood 487(8b). STC 15337.

4069. Lazarillo, de Tormes. P[histon?], W[illiam], trans. *[The most pleasaunt and delectable historie of Lazarillo de Tormes. Pt. 2, tr. by W. P.]*. [London]: [T. C[reede] f. J. Oxenbridge], [1596]. 4°. A2-4,B-H⁴ (wanting the tp).
A2, below, 'H'.
Wood 487(8a). STC 15340.

4070. Le Loyer, Pierre. [Jones, Zachary], trans. *A treatise of specters or straunge sights, visions and apparitions appearing sensibly unto men*. London: V. S[immes] f. M. Lownes, 1605. 4°. Ff. [8], 145, [1]. Parchment. Pastedowns and flyleaves, upper and lower, printer's waste paper (Sidney, *Apol. for Poetrie* (1595), STC 22534: E1ᵛ-E4ᵛ; E2 and E3ʳ⁻ᵛ (E2ᵛ has an uncorrected catchword, 'of' instead of 'mate'); and D2 and D3ʳ⁻ᵛ, D1ᵛ-D4ʳ).
[MS.] Wood B. 23. STC 15448.

4071. Le Mire, Aubert. *Notitia episcopatuum orbis Christiani . . . libri v*. Antverpiae: ex off. Plantiniana, ap. viduam & filios J. Moreti, 1613. 8°. Pp. [16], 418, [4]. Parchment.
Cover, upper, inside, 'b'; tp, bsm.
Wood 148. BL.

4072. Le Petit, John François. Grimeston, Edward, trans. *The Low-country common wealth*. [London]: G. Eld, 1609. 4° in 8's. Pp. [8], 303. Parchment with 2 clasp holes.
Wood 359. STC 15485.

4073. Le Vager, Jean, et al. *The voluntarie conversion, and severall recantations, of foure . . . from the errours of idolatrie and poperie*. London: R. Bradocke f. W. Jones, sold W. Aspley, 1604. 4°. Pp. [4], 44. Pasteboard (blue) with parchment spine. 1st upper and last lower flyleaves, marbled paper.
Flyleaf, upper, 2ndᵛ, AW wrote the titles of 10 printed works in this vol., within guidelines made with red ink.
[MS.] Wood D. 24(1). STC 5650.

4074. Le W[right], T[homas]. *A more exact character and perfect narrative of . . . Oliver Cromwell. Originally published as: An exact character or narrative of . . . Oliver Cromwell*. London: J. Jones, 1658. 4°.
Missing since 1994.
Wood 531(23). Wing L1853A.

4075. Leathermore. *Leather-more: or advice concerning gaming*. London: n.pub., 1668. 4°. 2nd ed. Pp. 11, [1].
Tp, AW wrote 'Jesus Bells. See p. 9'. P. 9, 'Bells' in margin (at 'in a Tower of St. Pauls'). Acquired 21 Dec. 1668, LT 2.146.
Wood 500(8). Wing L800.

4076. [Lee, E.]. *Legenda lignea: with an answer to mr. Birchleys Moderator [pleading for a toleration of popery]*. London: n.pub., 1653. 8°. Pp. [16], 238.
Missing in 1837. Dupl. at Wood 793.
Wood 791. Wing L839. *Clark, Folg.*

4077. [Lee, E.]. *Legenda lignea: with an answer to mr. Birchleys Moderator [pleading for a toleration of popery]*. London: n.pub., 1653. 8°. Pp. [14], 238. Calf with 2 fillets; rebacked.
Flyleaf, upper, 'a - 4' (?), and 'Pret: 6ᵈ' and tp, '1ˢ-4ᵈ.', none by AW. Dupl. at Wood 791 missing.
Wood 793 (not in Bodl. CD cat.). Wing L839.

4078. Leech, Humphrey. *A triumph of truth. Or declaration of the doctrine concerning evangelicall*

counsayles; lately delivered in Oxford. [Douai]: [L. Kellam], 1609. 12°. Pp. [14], 135, [1].
Missing. MS. Wood E. 2(70), p. 5, '1 Declaration of the doctrine concerning evangelicall counsayle . . . '.
MS. Wood E. 2(70), p. 5. STC 15363. ARCR 2.497. *O, Folg, Hunt.*

4079. [Legh, Gerard]. Argoll, Richard, ed. *The accedens of armory.* (London): (R. Tottel), (1568). 4°
in 8's. Ff. [6], 135, [2] (wanting t. leaf). Calf, with 3 fillets, 2 interior rectangles each with 3 fillets and
between, stamp decoration; stamp centrepiece; rebacked.
Pastedown, upper, 5 coats of arms, and scribbles, may be in AW's hand, and 'Antony Woo' [sic]. Also,
'Johannes Vincent me Jure tenet teste Me metipse' (John Vincent's books were acquired by R. Sheldon,
and AW apparently acquired this via Sheldon). Text, to lower pastedown, a few notes, lines in margin, and
underscoring, in more than 1 hand, but none in AW's hand. Inserted, loose, two 8° sheets of MS, corrections
for a work on armory, not in AW's hand.
Wood 355. STC 15389.

4080. Legh, Gerard. Argoll, Richard, ed. *The accedence of armorie.* (London): [W. Jaggard] (f. J. Jaggard), (1612). 4° in 8's. Newly corrected. Pp. [15], 241, [1]. Parchment with 2 clasp holes.
Pastedown, upper, AW wrote, 'The first impress at Lond. 1568', some scribbles, and a printed large upper
case 'A'. Tp, bsm. Text, some minor corrections, notes, and vertical lines in margins: A3, A5; pp. 1-16
undercoring, marks in margins, and some notes, not in AW's manner or hand; pp. 41, 53, 56-7, some coats
of arms coloured; pp. 51, 53, 73, 95-105, and, frequently, to p. 234, vertical lines in margins, in pencil, in
AW's manner. Flyleaf, lower[v] (formerly the upper flyleaf?), 'Thom – [illeg.] Barker his booke', lined out.
Wood 356. STC 15393.

4081. Leghorn. *From aboard the Van-herring. A letter from Legorn [1 Dec.].* [London]: n.pub., [1679]. Fol.
Pp. 4.
Wood 276a(164). Wing F2238.

4082. Leiden, University. *Rector et senatus academiae Lugduno-Bat. lectori salutem. [Beginning] Ordo*
lectionum hiemalium in academia Batava Leydensi. Lugd. Batavor.: B. & A. Elzevir, 1629. S.sh.
May have been in possession of G. Higgs, see Morrish, p. 8[144] and note 57 p. 51[187], and see notes at
Comptoir, Wood 498(14), item 61.
Wood 276a(517). Not in BL, NUC, BN. Not in A. Willems, *Les Elzevier* (Bruxelles, 1880).

4083. Leigh, Edward. *Selected and choice observations concerning the twelve first caesars.* Oxford: L.
Lichfield, f. W. Webb, 1635. 12°. Pp. [10], 209. Parchment.
Pastedown and flyleaf, upper, schoolboy scribbles. Some numbers and marks in text and margins. Flyleaves,
lower, drawing, scribbles and signatures of Edmund Salmon and Edward Salmon. Lent to O. Sedgwick,
March 1659, LT 1.306.
Wood 272. STC 15410. Madan 812. AO 3.927.

4084. Leigh, Edward. *A treatise of the divine promises; in five books.* London: A. Miller f. T. Underhill,
1650. 12°. 3rd ed. Pp. [18], 409, [39]. Calf with 2 fillets; rebacked.
Flyleaf, upper, 2nd[v], AW wrote '5 books of divine promises'. Flyleaves, lower, 2nd-3rd, scribbles or school
exercises, not by AW.
Wood 796. Wing L1015.

4085. Leigh, Edward. *A treatise of religion & learning, and of religious and learned men.* London: A. M.
f. C. Adams, 1656. Fol. Pp. [10], 373, [34] (interleaved). Calf with 3 fillets; rebacked. 1st and last flyleaves,
printer's waste paper.
Tp, bsm. Text, notes by a former owner, not by AW, e.g.,1st pp. [9], 91, 99, 165, 271, 286, 303, 324 (the
note), 340. From p. 93, AW made some minor annotation, vertical lines in margins, underscoring and a few
notes, in pencil, ink and red ink, e.g., 36 ('q[uaere]' at Richard Greenvill), 93, 113-4, 141-2, 160 (the note
on the interleaf may be by AW), 161, 165, 197-8, 211-2, 215, 217-8, 231, 236, 324 (not the note), 332, 357
('false' in margin), to the end, 371.
Wood 656. Wing L1013.

4086. Leigh, Edw[ard]. *Second considerations concerning the high court of chancery, and the . . . ordi-*
nance for the regulation . . . of that court. London: J. G. f. R. Marriot, 1658. 4°. Pp. [2], 13.
Wood 630(17). Wing L1002 (two).

4087. Leigh, Samuel. *Samuelis primitiae: or, an essay towards a metrical version of the . . . Psalmes.*
London: Tho. Milbourn f. author, 1661. 8°. Pp. [16], 135. Calf with 2 fillets.
Flyleaf, 2nd, AW wrote, 'Donavit Author'; tp, after name of author, 'Commoner of Merton Coll.' A5, A6,

A7^v, AW underscored names of those who wrote verses. LT 1.418.
Wood 96. Wing B2473A (two).

4088. Leigh, [Thomas]. Stoneleigh, baron of. *The case of the right honourable the lord Leigh, in answe*
to a printed paper entituled the case of dame Elizabeth. [London]: n.pub, [1677?]. S.sh.
See G. E. Cokayne, *The Complete Peerage*, ed. H. A. Doubleday and H. de Walden (London, 1929), 7.567
Wood 276b(46). Wing C1157C (rare).

4089. Leighton, Henry. *Linguae Gallicae addiscendae regulae.* Oxoniae: exc. H. H[all] impen. authori
or A. & L. Lichfield, 1659, 1662. 12° or 8°.
Missing. MS. Wood E. 2(70), p. 74, 'Leighton (M. A.) Ox. [Ox. lined out and above:] Scotland rather [anc
French Gramar – Ox'. Ed. not identified.
MS. Wood E. 2(70), p. 74. Wing L1026 and 1027 and 1027A. Madan 2448 and 2601. *O* and *O*.

4090. Leland, John. *Genethliacon illustrissimi Eäduerdi principis Cambriae, ducis Coriniae, et com*
tis Palatini: libellus. [Heading, part 2:] Syllabus, et interpretatio antiquarum dictionum. Londini: (ap. R
Wolfium), 1543. 4°. a-f^4,g^6. Parchment with 2 clasp holes.
Tp, 'Liber Antonii Woode Oxōn: ex dono Ven[erabilis]: V[iri]: Johannis Wilton S. T. B. nuper Coll: Mer
ton Capellani. Iunij VI. MDCLxiiiij.', and slightly later in time, 'Obijt Wiltonus xvii ejusdem mensis e
sepultus jacet in ecclesia Coll: Merton. /' (LT 2.38); and, not in AW's hand, 'pretium ijs viijd'. Text, som
underscoring and, e4^{r-v}, g2^{r-v}, notes, not in AW's hand. Lent to T. Gore, July-Aug 1668, Letters, 23 Jul
and 29 Aug. 1668, MS. Wood F. 42, ff. 66, 68.
Wood 479(1). STC 15443.

4091. Leland, John. *Assertio inclytissimi Arturii regis Britanniae.* Londini: [R. Wolfe] (ap. J. Herford)
1544. 4°. Ff. [4], 39, [1].
Ff. [4]^v, at index of authors are written f. nos. and a note, not in AW's hand. Text, ff. 3, 39^v notes, not i
AW's hand, and some underscoring. Flyleaves, lower, 23 pp. of ms. entries in Latin of places, cities, rivers
religious centres, in Britain, titled 'Brevis quaedam Britannicae insulae descriptio', not by AW. LT 2.38.
Wood 479(4). STC 15440.

4092. Leland, John. Κυκνειον ασμα. *Cygnea cantio. [Followed by] Commentarii in cygneam cantionem*
indices Britannicae antiquitatis. [London]: [R. Wolfe], [1545]. 4°. A^6,B-E^4; A-P^4 (2 pts.).
Text, poem, 1st B2-E2, AW wrote in margins the English names for Latin cities and places. 2nd A3^{r-v}, a
index of authors are written the dates of authors and one ref. to the text, not in AW's hand. Text afte
2nd A3, p. nos. entered, prob. not by AW; some underscoring.
Wood 479(3). STC 15444.

4093. Leland, John. Εγκωμιον της εν ειρηνης. *Laudatio pacis.* Londini: (ap. R. Wolfium), 1546 (Aug.)
4°. a-b^4.
Wood 479(2). STC 15442.

4094. Leland, John. Bale, John, ed. *The laboryouse journey & serche of Johan Leylande, for Englande*
antiquitees. (London): [S. Mierdman f.] (J. Bale), sold [R. Foster], (1549). 8°. A-H^8 (H8 blank). Calf with
5 fillets, 1 gold-stamped, and gold-stamped centrepiece (laurel).
Flyleaf, upper^v, 'Anthony Woode: 1658'. Tp, 'Ant: Woode Merton: Coll: Oxōn: 1658'. In index of writers
some brief notes, e.g. G4, G8, may be by AW. Acquired 29 Ap. 1658 out of G. Langbaine's study, LT 1.247
Lent to R. Bathurst 11 March 1659; to A[rthur] Crew 4 May 1659; again to Bathurst 21 March 1660, LT
1.271, 278, 307.
Wood 134(1). STC 15445.

4095. Leland, John. Κυκνειον ασμα *Cygnea cantio.* Londini: typ. & expens. J. Streater, 1658. 8°. Pp.
[13], 1-165, [4]. Pasteboard (brown) with calf spine. 1st upper and last lower flyleaves, marbled paper.
Flyleaf, upper, 3rd^v, AW wrote the titles of 2 printed works in this vol. (a later writer added as a separate
item the 2nd section of Gore, Wood 149(2)), within guidelines made with red ink. A1, '4'. Tp, AW wrote
'Ant: Woode: Merton Coll: Oxōn: 1658'. Acquired 16 Oct. 1658, 1^{s}2^d, LT 1.260.
Wood 149(1). Wing L1036.

4096. Leland, John, and Thomas Newton. *Principum, ac illustrium aliquot & eruditorum in Anglia*
virorum, encomia, trophaea, genethliaca & epithalamia. Quibus . . . adjuncta sunt, encomia . . . à Thoma
Newtono. Londini: ap. T. Orwinum, 1589. 4°. Pp. [4], 132 (2nd tp at P1, p. 113).
Tp^v, notes, not in Wood's hand. Passim, some underscoring and lines in margins, in ink and pencil, in
AW's manner. AW wrote identifications of persons, especially transliterations (and translations) of fanciful

Latinate names, e.g., pp. 33, at 'Volusegum, Archiepiscopum Isurocanum', 'Wolsey Archbp. of. York'; 111, at 'Henedrigum', AW wrote, 'Hedrig, Edrye, vel Etheridge.' Some scribbling, not in AW's hand (e.g., pp. 39-41, 132), and 'x' marks, prob. not by AW.
Wood 484(9). STC 15447.

4097. Lenthall, John. *A coppy of the speech made by sir John Lenthall to the lord-mayor & aldermen in the Guild-hall.* London: T. Leach, 1659. 4°. Pp. 8.
Wood 610(16). Wing L1065.

4098. Lenthall, William. *A copy of the speakers letter to the vice-chancellour and the heads of houses of the university of Oxford [8 Feb. 1641].* Oxford: L. Lichfield, 1642. 4°. Pp. [2], 14.
Tp, AW wrote after the year, '1641[2]. Feb. 8.', and below, 'This letter, Protestation & Declaration are not regestred in the University Regester. A. Woode [/] They should have bin inserted in Reg: R.' P. 11, AW wrote in margin, '7. Jan: 1641[2]'. LT 1.77.
Wood 514(11). Wing L1070. Madan 974.

4099. Lenthall, William*. *A letter to the hono*ble *William Lenthal . . . from the commissioners imployed by the parliament for the reducing of Newark.* London: f. E. Husband, 1646, 6 Apr. 4°. Pp. 8. Pasteboard (blue) with parchment spine; rebacked by R. H[arvey] in 1946.
Flyleaves, upper, 2nd-4th, AW wrote the titles of 42 printed works in this vol., within guidelines made with red ink (after 42, in pencil, 'Meditations', no. 43, was added to the list prob. after 1717 for the Whiteside cat. summarized the contents into '42 Pamphlets'). Most items after no. 10 have earlier nos. lined out; these earlier nos. reflected an earlier order in an unbound bundle. AW may have bought 14 of the pamphlets from the same seller, for the prices, 1d or 2d, prob. not by AW, are written on the upper right hand corner of the tpp (item nos. 1-4, 7-8, 11-13, 15, 18, 22, and 25-6) Tp, '1d'.
Wood 501(1). Wing L1737.

4100. Leslie, Alexander. Leven, earl of; et al. *A letter from generall Leven, the lord Fairfax, and the earle of Manchester . . . concerning the great victory . . . neer York.* London: E. Husbands, 1644, 12 July. 4°. Pp. 1-7.
Wood 377(21). Wing L1816.

4101. Leslie, Alexander. Leven, earl of. *A declaration of his excellency the earle of Leven: concerning the rising of the Scotish army from . . . Hereford.* London: M. B. f. R. Bostock, 1645, 11 Sept. 4°. Pp. [2], 6, [3].
Tp, AW lined out the former no., '18'.
Wood 378(20). Wing L1810.

4102. [Leslie, Henry]. Downe, bishop of. *The martyrdome of king Charles, or his conformity with Christ in his sufferings.* Hage: S. Broun, 1649. 4°. Pp. [2], 23 (i.e., 32).
Wood 364(34). Wing L1163.

4103. [Leslie, John]. Philippes, Morgan, pseud. *[A] treatise concerning the defence of . . . Marie queene of Scotland [cropped; and pt. 3] A treatise wherein is declared, that the regiment of women is conformable to the lawe of God.* Leodii [a. Louvain]: ap. G. Morberium [a. J. Fowler], 1571. 8°. Ff. [1], 50, [1], 51 (2nd tp. at 2nd [1]; wanting pt. 2).
Tp, 'In Bib. B[odl].', prob. by AW. Passim, some vertical lines in margins, and f. 34v, 'Regio', prob. not by AW.
Wood 255(2). STC 15506.

4104. L['Estrange], H[amon]. *The reign of king Charles. An history, . . . With a reply to some late observations [and] The observator observed [by Peter Heylyn].* London: F. L. a. J. G. f. H. Seile, sen. a. jr., a. E. Dod; 2nd work: T. C. f. E. Dod, 1656. Fol. 2nd ed. Pp. [10], 274, [6]; [2], 47, [1] (1 p. books sold by Dod) (wanting, *Observators rejoinder*).
P. 2nd [6], index, at Lord Wentworth, AW wrote 'p 89'. Tp of *Observator*, at 'To which is added, . . . the observators rejoinder', AW wrote, 'Where is it?'; 2nd p. 16, line in margin; p. 46, 'Vid. Dr. Heylins Hist. Quinq. Artic. cap. 6 ¶7.7.8.9' (may not be in AW's hand) (i.e., [MS.] Wood C. 45). Flyleaf, lowerv, 4 brief references, prob. not in AW's hand. AW wanted this fol. at a different location, see notes at Wood 244(1) and (4), items 1770, 3553.
Wood 407(2). Wing L1190.

4105. [L'Estrange, Roger]. Scot, Tho[mas], pseud. *No fool, to the old fool.* [London]: n.pub., 1659[60], 16 March. S.sh.

Wood 416(64). Wing L1279A (Wing, fool to).

4106. [L'Estrange, Roger]. *Rump enough: or, quaere for quaere, in answer to . . . No new parliament.* London: f. any man that loves peace, 1659[60], 14 March. 4°. Pp. [2], 6.
Tp, AW wrote 'parl', in pencil.
Wood 613(39). Wing L1300.

4107. [L'Estrange, Roger]. *Double your guards; in answer to . . . An alarum to the armies [4 April].* London: n.pub., 1660. 4°. Pp. '1-8', '7-9'.
Response to Wood 608(72).
Wood 608(27). Wing L1246A.

4108. [L'Estrange, Roger]. *The fanatique powder-plot, or the design of the rumpers . . . to destroy both parliament and people. . . . March 24. 1659.* [London]: n.pub., [1660]. S.sh.
ᵛ, AW wrote, 'Mar 59[60]', and '67' replaced a former no., '53' in pencil.
Wood 416(67). Wing L1247A.

4109. [L'Estrange, Roger]. *A free parliament proposed by the city to the nation . . . Decemb. 6. 1659 . . . January 3. 1659[60].* [London]: n.pub., [1660]. S.sh.
Wood 276a(231). Wing L1250B.

4110. L'Estrange, Roger. *Peace to the nation.* [London]: n.pub., [1660]. S.sh.
AW added the date, 'ffeb: 1659[60]'.
Wood 276a(249). Wing L1284A (3) ('O' not recorded in Wing).

4111. [L'Estrange, Roger]. *Physician cure thy self: or, an answer to . . . Eye-salve for the English army.* London: f. H. B., 1660. 4°. Pp. [2], 6.
Wood 608(7). Wing L1284B.

4112. [L'Estrange, Roger]. *A plea for limited monarchy, as it was established in this nation, before the late war. . . . to . . . general Monck.* London: T. Mabb f. W. Shears, 1660. 4°. Pp. 8.
Tp, AW altered the year to 16'59 ffeb'; and wrote below, '3ᵈ heape next before An Alarum to yᵉ Counties' (i.e., Wood 610(10), item 3108); the no. at the top, '20', is not by AW. This item, a large 4°, was folded to fit into the vol. after AW wrote the list of printed works on the upper flyleaf. Diff. ed. at Wood 632(75).
Wood 626(20). Wing L1285.

4113. [L'Estrange, Roger]. *A plea for limited monarchy, as it was established in this nation, before the late war. . . . to . . . generall Monck.* London: n.pub., 1660. 4°. Pp. 8.
AW altered the year to, 16'59. feb.' and wrote, 'Dupl.' Diff. ed. at Wood 626(20).
Wood 632(75). Wing L1285A (two).

4114. [L'Estrange, Roger]. *A rope for Pol. Or, a hue and cry after Marchemont Nedham. . . . of his horrid blasphemies . . . against the king's majesty, . . . in his weekly Politicus.* London: n.pub., 1660. 4°. Pp. [4], 45.
Tp, AW wrote, 'Marchem. Needham sculkd for a time till the act of oblivion was past.' and, in pencil, 'pamphlets 4 bundles' (?). P. [4], 9, 30, short vertical lines in margin.
Wood 622(24). Wing L1299A.

4115. L'Estrange, Roger. *Sir Politique uncased, or, a sober answer to a juggling pamphlet, entituled, a letter intercepted . . . by N. D. gent. . . . by D. N. gent. [sic].* London: n.pub., 1660. 4°. Pp. [2], 14.
Tp, AW altered the year, 16'59: March'. Flyleaf, lower, continuation of list of contents, 42-64 (incorrectly written LXII-LXIX, L-LXIV) from upper flyleaf (see note at Wood 610(1)).
Wood 610(64). Wing L1308A.

4116. [L'Estrange, Roger]. *To his excellency, general Monck. A letter from . . . Devon [28 Jan.].* London: f. Y. E., 1660. S.sh.
AW altered the year to 16'59'.
Wood 276a(238). Wing L1313A ('O' not recorded in Wing).

4117. L'Estrange, Roger. *Treason arraigned, in answer to plain English; being a trayterous . . . pamphlet, . . . to . . . general Monck.* London: n.pub., 1660. 4°. Pp. [3], '1-21', '21-28', '22-24'.
Wood 608(28). Wing L1318A.

4118. [L'Estrange, Roger]. *A word in season, to general Monk.* The Hague: f. S. B., 1660. S.sh.

AW altered the date to 16'59:ffeb:'.
Wood 276a(239). Wing L1328A.

4119. L'Estrange, Roger. *To the right honorable, Edward earl of Clarenden, . . . the humble apology of Roger L'Estrange*. London: f. H. Brome, 1661. 4°. Pp. [2], 6.
Wood 632(51). Wing L1314A.

4120. L'Estrange, Roger. *Truth and loyalty vindicated, from the reproches and clamours of mr. Edward Bagshaw [in a letter to Edward earl of Clarendon.]*. London: f. H. Brome a. A. Seile, 1662, 7 June. 4°. Pp. [12], 64.
Tp, name of former owner, Eliza. Hales, lined out (married George Sheldon; died 4 Oct. 1678, LT 3.99). Most annotation is in red ink: pp. 2-3, AW identified the author of a work mentioned, 'Dr Georg Morley', added cross refs., and numbered books titles by Edw. Bagshaw; 9, identification of brother of Bagshaw, 'Hen. Bagshaw', and a line in margin; 21, line at publications of E. Bagshaw (see AO 3.946-8); 28, 36, 48, 55, line in margins.
Wood 533(17). Wing L1320.

4121. L'Estrange, Roger. *Considerations and proposals in order to the regulation of the press*. London: A. C., 1663, 3 June. 4°. Pp. [16], 33 (wanting imprimatur).
Tp, AW wrote 'Dupl', in pencil. P. [10], 'He means S^r. Joh: Birkenhead, how truely, I know not', not in AW's hand. Dupl. at Wood 642(5).
Wood 608(44). Wing L1229.

4122. L'Estrange, Roger. *Considerations and proposals in order to the regulation of the press*. London: A. C., 1663, 3 June. 4°. Pp. [17], 33.
Dupl. at Wood 608(44).
Wood 642(5). Wing L1229.

4123. L'Estrange, Roger*. *An exclamation against Julian, secretary to the muses [R. L'Estrange]; with the character of a libeller*. [London]: n.pub., [1679 to 1688?]. Fol. Pp. 4.
P. 1, top, AW wrote, 'q[uaere]', in pencil.
Wood 417(105). Wing E3844.

4124. [L'Estrange, Roger]. *The history of the plot: or a brief and historical account of the charge and defence of Edward Coleman, esq; William Ireland [& 15 others]*. London: f. R. Tonson, 1679. Fol. Pp. [4], 88.
Tp, AW wrote, 'Collected and written by Roger L'estrange. Esq.', '2^s-6^d', and 'This came out soon after Sr Georg Wakemans triall'; ^{v}, 'He that was the author of this book was the author of another intit. The free borne subject or the Englishmans birthright &c. Lond. 1679. 4° – printed in Sept. [Wing L1248] [/] Ib. p. 15. – he saith thus upon perusal of the printed trials [/] I found severall gross mistakes (especially in the later of them) as in that of Mr Langhorne p. 39.40. Mr Lydcots name is used no less than 9 times as one of the St Omers witnesses, instead of Mr Hall to his great prejudice' and 12 more lines quoted from the same book, beginning with 'p. 14 thus the author of himself – I defie any man to produce another Gentleman in the kings dominions under my circumstances that hath suffered so many illegall, arbitrary . . . ' and 9 more lines. AW ended the quotations with, 'In the said booke he answers two pamphletts. The first is. Omnia comesta a Bello (for Belo) – a most virulent pamphlet against the Bishops [Wing O290] – & the other The Lord Lucas his speech [Wing L3391f.], not the speech it self but the appendix to it, written by a divellish hand –'. P. 29, in testimony, 'Grove, Pickering', lined out. Purchased from Vade in July or August 1679, see his record of purchase in MS. Wood F. 50, f. 11.
Wood 422(17). Wing L1258.

4125. [L'Estrange, Roger]. *A further discovery of the plot, drawn from the narrative . . . of Titus Oates*. London: f. H. Brome, 1680. Fol. Pp. [2], 6.
Wood 426(4). Wing L1251 ('O' not recorded in Wing).

4126. L'Estrange, Roger*. *Strange's case, strangly [sic] altered*. [London]: n.pub., [1680?]. S.sh. (mutilated at bottom).
Wood 417(33). Wing S5924.

4127. [L'Estrange, Roger*]. *Trialogue: or a threefold discourse betwixt the pope, the devil and Towzer [Roger L'Estrange]*. (London): (f. T. B.), [1681]. Fol. Pp. 8.
P. 1, notes, not by AW: at Towzer, 'Rog: L'Estrange' [but the final 'ge' was added by AW], and 2 identifications. P. 8, AW wrote '1679/80', in red ink.

Wood 417(20). Wing T2242.

4128. [L'Estrange, Roger]. *Considerations upon a printed sheet entituled the speech of the late lord Russel.* London: T. B. f. J. Brome, 1683. 4°. 3rd impr. Pp. 52.
Tp, AW wrote, '6ᵈ' and 'by Rog. L'estrange'; and p. 4, identification of printed 'Julian', 'Sam. Johnson author of the life of Julian [Wood 835(7), item 3891] was chapl. to Will. Lord Russell at the time of his death & about half an yeare before'. See item 5672 and the reference to the article by P. Hinds.
Wood 428(15). Wing L1232.

4129. [L'Estrange, Roger]. *A reply to the reasons of the Oxford-clergy against addressing.* London: H. Hills, 1687. 4°. Pp. 20.
Tp, AW wrote, 'The reasons of Oxf. clergy, & answer to them, were not at all published, but what are in this pamphlete.' LT 3.220.
Wood 515(34). Wing L1297.

4130. [L'Estrange, Roger]. *Some queries concerning the election of members for the ensuing parliament.* London: n.pub., 1690. 4°. Pp. 8.
Tp, AW wrote 'Ex dono Jac. Harrington Ex Æd.ch. 26 Feb. 1689[90] in taberna Corona ap. Oxon-'. P. 6, AW completed the name Sach'everel'. LT 3.327.
Wood 608(65). Wing L1308B.

4131. [Leti, Gregorio]. Compton, Henry, trans. *The life of donna Olimpia Maldachini . . . by abbot Gualdi.* London: W. Godbid, sold R. Littlebury, 1667. 8°. Pp. [8], 214.
Tp, AW wrote, 'By Mʳ Hen. Compton M. of A. of Christ church Oxōn. 1ˢ-3ᵈ'. Pp. 6, note, cropped; 7, line in margin, at a misspelling.
Wood 260(3). Wing L1334.

4132. Letter. *The coppy of a letter to generall Monck.* London: n.pub., 1660. 4°. Pp. 8.
AW altered the year to, 16'59', and, p. 8, wrote, 'ffeb: 1659'.
Wood 632(74). Wing C6163.

4133. Letter. *A letter from a friend, occasioned by the receipt of his majestie's . . . expresses [7 May].* [London]: n.pub., 1660. 4°. Pp. 7.
Tp, AW added after the year, 'May'.
Wood 632(48). Wing L1376.

4134. Letter. *A letter to a member of the . . . house of commons, speaking his humble desires of the receiving the king.* (London): n.pub., (1660). 4°. Pp. 8.
P. 8, AW added below the year, 'Aprill: Last:'.
Wood 632(47). Wing L1686.

4135. Letter. *A letter from a friend, . . . in answer to a letter . . . about abhorrers and addressers.* [London]: (f. J. Tonson), (1682). S.sh. Pp. 2.
Wood 276a(158). Wing L1377A (3) ('O' not recorded in Wing).

4136. Levellers. *The Levellers (falsly so called) vindicated, or, the case of the twelve troops (which by treachery in a treaty) was . . . defeated at Burford.* [London]: n.pub., [1649]. 4°. Pp. 12.
Wood 503(4). Wing L1800A.

4137. Levellers. *The Leveller: or, the principles & maxims concerning government and religion, . . . asserted by . . . Levellers.* London: f. T. Brewster, 1659. 4°. Pp. 16.
Wood 613(9). Wing L1799.

4138. Levellers, and Anabaptists. *A bloody independent plot discovered: prosecuted by the open malice of divers agitators, Levellers, Anabaptists.* [London]: n.pub., 1647. 4°. Pp. [2], 10.
Wood 612(64). Wing B3255.

4139. Lever, Thomas. *A sermon preached at Pauls crosse, the. xiiii. day of December.* (London): (Jhon Day), 1550. 8°. A-G⁸,H⁴. Parchment ms. with coloured initials (Latin commentary, 1 Cor. 4).
Tp, signatures of Rand: Parker and John Briten; ᵛ, symbol, and 'John Cotton pss [possesses?] this boke'.
Wood 799. STC 15546.3. STC, 1551.

4140. Lewis, [David]. *The last speech of father Lewis, who was executed at Hereford.* [London]: n.pub., [1679]. S.sh. (r-v).

^r, AW wrote the date, '(Aug. 1679)'; ^v, '27. Aug. 1679. David Lewes a Jesuit suffered death by hanging at Uske in Com. Monmouth – so in letters to M^r Jo. Hall of High Meadow – but in the beginning of this speech (which I doubt whether his or no) tis said he was executed at Hereford –'. LT 2.461.
Wood 425(14). Wing L1836.

4141. Lewis, William. *The information of William Lewis, gent. delivered at the bar of the house of commons [18 Nov.].* London: f. R. Taylor, 1680. Fol. Pp. [3], 31.
Tp, AW wrote the price, '1^s'. P. 24-5, lines in margin, at passages indicating sympathy of Scroggs to Catholics, and 'See Faria's information' (Wood 426(22, 28), items 2944f.), and, at a contrite passage, 'This is but dissimulation'.
Wood 426(26). Wing L1851.

4142. Lewkenor, Edward, ed. by (son of E. Lewkenor). *Threnodia in obitum d. Edouardi Lewkenor, . . . & d. Susannae conjugis charissimae. Funerall verses.* London: A. Hatfield, f. S. Macham a. M. Cooke, solde [M. Cooke], 1606. 4°. Pp. [4], 48.
P. [4, a blank], 3 ms. poems (30 lines in all, in English); flyleaves, lower, 1-7, poems, in English, signed G[eorge] S[adleir].
Wood 460(9). STC 15561.

4143. Lewkenor, Lewis. *The estate of English fugitives under the king of Spaine.* London: [T. Scarlet] f. J. Drawater, 1596. 4°. Newly corrected. Pp. [8], 136.
Printer's waste, lower^v, scribbles. All items in this vol. came from Francis Isaac, see Wood 587(1).
Wood 587(5). STC 15565.

4144. Lewkenor, Samuel. *A discourse . . . for such as are desirous to know of forraine cities. Containing a discourse of citties wherein flourish universities.* London: J. W[indet] f. H. Hooper, 1600. 4°.
Missing. 'An acct of the universities of Europe', in a list of 'Mr. Woods Duplicats', MS. Wood F. 51, f. 44, item 40.
MS. Wood F. 51(40). STC 15566.

4145. Ley, James. Marlborough, 1st earl of. *A learned treatise concerning wards and liveries.* London: G. Bishop a. R. White f. H. Shepheard a. H. Twyford, 1642. 8°. Pp. [14], 79 (cropped).
Tp, name of author underscored in red ink.
Wood 699(2). Wing M687.

4146. Leybourn, William. *Four tables of accompts ready cast up.* London: printed, sold R. Walton, [1690-5?]. S.sh.
Wood 276a(41) (not in Bodl. CD cat.). Wing L1914 (rare).

4147. Leycester, Peter. *An answer to the book of sir Thomas Manwaringe . . . entituled a defence of Amicia, daughter of Hugh Cyveliok earl of Chester.* [London]: n.pub., 1673. 8°. Pp. [2], 90 (t leaf cropped and without the Addenda).
Tp, after year, 'Ju'. Another note is cropped. See Wood 673(2), 673(4), items 4148, 4352; LT 2.188.
Wood 673(3). Wing L1942.

4148. Leycester, Peter. *Two books: the first being styled a reply to sir Thomas Manwaring's book entituled, an answer to sir Peter Leicesters's addenda. The other styled, sir Thomas Manwaring's law-cases mistaken.* London: n.pub., 1674. 8°. Pp. [6], 96, [6], 51 (2 tpp).
Tp, note at bottom, cropped. Bsm. See also Wood 673(2 and 3), items 4147, 4352. LT 2.188.
Wood 673(4). Wing L1944A ('O' not recorded in Wing).

4149. Leydanus, Florentinus. *Historia passionis novorum in Germaniae inferioris.* Ingolstadii: ex off. W. Ederi, 1582 (27 Augusti). 12°. Pp. 95.
Tp, '1582' entered after date in Roman numerals. Pp. 3-18, 32, some marks in margins, underscoring and a note, not by AW.
Wood 231(2). BL.

4150. Lichfield. *Articles for the delivering up of Lichfield-close, together with a list of the commanders.* London: f. E. Husband, 1646, 18 July. 4°. Pp. 12 (pp. 9-12 precede 1-8).
Tp, '1^d', prob. not by AW.
Wood 501(18). Wing A3825.

4151. Lilburn, John*. *The selfe afflicter. . . . the life of mr. John Lilburn.* [London]: f. T. Vere a. W. Gilbertson, 1657. 8°. Pp. [2], 14.

Tp, a correction. Pp. 1-4, 11-13, vertical lines in margins, in red ink, by AW, and in pencil. Wood 259(4). Wing S2447E (rare).

4152. Lilburne, [John]. *A more full relation of the great battell fought betweene sir Tho: Fairfax, and Goring, on Thursday last, 1645.* London: T. Forcet f. P. Cole, 1645. 4°. Pp. [2], 8. Tp, at '1645', AW wrote the date, 'July 14', in pencil; and lined out the former no., '11'. Wood 378(13). Wing L2144.

4153. Lilburne, John. *The proposition of liev. col. John Lilburne, prisoner in the Tower of London, made unto the lords and commons [2 Oct. 1647].* [London]: n.pub., [1647]. S.sh. 4°. Wood 612(52b). Wing L2166.

4154. Lilburne, John*. *The engagement vindicated & explained, or the reasons upon which leiut. [sic] John Lilburne, tooke the engagement.* London: J. Clowes, 1650. 4°. Pp. [2], 6. Wood 368(12). Wing L2101.

4155. [Lilly, William]. *The late storie of mr. William Lilly [purporting to be by col. Th., but probably by himself. An answer to G. Wharton in Merc. elenc., no. 3.].* London: n.pub., 1647/8, Jan. 4°. Pp. [2], 12. Tp, 'Prae: 3^d of Bowman Oxford Septem. 14 1654', prob. not by AW (nor by A. Allam, *pace* Clark, LT 3.167 (Allam was born in 1655)). Dupl. at Wood 612(67). Wood 622(15). Wing L559.

4156. [Lilly, William]. *The late storie of mr. William Lilly [purporting to be by col. Th., but probably by himself. An answer to G. Wharton in Merc. elenc., no. 3.].* London: n.pub., 1647/8, Jan. 4°. Pp. [2], 12. Dupl. at Wood 622(15). Wood 612(67). Wing L559.

4157. Lilly, William*. *A declaration of the several treasons, blasphemies and misdemeanors acted, spoken and published . . . by . . . William Lilly.* London: f. D. White, 1660. 4°. Pp. [4], 7. Tp, AW wrote 'A rope for Pol', in pencil, over an earlier pencil note (AW owned a copy of L'Estrange's *A rope*, Wood 622(24)). P. 2, at a quote from Lilly on the killing of the king, a line in the margin. AO 1.36. Wood 622(23). Wing D767.

4158. Lilly, William. *William Lilly student in astrologie, his past and present opinion touching monarchy . . . and . . . of the controversie between the Normans and the long-parliament.* London: n.pub., 1660. 4°. Pp. [2], 6. Tp, AW wrote after the year, 'May'. Wood 622(22). Wing L2236 (two) ('O' not recorded in Wing) (Wing, opinions).

4159. Lilly, William. *Strange news from the east, or, a sober account of the comet, . . . with an historical discourse of . . . comets.* London: f. B. H., 1677. 4°. Pp. 8. Tp, AW wrote, 'Will. Lilye died in June 1681', correcting an earlier note by another, 'He was deade halfe a yeare before it appeared.' LT 2.543. [MS.] Wood D. 28(23). Wing L2248.

4160. [Lily, William]. *A short introduction of grammar generally to be used.* Oxford: W. Turner, 1636. A-P^8 (interleaved blank leaves; P8 blank) (2nd tp at E5). Calf with 3 fillets, 2 cloth clasps, and edge hatching; spine, hatching (Oxford binding). Blind-stamped 'A W' on covers. Pastedown, upper, note by F. Madan (in 1919) pointing out fragments 'of one of the Theatre Press Keepsakes printed for [Anthon]y W[ood]' (see see Index, 'Wood, Anthony, bookplate'); flyleaf, upper, 1st, torn out, on remainder, traces of a drawing of an animal; 2nd, 'Anthony Wood'; ^{v}, 'Mary Wood 1647', 'Robert Wood'; and AW later wrote, 'Among Seldens books in the public library 8.L.14 Arts Seld. [still at same shelf-mark] is Will Lilies grammar printed at London 1574. which hath more things in it than this hath.' Some notes, in various hands, on interleaved blank leaves. Flyleaf, lower^v (inserted upside down): 'a gounde [?]: 4 Octo: being WednesDay: [sic] 1648' (may be by AW), 'Robert Wood 1647', 'Robert Le Diable', 'Anthony Wood', and 'Louis Pa–' [?]. LT 2.102. Wood 46. STC 15632 (two). Madan 831.

4161. Lily, William. Brookbank, Joseph, ed. *A breviate of our kings whole Latin grammar.* London: W. H. f. R. Thrale, [1660, Oct.]. 8°. Pp. [18], 52, [2]. Tp, 'Wanting', prob. not by AW, cropped. AW underscored the name of Brookbank, in red ink, and after and below the publisher wrote '1660' and 'December: IV: MDCLx:'. Bsm. See note at Wise, 8° A 153(1) Art., item 6648. This item is listed in MS. Wood E. 2(70), p. 16, 'Joseph Brookbank a breviate of the Lat.

Grammar'; see also AO 3.541.
8° A 153(2) Art. Wing L2254.

4162. Lily, William*. *Qui mihi Liliense burlesque redditum*. [London?]: n.pub., [1680]. S.sh. (mutilated at bottom).
3 minor corrections, may not be by AW. Dupl. at Wood 276a(558), missing.
Wood 417(31). Wing Q205.

4163. Lily, William*. *Qui mihi Liliense burlesque redditum*. [London?]: n.pub., [1680]. S.sh.
Missing in 1939. T is from the 1717 list (mutilated entry). Dupl. at Wood 417(31).
Wood 276a(558). Wing Q205. *BL.*

4164. Limerick. *A diary of the siege & surrender of Lymerick: with the articles*. London: f. R. Taylor, 1692. 4°. Pp. [4], 32.
Not listed on the front flyleaf. Tp, no. '38' not by AW (prob. added to the bundle after he finished the list of contents, see Wood 510(1)). P. 3, AW wrote in margin, 'Earl of Tyrconnell', twice.
Wood 510(38). Wing D1376.

4165. Linacre, Thomas. *'Grammar'*. ?: ?, ? Pp.?
Missing. MS. Wood E. 2(70), p. 16, 'Tho. Linacer – Grammar – another thing bound with it' (ed. not identified).
MS. Wood E. 2(70), p. 16. STC 15635ff.

4166. Lincoln. *A relation of a fight in the county of Lincolne, . . . Eleaventh [sic] day of April*. [Oxford]: [L. Lichfield], 1643. 4°. Pp. [2], 5.
Wood 376(4). Wing R786. Madan 1327.

4167. Lincoln. *The declaration of the gentry, . . . of Lincolne*. [London]: f. H. M., 1659[60]. S.sh.
AW added to year, 'ffeb.'
Wood 276a(208). Wing D678.

4168. Lincolnshire Gentleman. *The copy of a letter from a Lincolne shire gentleman; sent to his friend in the city of London*. [London]: n.pub., 1660. 4°. Pp. 7.
Tp, AW altered the year to 16'59[60]: feb:', and below t, added 'without date'.
Wood 632(28). Wing C6116.

4169. Lindanus, Willelmus. Evan, Lewis, trans. *Certaine tables sett furth . . . wherein is detected . . . the doting dangerous doctrine . . . of heretikes*. Antwerpe: A. Diest, 1565. 8°. A-E⁸.
Missing. MS. Wood E. 2(70), p. 21.
MS. Wood E. 2(70), p. 21. STC 15653. ARCR 2.245. *O, Folg.*

4170. Lindsay, David. Burrant, Robert, ed. *The tragical death of David Beatō, bischoppe of Sainct Andrews: Whereunto is joyned the martyrdom of maister George Wyseharte [by R. Burrant]*. (London): (J. Day a. W. Seres), [1548?]. 8°. A2-8,B⁶,C-E⁸,F⁶ (wanting the t leaf and cropped).
A bibliog. note is supplied by D. Hamer, July 1929. F6, date added, 1546.
Wood 736(5). STC 15683.

4171. [Lindsay, David]. *[A dialogue betweene experience and a courtier]*. [London]: [T. Purfoote], [1581]. 4° in 8's. Corrected. Ff. [3], 140 (misnumbering) (wanting the t leaf). Parchment with 2 clasp holes.
Sig. ii (1st surviving p.), 'A W: MDcLx: 1ˢ'. Ff. 27-143ᵛ, frequent notes, not in AW's hand. Dupl. at Wood 483(13).
Wood 323. STC 15678.

4172. Lindsay, David. *A dialogue betweene experience and a courtier*. London: T. Purfoote, 1581. 4° in 8's. Corrected. Ff. [4], 140 (misnumbering).
Dupl. at Wood 323.
Wood 483(13) (482(13) in Bodl. CD cat.). STC 15678.

4173. Lindsay, David. Brechen, bp. of. *A true narration of all the passages of the proceedings in the general assembly of the church of Scotland, holden at Perth [25 Aug. 1618]*. London: W. Stansby f. R. Rounthwait, 1621. 4°. Pp. [28], 136, 152, 125. Parchment.
Tp, AW wrote '1.2ᵈ.' and 'Sept: xiiii: MDClx:'. LT 1.331. On the spine, 'Proceedings at Perth B. 3J', may be by AW.
[MS.] Wood B. 31 (not in Bodl. CD cat.). STC 15657.

4174. Lineall, John. *Itur [sic] Mediteranium. A true accompt given of the proceedings of . . . lord Glin.* N.p.: f. the author John Lineall, sold J. Felton. iu [sic, i.e., in] Stafford, 1658. 4°. Pp. [2], 16.
Wood 465(3). Wing L2331.

4175. Lingard, Richard*. *An elegy and funeral oration, on the death of . . . Richard Lingard.* London: f. B. Tooke, 1671. Fol. Pp. [2], 6.
Wood 429(30). Wing E345 (rare).

4176. Lingard, Richard. *A letter of advice to a young gentleman leaving the university.* London: f. B. Tooker, 1671. 12°in 6's. Pp. [8], 62.
Tp, AW underscored the name of the author and wrote 'The 2^d. Edit: 1st came out 1670'. P. 1, AW wrote 'To Mr Joh. Lane a Gent.-Commonor of X^tch. Oxōn.' Pp. 3-5, 7-8, 11, lines in margin, in pencil.
Wood 792(5). Wing L2350.

4177. Lipsius, Justus. *Justi Lipsii de cruce libri tres.* Antverpiae: ex off. Plantiniana ap. vid. a. J. Moretum, 1595. 8°. 2nd ed. Pp. 137, [6]. Parchment.
Tp, signature 'Th. Cole 2^s.ij^d. decemb. 13. [15]95'.
Wood 880. BL.

4178. Lipsius, J[ustus]. *Diva virgo Hallensis.* Parisiis: ap. D. le Clerc, 1604. 4°. Ff. [4], 49, [7]. Parchment with 2 clasp holes.
Wood 306. BL.

4179. [Lisola, François Paul]. Coventry, William, also attrib. to. *Englands appeal from the private cabal at White-hall. To . . . parliament . . . by a true lover of his country.* [London]: n.pub., 1673. 4°. Pp. [2], 52.
Tp, AW wrote, 'Sr Will. Coventry, as the common report went.' AO 4.192f.
Wood 608(46). Wing L2372.

4180. Little Yarmouth. *Encouragements to builders and planters of Little Yarmouth.* London: f. S. Speed, 1668. S.sh.
On blank side, 'ffor Mr Henry Foulis at Lincolne Colledge in Oxon', not by AW. LT 2.180.
Wood 276a(292). Wing E725 (two).

4181. [Littleton, Adam]. *Tragi-comoedia Oxoniensis [in verse, on the proceedings of the university visitors].* [Oxford]: [H. Hall], [1648]. 4°. Pp. 8.
Tp, AW wrote 'Tragico-comoedia.', and below, 'A D: 1648 [/] By Adam Littleton student of Ch.ch [/] D^r [Thomas] Barlow saith it was written by Joh. Carrick of the same house'. Dupl. at Wood 615(21). LT 1.144; AO 4.404.
Wood 514(52). Wing L2574. Madan 1989.

4182. [Littleton, Adam]. *Tragi-comoedia Oxoniensis [in verse, on the proceedings of the university visitors].* [Oxford]: [H. Hall], [1648]. 4°. Pp. 8.
Tp, AW wrote 'dup', in pencil; at top 'It should have been written Tragico-com . . . '(cropped), by John Aubrey; below, lined out 'for Mr Anthony Wood'. P. 8, identifications of the 'Comite' and 'Asinus Smythaei' as the Earl of Pembroke and Mr. Smyth of Magdalen College, who met the Earl 'riding on an Asse', in margin (Thomas Smith, LT 1.268), not in AW's hand and prob. not in Aubrey's hand; below, 'This was writt (as I take it) by one . . . Cradock a (young) Student of Christ-church.', by Aubrey. Dupl. at Wood 514(52). LT 1.144; AO 4.404.
Wood 615(21). Wing L2574. Madan 1989.

4183. Littleton, Edward. *De juventute. Oratio habita in comitiis Oxoniensibus.* Londini: T. Newborough, 1689. 4°. Pp. [4], 72.
Tp, 'Donum Authoris, Maii . . 1694' (so also a note at Wood 533(4)). LT 3.454.
Wood 383(6). Wing L2576.

4184. [Littleton, Edward]. *The groans of the plantations: or a true account of their sufferings by the impositions upon sugar.* London: M. Clark, 1689. 4°. Pp. [2], 35.
Flyleaf, upper, AW wrote, 'Donu[m] Authoris [cropped at top] [/] Maii .. 1694.' (so also a note at Wood 383(6)). Tp, 'By Edw. Littleton somtimes of Alls. coll'.
Wood 533(4). Wing L2577.

4185. [Littleton, Edward]. *Observations upon the warre of Hungary.* London: printed a. sold R. Taylor a. T. Newborough, 1689. 4°. Pp. [8], 47.

Tp, AW wrote, 'Received from the Author Mr Edw. Littleton 4 Dec. 1694.' LT 3.473.
Wood 533(3). Wing L2580.

4186. Lively, Edward. *A true chronologie of the times of the Persian monarchie.* London: F. Kingston
f. T. Man, J. Porter, a. R. Jacson, 1597. 8°. Pp. 258, and S-2C⁸. Calf with 4 fillets; rebacked.
Tp, price, xviii^d, prob. not in AW's hand.
Wood 143. STC 16609.

4187. Ll[ewellyn], M[artin]. *[Men-miracles. With other poems. By M. Ll.].* [[Oxford]]: [[H. Hall]], [1646].
8°. Pp. [12], 152 (wanting A1-2, B1).
A3, at top, 'Llewellin', prob. not by AW, and 'Thomas B'. A4-5, and pp. 1, 7, signatures of John Lockstone
and Thomas Boeing. LT 1.129.
Wood 90(4). Wing L2625. Madan 1884.

4188. [Lloyd, David]. *The legend of captain Jones.* London: H. Moseley, 1659. 4°. Pp. [25], 71, [1].
Pasteboard (grey) with parchment spine.
Pasteboard, upper, inside, 'M. Sedgley 2^d.' (prob. the binder's price). Flyleaf, upper, 3rd^v, AW wrote the
heading, 'Wonderful persons & things', in pencil, and the titles of 7 printed works in this vol., in brown ink
and within guidelines made with red ink. Frontispiece foldout, 'The Legend of Captaine Jones', printed f.
E. Okes and F. Haley, 1671, which AW obtained from a later ed., Wing L2633; on ^v, are his instructions to
the binder, 'To be put before Capt. Jones Legend'. Tp, 'two parts', '9^d', 'This was the 2^d or 3^d edit.' (the
3rd ed.), and '1656' (date of the 2nd ed.). See LT 1.331.
Wood 246(1) (not in Bodl. CD cat.). Wing L2632.

4189. Lloyd, David. Εικων βασιλικη. *Or, the true pourtraicture of . . . Charls the II in three books.*
London: (J. Budenell) (J. Cadwel) f. H. Brome a. H. Marsh, 1660. 8°. Pp. [8], 86, 121, [2], 70 (3 tpp). Calf
with 2 fillets and 2 vertical fillets, gold-stamp crown over CR (Charles, Rex; upper, off-centre).
Flyleaf, upper, '74' and signature of Jh– Hoyeter (?), lined out.
Wood 250. Wing L2640 (Wing, Charles). FFMadan 134.

4190. Lloyd, David. *Modern policy compleated, or the publick actions . . . of . . . generall Monck.* London:
J. B. f. H. Marsh, 1660. 8°. Pp. [8], 64 (pp. 62-64, 3 pp. books sold by Marsh). Pasteboard (grey) with
parchment spine. Trace of upper flyleaf, marbled paper, lower flyleaf, marbled paper.
Flyleaf, upper^v, AW wrote the titles of 4 printed works in this vol., within guidelines made with red ink;
after hand pointer, 'Memorandum that I do here put into this vol. <u>Modern Policy Compleated</u> &c following,
because the latter halfe of it treats of his majesties restauration.' Tp, AW underscored the name of the
author, in red ink, added, 'Oriel Coll', and, at foot of page, 'Jan iv. mdclx' (i.e., 1661, LT 1.378). Tp^v, 'The
last half of this book treats of the Restauration of K. Ch. 2^d.' P. 1, at the 'Second Part', 'The first part is
mention'd in p. 64' (i.e., in Marsh's list of books).
Wood 236(1). Wing L2644.

4191. Lloyd, David. *The states-men and favourites of England since the reformation.* London: J. C[ottrell]
f. S. Speed, 1665. 8°. Pp. [15], 823, [1] (1 p. books printed f. Speed).
Missing in 1837. 'Observations on the Lives of the Statesmen & Favourites of England since the Reformation
– Lond. 1665' in Whiteside cat. Listed in MS. Wood E. 2(70), p. 47, 'Statesmen & favorites of England –
no author cities [? i.e., citations] produced therfore a plagiary', and an index. AW borrowed Lloyd's *The
worthies of the world* (1665) from A. Curteyne , 30 Dec. 1667, LT 2.122.
Wood 298. Wing L2648. *BL, Hunt, Folg.*

4192. [Lloyd, David]. *Wonders no miracles; or, mr. Valentine Greatrates gift of healing examined.* London: f. S. Speed, 1666. 4°. Pp. [2], 46.
Tp, AW wrote, 'By David Lloyd M.A. Sometimes of Oryall Coll: Oxōn'; former no., '2'. P. 14, vertical line
in margin, at Greatrakes twice hearing a voice from heaven. LT 2.79.
Wood 643(9). Wing L2649.

4193. Lloyd, John. *To the worshipful Hugh Chamberlen . . . An account of the situation, . . . of the
island of Tobago.* [London]: sold, J. Seller at his Shop on the West side of the Royal-Exchange, [1685 ca.].
S.sh. (r-v).
Wood 386(20). Not in Wing. Not in ESTCR.

4194. Lloyd, Lodowick. *The consent of time, disciphering [sic] the errors of the Grecians . . . also
. . . the beginning, continuance, . . . of kings, kingdomes . . . by Lodowik Lloid.* London: G. Bishop, a. R.
Newberie, 1590. 4°in 8's. Pp. [16], 722. Calf with 3 fillets, stamp centrepiece (Ker, plate VII, no. xv), and

edge hatching; spine, 4 bands and hatching (Oxford binding).
Tp, bsm.
Wood 474. STC 16619.

4195. Lloyd, Lodowick. *A briefe conference of divers lawes*. London: T. Creede, 1602. 4°. Pp. [4], 144 (p. 144 blank), [6]. Parchment.
Parchment, upper, inside, scribble. Flyleaf, upper, 1st, 'Robert Pedley his booke' and some multiplication, not in AW's hand; 2nd, monetary figures, not in AW's hand. Parchment, lower, inside, 'John Pedly'.
Wood 488(1). STC 16616.

4196. Lloyd, Lodowick. *The stratagems of Jerusalem: with the martiall lawes . . . as well of the Jewes, as of the gentiles*. London: T. Creede, 1602. 4°. Pp. [8], 352, [13].
A few annotations, mainly drawn hands, not in AW's manner, e.g., pp. 9, 100-103.
Wood 488(2). STC 16630.

4197. Lloyd, Lodowick. *The practice of policy*. London: S. Stafford, 1604. 4°. Pp. [4], 84.
Tp, author's name underscored in red chalk.
[MS.] Wood B. 39(2). STC 16627.

4198. Lloyd, Lod[owick]. *Hilaria: or the triumphant feast for the fift of August*. London: S. Stafford, 1607. 4°. A-C⁴ (C4 blank).
Wood 537(6). STC 16622 (two).

4199. Lloyd, Lodowick. *Linceus spectacles*. London: N. Okes, 1607. 4°. Pp. [8], 67.
Tp, 2 prices (iiii^d and ?) and the signature of Timo: Hutton.
Wood 619(9). STC 16623a.

4200. Lloyd, William. Killala, bp. of. *An historical account of church-government as it was in Great-Britain and Ireland . . . by the bishop of St. Asaph*. London: f. C. Brome, 1684. 8°. Pp. [68], 182, [2]. Includes a cat. of works by William Lloyd. Pasteboard (brown) with calf spine. 1st upper and last lower flyleaves, marbled paper.
Flyleaf, upper, 2nd^v, AW wrote the titles of 3 printed works in this vol., within guidelines made with red ink. Tp, AW underscored 'Bishop', in red ink, and wrote '1.9.' (the price), in pencil; p. [183], line in margin at catalogue of books by Lloyd, in red ink. Responded to by Mackenzie, item 4342.
Wood 200(1). Wing L2681.

4201. Llwyd, Humphrey. *Commentarioli Britannicae descriptionis fragmentum. Auctore Humfredo Lhuyd*. Coloniae Agrippinae: ap. J. Birckmannum, 1572. 8°. Ff. [8], 79.
Tp, scribbles. A2, 'Thomas Prichard, Oxōn 1609'. Ff. 9, 79^v, note and chart, not in AW's hand.
Wood 164(2). BL.

4202. Llwyd, Humphrey. Twyne, Thomas, trans. *The breviary of Britayne . . . by Humfrey Lhuyd*. (London): (R. Johnes), 1573. 8°. Ff. [22], 96. Calf with 2 fillets and stamp centrepiece (acorn design); rebacked, R. H., 1950.
Pastedown, upper, arms, in colour, 3 fleurs de lis counterchanged, and 'W. S. .1574'; in AW's hand: 'The armes of Will. Smyth Rogue [i.e., Rouge] Dragon, pursevant of Armes, who died 1. Oct. 1618. Ant. à Wood' (AO 2.233; W. H. Godfrey, *The College of Arms* (1963): 220-1); and, perhaps in AW's hand, 'p^t: 4^d'. Tp, 'W. Smythe 1574 12 September. 10^d'. Passim, some brief notes and underscoring, not in AW's hand, e.g., ¶ *4^v, errata (corrections are made in the text), ff. 24-24^v, 64-65^v, 78, 82^v; and, by AW, pasted to pastedown, lower, a slip, with drawing of arms of Dorchester and red ink guidelines. Acquired 29 Ap. 1658 out of G. Langbaine's study, LT 1.247-8. Lent to R. Bathurst 14 March 1660, LT 1.307.
Wood 165. STC 16636.

4203. Locke, Matthew. *His little consort of three parts:. . . for viols or violins. . . . Treble*. London: W. Godbid f. J. Playford, 1656. 4°, obl. ²,C⁴,cc² (including paper covers). Original paper covers enclosed by more recent binding.
Paper cover, upper^v, 'M. Locke', may be by AW.
Wood 277 (not in Bodl. CD cat.). Wing L2772 (rare) (Wing, fol.). See W.B. Squire, *Catalogue of printed music* (London, 1912).

4204. Locke, Matthew. *His little consort of three parts:. . . for viols or violins. . . . Bassus*. London: W. Godbid f. J. Playford, 1656. 4°, obl. ²,A⁶ (includes marbled paper covers) (1 p. books sold by Playford). Original marbled paper covers enclosed by later binding.

Marbled paper cover, 'M Locke', may be by AW. Tp, 'Ant: Woode: Merton: Coll Oxōn: A. D. M DC: Lvi'. A6, 5 music books sold by Playford are marked by lines or underscoring. LT 1.211. Wood 279 (not in Bodl. CD cat.). Wing L2771 (two).

4205. Locke, Matthew. *His little consort of three parts:. . . for viols or violins. . . . Treble and tenor.* London: W. Godbid f. J. Playford, 1656. 4°, obl. ^{2},B^4,bb^2 (includes blank flyleaves). Original marbled paper covers enclosed by later binding. B4, corrections. Wood 278 (not in Bodl. CD cat.). Wing L2773 (rare) (Wing, fol.).

4206. Locke, Matthew. *Observations on a late book, entituled, an essay to the advancement of music.* London: W. G., sold J. Playford, 1672. 8°. Pp. [4], 39, [1]. Missing in 1837. 'Observations on the s^d Book, by M. Lock – Lond. 1672' in Whiteside cat. Wood 120(3). Wing L2776. *O, Hunt.*

4207. Lockhart, William. *A letter sent from . . . dated at Dunkirk, Decemb. 31. 1659. superscribed, for . . . William Lenthall.* London: J. Streater a. J. Macock, 1659[60]. 4°. Pp. 8. Wood 632(63). Wing L2779.

4208. Loftus, Dudley. *The proceedings observed in order to, and in the consecration of the twelve bishops at . . . Dublin [27 Jan.].* London: J. C. f. J. Crook, 1661. 4°. Pp. 8. Tp, author's name underscored in red ink. P. 3, line in margin. Wood 510(31). Wing L2826 (two).

4209. Loftus, Edward. *The latest and truest newes from Ireland; or, a true relation of the happy victory . . . before Droheda, in a letter from a privy councellor in Dublin. Where unto is added another relation [by E. Loftus.].* London: f. H. S. a. W. Ley, 1642. 4°. Pp. [2], 6. Tp, below, '<u>12</u>', may not be by AW. Wood 507(38). Wing L2832.

4210. [Loggan, David]. *Juven. Sat. IV Ill. XVI [Verona].* [Oxford]: [W. Downing, f. F. Oxlad senior, J. Adams, a. F. Oxlad junior], [1673]. S.sh. (engr.). P. 72 of Holyday, *Juvenal* (1673). Wood 276a(12) (not in Bodl. CD cat.). Wing J1276. Madan 2979.

4211. Loggan, David. *Nova & accuratissima celeberrimae universitatis civitatisque Oxoniensis sceno-graphia.* [Oxford]: [e theatro Sheldoniano], [1674]. S.sh. 440 x 604 (untrimmed). AW wrote, 'Memorandum that this map or platforme of the University & Citie of Oxōn was mostly drawne by the hand (with a pencill) of David Loggan the universitie engraver an. 1673, engraven on a copper plate an. 1674, & published with the book of Maps of Colleges & Halls an. 1675. The said Dav. Loggan using my direction in the matter & an old [ma]p of Oxōn which I have in my hands, he in gratitude gave me this map in Aprill an. 1674 Ant. à Bosco' (cropped at bottom). The old map may be that of Agas, purchased 7 June 1658 from Davies (Agas not mentioned), see LT 1.254; and lent to D. Loggan (Agas not mentioned), 14 Oct. 1665, LT 2.49. The Agas map eventually went to Charlett, according to Hearne, 4.261. See LT 2.313, and H. Hurst, *Oxford topography* (OHS, 1899): 9. It is less likely that the 'old' map is the 1643 map of Hollar, see Wood 423(1), item 3640, and notes. Wood 276b(31). Wing L2838 (from *Ox. illustrata* (1675)). Madan 3035 (no. 2).

4212. Loggan, D[avid]. *Reverendissimo in Christo Patri & Domino dno. Gilberto divina providentia archiep: Cant:. . . universitatis Oxon. cancellario.* N.p.: n.pub., [1674?]. S.sh. 510 x 400mm. (engr.). Sheldonian seen from the south. A copy of this engraving was included in the presentation copies of AW's *Historia* (1674/5) at 2.25 (13 people and 3 dogs visible; framed by walls, each with 4 vases on top). It is different from that in Loggan, *Oxonia illustrata* (1675) (440 x 360mm.) (8 people and 2 dogs visible; framed by the Bodleian and the Clarendon Bldg.). Wood 276a(10) (not in Bodl. CD cat.). Wing W3385. Madan 2996 (i.e., Wood's *Historia*).

4213. Lombardus, Petrus. Armagh, abp. of. *De regno Hiberniae sanctorum insula commentarius.* Lovanii: ap. viduam S. Martini, 1632. 4°. Pp. [16], 492. Flyleaf, upper^v, AW wrote, 'v[ide] Fasti Lovanis p. 130' (i.e., in Wood 589, item 237, a brief vita of Lombard). Tp., prob. not in AW's hand, 'Hic liber spectat ad bibliothecam fratrum minorum Hibernorum Collegii S. Antonii Lovaniensis.' P. 429, AW wrote, at Robertus Dunlaerus, 'Rob: Dudleyus' and a brief note on Dudley, earl of Leicester. Wood 593. BL.

4214. London. *A breefe discourse, declaring and approving the . . . maintenance of the laudable customes of London: namely, . . . a reasonable partition of goods of husbands among their wives and children.* London: H. Midleton for R. Newberie, 1584. 8°. Pp. 48. Pasteboard (grey) with parchment spine. 1st upper and last lower flyleaves, marbled paper.
Each 8° leaf is pasted on a 4° template. Flyleaf, upper, 2nd^v, AW wrote the titles of 7 printed works in this vol., within guidelines made with red ink. Tp, by Jackson, 'Henrici Jacksoni Oxon. Coll Corp. Chrī. MDC.' and a letter or symbol, cropped at bottom (a star?). Light annotation (e.g., p. 12-3, 14-17, etc.) not by AW, and lines in margin and underscoring. LT 1.459 (see also 1.331).
Wood 590(1). STC 16747.

4215. London. *A plott against the citie of London discovered [8 Jan.].* London: J. Thomas, 1641. 4°. A^4.
Tp, AW wrote, 'Plots 13', in pencil; and A2, 'This is like the letter, that caused the discoverie of the gunpowder treason'.
Wood 373(13). Wing P2591.

4216. London. *A relation of a strange apparition in an ale-house . . . in the Strand; where a company of papists were at their exercises.* London: f. R. Smethrust [sic], 1641. 4°. Pp. [2], 5.
P. 5^v, scribbles, not by AW, covered by a slip.
[MS.] Wood B. 35(7). Wing R795.

4217. London. *The propositions made by the city of London, for the raising of a million of mony, for the quick subduing of the bloudy rebels in Ireland.* London: f. J. Borroughs a. J. Franke, 1642. 4°. A^4.
Wood 508(10). Wing P3790A ('O' not recorded in Wing) (Wing, Frank).

4218. London. *Strange and horrible news which happened betwixt St. Johns Street, and Islington.* London: f. T. Smith, 1642. 4°. A^4.
Wood 365(8). Wing S5818 (3) (Wing, John's).

4219. London. *A terrible plot against London and Westminster discovered.* London: f. J. Greensmith, 1642. 4°. A^4.
Tp, AW rubbed out a former no., '-9'; at t, wrote, 'written by an ignorant coxcomb to breed feares & jelousies in the giddy multitude'; at printed 'where Canterbury should have bin Sainted, and Wren made Cardinall', AW underscored it and wrote, 'very ridiculous & silly'; below, 'Col. Sr Tho. Lunsford (a Rom. Cath) was removed from the Lieutenancy of the Tower, in the Latter End of Dec. 1641, & Sr Thom Byron was put in his room.' A4^v, below a woodcut of 'Captaine Vaul the cruell Tyrant', AW wrote, 'see this picture at the latter end of Nu. 36 [there showing a Mr. Holk]' i.e., no. 36 in an earlier bundle, now Wood 373(52), item 3935.
Wood 373(44). Wing T774.

4220. London. *A true relation of two merchants of London, who were taken prisoners by the cavaliers.* [London]: f. H. Watson, 1642. 4°. A^4.
Tp, AW wrote, 'after Edghill fight'.
Wood 375(21). Wing T3075.

4221. London. *The virgins complaint for the losse of their sweet-hearts, by these present wars, . . . presented . . . by sundry virgins of the city of London.* London: f. H. Wilson, 1642[3], 31 Jan. 4°. Pp. 8.
Wood 654a(7). Wing V640 (Wing, wrong alpha order).

4222. London. *The discovery of a great plot intended against the city of London, . . . Also, the victory at Arundell castle, . . . Together with a full satisfaction . . . of the observing of holy dayes.* London: f. A. Coe, 1644, 8 Jan. 4°. A^4.
Tp, AW altered a former no., '53'; and wrote the date, 'Jan. 1643'.
Wood 376(59). Wing D1634.

4223. London. *A second powder-plot, discovered in . . . the lord generalls armie.* London: M. Simmons, 1644, 5 Sept. 4°. Pp. 1-7.
Tp, AW wrote the date, 'Aug. 26', recorded in the text after the 1st letter.
Wood 377(29). Wing S2328.

4224. London. *A paire of spectacles for the citie.* [London]: n.pub., 1648. 4°. Pp. 13 (really 15, misnumbering).
Tp, AW wrote, 'Smart characters of divers persons in this booke'. P. 5, printed name, 'Gravener', underscored; p. 7, line in margin; 2nd p. 7, 'Manchester' in margin.

Wood 609(15). Wing P196.

4225. London. *Londons wonder. Being a most true . . . relation of the taking and killing of a great whale.* London: f. F. Grove, 1658. 8°. A⁸ (A8 blank).
Wood 246(5). Wing L2957 (two).

4226. London. *Certain considerations propos'd by the city to the souldiery in and about London.* [London]: n.pub., [1659]. S.sh.
AW wrote, 'Decemb: 1659'.
Wood 276a(115). Wing C1692 (two).

4227. London. *A declaration of the maids of the city of London.* [London]: n.pub., [1659]. S.sh.
AW wrote, below, 'M DC Lix'.
Wood 654a(20). Wing D710.

4228. London. *The Londoners last warning [urging the restoration of Charles 2].* [London]: n.pub., [1659]. 4°. Pp. 8 (wanting the t leaf).
Tp, no. 68 in a former bundle. P. 8, AW wrote, 'printed Aug: 1659'.
Wood 610(11). Wing L2913.

4229. London. *London's new wonder: or, the great sleeper:. . . whereunto is annexed, the worlds wonder; . . . apparitions . . . at New-market-heath.* London: f. G. Horton, 1659. 4°. Pp. 8.
P. 8, AW wrote, 'This pamphlett came out about the middle of March 1658-9[1659]'.
[MS.] Wood B. 35(22). Wing L2945 (rare).

4230. London. *The remonstrance and protestation of the . . . people of . . . London, Westminster and other the cities . . . against those officers . . . who put force upon, . . . the parliament [13 Oct.].* London: n.pub., 1659. Fol. Pp. [2], 10 (with 2 dupl. leaves).
Tp, AW wrote 'Nov. 16 1659' in pencil; below, pencil mark, cropped.
Wood 657(46). Wing R972.

4231. London. *A declaration of all the watermen . . . of London. Or, a hue and cry after col. Whitton.* [London]: n.pub., [1660]. S.sh.
AW wrote 'Jan: 1659[60]'.
Wood 276a(210). Wing D604A (3) ('O' not recorded in Wing).

4232. London. *A declaration of the nobility and gentry that adhered to the late king, now residing in . . . London.* London: R. Norton, 1660. S.sh.
AW added to the year, 'Aprill:', and lines after the name of a subscriber, Adrian Scrope.
Wood 276a(224). Wing D716 ('O' not recorded in Wing).

4233. London. *The honest cryer of London.* [London]: f. G. Thompson, 1660. S.sh.
In printed '1660' AW lined out '60' replaced it with '59'.
Wood 416(44). Wing H2581.

4234. London. *The cities loyalty display'd: or the four famous and renowned fabricks . . . exactly described.* London: n.pub., 1661. 4°. Pp. [2], 5.
Wood 537(18). Wing C4330.

4235. London. *A letter from a gentleman at London, to his friend in the countrey.* [London]: n.pub., [1676]. 4°. Pp. 18, [2].
P. 1, AW wrote, 'Printed in the summer time at London 1676: Mʳ Will. Rogers who dispersed this pamphlet told me twas about Easter.-'. Pp. 2-14, AW wrote some brief notes (e.g., p. 2, '1675'), underscoring, and lines in margins; 5, at a passage on Jesuits, 'A proclamation from the K. & his counsell 10. Nov. 1675 for the apprehension of Sᵗ Germaine, & 200ˡⁱ to be given to him that shall take him, for assasianating [sic] Luzancy'; 15, 'Breval prb[end] of Westm[inster] 1675/6 & his char[acter]'; 18, 'When this pamphlet was printed, Will. Rogers before mentioned dispersed it, for which & the dispersing of others, he was brought before the K. & his councell in Aug. or Sept. 1676'. LT 2.337.
Wood 632(52). Wing L1379.

4236. London. *The London bully, or the prodigal son, displaying the principal cheats of our modern debauchees. [Adapted from Het kind van weelde, of De Haagsche lichtmis].* London: H. Clark f. T. Malthus, 1683. 12°. Pp. [10], 131.
A1, '9ᵈ', may be by AW.

Wood 824(4). Wing L2890 (rare).

4237. London. *The gentlewoman who lived in Red-lyon-court, is removed to Racquet-court, near Fleet-bridge.* [London]: n.pub., [1690?]. S.sh.
[MS.] Wood F. 50, f. 36. Wing G523aA (Wing, var., is now removed).

4238. London, Apprentices. *To his excellency the lord general Monck . . . the apprentices . . . of London [2 Feb.].* London: T. Ratcliffe, 1659[60]. S.sh.
ᵛ, now pasted down, AW wrote 'feb: 2: 59[60]'; and an illeg. note.
Wood 276a(237). Wing T1359.

4239. London, Army. *A list of the field-officers chosen and appointed for the Irish expedition, by the committee at Guild-hall London . . . under . . . Philip lord Wharton.* London: f. E. Paxton, 1642, 13 June. S.sh.
Wood 508(16). Wing L2442A (one) ('O' not recorded in Wing).

4240. London, Blackfriars. *Something written by occasion of that fatall . . . accident in the Blacke Friers [26 Oct.].* [London]: n.pub., 1623. 4°. Pp. [2], 30.
Tp, AW wrote, 'Another pamphlet concerning this matter is extant, called The dolefull evensong – I have it.' (Wood 643(1), item 3236).
Wood 643(2a). STC 3101.

4241. London, Cheapside. *The resolution of the round-heads to pull down Cheap-side crosse.* [London?]: n.pub., 1642. 4°. A⁴.
[MS.] Wood D. 31(41). Wing R1157B (two).

4242. London, Cheapside. *Cruel and barbarous news from Cheapside . . . of an horid fact, acted by an unhuman mistress.* [London]: f. W. P, 1676. 4°. Pp. [2], 5.
Wood 365(24). Wing C7415 (two).

4243. London, Clergy. *A serious and faithfull representation of the judgements of ministers of the gospell within . . . London. . . . Jan. 18. 1648.* London: M. B. f. S. Gellibrand a. R. Smith, 1649. 4°. Pp. [2], 14 (A-B⁴).
Wood 364(5). Wing S2604 (in t, 'of the ministers').

4244. London, Clergy. *To the reverend, learned, and grave divines, in . . . London.* [London]: n.pub., [1660]. S.sh.
AW wrote, 'January: 1659[60]'.
Wood 276a(171). Wing T1603 (3).

4245. London, Clergy. *A renuntiation and declaration of the ministers of congregational churches . . . in . . . London: against the late horrid insurrection.* London: P. Cole a. E. Cole, 1661. 4°. Pp. [2], 9.
Tp, AW altered the year to 166'0', and wrote the price, '2ᵈ'.
Wood 608(30). Wing R1042.

4246. London, Clergy. *A list of the praebendaries of the cathedral church of St. Paul London, . . . to preach . . . at St. Peter's church in Cornhil.* London: f. W. Kettilby, 1693. S.sh.
AW wrote 'Oxon.' after Oxford persons, e.g. Drs. Isham, Williams, Scott, Godolphin, Turner, Lancaster, and Sanders; and Mssr. Wigan and Masters. ᵛ, 'ffor Mʳ Harms. This present from the Author.'
Wood 276a(100). Wing L2489 (rare).

4247. London, Committee of Militia. *A narrative of the proceedings of the committee of the militia of London . . . concerning a letter, . . . to be sent to general Monck.* [London]: n.pub., [1659]. S.sh.
AW wrote the date, 'novemb. M DC Lix'.
Wood 276a(233). Wing N215.

4248. London, Common Council. *The humble petition, and remonstrance of divese [sic] citizens of London.* [Oxford]: f. W. Webb, 1643. 4°. Pp. [2], 6.
Tp, AW overwrote the former no., '29'; wrote 'qu[aere] whether not – [illeg.]', in pencil, and several dates, '1643', '1642', and 'December 7 12' (dates he also wrote in the text, pp. 2, 3,), and made a correction in the t.
Wood 375(26). Wing H3437. Madan 1209 (Wing, 1642[3]).

4249. London, Common Council. *The humble desires of the loyall hearted, . . . free-men . . . of London*

. . . for the peace. [London]: n.pub., [1648]. S.sh.
AW wrote, '1646-47', in pencil.
Wood 276a(191). Wing H3415.

4250. London, Common Council. *Aleyn mayor. At a common councel holden in the guildhall London [20 Dec.].* London: J. Flesher, [1659]. S.sh.
Wood 276a(111). Wing L2852N.

4251. London, Common Council. *The humble petition of the citizens of London, intended to be presented to the . . . lord mayor, aldermen, and commons, in common-council.* [London]: n.pub., [1659]. S.sh.
AW wrote, 'Octob: MDcLix'; ᵛ, 'Oct – 1659'.
Wood 657(47). Wing H3489A ('O' not recorded in Wing).

4252. London, Common Council. *To the right honourable, our right worthy and grave senatours, the lord mayor, . . . the most humble petition . . . of divers young men.* [London]: n.pub., [1659]. S.sh.
AW wrote, 'printed decemb: 1659'.
Wood 276a(107) (not in Bodl. CD cat.). Wing T1609.

4253. London, Common Council. *A true copy of the letter sent from the lord mayor, . . . Directed to . . . George Moncke [29 Dec. 1659].* London: n.pub., 1659[60]. S.sh.
Wood 276a(116). Wing T2647.

4254. London, Common Council. *Two letters; the one, sent by the lord mayor, aldermen, and common council of London, to . . . Monck . . . The other, his excellencies answer.* London: J. Macock, 1659[60]. 4°.
Pp. [2], 6.
Wood 632(68). Wing T3481.

4255. London, Common Council. *A common-councell holden the first day of May 1660.* [London]: J. Flesher, 1660. 4°. Pp. [2], 13 (p. [1] blank).
Wood 608(13). Wing L2852Q.

4256. London, Common Council. *A declaration and vindication of the lord mayor, aldermen and commons of . . . London. [30 Apr.].* London: J. Flesher, 1660. 4°. Pp. [2], 26.
Wood 608(29). Wing D559.

4257. London, Common Council. *A new declaration of the citizens of London to . . . Monck in Scotland. With his excellencies answer, and further resolution.* London: f. G. Horton, 1660. 4°. Pp. 8.
Tp, AW altered the year to, 16'59 Janua-' (cropped at side).
Wood 632(70). Wing N610A.

4258. London, Common Council. *To the [rig]ht honourable the council of state, . . . The humble petition of . . . citizens . . . of London . . . for the . . . securing of John Lambert.* [London]: n.pub., [1660]. S.sh.
Wood 276a(205). Wing T1618F (two) ('O' not recorded in Wing).

4259. London, Common Council. *To the right honourable the lord mayor, . . . The humble petition of the inhabitants in and about London.* London: f. T. M., [1660]. 4°. Pp. 7.
Tp, AW wrote, 'January 1659'.
Wood 610(49). Wing T1655B (rare) (Wing, [1659]).

4260. London, Common Council. *To the kings most excellent majesty. The humble petition . . . of London [12 Nov.].* London: f. F. Smith, 1680. S.sh.
Wood 276a(175). Wing T1520 ('O' not recorded in Wing).

4261. London, Common Council. *An act of common council for regulating the election of sheriffs, and for repealing the treasonable . . . acts . . . in the time of the late rebellion [6 June].* London: S. Roycroft, 1683. Fol. Pp. [2], 18.
Tp, AW wrote at top, 'London', in pencil.
Wood 657(35). Wing L2858.

4262. London, Common Council. *To his highness the prince of Orange. The humble address of the lord mayor.* London: n.pub., 1688. S.sh.
AW wrote the date, 'Dec. XI – 88'. LT 3.288.
Wood 529(13). Wing T1371.

4263. London, Court of Aldermen. *Pack mayor. . . . Ordered, that such of the rules and by-laws made*

. . . for regulation of hackney coachmen [Tuesday, 2 Jan. 1654]. (London): (J. Flesher), 1654[5]. 4°. Pp. 8.
Wood 590(7). Wing L2864F (two) ('O' not recorded in Wing).

4264. London, Covent Garden. *News from Covent Garden: Or, the town gallants vindication.* London:
f. J. T., 1675. 4°. Pp. 7.
Wood 500(11). Wing N953 ('O' not recorded in Wing).

4265. London, Fire. *The papists plot of firing discovered, in a perfect account of the late fire in Fetter-*
lane, London. London: f. A. B., 1679. 4°. Pp. [2], 6.
[MS.] Wood D. 28(25). Wing P318.

4266. London, Fire. *A true narrative of a sad and lamentable fire which happened . . . in Temple lane,*
London [27 Jan., Elias Ashmole]. [London]: f. D. M., 1679. 4°. Pp. 8.
LT 2.435.
[MS.] Wood D. 28(26). Wing T2771 (rare).

4267. London, Guildhall. *The proceedings at the guild-hall . . . July the 29th, 1680.* [London]: n.pub.,
[1680]. Fol. Pp. 4.
Wood 657(59). Wing P3559.

4268. London, Guildhall. *A true narrative of the proceedings at guild-hall . . . in the unanimous election*
of their four members to serve in parliament. (London): (f. F. Smith), (1681). S.sh. Pp. 2.
Wood 657(60). Wing T2809.

4269. London, Inner Temple. *A vindication of the proceedings of the gentlemen of the Inner-Temple.*
Cambridge: n.pub., 1662. 8°. Pp. [10], 27.
Wood 112(4). Wing V527 ('O' not recorded in Wing).

4270. London, Kings-Head Court. Gerbier, Balthazar possibly by. *A brief account of the grammar-*
lecture, in Kings-head court near the Theater Royal, . . . where children are . . . taught the Latine tongue.
(London): (T. M. f. the author), (1667). 4°. Pp. 8, [1] (may be wanting preliminary p. or pp. P. [1, last p.],
a appeal for support ends without the name of the solicitor).
Wood 310(8). Wing B4506aA. ESTCR 173269 (rare).

4271. London, Livery Companies. *The armes crest supporters & mottowes of all y[e] several companies*
& corporations . . . of London. London: P. Stent, n.d. Fol. Pp. [2] (engraving) (61 corporations plus 3
companies).
Wood 276a(65). Not in Wing. Not in ESTCR.

4272. London, Merchant Taylors' Hall. *An answer to the Whiggish poem on the loyal apprentices*
feast. (London): (f. A. Banks), (1682). S.sh. (r-v).
AW wrote '1682', in pencil.
Wood 417(96). Wing A3453.

4273. London, Prison. *A true relation of the cruell and unparallel'd oppression which hath been illegally*
imposed upon the gentlemen, prisoners in the Tower of London. [London]: n.pub., 1647. 4°. Pp. [2], 20.
Pasteboard (blue) with parchment spine.
Flyleaf, upper, AW wrote the titles of 12 printed works in this vol., within guidelines made with red ink.
AW assigned an Arabic number to each tp, and the Ashm. librarian entered the corresponding Roman
numeral, sometimes overwriting AW's nos.
Wood 500(1). Wing T2938.

4274. London, Prison. *Multum in parvo: or, a summary narrative . . . on behalfe of prisoners captived*
for debt. London: f. J. H., 1653. 4°. Pp. [2], 14.
Wood 500(3). Wing M3062.

4275. London, Tyburn. *The groanes and pangues of Tiburne.* [London]: printed at the mayors banqueting
house near Tyburne, 1648. 4°. Pp. 8.
Tp, date mutilated; AW wrote '1648'.
Wood 609(12) (not in Bodl. CD cat.). Wing G 2054 ('O' not recorded in Wing).

4276. London, Tyburn. *A true relation of the executions at Tyburn & Little-Brittain [22 Jan. 1678].*
[London]: f. P. Brooksby, [1678]. 4°. Pp. [2], 6.
Wood 365(28). Not in Wing. Should be at Wing T2950aA. Not in ESTCR.

4277. London, Westminster. *All the proceedings at the sessions of the peace holden at Westminster,* . . . *against Thomas Tydford, Elizabeth Sorrell [et al., 20 June].* London: T. Harper, 1651. 4°. Pp. 14. Wood 647(18). Wing A946 ('O' not recorded in Wing).

4278. London, Whitehall. *An account of the proceedings at White-hall, Guild-hall, and at the tower; together with its surrender upon . . . the king's . . . departure [11 Dec.].* [London]: n.pub., [1688]. S.sh. Wood 529(12). Wing A365.

4279. [London, William]. *The civil wars of France, during the bloody reign of Charls the ninth.* London: H. H. f. W. London, 1655. 12°. Pp. [20], 272 (unopened pp.). Tp, AW, wrote, '1^s-8^d-', bsms. Acquired 29 Mar. 1662, LT 1.435. Wood 219(2). Wing L2851.

4280. London's Account. *Londons account: or, a calculation of the arbytrary [sic] and tyrannicall exactions, taxations . . . during the foure yeers of this unnaturall warre.* [London]: n.pub., 1647. 4°. Pp. [2], 12. Wood 526(4). Wing L2915 (Wing, London's).

4281. Long, Thomas. *Dr. [Anthony] Walker's . . . account of the author [J. Gauden] of* Εικων βασιλικη *. . . and demonstrated to be false.* London: R. Talor, 1693. 4°. Pp. [2], ii, iv, 57 [really 63], [1] (1 p. cat. of books written by Long). Tp, 'Long', underscored in red chalk. Wood 363(9) (not in Bodl. CD cat.). Wing L2965. FFMadan 171.

4282. Longeville, Charles. *To the king's most excellent majesty, the humble petition of Charles Longeville [26 May 1685].* [London]: n.pub., [1685]. S.sh. (r-v). Wood 276b(71) (not in Bodl. CD cat.). Wing L2995 (rare).

4283. Longinus. Langbaine, Gerard, ed. Διονυσιου λογγινου *. . . Dionysii Longini . . . liber de grandi loquentia.* Oxonii: G. T[urner,] imp. G. Webb, 1636 and 1638. 8°. 2 eds. Missing. MS. Wood E. 2(70), p. 39, 'Dr Langbaynes notes on Longinus'. Ed. not identified. MS. Wood E. 2(70), p. 39. STC 16788 and STC 16789. *Folg.*

4284. Look About You. *Looke about you, or the fault-finder, and criticall observer.* [London]: n.pub., [1647]. 4°. Pp. 7. Wood 476(18) (not in Bodl. CD cat.). Wing L3009.

4285. Loredano, Giovanni Francesco. S., J., trans. *The life of Adam.* London: H. Moseley, 1659. 8°. Pp. [8], 86. Calf with 3 fillets and stamp decoration in corners (flower with point) (Ashm. binding). Flyleaf, upper, 4th, list of 7 printed works in this vol., written by Ashm. librarian. AW grouped this collection together and his Arabic nos. (1-5) are present on tpp (severe cropping may have eliminated nos. in items 6 and 7); Ashm. Roman numerals were added after 1695. Tp, AW wrote, '6^d'. Bsm. Acquired 12 Feb. 1669, LT 2.151. Wood 289(1). Wing L3067.

4286. Loritus Glareanus, Henricus. *Glareani* Δωδεκαχορδον. Basileae: (Per H. Petri), (1547, Sept.). Fol. Pp. (20), 470, (6). Parchment (backing, upper cover, a Middle English ms., ca. 1400). Flyleaf, lower^v, drawing, apparently AW's full-length profile of himself, striding; head, in ink, and body, in pencil. Tp, 'cuts' (?). Wood 396. BL.

4287. Lorraine, Henri de. Mayenne, duke of. *The duke of Mayennes ghost speaking to the princes, . . . of France.* Hage [really London?]: H. Jacobson [B. Alsop?], [1622] MDCCXXII. 4°. Pp. [2], 20. Tp, '4', over place of publication. Wood 345(21). STC 17728.7 (one) ('O' not recorded in STC).

4288. Lotius, [Eleasar]. *A speech of d^r. Lotius, to king Charles, the second of that name. [2nd t] Allocution d. d. Lotii.* [London]: n.pub., 1649, 23 Feb. 4°. ^{2},A^2 (Engl. and Lat. versions) (A^2 unopened). Wood 364(24) (not in Bodl. CD cat.). Wing L3084.

4289. Louis IV. France, king of, pseud. *A lively pourtraicture of the face of this common-wealth, . . . by Lewis the fourth.* [London?]: n.pub., 1659. 4°. Pp. [2], 14. Tp, a few scribbles in pencil, including a portion of a no. in a former bundle. Wood 613(4). Wing L2594A.

4290. Louis XIV. France, king of. *The treaty of peace between the crowns of France & Spain; concluded . . . the seventh of November, 1659. Rendred into English.* London: T. Newcomb, sold G. Bedell a. T. Collins, 1660. 4°. Pp. 44.
Tp, AW wrote 'This came out in ffeb: 1659[60]: 8ᵈ.' LT 1.302.
Wood 615(4). Wing L3139B.

4291. Louis XIV. France, king of. *A narrative of the progress of his most Christian majesties armes against the Dutch. . . . Likewise a letter from his said majesty.* [London]: T. Newcomb, 1672. Fol. Pp. 11.
Tp, 2 verses, not in AW's hand.
Wood 559(19). Wing N 221.

4292. Love, Christopher. Mʳ. *Love's case . . . taken in short-hand by John Hinde.* London: f. R. W. a. P. Cole, 1651. 4°. Pp. [2], 67. Pasteboard (blue) with parchment spine.
Flyleaf, upper, 2ndʳ⁻ᵛ, AW wrote the titles of 22 (really 23, he omitted item 14) printed works in this vol., within guidelines made with red ink. After the last entry, 'Will Anderton' (see the s.sh. concerning an execution, Wood 657(30), item 236, that AW had intended to insert here). Item 19 (no. 18 in AW's list) has been removed. The Bodl. CD cat. nos. are erratic after Wood 367(14). The Roman numerals, made by the Ashm. cataloguer, are correct.
Wood 367(1). Wing L3143.

4293. Love, Christopher. *A true and exact copie of mʳ Love's speech . . . at Tower-hill, Aug. 22.* [London]: n.pub., [1651]. 4°. Pp. 8.
Wood 367(2). Wing L3181.

4294. Love, Christopher. *Sum or substance of practical divinity; or, the grounds of religion in a catechistical way.* London: n.pub., 1654. 12°.
Missing. MS. Wood E. 2(70), p. 39, 'The sum of Practicall Divinity'. Details from AO 3.283.
MS. Wood E. 2(70), p. 39. Not in Wing. Not in ESTCR.

4295. Love, Christopher, and John Gibbons. *The true and perfect speech of mr. Christopher Love. . . on Tower-hill:. . . together with mr. [John] Gibbons speech.* London: J. Clowes, 1651. 4°. Pp. 7.
Wood 367(3). Wing L3182 ('O' not recorded in Wing).

4296. Lovekin, Thomas. *A true relation of a dangerous plot against the well-affected party of the town of Lynn, discovered by . . . Tho. Lovekin.* London: f. J. C., 1648. 4°. Pp. [2], 6.
Wood 502(6). Wing T2874.

4297. L[owe], E[dward]. *A short direction for the performance of cathedrall service.* Oxford: W. Hall f. R. Davis, 1661. 8°. Pp. 64. Obl. Parchment.
Tp, AW wrote, 'Edw. Low professor of the musicall praxis in the university of Oxon.'; and 'Jan: 1. 1660[1]'.
P. 4, mark in margin (at a reference to a source of a musical work). LT 1.420. For AW's sale of music mss. in 1667 to Lowe, see M. Crum, *Chelys*, 4(1972): 3.
Wood 118 (not in Bodl. CD cat.). Wing L3305. Madan 2563 ('O' not recorded in Wing).

4298. Lowick, Thomas. *The history of the life & martyrdom of st. George.* London: J. Best f. W. Crook, 1664. 4°. Pp. [4], 56 (p. 56 books sold by W. Crook).
Acquired 8 Aug. 1664, 6ᵈ, LT 2.19.
Wood 536(4). Wing L3320.

4299. Lowth, Simon. *A letter to dr. Burnet. Occasioned by his late letter to mr. Lowth [on S. Lowth's Of the subject of church-power].* (London): (f. R. Taylor), (1685). 4°. Pp. 7.
Flyleaf, upperᵛ, Latin dissertation topic, not by AW.
[MS.] Wood D. 29(13). Wing L3327.

4300. Lucan. May, Thomas, trans. *Lucan's Pharsalia.* ?: ?, ? Pp.?
Missing. MS. Wood E. 2(70), p. 55, 'Translation of Lucan Tho. May'. Ed. not identified.
MS. Wood E. 2(70), p. 55. STC 16886-16889, and 17711-2.

4301. Lucian of Samosata. Hickes, Francis, trans.; Hickes, Thomas, ed. *Certaine select dialogues of Lucian:. . . Whereunto is added the life of Lucian . . . by T[homas] H[ickes].* Oxford: W. Turner, 1634. 4°. Pp. [16], 196. Parchment.
Cover, lower, name of 'Evan Thomas Esquire C–' (Ch.Ch.?). Pastedown, upper, some figures and accounts, not by AW. Flyleaf, upper, torn out, a trace of annotation remains. AO 2. 491, 584.
[MS.] Wood C. 27. STC 16893. Madan 784.

4302. Lucian of Samosata. *Part of Lucian's dialogues, (not) from the original Greek, done into rhyme.* London: f. C. Corbet, 1684. Fol. Pp. [2], 2 (t leaf and no. 1 (pp. 1-2) of pt. 1. N.B., this is a separate imprint, p. [1ᵛ]: 'lay out a penny for the purchase, . . . a Sheet every Week by this *Printer*'). Wood 417(132). ESTCR 204313 (part of). See Wing L3432-3.

4303. Lucifer. *Lucifer's life-guard containing, a schedule list.* London: n.pub., 1660. S.sh. ᵛ, AW wrote, '1660', and '74' over a former no. '48' in pencil. Wood 416(74). Wing L3440.

4304. Lucretius. Barksdale, Clement, trans. *Noctes hibernae. Winter-nights exercises.* London: T. Warren, f. E. Thorn, at Oxford, 1653. 8°. Pp. 14. Tp, AW wrote, 'Author Clem. Barksdale.' and '2ᵈ'. Wood 84(5). Wing B803.

4305. Ludlow, [Edmund]. Probably not written by Ludlow. *A letter from major General Ludlow to sir E[dward] S[eymour] . . . upon the 30th of January, being the anniversary or general madding-day.* Amsterdam: n.pub., 1691. 4°. Pp. [2], 30. Pasteboard (blue) with parchment spine; traces of upper and lower marbled flyleaves. Flyleaf, upper, 1stᵛ, AW wrote, 'Note that the pamphlets following which were put out under the name of Maj. Gen. Ludlow, were commonly reported to be written by Joh. Philipps nephew, by the mother, to John Milton the great Anti-monarchist–'. 2ndʳ⁻ᵛ, AW wrote the titles of 16 printed works in this vol., within guidelines made with red ink. Item 1, tp, 'published at Lond. in the beginning of March 1690-1', and, in pencil, 'Jo. Philipps'. LT 3.357. Wood 363(1) (not in Bodl. CD cat.). Wing L1489.

4306. Ludlow, Edmund. Probably not written by Ludlow. *A letter from general Ludlow to dr. [Richard] Hollingworth.* Amsterdam: n.pub., 1692. 4°. Pp. viii, 72. Tp, AW wrote the price, '1ˢ'. See note at Wood 363(3), item 3651. LT 3.377. Wood 363(4) (not in Bodl. CD cat.). Wing L1469.

4307. Ludlow, Edmund. Probably not written by Ludlow. *Truth brought to light: or, the gross forgeries of dr. [Richard] Hollingworth.* London: n.pub., 1693. 4°. Pp. 40. Tp, AW wrote, 'Bought at Oxon. 2. Feb. 1692[3]'. LT 3.415. Wood 363(14). Wing T3153. FFMadan 173.

4308. Lunadoro, Girolamo, and Fioravante Martinelli. Cogan, Henry, trans. *The court of Rome [by G. Lunadoro]. . . . And a direction for such as shall travell to Rome [by F. Martinelli].* London: H. Herringman, 1654. 8°. Pp. [8], 275. Calf with 2 fillets; flyleaves, upper and lower, printer's waste paper. Tp, 'Codex Johannis Lee olim Mertonensis apud Oxōn, Aprilis 21°. A°. Dⁱ. MDCLV.' and 'pretium. 1ˢ - 8ᵈ'. Acquired 23 Nov. 1663, 1ˢ2ᵈ, LT 1.503; lent to R. Peyton, 29 Mar. 1664, LT 2.8. Wood 563. Wing C6591.

4309. L[upton], D[onald]. *Emblems of rarities: or choyce observations out of worthy histories.* London: N. Okes, 1636. 12°. Pp. [24], 478. Calf with 2 fillets. Pastedown and flyleaf, upper, signatures of Henry Foulis and '1658 at Notingham Septemb. pr: 12ᵈ'; 2nd, 'Mary Foulis Book'. LT 2.179. P. 3, cross in margin. Wood 226. STC 16942.

4310. Luther, Martin. *The last wil and last confession of Martyn Luthers faith.* [Wesel]: [von der Straten?], [1543]. 8°. A-D⁸ (without a t leaf). Tp, signature of Hum: Dyson. Wood 774(6). STC 16984.

4311. Luther, Martin. *The signs of Christs coming, and of the last day. Being the substance of a . . . sermon [Tröstliche Predigt von der Zukunft Christi] lately translated out of his Enarrations on the Gospels.* London: n.pub., 1661. 4°. Pp. [2], 34. Wood 643(5). Wing L3516.

4312. Lydiat, Thomas. *Numerus aureus melioribus lapillis insignitus factusque Gemmeus; è thesauro anni magni.* Londini: G. Jones, 1621. S.sh. Wood 276a(39). STC 17042 (two).

4313. Lyford, Edward. *[Hebrew: Sefer melitsat ha-shemot.] Or, the true interpretation and etymologie of Christian names.* London: T. W. f. George Sawbridge, 1655. 12°. Pp. [24], 237, [62]. Calf with 2 fillets;

rebacked.
Flyleaf, upper 1st, printer's waste paper; 2nd, 'John: Norman his booke 1655' and his price, '1ˢ4ᵈ'. Tp, bsm.
Wood 28. Wing L3543.

4314. Lyford, William. *Principles of faith & good conscience, digested into a catecheticall forme*. [London]: T. Harper, sold P. Nevil, 1642. 8°. Pp. [16], 294. Calf with 3 fillets and stamp A W; flyleaf, upper and lower, printer's waste paper.
Pastedown, upperᵛ (pasted down side), 'Edward Wood his Book by the gift of Mr. B– Ho– . . . of Trinity Colledge'. Flyleaves, upper and lower, scribbles, and shorthand, in more than one hand. Pastedown, lower, signature, 'Thomas –d', lined out.
Wood 807. Wing L3552.

4315. Lyme. *An exact and true relation in relieving the resolute garrison of Lyme*. [London]: f. M. Walbanke, 1644, 10 June. 4°. Pp. [2], 6.
Wood 377(12). Wing E3611 (Wing, Walbancke).

4316. Lynche, Richard, trans. [really written by]. *An historical treatise of the travels of Noah into Europe [from G. Nanni]*. London: A. Islip, 1601. 4°. A-O⁴.
Missing in 1837. See note at Wood 490(1). Listed in MS. Wood E. 2(70), p. 48, 'Rich Lynch travells of Noah into Europe – (1606) q[uarto?]' (only 1601 and 1602 editions are recorded in ESTCR).
Wood 490(4). See STC 17092. *O* (evidence erased), *Folg, Hunt*.

4317. Lynne, Walter. *?. ?: ?, ? 4°.*
Missing. MS. Wood E. 2(70), p. 48, 'his transl.'
MS. Wood E. 2(70), p. 48. Not identified. See STC 17115ff. and STC 4626.

4318. M., A. *Plain-dealing: or, a full and particular examination of a late treatise [by M. Clifford] entituled, Humane reason*. London: A. Clark f. H. Dickinson in Cambridge, 1675. 12°. Pp. 164, [1] (pp. 1-2 blank).
Tp, under initials, 'Marvell', in pencil, prob. not by AW. Wood 841(2-4) all respond to M. Clifford, Wood 841(1), item 1920.
Wood 841(3). Wing M4A.

4319. M., D. *A letter to a noble lord concerning a late prophane pamphlet [by T. Ashenden] entituled, the Presbyterians [sic] pater noster*. [London]: n.pub., [1681]. S.sh. (r-v).
ᵛ, AW wrote, 'In March. 1680/1 then published'.
[MS.] Wood D. 26(16). Wing M13.

4320. M., E. *An achrostickal epitaph on sir Edward Sprague [name in acrostic]*. [London]: n.pub., [1673]. S.sh.
ᵛ, AW wrote, 'Sʳ Edw. Spragg'.
Wood 429(25). Wing M14A (two).

4321. M., H. *The armies dutie; or, faithfull advice to the souldiers: given in two letters written . . . [signed H. M. and others] unto lord Fleetwood*. London: printed, sold Popes-head Alley, etc., 1659. 4°. Pp. 29.
Tp, no. 26 in a former bundle.
Wood 610(9). Wing M28.

4322. M., H. *A pair of spectacles for this purblinde nation with which they may see the army and parliament . . . brethren in iniquity*. London: n.pub., 1659. 4°. Pp. [2], 14.
Tp, no. 32 in a former bundle.
Wood 610(8). Wing M30.

4323. M., J. *A letter from a friend in Shropshire to . . . mr. Richard Baxter . . . in London*. (London): (f. A. Banks), (1681). S.sh. Pp. 2.
Wood 276a(162). Wing M38.

4324. M., R. *Newes of sʳ. Walter Rauleigh with the true description of Guiana*. London: [G. Eld] f. H. G[osson], sold J. Wright, 1618. 4°. Pp. [2], 45.
P. 45ᵛ, extensive notes on Raleigh's fleet, not in AW's hand.
Wood 386(5). STC 17148.3.

4325. M., R. *Micrologia. Characters, or essayes, of persons, trades, and places*. London: T. C[otes] f. M. Sparke, 1629. 8°. A⁴,B-D⁸. Pasteboard (grey) with parchment spine. 1st upper and last lower flyleaves,

purple paper; rebacked.
Flyleaf, upper, 3rd^v, AW wrote the titles of 6 printed works in this vol., within guidelines made with red ink. Tp, signature of 'Rob: Warner'.
Wood 868(1). STC 17146 (rare, 2 at O).

4326. M., S. *The loyal garland*. London: J. M. f. I. Deacon, 1685. 8°. Pp. 16.
Missing in 1837. 'Loyal Garland – 1685' in Whiteside cat.
Wood 94(3) (not in Bodl. CD cat.). Wing M79C (two). O, CM.

4327. M., S. *True tryal of understanding a book of riddles*. London: ?, 1688. Pp.?
Missing in 1837. 'True Tryal of understanding a Book of riddles – Lond. 1688' in Whiteside cat. See Wing M79E (1687).
Wood 64(11). Not in Wing. Not in ESTCR.

4328. M., T. *The true narration of the entertainment of his royall majestie, from the time of his departure from Edenbrough; till his receiving at London*. London: T. Creede f. T. Millington, 1603. 4°. A^2,B-E^4,G^2.
Wood 537(3). STC 17153.

4329. M., T. Morrice, Thomas, attrib. to. *Digesta scholastica, in gratiam puerorum edita*. Oxoniae: J. Lichfield et G. Wrench, 1617. 8°. Pp. [4], 52, 127, [1].
Missing. MS. Wood E. 2(70), p. 16. AOF 1.272.
MS. Wood E. 2(70), p. 16. STC 17152 (rare). Madan 457. *O*.

4330. M., T. *A particular list of divers of the commanders . . . taken prisoner . . . at Marston moore neer York*. London: f. R. Rounthwait, 1644. 4°. Pp. [2], 6.
Wood 377(20). Wing M84 (3).

4331. M., T. *Sir Thomas Fairfaxes taking of Dennis castle, and Felford haven*. [London]: f. M. Walbanke, 1646, 26 Mar. 4°. Pp. 7.
Tp, AW altered the former no., '60'.
Wood 378(63). Wing M85.

4332. Maastrich. *A narrative of the siege and surrender of Maestricht to the most Christian king [30 June]*. [London]: T. Newcomb, 1673. Fol. Pp. 12.
Wood 559(8). Wing N225.

4333. [Mabbut, George]. *Tables for renewing and purchasing of the leases*. Cambridge: J. Hayes, 1686. 8°. Pp. [23], 39.
Wood 21(6). Wing M113.

4334. MacConnor, Dermond. *The copy of a letter written from . . . one of the chiefetaines of the Irish rebels, unto the king of Spaine, for aide . . . Also, . . . another letter written from Lisbon*. London: f. R. Harford, 1642. 4°. Pp. [2], 6.
Tp, AW wrote after the year, '24. Dec. 1641', and, in pencil 'Dec ult 1641'. Dupl. at Wood 616(24).
Wood 507(19). Wing M117.

4335. MacConnor, Dermond. *The copy of a letter written from . . . one of the chiefetaines of the Irish rebels, unto the king of Spaine, for aide . . . Also, . . . another letter written from Lisbon*. London: f. R. Harford, 1642. 4°. Pp. [2], 6.
Tp, AW wrote 'Du[pl]', cropped at side. Bsm. Dupl. at Wood 507(19).
Wood 616(24). Wing M117.

4336. MacDonnel, Alexander. *The case of Alexander Mac Donnel esq; and the lady Elizabeth his wife*. [London]: n.pub., [1677]. Fol. Pp. 8.
AW wrote, '1676/7 { Febr.'
Wood 276b(86). Wing C875 (two).

4337. MacDonnell, William. *Anglia liberata, or, the rights of the people of England, maintained against the pretences of the Scotish king*. London: T. Newcomb f. R. Lowns, 1651. 4°. Pp. [4], 68 (3 tpp.).
Tp, at Mac-Donnel, 'Mac-dowel', in a modern hand. Bsms.
Wood 609(29). Wing A3178.

4338. [Machell, Thomas]. *That the northern counties which abound in antiquities and ancient gentry, may no longer be bury'd in silence*. [Oxford]: [H. Hall], [1677]. Fol. Pp. 4.

P. 1, scribbles, not by AW. P. 4, AW wrote, 'Thomas Machell of Cracanthorpe in Westmoreland. A.M. and Fellow of Queens Coll in Oxon. 1. Jan. 1676-7.' AO 4.532.
[MS.] Ashm. 1820a, ff. 226-7. Wing M127B (rare). Madan 3145 (AW's hand, not Machell's).

4339. Machiavelli, Nicolai. *Historiae Florentinae.* Argentorati: L. Zetzneri, 1610. 8°. Pp. [2], 494, [26]. Calf, speckled, with 2 fillets.
Tp, bsm. Pasted to a sheet at middle fore-edge, a slip identifying the author and work (for similar slips, also by a former owner, see Index, 'Slip with title').
Wood 208. BL.

4340. MacKenzie, George. *Religio stoici.* Edinburgh: f. R. Broun, 1663. 8°. Pp. 23, [1], 159, [1] (sigs. L 2,3, mutilated).
Tp, AW wrote the price '9ᵈ'. Bsm. Pp. 144-5, former slip with the title, by AW, used as backing. Acquired 27 Oct. 1663, LT 1.501.
Wood 870(3). Wing M197.

4341. [Mackenzie, George]. *A vindication of his majesties government . . . in Scotland.* Loudon [sic]: N. Thompson, f. S. Forrester, 1683. 4°. Rpt. of Edinburgh edition. Pp. [2], 29.
Tp, AW wrote, 'By Sʳ George Mackenzie', in pencil.
Wood 368(23). Wing M212 ('O' not recorded in Wing).

4342. Mackenzie, George. *A defence of the antiquity of the royal-line of Scotland.* London: f. R. C., sold A. Swalle, 1685. 8°. [8], xiv, [2], 190 (misnumbering).
Flyleaf, upperᵛ, AW wrote, 'The book following was written by Sʳ George Mackenzie in answer to the before mention'd book entit. <u>An historical account of church-government</u> &c [W. Lloyd, Wood 200(1), item 4200] [/] It was first published in the latter end of June 1685 - But before it was published it was animadverted upon by Dʳ. Edw. Stillingfleet (who had before seen the manuscript of it) in the preface to his book entit. Origenes <u>Britannicae</u> &c published in fol. at Lond. about the beginning of June 1685 [Wing S5615]. See in Athenae et Fasti Oxon vol. 2. p. ult.' (AOF 2.411). Tp, AW underscored Mackenzie's name, in red ink.
Wood 200(2). Wing M155.

4343. MacKenzie, George. *Moral gallantry. [Followed by] A moral paradox [and] A consolation against calumnies.* London: f. H. Sawbrige, 1685. 12°. Pp. [24], 124, [4], 89, [1], 36 (2 tpp).
Wood 752(5). Wing M178.

4344. Mackenzie, George. *The antiquity of the royal line of Scotland farther cleared and defended.* London: f. J. Hindmarsh, 1686. 8°. [14], 212, [8] (3 pp. books sold by Hindmarsh).
Tp, AW wrote, '1.6ᵈ'.
Wood 200(3). Wing M150.

4345. Macquerella, Mrs., pseud. *A dialogue between mistris Macquerella, a suburb bawd, mˢ Scolopendra, a noted curtezan, and mʳ Pimpinello . . . bemoaning . . . the act . . . against adultery.* London: f. E. Crowch, 1650. 4°. Pp. [2], 6.
Wood 654a(14). Wing D1318.

4346. Magnus, Olaus. Upsala, abp. of. *Historiae septentrionalium gentium breviarium.* Lugduni Batavorum: ap. A. Wyngaerd et F. Moiardum, 1645. 12°. Pp. [16], 589, [73]. Parchment over pasteboard.
Flyleaf, upper, A. Allam wrote 'pret: 2ˢ-0ᵈ We[st]: Bibl: Sept: die 18ᵛᵒ 1675'. LT. 3.167.
Wood 693. BL.

4347. Maguire, Connor. Enniskillen, 2nd baron of. *The last speeches and confession of the lord Maguire: the Irish rebell.* London: J. Coe, [1645]. 4°. Pp. [2], 14.
Tp, AW wrote, 'bred in Magd. Coll. in Oxon – see p. 1.' Dupl. at Wood 614(17b).
Wood 368(4). Wing E3128A.

4348. [Maguire, Connor]. Enniskillen, 2nd baron of. *[The last speeches and confession of the lord Maguire: the Irish rebell].* [London]: [J. Coe], [1645]. 4°. Pp. 14 (wanting t leaf).
Dupl. at Wood 368(4).
Wood 614(17b). Wing E3128A.

4349. Maguire, Connor*. Enniskillen, 2nd baron of. *The whole triall of Conner lord Macguire.* London: f. R. Austin, 1645. 4°. Pp. [2], 16, 32.
Wood 368(3). Wing W2063A.

4350. Maiden's Faithful Counsellor. *The maidens faithfull counsellour: or, the speediest way to get good husbands*. London: f. P. Brooksby, [1685-1688]. 8°. Pp. 24.
Wood 69(4). Wing M268[AB] (1996) (rare). Not in ESTCR.

4351. [Maidwell, Lewis]. *Soteria regi, et ecclesiae Anglicanae, cujus primatum reverendissimo domino Gulielmo Sandcrofto, &c. foeliciter commissum, . . . Ludovicus à Fonte Virgineo*. N.p.: n.pub., [1678-91]. Fol. Pp. 4.
Tp, after author 'Ludovicus' in t, 'Maidwell q[uaere]', in pencil, prob. by AW.
Wood 398(21). Wing M285C (one) ('O' not recorded in Wing).

4352. Mainwaring, Thomas. *A defence of Amicia, daughter of Hugh Cyveliok, earl of Chester. Wherein it is proved, that sir Peter Leicester, . . . hath without any just grounds declared the said Amicia to be a bastard*. London: f. S. Lowndes, 1673. 8°. Pp. [10], 80, [3] (3 pp. books sold by Lowndes).
Tp, price, '8ᵈ'. For more on the subject, see Wood 673(3 and 4), items 4147f. and LT 2.188 (see note at Wood 723a, item 3702, for information about a similar copy at Wood 723b, which is not included because it is an intrusion in the Wood collection).
Wood 673(2). Wing M300.

4353. Mall, pseud. *Mall and her master: or, a dialogue between a Quaker and his maid*. London: n.pub., [1675] (cropped at bottom). 4°. Pp. [2], 5. Calf with 3 fillets, stamp decoration inside corners, and roll decoration at inner, spine edge (Ashm. binding).
Flyleaf, upper, 1st, the titles of 13 printed works in this vol., by an Ashm. librarian. Numbering of works on tpp is in Roman numerals. 1st printed item, dupl. at Wood 645(22).
Wood 619(1). Wing M336.

4354. Mall, pseud. *Mall and her master: or, a dialogue between a Quaker and his maid*. London: n.pub., [1675]. 4°. Pp. [2], 5 (tp cropped at bottom).
Tp, AW wrote, '1675. May.' and at top, in pencil, 'Ridicula'. Dupl. at Wood 619(1).
Wood 645(22). Wing M336.

4355. Malpas, Cheshire. *Letters from the lord generall his quarters, . . . Also a great victorie at Malpesse*. London: J. Coe, 1644. 4°. A⁴.
Tp, AW wrote '26 Aug', in pencil.
Wood 377(30). Wing L1782A (3).

4356. Malvezzi, Virgilio. Carey, H., trans. *Romulus and Tarquin*. London: J. H[aviland] f. J. Benson, 1637. 12°. Pp. [12], 299. Calf with 2 fillets.
Cover, upper, inside, names, erased. Flyleaf, upper, signature of 'Edward Southcote'.
Wood 265. STC 17219.

4357. Malynes, Gerard. *The maintenance of free trade, according to the three essentiall parts of traffique; . . . an answer to a treatise of free trade*. London: J. L[egatt] f. W. Sheffard, 1622. 8°. Pp. [12], 105.
Tp, AW wrote, '8ᵈ'. Responds to Misselden, Wood 683(3), item 4496.
Wood 683(2). STC 17226.

4358. Manchester, Siege. *A true & exact relation of the several passages at the siege of Manchester*. London: f. E. Blackmore, 1642, 12 Oct. 4°. Pp. [2], 14.
Tp, AW overwrote the former no., '19'.
Wood 375(14). Wing T2462.

4359. Manilius, Marcus. Sherburne, Edward, ed. *The sphere of Marcus Manilius made an English poem; with annotations and an astronomical appendix*. London: f. Nathanael Brooke, 1675. Fol. Pp. [18], 68, [2], 221, [9].
Missing. On Jan. 13, AW recorded in his diary, 'sent a letter to Mr. Edward Sherburne to give him thanks for his Manilius . . . '. LT 2.477. Also listed in MS. Wood F. 51, f. 44.
LT 2.477. Wing M432.

4360. M[anley], T[homas]. *A short view of the lives of those illustrious princes, Henry duke of Gloucester, and Mary princess of Orange deceased*. London: f. a Soc. of Stationers, 1661. 8°. Pp. [7], 114.
Tp, two prices, '6ᵈ', '8ᵈ' (both prob. by AW); bsm.
Wood 245(2). Wing M446.

4361. Mansell, Roderick, collected by. *An exact and true narrative of the late popish intrigue*. London: f. T. Cockerill a. B. Alsop, 1680. Fol. Pp. [11], 75.

Tp, AW wrote the price, '2^s-6^d', in red chalk; bsm. b1^v and c1^v, mark in margin and underscoring. LT 2.466.
Wood 425(23). Wing M514.

4362. Mansfield, Miller of. *[The] pleasant history of the miller of Mansfield*. [London]: f. W. Gilbertson, 1651. 8°. A^8,B1-3 (cropped).
Wood 84(15). Wing P2551A (rare).

4363. Mansfield, Miller of. *The pleasant history of the miller of Mansfield*. London: f. F. Coles, J. Wright, T. Vere, a. W. Gilbertson, 1655. 8°. A^8,B^4.
Wood 254(4). Wing P2551B (rare).

4364. Manzini, Giovanni Battista. Burbury, John, trans. *The loving husband, and prudent wife; . . . st. Eustachius and Theopista, martyrs*. London: f. J. Martin a. J. Allestrye, 1657. 12°. Pp. [10], 203.
Backing, lower, remnant of a list of books, by AW.
Wood 818(3). Wing M556 (two).

4365. [Marbecke, Roger] (?). *A defence of tabacco: with a friendly answer to the late printed booke [by J. H.] called worke for chimny-'sweepers*. London: R. Field f. T. Man, 1602. 4°. Pp. 70.
Responds to J. H., [MS.] Wood D. 30(1), item 3356.
[MS.] Wood D. 30(2). STC 6468.

4366. Margery*. *Margery Good-Cow, . . . Or, a short discourse, shewing that there is not a farthing due . . . to old Oliver*. London: n.pub., 1659. 4°. Pp. 5.
Tp, no. 39 in a former bundle.
Wood 610(60) (not in Bodl. CD cat.). Wing M590.

4367. Markham, Gervase. *The art of archerie*. London: B. A[lsop] a. T. F[awcett] f. B. Fisher, 1634. 8°. Pp. [24], 172.
Missing in 1837.
Wood 729(1). STC 17333. O (Jesus), *Hunt*.

4368. Markham, Gervase. *Country contentments: or, the husbandmans recreations*. London: W. Wilson f. J. Harison, 1649. 4°. 6th ed. Pp. [8], 118.
[MS.] Wood C. 25(2). Wing M620.

4369. Markham, Gervase. *The English house-wife [issued as part of A way to get wealth, 1648]*. London: B. Alsop f. J. Harison, 1649. 4°. 5th ed. Pp. [10], 252.
[MS.] Wood C. 25(3). Wing M649.

4370. Markham, Gervase. *The inrichment of the weald of Kent: or, a direction to the husbandman, for the true ordering*. London: E. Purslow f. J. Harison, 1649. 4°. Revised ed. Pp. [4], 24.
[MS.] Wood C. 25(4). Wing M637.

4371. Markham, Gervase. *Markhams farewell to husbandry: or, the inriching of all sorts of barren and sterile grounds [issued as part of A way to get wealth, 1648]*. London: W. Wilson f. J. Harison, 1649. 4°. 4th ed. Pp. [12], 158.
[MS.] Wood C. 25(5). Wing M648.

4372. Markham, Gervase, and William Lawson. *Cheape and good husbandry for the well-ordering of all beasts and fowles [1st tp; the general tp is bound before C1:] A way to get wealth: containing si e [sic, i.e., altered from 'five' to 'six'] principall vocations, . . . The first five bookes gathered by G. M. The last by master W. L*. London: B. Alsop f. J. Harrison (B. A. f. J. Harison), 1648. 4°. 7th ed. Pp. [28], 188. Calf with 2 fillets, a vertical line of 2 fillets, and edge hatching; spine, hatching (Oxford binding). Flyleaves, upper and lower, printer's waste paper.
Flyleaf, upper, 2nd^v, AW wrote the titles of 7 printed works 'In hoc Volumine'. 1st tp, bsm.
[MS.] Wood C. 25(1). Wing M 611 and M675.

4373. Marmion, Shackerley. *The antiquary. A comedy . . . by Shackerly Mermion*. London: F. K. f. I. W. a. F. E., 1641. 4°. A1,B-K^4,L2.
Tp, AW wrote, 'publ. after the authours death'.
Wood 330(9). Wing M703.

4374. Marmion, Shackerley. *Cupid and Psiche. Or an epick poem of Cupid, and his mistress*. London:

J. Okes, f. H. Sheppard, 1638. 4°. A1-3,B-L⁴,M1 (wanting letterpress tp).
Tp, bsm.
Wood 330(3). STC 17444a.

4375. [Marnix van Sant Aldegonde, Philips van]. Gilpin, George, trans. *The bee hive of the Romish church. A worke of all good Catholikes to be read.* London: J. Dawson, 1623. Ff. [50], 364. Calf, with 3 fillets and stamp centrepiece; spine, 4 bands.
Tp, 'A: W' and 'ABosco'.
Jesus College G. 1. 22. STC 17448.

4376. Marprelate, Martin, pseud. *[Oh read over d. John Bridges, for it is a worthy worke [A defence of the government established in the Church of Englande]].* [Fawsley]: [Printed on the other hand of some priests [R. Waldegrave]], [1588, Nov.]. 4°. Pp. 44 (wanting the t leaf and all after sig. F3).
Passim, some scribbling, not by AW.
[MS.] Wood D. 31(53). STC 17454.

4377. Marriage. *An antidote against carnal love &c a sermon delivered in an eminent meeting house upon an unhappy marriage &c.* [?]: [?], [?]. 4°.
Missing in 1922, according to the Milford hand-list; see note at Wood 654a(1), item 4758.
Wood 654a(34). Not in Wing (prob. not Wing A3497 or Wing P3102). Not in ESTCR.

4378. Marriage. *An account of marriage or the interests of marriage considered and defended.* London: B. G. f. A. Bancks, 1672. 12°. Pp. [8], 82.
Tp, 'ABosco Oxon' in red ink.
Wood 750(2). Wing A209.

4379. Marsh, A. *The ten pleasures of marriage [and] A letter.* London: n.pub., 1682. 12°. 2 pts. Pp. [4], 218.
Missing in 1837.
Wood 749. Wing M727. *O, Hunt.*

4380. Marshall, Stephen*. *The godly man's legacy . . . exhibited in the life of . . . Written by way of letter.* London: n.pub., 1680. 4°. Pp. [6], 30.
Tp, AW wrote, '17. Jun. 1680. 6ᵈ. AW'; 'd.ot' at bottom corner (?). Pp. 20-1, 25, 28, lines in margin, in ink and pencil. LT 2.488.
Wood 532(9). Wing G937.

4381. Marshall, Thomas. *The catechism set forth in the book of common-prayer.* Oxford: at the theater, 1683. 8° in 4's. 5th ed. A⁴,A⁴-O⁴. Parchment over marbled paper.
Pastedown, upper, AW wrote '7. Febr. 1682[3] Given to me to [sic] Dʳ Thomas Marshall the authour'. LT 3.36. A2, correction; O2ᵛ, brief note torn out.
Wood 823. Wing M802.

4382. Marshall, W[illiam], sculpsit. *A table shewing the variety of places names in Palestine.* [Cambridge]: [R. Daniel f. T. Buck], [1636-50 ca.]. S.sh. Map, 355 x 300 mm. [printed border to printed border; different state printed in T. Fuller, *The historie of the holy warre* (1639), 370 x 310 mm.].
See Fuller, STC 11464 and Wing F2438f.
Wood 276a(55) (not in Bodl. CD cat.). STC 11464. Wing F2438f.

4383. [Marsin, M.]. *The womens advocate: or, fifteen real comforts of matrimony, being in requital of the late fifteen sham-comforts. With satyrical reflections on whoring, . . . Written by a person of quality of the female sex.* London: f. B. Alsop a. T. Malthus, 1683. 12°. 2nd ed. Pp. [10], 131 (misnumbering).
Tp, bsm.
Wood 750(5). Wing M813EA.

4384. Marstrand*. *A breefe conjecturall discourse, upon the hierographicall letters . . . found upon fower fishes, taken neere Marstrand.* London: E. Allde, 1589. 4°. A-B⁴,C1. Pasteboard (blue) with parchment spine.
Flyleaves, upper, 2nd and 3rd, AW wrote the titles of 33 printed works in this vol., within guidelines made with red ink. Tp, A2ʳ⁻ᵛ, B2ᵛ, and C1ᵛ (slips pasted over scribbles), scribbles in 2 hands, neither in AW's.
[MS.] Wood B. 35(1). STC 17488.7 (rare, 2 at O).

4385. Marten, Henry*. *Mr. Henry Martin his speech in the house of commons, before his departure thence.* [London]: n.pub., 1648. 4°. Pp. [2], 6.

Tp, AW wrote, 'A piece of roguerie.'
Wood 609(3). Wing M2267A.

4386. Martial. May, Thomas, trans. *Selected epigrams of Martial*. London: [H. Lownes] f. T. Walkley, 1629. 16°. A2-4,B-F⁸,G⁶.
Wood 79(7) (now Arch. G. f. 2(7)). STC 17494.

4387. Martiall, John. *A treatyse of the crosse gathred out of the scriptures*. Antwerp: J. Latius, 1564. 8°. Ff. [1], 169, [13].
Missing. MS. Wood E. 2(70), p. 4.
MS. Wood E. 2(70), p. 4. STC 17496. ARCR 2.513. O (two), *Folg, Hunt, Yale*.

4388. Martin, Robert, lieut. col. *A relation of the great victories . . . of the garrison of Plymouth*. London: T. P., 1644, 4 June. 4°. Pp. [2], 6.
Wood 377(10). Wing M836.

4389. Martin, Thomas. *Historica descriptio complectens vitam, ac res gestas . . . Gulielmi Wicami*. Oxoniae: e theatro Sheldoniano, 1690. 4°. Pp. [8], 132 (wanting frontisp.). Pasteboard (blue) with parchment spine; upper and lower flyleaves, traces of marbled paper.
Flyleaf, upper, 1st^v, AW listed the three vitae in this vol., within guidelines made with red chalk: 'Vita { Gulielmus Wykehami [/] Gul. Patteni [/] Henrici Chichlei' { Fundatoris coll. { Novi [/] Magd. [/] Om. An { Oxōn'. AO 1.502-3.
Wood 528(1). Wing M852. See Madan 168.

4390. Martyn, William. *Youths instruction*. London: J. Beale f. R. Redmer, 1612. 4°. Pp. [6], 109, [2].
Tp, AW wrote, '10ᵈ'. Text, p. 1, a note, and, to p. 14, marks in margins, not in AW's hand or manner.
Wood 309(2). STC 17530 (STC, wants f. R. Redmer).

4391. [Marvell, Andrew] (? at times attrib. to). *A seasonable argument to persuade all the grand juries . . . to petition for a new parliament. Or, a list of the principal labourers in the great design of popery*. Amsterdam: n.pub., 1677. 4°. Pp. 23.
Tp, AW wrote over Amsterdam, 'London', in red ink, and made frequent marks and lines in the margins at the names, underscored (passim), and made corrections or additions (pp. 4-5, 7, 9, 15, 18 (at Baptist May, 'a whore'), 20) (most cropped at side) and query or cross-reference abbreviations (7, 9, 13, 15, 16), in red and black ink and in pencil. LT 3.120.
Wood 608(50). Wing M885.

4392. M[arvel]l, A[ndrew] (? at times attrib. to). *A collection of poems on affairs of state [by A. M–l]*. London: n.pub., 1689. 4°. Pp. 36.
Tp, AW wrote, 'bought at Oxon 26 Feb. 1688[9] – 6', in pencil. LT 3.293.
Wood 382(6). Wing C5176.

4393. Mary 1*. *Memoirs of queen Mary's days. Wherein the Church of England, and all the inhabitants may plainly see . . . the sad effects which follow a popish successor*. [London]: n.pub., [1679]. Fol. Pp. 4.
Pp. 1 and 4, AW wrote '1680' in pencil.
Wood 660c(21). Wing M1669.

4394. Maryland. *A relation of Maryland; . . . with a map . . . his majesties charter to the lord Baltemore*. [London]: to bee had, at W. Peasley Esq; his house, or at J. Morgans house, 1635, 8 Sept. 4°. Pp. [2], 56, 25 (with map).
Wood 386(6). STC 17571.

4395. Mason, John, and William Swan. *Blood-thirsty Cyrus unsatisfied with blood. Or the boundless cruelty of an Anabaptists tyranny . . . in a letter of . . . with . . . Swans . . . answer . . . published by Thomas Ashton*. London: n.pub., 1659. 4°. Pp. 8.
Tp, former no. '75', in pencil; Thomas Ashton, underscored.
Wood 632(41) (not in Bodl. CD cat.). Wing M923B (rare).

4396. Mason, Margaret, pseud. *The tickler tickled: or the observator [Francis Smith] upon the late tryals of sir George Wakeman*. London: f. A. Brewster, 1679. Fol. Pp. [2], 8.
AW owned a copy of Smith's *Observations*, Wood 425(9a). LT 2.457. Purchased from Vade in July or August 1679, 3ᵈ, see his record of purchase in MS. Wood F. 50, f. 11.
Wood 425(9b). Wing T1159.

4397. Massachusetts. *A declaration . . . Concerning the execution of two Quakers [W. Robinson and M. Stevenson, 18 Oct.].* London: n.pub., 1659. S.sh. Rpt. of New England edition.
Wood 645(11). Wing M1001.

4398. Massachusetts. *The humble petition and address of the general court . . . unto . . . prince Charles the second [11 Feb.].* [Boston]: n.pub., [1660]. 4°. Pp. 8.
Wood 608(39). Wing H3426.

4399. Massey, Edward*. *Eben-ezer. A . . . relation of the severall . . . proceedings of . . . colonell Massy [7-25 May].* London: f. T. W., 1644. 4°. Pp. [2], 14.
Dupl. at Wood 612(18).
Wood 377(11). Wing E126A.

4400. Massey, Edward*. *Eben-ezer. A . . . relation of the severall . . . proceedings of . . . colonell Massy [7-25 May].* London: f. T. W., 1644. 4°. Pp. [2], 14.
Tp, AW wrote 'Dupl', in pencil. Dupl. at Wood 377(11).
Wood 612(18). Wing E126A.

4401. Massey, Edward*. *A new hue and cry after major general Massey and some others, who . . . escaped from the Tower of London [30 Aug.].* London: n.pub., 1652. 4°. Pp. [2], 6.
Wood 609(31). Wing N647 (two) ('O' not recorded in Wing).

4402. Massey, Edward*. *A letter from an eminent person in Gloucester, . . . giving an account of the late passages there, in reference to major Gen. Massey [2 Apr.].* London: J. Cottrel, 1660. 4°. Pp. [2], 6.
Wood 632(44). Wing L1445 (two).

4403. Massinger, Philip; Thomas Middleton, and William Rowley. *The excellent comedy, called the old law: or a new way to please you . . . Together with an exact and perfect catalogue of all the playes.* London: f. E. Archer, 1656. 4°. Pp. [2], 76 (wanting the catalogue; tp damaged).
AW himself removed the cat. and placed it among his catalogues; it is now at [MS.] Wood E. 28(2).
Wood 607(5). Wing M1048.

4404. Master, Thomas (same as Masters, items 4408-9). *Monarchia Britannica sub Elizabetha Jacobo: in oratione.* Oxonii: W. Hall, imp. J. Godwin, 1661. 4°. A-B⁴ (pages are misnumbered).
Diff. ed. at Wood 113(2), item 4406.
Wood 512(14). Wing M1056. Madan 2565.

4405. Master, Tho[mas] (same as Masters, items 4408-9). *Iter Boreale. Ad ipsius patrem Gulielmum Masterum.* [Oxford]: [H. Hall], 1675. 4°. Pp. [2], 20.
Flyleaf, upper, 'qu[aere] other things q[uaere] other sheets', in pencil. Tp, AW wrote, 'Oxon', and a note, 'published by George Ent, son of Georg E.', lined out (AO 3.83-6).
Wood 465(6). Wing M1055. Madan 3065.

4406. Master, Thomas; Henry Savile, and Henry Wotton. *Monarchia Britannica sub auspiciis Elisabethae . . . Caroli I.* Oxonii: e theatro Sheldoniano, 1681. 8°. Pp. [6], 54 (misnumbering; contains a 2nd F⁴; A1, H4, blank).
A1ᵛ, '17. Junii 1681. Given to me by the publisher Dr. Joh. Lamphire. - AWood – Monarchia Britannica was first published by Dr Lamphire, an. 1661. qu[arto]' (i.e., Master, Wood 512(14), item 4404, and see AO 3.85). P. 23, a 2nd tp, 'The first edit. of this came out at Oxon. 1658 in qu[arto] by the care of Dʳ Tho. Barlow' (i.e., Savile, *Oratio*, Wood 512(4), item 5769). Pp. 38, 'The exact contrary was the truth: For Charles was under the dominion of favourites from his very infancy', not by AW; and p. 41, 'The most foolish action of his life', not by AW. See LT 2.544 and Madan 2369.
Wood 113(2). Wing M1057.

4407. [Master, William]. Λογοι ευκαιροι, *essays and observations theologicall & morall. . . . Together with some meditations . . . By a student in theologie. [Followed by] Drops of myrrhe.* London: R. W. f. R. Davis in Oxon, 1653. 8°. Pp. [16], 107, [9], 27 (2 pts.).
In the list of contents on the upper flyleaf of the vol. AW identified the author. Tp, AW underscored 'Student in Theology'. AO 4.148.
Wood 868(4-5). Wing M1060. Madan 2231 (Wing, lists *Myrrhe* separately at M1058A).

4408. Masters, Thomas (same as Master, items 4404-6). *Mensa lubrica; Anglicè shovel-board.* Oxford: n.pub., n.d. 4°. Pp. [4].
Missing in 1837. 'Shovel Board' in Whiteside cat. Dupl. or diff. ed. at Wood 416(5). See AO 3.84.

Wood 440(3). Wing M1070A (1690?) or less likely, the Latin version, M1071 (1651). Madan 2154 (and see 2369). *Harv*, and *O*.

4409. Masters, Thomas (same as Master, items 4404-6). *Mensa lubrica; Anglicè shovel-board. In gratiam . . . Eduardi Herbert Baronis de Cherbury[.] Lusis Thomas Masters*. [Oxford]: n.pub., [1690?] and printed 'A. D. circiter 1636'. 4°. Pp. [4].
Tp, AW wrote, 'published againe by Dr R. Bathurst in the month of Dec. 1690'. Later librarians added 2 notes. Dupl. or diff. ed. at Wood 440(3) (missing). AO 3.84-5, LT 3.349.
Wood 416(5) (under 'Master' in Bodl. CD cat.). Wing M1070A (two). See Madan 2154.

4410. Mastix, Maligno, pseud. *The current of justice against the torrent of tyranny cleared from the muddy positions and bloody practices of king-quelling priests, and state-firing Jesuites. Presented to state-patriots and church-presbyters.* N.p.: n.pub., 1649. 4°. Pp. 21 (A1-3,B^4,C1-3).
Pp. 4, 7, 20-1, some corrections, may not be by AW.
Wood 586(16). Not in Wing. Not in ESTCR.

4411. Mather, Cotton. *Late memorable providences relating to witchcrafts and possessions.* London: f. T. Parkhurst, 1691. 8°. 2nd ed. Pp. [22], 144 (3 pp. books printed for Parkhurst). Calf, speckled, with 2 fillets and roll decoration at inner, spine edge.
Flyleaf, upper, 1st, AW wrote '17 Jan. 1690-1, recepi a Crescentio Mathero', and 2nd^v, 'Cotton Mather, the author of this book was son of Crescentius or Increase Mather.' Removed to and later restored from Mather 8° 17. LT 1.6; 3.349.
Wood 706. Wing M1118.

4412. Mather, Increase. *Diatriba de signo filii hominis, et de secundo messiae adventu.* Amstelodami: M. Browning juxta bursam, 1682. 8°. Pp. [8], 98, [6]. Calf, speckled, with 2 fillets; rebacked.
Pastedown, upper, AW wrote '17. Jan. 1690[1] recepi ab authore.' Removed to and later restored from Mather 8° 143. LT 1.6.
Wood 809. BL.

4413. Mather, Increase. *An essay for the recording of illustrious providences.* Boston in New-England: sold G. Calvert, 1684. 8°. With cancel t leaf. Pp. [24], 372, [9]. Calf, speckled, with 2 fillets and roll stamp decoration at inner edge.
Pasteboard, upper, AW wrote '17 [over 19] Jan. 1690[1] rec[epi] ab authore'. Flyleaf, upper, 'Liber Musei' by an Ashm. librarian. LT 3.349; 1.6. Removed to and later restored from Mather 8° 9^b.
Wood 797. Wing M1208.

4414. Mather, Increase. *De successu evangelij apud Indos in Novā-Angliā epistola.* London: Typis J. G., 1688. 8°. A^8. Parchment with 2 fillets over marbled paper.
Flyleaf, upper^v, AW wrote 'Jan. 17, 1690[1] rec[epi] ab authore'. Removed to and later restored from Mather 8° 12. LT 1.6.
Wood 716. Wing M1197.

4415. Matheus, excud. *S. Antonius. Abbas vixit sub Constantino magno anno 356.* N.p.: n.pub., n.d. S.sh. (engr.).
At top, 'xx-xxv not here [1881]'. Old Ashm. no. XXII was renumbered, XXV, in 1881.
Wood 276b(25). Not identified.

4416. Maton, Robert. *Israels redemption or the propheticall history of our Saviours kingdome on earth . . . With a discourse of God and Magog.* London: (R. Cotes) f. D. Frere, 1642. 8°. Pp. [15], 133, [2] (2 tpp).
Calf with 2 fillets; rebacked. Flyleaves, upper and lower, printer's waste paper (Apocrypha).
Pasted to a sheet at bottom edge, remnants of a slip identifying the author and work (for other slips, see Index entry 'Slip with title'). Tp, bsm.
Wood 882. Wing M1294.

4417. Matthias*. Germany, emperor of. *Newes from Francfort, concerning the election of the most mighty emperor Matthias . . . translated out of Dutch.* London: [G. Eld] f. H. Holland, 1612. 4°. A-B^4.
Tp, scribble, cropped at top.
Wood 615(9b). STC 17660.

4418. Matthieu, Pierre. Grimeston, Edward, trans.; Sylvester, Jos. trans. *The heroyk life and deplorable death of . . . Henry the fourth. . . . by P: Mathieu [and] The tropheis of the life . . . of . . . prince Henry.* London: G. Eld, 1612. 4°. Pp. [8], 190, 170, [29].

P. 140, note, not by AW. Probably acquired from the bookseller Robinson on 8 Jan. 1661, LT 1.380. Wood 337(2). STC 17661.

4419. Maudit, John. *A letter to . . . Monk containing the instrumental causes of the ruine of governments and common-wealths.* [London]: n.pub., [1660]. 4°. Pp. 7.
P. 7, AW wrote, 'ffeb:1659'.
Wood 632(76). Wing M1329.

4420. [Maurice, Henry]. *The antithelemite; or, an answer to certain quaeres of the d. of B. and to the considerations of an unknown author concerning toleration.* London: f. S. Smith, 1685. 4°. Pp. [2], 76.
Tp, above, no. 9 (?), in pencil, in a former bundle (cropped at top); below, AW wrote, 'The author Dr Hen. Maurice of Jesus Coll. in Oxon'.
Wood 611(13). Wing M1359.

4421. Maurice, Prince. *Articles of agreement betweene his excellency prince Maurice, and the earle of Stamford, upon delivery of . . . Excester [5 Sept.].* London: f. T. Walkley, 1643. 4°. Pp. [2], 5.
Wood 376(34). Wing M1357.

4422. May, Edward. *A most certaine and true relation of a strange monster or serpent found in the . . . heart of John Pennant.* London: G. Miller, 1639. 4°. Pp. [10], 40 (pp. unopened).
Tp, AW wrote, 'December: iv. MDclx:'; purchased for 6^d, LT 1.349.
[MS.] Wood B. 35(5). STC 17709.

4423. May, Thomas. *The reigne of king Henry the second.* London: A. M[athewes a. J. Beale] f. B. Fisher, 1633. A^2,B-N^8,O^2 (wanting M8).
Tp, AW wrote, 'by Thom. May'.
Wood 90(7). STC 17715.

4424. M[ay], T[homas]. *Historiae parliamenti Angliae breviarium.* Londini: typ. C. Snmptner [sic], venales off. T. Brusteri, [1650]. 8°. Pp. [4], 216. Calf with 2 fillets; rebacked.
Wood 195. Wing M1408.

4425. [Maynard, Thomas], et al. *London's liberties; or a learned argument of law & reason, . . . December 14. 1650 . . . at Guild hall, London, between Mr. Maynard, Mr. Hales, and Mr. Wilde on councell for the companies of London . . . And . . . freemen.* London: J. Cottrel f. G. Calvert, 1651. 4°. Pp. [8], 38.
Wood 590(6). Wing L2936A.

4426. [Mayne, Jasper]. *The citye match. A comoedye.* Oxford: L. Lichfield, 1639. Fol. (imperf.). Pp. [6], 62 (ends at R2).
P. 1, ':1694', may be in AW's hand.
Wood 657(2). STC 17750. Madan 924.

4427. Mayne, Jasper. *A late printed sermon against false prophets, vindicated by letter, from the causeless aspersions of mr. Francis Cheynell.* [London]: n.pub., [1647]. 4°. Pp. 60 (wanting the t leaf, sig. A2 mutilated).
Wood 617(6). Wing M1471.

4428. Mayne, Jasper. *A sermon against schisme: or, the seperations of these times.* London: f. R. Royston, 1652. 4°. Pp. [2], 22.
Tp, AW supplied, at a blank in the t, the name of author's opponent, 'John Pendarves'.
Wood 633(10). M1475.

4429. [Mayne, Zachary]. *The snare broken, or, the natural and eternal deity of the son of God.* N.p.: n.pub., 1692. 8°. Pp. 16.
Tp, AW wrote 'Zach Mayne'.
[MS.] Wood B. 36(9) (not in Bodl. CD cat.). Wing M1488 (rare).

4430. Mazzarini, Giulio. H[owell], J[ames], trans. *The last will and testament of the late renowned cardinal Mazarini [2nd tp] Some historical remarques of the life of Cardinal Mazarini.* London: P. Lillicrap f. W. Gilbertson, 1663 (1664). 12°. Pp. [9], 154.
Missing in 1837. 'The last Will & Testament of Cardinal Mazarini &c – Lond. 1663 [/] Some historical Remarks of the Life of Card: Mazarini – Lond. 1664' in Whiteside cat.
Wood 276. Wing H3084. *O* (two), *Clark, Yale*.

4431. Meara, Dermitius de. *Ormonius: sive, illustrissimi herois ac domini, d. Thomae Butleri, . . . commemoratio*. Londini: T. Snodhamus, 1615. 8°. Pp. [14], 144, [9].
Tp, 'Sum Barrelli pretium 4ᵈ'. P. 123, correction, prob. not by AW. P. 144, AW wrote, 'Ep. ded. must follow, see two leaves after' (to Walter Butler), AO 2.275.
Wood 82(3). STC 17761.

4432. Meg of Westminster*. *[The] life of [long Meg of Westminster]*. [London]: [J. M. f. G. Conyers], [1690?]. 12°. Pp. [12]. Imperf., fragment of tp and chapts. 7-14, only.
Flyleafᵛ, 'Found to have 3 leaves torn out. 1882'.
Wood 254(9). Wing L2033A (one) ('O' not recorded in Wing).

4433. Meier, Georg. Luther, Martin, praef. *Vitae patrum, in visum ministrorum verbi, quo ad ejus fieri potuit repurgatae*. Witembergae: (per P. Seitz), 1544. Ff. [8], 323, [21]. Calf with 2 fillets, 2nd rectangle with 3 fillets and stamp decoration in corners, stamp centrepiece, and 2 clasp holes.
Tp, bsm. F. [21]ᵛ, mark, prob. by AW.
Wood 294. BL.

4434. Memento. *Memento Mori[.] It is appointed for all men once to die, Heb: 9.27*. [London]: Sould by T. Wright, [1636?]. S.sh.
Wood 416(2). STC 26038.2 (rare) (STC, 'not traced').

4435. Memorare. *Memorare novissima. Dies irae, dies illa*. Oxford: L. Lichfield f. W. Smart, 1671. S.sh. 3rd ed. Parchment (green-blue) with new corners and backing.
Flyleaf, upper, 2nd-4th, AW wrote the titles of 133 printed works in this vol., within guidelines made with red ink. At item 68, 'deest Oct. 1840 W[illiam] K[irtland]' and, in a later hand, in pencil, 'Perhaps see 'dupl.' in no. 15' (see notes at Wood 416(15, 68), items 1083, 1086). Item (102) (see cat. item 1956), was removed after 1840 and before 1922. AW numbered the items in this vol. in his usual fashion, with the exception that a few have either 'numb.' or 'nu.' before the number (not recorded in this cat. after item no. 1). There are some earlier item nos. on tpp, in pencil, reflecting AW's earlier order. He overwrote or replaced these with new nos. On the recto sides of most s.shs. in this vol. he wrote the month and the year in his early formal manner. Most of these s.shs. also have dates on the verso sides, in his later hand 1st item, ᵛ, 'numb. 1'.
Wood 416(1). Wing M1682 (rare). Madan 2888.

4436. [Mennes, John], and J. S. *Wit restor'd in severall select poems not formerly publish't*. London: f. R. Pollard, N. Brooks, and T. Dring, 1658. 8°. Pp. [2], 1-138, [1-4], 139-189 (2nd tp, 2nd p. 1 (K6)).
Tp, bsm., 'h'. P. 103, at Wadham's butler: 'The first Butler of Wadham Coll. of kin to the founder.'
Wood 90(3). Wing M1719.

4437. Menz, Balthasar. *Syntagma epitaphiorum, quae in inclyta septemviratus Saxonici metropoli Witeberga, . . . conspiciuntur*. Magdeburgi: A. Seidner, sumt. A. Kirchneri, 1604. 8°. Pp. 135, 117, 111, 140 (4 tpp.). Parchment over pasteboard.
Pastedown, upper, note 'Liber Antonij Wood Oxon: ex officina Edv: Forest eiusdem Bibliopolae emptus A: 1659'. Tp, signature, 'Ant: Woode:'. Bsms., 'n 5.1' (shelf-mark?) and 'k'. LT 1.271.
Wood 101. BL.

4438. [Merbecke, John]. *The booke of common praier noted*. [London]: (R. Grafton), 1550. 4°. A²,B-R⁴,S². Calf with sets of 3 and 4 fillets, stamp decoration between the sets of fillets, and 2 clasp holes; rebacked. Backing, Latin and music parchment ms.
Flyleaf, upper, 4thᵛ, AW wrote, '1ˢ6ᵈ' and 'The book of common prayer noted: or musical notes set to the book of Common Prayer by Rog. Merbeck'; a note added later, not by AW: 'John consule caliem hujus libri'. Tp, 'ABosco' and bsm. S2, at end, after name of author, 'Organist of Windsore: he is mentioned by Mʳ Joh. Fox in his book of martyrs, in Qu. Maries raigne. ABosco'. LT 1.426, AOF 1.130.
Wood 314. STC 16441.

4439. Mercator, Gerard. *Literarum latinarum, quas Italicas cursoriasque vocant, scribendarum ratio*. Antverpiae: J. Richard, 1556. 4°. A-F⁴,G1-3 (2 leaves cut out at end, traces of annotation in English).
Tp, 'ABosco', and some scribbles.
Wood 499(2). Not in BL, BN, NUC, Adams.

4440. Merchant Taylors' School. *III. Election at the Merchant-tailors school. Junii 11*. [London]: n.pub., [1664]. S.sh.
Wood 276a(183). Wing M1744A (rare).

4441. Merchants. *The merchants new-royall-exchaunge: framed at Roan, and brought over to . . . England. Or, a law-booke for English merchants.* London: T. C[reede] f. C. Burbey, 1604. 8°. Pp. A⁴,B-F⁸,G⁴.
Pasteboard (blue) with parchment spine. 1st upper and last lower flyleaves have remnants of marbled paper; rebacked.
Flyleaf, upper, 2ndᵛ, AW wrote the titles of 3 printed works in this vol., within guidelines made with red ink. Tp, AW wrote '9ᵈ'. Bsm.
Wood 683(1). STC 16784.

4442. Mercurius Civicus. *A letter from Mercurius Civicus to Mercurius Rusticus: or, Londons confession . . . shewing, that . . . this . . . rebellion is principally to be ascribed to that rebellious city.* [Oxford]: n.pub., 1643. 4°. Pp. [2], 33.
Pp. 2-3, 8-9, 26, short vertical lines in margins, 2 in red ink, may be by AW.
Wood 632(10). Wing L1489A (olim B6323). Madan 1441.

4443. Mercurius Lepidus, pseud. *News from the Lowe-countreys. Or, Podex his encomium.* London: f. W. N, 1652. 8°. Pp. [2], 10, [2].
Tp, 'N B: Wᵐ', not in AW's hand. Dupl. (?) at Wood 66(3).
Wood 84(9). Wing N1009 (two).

4444. Mercurius Lepidus, pseud. *News from the Lowe-countreys. Or, Podex his encomium.* London: f. W. N, 1652. 8°.
Missing in 1837. 'News from the Low Countrys – Lond. 1652' in Whiteside cat. Dupl. (?) at Wood 84(9).
Wood 66(3). Wing N1009 (two).

4445. Mercurius Politicus. *The character of Mercurius Politicus.* [London]: n.pub., [1650?]. 4°. Pp. 8.
Wood 622(17). Wing C2021 ('O' not recorded in Wing).

4446. Mercurius Propheticus. *Mercurius propheticus. Or, a collection of some old predictions.* [London]: n.pub., 1643[4]. 4°. Pp. [4], 12.
Wood 646(6). Wing M1769.

4447. Meres, Francis. *Witts academy a treasurie of goulden sentences. [2nd tp] Wits commonwealth. The second part.* London: W. Stansby, sold R. Royston, 1634. 12°. Pp. [18], 741, [8]. Calf with 2 fillets and blind-stamped 'A W'.
Pastedown, upper, 'Robert Wood' and '1647'. Flyleaf, upper, 'Anthony Wood his booke 1645' and numerous scribbled notes in several hands; ᵛ, 'Anthony Wood his booke Wittnesse John Cowdrey 1645' (Wood was 13 years old in 1645), LT 1.255. 2nd tp, '1 Edit. 1598 London.', prob. in AW's hand. Passim, a few schoolboy notes in margins, mainly in Latin, scribbling (p. 446, 'Wood is a foole'), and some underscoring of person's names. Last p. ᵛ, a few words in French (by Robert Wood?). Flyleaf, lower, scribbles.
Wood 54. STC 17835.

4448. Merke, Thomas. Carlisle, bp. of. *The bishop of Carlile's speech in parliament, concerning deposing of princes [Oct. 1399].* London: n.pub., 1679. Fol. Pp. [2], 5, [1].
Dupl. at Wood 660c(19).
Wood 560(2). Wing M1827.

4449. Merke, Thomas. Carlisle, bp. of. *The bishop of Carlile's speech in parliament, concerning deposing of princes [Oct. 1399].* London: n.pub., 1679. Fol. Pp. [2], 5, [1].
Dupl. at Wood 560(2).
Wood 660c(19). Wing M1827.

4450. Merlin; Bede, and Becket, et al. *Sundry strange prophecies of Merline, Bede, Becket, and others.* London: f. M. Walbancke, sold J. Bell, 1652. 4°. Pp. [2], 34.
Wood 646(9). Wing S6180A.

4451. Merrett, Christopher, ed. *A collection of acts of parliament, charters, . . . concerning . . . grants to the colledge of physicians . . . Commanded by sir Edward Alston.* [London]: n.pub., 1660. 4° (cropped). Pp. [4], 135.
Tp, AW underscored *Alston* in t, in red ink. Passim, esp. pp. 1-5 (underscoring in red ink and, p. 3, a cross in margin at a reference to Oxford privileges), 6, 34, 80-125, some minor annotation, mainly corrections, and underscoring (in red ink). Some of the minor corrections may not be by AW and, p. 84, correction, and pp. 13 (cropped), and 128, notes, not by AW.
Wood 615(14). Wing M1836.

4452. Merry and Pleasant Dialogue. *A merry and pleasant dialogue, betwixt a courtier, a citizen, & a countryman, . . . for the . . . marriage, betwixt Charles II, . . . and queen Katharine . . . of Portugall.* N.p.: n.pub., 1662. 4°. Pp. [2], 6.
Wood 486(10). Not in Wing. Not in ESTCR.

4453. Merry Drollery. N., W.; C. B., R. S., and J. G., collected by. *Merry drollery, or a collection of jovial poems.* London: J. W. f. P. H., [1661?]. 8°. Pp. [4], 175.
AW wrote 'May 1661' and '1^{s}3^d.' Bsm.
Wood 326(2). Wing M1860 (two).

4454. Merry Drollery. N., W.; C. B., R. S., and J. G., collected by. *The second part of merry drollery, or a collection of jovial poems.* London: J. W. f. P. H., [1661?]. 8°. Pp. [4], 159.
AW wrote '1661' and '1^{s}3^d' (acquired 23 Oct, 1^{s}2^d, LT 1.416).
Wood 326(3). Wing S2295 (two).

4455. Merry Jest of the Fryer. *The merry jest of the fryer and the boy.* London: ?, 1655. Pp.?
Missing in 1837. 'A merry Jest of the Fryer & the Boy – Lond. 1655' in Whiteside cat. See STC 14522ff., Wing F2205ff., H1546C.
Wood 66(13). Not in Wing. Not in ESTCR.

4456. Mervyn, Audeley. *An exact relation of all such occurrences . . . in the . . . counties of Donegall, London-Derry, . . . since the beginning of this . . . rebellion . . . begun in October last [4 June].* London: f. T. Downes a. W. Bladen, [1642]. 4°. Pp. 2, 14.
Tp, former no., '19' lined out.
Wood 508(22). Wing M1880A.

4457. Mervyn, Audley. *A speech made . . . in the upper house of parliament in Ireland, . . . March the* 4th. *1640. At the impeachment of sir Richard Bolton [et al.].* [London]: n.pub., 1641. 4°. Pp. [2], 27.
Wood 507(2). Wing M1888A.

4458. Meterby, Sarah*. *A sad and lamentable account of one Sarah Meterby, who wickedly sold her self to the devil. [Followed by] Dreadful examples of God's . . . judgments.* [London]: f. J. Blare, 1692. 8°. Pp. 23, [1].
Wood 836(13). Not in Wing. Not in ESTCR.

4459. Methinks. *Methinks the poor town has been troubled too long. Or, a collection of all the new songs.* N.p.: n.pub., 1673. 8°. Pp. [8], 40.
Wood 326(4). Wing M1939.

4460. Mew, John. *Trotters journey-man on his amble to the gallowes or the confession of John Mew, before execution.* [London]: n.pub., [1660]. S.sh.
AW wrote, 'feb: 1659[60]'; several minor corrections in spelling.
Wood 416(56). Wing T2306B (rare).

4461. [Mews, Peter]. Winchester, bp. of (attrib. to). *Exaltatio alae. The ex-ale-tation of ale. Done into verse [Lat. and Eng.] by T. C. P.* [London]: n.pub., 1666. 8°. Pp. 32.
Wood 679(6). Wing M1955.

4462. [Mews, Peter]. Winchester, bp. of (attrib. to). *The ex-ale-tation of ale. Written by a learned pen.* London: J. R., 1671. 8°. Pp. 15.
P. 15^v, scribbles, 3 letters of the alphabet.
Wood 679(5). Wing M1954.

4463. [Mews, Peter]. Winchester, bp. of. *An account of the late visitation at St. Mary Magdal. colledge in Oxon. by . . . Peter l^d bish. of Winton [24 Oct.].* (London): (f. R. Taylor), (1688). Fol. Pp. 4.
AW apparently witnessed some aspects of the visitation and made 6 minor corrections and changes to this account: e.g., p. 1, at parentheses, 'This silly parenthesis might have been omitted'; at the end, p. 4, 'This simple paper containing many mistakes, was published (& I think written) by Nich. Cox Lately manciple of S. Edm. Hall. Oxon. & first of all exposed to view at Oxon. 4. Nov. 1688.' LT 3.280.
Wood 423(64). Wing M1951.

4464. Mexia, Pedro. Baildon, Joshua, trans. *The rarities of the world. Containing, rules . . . touching the beginning of kingdoms . . . by J. B. gent.* London: B. A. (B. Alsop), 1651 (1650). 4°. Pp. [8], 134, [1].
Tp, bsm.

Wood 496(2) (not in Bodl. CD cat.). Wing M1956 ('O' not recorded in Wing).

4465. [**Micanzio, Fulgentio**], trans. *The life of the most learned father Paul [Sarpi]*. London: f. H. Moseley a. R. Marriot, 1651. 8°. Pp. [9], 204. Pasteboard (brown) with calf spine. 1st and last flyleaves, marbled paper.
Flyleaf, upper, 3rd[v], AW wrote the titles of 2 printed works in this vol., within guidelines made with red ink.
Wood 233(1). Wing M1959.

4466. [**Micanzio, Fulgentio**]. *The policy of the Jesuits, their insinuation into the courts . . . and . . . noble families of Europe [tr. from the Instruttione a'prencipi della maniera]*. London: n.pub., 1658. 12°. A⁴,B-D¹²,E⁴ (last leaf blank). Pasteboard (grey) with parchment spine. 1st upper and last lower flyleaves, purple paper.
Flyleaf, 2nd[v], AW wrote the titles of 7 printed works in this vol., within guidelines made with red chalk. B1, '6x' in margin (or bx?).
Wood 876(1). Wing P2758.

4467. Michaelis, Sebastien. B., W., trans. *The admirable historie of the possession and conversion of a penitent woman. Seduced by a magician . . . Whereunto is annexed a pneumology*. London: [F. Kingston] f. W. Aspley, 1613. 4°. Pp. [54], 418, [10], 154, [34] (disruption after 1st quire, ¶⁴) (2 tpp). Pasteboard (blue) with parchment spine. 1st upper and last lower flyleaves, marbled paper; rebacked.
Tp, note, 'All most reverend Cossoners' and similar anti-Catholic comments, A3, B6, pp. 409, 2nd p. 154 (also 2 lines in a 2nd hand), and final leaf[r], none by AW. P. 3, a few words in the 2nd hand, not by AW. Acquired 16 Oct. 1662, LT 1.458.
[MS.] Wood B. 17. STC 17854a.

4468. Michel, Thomas. *The last newes from the armie [20 June]*. London: f. J. Neale, 1647, 21 June. 4°. Pp. [1-2], 1, [2-6].
Wood 501(32). Wing M1964. Madan 1935.

4469. Middendorpius, Jacobus. *Academiarum celebrium universi terrarum orbis libri VIII*. Coloniae Agrippinae: ap. G. Cholinum, 1602. 8°. Pp. [32], 630, 484, [20] (2nd tp at 2nd p.1). Calf with 2 fillets; rebacked.
Wood 174. BL.

4470. Middlesex. *A discoverie of six women preachers, in Middlesex, Kent, Cambridgshire, and Salisbury*. [London]: n.pub., 1641. 4°. Pp. [2], 5.
Wood 654a(5). Wing D1645.

4471. Middlesex. *A relation of the cruelties and barbarous murthers, . . . in the county of Middlesex*. London: n.pub., 1659. 4°. Pp. 8.
Wood 365(15). Wing R819 (two).

4472. Middlesex. *A catalogue of the names of such persons as are, . . . of the Romish religion, (not as yet convicted) . . . within the county of Middlesex*. London: n.pub., 1680. S.sh.
Note on blank verso, pasted down, 'Cit – papists Lond & West' (illeg.).
Wood 276a(93) (Wood 376a(93) in Bodl. CD cat.). Wing C1390.

4473. Middlesex, Grand Jury. *A copy of the presentment and indictment found . . . by the grand-jury of Middlesex, . . . Against collonel Matthew Alured*. London: f. E. Thomas, 1660. S.sh.
AW altered the date of publication to 16'59'.
Wood 276a(146). Wing C6219.

4474. Middlesex, Grand Jury. *The presentment and humble petition of the grand jury for . . . Middlesex [18 May]*. (London): (G. Croom), (1681). S.sh. (r-v).
Wood 657(49) (not in Bodl. CD cat.). Wing P3280.

4475. Middlesex, Grand Jury. *A true list of the names of the good men of . . . Middlesex, summoned to be of the grand-jury in the quarter sessions, . . . 1681*. (London): (f. R. Harbottle), (1681). Fol. Pp. 4.
Wood 276a(101). Wing T2733.

4476. M[iddleton], T[homas]. *The blacke booke*. London: T.C[reede] f. J. Chorlton, 1604. 4°. A-F⁴ (A1-2, F3-4 blank).
A1, 'E65', a shelf-mark in another collection (see Wood 614(9), item 3298, for a similar shelf-mark, 'E64',

by William Chester?). Tp, Josias N and scribble.
Wood 616(4). STC 17875.

4477. Middleton, Tho[mas]. *A copy of a letter sent from sir Tho. Middleton, . . . concerning the . . . siege at Oswestree, July 3.* London: f. E. Husbands, 1644, 10 July. 4°. Pp. 8.
Wood 377(22). Wing M1992.

4478. Midgly, William*. *A true narrative of a base and bloody act . . . on the body of one William Midgly.* London: H. R., 1678. 4°. Pp. 7.
Wood 365(27). Wing T2770 (rare).

4479. Midwives. *The mid-wives just petition: or, a complaint . . . Shewing . . . their sufferings . . . for their want of trading [a satire].* London: n.pub., 1643. 4°. A⁴.
Wood 654a(8). Wing M2005.

4480. Miege, Guy. *The present state of Denmark.* London: f. T. Basset, 1683. 8°. Pp. [8], 159.
Wood 666(4). Wing M2024.

4481. Mill, Humphrey. *The second part of the nights search.* London: f. H. Shepheard, a. W. Ley, 1646. 8°. Pp. [15] (A⁸, only). Parchment with 2 clasp holes.
Flyleaf, upper, 'Hen: Foulis Booke – 1652. Feb. 19. Pre: 0. [illeg.]'; note, rubbed out. LT 2.179.
Wood 232(1). Wing M2058.

4482. Mill, John. *A sermon preached on the feast of the annunciation [on Luke 1.28].* London: in the Savoy, by T. Newcomb, 1676. 4°. Pp. [4], 31 (p. [1] blank).
P. [1], 'Antonii a Wood Ex [lined out, and] Ex dono Authoris 7. Apr. 1676.'; tp, Mill underscored. See LT 2.343.
Wood 634(15). Wing M2059.

4483. Milton, John. *Areopagitica; a speech . . . for the liberty of unlicenc'd printing.* London: n.pub., 1644. 4°. Pp. [2], 40.
Pp. 21, 23, 25, marks in margin, in pencil and ink, prob. not by AW.
[MS.] Wood B. 29(5). Wing M2092.

4484. [Milton, John]. *Of education. To Samuel Hartlib.* [London]: [T. Underhill], [1644]. 4°. Pp. 8.
Pp. 3, 6, 8, marks in margin, in pencil, prob. not by AW.
[MS.] Wood B. 29(6). Wing M2132.

4485. M[ilton], J[ohn]. *Colasterion: a reply to a nameles answer against the doctrine and discipline of divorce.* [London]: n.pub., 1645. 4°. Pp. [2], 27.
Tp, after author's initials, 'Milton', in pencil, not by AW.
[MS.] Wood B. 29(4). Wing M2099.

4486. Milton, John. *The doctrine and discipline of divorce: restor'd to the good of both sexes, . . . The author I. M.* London: n.pub., 1645. 4°. 2nd time revis'd. Pp. [8], 82. Calf with 2 fillets and a vertical line of 2 fillets; rebacked.
Flyleaf, upper, 'pr[et] - 4ˢ-6ᵈ' and signatures or names of Edw. Rigby (2), Alice Rigby (3), and Lucy Hesketh. 2ndᵛ, AW wrote the titles of 8 printed works in this vol., unnumbered, within guidelines made with red ink, followed by 'All written by Joh. Milton.' (the name in red ink). Tp, after initials of the author, AW wrote 'Joh. Milton.', in red ink. Signature of a former owner, Ja: Hales. LT 1.319.
[MS.] Wood B. 29(1). Wing M2111.

4487. Milton, John. *Tetrachordon: expositions upon the foure chief places in scripture, which treat of mariage, or nullities in mariage.* London: n.pub., 1645. 4°. Pp. [8], 98 (misnumbering).
To p. 40, short horizontal pencil lines, not in AW's manner.
[MS.] Wood B. 29(3). Wing M2184.

4488. M[ilton], J[ohn]. Εικονοκλαστης *in answer to a book [by J. Gauden] intitl'd* Εικων Βασιλικη *. . . The author J. M.* London: M. Simmons, 1649. 4°. Pp. [12], 242.
Dupl. at Wood 492(3).
[MS.] Wood B. 29(8). Wing M2112.

4489. M[ilton], J[ohn]. Εικονοκλαστης *in answer to a book [by J. Gauden] intitl'd* Εικων Βασιλικη *. . . The author J. M.* London: M. Simmons, 1649. 4°. Pp. [12], 242.

Tp, bsm. B^{r-v}, line in margin and 2 corrections. Dupl. at [MS.] Wood B. 29(8).
Wood 492(3). Wing M2112.

4490. M[ilton], J[ohn]. *The tenure of kings and magistrates*. London: M. Simmons, 1649. 4°. 2nd ed. Pp. [2], 60.
[MS.] Wood B. 29(7). Wing M2182.

4491. [Milton, John] (? at times attrib. to). *The grand case of conscience concerning the engagement stated & resolved. Or, a strict survey of the solemn league & covenant*. London: J. Macock f. F. Tyton, 1650. 4°. Pp. 22.
Wood 609(26). Wing G1486A.

4492. M[ilton], J[ohn]. *The readie & easie way to establish a free commonweath, . . . the author J. M.* London: T. N., sold L. Chapman, 1660. 4°. Pp. [2], 18.
Tp, AW wrote after author's initials (underscored in red ink), 'Joh. Milton'; altered the year to 16'59[60]: ffeb' and in pencil, 'beg[inning]' (of Feb.? Thomason recorded 3 March).
Wood 626(7). Wing M2173.

4493. Milton, John. *Literae pseudo-senatūs Anglicani, Cromwellii, reliquorumque perduellium nomine ac jussu conscriptae*. N.p.: n.pub., 1676. 12°. Pp. [4], 234. Calf, mottled, with 2 fillets and stamp decoration in corners; rebacked.
Flyleaf, upper, 1st, A. Allam wrote 'Pret: 2^s-8^d W[est]: Bibliop: Sextilis [August] decimo octavo 1677'. LT 3.167.
Wood 709. Wing M2129.

4494. Milton, John. *Mr John Miltons character of the long parliament and assembly of divines. In MDCXLI*. London: f. H. Brome, 1681. 4°. Pp. [4], 11.
Tp, bsm.
Wood 620(36). Wing M2098.

4495. Minis, Mr. *Englands ioyalty, [sic] in joyfull expressions, for the city of Londons safety, being a . . . relation of . . . passages . . . lately divulged by one d. [Humphrey] Peake*. London: f. J. Harison, 1641. 4°. Pp. [2], 5.
[MS.] Wood D. 31(30). Wing M2194A (two). ESTCR 43455 (ESTCR, ioyalty in and safety being).

4496. Misselden, Edward. *Free trade. Or, the meanes to make trade florish*. London: J. Legatt for S. Waterson, 1622. 8°. 2nd ed. Pp. [16], 134, [1].
Backing, lower, title of a work, cropped, not in AW's hand. Answered by G. Malynes, Wood 683(2), item 4357
Wood 683(3). STC 17986.

4497. Missing. *?. ?: ?, ? 4°*.
Missing in 1995. Only a small fragment of a leaf remains. No title or description of contents is given in the Whiteside cat., 'A volume of pamphlets &c', at [MS.] Wood C. 32.
[MS.] Wood C. 32(4). Not identified.

4498. Missing. *?. ?: ?, ? 4°*. In a context of brief pamphlets in separate parchment bindings.
Missing in 1717. Vol. removed before the Whiteside cat. was prepared.
[MS.] Wood C. 50. Not identified.

4499. Missing. *?. ?: ?, ? 4°*.
Missing. The list of titles prepared by AW is also missing from this vol. The entry in the Whiteside cat. is 'A Volume containing 52 pamphlets &c Against B^{ps}, Orthodox Clergy, Cheapside cross &c Rich: Culmer agst ye Cath: Ch: of Cant:' (f. 86; for the last, see items 2116ff.). This item was is the context of works against bishops.
[MS.] Wood D. 31(18). Not identified.

4500. Missing. *?. ?: ?, ? Pp.?*
Missing since 1881. Apparently 5 items, or single sheets, were removed. See note at Wood 276b(25), item 4415. Items XX-XXI and XXIII-XXV are missing. Item XXII is still here, with its Ashm. Roman numeral, but it was later renumbered XXV. Items removed from this location would have Roman numerals on the upper right hand corner.
Wood 276b(20-24). Not identified.

4501. Missing. *?. ?: ?, ? 8°.*
Missing in 1717. Vol. removed before the Whiteside cat. was prepared.
Wood 449. Not identified.

4502. Missing. *?. ?: ?, ? 12°.*
Missing in 1717. Vol. removed before the Whiteside cat. was prepared.
Wood 692. Not identified.

4503. Missing. *Wish[?] in the titl[or tile] [illeg.]. ?: ?, ? Pp.?*
Missing. MS. Wood E. 2(70), p. 70, 'Amongst my duplicates is digitus Dei - [by Nedham, item 4614f.] &
by an unknowne hand is wish[?] in the titl[? or tile].'
MS. Wood E. 2(70), p. 70. Not identified.

4504. Mitton, Tho[mas]*. *Several letters of great consequence intercepted by colonel Milton.* London: f.
E. Husband, 1645[6], 17 Feb. 4°. Pp. 8.
Tp, AW wrote the price, '1^d', corrected 'Milton' to 'Mitton', and altered the former no., '41'.
Wood 378(44). Wing S2778.

4505. Mitton, Thomas. *A letter to . . . William Lenthal . . . concerning the surrender of Ruthin-castle.*
London: f. E. Husband, 1646, 14 Apr. 4°. Pp. 8.
Tp, '1^d', prob. not by AW.
Wood 501(2). Wing M2296.

4506. Modena. *A discourse of the dukedom of Modena.* London: J. C. f. W. Crook, 1674. 4°. Pp. [2], 30.
Wood 386(12). Wing D1603.

4507. [Molinos, Miguel de]. No-Body, ed. *The spiritual guide, which disintangles the soul, . . . With a
short treatise concerning daily communion.* [London]: n.pub., 1688. 12°in 6's. Pp. [30], 191, [7], [8], 38, [1]
(2 tpp.).
Tp, AW wrote '1^s-8^d. in qu[arto]'. LT 3.307.
Wood 836(6-7). Wing M2387.

4508. Molyneux, William. *Whereas there is an accurate account and description of Ireland designed
to be made publick in the English atlas undertaken by Moses Pitt . . . Quaeries . . . relating to Ireland.*
[Dublin]: gratis at the shop of Mr. D. Davis, Dublin; and M. Pitt, London, [1682]. S.sh.
Below, AW wrote 'July 1682'. A prospectus.
[MS.] Ashm. 1820a, f. 221 (not in Bodl. CD cat.). Wing M2407 (rare).

4509. Monantholius, Henricus. *De puncto primo geometriae principio liber.* Lugduni B. [Leiden]: ex
biblio. Commeliniano, [1600]. 4°. Pp. [8], 35 (cropped, and having the t leaf mounted).
Wood 499(10). BN.

4510. Monck, Christopher*. Albemarle, 2nd duke of. *To his grace Christopher duke of Albemarle,
&c. . . . A Pindarick poem.* Cambridge: J. Hayes, f. F. Hicks, 1682. Fol. Pp. [2], 10.
P. 3, 'Ashmolean Museum', in a later hand.
Wood 417(104). Wing T1361.

4511. Monck, George. Albemarle, duke of. *A declaration of general Monck touching the king of Scots;
and his proclamation, . . . upon his marching . . . for Berwick.* London: f. N. Bradley, 1659. 4°. Pp. 7.
Wood 610(37). Wing A843.

4512. Monck, George. Albemarle, duke of. *A declaration of the commander in chief of the forces in
Scotland, also another declaration of the officers . . . to the churches of Christ . . . together with 3 letters.*
Edinburgh: C. Higgins, 1659. 4°. Pp. 8.
Tp, AW wrote after the year, 'Oct. 20', in pencil.
Wood 610(33). Wing A844A.

4513. Monck, George. Albemarle, duke of. *A letter from gen. Monck . . . to the commissioners of
parliament in Ireland.* London: f. N. Brook, [1659]. S.sh. Rpt. of Dublin edition.
AW added the date, 'Decemb: 1659:'.
Wood 276a(335). Wing A850 (two). Steele 2.1.606.

4514. Monck, George. Albemarle, duke of. *A letter of November the 12th. . . . directed . . . to the
lord mayor, aldermen, and common-council of . . . London. Inciting them, . . . to give their assistance.*

[London]: n.pub., 1659. 4°. Pp. [1], 3.
Tp, former nos., '44' and '40', in pencil.
Wood 632(36). Wing A860A.

4515. Monck, George. Albemarle, duke of. *A letter sent by general Monck to vice admiral Goodson*
. . . Novemb. 29. London: J. Johnson, [1659]. S.sh.
Wood 276a(338). Wing A862.

4516. Monck, George. Albemarle, duke of. *A letter sent from general Monck. Dated at Caldstreame Dec.*
29. 1659. Superscribed to . . . William Lenthall. London: J. Streater a. J. Macock, 1659[60]. 4°. Pp. [2], 6.
Tp, former nos. '79' and '75' in pencil.
Wood 632(61). Wing A863.

4517. Monck, George*. Albemarle, duke of. *A narrative of the northern affairs, touching the proceedings*
of general Monck, and the lord Lambert. [London]: n.pub., 1659. 4°. Pp. 7.
Wood 503(28). Wing N201.

4518. Monck, George. Albemarle, duke of. *The northern queries from the lord gen: Monck his quarters;*
sounding an allarum, to all loyal hearts. [London]: n.pub., [1659?]. 4°. Pp. 8.
Tp, AW wrote the year 'M: DC Lix' (and again on p. 8), and, in pencil, the no. in a former bundle, '21'.
Wood 613(42). Wing N1297.

4519. Monck, George*. Albemarle, duke of. *The pedigree and descent of . . . George Monck.* London: f.
W. Godbid, 1659[60]. 4°. Pp. 15.
Tp, AW wrote after the year, 'Feb:'.
Wood 535(11). Wing P1048.

4520. Monck, George. Albemarle, duke of. *The speech and declaration of . . . delivered at White-hall*
. . . to the members of parliament . . . before the re-admission of the formerly secluded members [21 Feb.].
London: S. Griffin f. J. Playford, 1659[60]. 4°. Pp. [2], 6.
Wood 610(21). Wing A867.

4521. Monck, George. Albemarle, duke of. *A letter from . . . Monck, and the officers under his command,*
to the parliament [11 Feb.]. London: J. Macock, 1660. 4° (having sheet A reset). Pp. [2], 15 (i.e., pp. 1-6,
9-15).
P. 9, AW identified the authors of a 'bold Petition': 'of prais god Barebone & his sectaries'.
Wood 632(73). Wing A854.

4522. Monck, George. Albemarle, duke of. *The lord general Monck his speech delivered by him in the*
parliament on Munday, Feb. 6. 1659. London: J. Macock, 1660. 4°. Pp. [2], 5.
P. 3, underscoring of 'Phanatique', and in margin, AW wrote 'This word phanatique go[es] much in fashi[on]
after this'. LT 1.303 (Clark read 'comes').
Wood 610(63). Wing A869.

4523. Monck, George*. Albemarle, duke of. *A speech spoken to his excellency the lord general Monk, by*
one representing the genius of England at Drapers-hall [28 March]. [London]: n.pub., [1660]. S.sh.
AW wrote the year, '1660'.
Wood 398(4). Wing S4870 (3) ('O' not recorded in Wing).

4524. Monck, George. Albemarle, duke of. *To the reverend and honourable, the vice-chancelour and the*
body of the convocation in the university of Oxford [5 Apr.]. [Oxford?]: n.pub., [1660]. S.sh.
At 'Master of the Rolls', AW wrote, 'Will Lenthall lately speaker', and below, 'St Jeamses Apr: 5 1660'. ^{v},
AW wrote, '1660', in pencil, and 'L^d. Monks Letter for ye election of [Sr John, lined out and:] Lenthall to
be one of ye Univers: Burg:'. LT 1.312. Dupl. at Wood 515(25).
Wood 423(33). Wing A871A (rare, 2 at O). Madan 2509 (Wing, Vice-Chancellor).

4525. Monck, George. Albemarle, duke of. *To the reverend and honourable, the vice-chancelour and the*
body of the convocation in the university of Oxford [5 Apr.]. [Oxford?]: n.pub., [1660]. S.sh.
AW wrote, 'This letter was read in convocation 7. Ap. 1660 And because the presbyterians & fanaticall
partie were eager for Will. Lenthall, therfore they caused this letter to be printed & dispersed about the
university – '. LT 1.312. Dupl. at Wood 423(33).
Wood 515(25). Wing A871A (rare, 2 at O). Madan 2509 (Wing, Vice-Chancellor).

4526. Monck, George*. Albemarle, duke of. *Georgio Monck duci de Albemarle, . . . epitaphium.* N.p.:

n.pub., [1669]. S.sh. (mutilated, cropped on side and below).
Wood 429(29) (not in Bodl. CD cat.). Wing G534 or G535.

4527. Monck, George, and Charles 2. *A letter from . . . to king Charls . . . Together with king Charls his answer [30 Dec.]*. London: n.pub., 1660. 4°. Pp. 8.
Tp, AW altered the year to 16'59[60]: Januar:' and added 'ffictions'.
Wood 632(26). Wing A852A ('O' not recorded in Wing).

4528. Monck, George, and Thomas Morgan. *A true relation of the rowting of Middletons army in Scotland, . . . in two letters, one from general Monck, and the other from col. Morgan*. London: W. Du-Gard a. H. Hills, 1654. 4°. Pp. 8.
Wood 503(21). Wing T3039.

4529. Money, Mistresse*. *Death & burial of mistresse Money*. London: ?, 1658. Pp.?
Missing in 1837. 'Death & Burial of Mrs Money – Lond. 1658' in Whiteside cat. See Wing D500 (1664) and D501 (1678).
Wood 64(12). Not in Wing. Not in ESTCR.

4530. Money Well Bestowed. *Money well bestow'd. At the [blank space] in Oxford will be shown divers rarities, performed upon spits*. [London?]: n.pub., [1681]. S.sh. 4°.
Inserted in Wood Diaries 25, item 126, between B4-B5. AW wrote, 'Nov. 15. 1681', in pencil and later, 'Nov. 16. 1681' in ink. At blank space in line following heading, 'Chequer Inn', not by AW. LT 2.560 (printed text quoted in full).
[MS.] Wood Diaries 25b. Not in Wing. Not in ESTCR (not Wing M2414A, though the same topic).

4531. [Monipennie, John]. *Certaine matters composed together. The genealogie of all the kings of Scotland*. Edinburgh: R. Walde-grave, [1594?]. 4°. A4,B-K^4. Pasteboard (grey) with parchment spine. 1st upper and last lower flyleaves, marbled paper.
Flyleaf, upper, 4th^v, AW wrote the titles of 5 printed works in this vol., within guidelines made with red ink. Tp, scribble and price [?] and 'in Scotland', not in AW's hand.
Wood 594(1). STC 18017.

4532. M[onipennie], J[ohn]. *The abridgement or summarie of the Scots chronicles*. Edinburgh: J. W[reittoun] f. J. Wood, 1633. 8°. A-R^8 (R3-4 blank). Corrected. Parchment with 2 clasp holes.
Flyleaf, upper^v, AW wrote, 'One . . . . Monnipenny wrot a compendium of the Scots history'.
Wood 135. STC 18015.

4533. Monro, Robert. *A letter of great consequence; . . . to the . . . committee for the Irish affairs in England, concerning the state of the rebellion there*. [London]: f. E. Husbands, 1643, 8 July. 4°. Pp. 7.
Tp, former no., '34', lined out.
Wood 508(41). Wing M2453.

4534. Montagu, Edward*. Manchester, earl of. *Articles of high treason, and other high misdemeanors against { the lord Kymbolton [Edward Montagu, et al.]*. London: R. Barker, by the assignes of J. Bill, 1641[2]. 4°. Pp. [2], 4.
Wood 373(11a). Wing A3847.

4535. Montagu, Edward*. Manchester, earl of. *A true relation of the late fight betweene the right honourable the earle of Manchesters forces and the marquesse of Newcastles*. London: R. Cotes, 1643. 4°. Pp. [2], 8, [1].
Tp, AW altered a former no.
Wood 376(45). Wing T2982.

4536. Montagu, Edw[ard]. Manchester, earl of. *A letter from . . . Ed. lord Montagu . . . With a perfect narration of all the passages betwixt his majesty and those forces that brought him from Holdenby [10 June]*. London: f. J. Wright, 1647. 4°. Pp. [2], 6.
Wood 612(45). Wing M2467A.

4537. Montagu, Edward*. Manchester, earl of. *A letter to the earl of Manchester, concerning the whole carriage of the house of peeres in generall, . . . during these late distractions*. [London]: n.pub., 1648. 4°. Pp. [2], 22.
Tp, AW wrote, 'To be put among the lett[ers]', in pencil, cropped at side. Pp. 3-8, 10-1, 13, 16, 18, 20-2, mainly reference names (numerous to 'Manchester'), some identifications, and some earlier notes and lines in margins in pencil, (p. 11, at the passage, 'He is the *Mountebank* (my Lord) and you but his *Zany*; or

rather, he leads you, and tutors you like an *Ape* in a chaine, . . . ', AW wrote 'excellent', in pencil, which he later overwrote with 'Manchester', in ink); p. 11. AW retained a low opinion of Manchester, AOF 2.283-4.
Wood 632(22). Wing L1733.

4538. Montagu, Edward. Manchester, earl of. *The earl of Manchester's speech to his majesty, . . . With his majestie's . . . answer [29 May].* Edinburgh: J. Macock a. F. Tyton, 1660. 4°. Pp. [4], 4, [2], 3 (p. [1] blank) (2 tpp).
P. [1], AW wrote 'E. of Manchester' (see notes at Wood 608(1a) and 608(17), items 5161, 2726).
Wood 608(19,20). Wing M397.

4539. Montagu, Edward*. Sandwich, earl of. *Memoriae sacrum, Edvardi comitis Sandovici, . . . qui Maii 28 . in illā fatali Naumachiā sublatus est.* Londini: typ. J. Redmayne, 1672. S.sh.
ᵛ, AW wrote, '1672' and 'Edw. Earl of Sandwich 1672', partially covered by repair slips.
Wood 429(32). Wing M1682A.

4540. Montagu, Henry. Manchester, earl of. *Manchester al mondo. Contemplatio mortis, et immortalitatis.* London: J. Haviland f. F. Constable, 1635. 12°. Pp. [2], 211. Calf with 2 fillets; rebacked. Flyleaf, upper, printer's waste paper (cookery).
Tpᵛ and p. 211ᵛ and flyleaf, lower, name, blotted out, school scribbling and signature of Anthony Garret; none by AW.
Wood 801. STC 18026.5.

4541. Montelion. *Don Juan Lamberto: or, a comical history of the late times . . . By Montelion knight of the oracle [pts. 1. and 2].* London: J. Brudenell (T. Leach) f. H. Marsh, 1661. 4°. 2nd ed. ²,A-O⁴ (2 tpp) (3pp. and 1p. books sold by Marsh).
P. [1], AW wrote, 'Reported to be written by Th. Flatman.'; [2], in the woodcut, AW identified the 'Meek Knight' as 'Rich Cromwell'. A1-A2, AW identified characters in this satire as Jo. Lambert, Hen. Vane, and Will. Lylie (i.e., Lilly); G4, line in margin in the books sold by Marsh; K1ᵛ, at the woodcut, 'The picture of Will. Lylie the Almanack maker.'
[MS.] Wood C. 31(4). Wing M2492.

4542. Moore, Charles, and Henry Tichborne. *A certificate from the lord Moor and sir Henry Tichborne, shewing the certainty of the cleering of the harbour, and country, twenty miles about Tredagh.* London: f. J. Hunscott, 1642. 4°. A⁴. Pasteboard (blue) with parchment spine; rebacked.
Flyleaves, upper, 1st-3rd, AW wrote the titles of 52 printed works in this vol., within guidelines made with red ink; all on Ireland, 1642-44. AW did some rearranging of the pamphlets in this vol., and many show earlier prebound nos. in addition to his final numbering. Several, e.g. 3, 5, 9, 12-15, 19 also show a 3rd set of nos. at the bottom, underscored, which may not be by AW.
Wood 508(1). Wing M2534.

4543. Moore, Dr.* *Strange and wonderful news from . . . Wicklow in Ireland, or, a . . . relation of what happened to one dᵣ. Moore.* London: f. T. R., 1678. 4°. Pp. [2], 6.
P. 6, 4 lines description of a night visit by fairies, not by AW.
[MS.] Wood B. 35(30). Wing S5869A.

4544. Moore, Francis. *A gallant victory obtained by the lord Inchiqueen against the rebels; at Capogh-Queen.* London: f. W. S., 1647. 4°. Pp. [2], 6.
Tp, AW wrote after the year, '7 May'.
Wood 509(19). Wing M2541 ('O' not recorded in Wing).

4545. [Moore, Mary]. *Wonderfull news from the north. Or, a true relation of the . . . torments, inflicted upon the bodies of three children of mr. George Muschamp, . . . by witch-craft.* London: T. H., sold R. Harper, 1650. 4°. Pp. [4], 28.
[MS.] Wood B. 18(11). Wing M2581.

4546. Moore, Richard. Ο θησαυρος εν οστρακινοις σκευεσιν: *a pearl in an oyster-shel: . . . two sermons. [Followed by] Abel redivivus; or the dead speaker.* London: A. M. f. T. Parkhurst, 1675 (1674). 8°. Pp. [16], 117, [3] (3 pp. books sold by Parkhurst) (2 tpp.). Calf with 2 fillets; rebacked.
Flyleaf, upper, 1st, AW wrote '7 Feb. 1681[2]. ex dono Edw. Bracey'. LT 3.4.
Wood 810. Wing M2583.

4547. Moorhead, William. *Lachrimae sive valedictio Scotiae sub discessum. The tears and valediction of Scotland upon the departing of . . . George Monck.* London: H. Brugis, 1660. 4°. Pp. [8], 18 [double pp.,

1,1, 2,2, etc.].

Frontispiece[r], 'Monkes departure from Scotland', in pencil. Tp, signature of 'Wm. Peeters ex Dono W. Smart' [? last 4 words lined out]. P. 16, scribble, not in AW's hand.

Wood 383(3). Wing M2613.

4548. [More, Henry]. *Observations upon anthroposophia theomagica, and anima magica abscondita [by T. Vaughan]. By Alazonomastix Philalethes.* Parrhesia [London]: sold O. Pullen, 1650. 8°. Pp. [6], 94, [5]. Tp, AW wrote 'M[r] St–es', in pencil. AO 3.723. Responds to Wood 859(2), item 6298 (and 6301).

Wood 859(3). Wing M2667.

4549. [More, Henry]. *Free-parliament quaeres: proposed to tender consciences; . . . by Alazonomastix Philalethes.* [London]: n.pub., 1660. 4°. Pp. [2], 6. Tp, AW wrote 'Aprill:'.

Wood 608(8). Wing M2661A.

4550. More, Henry. Elys, Edmund, ed. *Letters on several subjects, . . . with several other letters. To which is added, . . . two letters.* London: W. Onely f. J. Everingham, 1694. 8°. Pp. [3], iv, 122, [2] (2 pp. books sold by Everingham). Parchment; a later binding over AW's original marbled paper.

P. [1], AW wrote, 'Recepi ab editore 17 Mar. 1694' (Edmund Elys, AO 4.472).

Wood 720. Wing M2664.

4551. More, John. Bownd, Nicholas, ed. *A table from the beginning of the world to this day.* Cambridge: J. Legate [sold, A. Kitson], 1593. 8°. Pp. [14], 237, [27]. Pasteboard (brown) with calf spine. 1st and last flyleaves, marbled paper; rebound in 1954.

Flyleaf, upper, 3rd[v], AW wrote the titles of 4 printed works in this vol., within guidelines made with red ink. Tp, bsm. Pp. 224-225, entries in tables, and flyleaf, lower, extensive notes, in different hands, none by AW. Possibly acquired 19 Apr. 1662, LT 1.436.

Wood 142(1). STC 18074.

4552. More, Sir Thomas. *De optimo reip. statu, deque nova insula Utopia, libellus . . . Epigrammata . . . Thomae Mori, pleraque è Graecis versa. Epigrammata. Des. Erasmi.* Basil: (ap. Jo. Frobenium), (1518, Dec.). 4°. Pp. [2], 355, [1]. 3 tpp. Parchment, soft.

Pastedowns, ms. with some coloured letters. Pastedown, upper, prices by 3 former owners, e.g. A. Allam, 'pret: o[s] 8[d] We[st] Bibliop Decembr die sexto 1615', scribbles, 2 names and erasures, LT 3.167. Flyleaf, upper, numbers, scribbles, and signature of John Jones; [v], AW wrote the titles of 3 printed works in this vol. Tp, signatures of 3 former owners, Leonardus Robinsonus, Jn. Augustine Seneschallus, and Joannes Campion. For pastedown, lower, see Erasmus, Wood 639(2). Pp. 19-20, 27, 34-5, 37, 107, 347, 353 notes or marks, not in AW's hand; 193ff. some underscoring; P. 24, arms, coloured; above, 'Seneschallorum stemmata', not in AW's hand; at side, in AW's hand, 'The arms of August. Steward de com. Cantab.'; below, description, not in AW's hand.

Wood 639(1). Adams M1757.

4553. More, Sir Thomas. James, Richard, ed. *Epistola Thomae Mori ad academiam Oxon. Cui adjecta sunt quaedam poemata [by R. James] in mortem Roberti Cottoni & Thomae Alleni.* Oxoniae: J. Lichfield imp. T. Huggins, 1633. 4°. Pp. [4], 18, [7]. Pasteboard (grey) with parchment spine.

Cover, upper, outside, 'Orationes', may be by AW. Flyleaf, upper, 2nd, AW wrote the titles of 16 printed works in this vol., within guidelines made with red ink. Tp, AW wrote, 'The publisher & author was Rich James CCC. Soc.', in red ink. Pp. 1, 3-4, 6-7, 10-1, brief notes and lines in margin, in pencil, prob. not by AW.

Wood 512(1). STC 18087. Madan 734.

4554. More, Sir Thomas. *The common-wealth of Utopia:. . . written by . . . sir Thomas Moore.* London: B. Alsop & T. Fawcet, sold W. Sheares, 1639. 12°. Pp. [4], 288 (imperf.). Parchment with 2 clasp holes.

Tp, signature, Robt. – (rubbed out); and 12[d] (may be by AW). A1, 'Liber Thomae Lloyd ex dono charissime Elisei Wynne de Glyn 1684[7?]' (see *The Dictionary of Welsh Biography* (1959), p. 1096, 1105), and scribbles. P. 142, 'David Ll[d] ex Aula B. M– [St. Mary Hall].', 143 'Ellis Wynne[,] John Burns[?]'. Dupl. at Wood 438.

Wood 253. STC 18098.

4555. More, Sir Thomas. *The common-wealth of Utopia:. . . written by . . . sir Thomas Moore.* London: B. Alsop & T. Fawcet, sold W. Sheares, 1639. 12°. Pp. [4], 305. Calf with 1 gold-stamp fillet.

Flyleaf, upper, with 'pretii', etc. removed (ink blottings on remaining flyleaf; the note to Wood 438 in LT

1.23 should be to Wood 436 (item 3983)). Dupl. at Wood 253.
Wood 438. STC 18098.

4556. More, Sir Thomas. *The historie of . . . Edward the V*[th]. London: f. W. Sheares, 1651. 12°. Pp.
[9], 461. Calf with 2 fillets.
Flyleaf, upper, 'AWood'. Frontispiece, 'I. p' (?).
Wood 264. Wing M2689.

4557. More, Thomas (died in 1685). *The English Catholike Christian, or, the saints utopia, a treatise
consisting of four sections.* London: R. Leybourn, 1649. 4°. Pp. [12], 36.
A2[v], a correction.
Wood 487(9). Wing D884.

4558. More, Thomas (died in 1685). *True old news as it may appeare by severall papers, and certificates
. . . &c.* London: E. G., 1649. 4°. Pp. [4], 20 (cropped).
Tp, AW wrote, 'Other writings of this authour see the short epistle following [i.e., A2[r]-3v]. He also trans.
into Engl –' (cropped at bottom, i.e., 'Vita et mors Edwardi II', see AO 4.179f., a translation 'not made
public'). A2[r-v], a correction and an underscoring.
Wood 487(10). Wing D885 (two).

4559. More, William, and Miles Smyth. *Very good newes from Ireland. Of three great victories [by W.
More] . . . Also papers concerning the remonstrance of the lord Inchequins officers [by M. Smyth].* London:
'printed for V, V.' [sic], 1647. 4°. Pp. [2], 6.
Tp, AW lined out a former no., '20'.
Wood 509(24). Wing M2694A ('O' not recorded in Wing).

4560. Morgan, Edward. *Edward Morgan, a priest, his letter to the kings . . . majesty, and . . . parliament
. . . who was drawne, hanged and quartered [26 April].* London: f. T. B., 1642. 4° (cropped). Pp. [2], 6.
Wood 616(25). Wing M2730.

4561. [Morgan, Matthew]. *An elegy on the death of the honourable mr. Robert Boyle.* Oxford: L. Lichfield, 1692. Fol. Pp. [2], 17.
Tp, AW wrote, 'D[r] Matth. Morgan', and, over a note in pencil, 'published in the beginning of March
1691[2]'; p. 17[v], 'R. Boyle 1691[2]'. LT 3.380.
Wood 429(49). Wing M2732.

4562. Morgan, Sheffery*. *The life and death of Sheffery Morgan, son of Shon ap Morgan.* [London]: f.
J. Deacon, n.d. 8°. Imperf. Pp. [2], 14 (A[8]). The final quire, B[4], pp. 17-24, is from a different source, a
version of Conscience, beginning '(17) [and a new line:] keepers in the Country gives such a' (end of line).
Tp, AW wrote, 'Bought at Oxon. 1688'. P. 10, a correction.
Wood 259(14). Wing L2009C (two).

4563. Morgan, Silvanus. *Heraldry epitomiz'd: and its reason essay'd.* London: printed and sold, W.
Bromwich, 1679. S.sh.
Coats and helmets are numbered, may not be by AW.
Wood 276a(64). Wing M2740 (two).

4564. Morgan, Tho[mas]. *Col: Morgan governor of Glocester's letter to . . . Lenthal . . . concerning the
total routing . . . at Stowe upon the Wold.* London: f. E. Husband, 1645[6], 24 Mar. 4°. Pp. 8.
Tp, AW wrote and later lined out the price, '1[d]', and altered the former no., '62'.
Wood 378(65). Wing M2747.

4565. [Morison, R.] (attributed to). Parker, Matthew, ed. *A defence of priestes mariages, stablysshed
by the imperiall lawes of the realme of Englande, agaynst a civilian, namyng him selfe Thomas Martin.*
(London): (J. Kingston, f. R. Jugge), [1567?]. 4°. Pp. [1-12], ff. 1-21, pp. 22-274, [1] (pp. 240-1, repaired)
(ends, Pp4).
Tp, AW wrote, 'Dr. Matthew Parker Archb. of Canterb. was author of this book – printed in the beginning
of Qu. Elizab. raigne', and 'D[r] Jo. Poynet the author. 1555 qu[aere]', all lined out (Poynet, or Ponet, wrote
on this topic in 1555).
Jesus College 2. Arch. 2. 17(2). STC 17518.

4566. Morley, Thomas. *A remonstrance of the barbarous cruelties . . . committed by the Irish rebels
against the protestants in Ireland.* London: E. G., 1644, 12 June. 4°. Pp. [2], 13.
Tp, a name and a sum of money and p. 13[v], 4 names, lined out; none by AW.

Wood 508(49). Wing M2800.

4567. Morrice, Thomas. *An apology for schoole-masters*. London: B. Alsop f. R. Flemming, 1619. 8°. A⁶B-C⁸,D1-7. Pasteboard (grey) with parchment spine.
Each 8° leaf is pasted on a 4° template. Flyleaf, upperᵛ, AW wrote the titles of 3 printed works in this vol., within guidelines made with red ink. Tp, signature of Will. Selby.
Wood 131(1). STC 18170 (3).

4568. M[orris] R[ichard]. *A letter to general Monck, in answer to his of the 23ᵗʰ [sic] of January, . . . to the gentlemen of . . . Devon. By one of the excluded members of parliament*. London: f. R. Lowndes, 1659[60]. 4°. Pp. 8.
Tp, AW wrote, 'The letter that this Answers is in merc: politicus: Jan: 26 [over '30']: 1659[60]:'; and identified the author, '(Rich. Morris)'. P. 8, 'Rich: Morris: Devon:'.
Wood 632(72). Wing M2809.

4569. Mosely, Edward*. *The arraignment and acquittall of sʳ. Edward Mosely . . . indited . . . for a rape*. London: E. G. f. W. L., 1647[8]. 4°. Pp. [2], 12.
Flyleaf, upper, on waste-paper, note, cropped.
Wood 368(5). Wing A3740.

4570. Mother Bunch's Closet. *Mother Bunch's closet newly broke open*. London: A. M[ilbourne] f. P. Brooksby, 1685. 12°.
Missing in 1837. 'Mother Bunche's Closet – Lond. 1685' in Whiteside cat.
Wood 66(16). Wing M2936A (rare). CM.

4571. Mowbray, Laurence. *The narrative of Lawrence Mowbray of Leeds, . . . concerning the bloody popish conspiarcy [sic]*. London: f. T. Simmons, a. J. Sampson, 1680. Fol. Pp. 36.
Tp, AW prob. wrote the price, '1ˢ'; also an 'i'.
Wood 425(28). Wing M2994 ('O' not recorded in Wing).

4572. Moyer, Sam[uel]. *The humble petition of many inhabitants . . . of London. Presented to the parliament by Sam. Moyer and others, May 12. 1659. Together with the answer*. London: f. T. Brewster a. L. Chapman, 1659. 4°. Pp. [2], 6.
Tp, no. 9 in former bundle.
Wood 610(48). Wing H3471.

4573. M[udie], A[lexander]. *Scotiae indiculum: or the present state of Scotland*. London: f. J. Wilkins, 1682. 12°. Pp. [24], 274, [2] (2 pp. books sold by J. Wilkins). Calf with 2 fillets plus 2 vertical fillets; rebacked.
Tp, AW wrote, after initials, 'Moodie'. LT 1.351.
Wood 568 (not in Bodl. CD cat.). Wing M3038 (Wing, Scoitae).

4574. Muggleswick, Petition. *A most lamentable information of part of the grievances of Mugleswick lordship in the bishoprick of Durham*. [London]: n.pub., [1642]. S.sh.
ᵛ, former no., '38'. See note on slip at item 2629.
Wood 373(49). Wing M2902.

4575. Muggleton, Lodowick*. *The heads of the blasphemous libel of Lodowick Muggleton labourer. Intituled, the neck of the Quakers broken*. N.p.: n.pub., [1681]. S.sh. Pp. 2.
P. 2, AW wrote the year, '1681'. The work referred to in the t is Wing M3048.
Wood 645(24). Not in Wing. Not in ESTCR.

4576. Mulcaster, Richard. *Positions wherein those primitive circumstances be examined, which are necessarie for the training up of children*. London: T. Vautrollier f. T. Chare [sic] or T. Vautrollier, 1581. 4°. Pp. [16], 302, [1].
Missing. MS. Wood E. 2(70), p. 6. Ed. not identified.
MS. Wood E. 2(70), p. 6. STC 18253 and 18253a. *Folg* and *O* (author underscored in red chalk), *Folg, Yale*.

4577. Mulerius, Carolus. *Linguae Italicae, compendiosa institutio*. Oxonii: imp. J. Crosley, 1667. 8°. Pp. 47 (A⁸,B⁴,C⁸,D⁴).
Tp, notes, in pencil, after AW's time. Pp. 15-6, some corrections, not by AW.
Wood 42(3). Wing M3053. Madan 2771.

4578. M[un], T[homas]. *A discourse of trade, from England unto the East-Indies*. London: N. Okes f. J.

Pyper, 1621. 4°. Pp. [6], 58.
[MS.] Wood C. 14(2). STC 18255.

4579. M[unday], A[nthony]. *A watch-woord to Englande to beware of traytours and tretcherous practises.* London: [J Charlewood] f. T. Hacket, 1584. 4°. Ff. [5], 47 (wanting sigs. A2,3).
Minor underscoring and note (e.g., f. 40ᵛ), not by AW.
Wood 586(2). STC 18282a.

4580. Munday, Anthony. *The English Romayne lyfe.* London: J. Charlwoode f. N. Ling, 1590. 4°. Pp. [4], 67, and a foldout.
Flyleaf, upperᵛ, AW wrote, 'Anth. Munday hath written another book - see p. 4. 8'; tp, 'A: Woode: Mert: Coll: Oxōn: 1656:'. Bsm. Text, pp. 4, 8, AW made hand pointers; 8, 'q[uaere]'; 2, 7, 8, 55, 60, some lines in margin in ink or pencil; 30, line in red ink and later he added '1581' in margin, see MS. Wood E. 2(70), p. 7, where he added '1581 printed'). P. 67, note on the fold-out woodcut of martyrdom of Rich. Atkins, 'of whome you may read the whole story in fox his booke of martyrs:'.
[MS.] Wood C. 44(4). STC 18273.

4581. Murders. *Three bloodie murders:. . . by Francis Cartwright upon William Storre, . . . The second, . . . by Elizabeth James.* London: [G. Eld?] f. J. Trundle, 1613. 4°. A-C⁴ (C4 blank).
Wood 365(4). STC 18287.

4582. Murford, Peter. *Newes from Southampton, or the copie of a letter to captain Thomas Harrison.* London: f. H. Overton, 1644. 4°. Pp. [2], 5.
Tp, AW lined out the former no., '57'; and wrote the dates, '1643', in pencil, and after '1644', '3 Feb.' AW prepared an earlier list of pamphlets beginning with this item, see note at [MS.] Wood D. 24(4).
Wood 376(63). Wing M3101 (3).

4583. Muriell, Christopher. *An answer unto the Catholiques supplication, . . . for a tolleration of popish religion in England.* London: R. R[ead] f. F. Burton, 1603. 4° (corrected). A-D⁴ (A1-2, D3-4, blank).
Tp, at author, line in margin, bsm?
Wood 611(16-17). STC 18292.3.

4584. Murray, Robert. *Corporation-credit, or, a bank of credit made currant [sic], by common consent in London.* London: J. Gain f. the office, 1682. 4°. Pp. 6.
Tp, AW wrote, 'By Rob. Moray who invented the peny-post'. P. 4, correction, not by AW. LT 3.31. AO 3.726, 1264.
Wood 628(6). Wing M3116.

4585. Muschamp, A. *Further intelligence from Ireland, declared in a letter.* London: R. Oulton & G. Dexter f. H Overton, 1642. 4°. Pp. [2], 5.
AW wrote after the year, '11. Mar. 1641'. Below, '26', may not be by AW.
Wood 507(44). Wing M3138.

4586. Myngs, Christopher*. *Upon the death of the truly valiant . . . sʳ Christoph: Minns wounded at sea.* Oxford: f. J. Godwin, 1666. S.sh.
In margin, 'sprung from Old Guy Warwick', not by AW; ᵛ, AW wrote, 'Sʳ Ch. Minnes 1666'.
Wood 429(24). Wing U109aA (rare). Madan 2747 (Wing, Sr and Minus).

4587. N., E. *Offices and places of trust not to be boucht [sic] or sold, . . . a letter [20 Sept.].* London: f. R. Marriot, 1660. 4°. Pp. [2], 13.
Tp, AW wrote, 'Last of the further bundell – –' (2 words illeg.), in pencil.
Wood 526(8). Wing N15.

4588. N., G. *A geographicall description of the kingdon of Ireland. As also declaring the right and titles of the kings of England unto that kingdom.* London: I. R. f. G. Emerson, 1642. 4°. Pp. [4], 104.
Wood 505(4) (504(4) in Bodl. CD cat.). Wing N18.

4589. N., N. Cogan, Henry, trans. *The scarlet gown, or the history of . . . cardinals of Rome.* London: H. Moseley, 1653. 8°. Pp. [17], 162, [20] (16 pp. books sold by Moseley). Calf with 2 fillets.
Wood 247. Wing N53.

4590. N., N. *America: or an exact description of the West-Indies.* London: R. Hodgkinsonne f. E. Dod, 1655. 8°. Pp. [14], 484, [2] (1 p. books printed by Dod).
Tp, bsm. Acquired 10 Feb. 1664, LT 2.5. See note at Wood 154(1), item 6173.

Wood 154(2). Wing N26.

4591. N., N. *Mutiny maintained: or, sedition made good, a discourse*. [London]: n.pub., [1659]. 4°. Pp. 16.
Tp, AW wrote, 'This came out in the beginning of Decemb: 1659:'. Nos. 47 and 4- (cropped at side) in former bundles.
Wood 610(4b). Wing N46.

4592. N., N. *A brief account, and seasonable improvement of the late earthquake in Northampton-shire*. (London): (f. N. Ponder), [1675-1676]. 4°. Pp. 8.
[MS.] Wood D. 28(21). Wing N29 (rare).

4593. N., N. *An account of the late proposals [for dissolving the ecclesiastical commission, &c.] of the archbishop of Canterbury, with some other bishops, to his majesty:. . . in a letter*. [London]: n.pub., [1688]. 4°. Pp. 4. Pasteboard (blue) with parchment spine.
Flyleaf, upper, 2nd, AW wrote the titles of 22 printed works in this vol., within guidelines made with red chalk. Pp. 1, AW wrote in the year at a date in the text, 28 September, '1688'; 4, at end, 'This paper was commonly sold in Oxon in the middle of Octob. 1688.' LT 3.279.
Wood 529(1). Wing N25.

4594. N., P.; H. Porter, and W. West. *The last newes from the prince of Wales: declaring his further proceedings against the par- parliaments [sic] forces [3 letters, 2 signed P. N., the 3rd H. Porter and W. West]*. London: n.pub., 1648. 4°. Pp.[2], 6.
Tp, AW wrote after the year, 'Aug. 19'.
Wood 502(52). Wing N65.

4595. N., S. Misopappas, Philanax, pseud. *Rawleigh redivivus; or the life & death of . . . Anthony late earl of Shaftsbury*. London: f. T. Malthus, 1683. 8°. Pp. [16], 88, 136, [8] (3 pp. books sold by T. Malthus).
Tp, AW wrote, 'in two parts.' Pp. 18-9, line in margin; 2nd p. 46, AW identified 'Lord P–s', as 'Peters', cropped; 2nd p. 48, underscoring.
Wood 433(2). Wing N72 (Wing, redivivus or) ('O' not recorded in Wing).

4596. [Nalson, John]. *The true protestants appeal to the city and countrey*. (London): n.pub., (1681). Fol. Pp. 4.
P. 3, correction of 'Committee of Safety' to 'Councill of State', not by AW.
Wood 276a(170). Wing N119.

4597. [Nalson, John]. *Reflections upon coll. Sidney's Arcadia; the old cause, being some observations upon his last paper*. London: f. T. Dring, 1684. Fol. Pp. 16.
Tp, AW wrote, '4ᵈ'.
Wood 428(22a). Wing N114.

4598. Nantwich, Cheshire. *Magnalia Dei. A relation of some of the . . . passages in Cheshire before the siege of Namptwich*. London: f. R. Bostock, 1644. 4°. Pp. [4], 22.
Tp, AW lined out the former no., '55'; underscored Tho. 'Fairfax' in the t and wrote the date, 'Feb. 1643', in pencil. Dupl. at Wood 612(26).
Wood 376(61). Wing M255.

4599. Nantwich, Cheshire. *Magnalia Dei. A relation of some of the . . . passages in Cheshire before the siege of Namptwich*. London: f. R. Bostock, 1644. 4°. Pp. [4], 22.
Tp, AW wrote 'Dupl', in pencil. Dupl. at Wood 376(61).
Wood 612(26). Wing M255.

4600. Nash, Tho[mas]. *Strange newes, of the intercepting certaine letters [G. Harvey's Foure letters], . . . as they were going privilie to victuall the Low Countries*. [London]: [J. Danker], 1592. 8°. A-L⁴,M²
(wanting sig. C⁴).
Tp, AW wrote above t 'The apologie of Pierce Penniless. Or' (i.e., Wood 721, also by Nash), and below, 'London 1593 in 4ᵗᵒ'. Recto leaves numbered, 1,3,5, etc. to 69, prob. by AW (he took no account of missing C⁴).
Wood 616(11). STC 18377.

4601. Nash, Thomas. *The apologie of Pierce Pennilesse*. London: J. Danter, 1593. 4°. A2-4,B-L⁴,M1-3. Parchment.
Tp, signature of Tho. Kettle. B4 to end, odd p. nos. written in pencil, prob. by AW. AW identified references,

D1, 'R. Green'; D4, 'Th. Lodge qu[aere]', and a few lines in margins at publications or at references to the university: D4 (in pencil), H1ᵛ and H2 (in ink), and G3 (marking by a line in red ink Stanyhurst and his 'lumbring boystrous wallowing measures'; in MS. Wood E. 2(70), pp. 51-2, AW wrote the names of three authors, Rob. Green, Gabr. Harvey, and R. Stanyhurst, discussed at leaves laid down in this item, e.g., 'R Stanyhurst the poet & his poems at a leaf laid downe in the apol. of Peirce Penniless', H4 and I2 (in red ink). Pastedown, lowerᵛ, brief note, '8 yewes & Lambes', not by AW.
Wood 721. STC 18378 (two).

4602. Nash, Tho[mas]. *The unfortunate traveller. Or, the life of Jacke Wilton*. London: T. Scarlet f. C. Burby, 1594. 4°. Corrected. A-M⁴.
[MS.] Wood C. 31(3). STC 18381.

4603. Nash, Thomas. *Pierce Pennilesse his supplication to the diuell*. London: (T. C[reede]) f. N. Ling, 1595. 4°. A-I⁴.
Wood 614(13). STC 18375.

4604. Nash, Thomas. *Have with you to Saffron-walden, or Gabriell Harveys hunt is up*. [London]: [J. Danter], [1596]. 4°. A2-3,B-X⁴ (wanting the t leaf and A4) (last leaf blank).
Text, D4 to end, odd-numbered pp. 1-135, in pencil, prob. by AW. I2, I3ᵛ, K3, L3ᵛ-L4. AW made vertical lines mainly at biographical details of Harvey, in red ink; M4ᵛ, N3ʳ⁻ᵛ, O4, Q1, V4ᵛ, X2ᵛ, the same, but mainly in pencil.
[MS.] Wood B. 30(3). STC 18369.

4605. Nash, Tho[mas]. *Nashes Lenten stuffe, . . . with . . . the praise of the red herring*. London: [T. Judson a. V. Simmes] f. N. L[ing] and C. B[urby], 1599. 4°. Pp. [8], 75.
Wood 487(7). STC 18370.

4606. Naudé, Gabriel. *News from France. Or, a description of the library of cardinall Mazarini: before it was utterly ruined*. London: f. T. Garthwait, 1652. 4°. Pp. [2], 6.
Naudé described the library of 40,000 volumes as one which 'without disparagement to the famous libraries of *Rome, Milan*, and *Oxford*, might passe, not only for the most goodly heap of Books that this age can shew, but likewise for the eighth wonder of the *World*.' (pp. 2, 4).
[MS.] Wood C. 26(16). Wing N248.

4607. Naudé, Gabriel. Evelyn, John, ed. *Instructions concerning erecting of a library*. London: f. G. Bedle, T. Collins, a. J. Crook, 1661. 8°. Pp. [16], 96.
Tp, '9ᵈ'.
Wood 68(3). Wing N247.

4608. Naunton, Robert. *Fragmenta regalia, or observations on the late queen Elizabeth, her times and favorits*. [London]: Printed, Anno Dom., 1641. 4°. Pp. 43.
Tp, AW wrote '2' at the bottom (formerly the 2nd item in a bundle). Bsm. P. 32, short line in margin at vignette of F. Greville. Diff. ed. at Wood 258(3).
Wood 486(7). Wing N249.

4609. Naunton, Robert. *Fragmenta regalia: or, observations on the late queen Elizabeth*. London: T. Mab a. A. Coles, f. W. Sheares, 1650. 12°. Pp. [2], 89.
Tp, bsm. Acquired 16 Jan. 1658, 6ᵈ, LT 1.235. Diff. ed. at Wood 486(7).
Wood 258(3). Wing N252.

4610. Nayler, James. *The power and glory of the lord, shining out of the north, or the day of the lord dawning*. London: f. G. Calvert, 1656. 4°. [2nd ed.]. Pp. [2], 26.
Wood 645(6). Wing N303.

4611. Nedham, Marchamont. *Match me these two: or the conviciton [sic] and arraignment of Britannicus and Lilburne. With an answer to . . . the parliament of ladies*. [London]: n.pub., 1647. 4°. Pp. [2], 14.
Responds to Neville, Wood 654a(9), item 4629.
Wood 654a(11). Wing M1077.

4612. [Nedham, Marchamont]. *[A plea for the king and kingdome, by way of answer to the late remonstrance of the army, presented to the house of commons on Novemb. 20.] (Signed Mercurius Pragmaticus)*. [London]: n.pub., [1648]. 4°. Pp. [2], 28 (wanting the t-leaf, A1).
Wood 609(17). Wing N402.

4613. Nedham, Marchamont. *The manifold practises and attempts of the Hamiltons, and particularly of the present duke of Hamilton . . . to get the crown of Scotland. Discovered in an intercepted letter*. London: n.pub., 1648. 4°. Pp. 23.
Missing since 1994. Listed in Whiteside cat.
Wood 531(13). Wing N396.

4614. [Nedham, Marchamont]. *Digitus Dei: or, God's justice upon treachery and treason; exemplifyed in the life and death of . . . James duke of Hamilton*. London: n.pub., 1649. 4°. Pp. 31.
Tp, AW wrote 'Dupl.'; 'By Marchamount Needham.', not by AW. Dupl. at Wood 531(12).
Wood 486(12) (not in Bodl. CD cat.). Wing N386.

4615. [Nedham, Marchamont]. *Digitus Dei: or, God's justice upon treachery and treason; exemplifyed in the life and death of . . . James duke of Hamilton*. London: n.pub., 1649. 4°. Pp. 31.
Missing since 1994. Listed in Whiteside cat. Dupl. at Wood 486(12).
Wood 531(12) (not in Bodl. CD cat.). Wing N386.

4616. [Nedham, Marchamont]. *The excellencie of a free-state: or the right constitution of a commonwealth [repr. from Mercurius politicus]*. London: f. T. Brewster, 1656. 8°. Pp. [8], 246, [5] (5 pp. books sold by Brewster). Pasteboard (grey) with parchment spine; last upper and lower flyleaves, marbled paper.
Tp, bsm. and below, 'lo' or 'lv'.
Wood 564(1). Wing N388.

4617. Nedham, Mar[chamont]. *Interest will not lie. Or, a view of England's true interest:. . . in refutation of . . . the interest of England stated*. London: T. Newcomb, 1659. 4°. Pp. 46.
Tp, former no. in a bundle '65' (in pencil). Responds to J. Fell, Wood 533(13), item 2969.
Wood 533(14). Wing N392.

4618. [Nedham, Marchamont]. *The downfall of Mercurius Britannicus, Pragmaticus, Politicus*. [London]: n.pub., 1660. S.sh.
AW wrote after the year, 'Aprill:'. In margin, after 'Ainsloe', AW wrote 'or Onslow', in red ink; and ᵛ, 'Ap. 1660'.
Wood 622(21). Wing D2087 (one) ('O' not recorded in Wing).

4619. [Nedham, Marchamont]. *Newes from Brussels, in a letter from a neer attendant on his majesties person*. N.p.: n.pub., 1660. 4°. Pp. 8.
Tp, former no. '4', and AW wrote the initials, 'M.N.' P. 8, AW wrote, 'This letter as was reported was writt by Sʳ Hen: Vane, Scot and Maior Salloway, printed by ['by' lined out] for Chapman a bookseller: how ['how' lined out] who upon the discovery of the matter, fled; wherupon a proclamation issued out against him under the penalty of paying a large summ of Money if he did appear by such a time: [/] It was writt after the inditement of the said persons by <u>March: Nedham</u>, and conveyed to the printer And boo[k]seller by prais god Barebone: [/] The Alarum to the officers and souldiers of the Armie was writt by the same persons://' (Wood 608(72), item 2504). Responded to by J. Evelyn, item 2861. See J. Raymond, 'The Cracking of the Republican Spokes', *Prose Studies*, 19 (1996): 265; AO 3.1186-7.
Wood 632(42). Wing N398A.

4620. Nedham, Marchamont. *The true character of a rigid presbyter:. . . To which is added, a short history of the English rebellion: compiled in verse*. London: by the assignes of J. Calvin, sold Z. Crofton, 1661. 4°. Pp. [6], 93, [1].
Flyleaf, upper, AW wrote, 'March. Needham published this meerly to curry favour at the kings restauration, when he had lost his credit so much, that he was many times in danger of his life-', and later, 'Here are two treatises in this booke-.'; tp, 'see the epistle to the reader' and below, '1ˢ', and 'A.Woode: July: V: MDCLXI'. LT 1.405.
[MS.] Wood D. 26(10). Wing N406.

4621. N[edham], M[archamont]. *A discourse concerning schools and school-masters, . . . By M. N.* London: f. H. H., 1663. 4°. Pp. [2], 161,A-B⁴,C1.
Tp, AW wrote the name of the author and, 'If Marchimont Needham was the authour then it agrees with his former profession, for I have been crediblie informed that he had been sometime . . . ' (cropped at bottom).
Wood 131(2). Wing N387.

4622. [Nedham, Marchamont]. *Honesty's best policy; or, penitence the sum of prudence:. . . in honour of the . . . earl of Shaftsbury's . . . submission for his offences*. [London]: n.pub., [1678]. 4°. Pp. 18.

Wood 608(51). Wing N390.

4623. Negative Voice. *A negative voyce: or, a check for your check: a message (by a black-rod) of non-concurrence, for the ballancing-house or co-ordinate senate.* [London]: n.pub., 1659. 4°. Pp. [2], 18.
Tp, AW wrote, 'first heap 23', in pencil.
Wood 626(17). Wing N414.

4624. Nepos, Corn[elius]. *The lives of illustrious men.* Oxon: f. H. Cruttenden, sold A. Stephens, 1684. 8°. Pp. [57], 272. Pasteboard (grey) with parchment spine. Traces of upper and lower flyleaves, marbled paper; rebacked.
Flyleaf, upper, 1st^v, AW wrote the titles of 5 printed works in this vol., within guidelines made with red chalk (really 2; all 4 sections of I. Walton, Wood 229(2), item 6437, are listed), and a note: 'These four last lives were given to me by the Author, on S. James day 1670' (i.e., Walton, 25 July). LT 2.197. P. 1, mark in margin at an Oxford translator, Tullie, of Queen's College, in pencil. Flyleaf, lower, in pencil, and erased, '12 Bks 56 –' (?). LT 3.86.
Wood 229(1). Wing N428.

4625. Netherlands. *Exceeding joyfull newes from Holland. . . . two great battels fought betweene the governour of Flanders . . . and the Hollanders [20-21 April].* London: f. J. Raymond, 1642. 4°. A⁴.
No. 52 in a former bundle.
Wood 614(43). Wing E3746.

4626. Netherlands. *Strange news from Holland. Being a true relation of a wonderful vision.* London: F. Neile, 1652. 4°. Pp. 6.
[MS.] Wood B. 35(21). Wing S5892 (rare).

4627. Neville, George*. *The title of George Nevil esq; Francis and Henry Nevil, to the . . . estate of the l^d. of Abergavenny.* [London]: n.pub., [1660 ca.]. S.sh.
Wood 276a(80). Not in Wing. Not in ESTCR.

4628. [Neville, Henry]. *The ladies, a second time, assembled in parliament. A continuation of the parliament of ladies.* [London]: n.pub., 1647. 4°. Pp. [2], 12.
P. 11, note, or scribble, not by AW.
Wood 654a(10). Wing N507.

4629. [Neville, Henry]. *The parliament of ladies. Or divers remarkable passages of ladies in spring-garden; in parliament assembled.* [London]: Pinted [sic], 1647. 4°. Pp. 16.
Tp, AW wrote, 'By Hen. Nevill esq.' Responded to by M. Nedham, item 4611.
Wood 654a(9). Wing N511.

4630. [Neville, Henry]. *Newes from the new exchange, or, the commonwealth of ladies, drawn to the life.* London: n.pub., 1650. 4°. Pp. [2], 21, [1] (misnumbering at end, 16, 3, 71, 21, 20, 2).
Diff. ed. at Wood 654a(15).
Wood 609(25). Wing N510. I.e., ESTCR 203016 ('O' not recorded in ESTCR).

4631. [Neville, Henry]. *Newes from the new exchange, or the common-wealth of ladies.* London: n.pub. Printed in the year, of Women without Grace, 1650. 4°. Pp. [2], 14 (A-B⁴).
Diff. ed. at Wood 609(25).
Wood 654a(15). Wing N510. I.e., ESTCR 232899.

4632. Neville, Henry. *Shufling, cutting, and dealing, in a game at pickquet: being acted from the year, 1653. to 1658. by O. P. and others.* [London]: n.pub., 1659. 4°. Pp. 8.
Tp, AW wrote the author's name, 'Harry Nevell', and 'dupl.' Dupl. at 531(29).
Wood 500(9). Wing N517.

4633. Neville, Henry. *Shufling, cutting, and dealing, in a game at pickquet: being acted from the year, 1653. to 1658. by O. P. and others.* [London]: n.pub., 1659. 4°. Pp. 8.
Missing since 1994. Dupl. at Wood 500(9).
Wood 531(29). Wing N517.

4634. [Neville, Henry]. Van Sloetten, Henry Cornelius, pseud. *The Isle of Pines . . . near Terra Australis, Incognita.* London: f. A. Banks a. C. Harper, 1668. 4°. Pp. [3], 31.
Tp, 'Hen. Nevill the Author' and 'When this was first published twas look'd upon as a sham'. P. 3, a correction.

Wood 386(11). Wing N506.

4635. [Neville, Henry]. *Plato redivivus: or, a dialogue concerning government*. London: f. S. I., sold, R. Dew, 1681. 8°. 2nd ed. Pp. [16], 293.
Flyleaf, lower, 1st^v, short titles of contents, not by AW.
Wood 564(2) (not in Bodl. CD cat.). Wing N515.

4636. New Advice. *New advice to a painter, &c. painter, once more thy pencil reassume*. N.p.: n.pub., [1679/80]. Fol. Pp. 4.
P. 4, AW wrote the year, '(1680)'. There is no entry for this item in the upper flyleaves, see Wood 417(1).
Wood 417(21b). Wing N533A.

4637. New Anatomy. *A new anatomie, or character of a Christian, or round-head*. London: f. R. Leybourne, 1645. 8°. Pp. [2], 13.
Wood 868(2). Wing N536.

4638. New England. *A true account of the most considerable occurrences that have hapned in the warre between the English and the Indians in New-England [5 May-4 Aug.]*. London: f. B. Billingsley, 1676. Fol. Pp. [2], 10 (misnumbering).
Wood 559(11). Wing T2385.

4639. New Litany. *A new letany for these times, fitted to most persons and occasions*. London: n.pub., [1659]. 4°. Pp. [2], 6.
Tp, AW wrote, 'Decemb: 1659'.
Wood 483(11a). Wing N656 (rare) (Wing, '1659').

4640. New Market Fair. *A tragi-comedy, called New-market-fayre, or a parliament out-cry: of state-commodities*. [London]: printed at you may goe look, 1649. 4°. 2nd ed. Pp. 8.
Tp, AW wrote 'To be bound with exchange of Nevile' (Wood 609(25) or 654a(15), items 4630f.).
Wood 615(24). Wing T2018A.

4641. New Market Heath. *The worlds wonder: being a true relation of the strange and dreadful apparitions seen in the air, . . . at New-market-heath*. London: f. G. Horton, 1659. 4°. Pp. 8.
[MS.] Wood D. 28(13). Wing W3591A (two) ('O' not recorded in Wing) (2 at O).

4642. New Model. *A new modell or the conversion of the infidell terms of the law, . . . The first century*. [London]: n.pub., 1652 [i.e., 1659]. 4°. Pp. [6].
Wood 609(30). Wing N677 ('O' not recorded in Wing).

4643. Newark. *Articles concerning the surrender of Newark to the commissioners of both kingdoms*. London: f. E. Husband, 1646, 11 May. 4°. Pp. 7.
Wood 501(9). Wing A3814.

4644. Newark, and John Belasyse. *The second summons to Newark sent from the committee of both kingdoms, together with the governours [J. Belasyse's] answer thereunto*. London: f. E. Husband, 1646, 4 May. 4°. Pp. 7.
Tp, '1^d', prob. not by AW.
Wood 501(7). Wing S2335.

4645. Newbery, William, and William Edmunds. *A letter to d^r. Fowler, . . . In answer to his late vindicatory preface*. London: n.pub., 1685. Fol. Pp. [2], 6.
P. 3, 5, brief notes by 'Ar. Charlett:', whose signature is on p. 6.
Wood 657(27) (not in Bodl. CD cat.). Wing N845.

4646. Newbury. *A most certain, strange, and true discovery of a witch, . . . taken by . . . parliament forces, . . . sayling . . . over the river at Newbury*. [London]: J. Hammond, 1643. 4°. Pp. 7.
Missing in 1839; see note by Kirtland at [MS.] Wood B. 18(1), item 1148.
[MS.] Wood B. 18(4). Wing M2870. O.

4647. Newcastle, Siege. *A full relation of the Scots besiedging Newcastle*. London: B. Alsop, 1644. 4°. A^4.
Missing in 1922. See also note at Wood 376(1).
Wood 376(71). Wing F2369. *Yale* (cropped at top).

4648. [Newcome, Henry]. Wolseley, Charles, preface by. *A faithful narrative of the life and death of*

. . . *John Machin*. London: f. N. Simmons, 1671. 8°. Pp. [10], 96.
Flyleaf, upper, ᵛ, AW wrote, 'One Joh. Machen a Yorksh. man borne became a student in Magd. Hall, Oxon. an 1590. aged 19' (a later person expanded 'becāe' to 'became'). Tp, '.6' (6ᵈ?). P. 95, AW added the date of death, '1664'.
Wood 292(7) (not in Bodl. CD cat.). Wing N896.

NEWSBOOKS (items 4649-4757, and See Index, 'Newsbooks')

4649. A la Mode. *Al-a-mode [sic] of Paris, or, the diurnall in verse. Numb. 1 [29 Dec. 1659].* [London]: n.pub., 1659. Fol. Pp. 4.
Wood 416(23). N & S 1A.1 (3).

4650. A la Mode. *Al a mode [sic] de Paris: or the diurnall in verse from Holland. Numb. 1 [Jan.].* [London]: n.pub., [1660]. 4°. Pp. 8.
Wood 483(17). N & S 1.1 ('O' not recorded in N & S).

4651. Army, Fairfax 2. *An exact and perfect relation of the proceedings of the army under the command of sir Thomas Fairfax. Numb. 2. [6-11 July].* London: f. S. Gellibrand, 1645, 14 July. 4°. Pp. 8.
Tp, AW overwrote the former no., '8'.
Wood 378(10). N & S 565.2.

4652. Army, Fairfax 3. *A continuation of the proceedings of the army under the command of sir Thomas Fairfax. Numb. 3 [11-19 July].* London: f. S. Gellibrand, 1645, 26 July. 4°. Pp. [2], 22.
Tp, AW lined out the former no., '9'.
Wood 378(11). N & S 565.3.

4653. [Birkenhead, John], and [Peter Heylyn]. *Mercurius aulicus, a diurnall, communicating the intelligence, and affaires of the court, to the rest of the kingdome. Sunday-Saturday. 1st weeke-52nd weeke. [1 Jan. 1642[3] to 30 Dec. 1643].* Oxford: H. Hall f. W. Webb, 1642[3]-1643. 4°. Pp. 1-750. Pasteboard (blue) with parchment spine.
Acquired 27 Jan. 1658, 9ˢ, LT 1.235. Flyleaf, upper, 4thᵛ, AW wrote, 'Merc. Aul 4° M. 12 Art. BS in bib. bod 1645', in pencil. P. 1, under t, 'Or Oxford Diurnall, as in some copies it is printed'; at Jan. 1, '1642/3'. AW wrote a very few minor notes, pp. 128, 'Ld Visc. Camden'; 133, lines in margin; 138, a correction, 'Cromwel was commanded' for 'Cromwel was demanded'; 153, at March 26, the year 'an. 1643'; 184-5, 192, line in margin, in red ink, at Doctor Homes, Mr. Hampden, and Sir Rob. Pye; 330, a cross-ref. to p. 192 and a correction, etc. to end. There is an longer note at p. 619, 'Joh. Bond son of Dennis Bond Alderman of Dorchester, & a Disciple of Mʳ Whites'.
Wood 623. N & S 275.000A, 275.101A-275.152. Madan 2043.

4654. [Birkenhead, John], and [Peter Heylyn]. *Mercurius aulicus, communicating the intelligence and affaires of the court, to the rest of the kingdome. Sunday-Saturday. 1st weeke to 47th weeke, and the last, unnumbered. [31 Dec. 1643 to 23 Nov. and 29 Dec. 1644 to 5 Jan. 1644[5]].* [Oxford]: [H. Hall f. W. Webb], 1643-1644[5]. 4°. Pp. 751-1328. Pasteboard (blue) with parchment spine (only traces of parchment remain); rebacked with leather spine.
Very little annotation: e.g., pp. 751, '10.11.14 17' (date of rebacking?) at top, in pencil, not in AW's hand; 786, 792, 1022, 1050, 1059 (i.e., following 1056), 1087 (cross-ref. of Capt. Keame to p. 1095), 1091, 1095-6 (on long hair), 1123 (Keame), 1144-6, 1165, 1184, 1209, line in pencil, mainly. Wood mentioned his vol. 3 in this series, but it is not among his current books, see MS. Wood E. 2 (70), p. 75.
Wood 624. N & S 275.201A-247A, 275.301. Madan 2043.

4655. Charles 2. *His majesties message to the . . . commons . . . relating to Tangier. And the humble address of the commons . . . in answer. Numb. 28 [29 Nov.].* London: f. J. Wright a. R. Chiswel, 1680. Fol. Pp. [2] and 71-86.
P. [1], a summary of the t of this item, not in AW's hand.
Wood 559(15). N & S 647.28.

4656. City Mercury. *The City Mercury: from the office at the Royal Exchange. . . . A weekly advertisement of books. Numbs. 262, 274 [6 Jan. 1680[1], 14 Ap. 1681].* (London): (R. Everingham), 1681. Fol. (r-v).
Wood 658(818, 819a). N & S 299.262, 274 (rare).

4657. Civitas Oxon. *Civitas Oxon. A bill of all the burials from . . . the VI*[th] *of August to . . . the XIV*[th].
[Oxford]: n.pub., (1641). S.sh.
Buried within wall, 10; in suburbs 3.
Wood 507(49). N & S 046.64108 (rare) Wing O853. Madan 2042.

4658. Civitas Oxon. *Civitas Oxon. (14) A bill of all that deceased . . . from the 18. of October to the 25.
1644.* [Oxford]: [L. Lichfield], (1644). 4°. S.sh.
Buried within walls 16; in suburbs, 15 (19 of the 31 of the plague). AW did not include this item on his
list on the upper flyleaf.
Wood 514(15b). N & S 046.64414. Madan 2062.

4659. Continuation of the Diurnal. *A continuation of the diurnall passages in Ireland, declared in two
letters. The one . . . from the lord Antrim . . . The other was sent to sir R. K. Numb. 2.* London: f. F.
Coules a. T. Banks, 1641[2]. 4°. Pp. [2], 6.
Wood 507(37). N & S 063.2.

4660. Continuation of the True Diurnal. *A continuation of the true diurnall of passages in parliament.
Numb. 2 [17-24 Jan. 1641].* [London]: printed . . . and are to bee sold by Stationers, [1641[2]]. 4°. A[4].
Wood 373(18). N & S 069.2.

4661. Continuation of the True Diurnal. *A continuation of the true diurnall of passages in parliament
from February 7. to February 14. Numb. 5. Monday 7 February. 1641. [Begins:] Upon a Petition from.*
N.p.: n.pub., 1641[2]. 4°. Pp. 33-40 (E[4]).
Wood 373(23). Not in N & S (should be at 105.5).

4662. Continuation of the True Diurnal. *A continuation of the true diurnall of proceedings in parlia-
ment. Numb. 9 [7-14 Mar.].* [London]: n.pub., (1641[2]). 4°. Pp. 65-72.
On a slip, inserted before tp, 'Darbysh. petit' (inserted at Wood 373(38), item 2231), and in pencil, '14
Mar. 1641[2]'. Tp, AW rubbed out the former no., '29'; below, a 2nd no. '14'.
Wood 373(37). N & S 071.09.

4663. Continuation of the True Diurnal. *A continuation of the true diurnall, of all the passages in
parliament. Numb. 10 [14-21 Mar.].* [London]: n.pub., [1642]. 4°. Pp. 73-80.
Tp, AW overwrote a former no. to make '41'; below, a no., '19'. Also, a former no., '28'.
Wood 373(41). N & S 068.10B..

4664. Continuation of True Intelligence. [Ashe, Simeon, and William Goode]. *A continuation of the
true intelligence. Numb. 5. [16 June-10 July].* London: f. T. Underhill, 1644. 4°. Pp. 8.
Wood 377(23). N & S 492.5.

4665. Continuation of True Intelligence. Ashe, Sim[eon]. *A continuation of true intelligence from the
armies in the north. Numb. 6 [10-27 July].* London: f. T. Underhill, 1644. 4°. Pp. [2], 1-6, 9-16.
Wood 377(25). N & S 492.6.

4666. Diurnal Occurrences in Parliament. *The diurnall occurrances in parliament. Numb. 2 [17-24
Jan.].* [London]: f. F. Coules a. T. Banks, 1641. 4°. Pp. 8.
Wood 373(17). N & S 099.02.

4667. Diurnal Occurrences in Parliament. *Diurnall occurrences in parliament [30 May-6 June].* [Lon-
don]: n.pub., (1642). 4°. Pp. 8.
Tp, AW lined out 1 former no., '69', altered '19' to '18', and let '81' stand; note by later librarian, 'H[ope]
A[dds.] 1127', in pencil. Flyleaf, lower, a note that this item was restored in Jan. 1932.
Wood 374(18). N & S 100.1.

4668. Diurnal Occurrences: Or. *The diurnall occurrances: or, the heads of proceedings in parliament
[13-20 Dec.].* [London]: f. T. Bates a. F. Coules, 1641. 4°. Pp. [2], 6.
Wood 507(14). N & S 103.1.

4669. Diurnal Occurrences, Or. *Diurnall occurrences, or, the heads of the proceedings in both houses.
Numb. 5 [31 Jan.-7 Feb.].* London: f. J. Thomas, 1641[2]. 4°. A[4]. To be with item 4673, below.
Wood 373(21). N & S 181.205.

4670. Diurnal Occurrences, Touching. *The diurnal occurrances, touching the daily proceedings in
parliament [3-10 Jan.].* London: f. J. Hamond, 1642. 4°. Pp. [2], 6.

Tp, AW marked the date; and '18', in a modern hand. P. 1, AW underscored 'Mandevile', and wrote in margin, 'Kimbolton'.
Wood 373(11b). N & S 106.3.

4671. Diurnal, Or. *The diurnall: or, the heads of all the proceedings in parliament [6-13 Dec.] . . . Wherein they voted Oneale guilty of high treason*. London: f. J. W. a. T. B, 1641. 4°. Pp. [1], 7.
Wood 507(13). N & S 109.1.

4672. Diurnal out of the North. *July, 19. A diurnall out of the north:. . . at Yorke and Beverley, . . . until . . . 16. of July*. (London): (T. Fawcet f. D. C.), (1642, 18 July). 4°. Pp. 8.
Wood 374(28). N & S 110.1.

4673. Diurnall Occurrences. *Diurnall occurrences. Numb. 4 [24-31 Jan.]*. London: f. J. Thomas, 1641[2]. 4°. A⁴. To be with item 4669, above.
Wood 373(19). N & S 181.204.

4674. England, King's and Queen's Commissions. *The proceedings on the king and queens commissions of the peace, and oyer and terminer [3-5 Sept. 1690]*. (London): (f. L. Curtiss), (1690). Fol. Pp. 4 (cropped).
Wood 657(63). N & S 9.69009.

4675. English Guzman. *The English Guzman: or, captain Hiltons memoirs, the grand informer. Numb. 1 [n.d.]*. (London): (f. R. Oswel), (1683). Fol. Pp. [4].
Wood 422(10). N & S 131.1.

4676. Gifford, Bonaventure*, and Obadiah Walker*. *A dialogue between father [Bonaventure] Gifford, the late popish president of Maudlin, and Obadiah Walker master of University . . . in Newgate*. N.p.: n.pub., [1689?]. S.sh. (r-v).
ᵛ, AW wrote, 'Feb. 22 an. 1688[9] – bought at Oxōn'. LT 3.299.
Wood 276a(565). N & S 091A.1 (two).

4677. Houghton, John, ed. *A collection for improvement of husbandry and trade. Vol. 6. Numb. 123 [30 Nov.1694]*. [London]: n.pub., 1694. S.sh. (r-v).
Wood 276a(43). N & S 049.123.

4678. Intelligencer. L'Estrange, Roger, ed. *The intelligencer. Monday. Numbs. 1-18 [31 Aug. to 28 Dec. 1663]*. London: R. Hodgkinson, 1663. 4°. Pp. 1-144.
The intelligencer (Monday) and *The newes* (Thursday) (see 521(3)) are interleaved. See notes at Wood 521(1 and 3), items 4708, 4712. On a flyleaf inserted after p. 538 of no. 33 of the *Mercurius publicus* (Wood 521(1)), he wrote, 'Mʳ Henry Muddiman desisting from writing Merc: Publicus, Mʳ Roger L'strang [sic] by order succedes [sic] in writing the Intelligencer and the Newes.' AW went through each number and made very brief annotations, mainly but not always in the form of pencil lines, at domestic matters, e.g. (from pp. 1-50, and the pattern continues throughout this newspaper), at book advertisements (p. 24); and at biographical details (pp. 46, at the 29 Sept. Oxford convocation; 48, at Richard Fanshaw being sworn as a member of the Privy Council).
Wood 521(2). N & S 201.1001-1018.

4679. Intelligencer. [L'Estrange, Roger, ed.]. *The intelligencer, published for satisfaction and information of the people. Monday [alternating with] The newes, published for satisfaction and information of the people. Thursday. Numbs. 1-102 [4 Jan. [1664]-29 Dec. 1664]*. London: R. Hodgkinson, 1664. 4°. Pp. 838 (some p. and numb. sequences are some times erratic).
On a slip (62 x 95mm.), loose, AW wrote, 'Note that some titles of book [sic] for this yeare I have removed for 1663'. Flyleaf, upper, 4thᵛ, 'Ant: Woode, Oxōn 1664.' Text, pencil lines in margins at advertisements of books newly published, e.g., pp. 28, 54, 67, 71, 76, 84, 92, 100 ('J. Pierce [lined out] q[uaere]. Whitby [added later in red ink]', 118, 131, 140, 188, 196, 203, 211, 219, 259, 275 ('q[uaere]' in pencil and 'Lond. 1664. vit.' in ink), 284, etc., to end (p. 443, identification of E. L., 'Edw. Lowe'); see also lines at material often relevant to England or Oxford, e.g., pp. 1, at 1663, '[-4]', pp. 9, 71, 272, 353, etc. to end (p. 584, at a story of the regicides in Switzerland, 'I remember this story was afterward contradicted. See p. 589'). P. 838. 'Here endeth the newes of Mʳ Roger L'estrang. for the year 1664'. All the pages show that 2 folds were made at one time, before being bound.
Wood 391. N & S 201.2001-2102.

4680. Intelligencer. [L'Estrange, Roger, ed.]. *The intelligencer, published for satisfaction and information*

of the people. Monday. [alternating with] The newes, published for satisfaction and information of the people. Thursday. Numbs. 1-95 [2 Jan. 1664[5]-23 Nov. 1665] [At 2 Dec. 1665:] Numbs. 1-9, 10, 2-9 [2 Dec. 1665-29 Jan. 1665[6]]. London: R. Hodgkinson, 1665. 4°. Pp. 1178, 2, 72, 72 (some p. and numb. sequences are erratic).
Flyleaf, upper, 4th^v, 'Anth: Woode. 1665'. Text, pencil lines in margins at advertisements of books newly published, e.g., pp. 37, 61, 84, 93, 109, 118, 149, 181, 203, 237, 260, 285, 293, 299, 309, 315, 396, 421, (2nd p.) 415, 437, etc.; see also lines at material often relevant to England or Oxford, e.g., pp. 40, 48, 134, 208 ('see pag 235'), 657, 1127; 2nd pp. 8, 48, 64. Flyleaf, lower, 1st, 'Rog. L'estrange desisted from writing the Newes – Becaus the Gazets which came out twice in the week took up all.'
Wood 392(1, 3). N & S 201.3001-5009.

4681. London Gazette. Muddiman, Henry, ed., et al. *The London gazette. Thursday to Monday. Monday to Thursday. Numbs. 247-454 [26 March 1668-24 March 1669[70]].* London: T. Newcomb, 1668-1669[70]. Fol. Ff. 247-454. Calf, mottled, with 2 fillets; 2nd rectangle formed by roll decoration and stamp decoration inside and outside corners; rebacked by 'RH[arvey] 1.12.58'. This is AW's 1681 binding.
Flyleaf, upper, 1st, 'Vol. 2 [/] 25. Jan. 1680[1] [/] paid to Rog. Bartlet of Oxon boke-binder for the binding of this book 2^s - 4^d being part of the legacie (40^s) that Mr Pet Nicolls Fellow of Merton College left to me [/] Ita testor Anton. à Wood. Oxōn. [/] In this volume are contained 301 Gazets, & every Gazette cost me one penny, (for I had them taken up at London by a freind at the best hand) so that all put togeather, come to eighteen shillings & 4^d besides binding [/] Ita testor Ant. à Wood', and the sums in the right margin. LT 2.413. In this nearly perfect collection there is minor annotation: no. 269^v, line at a Whitehall dateline, 14 June, at death of Charles Lord Viscount Fitzharding and his successors, Thomas Clifford and Francis Lord Neuport. For the preceding years, 1665-1668, see the *Oxford Gazette*, and *London Gazette*.
Wood 542. N & S 471.0247-0454.

4682. London Gazette. Muddiman, Henry, ed., et al. *The London gazette. Thursday to Monday. Monday to Thursday. Numbs. 455-662 [24 March 1669[70]-25 March 1672].* London: T. Newcomb, 1670-1672. Fol. Ff. 455-662. Calf, mottled, with 2 fillets; 2nd rectangle formed by roll decoration and stamp decoration inside and outside corners; rebacked by 'RH[arvey] 1.12.58'. This is AW's binding.
Flyleaf, upper, 3rd, 'vol. 3'. In this nearly perfect collection there is minor annotation, e.g., nos. 479^{r-v}, at an event and at a book advertisement; 521^v, at at advertisement of a book by J. Glanvill; 537, underscoring of death of the bishop of Dromore.
Wood 543. N & S 471.0455-0662.

4683. London Gazette. Muddiman, Henry, ed., et al. *The London gazette. Thursday to Monday. Monday to Thursday. Numbs. 663-871 [25 March 1672-26 March 1674].* London: T. Newcomb, 1672-1674. Fol. Ff. 663-871. Calf, mottled, with 2 fillets; 2nd rectangle formed by roll decoration and stamp decoration inside and outside corners; loose boards. This is AW's binding.
Flyleaf, upper, AW wrote, 'Binding 2^s - 6. [/] Rebound 1^s - 6. [/] Apr. 3. 1694.' In this nearly perfect collection there is minor annotation, e.g., nos. 681^v, line in margin at a book advertisement (Tomkins, T., *Musica Deo sacra*), in pencil; 686, no. on slip used to reinforce inner margin, prob. not in AW's hand; 686^v, 690^v, 691^v, 726^v, 727^v, and 730^v, etc., line at book advertisement, in pencil.
Wood 544. N & S 471.0663-0871.

4684. London Gazette. Muddiman, Henry, ed., et al. *The London gazette. Thursday to Monday. Monday to Thursday. Numbs. 872-1080 [26 March 1674-27 March 1676].* London: T. Newcomb, 1674-1676. Fol. Ff. 872-1080. Calf, mottled, with 2 fillets; 2nd rectangle formed by roll decoration and stamp decoration inside and outside corners; rebacked. This is AW's binding.
Pastedown, upper, blotting of 'Vol 5', which AW had written on a now removed flyleaf; a scribble, and the no. of issues, not in AW's hand. In this nearly perfect collection there is minor annotation, e.g., nos. 876^v, 881^v, 889^v, 890^v, 905^v, line in margins at a book advertisement, in pencil; 935^v, a correction of a name, in a list.
Wood 545. N & S 471.0872-1080.

4685. London Gazette. Muddiman, Henry, ed., et al. *The London gazette. Thursday to Monday. Monday to Thursday. Numbs. 1081-1288 [27 March 1676-25 March 1678].* London: T. Newcomb, 1676-1678. Fol. Ff. 1081-1288. Calf, mottled, with 2 fillets; 2nd rectangle formed by roll decoration and stamp decoration inside and outside corners; loose boards. This is AW's binding.
Flyleaf, upper, AW wrote, 'Vol. 6'. In this nearly perfect collection there is minor annotation, e.g., nos. 1084^v, 1089^v, line at book advertisement, in ink; 1093^v, the same, in pencil; 1119^v, the same, in red ink and pencil; 1145^v, the same, in pencil; 1146^v, the same, in red ink; 1147^v, the same, in pencil; etc. No. 1256,

slip to repair inner margin, 2 lines of Greek visible; 1226$^\mathrm{v}$, line in margin at book advertisement, in pencil; 1268$^\mathrm{v}$, 1271$^\mathrm{v}$, line in margin, in pencil over red ink.
Wood 546. N & S 471.1081-1288.

4686. London Gazette. Muddiman, Henry, ed., et al. *The London gazette. Thursday to Monday. Monday to Thursday. Numbs. 1289-1497 [25 March 1678-25 March 1680]*. London: T. Newcomb, 1678-1680. Fol. Ff. 1289-1497. Calf, mottled, with 2 fillets; 2nd rectangle formed by roll decoration and stamp decoration inside and outside corners; rebacked. This is AW's 1688 binding.
Flyleaf, upper, 1st, AW wrote, 'Dec. 24. an. 1688 2$^\mathrm{s}$ - 6.' and 'Vol. 7'. In this nearly perfect collection there is minor annotation, most are lines, in pencil, ink or red ink, at book advertisements: nos. 1289$^\mathrm{v}$, at beginning of 3 book advertisements, AW wrote, 'An account of the growth of popery, was written by And. Marvell.'; 1293$^\mathrm{v}$, 1298$^\mathrm{v}$, 1385$^\mathrm{v}$ (correction), 1393$^\mathrm{v}$, 1396$^\mathrm{v}$ (in red ink), 1424$^\mathrm{v}$, 1408$^\mathrm{v}$, 1497$^\mathrm{v}$ (line in margin at a U. of Cambridge event).
Wood 547. N & S 471.1289-1497.

4687. London Gazette. Muddiman, Henry, ed., et al. *The London gazette. Thursday to Monday. Monday to Thursday. Numbs. 1498-1705 [25 March 1680-23 March 1681[2]]*. London: T. Newcomb, 1680-1682. Fol. Ff. 1498-1705 (one issue has 2 leaves, unnumbered). Calf, mottled, with 2 fillets; 2nd rectangle formed by roll decoration and stamp decoration inside and outside corners; repaired. This is AW's binding.
In this nearly perfect collection there is annotation, all in the form of lines, usually in pencil, at Whitehall events or announcements: nos. 1501$^\mathrm{v}$, 1502$^\mathrm{v}$, 1504$^\mathrm{v}$, 1507$^\mathrm{r-v}$, 1508$^\mathrm{v}$, 1509$^\mathrm{v}$ (on restrictions for printing of newsbooks), 1511$^\mathrm{v}$, 1515$^\mathrm{v}$, 1519, 1522$^\mathrm{v}$ (imprisonment of Edward Peters), 1526$^\mathrm{v}$, 1534$^\mathrm{v}$, 1537$^\mathrm{v}$, 1541$^\mathrm{v}$, etc. 1656$^\mathrm{v}$, brief note at a report of a U. of Cambridge presentation of a book, 'View of the late Troubles in England', to the King, 'Dugdale', i.e., William Dugdale (Oxford, 1681).
Wood 548. N & S 471.1498-1705.

4688. London Gazette. Muddiman, Henry, ed., et al. *The London gazette. Thursday to Monday. Monday to Thursday. Numbs. 1706-1914 [23 March 1681[2]-24 March 1683[4]]*. London: T. Newcomb, 1682-1684. Fol. Ff. 1706-1914 (some issues have 2 leaves, unnumbered). Calf, mottled, with 2 fillets; 2nd rectangle formed by roll decoration and stamp decoration inside and outside corners; loose boards. This is AW's 1688 binding.
Flyleaf, upper, 1st, AW wrote, '2$^\mathrm{s}$ - 6. Dec. 24. an. 1688', and 'vol. 9'. In this nearly perfect collection there is minor annotation, all in the form of lines, in pencil or ink, at events or announcements: nos. 1710$^\mathrm{v}$, 1726$^\mathrm{v}$ (an Oxford event), 1731$^\mathrm{v}$, 1734$^\mathrm{v}$, 1738$^\mathrm{v}$ (book advertisement), 1741$^\mathrm{v}$ (cross mark, not by AW), 1750$^\mathrm{v}$ and 1768$^\mathrm{v}$ (Whitehall event), etc.
Wood 549. N & S 471.1706-1914.

4689. London Gazette. Muddiman, Henry, ed., et al. *The London gazette. Thursday to Monday. Monday to Thursday. Numbs. 1915-2123 [24 March 1683[4]-25 March 1686]*. London: T. Newcomb, 1684-1686. Fol. Ff. 1915-2123 (some issues have 2 leaves, unnumbered). Calf, mottled, with 2 fillets; 2nd rectangle formed by roll decoration and stamp decoration inside and outside corners; rebacked. This is AW's binding.
In this nearly perfect collection there is minor annotation, in the form of a line in the margin, in pencil and pen, e.g., nos. 1922$^\mathrm{v}$, at 2 book advertisements and at a Whitehall swearing in of S. Goldophin; 1924$^\mathrm{v}$; 1929$^\mathrm{v}$ and 1930$^\mathrm{v}$, at book advertisement; 1945$^\mathrm{v}$, at a U. of Cambridge appt. to N. Stagins; 1953$^\mathrm{v}$, at an advertisement of an Oxford book; 1959$^\mathrm{v}$, at Windsor, appt. of the Earl of Rochester and [S.] Godolphin (see also 2009 and 2010, 2nd leaves$^\mathrm{v}$); 1960$^\mathrm{v}$, 1968$^\mathrm{v}$, book advertisement, etc.
Wood 550. N & S 471.1915-2123.

4690. London Gazette. Muddiman, Henry, ed., et al. *The London gazette. Thursday to Monday. Monday to Thursday. Numbs. 2124-2332 [25 March 1686-26 March 1688]*. London: T. Newcomb, 1686-1688. Fol. Ff. 2124-2332 (some issues have 2 leaves, unnumbered). Calf, mottled, with 2 fillets; 2nd rectangle formed by roll decoration and stamp decoration inside and outside corners; rebacked. This is AW's binding.
In this nearly perfect collection (with some foxing) there is minor annotation, in the form of a line in the margin, in pencil and ink, e.g., nos. 2131$^\mathrm{v}$, a Whitehall announcement; 2132$^\mathrm{v}$, Dublin and Westminster items; 2133$^\mathrm{v}$, Whitehall item concerning John Powell and H. Finch; 2144$^\mathrm{v}$, book advertisement; 2148$^\mathrm{v}$, at sale of library of Rich. Weston; 2149$^\mathrm{v}$, at Westminster, trial of Sam. Johnson; 2187$^\mathrm{v}$, book advertisement, Tho. Farmer, *Consort of music*; 2188$^\mathrm{v}$, book advertisement, etc.
Wood 551. N & S 471.2124-2332.

4691. London Gazette. Muddiman, Henry, ed., et al. *The London gazette. Thursday to Monday. Monday to Thursday. Numbs. 2333-2542 [26 March 1688-24 March 1689[90]]*. London: T. Newcomb, ended with numb. 2365; E. Jones, 1688-1690. Fol. Ff. 2333-2542 (some issues have 2 leaves, unnumbered). Calf, mottled, with 2 fillets; 2nd rectangle formed by roll decoration and stamp decoration inside and outside corners; rebacked. This is AW's binding.

In this nearly perfect collection there is minor annotation, in the form of a line in the margin, in pencil and ink, e.g., nos. 2349^v, book advertisment, 2362^v, Whitehall event, appt. of Oxford judges; 2364^v, Whitehall appt. to Privy Council of T. Strickland; 2374^v, Windsor, knighthood of Gilbert Gerard Cossine & Samuel Gerard; 2376^v, Whitehall licensing of plays; 2386^v, Whitehall investiture with Garter, Ormond; 2390^v, Whitehall, consecration of T. Hall, Bp. of Oxford; 2394^v, Whitehall appointment; 2397, marks and AW's correction at appointment of an Oxford sheriff, William Glyn, 'He did not stand' and 2398^v, a similar comment at sheriff, W. Walter, and addition for Oxon of 'Sr Farmeden Peniston was his sherriff this year'; 2408^v, Whitehall event, etc.

Wood 552. N & S 471.2333-2542.

4692. London Gazette. Muddiman, Henry, ed., et al. *The London gazette. Thursday to Monday. Monday to Thursday. Numbs. 2543-2751 [24 March 1689[90]-24 March 1691[2]].* London: E. Jones, 1690-1692. Fol. Ff. 2543-2751. Calf, mottled, with 2 fillets; 2nd rectangle formed by roll decoration and stamp decoration inside and outside corners; rebacked by 'RH[arvey] 18.5.50'. This is AW's binding.

In this nearly perfect collection (but frequent foxing) there is minor annotation, all in the form of lines, in pencil or pen, at events or announcements: nos. 2563^v, involving Sir John Trever and William Rawlinson; 2591^v, at Lords Justices of Ireland; 2610^v and 2618^v, Whitehall; 2612^v and 2647^v, book advertisement.

Wood 553. N & S 471.2543-2751.

4693. London Gazette. Muddiman, Henry, ed., et al. *The London gazette. Thursday to Monday. Monday to Thursday. Numbs. 2752-2960 [24 March 1691[2]-26 March 1694].* London: E. Jones, 1692-1694. Fol. Ff. 2752-2960. Calf, mottled, with 2 fillets; 2nd rectangle formed by roll decoration and stamp decoration inside and outside corners; loose boards. This is AW's 1694-5 binding.

Flyleaf, upper, 1st (loose), 'Binding & – [paper? fading and stained] [/] 3^s - 6' in pencil, prob. in AW's hand. In this nearly perfect collection, there are only a few annotations: nos. 2752, correction of the year to 1692; 2858^v, correction of day of week; 2877^v, AW marked with a line in pencil the advertisement for subscriptions to 'Monumenta Britannica: By Mr. Tho. [sic] Aubrey'. AW, possibly, inserted a blank leaf before no. 2893, which has printed news item: 'Oxford, July 31, 1693' and 'On the 29th Instant Antony A- [sic] Wood was Condemned in the Chancellors Court of the University of Oxford, for having Written and Published in the Second Volume of his Book, Entituled, Athenae Oxoniensis divers infamous Libels against the Right Honourable Edward late Earl of Clarendon, . . . '. LT 3.429 and 4.47. AW made no notes on this page. Landen, Wood 554(2), item 4020, an 8-page pamphlet, was inserted after no. 2893. No. 2907, corrected to 2908, prob. not by AW.

Wood 554(1). N & S 471.2752-2960.

4694. London Gazette. Muddiman, Henry. ed., et al. *The London gazette. Thursday to Monday. Monday to Thursday. Numbs. 2961-3272 [March 1694-22 March 1696].* London: E. Jones, 1694-1696. Fol. Ff. 2961-3272. Calf, smooth, with 2 fillets; 2nd rectangle formed by roll decoration and stamp decoration inside and outside corners; loose board.

There is no annotation in this collection of the London *Gazette*. It contains issues dated after the death of AW on 29 Nov. 1695. Since AW had the vols. bound in 2-year segments, he would not have had any portion of this consignment bound. The upper pasteboard, curiously, has the book-plate of Richard Rawlinson, as do succeeding vols, 556-8, which continue the run of London *Gazettes* to 1704. The volumes apparently came to the Museum before 1717 for they are entered in the Whiteside cat. All have binding similar to that of earlier vols. (Wood 541-554, but the boards are a smooth, not mottled, calf, some of the pp. are cropped, and some stitching shows). Vol. 557 has a slightly larger format because the pages were uncut along the margins.

Wood 555. N & S 471.2961-3272.

4695. Loyal Protestant. *The loyal protestant, and true domestick intelligence, . . . 9 March, 1681; 15 March, 1681-20 March, 1683. no. 1, 3-247 [Tues., Sat.].* London: N[ath.] Thompson, 1681. S.sh. Fol.

Missing. AW recorded in his diary, 17 and 31 August 1681, that he has this newsbook 'in my other study among Oxon papers, bundell 4', LT 2.551, 554; also mentioned, 3.19, 25. First published as *Domestic intelligence* (1679) (at the General Sessions, . . . the 31st of August, . . . in the Old Bayly, . . . we the Grand-Jury . . . do . . . present, That one N. Thompson . . . has . . . printed and published . . . a . . . seditious paper . . . entituled, The Loyal Protestant and true domestic intelligence, tending to the advancement . . . of Popery).

LT 2.551. N & S 245.001ff..

4696. Mercurius Academicus. *Mercurius academicus: communicating the intelligence and affairs of Oxford. No.1 [by Thomas Swadlin, Monday [3 Ap.] in Easter-week to 15 Ap.].* [London]: n.pub., [1648]. 4°. Pp. 8.
P. 8, AW wrote, just prior to binding, 'I could never learne that any other numbers of this Merc. Acad. were afterwards published.' LT 1.143.
Wood 514(41). N & S 261.1 ('O' not recorded in N & S). Madan 1977.

4697. Mercurius Anti-Britannicus. *Mercurius anti-britanicus [by sir J. Birkenhead et al.] [Unnumbered] [n.d., ca. 4 Aug].* [Oxford]: [L. Lichfield], [1645]. 4°. [No. 1]. Pp. 7.
Restored to this location from Hope adds. 1133 in 1932.
Wood 622(9). N & S 267.1. Madan 2064.

4698. Mercurius Anti-Britannicus. *Mercurius anti-britanicus; or, the second part of the king's cabinet vindicated [by sir J. Birkenhead et al.] [Unnumbered] [n.d., ca. 22 Aug].* [Oxford]: [L. Lichfield], [1645]. 4°. [No. 3.] Pp. '21-32'.
Waste paper, upper[v], upside down, Latin disputation topic, 'Et differentia sit realis' (?), not by AW. Tp, AW wrote the year,1645; and 'Dupl' (not in AW's hand).
Wood 622(10). N & S 267.3. Madan 2064.

4699. Mercurius Civicus. *Mercurius civicus, or the cities intelligence. Numb. 1 [19 March 1660] [Tues.].* London: J. Remayne, 1660. 4°.
Missing. In diary, AW wrote, 'See 'Mercurius Civicus' among my pamphletts, March 18 (Su.) 1659[60]'. LT 1.307.
LT 1.307. N & S 300.01.

4700. Mercurius Elencticus. *Mercurius elencticus communicating the unparallell'd proceedings at Westminster. Numb. 41 [30 Aug. to 6 Sept.].* N.p.: n.pub., 1648. 4°. Pp. 327-331, [332-334].
Tp, AW wrote in margin, 'Kent'.
Wood 502(65). N & S 312.41.

4701. Mercurius Politicus. [Nedham, Marchamont, and J. Canne, eds.]. *Mercurius politicus, comprising the sum of forein [sic] intelligence, . . . of England, Scotland, & Ireland. . . . Thursday. Numbs. 340-2 [11 Dec. 1656-1 Jan. 1656[7]].* London: T. Newcomb, 1656-1657. 4°. Pp. 7439-7486 [3 issues only, on Thursdays, alternating with the Monday issues of *The publick intelligencer*, Numbs. 62ff. (1656f.) (i.e., Wood 389(2) and continues at Wood 522, q.v]. Pasteboard (blue) with parchment spine.
P. 7439, beneath 2 pasted on slips, 'Decemb: 20: 1656: I made a bargaine with M[r] Forrest, to give 2[s] a quarter for Newes Bookes taking them of him, the next day they come to Oxford, being every Wednesday and Saturday: whereof this is the first:'. P. 7455, 'the 3[d]' (the 2nd is the Monday issue of *The publick intelligencer*). See LT 5.45 and refs. there.
Wood 389(1). N & S 361.340-2.

4702. Mercurius Politicus. [Nedham, Marchamont, and J. Canne, eds.]. *Mercurius politicus. Thursday. Numbs. 343-396 [1 Jan. 1656[7] to 31 Dec. 1657].* London: T. Newcomb, 1657. 4°. Pp. 7487-8020, 1583-1664, 1-208.
Flyleaves, upper (loose) and lower, printer's waste paper (upper, 2 sheets, Arthurian prophecies, not identified; lower, 2 tpp, Bacon, *Sylva Sylvarum: . . . Natural*, ed. W. Rawley, both cropped at bottom]. Flyleaf, upper, 2nd, 'Anthony Woode Oxōn'. AW obtained these through the bookseller, Mr. Forrest, on Saturdays, a day after they arrived in Oxford (see note at Wood 389(1), item 4701). AW wrote consecutive odd nos. on each tp, i.e., the Thurs. issues in this vol., beginning at 7, to 103 (3 Dec., numb. 393). The 1st 3 issues of *Mercurius* are at Wood 389(1). The issues on which he wrote the even nos., the Monday *Publick intelligencer*, are at Wood 389(2), item 4738. He received the latter on Wednesdays and numbered them to 104 (again, the last 2 are unnumbered). AW went through each number and made very brief annotations, mainly but not always in the form of pencil lines: at domestic matters, e.g. (from pp. 7487-7650, and the pattern continues throughout this vol.), at book advertisements (pp. 7557, 7061 [i.e. 7601], 7621, 7635-6, etc.); and at biographical details (7493, at Henry Vane, Mr. Feak, and William Lawrence; 7518, at David Jenkins). At numb. 374, p. 7957, a loose fol. leaf, with 8 ms. lines, cursive, not in AW's hand: '1657 - July 29. This day the most Noble Lord the Lord Richard Cromwell was installed Chanceler of the most famous University of Oxon. The manner thus. About 4 a'clock afternoon, D[r] John Owen Vice-Chancelor of the University, with the Heads of Houses in their Scarlets, the Proctors, and a great number of Masters of Arts, representing the Body of the University, came hither to the Lodgings'.
Wood 522. N & S 361.343-396.

4703. Mercurius Politicus. [Nedham, Marchamont, and J. Canne, eds.]. *Mercurius politicus. Thursday. Numbs. 398 [sic, i.e., 397]-547 [sic, i.e., 447] [31 Dec. 1657-30 Dec. 1658]*. London: T. Newcomb, 1657-1658. 4°. Pp. 209-732 [sic, i.e., 932], 133-164, 1-128 (much misnumbering). Pasteboard (blue) with parchment spine.
Flyleaves, upper printer's waste paper, 2 sheets, running head 'Europe's Calamity, Englands Glory . . . Discovering the Fate of Great Britain'; and lower, 2 sheets, on kingship. Upper, 2nd^v, 'Anthony Woode Oxon, 1660'. AW went through each number and made very brief annotations, mainly but not always in the form of pencil lines, at domestic matters, e.g. (from pp. 209-350, and the pattern continues throughout this vol.), at book advertisements (pp. 266 (3 marked); 283 (4 marked including 1 by Lewis Du Moulin and 1 by W. Prynne); 347; 522 (Browne, *Sepulchral Urns*), etc., to end); and at biographical matters (224, at a wild man blown ashore at St. Andrews; 252, at a ref. to a book called *Killing no Murder* [eventually acquired, Wood 631(14), item 6204]; 314, at a proposition by G. Downing).
Wood 523. N & S 361.397-547.

4704. Mercurius Politicus. [Nedham, Marchamont, and J. Canne, eds.]. *Mercurius politicus. Thursday. Numbs. 548-615 [30 Dec. 1658-12 Ap. 1660]*. London: T. Newcomb, 1658-1660. 4°. Pp. 129-1254.
Flyleaves, upper (2), and lower (2), printer's waste paper. Upper, 2nd^v, 'Anthony Woode, Oxōn. 1660'. Lower, 1st, 'Marchiomont [sic] Needham gives of[f] writing, or rather prohibited about this time. & Merc: Publicus goes forward, who [sic] began in the beginning of the yeare 1660.'; and later 'See Merc. Publicus num: 13 p. 193. v. mer. 14.' (i.e., 22 March to 29 March 1659[60], and 29 March to 5 April, numb. 14, p. 209 in Wood 393); and 'Needham was prohibited v. p. 437 - ubi' (i.e., numb. 567, 'Friday May 13' in this vol.). AW went through each number and made very brief annotations, mainly but not always in the form of pencil lines, at domestic matters, e.g. (from pp. 129-272, and the pattern continues throughout this vol.), at book advertisements (pp. 204-5, AW marked 3 books and also wrote in the p. nos. at top; 237, at a romance by J. D., and at *A treatise of civil power* by John Milton, AW wrote 'Milton' in the margin; 252, also a correction, M. Wr to M. Wren; 269); and at biographical matters (pp. 135; 144, at elections of J. Rushworth and H. Nevil; 159, at election of Matthews and H. Mildmay; 165 (AW wrote in the p. no. at top), at elections for Portsmouth and Woodstock; 173; 183; 192, at election of Thomas and John Wroth; 198; 215; and 232, at a murder).
Wood 524. N & S 361.548-615.

4705. Mercurius Publicus. [Muddiman, Henry, and G. Dury, eds.]. *Mercurius publicus: comprising the sum of forraign intelligence; with the affairs now . . . in England . . . Thursday. Numbs. 1-54 [29 Dec. 1659-3 Jan. 1661]*. London: J. Macock (numbs. 1-15); T. Newcomb (numb. 16); J. Macock, a. T. Newcomb (numb. 17-53); R. Hodgkinsonne, a. T. Newcomb (numb. 54), 1659-1661. 4°. Pp. 846 (some p. and numb. sequences are erratic; 697-704 were removed). Pasteboard (blue) with parchment spine.
Flyleaf, upper, 2nd^v, 'Anth: Woode, 1661'. AW went through each number and made very brief annotations, mainly but not always in the form of pencil lines, at book advertisements and domestic matters, e.g. (from pp. 1-144, and the pattern continues throughout this vol.), at book advertisements (pp. 88-9); at biographical matters (pp. 9, at 3 names of person appointed to be a council of state; 19, at a letter from L. Fairfax; 28; 32, at A. A. Cooper; 48; 140), and corrections (p. 22, of Lyscot to Lydcot). See also book advertisements marked at pp. 169, 204-5, 221, 265 (lines, in pencil, and 'v. prox. pag', in ink), 280, 293, etc. to 839; at material often relevant to England or Oxford, e.g., pp. 272, 325, etc. to p. 810 (p. 810, AW wrote 'By privat letters from there also it was certified that the river Dee went back 12 mil: and was also dry:'); or identifications, e.g., pp. 342-3, 367, 396, 552. Correction, p. 22. For pp. removed from this vol., see note on waste paper at Wood 521(1), item 4708.
Wood 393. N & S 378.101-54.

4706. Mercurius Publicus. [Muddiman, Henry, and G. Dury, eds.]. *Mercurius publicus, comprising the sum of all affairs now in agitation in England. . . . Thursday. Numbs. 1-53 [3 Jan. 1661-2 Jan. 1662]*. London: R. Hodgkinsonne, a. T. Newcomb (numb. 1-2); R. Hodgkinson (numb. 3-6, 52); R. Hodgkinsonne, a. D. Maxwell (numb. 7); D. Maxwell (numb. 8-15); R. Hodgkinson (16); D. Maxwell (numb. 17-46); P. Lillicrap (numb. 47-51, 53), 1661-1662. 4°. Pp. 824 (some p. and numb. sequences are erratic). Pasteboard (blue) with parchment spine.
Flyleaf, upper, 2nd^v, 'Anth: Woode. Oxon.' Text, mainly pen or pencil (a few in red chalk) marks in margins at advertisements of books newly published, e.g., pp. 25, 57, 76, 92 (and 'q[uaere]'), 105, 137, etc. to end; or at material often relevant to England or Oxford, e.g., pp. 17, 51, 64, 67, 70, 77, 80, 128, 137 (at Lues Venerea: Or, a perfect Cure of the French Pox), etc. to end. Identification or 'q[uaere]', e.g., pp. 156, 218, 337 (misnumbering), 361, 377, 501, 505.
Wood 394. N & S 378.201-53.

4707. Mercurius Publicus. Muddiman, Henry, and G. Dury, eds. *Mercurius publicus. Thursdays. Numbs. 1-52 [2 Jan. 1661[2] to 1 Jan. 1662[3]*. London: P. Lillicrap, or R. Hodgkinson, 1662. 4°. Pp. 854 (much misnumbering). Pasteboard (blue) with parchment spine.
Flyleaves, upper and lower, printer's waste. Flyleaf, upper, 1st, 'Anth. à Wood 1670'; 2nd^v, 'Anth: Woode Oxōn. 1662'. He went through each number and occasionally made very brief annotations, mainly but not always in the form of pencil lines, e.g. (from pp. 1-116, and the pattern continues throughout this vol.), at book advertisements (pp. 9, 25, 59, 73, 75, 91-2, 100, 105, 108); at biographical details (23, at a matter concerning William Strode; 62, at mention of H. Waller, E. Harvey, and R. Lilburn coming before the House; 102-3, at the consecration of Henry Lord Bishop of Chester); wrote cross-refs. (116); identified persons referred to by initials (108); and wrote in the year (104). See also p. 201, where he marked 4 book advertisements and at one by Edward Lake, wrote 'printed 1662 in qu[arto]'; or p. 792, Dr. Dalby corrected to 'Dolben'. Vol. loaned to – Godwyn, 5 Jan 1664, LT 2.2.
Wood 520. N & S 378.301-52.

4708. Mercurius Publicus. Muddiman, Henry, and G. Dury, eds. *Mercurius publicus. Thursday. Numbs. 1-33. [1 Jan. 1662[3] to 20 Aug. 1663]*. London: R. Hodgkinson, et al., 1663. 4°. Pp. 1-538 (frequent misnumbering). Pasteboard (blue) with parchment spine.
Flyleaves, upper, 1st 2, and lower (after Wood 521(2), item 4678), last 2, newspaper leaves (from the *Merc. publ.*, no. 44, Oct. 25, pp. 697-8 and 703-4, and Oct. 11, no. 42, Oct. 1660, pp. 667-670). Flyleaf, upper, 1st, 'Wood', and, in pencil, 'After 33. nu[.] R. Lestrange begins' (see also note at Wood 521(2) where he also noted the change – that *Merc. publ.* was succeeded by *The intelligencer* (Monday) and *The news* (Thursday)). The upper flyleaves of 'printer's waste' were supplied by AW from his stock of rejected sheets, but he, or his binder, mistakenly took a sheet (pp. 697-8 and conjoint 703-4) which belonged to issues in his collection of *Merc. publ.* now at Wood 393. In that vol. pp. 697 to 704 are wanting. He marked 2 book advertisements on p. 705, just after the absent sheets. On the p. 697, the upper flyleaf in Wood 521, he marked 5 book advertisements and wrote the name of the author, Jo. Tombes, at one entry. The lower flyleaves come from a stack of genuinely rejected waste paper, for the sheet with pp. 667-8 and 669-670 is present in Wood 393. Flyleaf, upper, 4th^v (a loose leaf), 'Ant: Woode. Oxon.' AW went through each number and made very brief annotations, mainly but not always in the form of pencil lines, at domestic matters, e.g. (from pp. 1-135, and the pattern continues throughout this newspaper), at book advertisements (pp. 9, 25, 57, 60, 73, 89, 93, 109); at biographical details (14, at E. Calamy sent to Newgate Gaol; 24, at a play written by W. Clerke; 34, E. Bagshaw sent to the Tower; 37; 72; 81, at death of R. Sanderson; 79-80; see also 206, 411); and a few times wrote in the year or 'qu[aere]' (89, 135; see also p. 254, where he corrected 'the beginning of March last' to 'Mar. 1661/2 rather [/] 1662/3'). For the note on the blank flyleaf after the last p., 538, see *Intelligencer*, Wood 521(2).
Wood 521(1). N & S 378.401-33.

4709. Mock-press. *The mock-press: or, the encounter of Harry Lungs, and Jasper Hem, two . . . pamphleteers. Numb. 1.* (London): (f. C. B.), (1681). S.sh. (r-v).
Wood 417(52). N & S 412.1. Wing M2299.

4710. Moderate Intelligencer. Manuscript. *'The Moderate Intelligencer impartially communicating martial affaires in the kingdome of England. Num. 161. from Thursday 13 to Thursday 20. Aprill. 1648. Oxford Apr. 17. [/] The earl of Pembroke cancellour of this university came last Tuesday . . . '*. Oxford: n.pub., 1648, 17 Apr. 4°. Pp. [4].
This ms. copy of a newsbook, has, on p. [4], AW's note pertaining to the next item concerning university visitors, Wood 514(46), item 4994.
Wood 514(45). N & S 419.161.

4711. Moderate Intelligencer. Manuscript. *The moderate intelligencer impartially communicating martial affaires, . . . num. 234. From Thursday Sept. 6 to Thurs. Sept. 13. an. 1649 [/] Oxford Sept. 8.* [London]: [R. W[hite]], 1649. 4°. Pp. 3.
Ms. copy of an issue concerning Levellers and Col. Ingoldsby.
Wood 515(7). N & S 419.234.

4712. News. L'Estrange, Roger, ed. *The newes. Thursday. Numbs. 1-18. [3 Sept. 1663-31 Dec. 1663]*. London: R. Hodgkinson, 1663. 4°. Pp. 1-144.
The newes (Thursday), and *The intelligencer* (Monday) (see Wood 521(2), item 4678) are interleaved. AW went through each number and made very brief annotations, mainly but not always in the form of pencil lines, at domestic matters, e.g. (from pp. 1-50, and the pattern continues throughout this newspaper), at book advertisements (after p. 50, e.g., 68, 92); at biographical details (7, at Gilbert Sheldon, Archbishop

of Cant.; 16, the burial of a 'phanatique'; 24, a solemnity at Bow Church). For the flyleaves at the end of this item, see Wood 521(1), item 4708.
Wood 521(3). N & S 450.01-18.

4713. [News from Parnassus]. *Advice from Parnassus. . . . from January 26. to February 2. 1680. Numb. 2.* (London): (f. H. L.), (1680[1]). S.sh. (r-v).
AW wrote the name of the editor, 'Roger L'estrange' and, in the text, underscored 'Rugiero'.
Wood 417(32). N & S 445.2.

4714. Occurrences. *Occurrences from Ireland from the 2. of April, to the 22. Tuesday May 3. 1642. Numb. 3. [signed R. C. [Robert Cole?]].* London: f. H. Twyford, 1642. 4°. A⁴.
Wood 508(18). N & S 464.

4715. Oxford Gazette, and London Gazette. Muddiman, Henry, ed., et al. *The Oxford gazette. Monday-Thursday, Thursday-Monday. Numbs. 1-23 [7 Nov. [1665]-1 Feb. 1665[6]]. [Continued as] The London gazette. Thursday-Monday, Monday-Thursday. Numbs. 24-246 [1 Feb. 1665[6]-26 March 1668].* Oxford; London: L. Lichfeild; after 25 Jan., T. Newcomb, 1665-1668. Fol. Ff. 1-246. Calf, mottled, with 2 fillets; 2nd rectangle formed by roll decoration and stamp decoration inside and outside corners. Extensive repairs to make margins even, apparently by Bartlett in 1681 or by a binder in 1688.
Pastedown, upper, AW wrote, 'Lord Orrery - Nu. 69 [/] Sʳ Will. Berkley. nu. 70. [/] Sʳ Th. Clifford nu. 74'; flyleaf, upper, 1st, '25 Jan. 1680[1] [/] Given to Roger Bartlet book-binder, for binding of this booke 2ˢ - 4ᵈ, being part of the Legacie that Mʳ Peter Nicolls Fellow of Merton Coll. lefte to me. Ita testor [/] Antonius à Wood. [/] In this volume are contained 246 Gazetts: and Every Gazette, cost me at least 1ᵈ - ob. so that all put togeather come to two pound 7ˢ & 10ᵈ – besides binding. [and totals written in right margin] 2ˢ. 4ᵈ' and 2ˡⁱ - 7ˢ - 10ᵈ' [and below:] Taken in peices & new bound again Dec. 21 - 2ˢ - 6. an. 1688'.
LT 2.413. In this nearly perfect collection there is minor annotation: no. 1, at top, AW wrote the editor, 'Mʳ Hen: Muddiman'; line in margin, usually in pencil, at various news items, e.g., nos. 66ᵛ (an audience before the king), 72 (at a controversy involving Edm. Warcup), 110ᵛ (T. Clifford sworn in as member of Privy Council), 112ᵛ (Irish affairs, and death of James Ware), and 191ᵛ (royal reception of Lord Hollis and H. Coventry, returning from Breda). See also LT 2.49-50. Pasted to the lower flyleaf is the London reprint of *The Oxford gazette* Numb. 3 [20 Nov.-23 Nov. 1665], given by W. Osler in Dec. 1915.
Wood 541. N & S 471.0001A-0021A; 471.0022-0246.

4716. Packet of Letters. [Ashe, Simeon, and William Goode, by]. *A particular relation of the severall removes, of the . . . earle of Manchesters army. Numb. 1 [20 Apr.-6 May].* London: f. T. Underhill, 1644. 4°. Pp. 8.
Wood 377(8). N & S 492.1.

4717. Packet of Letters. [Ashe, Simeon, and William Goode, by]. *A particular relation of the severall removes, of the . . . earle of Manchesters army. Numb. 1 [20 Apr.-6 May].* London: f. T. Underhill, 1644. 4°. Pp. 8.
Tp, AW wrote 'Dupl', in pencil. Dupl. at Wood 377(8).
Wood 612(17). N & S 492.1.

4718. Packet of Letters from Scotland. *Packets of letters from Scotland, . . . to members of the house of commons concerning the transactions of the parliament of Scotland. Num. 5 [17 Ap.].* London: R. Ibbitson, 1648. 4°. Pp. [2], 6. Pasteboard (blue) with parchment spine.
Flyleaves, upper, 2nd-5th, AW wrote the titles of 75 printed works in this vol., within guidelines made with red ink. All concern the civil war. Nos. 45 and 46 were not present in Dec. 1840, according to W. Kirtland. AW himself wrote, at no. 45, 'see afterwards.' and 'Vide Nu. 63'. He had noted his dupl. of Colchester, (45) at (63) and removed (45) from the vol. and placed it in an unbound bundle which was later bound by the Ashm. It is now at Wood 609(14), item 1936 (see also the note at Wood 502(46a), item 5777). A new no. 46 (46b in this cat.) was inserted 15 July 1874 by W. H. Allnutt. Nos. 53 and 69 were absent in 1922 (i.e., they are not in the Milford hand-list). No. 53 was apparently a dupl. of no. 47, and prob. removed for that reason. From nos. 2-59, there is some overwriting of nos. on the printed items; the earlier nos. reflect an earlier order in an unbound state. The final order is roughly chronological from April 1648 to October 1648 Tp, AW wrote after the year, 'Ap. 15'.
Wood 502(1). N & S 480.05.

4719. Packet of Letters from Scotland. *Packets of letters from Scotland, Lincolne, and Lancashire, to members of the house of commons concerning the transactions of . . . Scotland. Num. 17 [11 July].* London: R. Ibbitson, 1648. 4°. Pp. [2], 6.

Tp, AW wrote after the year, 'Jun. 29'.
Wood 502(33). N & S 480.17.

4720. Packet of Letters from Scotland. *Packets of letters from Scotland, . . . to members of the house of commons concerning the transactions of . . . Scotland. Num. 20 [31 July].* London: R. Ibbitson, 1648. 4°. Pp. [2], 6.
The new no. 46, i.e., 46b, was inserted 15 July 1874 by W. H. Allnutt (see note at Wood 502(1), item 4718). Scarborough, Wood 502(46a), item 5777, was stolen before 1840.
Wood 502(46b). N & S 480.20.

4721. Packet of Letters from Scotland. *Packets of letters from Scotland, . . . to members of the house of commons concerning the transactions of . . . Scotland. Num. 23 [21 Aug.].* London: R. Ibbitson, 1648. 4°. Pp. [2], 6.
Tp, AW wrote after the year, 'Aug. 19'.
Wood 502(54). N & S 480.23.

4722. Packet of Letters from Scotland. *Packets of letters from Scotland, . . . to members of the house of commons concerning the transactions of the kingdomes. Numb. 31 [17 Oct.].* London: R. Ibbitson, 1648. 4°. Pp. [2], 6 (one leaf unopened).
Tp, AW wrote after the year, 'Oct. 9'.
Wood 502(73). N & S 480.31.

4723. Parliament. *The humble address of the commons in parliament presented to his majesty, to remove George earl of Hallifax [pp. (63-4) Numb. 24, 26 Nov.].* (London): (f. J. Wright a. R. Chiswell), (1680). S.sh. Pp. '63-64'.
Wood 276a(172). N & S 647.24.

4724. Parliament, Votes. *(Numbs. 59, 60, 60, 62, 61, 6 [really 64]). Votes of the house of commons, Lunae 21. Die Martii. 1681 [and 23, 24, 25, 26 and 26 March].* Oxford: L. Lichfield, f. G. Kunholt, 1681. S.sh. [6] (r-v).
On these sheets the nos. 9-14, in pencil, indicates their place in a former bundle.
Wood 276a(136-141). N & S 648.1 (Wing E2765).

4725. Perfect Diurnal. *A perfect diurnall of the passages in parliament [21-28 Febr.].* [London]: n.pub., (1641[2]). 4°. Pp. 8 (E⁴).
Tp, below, a former no., '2'.
Wood 373(27). N & S 507.05.

4726. Perfect Diurnal. *A perfect diurnall of the passages [28 Feb.-7 Mar.].* [London]: n.pub., (1641[2]). 4°. Pp. 8.
Tp, below, a former no., '8'.
Wood 373(30). N & S. 507.06.

4727. Perfect Diurnal. *A perfect diurnall of the passages in parliament. Numb. 7 [7-14 Mar.].* (London): (f. W. Cooke), (1641[2]). 4°. Pp. 7.
On a slip, inserted before tp, 'Hampsh. petit', and in pencil, 'Mar. 11 1641[2]' (the Hampshire petition is not identified). Tp, AW altered a former no., '37', to '36'; below, a 2nd no., '13'.
Wood 373(36). N & S 507.07.

4728. Perfect Diurnal. *A perfect diurnall of the passages in parliament. Numb. 11 [21-28 March].* [London]: f. W. Cook, [1642]. 4°. Pp. 8.
Tp, AW rubbed out a former no.
Wood 373(43). N & S 507.11B.

4729. Perfect Diurnal. *A perfect diurnall of the passages in parliament. Numb. 12 [28 March-4 Apr.].* [London]: n.pub., 1642. 4°. Pp. 8.
AW altered a former no., '37', to '48'. Below, a no., '29'.
Wood 373(48). N & S 507.12.

4730. Perfect Narrative 1. *A perfect narrative of the whole proceedings . . . in the tryal of the king. Numb. 1 [20-22 Jan.].* London: f. J. Playford, 1648[9], 23 Jan. 4°. Pp. 16.
Lat. version at Wood 670(3).
Wood 364(10). N & S 518.1.

4731. Perfect Narrative 2. *A continuation of the narrative . . . of the high court . . . concerning the trial of the king. Numb. 2 [23 Jan.].* London: f. J. Playford, 1648[9], 25 Jan. 4°. Pp. 8.
Dupl. at Wood 609(6). Latin version at Wood 670(3), item 6358.
Wood 364(12). N & S 518.2.

4732. Perfect Narrative 2. *A continuation of the narrative . . . of the high court . . . concerning the trial of the king. Numb. 2 [23 Jan.].* London: f. J. Playford, 1648[9], 25 Jan. 4°. Pp. 8.
Tp, AW wrote 'Dupl', in pencil. Dupl. at Wood 364(12). Latin version at Wood 670(3), item 6358.
Wood 609(6). N & S 518.2.

4733. Perfect Narrative 3. *A continuation of the narrative . . . concerning the tryal of the king. Numb. 3 [27 Jan.].* London: f. J. Playford, 1648[9], 29 Jan. 4°. Pp. 15.
Between pp. 6-7, AW inserted 2 sheets and covered 3 pp. with notes: 'Bulstr[ode] Whit[e]lock in his Memorials of English Affaires &c. printed 1681, p 368. a. sub an. 1648' (i.e., Wing W1986, published in 1682; see also AO 3.1045), after which he quoted and summarized a description of the trial and some participants. P. 9, correction. Dupl. at Wood 609(7). Latin version at Wood 670(3), item 6358.
Wood 364(14). N & S 518.3.

4734. Perfect Narrative 3. *A continuation of the narrative . . . concerning the tryal of the king. Numb. 3 [27 Jan.].* London: f. J. Playford, 1648[9], 29 Jan. 4°. Pp. 15.
Tp, no. 2 in a former bundle; AW wrote 'Dupl', in pencil. Dupl. at Wood 364(14). Latin version at Wood 670(3), item 6358.
Wood 609(7). N & S 518.3.

4735. Philalethes, Mercurius, pseud. *Part. III. Select city quaeries.* London: n.pub., 1660 [11 April]. 4°. Pp. [2], '17-21'.
Tp, AW wrote, 'Aprill:'.
Wood 608(33). N & S 596A.3.

4736. Publick Advertisements. *Publick advertisements: (with privilege.). No.1 [25 Jun.].* London: T. Newcomb, [1666]. 4°. Pp. [4].
[MS.] Wood D. 22(9). N & S 572.1 (two).

4737. Publick Intelligence. [L'Estrange, Roger, ed.]. *Publick intelligence. Tuesday. Numb. 1 [28 Nov.].* London: R. Hodgkinson, 1665. S.sh. (r-v).
Wood 392(2). N & S 574.1.

4738. Publick Intelligencer. [Nedham, Marchamont, and John Canne, eds.]. *The publick intelligencer, communicating the chief occurrences . . . within the dominions of England, Scotland, and Ireland: Monday. Numbs. 62-114 [15 Dec. 1656-28 Dec. 1657].* London: T. Newcomb, (1656-1657). 4°. Pp. 1053-1948; 1-206 (some p. and numb. sequences are erratic).
Tp, p. 1053, 'the 2ᵈ:'; 1069, 'the 4ᵗʰ' and after that, on tpp, 6, 8, 10 (see note at Wood 389(1)). AW numbered subsequent newsbooks in this vol. until '104' (p. 145), the 3rd from the last. AW had some 104 issues of *The publick intelligencer* and 3 of *Mercurius politicus* bound in this vol. Text, very few marks, and none in the 1st 100 pp. Later, mainly black ink lines in margins at advertisements of books newly published, e.g., pp. 1164, 1241 (AW identified unnamed author, 'Jo. Murcot' in red ink), 1324 (in ink, red and black), 1420, 1451, 1498, 1531, 1894, 1928, 61, 125; and a correction, p. 1580.
Wood 389(2). N & S 575.062-114.

4739. Publick Intelligencer. [Nedham, Marchamont, and John Canne, eds.]. *The publick intelligencer, communicating the chief occurrences and proceedings within the dominions of England, Scotland, and Ireland: Monday. Numbs. 115-155 [28 Dec. 1657-21 Dec. 1658].* London: T. Newcomb, 1657-1658. 4°. Pp. 193-927, 128-164, 1-80 (some p. and numb. sequences are erratic; wanting numb. 146 [4 Oct.-11 Oct.]). Pasteboard (blue) with parchment spine.
Very few marks; these are pencil lines in margins at advertisements of books newly published, e.g., pp. 250, 267, 283, (2nd p.) 298, 490, 523, (2nd p.) 561, 614, (2nd p.) 635, etc.
Wood 390. N & S 575.115-155.

4740. Remarkable Occurrences. *The heads of all the proceedings in both houses of parliament, from the 23. of May.* London: f. J. Smith, a. A. Coe, 1642. 4°. A⁴.
Tp, AW altered a former no., '61' and let a 2nd stand, '74'. A3, at Muyleswick [Muggleswick], he wrote 'in the county pal. of Durh.'
Wood 374(6). N & S 581.2. Wing H1283.

4741. R[eynolds], E[dward]. *The divine penitential meditations and vowes of his late sacred majestie in his solitude at Holmby-house. Numb. 1 . . . By E. R. [18 June]*. London: [J. Clowes], 1649. 4°. Pp. [8], 8. Wood 483(11b). ESTCR 204961. N & S 111A.1. FFMadan 90.

4742. Royal Society. Oldenburg, H., ed. *Philosophical transactions, giving some accompt of the present undertakings, studies and labors of the ingenious in many considerable parts of the world*. London: n.pub., 1665ff. 4°. 5 vols. with numbers from 1665 to at least 1670.
Missing. 'Transactions of Philosophy,' nos. 1, 2, acquired 22 Apr. 1665, 8^d, LT 2.33. Nos. 18-20, acquired 11 Feb. 1667, 1^{s}4^d, LT 2.98. Some nos. acquired 8 Mar. 1670, 3^s, LT 2.189; and 14 June 1670, 1^{s}6^d, LT 2.194. 37 nos. lent to G. Croke, 20 and 30 June 1668, LT 2.139. Sold 5 vols. to R. Plot, 7 Mar. 1686, 1^{li},5^s, LT 3.181.
LT 3.181. N & S 539.01000ff. *O*.

4743. Royal Society. *A general index or alphabetical table to all the Philosophical transactions, from the beginning to July 1677*. London: J. M. f. J. Martyn, 1678. 4°. Pp. [2], 38. Calf with 3 fillets, stamp decoration inside corners (2 leaves and sunflower sprouting fleur-de-lis), and roll decoration at inner, spine edge (Ashm. binding).
Flyleaf, upper, 2nd^v, list of 7 printed works in this vol., by an Ashm. librarian. Many notes in this vol. were cropped when it was carelessly rebound. P. 37, correction, may not be in AW's hand.
Wood 534(1). N & S 539.12136B. Wing G500.

4744. Scotland, Army. *A true relation of the proceedings of the Scottish Army. Numb. 5 [12-25 Mar.]*. London: f. R. Bostock a. S. Gellibrand, 1644. 4°. Pp. [2], 6.
Tp, AW wrote the year, '1643' and '44', and overwrote the latter with a former no., '69', and still later, lined out '69'.
Wood 376(70). N & S 592A.5.

4745. Some Special Passages. *Some speciall passages from, London, Westminster, Yorke. Numb. 2 [17-24 May]*. [London]: n.pub., 1642. 4°. A^4 (A4 blank).
Tp, AW lined out 1 former no., '60', and let a 2nd stand, '69'; and classified the item, 'Anglia', in pencil. Blank leaf, lower^v, 'A. Remonst of the State of the Kingdom by the Parliament – 6 shetes', prob. not in AW's hand (AW's copy is at Wood 374(1), item 2624).
Wood 374(5). N & S 606.02.

4746. Some Special Passages. *Some speciall passages from London, Westminster, Yorke. Numb. 3 [24-31 May]*. N.p.: n.pub., (1642). 4°. Pp. 17-24.
Tp, AW lined out a former no., '67', and left a 2nd stand, '78'.
Wood 374(12) (restored from Hope adds. to its Wood shelf-mark in 1932). N & S 606.03A.

4747. Some Special Passages. *Some speciall passages from Westminster, London, Yorke. Numb. 7 [5-12 July]*. [London]: n.pub., (1642). 4°. G^4.
G1, line in margin.
Wood 374(27). N & S 606.07B.

4748. Some Special Passages. *Some speciall passages from Hull, Anlaby, and Yorke. Numb. 10 [1 Aug.]*. London: R. O. a. G. D., 1642. 4°. Pp. 7.
Tp, AW lined out the former nos., '75', '78'.
Wood 374(31). N & S 606.10.

4749. Three Great Overthrowes. *Three great overthrowes: one in the Palatinate, . . . The other before Haggenaw, . . . and the last in Languedock . . . out of two letters*. [London]: [B. Alsop], 1622, 4 May. 4° (wanting pp. 1-2). Pp. ['3-5'], '6-22'.
Wood 615(7) (Wood 617(7) in Bodl. CD cat.). STC Newsbooks 44.

4750. True and Brief Relation. [Heylyn, Peter, ed.]. *A true and briefe relation of the great victory obtained by sir Ralph Hopton, . . . January 19*. [Oxford]: H. Hall f. W. Webb, 1642[3]. 4°. Pp. 36-42 (F^4).
Tp, AW overwrote a former no. with '30', and added 'written by Dr Pet. Heylyn.'
Wood 375(30). N & S 275.103A. Madan 2043.

4751. True Diurnal. *A true diurnall of the last weekes passages. Numb. 3 [24-31 Jan.]*. London: f. J. Wright, 1641[2]. 4°. Pp. [2], 5.
Wood 373(20). N & S 624.3 (3).

4752. True Diurnal. *A true diurnall of the passages in parliament [7-14 Mar.]*. [London]: n.pub., (1641[2]).

4°. Pp. 7.
Tp, AW altered a former no. and lined out a former no., '35'.
Wood 373(35). N & S 625.1.

4753. True Diurnal Occurrences. *The true diurnal occurrances: or, the heads of the proceedings in parliament [7-14 Feb.].* London: f. J. Hammond, 1642. 4°. A⁴.
Wood 373(22). N & S 621.3.

4754. [Tyrrell, James]. *Bibliotheca politica: or an enquiry into the ancient constitution of the English government; . . . in thirteen dialogues.* London: f. R. Baldwin, 1694 (14 tpp, 1691/2 to 1694). 4°. Pp. [14], 968, [32] (some pp. unopened) (misnumbering) (14 tpp. and an index). Pasteboard (blue) with parchment spine; 1st upper and last lower flyleaves, marbled paper.
The 'Dialogues' came out over a period of two years, and AW recorded when he received certain ones (frequent misnumbering): 1st (to 5th), p. [7], 'Aug. 6 an. 1692'; 6th and 7th, pp. 368 and 435, 'Given by the author Apr. 7. 1693'; 8th (to 11th), p. 539, 'Given to me by the author May 13 1693'; 12th and 13th, pp. 835 and after 900, 'ex dono Authoris 12. May 1694' (also after p. 900, 'Ap[r.]' after imprint date); 1st p. 372, at an advertisement of a book, AW wrote 'By Jam. Tyrrell'. LT 3.397-8.
Wood 625. N & S 24.00-24.14. Wing T3582.

4755. Universal Intelligence. *The Universal intelligence. Tuesday. Numb. 1 [11 Dec.] [by John Wallis].*
N.p.: n.pub., 1688. S.sh. (r-v).
ᵛ, AW took issue with some facts in the report of Lovelace's coming to Oxford (5 Dec.) and wrote in margin, e.g., at printed '300. Horse', 'not 200'; at '2 a Clock', 'three in the morn.'; at '1000. Men in Arms', 'false'; at 'above a hundred of the scholars', '200 of the rabble'; at 'Myter Tavern', 'Miter inne'; and below, 'This is a most ridiculous & silly thing'. LT 3.286-7.
Wood 529(11). N & S 644.01.

4756. Weekly Discovery. *The weekly discovery of the mystery of iniquity: in . . . the late unnatural rebellion in England, anno 1641 [Numb.1].* London: f. B. Tooke, 1681. S.sh. (r-v).
Wood 503(32). N & S 681.01.

4757. Weekly Discovery. *The weekly discovery of the mystery of iniquity: in . . . the late unnatural rebellion in England, anno 1641 [Numb. 2., 12 Feb. 1680].* London: f. B. Tooke, 1681. S.sh. (r-v).
Wood 503(33). N & S 681.02.

End of NEWSBOOKS (items 4649-4757)

4758. Niccholes, Alexander. *A discourse, of marriage and wiving: and of the greatest mystery therein contained: how to choose a good wife from a bad.* London: N.O[kes] f. L. Becket, 1615. 4°. Pp. [8], 55 (mutilated and having the t leaf mounted). Pasteboard (blue) with parchment spine; rebacked.
Flyleaf, upper, 2nd-3rd, AW wrote the titles of 34 printed works in this vol., within guidelines made with red ink. Kirtland wrote at no. 30, 'deest 1841 W. K', and Milford wrote in his hand-list that no. 34 was missing in 1922. AW renumbered items on tpp from no. 4-33, in ink, over former nos. 3-32, in pencil. 1st item, tp, former no. 3.
Wood 654a(1). STC 18514.

4759. Nichols, John. *A declaration of the recantation of.* London: C. Barker, 1581. 8°. A-M⁸,N².
Missing. MS. Wood E. 2(70), p. 5: 'His recantation – his pilgrimages wherin are many things of the author'.
Ed. not identified. Lent to H. Foules, 17 Oct. 1668, LT 2.145.
MS. Wood E. 2(70), p. 5. STC 18533 and 18533.5. O(imperf.), *Folg, Union,* and *O* (imperf.).

4760. Nichols, John. *John Niccols pilgrimage, whrein [sic] is displaied the lives of the proude popes.*
London: T. Dawson f. T. Butter a. G. Isaac, 1581. 8°. *⁸,A-R⁸.
Missing. MS. Wood E. 2(70), p. 5: 'His recantation – his pilgrimages wherin are many things of the author'.
Lent to H. Foules, 17 Oct. 1668, LT 2.145.
MS. Wood E. 2(70), p. 5. STC 18534. *O, BL.*

4761. Nicodemus. Warrin, John, ed. *Nichodemus his gospel.* [Rouen]: J. Cousturier, [1635 ca.]. 8°. Pp. [6], 73.
Wood 871. STC 18571. ARCR 2.793.

4762. Nicolls, Ferdinando. *The life and death of mr. Ignatius Jurdain.* London: f. T. Newberry, 1655.

12°. 2nd ed. [34], 86.
Wood 196(3). Wing N1140.

4763. Nineteen Cases. *Nineteen cases of conscience. Submissively tendred to mr. Hugh Peters, and . . . the triars.* London: n.pub., 1659. 4°. Pp. 8.
Tp, no. '43', in pencil, in a former bundle (cropped at side).
Wood 613(48). Wing N1163.

4764. N[ixon], A[nthony]. *A true relation of the travels of m. Bush, . . . who with his owne handes . . . made a pynace, in which hee past by ayre, land, and water: from Lamborne, . . . to . . . London.* London: T. P[urfoot] f. N. Butter, 1608. 4°. A², B-D⁴,E1-3 (wanting all after sig. E3). Pasteboard (blue) with parchment spine; upper and lower flyleaves, traces of marbled paper.
Flyleaf, upper, 2ndᵛ, AW wrote the titles of 7 printed works in this vol., within guidelines made with red ink.
Wood 465(1). STC 18325 (two) ('O' not recorded in STC).

4765. Nixon, Anthony. *Londons dove: or a memoriall of the life and death of maister Robert Dove.* London: T. Creede, f. J. Hunt, sold E. Marchant, 1612. 4°. A2-4,B-D⁴. Pasteboard (blue) with parchment spine. Rebacked 'H. C. 24.4.[19]50'.
Flyleaf, upper, 2nd, AW wrote the titles of 15 printed works in this vol., within guidelines made with red ink; 3rd, is a misplaced leaf from Wood 532(2), item 5147. Tp, bsm. B4, word in margin, not by AW.
Wood 532(1). STC 18588.5.

4766. Norden, John. *Speculum Britanniae. The first parte an historicall, & chorographicall discription of Middlesex.* [London]: [Eliot's Court Press], 1593. 4°. Pp. [8], 48, [4] (with 3 maps, including London by Pieter Vanden Keere). Pasteboard (blue) with parchment spine.
Flyleaf, upperᵛ, AW wrote the titles of 7 printed works in this vol., within guidelines made with red ink. Tpᵛ, AW wrote 'John Norden hath also published A chronographical description of Hertfordshire – printed much about the same time with this – It is dedicated to Sʳ Edw. Seymoure Earl of Hertford, & containes but 4 sheets besides the title, pref. & Epist.' (STC 18637).
Wood 467(1). STC 18635.

4767. Norden, Jo[hn]. *The surveyors dialogue. Divided into five bookes.* London: [S. Stafford] f. H. Astley, 1607. 4°. Pp. [14], 244.
Pastedown, upper, 3 brief notes to pp. 58, 116 and 138, not by AW. Flyleaf, upper, signature, 'Jo: Aubrey', price, and his note on a 3rd ed. of this book, 1618. LT 2.117. Tp, name of Norden written after initials, not by AW. Pastedown, lower, signatures, 'James Whetcombe'.
[MS.] Wood C. 20. STC 18639.

4768. Norden, John. *Anglus descripsit. A guide for cuntrey men. In the famous cittey of London.* [London]: sold by P. Stent, 1653. S.sh. 290 x 380 mm (untrimmed).
This prob. belongs with Wood 276b(35), both included in an ed. of Norden, *Speculum Britanniae* (STC 18635).
Wood 276b(34). BL Map.

4769. [Norden, John]. *Westminster.* [London]: n.pub., [1653?]. S.sh. 190 x 284 mm. (untrimmed).
This prob. belongs with Wood 276b(34), both included in an ed. of Norden, *Speculum Britanniae* (STC 18635).
Wood 276b(35). BL Map.

4770. N[orris], S[ylvester]. *An appendix to the antidote. Conteyning a catalogue of the visible and perpetuall succession of the Catholique professours of the Roman church.* [St. Omer]: [English College Press], 1621. 4°. Pp. 107.
[MS.] Wood B. 40(9). STC 18658.5. ARCR 2.572.

4771. Northampton. *A true and punctuall relation of the severall skirmishes performed, betweene the Northamptonshire forces and a party . . . under the command of prince Rupert.* London: f. J. Wright, 1643, 28 Oct. 4°. Pp. [2], 6.
Tp, AW altered a former no.
Wood 376(48). Wing T2574.

4772. Northampton. *The humble address, and hearty desires of the gentlemen, ministers . . . of Northampton . . . to . . . Monk [24 Jan. 1659[60]].* [London]: n.pub., [1660]. S.sh.

Note, 'Another copy with date 1660', in a modern hand.
Wood 276a(247). Wing H3373 (one) ('O' not recorded in Wing).

4773. Northampton, and Oxfordshire. *The petitions of Northampton-shire and Oxford-shire*. London: R. Olton a. G. Dexter f. B. Allen a. J. Bull, 1642. 4°. Pp. [2], 5, [1].
Tp, AW overwrote former nos., '15' and '18' (in pencil and in ink), with '24'; below, 'Feb 10. 1641[2]', in pencil.
Wood 373(24). Wing P1865.

4774. Norton, John. *Abel being dead yet speaketh; or, the life & death of . . . m^r John Cotton*. London: T. Newcomb f. L. Lloyd, 1658. 4°. Pp. 51, [5] (5 pp. books printed a. sold by L. Lloyd).
Wood 532(5). Wing N1313.

4775. Norton, Ralph. *A letter concerning the storming . . . of the castle of the Devises*. London: f. E. Husband, 1645, 25 Sept. 4°. Pp. 7.
Tp, AW lined out the former no., '24'.
Wood 378(27). Wing N1326.

4776. Norton, Thomas. *All such treatises as have been lately published by Thomas Norton*. London: J. Daye, [1570]. 8° in 4's. 1,A-C^8,D^4; A-O^4; A-B^4,C^2; A-B^4,C^2; A-B^4 (5 pts., wanting pt. 6). Calf with 3 fillets and stamp centrepiece; flyleaf, upper and lower, printer's waste paper.
Flyleaf, upper, scribble, not by AW. Tp, AW wrote 'This first treatise was printed an. 1569. The rest soon after'; ^{v}, in list of parts, after last, AW wrote 'not here'. A1, AW underscored the name of the author in red ink. Text, some scribbles, frequent marks in margin and underscoring and a few notes, not by AW.
Wood 821. STC 18677.

4777. Norwood, Robert. *The case and trial of capt. Robert Norwood . . . truely and impartially stated, . . . Together with some observations upon the law and its professors*. [London]: n.pub., [1652]. 4°. Pp. 24.
Tp, AW wrote 'Fanaticisms', in pencil. Below, 'Lond 1652', not in AW's hand. P. 3, AW wrote in margin, 'Tho. Andrews was L. mayor'.
Wood 647(16). Wing N1380A.

4778. Nottingham. *A petition presented to the parliament from . . . Nottingham. Complaining of grievances under the ecclesiasticall government*. [London]: n.pub., 1641. 4°. Pp. [4], 28.
[MS.] Wood D. 31(10). Wing P1849.

4779. Nottingham. *To the kings most excellent majesty. A petition presented . . . at York, the first of April by the inhabitants of . . . Nottingham*. London: f. J. Hunscott, 1642, 13 April. S.sh.
^{v}, AW lined out a former no, '36'.
Wood 373(47). Wing T1496bA (Wing, 1642[3]).

4780. Nottingham. *The declaration of the county of Nottingham . . . by way of address to . . . lord general Monck [23 Feb. 1659[60]]*. London: I. B., 1660. S.sh.
AW altered the year to 16'59'.
Wood 276a(215) (not in Bodl. CD cat.). Wing D661B (one) ('O' not recorded in Wing).

4781. Nottingham. *The case of the burgesses of Nottingham, in reference to the surrendring of their charters*. (London): (f. B. Aylmer), (1682). Fol. Pp. 4.
Wood 276b(91). Wing C1023E.

4782. Nowell, Alexander. [Whitaker, William, trans.]. Χριστιανισμου στοιχειωσις . . . *Christianae pietatis prima institutio [Greek and Latin]*. Londini: ap. J. Dayum, 1578. 8°. A-Q^8. Calf with 3 fillets and stamp centrepiece; rebacked.
Pastedown, upper, pasted down side, notes, not by AW. Tp, signature of Edward Wood, lined out; scribbles, in Greek; 'A. W.'; and a signature of an earlier owner, Thomas Astell (?). Tp backed with a leave with scribbles on the pasted down side. Text, passim, schoolboy scribbles, and signatures by Anthony Wood (several, some lined out; for date, see L4, 'Liber Anthonius Wood / amen 1645 /'), Edward Wood (L2), Christopher Wood, and Robert Holman. I4, 'Anthony Wood his Booke witness Walter Condery [?] and Adrian Barry [?] and Robert Holman and John Holman and Christopher Wod anen [i.e., amen]. 1648' (see also Q2^v and Q8).
Wood 780. STC 18728.

4783. [Numan, Philips]. Chambers, Robert, trans. *Miracles lately wrought by the intercession of the glorious Virgin Marie, at Mont-Aigu, . . . in Brabant*. Antwerp: A. Conings, 1606. 8°. Pp. [86], 296, [2].

Parchment.
Flyleaf, upper, 2 notes by Ashm. readers or librarians, followed by 'this is not Ant: a Wood wryte [sic]'.
Tp, AW wrote 'AW MDClx. 1ˢ-2ᵈ'. P. 3, lines mutilating text.
Wood 825. STC 18746.

4784. [Nye, John]. *Mʳ Sadler re-examined, or, his disguise discovered.* London: f. N. Webb a. W.
Grantham, 1654. 4°. Pp. [2], 13.
Tp, AW wrote, 'Said to be written by Philip Nye, or, else with his help, by one of his creatures'. Below,
'Ent. in cat.', in a later hand. AO 3.965.
Wood 476(13). Wing N1480.

4785. O., J. *Bradshaw's ultimum vale, . . . a sermon preach'd at his interrment. By J. O. d.d. [purporting
to be John Owen].* Oxon [really London]: n.pub., 1660. 4°. Pp. 15.
Tp, author's initials underscored in red ink. In a later hand, 'Entered. – ' [?].
Wood 608(38). Wing O3. Madan 2512.

4786. Oates, Titus. *The king's evidence justifi'd: or doctor Oates's vindication of himself, and the reality
of the plot, against a traiterous libel, called the compendium [by R. Palmer, earl of Castlemain].* London: f.
J. Edwin, 1679. Fol. Pp. [2], 53.
Tp, AW wrote '1ˢ.6' and 'Octob.' P. 43, at Odeschalchi and Princess of Rossana, lines in margin.
Wood 422(16). Wing O46.

4787. Oates, Titus*. *A poem upon mr. Tytus Oates, the first discoverer of the late popish plot.* London:
f. H. Brome a. R. Chiswell, 1679. S.sh. with engraving.
Tp, AW wrote the month, 'June'. LT 2.457.
Wood 425(20). Wing P2712A ('O' not recorded in Wing).

4788. Oates, Titus. *A true narrative of the horrid plot and conspiracy of the popish party against the life
of his sacred majesty.* London: f. T. Parkhurst, a. T. Cockerill, 1679. Fol. Pp. [13], 68.
P. [1], beneath the engraving of Oates, AW wrote, 'Anigr[am] Testis ovat.' P. [2], notes from, 'A modest
vindication of Tit. Oates the Salamanca Doctor from perjury: Or an essay to demonstrate him only for-
sworne in severall instances – by Adam Elliot M. A & priest of the church of England – somtimes of Caius
coll. Cambr. Lond. 1682 fol. [Wing E543] [/] p. 27. Tit. Oates borne at Okeham in Rutlandsh. p. 1. entred
into Caius Coll. with the plague 1665 – remarkable for a canting fanatical way conveyed to him with his
anabaptistical Education; & in our academical exercises, when others declaimed, Oates alwaies preached
– p. 2 he staied not above an yeare in Cajus, but removed to Sᵗ Johns Coll. Ib p. 2 Oates afterwards a
school-boy & no Jesuit at Sʳ Omers. – turned away thence for a blockhead p. 20. [blank] p. 32. Oates
vicar of Bobbing in Kent. before he went to the ch. of Rome – Out of the said book might be extracted
Oates his life q[uaere].' P. 3, AW underscored the name, 'Earl of Clarendon', in red crayon; below, 'Titus
Oates, son of Sam. Oates weever: which Sam. having been a preacher, Anabaptist & notorious sectarie,
is mentioned in Tho. Edwards his Gangrena part. 2. p 17. 121. One Oates a carpenter see there also p
72' (i.e., Wood 655(3), item 2403). (AW collected much information on Oates, see, e.g., LT 2.417-8; 3.36).
Tp, AW underscored 'D.D.' after Oates's name, and wrote the price, '2ˢ-6'. P. (8), at printed 'Milton was
a knowne frequenter of a Popish Club', AW wrote, 'qu[aere]'. P. 20, line in margin, in pencil, at story of
Father Warren reconciling Lord Chancellor Hyde to the Church of Rome on his deathbed.
Wood 424(13). Wing O59.

4789. Oates, Titus. *Articles of high misdemeanor . . . against sir William Scroggs.* (London): (R.
Janeway), (1680). Fol. Pp. 4.
Wood 276a(281). Wing O31A.

4790. [Oates, Titus*]. *An exact and faithful narrative of the horrid conspiracy of Thomas Knox, William
Osborn, and John Lane, to invalidate the testimonies of dr. Titus Oates, and mr. William Bedlow.* London:
f. T. Parkhurst, T. Cockerill, a. B. Alsop, 1680. Fol. Pp. [7], 36. Pasteboard (blue) with parchment spine.
Flyleaf, upper, 1st, AW wrote, 'Sʳ Will. Dolben Kᵗ nu 30' (i.e., Wood 426(30), item 6197). 4thᵛ, AW wrote
the titles of 35 printed works in this vol., within guidelines made with red ink; above, 'Third Volume Of
tryals, narratives, dying speeches[,] depositions, inform. &c concerning the popish plot.'; below, 'All plac'd
according to time/'. All 35 items are present in this vol. AW had difficulty in arranging the items and
finally did so according to 'time'. Numerous items have 3 nos. on tpp or flyleaves. On a few (e.g., 18, 28,
29), the final nos. are not in his hand. The binder may have written these, following AW's order on the
upper flyleaf.
Wood 426(1). Wing O41.

4791. Oates, Titus*. *The character of an ignoramus doctor [T. Oates].* (London): (M. T.), (1681). S.sh. (r-v).
ᵛ, AW wrote the month, 'Oct. or Decemb.'
Wood 417(72). Wing C2009.

4792. Oates, Titus*. *A dialogue between two porters, upon dᵣ O–s's removing from White-hall into that city. Robin and Nick.* (London): (f. A. Banks), (1681). S.sh. Pp. 2.
Dupl. at Wood 417(68).
Wood 276b(120) (old no., (98), in Bodl. CD cat.). Wing D1344.

4793. Oates, Titus*. *A dialogue between two porters, upon dᵣ O–s's removing from White-hall into that city. Robin and Nick.* (London): (f. A. Banks), (1681). S.sh. Pp. 2.
AW identified Oates and ᵛ, added the month, 'Sept.' Dupl. at Wood 276b(120).
Wood 417(68). Wing D1344.

4794. Oates, Titus*. *A dialogue betwixt the devil and the ignoramus doctor [T. Oates].* [London]: n.pub., [1681?]. S.sh. (r-v).
ᵛ, AW wrote '1681 in Decemb.'
Wood 417(71). Wing D1355 (Wing, 1679?).

4795. Oates, Titus*. *A hue and cry after dr. T. O.* London: f. Alex. Banks, 1681. S.sh.
AW added the month, 'Sept.'
Wood 417(69). Wing H3274.

4796. Oates, Titus*. *A dialogue between a Yorkshire-alderman and Salamanca-doctor . . . about swearing.* (London): (f. J. Smith), (1683). S.sh (r-v).
Wood 276a(566). Wing D1300.

4797. Oates, Titus*. *The tragick-comedy of Titus Oates, who sometime went under the notion of the Salamanca doctor.* London: Printed by J. M., publ. by R. Taylor, 1685. S.sh.
AW wrote, 'published before he stood in the pillory as tis said–'. LT 3.143.
Wood 421(3). Wing T2014.

4798. Oates, Titus*. *The tryals, convictions & sentence of Titus Otes, upon two indictments. [Part 2] Die Sabbato 9ᵖ Maii, anno Domini, 1685. in Banco regis. Dominus rex versus Oats.* London: f. R. Sare, sold R. Taylor, 1685. Fol. Pp. [3], 94, [2], 60. Pasteboard (blue) with parchment spine.
Flyleaf, 2ndʳ⁻ᵛ, AW wrote the titles of 17 printed works in this vol. (really 14, AW twice included parts of items as separate items), within guidelines made with red ink. On several items, AW recorded a no. in pencil (e.g., 42, 45, 48, 49, 50) which reflects an earlier order (not recorded at entries of items in this vol.). Tp, in t, at Jeffreys, baron of Wem, AW wrote, 'He was made Baron of Wem about 3 dayes before.'; below, 'Sʳ Rob. Sawyer Attorney Gen. [/] Heneage Finch Sollicit. Gen. published at least a month after the triall.' Part 2, pp. 24, 41, 50, 52, 60, some notes on the trial, and/or lines in margins, e.g., 41, AW underlined Oates's address to a female witness, 'Sweet-heart', and at absence of witnesses, noted, 'Oats his witnesses shrink from him.'; 50, identification of a peer, 'Earl of Shaftsbury'; 52, at an attack on lying Presbyterians, hand pointer in margin; 60, at judgments to be carried out, 'This was done [/] and this also [/] and this also [and twice more]'. LT 3.143.
Wood 421(1-2). Wing T2249.

4799. Oates, Titus. *Otes's letter. For . . . sir Leoline Jenkins . . . Feb. 28. 1683 [and] Otes's petition, to the kings . . . majestie.* [London]: n.pub., [1683/4]. S.sh. (r-v).
Wood 276a(159-160). Wing O48A.

4800. O'Brien, Murrough. Inchiquin, 1st earl of. *A manifestation directed to the . . . houses of parliament . . . from the lord Inchequin [et al.] containing the reasons of their now opposing the cessation with the . . . Irish rebels.* London: f. J. Wright, 1644, 10 Aug. 4°. Pp. [2], 10.
Tp, former no., '44', lined out.
Wood 508(51). Wing M424.

4801. O'Brien, Murrough*. Inchiquin, 1st earl of. *Articles exhibited to the . . . house of commons . . . against the lord Inchiquine . . . Together with a full answer their [sic] unto.* London: f. H. Tuckey, 1647. 4°. Pp. [4], 10 (i.e, 16, misnumbering) (p. unopened).
P. 7, 14 words lined out.
Wood 509(28). Wing A3824 ('O' not recorded in Wing).

4802. O'Brien, Murrough. Inchiquin, 1st earl of. *More victoryes obtained in Ireland by . . . lord Inchquine, . . . The relations in a letter.* London: f. R. Bostock, 1647. 4°. Pp. [2], 6.
Tp, AW lined out a former no., '19'.
Wood 509(23). Wing I134A ('O' not recorded in Wing).

4803. O'Brien, Murrough. Inchiquin, 1st earl of. *Two letters sent from . . . unto the speaker of the . . . commons, concerning two great victories . . . in Ireland.* London: f. J. Wright, 1647. 4°. Pp. [2], 6.
Tp, former no., lined out.
Wood 509(20). Wing I137.

4804. O'Brien, Murrough. Inchiquin, 1st earl of. *A letter to the honorable William Lenthal . . . . concerning the . . . proceedings of the lord Inchiquine in . . . Ireland [12 Sept.].* London: f. E. Husband, 1647, 28 Sept. 4°. Pp. 8.
Missing in 1841, see Wood 509(1), item 2361. AW wrote the t on the upper flyleaf.
Wood 509(26). Wing I132. *O, Folg.*

4805. O'Brien, Murrough*. Inchiquin, 1st earl of. *The declaration and ingagement of the protestant army in . . . Mounster. Under . . . baron of Inchiquin.* London: n.pub., 1648. 4°. Rpt. of Cork edition. Pp. [2], 6.
Tp, AW lined out a former no., '40'.
Wood 509(30). Wing D530.

4806. Ockland, Christopher, and Alexander Neville. *Anglorum praelia ab anno Domini. 1327. . . . usque ad annum Domini 1558. Hiis Alexandri Nevilli Kettum.* Londini: R. Nuberie, ex asignat. H. Bynneman, 1582. A⁴,B-L⁸,M⁴,N²,M3-4,N⁴,M5-8,O-T⁸,V⁴ (Kettus is numbered 1-97). Parchment.
Pastedown and upper flyleaves, notes in hands of former owners, Edmund Speccott (and Speccatus, and xvi^d), Johannes Culme (1597), Nicolaus Culme (1600), and Johannes Palimoquo. Margins of *Kettus*, some notes on persons mentioned in text, e.g., pp. 6-8, 11, 15, 21, 25-27 (some word play – 'Wyndhamiae' in text (p. 6) and note: 'They were not so wise or honest as in time to Wynde home./'; 'Hethersetum' in text (p. 8) and note: 'hither set a sett of knaves.'), not in hand of AW.
Wood 100. STC 18773.

4807. Office of General Remembrance. *The office of generall remembrance. Of matters of record, created by his majesties letters pattents for ease of his subjects in their searches.* London: G. Eld f. the Remembrancers Generall, [sold] R. Wilson, 1617. 4°. A-G⁴ (last leaf a foldout).
[MS.] Wood B. 39(9). STC 18788.

4808. Ogilby, John. *The relation of his majestie's entertainment passing through the city of London, to his coronation.* London: T. Roycroft, f. R. Marriott, 1661. Fol. Pp. [5], 38.
Wood 398(18). Wing O181.

4809. O[gilby], J[ohn]. *The Holland nightingale, or the sweet singers of Amsterdam; being a paraphrase upon the fable of frogs.* [London]: f. R. Clavill, 1672. S.sh.
Wood 416(121). Wing O172D.

4810. [Oldham, John]. *Garnets ghost[,] addressing to the Jesuits, . . . after the murther of sir Edmund-Bury Godfrey.* [London]: n.pub., [1679]. Fol. Pp. 4 (mutilated at top).
Wood 417(2). Wing O235.

4811. [Oldham, John]. *The clarret [sic] drinker's song: or the good fellows design.* (London): n.pub., (1680). S.sh. (r-v). See Plate VIII.
At top, AW wrote '1680'; ᵛ, at the date, 'This was printed in John Oldhams poems, publish [sic] an . .'
Wood 417(28). Wing O233.

4812. Oldisworth, Giles. *In eruditissimos sacrorum bibliorum polyglottorum compilatores: poema.* N.p.: n.pub., [1670 ca.]. S.sh.
Wood 416(79). Wing O253A (rare).

4813. [Oldisworth, Michael]. *The speech (without an oath) of Philip Herbert . . . at his admittance . . . into the . . . house of commons, . . . April the 6th, 1649.* [London]: n.pub., [1680]. Fol. Pp. 4.
Missing since 1994.
Wood 531(19). Wing O257A.

4814. Olivier, Jacques. [Bancke, Richard, trans.]. *A discourse of women, shewing their imperfections*

alphabetically. . . . out of the French. London: f. R. T., 1673. 12°. Pp. [4], 185. Calf with 2 fillets.
Tp, 'by Mr Richard Bancke', not in AW's hand, though AW underscored Bancke in red ink.
Wood 738. Wing O284c (olim D1612).

4815. One Argument. *One argument more against the cavaliers; taken from their violation of churches.*
[London]: n.pub., [1643]. 4°. Pp. 20.
Tp, AW wrote the year, '1643'; p. 6, at printed 'Do. Laur.', 'Tho. Laurence'.
Wood 476(17). Wing O333.

4816. O'Neale, Daniel*. *Treason discovered: or the impeachment of Daniel Oneale, . . . one of the commanders . . . against Scotland, . . . and his answer.* London: f. J. Greensmith, 1641. 4°. Pp. A⁴.
Tp, AW wrote 'Scotla[nd]' (cropped at top and side), in pencil, and '1640'.
Wood 614(23). Wing T2075.

4817. O'Neill, Phelim, et al. *The rebells letter to the pope. Wherein they present unto him their late purchases by the sword in Ireland.* London: n.pub., 1642, 20 Jan. 4°. Pp. [2], 6.
Tp, AW wrote after the t, '20 Dec. 1641'.
Wood 507(18). Wing R602.

4818. Onslow, Denzil*. *The memorable case of Denzil Onslow . . . tryed at the assizes . . . touching his election at Haselmere in Surrey.* (London): (f. R. Baldwyn), (1681). Fol. Pp. 8.
Wood 657(54). Wing M1676.

4819. Oprecht Verhaal. *Oprecht verhael van de justitie gedaen over drie misdadigers . . . gejusticeert . . . 28 January, 1669. [In verse, and p. [3] begins:] Verhael vaude [sic] verscheyde tydingen uyt West-phelen wegens den Bisschop van Munster.* Amsterdam: J. Koster, [1669?]. 4°. Pp. [4].
Wood 615(19). Not in BL. Not in BN. Not in NUC.

4820. Opsopoeus, Vincentius, and Matthaeus Delius. *De arte bibendi . . . quibus adjunximus de arte jocandi.* Francoforti ad Moenum: (ex off. haered. C. Egenolphi, imp. A. Loniceri, J. Cnipii Andronici secundi, P. Steinmeyeri), 1582. 8°. A-O⁸. Parchment with 2 clasps, leather.
Flyleaf, upper^v, bsm. and scribble, 'haste'; tp, bsm. A very few marks in margin and underscorings, e.g., K7, K8, prob. not by AW.
Wood 92(1). Adams O 211.

4821. Oraeus, Henricus. *Nomenclator praecipuorum . . . ecclesiae doctorum, . . . metropolitarum . . . Cui accesserunt . . . series Romanorum pontificum atque imperatorum.* Hanoviae: sumpt. D. a. D. Aubriorum & C. Schleichii, 1619. 12°. Pp. 177, [2]. Parchment.
Flyleaf, upper, 2nd, AW wrote 'Guido Bonatus lived 1220 q[uaere]'. Pp. 152-161, marks in pencil, may not be by AW. Flyleaf, lower^r-v, notes, not by AW.
Wood 892. BL.

4822. Orléans, Jesuit College. *Deo opt. max. quod felix, faustum, fortunatumque sit rei literariae universae; adversus morosam antiquariorum nationem, qui ut veterum exaggerent, nostrorum hominum elevant industriam, artes omnes nullā unquam vehementiùs, quam hac aetate viguisse demonstrabit eloquentiae professor in regio aurelian. Collegio Societatis Jesu ad solennem scholarum instaurationem . . . Dies vobis dicitur XVIII. Octobris qui D. Lucae sacer est. [1659, 18 Oct.].* N.p.: n.pub., [1659]. S.sh.
Wood 276a(27) (not in Bodl. CD cat.). Not in BL. Not in BN.

4823. Ortelius, Abraham. *Tusciae antiquae typus. Ex conatibus geographicis Ab. Ortellii.* N.p.: Cum privilegio imperiali et Belgico ad decennium, 1584. S.sh. 436 x 555 (untrimmed) (repaired with a piece of a parchment ms.).
Wood 276b(7). BL Map.

4824. Ortelius, Abrah[am]. *Alexandri magni Macedonis expeditio. Ingenio, iudicio, et eruditione praestanti, domino Henrico Schotto, . . . dedicab. Abrah. Ortelius.* [Antwerp]: cum privilegio imp. et ordinum Belgicor. ad decennium, 1595. S.sh. (no text on ^v). 436 x 557 mm (untrimmed).
Wood 276b(12). BL Map.

4825. Orthography. *Orthography.* N.p.: N.d., n.pub. S.sh.
Missing in 1939 (a delete sign before the entry in the 1717 list). Possibly Wing R314 (rare, BL T) which has the t, Orthography. 1 of consonants, or the alphabet (London 1648).
Wood 276a(22). Not identified.

4826. [Osborne, Francis]. *A perswasive to a mutuall compliance under the present government. Together with a plea for a free state compared with monarchy.* Oxford: [L. Lichfield], 1652. 4°. Pp. [6], 41.
Each small 4° leaf is pasted on a 4° template. Tp, AW wrote 'This book was writt by ffranc: Osbourne ye Author of ye Advice to a son:' (Wing O508, 1656). LT 2.5. AO 1.706.
Wood 626(2). Wing O517. Madan 2201.

4827. [Osborne, Francis]. *Historical memoires on the reigns of queen Elizabeth, and king James.* London: J. Grismond, sold T. Robinson in Oxon., 1658. 12°. Pp. [22], 108, [20], 148 (3 tpp). Calf with 3 fillets and stamp decoration in corners (flower and point) (Ashm. binding); rebacked.
Flyleaf, upper, 3rd, list of 5 printed works in this vol. (really 4, 2 entries for item (1)), by an Ashm. librarian (same hand in Wood 276a). Lines in margin and note at 2nd pp. 72-7, at Philip Herbert, earl of Montgomery (later chancellor of Oxford University), Parsons the Jesuit, and Philip Sidney. P. 88, 'Fox' and 'pox' entered in blanks in a poem. Pp. 100, 124, line in margin. Acquired 22 Apr. 1658, 7^d, LT 1.242.
Wood 251(1). Wing O515. Madan 2401.

4828. Osborne, Francis. *A miscellany of sundry essayes.* London: J. Grismond [f. R. Royston], 1659. 12°.
Missing. Acquired 10 Feb. 1664, LT 2.5. AO 1.705-7.
LT 2.5. Wing O516, 516A.

4829. Osborne, Richard. *A true coppy of two severall letters sent by master Richard Osborne . . . touching a designe to poyson his majesty.* [London]: n.pub., 1648. 4°. Pp. [2], 5.
P. 2, at 'Captain Rolfe', AW wrote 'Edm. Rolfe'.
Wood 632(18). Wing O529A (two).

4830. Osborne, Richard. *Two letters sent by . . . With an answer.* London: f. A. H., 1648. 4°. Pp. [2], 6.
Wood 632(19). Wing O530.

4831. Osborne, Thomas*. Leeds, duke of. *Articles of impeachment of high treason against Thomas, earl of Danby.* [London]: n.pub., [1678]. 4°. Pp. 9.
Missing. Lent to W. Fulman, 1 Jan. 1679, LT 2.432.
LT 2.432. Wing A3858.

4832. Osborne, Thomas*. Leeds, duke of. *The sentiments. A poem to the earl of Danby in the Tower.* London: f. J. Vade, 1679. Fol. Pp. 11.
Tp, AW wrote, 'received from Lond. 24. Aug. 1679', and '3^d.'. Purchased from Vade in July or August 1679, see his record of purchase in MS. Wood F. 50, f. 11.
Wood 417(16). Wing S2558.

4833. Osorio da Fonseca, Jeronimo. Shacklock, Richard, trans. *An epistle of Hieronimus Osorius . . . in Portugale, to . . . princesse Elizabeth . . . quene.* Antwerp: J. Latius, 1565. 8°. Ff. 78, [1] (wanting the errata leaf). Pasteboard (grey) with parchment spine. 1st upper and last lower flyleaves, marbled paper.
Flyleaf, upper 3rd^v, AW wrote the titles of 4 printed works in this vol., within guidelines made with red ink. Tp, 'I have another copie of this -' (perhaps he was referring to W. Haddon, Wood 800(2), item 3366), and 'H1' (shelf-mark?). Some underscoring and section numbers in margins, not in AW's manner.
Wood 800(1). STC 18888. ARCR 2.700.

4834. Osorio da Fonseca, Jeronimo. [Matalius, J., ed.]. *Hieronymi Osorii Lusitani, . . . de regis institutione et disciplina; libri VIII.* Coloniae Agrippinae: ap. haer. A. Birckmanni, 1574. Ff. [8], 318, [11]. Calf with 3 fillets and blind-stamp centrepiece (Ker, VII, no. xv), 2 clasp holes; spine, 4 bands, repaired (Oxford binding).
Flyleaf, upper, waste paper, notes, and flyleaf, and waste paper, lower, notes and scribbles, not in AW's hand. Text, to f. 17, some marks in margin, in ink and pencil.
Wood 458. BL.

4835. Otway, [Thomas]. *The epilogue. Written by mr. Otway to . . . Venice preserv'd, . . . upon . . . the duke of York's coming to the theatre, . . . April 21.* [London]: (f. J. Hindmarsh), (1682). S.sh. (r-v).
Wood 276a(562). Wing O547.

4836. [Otway, Thomas]. *Prologue to a new play, called Venice preserved; or the plot discovered [and] Epilogue to the same.* (London): (f. A. Banks), (1682). S.sh. (r-v).
Wood 276a(563-4). Wing O559.

4837. Otway, Tho[mas]. *The prologue to the City heiress, or, sir Timothy Treatall [by A. Behn]*. (London): (f. J. Tonson), (1682). S.sh. (r-v).
Wood 417(92). Wing O561.

4838. Overbury, Thomas*. *The just downefall of ambition,. [sic] adultery. Murder, . . . Westons, and mistris Turners last teares, shed for the murder of sir Thomas Overbury*. London: f. R. H[iggenbotham], [1615]. 4°. A2-4,B-D⁴.
Wood 365(5). STC 18919.7 (two).

4839. Overbury, Thomas*. *Sir Thomas Overburie his wife. With additions of new characters*. London: [J. Legat] f. R. Allot, 1628. 8°. 13th impr. A-V⁸. Parchment.
Passim, a few brief notes and hand pointers, to F7ᵛ, not by AW.
Wood 740. STC 18916.

4840. Overbury, Tho[mas], copied by. *The arraignment and conviction of sʳ Walter Rawleigh, . . . 17. of November 1603*. London: W. Wilson, f. A. Roper, 1648. 4°. Pp. [2], 38. Pasteboard (blue) with parchment spine; flyleaves, upper and lower, marbled paper.
Flyleaf, upper, 3rdʳ⁻ᵛ, AW wrote the titles of 28 printed works in this vol. (really 29, AW omitted item 25), within guidelines made with red ink. P. 37, note in pencil, prob. not by AW.
Wood 368(1). Wing A3744.

4841. Overbury, Thomas. *Observations upon the Provinces United and on the state of France*. London: T. Maxey f. R. Marriot, 1651. 8°. Pp. [3], 80.
Flyleaf, upper, year and t of this item, not in AW's hand. Tp, Overbury underscored in red ink.
Wood 666(2). Wing O609.

4842. Overbury, Thomas*. *A true and historical relation of the poysoning of sir Thomas Overbury . . . . Also, . . . passages . . . and . . . large speeches*. London: T. M. & A. C. f. J. Benson a. J. Playford, 1651. 8°. Pp. [2], 127 (misnumbering).
Tp, AW wrote, 'Septem: 11. 1660'. See LT 1.331-2. Pp. 26, underscoring, in red ink; 27, at 'at Newmarket', AW wrote, 'at Whitehall say others'; 35, a pointer in margin to a date in the text; 103, a line in margin, in pencil.
Wood 289(7). Wing T2487.

4843. Overbury, Tho[mas]. *A true and perfect account of the examination . . . and execution of Joan Perry, . . . for the . . . murder of William Harrison*. London: f. R. Reynolds, 1676. 4°. Pp. 4, 23.
Flyleaf, upper, 'In Posterum', (R. Sheldon's autograph book motto), and price, '0-6'. Tp, AW identified T. O and T. S. in t as Th. Overbury and Th. Shirley and wrote, 'Sʳ Tho. Overbury of Bourton on the hill in Glouc. the authour', all in red ink; pp. 11-12, identified C. T. as Sʳ Christopher Turner, and R. H. as Sʳ Robert Hyde; 13, (27 lines in all), 'John Perry hung in chaines on the same gallowes [/] Richard & Joane Perry were after execution taken downe & buried under the gallowes: – Three dayes after a gentlewoman pretending to understand witches hired a man to dig up the grave that shee might search Joans body – shee being on horse back, drew up to the grave when 'twas opened, but the horse startling at the sight of the body in grave [sic], ran away under the gallowes & her head hitting against Johns feet struck her off from the horse into the grave – [/] After Harrisons return John was taken downe & buried – And Harrisons wife soon after (being a snotty covetuous [sic] Presbyterian) hung her self in her owne house –why, the reader is to judge. [/] Upon Harrisons return to London, Sʳ R[obert] Hyde was at Glocester in his circuit, & one that had seen Harrison there brought the news to Glouc. which comming to the Hearings of Hyde he became somewhat passionate, [Hyde] commanding his servant to call the messenger, chid him for bringing false news & commanded the jailer to commit him to prison –'. LT 1.452; 3.104.
Wood 365(25). Wing O614.

4844. Overton, R[ichard]. *Articles of high treason exhibited against Cheap-side crosse [in verse]*. London: f. R. Overton, 1642. 4°. Newly printed. Pp. [2], 6.
[MS.] Wood D. 31(42). Wing O623.

4845. Overton, Richard. *New Lambeth fayre newly consecrated and presented by the pope himselfe*. London: R. O. a. G. D., 1642. 4°. A-B⁴.
Wood 483(19). Wing O631A.

4846. [Overton, Richard]. *A remonstrance of many thousand citizens, . . . to their own house of commons*. [London]: n.pub., 1646. 4°. Pp. 20.
Wood 368(8). Wing O632B.

4847. [Overton, Richard]. *The paper called the agreement of the people taken into consideration . . . by the ministers of Christ in . . . Lancaster.* London: f. L. Fawne, 1649. 4°. Pp. [2], 36.
Pp. 4, 6, 7-10, 12-14, pencil lines in margins; 8, 14-6, notes in ink, not by AW (cropped at side); 34-6, some lines in margins at names of testifying ministers.
Wood 609(18). Wing P279.

4848. Overton, Richard. *The baiting of the great bull of Bashan unfolded.* London: n.pub., 1649 [2 July]. 4°. A⁴.
A2ᵛ, pencil line in margin at a purple passage on the link between melancholy and covetousness.
Wood 368(10). Wing O624.

4849. Ovid. *P. Ovidii Nasonis metamorphoseos libri moralizati . . . cum commentarius [R. Regius] ac cum Lactantii Firmiani argumentis: et tropologica ennarratione per P. Lavinium adjecta.* (Lugduni): (imp. J. Huguetan in edibus J. Myt), (1516, 22 June). 4° in 8's. Ff. [5], 194, [6] (wanting t. leaf); f. [1], a2, mutilated. Pasteboard (blue) with parchment spine.
Notes of former owners, f. [1], 'Oxoniae imprimatur impensis William Smith [1632]'; lower ff. [4-6]ᵛ, signatures of William Daudre, e.g., 'William Daudre His Boocke amen anno domino 1637', 'Ex libris Guelielmi Napper [Napier] 1629', and 'Lambert Thomas' (see also 1st f. [5], illeg.) Text, some notes in various hands, none in AW's hand. LT 2.128 (on 3.188 the citation to Wood 404 is incorrect).
Wood 404. *Bibl. Lyon.* 11.291.

4850. Ovid. Peend, Thomas de la, trans. *The pleasant fable of Hermaphroditus and Salmacis.* (London): (T. Colwell), 1565. 8°. A-C⁸. Bound with 87(1) before Wood acquired this volume.
Tp, scribble [?], '89.' and 'Wood 87', not by AW. Ms. pagination and dating continue from the preceding item, 87(1).
Wood 87(2). STC 18971.

4851. Ovid. Underdowne, Thomas, trans. *Ovid his invective against Ibis.* London: T. East and H. Middleton, 1569. 8°. A1-7,B-M⁸ (wanting A8). Parchment.
Tp, 'ABosco'. In text, p. nos. added, numerous lines and underscorings, and hand pointers and dates of events mentioned in text written in margins, which continue through next 2 items; not by AW. B1, signature of Richard Dier.
Wood 87(1). STC 18949.

4852. Owen, John (1560?-1622). Vicars, John, trans. *Epigrams of that most wittie and worthie epigrammatist.* London: W. S[tansby] f. J. Smethwicke, 1619. 8°. A-G⁸.
Missing in 1837. 'Owen's Epigrams translated by John Vicars – Lond. 1619' in Whiteside cat.
Wood 74. STC 18993 (3). O, Hunt, Harv.

4853. Owen, John (1560?-1622). *Epigrammatum . . . Libri decem.* Londini: ex off. A. Math[ewes,] sumpt. S. Waterson, 1633. 12°. Pp. [4], 254 (2 tpp).
Missing. Listed as dupl. in MS. Wood E. 2(70), p. 55, 'Epigrammatum – 1647. 1633. dupl. Joh. Owen'. The 1647 ed., Wood 76(1), has been missing since 1922. The 1633 ed. is listed in MS. Wood F. 51, f. 44. MS. Wood E. 2(70), p. 55. STC 18991. O, Folg, Hunt.

4854. Owen, John (1560?-1622). *Epigrammatum.* Amsterodami: Elzevir, 1647. 24°. Pp. [3], 212.
Missing since 1922. 'Oweni Epigrammata – Amster. 1647' in Whiteside cat. In MS. Wood E. 2(70), p. 55, 'Epigrammatum – 1647. 1633. dupl. Joh. Owen'. The dupl. of 1633 ed. is listed in MS. Wood F. 51, f. 44.
Wood 76(1). O, BL.

4855. Owen, John (1616-1683). *Of schisme the true nature of it discovered and considered.* Oxford: L. L. f. T. Robinson, 1657. 12°. Pp. [4], 280, [2].
Missing. 19 Oct. 1657, 'I exchanged these following bookes in sheets with Mr. Forrest, for . . . [sic]: . . . Owen of schishme [sic] 8° . . . All amounting to a crowne', LT 1.230.
LT 1.230. Wing O780. Madan 2348.

4856. O[wen], J[ohn] (1616-1683). *Unto the questions sent me last night, I pray accept of the ensuing answer, . . . concerning the power of the supream magistrate about religion.* (London): (f. F.Tyton), (1659). 4°. Pp. 8.
Tp, AW wrote, at top, '58', and at bottom, '2ᵈ heap 55', in pencil. P. 8, after printed 'J. O.', 'Jo. Owen.', in red ink.
Wood 370(9). Wing O820.

4857. Owen, John* (1616-1683). *An elegy on the death of . . . John Owen [24 August].* London: f. R. Janeway, 1683. S.sh.
LT 3.66-7.
Wood 276a(536). Wing E390.

4858. Owen, Lewis. *The running register: recording a true relation of the state of the English colledges, seminaries . . . in all forraine parts.* London: [F. Kingston] f. R. Milbourne, 1626. 4°. Pp. [8], 118.
Tp, AW wrote, 'The Engl. Coll. at Lisbon is here omitted.' Pp. 11, 2 corrections, the 2nd by AW; 19, note, 'Dr Smith' at printed 'Doctor Smith'; 20, 46, 48, 51, 67, 78, etc., to 109, short line in margins; 57, 'Lew. Owen at Valladolid 1605'. See note on Owen at Wood 419, item 2365.
[MS.] Wood D. 24(5). STC 18996.

4859. Owen, Lewis. *The unmasking of all popish monks, friers, and Jesuits.* London: J. H[aviland] f. G. Gibs, 1628. 4°. Pp. [8], 164.
Tp, former no., '5'. Bsm. Acquired 2 Sept. 1657, 10^d, LT 1.226.
[MS.] Wood D. 24(6). STC 18998.

4860. Owen, William. *The last true intelligence from Ireland. Being a letter sent from Chester [2 Ap.].* [London]: T. Paine f. J. Sweeting, 1642. 4°. Pp. 8.
Wood 508(6). Wing O833.

4861. Oxenham, James*. *A true relation of an apparition in the likenesse of a bird . . . that appeared . . . over the death-beds . . . of the children of mr. James Oxenham.* London: I. O. f. R. Clutterbuck, 1641. 4°. A-C^4.
Tp, AW wrote, 'I remember I have read this storie in Ja. Howells familiar letters.' (i.e., item 3702).
[MS.] Wood B. 35(6). Wing O842.

4862. Oxford, City. Manuscript. *Drawings of cities, buildings, and notes.* N.p.: n.pub., n.d. Fol. Pp. [4].
Item 114: not in AW's hand, a 14-line statement in Latin, cropped at side, and ^v, a drawing of Queen's Lane and adjacent area, 'Edm. Hall' to 'Black hall Herts Hall'. The other mss. are in AW's hand. Fol. 115: a fragment, notes on the site preparation for the Sheldonian Theatre in 1663-4, and ^v, 'This is the ichnography of Merton Coll choire, before the pavement & gravestones were pulled up & stalls pulled downe 1671' (reproduced, LT 1.450-1; and, A. Bott, *The Monuments in Merton College Chapel* (1964): after p. 12). Fol. 116: drawing and 'The draught of the old building which stood in the middle of University Coll. quadrangle . . . all pulled doune 1668' and details (reproduced, LT 2.148, plate II; and W. Carr, *University College* (London, 1902): 66. Fol. 117: drawing and 'Ousney prospect of the north side of the ruins of Osney church – 1574', and, 'This tower should be higher'.
Wood 276b(114-117).

4863. Oxford, City. *A true confutation of a false and lying pamphlet entituled, a divelish designe by the papists [7 Feb.].* [Oxford]: n.pub., [1641]. S.sh.
Wood 276a(307). Wing T2608 (rare). Madan 976.

4864. Oxford, City. *A true relation of a divelish designe by the papists: to blow up the city of Oxford [13 Jan. 1641[2]].* London: f. I. W., 1641[2]. 4°. A^4.
Tp, AW wrote beside the t, 'All false', and below, 'AW', and 'Jan: 13. 1641[2]'. LT 1.77.
Wood 514(7). Wing T2875. Madan 975.

4865. Oxford, City. *A true and most sad relation of the hard usage . . . used on captain Wingate, captaine Vivers . . . with others of the parliament souldiers, &c. prisoner [sic] at Oxford, under the custody of one Smith.* London: f. G. Hutton, 1642[3], 13 Feb. 4°. Pp. 8.
Tp, 'm' written over printed 'w' in name of Edward Chillendon.
Wood 514(12). Wing T2512. Madan 1233.

4866. Oxford, City. Map. *Oxforde as it now lyeth fortified by his ma^ties forces.* N.p.: n.pub., [1644]. S.sh. 303x 396 mm. (untrimmed).
AW added the date, 'an. 1644' and below, wrote 'This map is made very false' (north and south reversed). LT 1.112.
Wood 276b(30). Madan 1653.

4867. Oxford, City. Glemham, Thomas, governor. *By the governour. I desire that present notice may be given [12 Jan. 1645].* Oxford: L. Lichfield, 1645. S.sh.

AW wrote '1645' in pencil.
Wood 276a(342). Wing G850 (rare). Madan 1834. Steele 2640.

4868. Oxford, City. *An oath to be administered unto all officers and souldiers . . . within the garrison of Oxford*. Oxford: L. Lichfield, 1645. S.sh.
Wood 276a(308). Wing O79. Madan 1764.

4869. Oxford, City. *Oxford, this 19th of August, 1645. Whereas by a former order . . . fortifications*. Oxford: L. Li[chfield], [1645]. S.sh. (mutilated).
Wood 276a(341). Wing E930C (rare). Madan 1807. Steele 2626.

4870. Oxford, City. *Articles concerning the surrender of Oxford [20 June]*. Oxford: L. Lichfield, 1646. 4°. Pp. [2], 10.
Pp. 6-8, wavy lines in margin, not in AW's usual manner. Dupl. at Wood 501(16) and Wood 612(44).
Wood 514(19a). Wing A3815. Madan 1877.

4871. Oxford, City. *Articles concerning the surrender of Oxford [20 June]*. Oxford: L. Lichfield, 1646. 4°. Pp. [2], 10.
Tp, AW wrote 'Dup' in pencil. Dupl. at Wood 514(19a) and Wood 612(44).
Wood 501(16). Wing A3815. Madan 1877.

4872. Oxford, City. *Articles concerning the surrender of Oxford [20 June]*. Oxford: L. Lichfield, 1646. 4°. Pp. [2], 10.
Dupl. at Wood Wood 501(16) and Wood 514(19a).
Wood 612(44). Wing A3815. Madan 1877.

4873. Oxford, City. *Articles to be propounded and treated upon, touching the rendring of the garrison of Oxford [drawn up by members of the privy council and the governor] [19, 22 May]*. [Oxford]: [L. Lichfield], [1646]. 4°. Pp. 8.
Wood 514(18). Wing A3887 (rare) (Wing, Madan 1863). Madan 1868.

4874. Oxford, City. *Civitas Oxon. ss. The oath of every free-man of . . . Oxford*. Oxford: L. Lichfield, 1646. S.sh.
v, AW wrote, '1646 Copy of the freemans Oath of Oxon'. Dupl. at Wood 423(22).
Wood 276a(309). Wing O854 (rare, 2 at O). Madan 1886.

4875. Oxford, City. *Civitas Oxon. ss. The oath of every free-man of . . . Oxford*. Oxford: L. Lichfield, 1646. S.sh.
In a blank, the name of 'Charles' is written in, not in AW's hand. v, '1645' is visible through the protective sheet. Dupl. at 276a(309).
Wood 423(22). Wing O854 (rare, 2 at O). Madan 1886.

4876. Oxford, City. *Orders and instructions . . . for the commissioners appointed to treat for the surrender of . . . Oxford to the parliament*. London: f. M. Walbancke, 1646, 23 May. 4°. Pp. [2], 6.
Tp, '1d', prob. not by AW.
Wood 501(13). Wing E2914. Madan 1867.

4877. Oxford, City. *A full and true relation of the several actions and particulars of what was . . . done in Oxford [28 June]*. London: f. E. Husband, 1646, 1 July. 4°. Pp. 7.
Dupl. at Wood 514(20).
Wood 501(17). Wing F2330. Madan 1892.

4878. Oxford, City. *A full and true relation of the several actions and particulars of what was . . . done in Oxford [28 June]*. London: f. E. Husband, 1646, 1 July. 4°. Pp. 7.
Dupl. at Wood 501(17).
Wood 514(20). Wing F2330. Madan 1892.

4879. Oxford, City. *The humble petition of the major, aldermen . . . of Oxon . . . to the . . . commons . . . With their grievances*. London: f. G. Calvert, 1649. 4°. Pp. 8.
Dupl. at Wood 609(19). LT 1.152.
Wood 515(4). Wing H3558. Madan 2011.

4880. Oxford, City. *The humble petition of the major, aldermen . . . of Oxon . . . to the . . . commons . . . With their grievances*. London: f. G. Calvert, 1649. 4°. Pp. 8.

Tp, AW wrote 'Dup', in pencil. Dupl. at Wood 515(4). LT 1.152.
Wood 609(19). Wing H3558. Madan 2011.

4881. Oxford, City. *Civitas Oxon.* } *ss. The oath of every free-man of the city of Oxford.* Oxon.: W. Hall, 1665. S.sh.
Wood 515(32). Not in Wing (should be at O853A). Not in N & S. Not in ESTCR. Madan 2712.

4882. Oxford, City. *The case of the city of Oxford: shewing how far the said city is concerned to oppose the confirmation of charters, . . . of the university by parliament.* N.p.: n.pub., [1690]. Fol. Pp. 4.
P. 1, 2 corrections. P. 4, AW wrote, 'Some few copies of this were printed in the beginning of January 1689[90]', and, in another hand, 'To be heard at the Barr of the house on Wednesday the 15th. of January 1689[90]. Oxford.', to which AW added, 'Defer'd thence till the 20.' LT 3.322.
Wood 423(65). Wing C1034 (Wing, [1691?]).

OXFORD. UNIVERSITY (items 4883-5088)

4883. Oxford, All Souls. *William Powell alias Hinson . . . plaintiffe; the warden and fellows of All-Soules colledge in Oxford defendants. In the chancellors court of the university of Oxford [10 Nov.].* [London?]: n.pub., [1656]. 4°. Pp. 8.
Wood 515(16). Wing P3098A (rare). Madan 2291.

4884. Oxford, Christ Church. *The case truly stated betwixt the dean and chapter of Christs Church in Oxford, and William Adkins butcher, concerning Frideswides medow near Oxford.* [Oxford]: n.pub., [1667?]. S.sh.
AW wrote '1661', in pencil, and below, another person wrote over an earlier pencil note (by AW?), 'circa 1667 tried at Gildhall at an assise'; ^{v}, '1661 2', in pencil. LT 2.55.
Wood 423(37). Wing C1207 (two). Madan 2777.

4885. Oxford, Magdalen. *Priest. [/] The just shall be had in everlasting remembrance. [/] [prayer . . .] by the hands of our Founder William Wainflett and all other our Benefactors:. . . [last line:] Mag. coll. Oxon. [overleaf] Commemorationes solenniores.* [Oxford]: n.pub., [1660?]. S.sh. (r-v).
Madan (2519) listed a variant printed on only one side of a s.sh.: "English black-letter leaded. – An English form of commemoration, consisting of two Versicles and Responses, and one Prayer mentioning 'our Founder William Wainflet and all other our Benefactors'. This is followed by 'Mag. Coll. Oxon.' in large type, and 'Proper Psalms, 145, 146, 147. Lesson Ecclesiaticus, chap. 44'." AW's copy is not English black-letter leaded, and ends at 'Mag. Coll. Oxon.' The device above, described by Madan as "Royal Arms crowned (with 'C. R.'), and two supporters (Lion and Unicorn) . . . ", is similar, but AW's copy does not have 'C. R.' Wing lists the 2 sides as separate printed items. Wing O992Q 'Form of commemoration of the founder' [1660]) and O992R 'Form of prayer for commemoration of founder' [1693]. Wing O992Q = Madan 2519. For the item printed on the verso side, see Oxford, Magdalen (1693?), Wood 276a(514).
Wood 276a(513). Wing O992Q (rare). See Madan 2519.

4886. Oxford, Magdalen. *Priest. The just shall be had in everlasting remembrance. Answer. Neither shall they fear any evil report.* [Oxford]: n.pub., [1660?]. S.sh.
AW wrote, 'The forme of commemoration to be used at certaine times in the yeare by the societie of Magd Coll. for their Founder–'. Dupl. at Wood 515(24).
Wood 423(36). Wing O992Q (rare, 2 at O) (Wing, [1660]). Madan 2519.

4887. Oxford, Magdalen. *Priest. The just shall be had in everlasting remembrance. Answer. Neither shall they fear any evil report.* [Oxford]: n.pub., [1660?]. S.sh. (ornament, CR, and 25 lines).
AW wrote, 'The forme of commemoration to be used at certaine times in the yeare by the societie of Magd. Coll. Oxon. for their Founder'. Dupl. at Wood 423(36).
Wood 515(24). Wing O992Q (rare, 2 at O) (Wing, [1660]). Madan 2519.

4888. Oxford, Magdalen. *Commemorationes solenniores [/] d^{mi} fundatoris & benefactorum [/] habendae in coll. Magd. Oxon. [/] 1. Obitus Johannis Claymond, Johannis Higden, [/] & Robert Morwent primo die lunae in Quadragesima. . . . [12. names; overleaf] Priest. The just shall be had.* [Oxford]: n.pub., [1693?]. S.sh. (r-v).
On sheet with another item. See note at Oxford, Magadalen (1660?), Wood 276a(513).
Wood 276a(514). Wing O992R (rare).

4889. Oxford, Merton College. *Merton colledge case.* [London?]: n.pub., [1625]. S.sh. Obl.
Note in margin, not in AW's hand.
Wood 423(12). STC 19049. Madan 513.

4890. Oxford, New College. *[The draught or view, with the ichnography, of the new buildings beyond &
on the east side of New College great quadrangle].* N.p.: n.pub., [1682]. S.sh.
The t is that written by AW on the sheet. LT 3.5.
Wood 423(55) (not in Bodl. CD cat.). Not in Wing. Not in ESTCR.

4891. Oxford, Trinity College. Kettle, R., praesidens. *Decretum de gratiis collegio rependendis [12 Dec.
1602].* [London?]: n.pub., [1602]. S.sh. (43 lines; above, woodcut).
Dupl. or diff. ed. at Wood 423(13) (which may have been removed to here; there is a second no. '13' at
Wood 276b). STC 19051, 'Post 1640', but with 47 lines of print. Madan 213, 43 lines of print and year,
1602. A similar item at G.A. Oxon. C.287(1), ca. 1700, has 52 lines).
Wood 276b(13). Wing O992T (rare). STC 19051. Madan 213.

4892. Oxford, Trinity College. *'Decretum de gratiis collegio s. s. Trin. rependendis'.* [London]: n.pub.,
[1602?]. S.sh.
Missing in 1922. T from upper flyleaf. Dupl. or diff. ed. at Wood 276b(13).
Wood 423(13). Wing O992T (rare). Madan 213.

4893. Oxford, University. *Cōpendium questōnū de luce et lumine.* [Oxford]: (in celiberima universitate
Oxoniensi per me J. Scolar), (1518, 5 June). A-B⁴.
LT 3.344.
Jesus College 1. Arch. 2. 25(3). STC 5607. Madan 30.

4894. Oxford, University. *Academiae Oxoniensis pietas . . . Jacobum Angliae Scotiae Franciae & Hiberniae regem.* Oxoniae: Jos. Barnesius, 1603. 4° in 8's. Pp. [4], 176 (wanting all after sig. L⁸). Calf with
3 fillets, stamp decoration inside corners, and roll decoration at the inner, spine edge (Ashm. binding);
rebacked.
Flyleaf, upper, 1st, 'E Libris Musei Ashmoleani.'; 2nd^v, list of 11 printed works in this vol., by an Ashm.
librarian. 1st item, pp. 96, 101, 115, 119, 120, 175, some underscoring or vertical lines at author's names,
some in AW's manner. Some pen and pencil marks and notes in text not in AW's hand, e.g., pp. 92-3, and
109, at 'Vive Jacobe diu.', in margin: 'Carole vive diu.'; 176, signature of 'Robert Scaife'.
Wood 484(1). STC 19019. Madan 230.

4895. Oxford, University. *The answere of the vicechancelour, the doctors . . . to the humble petition
. . . desiring reformation of certaine ceremonies and abuses of the church.* Oxford: J. Barnes, sold by S.
Waterson [London], 1603. 4°. Pp. [16], 32.
Tp, scribbles. Diff. ed. (1604; dedicated to King James) at Wood 516(1).
Wood 614(3). STC 19011. Madan 233.

4896. Oxford, University. *The answere of the vicechancelour, the doctors . . . to the humble petition
. . . desiring reformation of certaine ceremonies and abuses of the church.* Oxford: J. Barnes, sold S.
Waterson [London], 1604. 4°. A-E⁴,F². Pasteboard (grey) with parchment spine; rebound.
Flyleaf, upper, 1st, a recent note, 'Found on stub opposite 1966' referring to a slip, now pasted in, on which
AW wrote, 'To be sewed on bords. [/] not glewed [/] parchment on the back side' (the binder followed these
instructions); 3rd^v, AW wrote the titles of 12 printed works in this vol., within guidelines made with red
ink. Some numbering in the vol. was later altered: item no. 7 to 6*, and item no. 12 to 10*. The vol. still
holds 12 printed works in AW's original order. 1st item, diff. ed. at Wood 614(3).
Wood 516(1). STC 19013. Madan 248.

4897. Oxford, University. *Britanniae natalis.* Oxoniae: J. Lichfield, 1630. 4°. Pp. [4], 78.
Pp. 63, 72, at Fr. Goldsmith and at A. Annesley, line in margin, in red ink; a few underscorings, e.g., pp.
64, 70.
Wood 484(3). STC 19032. Madan 651.

4898. Oxford, University. Potter, Christopher, issued by. *To all Christian people to whom these presents
shall come to be read: Christopher Potter . . . sendeth greeting.* [Oxford]: n.pub., [1640]. S.sh.
Template sheet with blanks for insertion of names. Below, date in a modern hand.
Wood 276a(343). STC 19014.5 (rare). Madan 949.

4899. Oxford, University. *An answer to the petition sent from the universitie of Oxford to . . . parliament*

[on behalf of episcopacy and cathedrals]. London: n.pub., 1641. 4°. Pp. 12.
LT 1.51.
Wood 514(4). Wing A3430. Madan 985.

4900. Oxford, University. Προτελεια *Anglo-Batava pari plusquàm virgineo Guiliellmo Aravsii, & Mariae Britanniarum, academia Oxoniensi procurante*. Oxoniae: L. Lichfield, 1641. 4°. ¶⁴,2¶²,A-D⁴,E²,a-b⁴,c².
Flyleaf, lower, 1st, 'Liber Musaei Ashm: Oxōn', not in AW's hand.
Wood 320(9). Wing O942. Madan 964*.

4901. Oxford, University. *To the high and honorable court of parliament, the humble petition of the university of Oxford, in behalfe of episcopacy and cathedralls*. [London]: n.pub., [1641]. S.sh.
A 2-word corrective addition, Easterne 'and westerne' Churches, prob. not by AW. ᵛ, a 25-line ms. summary of the answer by his majesty to the vice-chancellor, and signed, 'Testor Ego C. P.' by the vice-chancellor Christopher Potter. Below, AW wrote '– his mᵗⁱᵉˢ 1640/1', cropped, and, '1641'. LT 1.51.
Wood 514(3). Wing O986B (two). Madan 983.

4902. Oxford, University. *To the high court of parliament, the humble petition of all colledges and halls*. [Oxford]: n.pub., [1641]. S.sh.
AW wrote, 'Delivered to his maj. by the vicechʳ. ult Apr. 1641'.
Wood 423(18). Wing O987 (two). Madan 977.

4903. Oxford, University. *To the high . . . court of parliament, the humble petition of the university of Oxford, in behalfe of episcopacy and cathedralls*. Oxford: L. Lichfield, 1641. 4°. Pp. [2], 6.
Wood 514(2). Wing O985. Madan 981.

4904. Oxford, University. *A true relation of the late conference held at Oxford between the Presbyterians and the Independents*. [London]: n.pub., 1646. 4°. Pp. [2], 5.
Tp, '3. 1. 2-'(?), lined out; an early shelf-mark(?) '2.46' [or 'Q.46']. P. 5ᵛ, '2.46' or 'Q.46'.
Wood 514(21). Wing T2978. Madan 1907.

4905. Oxford, University. *The remonstrance of the kingdome of England to the universities of Oxford and Cambridge. With a review of the covenant*. [Oxford?]: f. the publique good, 1647. 4°. A².
Wood 612(69). Wing O1005 (two). Madan 1966.

4906. Oxford, University. *The case of the university of Oxford: or, the sad dilemma that all the members thereof are put to, . . . In a letter . . . to mr Selden*. [London]: [f. R. Royston], 1648. 4°. Pp. [2], 6.
Dupl. at Wood 614(4) and Wood 631(1).
Wood 514(40). Wing C1173. Madan 1992.

4907. Oxford, University. *The case of the university of Oxford: or, the sad dilemma that all the members thereof are put to, . . . In a letter . . . to mr Selden*. [London]: [f. R. Royston], 1648. 4°. Pp. [2], 6.
Dupl. at Wood 514(40) and Wood 631(1).
Wood 614(4). Wing C1173. Madan 1992.

4908. Oxford, University. *The case of the university of Oxford: or, the sad dilemma that all the members thereof are put to, . . . In a letter . . . to mr Selden*. [London]: [f. R. Royston], 1648. 4°. Pp. [2], 6. Calf with 3 fillets, stamp decoration inside corners (2 leaves, sunflower sprouting fleur-de-lis), and roll decoration at inner, spine edge (Ashm. binding). Most items were cropped in the binding.
Flyleaf, upper, 2nd, the titles of 20 printed works (actually 19, nos. 8-9 are 1 item) in this vol., by an Ashm. librarian (same hand in Wood 276a). Numbering of works on tpp is in Roman numerals (nos. 1-4 also have Arabic numbers, though prob. not by AW). Tp, AW wrote 'Dupl', in pencil. Dupl. at Wood 514(40) and Wood 614(4).
Wood 631(1). Wing C1173. Madan 1992.

4909. Oxford, University. *Oxonii lachrymae, Rachell weeping for her children, or, a . . . relation of the present grievances . . . a letter [signed Philanax Anonomus]*. London: n.pub., 1649. 4°. Pp. 8.
Pp. 4-8, AW wrote some notes, corrections, underscored and made marks in margin, e.g., p. 6 at loyalists expelled, 'Those crossed thus † either kept their places or got into other colleges.' (p. 6, below, 3-word note, not in AW's hand); 8, at a reference to a catalogue which the author will send, 'That I desire much to see.' Flyleaf, lower, on a slip pasted on, AW wrote, 'Turn'd out from Q. Coll' and six names, Joh. Pierson, F. Gibson, J. Grigge, R. Fletcher, Tho. Tarne, and E. Wilkinson. LT 1.142.
Wood 514(54). Wing O998. Madan 2012.

4910. Oxford, University. *To our reverend brethren the ministers of the gospel in England and Wales*.

[London]: n.pub., (1649, 22 Oct.). S.sh (r-v).
Wood 423(29). Wing T1383A (two). Madan 2018.

4911. Oxford, University. *Musarum Oxoniensium* Ελαιοφορια . . . *Sive, ob faedera, auspiciis Oliveri . . . protectoris.* Oxoniae: L. Lichfield, 1654. 4°. Pp. [4], 1-68, 89-104; A-L⁴.
Pp. [1], [3], 1, 104, scribbling, not by AW. Pp. 11, 25, 45, 49, 51, 58-9, and 67, identifications of authors or their offices, by AW. See item 995, and for a satire, Wood 515(13), item 3799, and Madan 2246.
Wood 484(4). Wing O902. Madan 2243.

4912. Oxford, University. *Sundry things from severall hands concerning the university of Oxford: viz. I. A petition from some well-affected therein.* London: T. Creake, 1659. 4°. Pp. [2], 10.
Tp, AW wrote, 'Reported to be written by Joh. Wagstaff of Oriel Coll. but false.' P. 8, at the John Wallis 'case', line in margin. Dupl. at Wood 610(45). LT. 1.295; AO 3.1114; AOF 2.220.
Wood 515(22). Wing S6181. Madan 2430.

4913. Oxford, University. *Sundry things from severall hands concerning the university of Oxford: viz. I. A petition from some well-affected therein.* London: T. Creake, 1659. 4°. Pp. [2], 10.
Tp, no. in a former bundle, '31', in pencil. Dupl. at Wood 515(22). LT. 1.295; AO 3.1114; AOF 2.220.
Wood 610(45). Wing S6181. Madan 2430.

4914. Oxford, University. Sheldonian. *To the right worshipful the heads of the respective colleges . . . a convocation in the theatre, for the university's being invested in the possession of it [John Fell, vice-chancellor].* Oxoford [sic]: H. Hall, 1669. S.sh.
Date entered, July 9, 1669, in a modern hand.
Wood 276a(384). Wing O987L (rare). Madan 2836.

4915. Oxford, University. *A certificat in order to the collecting and reporting [by C. Wase] the state of the present English free-schools [16 Aug.].* [Oxford]: n.pub., [1673]. S.sh. 4°.
LT 2.268.
Wood 658(798). Wing O865 (rare) (Wing, 1673). Madan 2984.

4916. Oxford, University. Sheldonian. *A discription of the painting of the theater in Oxford.* Oxford: L. Lichfield, 1673. S.sh.
AW wrote, 'published at the Act time. At the same time also in 1674' (the latter is Wing D1165A). LT 2.266.
423(50). Wing D1165 (rare). Madan 2956.

4917. Oxford, University. *A pandarique [sic] ode on the vice-chancelor's [J. Lloyd] return to Oxon.* [London]: (f. C. Corbet), (1683). S.sh. Pp. 2.
AW wrote '1683', in pencil. Dupl. at Wood 417(116).
Wood 423(57). Wing P2254A (Wing, Chancellor's).

4918. Oxford, University. *A pandarique [sic] ode on the vice-chancelor's [J. Lloyd] return to Oxon.* [London]: (f. C. Corbet), (1683). S.sh. Pp. 2.
P. 2, AW wrote the month, 'May'. Dupl. at Wood 423(57).
Wood 417(116) (517(116) in Bodl. CD cat.). Wing P2254A (Wing, Chancellor's).

4919. Oxford, University. *The humble address and recognition of the university of Oxford presented to . . . James II.* Oxford: at the theater, 1685. Fol. Pp. [4].
AW noted the year to be '4' that is, in his o.s., '1684', beside the year of the act of convocation, and 'This was set before the book of verses, on the Kings inauguration.'
Wood 423(60). Wing O887.

4920. Oxford, University Carrier. *Orders concerning the rates, and demands of carriers, . . . betwixt . . . Oxford, and . . . London [1 Sept.].* [Oxford]: [H. Hall], [1666]. S.sh.
AW wrote '1666', in pencil.
Wood 276a(352). Wing O903E (rare). Madan 2751.

4921. Oxford, University Carrier. *'Thomas More's paper of a flying coach'.* N.p.: n.pub., [1669 or later]. S.sh.
Missing. T is from the 1717 list. See Wood 276a(355a-b, 359, 369). LT 2.153, 219f., 223, 245. This item may be a duplicate or a copy not listed in Madan (2835, 2894, 2898, 2935).
Wood 276a(366). Not identified.

4922. Oxford, University Carrier. *Whereas the appointment, ordering, . . . of all carriers . . . trading [5 Apr.].* [Oxford]: [L. Lichfield?], [1669]. S.sh.
See LT 2.153.
Wood 276a(355a). Wing O992F (rare) (Wing, 1660). Madan 2835.

4923. Oxford, University Carrier. *Whereas Edward Bartlet hath without licence from me, presumed to set up a flying coach . . . July 20.* [Oxford]: n.pub., [1670]. S.sh.
LT 2.196.
Wood 276a(358). Wing O992C (rare). Madan 2857.

4924. Oxford, University Carrier. *By order from mr vice-chancellour. These are to give notice that whereas Thomas Dye and John Fosset hath without license from mee [P. Mews, 27 Apr.].* [Oxford]: n.pub., [1671]. S.sh.
LT 2.221.
Wood 276a(365). Wing O863D (rare). Madan 2897.

4925. Oxford, University Carrier. *Oxford one day stage-coach . . . begins Munday next, being the 17th instant April.* [Oxford]: n.pub., [1671]. S.sh. 4°.
AW wrote at top, '1671', in pencil, and added, at bottom, over a 2nd pencilled '1671', in ink, 'This coach was silenced by the Vicechanc: Order stuck up on every corner in Oxōn Apr: 15. 1671. because it was set up without his leave.' LT 2.221.
Wood 276a(363) (not in Bodl. CD cat.). Wing S5740 (rare). Madan 2910.

4926. Oxford, University Carrier. *To London every day. . . . The stage begins . . . 15. of May.* [Oxford]: n.pub., [1671]. S.sh. obl. 16°.
AW wrote '1671', in pencil. LT 2.223.
Wood 276a(355b). Wing T1379C (rare). Madan 2898.

4927. Oxford, University Carrier. *Whereas the appointment, ordering, . . . of all carriers . . . trading . . . April 1. 1670.* [Oxford]: n.pub., [1671]. S.sh.
AW altered the date to 167 '1' and wrote '1671'. LT 2.219-20.
Wood 276a(359). Wing O992G (rare). Madan 2894.

4928. Oxford, University Carrier. *By order from mr. vice-chancellor. These are to give notice, that whereas Thomas Dye and John Fosset, have without license from me . . . 22 Feb. 1671.* [Oxford]: [at the Sheldonian], [1672]. S.sh.
Wood 276a(362). Wing O863F (rare). Madan 2934.

4929. Oxford, University Carrier. *By order from mr vice-chancellor. Whereas Thomas Dye and John Fosset, have without licence from mee [P. Mews, 22 Apr.].* [Oxford]: [at the Sheldonian], [1672]. S.sh.
Wood 276a(370). Wing O863H (rare). Madan 2936.

4930. Oxford, University Carrier. *Whereas the appointment, ordering . . . of all carriers . . . doth of right belong . . . to the chancellor, . . . Thomas Moore, and Edward Bartlet jun. licensed carriers of the said university [P. Mews, 19 Apr.].* [Oxford]: [at the Sheldonian], [1672]. S.sh. obl.
For more, see LT 2.245.
Wood 276a(369). Wing O992H (rare) (Wing, no location recorded). Madan 2935.

4931. Oxford, University Carrier. *Whereas the carriers between the university of Oxford, and the city of London, . . . exacted what rates they pleased . . . It is therefore now ordered [4 Dec.].* [Oxford]: n.pub., [1674]. S.sh.
Wood 276a(318). Wing O992I (rare). Madan 3019.

4932. Oxford, University Encomia. Kingsmill, William, ed. *Encomion Rodolphi Warcopi [Aug. 1605].* Oxoniae: J. Barnesium, 1605. 4°. A-E⁴ (E4 blank).
A3, C1, at names of authors of poems, W. Kingesmillus and Jo. Reinoldes, line in margin.
Wood 460(7). STC 19049.5. Madan 263.

4933. Oxford, University Encomia. Magdalen. *Beatae Mariae Magdalenae lachrymae, in obitum . . . Gulielmi Grey.* Oxoniae: J. Barnesius, 1606. 4°. Pp. [4], 42.
P. 14, correction, at 1606, '1605-6'; 36, at Gualt. Rauleigh, line in margin.
Wood 460(8). STC 19046. Madan 277.

4934. Oxford, University Encomia. [Martin, James, ed.]. *Eidyllia in obitum fulgentissimi Henrici*

Walliae principis duodecimi. Oxoniae: Jos. Barnesius, 1612. 4°. A-D⁴,E².
Wood 484(2). STC 19020. Madan 342.

4935. Oxford, University Encomia. Merton. *Bodleiomnema. (Memoriae sacrum. Viro clarissimo,*
. . . Thomae Bodleio. . . . Oratio funebris . . . à Johanne Halesio). Oxoniae: J. Barnesius, 1613. 4°.
[4], 84, [18]. Parchment.
Flyleaf, upper, 1st^v, list of 9 printed works in this vol., not in AW's hand; 2nd, 'George: Sadleir', and, AW
wrote, 'He hath severall copies of verses here in ms.' (LT 1.426; see also 2.129, possibly acquired 3 Mar.
1668). After last p., blank sheet^r-v, a 46-line MS. poem, in English, unsigned, but by George Sadleir, with
heading, 'An extemporall compassion on some passages in the Funebria Sacra'. Sadleir owned this vol. and
wrote other poems on flyleaves; see Wood 460(3 and 9).
Wood 460(1). STC 19048. Madan 374.

4936. Oxford, University Encomia. Exeter. *Threni Exoniensium in obitum . . . Johannis Petrei, baronis*
de Writtle. Oxoniae: J. Barnesius, 1613. 4°. Pp. [4], 48.
P. 5, a correction. Pp. 18, 22, and 41, at Jo. Balcanquall, Joh. Bayly, and Nic. Hunt, lines in margin, in
red ink.
Wood 460(2). STC 19044. Madan 372.

4937. Oxford, University Encomia. *Camdeni insignia.* Oxoniae: J. Lichfield a. J. Short, 1624. 4°. ²,A-
F⁴,G² (wanting ¶,2¶⁴,3¶²).
A2^v, at Samuel Fell, AW wrote, 'ch.ch. in Ox.'; B4^v, correction; E2, at Joh. Donne, lines in margin; E3 line
in margin, in red ink. After 1st flyleaf, upper, bibliog. note on contents of this item by a later librarian.
Wood 484(7). STC 19028. Madan 517.

4938. Oxford, University Encomia. *Schola moralis philosophiae Oxon. In funere [Thomae] Whiti pul-*
lata. Oxoniae: J. Lichfield a. J. Short, 1624. 4°. Pp. [2], 6 (wanting 'Oratio funebris', per G. Price).
There are 2 entries for this single work. The other part, the last 4 leaves, is at Wood 512(8), item 4939.
Slip added, with bibliog. information by a later librarian.
Wood 484(6). STC 19029. Madan 518.

4939. Oxford, University Encomia. Price, William, academic. *Schola moralis philosophiae Oxon. In*
funere [Thomae] Whiti pullata [Heading:] Oratio funebris habita Oxoniae, . . . per G. Price [22 Apr. 1624].
[Oxoniae]: [J. Lichfield a. J. Short], [1624]. 4°. A⁴, only.
There are 2 entries for this single work. The other part, pp. [2], 6, is at Wood 484(6), item 4938.
Wood 512(8). STC 19029. Madan 518.

4940. Oxford, University Encomia. *Verses on the death of . . . Bevill Grenvill.* [Oxford]: [L. Lichfield],
1643. 4°. Pp. [2], 22.
P. 3, correction in a poem.
Wood 319(3). Wing 0990. Madan 1436.

4941. Oxford, University Press. *A proposal tending to the advancement of learning by . . . encourage-*
ment of the press. [Oxford]: [at the Sheldonian], [1675]. S.sh. (r-v).
Year, not in AW's hand; ^v, AW wrote the year, '1675'. Also, 'proposalls to encourage the presse att Oxford',
not in AW's hand. Later ed. at Wood 423(54). LT 2.333.
Wood 423(51). Wing P3710 (two). Madan 3069.

4942. Oxford, University Press. *A proposal tending to the advancement of learning by . . . encourage-*
ment of the press. [London]: [at the Sheldonian], [1681]. S.sh. (r-v).
AW wrote the year, '1681', in pencil; below, year, not in AW's hand. Earlier ed. at Wood 423(51).
Wood 423(54). Wing P3711 (rare). See Madan 3069.

4943. Oxford, University Press. *Friendly advice to the correctour of the English press at Oxford con-*
cerning the English orthographie. London: f. R. Clavell, 1682. Fol. Pp. [2], 10.
AW wrote, 'AW', in pencil, and 'published about 10. Apr. 1682'. Pp. 1, initials of the public orator, 'D. S.',
altered to 'D^r. South'; 6, underscoring; 7, William Slater, underscored, and line in margin at controversy
over the city name, Ousford vs. Oxford. A few later pencil lines in margins. LT 3.12; 2.170.
Wood 423(56). Wing F2215.

4944. Oxford, University Statutes. *Decretum . . . damnans propositiones neotericorum [D. Paraeus et*
al.] infra-scriptas, sive Jesuitarum, sive Puritanorum, sive aliorum cujuscunq; generis scriptorum. Oxonii:
J. Lichfield & J. Short, 1622. 4°. A⁴,B² (A1 blank).

Flyleaf, upper, AW wrote, 'See in H. Grotius', a reference to a work outside of this vol. B1, pencil line around a paragraph (quoted in *Hist. and Antiq.*, 2.346-7; AO 1.3).
Wood 516(4). STC 19014 (STC, Oxoniae). Madan 499.

4945. Oxford, University Statutes. [Turner, P[eter] (younger), engraver]. *Carolus R. Ordo sive series electionis procuratorum in singulis coll. academiae Oxoniensis [a chart. With] Statuta*. Oxoniae: J. Lichfield, imp. G. Davis, 1629. S.sh. Obl. [2] (*Statuta* is cut in 2 and pasted at sides of the *Ordo*; all corners of *Statuta* are supported by slips).
ᵛ, AW wrote the year, '1629'. Acquired 8 Oct. 1658, 6ᵈ, LT 1.260. Dupl. of *Statuta* at Wood 276a(310).
Wood 423(14). STC 19009 and 19008 (issued together). Madan 628-9.

4946. Oxford, University Statutes. *Statuta. I Schedula sive repertorium seriei & circuitus praedicti*. Oxoniae: J. Lichfield, imp. G. Davis, 1629. S.sh.
Dupl. with Wood 423(14).
Wood 276a(410). STC 19008. Madan 629.

4947. Oxford, University Statutes. *A proclamation, for the well ordering of the market in the cittie of Oxford*. (Oxford): (J. Lichfield), (1634). Fol. Pp. [3].
P. 1-2, slight marks or horizontal lines in margin. P. 3ᵛ, on pasted down side, a heading for this document, not in AW's hand.
Wood 276a(310). STC 19004. Madan 769.

4948. Oxford, University Statutes. [Crosfield, T., ed?]. *Synopsis seu epitome statutorum, eorum praesertim, quae juventuti academ. Oxon: maxime expedit pro doctrinā & moribus habere cognita*. Oxonii: G. Turner, imp. G. Webb, 1635. S.sh.
ᵛ, AW wrote the year, '1635', in pencil.
Wood 423(15). STC 19006. Madan 797.

4949. Oxford, University Statutes. [Crosfield, T., compiler]. *[Statuta selecta è corpore statutorum universitatus Oxon.] Speculum academicum: quadratura circuli, sive cyclus praelectorum in schema redactus*. [Oxford]: [typ. G. Turner pro G. Webb], [1638]. 8°. S.sh. (one p. only, 'pag. 20').
LT 1.131.
Wood 423(16). STC 19007. Madan 876.

4950. Oxford, University Statutes. *5. Elizabeth. The oath of supremacy to be taken by everyone that is matriculated being sixteen years of age or more*. [Oxford]: n.pub., [1640?]. S.sh. 4°. Pasteboard (blue) with parchment spine; rebacked.
Flyleaf, upper, 1st, 'Binding - 5ᵈ· Feb. 8. an. 1689[90]'; 3rd-4th, AW wrote 'Oxoniensia Vol. - - - -' (i.e., vol. 4, for it is so cross-referenced at Wood 645(1), item 3078), in pencil, and the titles of 34 printed works in this vol., within guidelines made with red ink. AW listed 2 items, 30 and 31, as a single item. There are two items at 28. At AW's no. 33, now catalogued as item no. 33b, there is a later note (1922) in the margin, 'Not in the vol.', hence 35 items remain in the vol. The Ashm. Roman numerals replace, at times obliterate, AW's numbering on the tpp in this vol.
Wood 515(1). Not in STC. Not in Wing. Not in ESTCR 181146. Madan 948.

4951. Oxford, University Statutes. S., W., ed. *Oxon: studia. Quadratura circuli, Anglor: Athenae. Studiorum & exercitii academici, pridem editi*. Londini: ap. O. Pullein, & T. Slater, 1643. S.sh.
Wood 423(19). Wing O997A (rare). Madan 1577.

4952. Oxford, University Statutes. *Jan. 9. 1651. By the vicechancellour and heads of houses of the university of Oxford. Whereas*. Oxford: L. Lichfield, 1651[2]. S.sh.
Wood 276a(319). Wing O863A (rare). Madan 2155.

4953. Oxford, University Statutes. *March 22. 1651. By the vice-chancellour and heads of houses. Whereas by the rude carriage*. Oxford: L. Lichfield, [1652]. S.sh.
Issued by vice-chancellor Daniel Greenwood, concerning 'coursing', LT 1.297.
Wood 276a(344) (not in Bodl. CD cat.). Wing O863B (rare). Madan 2156.

4954. Oxford, University Statutes. *Oxon. July 5ᵗʰ. 1652. The vice-chancellour and heads of houses*. Oxford: L. Lichfield, 1652. S.sh.
Wood 276a(345). Wing O903B (rare) (Wing, 1653). Madan 2187.

4955. Oxford, University Statutes. *Mart. 20. 1660. Quandoquidem compertum est intra academiae limites, factiosos nonnullos & turbones oberrare*. Oxon: typ. acad. Lichfieldianis, [1660]. S.sh.

Wood 276a(346). Wing O961 (rare, 2 at O). Madan 2426.

4956. Oxford, University Statutes. *Paul Hood, doctor of divinity, . . . Whereas the statues certaine require . . . scholasticall, and decent habits [8 Oct.].* [Oxford]: [A. Lichfield], [1660]. S.sh.
AW wrote '1660', in pencil.
Wood 276a(347). Wing O934A (rare, 2 at O). Madan 2516.

4957. Oxford, University Statutes. *Advertisements from the delegates of convocation for his majesties reception.* [Oxford]: n.pub., [1663, Sept.]. S.sh.
At top, AW added, 'Dup 1663', in pencil (for statutes with the same title, 1687 and 1695, see items 4984, 4990). An editorial addition, 'That none of the Masters of Arts that have . . . ' not in AW's hand, lined out. Below, AW wrote 'this paper came out in Oxon Sept: 22: 1663'. Later, he added 'Registred in convocation book. p. 170-171'. LT 1.489, 491.
Wood 276a(326). Wing O859. Madan 2644.

4958. Oxford, University Statutes. *Walter Blandford, doctor in divinity, . . . Whereas all undergraduates, . . . are strictly accomptable [26 Jan. 1663].* [Oxford]: [A. or L. Lichfield], [1664]. S.sh.
AW wrote '1663[4] Dup', in pencil. Dupl. at Wood 276a(349).
Wood 276a(348). Wing O992B (rare, 2 at O) (Wing, 1669). Madan 2665.

4959. Oxford, University Statutes. *Walter Blandford, doctor in divinity, . . . Whereas all undergraduates, . . . are strictly accomptable [26 Jan. 1663].* [Oxford]: [A. or L. Lichfield], [1664]. S.sh.
AW wrote, '1663[4]', in pencil. Dupl. at Wood 276a(348).
Wood 276a(349). Wing O992B (rare, 2 at O) (Wing, 1669). Madan 2665.

4960. Oxford, University Statutes. *Rules and orders made by the vice-chancellor of the university of Oxford . . . for the good [against the plague].* [Oxford]: n.pub., [1665]. S.sh.
AW added after the year, 'Aug: 25.' LT 2.44.
Wood 276a(313). Wing O962 (rare). Madan 2713.

4961. Oxford, University Statutes. *Cum de vestitu & habitu scholastico . . . Aug. An: Dom. 1666 [27 Aug.].* Oxon: H. Hall, [1666]. S.sh.
AW wrote, 'Regestred in the convocation book which begins 1659. p. 220'. LT 2.84-5.
Wood 276a(320). Wing O871A (rare). Madan 2750.

4962. Oxford, University Statutes. *Robert Say, doctor of divinity, . . . Whereas the statutes . . . require certain scholastical, and decent habits [13 Feb.].* [Oxford]: [A. or L. Lichfield], [1666]. S.sh.
AW wrote 'Dupl', in pencil. AW may have been referring to a similar document issued in 1660 now at Wood 276a(347), item 4956.
Wood 276a(350). Wing O961B (rare). Madan 2749.

4963. Oxford, University Statutes. *Octob: 21. 1667. Prizes of wines set.* [Oxford]: [W. Hall], [1667]. S.sh.
LT 2.120.
Wood 276a(354). Wing O939A (rare). Madan 2776.

4964. Oxford, University Statutes. *Orders for the reception of . . . the prince of Orange.* [Oxford]: n.pub., [1670]. S.sh.
AW wrote, 'A copy of this paper was stuck up in the Common Refectory of every Coll. and Hall Dec. 8. in the morn. 1670, in expectation of the said prince in the evening, but he came not - Registered in convoc. book p. 304'. LT 2.206-7.
Wood 276a(329) (not in Bodl. CD cat.). Wing O903G (rare). Madan 2858..

4965. Oxford, University Statutes. *By order from mr vice-chancellor, and mr major. April 26. 1671. These are to give notice . . . Pet. Mews vice-chancel. Roger Griffin deputy major.* [Oxford]: n.pub., [1671]. S.sh.
AW wrote 'Oxōn', twice. LT 2.222.
Wood 276a(364). Not in Wing. Not in ESTCR. Madan 2896.

4966. Oxford, University Statutes. *Orders agreed upon by the heads of houses for the preventing and quenching of fire . . . Octob. 23.* [Oxford]: n.pub., [1671]. S.sh.
LT 2.222.
Wood 276a(316). Wing O903D (rare). Madan 2901.

4967. Oxford, University Statutes. *Orders and directions agreed upon by . . . justices of the peace of . . . Oxford.* [Oxford]: n.pub., [1671]. S.sh.
Added above regnal year, '(Apr. 27)' and below, '1671', in blue crayon, not by AW. Dupl. at Wood 276a(315). LT 2.222.
Wood 276a(314). Wing O392 (rare, 2 at O). Madan 2899.

4968. Oxford, University Statutes. *Orders and directions agreed upon by . . . justices of the peace of . . . Oxford.* [Oxford]: n.pub., [1671]. S.sh.
'1671' in the margin, may be by AW; below, AW wrote, 'These orders were stuck up on every corner, & every Inn dore June 9, 1671'. Dupl. at Wood 276a(314). LT 2.222.
Wood 276a(315). Wing O392 (rare, 2 at O). Madan 2899.

4969. Oxford, University Statutes. *Whereas formerly the practical musick . . . hath been much disturb'd . . . P. Mews vice-cancel. [6 July].* [Oxford]: n.pub., [1671]. S.sh.
LT 2.225.
Wood 276a(367) (not in Bodl. CD cat.). Wing O992D (rare). Madan 2900.

4970. Oxford, University Statutes. *Orders and directions for the cleansing of the ways, streets and passages in and about the university and city of Oxford.* [Oxford]: [at the Sheldonian], [1672]. S.sh.
At bottom, AW wrote, 'printed Apr. 28. an. 1672'.
Wood 276a(317). Not in Wing. Madan 2937. Not in ESTCR.

4971. Oxford, University Statutes. *Whereas Tuesday next, . . . is . . . appointed to be observed as a day of fasting . . . that the guilt of the . . . blood of Charles the first . . . Jan. 27. 1671.* [Oxford]: [at the Sheldonian], [1672]. S.sh.
AW wrote, 'Memorandum that this programma was printed under the same forme Jan 27. aᵒ 1670 & stuck up on all common places in the University. Some there were also that were printed without the Vice-chanc. name; to the end that the Maior of the City might put his hand to them: which he did & they were stuck up on all common places of the City.' LT 2.215.
Wood 276a(360). Wing O992J (rare). Madan 2932.

4972. Oxford, University Statutes. *Cum statutum universitatis exigat . . . Novemb. 24.* [Oxford]: n.pub., [1674]. S.sh.
See LT 2.298.
Wood 276a(322). Wing O871C (rare). Madan 3018.

4973. Oxford, University Statutes. *Prizes of wines set and appointed by the vice-chancellor [Ra. Bathurst, 19 Feb. 1673].* [Oxford]: n.pub., [1674]. S.sh.
Above, AW wrote '1673', outlined the university seal, and wrote 'The University Armes' inside; at the price of Canary wines (2 shillings the quart), he wrote, 'Before for severall yeares at 2ˢ.2ᵈ. to the great resentment of all: who to make even money would either spend more or give the Drawer the rest. This price was raised upon pretence of carriage.' After the price of French wines (1 shilling the quart), 'Before for severall years 1ˢ.1ᵈ.' See LT 2.281-2.
Wood 276a(372). Wing O939B (rare). Madan 3017.

4974. Oxford, University Statutes. *April 18. 1676. Whereas on Friday last, April 14ᵗʰ, at midnight, several outrages were committed [Ra. Bathurst vice-chancellor].* [Oxford]: n.p, [1676]. S.sh.
Below, AW wrote, 'Stuck up in all publick places in Oxford'. LT 2.343-4.
Wood 276a(374). Wing O992E (rare). Madan 3115.

4975. Oxford, University Statutes. *Orders for the reception of . . . James, duke of Ormond.* [Oxford]: [at the Sheldonian], [1677]. S.sh. Proof copy, uncorrected, 35 lines and no signature.
ᵛ, note, apparently to AW, '2 a clock If you come within this hour, you will find T[homas] Tully, & N[athaniel] Ellison either at the Bacchelours Garden at CCC or else at my chamber N. E.' (prob. N. Ellison). Diff. ed. at Wood 276a(325). LT 2.387.
Wood 276a(324). Wing O903F (rare). Madan 3150.

4976. Oxford, University Statutes. *Orders for the reception of . . . James, duke of Ormond.* [Oxford]: [at the Sheldonian], [1677]. S.sh. 39 lines and printed signature of Hen: Clerke, vice-chancellor.
AW wrote, 'Stuck up in all Refectories of College & halls 4. Aug. in the morn. 1677'. Diff. ed. at Wood 276a(324). LT 2.387.
Wood 276a(325). Wing O903F (rare, 3 at O). Madan 3150.

4977. Oxford, University Statutes. *John Nicholas, doctor in divinity, and vice-chancellour . . . Whereas all undergraduates . . . are strictly accomptable in all their matters of bargaine . . . [template, no month or day]*. [Oxford]: n.pub, [1678]. S.sh.
Wood 276a(376). Wing O889A (rare). Madan 3190.

4978. Oxford, University Statutes. *Orders to be observed while his majestie . . . continue in Oxford*. [Oxford]: n.pub., [1681]. S.sh.
AW wrote, 'These orders were printed 7. March (Munday) 1680[1]. & forthwith sent to the Colleges & Halls, to be posted up.' LT 2.517.
Wood 276a(328). Wing O903H (rare).

4979. Oxford, University Statutes. *Univers. Oxon. The prices of provision, appointed by the reverend Timothy Halton . . . vice-chancellor . . . his majesties clerk of this market*. [Oxford]: n.pub., [1681]. S.sh.
AW wrote, 'Stuck up in all public places 13. March 1680[1]'. After each item, a line and the price, entered in hand, may not be by AW. LT 2.520.
Wood 276a(377). Wing O939 (rare). ESTCR 232112.

4980. Oxford, University Statutes. *The judgment and decree of the university of Oxford past in their convocation July 21. 1683, against certain pernicious books*. [Oxford]: at the theater, 1683. Fol. Pp. [2], 9.
Tp, AW wrote the price, '3ᵈ', and pp. 3-6, some 25 notes in dark ink and reference letters and underscoring in red ink, identifying authors of works to be burned, e.g., p. 3, at Lex Rex, '(a) written by Sam. Rutherford'; p. 4, at Jenkin's Petition, '(b) Will. Jenkyns M. A Cambr. his petition to save himself having assisted K. Ch. 2. with moneys when he came out of Scotland into Engl.'; and p. 6, at Protestant Reconciler, 'Prot. Reconciler, the 1st part, written by Dan. Whitby'. LT 3.62-4 and notes 4, 5; 3.96.
Wood 423(58). Wing O891.

4981. Oxford, University Statutes. *Comitia habita in universitate Oxoniensi Ap. 23. . . . Die inaugurationis . . . principis Jacobi II. et . . . reginae Mariae*. [Oxford]: e theatro Sheldoniano, 1685. S.sh.
AW made made notes, in ink, one over a previous, briefer, note in pencil. 'See the orders that came out the day before'; at first carmines, 'very well'; at second, U. Corbet, T. Sprot. and R. Barber, 'These three took from each other as in Carm. Amoebeo [in a responsive song]' over an earlier note in pencil; at Jerv. Eyre, immediately following, 'Eyre shut up their discourse'; and after this set of carmines, 'Vocal & instrumental musick, from the musick Gallery'. LT 3.141.
Wood 276a(408). Wing O866 (rare).

4982. Oxford, University Statutes. *The heads of the respective colleges and halls . . . April 23. the day of his majesties coronation*. [Oxford]: n.pub., 1685. S.sh.
Below, AW wrote, 'stuck up in all public refectories 22. Apr'. LT 3.140. Date entered in Roman numerals, not by AW. Diff. ed. at Wood 276a(378).
Wood 276a(373). Wing O988 (rare) (Wing, diff. ed. not recorded).

4983. Oxford, University Statutes. *To the right worshipfull the heads of the respective colleges and halls . . . on Thursday April 23. the day of his majesties coronation*. [Oxford]: n.pub., 1685. S.sh.
Date entered in Roman numerals, not by AW. Diff. ed. at Wood 276a(373).
Wood 276a(378). Wing O988 (rare) (Wing, diff. ed. not recorded).

4984. Oxford, University Statutes. *Advertisements from the delegates of convocation for his majesties reception*. [Oxford]: n.pub., [1687]. S.sh.
AW wrote, 'This paper was stuck up in all refectories in the University about a week before the K. came to Oxon.' and in pencil '1687'. In a later hand, '(Sept. 1687)'. LT 3.224.
Wood 276a(327). Wing O 860 (two) ('O' not recorded in Wing).

4985. Oxford, University Statutes. *Doctors in all faculty's appointed to meet the king [26 Aug.]*. [Oxford]: n.pub., [1687]. S.sh.
Lines at 4 names of academics in the 1st group, and the count '24'; after the 2nd group, AW wrote, 'Mʳ – [Harvey] Broughton of S. Alb. Hall put in for a voluntier'. LT 3.224, 226.
Wood 276a(379). Wing O874 (3).

4986. Oxford, University Statutes. *At a meeting of the heads of houses. Mar. 22. 1688. Whereas the gowns, capps, and habits*. [Oxford]: n.pub., [1688]. S.sh.
Wood 276a(380). Wing O861 (rare).

4987. Oxford, University Statutes. *Comitia habita in universitate Oxoniensi Apr. 11. . . . Die inau-*

gurationis . . . principis Wilhelmi et . . . reginae Mariae. [Oxford]: e theatro Sheldoniano, 1689. S.sh.
LT 3.301.
Wood 276a(409). Wing O867 (two).

4988. Oxford, University Statutes. *A model of a college . . . for the education of some youths of the Greek church.* [Oxford]: n.pub., [1689]. S.sh.
'[1689]' in blue crayon, not by AW. On the education of Greek students at Oxford in 1677, see LT 2.379.
Wood 276a(381). Wing M2314.

4989. Oxford, University Statutes. *'Orders of the Regulating of Habitts. an. 1690. Januarii. Edds. V. Can.'*. [Oxford]: [n.pub.], [1690]. S.sh.
Missing in 1939. T is from 1717 list.
Wood 276a(323). Not identified. See Wing O987J.

4990. Oxford, University Statutes. *Advertisements from the delegates of convocation for his majesties reception.* Oxford: at the theater, 1695. S.sh.
AW wrote, 'publish'd Nov. 8 1695' (AW's last dated entry in a printed item; he died 29 Nov.). LT 3.494.
Wood 276a(330). Wing O860A (rare, 2 at O).

4991. Oxford, University Visitors. *[Begin.] Nos quorum nomina literis praesentibus subscripta sunt [a summons, by the parliamentary visitors, to the members of the university to appear before them in convocation on July [really June] 4th] [15 May].* [London]: n.pub., [1647]. S.sh.
Correction in text, at Julii, 'Junii'. Signed in ms. by 11 persons, see *Hist. and Antiq.*, 2.504ff. ᵛ, 'received May 24. after dinner published at night to the company', not by AW.
Wood 514(28). Wing N1386 (rare) (see also Wing O903A). Madan 1923.

4992. Oxford, University Visitors. *A letter from a scholar in Oxford, to his friend in the countrey: shewing what progresse the visitors have made in the reformation.* [London]: n.pub., 1647. 4°. Pp. [2], 5.
P. 2, scribble and line.
Wood 514(32). Wing L1435. Madan 1936.

4993. Oxford, University Visitors. *April 13. 1647. Ordered by the lord chancellour and visitours . . . that no fellow . . . or member of Magdalen colledge shall enjoy any benefit . . . untill they give satisfaction to the visitours [and satirical remarks, in Lat.] [ᵛ, 2 orders relating to the university, from parliament and from T. Fairfax, 18 Feb. 1647 and 31 Mar. 1648 respectively].* [London]: n.pub., [1648]. S.sh. (r-v).
Wood 514(29). Wing O903C (rare). Madan 1974.

4994. Oxford, University Visitors. *Die Martis, viz: primo die Junii, ann: Dom: 1647. Considente domo. [An account of some of the proceedings of the parliamentary visitors at Oxford university between 1 June 1647 and 7 April 1648].* [Oxford]: n.pub., [1648]. 4°. A⁴.
AW's note on p. [4] of the preceding item (i.e., Wood 514(45), item 4710) gives this information: 'Note that the Narrative following being privately in the press at Oxon. was stop'd from going any farther by the visitors command – with much adoe I got these two sheets following of the said narrative: – I could never see any other printed copie of it, or any of the MS copie that followed[.] This that I got, I cannot now tell justly from whence I had it, unless from Dʳ Langbaines papers – qu[aere]'. AW's two sheets are the only copies known. LT 1.142.
Wood 514(46). Wing C5904 (rare). Madan 1976.

4995. Oxford, University Visitors. *Halifax law translated to Oxon: or, the new visitors justice, . . . concerning the late reformation begun there by the e. of Pembroke [17 Ap.].* [London]: n.pub., 1648. 4°. A⁴.
A3, A4, AW made 3 corrections. Dupl. at Wood 632(23).
Wood 514(43). Wing H323. Madan 1985.

4996. Oxford, University Visitors. *Halifax law translated to Oxon: or, the new visitors justice, . . . concerning the late reformation begun there by the e. of Pembroke [17 Ap.].* [London]: n.pub., 1648. 4°. A⁴.
AW wrote 'Dupl', in pencil. Dupl. at Wood 514(43).
Wood 632(23). Wing H323. Madan 1985.

4997. Oxford, University Visitors. *Lord have mercy upon us, or the visitation at Oxford: begun Aprill the 11. 1648.* Pembrook and Mongomery [really London]: n.pub., 1648. 4°. Pp. 8.
P. 6, underscoring. Dupl. at Wood 609(2).
Wood 514(42). Wing L3047. Madan 1981.

4998. Oxford, University Visitors. *Lord have mercy upon us, or the visitation at Oxford: begun Aprill*

the 11. 1648. Pembrook and Mongomery [really London]: n.pub., 1648. 4°. Pp. 8 (mutilated by fire).
Tp, AW wrote the former no. in a bundle, '23', and, in pencil, 'dup'; p. 4, 'Even Nixon Ruffe & all' (at a
phrase now destroyed by fire). Dupl. at Wood 514(42).
Wood 609(2). Wing L3047. Madan 1981.

4999. Oxford, University Visitors. *To the honourable visitours appointed by both houses of parliament
for the regulating . . . of the university of Oxford*. [London]: n.pub., [1648]. Fol. Pp. [4].
P. [1], AW wrote 'Dupl' and '1647', in pencil. Related item at Wood 514(30).
Wood 423(23-6). Wing T1484A (rare, 2 at O). Madan 1973 (Wing, [Oxford]).

5000. Oxford, University Visitors. *To the honourable visitours . . . of the university of Oxford. The
petition of your freinds [sic] . . . [2 June 1647]. [Followed by] The protestation of the well-affected [against
S. Fell as vice-chancellor]*. [London]: n.pub., [1648]. S.sh. (r-v).
Related item at Wood 423(23).
Wood 514(30). Wing O987A (rare) (Wing, 1647). Madan 1975.

5001. Oxford, University Encaenia Orders. *To the right worshipful, the heads of the respective colleges
. . . during the solemnity now approaching, all doctors are to wear [P. Mews, 7 July]*. [Oxford]: n.pub.,
[1671]. S.sh.
A set of orders for arrangements of the Act, Wood 276a(385-393), the last is for 1693. LT 2.225.
Wood 276a(385). Wing O987D (rare). Madan 3292.

5002. Oxford, University Encaenia Orders. *To the right worshipful the heads of the respective colleges
. . . during the solemnity now approaching, all doctors are to wear [P. Mews, 4 July]*. [Oxford]: n.pub.,
[1672]. S.sh.
Wood 276a(386). Wing O987E (rare). Madan 3292.

5003. Oxford, University Encaenia Orders. *To the right worshipful the heads of the respective colleges
. . . during the solemnity now approaching, all doctors are to wear [P. Bath and Wells vice-chancel., 8
July]*. [Oxford]: n.pub., [1673]. S.sh.
Wood 276a(387). Wing O987F (rare). Madan 3292.

5004. Oxford, University Encaenia Orders. *To the right worshipful the heads of the respective colleges
. . . during the solemnity now approaching, on the tenth of July, all doctors are to wear [Ra. Bathurst
vice-chancel, 8 July]*. [Oxford]: n.pub., [1674]. S.sh.
LT 3.300.
Wood 276a(388). Wing O987G (rare). Madan 3292.

5005. Oxford, University Encaenia Orders. *To the right worshipful the heads of the respective colleges
. . . during the solemnity now approaching, on the ninth of July, all doctors are to wear [Rad. Bathurst, 9
July]*. [Oxford]: n.pub., [1675]. S.sh.
Wood 276a(389). Wing O987H (rare). Madan 3292.

5006. Oxford, University Encaenia Orders. *To the right worshipful the heads of the respective colleges
. . . during the solemnity now approaching, on the twenty first day of May, all doctors are to wear*. [Oxford]:
n.pub., [1683]. S.sh.
AW wrote, 'This was stuck up in all publick places on Munday 21. May 1683'. LT 3.60.
Wood 276a(390). Not in Wing. Not Wing O987I (rare), which is Wood 276a(391). Madan 3292. Not in
ESTCR.

5007. Oxford, University Encaenia Orders. *To the right worshipful the heads of the respective colleges
. . . during the solemnity now approaching, on the sixth day of July, all doctors are to wear*. [Oxford]:
n.pub., [1683]. S.sh.
AW wrote the date, '7. July 1683'.
Wood 276a(391). Wing O987I (rare). Madan 3292.

5008. Oxford, University Encaenia Orders. *To the right worshipful the heads of the respective colleges
. . . during the solemnity now approaching, on the seventh day of July, all doctors are to wear*. [Oxford]:
n.pub., [1684?]. S.sh.
Earlier note, erased, but date of 1684 is visible. Modern note, '[about 1690?]' with a later comment, 'no,
earlier'.
Wood 276a(392). Wing O987J (rare). Madan 3292.

5009. Oxford, University Encaenia Orders. *[T]o [1st letter is 'm' upside down] the right worshipful*

*the heads of the respective colleges . . . during the solemnity now approaching, on the seventh day of July,
all doctors are to wear.* [Oxford]: n.pub., [1693]. S.sh.
Below, AW wrote 'July 7 1693', and, in pencil, '1693'.
Wood 276a(393). Wing O987K (rare). Madan 3292.

5010. Oxford, University Encaenia. *Carmen Pindaricum in theatrum Sheldonianum in . . . encaeniis
[9 July].* Oxonii: e typog. Sheldoniana, excud. H. Hall, imp. J. Crosley, 1669. 4°. Pp. [4], 28 ([4] blank).
Tp, AW wrote, 'published the 16. Octob. 1669 6ᵈ·' and below, 'published Oct 16. 69', in pencil. LT 2.172.
Wood 512(16) (not in Bodl. CD cat.). Wing O702. Madan 2816.

5011. Oxford, University Encaenia. Fell, John, by. *In laudem musices carmen Sapphicum.* [Oxford]: [e
theatro Sheldoniano], [1672]. S.sh.
AW wrote, 'These verses were made by Dʳ John Fell Deane of Ch. Ch. Dispersed among the people in the
Theater before the Encaenia began, 5 July 1672. Afterwards spoken from the Musick Gallery by [blank,
i.e., John] Panker* a commoner of Ch. Ch. then (so much of it that is printed in Ital. character) sung by
severall there present: the composition of which musick was performed by Mʳ [blank, i.e., Henry] Alridge
[sic] Student of Ch. Ch. It was well performed & gave great content.', and for the note reference '*or
Penkhurst'. LT 2.248. Dupl. at Wood 423(48).
Wood 276a(534). Wing F612 (rare, 2 at O). Madan 2927.

5012. Oxford, University Encaenia. Fell, John, by. *In laudem musices carmen Sapphicum.* [Oxford]: [e
theatro Sheldoniano], [1672]. S.sh.
On preceding blank leafᵛ, AW wrote, 'The verses following (In Laudem Musices) were made by Dʳ Joh.
Fell Deane of ch. ch – Dispersed in printed papers among the scholars in the Sheldonian theater at Oxon
just before the Encaenia began, 5. July 1672 – [/] Afterwards they were spoken from the musick gallery
by one John Penkherst (commonly called Penker) a commoner of ch. church: At which time, so much of it
that is in Italick character, was sung by several masters of musick, scholars, & choiristers in divers parts:
All admirably well performed, & so consequently gave great content – [/] The musick to which the verses
were sung was composed by Hen. Aldridge student of Ch. ch – (The same who became Deane of that
house in 1689)'; text, word filled at bottom, not by AW. LT 2.248. Dupl. at Wood 276a(534) (with similar
annotation but a 1st draft of the above).
Wood 423(48). Wing F612 (rare, 2 at O). Madan 2927.

5013. Oxford, University Encaenia. *Theatri Oxoniensis encaenia Jul. 10. an. 1674. celebrata.* Oxon:
e theatro Sheldoniano, 1674. S.sh.
AW attended the celebration and on this program recorded some of his responses to presentations, much
of which was later lined out; most is still legible: e.g., at Georgius Rainsford, 'Well'; at Ambrosius Brown,
'Well'; at Richardus Russel, 'Well, in the middle of the Theatre'; at Jacobus Parkinson, underscored, 'verie
well, expelled from CCColl the Lent going before'; at Antonius Carey, Vicecomes Falkland, 'verie well, in
the middle'; at Thomas Newport 'much like a man, but his voice a little too low'; at Thomas Herbert,
Comitis Pembrochiae, 'He spoke indifferently well but understood not what he said'; after Pembroke, 'a
little crash of instrumentall musick.'; at Philippus Percival Baronettus, 'Well'; and after, 'musick both
vocall & instrumentall for above half an houre, of Mr. [Henry] Aldriges compos.'; at Vitae instituendae
delectus, 'Lord Falkland againe verie well but his voice a little harsh because in breaking'; at Tho. Moorer,
'verie well but too fast'; and, at Robertus Tracey, 'so so & too long in the middle'. LT 2.288-9.
Wood 276a(394). Wing O971 (rare). Madan 3293.

5014. Oxford, University Encaenia. *Theatri Oxoniensis encaenia Jul. 9. an. 1675. celebrata.* Oxon.: e
theatro Sheldoniano, 1675. S.sh.
AW attended the celebration and on this program recorded some of his responses to presentations, much
of which was later lined out, but most is still legible: e.g., 'Well'; 'Well but not his owne [all lined out]';
'Well, but not his owne [all lined out]'; at Gulielmus Talbot, 'spoke like a child, but not his own. [all lined
out, and] Fit Dec. Wigorn 1691' (added later); at Thomas, Killmuriae Vicecomes, ex Aede Christi, 'well
but not his own [all lined out, and] in the middle of the Theatre'; 'The musick both instrumentall & vocall.
The vocal was set by Mr Aldridg of Ch.Ch. to the Latter part of the Lord Kilmurreys verses'; at Johannes
Bury, 'Spoken very effectively & sensibly [all lined out]'; at Johannes Parsons, 'well & manly but little or
nothing his owne [all lined out]'. LT 2.318.
Wood 276a(395). Wing O972 (rare). Madan 3293.

5015. Oxford, University Encaenia. *Theatri Oxoniensis encaenia Jul. 7. an. 1676. celebrata.* Oxon.: e
theatro Sheldoniano, 1676. S.sh.
AW wrote 2 comments in the margins: at Hawtaine Morgan, 'performed his part verie simply & conceitedly,

in the middle [all lined out]' and 'Musick.' He added below: 'I was at the Bathe in the Act time, [from here on, lined out:] & therefore can not pass my censure on the speakers'. AW was at Bath until 14 July, LT 2.351.
Wood 276a(396). Wing O973 (rare). Madan 3293.

5016. Oxford, University Encaenia. *Comitia philologica, habita Aug. 6 Anno 1677. In gratulatione solenni ob adventum expectatissimum . . . Jacobi [Butler] Ormondiae ducis.* [Oxford]: [at the Sheldonian], [1677]. 1,S-X² (X2 blank).
See Wood 276a(405 and 406a), items 5017f. LT 2.384.
Wood 423(53). Wing O871. Madan 3152.

5017. Oxford, University Encaenia. *Comitia philologica in gratulatione solenni academiae Oxon: ob . . . cancellaraii (James Butler) adventum expectatissimum. Aug. 6.* Oxon.: e theatro Sheldoniano, 1677. S.sh.
AW made 4 annotations: after the 2nd of 4 speeches, 'Musick vocall & instrumentall'; at Jo. Percival (Christ Church), 'very well & much like a man.'; one word underscored; and, at end, 'After these speeches were done the Orator concluded'. Dupl. at Wood 276a(405), and see Wood 423(53), item 5016. LT 2.387. The next item, Wood 276a(406b) (*Ordo baccalaureorum*, of bachelors who were to take part in final disputations, 1718/9), is not on the 1717 list and was added after 1695.
Wood 276a(406a). Wing O870 (two). Madan 3151, 3293.

5018. Oxford, University Encaenia. *Comitia philologica in gratulatione solenni academiae Oxon:. . . Aug. 6.* Oxon.: e theatro Sheldoniano, 1677. S.sh.
AW wrote, 'dup 1677', in pencil. Dupl. at Wood 276a(406a), see note there. LT 2.387.
Wood 276a(405). Wing O870 (two). Madan 3151, 3293.

5019. Oxford, University Encaenia. *Theatri Oxoniensis encaenia Jul. 6. an. 1677. celebrata.* Oxon.: e theatro Sheldoniano, 1677. S.sh.
AW wrote, 'These speeches & verses spoke in the Theatre in the Encaenia were all published ex[c]ept those of Ch. Wroughton 4. Aug. 1677. [and added later:] Wroughtons were added after.' (Wroughton's was printed separately, see items 5020 and 5021, Madan 3148-9, and LT 2.384). 2 short comments, lined out, and 'Musick.'
Wood 276a(397). Wing O977. Madan 3293.

5020. Oxford, University Encaenia. *[Theatri Oxoniensis encaenia, sive comitia philologica. Julii 6, anno 1677. celebrata].* [Oxon.]: [e theatro Sheldoniano], [1677]. Fol. A2,B-P²,1 (wanting tp).
Note on want of tp, and below, year, not in AW's hand. In text, A2, AW wrote an addition, 'Car. Wroughton A. bac. et Coll. Mert. soc. – lemma habuit, Bodleius'. See references listed at LT 2.384, and the next item, Wood 657(73).
Wood 423(52). Wing O974. Madan 3148.

5021. Oxford, University Encaenia. Wroughton, Charles, by. *Bodleius.* [Oxford]: [at the Sheldonian], [1677, after 6 July]. Fol. Pp. [4] (the two leaves, quire G, has catchwork MAJOR, on G2ᵛ).
G1, AW wrote, 'Dupl', in pencil. See LT 2.384 and references there, including to *Theatri Oxoniensis encaenia*, Wood 276a(397), where this item was intended to be inserted (a note by F. Madan, 2 Feb. 1927, explains that this oration in praise of Bodley, delivered at the encaenia 6 July 1677 by C. Wroughton, apparently was printed too late to be included).
Wood 657(73). Wing W3732 (rare). Madan 3149.

5022. Oxford, University Encaenia. *Theatri Oxoniensis encaenia Jul. 11. an. 1679. celebrata.* [Oxford]: e theatro Sheldoniano, 1679. S.sh.
AW marked 2 music interludes, and, in red ink, 2 'pro' and 'con' debaters. At Christian Howard, Johannes Berkely and Daniel Harvey, AW wrote, 'They tooke the matter from one another & [from here on, lined out:] twas like the telling of tales or news by turns'. There are other marks in red ink. LT 4.456.
Wood 276a(398). Wing O978 (rare). Madan 3293.

5023. Oxford, University Encaenia. *Theatri Oxoniensis encaenia Jul. 9. an. 1680. celebrata.* [Oxford]: e theatro Sheldoniano, 1680. S.sh.
In red ink, pencil, and dark ink, AW recorded the place of speeches, 'in rostro', 4 times; music interludes, 'musick from the gallery', twice; and one 'pro' and 'con' debate. At the 1st exercise, on philology, he wrote, 'The matter they spake was verie good. They spoke round, like the telling of tales or newes' (last 7 words lined out). At Joan. Loving, 'very well & much like a poet - in rostro'. At the 'carmine heroico' 'Clusius

Oxoniensis renatus', he wrote, 'Great Tom of Oxon re-cast'. LT 2.490.
Wood 276a(399). Wing O979 (rare). Madan 3293.

5024. Oxford, University Encaenia. *Theatri Oxoniensis encaenia Jul. 8. an. 1681. celebrata.* [Oxford]: e theatro Sheldoniano, 1681. S.sh.
A mark in margin at Robertus Bulkley, and Georgius Cholmondeley is underscored. At Thomas Hoy, AW wrote, 'verie well'; at Ludovicus de Borbon, underlined in red ink, 'He spoke as if he understood it not.' (all lined out); after Borbon, underscored, 'Here followed instr. & vocall musick.'; the same, after Cholmondeley, just before the close of the program. LT 2.547.
Wood 276a(400). Wing O980 (rare). Madan 3293.

5025. Oxford, University Encaenia. *Theatri Oxoniensis encaenia Jul. 7. an. 1682. celebrata.* [Oxford]: e theatro Sheldoniano, 1682. S.sh.
AW noted position of speakers, 'middle' or 'in the middle', 5 times, and musick interludes, 2 times; at Ric. Dighton, 'In the middle a very little boy Grandson to Dr Rich Baylye'. LT 3.23.
Wood 276a(401). Wing O981 (rare). Madan 3293.

5026. Oxford, University Encaenia. *Theatri Oxoniensis encaenia Jul. 6. an. 1683. celebrata.* [Oxford]: e theatro Sheldoniano, 1683. S.sh.
At Jonathan Langley, AW wrote, 'Fil. nat. max [?] D. Hen. Langley de Shrosbury' (AO i.xxxv), and at Ed. Reinolds, a similar note; he noted the position of the speaker, 'in the middle', 7 times, and recorded two music interludes, e.g., 'Musick followed from the gallery instrumentall & vocal'. LT 3.60.
Wood 276a(402). Wing O982 (rare). Madan 3293.

5027. Oxford, University Encaenia. *Theatri Oxoniensis encaenia Jul. 11. an. 1684. celebrata.* [Oxford]: e theatro Sheldoniano, 1684. S.sh.
AW made 14 judgements of presentations, all lined out, e.g., 'incomparably well', 'verie well', 'well', 'indifferent', 'verie ill'. At the presentation of Gul. Cater, 'Horti Botanici querela', not lined out: 'because the frost last winter kill'd most of the trees.'; also, one correction and one record of 'musick'. LT 3.105. But Wood was in Beoley and at Skilts, another Sheldon home a few miles south of Beoley, on 10 July, and seems to have stayed away from Oxford until the end of the month, LT 3.98.
Wood 276a(403). Wing O983 (rare). Madan 3293.

5028. Oxford, University Encaenia. *Theatri Oxoniensis encaenia Jul. 7. an. 1693. celebrata.* [Oxford]: e theatro Sheldoniano, 1693. S.sh.
AW noted the position of the speaker, 'in rostro', 6 times, and the interludes of musick, 2 times. All, ink over pencil marks. LT 3.427. Wood 276a(404a) is followed by 404b and c, encaenia programs of 1696 and 1697, both were added after 1717 (not in the 1717 list).
Wood 276a(404a). Wing O984. Madan 3293.

5029. Oxford, University Lent Exercises. *Quanquam statua academiae summis rogata auspiciis, gravissimis sancita poenis [16 Feb. 1666].* [Oxford]: [H. Hall], [1667]. S.sh.
AW wrote '1666 Dup', in pencil. Dupl. at 276a(353). LT 2.100.
Wood 276a(351). Wing O961A (rare, 4 at O). Madan 2775.

5030. Oxford, University Lent Exercises. *Quanquam statua academiae summis rogata auspiciis, gravissimis sancita poenis [16 Feb. 1666].* [Oxford]: [H. Hall], [1667]. S.sh.
Dupl. at 276a(351). LT 2.100.
Wood 276a(353). Wing O961A (rare, 4 at O). Madan 2775.

5031. Oxford, University Lent Exercises. *Ut exercitia academica & praesertim quadragesimalia solennius in posterum peragantur . . . Feb, 17. 1669.* [Oxford]: n.pub., [1670]. S.sh.
AW wrote '1669', in pencil.
Wood 276a(356). Not in Wing. Not in ESTCR. Madan 3294.

5032. Oxford, University Lent Exercises. *Programma die Martii 13. 1670. Ut exercitia academica & praesertim quadragesimalia solennius in posterum peragantur.* [Oxford]: n.pub., [1671]. S.sh.
Wood 276a(357). Not in Wing. Not in ESTCR. Madan 3294.

5033. Oxford, University Lent Exercises. *Programma die Febr. 22. 1671. Ut exercitia academica & presertim quadragesimalia solennius in posterum peragantur.* [Oxford]: n.pub., [1672]. S.sh.
Wood 276a(361). Not in Wing. Not in ESTCR. Madan 3294.

5034. Oxford, University Lent Exercises. *Ut exercitia academica & praesertim quadragesimalia solen-*

nius in posterum peragantur [12 Feb. 1672]. [Oxford]: n.pub., [1673]. S.sh.
Wood 276a(368) (not in Bodl. CD cat.). Not in Wing. Not in ESTCR. Madan 3294.

5035. Oxford, University Lent Exercises. *Ut exercitia academica, & praesertim quadragesimalia, solennius peragantur [Rad. Bathurst, 29 Jan. 1673].* [Oxford]: n.pub., [1674]. S.sh.
AW marked by 2 vertical lines a new passage inserted in this annually printed document.
Wood 276a(371). Not in Wing. Not in ESTCR. Madan 3294.

5036. Oxford, University Lent Exercises. *Ut exercitia academica, & praesertim quadragesimalia, solennius peragantur . . . 167 [sic].* [Oxford]: n.pub., [1677]. S.sh.
An announcement with date '167' to which AW added '7. Febr.' and 167'7', and below, 'Such a paper comes out every yeare about a week before Lent begins'. Signed by 'Johannes Nicholas' above the printed 'Vice Cancell.' LT 2.100.
Wood 276a(375). Not in Wing. Not in ESTCR. Madan 3294.

5037. Oxford, University Determinations. *Ordo baccalaureorum determinantium in acad: Oxon: per quadragesimam ann. 1667/8 [Philos: nat. – rhet.].* [Oxford]: n.pub., 1668. S.sh.
This is the first of a series of calendars for bachelors to take part in disputations throughout Lent, 'determinantes in Quadragesima'. The 24 items in AW's collection, 1668 to 1695, are complete except for 1669, 1671, 1673, and 1679. His copies are the only ones known to have survived. LT 2.129.
Wood 276b(52). Wing O904 (rare). Madan 3291 (Madan missed Wood copies for 1672 and 1674).

5038. Oxford, University Determinations. *Ordo baccalaureorum determinantium in universit. Oxon. per quadragesimam. ann. 1669/70.* Oxonii: excud. H. Hall, [1670]. S.sh.
Wood 276b(44). Wing O905 (rare). Madan 3291.

5039. Oxford, University Determinations. *Ordo baccalaureorum determinantium in universitate Oxoniensi per quadragesim. ann. 1671/2.* Oxonii: theatro Sheldoniano, 1672. S.sh.
Wood 276b(47). Wing O906A (rare). Madan 3291.

5040. Oxford, University Determinations. *Ordo baccalaureorum determinantium in universitate Oxoniensi per quadragesim. ann. 1673/4.* [Oxford]: ex off. L. Lichfield, [1674]. S.sh.
Wood 276b(45). Wing O907 (rare). Madan 3291.

5041. Oxford, University Determinations. *Ordo baccalaureorum determinantium in universitate Oxon. per quadragesim. ann. 1674/5.* [Oxford]: ex off. L. Lichfield, [1675]. S.sh.
Dupl. at Wood 276b(48).
Wood 276a(382). Wing O908 (rare, 2 at O). Madan 3291.

5042. Oxford, University Determinations. *Ordo baccalaureorum determinantium in universitate Oxon. per quadragesim. ann. 1674/5.* [Oxford]: ex off. L. Lichfield, [1675]. S.sh.
AW wrote, '1674[5]'. Dupl. at Wood 276a(382).
Wood 276b(48). Wing O908 (rare, 2 at O). Madan 3291.

5043. Oxford, University Determinations. *Ordo baccalaureorum determinantium in universitate Oxon. per quadragesim. ann. 1675/6.* [Oxford]: ex off. Lichfieldiana, 1676. S.sh.
Wood 276b(49). Wing O909 (rare). Madan 3291.

5044. Oxford, University Determinations. *Ordo baccalaureorum determinantium. In universitate Oxon: per quadragesim. ann. 1676/7.* [Oxford]: ex off. Lichfieldiana, 1677. S.sh.
Wood 276b(50). Wing O910 (rare). Madan 3291.

5045. Oxford, University Determinations. *Ordo baccalaureorum determinantium. In universitate Oxon: per quadragesim. ann. 1677/8 [Nat. ph. – anat.].* [Oxford]: n.pub., [1678]. S.sh.
Wood 276b(51). Wing O911 (rare). Madan 3291.

5046. Oxford, University Determinations. *Ordo baccalaureorum determinantium in universitate Oxon. per quadragesim. ann. 1679/80.* Oxonii: ex off. L. Lichfield, 1680. S.sh.
Wood 276b(53). Wing O912 (rare). Madan 3291.

5047. Oxford, University Determinations. *Ordo baccalaureorum determinantium in universitate Oxon. per quadragesim. ann. 1680/1.* [Oxford]: n.pub., [1681]. S.sh.
In the t, AW lined out '81'; and wrote below, '† Those that have this marke to them were not presented on Egg-Saturday 12. Feb. 1680[81]. All these were to determine from Thursday 17. Feb. to March 7. 1680[81].

because the K was to come soone after, & the Parliam. to sit 21. March. The Div. Schoole was made use of this Lent, because the Arts. [i.e., Astronomy] Geom. & Greek schooles were making ready for the Lords - yet they are here put downe –', and, '200 bac. wanting 8'. Dupl. at Wood 276b(54) with a similar note. There is a 3rd version in his diary entry, 11 Feb. 1681, LT 2.517.
Wood 276a(383). Wing O913 (rare, 2 at O). Madan 3291.

5048. Oxford, University Determinations. *Ordo baccalaureorum determinantium in universitate Oxon. per quadragesim. ann. 1680/1.* [Oxford]: n.pub., 1681. S.sh.
Below, AW wrote, '† Those names that have this marke † put after them, were not presented on Egg-Saturday 12 Feb. 1680[1]. – All these Bachelaurs were to determine from Thursday 17 Feb to 7. Mar. 1680 because the King was to come soon after, & the Parliament was to sit 21. March – The Divinity School was made use of this Lent, because the Astronomie, Geometrie & Greek Schooles, were making ready for the Lords to sit in – However their names were here put downe – 200 bach. wanting 8.' (i.e., 192; in diary entry of 11 Feb. 1681, LT 2.517). Dupl. at Wood 276a(383), with a similar note.
Wood 276b(54). Wing O913 (rare, 2 at O). Madan 3291.

5049. Oxford, University Determinations. *Ordo baccalaureorum determinantium in universitate Oxon. per quadragesim. ann. 1681/2.* [Oxford]: n.pub., [1682]. S.sh.
Wood 276b(55). Wing O914 (rare). Madan 3291.

5050. Oxford, University Determinations. *Ordo baccalaureorum determinantium in universitate Oxon. per quadragesim. ann. 1682/3.* [Oxford]: n.pub., [1683]. S.sh.
AW wrote, 'numb. 120' (of determinants by his count).
Wood 276b(56). Wing O915 (rare). Madan 3291.

5051. Oxford, University Determinations. *Ordo baccalaureorum determinantium in universitate Oxon. per quadragesim. ann. 1683/4.* [Oxford]: n.pub., [1684]. S.sh.
Wood 276b(57). Wing O916 (rare). Madan 3291.

5052. Oxford, University Determinations. *Ordo baccalaureorum determinantium in universitate Oxon. per quadragesim. ann. 1684/5.* [Oxford]: n.pub., [1685]. S.sh.
Wood 276b(58). Wing O917 (rare). Madan 3291.

5053. Oxford, University Determinations. *Ordo baccalaureorum determinantium in universitate Oxon. per quadragesim. ann. 1685/6.* [Oxford]: n.pub., [1686]. S.sh.
Wood 276b(59). Wing O918 (rare). Madan 3291.

5054. Oxford, University Determinations. *Ordo baccalaureorum determinantium in universitate Oxon. per quadragesim. ann. 1686/7.* [Oxford]: n.pub., [1687]. S.sh.
Wood 276b(60). Wing O919 (rare). Madan 3291.

5055. Oxford, University Determinations. *Ordo baccalaureorum determinantium in universitate Oxon. per quadragesim. ann. 1687/8.* [Oxford]: n.pub., [1688]. S.sh.
Wood 276b(61). Wing O920 (rare). Madan 3291.

5056. Oxford, University Determinations. *Ordo baccalaureorum determinantium in universitate Oxon. per quadragesim. ann. 1688/9.* [Oxford]: n.pub., [1689]. S.sh.
Wood 276b(62). Wing O921 (rare). Madan 3291.

5057. Oxford, University Determinations. *Ordo baccalaureorum determinantium in universitate Oxon. per quadragesim. ann. 1689/90.* [Oxford]: n.pub., [1690]. S.sh.
Wood 276b(63). Wing O922 (rare). Madan 3291.

5058. Oxford, University Determinations. *Ordo baccalaureorum determinantium in universitate Oxon. per quadragesim. ann. 1690/1.* [Oxford]: n.pub., [1691]. S.sh.
Wood 276b(64). Wing O923 (rare). Madan 3291.

5059. Oxford, University Determinations. *Ordo baccalaureorum determinantium in universitate Oxon. per quadragesim. ann. 1691/2.* [Oxford]: n.pub., [1692]. S.sh.
Wood 276b(65). Wing O924 (rare). Madan 3291.

5060. Oxford, University Determinations. *Ordo baccalaureorum determinantium in universitate Oxon. per quadragesim. ann. 1692/3.* [Oxford]: n.pub., [1693]. S.sh.
Wood 276b(66). Wing O925 (rare). Madan 3291.

5061. Oxford, University Determinations. *Ordo baccalaureorum determinantium in universitate Oxon. per quadragesim. ann. 1693/4*. [Oxford]: L.Lichfield, [1694]. S.sh.
Wood 276b(67). Wing O926 (rare). Madan 3291.

5062. Oxford, University Determinations. *Ordo baccalaureorum determinantium in universitate Oxon. per quadragesim. ann. 1694/5*. [Oxford]: L. Lichfield, [1695]. S.sh.
AW wrote, 'All those that have the cross-Daggers added to their names were absent on Egg-Saturday when they were to be presented ad Determinandum.' LT 3.479.
Wood 276b(68). Wing O927 (rare). Madan 3291.

5063. Oxford, University Questions. *Quaestiones in sacra theologia discutiendae Oxoniae in vesperiis, nono die Julii*. [Oxford]: [J. Barnes], [1614]. Fol. Pp. [2].
Some marks in margins, Roman numerals, and underscoring, not by AW. On the series of Oxford *Quaestiones*, Wood 276a(412) to 276a(437), see LT 2.165.
Wood 276a(412). STC 19016.2 (rare). Madan 3288 (and 1.225).

5064. Oxford, University Questions. *Quaestiones in sacra theologia discutiendae Oxonii in vesperiis, undecimo die Julii*. [Oxford]: n.pub., [1618]. Fol. Pp. [2].
Wood 276a(413). STC 19016.4 (rare). Madan 3288 (and 1.225).

5065. Oxford, University Questions. *Quaestiones in sacra theologia discutiendae Oxonii in vesperiis, decimo die Julii*. [Oxford]: n.pub., [1619]. S.sh.
Wood 276a(414). STC 19016.5 (rare). Madan 3288 (and 1.225).

5066. Oxford, University Questions. *Quaestiones in sacra theologia discutiendae Oxonii in vesperiis, sexto die Julii*. [Oxford]: n.pub., [1622]. Fol. Pp. [2].
Wood 276a(415). STC 19016.7 (rare). Madan 3288 (and 1.225).

5067. Oxford, University Questions. *Quaestiones in sacra theologia discutiendae Oxonii in vesperiis, duodecimo die Julii*. [Oxford]: n.pub., [1628]. S.sh.
Wood 276a(416). STC 19016.10 (two). Madan 3288 (and 1.225).

5068. Oxford, University Questions. *Quaestiones in sacra theologia discutiendae Oxonii in vesperiis, septimo die Julii*. [Oxford]: n.pub., [1632]. S.sh.
Wood 276a(417). STC 19016.13 (rare). Madan 3288 (and 1.225).

5069. Oxford, University Questions. *Quaestiones in sacra theologia discutiendae Oxonii in vesperiis, duodecimo die Julii*. [Oxford]: [W. Turner], [1634]. S.sh.
On blank side, pasted down, note, not in AW's hand.
Wood 276a(419). STC 19016.16 (rare). Madan 3288 (and 1.225).

5070. Oxford, University Questions. *Quaestiones in sacra theologia discutiendae Oxonii in vesperiis, undecimo die Julii*. [Oxford]: L. Lichfield, [1635]. Fol. Pp. [2].
Wood 276a(418). STC 19016.17 (rare). Madan 3288 (and 1.225).

5071. Oxford, University Questions. *Quaestiones in sacra theologia discutiendae Oxonii in vesperiis, undecimo die Julii*. [Oxford]: n.pub, [1640]. S.sh.
Wood 276a(420). STC 19016.19 (rare). Madan 3288 (and 1.225).

5072. Oxford, University Questions. *Quaestiones in sacra theologia discutiendae Oxonii in vesperiis decimo die Julii*. Oxoniae: L. Lichfield, 1652. S.sh.
Wood 276a(421). Wing O944 (rare). Madan 3288 (and 1.225).

5073. Oxford, University Questions. *Quaestiones in s. theologia discutiendae Oxonii in vesperiis sexto die Julii*. Oxoniae: typ. Lihfieldanis [sic], 1661. S.sh.
Wood 276a(423). Wing O944D (3). Madan 3288 (and 1.225).

5074. Oxford, University Questions. *Quaestiones in sacra theologia discutiendae Oxonii in vesperiis undecimo die mensis Julii*. Oxoniae: typ. Lichfieldianis, 1663. S.sh.
Wood 276a(424). Wing O945 (two). Madan 3288 (and 1.225).

5075. Oxford, University Questions. *Quaestiones in s. theologia discutiendae Oxonii in vesperiis, decimo die mensis Julii*. Oxoniae: typ. Lichfieldianis, 1669. S.sh.
Wood 276a(422). Wing O946 (rare). Madan 3288 (and 1.225).

5076. Oxford, University Questions. *Quaestiones in s. theologia discutiendae Oxonii in vesperiis, octavo die mensis Julii.* Oxonii: L. Lichfield, 1671. S.sh.
Wood 276a(425). Wing O947 (rare). Madan 3288 (and 1.225).

5077. Oxford, University Questions. *Quaestiones in s. theologia discutiendae Oxonii in vesperiis, duodecimo die mensis Julii.* Oxonii: L. Lichfield, 1673. S.sh.
On blank side, pasted down, traces of accounts, 'Mother', and 'Nephew', may be in AW's hand.
Wood 276a(426). Wing O948 (rare). Madan 3288 (and 1.225).

5078. Oxford, University Questions. *Quaestiones in s. theologia discutiendae Oxonii in vesperiis undecimo die mensis Julii.* Oxonii: L. Lichfield, 1674. S.sh.
Wood 276a(427). Wing O949 (two). Madan 3288 (and 1.225).

5079. Oxford, University Questions. *Quaestiones in s. theologia discutiendae Oxonii in vesperiis, decimo die mensis Julii.* Oxonii: L. Lichfield, 1675. S.sh.
Wood 276a(428). Wing O950 (two). Madan 3288 (and 1.225).

5080. Oxford, University Questions. *Quaestiones in s. theologia discutiendae Oxonii in vesperiis. Octavo die mensis Julii.* Oxonii: L. Lichfield, 1676. S.sh.
Wood 276a(429). Wing O951 (rare). Madan 3288 (and 1.225).

5081. Oxford, University Questions. *Quaestiones in s. theologia discutiendae Oxonii in vesperiis. Septimo die mensis Julii.* Oxonii: L. Lichfield, 1677. S.sh.
ᵛ, AW wrote '1677'.
Wood 276a(430). Wing O952 (two). Madan 3288 (and 1.225).

5082. Oxford, University Questions. *Quaestiones in s. theologia discutiendae Oxonii in vesperiis. Duodecimo die mensis Julii.* Oxonii: L. Lichfield, 1679. S.sh.
ᵛ, AW wrote '1679'.
Wood 276a(431). Wing O954 (rare). Madan 3288 (and 1.225).

5083. Oxford, University Questions. *Quaestiones in s. theologia discutiendae Oxonii in vesperiis. Decimo die mensis Julii.* Oxonii: L. Lichfield, 1680. S.sh.
ᵛ, AW wrote '1680'.
Wood 276a(432). Wing O955 (two). Madan 3288 (and 1.225).

5084. Oxford, University Questions. *Quaestiones in s. theologia discutiendae Oxonii in vesperiis: Nono die mensis Julii.* Oxonii: L. Lichfield, [1681] (mutilated). S.sh.
Wood 276a(433). Wing O956 (rare). Madan 3288 (and 1.225).

5085. Oxford, University Questions. *Quaestiones in s. theologia discutiendae Oxonii in vesperiis. Octavo die mensis Julii.* [Oxford]: L. Lichfield, 1682. S.sh.
ᵛ, AW wrote '1682'.
Wood 276a(434). Wing O957 (rare). Madan 3288 (and 1.225).

5086. Oxford, University Questions. *Quaestiones in sacra theologia discutiendae Oxonii in vesperiis. Septimo die mensis Julii.* Oxonii: L. Lichfield, 1683. S.sh.
Wood 276a(435). Wing O958 (two). Madan 3288 (and 1.225).

5087. Oxford, University Questions. *Quaestiones in s. theologia discutiendae Oxonii in vesperiis, duodecimo die mensis Julii.* [Oxford]: L. Lichfield, 1684. S.sh.
Wood 276a(436). Wing O959 (rare). Madan 3288 (and 1.225).

5088. Oxford, University Questions. *Quaestiones in s. theologia discutiendae Oxonii. In vesperiis. Octavo die mensis Julii.* [Oxford]: e theatro Sheldoniano, 1693. S.sh.
Wood 276a(437). Wing O960 (rare). Madan 3288 (and 1.225).

End of OXFORD. UNIVERSITY (items 4883-5088)

5089. Oxfordshire. *Two petitions of the knights, gentlemen, . . . in the county of Oxford [10 Feb.].* London: f. J. Wright, 1641[2]. 4°. Pp. [2], 3, 2.
AW rubbed out a former no. Bsm.

Wood 373(25). Wing T3512.

5090. Oxfordshire. *To the honourable the knights citizens . . . of the house of commons, . . . The humble petition of . . . the county of Oxford.* [Oxford]: n.pub., [1642]. S.sh. 4°.
Scribbles, not in AW's hand. Dupl. at Wood 373(26).
Wood 276a(188). Wing T1459A (two). Madan 978. Steele 2020.

5091. Oxfordshire. *To the honourable the knights citizens . . . of the house of commons, . . . The humble petition of . . . the county of Oxford.* [Oxford]: n.pub., [1642]. S.sh. 4°.
ᵛ, AW wrote, 'Oxfordsh. petit'. Dupl. at 276a(188).
Wood 373(26). Wing T1459A (two). Madan 978.

5092. Oxfordshire. *An explanation of the agreement of the 21. of Decemb. last, betwixt his majesty and the inhabitants of . . . Oxon.* Oxford: L. Lichfield, 1642, 16 Jan. 4°. Pp. [2], 6.
Tp, AW wrote 'dup', in pencil, and overwrote that with the item no. There is no duplicate in the Wood collection. Below, he wrote, 'see the agreement in Oxoniensia vol' and 'vide inter Oxoniensia'; now at Charles 1 (1642), Wood 516(6), item 1732.
Wood 375(28). Wing E3883 (two). Madan 1187.

5093. Oxfordshire. *The humble representation and petition of divers . . . of the county of Oxon. Presented to . . . the Commons, . . . April 6 . . . With the speeh [sic] of mr. Butler.* London: f. G. Calvert, [1649]. 4°. Pp. [2], 6.
Wood 515(3) (513(3) in Bodl. CD cat.). Wing H3631. Madan 2011 (in note).

5094. Oxfordshire. *The declaration of the county of Oxon to . . . Monck.* London: f. J. Starkey, 1660. S.sh.
AW altered the year to 16 '59'.
Wood 276a(236). Wing D662.

5095. Oxfordshire. *A declaration of the nobility, . . . of the county of Oxon.* London: f. T. Bassett, 1660. S.sh.
AW added to the year, 'Aprill: 28'.
Wood 276a(221). Wing D721.

5096. Oxfordshire. *May it please you sir to take notice, that there is a commisssion under the greate seale of England . . . to redresse the misimployment of lands [19 Aug. 1667].* [Oxford?]: n.pub., [1667]. S.sh.
AW wrote the year, '1669 - 68', in pencil; a later librarian wrote, 1667. ᵛ, 'These for the right woˡˡ: John Lamphire Doctor in physick.', not in AW's hand (AOF 2.235).
Wood 423(43). Wing M1417B (two). Madan 2774.

5097. Oxfordshire. *A letter from a person of honour at London, in answer to his friend in Oxford-shire. Concerning the ensuing election of knights of the shire.* [London]: n.pub., [1690]. S.sh. (r-v).
AW wrote, 'This paper was put ito my hands by Jam. Harrington of ch.ch. Mar. 8. an. 1689[90] -', 'The Election was 10 March, 1689[90].', both in red ink, and 'Dat. about the beginning of March. 1689[90] – priᵈ on the 10 of the same month began the election'. LT 3.327.
Wood 423(67). Wing L1420A (rare) (Wing, Oxfordshire).

5098. Oxfordshire. *A presentment of the grand jury for the body of the county of Oxon. at the assizes [5 Mar.].* [Oxford]: n.pub., [1690]. S.sh.
Response to Wing L1656. This item, numbered '3' prob. by AW, also has '68' in a recent hand. It was apparently added to this vol. sometime after 1922 (it is not listed on the upper flyleaves; the Whiteside cat. has only '67, Pamphlets on Several Occasions' for the contents of this vol.; and it is not in the Milford hand-list). Pasteboard cover, lower, note, lined out.
Wood 423(68). Not in Wing (should be at P3281A). Not in ESTCR.

5099. Oxfordshire Feast. *Oxford-shire. 1662. Sir, For the continuance of our mutual society.* [London]: [f. R. Royston], [1662]. S.sh.
With 6 stamped wax seals. LT 1.462-3. A ticket for the 1686 feast is at Wood Diaries 30b; see the following item.
Wood 276b(119). Wing S3877. Madan 2582.

5100. Oxfordshire Feast. *Sir, for the continuance of mutual society, and to promote a charitable relief for the poor.* [Oxford]: n.pub., [1686]. S.sh. 4°.
Inserted, Wood Diaries 30 (item 213), f. 61. AW wrote, 'I gave 2ˢ-6ᵈ for this Ticket 25 Oct. 1686 AWood'

and 'For my dinner in the councill chamber at gild hall 2^s-0'; with a wax seal. For other such Oxfordshire feasts, see Wood 276b(119); LT 1.462; 2.154, 201, 255; 3.109, 199, 225, 279, 312, 374, 433, 471. [MS.] Wood Diaries 30b. Not in Wing. Not in ESTCR (but see Wing S3877 and Madan 2582).

5101. Oxfordshire, Map. *A map of Oxford, Buckingham, and Berkshire.* N.p.: n.pub, n.d. S.sh.
Missing in 1939.
Wood 276a(60). Not identified.

5102. Oxfordshire, Map. '*A map of Oxford-shire*'. N.p.: ?, n.d. S.sh.
Missing in 1939.
Wood 276a(62). Not identified.

5103. P., G. *Libellus de memoria.* Londini: R. Walde-grave, 1584. 8°. A-D^8,E^2. Pasteboard (grey) with parchment spine (over original red paper covers which are now flyleaves).
Flyleaf, upper, 3rd^v, AW wrote the titles of 4 printed works (really 3) in this volume, within guidelines made with red ink. Tp, AW wrote '4^d'. Some notes on a leaf pasted to the back of the tp, illeg. ('placed', 'a play', 'game of chess play'). Also, some Latin notes on a leaf pasted to the final leaf, E2^v. At E1, wastepaper used to support backing has a note by AW, 'game at chesse play per Barbier', i.e., Wood 440(1) (vol. 440 was stolen).
Wood 36(1). STC 19065.

5104. P., G. *Englands murthering monsters set out in their colours, in a dialogue between Democritus and Heracclitus [sic].* [London]: n.pub., [1660]. S.sh.
AW wrote, 'Januar 1659[60]'; ^{v}, 'Jan. 59', and a former no. '26' in pencil was replaced by '42' on a slip used to repair the s.sh.
Wood 416(42). Wing P22 (two).

5105. P., G. *A word of exhortation to our separating brethren of whatever denomination, especially . . . Anabaptists.* Oxford: W. Hall, 1663. 4°. Pp. [2], 12.
Wood 617(19). Wing P25. Madan 2645.

5106. P., H. *The coffin opened: or, self-interest discovered, to be laid up in the coffin, under the name of the good old cause. In answer to . . . A coffin for the good old cause.* (London): (f. J. Johnson), (1660). 4°. Pp. 8.
P. 8, AW altered the year, 16'59'. Responds to Wood 613(29), item 2801.
Wood 613(30). Wing P26.

5107. P., P. *A warning-peece for England. Being a discovery of a jesuiticall design, to dismember Wales from England.* London: f. N. Ekins, 1655. 4°. Pp. [4], 32.
Wood 478(5). Wing P94.

5108. P., R. *The bishops looking-glasse, or the clergies prospective.* London: f. F. Coules a. W. Ley, 1641[2]. 4°. Pp. 6.
[MS.] Wood D. 31(28). Wing P96.

5109. P., R. *A discreet and judicious discourse betweene wisdome and pietie.* London: n.pub., 1642. 4°. Pp. [2], 6.
Tp, below, a 2nd no., '10'.
Wood 373(31). Wing P98.

5110. P., S. *The rumps last will and testament.* London: J. Tailor, 1660. 4°. Pp. 8.
Tp, AW altered the year to 16'59: March' and wrote, in pencil, no. in a former bundle, '4-' (cropped).
Wood 613(36). Wing P106.

5111. P., W. *One sheet, or, if you will a winding sheet for the good old cause.* London: n.pub., 1659. 4°. Pp. 8.
Tp, AW wrote the no. in a former bundle, '1-', in pencil (cropped at side), and after author's initials, 'Not written by Will Prynne', in red ink.
Wood 613(21). Wing P134.

5112. P., W. *The character of that glorious martyred king, Charles I.* London: f. T. B., 1660. 4°. Pp. [2], 6.
Wood 364(37). Wing P125.

5113. P., W. *Animadversions on the speech read by the late lord Stafford at the place of execution*. London: f. R. Janeway, 1681. Fol. Pp. [2], 18.

Tp, AW wrote the price, '6ᵈ', and 'W. Philips, auth. q[uaere]', lined out. P. 1, AW argues against the anti-Stafford author: 'Yᵒ may thinke so, but all did not', 'That is onlie supposed by yᵒ, yᵒ cannot prove it.', 'All this signifies nothing unless yᵒ can prove that he did not make his speech', and 'Archb. Laud when he suffered, read his speech; must it be thought therfore that he did not make it? But your reply perhaps, by saying, he was old, for he was about 73. This Lord was as old if not older, & hee had been a prisoner tow [i.e., two], & Laud almost 4, yeares, before they suffered – But I perceive wee want a great deale of charity'. P. 3, underscoring. LT 2.506.
Wood 427(7). Wing P123.

5114. Pagit, Eusebius. *The historie of the Bible, briefely collected by way of question and answer*. London: J. L[egat,] sold by S. Waterson, 1627. 8°. Pp. 47 (misnumbering).

Tp, AW wrote 'Ant: Woode: Merton: Coll: Oxōn: 1657' (year lined out), and underscored the name of the author. P. 5, scribble.
Wood 875(3). STC 19108.

5115. Painter, William. *The pallace of pleasure beautified . . . with pleasaunt historyes*. London: T. Marshe, 1569. 4°. Ff. [12], 264. Parchment, now pasted on new parchment boards (by L.F. 13.4.[19]57). Ms. waste paper, upper and lower, music with notes and Latin hymn with gold initials (see Ernest H. Sanders, 'Tonal aspects of 12th-century English polyphony', in *French and English polyphony* (Variorum Collected Studies Series CS637, Ashgate, 1998).

Ms. wastepaper, 2ndʳ, signatures of Thomas Leii, Edward Ferrers, Robert Vincente. Dated by Lee, 1587; 2ndᵛ, AW wrote, '1660 Feb. 9 With this may be bound pettyes pallace of pleasure' (now [MS.] Wood C. 33); and 'Women are wordes / Men are dedes', not by AW. Tp, signatures of Ferrers and Lee, and one line, 'hony is swete but cunning is swetter: And gold is good yet learning ys better.', not by AW. F. 264ᵛ, and ms. wastepaper, lower, scribbles, accounts, and verse by Ferrers and another, and a signature of Richard Lane.
Wood 591. STC 19122.

5116. Palladio, Andrea. *Les antiquitez de la ville de Rome*. Arras: ?, 1612? Pp.?
Missing. Gore, f. 322ᵛ. See Franzini and Palladio, Wood 162 and Wood 218(1), items 3090f.
Gore 322. Not in BL.

5117. [Palmer, Edward]. *An elegy on the death of mr. James Bristow*. Oxford: W. H[all] f. F. Oxlad, Jun., 1667, Jun. 4°. Pp. 10.

Tp, AW wrote, 'written by Edw. Palmer of Qu. Coll. Commoner, lately School-Fellow with Jam. Bristow at Eaton neare Windsore. See in the Fasti of the second vol. of <u>Ath. Oxon.</u> p. 835, an. 1665. & page 845, an. 1668' (AOF 2.281, 301). Acquired 28 Dec. 1667, 2ᵈ, LT 2.122-3.
Wood 319(7). Wing P224. Madan 2778.

5118. Palmer, Roger. Castlemaine, earl of. *An account of the present war between the Venetians & Turk*. London: J. M. f. H. Herringman, 1666. 8°. Pp. [18], 93.

Tp, AW wrote, 'Roger Palmer E. of Castlemaine', bsm.
Wood 156(3). Wing C1238.

5119. [Palmer, Roger]. Castlemaine, earl of. *A full answer and confutation of a scandalous pamphlet [by W. Lloyd], called, a seasonable discourse, shewing, the necessity of maintaining the established religion in opposition to popery*. [Antwerp]: n.pub., 1673. 4°. Pp. [4], 24 (cropped).

Tp, AW wrote, 'E of Castlemain', in pencil. Listed as dupl. in MS. Wood E. 2(70), p. 61.
[MS.] Wood B. 40(11). Wing C1243.

5120. Palmer, Roger. Castlemaine, earl of. *The compendium: or, a short view of the late tryals, in relation to the present plot*. London: [Mathew Turner], 1679. 4°. Pp. [1], 88.

P. [1], errata sheet, AW wrote, 'This compendium was published in Septemb. 1679. & the bookseller that sold it, being called into question by the Lords of his Majesties privy council, was by them committed to Newgate, 24 of the said month – (Mathew Turner[)] [/] Roger Earl of Castlemain was author of this compendium – see the narrative of the popish designe, published by Tho. Dangerfeild alias Willoughby an. 1679. p. 23' (i.e., Wood 425(25)); 2 corrections added to the errata, not by AW; and a later person wrote 'sum e Libris Musaei Ashmolaeani'. Tp, AW wrote 'In Septemb. The printer imprison'd by order of Councill'; p. 5, AW made a correction. LT 2.463, 465.
Wood 422(15). Wing C1241.

5121. Palmer, Roger*. Castlemaine, earl of. *The tryal of Roger earl of Castlemaine for high treason . . . before the lord chief justice Scroggs [23 June 1680]*. London: f. S. G., a. N. E., sold R. Taylor, 1681. Fol. Pp. 68.
Tp, AW wrote, 'This was not published immediately after the triall, but half an yeare after in Jan 1680-81. purposely to bring an odium upon Lord Ch. Justice Scroggs, for his partiality (as by many it was thought) in this triall – & baiting Oates &c.', '1.6ᵈ'. Bsm. LT 2.515.
Wood 427(12). Wing T2214.

5122. Palmerin, de Oliva. Munday, Anthony, trans. *The first part. Shewing the mirrour of nobilitie*. London: f. [by] B. Alsop a. T. Fawcet, 1637. 4°. A2-8,B-2A⁸,2B7. Calf with 3 fillets and edge hatching; spine, 4 bands and hatching (Oxford binding).
Wood 346. STC 19160.

5123. Panke, John. *A short admonition by way of dialogue*. Oxford: J. Barnes, sold S. Waterson [London], 1604. 8°. A-D⁸,E⁴ (pp. [72]).
Missing. MS. Wood E. 2(70), p. 56.
MS. Wood E. 2(70), p. 56. STC 19172 (3). Madan 254. O, BL, Harv.

5124. [Panton, Edward]. *News from hell: or a speech of a ghost of one of the old kings of Ormus . . . a mirror for monarchs . . . by E. F.* London: f. the booksellers, 1680. 4°. Pp. 8.
Wood 417(26). Wing P275.

5125. Paradin, Claude. S., P., trans. *The heroicall devises of m. Claudius Paradin . . . Whereunto are added the lord Gabriel Symeons and others*. London: W. Kearney, 1591. 16°in 8's. Pp. [10], 352 (to Y8, wanting Z, Aa, at end). Parchment over pasteboard.
Tp, name of former owner, Robart Aldewell (? illeg.).
Wood 437. STC 19183.

5126. Paradox. *A paradox against liberty. Written by the lords, during their imprisonment in the Tower. A poem*. London: f. J. Vade, 1679. Fol. Pp. 11.
Tp, AW wrote 'July', and '6ᵈ'. Purchased from Vade in July or August 1679, see his record of purchase in MS. Wood F. 50, f. 11.
Wood 417(15). Wing P329A.

5127. P[arker], H[enry]. *The true portraiture of the kings of England; . . . To which is added the political catechism. The author . . . is unknown to me . . . H. P.* London: n.pub., 1688. 4°. Pp. [4], 63. Calf with 3 fillets, stamp decoration inside corners (flower with 2 leaves), and roll decoration at inner, spine edge (Ashm. binding).
Flyleaf, upper, list of 17 items in this vol. by an Ashm. librarian (same hand in Wood 276a). Tp, traces of a note by AW, cropped at bottom.
Wood 486(1). Wing P430.

5128. [Parker, Martin]. *[Robin] Conscience: or, conscionable Robin*. London: by T. F. f. F. Coles, [1662]. 8°. 1,A⁸,B⁴ (cropped at top and bottom).
Wood 84(16). Wing P445 (one) ('O' not recorded in Wing).

5129. [Parker, Martin]. *Robin Conscience*. London: ?, 1684. 8°.
Missing in 1837. 'Robin Conscience – Lond. 1684' in Whiteside cat. See Wing P445 (1662).
Wood 66(15). Not in Wing. Not in ESTCR.

5130. Parker, Martin. *A true tale of Robin Hood*. [London]: f. J. Clark, W. Thackeray, a. T. Passinger, 1686. 8°. A2-8,B⁴.
Wood 284(2). Wing P447 (two).

5131. [Parker, Matthew]. Canterbury, abp. of, [Stubbs, J., trans.?]. *The life of the 70. archbishopp off [sic] Canterbury presentlye sitting Englished*. [Zürich?]: [C Froschauer?], 1574. 8°. A-D⁸,E1-7; plus a table at end (imperf., wanting leaves after E). Pasteboard (grey) with parchment spine. 1st upper and last lower flyleaves, marbled paper.
Parchment spine, AW listed the subject of this collection, 1-7, 'Lives of Archbishops and Bishops and Richlieu.' Flyleaf, upper, 2ndᵛ, AW wrote the titles of 7 printed works in this vol., within guidelines made with red ink. After the 1st entry, AW wrote, 'by a Seperatist' (sic). This leaf was pasted over a second leaf, with 6 entries (lacking the life of 'Richlieu'); Tp, 2 Latin tags, not in AW's hand. Text, AW wrote in the odd nos. (and a few even nos.). On A3ᵛ-A6, and E2ᵛ, underscorings, in AW's manner; C6-E7ᵛ, underscoring,

marks and notes in margins, most, not in AW's hand or manner. At end, 'A Table', appended and folded, containing a list of British prelates, AW underscored numerous entries and added several brief notes. Below, he wrote: 'This was printed beyond the sea – taken out of [M. Parker's] Antiquitates Britannicae – by some preist or Nonconf sent into England, about the time when Archb. Parker died'. Acquired 29 Ap. 1658 out of G. Langbaine's study, LT 1.247-8 (and note). Prob. lent to R. Bathurst 14 March 1660, LT 1.307. Wood 307(1). STC 19292a.

5132. Parker, Matthew. Canterbury, abp. of. *An admonition to all such as shall [/] intend hereafter to enter the state of ma- [/] trimony, godlily and agreeably to lawes*. [Oxford]: [W. Turner], [1630?]. S.sh. Wood 276a(285). STC 19289.5 (line 2 ends: 'of ma-').

5133. Parker, Sam[uel]. *A free and impartial censure of the Platonick philosophie; with an account of the Origenian hypothesis*. Oxford: H. Hall f. R. Davis, 1667. 8°. 2nd ed. Pp. [12], 242 (tpp at A2, A4 and I8).
Wood 127(3). Wing P464. Madan 2779.

5134. Parkhurst, John. *Ludicra sive epigrammata juvenilia*. Londini: J. Day, 1573. 4°. Pp. [24], 198.
Flyleaf, upper[v], AW wrote, 'In D. Johannis Parkhurst episcopi de Norwich in Anglia dignissimi obitum epicedia, per Rodolphum Gualter = habeo' (Wood 460(3), item 6433) and 'This book following did belong to M[r] Nath. Crew of Linc. Coll., (afterwards Bp of Durham) who exchanging it, among others, for other books, of Joseph Godwin a bookseller, living at the upper end, I afterwards bought it of him' (13 Aug. 1662, 1[s], LT 1.450). Tp, signature of 'Nath Crew' (cropped), and bsm. Passim, some notes, scribbles and marks in text, some in Nathaniel or Thomas Crew's hand, pp. 51, 111, 198, or yet another's, pp. 81, 105. For AW's hand, see p. 85, at 'Ioannem Halesium' (marked in red ink), 'Joh. Hales v. Stows survey of London p.' (Wood 472, item 6060), and p. 175.
Wood 334(2). STC 19299.

5135. Parkinson, [James]*. *An account of mr. Parkinson's expulsion from the university of Oxford . . . in vindication of him from the . . . aspersions . . . in . . . the history of passive obedience [by Abednego Seller]*. London: f. a. sold R. Baldwin, 1689. 4°. Pp. 20 (p. 20 books printed for R. Baldwin).
Tp, AW wrote in the Christian name of Parkinson; at 'Passive Obedience, 'written by D[r] George Hicks Deane of Worcester' (in AO 4.572, AW qualified this, 'The said *History* was said to be written by Dr. Geor. Hickes'); below, 'Bought at Oxon. in the beginning of Nov. 1689'; and [v], 10 identifications of persons cited in the text only by initials of surnames. Pp. 14, 19, a correction, a date, and an identification in margins. LT 3.68-72.
Wood 517(5). Wing P492.

5136. [Parkinson, James]. *The fire's continued at Oxford: or, the decree of the convocation for burning the naked gospel [by A. Bury], considered*. [London]: n.pub., [1690]. 4°. Pp. 15.
P. 15, AW wrote, 'This pamplet [sic] which was written by James Parkinson somtimes Fellow of Linc. Coll. was first expos'd to sale at Oxon, 20 Sept. 1690, having been printed at London'. At Parkinson, AW added, in red ink, 'q[uaere]'. LT 3.329-30, 337-41.
Wood 631(4). Wing P494.

5137. Parr, Richard. *The judges charge; delivered in a sermon*. London: J. C. f. N. Brook, 1658. 8°. Pp. [8], 32.
Missing. MS. Wood E. 2(70), p. 39.
MS. Wood E. 2(70), p. 39. Wing P547. *O, Folg, Union*.

5138. Parr, Susanna. *Susanna's apologie against the elders. Or a vindication of Susanna Parr*. [Oxford]: [H. Hall f. T. Robinson], 1659. 4°. Pp. [10], 114.
Tp, AW wrote 'Anth: Woode: Merton: Coll: MDc:Lix' and below, in pencil, 'qu[aere] whether – [1 word illeg.] Presbyt.' Acquired 10 May 1659, 3[d], LT 1.278.
Wood 888(3). Wing P551. Madan 2455.

5139. P[arrot], H[enry]. *Epigrams*. London: R. B[radock], soulde J. Helme, 1608. 4°. A-H[4].
Missing. MS. Wood E. 2(70), p. 54.
MS. Wood E. 2(70), p. 54. STC 19330 (3). *BL, Hunt*.

5140. Parrot, Henry. *[Laquei ridiculosi or springes for woodcocks]*. [London]: [[T. Snodham] f. J. Busby], [1613]. 8°. A2-3,B-P[8],Q1-7 (cropped and wanting tp).
Sig. Q1, signature, Thomas Shephy (? smudged); Q6[v], name, illeg.; Q7[v], 2 cooking recipes, in a secretary hand.

Wood 79(8) (now Arch. G. f. 2(8)). STC 19332.5.

5141. Parry, William*. *A true and plaine declaration of the horrible treasons, practised by William Parry. [Followed by] A prayer for all kings, princes.* London: C. B[arker], [1585]. 4°. Pp. [2], 53, [1], 7.
Tp, year, '1584' and flourish, prob. not by AW. Acquired 29 Ap. 1658 out of G. Langbaine's study, LT 1.247.
Wood 586(7). STC 19342a.5.

5142. Pascal, Blaise. Davies, John, trans. *Les provinciales: or, the mysterie of Jesuitisme, discover'd in certain letters [by Louis de Montalte].* London: J. G. f. R. Royston, 1657. 12°. Pp. [22], 409, [7] (2 pp. books by J. Taylor). Calf with 2 fillets; rebacked.
Flyleaf, upper, A. Allam wrote 'Pret: 1ˢ-4ᵈ Oxl[ad]:Sᵒʳ [senior] Bibliop: Sextilis [August] vicesimo 1ᵐᵒ 6/', and AW wrote 'Antonius Wood è Coll Merton'. LT 3.167. Flyleaf, lower, 1stᵛ, measurements, not by AW.
Wood 826. Wing P643.

5143. Pasor, Georgius. *Lexicon Graeco-Latinum. In novum . . . testamentum.* N.p.: n.pub., 1623. 8°. Pp. [16], 770, [169]. Calf with two fillets and gold stamp roll on edges of boards; spine, 4 bands.
Waste paper slip, upper, scribbles. Flyleaf, upper, notes, 'one printed 1622 conteining the new list in greek with Casaubons notes and others. as also the etymologies of proper names in the end', not in AW's hand, and 'Johannes Herford . . . de Patre meo . . . 1650'.
Wood 41. Not in BL, NUC, BN (see STC 19443-4).

5144. Patrick, Saint. Ware, James, ed. *Opuscula.* Londini: ap. J. Crook, 1656. 8°. [22], 151, [6].
Tp, AW wrote, '1ˢ3ᵈ'. Acquired 11 Nov. 1663, LT 1.503.
Wood 206(2). Wing P726.

5145. P[atrick], S[ymon]. Ely, bp. of. *A brief account of the new sect of latitude-men together with some reflections upon the new philosophy.* London: printed, sold St. Pauls Church-yard, . . . Oxford a. Cambridge, 1662. 4°. Pp. 24.
Tp, 'AWood:' and '4ᵈ'. Acquired 19 Aug. 1662, LT 1.452.
Wood 607(4). Wing P754. Madan 2583.

5146. Patrizi, Francesco. Nicodonus, Jo., ed. *Francisci Patricii . . . de regno et regis institutione libri novem.* Parisiis: ap. J. Hulpeau, 1578. 16°. Ff. [10], 380, [35]. Calf with 4 fillets; oval stamp centrepiece.
Flyleaves, upper, a few scribbles and Latin phrases, not in AW's hand; 2ndᵛ, AW wrote in pencil, 'In bib. Bod'. Tp, signature of Tho. Cleyton; bsm. LT 1.132.
Wood 576. Not in BL, NUC, BN.

5147. Paule, George. *[The life of . . . John Whitgift].* [London]: [T. Snodham], [1612]. 4°. Pp. [4], 94 (wanting title leaf at beginning; the 1st extant leaf serves as a flyleaf, upper, 3rd, in this vol., Wood 532).
Wood 532(2). STC 19484.

5148. Peacham, Henry (1546-1634). *The garden of eloquence conteyning the figures of grammer and rhetorick.* London: H. Jackson, 1577. 4°. A-U⁴.
Missing. MS. Wood E. 2(70), p. 6.
MS. Wood E. 2(70), p. 6. STC 19497. *O, Folg, Hunt, Yale* (tp repaired).

5149. [Peacham, Henry] (1576-1643). *Coach and sedan, pleasantly disputing for place and precedence [signed Mis-amaxius].* London: R. Raworth f. J. Crowch, sold E. Paxton, 1636. 4°. A-G⁴.
Wood 614(8) (614(18) in Bodl. CD cat.). STC 19501.

5150. Peacham, Henry (1576-1643). *The compleat gentleman.* London: E. Tyler f. R. Thrale, 1661. 4°. 3rd imprint. Pp. [11], 455 (2nd tp at p. 305). Pasteboard (blue) with parchment spine.
Flyleaf, upper, 3rdᵛ, AW wrote the titles of 4 printed works in this vol., within guidelines made with red ink (AW included 2 works at (1) and omitted (4)). Tp, '4ˢ-6ᵈ in sh[eets]' (acquired 26 July 1661, LT 1.405), and 'v. p. 244 [and in different ink and possibly not by AW:] & 129' (on p. 244, AW marked the passage concerning the author's brother, Richard Peacham); on p. 129 there are no marks though there is a printed paragraph on H. Holbein). P. 215, at Gilbert Sheldon's arms, AW wrote, 'The author is here out in his Heraldry', and, p. 216, at a statement that Sheldon is a 'generous Branch' (underscored by AW) of the Beoley Sheldons, he wrote 'How doe yo[u] prove that? He himselfe knew no such matter.', in red ink, and added 'Brayles' (Brailes, Worc.) in margin at a list of Sheldon's possessions. P. 243, at 1459, the year of birth of William de Wainflet and p. 447, at a reference to the coat of Bishop Fox (also underscored), AW wrote 'q[uaere]'. See also LT 1.477.

Wood 605(1). Wing P943.

5151. Peake, Humfrey. *Meditations upon a seige.* [Oxford]: [H. Hall], 1646. 8°. Pp. [8], 157.
Tp, AW wrote a former no. in a bundle, '28'. This item was prob. added to Wood 501 after 1695, see note at Wood 501(1), item 4099.
Wood 501(43). Wing P966B (two). Madan 1891 ('O' not recorded in Wing).

5152. P[ecke], T[homas]. *Advice to Balam's ass; or, Momus catechised. In answer to . . . John Heydon, author of advice to a daughter.* London: E. B. f. H. Marsh, 1658. 8°. Pp. [6], 65, [2].
Acquired 9 June 1664, 6ᵈ, LT 2.14.
Wood 843(6). Wing P1039.

5153. Pecock, Reginald. Wharton, Henry, ed. *A treatise proving scripture to be the rule of faith.* London: f. J. Adamson, 1688. 4°. Pp. [3], xl, xli, [3].
1st leaf, 'For Mʳ Wood.', after which AW wrote, 'From Mʳ Arth. Charlet 2. March 1687/8'. 1st iii-xv, lines in margin, in pencil, not in AW's manner.
[MS.] Wood B. 36(10). Wing P1043.

5154. Pedigree of Popery. *The pedigree of popery; or, the genealogie of antichrist.* [London?]: n.pub., 1688. S.sh.
AW wrote, 'A silly thing.', and 'Latter end of Nov.'
Wood 417(157). Wing P1050.

5155. Peeke, Richard, and J. D. *Three to one: being, an English-Spanish combat, performed by a westerne gentleman . . . against 3 Spanish rapiers and poniards [15 Nov. 1625]. [Followed by] Certain verses, written by a friend [J. D.].* London: [A. Mathewes] f. J. T[rundle], 1626. 4°. A2-4,B-E⁴ (wanting the t leaf, A1, supplied in photogr. facs.; E4 blank).
Wood 511(15). STC 19529.

5156. [Peers, Richard]. *A poem, in vindication of the late publick proceedings. By way of dialogue, between a high tory and a trimmer.* [London]: n.pub., 1689. Fol. Pp. [2], 9.
Tp, AW wrote 'Rich. Peers'. On authorship of this poem, see AO 4.291.
Wood 417(158). Wing P2677 (Wing, no author given).

5157. Peers, Richard, and [Gerard Langbaine (younger)], compilers. *A catalogue of all graduats in divinity, law, and physick:. . . in the university of Oxford [10 Oct. 1659 and 14 July 1688] [and] Proceeders between 14. of July 1688. And the 14. of July 1689.* Oxford: at the theater f. H. Clement, 1689. 8°. Pp. [8], 167, [1], and '169 to 176' (Y-Z²).
Tp, AW wrote 'published in the very beginning of Jan. 1688[9].' to replace an earlier similar note, cropped at bottom. Pp. 1, 4-5, 13-6, 20-2, 33, 35, 37-9 etc. to 172, various annotations: corrections, underscoring, additional information. After p. 167 at new section, 'The following additions were made by Gerard Langbaine 1691'. AO 4.367.
Wood 862(2) (not in Bodl. CD cat.). Wing P1055.

5158. [Peirce, Edmond]. *Vox verè Anglorum: or Englands loud cry for their king, by a hearty well-willer.* [London]: n.pub., 1659. 4°. Pp. 15.
Tp, former no. in a bundle '67' (in pencil).
Wood 533(15). Wing P1066.

5159. Peirce, Edmond. *Anglorum singultus: or, the sobbs of England, poured out. To . . . George Monke.* London: f. D. L., 1660. 4°. Pp. 11.
Tp, AW altered the year to, 16'59: Jan:'.
Wood 632(71). Wing P1059.

5160. [Peirce, Edmond]. *Englands monarchy asserted, and proved to be the freest state, . . . With a word to . . . general Monck.* London: W. G. f. R. Lowndes, 1660. 4°. Pp. [2], 12.
Tp, AW altered the year to 16'59[60]: ffeb:'; and wrote, in pencil, the no. in a former bundle, '20'.
Wood 626(8). Wing P1061.

5161. [Peirce, Edmond]. *The Jesuits grand design upon England clearly discovered in a letter lately written [27 March, 1660] from a father of that society [signed J. M. Really by E. Peirce].* [London]: n.pub., [1660]. 4°. Pp. 8. Rough calf with 3 fillets, stamp decoration inside corners (tulip sprouting a pin), and roll decoration at inner, spine edge (Ashm. binding); rebacked.
Flyleaf, upper, 2nd, titles of 72 printed works in this vol., by an Ashm. librarian (same hand in Wood

276a). Numbering of works on tpp is in Roman numerals. From AW's notes at Wood 608(17) and 608(19), items 2726, 4538, it can be seen that he intended a specific order of a short series of these pamphlets. There are also a number of 1660 pamphlets on which he wrote dates March to July in his early hand. These are in chronological order (except 33). Only 3 items have former nos., 1b, 4, 70.
Wood 608(1a). Wing P1063 (4).

5162. Pemble, William. *A briefe introduction to geography*. Oxford: J. Lichfield f. E. Forrest, 1630. 4°. Pp. [4], 46.
Wood 386(3). STC 19571. Madan 662.

5163. Pembroke Castle. *A great and bloudy fight at Penbrook [sic] castle between the parliaments forces . . . and the kings forces*. London: n.pub., 1648. 4°. Pp. [2], 6.
Tp, AW wrote after the year, 'Jul. 4' and below, in pencil, 'July'.
Wood 502(35). Wing G1637.

5164. Penkethman, John. *Additions to Hoptons concordancy*. London: A. Griffin f. A. Hebb, 1635. 8°.
A⁸,B⁴ (last leaf blank).
Wood 18(2). STC 13781.

5165. Penkethman, John. *Artachthos or a new booke declaring the assise or weight of bread*. London: E. Griffin a. E. Bishop, sold J. Penkethman (E. G. a. R. B.), 1638. 4°. A-L⁴.
[MS.] Wood C. 14(13). STC 19598.

5166. Penn, William. *The peoples { ancient and just } liberties asserted, in the tryal of William Penn, and William Mead*. [London]: n.pub., 1670. 4°. Pp. 62.
Tp, AW wrote the year, '1670'. Response at Wood 645(19), item 6034.
Wood 645(18). Wing P1334C.

5167. Penn, William*. *A brief account of the province of Pennsylvania. Lately granted by the king . . . to William Penn*. (London): (f. B. Clark), (1681). Fol. Pp. 8. Pasteboard (blue) with parchment spine.
Flyleaf, upper, 2nd, AW wrote the titles of 23 printed works in this vol. (2 items at no. (2) and (12 and (13) are really one item), within guidelines made with red ink.
Wood 559(1) (not in Bodl. CD cat.). Wing P1255.

5168. Penn, William. *A brief account of the province of Pennsilvania in America, lately granted . . . to William Penn, &c*. [London]: n.pub., [1681]. S.sh. (r-v).
Wood 559(2b) (not in Bodl. CD cat.). Wing P1256.

5169. Penn, William. *The frame of the government of the province of Pennsilvania in America*. [London]: [A. Sowle], 1682. Fol. Pp. [4], 11.
Wood 559(3). Wing P1292.

5170. Penn, William*. *Ulmorum Acherons; or the history of William Pen's conversion from a gentleman to a Quaker. Or a stop to the call of the unconverted*. London: f. T. Lee, 1682. 4°. Pp. [2], 6.
Flyleaf, upperᵛ, Latin sentence, by Ashm. librarian (?), 'Dabit Deus his quoque finem'.
Wood 645(25). Wing U21.

5171. Penn, William. *William Penn's last farewel to England: being an epistle*. London: f. T. Cooke, 1682. 4°. Pp. [2], 6.
Marbled flyleaf, lowerʳ, unmarbled side (bound upside down): 'Ar Charlet ded[it] 27 Ap 90', which belonged at one time to the book, Proast (1690), at Wood 611(19), item 5364, which has left the trace of an impression of the tp, reversed, on this flyleaf; ᵛ, on the marbled side, 'Mʳ Proast' (also upside down).
Wood 645(26). Wing P1317.

5172. Penn, William. *A letter from William Penn proprietary and governour of Pennsylvania . . . to the committee of the free society of traders*. London: printed and sold A. Sowle, 1683. Fol. Pp. [2], 10 (plus 1 sheet, a map of Philadelphia).
Wood 559(4). Wing P1320.

5173. Penn, William. *Considerations moving to a toleration, and liberty of conscience. . . . Occasioned by an excellent discourse [A short discourse] . . . publish'd by the duke of Buckingham*. London: f. R. Hayhurst, 1685. 4°. Pp. [8], 12.
Tp, no. '(8)', in pencil, in a former bundle. Responds to Villiers, Wood 611(7), item 6333.
Wood 611(11). Wing P1269.

5174. [**Penn, William**]. *A defence of the duke of Buckingham, against the answer to his book, and the reply to his letter. By the author of the late considerations.* (London): (f. W. C.), (1685). 4°. Pp. 8.
Tp, no. '(7)', in pencil, in a former bundle.
Wood 611(12). Wing D816A.

5175. [**Penn, William**]. *A defence of the duke of Buckingham's book of religion & worship, from the exceptions of a nameless author [in a short answer to the d. of Buckingham's paper]. By the Pensilvanian.* London: f. A. Banks, 1685. 4°. Pp. [4], 31.
Tp, no. '(5)', in pencil, in a former bundle; after Pensilvanian, AW wrote, 'qu[aere]'.
Wood 611(9). Wing P1275.

5176. Pennsylvania. *The articles, settlement and offices of the free society of traders in Pennsilvania.* London: f. B. Clark, 1682. Fol. A-D².
Wood 559(2a). Wing A3885.

5177. Penruddock, John*. *The triall of the honourable colonel John Penruddock of Compton in Wiltshire and his speech; . . . 16. day of March.* N.p.: n.pub., 1655. 4°. Pp. [2], 17.
Flyleaf, upper^{r-v}, AW wrote 64 lines on events leading to Penruddock's capture: '1654 - The Anabaptists being much discontented at Olivers proceedings in making himself protector & aiming at Monarchy, (to which alwaies he before did pretend to be an enimy) & therefore had cashired some of the activst men of that party - The cavaliers thereupon took opportunity to joyne with them to pluck him downe – They had several meetings & caballs & at length appointed that insurrections should be made in severall counties – in Merionethsh. Nottinghamsh. Shrewsbury – but their plots being underhand betrayed by one [blank] Manning belonging to K. Ch. 2 beyond the sea, their risings were nipt in the beginning – . . . [etc., last paragraph:] In the beg. of Apr. 1655 were appointed 70 commissioners of Oyer & terminer & goale delivery for the counties of Wilts, Dorset, Somerset & Devon & the countie of the city of Exon.' (transcribed in full in LT 1.194-5). P. 12, vertical line in margin; p. 17^v, not in AW's hand: 'Charles' (twice) and 'To my friend Mr James Perrott with a bundle' (for Perot, see LT 3.188-9).
Wood 367(12). Wing P1431.

5178. [**Penton, Stephen**]. *The guardian's instruction, or, the gentleman's romance. Written for . . . the gentry.* London: f. the authour, sold S. Miller, 1688. 12°. Pp. [15], 90, [2].
Tp, AW wrote 'By Steph. Penton'.
Wood 754(5). Wing P1439.

5179. Percey, William. *The compleat swimmer: or, the art of swimming.* London: J. C[ottrell] f. H. Fletcher, 1658. 8°. Pp. [11], 83.
Tp, AW wrote '2^d', and 'Taken out of Sr Everard Digby de arte natandi' (STC 6839), in red ink. Bsms.
Wood 728(3). Wing P1454.

5180. Percy, Algernon; O. Saint-John, and Henry Vane. *A cunning plot to divide and destroy, the parliament.* London: P. Cole, 1643[4], 16 Jan. 4°. Pp. [2], 56.
First blank p., '16', lined out and replaced by '10 Jan.' (date of publication, and date of authorization to publish). Tp, AW underscored names, and after 'Master Riley', wrote, 'Theoph. Riley'.
Wood 376(57). Wing C7586.

5181. Percy, James. *A short account of the proceedings of James Percy late of Ireland, in pursuance of his native right to the earldome of Northumberland.* [London]: n.pub., [1674]. S.sh.
Wood 276b(85). Wing P1459 (rare).

5182. Percy, James. *The case of James Percy, claymant to the earldom of Northumberland.* London: n.pub., 1685. Fol. Pp. [4], 10.
Wood 276b(70). Wing C923.

5183. Percy, James. *To the high and noble prince, Henry, duke of Norfolk, earl marshal of England, in court of chivalry.* [London]: printed to attend the Court of Chivalry, 1687, 21 Oct. S.sh.
Wood 276b(110). Wing P1461A (rare).

5184. Perfect Collection. *A perfect collection of all the songs now in mode either at the court or, theatres.* London: n.pub., 1675. 8°. With new additions. Pp. [4], 12, 48.
Wood 326(6). Wing P1476 (rare).

5185. Perfect Collection. *A perfect collection of the several songs now in mode either at the court, or, theatres.* [London]: n.pub., 1675. 8°. 'All New'. Pp. [8], 48.

Wood 326(5). Wing P1477 (rare).

5186. Perkins, Jos[eph]. *Iter australe. Curatus quidam lassatus itineribus ad urbem Sarum.* Londini: impensis authoris, 1688. S.sh.
Wood 417(156). Wing P1556 (two).

5187. Perkins, William. *The foundation of Christian religion, gathered into six principles.* London: J. Legat, 1645. 8° (cropped). Pp. [8], 47.
Tp, signature of former owner, 'Robert –and (?) [his] booke' 1648 (cropped at side).
Wood 795(2). Wing P1564B (two).

5188. Perlunkett, Thomas, and Robert Moulton. *A true relation of some notable passages faithfully performed on the coasts of England and Ireland . . . two letters.* London: F. Leach f. L. Blackelock, 1643, 8 July. 4°. Pp. [2], 6.
Tp, AW wrote below, 'Jul 7. 43', in pencil; former no., '36', lined out.
Wood 508(43). Wing T2917.

5189. [Perrault, François]. *The devill of Mascon. Or, a true relation . . . at Mascon in Burgundy, . . . now made English.* Oxford: H. Hall, 1658. 8°. 2nd ed. Pp. 32, [4].
Wood 707(6) (not in Bodl. CD cat.). Wing P1685. Madan 2408.

5190. P[errinchief], R[ichard]. *A messenger from the dead, or, conference . . . between the ghosts of Henry the 8. and Charls the first.* London: f. T. Vere, a. W. Gilbertson, 1658. 4°. Pp. 20.
P. 1, AW gives the source of this item, 'Nuntius a mortuis, hoc est*, stupendum . . . printed at Lond. 1657. oct. Note that from this Lat. book, printed at Lond. 1657, is the silly pamphlet following, taken', and the footnote, '(*)putidum, mendacium, in subsidium causae pontificiae harum artium indigae, et alias ruiturae, confictum.' (See Wing P1598-1599A for Paris and London eds.; Wing P1599, Latin edition; Wing P1599A, 1st English translation). LT 1.234.
Wood 364(36). Wing P1597.

5191. [Perrinchief, Richard]. *The royal martyr: or, the life and death of king Charles I.* London: J. M. f. R. Royston, 1676. 8°. Pp. [15], 311, 9 (1 p. books sold by Royston). Calf, speckled, with 2 fillets and 2nd rectangle with three fillets and stamp decoration in corners.
Leaf fragment, upper, Andrew Allam wrote, 'Pret: 5s-0d Oxl[ad]: Ju or Bibliop: Quintilis desimo nono [16]76'.
See note at Wood 363(16), item 6377, and LT 2.270; 3.167.
Wood 238(1) (not in Bodl. CD cat.). Wing P1601. See FFMadan 65.

5192. Perrinchief, Rich[ard]. *The Sicilian tyrant: or, the life of Agathocles.* London: J. Grover f. R. Royston, 1676. 8°. Pp. [17], 278.
Wood 238(2) (not in Bodl. CD cat.). Wing P1607.

5193. [Persons, Robert]. Anon. Arundell, Charles, also attrib. to; Morgan, Thomas, also attrib. to. *[The copie of a leter, wryten by a master of arte of Cambridge . . . about the present state, and some procedinges of the Erle of Leycester].* [Paris]: n.pub., 1584. 8°. Pp. 9-199, [1], wanting all before sig. A6 and last leaf. Parchment over pasteboard, 2 clasp holes (green colouring on edges).
Pastedown, upper, 3 notes concerning the printing and authorship, the 1st 2 by AW: 'Leycsters comonwealth. This book being printed beyond the seas at [blank] was at its first arrivall into England called Green [correction over lined out Blew] coat, because all that came from thence their leaves were coloured Greene [correction after lined out blew].', and later, 'See in the Life of Parsons by Dr. James: p. 59' ([MS.] Wood D. 24(2)), and 'Some report that Rob: Persons the Iesuit was the author of it, but most that [blank] Ld Burleigh, had the cheifest hand in it. who was a great enemy to the E. of Leycester' (see AO 2.74-5, where AW incorporated some of the above information). The 3rd note, the correct t, is in a different hand. P. 12, a scribble; 115, 127, 138, 150-1, notes, cropped, not in AW's hand. Last p., apparently a signature, illeg. AW wrote in MS. Wood E. 2(70), p. 31, 'common wealth & other matters by Rob. Parsons – 1641. I have it in 8°'. AW acquired either this or the diff. ed. on 21 Sept. 1663, 1s10d, LT 1.487. See note at the diff. ed., Persons, *Leycesters* (1641), Wood 535(2a), item 5199.
Wood 456. STC 5742.9. ARCR 2.31.

5194. [Persons, Robert]. *A treatise of three conversions of England . . . by N. D.* [St. Omer]: [F. Bellet], 1603. 8°. Pp. [74], 658, [32]. Parchment, with 2 clasp holes.
Flyleaf, upper, AW wrote, 'Two parts of the Conversions are in this vol.' (dark ink) and later, 'These conversions are answered by Mat. Sutcliff – I have them' (light ink) (Wood 322, item 6091) ; and 'A Wood' (pencil, may not be by AW).

Wood 223. STC 19416. ARCR 2.638.

5195. Persons, Robert. *A relation of the triall made . . . betweene [M. Peron] the bishop of Eureux and the l. Plessis Mornay. . . . By N. D.* [St. Omer]: [F. Bellet], 1604. 8°. 'Newly reuewed', [sic]. Pp. 237. P. 58, at printed 'Jewells wrytyngs', AW wrote 'See in the 2 vol. of the 3. conversions p 277' (i.e., Wood 872). Other notes are not by AW, e.g., 96, 200. There are also underscorings and lines in margin, prob. not by AW. Diff. ed. is at pt. 2 of Wood 872.
Wood 863(2). STC 19413. ARCR 2.635.

5196. Persons, Robert. D., N., by. *A review of ten publike disputations or conferences held . . . under k. Edward & qu. Mary, . . . By N. D.* [St. Omer]: [F. Bellet], 1604. 8°. Pp. 370. Parchment, limp. Pastedown, upper, AW wrote 'This is at the end of the 3. part of Conversions which I have.' (Wood 856). Tp, after initials N. D., AW wrote 'Rob. Persons' and below at imprint, 'Audomari' (St. Omer). Initials of an earlier owner, 'S. L.' Text, some underscoring and marks and lines in margin and a few brief notes. The notes and marks in margins are not by AW, but a few of the underscorings and lines in margin may be his, e.g., p. 71. Dupl. of pt. 2 is at Wood 856.
Wood 863(1). STC 19414. ARCR 2.636.

5197. Persons, Robert. D., N., by. *The third part of a treatise, intituled: of three conversions of England: conteyninge. An examen of the calendar . . . of Protestant saints, . . . divised by John Fox, . . . The first six monethes. Wherunto . . . is annexed a defence of a certaine triall, made . . . betweene monsieur Peron bishop of Eureux, and monsieur Plessis Mornay . . . By N. D.* [St. Omer]: [F. Bellet], 1604. 8°. Vol. 2. 2 pts. Pp. [146], 530, [14], 237. Parchment.
Pastedown, upper, AW wrote 'Vol. 2' (other notes and signature, in pencil, are not by AW). Diff. ed. of pt. 2 is at Wood 863(2).
Wood 872. STC 19416. ARCR 2.638.

5198. Persons, Robert. D., N., by. *The third part of a treatise intituled of three conversions of England. Conteyninge an examen of the calendar . . . of protestant saintes, . . . devised by Fox, . . . The last six monethes. Wherunto is annexed, . . . a re-view of ten publike disputations. . . . By N. D.* [St. Omer]: [F. Bellet], 1604. 8°. Vol. 3. 2 pts. Pp. [116], 465 (i.e., 475, misnumbering), [21], 370. Parchment.
Pastedown, upper, AW wrote 'When these 3 books came out first they were 20ˢ price. [/] Mʳ Wilton' (i.e., information from John Wilton); 'At the end is a veiw of 10 publick disputations'; and 'vol 3'. Flyleaf, upper, 10ᵈ, not in AW's hand. Tp, at N. D., AW wrote 'Robert Parsons'. Dupl. of pt. 2 is at Wood 863(1), item 5193.
Wood 856. STC 19416. ARCR 2.638.

5199. [Persons, Robert]. Anon. Arundell, Charles, also attrib. to; Morgan, Thomas, also attrib. to. *Leycesters common-wealth: conceived, spoken and published.* [London]: n.pub., 1641. 4°. Pp. [8], 182.
Tp, AW wrote, 'In this book are represented the Life & actions of Robert Earl of Leycester, who died, 1588'. P. 27, lines in margin, in pencil. Sometimes issued, as here, with Rogers, *Leycesters Ghost*, Wood 535(2b), item 5597. AW acquired either this or the diff. ed. on 21 Sept. 1663, 1ˢ10ᵈ, LT 1.487. He probably listed a copy (as an 8°) in MS. Wood E. 2(70), p. 31, 'Leicesters common wealth & other matters by Rob. Parsons – 1641. I have it in 8°'. Diff. ed. (1584) is at Persons, Wood 456 (1584).
Wood 535(2a). Wing L968 (see ARCR 2.31).

5200. [Persons, Robert]. *A treatise concerning the broken succession of the crown of England.* London: n.pub., 1655. 4°. Pp. 167.
Tp, AW wrote, 'Md [Memorandum] that F. Rob. Persons put out a book an[.] 1594 de successione Regni Angliae, qu[aere] the last pag. of this booke.' (i.e., pp. 166-7, the printed 'by Father Parson's the Jesuit, under the name of Doleman'); and below, 'Anton à Wood. Oxōn. 1669'. See LT 2.181 and ARCR 2.167.
Wood 533(11). Wing P574.

5201. Peryn, William. *Spirituall exercyses and goostly meditacions, and a neare waye to come to perfection.* [Adapted from the Exercitia of N. van Ess]. London: [J. Kingston f.] J. Waley, 1557. 8°. 4,A-U⁸ (last 2 leaves blank). Parchment over pasteboard.
Flyleaf, upper, 1stᵛ, 'Mary S–den' (?, lined out). 2nd, 'Thomas Haythe And Mary hys Wyfe, Amen'. 4thᵛ, AW wrote 'in bib Bod', in pencil.
Wood 784. STC 19784.

5202. Pestell, William. *A congratulation to his sacred majesty.* London: n.pub., 1661. 4°. Pp. 7.
Wood 319(12). Wing P1676A (two) ('O' not recorded in Wing).

5203. Pet, Edmond*. *Lamentable newes, shewing the wonderfull deliverance of maister Edmond Pet.* London: T. C[reede] f. W. Barley, 1613. 4°. A⁴.
[MS.] Wood D. 28(5). STC 19792.

5204. Peter, Saint. *News from heaven: or a dialogue between s. Peter and the five Jesuits last hang'd.* [London]: n.pub., [1679]. Fol. Pp. 4.
LT 2.457.
Wood 424(28). Wing N964.

5205. Peters, [Hugh]. *A full and last relation, of all thing concerning Basing-house.* London: J. Coe, 1645. 4°. Pp. [2], 6.
Tp, AW wrote the date, 'Oct', in pencil; the price, '1ᵈ'; and lined out the former no., '28'.
Wood 378(31). Wing P1702.

5206. Peters, Hugh. *Master Peters messuage [sic] from sir Thomas Fairfax.* London: f. M. Walbancke, 1645[6], 22 Mar. 4°. Pp. [2], 15.
Tp, AW wrote the price, '2ᵈ', lined it out, and altered the former no., '61'.
Wood 378(64). Wing P1710A.

5207. Peters, Hugh. *Mʳ Peters last report of the English wars.* London: M. S. f. H. Overton, 1646. 4°. Pp. 15.
Tp, '2ᵈ', prob. not by AW. AW wrote 'June or July.', in pencil.
Wood 501(26). Wing P1707.

5208. Peters, Hugh*. *Hugh Peters's dreame.* [London]: n.pub., [1659]. 4°. Pp. 8.
P. 8, AW wrote the date, 'M DC: Lix'.
Wood 613(5). Wing H3302A.

5209. Peters, Hugh. *The case of mr. Hugh Peters.* London: S. Speed, [1660]. 4°. Pp. [2], 8.
Tp, AW wrote, at 'written by his own hand', 'qu[aere].'
Wood 369(4). Wing P1695.

5210. Peters, Hugh*. *The tales and jests of mr. Hugh Peters. . . . Together with his sentence, and . . . execution.* London: f. S. D., 1660. 4°. Pp. [10], 32.
Wood 486(17). Wing P1721.

5211. Peters, Hugh*. *Spectrum anti-monarchicum. Or, the ghost of Hugh Peters.* [London]: n.pub., [1679]. Fol. Pp. 3.
Wood 417(125). Wing S4848 (Wing, : or,).

5212. Petre, William, 4th baron. *The declaration of the lord Petre upon his death, touching the plot, in a letter.* (London): (T. B. f. R. Mead), (1684). S.sh. (r-v).
AW wrote, 'This William Lord Petre died in the Tower of Lond. 4. January 1683[4]. after 5. yeares, & severall weeks imprisonment there.'; ᵛ, 'Received in a Letter dat. at Lond. 10. Jan. 1683[4] from Mʳ Arth. Charlett proctor of the Universitie of Oxōn – AWood.' LT 3.85-6.
Wood 427(48). Wing P1877.

5213. Petrucci, Ludovico. *Apologia equitis Ludovici Petrucci contra calumniatores suos. Una cum responsione ad libellum à Jesuitis contra . . . Leonardum Donatum.* [London]: [Eliot's Court Press], [1619?]. 4°. Cropped at bottom. A-E⁴,F² (wanting all after F2).
Tp, AW wrote, 'Oratio ad finem [cropped] Emblemata et Poemata' (reminding himself of works printed at the end of this item). E4ᵛ, F1, AW wrote in margin English names for printed Latin names and underscored 2 names, Rogerus Pinke and Thomas Wood.
Wood 483(24). STC 19812.5 (two).

5214. Pe[tt], Pe[ter]. *In obitum Joannis Reynoldi.* [London]: typ. G. Godbid, 1657. S.sh.
After initials of author, AW wrote, 'Peter Pett'.
Wood 429(11). Wing P1883A (rare).

5215. Pettie, George. *A petite pallace of Pettie his pleasure, conteyning many pretie histories.* London: G. Eld, 1608. 4°. A-Z⁴,¶⁴ (last leaf blank). Parchment.
Flyleaf, upper, 1st, the title, a Latin tag (copied from the tp, Horace, *Ars poet.*, 343), and 'Containing many pretty historyes by line set forth in comely coloures and delightfull discourse [/] John Crofts his book' (LT 1.329), and 'Humfrey', none by AW; another signature of Crofts and one of 'Filadelpha Carey'.

Tp, AW wrote, 'A. W.' and 'By George Pettie son of Jo: Pettie of Tetsworth Com: Oxon: gener:'. LT 1.32; AO 1.553. Flyleaf, lower[v], the title, not in AW's hand, and the signature of 'M[rs] Phillidelpha Cary'. [MS.] Wood C. 33. STC 19822.

5216. Petty, William*. *A brief of proceedings between s[r.] Hierom Sankey and d[r.] William Petty.* London: n.pub., 1659. Fol. Pp. [4], 8.
P. 3, eleven words of printed text, lined out.
Wood 657(58). Wing P1915A. G. Keynes, *Petty* (1971), no. 4.

5217. Petty, William. *Reflections upon some persons and things in Ireland, by letters to and from d[r] Petty.* London: f. J. Martin, J. Allestreye, a. T. Dicas, 1660. 8°. Pp. [2], 185, [13]. Calf with roll decoration at edges and stamp decoration in corners.
Wood 712. Wing P1936. G. Keynes, Petty (1971), no. 5.

5218. [Petty, William]. *A treatise of taxes & contributions.* London: f. N. Brooke, 1662. 4°. Pp. [16], 75, [3].
Tp, AW wrote below the year, '& in 1667', in pencil. Pp. 5-6, 18, 22, 32-4, 39-41, etc., to end, corrections entered from errata, not in AW's hand. Pp. 43-4, line in margin. See AW's note on Petty at Cotton, Wood 526(1), item 2028.
Wood 526(10). Wing P1938. G. Keynes, Petty (1971), no. 8.

5219. Peyton, Edward. *The divine catastrophe . . . of the house of Stuarts.* London: f. G. Calvert, 1652. 8°. Pp. [6], 149. Calf with 2 fillets; rebacked.
Flyleaf, upper[v], 'parte mandita alterā', not by AW, and AW wrote, 'Full of lies, mistakes, nonsense etc [/] The author speaks of himself p 22. 26. 61. 62. 119 118 139' (see AO 3.320-1). Text, some vertical pencil lines in margins and a few underscorings, e.g., 13, 19, 22-3, 26, 28, etc.
Wood 194. Wing P1952.

5220. Phelps, Thomas. *A true account of the captivity . . . at Machaness in Barbary.* London: H. Hills, Jun. f. J. Hindmarsh, 1685. 4°. Pp. [4], 27.
Wood 387(12). Wing P1982.

5221. Philastrogus, pseud. *Lillies ape whipt by Philastrogus [a criticism of N. Culpeper's ephemeris for the year 1652].* [London?]: f. W. I. C. I. G. W., [1652]. 4°. Pp. [2], 6.
Tp, a note in two hands, AW's supplementing an earlier, in double brackets: 'viz: Nich. [Culpeper] Figure-flinger'.
Wood 622(16). Wing L2203.

5222. Philipot, John. *[The examination of the constante martir of Christ, John Philpot] [With] Jesus is God with us. An apologie of Johan Philpot written for spitting upon an Arrian.* [London]: [(H. Sutton)], [(1559)]. 8°. 2 pt. Ff. 8 and unnumbered ff. (A2-8,B-O⁸,A-B⁸,C⁶) (wanting the t leaf).
Some notes, many by the former owner Henry Jackson, and frequent lines in margin in pencil; prob. none by AW. LT 1.459-60 (see also 1.331).
Wood 789(3). STC 19893a.

5223. Philipot, John. *The catalogue of the chancellors of England. By J. P. Summerset herald.* London: T. Cotes, sold A. Crooke, 1636. 4°. 2 pts. Pp. [10], 82, [2], 85.
Missing in 1837. See Wood 490(1).
Wood 490(5). STC 19846. *O, Folg, Hunt.*

5224. Philipps, Fabian. *The reforming registry, or a representation of the very many mischiefs and inconveniences which will unavoidably happen by the needless, . . . way of registries.* London: T. Newcomb f. the author, sold A. Roper, 1662. 4°. Pp. [2], 100.
Wood 630(23). Wing P2014.

5225. [Philipps, Fabian]. *The pretended perspective-glass; or some reasons . . . against the proposed registring reformation.* London: n.pub., 1669. 4°. Pp. [2], 16.
Tp, AW wrote, 'Fabian Philipps Esq. (phelicer) the authour.' Lower flyleaf, 'Ex dono Authoris ffab. Ph . . . [lined out] 1670', not in AW's hand.
Wood 630(21). Wing P2013.

5226. Philipps, H[enry]. *The grandeur of the law: or, an exact collection of the nobility and gentry.* London: f. A. Jones, 1684. 8°. Pp. [8], 276, [10].
Flyleaf, upper, AW wrote, '1.q[uaere]', in pencil, and 'The first foundation of this book seems to be laid

on the series or Cat. of Lord chancellours, Treasurers, justices &c at the end of Sr Will. Dugdales Orig. jurid. [/] For those names that he† [in margin: '† the authour'] hath seen these, which are now names of quality, he takes to be the original of such families that beare the same names. [/] The Nobility in this book, which have taken there use from the Law, is taken from Dugdales Baronag'. AW wrote notes (some critical, some cropped), corrections, underscorings and lines in margins, e.g., pp. 2 (at Sir John Cavendish, 'But it may be a question whether he was raiser of the family'), 3 (at the first reputable person of the family, Sir Richard Sackvill, 'They were noted gentlemen before his time'), 4, 19, 24, 124 (at a descendant of Sir Thomas Wood Knight, 'How do yo[u] prove that?'), 128, 139-40, 172, 191, 216 (at Nevill Brome, 'This person is not fit to [be] mentioned as being verie inconsiderable'), 236-8, 256-7.
Wood 251(3). Wing P2022.

5227. Philipps, Sam[uel]. *To the learned and worthy artist mr. Grinsted Gibbons.* (London): (f. J. Norris), (1684). Fol. Pp. 4.
Wood 416(133). Wing P2024.

5228. Philips, [Robert]. *The coppy of a letter of father Philips, the queenes confessor, . . . to mr. Mountague.* [London]: n.pub., 1641. 4°. Pp. [2], 5, [1].
Tp, AW wrote, 'Walt. Mountague Abbat of Nanteul afterwards of Pontois'. P. 5, lines at date and at name of author.
Wood 373(4). Wing P2039.

5229. Philips, Robert*. *The impeachment and articles of complaint against father Philips the queenes confessor. Lately committed to the Tower . . . Novemb. 2. 1641.* London: f. A. I. or n.pub., 1641. 4°. A^4 (pp. 343-346).
Missing in 1839; see note at Wood 373(1) and Plate I. Ed. not identified.
Wood 373(5). Wing I92 and I93. O (two), *Clark*, and *Hunt, Folg.*

5230. Phillips, Edward. *Theatrum poetarum, or a complete collection of poets.* London: f. C. Smith, 1675. 12°. Pp. [32], 192, 261, [2] (2 pp. books sold by C. Smith). Calf with 2 fillets; rebacked.
Flyleaf, upper, 1st, '1. Aug. 1681 Bought of Tho. Vicars [above Vicars, 'Fichus'] a stationer newlie set up on Holywell – 1^s-6^d ABosco' (LT 2.549). 2nd^r-v, AW wrote the names of some 40 'poets omitted [/] Sr Will. Lower K^t [/] Joh. Owen [/] Joh. Vicars . . . Tho. Ford 1660. See what I have said in Th. Ford the Divine of Magd. hall . . . Sam. Butler Alias Hudibras[,] Jo[.] Ogilby[,] Rob. Whetstone' in this collection. In Modern Poets section, lines in margins, underscorings, and notes, in red and dark inks and pencil, mainly identifications, cross-refs., 'q[uaere]' letters, or corrections, e.g, 2nd p. 17, line(s) at Barnabas Brissonius; 19, at Jonson; 24 at Marlowe; to p. 260 at Countess of Pembroke; notes on p. 114, at a reference to John Philips, 'the Maternal Nephew and Disciple of an Author of most deserved Fame late deceas't', AW named the unidentified author: 'John Milton a rogue', and added below, 'This Joh. Philips is yonger brother to the authour'; on p. 170, Wood corrected, at Shackerley Marmion: 'Edw. Sharpham was authour of the Flere, & Tho. Heywode of the Faire maide –'.
Wood 88. Wing P2075.

5231. Phillips, John. *[A summons to repentance].* [London]: [H. Jackson], [1584]. 8°. *2-3,A2-8,B-C^8,D1-7 (wanting the t leaf and sig. A1; cropped). Calf with 3 fillets, stamp decoration (dragon) inside corners and roll decoration on spine (Ashm. binding).
Flyleaf, 2nd, the titles of 7 printed works (really 8) in this vol. by an Ashm. librarian (in 2 hands, the earlier, same in Wood 276a, and the more recent is that of Hausted's who prepared the Whiteside cat.). D7^v, scribbles.
Wood 795(1). STC 19874.5 (rare).

5232. [Phillips, John]. *An introduction to astrology.* London: sold, Henry Marsh, 1661. 8°. Pp. [4], 60.
Tp, AW wrote the price, '6^d'; bsm. AW bound this in a vol. with almanacs.
Wood 15(6) (not in Bodl. CD cat.). Wing P2087.

5233. Phillips, John. *The religion of the hypocritical Presbyterians [in verse].* London: n.pub., 1661. 4°. Pp. [2], 22.
[MS.] Wood D. 26(9). Wing P2097.

5234. [Phillips, John]. *Jockey's downfall: a poem on the late total defeat given to the Scotish covenanters, . . . June 22.* London: n.pub., 1679. S.sh.
AW identified the author, 'ie. Joh. Philipps', and ^v, wrote '1679'.
Wood 417(6). Wing P2088.

5235. P[hillips], J[ohn]. *Dr. Oates's narrative of the popish plot, vindicated: in an answer to . . . a vindication of the English Catholicks [by J. Warner].* London: f. T. Cockerill, 1680. Fol. Pp. [4], 52 (mis-numbering).
Wood 426(13). Wing P2083.

5236. Phillipson, John. *Mock-majesty: or, the siege of Munster. A true story . . . wherewith king John Becock, . . . and . . . the Anabaptists, pleased themselves. [A trans. of part of J. Sleidan's commentaries].* London: f. J. S. a. L. C., 1644[5]. 4°. Pp. [8], 24.
Wood 647(13). Wing P2120.

5237. Phillpott, Nicholas. *Reasons & proposalls for a registry or remembrancer of all deeds and incum-brances of real estates.* Oxford: W. Hall f. R. Davis, 1671. 4°. Pp. [2], 10.
Tp, AW wrote, 'This came out about yᵉ middle of Febr. 1670', and at author, 'London'.
Wood 630(25). Wing P2121. Madan 2903.

5238. Philo-Basileuticus Verax, pseud. *Orthodox state-queries.* [London]: f. Philo-Basileuticus Verax, [1660]. S.sh.
AW added the date, 'ffeb: 1659[60]'.
Wood 276a(280). Wing O504.

5239. Philocrates, pseud. *The loyall sacrifice: presented in the lives and deaths of . . . sir Charls Lucas, and sir George Lisle.* [London]: n.pub., 1648. 12°. Pp. [19], 96, [16].
A8, A9, A9ᵛ, AW identified initials after 3 dedications: 'G. W.', 'Georg Wharton'; 'E. A.', 'perhaps Elias Ashmole.', and 'J. H.', 'James Howell. q[uaere].' Flyleaf, lower, 1stᵛ, AW wrote, 'the picture' (prob. referring to the vivid frontispiece of the execution of 2 royalists), lined out.
Wood 581(2). Wing L3364.

5240. Physical Dictionary. *A physical dictionary: or, an interpretation of . . . words . . . used in physick, anatomy, chirurgery and chemistry.* London: G. D. f. J. Garfield, 1657. 8° (some leaves, cropped). A-O⁸ (2 pp. books sold by Garfield; 1st and last leaves blank). Pasteboard (blue) with parchment spine. 1st upper and last lower flyleaves, slips of marbled paper pasted on brown paper.
Tp, AW wrote '1ˢ'. Acquired 4 Jan. 1662, LT 1.428.
Wood 702(1). Wing P2143.

5241. Pickering, Edmond. *Edmond Pickering painter to the hono:ᵇˡᵉ cittie of London, is now removed.* [London]: n.pub., [1681]. S.sh. (engr.). Red cloth over pasteboard (1939); 2 modern flyleaves.
Wood 276a is the shelf-mark of six large guardbooks of blank leaves, 55 x 47 cm. (22 x 18.5 in.), on which are pasted 553 items. The contents in this vol. were gathered together in 1717 and, along with the contents of Wood 276b, replaced a former vol. at Wood 276 (Mazzarini, *Last will*), which had been lost or removed. An Ashm. librarian, perhaps in 1837, described the replacement as 'Miscellaneous Prints Papers &c a large Parchment. Fol.' (in Library Records d. 1071, ff. 19ᵛ). Wood 276a contains letterpress, mainly single sheets, but also engravings and 2-4 page items. These are of irregular sizes, and the physical dimensions are not recorded (one of the largest is Wood 276a(50), 76.5 x 51.5 cm.; some were cut to fit on to the blank sheets in these vols.). In this catalogue, the order of items is Wood 276a(1-576). The difference between the no. of items, 553, and the nos. of the items, 1-576, results mainly from giving multiple nos. to single items. On the 1st leaf in Wood 276a, vol. 1, a note explains the general order of items after they were rebound in 1939: 'Divided (Aug. 1939) as follows: [i] 1-190 [ii] 191-362 [iii] 363-577'. Each subdivision, [i], [ii], [iii] contains 2 vols. and these are numbered consecutively, i-vi. Hence Wood 276a[i] includes item nos. 1-76 in vol. 1 and 77-190 in vol. 2; Wood 276a[ii], item nos. 191-272 in vol. 3 and 273-362 in vol. 4; and Wood 276a[iii], item nos. 363-446 in vol. 5 and 447-576 in vol. 6. The current Bodleian Library CD Catalogue uses four different shelf-marks, e.g.: Wood 276(540), Wood 276a(100), Wood 276a(i,280), and Wood 276a(f.72) and is incomplete, omitting 49 items (in addition to maps and engravings which are not, as a general rule, in the CD Catalogue). 2 mss. are included, (Wood 276a(57) and Wood 276a(537) (a ms. poem is included with the printed item at Wood 276a(539-40).
The first vol. of Wood 276a begins with a ms. list, prepared in about 1717, of 576 items on 2 sheets, 45 x 31 cm. (18 x 12 in.), from 'i. A Coat of Arms drawne by Edmund Pickering' to 'CCCCCLXXVI. A mapp of Africa. Finis'. This list was not, as was Library Records d. 1071, in the hand of John Hausted, but by the same Ashm. librarian who prepared the tables of contents of many Wood bundles bound in calf by the Ashm. Museum (33 are noted in this catalogue by 'same hand in Wood 276a'). The 1st sheet in vol. i is pasted to a blank leaf; the second, r-v, is attached to a blank leaf. The 1st sheet lists items I to CLVII; the 2nd sheet, slightly damaged around the edges, lists items CLVIII to CCCXX on the recto side and CCCXXI to CCCCCLXXVI on the verso. The order of the items in Wood 276a was slightly revised in

1939. There are four non-Wood intrusions, that is, items added after 1717. They are not recorded here; see notes at Wood 276a(404a, 406a and 576). Volumes later added to the Wood collection, Wood 276c (now MS. Ashm. 1819), Wood 276d (now MS. Ashm 1818), and Wood 276e (now MS. Ashm. 1820 b), were also intrusions. Item 1, AW added the date, '1681'.
Wood 276a(1) (not in Bodl. CD cat.). Wing E177A (rare).

5242. Pictures. *Pictures . . . with their characters.* N.p.: n.pub., n.d. Pp.?
Missing since 1841. In Whiteside cat., 'The Pictures of P. Smart, Hen: Burton, Dr Leighton, Dr Joh: Bastwick, Wm Prynne, Jo. Lilbourn wth their Characters'. In list on upper flyleaf, 'deest 20 Mar 1841 W. K[irtland]' (noted by T.A. Birrell before the vol. was lost in 1994).
Wood 531(1). Not identified.

5243. Pie, Thomas. *An houreglasse contayning I a computation from the beginning of time to Christ.* London: [R. Robinson f.] J. Wolfe, 1597. 4°. Pp. [14], 98, [8]. Parchment with gold-stamp fillet and centre-piece.
Tp, AW wrote after the author, 'Coll. Merton' (later lined out). Flyleaf, lower^v, '3e/k' (a shelf-mark).
[MS.] Wood C. 37. STC 19900.

5244. Pie, Thomas. *Epistola ad . . . Johannem Housonum . . . qua dogma ejus . . . de Judaeorum divortiis refutatur.* London: A. Hatfieldus, 1603. 4° (mutilated). Pp. [2], 58.
Tp, price by former owner, 6^d, cropped; a salutation to a friend, William Moore, by R. Crakanthorp; and a signature of an owner, Johannes Morris. Text, some scribbles, not by AW. Responds to J. Howson, Wood 636(1-2), item 3708. LT 3.29.
Wood 636(4). STC 19899.

5245. [Pierce, Thomas]. Philomusus, Basilius, pseud. *A third and fourth part of Pegasus [the work by T. Barlow and T. Pierce]: taught by Bankes his ghost to dance in the Dorick moode [1 July].* [London]: [f. R. Royston], 1648. 4°. Pp. [2], 6.
Tp, AW wrote, 'Tho. Pierce of Magd. Coll. the author', in red ink. Flyleaf, upper, a slip was pasted over 6 lines of notes on Pegasus, not in AW's hand. Dupl. at Wood 632(21).
Wood 514(50). Wing P2205. Madan 1997.

5246. [Pierce, Thomas]. Philomusus, Basilius, pseud. *A third and fourth part of Pegasus [the work by T. Barlow and T. Pierce]: taught by Bankes his ghost to dance in the Dorick moode [1 July].* [London]: [f. R. Royston], 1648. 4°. Pp. [2], 6.
Tp, AW wrote 'Dupl', in pencil. Dupl. at Wood 514(50).
Wood 632(21). Wing P2205. Madan 1997.

5247. [Pierce, Thomas]. *Caroli* Του μακαριτου παλιγγενεσια. [London]: n.pub., 1649. 8°. Pp. [2], 11.
Flyleaf, upper, some scribbles, pasted over with a 2nd leaf; tp, AW wrote, 'M^r, afterwards Dr Peirce (Tho.) the author'.
Wood 364(32). Wing P2165A. FFMadan 105.

5248. Pierce, Thomas*. *Certain queries upon d^r. Pierces sermon at Whitehall Feb.1.* London: n.pub., 1663. 4°. Pp. 12.
Tp, AW wrote, 'These queries were answered by Joh Dobson of Magd. Coll.' (i.e., Wood 633(7)). P. 12, scribble, 'for Ch^r Marke Downe' (?). LT 1.487-9.
Wood 633(6). Wing C1745 ('O' not recorded in Wing).

5249. Pierce, Thomas. *The primitive rule of reformation: delivered in a sermon . . . at Whitehall, Feb.1. 1662. In vindication of our church against the novelties of Rome.* Oxford: H. H. f. R. Royston [London] a. R. Davis in Oxon, 1663. 4°. 6th ed. Pp. [8], 37. See note at item 3124.
Wood 633(5). Wing P2192. Madan 2646.

5250. [Pierce, Thomas]. *A true accompt of the proceedings (and of the grounds of the proceedings) of the president . . . of St. Mary Magdalen college . . . against dr. [Thomas] Yerburie.* [London]: n.pub., [1663]. Fol. Pp. 11.
P. 11^v, 'Miscellanies' and 'Dr Peirce President of Madg: his proceed: justified. 1663', not in AW's hand; and AW wrote, 'Dr Yerbury hath an answer to this q[uaere]'. See item 446; AO 4.2, 3, 304; LT 1.473, 487ff.
Wood 423(40). Wing P2206. Madan 2626.

5251. [Pierce, Thomas]. *Death consider'd as a door to a life of glory.* London: f. the author's private use, [1690?]. 4°. Pp. [2], 126. Parchment.

Tp, AW wrote, 'Dr Tho Pierce', in pencil. P. 45, 51, identifications of biblical passages, not by AW. [MS.] Wood C. 41. Wing P2175.

5252. Pierius, Christianus. *Pöema thaumasticon sive paradoxicon, hoc est: admirandum ac inopinatum.* Franc(oforti): ap haer. C. Egenolphi, (imp. A. Loniceri, J. Cnipii Andronici secundi, P. Steinmeyeri), 1583. 8°. A-C^8.
Flyleaf, lower^r, 'Be it known to all men', not by AW.
Wood 92(3). VD P2741.

5253. Pierpoint, Henry. Dorchester, marq. of. *The reasons why the l^rd. marquiss of Dorchester printed his letter [25 Feb. 1659].* [London]: n.pub., 1659[60], 20 March. S.sh.
Wood 276a(252). Wing D1919.

5254. Pierpoint, Henry. Dorchester, marq. of. *A true and perfect copy of a letter . . . to the lord Roos . . . Feb. 13. 1659.* [London]: n.pub., [1660]. S.sh.
^v, AW wrote, 'Marq. of Dorchester'.
Wood 276a(250). Wing D1920 ('O' not recorded in Wing).

5255. [Pilkington, James]. *The burnynge of Paules church in London in . . . 1561.* London: W. Seres, (1563, 10 March). 8°. A-R^8,S^4. Parchment with 2 leather clasps.
Flyleaves, upper, 2 prices, 6^d and 4^d, in unidentifiable hands. Text, a few marks in margins and underscorings, prob. not in AW's hand. Cover, lower, inside, slip pasted, to classify and to indicate contents of a group of books: 'Lightning & Earthquakes Fiers', in AW's hand.
Wood 221. STC 19931.

5256. Pimenta, Niccolò. B[usaeus], J[oannes], trans. *Exemplum epistolae p. Nicolai Pimentae . . . ad . . . Claudium Aquavivam . . . de statu rei Christianae in India Orientali . . . 1600.* Moguntiae: ap. J. Albinum, 1602. 8°. Pp. 123, [1].
Wood 835(2). BL.

5257. Pincierus, Johannes. *Aenigmatum libri tres.* [Herborn.]: ex off. C. Corvini, 1605. 8°. Pp. [16], 395, [19]. Parchment.
Tp, '1^s2' (cropped at side, prob. not by AW), bsm.
Wood 65. BL.

5258. P[inke], R[obert]. *Quaestiones selectiores in logica, ethica, physica, & metaphysica, inter authores celebriores repertae. Collectore R. P.* Oxoniae: excud. L. Lichfield, 1680. 4°. Pp. [2], 27.
Tp, at R. P., AW wrote, 'Rob Pynke Coll. Novi Custode', and below, 'Ant. à Wood, ex dono D^ni Joh. Lamphire editoris, die S. Valentini, 1679[80]'. AO 3.262.
Wood 607(2). Wing P2268. Madan 3275.

5259. Pinke, Robert, and Philip Herbert. Pembroke, 4th earl of. *A letter sent from the provost vice-chancellour of Oxford to the . . . earle of Pembrooke, lord chancellour [12 Sept.] . . . with his lordships answer [13 Sept.].* London: L. N. f. E. Husbands a. J. Franck, 1642, 13 Sept. 4°. Pp. [2], 7.
Wood 514(9). Wing P2267. Madan 1038.

5260. Pirckheimer, Bilibaldus. Est, William, trans. *The praise of the gout, or, the gouts apologie.* London: G. P[urslowe] f. J. Budge, 1617. 4°. Pp. [6], 37.
Tp, bsm. Dupl. at Wood 615(15).
Wood 498(8). STC 19947.

5261. Pirckheimer, Bilibaldus. Est, William, trans. *The praise of the gout, or, the gouts apologie.* London: G. P[urslowe] f. J. Budge, 1617. 4°. Pp. [2], 37 (wanting pp. [3-6]).
Dupl. at Wood 498(8).
Wood 615(15). STC 19947.

5262. Pisani, Fabricio. *A late letter from the citty of Florence, . . . touching these present distempers of England.* London: n.pub., 1660. 4°. Pp. 12.
Tp, former nos., '68' and '67', in pencil.
Wood 632(50). Wing P2283.

5263. Pits, John. Bishop, W., ed. *Ioannis Pitsei Angli, . . . Relationum historicarum de rebus Anglicis tomus primus quatuor parte complectens.* Parisiis: ap. R. Thierry & S. Cramoisy, 1619. 4°. Pp. 990.
Missing. 'De scriptoribus angliae', acquired from Langbaine's study, 29 Apr. 1658, 7^s, LT 1.247.

LT 1.247. BL, *Hunt.*

5264. Pits, John. *Relationum historicarum de rebus Anglicis.* Parisiis: ap. R. Thieris & S. Cramoisy, 1619. S.sh. (r-v) (tp and ᵛ, description of 4 parts, only).
Wood 658(781). BL.

5265. Pits, Thomas. *The confession of Thomas Pits: who was executed . . . 12. of October for endeavouring to betray Russell-hall.* London: f. J. Raworth, 1644, 14 Oct. 4°. Pp. 8.
Tp, AW wrote, 'i e cavaliers having been employed so to doe by Sʳ. Rich. Leveson'.
Wood 366(17). Wing P2300.

5266. Plague. *Sundrie approoved remedies against the plague.* London: E. Allde f. E. White, [1603?]. Fol. S.sh.
Wood 276a(32) (not in Bodl. CD cat.). STC 20874.5 (rare).

5267. Plainman, Peirce, pseud. *A latter discovery of Ireland: or, a Shamrokshire gallemaufery.* London: n.pub., 1646. 4°. Pp. [8], 96.
Tp, after lined out '1646', AW wrote, '1646' in red ink. Note, not in AW's hand: 'this booke should have com forth 4 yeares since miscaried thorough the Stationers default'. Other notes, none by AW are: pp. [7-8], corrections; 10, short note; 28, on Irish having pads instead of saddles, 'soe formerly'; 96 'to answer all objections this booke is lycensed by Sʳ Nathaniell Brent and may shortly com forth'.
Wood 505(5). Not in Wing. Not in ESTCR.

5268. Plaistow. *Strange and fearfull newes from Plaisto. In the parish of West-Ham.* London: I. H., [1645]. 4°. Pp. 8.
Tp, AW wrote, 'No date to this pamphlet'.
[MS.] Wood B. 35(15). Wing P5816 (Wing, news).

5269. Plat, Hugh, and D. B. [Boate, Arnold, ed. (also attrib. to)]. *The jewel house of art and nature. . . . Whereunto is added, a . . . discourse of minerals, stones, gums, and rosins; . . . by D. B.* London: E. Alsop, 1653. 4°. Pp. [8], 232.
Tp, bsms. Pp. 1, 25, 27-9, etc., to 77, 168, 191, a few cross marks, most erased, in margin at some new sections, not in AW's usual style.
Wood 618(9). Wing P2391 ('O' not recorded in Wing).

5270. Plattes, Gabriel. *A discovery of infinite treasure, hidden since the worlds beginning.* London: J. L[egat], sold G. Hutton, 1639. 4°. Pp. [34], 92 [1]. Pasteboard (grey)with parchment spine. 1st upper and last lower flyleaves, marbled paper. Leaves show previous thread holes.
Flyleaf, 3rdᵛ, AW wrote the titles of 2 printed works in this vol., within guidelines made with red ink. Tp, AW wrote the price, '1ˢ'.
Wood 496(1). STC 19998.

5271. [Playford, John]. *The dancing master: or, plain and easie rules for the dancing of country dances.* London: f. J. Playford, 1652. 4°. Pp. [6], 111. Obl. 2nd ed. Calf with 3 fillets, 1 metal clasp.
Tp, bsm. Pp. 12-14, 16-17, etc. to end, a cross mark at some tunes; p. 109, 'C. 2 - p - 49', a reference note?
Wood 125. Wing P2468 (two).

5272. Playford, John. *An introduction to the skill of musick.* London: f. J. Playford, 1654. 8°. 3 items were in this missing vol.
Missing in 1837. 'An Introduction to the Skill of Musick – Lond. 1654'. See Wing P2478 (1655) and ESTCR 2098.
Wood 120(1). Not in Wing. Not in ESTCR.

5273. Playford, John. *Court-ayres: or, pavins, almains, corant's, and sarabands, of two parts [treble only].* London: f. J. Playford, 1655. 4°. Pp. [2], 112. Obl. Parchment over paper.
Cover, upper, inside, and flyleaf, upper, scribbles and signatures of 'Christopher Coward ex C.C.C. Oxōn.', LT 1.274. Tp, bsm.
Wood 121 (not in Bodl. CD cat.). Wing P2466.

5274. Plessington, William. *The speech of mr. William Plessington, who was executed at Chester [19 July].* [London]: n.pub., [1679]. S.sh (r-v).
LT 2.456, and see note at item 6383.
Wood 425(10). Wing P2567.

5275. Pliny (the younger). Stapleton, Robert, trans. *Pliny's panegyricke: a speech in senate.* Oxford: [H. Hall], 1644[5]. 4°. Pp. [16], 60, [1].
Missing. MS. Wood E. 2(70), p. 11.
MS. Wood E. 2(70), p. 11. Wing P2579. Madan 1745. *Hunt* (London ed.), *Folg.*

5276. Plot Lately Discovered. *A plot lately discovered for the taking of the Tower, by negromancie.* London: n.pub., 1641. 4°. Pp. [2], 5.
Tp, AW wrote, 'A ridiculous & impertinent pamphlet' in ink over an earlier note: 'Lyes & ignorance', in pencil.
Wood 373(6). Wing P2600.

5277. P[lot], R[obert]. *Quaer's [sic] to be propounded to the most ingenious of each county in my travels through England.* [Oxford?]: n.pub., [1674]. 4°. Pp. [3].
Above, AW (prob.) wrote '1674'. This is prob. a Wood item for it is in a group of 4 letterpress items, all on similar antiquarian topics, removed before 1716 from AW's collection and placed in MS. Ashm. 1820a, ff. 221-227. The annotations in the other 3 items are in the hand of AW. Lines in margin and note, not by AW.
[MS.] Ashm. 1820a, f. 222. Wing P2589 (rare). Madan 3022.

5278. P[lot], R[obert]. *Enquiries to be propounded to the most ingenious of each county in my travels through England and Wales, in order to their history of nature and arts.* N.p.: n.pub., [1679]. Fol. Pp. [4].
P. [1], annotation not by AW; p. [4], AW wrote 'Robert Plott' after the printed initials and 'Oxōn 14. Febr. 1678/9'.
[MS.] Ashm. 1820a, ff. 224-5. Wing P2584. Madan 3220.

5279. Plutarch, and Basilius Magnus. Grotius, Hugo, ed.; Potter, Johannes, notas. Πλουταρχος χαιρωνεως *[Plutarchi Chaeronensis liber; Basilii Magni oratio ad juvenes; Catalogus librorum in theatro Sheldoniano Oxon. impressorum].* Oxonia: εχ θεατρος εν Οξονια, [1694] αχζδ. 4°. Pp. [8], 105, [2], 41, [3], and U⁸ ('Catalogus'; U8 blank). Calf with 2 fillets; stamp decoration inside and around a central light calf panel.
U⁸, in margins of 'Catalogus', numerous marks in margins, in pencil.
Wood 117. Wing P2632.

5280. Plymouth. *Joyfull newes from Plimouth, being an exact relation of a great victory.* London: f. L. Smith, 1643. 4°. A⁴.
Tp, AW lined out the former no., '9'; and wrote below, 'In Apr. 1643 as it seemes'.
Wood 376(10). Wing J1141 (two) ('O' not recorded in Wing).

5281. Plymouth. *A true narration of the most observable passages, in and at the late seige of Plymouth, from the fifteenth day of September.* London: L. N. f. F. Eglesfeild [sic], 1644. 4°. Pp. [2], 20.
Tp, AW altered a former no., '50'; below, at date, AW wrote '43'.
Wood 376(54). Wing T2763 (Wing, Eglesfield).

5282. Plymouth. *A continuation of the true narration of the most observable passages in and about Plymouth, from January 26. 1643 till this present.* London: I. D. f. F. Eglesfield, 1644, 10 May. 4°. Pp. 12.
Tp, AW wrote, in the title after 'present', 'Apr.'
Wood 377(7). Wing C5973.

5283. [Pococke, Edward]. *An answer to the satyr against mankind.* [London]: n.pub., [1679?]. Fol. Pp. 4.
Responds to J. Wilmot, Wood 417(7), item 6622.
Wood 417(8). Wing P2659A.

5284. Poem. *A poem, upon the transactions between a landlord and his tenant Day, who privately departed from him by night. By a gent. of Lincoln's-Inne.* (London): (f. J. Norris), (1684). Fol. Pp. 4.
P. 1, AW wrote the year, '1684'.
Wood 417(128). Wing P2717.

5285. Poems 1. *A collection of the newest and most ingenious poems, songs, catches, &c. Against popery.* London: n.pub., 1689. 4°. Pp [2], iv, 23.
Tp, AW wrote, 'published in Lond. in the latter end of Dec. 1688 6ᵈ'. LT 3.293.
Wood 382(4). Wing C5205.

5286. Poems 2. *A second collection of the newest and most ingenious poems, satyrs, songs, &c. Against*

popery and tyranny. London: n.pub., 1689. 4°. Pp. 31 (1-2 blank).
Tp, AW wrote, '14. Feb. 1688[9] – 6^d – Ox.' LT 3.293.
Wood 382(5). Wing S2266.

5287. Poems 3. *A third collection of the newest and most ingenious poems, satyrs, songs, &c. Against popery and tyranny.* London: n.pub., 1689. 4°. Pp. 32 (1-2 blank).
Tp, AW wrote, 'Bought at Oxō. 12. March 1688[9]. – 6^{d}'. LT 3.293.
Wood 382(7). Wing T902.

5288. Poems 4. *The fourth (and last) collection of poems, satyrs, songs, &c.* London: n.pub., 1689. 4°. Pp. [2], 33 (i.e., 34).
Tp, AW wrote, 'Bought at Oxon 30. Mar. 1689'. LT 3.293.
Wood 382(8). Wing F1684.

5289. Poet's Jests. *The poets jests.* [London]: [J. Back?], [1680?]. Pp.?
Missing in 1837. 'The Poets Jests – ' in Whiteside cat. For bibliog. data see Wood 284(5), item 5764, list of books published by Back, c. 1680.
Wood 66(5). Not in STC. Not in Wing. Not in ESTCR.

5290. Poland, Satire. *Great news from Poland: being an impartial account of the election of a new king.* (London): (f. the assigns of F. S.), (1683). S.sh. (r-v).
Wood 276a(258). Wing G1729 ('O' not recorded in Wing).

5291. Poland, Satire. *The saints liberty of conscience in the new kingdom of Poland.* (Warsaw) [London]: n.pub., (1683). Fol. Pp. 4.
Wood 276a(257). Wing S363 (3) ('O' not recorded in Wing).

5292. Polden, Morgan. *To the right honourable the lords assembled in parliament . . . Septemb. 20. 1644.* [London]: n.pub., [1644]. S.sh.
^{v}, (Wood 276a(71)), elaborate genealogies of John de Lacy, Basker, Baskerville, Spenser, and Langham, not in AW's hand.
Wood 276a(70-71). Wing P2746C (rare).

5293. Pole, Reginald. *'De generali concilio – q[uaere] C. Pole'.* ?: ?, [1562-9?]. Pp.?
Missing. MS. Wood E. 2(70), p. 25. Not identified.
MS. Wood E. 2(70), p. 25. Part of STC 20088? See AO 1.292.

5294. Poleman, John, ed. *All the famous battels that have bene fought in our age throughout the worlde.* London: H. Bynneman & F. Coldock, [1578]. 4°. Pp. [4], 337, [3]. Parchment (letterpress, on history and theology, now fragments, once served as pastedowns).
Wood 596. STC 20089.

5295. Polemann, Joachimus. H., F., trans. *Novum lumen medicum; wherein the . . . doctrine of . . . Helmont concerning the great mystery of the phoolosophers [sic] sulphur. Is fundamentally cleared.* London: J. C. f. J. Crook, 1662. 8°. Pp. [8], 206.
Tp, AW wrote the price, '1^s'.
Wood 680(3). Wing P2748.

5296. Polemon, [Antonius], and Himerius. Stephanus, Henricus, ed. Πολεμωνος ιμεριου *Polemonis, Himerii, & aliorum quorundam declamationes.* [Geneva]: excud. H. Stephanus, H. Fuggeri typog., [156]7 (mutilated). 4°. Pp. [4], 91.
Passim, notes in Greek (some cropped) and in Latin, not in AW's hand. P. 91^v, geometric drawings, prob. not by AW.
Wood 380. BL.

5297. Polyander a Kerckhoven, Joannes. *Miscellaneae tractationes theologicae.* Lugduni Batavorum: ex off. B. & A. Elzevir, 1629. 8°. Pp. [16], 284. Calf with 3 fillets.
Flyleaf, upper, 1st, 'Pretium o^{ll} 1^S 3^D', not by AW. Tp, bsm. Pastedown, lower, T:6 [/] c:gar', 'T:C' (shelfmarks?), not by AW.
Wood 696. Not in BL.

5298. Pontaeus, John. *By special approbation. The compounded balm, or balsome, made by m. John Pontaeus, a chymicall physitian.* [London]: n.pub., [1670-1695]. S.sh.
[MS.] Wood F. 50, f. 37. Not in Wing. Not in ESTCR.

5299. Ponticus, Ludovicus Virunius, and Giraldus Cambrensis. Powell, David, ed. *Britannicae historiae libri sex, quibus praefixius est catalogus regum Britanniae: per Davidem Pouelum. [2nd tp] Itinerarium Cambriae.* Londini: E. Bollifantum, imp. H. Denhami & R. Nuberii, 1585. 8°. Pp. [14], 284, [5]. Missing in 1837.
Wood 161. STC 20109. *Folg, NYPL.*

5300. Poole. *A true relation of a plot to betray the towne of Poole . . . 29 September.* London: L. N. f. L. Blaikelocke, 1643. 4°. Pp. [2], 5.
Tp, AW lined out a former no. '39'.
Wood 376(42). Wing T2890.

5301. Poole, Mat[thew]. *A model for the maintaining of students of choice abilities at the university, and principally in order to the ministry.* London: J. H. f. J. Rothwell, 1648 [really 1658]. 4°. Pp. [10], 23. Calf with 3 fillets, stamp decoration (flower) inside corners, and roll decoration at inner, spine edge (Ashm. binding).
Flyleaf, upper, 2nd, the titles of 13 printed works in this vol., by an Ashm. librarian (same hand in Wood 276a). Diff. ed. at Wood 515(19).
[MS.] Wood B. 37(1). Wing P2841. Madan 2368.

5302. Poole, Mat[thew]. *A model for the maintaining of students . . . at the university, and principally in order to the ministry.* [London]: n.pub., 1658. 4° (small). Pp. [6], 21.
Tp, 'By Mat. Poole', may not be by AW. LT 1.295. Diff. ed. at [MS.] Wood B. 37(1).
Wood 515(19) (not in Bodl. CD cat.). Wing P2842. Madan 2367.

5303. P[oole], M[atthew]. *A letter from a London minister to the lord Fleetwood [13 Dec.].* London: f. T. V., 1659. 4°. Pp. [2], 6.
Tp, former no., '6-' (cropped), in pencil. Tp and p. 6, AW wrote 'M. Poole' and 'math: poole'.
Wood 632(64). Wing P2840.

5304. Poole, William. *The country farrier. Teaching divers and sundry approved medicines, to cure all sorts of cattell.* London: T. Fawcet, 1652. 8°. Pp. [10], 56, [12], 8, [1]. Pasteboard (blue) with parchment spine. 1st upper and last lower flyleaves, purple paper; rebacked.
Flyleaf, upper, 2nd^v, AW ruled the guidelines in red ink but entered no list of contents.
Wood 727(1). Wing P2857 (rare).

5305. [Pope, Walter]. *The memoires of monsieur Du Vall.* London: f. H. Brome, 1670. 4°. Pp. [2], 21.
Tp^v, AW wrote, 'This pamphlet was written by Dr Walter Pope Med. D^r. sometimes Fellow of Wadham Coll. & Proctor of the University of Oxford. written upon offence taken from a Gentle-woman, who, having a respect for his person, left him upon the sight & company of Du Vall. [/] This pamphlett took so well & sold so much that tis thought there were 10000 of them printed [/] Dec. 23. an. 1668. his majestie was pleased in Council to order his proclamation to be issued out for the prevention of Robberies, murders & Burglaries & for the apprehension of Edw. Madox alias Morgan, Joh. Blanchard alias Major, Lodowick alias Lewis alias Peter De Vall &c. see afterward p. 7. [/] In another proclamation date Nov. 17. an. 1669 he among other Robbers is set downe first of all by the name of Lewis alias Lodowick alias Claud de Val alias Browne – see in this pamphlet p. 7. [/] Dec. 24. 1669 was taken in the night time by Mr Joh. Bennet Head-Bailiff of Westmi[n]ster, Claud de Val alias Georg Browne a notorious high way robber, & was then committed to Newgate.' (LT 2.185). Passim, some comments, dates, and marks in margins, mainly in ink, e.g. p. 1, at the 'Occupations' of du Vall's parents, 'by filching & stealing'; p. 3, at a comic story of baptism and burial at Domfret, Normandy, at a reference to the Register Book, AW wrote, 'Noe Register there', in pencil; p. 11, at a comment on women bewitched by 'a Dapper Fellow with fine black Eyes,' and who had 'run to the King to beg his life', AW wrote, 'Excellent good'; p. 15, at du Vall's speech of repentance, 'he received extreame unction upon the Ladder by a popish preist'.
Wood 372(10). Wing P2912.

5306. P[ordage], S[amuel]. *The loyal incendiary, or the generous boutefieu [sic]. A poem.* (London): (W. Davis), (1684). Fol. Pp. 6.
P. 1, AW wrote the year, '1684', in pencil.
Wood 417(131). Wing P2972.

5307. Porta, Giovanni Battista della. *Magiae naturalis, sive de miraculis rerum naturalium, libri IIII.* Coloniae: ap. J. Birckmannum & W. Richvvinum, 1562. 12°. Ff. [8], 307, [7]. Calf with 3 fillets, an inner rectangle with gold-stamp decoration outside corners, centrepiece, and clasp holes; rebacked. Pastedown,

lower, printer's waste paper.
Tp, AW wrote, 'in bib. b[odleian]'. F. 3, underscoring.
Wood 690. VD P4327.

5308. Portsmouth. *A true relation of the severall passages . . . of colonell Goring at Portsmouth.* London: E. G. f. J. Benson, [1642]. 4°. Pp. 8.
Tp, AW lined out the former no.; and wrote the date, '1642. Aug'.
Wood 374(33). Wing T3046.

5309. Portsmouth. *A declaration of all the passages at the taking of Portsmouth.* London: f. J. Sweeting, 1642, 15 Sept. 4°. Pp. 8.
Missing in 1839; see note at Wood 375(1), item 1720.
Wood 375(8). Wing D604. *Hunt, Folg.*

5310. Portsmouth. *A true relation of the passages which happened at . . . Portsmouth.* London: f. J. Hunscot, 1642, 21 Sept. 4°. Pp. [2], 12.
Tp, AW rubbed out the former no., '17'.
Wood 375(7). Wing T3015.

5311. Portsmouth, Duchess of*. *Articles of high-treason . . . against the dutches of Portsmouth [Kérouaille, L. R. de].* [London]: n.pub., [1680]. S.sh. (r-v).
Wood 276a(283). Wing A3846.

5312. Portugal. *The history of Portugal.* London: J. Redmayne, 1662. 12°. Pp. [4], 125, [3].
Tp, AW wrote, '7ᵈ'; bsm. ᵛ, he wrote, 'This book was published upon the marriage of K. Ch. 2. with Donna Catherina of Portugall'.
Wood 167(3). Wing H2135 (3).

5313. Possevino, Antonio. *Apparatus ad omnium gentium historiam.* Venetiis: ap. J. B. Ciottum Senensem, 1597. Ff. [24], 260. Calf with 3 fillets and edge hatching; spine, 4 bands and hatching (Oxford binding).
Text, a few notes and marks, e.g., at f. 69, not by AW.
Wood 175. BL.

5314. Potter, Francis. *An interpretation of the number 666 [with Mr. Medes testimony on it].* Oxford: L. Lichfield [sould R. Mynne & G. Bedell [London]], 1642 or 1647. 4°. Pp. [18], 214.
Missing. MS. Wood E. 2(70), p. 2, 'Franc. Potter of the number of 666 – with Mʳ Medes testimony on it'.
Ed. not identified.
MS. Wood E. 2(70), p. 2. Wing P3028 and P3029. Madan 1032 and 1965*.

5315. Potts, Thomas. *The wonderfull discoverie of witches in the countie of Lancaster. . . . Together with the . . . triall of Jennet Preston, at . . . Yorke.* London: W. Stansby f. J. Barnes, 1613. 4°. ⁴,A-Z⁴.
Missing. Listed in MS. Wood E. 2(70), p. 23: 'dupl. bound up with Gifford'. Perhaps disposed of when AW had G. Gifford rebound, shortly before 1695; it was not in that vol., [MS.] Wood B. 20, when AW prepared the list on the upper flyleaf. A copy is at [MS.] Wood B. 18(2), item 5316.
MS. Wood E. 2(70), p. 23. STC 20138. *O, Folg* (no tp), *Hunt.*

5316. Potts, Thomas. *The wonderfull discoverie of witches in the countie of Lancaster. . . . Together with the . . . triall of Jennet Preston, at . . . Yorke.* London: W. Stansby f. J. Barnes, 1613. 4°. ⁴,A-Z⁴ (1st and last leaves blank).
[MS.] Wood B. 18(2). STC 20138.

5317. Povey, Thomas*. *A fuller answer to the moderatour [T. Povey], wherein his argument of advantage and disadvantage is so opened, as that he is laid open too.* [London]: n.pub., (1643). 4°. Pp. 20.
Tp, no. 3 in a former bundle.
Wood 617(10). Wing F2487.

5318. [Powell, John]. *The assise of bread: with sundry good and needful ordinances for bakers, . . . newly corrected and enlarged.* London: f. A. Crook, 1661. 4°. A-G⁴ (Pp. 56).
Tp, AW wrote, '6ᵈ' and 'An edition of this came out in 1630, in 4ᵗᵒ. But it hath not in it so much as this'.
Acquired 23 Sept. 1664, LT 2.22.
[MS.] Wood C. 14(14). Not in Wing. Not in ESTCR. Should be at Wing P3058aB (2 at O).

5319. Powell, Robert. *The life of Alfred . . . with a parallell of . . . k. Charles.* [London]: R. Badger f. T. Alchorn, 1634. 12°. Pp. [34], 156. Calf with 1 gold-stamp fillet.

Flyleaf, upper, random notes, 'which signifies to dreame another is with what to dreame of himselfe' (?), not in AW's hand; 2nd^v, 'Anthonii à Woode. Oxōn 1670.' Pp. 148f., underscoring. Flyleaf, lower^v, some additions. A copy acquired 14 Nov. 1666, 8^d, LT 2.93.
Wood 266. STC 20161.

5320. Powell, Rob[ert]. *Depopulation arraigned, convicted and condemned, by the lawes of God and man.* London: R. B[adger], 1636. 8°. Pp. [8], 118, [24]. Pasteboard (blue) with parchment spine. 1st upper and last lower flyleaves, marbled paper.
Flyleaf, upper, 2nd^v, AW wrote the titles of 6 printed works in this vol., within guidelines made with red ink. Tp, signature of Rg Prichard (?); ^v and to p. 20, and 52-105, sporadic notes, not by AW.
Wood 730(1). STC 20160.

5321. Powell, Thomas (died ca. 1635). *Direction for search of records remaining in the chancerie. tower. exchequer, with the limnes thereof.* London: B. A[lsop] f. P. Man, 1622. 4°. Pp. [14], 78.
[MS.] Wood B. 39(3). STC 20166.

5322. Powell, Thomas (died ca. 1635). *The attornies almanacke.* London: B. A[lsop] & T. F[awcet] f. B. Fisher, 1627. 4°. Pp. [6], 72.
[MS.] Wood B. 39(4). STC 20165.

5323. Powell, Thomas (died ca. 1635). *The attourney's academy.* London: [B. Alsop a. T. Fawcet] f. B. Fisher, 1630. 4°. 3rd impress. Pp. [12], 230, [61]. Parchment with 2 clasp holes.
Flyleaf, upper, 2 lines, not by AW. Tp, bsm. Pastedown, lower, and flyleaf lower^v, signatures of John Harrison, and 'Anno dnj. 1638. pret. 3^s-2^d'.
Wood 362. STC 20164a.

5324. [Powell, Thomas] (died 1666). *Humane industry: or, a history of most manual arts.* London: f. H. Herringman, 1661. 8°. Pp. [16], 188.
Tp, AW wrote 'Jan. iv: MDCLx [i.e., 1661]. written by Dr Tho. Powell – see Hist. et antiq. Oxon. lib. 2. p. 320.a. in Coll. Jesu'.
Wood 730(3). Wing P3072.

5325. Powell, Vavasor*. *The life and death of mr. Vavasor Powell.* [London]: n.pub., 1671. 8°. Pp. [8], 208, [1] (misnumbering). Calf with 2 fillets.
Flyleaf, upper, 1st, in ink, 'AWood. 2^s-4. bound.' 2nd^v, in pencil 'if not of Jesus Coll. then bring him in into Jes. Coll.' (unresolved also in AO, see 3.911-8). Notes, corrections, dates, and marks in margins, pp. 2 (underscoring of an oblique reference to the anonymous author), 16, 106-7, 120 ('Titles of books written by him' and 'There is another book published by Edw. Bagshaw – see also p. 132'), 126, 130, 132-3, 208 (at epitaph, 'Something wanting in this Epitaph.', see his later version, AO 3.917). LT 1.293.
Wood 300. Wing L2003. ESTCR 26670.

5326. P[ownoll], N[athaniel]. *The young divine's apology for his continuance in the university. With his . . . meditation on the calling of the ministery.* Oxford: [H. Hall] f. T. Robinson, 1658. 8°. Pp. [8], 68. Calf with 3 fillets, stamp decoration (dragon) inside corners, and roll decoration on spine (Ashm. binding).
Flyleaf, upper, 2nd ^v, the titles of 13 printed works in this vol. (really 11, 2 entries for items 6 and 10), by an Ashm. librarian. Tp^v, AW wrote 'This Apology and meditation on the ministrie were printed with the authours meditation on the first of the 7. penitentiall psalmes, & his dayly sacrifice at Cambridge 1612 in 12°. with the epistle Ded. of G. Fletcher to John King B. of London.' Acquired 8 Aug. 1664, 4^d, LT 2.19. AO 2.85.
Wood 836(1). Wing P3116. Madan 2409.

5327. Poyer, John* (died 1649). *Colonell Poyers forces in Wales totally routed. By . . . collonel Horton.* London: B. A., 1648, (11 May). 4°. Pp. [2], 1[-6].
Wood 502(7). Wing C5411.

5328. Poyntz, John. *A true relation of the taking of Roger Manwering bishop of St. Davids coming from Ireland.* London: T. Banks, 1642 (2, inverted), 9 July. 4°. Pp. [2], 6.
Tp, AW lined out the former no., '70'; at 'Pointz', he wrote 'q[uaere]', and below, 'silly things in this pamphlet'.
Wood 374(24). Wing P3133 (Wing, Manwering,).

5329. Poyntz, John. *The present prospect of the famous and fertile island of Tobago.* London: G. Larkin f. the author, sold T. Malthus, 1683. 4°. Pp. [2], 47.

Tp, signature 'Jo. Aubrey R[egiae] S[ocietatis] S[ocius] ex dono A–', lined out. This item was in AW's possession when bound.
Wood 386(19). Wing P3130.

5330. Poyntz, Sydenham*. *The kings forces totally routed by . . . Poyntz . . . on Routon-heath [24 Sept.].* [London]: f. E. Husband, 1645, 29 Sept. 4°. Pp. 15.
Tp, AW altered the former no., '26'. Dupl. at Wood 612(32).
Wood 378(29). Wing K595.

5331. Poyntz, Sydenham*. *The kings forces totally routed by . . . Poyntz . . . on Routon-heath [24 Sept.].* [London]: f. E. Husband, 1645, 29 Sept. 4°. Pp. 15.
Tp, AW wrote 'Dupl', in pencil. '2ᵈ', in ink, may not be in AW's hand. Dupl. at Wood 378(29).
Wood 612(32). Wing K595.

5332. Poyntz, Sydenham*, and Chr. Copley*. *A great victory obtained by generall Poyntz and col: Copley . . . at Sherborn in Yorkshire [15 Oct.].* London: f. E. Husband, 1645, 21 Oct. 4°. Pp. 15.
Tp, AW altered the former no., '31'. Dupl. at Wood 612(33).
Wood 378(34). Wing G1773.

5333. Poyntz, Sydenham*, and Chr. Copley*. *A great victory obtained by generall Poyntz and col: Copley . . . at Sherborn in Yorkshire [15 Oct.].* London: f. E. Husband, 1645, 21 Oct. 4°. Pp. 15.
Tp, AW wrote 'Dupl', in pencil. '2ᵈ', in ink, may not be in AW's hand. Dupl. at Wood 378(34).
Wood 612(33). Wing G1773.

5334. Poyntz, [Sydenham], and Oliver Cromwell. *Severall letters from col. gen. Poyntz. lieu. gen. Cromwell. [et al.] . . . of the . . . victory neere Sherborne.* London: f. J. Wright, 1645, 27 Oct. 4°. Pp. [2], 6.
Tp, AW underscored 'Cromwell', in red ink, and altered the former no., '32'.
Wood 378(35). Wing S2771.

5335. Poyntz, [Sydenham], and Colonel Parsons. *A letter from colonell generall Poynts, . . . with a perfect narration of colonell Parsons.* London: f. J. Wright, 1645, 30 Sept. 4°. Pp. [2], 6.
Tp, AW overwrote the former no., '27'.
Wood 378(30). Wing P3135.

5336. Prague. *A true relation of the bloudy execution, . . . in Prague . . . 11. of June . . . Translated out of the Dutch copye.* [London]: n.pub, 1621, 21 July. 4°. A-C⁴.
Dupl. at Wood 615(12).
Wood 365(6). STC 20181.

5337. Prague. *A true relation of the bloudy execution, . . . in Prague . . . 11. of June . . . Translated out of the Dutch copye.* [London]: n.pub., 1621, 21 July. 4°. A-C⁴.
Dupl. at Wood 365(6).
Wood 615(12). STC 20181.

5338. Praise of Music. *The praise of musicke.* Oxenford: J. Barnes, 1586. 8°. Pp. [8], 152. Parchment wrapper.
Tp, 'Thomas Whorwood: hunc librum possidit'. Flyleaf, lower, mostly torn out, but traces of a drawing remain (AO 1.686-7). See *Music & Letters,* 55 (1974): 444-53.
Wood 25. STC 20184. Madan 81.

5339. Prance, Miles. *The additional narrative of mʳ. Miles Prance . . . the discoverer of the murther of sʳ. Edmondbury Godfrey.* London: f. F. Smith, T. Basset, J. Wright, R. Chiswel, a. S. Heyrick, 1679. Fol. Pp. 54, [1].
Tp, AW wrote the price, '1.6', and p. 11, at 'Pensions *were assigned to the* Fryars', he underscored Fryars and wrote, 'The Fryers had no pensions allowed, because the[y] professed povertie & begging.' Purchased from Vade on 1 Nov. 1679, see his record of purchase in MS. Wood F. 50, f. 11. LT 3.185.
Wood 425(19). Wing P3170.

5340. Prance, Miles. *A true narrative and discovery of several very remarkable passages relating to the horrid popish plot.* London: f. D. Newman, 1679. Fol. Pp. [9], 40.
1st blank p., AW wrote the price, '1ˢ.8ᵈ'. LT 3.185.
Wood 424(19). Wing P3177.

5341. Prance, Miles. *Mr. Prance's answer to mrs. Cellier's libel, and divers other false aspersions cast upon him: containing likewise a vindication of sir William Waller*. London: f. L. Curtis, 1680. Fol. Pp. [2], 18.
Wood 426(10). Wing P3171.

5342. Presbyter, John, pseud. *The last will and testament of sir John Presbyter, who dyed of a new disease, called the particular charge of the army*. [London]: n.pub., 1647. 4°. 2nd ed. Pp. [2], 6.
See Plate VIII.
[MS.] Wood D. 26(6). Wing L527 (Wing, London).

5343. Presbyterian. *The cloak in its colours; or the Presbyterian unmasked, . . . Together with a brief answer to their . . . queries*. London: N. T., 1679. 4°. Pp. 12 (wanting the 'answer').
Tp, AW wrote, 'where is the answer'.
[MS.] Wood D. 26(13). Wing C4719A.

5344. Presbytery. *Presbytery. [Text begins: The Presbyterians entered into a covenant]*. [London?]: n.pub., [1663?]. 4°. Pp. 7.
P. 1, AW wrote, '1662'.
[MS.] Wood D. 26(11). Wing P3229B (two).

5345. [Preston, Thomas]. Widdrington, Roger, alias. *An adjoynder to the late catholike New-yeares gift, or explication of the oath of allegiance [signed E. I.]*. London: [Eliot's Court Press], 1620. 8°. Pp. [38], 118.
Missing. MS. Wood E. 2(70), p. 10 (twice).
MS. Wood E. 2(70), p. 10. STC 14050. ARCR 2.654. *NYPL*.

5346. Preston, Thomas*, and Thomas Green*. *Appellatio qua . . . Thomas Prestonus, & Thomas Greenaeus . . . ab . . . cardinalibus ad indicem deputatis ad . . . pontificem . . . provocarunt*. [London] Augustae: ap. B. Fabrum [really E. Griffin], 1620. 4°. Pp. [6], 34.
Corrections from errata, entered. Flyleaf, lower^v, list of 5 works, not in AW's hand.
Wood 651(2). STC 20286.3.

5347. Preston, Thomas, and Thomas Green. *Reverendorum patrum d. Thomae Prestoni . . . & . . . Thomae Greenaei . . . ad . . . Gregorium decimum quintum, . . . supplicatio [renewing their appeal]*. [London] Augustae: ap. B. Fabrum [really E. Griffin], 1621. 4°. Pp. [2], 96. Parchment with gold-stamp decoration: outer and inner rectangle fillets with stamp decoration at corners of inner rectangle and centrepiece; 2 clasp holes; gold fore-edges.
Flyleaf, upper, Sheldon's motto, 'In Posterum' and, by AW, in pencil, 'Ex dono Rad. Sheldon June 1681', LT 2.541; 3.104. Tp, price, '2-6', not by AW. Text, p. 71, AW identified a work by J. Gerson; corrections, some from errata, e.g., pp. 70-1, 73, 80-1, 83, 93, 96.
Wood 651(1). STC 20286.7.

5348. P[rice], J[ohn]. *Some few and short considerations on the present distempers*. [London]: n.pub., [1642]. 4°. Pp. 8.
P. 1, J. P. altered to J. B.
Wood 614(20) (not in Bodl. CD cat.). Wing P3347.

5349. Price, John. *A description of Wales by s^r John Prise*. Oxford: W. Hall, 1663. 4°. Pp. [2], 15 (wanting all after p. 15).
Tp, AW wrote, 'This edit. was published by Tho. Ellis of Jes. Coll.' P. 15, line in margin at corrections to another printed item, T. Vaughan, *British antiquities revived* (AW entered these corrections, see Wood 478(3), item 6297). AO 1.217; 3.710, 729, 993-4.
Wood 478(2). Wing P3333. Madan 2647.

5350. Price, John. *The mystery and method of his majesty's happy restauration*. London: f. J. Vade, 1680. 8°. Pp. [20], 162, [2] (2 pp. books sold by Vade).
Tp, AW wrote, '(K.Ch.2)'; and, over the same in pencil, '1^s-3^d- Jan. 1681[2]'. Dedication, AW added some p. nos. and lines in margins, e.g., A8^v, pp. 17, 118-9, 131 (note in pencil), 151. LT 1.328; 2.498.
Wood 236(2). Wing P3335.

5351. P[rice], L[aurence]. *The witch of the woodlands: or, the coblers new translation*. London: f. J. Stafford, 1655. 8° (slightly cropped). Pp. 22, [2] (A⁸,B⁴).
Diff. ed. at Wood 707(8).
Wood 704(2). Wing P3391 (two).

5352. Price, Laurence. *Corydon's complements: or, the shepherd's academy.* London: J. M. f. W. T[hack]-eray, [1656]. 8°. A^8,B^4.
Flyleaf, upper^v, scribble, not by AW.
Wood 69(9). Wing P3355BA (rare) (Wing CD). Not in ESTCR.

5353. P[rice], L[aurence]. *The witch of the woodlands: or, the cobler's new translation.* [London]: J. Millet, sold J. Gilbertson, [1670?]. 8°. Pp. 22, [2].
Tp, AW wrote '1655' (this is the date of the earlier ed., at Wood 704(2)).
Wood 707(8). Wing P3392 (two).

5354. Price, Laurence. *Make room for Christmas all you that do love him: or, remember your Christmas-box.* London: T. Vere, 1675. 8°. Pp. [4], 12.
Flyleaf, upper^v, scribble, 'Albanus Thomas' (Thomas White?).
Wood 110(7) (not in Bodl. CD cat.). Wing P3374aA. ESTCR 188726.

5355. [Price, Laurence]. *Variety of new merry riddles.* London: ?, 1678. Pp.?
Missing in 1837. 'Variety of new merry Riddles – Lond. 1678' in Whiteside cat. See Wing P3386A (1684).
Wood 64(7). Not in Wing. Not in ESTCR.

5356. [Price, Laurence]. *The five strange wonders of the world.* N.p.: ?, 1682. Pp.?
Missing in 1837. 'The Five Strange wonders of the World – Lond. 1682' in Whiteside cat. See Wing P3364A-B (1674, 1683).
Wood 64(6). Not in Wing. Not in ESTCR.

5357. Price, Laurence. *The famous history of Valentine and Orson.* London: f. M. W., sold D. Newman a. B. Alsop, 1683. 8°. A^8,B^4.
Wood 259(2). Wing P3362 (rare).

5358. Pride, Thomas. *The beacons quenched: or the humble information . . . concerning the Machivilian [sic] design of the Presbyterians.* London: H. Hils, sold G. Calvert a. W. Larner, 1652. 4°. Pp. [2], 5-16 (imperf.).
Tp, bsm. P. 14, AW wrote the Christian name, 'Edm.' of Calamy and the work attacked, 'See the Beacon Flaming p. 2', by F. Cheynell, Wood 609(47), item 1862. Pride's pamphlet responds to L. Fawne, *A beacon,* Wood 609(33), item 2960.
Wood 609(46). Wing P3409.

5359. Pride, Thomas. *The last words of Thomas lord Pride.* [London]: n.pub., [1659]. 4°. Pp. 8.
P. 8, AW wrote, 'This came out January: 1658[9]'.
Wood 609(44) (not in Bodl. CD cat.). Wing L534A (Wing, Thomas, Lord and [1659?]).

5360. Pride, Thomas*. *The last speech and dying-words of Thomas . . . Pride; . . . by T. S. late clerk to his lordships brewhouse.* London: f. C. W., 1680. 4°. Pp. 12.
Wood 608(52). Wing L505aA.

5361. P[rideaux], J[ohn]. *Alloquium serenissimo regi Jacobo Woodstochiae habitum [24 Aug. 1624) [Signed J. P. V. Ox.].* [Oxford]: n.pub, [1624]. 4°. A^4.
A1, 'H1' (a shelf-mark?). A4, AW wrote after initials, 'Jo. Prideaux Vicecanc. Oxōn.'
Wood 512(9). STC 20343.7 (rare). Madan 519.

5362. Prideaux, Jo[hn]. *Tabulae ad grammatica Graeca introductoriae [and] Tyrocinium ad syllogismum legitimum contexendum [and] Heptades logicae.* Oxoniae: L. Lichfield, impens. E. Pearse a. T. Allam, 1639. 4°. 3rd ed. A-E^4,G2,H-I^4 (2nd tp at E2; 3rd tp at H1).
Tp, scribble and 'Mary'. Possibly lent to – French, 5 Mar. 1664, LT 2.7; AO 3.267.
Wood 310(4-5). STC 20364. Madan 925.

5363. Prideaux, Mathias, and John Prideaux. *An easy and compendious introduction for reading all sorts of histories:. . . in which is added a synopsis of councels by John Prideaux.* Oxford: f. L. Lichfield, sold T. Robinson, 1655 (1654). 4°. 3rd ed. Pp. [6], 351, [35]; [2], 58, [4]. Pasteboard (blue) with parchment spine.
Flyleaf, upper, 2nd^v, AW wrote the titles of 3 printed works in this vol. (really 4), within guidelines made with red ink. Tp, AW wrote, 'the 4th [ed.] came out 1664.' AO 3.199, 268.
Wood 473(1). Wing P3442 (P3436A). Madan 2280 (2261).

5364. [Proast, Jonas]. *The argument of the letter concerning toleration [by J. Locke] briefly consider'd*

and answer'd. Oxford: at the theatre, f. G. West a. H. Clements, 1690. 4°. Pp. [4], 28.
P. 23, line in pencil, not in AW's usual style. Prob. a gift of A. Charlett; see Wood 645(26), item 5171.
Wood 611(19). Wing P3538.

5365. Proast, Jonas. *The case of Jonas Proast, M.A. chaplain of All Souls college [2 letters to explain why he considered his dismissal by L. W. Finch from the chaplaincy to be unjust].* [Oxford]: n.pub., [1690]. Fol. Pp. 4.
P. 4, AW wrote, 'Nov. xi an. 1690 dedit mihi ap. London Jonas Proast – publ. in octob.' LT 3.263.
Wood 657(55). Wing F940 (Wing, [1693]).

5366. Prophecies. *Seven severall strange prophesies: full of wonder and admiration.* London: f. R. Harper, 1642. 4°. A⁴.
Tp, face, drawn, copied from illustration of Mother Shipton.
Wood 646(5). Wing S2739.

5367. Prophecies. *The mystery of prophesies revealed, by which the restoring of k. Charls . . . is . . . convinced.* London: n.pub., 1660. 4°. Pp. 8.
Tp, AW wrote after the year, 'Aprill'.
Wood 646(11). Wing M3190 (two).

5368. Prophet. *A strange prophet now in England. Being a true relation, sent to a person of quality, now in Oxford.* [London]: n.pub., [1679?]. S.sh.
Above, AW wrote 'ridiculous', in pencil; below, 'qu[aere] when', in pencil, and 'No date – qu[aere]', in ink. Below, 'ballus' or 'Pallu-' (?).
Wood 417(13). Wing S5917A (rare).

5369. Proposal. *A proposal for a yearly increase of wealth, by subscriptions to advance money upon lives.* [London]: [at Mr. Hill's] [bibliog. data, trimmed at foot], [1682]. S.sh. (r-v).
AW did not enter this work on the upper flyleaf.
Wood 628(7). Wing P3690.

PROSPECTUSES AND SPECIMEN PAGES (items 5370-5418)(and item 4508)

5370. Aubrey, John. *Proposals for printing Monumenta Britannica, . . . containing four parts.* [London]: n.pub., [1693]. S.sh. (r-v).
Aubrey's note: 'For Mʳ Anthony à Wood'. LT 3.420. Dupl. at Wood 276b(121), Wood 658(780), Wood 658(811a and 811b), and Wood 660b(16b and 16c).
Wood 276b(121). Wing A4189 (rare) (6 at O) (Wing, 1690?).

5371. Aubrey, John. *Proposals for printing Monumenta Britannica, . . . containing four parts.* [London]: n.pub., [1693]. S.sh. (r-v); tp and p. 25.
Tp, at a list of the 'four parts', AW put single brackets around I., II., and III. and wrote in margin, 'Where is the fourth part?'; below, 'Apr. 10. an. 1693'. LT 2.265 and 3.420. Dupl. at Wood 276b(121), Wood 658(811a and 811b), and Wood 660b(16b and 16c).
Wood 658(780). Wing A4189 (rare, 6 at O) (Wing, 1690?).

5372. Aubrey, John. *Proposals for printing Monumenta Britannica, . . . containing four parts.* [London]: n.pub., [1693]. S.sh. (r-v); tp and p. 25.
LT 3.420. Dupl. at Wood 276b(121), Wood 658(780), Wood 658(811a and 811b).
Wood 660b(16b and 16c). Wing A4189 (rare, 6 at O) (Wing, 1690?).

5373. Aubrey, John. *Proposals for printing Monumenta Britannica, . . . containing four parts.* [London]: n.pub., [1693]. S.sh. (r-v); tp and p. 25.
LT 3.420. Dupl. at Wood 276b(121), Wood 658(780), Wood 660b(16b and 16c).
Wood 658(811a and 811b) (2 copies) (not in Bodl. CD cat.). Wing A4189 (rare, 6 at O) (Wing, 1690?).

5374. Barrow, Isaac. *Proposals for the first volume of the works of . . . Isaac Barrow . . . publish'd by . . . dr. Tillotson.* [London]: f. B. Aylmer, [1682]. S.sh. Pp. 2.
See Wood 657(8), item 882, for the intro. Possibly a gift from Aubrey, see P. Lindenbaum, 'Brabazon Aylmer' *The Library* 7th series, 3 (2002): 42.
Wood 658(804) (not in Bodl. CD cat.). Wing B952 (rare).

5375. Bernard, Edward. *Librorum manuscriptorum academiarum Oxoniensis & Cantabrigiensis [list of contents and entry of J. Leland and R. Dodsworth in a proposed work, Aug. 1694].* [Oxford]: n.pub., [1694]. Fol. P. 1 (cropped) and p. nos. 235, 236, 233, 234 (proof-sheets).
Pp. 235, 234, narrative introduction and final paragraph are corrected in ms. (cropped), not by AW, though a single correction on p. 235 may be by AW, of William Burton's home at 'Linsiaco', to 'Lindliaco' (not entered in the final copy, published in 1697). P. 234, 'To Mr Anthony Wood at his House over against Merton College –[?].' Diff. ed., 8°, at Wood 896(9); LT 3.455.
Wood 658(815b). Not in Wing. Not in ESTCR (variant of Wing B1988; ESTCR 33780 and 231448).

5376. Bernard, Edward. *Librorum manuscriptorum academiarum Oxoniensis & Cantabrigiensis . . . Tomis duobus in fol. [last item on ^{v}: '27. Hospitii Lincolniensis. [/] Omnes isti catalogi typis Sheldoniis jam impressi sunt. [/] Rogantur . . . supplere. [/] Oxon. June 8. 1694. [/] Edv. Bernardus.* (Oxon.): (typ. Sheldoniis), (1694, 8 June). S.sh. (r-v), 8°.
Diff. ed., fol. with specimen pp., at Wood 658(815b). LT 3.455.
Wood 896(9) (not in Bodl. CD cat.). Not in Wing. Not in ESTCR (variant of Wing B1988; ESTCR 33780 and 231448)..

5377. Blome, Richard. *There is now in the press, a geographical discription of England [proposals for printing].* [Oxford]: n.pub., [1671]. S.sh.
Published in 1673, LT 2.539.
Wood 658(815a). Wing B3219aA (rare) (olim Wing T868). Not in Madan.

5378. Camden, William. *New proposals for printing by subscription, Cambden's Britannia [20 Apr.].* [London]: n.pub., [1693]. Fol. Pp. [4].
P. 4, '1693', in pencil, prob. not by AW.
Wood 658(806). Wing C373 (rare).

5379. Chauncy, Henry. *Proposals for printing a book entituled, The history and antiquities of Hertfordshire.* [London]: n.pub., [1695?]. Fol. Pp. [4].
Wood 658(812). Wing C3742 (rare) (Wing, [1700]).

5380. Dupin, Louis Ellies. Wotton, W., trans. *Proposals for printing by subscription Bibliotheca patrum: or, a new ecclesiastical history.* [London]: n.pub, [1692]. Fol. Pp. [4].
P. [2], centre, '1692' in pencil, prob. not by AW.
Wood 658(803). Wing D2646 (rare).

5381. England, History. *January, 1694/5. Proposals for printing a compleat history of England.* [London]: n.pub., [1695]. S.sh. (r-v).
AW added, 'Jan. 1694[5]'.
Wood 276a(569) (now placed after 576). Wing P3732 (two).

5382. Gibbon, Nicholas. *The scheme or diagramme adjusted.* [London]: f. private hands, [1680?]. Fol. Pp. 30, [1].
Missing. MS. Wood E. 2(70), p. 1, 'his scheem – in 2. sheets'. AW mentions in AO 4.788 the 'Scheme' of '8 sh. in fol.' and Gibbon's plans to publish this work. It was never published.
MS. Wood E. 2(70), p. 1. Wing G655.

5383. Gratius, Ortwinus. *Whereas there was printed out at Colen by Orthuinus Gratius [proposals for reprinting by subscription, Fasciculus rerum expetendarum & fugiendarum].* [London]: n.pub., [1688, 28 June]. Fol. Pp. [8].
P. [1], AW wrote, 'This paper was sent to Oxōn in the beginning of July 1688'. Dupl. at Wood 658(802) (imperf.).
Wood 658(788). Wing G1584 (rare).

5384. Gratius, Ortwinus. *Whereas there was printed out at Colen by Orthuinus Gratius [proposals for reprinting by subscription, Fasciculus rerum expetendarum & fugiendarum].* [London]: n.pub., [1688, 28 June]. Fol. Pp. [4] (wanting pp. [1-2], [7-8]).
P. 1, scribbles in margin, 'in Oxon', 'Blagrave', 'Clavell', not in AW's hand. Dupl. at Wood 658(788).
Wood 658(802). Wing G1584.

5385. Grew, Nehemiah. *Whereas a book entituled, Musaeum regalis societatis.* [London]: n.pub., [1680]. Fol. Pp. [3].
Correction, at date of the meeting of the Royal Society in 1680, from 16 February to 26 February.

Wood 658(794). Wing G1962 (two).

5386. Guidott, Tho[mas]. *Propositions touching printing a book, entituled, De thermis Britannicis.* [London]: n.pub., [1686]. Fol. Pp. [3].
P. 3, on specimen p., AW wrote, 'This specimen was published in May 1686' (see also item 3341 for the tp (1691) to this work).
Wood 658(808). Wing G2197 (rare).

5387. Gunton, Simon. Patrick, Symon, ed. *The history of the church of Peterburgh [proposals for printing, 19 August 1684 of Wing G2246].* London: f. R. Chiswell, [1684]. Fol. Pp. [2], 2.
Wood 658(784b). Not in Wing. Not in ESTCR.

5388. Harding, Thomas. *There is a very large historie of the church [proposal by bishop Ussher and others for the publication of T. Harding's history of the church.].* [London]: n.pub., [1651]. S.sh.
Signature of W^m duGard and a note on the quantity of leaves and sheets, prob. by Dugard. See Wood 276b(111).
Wood 658(799). Wing T865 (rare).

5389. Harding, Thomas. *Annales. An English manuscript.* (London): (Euclid Speidell), [1695]. S.sh. Obl. 4°.
AW wrote, 'Sept. 1695' and underscored, 'University of Oxford.' LT 3.490 and Wood 658(799).
Wood 276b(111). Wing H700aA (rare).

5390. Holwel, John. *Proposals for printing of Holwell's book of dialling.* [London]: n.pub., [1684]. S.sh.
AW wrote, below, '1684'.
Wood 658(789). Wing P3735 (rare).

5391. Howell, William. *Proposals for printing the manuscripts of dr. William Howell, late chancellour of Lincoln.* [London]: n.pub., [1684]. S.sh.
Wood 658(786a) (not in Bodl. CD cat.). Wing P3736 (rare).

5392. Jackson, Richard, pseud. *Proposals for the imprinting of Brigantia Lancastriensis restaurata, or history of the . . . county palatine of Lancaster, composed by Richard Keurden.* N.p.: n.pub., [1688]. S.sh. (r-v).
^v, AW wrote at end, 'q[u]i mihi hoc specimen donavit 2 Aug. 1688'; 2 words supplied at crease, in pencil, not by AW. AOF 2.94, 275; see also LT 2.484; 5.19, and *The Manchester courier*, 28 January 1876, no. 268, p. 6, which is pasted on to this item.
Wood 658(813). Not in Wing. Not in ESTCR.

5393. Josephus, Flavius. *Antiquitatum Judaicarum libri quatuor priores, et pars magna quinti, Gr. Lat. [illustr. notis E. Bernardi; specimen p. of the Antiquitates, with details of authorities].* [Oxford]: sumt. J. Crosley, H. Clements & J. Howell, [1694]. Fol. 2Y1-2, pp. 353-4.
2Y1, AW wrote, 'Donavit mihi Edw. Bernard 30 Aug. 1694'. LT 3.466.
Wood 658(774). Wing J1082 (rare).

5394. Keepe, Henry. *By Henry Keepe, . . . Having in the year 1681 [proposals for publishing an illustrated work on the history of Westminster Abbey].* N.p.: n.pub., [1683]. S.sh. (r-v).
^v, AW wrote 'This paper was sent to Oxon in the middle of Oct 1683'. LT 3.76.
Wood 658(800). Wing K125 (rare).

5395. Molyneux, William. *Whereas there is an accurate account and description of Ireland designed to be made publick in the English atlas undertaken by Moses Pitt . . . Quaeries . . . relating to Ireland.* [Dublin]: gratis at the shop of D. Davis, [1682]. S.sh.
Wood 658(787). Wing M2407 (rare).

5396. Morgan, William. *Proposals . . . for vending mr. Ogilby's works in a standing lottery, to enable him to finish Britannia.* [London]: n.pub., [1677]. S.sh.
AW wrote, 'Hillary Terme 1676/7'.
Wood 658(786b). Wing M 2755 (two).

5397. Ogilby, John. *The translation of Homer's works into English verse being undertaken.* [London]: n.pub., [1660]. S.sh.
Wood 658(790). Wing O183 (rare).

5398. Ogilby, John. *An accurate description of Africa*. London: T. Johnson f. the author, 1669. Fol. Pp. [2], 4 (t leaf and 4 pp. only).
Wood 658(785) (not in Bodl. CD cat.). Wing O162 (rare).

5399. Ogilby, John. *A proposal concerning an English atlas [10 May]*. [London]: n.pub., [1669]. S.sh. (cropped at bottom).
Wood 658(792). Wing O179 (rare).

5400. Ogilby, John. *Queries in order to the description of Britannia [19 queries]*. N.p.: n.pub., [1673]. S.sh.
A 20th query scribbled in, was written more clearly by AW, 'old words & proverbs'; below, AW wrote 'Received in a letter from Mᴿ Joh. Awbrey from Lond. 18. June 1673. AWood'. A copy at MS. Aubrey 4 (f. 243) has two categories added in hand by Aubrey, '20. Obsolete and peculiar Words. [/] 21. Old Customes./'. LT 2.265.
Wood 658(793). Wing O180 (two).

5401. Pitt, Moses. *[Begins:] Whereas his most sacred majesty has been graciously pleased, for the promoting of this design, to permit that his collections of maps . . . may be perus'd [3 May 1678; and,* ᵛ*, a list of subscribers beginning with 'Ailesbury' and ending with 'Peter Wyche'; and a final sentence:] 'We whose Names are underwritten, do subscribe for [blank] Book compleat, according to the true intent and meaning of these Proposals'*. N.p.: n.pub., [1678]. S.sh. (r-v).
ʳ, 'May 1678', prob. not by AW.
Wood 658(791c) (not in Bodl. CD cat.). Not in Wing. See Wing P2308. Not in ESTCR. Madan 3253.2.

5402. Pitt, Moses. *Proposals for printing a new atlas [begins] Moses Pitt of London . . . He the said*. [London]: n.pub., [1678]. S.sh. (r-v).
AO 4.442, 534, 749.
Wood 658(791b). Wing P2308. Madan 3253.1.

5403. Pitt, Moses. *Moses Pitt of London, bookseller, being encouraged by his most sacred majesty [a prospectus, with subscribers' names, for the English atlas]*. N.p.: n.pub., [1679?]. S.sh.
ᵛ, '1678' and 'Atlas', not by AW.
Wood 658(795). Wing P2308B (two) ('O' not recorded in Wing). Madan 3253.3.

5404. Pitt, Moses. *A catalogue of the subscribers names to the English atlas, now printing at the theater in Oxford*. [London]: n.pub., [1680]. Fol. Pp. [4].
Wood 658(791a). Wing C1411aA (one) ('O' not recorded in Wing). Madan 3253.4.

5405. Plot, Robert. *Whereas Robert Plot, doctor of laws of the university of Oxford, has . . . travell'd over the whole county of Stafford*. N.p.: n.pub., [1681]. S.sh. (r-v).
AW wrote above, '10. Jan. 1680[1].' AW's name is not present in the list of 200 current subscribers. LT 2.511.
Wood 276a(570) (now placed after 576) (not in Bodl. CD cat.). Not in Wing. Not in ESTCR.

5406. Poole, Matthew. *A brief description of a design concerning a synopsis of the critical and other commentatours [sic] upon the holy scripture*. [London]: n.pub., [1667]. Fol. Pp. IV, 8.
P. I, AW wrote, 'Ex dono Rad: Bathurst M.D. Coll: Trin Oxon Praesidis: Dec. 16. 1667'. Pp. 1-4, corrections in the heading. P. 7, '1667', in pencil, not by AW. LT 2.123.
Wood 658(784). Wing P2827 ('O' not recorded in Wing).

5407. Poole, Matthew. *A just vindication of mr. Poole's designe for printing of his synopsis . . . against the pretences of mr. Cornelius Bee*. [London]: n.pub., [1667]. 4°. Pp. 4.
P. 1, former no., '5'.
Wood 658(784f). Wing J1242A (one) ('O' not recorded in Wing).

5408. Poole, Matthew. *A just vindication of mr. Poole's designe for printing of his synopsis of critical and other commentators; against the pretences of mr. Cornelius Bee, book-seller [Followed by, on p. 4:] An account of some considerable additions to mr. Pooles work [and signed 'M. P.']*. [London]: n.pub., [1668] (includes 3 notes of attestation, dated 18, 22, and 14 Apr.1668). Fol. Pp. [4].
P. 2, 3 scribbles of 'Constantinus', not by AW.
Wood 658(807). Not in Wing. Not in ESTCR (not Wing J1242 and ESTCR 218074 which cite the BL copy, also at Wood 658(784f)).

5409. Poole, Matthew, and Cornelius Bee. *An advertisement concerning mᴿ. Poole's synopsis, &c.*

[Wing P2853]. There being some supernumerary books printed [signed M. Poole, C. Bee, 31 March 1670]. [London]: n.pub., [1670]. S.sh. 4°.
Advertisement for subscription to already printed vol. 1 and forthcoming vols. 2 and 3.
Wood 658(784e). Not in Wing. Not Wing P2819A. Not in ESTCR.

5410. Sammes, Aylett. *Proposals concerning the printing of a chronological history of England.* [London]: n.pub., 1677. S.sh.
Line in margin at author's name.
Wood 658(801). Wing S536 (rare).

5411. Skinner, Stephen. *Etymologicon linguae Anglicanae, seu explicatio [subscription form for, and specimen of].* London: typ. T. R. pro H. Brome, R. Clavel, & B. Tooke, 1669. Fol. Pp. [4].
P. [1], correction, prob. not by AW.
Wood 658(796). Wing S3946A (two) ('O' not recorded in Wing).

5412. Stow, John. *The model of a design to reprint Stow's Survey of London. With large additions and improvements.* [London]: n.pub., 1694, August. S.sh. (r-v).
Wood 658(810). Wing M2316 (rare).

5413. Tanner, Thomas. St. Asaph, bp. of. *An account of the book, entituled, Notitia monastica.* [Oxford]: n.pub., [1694]. Fol. Pp. [2].
P. [2], AW wrote 'This is the undertaking of Tho. Tanner B.A. of Qu. Coll– From Dr Charlet 24. May 1694.' LT 3.452-3.
Wood 658(782). Wing A255 (rare) (Wing, n.p.).

5414. [Thacker, Robert]. *A new map of Tangier, six foot long.* [London]: [for subscription, Clavel's shop], [1681]. S.sh.
LT 3.207.
Wood 386(17) (not in Bodl. CD cat.). Not in Wing. Not in ESTCR.

5415. Thucydides. *Proposals for subscription to Thucydides Gr. Lat. folio, now printing at the theater in Oxford.* [Oxford]: [at the theater], [1695]. Fol. Pp. [1-2] and specimen pp., 161-2.
P. [2], '1695', in pencil, not in AW's hand.
Wood 658(779). Wing T1135 (rare).

5416. Wantner, Abel. *To the nobility, clergy, and gentry of . . . Gloucester.* [London]: n.pub., [1684]. Fol. Pp. 3, [1] (last blank).
Date given in printed text, p. 3, 'which is now . . . ready for the Press this Michaelmas, 84'. Diff. ed. at Wood 658(786c).
Wood 276a(571-2). Wing W714 (two) (Wing, 1686). ESTCR 24108.

5417. Wantner, Abel. *To the nobility, clergy, and gentry of the city and county of Gloucester. Abel Wantner . . . most humbly certifieth [proposals for printing a history of Gloucester].* [London]: n.pub., [1686]. Fol. Pp. 4.
Diff. ed. at Wood 276a(571-2).
Wood 658(786c). Wing W714 (two) (Wing, 1686). ESTCR 217149.

5418. Wood, Anthony. *Proposals for printing Athenae Oxonienses, and Fasti Oxonienses.* [London]: [T. Bennet], [1690]. Fol. Pp. [4].
Includes printed entries of H. Savile and W. Camden. '1691' in pencil, not by AW. This should be dated about 7 October 1690, see LT 3.342.
Wood 658(814). Wing P3734 (rare).

End of PROSPECTUSES AND SPECIMEN PAGES (items 5370-5418)

5419. Prynne, William. *Healthes: sicknesse. Or, a compendious . . . discourse, proving, the drinking . . . of healthes, to be sinfull.* London: [A. Mathewes], 1628. 4°. Pp. [32], 95.
Pp. 68-94, some hand pointers, an underscoring, and a brief note (74, 'stage-play's'), not by AW. [MS.] Wood D. 30(7). STC 20463.

5420. [Prynne, William]. *Newes from Ipswich. Discovering certaine late detestable practises of some domineering lordly prelates [signed Matthew White, 12 Nov.].* Ipswich: n.pub., 1636. 4°. 'Edition 3'. ¶⁴.

Pasteboard (blue) with parchment spine. 1st upper and last lower flyleaves, marbled paper.
AW's list of contents was removed. Tp, AW wrote, 'Will Prynne the authour.' (cropped at bottom). Diff. ed. at [MS.] Wood D. 31(2), item 5423a.
[MS.] Wood D. 31(1). STC 20470.

5421. Prynne, William. *The antipathie of the English lordly prelacie*. London: f. M. Sparke senior, 1641. 4°. Pp. [30], 337. Calf, speckled, with 2 fillets.
Flyleaf, upper, and tp, signature of 'Dorothy Poole'.
[MS.] Wood C. 42 (not in Bodl. CD cat.). Wing P3891.

5422. [Prynne, William]. *A new discovery of the prelates tyranny, in their late prosecutions of m*[r] *William Pryn . . . John Bastwick . . . Henry Burton*. London: f. M. S., 1641. 4°. Pp. [2], 226, [1] (misnumbering, wanting 1 portrait). Calf with 2 fillets.
AW renumbered pp. 7-9 as 1, 2, and 3.
Wood 603. Wing P4018.

5423a. [Prynne, William]. *Newes from Ipswich: discovering certaine late detestable practices of some dominiering lordly prelates [signed Matthew White]*. [London]: f. T. Bates, 1641. 4°. Rpt. A[4].
Diff. ed. at [MS.] Wood D. 31(1), item 5420.
[MS.] Wood D. 31(2). Wing P4021A.

5423b. Prynne, William. *The doome of cowardize*. London: f. M. Spark, senior, 1643.
Missing. See note, 'habeo', at [MS.] Wood D. 22(7), item 1602.
Wing P3947.

5424. Prynne, William. *[An humble remonstrance against the tax of ship-money lately imposed] [pt. 2:] 'The opening of the great seale of England'*. Lodon [sic]: f. M. Sparke, senior, 1643. 4°. Pt. 2 only. Pp. [2], 32, [1] (A[2],B-E[4]).
1st part is at Wood 527(4).
Wood 629(2). Wing P4026.

5425. Prynne, William. *An humble remonstrance against the tax of ship-money lately imposed*. London: f. M. Sparke senior, 1643. 4°. Pt. 1 only. Pp. [2], 34.
Tp, bsm. 2nd part is at Wood 629(2).
Wood 527(4). Wing P3982.

5426. [Prynne, William]. *Romes master-peece. Or, the grand conspiracy of the pope and his Jesuited instruments . . . revealed . . . to Andreas ab Habernfeld [letters from him and sir W. Boswell to W. Laud, ed. by W. Prynne]*. London: f. M. Sparke, senior, 1643. 4°. Pp. [2], 36, [1] (misnumbering).
Former owner, W. Laud. Tp, at Prynne, Laud wrote '(whom I beleeve is the Author of thiss [sic] Tract./'; AW wrote, 'Liber Antonii à Wood Oxon. 1675'. Tp[v], AW wrote, 'All the scorings in this book, & written notes in the margin thereof, were made & done by that blessed Martyr Dr Will. Laud Archb. of Canterb. while he was a prisoner in the Tower of London'. Pp. 1-2, 7-10, 25, 27-29, 31-36, notes (all cropped in margin) and/or underscoring in hand of Laud, who responded vigorously to Prynne. LT 2.333. AW acquired this copy 7 years after the death of Richard Bayly, president of St. John's. Wood lent this pamphlet to Henry Wharton, who published it in 1695 with Laud's notes and other works by Laud (Wing L586). See AO 3.137-8; 3.859.
Wood 533(6). Wing P4055.

5427. Prynne, William. *A breviate of the life, of William Laud . . . extracted (for the most part) verbatim, out of his owne diary, and other writings, under his owne hand*. London: F. L[each] f. M. Spark senior, 1644. Fol. Pp. [7], 35.
Frontis.[r], 'Francis Markham', blotted out (and also blotted out on p. 35[v]; died in 1668, see LT 2.412). AW made extensive annotations, lines in margins, underscoring, double brackets, most in red ink but some in pencil and dark ink, on every p., 1-31, except p. 5. His frequent comments are critical of Prynne's methodology: his additions to the diary, p. 1, at printed 'extracted for the most part out of his own Diary', AW wrote 'By which it appears that there be some envious matters of your owne put in', and at a description of Laud's humble birthplace, the printed 'in a Cottage, just over against the Cage', AW wrote, 'This is of Prynns putting & not in the Diary – envious reflections'; and similar notes on pp. 2-3, 7-11, 13, 24. Of his attempts to sway the reader by his use of 'large character' or 'another character', that is, upper case or italic: pp. 3, 'Prynne put this in a larg character to make the reader believe it some scandalous matter.'; 4, 'Prynne puts this in another charact. to make it envious'; 22, 'What is the meaning that this

is put in another char?'. Of his use of 'saint': p. 21, at use of 'Saints' in text, AW wrote sarcastically, 'S^{tts}. ie. Prynne, Burton, & Bastwicke'. And of his lack of precision: pp. 3, at printed 'On Munday morning', he wrote, 'What day of the month was that?'; 6, a correction, 7, 23, 27, 'at January 17', AW wrote, '27 January see pag. 33'). AW identified persons on pp. 3, 'Rich Baylie his chapl.', 6, 'Henry' Burton, 13, 16, 19, 27, 29, 30. AW used the notes in this book for AO 3.125 and 139; 3.874.
Wood 657(7). Wing P3904.

5428. [Prynne, William]. *A checke to Brittanicus [Mercurius Britannicus], for his . . . flattery . . . in justifying condemned Nat: Fiennes.* London: J. Dawson f. G. Hutton, 1644. 4°. Pp. 8.
Tp, AW wrote, 'Dupl'. Dupl. at Wood 612(27).
Wood 533(7). Wing P3926.

5429. [Prynne, William]. *A checke to Brittanicus [Mercurius Britannicus], for his . . . flattery . . . in justifying condemned Nat. Fiennes.* London: J. Dawson f. G. Hutton, 1644. 4°. A⁴ (cropped at side).
Tp, AW wrote 'Dupl'. Dupl. at Wood 533(7).
Wood 612(27). Wing P3926.

5430. Prynne, William. *Canterburies doome. Or, the first part of a compleat history of the . . . charge, tryall, condemnation, execution of William Laud. . . . Wherein . . . trayterous artifices to usher in popery by degrees, are cleerly detected.* London: J. Macock f. M. Spark senior, 1646. Fol. Pp. [38], 17-565 (wanting pp. 49-50, 55-6). Calf with 3 fillets plus 3 vertical fillets, and roll decoration on edges of boards; spine, 5 bands and hatching.
Flyleaf, upper, printer's waste paper, AW wrote, ' Mr Joh. He[a]rne [/] Math. Hales Lync. Inn [/] [Rich.] Gerrard of Grey I-' (all 3 were members of the council assigned for the archbishop, AO 3.128). Flyleaf, upper, 2nd, 2 scribbles or drawings of a capitol(?) or an ornament, and some enigmatic abbreviations and nos., 'Bo } 21 [/] ha } 10' etc. Tp, bsm., '6.8x'. Text, beginning with the table, and, after p. 48, fairly frequent annotation (AW went through some sections carefully) in the form of lines in margins at names and topics, names, corrections, and reference nos. Pp. 49-50, 55-6 supplied in ms., not in AW's hand. Pp. 427, 429-30, AW wrote 3 notes on the lack of clarity in the text concerning a book by Sancta Clara (i.e., C. Davenport, see items 2175-82), with a longer note at printed 'Saint *Giles* was the Author of *Sancta Clara's* book', 'Of what book? of the exposition of the articles or of Deus natura et grā – Here is a great deale of confusion'. LT 2.507.
Wood 540. Wing P3917.

5431. Prynne, William. *A full vindication and answer of the XI. accused members . . . to . . . A particular charge . . . in the name of sir Thomas Fairfax.* London: n.pub., 1647. 4°. Pp. 42.
Tp, AW wrote 'Du-' (cropped) and nos. '56' and '46' in former bundles. Dupl. at Wood 620(5).
Wood 608(70). Wing P3968.

5432a. Prynne, William. *A full vindication and answer of the XI. accused members . . . to . . . A particular charge . . . in the name of sir Thomas Fairfax.* London: n.pub., 1647. 4°. Pp. 42.
Dupl. at Wood 608(70).
Wood 620(5). Wing P3968.

5432b. Prynne, William. *The levellers levelled.* T. B. f. M. Spark, 1647.
Missing. See note, 'habeo', at [MS.] Wood D. 22(7), item 1602.
Wing P4001.

5433. Prynne, William*. *A moderate answer to a late printed pamphlet [by W. Prynne] intitled nine queries upon the printed charge . . . against the XI members.* London: n.pub., 1647. 4°. Pp. 8.
Tp, nos. 5- and 47 (both lined out) in former bundles.
Wood 620(6). Wing M2323 ('O' not recorded in Wing).

5434. Prynne, William. *The university of Oxfords plea refuted. Or, a full answer to a late . . . paper intituled the priviledges of the university of Oxford in point of visitation.* London: T. B. f. M. Spark, 1647. 4°. Pp. [2], 64.
Responds to J. Fell, Wood 514(33), item 2968. Tp, bsm. Pp. 7, 9, 10, 12, 21, 27-9, 35, AW wrote notes, cross-references to the text and to mss., corrections, lines in margins, and dates, e.g.: 9, at complaint by scholars, to Archb. Arundel, against the Chancellor for procuring a bull concerning visitation, in time of Richard 2: 'Those articles were put up by the Civilians and canonists of the univers[ity] in relation to their old quarrell had with the Theologues & artists. ut in eod. Reg[istro]: Arundell patet', 'v[ide] p. 6. at the bottome', and in an argument about who, in tradition, had the authority to appoint visitors to the

university, 'they did not procure but produce the bull of p. Boniface the 3. & is the same yo[u] mentioned before p. 6. et. 7.'; and on the same topic, 10, 'this is very false. for only a certaine number of civ: & canonists who were now enimies to the Theologues & Artists, did among other greivances, put in the procuration of that Bull because that it was an obstacle to a visitation of the Univers. which they then expected to the end of that the said greivances might be reformed. See p. 9. Let any man iudg whether the generality of the scholars would be against the granting of privileges to them. v[ide] [an 'o' with a cross, i.e., inverted sigil of Venus [i.e., AW's symbol for MS. Twyne XXIV, LT 4.216] (see *Hist. and Antiq.*, 2.501ff.). Wood 514(34). Wing P4121. Madan 1960.

5435. [**Prynne, William**]. *The petition of right of the free-holders and free-men of . . . England: humbly presented to the lords and commons.* [London]: n.pub., 1648[9]. 4°. Pp. 23.
Tp, bsm.
Wood 609(13). Wing P4029.

5436. [**Prynne, William**]. *The second part of the narrative concerning the armies force and violence upon the commons house.* London: n.pub., 1648. 4°. Pp. 8.
Wood 620(12). Wing P4074A ('O' not recorded in Wing).

5437. [**Prynne, William**]. *A true and ful relation of the officers and armies forcible seising of divers eminent members of the commons house, Decemb. 6. & 7. 1648.* London: n.pub., 1648. 4°. Pp. 15.
Tp, AW wrote 'Will. Prynne hath such another in this extant - ' (i.e., Wood 620(12)). No. '4' (prob. the no. in a former bundle).
Wood 620(11). Wing P4110.

5438. Prynne, William. *A brief memento to the present unparliamentary junto.* London: n.pub., 1649. 4°. Pp. 16.
Tp, AW wrote, 'Jan. 1. 1648[9].'
Wood 364(2). Wing P3911.

5439. Prynne, William. *The first part of an historical collection of the ancient parliaments of England from . . . 673, till . . . 1216.* London: f. R. Hodges, 1649. 4°. Pp. 31.
Tp, AW wrote below, 'I could never see or learn that a second part was ever published'; and in margin in pencil, 'qu[aere] in Pryn['s] life for the 2d part' (faint).
Wood 518(6). Wing P3957.

5440. Prynne, William. *A new discovery of some Romish emissaries, Quakers; as likewise of some popish errors.* London: printed f. the author, sold E. Thomas, 1656. 4°. Pp. [2], 56 [1].
Tp, author's name underscored.
Wood 645(4). Wing P4017.

5441. Prynne, William. *The second part of a short demurrer to the Jewes long discontinued barred remitter into England.* London: f. E. Thomas, 1656. 4°. Pp. [4], 147, [1] (unnumbered pp. and misnumbering) (issued with Wood 637(4)).
Pp. 6, 13, 14ᵛ, etc. to 57, marks and 2 brief notes in margin, not by AW; 94-129, some marks in margin, in pencil, not by AW. Acquired, with part 1, 12 Aug. 1661, 2ˢ, LT 1.407.
Wood 637(5) (not in Bodl. CD cat.). Wing P4073.

5442. Prynne, William. *A short demurrer to the Jewes long discontinued barred remitter into England.* London: f. E. Thomas, 1656. 4°. 2nd ed. Pp. [12], 182 (i.e., 128, misnumbering) (issued with the preceding item, Wood 637(5)).
Acquired, with part 2, 12 Aug. 1661, 2ˢ, LT 1.407.
Wood 637(4). Wing P4079.

5443. [**Prynne, William**]. *King Richard the third revived. Containing a memorable petition . . . contrived by himself . . . to importune and perswade him to accept of the kingship.* London: f. W. Leak, 1657. 4°. Pp. [2], 9.
Tp, bsm.
Wood 609(42). Wing P3990.

5444. Prynne, William. *Eight military aphorismes.* London: f. the author, sold E. Thomas, 1658. 4° (wanting A3,4). Pp. [2], 32.
Tp, 'Prynne' underscored.
Wood 635(3). Wing P3948.

5445. [**Prynne, William**]. *An answer to a proposition [by J. Harrington] in order to the proposing of a commonwealth or democracy.* London: n.pub., 1659. 4°. Pp. [2], 6.
Tp, AW wrote, 'first heape 57', in pencil.
Wood 626(18). Wing P3889.

5446. [**Prynne, William**]. *Beheaded dr. John Hewytts ghost pleading, yea crying for exemplarie justice.* London: n.pub., 1659. 4°. Pp. [2], 18.
Tp, 'By Mʳ. W. Prynne', prob. by AW.
Wood 367(18). Wing P3900.

5447. Prynne, William. *A brief necessary vindication of the old and new secluded members, from the false . . . calumnies; . . . from the . . . subversions 1. Of John Rogers . . . 2. Of M: Nedham.* London: printed, sold E. Thomas, 1659. 4°. Pp. [2], 62.
Tp, Prynne underscored in red ink.
Wood 610(24). Wing P3913.

5448. Prynne, William*. *The character or ear-mark of mr. William Prynne.* London: n.pub., 1659. 4°. 2nd ed. Pp. [2], 5.
Tp, no. 24 in a former bundle (cropped at bottom).
Wood 610(56). Wing C2033.

5449. Prynne, William. *Concordia discors, or the dissonant harmony of sacred publique oathes, protestations, leagues, . . . lately taken . . . without scruple of conscience.* London: f. E. Thomas, 1659. 4°. Pp. [2], 45.
Tp, bsm.
Wood 610(55). Wing P3928.

5450. [**Prynne, William**]. *The curtaine drawne, or the parliament exposed to view. The names . . . secluded . . . in 1648.* (London): (f. H. Brome), (1659). 4°. Pp. 8.
Tp, AW wrote the year, '1648'. Dupl. at Wood 620(27).
Wood 487(2). Wing P3935 (Wing, drawne;).

5451. [**Prynne, William**]. *The curtaine drawne, or the parliament exposed to view. The names . . . secluded . . . in 1648.* (London): (f. H. Brome), (1659). 4°. Pp. 8.
Tp, AW wrote 'dupl', in pencil. Pp. 1, 3, 6, line in margin; 8, 'From . . . ' six words in all, illeg. (faint). Dupl. at Wood 487(2).
Wood 620(27). Wing P3935 (Wing, drawne;).

5452. [**Prynne, William**]. *The remonstrance of the noble-men, . . . and commons . . . who desire to shew themselves faithfull . . . to the good old cause.* [London]: n.pub., [1659]. S.sh.
AW wrote the date, 'November: M: Dc Lix'.
Wood 276a(232). Wing P4051.

5453. Prynne, William. *The re-publicans and others spurious good old cause, . . . anatomized.* [London]: n.pub., 1659. 4°. Pp. [2], 18.
Tp, AW underscored 'Prynne' in red ink.
Wood 613(20). Wing P4052.

5454. [**Prynne, William**]. *Seven additional quaeres in behalf of the secluded members, propounded to the twice-broken rump now sitting.* [London]: n.pub., [1659 to 1660]. 4°. Pp. 8.
P. 1, above, AW wrote the current item no. over a previous one, no. '78' (?) in a former bundle, and 'Parl sec', all in pencil; 'Will. Prynne the authour –', in red ink; and '27. Dec.' P. 8, 'Decemb: 1659'.
Wood 620(29) (Wood 620(2a) in Bodl. CD cat.). Wing P4077.

5455. Prynne, William. *A short, legal, medicinal, . . . prescription, to recover our kingdom, church, nation from their present . . . confusion.* London: printed, sold E. Thomas, 1659. 4°. Pp. [2], 9.
Tp, AW wrote 'Oct. ult', in pencil.
Wood 613(7). Wing P4080.

5456. [**Prynne, William**]. *Six important quaeres, propounded to the re-sitting rump of the long parliament.* [London]: n.pub., [1659]. S.sh.
AW wrote 'Will: Prinne: Decemb: 1659'.
Wood 620(28). P4083.

5457. Prynne, William. *Ten considerable quaeries concerning tithes, the present petitioners . . . for their total abolition*. London: f. E. Thomas, 1659. 4°. Pp. [2], 6.
Tp, AW underscored the author's surname, in red ink, and wrote at bottom a former location, 'First heap 27', in pencil.
Wood 370(7). Wing P4100 (Wing, 'O' is a 'var.').

5458. [Prynne, William]. *Ten quaeries, upon the ten new commandements . . . of the officers of the armies [22 Dec.]*. [London]: n.pub., [1659]. 4°. Pp. 8.
Tp, AW wrote, 'Will. Prynne the author-' in red ink, and, in pencil, former nos. in bundles, '65' and '6-' (cropped at side).
Wood 613(58). Wing P4101.

5459. [Prynne, William]. *To the right honourable, the lord mayor, . . . The humble petition and address of the sea-men, and water-men*. [London]: n.pub., [1659]. S.sh.
AW wrote, 'Decemb: 1659'.
Wood 276a(109). Wing P4106B.

5460. Prynne, William*. *To the supream authority of England, Scotland, & Ireland, . . . The humble petition . . . for as much as William Prynne*. [London]: n.pub., [1659]. S.sh.
This is the 'Petition against Prynns scribling - on sheet on one side' that AW entered in his catalogue of 1681, MS. Wood E. 2(70), p. 32. AO 3.853.
Wood 276a(200). Wing T1723B.

5461. Prynne, William. *A true and perfect narrative of what was done, spoken by and between mr. Prynne*. [London]: n.pub., 1659. 4°. Pp. [2], 99 (misnumbering).
Tp, 'Bund 1', in pencil. Bsm.
Wood 620(20). Wing P4113.

5462. [Prynne, William]. *The true good old cause rightly stated, and the false un-cased*. [London]: n.pub., [1659]. 4°. Pp. 8 (cropped).
Tp, AW wrote 'Will. Prynne the author', in red ink.
Wood 613(17). Wing P4114.

5463. [Prynne, William]. *A brief narrative of the manner how divers members of the house of commons, . . . were again forcibly shut out*. London: f. E. Thomas, 1660. 4°. Pp. [2], 10.
Tp, AW wrote '27 Dec', in pencil, and below, 'Will. Prynn the author', in red ink.
Wood 620(26). Wing P3912.

5464. Prynne, William. *The case of the old, secured, secluded, and now excluded members, . . . stated*. (London): (printed, sold E. Thomas), (1660). 4°. Pp. 8.
Tp, AW wrote 'Bund 3 Parl Jan 1[659]', in pencil (cropped at side). P. 8, AW altered the year to 16'59:Januar:'.
Wood 620(31) (Wood 623(31) in Bodl. CD cat.). Wing P3921.

5465. Prynne, William. *Conscientious, serious theological and legal quaeres, propounded to the . . . anti-parliamentary Westminster juncto*. London: printed, sold E. Thomas, 1660. 4°. Pp. [2], 48, [1].
AW wrote, 'This came out in Novemb: 1659' and, in pencil, former nos. '46' and '42'.
Wood 631(11). Wing P3930.

5466. [Prynne, William]. *A full declaration of the true state of the secluded members case. In vindication of themselves*. London: printed, sold E. Thomas, 1660. 4°. Pp. [2], 54, [4] (35-50 unopened).
Tp, AW wrote 'Bund 3 Parl' and 'Jan. 5', in pencil; altered the year to 16'59'; and, later, 'By William Prynne.' and 'published about the latter end of Jan. 1659'. Pp. 2nd [1-3], marks at most names of secluded members, not in AW's usual manner.
Wood 620(32). Wing P3965.

5467. [Prynne, William]. *The long parliament twice defunct: or, an answer to [by W. Drake] The long parliament revived*. London: f. H. Brome, 1660. 4°. Pp. [8], 40 (some pp. unopened).
Wood 620(35). Wing P4003.

5468. P[rynne], W[illiam]. *A plea for s^r George Booth, and the Cheshire gentlemen. Briefly stated in a letter to sir Arthur Hesilrrigge*. [London]: n.pub., [1660]. S.sh.
AW wrote, 'Januar: 1659'.
Wood 503(30). Wing P4031.

5469. [**Prynne, William**]. *The privileges of parliament which the members, army . . . have taken the protestation and covenant to maintain . . . Reprinted for consideration . . . 5th. of January, 1659.* [London]: n.pub., [1660]. 4°. Pp. 8.
Tp, AW wrote 'Bund 3. Parl', in pencil; at 'Reprinted' in t, 'When the first edit. came out, I find not.'; and 'Will Prynne the authour'.
Wood 620(30). Wing P4040.

5470. [**Prynne, William**]. *Three seasonable quaeres, proposed to all those cities, . . . forcibly excluded, . . . by those now acting in Westminster.* London: f. E. Thomas, 1660. S.sh.
AW altered the date to 16'59: Janu:' and later added 'By Will. Prynn'.
Wood 276a(227). Wing P4105.

5471. Prynne, William. *Brevia parliamentaria rediviva. In XIII. sections.* London: f. the author, sold E. Thomas, 1662. 4°. Pp. [24], 398, [1].
Tp, AW wrote the price, '4ˢ'.
Wood 518(9). Wing P3902.

5472. Prynne, William. *The Quakers unmasked, and clearly detected to be but the spawn of Romish frogs [22 Jan.].* London: f. E. Thomas, 1664. 4°. 2nd ed. Pp. [2], 38, [1].
Tp, name of author, underscored in red ink. P. 2, mark in margin, prob. not by AW.
Wood 645(16). Wing P4047.

5473. [**Prynne, William, and Edward Sexby**], et al. *The hypocrites unmasking; or, a cleare discovery of the . . . hypocrisy of the officers and agitators in the army . . . to relieve Ireland.* London: n.pub., 1647. 4°. Pp. 8.
Tp., former no., '15', lined out.
Wood 509(17). Wing P3984.

5474. [**Przipcovius, Samuel**]. *The life of that incomparable man, Faustus Socinus Senensis.* London: f. R. Moone, 1653. 8°. Pp. [7], 61, [7] (2 tpp).
Wood 292(2-3) (not in Bodl. CD cat.). Wing P4136.

5475. Pudsey, George. *The speech of sˢ George Pudsey kᵗ at the time of his being sworn. Recorder of . . . Oxford [8 Jan. 1684].* Oxon: f. A. Stephens, 1684. Fol. A-B².
Wood 423(59) (Wood 723(59) in Bodl. CD cat.). Wing P4167.

5476. Pudsey, George. *The speech of sir George Pudsey, serjeant at law, recorder of the city of Oxford [30 Sept.].* (London): (f. T. Goodwin), (1685). S.sh. Pp. 2.
Wood 423(61). Wing P4169.

5477. Pudsey, George. *The speech of sir George Pudsey . . . to the king, upon his majesty's coming to Oxford Sept. 3.* Oxon.: H. Cruttenden, 1687. Fol. Pp. [4].
Pp. [3]-[4], AW wrote 3 satiric notes, e.g.: at printed 'No sooner Your Majesty ascended the Throne . . . but you were proclaimed a Favourite of heaven, the Wicked were taken in their own Nets', he wrote, 'was Joseph made second in Potiphers court but blessings flowed upon his master for his sake; so no sooner'.
LT 3.229. Dupl. at Wood 657(45).
Wood 423(62). Wing P4170.

5478. Pudsey, George. *The speech of sir George Pudsey . . . to the king, upon his majesty's coming to Oxford Sept. 3.* Oxon.: H. Cruttendon, 1687. Fol. Pp. [4].
Tp, AW wrote 'Dup' in pencil. Dupl. at Wood 423(62).
Wood 657(45). Wing P4170.

5479. Puget de la Serre, Jean. H[awkins], H[enry], trans. *The sweete thoughts of death, and eternity. Written by Sieur de la Serre.* Paris [i.e., St. Omer]: [English College Press], 1632. 8°. 2 pts. Pp. [8], 175, [1], 168.
Missing. MS. Wood E. 2(70), p. 5, J. Henshaw, *Horae succisivae* was 'bound with a discourse of eternity Hawkins qu[aere] cat.' (see also note at item 3513).
MS. Wood E. 2(70), p. 5. STC 20492. ARCR 2.392. *O, Folg, Hunt.*

5480. P[ugh], R[obert]. *Elenchus elenchi: sive animadversiones in Georgii Batei, Cromwelli parricidae aliquando protomedici, elenchum motuum nuperorum in Angliā.* Parisiis: n.pub., 1664. 8°. Pp. [8], 61, [7] (misnumbering).
Tp, AW wrote, 'Rob. Pugh, Jesuita'; bsm. Pp. 17, 20-1, marks in margin.

Wood 112(2). Wing P4186E ('O' not recorded in Wing).

5481. P[ugh], R[obert]. *In nobilissimi juvenis Sidnaei Montacuti immaturum obitum, . . . Ode [V. cal. June 1672].* [London]: n.pub., [1672]. S.sh.
AW wrote at t, 'Son of Edw. E. of Manchester qu[aere]'; below, at R. P., 'Capt: Robert Pugh, è Soc. Jesu.', not by AW. ᵛ, AW wrote, 'Sidney Mountagu 1672.' LT 2.435, AO 3.829.
Wood 429(33). Wing P4187 (two).

5482. Pye, Robert, and James Ennis. *A more exact relation of the siege laid to . . . Leicester . . . Delivered in to . . . the house of commons by sir Robert Pye . . . and major James Ennis, June 10.* London: J. Field f. L. Chapman, 1645. 4°. Pp. 8.
Tp, AW wrote the price '1ᵈ', and overwrote the former no., '4'.
Wood 378(5). Wing P4255.

5483. Pym, John. *The heads of a conference delivered by mr Pymm, at a committee of both houses [24 June].* [London]: n.pub., 1641. 4°. Pp. [2], 6.
Tp, no. 8 in a former bundle; at imprint, 'elswhere', in pencil (also printed in *Diurnall occurrences*, in Wood 494(1), item 2603), and Pymm underscored in red ink.
Wood 614(26) (not in Bodl. CD cat.). Wing P4268A.

5484. Pym, John. *March 17. Master Pyms speech in parliament. Wherein is expressed his zeal . . . to the publike good.* London: f. A. Coe a. M. Boat, 1641. 4°. Pp. 8.
Wood 614(31). Wing P4289.

5485. Pym, John. *Two speeches made by . . . the one after the articles of charge against the earle of Strafford were read. The other, after . . . sir George Ratcliffe.* London: f. J. Bartlet, 1641. 4°. Pp. [2], 8.
Tp, no. 7 in a former bundle; 'Pymm' underscored in red ink. Bsm. Pp. 1, 6, line in margin at names of Strafford and Ratcliffe, in red ink.
Wood 614(33). Wing P4302.

5486. Pym, John*. *A short view of the life and actions of the late deceased John Pim.* [London]: J. Hammond, [1643]. 4°.
Missing since 1994. In Whiteside cat.
Wood 531(3). Wing S3639 ('O' not recorded in Wing).

5487. [Pyne, John]. *Anagrammata regia. In honorem . . . regis Caroli conscripta.* Londini: [W. Stansby], [1626] (in an anagram). 4°. A2-4,B-D⁴,E1-3.
Each 8° leaf is pasted on a 4° template. A1, torn out; the fragment remaining has traces of annotation. Tp, uncoding the date of publication from the upper-case letters in an anagram (similar uncoding on E3), prob. by AW. Perhaps acquired 2 Nov. 1667, 8ᵈ, LT 2.120.
Wood 318(2). STC 20521.2.

5488. Quakers. *Here followeth a true relation of some of the sufferings inflicted upon the . . . Quakers, . . . in Oxford.* [London?]: n.pub., [1654]. 4°. Pp. 8.
Flyleaf, upperᵛ, 'This simple pamphlet following containing a relation of the suffering of certaine Quakers done by Oxford scholars, then under the government of Presbyterians & Independents, was published in 1654, in the raigne of Oliver. [/] The Quakers came first to Oxon. in that yeare, & had their meetings in an old stone-house almost opposite to the common gate of New-Inne (in which house Rich. Beatrice [i.e., Betterus] Chirurgion & Quaker then lived) as they journied from the north parts of England to London – The said Rich Batrice [sic] one of the chief Quakers in Oxon. lived to the beginning of K. Jam. 2. [/] Some but not all things in this pamphlet are true.' LT 1.190.
Wood 515(14). Wing H1547. Madan 2250.

5489. Quakers. *The saints testimony finishing through sufferings: or, the proceedings . . . in Banbury.* London: f. G. Calvert, 1655. 4°. Pp. [2], 44.
Pp. 3, 8, 13, etc., corrections in text.
Wood 645(3). Wing S365.

5490. Quakers. *The devil turned Quaker: or, the damnable . . . doctrines . . . of these . . . people; called, Quakers:. . . Especially, . . . of one James Neyler [sic].* London: f. J. Andrews, 1656. 8°. A⁸.
Wood 645(5). Wing D1222 (rare).

5491. Quakers. *A true relation of the persecutions of the . . . Quakers, in the town of Aroundel in . . . Sussex.* London: f. T. Simmons, 1659. 4°. Pp. [1], 8.

Wood 645(10). Wing T3015A (one) ('O' not recorded in Wing).

5492. Quakers. *For the king, and . . . parliament. Being a short declaration of the cruelty inflicted upon some . . . Quakers, in Merionyth shire [3d month 1660].* [London?]: n.pub., [1660?]. 4°. Pp. 8.
Pp. 1, 7, 2 locations, not in AW's hand.
Wood 645(15). Wing F1434 (two) ('O' not recorded in Wing).

5493. Quakers. *A short relation of some part of the sad sufferings, . . . inflicted on . . . Quakers, for meeting.* [London?]: n.pub., 1670. 4°. Pp. 76.
P. 11, at Robert Copput, AW wrote, 'Rob. Cophoc (commonly call'd <u>Robhooks</u> pothooks) somtimes chapl. of C. C. coll.' (i.e., Coppocke).
Wood 645(17). Wing S3619.

5494. Quakers. *To the king and both houses of parliament the suffering condition of the peaceable people, called Quakers.* [London]: n.pub., [1685?]. Fol. Pp. 3.
Wood 645(23). Wing T1491 (Wing, Parliament . . . the suffering).

5495. Quakers; Fifth Monarchy, and Anabaptists. *To the supreme authority of the nation: an humble petition on behalf of many thousands of Quakers, Fifth-Monarchy men, Anabaptists.* London: D. Maxwell, 1660. S.sh.
AW altered the year to 16'59: feb:'.
Wood 276a(262). Wing T1729 ('O' not recorded in Wing).

5496. Quarles, Fran[cis]. *Argalus and Parthenia.* London: J. Marriott, [1635 ca.]. 4°. Pp. [7], 152, [1].
Text, some underscoring, horizonal lines, and other marks, in pencil, not in AW's manner.
Wood 330(4). STC 20528 (3).

5497. [Quarles, Francis]. *The shepheards oracle: delivered in an eglogue.* [Oxford]: n.pub., 1644. 4°. Pp. [2], 14. Calf with 3 fillets and 2 clasp holes; spine rebacked (Oxford binding?).
Flyleaf, 2nd^v, AW wrote in his early hand, 'The severall bookes contained in this volume:' a list of 10 printed works, with Arabic nos. (two entries have authors added at a later date (a different hand?), (4) and (8)), and below, 'Anthoni: Woodi : Februari 27 [all lined out, and] 27: 1656/7 [? prob. '6/7'; over which:] 27: 1666/7' (Clarks accepts the year 1667 for the acquisition, LT 2.99, but the hand is clearly that of AW before 1660, with many secretary letters). AW's mother died on 28 February 1667 and one book in this collection has her signature (Wood 330(8), item 915). It is likely that AW made an inventory of this vol. when still in his mother's possession. He received it upon her death and changed the date to 1667. The contents were in the current order from 1657, but some items were disturbed in a rebinding. E.g., some of the some Arabic numerals (1, 3, 4, 5, 6, 9), possibly written by AW at the bottoms of tpp, were cropped; and leaves were removed from item 7. Roman numerals are at the tops of tpp. AW listed 7 of these in his cat. of 1681 in the following order: 3, 2, 9, 5, 6, 7, 10 (MS. Wood E. 2(70), p. 50), which is puzzling.
Wood 330(1). Wing Q114. Madan 1653.

5498. Quarles, Francis. *Boanerges and Barnabas, or judment and mercy.* London: f. R. Royston, 1657. 12°. 4th ed.
Missing. 'Barnabas & Boanerges,' acquired 6 March 1658, 1^s2^d, LT 1.238 (Clark gives 4th ed., 1657).
LT 1.238. Wing Q54.

5499. Quarles, John. *Regale lectum miseriae: or, a kingly bed of misery:. . . with an elegie upon the martyrdome of Charls . . . and . . . upon lord Capel.* [London]: n.pub., 1649. 8°. Pp. [4], 66 (2 tpp).
Tp, below, '6'. Dupl. at Wood 898(2) imperf.
Wood 670(4). Wing Q135.

5500. [Quarles, John]. *[Regale lectum miseriae: or, a kingly bed of misery:. . . with an elegie upon the martyrdome of Charls . . . and . . . upon lord Capel].* [London]: n.pub., [1649]. 8°. Pp. [2], 58 (wanting the t leaf and all after sig. D7).
Dupl. at Wood 670(4).
Wood 898(2). Wing Q135.

5501. Quevedo y Villegas, Francisco Gomez de. Messervy, Edward, trans. *Hell reformed or a glasse for favorits. . . . by D: F: Q: V:.* London: E. Griffin f. S. Burton, 1641. 8°. Pp. [24], 112.
Tp, AW wrote 'MDClx: vi^d:'. A5, B1, words, not by AW. P. 103, part of heading lined out and 'for Reformation.' written below, may be in AW's hand.
Wood 664(2). Wing Q189.

5502. Quinones de Benavente, Juan de. Chamberlayne, Edward, trans. *The Spanish Otes, or, the unparallel'd imposture of Michael de Molina*. London: J. Bennet, sold W. Davis, 1685. 4°. Pp. [2], 5.
Wood 586(22). Wing M2386.

5503. R., M. *An exact accompt of the receipts, . . . expended by the committee of safety*. London: f. J. Hanzen, 1660. Fol. Pp. 11.
AW wrote '1659' in pencil, and in printed 1660 lined out '60'.
Wood 416(59). Wing R44.

5504. R., N. *Proverbs English, French, Dutch, Italian, and Spanish*. London: f. Simon Miller, 1659. 12°.
Pp. [8], 151, [7] (6 pp. books sold by S. Miller).
Wood 60(3). Wing R56.

5505. R., T. *A confutation of the tenne great plagues, prognosticated by John Doleta . . . to happen in . . . 1587*. London: R. Walde-graue, [1587]. 8°. A-B⁸ (B8 blank).
Wood 583(6). STC 20589 (rare).

5506. R., T. *A message of peace: in a letter . . . about the use of the liturgie. Together with a friendly letter sent to sir Edward Deering*. London: S. Saterthwait, 1642. 4°. Pp. [2], 6.
Tp, a former no., '3-'.
Wood 632(2). Wing R88.

5507. R., T. *An extract of a letter from a person of quality at Bruxels . . . March 5*. [London]: f. T. Bassett, 1660. S.sh.
Wood 276a(189) (Wood 274a(189) in Bodl. CD cat.). Wing R82.

5508. R., W. *No parliament but the old: or, a new-years gift for the late interrupted parliament*. London: J. Clowes, 1659. S.sh.
AW added to date, 'Decemb'.
Wood 276a(228). Wing R99A ('O' not recorded in Wing).

5509. Rainolds, John. *Orationes*. ?: ?, [1587 to 1628]. 12°.
Missing. MS. Wood E. 2(70), p. 46, 'Orationes 12.' Ed. not identified.
MS. Wood E. 2(70), p. 46. STC 20612.3-20615.5.

5510. Rainolds, John. *A defence of the judgment of the reformed churches, that a man may . . . put awaie his wife for her adulterie, . . . wherin both R. Bellarmin the Jesuites treatise [Disputationes de controversiis] and an English pamphlet . . . are côfuted*. [Dort]: [G. Waters], 1609. 4°. Pp. [6], 94.
Tp, 'Pret. 6ᵈ . . . Oᵉʳ: 1618' cropped at top and side, not in AW's hand.
Wood 636(3). STC 20607.

5511. Rainolds, John. *The overthrow of stage-playes, by the way of controversie betwixt D. [William] Gager and D. Rainoldes. . . . letters betwixt . . . Rainoldes, and Doct. [Albericus] Gentiles*. Oxford: J. Lichfield f. E. Forrest a. W. Webbe, 1629. 4°. 2nd ed. Pp. [8], 190, [1].
Missing. MS. Wood E. 2(70), p. 49. Ed. not determined, though AW knew the 1629 ed., AO 2.15.
MS. Wood E. 2(70), p. 49. STC 20618. Madan 645. *O, Folg, Hunt, NYPL*.

5512. Rainolds, John. Leycester, John, trans. *An excellent oration . . . translated . . . by J. L.* London: T. Harper f. T. Slater a. W. Aderton, 1638. 12°. Pp. [14], 145, [2]. Calf with 1 fillet, gold stamped.
Tp, AW identified Rainolds' college, 'C. C. Coll', in red ink. P. 1 oration dated: 'after the feast of St. Mich 1573'.
Wood 49. STC 20610.

5513. [Raleigh, Carew]. *Observations upon some particular persons and passages, in a book [by sir W. Sanderson] . . . intituled, a compleat history*. London: f. G. Bedell a. T. Collins, 1656. 4°. Pp. [2], 21.
Tp, AW wrote the name of the author, 'Mʳ Carew Rawley p. 2'; and below, 'Ant: Woode: Merton: Coll: Oxōn: M:DC:Lix:'. P. 21, at end, 'Criticus.-.-.-' prob. not by AW.
Wood 660e(3). Wing R149.

5514. Raleigh, Walter. *A report of the truth of the fight about the iles of Açores, this last sommer. Betwixt the Revenge, . . . and an armada of the king of Spaine*. London: [J. Windet] f. W. Ponsonbie, 1591. 4°. A2-4,B-C⁴,D1-3 (the final leaf mutilated).
D1, hand and line in margin, prob. not by AW.
Wood 511(4). STC 20651.

5515. Raleigh, Walter. *The life and death of Mahomet, the conquest of Spaine*. London: R. H[odgkinson] f. D. Frere, 1637. 12°. Pp. [9], 274, [1]. Parchment with 2 clasp holes.
Tp, bsm. A4, correction.
Wood 262. STC 20647.

5516. Raleigh, Walter. *The perogative [sic] of parliaments in England. Proved in a dialogue*. [London]: [T. Cotes], 1640. 4°. Pp. [8], 65, [1]. Pasteboard (blue) with parchment spine (rebacked by H. C. 28. 8. [19]48).
Flyleaf, upper, 2nd, AW wrote the titles of 9 printed works in this vol., within guidelines made with red ink (he omitted 3a). Tp, AW wrote, 'The first edition of this booke came out at Midleburge A: D^{ni} 1628.' (a false imprint, i.e., London).
Wood 518(1). STC 20650.

5517. Raleigh, Walter. *The prince, or maxims of state*. London: n.pub., 1642. 4°. Pp. [7], 46.
Missing in 1837. Wood 490, which held 5 printed works, all recorded in the Whiteside cat., was marked as missing in the 1837 inventory.
Wood 490(1). Wing R179. *O, Hunt, Folg.*

5518. Raleigh, Walter. *The cabinet-council: containing the cheif arts of empire, . . . published by John Milton*. London: T. Newcomb f. T. Johnson, 1658. 8°. Pp. [9], 199.
Missing. MS. Wood E. 2(70), p. 40.
MS. Wood E. 2(70), p. 40. Wing R156. *Hunt, Folg, Union.*

5519. Raleigh, Walter. *The marrow of history*. London: f. J. Place a. W. Place, 1662. 12°. 2nd ed. Pp. [24], 574. Calf, rough, with 3 fillets and stamp decoration (dragons) in corners; rebacked (Ashm. binding).
Flyleaf, upper, list of 4 printed works in this vol., written by an Ashm. librarian. Tp, bsm. A3^v, A4, corrections, prob. not by AW.
Wood 225(1). Wing R173.

5520. Raleigh, Walter. *The pilgrimage . . . after his condemnation, the day before his death*. (London): (G. Larkin), (1681). S.sh. (r-v).
'Raleigh' underscored in red ink.
Wood 417(75). Wing R178.

5521. Raleigh, Walter, and [John Keymor]. *Maxims of state. With instructions to his son, . . . Whereunto is added observations touching trade and commerce with the Hollander*. London: f. W. Shears, Junior (2nd tp, T. H., sold W. Sheeres, 1653), 1656. 8°. Pp. [10], 202, [8], 80 (2 ttp). Calf with 2 fillets and a vertical fillet; rebacked.
Pastedown, upper, Sheldon's book plate, a single sheldrake. Flyleaf, upper, a shelf-mark, 'E. 21' (Sheldon's?). Tp, 'Geo. Sheldon'. LT 2.510.
Wood 450. Wing R176 (and K391).

5522. [Ramesey, William]. *The gentlemans companion: or, a character of true nobility, and gentility:. . . by a person of quality*. London: T. M. f. T. Sawbridge, 1676. 12°. Pp. [6], 264, [2] (2 pp. books printed f. Sawbridge).
Flyleaf, upper, 'Ant. à Wood 16. Sept. 1676. 1^s - 4^d'; ^{v}, AW tried to deduce the name of the author: 'The Authour [/] A gentleman borne, & of an anbient [sic] & honorable family. - v. pag. 3. [/] Hath writ another book beside this, vide p. 100. in marg. [/] No papist, - p. 36. 37. &c [/] Nor no Fanatick p. 39 &c. [/] A Cambridg man p 132'. Pp. 1, 3, lines in margin, in red ink; 37, note, not by AW; 131-2, line in margin or underscoring, and a correction.
Wood 752(4). Wing R207.

5523. Randolph, Bernard. *The present state of the Morea, called anciently Peloponnesus*. London: f. the author, sold T. Basset, J. Penn, a. J. Hill, 1686. 4°. Pp. [2], 26.
Tp, after the t, AW added, 'and by the Turks Mora'.
Wood 386(21). Wing R235.

5524. Randolph, Thomas. *Poems, with the muses looking-glass*. London: f. F. Bowman, sold W. Roybould, 1652. Pp. 502. 8°.
Missing in 1837. 'Randolphs Poems – Oxon. 1652' in Whiteside cat. Listed in MS. Wood E. 2(70), p. 51, 'Poems & playes – 1652'.
Wood 77. Wing R243. *O.*

5525. Ranters. *The arraignment and tryall with a declaration of the Ranters.* [London]: B. A., 1650. 4°. Pp. [2], 6.
Wood 647(17b). Wing A3748 ('O' not recorded in Wing).

5526. Ranters. *The routing of th [sic] Ranters.* [London]: B. A., [1650]. 4°. Pp. [2], 6.
Wood 647(8). Wing R2055 ('O' not recorded in Wing) (Wing, the).

5527. Ranters. *Strange newes from Newgate and the Old-Baily: or the proofs, . . . of I. Collins, and T. Reeve, two of the Ranters.* London: B. Alsop, 1651. 4°. Pp. [2], 6.
Wood 647(17c) (not in Bodl. CD cat.). Wing S5897..

5528. Rapin, René, and Charles Maraguetel de Saint Denis Saint-Evremond. Dancer, John, trans. *The comparison of Plato and Aristotle. With the opinions of the fathers on their doctrine . . . Together with judgment on Alexander & Caesar.* London: T. R. a. N. T. for D. Newman, a. J. Edwin. 2nd item, A. Maxwell, f. J. Edwin, 1673, (1672). 8°. Pp. [26], 214; 78 (3 tpp). Calf with 2 fillets; rebacked.
See AW's note at J. Dauncey, Wood 235(5), item 2168.
Wood 288 (not in Bodl. CD cat.). Wing R260 and S303A.

5529. Rarity and Wonder of the World. *'The rarity and wonder of the world, viz. A living child about eight years old, that is neither perfect man, woman, nor hermophrodite . . . in White-hall, on Friday the 8th of September, 1676. and is now to be seen at any hour in the day at'.* N.p.: n.pub., [1676]. S.sh. (14 lines).
Wood Diaries 21a, f. 25. AW filled in at end of title, 'a house overagainst [sic] the gild hall Oxon. 4. July 1677 & so forward'; in margin, 'the childs name is . . . Macconaught'; ᵛ, 'This was originally begot by a man, but a mastie dog or monkie gave the semen some sprinkling.' LT 2.378 (quoted in entirety).
[MS.] Wood Diaries 21b (not in Bodl. CD cat.). Not in Wing. Not in ESTCR.

5530. [Rastell, John]. Blount, Thomas, intro. *Les termes de la ley: or, certain difficult . . . words and terms of the common lawes . . . of this realm . . . expounded [in Law Fr. and Engl.].* London: J. Streater f. the Co. of Stationers, 1659. 8°. Ff. [7], 271.
Tp, 'A. Wood' and a former no., lined out; ᵛ, AW wrote, 'William Briscoe his book. Given to him by Anthony à Wood of Merton Coll. in Oxōn, 16. July 1675, at what time the said Mʳ Briscoe left that college - [/] Nescio qua natale solum dulcedine cunctos [/] Ducit et immemores non sinit esse sui. [/] Ant. à Wood.' (Ovid, *Pont.* 1.3.35). Briscoe matriculated in 1673 at the age of 18 and left two years later to become a student at Lincoln's Inn. The two seem not to have retained the earlier friendship (see LT 2.319). AW acquired 'The termes of the Law', 1 June 1661, 2ˢ6ᵈ, LT 1.401.
Wood 677(2). Wing R289.

5531. [Rastell, William]. *A table . . . of the yeres of the kynges of Englande.* London: J. Waley, 1562. (1563, Marcii). 8°. A-L⁸, and 24 blank leaves. Parchment.
Cover, upperᵛ, 'Ant. Woode' and note by the former owner, or references to, 'Comes Leycestr / Comt [/] William Thomas de civitat Oxōn [/] yeoman'; sig. A1, 'Ant: Woode: Coll. Merton Oxon: A: 1660 [/] This booke was written by William Rastall. & published the 2ᵈ time. 1607'. Not in AW's hand, entries from 1562 to L8ᵛ, and at L8ᵛ, 'The best counting is by the yere of our lorde and not by the raigne of the princes./'. AW continued the record of regnal years on the 1st 14 blank leaves inserted after the text, from 1557 to 1665[6] where the final entry is: 'January 30. day 18. Car. 2'; cover, lower, scribbles, 'Wood ow [/] oweth', and name, 'William Busby[?]', rubbed out. LT 2.306.
Wood 7. STC 20735.

5532. Rastell, William. *A table collected of the yeares of our Lord God, . . . from the first yeare of William the conquerour.* London: W. J[aggard] f. T. Adams, 1607 (1606). 8°. A-M⁸ (M8 blank) (waste paper, Bright, *Treatise of Melancholie*, pp. 197-8, 203-4 (N3). Parchment.
Cover, upperᵛ, 'Ant Woode 166j'. Waste paper, upper, scribbles, the author's name, some in AW's hand. Tp, 'Robert Selbie et fratrorum'. M5-7, from 1608 to 1621, years of King James, 6 to 19, entered; may not all be in AW's hand.
Wood 136. STC 20741.

5533. Rastell, William. Booker, J., corr. and aug. *A table collected of the yeares.* London: R. B[adger] f. A. Hebb, 1639. 8°. Pp. [6], 100.
Some entries in text, from the death of Charles I, corrected, and AW wrote tables to the year 1669 on the blank p. [101].
Wood 18(3). STC 20743.

5534. Ratcliff. *A true narrative of the late dreadful fire which happened near Limus in Ratcliff [18 Sept.].* London: f. D. M., 1678. 4°. Pp. 8.
[MS.] Wood D. 28(24). Wing T2797 (rare) (Wing, '(not found)').

5535. Ratcliff Highway. *A strange and wonderfull relation of an old woman that was drowned at Ratcliff high-way . . . Whereunto is added, the old woman's dream.* London: f. W. Thackery, [1680?]. 8°. Pp. 16.
Wood 704(3). Wing S5876A (rare).

5536. Raue, Christian. *Sesqi-decuria epistolarum adoptivarum.* London: W. Wilson f. T. Jackson, 1648. 12°. Pp. 35 (A^{12},B^6).
Wood 33(2). Wing R315.

5537. Raue, Christian. *A discourse of the oriental tongues. . . . with a generall grammer.* London: W. Wilson f. T. Jackson, 1649. 12°. Pp. [8], 243, [2 large leaves, folded] [12] (2nd tp at p. 95). Calf with 3 fillets and with 2 vertical fillets.
Calf board, upper, inside, 6 page references, in pencil; flyleaf, upper, 1st, notes on similar books, not in AW's hand; pp. 63-86, 196-7, pencil lines in margins.
Wood 33(1). Wing R310.

5538. Ravaillac, François*. Trans. from French. *The terrible and deserved death of Francis Ravilliack.* London: [R. Blower a. E. Allde] f. W. Barley and J. Baylie, 1610. 4°. Pp. [2], 13.
Wood 365(3). STC 20755.

5539. Ravisius, Joannes. *Officina, vel potius naturae historia.* Basileae: ap. B. Westhemerum, 1538, Septembri. 8°. Pp. [12], 804, [10]. Parchment, with brown paper pasted over, and modern calf spine; pastedowns, printers' waste paper; flyleaves, parchment ms., Latin. Rebound by W, 2 Ap. [19]68.
Pastedown, upper, shelf-mark, 'E: 1: 7'. Flyleaf (former pastedown), upper, names (prob. not signatures), 'Lady Digbie' and 'James Pembroke'. Tp, three signatures: 'Liber Richardi King pretium 2^s', 'Thom: Widdowes' and A– – (rubbed out); phrase, 'Blessed are they . . . ', not in AW's hand; and scribbles; a2, 'V:Vis InteLLIgensiAM – [?]per LEge' (i.e., William Le[e]). Notes, passim to p. 203, prob. in King's hand. Pasteboard cover is made up of pressed pages of an earlier printed book; pastedowns, upper and lower, now disengaged from boards, are parchment ms. leaves.
Wood 38. BL.

5540. Rawlidge, Richard. *A monster late found out and discovered. Or the scourging of tiplers.* Amsterdam [i.e., London]: n.pub., 1628. 4°. Pp. [10], 30, [16].
Tp, 'B' (?).
[MS.] Wood D. 30(8). STC 20766.

5541. Raymond, Jo[hn]. *An itinerary contayning a voyage, made through Italy, in the yeare 1646, and 1647.* London: f. H. Moseley, 1648. 12°. Pp. [44], 284, [2]. Pasteboard (brown) with calf spine. 1st and last flyleaves, marbled paper.
Flyleaf, upper, 3rd^v, AW wrote the titles of 2 printed works in this vol., within guidelines made with red ink. Tp, he wrote 'Iuly iij: MDCLXI' and '2^s' (see LT 1.404-5).
Wood 153(1). Wing R415.

5542. Reading, John. *A speech made before the king's most excellent majesty Charles the second, on the shore where he landed at Dover [25 May].* [London]: n.pub., 1660. S.sh.
AW underlined the name of the author, in red ink; 3 corrections. ^{v}, scribble, 'Thomas'.
Wood 398(11). Wing R453 (rare).

5543. Reading, Nathaniel*. *The tryal of Nathaniel Reading esq; for attempting to stifle the kings evidence as to the horrid plot.* London: f. R. Pawlet, 1679. Fol. Pp. [3], 71.
Tp, AW wrote the price, '2^{s}0'. P. 48, note at printed 'M. Griffith' [sic], 'Edw. Griffyn was steward to Ralph Sheldon of Beoly in com. Wyg. But he left his service in Dec. 1677', and at 'Mr. Reading,' 'If Mr Reading had been suffered to go on he would have ript up all the false information that Bedlo had given in, purposly to invalidate the Testimonie against him – He began first with Mr Griffin, & would have gon on to Mr Sheldon, whom Bedlo (upon provocation) accused, as being appointed and allotted to be a Colonell of horse if the plot had gon on, but interrupted as yo[u] see by the Lord cheif justice.' P. 49, 'The Nephew named . . . . [blank] Gryffyn lives at Bickmarsh in com. Warw.'
Wood 424(14). Wing T2205.

5544. Recovery. *The recovery.* [London]: n.pub., [1682?]. S.sh.

Note by a later librarian of his copying of '1681 Dec. or Jan.' from a note at bottom edge, now lost.
Wood 417(81). Wing R654.

5545. Reformado. *The reformado, precisely charactered by a transformed church-warden, at a vestry, London.* [London]: n.pub., 1643. 4° (date cropped at bottom). A-B⁴,C² (C2 blank).
B1ᵛ-B2, some underscoring of words, in pencil, prob. not by AW.
Wood 612(12). Wing R736.

5546. Reformation. *The reformation. A satyr.* (London): (f. C. Corbet), (1684). S.sh. (r-v).
AW wrote the year, '1684', in pencil.
Wood 417(130). Wing R740.

5547. Register's Intelligence. *The register's intelligence, and advertisement-office.* [London]: The Office is kept at the Pea-hen, next door to the Shears, over against Somerset-house, [1680 ca.]. S.sh.
Wood 276a(290). Not in Wing. Not in N & S. Not in ESTCR.

5548. Reno, Jacobus de. *Tractatus brevis . . . in laudem musice artis et de ejus utilitatibus.* (Antwerpiae): (per me G. Leonis), (1491, 5 Julii). 8°. d-e⁸ (e8 blank)(2nd part, only).
In text, some underscoring; e8ᵛ notes, not in AW's hand; and flyleaf, lower, perhaps a former shelf-mark, P/1ᵐ, and, 'To my frende Robarte Jackson at Baldon, these li[bri] Primo Maii' (and initials, illeg.), not in AW's hand.
Wood 24(2). Proctor 9398.

5549. Reusnerus, Nicolas. *Aureolorum emblematum liber singularis.* Argentorati: ap. B. Jobinum, 1591. 8°.)(⁸,A-G⁸,H1-7. Rough calf with 3 fillets and stamp decoration (dragon) in corners (Ashm. binding); rebacked.
Flyleaf, upper, 2nd, list of 9 printed works in this vol., by an Ashm. librarian.
Wood 79(1) (now Arch. G. f. 2(1)). BL.

5550. Revius, Jacobus. *Historia pontificum Romanorum.* Amstelodami: ap. J. Janssonium, 1632. 8°. Pp. [8], 322, [30]. Parchment over pasteboard.
Wood 249. BL.

5551. Reynard*. *The most pleasant history of Reynard the fox.* [London]: f. J. Conyers, sold J. Blare, [1688 ca.]. 8°. Pp. 23, [1].
Tp, a librarian wrote, '(c. 1688.)', in pencil.
Wood 259(3). Wing M2914A (rare) (Wing, [1700?]).

5552. Reynell, Edward. *An advice against libertinism.* London: f. A. Roper, 1659. 12°. Pp. [2], 113.
Tp, AW underscored the name of the author, in red ink. Bsm.
Wood 788(2). Wing R1216.

5553. Reynolds, Edward. Norwich, bp. of. *A treatise of the passions and faculties of the soule of man.* London: f. H. Cripps a. E. Farnham, 1658. 4°. Pp. [18], 553. Calf with 2 fillets; rebacked.
Flyleaf, upper, scribble, 'Gwiria gair . . . '(?, not in AW's hand). Bsms. pp. 5, 192 marks in margin and a word, prob. not by AW.
Wood 654b. Wing R1298.

5554. Reynolds, John. *Vox coeli, or, newes from heaven. Of a consultation there held by . . . king Hen. 8. [et al.] . . . wherein Spaines ambition and treacheries . . . are unmaskd . . . by S. R. N. I.* Elesium [sic, i.e., London]: [N. Jones], 1624. 4°. Pp. [20], 60.
Flyleaf, upperᵛ, scribble, 'John'. Tp, bsm.
Wood 511(12). STC 20946.8.

5555. Reynolds, John. *A discourse upon prodigious abstinence: occasioned by the twelve months fasting of Martha Taylor.* London: R. W. f. N. Simmons a. f. D. Newman, 1669. 4°. Pp. [7], 37.
On this publ., see note at T. Robins, Wood 246(7), item 5586.
[MS.] Wood B. 35(26). Wing R1314.

5556. [Reynolds, John]. *Perfet [sic] directions for all English gold.* London: N. Okes f. B. Fisher, 16[31] (cropped). 8°. A-C⁸.
Wood 21(4). STC 20948.

5557. Rhauus, Georgius, and Johannes Galliculus. *Enchiridion utriusque musicae practicae a Geor-*

gio Rhauuo congestum. Isagoge Johannis Galliculi de cantus compositione. (Lipsiae): (ex aed. V. Schuman), (1520, Maio). 8°. a⁸,b-m⁴; a⁸,b-n⁴; A⁸-E⁴ (E4 blank) (2nd tp at 2nd a1; 3rd tp at A1). Calf over wood boards, blind-stamped (2 saints on each side), two clasps.
Flyleaf, upper, 'Ant: Wood.', lined out, and '4ᵈ'; musical score, not in AW's hand. Tp, '6ᵈ'. Some underscoring and notes in text, in red ink, not in AW's usual manner. Robarte Jackson was the former owner, see Wood 24(2), item 5548.
Wood 24(1). BL.

5558. Ribadeneira, Pedro de. Schottus, Andreas, trans. *Vita P. Jacobi Laynis secundi societatis Jesu generalis Alphonsi item Salmeronis.* Coloniae Agrippinae: sumpt. A. Mylii Birckmanni, 1604. [16], 259, [1]. Parchment.
Tp, bsm. Text, some notes and marks in margin, not by AW.
Wood 281. BL.

5559. Rich, Barnaby. *Allarme to England, foreshewing what perilles are procured, where the people live without regarde of martiall lawe.* (London): (C. Barker), 1578. 4°. Pp. *-**⁴,A-I⁴,K².
Wood 635(5). STC 20978.

5560. Rich, Barnaby. *A path-way to military practise. . . . Whereunto is annexed a kalender of the imbattelinge of men.* London: J. Charlewood f. R. Walley, 1587. 4°. A-L⁴. Parchment; flyleaves, 1st upper and last lower, parchment ms., Latin.
Flyleaf, upper, 8 figures totaling '7 - 10'; ᵛ, elaborate notes on warfare, English and Latin, not by AW. Tp, a reference to a 1626 edition by Norton and Bill, not by AW. B3, a correction. Flyleaves, lower, 2-8, elaborate notes, English and Latin, on the Roman army, not by AW.
[MS.] Wood C. 23. STC 20995.

5561. Rich, Barnaby. *A souldiers wishe to Britons welfare.* London: [T. Creede] f. J. Chorlton, 1604. 4°. Pp. [6], 76.
Flyleaf, upper, AW wrote, 'See bundle of (soldiers & wars)'.
Wood 635(6). STC 21000 (rare).

5562. Rich, Barnaby. *A new description of Ireland.* London: [W. Jaggard] f. T. Adams, 1610. 4°. Pp. [16], 116. Pasteboard (blue) with parchment spine.
Pastedown, upper, note on binding, partially covered by paper, '8 Nov. 1692'. Loose leaf pasted on flyleaf, 1stᵛ; ʳ of loose leaf, AW wrote notes on 'Barnabe Riche', 2 books published by Rich, 'Allarme to England' 1578 (Wood 635(5)), and 'A pathway to military practice' 1587 ([MS.] Wood C. 23), and brief summaries, followed by some biographical details, 'Barnab. Riche soldier, servant to the right honorable Sʳ Christop. Hatton Kt', and 'Twenty four yeares before 1587 Barn. Riche undertook armes & served at Newhaven under Ambrose Earl of Warwick; (a father alwaies to soldiers) since which time Riche had either practiced by experience, seen by example, or gathered by History concerning Martiality', and ᵛ, 'Barn. Rich boasted in a book by him written, that it was the 36 book that he had wrot – See The Surfeit to A. B. C. – Lond 1656 Oct. or Nv. p. 55' (by P. King, 1656; Wood 739(3), item 3974). 2ndᵛ, AW wrote the titles of 4 printed works in this vol., written within guidelines made with red ink.
Wood 505(1). STC 20992.

5563. Rich, Barnaby. *A true and a kinde excuse, written in defence of that booke, intituled a newe description of Irelande.* London: [T. Dawson] f. T. Adams, 1612. 4°. Ff. [3], 25.
Tp, bsm.
Wood 505(2). STC 21003.

5564. Rich, Barnaby. *The Irish hubbub, or, the English hue and crie.* London: f. J. Marriot, 1619. 4°. Pp. [6], 61.
Tp, bsm.
Wood 505(3). STC 20990.

5565. Rich, Jeremiah. *Semigraphy: or, arts rarity.* London: J. G., sold N. Brook, 1654. 8°. Pp. [13], 39. Missing in 1837.
Wood 729(2). Wing R1351. *BL, Hunt.*

5566. Rich, Robert. Warwick, earl of. *The valiant resolution of the sea-men, listed under the commaund of the earle of Warwicke.* London: f. T. Hanson, 1642, 16 Nov. 4°. A⁴.
Tp, AW lined out the former no., 'E9' (a shelf-mark?), underscored the name, 'Lord Robert' in a 2ndary t, and wrote the month, 'Nov.'

Wood 375(22). Wing V38.

5567. Rich, Robert. Warwick, earl of. *A letter sent from . . . Robert earl of Warwick: to . . . the speaker . . . concerning . . . the siege, of Lyme.* [London]: R. Best, 1644, 18 June. 4°. Pp. 8.
Wood 377(13). Wing W1006.

5568. Richard Plantagenet*. York, duke of. *An impartial account of Richard duke of York's treasons, . . . to which is added the true picture of a popish successor.* London: f. A. Banks, 1682. Fol. Pp. [2], 21.
Wood 660c(30). Wing I64.

5569. Richard, Thomas. *May the second, 1642. The warlike, noble and prosperous proceedings of the protestant army in, Ireland. Being the true copy of a letter.* London: f. J. Wright, 1642. 4°. A⁴.
Tp, below, '51'.
Wood 508(12). Wing R1369.

5570. R[ichards], W[illiam]. *Wallography; or the Britton describ'd.* London: f. O. Blagrave, 1682. 8°. Pp. [xiv], 127.
Flyleaf, upper, AW wrote, 'Will. Richards of Trin. Coll. the authour–' and '9ᵈ – to H. Clement Feb. 1681[2]. Full of Drollery & Roguery'. LT 3.6.
Wood 155(4). Wing R1375C.

5571. Richardson, John. *In honour of Abingdon or on the seaventh day of Septembers solemnization.* [Oxford]: n.pub., 1641. 4°. A⁴.
Tp, 3-4 numbers (?). LT 1.455.
Wood 537(14b). Wing R1387. Madan 1002.

5572. [Richardson, Samuel]. *Of the torments of hell. The foundation and pillars thereof discovered, searched, shaken and removed.* London: n.pub., 1658. 12°. Pp. [10], 194. Pasteboard (blue) with parchment spine. 1st upper and last lower flyleaves, marbled paper.
Flyleaf, upper, 3rdᵛ, AW wrote the titles of 2 printed works in this vol., within guidelines made with red ink, and below, 'The Torments of Hell was answer'd by Joh. Brandon. [Wing B4251, in 1678] I have been informed that the Torments of Hell was written by one Sam. Richardson an Anabapt. [/] qu[aere] of Mʳ All' (Allam).
Wood 788(1). Wing R1411.

5573. Richelieu, Armand Jean du Plessis*, cardinal. *A synopsis, or contract view, of the life of John Armand, cardinall of Richlieu, . . . to bee engraven on his tombe. First written in Latine, and now . . . into English.* [London]: n.pub., 1643. 4°. Pp. [2], 6.
Flyleaf, upper, waste paper, a Latin examination topic, 'An res singularii addat aliquid .. naturam universalem 8', not in AW's hand. Tp, 'I have this Card. Life elswhere in 8°' (i.e., Wood 307(2), item 2367).
Wood 535(8). Wing S6387 ('O' not recorded in Wing).

5574. Ricraft, Josiah. *A survey of Englands champions.* London: R. Austin, sold J. H., 1647. 8°. Pp. [6], 128 (misnumbering). Pasteboard (grey) with parchment spine. 1st and last flyleaves, marbled paper.
Flyleaves, upper, 2ndᵛ and 3rd, AW wrote the names of 47 persons mentioned in text and p. nos. of text. Pp. 72-83, AW wrote in margins names of those mentioned in text; pp. 85-115, the years of the chronology in the text and a correction; and pp. 122-3, corrections of numbers.
Wood 304(1). Wing R1436.

5575. R[id], S[amuel]. *Martin Mark-all, beadle of Bridewell.* London: [E. Allde] f. J. Budge, a. R. Bonian, 1610. 4°. ¶²,A2-4,B-G⁴ (wanting A1).
Wood 371(4). STC 21028.5.

5576. Rider, John. Holyoke, Francis, ed. *Riders dictionarie corrected and augmented.* London: A. Islip, 1606. 4° (imperfect). 1-3,A-4D⁸, 4E1-6. Calf, speckled, with 2 gold-stamp fillets; rebound.
Pastedown, upper (a former flyleaf), is covered with scribbling by AW and former owners, e.g., 'Anthony Wood his booke [/] amen July: 25: 1645', 'John Jones his book 173–' (?), 'Greenbarrow' (4 times), 'Robert Holman: amen. 1643' and, 'Curiosities of the College', etc. Tp, more scribbles, including 'Edward Wood his bok' and 'Robert', 3 times, and several notes, too faint to be read. Text, schoolboy scribbles, various kinds of marks, signatures (2G8ᵛ, Edward and Anthony Wood), and clichès, in various hands. Pastedown, lower, scribbles, and signatures of Edward and Anthony Wood. LT 1.48.
Wood 308. STC 21032.

5577. Ridley, Nicholas. *Certen godly, learned, and comfortable conferences, betwene Nicolas Rydley*

. . . and M. Hughe Latymer. Whereunto is added. A treatise agayst transubstantiation. [Emden] or [Strassburg] or London: [heirs of W. Rihel] or J. Awdeley, 1556 or 1574 (14 Oct.). 8°.
Missing. MS. Wood E. 2(70), p. 9. Ed. not identified.
MS. Wood E. 2(70), p. 9. STC 21247.3 to 21050.

5578. Ridley, Thomas. G[regory], J[ohn], ed. *A view of the civile and ecclesiasticall law.* Oxford: W. Hall f. E. Forrest, 1662. 8°. 3rd ed. Pp. [12], 397, [32]. Pasteboard (blue) with parchment spine. 1st upper flyleaf, remnant of marbled paper, and last lower flyleaf, marbled paper.
AO 3.205.
Wood 676. Wing R1454A. Madan 2606.

5579. Ringhieri, Innocenzio. Louveau, Jean, trans. *Dialogue de la vie et de la mort.* Lyon: R. Granjon, 1558. 8°. 2nd ed. A-L⁸. Parchment.
Wood 853. BL. BL (1557).

5580. Ritschel, George. *Dissertatio de ceremoniis Ecclesiae Anglicanae.* London: excud. R. White, impen. J. Nevill, 1661. 8°. Pp. [14], 128. Calf with 2 fillets and stamp decoration inside corners; rebacked.
Wood 808. Wing R1544.

5581. Rively, Benedict. *A sermon preach'd . . . at the funeral of . . . Edward lord bishop of Norwich [28 July 1676; on Job 30.23].* London: f. S. Lowndes a. W. Oliver in Norwich, 1677. 4°. Pp. [3], 34.
Tp, AW underscored 'Riveley' (on Edward Reynolds, bp., AO 3.1083ff.).
Wood 634(2). Wing R1548.

5582. Rivers, Marcellus, and Oxenbridg Foyle. *Englands slavery, or Barbados merchandize; represented in a petition to the high and honourable court of parliament.* London: n.pub., 1659. 8°. Pp. 23. Calf with 3 fillets and 2nd vertical line of 3 fillets, stamp decoration inside corners (dragons) (Ashm. binding). Flyleaf, upper, 2nd, the titles of 7 printed works in this vol. by an Ashm. librarian (same hand in Wood 276a). Below, and on tp, signature of John Jones.
Wood 666(1) (not in Bodl. CD cat.). Wing R1553 (one) ('O' not recorded in Wing).

5583. Roberts, Alexander. *A treatise of witchcraft. . . . With a true narration of the witchcrafts which Mary Smith . . . did practise.* London: N. O[kes] f. S. Man, 1616. 4°. Pp. [8], 80.
Tp, bsm.
[MS.] Wood B. 21(3). STC 21075.

5584. Roberts, Francis. *A communicant instructed: or, practical directions for worthy receiving of the lords-supper.* London: T. R. a. E. M. f. G. Calvert, 1653. 8°. 2nd ed. Pp. [22], a foldout, 243, [13] (2 pp. books sold by Calvert). Calf with 2 fillets and a vertical line of 2 fillets.
Pastedown, upper, AW wrote 'Here wants the picture'. Tp, AW underscored the name of the author in red ink. Passim, some short horizontal lines in margins, not in AW's manner.
Wood 861. Wing R1590.

5585. Robertus, Prior of Shrewsbury. Falconer, John, trans. *The admirable life of saint Wenefride virgin, martyr, abbesse.* [St. Omer]: [English College Press], 1635. 8°. Pp. [33], 275, [11]. Parchment.
Flyleaf, upper, 4thᵛ, 'Anthony à Wood. This book was given to me by Edw. Griffin of Bickmarsh in Warwickshire esq. August an. 1675', 'Robertus Salopiensis ord. s. Bened. monachus qui clar. 1140. temp. Steph. Regis hunc librum Lat. scripsit.', 'The Life of S. Winnefride was translated by Will. Caxton - temp H. 7. pr. in fol.' LT 2.342.
Wood 285. STC 21102. ARCR 2.268.

5586. Robins, T[homas]. *New news from Darby-shire. Or the wonder of wonders.* London: f. T. P[assinger], 1668. 8°. Pp. 16.
Flyleaf, upperᵛ, note by later writer: 'See a discourse on this Fasting Girl in the 4ᵗᵒ Vol. in this Room mark'd B.35. tis by J. Reynolds, offerd to the Rˡ Society; where the acct of the cause is somewhat different. See there, p. 33. He says, T. Robins, B. of D. signifies Ballad maker of Derby See Harl. Cat. of Pamph. 59' (i.e., by J. Reynolds, [MS.] Wood B. 35(26), item 5555). Tp, 'AW 1668'. LT 2.148.
Wood 246(7). Wing R1657 (two) (Wing, News from).

5587. Robins, Thomas. *The arraigning & indicting of sir John Barleycorn.* London: f. T. Passenger, 1675 or [1680?]. 8°. Pp. 21, [3].
Missing in 1837. 'The Arraining [sic] & indicting Sʳ John Barly Corn –' in the Whiteside cat. Ed. not identified.

Wood 66(11). Wing R1648 (two) or R1648A (rare). CM, *Hunt*, and CM.

5588. Robinson, Henry. *Certain proposalls in order to the peoples freedome and accommodation . . . With the advancement of trade and navigation*. London: M. Simmons, 1652. 4°. Pp. [2], 27.
Wood 630(11). Wing R1670.

5589. Robinson, Henry. *Certaine proposals in order to a new modelling of the lawes, and law-proceedings, for . . . justice*. London: M. Simmons, 1653. 4°. Pp. [2], 16, 26.
Tp, at author's name, 'and' (?), not in AW's hand.
Wood 630(10). Wing R1669.

5590. Robinson, Thomas. *The anatomie of the English nunnery at Lisbon in Portugall. Dissected . . . by . . . a yonger brother of the couent [sic]*. [London]: [G. Eld,] sould R. Milbourne a. P. Stephens, 1623. 4°. Pp. [7], 32.
[MS.] Wood D. 24(3). STC 21124.

5591. Robinson, William. *Stafford-shires misery, set forth in a true relation*. London: G. Dexter, 1643, 20 July. 4°. Pp. [2], 8.
Tp, AW altered one former no., '19' and lined out a 2nd, '18'.
Wood 376(21). Wing R1723.

5592. Rodrigues de Sá e Menezes, João. Milton, John, by (?). *Panegyrici Cromwello scripti. Unus à legato Portugallici regis. Alter à quodam Jesuita*. [Leiden]: n.pub., 1654. 4°. Pp. 46. Pasteboard (blue) with parchment spine. 1st upper and last lower flyleaves, marbled paper.
Flyleaf, upper, 'Evans Thomas Omn. Anim: Coll: Sub Custos Musai 1793.' (apparently a reader in the Ashmolean); ᵛ, AW wrote the titles of 7 printed works in this vol., within guidelines made with red chalk.
Tp, drawing, a harp. Pp. 9, 21, mark in margin.
Wood 383(1). BL.

5593. R[ogers], J[ohn]. *The displaying of an horrible secte of . . . heretiques, naming themselves the Familie of Love, with the lives of their authours*. London: [H. Middleton] f. G. Bishop, [1578]. 8°. Newely set foorth. A-I⁸,K1-3.
Tp, note cropped at bottom. C1, symbols in margin (?, cropped). Acquired 29 Ap. 1658 out of G. Langbaine's study, LT 1.247-8.
Wood 795(4). STC 21181.5.

5594. R[ogers], J[ohn]. *Mr. Pryn's good old cause stated and stunted 10. years ago*. London: J. C. f. L. Chapman, 1659. 4°. Pp. [2], 20.
P. 20, AW wrote the author's name after initials, I. R'ogers'.
Wood 613(18). Wing R1812.

5595. Rogers, Lydia. *A more exact relation of the most lamentable and horrid contract which Lydia Rogers . . . made with the divel . . . To which is added a true narration of a weaver*. [London]: f. T. Vere a. W. Gilbertson, 1658. 8°. Pp. [3], 12.
Wood 707(10). Not in Wing. Not in ESTCR.

5596. [Rogers, Thomas]. *Miles Christianus or a just apologie of all necessarie writings and writers, . . . which . . . build up the church of Christ in this age and . . . are unjustly depraved [in A shorte catechisme, by M. Mosse]*. London: J. Wolfe, 1590. 4°. Pp. [4], 36 (tp is mutilated).
Wood 619(6). STC 21238.

5597. [Rogers, Thomas]. *Leycesters ghost*. [London]: n.pub., 1641. 4°. Pp. [2], 35.
See note at R. Persons (1641), Wood 535(2a), item 5199.
Wood 535(2b). Wing R1837A ('O' not recorded in Wing).

5598. Rohan, Henri, duc de; Hunt, Henry, trans. *A treatise of the interest of the princes and states of Christendome*. London: R. Hodgkinsonne, 1641. 12°. Pp. [24], 146, [4]. Parchment.
Tp, 'pretium – 1ˢ·' (?), prob. not by in AW.
Wood 452. Wing R1868.

5599. Rolph, Edmond. *The case of major Edmond Rolph [23 Aug.]*. [London]: n.pub., [1648]. S.sh.
Wood 276a(106). Wing R1890.

5600. Rome. *Guida angelica perpetua per visitar le chiese che sono dentro e fuori di Roma . . . nei giorni*

delle feste. Roma: per R. Alberto Tani, 1668. 12°. Pp. 96 (pp. 49-53 unopened). Parchment.
Tp, 'Ant. à Wood ex dono Radulphi Sheldon de Beoly, Arm. 25 Mar. 1676.-'. LT 2.341.
Wood 771. Not in BL.

5601. Rome's Wickedness. *Romes wickednes. Or, wicked Rome, with her seven deadly sins [signed Anonymus]*. London: A. M[athewes] f. J. Wright, the younger, 1637. 8°. Pp. [4], 39.
Tp, AW wrote 'An edition of this in 8° came out in 1624' (STC 21302a; and 1623, STC 21302). Bsm.
Wood 876(3). STC 21303 (two).

5602. Roos, John Manners. Rutland, 8th duke of. *A true and perfect copy of the lord Roos his answer to the marquesse of Dorchester's letter [25 Feb. 1659]*. [London]: n.pub., [1660]. S.sh.
To 'Roos', AW added 'John Lord'; ᵛ, Roos's name.
Wood 276a(251). Wing R2400.

5603. Rosamond*. *The life and death of Rosamond, king Henry the seconds concubine*. [London]: f. W. Thackeray, a. T. Passenger, [1686-88]. 8°. A⁸,B⁴.
Tp, AW wrote, 'Bought at Oxon. 1688'.
Wood 254(3). Wing L2009B (rare).

5604. Rosamond of Scotland*. *The lovers quarrel: or Cupids triumph: being the . . . history of fair Rosamond of Scotland*. London: f. F. Coles, T. Vere, J. Wright, a. J. Clarke, 1677. 8°. A⁸,B⁴. Pasteboard (grey) with parchment spine; rebound.
Flyleaves, upper, 1stᵛ and 2nd, AW wrote the titles of 15 printed works in this vol., within guidelines made with red ink (1-15 in Arabic numbers; the items in vol. are numbered in Roman numerals (prob. not by AW)). 11 of these are known to exist only in the Bodl. and 4 are known to exist in the Bodl. and at one other location. See Plate III. Tp, '4' (? a scribble).
Wood 259(1). Wing L3257B (rare).

5605. Rosewell, Walter. *The serpents subtilty discovered, or a true relation of what passed in the cathedrall church of Rochester between divers ministers and Richard Coppin*. London: A. M. f. J. Cranford, 1656. 4°. Pp. [12], 16.
Tp, bsm.
Wood 647(22). Wing R1943.

5606. Ross, Alexander. *Som animadversions . . . upon sʳ Walter Raleigh's historie*. London: W. Du-gard f. R. Royston, [1650]. 12°. Pp. [10], 72.
P. 1, correction.
Wood 225(2). Wing R1981.

5607. Ross, John. *Tangers rescue; or a relation of the late memorable passages at Tanger*. London: f. H. Hills, 1681. 4°. Pp. [4], 36.
Wood 386(16). Wing R1988.

5608. Rosseter, Edward*. *An impartiall and true relation of the great victory obtained . . . by the conjoyned forces of Lincolne, Nottingham, Lecester, Derby, and Rutland, under . . . col. Edw. Rosseter*. London: E. Griffin, 1648, 12 July. 4°. [A]⁴.
Tp, AW wrote after the date, 'Jul. 5'.
Wood 502(36). Wing I80A.

5609. Rossington, James. *To the right honourable the house of commons assembled in parliament, the humble petition*. [London]: n.pub., [1675]. S.sh.
AW wrote, 'This I found in Dʳ Lowers privy house 24. May 1675 in Bow Street, Lond.' AW was in London, 19-28 May, see LT 2.314.
Wood 276a(173). Wing R1995A (rare).

5610. [Rosso, G. Raviglio]. [Contile, Luca, ed.]. *Historia delle cose occorse nel regno d'Inghilterra, in materia del duca di Notomberlan dopo la morte di Odoardo VI*. Venetia: nell' Academia Venetiana, 1558. 8°. Pp. 68.
Wood 84(3). BL.

5611. Rother, M. E. *Memoriam vesperiarum et comitiorum in theatro Oxoniensi . . . 6, 7, & 9. Jul: amico suo dn. Paulo Brand . . . 12. Aug*. Oxonii: n.pub., [1677]. S.sh.
AW wrote the year, '1677' in pencil. See Madan and LT 2.378.
Wood 276a(407). Wing R1998 (rare). Madan 3160.

5612. Rous, Francis. *A speech made before the lords in the upper house . . . [16 March] Against dr. Cossens, . . . upon the complaint of mr. Peter Smart.* London: f. J. Wright junior, 1641. 4°. Pp. [2], 6. Tp, AW underscored the name of the author, in red ink. Bsm. [MS.] Wood D. 31(26). Wing R2028.

5613. Rouse, Francis. *Archaeologiae Atticae libri tres.* ?: ?, 1637-1685. Pp.? Missing. MS. Wood E. 2(70), p. 48, 'Archeologiae atticae'. Ed. not identified. MS. Wood E. 2(70), p. 48. STC 21350 and Wing R2032-2041.

5614. Rouse, J[ohn]. *Rouse his case, . . . written with his own hand in Newgate.* London: J. Grantham, by the order of the Widdow Rouse, 1683. Fol. Pp. [2], 16. On blank sheet before tp, 'inter 2 & 3', in pencil; placed finally between items 4 and 6. Tp, AW wrote, '5ᵈ'; p. 13, AW identified Mrs. Rouse's 'good Father', 'Hen. Cornish sometime Canon of ch. ch. now a Nonconformist minister—'. Wood 428(5). Wing R2047.

5615. Row, William. *The fatal blow given to the earle of Newcastles armie, by the Scots.* [London]: A. Coe, 1644. 4°. Pp. [8]. Pp. 4-5, nonsense scribbles, not by AW. Wood 377(5). Wing R2061 (two).

5616. Rowe, Matthew. *An exact and full relation of the great victory . . . at Dungons-hill in Ireland, . . . by . . . Michael Jones [8 Aug.].* London: f. E. Husband, 1647, 19 Aug. 4°. Pp. 16. Tp, AW lined out a former no., '18', and below, wrote, 'If [?] Dup. –'. Dupl. at Wood 612(49). Wood 509(22). Wing R2068.

5617. Rowe, Matthew. *An exact and full relation of the great victory . . . at Dungons-hill in Ireland, . . . by . . . Michael Jones [8 Aug.].* London: f. E. Husband, 1647, 19 Aug. 4°. Pp. 16. Tp, no. 3 in a former bundle. AW wrote 'Dupl', in pencil. Dupl. at Wood 509(22). Wood 612(49). Wing R2068.

5618. Rowland, David, trans. *A comfortable ayde for schollers, full of variety of sentences [from Grifoni, Giovanni Andrea, Specchio].* London: T. Marshe, 1578. 8°. Pp. [8], 143, [16]. Missing. MS. Wood E. 2(70), p. 16, 'Lond. 1578 – 8°. parch. cover'. BL copy is cropped at top. MS. Wood E. 2(70), p. 16. STC 21357 (rare, *BL*).

5619. Rowlands, Richard. [Verstegan, Richard, alternate name]. *[The post of the world. Wherein is contayned the antiquities and original of the most famous cities in Europe]. (The post for diuers partes of the world).* London: published by R. Rowlands. Imprinted T. East, 1576. 4°. Pp. [8], 112 (wanting the almanack at the beginning). Flyleaf, upperᵛ, AW wrote, 'One Rich. Rowland was a poore scholar under Mʳ Tho. Bernard canon of ch. ch. in Oxon, an. 1564'. P. 112, details of death and burial after printed entry of Queen Elizabeth, not by AW: 'died the 24 of March 1602[3] buried at Westminster the 28 of Aprill 1603 being the thursday in Easter weeke'. Wood 142(4). STC 21360.

5620. Rowlands, Richard. [Verstegan, Richard, alternate name]. *A restitution of decayed intelligence: in antiquities. Concerning the . . . English nation, . . . by R. V.* Antwerp: R. Bruney, sold J. Norton a. J. Bill, London, 1605. 4°. Pp. [24], 338, [13] (wanting sig. Y⁸, pp. 169-176). Parchment with clasp holes. Parchment, upper, inside, 'Henry Foulis booke: July 16: 1651 Praetium M [?] oᵈ' pasted over with AW's book-plate, which itself is badly mutilated (7 x 9 cm.; most of fringe decoration, acorns and stems, survives, along with a portion of the bottom line, 'Book. 16.'; see Index, 'Wood, A., bookplate'). Pastedown, upper, torn out. Tp, AW wrote, 'Another Edit. of this at Lond. 1653. in a Larg oct[avo] but not well corrected'. Tpᵛ, note by Foulis, 'Henricus si addis Foulis sit possessor honestus / Hujus codiculi: nam mihi Βυρσα dedit.' with date and price; below, signature of E J LeOgle (?). In intro. AW numbered pp. 1, 3 and 5. Text, sporadic annotation: brief note (p. 23, not by AW), underscoring and lines and marks (p. 81, hand) in margins. 2nd p. 13ᵛ, AW wrote, 'Harlots a sect in K. Hen. III. time. vid. Fox. Acts. Mon. tom. 1. pag. 435.' Pastedown, lower, inside, 18 lines of verse, badly mutilated, not in AW's hand. LT 2.180. Wood 598. STC 21361.

5621. R[owlands], Samuel. *The letting of humours blood in the head-vaine.* London: W. White f. W. F[erbrand], 1600. 8°. A-E⁸,F1-3. P. nos., 1-85, written in pencil, not by AW.

Wood 84(11). STC 21393.

5622. Rowlands, Samuel. *The famous history of Guy earle of Warwick*. London: J. Bell f. T. Vere, 1649. 4°. A-Q⁴.
Flyleaf, upper, 2nd^v, AW wrote, 'One Joh. Lane wrot an heroick poem called Guy of Warwick'.
Wood 321(3). Wing R2084 (rare).

5623. R[owlands], S[amuel]. *Doctor Merry-man: or nothing but mirth*. London: E. Crowch, f. F. Coles, T. Vere, a. J. Wright, 1671. 4°. A-C⁴. Pasteboard (blue) with parchment spine.
Flyleaf, upper, simple division and multiplication figures, prob. not by AW; ^{v}, AW wrote the titles of 8 printed works in this vol., within guidelines made with red ink, and concluding with: 'Memorandum that I have two volumes in fol. endorsed, <u>Poems, Songs, Elegies, several things in prose</u> &c. The first vol. contains 132 several things, & the second 183, among which also are Ballads [i.e., Wood 416-7]. But those being all printed in folio sheets & papers, cannot be bound with these following [i.e., Wood 382] – Nor a thick octavo book endorsed <u>Songs, Drollerie</u>, containing 7 seve[r]all octavo books bound together – [i.e., Wood 326]' (LT 1.18). 1st item, each 8° leaf is pasted on a 4° template. B3^v, in margin, 'Stolen from Chaucer [and signed] Wms.', in red chalk, possibly by AW.
Wood 382(1). Wing R2082 (rare).

5624. Rowney, Thomas. *The case of Thomas Rowney gent. executor of Edward Twyford*. [London?]: n.pub., [1680]. S.sh.
^{v}, note, cropped, 'Mr Ro– Case', not in AW's hand.
Wood 276b(69). Wing C1188A (two).

5625. Roy, William, and William Barlow. O., N., ed. *Rede me and be nott wrothe for I saye no thynge but trothe [a satire in verse on T. Wolsey]*. [Strassburg]: [J. Schott], [1528]. 8°. A-I⁸. Calf with 4 fillets; backing, upper, printer's waste paper (Psalms in Eng.).
Pastedown, upper, 1st, shelf-mark, 'C: l: Lib: 7'; 2nd^v, AW wrote the titles of 7 printed works (really 8, including the fragment, Stoughton (1604), at 774(3b), item 6058) in this vol., 'Libri in hoc volumine'. Tp, signature of an earlier owner, Hum Dy[son], cropped. Text, scribbles, a note, a drawing and signatures, e.g., Thomas –, most are cropped and none are by AW.
Wood 774(1). STC 1462.7.

5626. Royal College of Physicians. *Certain necessary directions, as well for the cure of the plague as for preventing the infection*. Oxford: W. Hall f. R. Davis, 1665. 4°. Rpt. Pp. [8], 24.
Wood 498(9). Wing C1709. Madan 2714.

5627. Royal College of Physicians. *An exact account of all who are the present members of the kings college of physicians*. Londgn [sic]: f. H. Brome, 1673. S.sh.
AW made 2 corrections of names and 6 marks in margins beside names and added 2 pieces of information.
Wood 276a(301). Wing E3560 (rare).

5628. Royal College of Physicians. *An exact account of all who are the present members of the king's college of physicians*. London: n.pub., 1676. S.sh.
Wood 276a(302). Wing E3561 (two).

5629. Royal College of Physicians. *The names of the fellows of the king's college of physicians*. London: n.pub., 1683. S.sh.
Lines in margins at 19 names; an underscoring. Dupl. at Wood 276b(42).
Wood 276a(303). Wing N132 (two).

5630. Royal College of Physicians. *The names of the fellows of the king's college of physicians*. London: n.pub., 1683. S.sh.
Dupl. at Wood 276a(303).
Wood 276b(42). Wing N132 (two).

5631. Royal College of Physicians. *The case of the college of physicians, London [concerning a proposed new charter]*. [London]: n.pub., [1688?]. Fol. Pp. 2 (2 leaves).
Wood 657(69). Wing C1042A.

5632. Royal College of Physicians. *An historical account of proceedings betwixt the college of physicians and surgeons, since their incorporation*. [London?]: n.pub., [1690?]. Fol. Pp. 8.
Wood 657(72). Wing H2095.

5633. Royal College of Physicians. *The physicians reply to the surgeons answer.* [London?]: n.pub., [1690]. Fol. Pp. 4.
Wood 657(71). Wing P2147aA ('O' not recorded in Wing).

5634. Royal College of Physicians. *The oath taken by the censors, who are the examiners of the college, . . . upon . . . their admission [Followed by] The statute concerning the admission.* [London]: n.pub., [1695]. S.sh.
This should be dated 1695 or earlier, since it was in AW's possession.
Wood 657(68). Wing O75D (two) (Wing, [1700]).

5635. Royal College of Physicians, and Charles Goodall. *The royal college of chysicians of London founded and established by law; as appears by letters' patents, acts of parliament, . . . and an historical account of the college's proceedings against empiricks.* London: M. Flesher f. W. Kettilby, 1684. 4°. Pp. [11], 1-288, [52], 305-472, [11]. 2 tpp. Calf with 2 fillets, stamp decoration inside corners (tulip).
Tp, bsms.
Wood 495. Wing G1091.

5636. Royal Game. *The royal game of ombre.* London: f. T. Palmer, 1665. 8°. Pp. [1], 13, [1].
Missing in 1837; in Whiteside cat., 'Ombre, London 1665'.
Wood 440(2). Wing R2130B (rare). *BL.*

5637. Royal Martyrs. *Royal martyrs: or, a list of the lords, knights, . . . that were slain in the late wars, . . . As also of those executed.* London: T. Newcomb, 1660. S.sh.
Some 'X' marks after names; in margin below, the names of 2 additional martyrs, not in AW's hand.
Wood 503(34). Wing R2134.

5638. Royal Society. '*A moneo for John Aubray – [illeg.] present at the election of officers for the Royal Society*'. N.p.: n.pub., n.d. S.sh.
Missing in 1939. T is from the 1717 list.
Wood 276a(298). Not identified.

5639. Royal Society. *A list of the fellows of the Royal Society, . . . ten are to be chosen . . . November 30th 1663.* [London]: n.pub., [1663]. S.sh.
Wood 276a(293). Wing L2423.

5640. Royal Society. *A list of the Royal Society. His sacred majesty king Charles II. Founder . . . ten are to be chosen . . . November 30th 1667.* London: f. J. Martyn, 1667. S.sh.
Wood 276a(294). Wing L2425 (two).

5641. Royal Society. *A brief vindication of the Royal Society: from the late invectives and mis- representations of mr. Henry Stubbe.* London: f. J. Martin, 1670. 4°. Pp. [2], 10.
LT 1.354.
Wood 640(4). Wing B4656A.

5642. Royal Society. *A list of the Royal Society. His sacred majesty king Charles II. Founder . . . ten are to be chosen . . . November 30th 1674.* London: f. J. Martyn, 1674. S.sh.
'Sr Jonas Moore K^t was admitted Decemb: . . . . 1674', not by AW.
Wood 276a(295). Wing L2427 (two).

5643. Royal Society. *A list of the Royal Society. . . . ten are to be chosen . . . the first of December, 1690.* London: T. James, 1691. S.sh.
Wood 276a(296). Wing L2439.

5644. Royal Society. *A list of the Royal Society . . . ten are to be chosen . . . the first of December, 1691.* [London]: n.pub., 1692. S.sh.
Missing in 1939. T is from 1717 list.
Wood 276a(297). Wing L2439A (rare). BL (not located).

5645. Royal Society. *A list of the Royal Society. . . . Ten are to be chosen . . . . the thirtieth of November, 1693.* London: T. James, 1694. S.sh.
AW wrote 2 'q[uaere]' notes and underscored 'M. D.' after Robert Hook and Robert Pitt. ^{v}, 'For Mr Anthony Wood. To be delivered to the Reverend Dr Charlet.' LT 1.354.
Wood 276a(299). Wing L2440 (rare).

5646. Royal Society. *A list of the Royal Society. . . . Ten are to be chosen . . . . the thirtieth of November, 1694*. London: T. James, 1695. S.sh.
Wood 276a(300) (not in Bodl. CD cat.). Wing L2440A (one) ('O' not recorded in Wing).

5647. Royal Story. *A royall story, for loyall readers*. [London]: n.pub., 1651. 8°. Pp. ²,*-**⁸,² (last leaf blank). Pasteboard (grey) with parchment spine. 1st and last flyleaves, marbled paper.
Flyleaf, upper, 3rdᵛ, AW wrote the titles of 6 printed works in this vol. (really 5, AW included 2 sections of Wood 235(2)), within guidelines made with red ink. The entries are followed by, 'Among these books, Boscobel is first to be prefer'd, as to K. Ch. 2. his escape from Worcester battle.' (i.e., Wood 235(2), by T. Blount, item 1015, over Wood 235(3), item 1794). Tp, '4ᵈ'. LT 1.327.
Wood 235(1). Wing R2153 (rare) (Wing, punct. differs).

5648. Rules of Civility. *Rules of civility or, the art of good-breeding*. [London]: f. J. Blare, at the Sign of the Looking-Glass, on London-Bridge, [1683 or later?]. 8°. A⁸,B⁴. Pasteboard with calf spine, modern, by H[arvey], 5 May 1951.
Flyleaf, upper, AW wrote the titles of 10 printed works in this vol., within guidelines made with red ink. The 11th, Rules, is not by AW and is an error. B4ᵛ, last 2 lines of printed text blurred, entered by AW.
Wood 69(1). Wing 2259aA.5. ESTCR 188738.

5649. Rumsey, Walter. *Organon salutis. An instrument to cleanse the stomach, as also divers new experiments of the virtue of tobacco and coffee [signed Will. Rumsey]*. London: R. Hodgkinsonne f. D. Pakeman, 1657. 8°. Pp. [24], 56.
Each small 8° leaf is pasted on an 8° template. A3, AW blotted out last 3 letters in printed forename 'Will.' Rumsey and inserted 'Walter'; A4, similar lining out; p. 2, he added at top, 'chapt.' before '1'.
Wood 679(4). Wing R2280.

5650. Rupert, Prince*. Rhine, count palatine of the. *His highnesse prince Ruperts late beating up the rebels quarters at Post-comb & Chinner in Oxford-shire*. Oxford: L. Lichfield, 1643. 4°. Pp. [2], 17.
A slip before tp, with AW's notes, torn out. Tp, AW altered a former no. P. 1, vertical line in margin; on p. 7ᵛ, wrote the date, '18. Jun'.
Wood 376(14). Wing H2076B. Madan 1400.

5651. Rupert, Prince*. Rhine, count palatine of the. *Prince Ruperts burning love to England: discovered in Birminghams flames*. London: f. T. Underhill, 1643. 4°. Pp. 8.
Tp, AW wrote the month, 'Apr'. P. 3., date at 'On Easter Monday', '3 Ap. 1643'. P. 5, underscoring and note, 'Vncle Peake/' at the story of the robbing of Thomas Peake, prob. not be in AW's hand. P. 8, note, not in AW's hand, 'Mʳ Roberts minister ecclesiae prope portum Sancti Augustini London/'.
Wood 376(3). Wing P3489.

5652. Rupert, Prince*. Rhine, count palatine of the. *His highnesse prince Rupert's raising of the siege at Newarke upon Trent, March the 21, 1643. Written by an eye witnesse*. [Oxford]: n.pub., [1644]. 4°. Pp. 1-8 (includes 2 leaves of A2).
P. 1, AW altered the former no., '62'.
Wood 376(69). Wing H2077 ('O' not recorded in Wing). Madan 1587.

5653. Rupert, Prince*. Rhine, count palatine of the. *A dog's elegy, or Rupert's tears*. London: f. G. B., 1644, 27 July. 4°.
Missing in 1839; see note at Wood 377(1), item 1225.
Wood 377(26). Wing D1830 (3).

5654. Rupert, Prince. Rhine, count palatine of the. *A declaration of his highnesse prince Rupert. With a narrative of . . . Bristoll*. London: E. Griffin, 1645. 4°. Pp. [2], 34.
Tp, AW wrote the month, 'Sept.', in pencil; and overwrote the former no., '20'.
Wood 378(23). Wing R2294.

5655. Rupert, Prince*. Rhine, count palatine of the. *Historical memoires of the life and death of . . . Rupert, prince palatine of the Rhine, duke of Cumberland*. London: f. T. Malthus, 1683. 8°. Pp. [17], 80.
Tp, AW wrote, '6ᵈ'. LT 2.495.
Wood 245(4). Wing H2104.

5656. R[ushworth], J[ohn], (probable author). *A full and exact relation of the storming and taking of Dartmouth*. London: f. E. Husband, 1645[6], 23 Jan. 4°. Pp. 8.
Tp, AW wrote the price, '1ᵈ', and lined out the former no., '39'.

Wood 378(42). Wing F2279.

5657. R[ushworth], J[ohn]. *A true relation of the fight at Bovy-Tracy, between the parliaments forces under the command of sir Tho: Fairfax.* London: f. E. Husband, 1645[6], 15 Jan. 4°. Pp. 7.
Tp, AW lined out the former no., '38'.
Wood 378(41). Wing R2336.

5658. R[ushworth], J[ohn]. *A true relation concerning the late fight at Torrington.* London: f. E. Husband, 1645[6], 20 Feb. 4°. Pp. 8.
Tp, AW overwrote the price, '1ᵈ' with the former no., '46', and altered that no.'
Wood 378(49). Wing R2334A.

5659. R[ushworth], J[ohn]. *A more full and exact relation (being the third letter . . .) of the several treaties between sir Tho. Fairfax and sir Ralph Hopton.* London: f. E. Husband, 1645[6], 18 Mar. 4°. Pp. 8.
Tp, AW wrote and later lined out the price, '1ᵈ', and lined out the former no., '58'.
Wood 378(61). Wing R2327.

5660. Rushworth, Jo[hn]. *Sir Thomas Fairfax's proceedings in the west . . . since he advanced to Bodman.* London: f. E. Husband, 1645[6], 7 Mar. 4°. Pp. 8.
Tp, AW wrote and later lined out the price, '1ᵈ', and altered the former no., '54'.
Wood 378(57). Wing R2330A (Wing, 1645).

5661. R[ushworth], J[ohn]. *A true relation of the storming Bristoll, . . . by sir Thomas Fairfax' army . . . 11. of this instant Septemb.* London: f. E. Husband, 1645, 13 Sept. 4°. Pp. 24.
Tp, AW altered the former no., '21'; trace of a price (?), cropped.
Wood 378(24). Wing R2336A.

5662. [Rushworth, John]. *The taking of Tiverton, . . . by sir Thomas Fairfax, . . . Octob. 19.* London: f. R. A., 1645, 23 Oct. 4°. Pp. [2], 6.
Tp, AW overwrote the former no., '34'.
Wood 378(37). Wing R2332.

5663. R[ushworth], J[ohn]. *Sir Ralph Hoptons and all his forces comming in to the parliament.* London: f. E. Husband, 1646, 16 Mar. 4°. Pp. 8.
Tp, AW wrote and later lined out the price, '1ᵈ', and altered the former no., '56'; and wrote after the date of publication, '1645', in pencil.
Wood 378(59). Wing R2330.

5664. R[ushworth], J[ohn]. *The severall fights neere Colchester in Essex. Also major generall Lamberts victories in the north.* London: f. R. Smithurst, 1648. 4°. Pp. [2], 6.
Wood 502(27). Wing R2329.

5665. Rushworth, John. *A true relation of the surrendring of Colchester to . . . Fairfax. A letter [28 Aug.].* London: R. W. f. J. Partridge, 1648. S.sh.
Wood 502(62). Wing R2337.

5666. R[ushworth], J[ohn]. *15 Junii, 1648. The particulars of the fight at Colchester.* London: f. E. Husband, 1648, 17 June. 4°. Pp. 8.
Tp, AW wrote after the year, 'Jun. 15'.
Wood 502(24). Wing R2328.

5667. Rushworth, William. White, Thomas, ed. *Rushworth's dialogues. . . . Corrected and enlarg'd by Thomas White.* Paris: chez J. Billaine, 1654. 12°. Last ed. Pp. [38], 280. Calf with 2 fillets.
Flyleaf, upper, 1st, 'T. B.' and below, AW wrote 'May 4. Ant. Wood. ex dono Th. Blount Interioris Templi Maii 4. 1670.'; 3rdᵛ, 'Will. Rushworth (somtimes called Charls Rosse) was author of the 3 Dialogues contained in this vol. & Thomas White or de Albiis was author of the fourth. [/] Will. Richworth [sic] – vide Cat. Bod.' Tp, under printed 'White', AW wrote 'Or de Albiis // He writ the 4ᵗʰ dialogue –'. LT 2.191.
Wood 820. Wing R2338B.

5668. Russell, William. Bedford, earl of. *A letter written from the right honorable the earle of Bedford, to a lord of the house of peeres, . . . about Sherborn castle.* London: f. H. Perry, 1642, 15 Sept. 4°. A⁴.
Tp, AW wrote the date, 'Sept 12'.
Wood 375(10). Wing B1672.

5669. Russell, William, lord, et al. *The last speech & behaviour of William late lord Russel, upon the scaffold . . . July 21. . . . Also the last speeches, . . . of capt. Thomas Walcot, John Rouse gent. & William Hone joyner [20 July].* London: J. C. a. F. C. f. T. Fox, 1683. Fol. Pp. [2], 14.
Tp, AW wrote, '6ᵈ'.
Wood 428(7). Wing L504 (Wing, Russell).

5670. Russell, William*, lord, et al. *The proceedings against the lord Russel, upon his tryal [13 July] . . . As also the tryals of William Hone, the joyner, John Rouse, and William Blake.* [London]: (f. L. Curtis), (1683). S.sh. Pp. 1-2.
Wood 428(3). Wing P3553 ('O' not recorded in Wing).

5671. Russell, William*, lord. *A satyr on the pretended ghost of the late lord Russel.* (London): (f. E. Golding), [1683]. S.sh. (r-v).
AW wrote the year, '1683', in pencil.
Wood 417(124). Wing S718B.

5672. Russell, William, lord. *The speech of the late lord Russel, to the sheriffs [21 July].* (London): (J. Darby, by direction of the Lady Russel), (1683). Fol. Pp. 4.
Tp, AW wrote, '2ᵈ'; and p. 4, 'This speech was published within few houres after the Lord Russells death, & two dayes after Dʳ Jo. Tillotson & Dʳ Gilb. Burnet were summoned before the councell, to give an account whether it was the same speech that he delivered in writing on the stage, & whether Dʳ Burnet had not a hand in it'. LT 3.118; and P. Hinds, 'Roger L'Estrange', *The Library*, 7th ser., 3 (2002): 5ff.
Wood 428(11). Wing R2356.

5673. Russell, William*, lord. *A vindication of the lord Russell's speech and innocence, in a dialogue betwixt a whig & tory.* [London]: N. Thompson, 1683. 4°. Pp. [2], 22.
P. 4, a correction.
Wood 428(16). Wing V515 ('O' not recorded in Wing).

5674. Rutherford, Samuel. *Joshua redivivus, or mʳ Rutherfoord's letters.* [Rotterdam]: n.pub., 1664. 8°. Pp. [48], 576. Parchment over boards.
Pastedown, upper, 'Pret: 5ˢ-6ᵈ. 1684' and a reference, none in AW's hand. Passim, underscoring, marks in margin and, at end, an index of recipients of letters, not in AW manner and hand. Numbers in 1st section, 1-45, may be in AW's hand.
Wood 717. Wing R2381.

5675. Ruthven, John*. Gowrie, earl of. *The earle of Gowries conspiracie against the kings majestie of Scotland [5 Aug.].* London: V. Simmes, 1600. 4°. Pp. A-D⁴.
Acquired 29 Ap. 1658 out of G. Langbaine's study, LT 1.247.
Wood 586(11). STC 21466.3.

5676. Ruthven, Patrick, Forth, earl of; and **Charles 1**. *The copy of . . . the earle of Forth's letter to the earle of Essex: and the copy of his majesties letter to . . . parliament [3 March].* Oxford: L. Lichfield, 1643[4], 7 March. 4°. Pp. [2], 5.
Tp, former no., '27'.
Wood 632(7). Wing F1614. Madan 1554.

5677. [Rycaut, Paul]. *A narrative of the success of the voyage of . . . Heneage Finch . . . from Smyrna to Constantinople.* London: J. R., 1661. 4°. Pp. [2], 11.
Wood 387(9). Wing N227 ('O' not recorded in Wing).

5678. Ryff, Petrus. *Quaestiones geometricae, in Euclidis et P. Rami Στοιχηειωσιν, . . . quibus geodaesiam, adjecimus.* Francofurti: in off. Wecheliana, ap. D. & D. Aubrios, & C. Schleichium, 1621. 4°. Pp. 135, [1].
Wood 481(2). BL.

5679. [Ryves, Bruno]. *Micro-chronicon: or, a briefe chronology of the time and place of the battels.* [London]: n.pub., 1647. 8°. A1-3,B-G⁸,H⁶ (A3 blank; H5, an extra leaf).
Passim, AW made underscorings, wrote brief notes and cross-references, in dark ink, in red ink, and in pencil, e.g., F1, 'See 5 pages following' and F3, 'see 4 pages backward'. H3, at death of Col. Meldrum at Alresford, he wrote, 'see in the former p.', where, H2ᵛ, Sir John Meldrum died at the siege of Scarborough Castle. Between E6 and E7, a loose slip of paper, on which AW wrote information about a person mentioned in the text at E7, 'Williams, the Apostate-Archbishop of Yorke' (marked by a vertical line in the margin):

'This he did like a poore spirited man when he saw the kings cause decline – Archb. Williams'.
Wood 207(4) (not in Bodl. CD cat.). Wing R2451.

5680. [Ryves, Bruno]. *[Frontispiece] Mercurius rusticus, the countrys complaint recounting the sad events of this unparraleld warr. [Tp] Mercurius rusticus: or, the countries complaint of the murthers. [2nd tp] Mercurius rusticus: or, the countries complaint, of the sacriledges.* (Oxford): n.pub., 1648 (1646). 8°. Pp. [14], 1-202, [8], 203-262 (wanting A^8) (2 tpp).
Wood 207(2). Wing R2446. Madan 1890 A + B (on p. 432).

5681. S., E. *A letter of advice, from a secluded member of the house of commons, to . . . Thomas lord Fairfax.* [London]: n.pub., 1649. 4°. Pp. [2], 5. Pasteboard (grey) with parchment spine.
Flyleaf, upper, 3rd^{r-v}, AW wrote the titles of 37 printed works in this vol., within guidelines made with red ink. Tp, 'Lib. T[homas] B[arlow] è Coll. Reg. Oxon' and p. 3, brief note, in Barlow's hand. LT 1.189.
Wood 364(1) (not in Bodl. CD cat.). Wing S18.

5682. S., E. *The witty rogue arraigned, condemned, & executed. Or, the history of . . . Richard Hainam.* London: f. E. S., 1656. 4°. Pp. [8], 47 (H^2, following A^4, belong to Fidge, Wood 372(2)).
Tp., faintly printed letters made legible with ink. P. [5], at the speech of Hainam 'immediately before his fatal leap from off the Ladder', AW wrote, 'This must be at the latter end' (catchwords suggest that this leaf is correctly placed). Flyleaf, lower^{r-v}, AW wrote 63 lines of a history of Richard Hainam. It begins, 'Jul. 3 Tuesday 1655 in the night, the French Embassadors house in Westm. was broken open . . . '. AW took some of the following details (lines 35ff.) from 'Mercurius Politicus. from Thursday June 12 to Thursday June 19 an. 1656 thus. – June 17 This day was executed the famous Theif called Hannam, . . . '. AW concluded the story of his capture on a second flyleaf, now inserted at the beginning of this item: Hainam with a dagger- 'knife stab'd Mr Langhorne in the back, and twice thro the Arme, intending to have killed him, & againe made his escape thorow and over the Houses, till he came into Serjeant Probies yard, who most valiantly encountred him, & first wounded him in the thigh; afterwards was stab'd in the belly by Hannam, yet at last, help comminge in, he was taken & carried prisoner to Newgate; from whence June 17 Tuesday, he was conveyed in a cart to the Rounds [sic] in Smithfield & there hanged; as a just reward of all his villanies. He confest not any thing material, only seemed to excuse the Box-maker where he lay, & acknowledged he went there under the name of Richardson, a working Gold-smith.'
Wood 372(3). Wing S20 ('O' not recorded in Wing).

5683. S., G. *A true relation of the sad passages, between the two armies in the west.* London: Publ. by G. S. Printed f. L. C., 1644, 2 Oct. 4°. Pp. 12.
Wood 377(33). Wing S28.

5684. S., G. *A letter out of Flanders. . . . to a noble-man in England: wherein divers observations of his majesties personal deportments, . . . are declared.* London: f. M. Thatcher, 1660. 4°. Pp. 8.
Tp, AW added to the year, 'March:'.
Wood 632(43). Wing S27.

5685. [S., I.]. *Elegies on the death of . . . John Hampden.* London: L. Norton, f. I. T., 1643, Oct. 16. 4°. A^4.
Tp, AW wrote, 'A grand rebell of Bucks.'; 'by. J. S.', may not be by AW.
Wood 319(2). Wing E339 (two) ('O' not recorded in Wing).

5686. S., I. *A brief and perfect journal of the late proceedings . . . of the English army in the West-Indies [to 24 June].* London: n.pub., 1655. 4°. Pp. 27.
Flyleaf, lower, waste paper with a Latin disputation topic, not by AW. Dupl. at Wood 559(6), missing.
Wood 503(22). Wing S35.

5687. S., I. *A brief and perfect journal of the late proceedings . . . of the English army in the West-Indies [to 24 June].* London: n.pub., 1655. 4°. Pp. 27.
Missing in 1922. Flyleaf, upper, 2nd, 'Journall of the late proceedings & success of the English Army in the West Indies - 1655'. Dupl. at 503(22).
Wood 559(6). Wing S35.

5688. [S., J.]. *[The famous history of the valiant London-prentice].* [London]: [f. J. Back], [1692]. 12°.
Fragments of 3 pp. survive.
'Found to be thus fragmentary 1882'. T is on list at Wood 254(1), item 3188.
Wood 254(7). Wing S60 (one).

5689. S., L. *A letter to a noble peer of the realm [Arthur Capel], about his late speech and petition to his majesty.* [London]: n.pub., [1681]. S.sh. Pp. 2.
Wood 276a(151). Wing S109A.

5690. S., M. *A discourse concerning the rebellion in Ireland.* London: f. R. Lownes, 1642. 4°. Pp. [2], 26.
Tp, top left, 'C 29' (or 'C 24').
Wood 508(37). Wing S113.

5691. S., N. *A new and further narrative of the state of New-England, being a continued account of the bloudy Indian-war [March-Aug.].* London: J. [B. f. D. Newman], 1676. Fol. Pp. [2], 14 (t leaf mutilated).
Tp, initials, 'R. S.' P. 13, scribbles, prob. not by AW.
Wood 559(10). Wing S120.

5692. S., R. *Very sad and bloody newes from Ireland, of the losse of Bunratty . . . and Roscomon.* London: J. Coe, 1646. 4°. Pp. [2], 6.
Tp, AW wrote '20 24 } Jul', in pencil; price, '1ᵈ', lined out, may not be by AW.
Wood 509(7). Wing S140 ('O' not recorded in Wing).

5693. S., R. *Avona; or a transient view of the benefit of making rivers of this kingdom navigable . . . By R. C.* London: T. R. & N. T. f. J. Courtney in Sarum, 1675. 8°. Pp. [2], 33.
Text, corrections, not by AW. Flyleaf, lowerᵛ, AW wrote 'Mart. Marprelate', on a sheet once used to identify a bundle (see [MS.] Wood D. 31(3) and (53), items 2253 and 4376).
Wood 730(6). Wing S125.

5694. S., T. *The declaration of the citizens of Edenborough, concerning the maintaining of a warre for the king, . . . Likewise, the proceedings of the northern army.* London: f. I. C., 1648. 4°. Pp. [2], 6.
Tp, AW wrote after the year, 'Jun.17'.
Wood 502(28). Wing S155.

5695. S., T. *A letter to his excellency the lord general Monck.* London: n.pub., 1659[60]. S.sh.
AW added to year, 'Feb:'. Text, one word, 'Fanatiques', underscored.
Wood 276a(240). Wing S170 ('O' not recorded in Wing).

5696. [S., T.]. *An account of the proceedings aganst [sic] the rebels, at Dorchester . . . at an assize [4-5 September].* (London): (E. Mallet), (1685). S.sh. (r-v).
Former no. '37' in pencil; after 'Rebels' in t, AW wrote, 'Lately under James Duke of Monmouth'. LT 3.159.
Wood 660c(10). Wing S151A.

5697. S., T. *An account of the proceedings against the rebels at an assize holden at Exeter [14 Sept.].* (London): (E. Mallet), (1685). S.sh. (r-v).
Former no. '39' in pencil, and no. '10' in ink.
Wood 660c(12a). Wing S151.

5698. Sá, Pantaleao. *A narration of the late accident in the New-exchange [21-22 Nov.].* London: n.pub, 1653. 4°. Pp. 14.
Flyleaves, upper, AW wrote a 4-page ms. description of the event, not derived from this pamphlet, and beginning, 'Nov. 21 Munday 1653 three of the Portugal embassadors family, . . . ', and ending at an entry of 5 July and 10 July 1654, concluding: 'A verie observeable hand of providence, that the said two persons, who began the aforesaid quarrel in the Exchange, in prosecution whereof murther was committed, should meet thus to die at the same time & place, for different crimes–'. Tp, 'dupl.' Dupl. at Wood 609(35).
Wood 365(12). Wing S210.

5699. Sá, Pantaleao. *A narration of the late accident in the New-exchange [21-22 Nov.].* London: n.pub., 1653. 4°. Pp. 14.
After this item a pamplet of 8 leaves was torn out. This theft occurred before the list of contents, 48 items, was written on the upper flyleaf of this vol. by an Ashm. librarian in about 1717 (see Wood 609(1), item 6530). The Whiteside cat. has only, for this vol.: 'Pamphlets &c 48'. Dupl. at Wood 365(12a).
Wood 609(35) (not in Bodl. CD cat.). Wing S210.

5700. Sacchettus, Joannes Baptista. *Privilegia prothonotariorum apostolicorum.* Romae: ex typ. R. Cam. Apost., 1651. 8°. Pp. 30.
Pastedown, upper, 'Sum J. Aubrey R[egiae] S[ocietatis] S[ocius]'. Flyleaf, upper, former owner, 'Robertus Pugus de Penrin creatus Protonotarius Apostolicus Sᵐⁱ. Dⁿⁱ Nci Innocentii Papa X Brevi dato 20ᵐᵒ. Decemb

anno 1653./', not by AW (see LT 2.435 and AO 3.697, 829-30).
Wood 860. BL.

5701. [Sacheverell, George]. *[Hudibras] on [Edmund] Calamy's imprisonment, and [Robert] Wild's poetry.* [London]: n.pub., [1663]. S.sh. (mutilated).
Dupl. at Wood 416(97). 1 of 2 copies acquired 3 Feb. 1663, LT 1.468.
Wood 276a(532). Wing H3256.

5702. [Sacheverell, George]. *Hudibras on [Edmund] Calamy's imprisonment, and [Robert] Wild's poetry.* [London]: n.pub., [1663]. S.sh.
ᵛ, AW wrote the year, '1662[3]'. 1 of 2 copies acquired 3 Feb. 1663, LT 1.468. Dupl. at Wood 276a(532).
Wood 416(97). Wing H3256.

5703. Sacro-Bosco, Johannes de. Burgersdicius, F. ed. *Sphaera.* Lugduni Batavorum: ex off. Bonaventurae & A. Elzevir, 1639. 8°. Pp. 117, [2]. Parchment.
Tp, AW wrote the price, 'pretium -1ˢ-6ᵈ'. Bsm. An intrusion of 3 vols., at Wood 11a, 11b, and 11c is not included in this cat. (*New baronage of England*, (1769), gift of J. Peshall).
Wood 11. NUC.

5704. Sadler, Anthony*. *Inquisitio Anglicana: or the disguise discovered. Shewing the proceedings of the commissioners at White-hall, . . . in the examinations of Anthony Sadler.* London: J. Grismond, f. R. Royston, 1654. 4°. Pp. [6], 17.
Tp, AW wrote, '1653', 'Anth. Sadler of Oxon. see p. 14'. Below, 'Ent. in cat', by a later librarian.
Wood 476(12). Wing S265 (Wing, or, the).

5705. Sadler, Anthony*. *Strange news indeed: from Mitcham in Surry. Of the treacherous and barbarous proceedings, of master Robert Cranmer . . . against Anthonie Sadler.* London: f. the authour, 1664. 4°. Pp. 8.
AO 3.1267-9.
Wood 476(14). Wing S272 (two).

5706. Sadler, Anthony. *Schema sacrum in ordine ad ordinem ecclesiae Anglicanae ceremoniarum.* London: f. H. Twyford, 1683. S.sh. (mutilated).
Wood 276a(287). Wing S271 (two).

5707. Sadler, Thomas. *Sadler's memoir's: or, the history of the life and death of . . . Thomas Sadler.* [London]: f. P. Brooksby, 1677. 4°. Pp. [2], 17, [1].
Tp, AW changed the date to 167'6/'7. LT 2.366.
Wood 372(15). Wing S282 (two) ('O' not recorded in Wing) (Wing, [1677]).

5708. Sadler, Thomas Vincent. *The childes catechism.* Paris [really London]: n.pub., 1678. 8°. Pp. [6], 49. Paper, marbled (prob. by AW).
Tp, AW wrote 'written by T. Vincent alias Vincent Sadler, a Benedictin monk.'; after the city of publication, 'alias London.'; and 'Antonii à Wood ex dono Rad. Sheldon de Beolie Arm. 2° Oct. 1679'. LT 2.464; LT 2.321.
Wood 813. Wing C3875 (rare).

5709. Saint Evremond, Charles Marguetel de Saint Denis, seigneur de. *Mixt essays upon tragedies, comedies, Italian comedies, English comedies and opera's [sic].* London: f. T. Goodwin, 1685. 4°. Pp. [8], 28.
Wood 615(18). Wing S307.

5710. Saint John, Oliver. *Mʳ Sᵗ-John's speech to the lords . . . Concerning ship-money [7 Jan. 1640].* [London]: [T. Harper], 1640[1]. 4°. Pp. [2], 45.
Tp, bsm.
Wood 527(3). STC 21589.7. Wing S331.

5711. Saint Jure, Jean Baptiste. S[heldon], E[dward], trans. *The holy life of monʳ. de Renty . . . councellor to king Lewis the 13ᵗʰ.* London: f. J. Crook, 1658. 8°. Pp. [15], 358. Calf with 2 gold-stamp fillets and gold-stamp decoration in corners (flower, 2 pedals, cp. Wood 241, item 6222, also from Sheldon).
Flyleaf, upper, 2nd 'Ja' (a Sheldon mark?). Tp, signature of 'Marie Sheldon'. LT 2.510.
Wood 301. Wing S334.

5712. Saint Leger, William. *A true copy of a letter from sir W. Saintliger . . . to the lord lieutenant of*

Ireland [25 Ap.]. London: E. G. f. J. Franke, 1642. 4°. A⁴.
Tp, AW wrote, 'Ap. 2'. Below, '<u>50</u>'.
Wood 508(3). Wing S338A.

5713. Salesbury, William. *A playne and a familiar introduction, teaching how to pronounce the letters in the Brytishe tongue . . . Welshe.* London: H. Denham f. H. Toy, 1567, 17 May. 4°. A-G⁴.
Missing. MS. Wood E. 2(70), p. 6.
MS. Wood E. 2(70), p. 6. STC 21615. *Folg, Hunt, Harv* (no tp).

5714. Saligniaco, Bartholomaeus de. *Itinerarii Terre Sancte.* Lugd.: Gilbert de Villiers, (1525, 28 August). Ff. 70, [9]. Parchment over sheets.
Flyleaf, upper, 3rdᵛ, 'In Bib B[odleian]', lined out. Tp, date of publication entered, '1525'. Text, some marks in margins, not in AW's manner. K7ᵛ, scribbles. Flyleaf, lower, 2ndᵛ, 'Novemb 7 - 1654 Lent Rich. Carr A Compleat Gentleman by Mr. [Henry] Peacham', in pencil, not by AW. Wood owned a 1661 edition of Peacham, Wood 605(1)). 3rdᵛ, torn out sheet with traces of notes, not in AW's hand.
Wood 160. BL.

5715. [Salkeld, John]. *A treatise of paradise. And the principall contents thereof.* London: E. Griffin f. N. Butter, 1617. 8°. Pp. [16], 359.
Missing. Listed as dupl. in MS. Wood E. 2(70), p. 61. Dupl. at Wood 858.
MS. Wood E. 2(70), p. 61. STC 21622. *O, Folg, Hunt, NYPL.*

5716. [Salkeld, John]. *A treatise of paradise. And the principall contents thereof.* London: E. Griffin f. N. Butter, 1617. 8°. Pp. [16], 359. Parchment.
Flyleaf, upper, '23'. Tp, former no. '44' over '43'. Listed as dupl. in MS. Wood E. 2(70), p. 61.
Wood 858. STC 21622.

5717. Sallust. Crosse, William, trans. *The workes of Caius Crispus Salustius.* London: [Eliz. Allde,] sold T. Walkley, 1629. 12°. Pp. [12], 692.
Missing in 1837. 'Salust Translated – 1629' in Whiteside cat. Listed in MS. Wood E. 2(70), p. 10. Bliss, in his copy, Bliss A231, wrote, 'The translator was not known to Anthony Wood'. This is not true.
Wood 192. STC 21624. *O.*

5718. Salmon, James . *Bloudy newes from Ireland, or the barbarous crueltie by the papists.* London: f. M. Rookes, 1641. 4°. A⁴.
Wood 507(8). Wing S412 (Wing, creueltie).

5719. Salmon, Thomas. *An essay to the advancement of musick.* London: J. Macock, sold J. Car, 1672. 8°. Pp. [17], 92, [1] (1 p. books sold by Carr [sic]).
Missing in 1837. 'An Essay to the advancement of Musick – Lond. 1672' in Whiteside cat. Listed in MS. Wood E. 2(70), p. 62.
Wood 120(2). Wing S417. *O* (two), *Hunt, Clark, Folg.*

5720. Salter, James. *Caliope's cabinet opened. Wherein gentlemen may be informed how to adorn them-selves.* London: G. M. f. W. Crooke, 1665. 8°. Pp. [4], 66, [2].
P. 51, at virtuous stones, 'fabulous', prob. by AW. Flyleaf, lowerᵛ, '1664. 6ᵈ', may be by AW. Acquired 28 Feb. 1665, LT 2.30.
Wood 442(2). Wing S465.

5721. Salter, Robert. *Wonderfull prophecies from the beginning of the monarchy of this land.* London: W. Jones, 1627. 4°. Pp. [8], 48.
Tp, outline of a crude horoscope(?).
Wood 646(3). STC 21631.

5722. Saltonstall, Wye. *Clavis ad portam, or a key fitted.* Oxford: W. Turner, 1634. 8°. A1,A4-8,B-F⁸ (wanting A2-3. F8 blank). Calf with 3 fillets; spine, 4 bands.
On slip, pasted to upper board, AW wrote 'vide 8°.G.117.Art.' (the Bodl. shelf-mark of a copy of the 2nd work in this vol., Wood 35(2), item 3985). On opposite side of this slip and on board, beneath, scribbles.
Wood 35(1). STC 21641. Madan 790.

5723. Saltonstall, Wye. *Picturae loquentes, or pictures drawne forth in characters.* London: T. Coles, sold W. Hope, 1635. 12°. A-G¹²,H⁶.
Missing in 1837. Listed in MS. Wood E. 2(70), p. 26, 'Wye Saltonstall picture & characters 1635', and in the Whiteside cat., 'Picturae Loquentes - Lond: 1635'.

Wood 734. STC 21646 (4). *O, BL, Hunt.*

5724. Salway, [Richard]. *To the right worshipful the master, . . . of the company of grocers. The . . . petition of major Salloway.* [London]: f. H. James, [1660]. S.sh.
AW wrote 'Rich' before Salloway, in pencil, and, at end, 'Jan: 1659[60]'.
Wood 276a(195). Wing T1722B (3).

5725. Salyus, Amedeus. *Breviarii Christianae chronologiae.* Lugdun.: Franciscus La Bottiere, bibliop. Lugdun., [1623 or later]. S.sh.
ᵛ, AW wrote, 'Salyus his breviarii Christian Chronolo' [cropped].
Wood 276a(50). Not in BL, NUC, BN.

5726. Sam. Datchet, ferryman of. *A dialogue betwixt Sam. The ferriman of Dochet, Will. A waterman of London, and Tom. A bargeman of Oxford, upon the kings calling a parliament to meet at Oxford.* London: n.pub., 1681. 4°. Pp. 31.
Missing. Tp, AW wrote 'Oxon Dupl', in pencil, at Wood 608(61). No dupl. in the AW collection.
Not located. Wing D1353.

5727. Sam. Datchet, ferryman of. *A dialogue betwixt Sam. The ferriman of Dochet, Will. A waterman of London, and Tom. A bargeman of Oxford, upon the kings calling a parliament to meet at Oxford.* London: n.pub., 1681. 4°. Pp. 31.
Tp, AW wrote 'Oxon Dupl', in pencil. No dupl. in the AW collection.
Wood 608(61). Wing D1353.

5728. Sambucus, Joannes. *Emblemata, et aliquot nummi antiqui operis.* Antverpiae: ex off. C. Plantini, 1576. 4th ed. 16°. Pp. 362. Calf with 3 fillets. Binding has cut off some notes.
Tp, pp. 21, 65, 352, notes, scribbles, presumably by the former owner 'Jhon Smithe', some cropped. Some emblems are marked, 18, 21, 44, 46, etc.
Wood 73. NUC.

5729. Sampson, Thomas. *A warning to take heede of Fowlers psalter.* London: T. Vautrollier f. G. Bishoppe, 1578. 8°. Pp. 111.
Missing. MS. Wood E. 2(70), p. 9.
MS. Wood E. 2(70), p. 9. STC 21685 (4). *BL, Folg.*

5730. Samson, Tho[mas]. *A narrative of the late popish plot in Ireland, . . . with the . . . tryal of the earl of Tyrone, and others.* London: f. S. Lee a. D. Major, 1680. Fol. Pp. [7], 32.
1st blank p., AW wrote 'oct. 1680', and tp, 'Octob.' and 'came out in Oct.'
Wood 422(18). Wing S542.

5731. Samuel, Marochitanus. Hominis, A[lphonsus] Boni, trans. *Tractatus rabby Samuelis errorē judeorū indicās.* [Paris]: venundantur a P. Gaudoul, [c.1520]. 8°. A-C⁸, D⁴ (last leaf blank).
Tp, AW wrote 'AWoode: Oxōn: MDclix.' P. nos. 1-16, some underscoring and a few brief notes, e.g., D2-3, underscoring and date, 1239, not by AW.
Wood 795(6). BL.

5732. Samwaies, P[eter]. *The wise and faithful steward. Or, a narration of the . . . death of mr. Beniamin Rhodes.* London: W. Godbid, 1657. 8°. Pp. [30], 88.
Wood 289(5) (not in Bodl. CD cat.). Wing S546A.

5733. Sancroft, William*. Canterbury, abp. of. *The proceedings and tryal in the case of . . . William lord archbishop of Canterbury, and . . . William lord bishop of St. Asaph [and 5 others].* London: f. T. Basset, a. T. Fox, 1689. Fol. Pp. [7], 140.
Tp, AW wrote 'Jan. 18. 1688[9] – 4ˢ-0'; pp. 1-2, notes on the Att. Gen and Sol. Gen.: 'Sʳ Tho. Powis was made Attorney Gen. in the place of S. Rob. Sawyer, xi. Dec. 1687' and 'Wil. Williams Esq. made Sol. Gen. xi. Dec. 1687. afterwards Kᵗᵉᵈ [on 12 Dec.]'; pp. 17, 19, 25, 31-2, lines in margins. LT 3.267.
Wood 421(10). Wing P3555A.

5734. Sancroft, William. Canterbury, abp. of. *A vindication of the arch-bishop and several other bishops, from the imputations . . . by the author of the modest enquiry.* [London]: n.pub., 1690. S.sh. (r-v).
ᵛ, AW wrote, 'about 18 Jul.' LT 3.336.
[MS.] Wood D. 31(24). Wing V496A (rare).

5735. Sanctorius, Sanctorius. *Ars . . . De statica medicina et de responsione ad staticomasticem.*

Lugduni Batavorum: ap. D. Lopes de Haro, 1642. 12°. Pp. [20], 135. Calf with 2 fillets; flyleaf, lower, printer's waste paper.
Pastedown, upper, 'John Lydall Trin: Coll: Oxōn.' and a reference. Flyleaf, upper, 1st, 'Jo: Aubrey. p[rt]. 10[d]. 1653.', and a signature of Lydall, after which Aubrey wrote 'my dearly honoured friend.' (Lydall, ca. 1626-1657, was Aubrey's contemporary at Trinity College). Tp, a price '0-3'. Text, marks in margins, some underscoring and a few notes and references in ink and pencil, by Lydall; flyleaf, lower, 2nd and pastedown, lower, notes by Lydall (some quoted in LT 1.229-30).
Wood 850. Not in BL.

5736. Sanders, Nicholas. Rishtonus, Edwardus, ed. *Vera et sincera historia schismatis Anglicani, . . . aucta per E. Rishtonum. Nunc postremùm . . . castigatius edita*. Coloniae Agrippinae: ap. P. Henningium, 1628. 8°. Pp. [16], 348, [22], 142. Pasteboard (blue) with parchment spine; rebound.
Flyleaf, upper, 2nd[v], the titles of 3 printed works in this vol., by an Ashm. librarian. 1st item, tp, bsm. Acquired 20 Apr. 1661, 10[d], LT 1.389.
Wood 890(1). BL.

5737. Sanderson, John. *Institutionum dialecticarum libri quatuor*. Oxoniae: Jos. Barnesius, 1602. 8°.3rd ed. Pp. [4], 228.
Tp, 'Many are the afflictions' and scribbles, apparently by a former owner, 'Robert Knight'. P. 228, more scribbles by the same person: 'Finis', etc.
Wood 42(6). STC 21698. Madan 225.

5738. Sanderson, Robert. Lincoln, bp. of. *Reasons of the present judgement of the university of Oxford, concerning the solemne league and covenant, the negative oath, . . . approved by . . . convocation [1 June]*. [London]: n.pub., 1647. 4°. Pp. [8], 35.
Tp, AW wrote, 'Reprinted in 1660 when the Kings commissioners sate at Oxon. to reforme the universitie.'; below, 'translated into several languages', in pencil. LT 2.50. Dupl. at Wood 614(19) (imperf.).
Wood 514(31). Wing S623. Madan 1926.

5739. Sanderson, Robert. Lincoln, bp. of. *[Reasons of the present judgement of the university of Oxford, concerning the solemne league and covenant, the negative oath]*. [London]: n.pub., [1647]. 4°. Pp. 35 (wanting all before sig. B1).
Tp, AW wrote 'Dup', in pencil. An Ashm. librarian wrote 'see Wood 514.29'. Dupl. at Wood 514(31).
Wood 614(19). Wing S623. Madan 1926.

5740. [Sanderson, William]. *Aulicus coquinariae: or a vindication in answer to . . . the court and character of king James*. London: f. H. Seile, 1650[1]. 8°. Pp. [8], 205. Calf with 2 fillets and also 2 vertical fillets.
Flyleaf, upper, 2nd[v], AW wrote, 'written by Godf[rey] Goodman Bishop of Gloc.' (i.e., the author of the work responded to, AO 2.867). A2[v]-A3, A4, some vertical lines in margin. Acquired 25 Oct. 1666, 1[s], LT 2.89.
Wood 263. Wing S645.

5741. Sanderson, William. *A compleat history of the lives and reigns of Mary queen of Scotland, and of her son and successor, James the sixth*. London: f. H. Moseley, R. Tomlins, a. G. Sawbridge, 1656. Fol. Pp. [20], 1-262, [14], 265-599, [3] (wanting the plates; 2 tpp). See note at item 716.
Wood 660e(2). Wing S647.

5742. Sanderson, William. *Post-haste: a reply to Peter (Doctor Heylin's) appendix. [2nd tp] Peter pursued, or dr. Heylin overtaken, arrested [3rd tp] The arraignment of dr. Peter Heylin's advertisement on the three histories*. London: f. the author (T. Leach), 1658. 4°. Pp. [4], 1-24, [4], 25-56. 3 tpp. (A2,B-D4,²,E-H4).
1st tp, AW wrote, 'This is concerning Hist. of K. Ch. 1. written by Wil Sanderson. D[r] Prideaux mentioned here & Hist of S. George' (cropped at bottom); p. 13, 'Of the Historie of S. George' and short line in margin; 2nd tp (after p. 24), in pencil, 'Here be some sheets wanting'; p. 29, 'This is in D[r] Heylyn[s] Diarie' (cropped at side).
Wood 486(14-16). Wing S650 (and S649; see ESTCR 5219 and 5263).

5743. Sandys, Edwin. *Europae speculum or, a view or survey of the state of religion in the westerne parts of the world*. London: T. Cotes f. M. Sparke, sold G. Hutton, 1637. 4°. Rpt. Pp. [8], 248 (some pp. unopened). Pasteboard (blue) with parchment spine. 1st upper and last lower flyleaves, marbled paper.
Flyleaf, upper, 3rd[v], AW wrote the titles of 3 printed works in this vol., within guidelines made with red

ink. He wrote Arabic nos. on tpp. 1st tp, AW underscored t and year, in red ink. Bsms. P. [3], name of printer of earlier ed., 'for one Simon Waterson, 1605', lined out.
Wood 627(1). STC 21721.

5744. Sandys, Edwin. *A vindication of colonell Sandys his honour and loyalty.* [Oxford]: [L. Lichfield?], 1642. 4°. Pp. [2], 13.
P. 1, AW underscored the surname of John Rushworth and wrote, 'qu[aere]'.
Wood 375(13). Wing S671. Madan 1049.

5745. [Sandys, Edwin], and Robert Tailour. *Sacred hymns. Consisting of fifti select Psalms of David . . . turned into English verse. And by Robert Tailour, set to be sung in five parts.* London: T. Snodham, 1615. 4°. Pp. [4], 136, [2]. Parchment.
Spine, 'Psalms with curious music', may in AW's hand. Flyleaf, upper, 'Liber Henrici Sandys. Ex dono Patris', and 'Mʳ Henry Tozer' (AO 3.273), both lined out. Cover, upper, outside, and pp. [3], 4-6, 103, an addition, 'with heaven', 2 notes, and some marks; the script is not by AW. On the translator, Sandys, see AO 2.474. Acquired 25 July 1662, 6ᵈ, LT 1.444.
Wood 381. STC 21723.

5746. Sandys, George. *Sandys travailes.* London: R. Cotes, sold J. Sweeting, 1652-1680. Fol. 5th to 7th eds.
Missing. MS. Wood E. 2(70), p. 45, 'Traviells [sic] by – George Sandys'. Ed. not identified. 27 Aug. 1664, AW paid 'to Ned Forest for borrowyng of Sands 'Travells,' 6ᵈ' (LT 2.19). AW either kept the borrowed book or acquired a copy.
MS. Wood E. 2(70), p. 45. Wing S677-680.

5747. Sanford, John. *A grammer or introduction to the Italian tongue.* Oxford: J. Barnes, sold S. Waterson [London], 1605. 4°. Pp. [8], 40 (imperf., wanting all after p. 40). Pasteboard (blue) with parchment spine.
Flyleaf, upper, 2ndᵛ, AW wrote the titles of 10 printed works (really 9, 2 sections of (4) are entered as separate items) in this vol., within guidelines made with red chalk.
Wood 310(1). STC 21735. Madan 273.

5748. Sanford, John. Προπυλαιον, *or an entrance to the Spanish tongue.* London: T. Haveland, f. N. Butter, 1611. 4°. Pp. [8], 64.
Wood 310(3). STC 21738.

5749. S[ansbury], J[ohn]. *Ilium in Italiam. Oxonia ad protectionem regis.* Oxoniae: J. Barnesius, 1608. 16°. A-C⁸.
Missing. Lent to Gore, recorded in a letter, 17 Jan. 1670., MS. Wood F. 42, f. 79. See also AO 2.58.
MS. Wood F. 42, f. 79. STC 21743. Madan 301. *O, BL.*

5750. Sarcerius, Erasmus. Taverner, Richard, trans. *Cōmon places of scripture ordrely . . . set forth.* London: T. East, 1577. 8°. Ff. 2-192 (wanting the t leaf). Calf, speckled and 2 gold-stamp fillets with small gold-stamp decoration in corners.
Flyleaf, upper, AW wrote the bibliog. data for the tp, 15 lines, and below, 'dup.' (no dupl. in Wood's current collection). Ff. 2 and192ᵛ, brief note and price, xᵈ, by a former owner.
Wood 803. STC 21756.

5751. Sares, John. *The chiefe heads of mr. John Sares speech, . . . at the time of his execution at West-Chester; . . . 20ᵗʰ· day of October 1651.* [London]: n.pub., [1652]. S.sh.
Wood 367(13). Wing S690.

5752. Sarpi, Paolo. Gentilis, R., trans. *The history of the inquisition, composed by . . . Paul Servita.* London: f. H. Moseley, 1655. 8°. Pp. [5], 147.
Marbled paper, lower, overlap, 'Inqui' and 'Servita' (to note the contents). Acquired 21 Dec. 1663, 1ˢ, LT 1.507.
Wood 233(2). Wing S697.

5753. Sarpi, Paolo. Denton, William, trans. *A treatise of matters beneficiary.* London: T. Hodgkin, sold W. Crook a. R. Bently, 1680. Fol. Pp. [8], 84. Pasteboard (blue) with parchment spine.
Pasteboard, upper, inside, a former shelf-mark, W. 559. This was a number assigned before 1717; the Whiteside cat. established the permanent shelf-marks in 1717 (Wood 559 now holds 23 pamphlets). Flyleaf, upperᵛ, AW wrote the titles of 4 printed works in this vol., within guidelines made with red ink. Below,

AW wrote, '1690 Some of the works of Dr Will. Denton, put into my hands by . . . . [Richard?] Parker B.A. of Merton Coll. by order from the Author-'. AO 4.307f. (see LT 3.361).
Wood 660f(1). Wing S701.

5754. Sartorius, Joannes. *Johannes Sartorius. Amsterodamus.* N.p.: n.pub., n.d. Fol. (small), B7 (only) (engr.).
1 leaf only.
Wood 276b(26). Not identified.

5755. Saul, Arthur. Barbier, J[ean], ed. *The famous game of chesse-play.* London: B. Alsop f. R. Jackson, 1618. 8°. A⁸,a⁴,B-F⁸,G⁴.
Missing in 1837. 'The game of chess play' in Whiteside cat. In Wood 36, at sig. E1, there is a slip, used to support the backing, with AW's note, 'game at chesse play per Barbier'.
Wood 440(1). STC 21773. O (cropped on all sides).

5756. [Sault, Richard]. *A conference betwixt a modern atheist, and his friend: by the methodizer of the second Spira.* London: f. J. Dunton, 1693. 12°. Pp. [12], 56, [4] (4 pp. books printed for Dunton).
Wood 879(3). Wing S732.

5757. [Sault, Richard]. *The second Spira: being a fearful example of an atheist, who had apostatized from the Christian religion, and died in despair, by J. S. [ed., or rather written, by R. Sault].* London: f. J. Dunton, 1693. 12°. 6th ed. Pp. [14], 56, [2] (3 pp. books printed for Dunton).
Wood 879(2). Wing S733C.

5758. S[aunders], Ed[mund]. *Summus Angliae seneschallus: or, a survey of the lord high-steward of England, his office, . . . In a letter.* London: n.pub., 1680. 4°. Pp. 36.
Tp, 'Dup' in pencil (cropped). Dupl. at Wood 629(4).
Wood 632(55). Wing S745.

5759. S[aunders], Ed[mund]. *Summus Angliae seneschallus: or, a survey of the lord high-steward of England, his office, . . . In a letter.* London: n.pub., 1680. 4°. Pp. 36.
Dupl. at Wood 632(55).
Wood 629(4). Wing S745.

5760. Saunders, Edmund*. *An elegy on the death of sir Edmond Saunders, late lord chief justice [19 June 1683].* London: f. J. Norris, 1683. S.sh.
AW wrote, 'Buried in Temple Church', in red ink; ᵛ, 'Sr Edm. Saunders 1683'. LT 3.59, and item 1115.
Wood 429(38). Wing E380.

5761. [Saunders, Jonathan]. *A narrative of a strange and sudden apparition of an arch-angel at the Old-Bayly, on Monday March the seventh, 1680.* [London]: n.pub., 1680/1. Fol. Pp. [2], 2.
Wood 276a(574). Wing S746B (Wing, printed in Truro).

5762. Saunders, Richard, and Dr. Coelson. *Two groatsworth of wit for a penny. Or the English fortune-teller.* [London]: f. J. Conyers, [1680?]. 8°. Pp. 16.
Wood 69(3). Wing T3452A ('O' not recorded in Wing).

5763. Savage, Henry. *Balliofergus, or a commentary upon the foundation, founders and affaires, of Balliol colledge.* Oxford: A. & L. Lichfield, 1668. 4°. Pp. [8], 129, [7].
Tp, 'Antonii Woode, ex dono Authoris, Maii xxi. MDCLXIIX' (LT 2.136 and LT 1.315). AW wrote several notes, most cropped at side, e.g., pp. 10 and 11, 'q[uaere]'; 25 (note badly cropped); 28 at the printed 'which my Friend, . . . supposing it not to be so', AW wrote 'Mr Anthony Woode [/] He doth not [one]ly suppose it [He] knowes it to [be] true by record.'; 28-9, at a similar printed statement, AW wrote, 'I can pr[ove] by many [cropped] that is is s[o]'; 29, 2 apparently similar notes (both cropped); 33, 2 identifications; etc., 51-2 to end, e.g., 69, 'Nothing at all to the purpose' and 2nd p. [3] (or 132), at 'which I owe to the Town Archives', AW wrote, 'tis false, you had them of Mr Ant: Woode.' AW inserted between pp. 114-5, at a section on Hen: Bright, a blank leaf, now bound, with his recording of Bright's epitaph, 'Worcester Cathedrall on a brass plate against a pillar there.' [and 19 more lines; he added later:] 'See Fullers Worthies in Worcestrensis p. 177 where he hath this epit[aph] [/] He was preb. of Worcester'.
Wood 534(5). Wing S759. Madan 2794.

5764. Savage, Thomas*. *The wicked life and penitent death of Tho. Savage.* [London]: f. J. Back, [1680?]. 8°. Pp. [4], 20 (2 tpp) (2 pp. books printed for Back).
Wood 284(5). Wing W2078 (two).

5765. Savage, Thomas*. *The murtherer turned true penitent; . . . Tho. Savage.* [London]: f. P. Brooksby, [1688]. 8°. Pp. 24.
Tp, AW wrote, 'executed 28 Oct. 1668' and a 2nd note, cropped at bottom.
Wood 284(6). Wing M3096 (rare).

5766. Savile, George. Halifax, marq. of. *Observations upon a late libel, called a letter from a person of quality to his friend, concerning the kings declaration.* [London]: (f. C. Mason), (1681). Fol. Pp. 8.
Wood 657(22). Wing H317 ('O' not recorded in Wing).

5767. [Savile, George]. Halifax, marq. of. *A seasonable address to . . . parliament concerning the succession; the fears of popery, and arbitrary government.* London: n.pub., 1681. 4°. Pp. [2], 20.
Pp. 3, 7-9, 12-14, 17-9, AW identified, mainly, initialed references (most cropped at outer edge); and some underscoring. Diff. ed. at Wood 608(59).
Wood 608(56). Wing H320 (Wing, records a variant only at Yale).

5768. [Savile, George]. Halifax, marq. of. *A seasonable address to . . . parliament concerning the succession; the fears of popery, and arbitrary government.* London: n.pub., 1681. 4°. Reset ed. Pp. [2], 20.
Tp, AW wrote 'Dupl.', in pencil. Diff. ed. at Wood 608(56).
Wood 608(59) (not in Bodl. CD cat.). Wing H320 (Wing, records a variant only at Yale).

5769. Savile, Henry. *Oratio, coram reginae Elizabetha Oxoniae habita; aliaeque doctiss: virorum opellae posthumae.* Oxoniae: typ. Lichfieldianis, 1658. 4°. Pp. [8], 34 (p. [8] blank).
Tp, AW wrote the price, '4ᵈ'; below, 'published by Dʳ Barlow', in pencil; and bsm. P. 7, AW wrote in the margin at a Greek t, 'in passionem Xᵗⁱ carmina Graeca.' P. 19, at 'Langbain,' mark in margin, in pencil (a section, 'Mensa lubrica', was published separately, see T. Masters, Wood 416(5) and Wood 440(3), items 4408-9). Diff. ed. is at T. Master, Wood 113(2) and 512(14), items 4406, 4404. Acquired 29 Aug. 1662, LT 1.454 (see also LT 2.239).
Wood 512(4). Wing S774. Madan 2369.

5770. [Savile, Henry]. *Advice to a painter, &c.* [London]: n.pub., [1679?]. Fol. Pp. 4.
AW wrote the date, '(1679)'. A name underscored and written in the margin, 'Darby', prob. not by AW.
Wood 417(11). Wing S774A.

5771. Sawyer, Thomas. *Antigamus or a satyr against marriage.* [Oxford]: n.pub., [1681]. 4°. Pp. 6.
Flyleaf, upper, AW wrote, 'Sayer of Magd. Coll' in pencil, and in ink, 'Tho. Sawyer of Magd. Coll was the author of Antigamus following – see Ahenae [sic] et Fasti Oxon vol. 2. p. 884', i.e., AOF 2.1680, where AW gave a publ. date of 1681.
Wood 654a(32). Wing S786 (rare) (Wing, Antigamus; or, and [1691]).

5772. Saxon. *The picture of a Saxon taken from Trajan's pillar in Rome.* N.p.: n.pub., n.d. S.sh. (engr.).
Missing in 1939 (a delete sign before the entry in the 1717 list).
Wood 276a(4). Not identified.

5773. Saxton, Christopher. *The kingdome of England 'Described by Christopher Saxton, augmented by John Speed. Abraham Goos . . . sculpsit Anno 1632 [or 1630]'.* [London]: solde by G. Humble, n.d. S.sh.
441 x 566 mm (untrimmed; mutilated and repaired).
Reprinted in Speed, *Theatre*.
Wood 276b(6). See STC 23041ff..

5774. Sayer, John. *The case of the widdow and children of John Sayer esq; deceased, and William Lightfoot.* [London?]: n.pub., [1690]. S.sh.
Wood 276b(95). Wing C1178A (two).

5775. Sayer, Joseph. *A sermon [on Rom. xiii. 5] preached at Reading, Feb. 25. 1672, at the assizes.* London: f. H. Brome, 1673. 4°. Pp. 40.
Tp, AW underscored 'Sayer', in red ink. Text, some horizontal lines in margins, prob. not by AW.
Wood 633(14). Wing S797.

5776. Scap. *Lexicon.* Lugd.: ?, 1602. 4°.
Missing. In a list of 'Mr. Woods Duplicats', MS. Wood F. 51, f. 44, item 3.
MS. Wood F. 51(3). Not identified.

5777. Scarborough. *A great and bloudy fight at Scarborough-castle.* London: f. G. W., 1648, [July?]. 4°.
Pp. [2], 6.

Missing since 1840. See Wood 502(1), item 4718. AW wrote the t on the upper flyleaf as: 'Bloody fight at Scarborough in Yorksh'. It was replaced in 1874 by the present no. 46 (Packet of Letters, numb. 20 (Newsbooks), i.e., 46b, item 4720 in this cat.). No. 45 (Colchester) is also recorded by Kirtland as missing, both on the upper flyleaf and on a blank leaf inserted before the present item 46 (i.e., 46b). But on the upper flyleaf, AW added after the entry, 'see afterwards', and in the margin drew a hand pointer and wrote, 'Vide Nu. 63' (item 1935) which is a dupl. of no. 45 (Colchester). AW himself removed the former no. 45 and placed it in an unbound bundle, later bound by the Ashm. and now at Wood 609(14), item 1936. The former number, '45', is still on the tp.
Wood 502(46a). Wing G1638 (two). *BL, Clark.*

5778. Scargill, Daniel. *The recantation of Daniel Scargill, publickly made before the university of Cambridge.* [Cambridge]: by the printers, 1669. 4°. Pp. 8.
Tp, AW wrote, 'For being an Hobbist & Atheist: see in Hobs life published in Lat. 1680 -' and the price, '2ᵈ'. AO 3.1213.
Wood 608(45). Wing S823A.

5779. [Schoppe, Caspar]. *Alphonsi de Vargas Toletani [pseud.] relatio ad reges & principes christianos de stratagematis . . . societatis Jesu.* [Padua?]: n.pub., 1636. 4°. Pp. 111. 4 pts.
Wood 619(5) (not in Bodl. CD cat.). BL.

5780. Schouten, Willem Cornelis. P[hilip], W., trans. *The relation of a wonderfull voiage . . . south from the straights of Magelan, in Terra Del-fuogo.* London: T. D[awson] f. N. Newbery, 1619. 4°. Pp. [8], 82.
Flyleaf, waste paper, a disputation topic, 'An oppositio contradictoria sit omnium maxima.' and '43', not by AW. Tp, AW wrote, '4ᵈ'; and a scribble, not in AW's hand. Acquired 16 Apr. 1667, LT 2.131.
Wood 387(4). STC 21828.

5781. Schurman, Anna Maria van. B[arksdale], C[lement], trans. *The learned maid; or, whether a maid may be a scholar?.* London: J. Redmayne, 1659. 8°. Pp. [7], 55. Pasteboard (brown) with calf spine; 1st upper and last lower flyleaves, marbled paper; rebacked.
Flyleaf, 2nd, AW wrote the titles of 5 printed works in this vol., within guidelines made with red ink. Tp, AW wrote, '3ᵈ.' and 'Translated, & published by Clem. Barksdale of Winchcombe'.
Wood 130(1). Wing S902.

5782. S[cobell], H[enry]. *The power of the lords and commons in parliament in point of judicature briefly discours'd.* London: n.pub., 1680. 4°. Pp. 11.
Tp, AW altered the date to 1679. P. 3, at the French king (Louis 14) being 'the most potent monarch in Europe', AW wrote, 'how does that appeare.'
Wood 518(8). Wing S927.

5783. Scot, Patrick. *Vox vera: or, observations from Amsterdam. Examining the late insolencies of some pseudo-Puritans, separatists.* London: B. Alsop, 1625. 4°. Pp. [6], 62 (imperf., A2ᵛ, A3ʳ blank).
Wood 647(2). STC 21863.

5784. Scot, Philip. *A treatise of the schism of England. Wherein particularly mr. Hales and mr. Hobbs are modestly accosted.* [London] Amsterdam: n.pub., 1650. 12°. Pp. [8], 273, [1]. Calf, mottled; 3 fillets.
Wood 772. Wing S942.

5785. Scot, Reginald. *A perfite platforme of a hoppe garden, and necessarie instructions for the making . . . thereof . . . by Reynolde Scot.* London: H. Denham, 1576. 4°. Newly corrected (wanting sig. A1, blank). Pp. [12], 63, [1].
Tp, AW wrote 'Septemb: xxij: A: D: MDCLx:'. LT 1.332.
Wood 618(2). STC 21866.

5786. Scot, Thomas, pseud. *The last will and testament of Carolus Gustavus king of Sweden, &c. translated out of the Swedish.* [London?]: f. W. Leadsom, 1660. 4°. Pp. 7.
Tp, AW altered the year to 16'59: March'.
Wood 610(14). Wing L515 ('O' not recorded in Wing).

5787. Scotch Presbyterian. *The Scotch presbyterian weather-cock pearch'd upon our English steeples: . . . presbyterian government in Scotland [in verse].* [London]: n.pub., 1647. 4°. Pp. [2], 6.
[MS.] Wood D. 26(7). Wing S960.

5788. Scotchman. *A true relation of a Scotchman, who comming into the church of St. Olaves . . . in*

London, . . . did much disturb them [5 Sept.]. London: T. Harper, 1641. 4°. A⁴.
Tp, bsm.
Wood 647(4). Wing T2891 (two) ('O' not recorded in Wing).

5789. Scotland. *Respublica, sive status regni Scotiae et Hiberniae. Diversorum autorum.* Lugd. Bat.: ex off. Elzeviriana, 1627. 16°. Pp. 280, [1].
Wood 196(2). BL (A. Willems, *Les Elzevier* (Brussels, 1880), no. 287).

5790. Scotland. *The charge of the Scottish commissioners against Canterburie [William Laud] and the lievetenant of Ireland [Thomas Wentworth].* London: f. N. Butter, 1641. 4°. Pp. [2], 53.
See note at Wood 366(1), item 6505.
Wood 366(19). Wing C4201L.

5791. Scotland. *Letters and papers from the committe [sic] of estates, and commissioners of Scotland, concerning the king . . . giving his consent to the surrender of Newarke to the parliament. 6th [really 5th] and 8th May 1646.* London: f. L. Chapman, 1646. 4°. Pp. 8 (pp. unopened).
Wood 501(10). Wing S1290.

5792. Scotland. *The answer of the commissioners . . . of Scotland, to both houses of parliament, upon the new propositions of peace, and the foure bills [17 Dec.].* London: f. R. Bostoch, 1647. 4°. Pp. 32.
Tp, AW wrote 'Dec. 17'; 'Four dethroning Bills' may be in AW's hand.
Wood 612(56b). Wing S1180.

5793. Scotland. *A letter from the parliament of Scotland, to . . . William Lenthall . . . Edenburgh, 26 Junii 1649.* [London]: n.pub., [1649]. S.sh.
Wood 276a(253). Wing S1284.

5794. Scotland. *A letter sent from the commissioners of Scotland, to . . . Monck, in the behalf of themselves and the whole nation [3 Mar. 1660].* London: f. D. White, 1660. 4°. Pp. 6.
AW altered the year, twice, to, 16'59'.
Wood 632(77). Wing S999B.

5795. Scotland. *A true relation of the inhuman cruelties lately acted by the rebels in Scotland.* London: A. M. a. R. R, 1679. 4°. Pp. [2], 6.
Wood 365(31). Wing T2971.

5796. Scotland. *A breviate of the state of Scotland in its government.* London: f. R. Chiswell, 1689. Fol. Pp. [2], 16.
Tp, AW wrote the price, '6ᵈ'.
Wood 559(23). Wing B4415.

5797. Scotland, Army. *A true relation of the late proceedings of the Scottish army, sent from his excellency the lord generall Lesley's quarters [8 Feb.].* London: f. R. Bostock, a. S. Gellibrand, 1643[4]. 4°. Pp. [2], 13.
Tp, AW lined out the former no., '58'.
Wood 376(64). Wing T2990.

5798. Scotland, Army. *A true relation of the proceeings [sic] of the Scotch army . . . until 30. July.* London: M. B. f. R. Bostock, 1645, 4 Aug. 4°. Pp. [2], 5.
Tp, AW altered the former no., '16'.
Wood 378(18). Wing T3025.

5799. Scotland, Army. *Truths discovery of a black cloud in the north: shewing some . . . proceedings of the Scotch army against the well-affected in the north of England.* [London]: n.pub., [1646]. 4°. Pp. 12.
Tp, above, 'B'.
Wood 501(19). Wing T3168.

5800. Scotland, Army. *A declaration of the Scottish army, concerning their present designe . . . to preserve and defend the kings majestie, and to gain his libertie from the Isle of Wight.* London: J. C. f. I. I., 1648. 4°. Pp. [2], 6.
Wood 502(2). Wing D764A ('O' not recorded in Wing).

5801. Scotland, Church of. *The ordoure and doctrine of the generall fast, appointed be the generall assemblie . . . [25 Dec. 1565, followed by] Certaine chapters and partes of the scriptures used . . . in the*

tyme of Godes visitatiō be the pest. Edinburgh: R. Lekprevik, 1574. 8°. A-D⁸,E⁴,F².
Tp, signature of Hum: Dyson, and scribbles in 2 hands; ᵛ, scribbles. Text, some scribbles, none by AW.
Wood 774(2). STC 22043.

5802. Scotland, Church of. *The confession of the true & Christian fayth, according to Gods word, and actes of parliament, holden at Edenburghe [28 Jan. 1581].* London: R. Waldegrave, [1581]. 8° in 4's. A-F⁴.
Tp, signature of Hum: Dyson.
Wood 774(5). STC 22022.

5803. Scott, James*. Monmouth, duke of. *For the right noble and potent prince James duke of Bucclengh [sic] and Monmouth, . . . The humble supplication of the non-conformists . . . now in arms . . . [signed] R. Hamilton.* N.p.: n.pub., [1679?]. S.sh.
Correction in t to Buccleugh.
Wood 660c(8). Wing F1438A (one) ('O' not recorded in Wing).

5804. Scott, James*. Monmouth, duke of. *A relation of the birth, as well as of several remarkable passages during the minority of the . . . duke of Monmouth, . . . with . . . his . . . victories.* [Edinburgh?]: n.pub., [1679]. Fol. Pp. 8.
P. 7, AW wrote, at '79', '1679'.
Wood 660c(2). Wing R816.

5805. Scott, James*. Monmouth, duke of. *A true account of the great victory obtained over the rebels in Scotland, . . . under the command of . . . the duke of Monmouth. In a letter [22 June].* [London]: n.pub., [1679]. Fol. Pp. 4.
Wood 660c(3). Wing T2370.

5806. Scott, James*. Monmouth, duke of. *A true narrative of the duke of Monmouth's late journey into the West, in a letter.* (London): (printed, sold R. Janeway), (1680). Fol. Pp. 4.
Wood 660c(4a). Wing T2786.

5807. Scott, James. Monmouth, duke of. *[Begin] Whereas Nat. Thompson hath lately [A statement, dated 2 Nov. 1681 and signed Monmouth, F. Grey, Herbert, occasioned by imputations in the Public intelligence of 25 Oct.].* [London]: n.pub., [1681]. S.sh.
Wood 660c(26). Wing W1628.

5808. Scott, James*. Monmouth, duke of. *The duke of Monmouth's case, with all the very strange crimes, and great misdemeanors alledged against his grace.* (London): (f. J. C.), [1682]. S.sh. (r-v).
Wood 660c(4b). Wing D2509.

5809. Scott, James*. Monmouth, duke of. *A true and impartial account of the duke of Monmouth's being taken into custody [25 September].* (London): (f. A. Johnson), (1682). Fol. Pp. 4.
Wood 660c(5). Wing T2491.

5810. Scott, James*. Monmouth, duke of. *An account of what passed at the execution of the late duke of Monmouth [15 July].* (London): (f. R. Horne, J. Baker, a. B. Tooke), (1685). Fol. Pp. 4.
Pp. 1, former no '36', in pencil; 4, AW wrote below imprint, 'published about 25 Jul. 85'. LT 3.154.
Wood 660c(9). Wing A433.

5811. [Scott, Thomas]. *Vox populi. Or newes from Spayne, translated according to the Spanish coppie.* [London?]: n.pub., 1620. 4°. A-C⁴,D².
Tp, AW wrote in pencil, '2 part with Gondamares picture' (i.e., the Spanish ambassador, marq. de Gondomar; the picture has been removed from part 2, Wood 511(9), item 5817; below, 'Dp [or Op]. 201' (?).
Wood 511(8). STC 22100.

5812. [Scott, Thomas]. *The Belgicke pismire: stinging the slothfull sleeper, and awaking the diligent to fast, watch.* London [really Holland]: n.pub., 1622. 4°. Pp. [12], 99, [1].
Tp, bsm.
Wood 617(21). STC 22069a.

5813. [Scott, Thomas], trans. *Newes from Pernassus. The politicall touchstone, . . . whereon the governments of the greatest monarchies of the world are touched [selections from T. Boccalini, Pietra del paragone politico].* Helicon [i.e. Holland]: n.pub., 1622. 4°. Pp. ['3-4'], '5-92', [3] (wanting pp. [1-2]).
Tp, bsm.
Wood 615(9a). STC 22080.

5814. [Scott, Thomas]. [Hexham, H., by?]. *An experimentall discoverie of Spanish practises. Or the counsell of a well-wishing souldier.* [London]: n.pub., 1623. 4°. Pp. [2], 54.
Diff. ed. at Wood 615(5).
Wood 511(10). STC 22077.5.

5815. [Scott, Thomas]. [Hexham, H., by?]. *An experimentall discoverie of Spanish practises or the counsell of a well-wishing souldier.* [London]: n.pub., 1623. 4°. Pp. [2], 54.
Diff. ed. at Wood 511(10).
Wood 615(5). STC 22077.3.

5816. [Scott, Thomas]. *Certaine reasons and arguments of policie, why the king of England should . . . enter into warre with the Spaniard.* [London]: n.pub., 1624. 4°. A-B⁴.
Wood 511(11). STC 22073.6.

5817. S[cott], T[homas]. *[The second part of vox populi, or Gondomar appearing in the likeness of Matchiavell in a Spanish parliament. Tr. out of the Span. coppie, or rather written by a well-willer to England and Holland [signing himself T. S. of U. Issued as part of the workes of Thomas Scot, 1624]].* [Goricom, [Gorinchem], i.e., London]: [A. Janss, i.e., W. Jones], [1624]. 4°. 2nd ed. Pp. [4], 1-52, 55-60 (wanting the t leaf and sig. H1).
Leaves were removed after AW wrote the note in Scott, Wood 511(8), item 5811.
Wood 511(9). STC 22104.

5818. [Scott, Thomas]. *Robert earle of Essex his ghost, sent from Elizian: to the nobility, gentry, and communaltie of England. [Followed by] A post-script.* Paradise [i.e., London]: [J. Beale?], 1624 [with a misdated tp]. 4°. Pp. [2], 18, [2], 11 (2 tpp).
Tp, title written (cropped at side) and 'S T', not by AW. Below, note cropped at bottom, not by AW.
Prob. acquired 29 Ap. 1658 out of G. Langbaine's study, LT 1.247.
Wood 586(10b). STC 22084a.

5819. Scott, William. *An essay of drapery: or, the compleate citizen. Trading justly.* London: E. All-de f. S. Pemell, 1635. 12°. Pp. [12], 169, [2].
Wood 739(2). STC 22109.

5820. Scotus, Romoaldus. *Summarium rationum, quibus cancellarius Angliae et prolocutor Puckeringius Elizabethae . . . persuaserunt occidendam esse . . . Mariam Stuartam Scotiae reginam:. . . His additum est supplicium et mors reginae Scotiae.* Coloniae: sumpt. P. Henningii, 1627. 8°. Pp. [2], 109, [7].
Wood 890(2) (listed with R. Turner, Wood 890(3), item 6254, in Bodl. CD cat.). BL.

5821. [Scroggs, William*]. *Good deeds ill requited: or, an answer to innocence unveil'd. Being a poem in vindication of dr. Oates and mr. Bedloe.* [London]: n.pub., [1679?]. S.sh. (r-v).
Wood 417(30). Wing G1042.

5822. Scroggs, William. *The answer of sir Willam [sic] Scroggs, kᵗ lord chief justice . . . to the articles of dr. Titus Oates, and mr. William Bedlow [21 Jan. 1679].* N.p.: n.pub., [1680]. S.sh. Pp. '3-4'.
Wood 276a(282). Wing O31A (part of).

5823. Scroggs, William*. *Innocence unveil'd: or, a poem on the acquittal of the lord chief justice Scroggs.* [London]: n.pub., [1680]. S.sh. (r-v).
AW wrote the year, '(1680)', in pencil (AO 4.115ff.).
Wood 417(29). Wing I194.

5824. Scroggs, William*. Philo-dicaios, signed by. *The triumphs of justice over unjust judges:. . . humbly dedicated to the lord chief Scroggs.* London: f. B. Harris, 1681. Fol. Pp. [4], 36.
Wood 426(34). Wing T2297.

5825. Scudamore, Barnabas. *A letter sent to the right honourable the lord Digby, from sir Barnabas Scudamore . . . concerning the late siedge of . . . Hereford.* Oxford: L. Lichfield, 1645. 4°. Pp. [2], 10.
Tp, AW wrote the date, 'Aug. 29.', and altered the former no.
Wood 378(21). Wing S2130. Madan 1815.

5826. Scudery, Madeleine de, of Almahide. *The history of Philoxypes and Polycrite, as it was told by Leontides to the great Cyrus. Englished out of French, by an honourable anti-Socordist.* London: H. Moseley, 1652. 8°. Pp. [2], 187.
Missing. In a list of 'Mr. Woods Duplicats', MS. Wood F. 51, f. 44, item 16.

MS. Wood F. 51(16). Wing S2159A. *O.*

5827. Seagar, Francis, and Robert Crowley. *The schoole of vertue, and booke of good nurture, . . . Newly perused. Also certaine prayers and graces by R. C.* London: M. Flesher f. R. Bird, [1635 ca.]. 8°. A2-8,B-C⁸. Pasteboard (blue) with parchment spine. 1st upper and last lower flyleaves, marbled paper.
Flyleaf, upper, 2nd, figures, a subtraction; 3rdᵛ, AW wrote the titles of 5 printed works in this vol., within guidelines made with red ink. Tp, AW wrote 'Rob. Crowley the author - see the first vol. of Ath. et Fasti Oxon p. [blank]' (AO 1.542ff.). B⁸, an early signature, 'Anthony Wood'; C7ᵛ, 'Mary Wood'.
Wood 792(1). STC 22138.5 (rare).

5828. Seasonable Advertisement. *A seasonable advertisement to the honourable city of London. Gentlemen, after so many no less unlawfull.* N.p.: n.pub., [1660 ca.]. S.sh.
Wood 276a(276). Wing S2205A.

5829. Sedgwick, Joseph. *A sermon [on 1 Cor. 14.1] preached at Sᵗ. Marie's in the university of Cambridge May 1ˢᵗ, 1653. Or, an essay to the discovery of the spirit . . . that disturbs . . . the universities: Together with an appendix, wherein mʳ. Del's stumblingstone is briefly repli'd unto.* London: R. D. f. E. Story, in Cambridge, 1653. 4°. Pp. [6], 57 (2 tpp).
Flyleaf, upper, 1stᵛ, astrological symbols and numbers. Tp, AW underscored the name of the author, in red ink.
[MS.] Wood B. 24(4). Wing S2362. Madan 2214.

5830. Selby, James*. *The unhappy citizen. A faithful narrative of the life and death of James Selby.* London: f. E. Brand, [1691]. 4°. Pp. 12.
Tp, AW wrote, 'Bought at Oxōn 14. May 1691' (Selby was executed on 2 May 1691).
Wood 173(5). Wing U66A. ESTCR 188778.

5831. [Selby, Richard]. Rubeus [Reed/Read], Joannes, ed. *Tabula votiva appensa tholo s. Scholasticae . . . A p. Joanne Rubeo.* Romae: ex typog. J. Dragondelli, 1659. 4°. Pp. [18], 172, [4].
Tp, after Rubeo, AW wrote, '– ie Read, de com. Ebor.'; below, 'Antonii à Wood. Oxon. ex dono Sereni Cressey, per manus D. Rad. Sheldon de Beoly, 21. July 1671'. LT 2.227 (AW's first gift from Sheldon).
Wood 644(3). Not in BL.

5832. Selden, John. *Marmora Arundelliana; sive saxa Graecè incisa . . . Publicavit . . . Joannes Seldenus.* Londini: G. Stanesbeii, 1628. 4°. Pp. [18], 182, [2].
LT 2.119.
Wood 318(4). STC 823. Madan 600.

5833. Selden, John. *The priviledges of the baronage of England, when they sit in parliament.* London: T. Badger f. M. Wallbanck, 1642. 8°. Pp. [6], 167.
Tp, 'ABosco', in red ink, and an illeg. note. Pp. 8-9, correction, and at a reference to bishop of Bristol (J. Thornborough) and a book he wrote, line in margin; 83, correction.
Wood 457(2). Wing S2434.

5834. Selden, John. Θεανθρωπος: *or, God made man. A tract proving the nativity . . . to be on the 25. of December.* London: J. G. f. N. Brooks [sic], 1661. 8°. Pp. [8], 91, [20] (20 pp. books sold by Brook [sic]) (wanting the frontisportrait).
Tp, AW wrote 'December: 1660.' 1st p. [7] at the 'Epitaphium' for Selden, AW wrote 'This epitaph is in the Inner Temple church, & I have printed it in his life, in Hert hall, in the Hist. & antiquities of the Univers. of Oxon.' (i.e., *Historia et antiquitates*; see also AO 3.378-9). Pp. [1-20], AW wrote in odd p. nos. (3-19); in the 20 pp. of books sold by 'Brook' he marked 28 items in some way (lines, underscoring, author's name, identification). Acquired 9 Jan. 1661, 1ˢ, LT 1.380.
Wood 883(2). Wing S2439.

5835. Selden, John. Milward, Richard, ed. *Table-talk: the discourses of John Selden.* London: f. E. Smith, 1689. 4°. Pp. [4], 60.
Tp, AW wrote, 'Jan. 23.1688[9] – 1ˢ – 0.', LT 3.296.
Wood 533(19). Wing S2437.

5836. [Seller, Abednego]. *A plain answer to a popish priest questioning the orders of the Church of England.* London: f. J. Howell in Oxford, 1688. 4°. Pp. [2], 6.
Tp, AW wrote, 'Abednego Sellers the author – Ex dono Arth. Charlet e coll. Trin. Maii . . . ' (cropped at

side and bottom).
[MS.] Wood B. 40(12). Wing S2458.

5837. Seller, John. *A new systeme: of geography, . . . accommodated with new mapps.* [London]: sold at his shop, [1685]. 8°. Pp. [4], 112, plus coloured maps. Calf, speckled, with 2 fillets.
Pastedown, upper, numbers, not by AW; flyleaf, lower, last, a subtraction.
Wood 665. Wing S2477.

5838. Seneca, Lucius Annaeus. Heywood, Jasper, trans. *The seconde tragedie of Seneca entituled Thyestes.* London: in the hous late T. Berthelettes, 1560, 26 March. 8°. *-**⁸, A-D⁸,E⁶.
Missing. MS. Wood E. 2(70), p. 53, 'The 2d Tragedie of Seneca – 1560 – Jasp. Heywood'.
MS. Wood E. 2(70), p. 53. STC 22226. *O, Folg, Hunt.*

5839. Seneca, Lucius Annaeus. Golding, Arthur, trans. *The woorke of . . . Lucius Annaeus Seneca concerning benefyting.* London: [J. Kingston f.] J. Day, 1578. 4°. Tp is a cancel. Ff. [4], 120. Parchment.
Tp, 'John Knighte hys boke, by the guyfte of Mr Arthure Robyns.' Text, some underscoring and marks in margin, not in AW's manner. Flyleaves, lower, two 8-line poems, one in English and one in Latin, in 2 hands, neither in AW's.
[MS.] Wood B. 28(b). STC 22215.

5840. Seneca, Lucius Annaeus. Newton, Thomas, trans. *Seneca his tenne tragedies.* London: T. Marsh, 1581. 4°. Ff. [3], 217.
Missing. MS. Wood E. 2(70), p. 51, 'Seneca in English – 1581 – Tho Newton he hath put out Leylands epigrams - q[uaere; i.e., STC 15447] . . . In this booke are 3. playes of Jasper Heywood . . . four playes by Joh. Studley [i.e. translated by] – This booke must be perused – & the epistles before every play'. See AO 2.10, 1.664.
MS. Wood E. 2(70), p. 51. STC 22221. *Folg* (4 copies), *Hunt, NYPL.*

5841. Seneca, Lucius Annaeus. Farnaby, Thomas, ed. *L. & M. Annaei Senecae tragoediae.* London: F. Kyngston, imp. P. Stephani & C. Meredith, 1634. 8°. 3rd ed. Pp. [8], 391, [9].
Missing. MS. Wood E. 2(70), p. 10, 'Tho. Farnabie his edit. & revise of Senecaes [sic] tragedies 1634'.
MS. Wood E. 2(70), p. 10. STC 22220. *Hunt, Yale.*

5842. Seneca, Lucius Annaeus. Sherburne, Edward, trans. *Troades: or the royal captives, a tragedy.*
London: A. Godbid a. J. Playford f. S. Carr, 1679. 8°. Pp. [6], 118, [10].
Missing. MS. Wood E. 2(70), p. 60.
MS. Wood E. 2(70), p. 60. Wing S2528. *O, Hunt, Harv.*

5843. [Sergeant, John]. *The method to arrive at satisfaction in religion [signed N. N.].* [London]: n.pub., [1671]. 12°. Pp. [8], 37.
Each 12° leaf is pasted on an 8° template. Tp, AW wrote 'John Sarjeant [and above, Sargeant], the author. i67i.'
Wood 869(3). Wing S2578.

5844. Sergeant, John, and David Maurice. *The informations of John Sergeant, and David Maurice,* } *gentlemen; relating to the popish-plot.* London: f. G. Kunholt, 1681. Fol. Pp. [3], 7.
1st blank, AW wrote the price, '4ᵈ'.
Wood 427(15). Wing S2572.

5845. Sergier, Richard, trans. *The present state of Spaine. Translated out of French.* London: P. S[hort] f. R. Serger, 1594. 4°. 1,*,A2-4,B-E⁴,2E²,F-G⁴,H1.
C3, underscoring and line in margin, not by AW.
Wood 511(5a). STC 22997.

5846. Serres, Jean de. Golding, Arthur, trans. *The lyfe of . . . capteine . . . Jasper Colignie Shatilion.* London: T. Vautrollier, 1576. 8°. A-G⁸,H⁶.
Tp, bsm.
Wood 292(4). STC 22248.

5847. Serres, Jean de, and Pierre de La Place. Timme, Thomas, trans. *The three partes of commentaries, . . . the civill warres of Fraunce, under the raignes of Henry the second . . . Charles the ninth . . . with an addition of the cruell murther of the admirall Chastilion.* London: F. Coldocke (H. Middleton f.), 1574. 4°. Pp. [16], 271, [24], 267, [5], 494 [i.e. 309], ff. 38 (misnumbering; 3 tpp). Calf with 3 fillets,

3 inner rectangles and stamp decoration with 'IOHA', 'MAR', 'ERAS' and 'PHIL' and heads in margins; metal clasp fittings.
Flyleaf, upper[v], 'm' over 'a', bsm? F. 38[v] (last leaf), practice in the Hebrew alphabet, prob. not by AW.
Wood 340. STC 22241.5.

5848. [Settle, Elkanah]. *The prologue to pastor Fido. . . . The epilogue.* [London]: n.pub., [1677]. S.sh. Obl.
AW wrote, 'written by Elkanah Settle 1677'.
Wood 416(132). Wing S2713 (rare).

5849. [Settle, Elkanah]. *The life and death of major Clancie, the grandest cheat of this age.* London: D. Mallet, 1680. 4°. Pp. [8], 150.
Tp, bsms. AW inserted a blank leaf after quires A and B on which he added details about the colourful but 'sharking' Major, whom he knew very well, for he was a lodger with Mary Wood, at AW's own residence, during the plague year, 1665. At the same time the King and Queen kept their courts in Oxford. The 44-line passage is quoted in full at LT 2.48-9. Flyleaf, lower, 1st, a classification of all the printed works in this bundle before it was bound: 'Murders Robberies –', prob. not by AW; last, a drawing and below it, 'Major Clancie', prob. not by AW.
Wood 173(6). Wing S2696A.

5850. Settle, Elkanah*. *A character of the true blue protestant poet: or, the pretended author of the character of a popish successor.* (London): (f. A. Banks), (1682). Fol. Pp. 4.
Tp, at 'poet', AW wrote, 'Elkanah Settle'; p. 4, after year, 'Aprill'. LT 3.141.
Wood 657(12). Wing C2028.

5851. [Settle, Elkanah]. *Animadversions on the last speech and confession of the late William lord Russel.* (London): (f. T. Graves), (1683). Fol. Pp. 4.
Tp, AW wrote, '3[d]'. P. 4, 'Said to be written by Elkanah Settle the poet/'.
Wood 428(13). Wing S2656.

5852. [Settle, Elkanah]. *Animadversions upon a paper, entituled, the speech of the late lord Russel.* (London): (for T. Dring), (1683). Fol. Pp. 4.
Tp, AW wrote, '2[d]'.
Wood 428(12). Wing S2658.

5853. [Settle, Elkanah]. *Remarks on Algernoon [sic] Sidney's paper delivered to the sherriffs.* (London): (f. W. C., sold W. Davis), (1683). Fol. Pp. 4.
P. 4, after printed date, AW wrote, 'in the latter end of Dec.', and, 'Elk. Settle the author'. LT 3.82.
Wood 428(21). Wing S2715.

5854. [Settle, Elkanah]. *The notorious impostor, or the history of the life of William Morrell, alias Bowyer.* London: f. A. Roper, 1692. 4°. Pp. [4], 36.
Tp, AW wrote, 'Bought of H[arry] Cl[ement] in the beg[.] of Mar. 1691[2]. It was also printed in 8°, an. 1694 for a pocket book'. LT 3.384.
Wood 372(17). Wing S2703 ('O' not recorded in Wing).

5855. [Settle, Elkanah]. *The second part of The notorious imposter, . . . William Morrell, alias Bowyer.* London: f. A. Roper, 1692. 4°. Pp. [4], 36.
Tp, AW wrote, 'of H[arry] Cl[ement] in the beg[.] of Mar. 1691', in red ink.
Wood 372(18). Wing S2717aA (two) ('O' not recorded in Wing).

5856. Seven Arguments. *Seven arguments plainly proving that papists are trayterous subjects.* [London]: n.pub., 1641. 4°. Pp. 15. Calf with 3 fillets, a vertical line of 3 fillets, and edge hatching; spine, 4 bands and hatching (Oxford binding; similar to S. Gibson, *Early Oxford Bindings* (OBS, 1903), plate xxx, no. 5, bound about 1645).
Tp, AW wrote, 'Ant: Woode: Coll: Mertō:' and later, 'Oxōn 1656:' (with, later still, 16'6'6 written over 16'5'6). AW acquired this vol. of 4 items in 1656. Bsm. LT 1.211.
[MS.] Wood C. 44(1). Wing S2735.

5857. [Severn, Thomas], and Charles Potter. Πυθαγορας μετεμψυχος. *Sive theses quadragesimales in scholis Oxonii publicis Mart: V. & XXVI. pro forma discussae. A.D. M.DC.XL.IX./L . . . Respondente Carolo Potter.* Oxonii: H. H[all] impen. R. Davis, 1651. 12°. Pp. [6], 137, [17]. Calf with 2 fillets; flyleaves, upper and lower, printer's waste paper. Rebacked.

Tp and A3, note, or letters of the alphabet, cropped at bottom. AO 3.648-9 and LT 1.243.
Wood 689. Wing S2817. Madan 2177.

5858. Severus, Sulpicius. Sleidanus, Johannes ed. *Sacra historia continuata ex Johannis Sleydani libro de quatuor summis imperiis*. Lugduni Batavorum: ex off. B. & A. Elzevir, 1626. 8°. Pp. 271. Calf, mottled, with 3 fillets and edge hatching; spine, 4 bands and hatching (Oxford binding).
Tp, at top, former no., '23' (?). Bsm.
Wood 847. BL. BL, 'Historia sacra'.

5859. S[hadwell], T[homas]. *On the most noble James [Murray], earl of Annandale*. [London]: n.pub., [1659]. S.sh.
AW wrote, 'He died before the restauration of K. Ch. 2'; ᵛ, 'Jam. E. of Annandale'; below, 3 references to Latin works, partially covered by binding, not by AW.
Wood 429(10). Wing S2864 (two).

5860. Shakespeare, William. *Venus and Adonis*. London: J. H[aviland], sold F. Coules, 1630. 8°. A-C⁸,D⁴ (D4 blank).
Sig. A1, AW wrote, 'Written by Will. Shakspeare.'
Wood 79(9) (now Arch. G. f. 2(9)). STC 22364 (rare).

5861. Shakespeare, William. *[Poems]*. [London]: [T. Cotes, sold J. Benson], [1640]. 8°. A2-8,B-L⁸, M1-2 (wanting 1,A1,*⁴,M3-4). Calf, two fillets on upper and lower boards; rebacked.
Sigs. L8 to end, signatures, e.g., Elizabeth, Frances, and Susnna [sic] Ayliffe, Ayliffe, Aylife.
Wood 80. STC 22344.

5862. Shakespeare, William. *The tragoedy of Othello*. London: W. Leak, 1655. 4°. 4th ed. Pp. [2], 92 (imperf., ends at p. 92).
Tpᵛ, the 'Dramatis Personae', men (9) and women (3), of a performance, not by AW.
Wood 320(7). Wing S2939.

5863. Sharp, James*. St. Andrews, abp. of. *A true account of the horrid murther committed upon his grace, the late lord archbishop of Saint Andrews*. London: T. N. f. A. Forrester, 1679. Fol. Pp. 7.
Wood 422(4). Wing T2375 (Wing, John Sharp).

5864. Sharp, James*. St. Andrews, abp. of. *A true relation of what is discovered concerning the murther of the archbᵖ of St. Andrews*. [London]: n.pub., [1679]. Fol. Pp. 4.
Tp, AW wrote, '1679: v. Gazet.', in pencil. Dupl. at Wood 657(14).
Wood 422(5). Wing T3080.

5865. Sharp, James*. St. Andrews, abp. of. *A true relation of what is discovered concerning the murther of the archbᵖ of St. Andrews*. [London]: n.pub., [1679]. Fol. Pp. 4.
Tp, AW wrote 'Dupl' in pencil. Dupl. at Wood 422(5).
Wood 657(14). Wing T3080.

5866. Sharpe, Leonell. *Oratio funebris in honorem Henrici . . . Walliae principis propriam atque intimam ejus effigiem praeferens*. Londini: G. Hall, 1612. 4°. Pp. [6], 16.
Tp, after the author, AW wrote 'Cantab.'
Wood 616(13). STC 22375.

5867. Shaw, Hester. *A plaine relation of my sufferings, by that . . . combustion, which happened in Tower-street . . . 4. of January 1650*. London: n.pub., 1653. 4°. Pp. [4], 15.
Tp, '(Hester Shaw)', prob. not by AW.
[MS.] Wood D. 28(12). Wing S3019.

5868. S[heafe], T[homas]. Gouge, William, ed. *Vindiciae senectutis, or, a plea for old-age*. London: G. Miller, 1639. 8° (tp a cancel). Pp. [25], 210, [10].
AW added the name of the author at the list of contents on the upper flyleaf.
Wood 747(2). STC 22391.8.

5869. Sheep's Skin. *The sheeps skin pull'd off from the wolfs back: or the uncasing of the knight*. [London]: n.pub., [1680]. S.sh. (r-v).
AW wrote the year, '1683', in pencil.
Wood 417(119). Wing S3056 (Wing, wolf's).

5870. [**Sheeres, Henry**]. *A discourse touching Tanger*. London: A. Godbid, 1680. 8°. Pp. 53.
Diff. ed. at Wood 386(14).
Wood 158(4). Wing S3058A.

5871. [**Sheeres, Henry**]. *A discourse touching Tanger*. London: n.pub., 1680. 4°. Pp. 40 (1-2 blank).
Tp, bsm. Diff. ed. at Wood 158(4).
Wood 386(14). Wing S3057.

5872. Sheffield, John. Buckingham, duke of. *An essay upon poetry*. London: f. J. Hindmarsh, 1682. 4°.
Pp. [2], 21.
Tp, 'By the Earl of Mulgrave', not in AW's hand, but by the same person who wrote the note in the
preceding item, Boileau-Despréaux, Wood 320(4), item 1032.
Wood 320(5). Wing B5339.

5873. Sheldon, Gilbert, Canterbury, abp of. *Gilbertus Sheldon archiepiscopius Cantuariensis*. N.p.:
n.pub., n.d. S.sh. (engr.).
There is no item at Wood 276a(7).
Wood 276a(8) (not in Bodl. CD cat.). *Engraved Portraits*, 4.80.

5874. [**Sheldon, Ralph**]. *[Book-plate]*. N.p.: n.pub., n.d. S.sh. 8° (engr.).
Ralph Sheldon's book-plate, a sheldrake, alone. See LT 3.104 and facing Plate I.
Wood 276b(40). BL *Cat. of Br. and Amer. Book Plates* (A. W. Franks Collection, ed. E. R. J. Gambier
Howe, 1904), cp. nos. 26649, 26651.

5875. [**Sheldon, Ralph**]. *[Coat of Arms]*. N.p.: n.pub., n.d. S.sh. 4° (engr.).
Ralph Sheldon's coat of arms, 3 sheldrakes. See LT 3.104 and facing Plate I.
Wood 276b(41).

5876. Shepery, John. *Hyppolitus Ovidianae Phaedrae respondens*. [Oxford]: excud. Jos. Barnesius, [1586].
8°. *8,A-D8. Pasteboard (brown) with calf spine; 1st flyleaf, trace of blue leaf; last flyleaf, blue leaf (Ashm.
rebinding).
Backing, upper, trace, 'Museo Ashm'; flyleaf, upper^v, AW wrote the titles of 7 printed works in this vol.,
within guidelines made with red chalk. Tp, AW wrote, 'An. 1584'. Bsm. Text, pencil lines in margins.
Wood 113(1). STC 22405. Madan 84.

5877. Shepery, John. *Summa et synopsis Novi Testamenti distichis ducentis sexaginta, . . . compre-
hensa:. . . à Laurentio Humfredo recognita*. Oxoniae: ex off. typ. J. Barnesii, 1586. 8°. A-C8,D6.
Missing. MS. Wood E. 2(70), p. 1. AO 1.135. Acquired 21 Sept. 1668, LT 2.143.
MS. Wood E. 2(70), p. 1. STC 22406. Madan 85. *O, Folg.*

5878. Sheppard, S[amuel]. *The yeare of jubile: or, Englands releasment, . . . under the command of
. . . sir Thomas Fairfax*. London: f. R. L., 1646. 4°. Pp. [4], 64.
Wood 501(20). Wing S3172 (Wing, or Englands).

5879. Sheppard, S[amuel]. *The committee-man curried, a comedy*. [London]: n.pub., 1647. 4°. Pp. [2],
13.
Wood 615(22a). Wing S3160.

5880. S[heppard], S[amuel]. *The second part of the committee-man curried*. [London]: n.pub., 1647. 4°.
Pp. [2], 12.
Wood 615(22b). Wing S3168.

5881. S[heppard], S[amuel]. *The secretaries studie: containing new familiar epistles*. London: T. H. f.
J. Harrison, 1652. 8°. Pp. [14], 279. Calf, speckled, with 3 fillets.
Flyleaves, upper, 1st-2nd, a draft of a letter, not by AW. Flyleaf, lower, 1st^v, name of AW, in pencil, lined
out; 2nd^v, 'Anthony Wood his booke 1656' and scribbled clauses in Latin and English.
Wood 711. Wing S3169.

5882. S[heppard], S[amuel]. *Fortunes tennis-ball: or, the . . . history of Dorastus and Fawnia*. [London]:
A. M. f. J. Deacon, 1688. 8°. A8,B4.
Wood 259(10). Wing S3165 (rare).

5883. Sheppard, W[illiam]. *The parsons guide: or the law of tythes*. London: f. W. Lee, H. Twyford, T.
Collins, J. Place, a. T. Basset, 1670. 12°. 2nd ed. Pp. [16], 99. Pasteboard (blue) with parchment spine;

upper and lower flyleaves, marbled paper. Rebacked.
Flyleaf, upper, 2nd[v], AW wrote the titles of 10 printed works in this vol., within guidelines made with red ink. Tp, '+' in bottom left corner.
Wood 370(1). Wing S3206.

5884. Sheringham, Robert. *De Anglorum gentis origine disceptatio*. Cantabrigiae: J. Hayes, imp. E. Story, 1670. 8°. Pp. [32], 488, [21].
Tp, AW wrote the price, '4ˢ6ᵈ in q.' (quires?) Text, several long notes in Latin, all are cropped, prob. by AW: pp. 10, 11 (2 sources for textual references to Pitseus: 'sic Th. James in Ecloga', 17, 38-40, 43 (extensive notes on Bede, Isle of Wight and early settlements of Germanic tribes, some in Old English and Greek), 51 (Greek source for name, Cimmerii, with a quotation in Greek), 153, 183 (origin of Getas, Gothas), 331 (comment on origin of the word, Eostrem, i.e., Easter), 363-4, 367-8, 373, and 381 (notes on ancient origins, relating to Berossus, and biblical passages, especially in Genesis 8), 397, 433 (extensive note on Tarsus), 436 (on the chronology of Abraham and Noah). Clark, LT 2.398, cited this item but wrote nothing of the annotation.
Wood 206(3). Wing S3236.

5885. Sherley, Thomas. *The case of Thomas Sherley esq; one of his majesties physitians in ordinary*. [London]: n.pub., [1678]. S.sh. (r-v).
AW wrote, '1678'; [v], 'This to be taken out of the letter When I have don', in red ink (AO 2.498 and 4.77). Also, a ms. copy of printed genealogy, not in AW's hand.
Wood 276b(83). Wing C1190 (rare).

5886. Sherlock, Ric[hard]. *Mercurius Christianus. The practical Christian, a treatise explaining the duty of self-examination*. London: R. Norton f. R. Royston, 1673. 12°. Pp. [15], 287, [1] (1 p. books printed f. Royston). Calf with one fillet.
Front edge, later signature, W. Stott 1766. Flyleaf, upper, 1st, 'Liber nescio cujus', by a later writer; 2nd[v], AW wrote 'Ant. à Wood. ex dono Authoris j Junii 1673.' LT 2.264.
Wood 831. Wing S3242.

5887. Sherlock, R[ichard]. *The second part of the practical Christian consisting of meditations, and Psalms illustrated with notes, or paraphrased*. London: R. N. f. R. Royston, 1675. 12°. Pp. [23], 347, [1]. Calf with 2 fillets; marbled edges.
Flyleaf, upper, 2nd[v], AW wrote 'Antonii à Wood ex dono authoris 3° [or 30] Junii 1675.' LT 2.316.
Wood 849. Wing S3255A (rare).

5888. [Shirley, John]. *The life of the valiant & learned sir Walter Raleigh, knight. With his tryal at Winchester*. London: J. D. f. B. Shirley, a. R. Tonson, 1677. 8°. Pp. 243, [1] (1 p. books sold by R. Tonson). Calf with 3 fillets and floral decoration (2 leaves, 4 pedalled flowers) in corners (Ashm. binding).
Flyleaf, upper, 4th[v], titles of 4 books in this vol., by an Ashm. librarian. Arabic nos., prob. by AW (some cropped), on the individual books in the vol. indicate that they were together before being bound by the Ashm. Tp, AW wrote 'written by Jo. Shirley A.m.'
Wood 433(1). Wing S3495.

5889. Shore, Jane*. *The history of mrs. Jane Shore. Concubine to k. Edward the fourth*. London: f. J. Clarke, W. Thackeray, & T. Passinger, [1688]. 8°. A⁸,B⁴.
Tp, AW wrote, 'Bought at Oxon. 1688'.
Wood 254(6). Wing H2125 (rare).

5890. Short Discourse. *A short discourse upon the desires of a friend: wherein . . . the perfect settlement of this nation*. London: f. H. H., 1660. 4°. Pp. [2], 13.
Tp, AW altered the year to '59: ffeb:'.
Wood 610(5). Wing S3590.

5891. Short, Richard. Περι ψυχροποσιας, *of drinking water. . . . Whereunto is added*, θερμοποσιας, *of warm drink*. London: f. J. Crook, 1656. 8°. Pp. [30], 173 (wanting the t leaf) (105-112 unopened).
AW copied information from a t-leaf to a blank leaf and inserted it here. A3, at printed '*Gregorie Oxoniensis, the late librarie keeper in Oxford*', AW wrote, 'no such person was libr. keeper unless of ch. ch. who was Joh. Gregory of that house.'
Wood 679(8). Wing S3528.

5892. Short Table, Italian and Spanish. *A short table, contayning the most usuall and hard wordes in the Italian tongue [and] in he [sic] Spanish tongue*. N.p.: n.pub., n.d. Fol. Pp. [8].

Some underscoring and entries in word lists, in two hands, in ink and pencil, neither in AW's hand. Wood 276a(25-6) (not in Bodl. CD cat.). Not identified.

5893. [Shower, Bartholomew]. *An antidote against poison: composed . . . upon the paper printed by the direction of the lady Russel.* (London): (f. C. Mearne), (1683). Fol. Pp. 7.
Tp, AW wrote, '3ᵈ' and 'Lady Rachell [Wriothesley] dau. & coheire of Thom. E. of S[out]hampt.'; p. 7, 'Said to be written by Heneage Finch Sollicitor Generall –'.
Wood 428(14). Wing S3648.

5894. Shrewsbury. *A letter from Shrewsbury, setting forth the design which the Anabaptists and Quakers had to secure the castle.* London: f. T. H., [1660]. S.sh.
AW altered 1660 to 16'59'.
Wood 503(31). Wing L1506 (two).

5895. Shropshire. *Shropshires misery and mercie. Manifested in the defeat given to the lord Capels ravenous . . . army.* London: f. T. Und[erhil], [1643], 8 Nov. 4°. Pp. [2], 6 (tp mutilated).
Tp, AW altered a former no.; below '1643' and in pencil, '1647 - q[uaere]'. Tpᵛ, 'for Mʳ Robert Warner, these deliver in Warwick', not in AW's hand.
Wood 376(46). Wing S3699.

5896. Shropshire, Declaration. *A declaration of the gentry of the county of Salop.* London: f. D. Pakeman, 1660. S.sh.
AW added to the year, 'Aprill:'.
Wood 276a(222). Wing D680A (two) ('O' not recorded in Wing).

5897. [Sibbald, James]. *The manner of the beheading of duke Hambleton, the earle of Holland, and the lord Capell [9 March 1648].* London: f. R. Ibbitson, [1649]. 4°. Pp. [2], 6.
Wood 366(33). Wing S3719.

5898. Sibscota, George. *The deaf and dumb man's discourse.* London: H. Bruges f. W. Crook, 1670. 8°.
Pp. [2], 89, [5] (5 pp. books printed for W. Crook).
Tp, price, '1'.
Wood 37(3). Wing S3748B.

5899. Sictor, Joh[n]. *Epitaphium honorabilis & consultissimi viri, domini Nathanaelis Brent [died, 6 Nov. 1652; buried, 17 Nov. 1652].* N.p.: n.pub., [1652?]. S.sh.
AW wrote, 'The figures for 1652. are contained I think in the two first verses'; a later writer lined out 'verses', and added, 'lines' (reading of upper case letters in the 2 verses); ᵛ, 'Sʳ Nath Brent 1651-2'; also, several sets of numbers or accounts which may not be by AW: '71 - 2 - 0', '76 - 4 - 6', '1569.3', and '3 1 10'. LT 1.162; LT 2.368ff.
Wood 429(7). Wing S3754A (rare).

5900. Sidney, Algernon. *The very copy of a paper delivered to the sheriffs, upon the scaffold . . . Decemb. 7. 1683 by Algernoon Sidney.* (London): (f. R. H., J. B., a. J. R., sold W. Davis), (1683). Fol. Pp. 3.
P. 3, AW wrote, 'After this speech was delivered by the authour to the said Sheriffs, they delivered it to his majestie to be read, whereupon, as the report went, a proclamation issued out to prohibit the printing thereof: but afterwards it came out by authority, otherwise it would have been printed beyond the seas.' LT 3.82.
Wood 428(20). Wing S3766.

5901. Sidney, Algernon*. *The arraignment, tryal & condemnation of Algernon Sidney, esq; for high-treason.* London: f. B. Tooke, 1684. Fol. Pp. [3], 65.
On a slip pasted to p. [1ᵛ], AW wrote notes on the life of 'Algernon Sydney [/] A yonger son of Rob. Sydney Earl of Leycester - & yonger brother to Philip Visc. L'isle [/] Sided with the parl. 1641 [/] Had a commission granted him to be a Colonel [/] Went into Irel. to do service there against the Rebells - was rewarded for so doing with Major Tho. Harrison [/] Nominated one of the Kings Judges [trial of Charles 1] but did not sit', and 6 more lines, including 2 sources: Whitlock p. 681 (i.e., B. Whitelocke (1682), Wing W1986) and list of parliament men, 1648. LT 3.82.
Wood 428(19). Wing A3754.

5902. Sidney, Philip. *An apologie for poetrie.* London: [J. Roberts] f. H. Olney, 1595. 4°. A1,3-4,B-K⁴,L1-3 (wanting A2). Pasteboard (blue) with parchment spine. 1st upper and last lower flyleaves, marbled paper (bound after 1691).

Flyleaf, 2nd, 'E Libris Antonii A Wood', not by AW; ᵛ, AW wrote the titles of 3 printed works in this vol., within guidelines made with red ink, and 'Note that Sʳ Joh. Harrington of Kelston neare Bathe, hath written <u>An apologie for poetry</u>, in. 3. sh. in fol. or thereabouts, set before his <u>Orlando furioso</u>'; B1, B2, Latin tags; passim, a few underscorings, marks in margin and corrections, none in AW's hand. See [MS.] Wood B. 23, item 4070, for proof sheets of the *Apologie* used as waste paper in binding.
Wood 116(1) (not in Bodl. CD cat.). STC 22534.

5903. Sidney, Philip. *An apologie for poetrie*. London: [J. Roberts] f. H. Olney or f. W. Ponsonby, 1595. 8°. A-L⁴.
Missing in 1837. Dupl. or diff. ed. at Wood 116(1). Ed. not identified. See [MS.] Wood B. 23 (item 4070) for proof sheets of the *Apologie* used as waste paper in binding.
Wood 887b(1). STC 22534 and 22534.5. *Folg, Hunt, NYPL,* and *Hunt.*

5904. Sidney, Philip. Leicester, earl of. *An armie for Ireland, conducted by the lord Lithe, . . . Being a vote of both houses in parliament for the sending of speedy ayd into Ireland*. London: f. J. Greensmith, 1642. 4°. A⁴.
Tp, at Lithe, AW wrote 'L'isle' (i.e., P. Sidney, 1619-98).
Wood 507(41). Wing L965.

5905. Sidney, Philip; Edmund Spenser; Robert Southwell, and Michael Drayton. *Works & remaines*. ?: ?, 1594, 1595. Pp.?
Missing. MS. Wood E. 2(70), p. 50, 'Ph. Sidney [/] Edm. Spenser [/] Rob. Southwell [/] Mich. Drayton Works & remaines – 1594. 95'.
MS. Wood E. 2(70), p. 50. Not identified.

5906. Sidney, Robert*, Leicester, earl of. *A list of the old and new regiments of horse and foot, under . . . Robert Sidney, earle of Leicester*. London: f. T. Walkley, [1642] 15 Jun. 4°. A⁴.
Tp, AW wrote the year, '42 – q[uaere]', and a brief note, illeg., in pencil.
Wood 508(17). Wing L2480 ('O' not recorded in Wing).

5907. Simlerus, Josias, and Joannes Guilielmus Stuckius. *Narratio de ortu, vita, et obitu . . . . d. Henrici Bullingeri. Item oratio funebris, auctore d. Joanne Guilielmo Stukio*. Tiguri: Froschoverus, 1575. Ff. 84, 24 (2nd tp at 2nd f. 1). Parchment with clasp holes.
Flyleaf, upper, signatures, e.g., 'Christopher Colson his booke' and scribbles. Tp, AW wrote the date of acquisition, 'Sept: XIV: MDclx'; also a shelf-mark, 'G1' (?), prob. written by Colson. Ff. 31ᵛ, 32, 66ᵛ, minor annotation, not by AW. Flyleaf, lower, 2ndᵛ, scribbles, not by AW, lined out.
Wood 349. BL.

5908. Simpson, Christopher. *The division-violist: or an introduction to the playing upon a ground*. London: W. Godbid, sold J. Playford, 1659. Fol. Pp. [10], 67 (wanting the portrait). Calf with 3 fillets, stamp decoration inside corners (2 leaves and sunflower sprouting fleur-de-lis), and roll decoration at inner, spine edge (Ashm. binding); rebacked; some cropping, passim.
Pastedown, upper, an Ashm. librarian wrote the shelf-mark twice and below, '1701' (prob. shortly after binding). Flyleaf, upper, 2ndʳ⁻ᵛ, list of 62 printed works in this vol., written by an Ashm. librarian (same hand in Wood 276a). The Whiteside cat. has '657 – A Volume of Pamphlets &c 62' and '73' added later in pencil. After the list on the flyleaf Milford added 'LXXIII Eleven more pamphlets 73 RTM 1922'. Apparently a loose bundle of AW pamphlets was later incorporated into this vol. Item nos. are mainly in Roman numerals. 1st item, p. [8], correction, may not be by AW.
Wood 657(1a). Wing S3813.

5909. Simpson, Margaret*. *Dreadful news from Southwark: or, . . . how one Margaret Simpson . . . with Elizabeth Griffin, . . . were . . . struck dead with a thunder-bolt*. [London?]: n.pub., [1680?]. Fol. Pp. 4.
Tp, AW wrote, '168–' [sic].
[MS.] Wood D. 28(29). Wing D2153.

5910. Simpson, Sydrach. *The anatomist anatomis'd. Or, a short answer to some things in the book [by A. Forbes] intituled, An anatomy of Independencie*. London: f. P. Cole, 1644. 4°. Pp. 12.
Wood 617(12). Wing S3821.

5911. Skinner, Robert. Oxford, bp. of. *Articles of visitation and enquiry concerning matters ecclesiasticall:. . . in the first episcopal visitation of Robert, bishop of Oxon*. Oxford: W. Hall, 1662. 4°. Pp. [2], 13.
Wood 516(10). Wing C4073. Madan 2612.

5912. Skippon, Philip. *To the honourable citie of London. The humble petition of Philip Skippon*. London: f. W. Waterson, [1660]. S.sh.
AW wrote 'Jan: 1659[60]'.
Wood 276a(198). Wing T1408A.

5913. Skory, Edmund. *An extract out of the historie of the last French king Henry the fourth*. London: R. Barker [sold J. Budge], 1610. 4°. A2-4,B-C⁴,D1-3. Pasteboard (grey) with parchment spine. Traces of upper and lower flyleaves in marbled paper.
Flyleaf, upper, 2nd^v, AW wrote the titles of 2 printed works in this vol., within guidelines made with red ink. Tp, repaired before AW's binding, with support covering a note or scribble, not by AW. A 2nd repair, before initial binding, is a support slip pasted to the final leaf.
Wood 337(1). STC 22629.

5914. Slatyer, G., exornavit. L., J. V., fecit. *The type of trew nobilitye Or ye armes of a Ch[ris]tian emblazoned*. N.p.: n.pub., n.d. S.sh. May be a frontispiece (engr.).
Possibly from William Slatyer, *The compleat Christian* (1643), see Wing S3983. A comment on removed items (37-8): 'xxxvii-xxxviii not here [1881]'.
Wood 276b(39). Not identified.

5915. Sleidanus, Johannes. *The key of historie. Or, a most methodicall abridgement of the foure chiefe monarchies, Babylon, Persia, Greece, and Rome*. London: M. Flesher, f. W. Sheeres, 1627. 12°. Pp. [30], 377 (2 tpp). Parchment.
Tp, bsm.
Wood 187. STC 19850.

5916. Sleidanus, Johannes. *De quatuor summis imperiis libri tres: postrema ed*. Amstelodami: ap. D. Elzevirium, 1667. 16°. Pp. 237, [25]. Calf with 2 fillets.
Wood 895. BL.

5917. Slingsby, Henry*, et al. *The several tryals of sir Henry Slingsby k^t. John Hewet d. d. and John Mordant esq*. London: n.pub., 1658. 4°. Pp. 30.
P. 29, an identification, 'Dr Barwick afterwards Dean of St Paul's', prob. not by AW.
Wood 367(15). Wing S2814.

5918. [Smalridge, George]. Bristol, bp. of. *Auctio Davisiana Oxonii habita*. Londini: prostant venales ap. J. Tonson, 1689. 4°. Pp. [4], 15.
Tp, AW wrote, 'George Smalridge A. bac. et Alumnus Æd. ch. Author' and 'Bought at Oxon. 4. May 1689. being then newly come from London'. Pp. [4], 1, AW identified and gave the names of the fathers of the 6 characters, K, B, S, D, C, W, in the verse dialogue: Arth. Kay, Walt. Bacon, Edw. Stradling, George Dixon, Christop. Codrington, and Will. Woodward, all of Christ Church. LT 3.302; AO 4.667.
Wood 517(4). Wing S4010B.

5919. Smet, Heinrich. *Prosodia . . . promptissima, quae syllabarum positione & diphthongis carentium, quantitates sola veterum poetarum auctoritate, adductis exemplis demonstrat*. London: excusum impens. Soc. Stationar., 1648. 8°. 16th ed. Pp. [32], 655. Calf with 2 fillets and a vertical line of 2 fillets.
Pastedown, upper, signature 'John Wheare His Booke 1671' and scribbles; flyleaf, upper^{r-v}, signatures 'Robert Clarke', 'Christopher Young owes [sic] this 1649', and scribbles. Tp, 'J.A. -' (6 or E?). Text, a few scribbles (names, pp. 170, 242, 318), not by AW. P. 654 to pastedown, lower, some notes and scribblings, prob. none by AW; 654, 'Henry Playford'; flyleaf, lower^v, Christopher Young.
Wood 886. Wing S4016.

5920. Smet, Heinrich. *Henrici Smetii Alostani prosodia in novam formam digesta*. Genevae: sump. J. Stoër, 1664. 8°. Ed. postrema emendatior. Pp. [16], 526. Calf with 2 fillets, stamp initials 'G M'; rebacked.
Tp, scribbles; ^v, scribbles, 'W' and cartoons. In the intro. some scribbles and the letter 'W'; text, a few scribbles.
Wood 662. Not in BL.

5921. [Smith, Francis]. Tickle-foot, Tom, pseud. *Some observations upon the late tryals of sir George Wakeman*. London: f. A. Brewster [i.e., F. Smith], 1679. Fol. Pp. 9 [really pp. 11].
Tp, AW wrote the price, '3^d.' P. 4, 'All this is very silly stuffe, & scarce becomes a schoolboy to write it', and a note on a pun at 'Chapmen': 'The apothecaries name is Chapman'. P. 7 [really p. 9], a brief note on a reference to the judge: 'Lord Cheif justice Scroggs, was the son of a Butcher.' LT 2.457. Responded to by M. Mason, Wood 425(9b), item 4396.

Wood 425(9a). Wing S4540.

5922. Smith, Francis*. *An account of the injurious proceedings of sir George Jeffreys k^{nt.} late recorder of London, against Francis Smith, bookseller [16 Sept. 1680].* London: f. F. Smith, [1681]. Fol. Pp. [4], 20.
Tp, AW wrote the year, '1688-89'.
Wood 421(17). Wing S4024.

5923. Smith, John, clock maker. *Equation of time demonstrated to the meanest capacity.* [London]: n.pub., [1678]. S.sh.
Wood 276a(40). Wing S4104 (two) (Wing, S. Crouch, publ.).

5924. Smith, John, of Walworth. *The narrative of mr. John Smith of Walworth . . . of the . . . popish plot.* London: R. Boulter, 1679. Fol. Pp. [7], 35.
Tp, AW wrote the price, '1ˢ'.
Wood 425(22) (not in Bodl. CD cat.). Wing S4127.

5925. Smith, John, of Walworth. *No faith or credit to be given to papists. . . . on the perjury of Will. [Howard] viscount Stafford, . . . in relation to mr. Stephen Dugdale, and mr. Edward Turbervill.* London: f. T. Cockerill, 1681. Fol. Pp. [4], 32.
Wood 427(8). Wing S4128.

5926. Smith, John*, and Edward Jackson*. *A true relation of the execution of John Smith, alias Ashburnham, (for murder) . . . and of Edward Jackson, executed the same day [26 May].* (London): (G. Croom), (1684). Fol. Pp. 4.
Wood 422(11) (not in Bodl. CD cat.). Wing T2947.

5927. Smith, R. *A wonder of wonders: or, a metamorphosis of fair faces voluntarily transformed into foul visages. . . . By . . . Miso-spilus.* London: J. G. f. R. Royston, 1662. 4°. Pp. [8], 31.
Wood 653(5). Wing S4149.

5928. Smith, Richard. *A defence of the sacrifice of the masse.* (London): (J. Herforde), 1546. 8°. Ff. [3], 190, [1]. Parchment.
Some marginal notes, and 2nd f. [1ᵛ], and flyleaf, lowerᵛ, notes and scribbles, e.g., 'To my mishappe alas I ffynde . . . ', not by AW.
Wood 829. STC 22820a.

5929. Smith, Samuel. *Aditus ad logicam.* ?: ?, 1613ff. Pp.?
Missing. MS. Wood E. 2(70), p. 11. Ed. not identified.
MS. Wood E. 2(70), p. 11. STC 22825-33. Wing S4194-6. Madan 2027.

5930. Smith, Thomas (1513-1577). [Laet, Joannes de, ed.]. *De republica Anglorum libri tres. Quibus accesserunt chorographcia illius descriptio.* Lug. Batavorum: ex off. Elzeviriana, 1630. 8°. Pp. [12], 404, [12]. Calf with 3 fillets.
Tpᵛ, a brief vita of Thomas Smith by a former owner, Ni: Overb[ury] (AO 2.133).
Wood 448. BL.

5931. Smith, Thomas (1513-1577). *The common-wealth of England. And the manner of governement thereof. . . . With new additions of the chiefe courts.* London: W. Stansby f. J. Smethwicke, 1633. 12°.
Newly corrected. Pp. [14], 285, [2]. Parchment with 2 clasp holes.
Wood 578. STC 22865.

5932. Smith, Thomas (1513-1577), and **James 1**. *An old mould to cast new lawes by; . . . Reprinted out of the common-wealth of England, . . . Together, with king James his declaration . . . of the kings power in . . . Scotland.* [Oxford]: [L. Lichfield, 1643]. 4°. Pp. [2], 10.
Former t on tp, underscored. Below, 'X'.
Wood 630(2). Wing S4218 (Wing, listed under Smith, Susannah). Madan 1579.

5933. Smith, Thomas (1558-1625), gaoler. *Sir Thomas Smithes voiage and entertainment in Rushia.* London: [J. Roberts a. W. Jaggard] f. N. Butter, 1605. 4°. A-B², C-N⁴, M1-3 (G1, wanting).
Tp, 'pretium – vjᵈ' not in AW's hand. A2, B1, scribbles; AW supplied a sheet at the place of the missing G1 and transcribed the text, r-v.
Wood 387(2). STC 22869.

5934. Smith, Thomas (1638-1710). *Septem Asiae ecclesiarum notitia.* Londini: excud. T. R., 1676. 4°.

Pp. [4], 44.

Missing. MS. Wood E. 2(70), p. 60, 'Th. Smith Magd. Coll. Septem Asiae ecclesiarum notitita. Edit. 1ª. 1672 – 3ª Edit. 1676 – [and, added later] preb. of Haylesbury [Heyghtbury] in Wilts by the favor of Dʳ Pierce . . . Apr. 1683 [1687?]' (AO 4.598-9). The t in his ms. suggests that he owned the 1676 ed.

MS. Wood E. 2(70), p. 60. Wing S4247. O, Hunt, Folg.

5935. Smith, Tho[mas] (1638-1710). *A sermon about frequent communion [17 Aug. 1679].* London: f. S. Smith, 1685. 4°. Pp. [4], 34.

Pp. 26-8, 30, 33, some marks, in pencil, may not be by AW.

Wood 633(16). Wing S4248.

5936. Smith, William, vice-admiral. *Severall letters of great importance, and good successe. Lately obtained against the fellowship of Bristow.* London: f. L. Blaiklock, 1643. 4°. Pp. [1], 7.

Tp, AW wrote the date, 'Aug 1643', in pencil, and lined out a former no., '28'. Dupl. at Wood 632(12).

Wood 376(31). Wing S2779.

5937. Smith, William, vice-admiral. *Severall letters of great importance, and good successe. Lately obtained against the fellowship of Bristow.* London: f. L. Blaiklock, 1643. 4°. Pp. [1], 7.

Tp, AW wrote in pencil, 'Duplic Auct.' Dupl. at Wood 376(31).

Wood 632(12). Wing S2779.

5938. Smith, William, of Bath. *Of the celebration of the king's coronation-day, in . . . Bathe. . . . in a letter.* London: n.pub., 1661, 29 Apr. 4°. Pp. 6, [1].

Tp, AW wrote 'A. à W. Ex dono J. . . . Pearce civ. Bathoni // 7. Jun. 1678', LT 2.407.

Wood 537(17). Wing S4275 (two).

5939. Smith, William. Clare College, Cambridge. *Johanni Poloniae regi, . . . carmen panegyricum.* Londini: J. Gellibrand, 1679. 8°. Pp. 40.

Some marks and scribbles in margins. Flyleaf, lowerᵛ, an addition, not by AW.

Wood 113(7). Wing S4276.

5940. [Smith, William], of Islington. *Contrivances of the fanatical conspirators, . . . of the popish-plot . . . with depositions . . . this present horrid rebellion hath been design'd by the republicans many years.* London: f. the author, sold by booksellers of London and Westminster, 1685. Fol. Pp. 34.

Flyleafᵛ, AW wrote notes from 'Medulla Historiae Anglicanae, being a comprehensive History of the Lives & reignes of the monarchs of England – Lond. 1687. in oct. 3ᵈ edit.' (by W. Howell, Wood 601, item 3705), and 'p. 447. Will. Smith somtimes a school mʳ in Islington & a principal evidence that swore Tit. Oates to be in London when a cloud of witnesses & persons of quality too, asserted him to have been at S. Omer at that time the consults, (at which he said he was present in London) were held, did afterwards retract all & published a Narrative, giving Account of the manner how he was drawne in to do so ill a thing, as to beare fals witness against his Neighbour'. Tp, at the 'horrid rebellion', 'Monmouths rebellion in the west – see' (Wood 660c(4a), item 5806); at the unnamed author, 'Will. Smith'; and 'published in Nov. 1685. 1ˢ'. Text, pp. 3-4, 5-6, 11, 22, 29, 31-2, 34, some underscoring and notes in margins, e.g., p. 6, at John Philips, 'brother of Edw. Philips I thinke & both the Nephews of Jo. Milton'; 11, at Gadbury and Fisher, 'Jo. Gadbury the Almanack maker & Maj. Payne Fisher, a poor poet.' (financially poor); 31, underscored 'Aaron Smith' and 'Raree Show', the ballad Smith claimed to have made (Wood 417(45), item 413); 32, at printed 'the King was drunk', 'The Parl. was dissolved between 10 & 11 in the morn. And tis very strange, that the K. being alwaies accounted a sober man, should be drunk in a morning'. LT 3.170.

Wood 421(4). Wing S4268A.

5941. Smithfield Jockey. *The Smithfield jockey: or, the character and original of a horse-courser [with an additional t leaf reading A whip for a jockey, printed for R. H.].* London: f. W. D., 1677. 8°. Pp. [4], 29 (t leaf mutilated).

Wood 868(7). Wing S4353 (two).

5942. Smithson, Samuel. *The famous history of Guy earl of Warwick.* London: f. F. Coles, T. Vere, J. Wright, a. J. Clark, [1674-79]. 8°. A⁸,B⁴.

Flyleaf, upper, 2nd-3rd, AW wrote the history of Guy of Warwick: 'Of Guy Earl of Warwick from the [blank] vol. of Joh. Lelands Itineraries, ms. in bib. Bod[leian] – There is a right goodly chappal of S. Mary Magd. upon Avon river ripa dextra somu-[?] a mile above Warwick – This place of some is called Gibcliffe, of some Guycliffe, & old fame remaineth with the people there, that Guido Earl of Warwick in K. Ethelstans (or Athelstans) dayes had a great devotion to this place & made an oratorie there. . . . ' (and 52 more lines).

Tp, he wrote, 'Bought at Oxon. 1687'.
Wood 254(2). Wing F375 (rare).

5943. Smithurst, Benjamin. *Britain's glory, and England's bravery. Wherein is shewed the degrees of honour . . . To which is added a continuation of the historian's guide.* London: f. W. Crook, 1689. 12°. Pp. [13], 172, 17, [2].
1st p. 13, corrections, not in AW's hand. Gift from E. Ashmole, 30 Nov. 1689, LT 3.295.
Wood 442(3). Wing S4356.

5944. Smythe, John. *Instructions, observations, and orders mylitarie [p. 1: Certen Instructions, observations and orders military, by sir Iohn Smythe, knight, 1591].* London: [J. Danater a. P. Short f.] R. Johnes, 1595. 4° (wanting all before sig. B1; bibliog. data is from STC 22885). Pp. 220, followed by 'The Table', A², and a 2nd 'The Table', A².
Wood 635(2). STC 22885.

5945. Sober and Seasonable Queries. *Sober and seasonable queries humbly offered to all good protestants.* [London]: n.pub., [1679?]. Fol. Pp. 4.
In [MS.] Wood E. 27(2) (item 1599; see Plate VIII) AW wrote of the 2nd ed., 'The 2d Edition with considerable additions by another authour – printed in Aug. 1679. 4° beyond sea as it seemes'.
Wood 276a(274). Wing S4402.

5946. Solemn League and Covenant. *[The anti-covenant, or, a sad complaint concerning the new oath or covenant, . . . a letter, . . . by a . . . lover of the parliament].* [Oxford]: [H. Hall], [1643]. 4°. Pp. 1-50 (wanting the t leaf).
Wood 612(72). Wing S3490. Madan 1410.

5947. Solemn League and Covenant. *[The anti-confederacy, or a discovery of the iniquity and hypocrisie of the solemne league and covenant].* [Oxford]: [H. Hall], [1644]. 4° (wanting [6] pp. before p. 1). Pp. 1-70.
Wood 612(71). Wing A3487. Madan 1694.

5948. Solemn Mock Procession. *[Th]e solemn mock procession of the pope, cardinalls, Jesuits, fryers, &c: through y*ᶜ*. city of London, November y*ᶜ*. 17*ᵗʰ. London: sold at the Kings-Arms, a. at the Feathers, [1679]. S.sh. (mutilated).
AW wrote the year, '1679'. ᵛ, '14 really no. 19', in a modern hand (see note at Wood 417(1)).
Wood 417(14a). Wing S4451C.

5949. Solemn Mock Procession. *The solemn mock-procession: or the tryal & execution of the pope and his ministers [17 Nov.].* London: f. N. Ponder, L. Curtis, J. Wilkins, a. S. Lee, 1680. 4°. Pp. [2], 6.
LT 2.500: 17 Nov. is the anniversary of Q. Elizabeth's accession.
[MS.] Wood B. 40(14). Wing S4452D.

5950. Somerset. *Certain and true news from Somerset-shire; with the besieging of sr Ralph Hopton's house. Likewise the manner of taking of sir Edward Rodney [et al.].* London: f. J. Underwood, 1642, 15 Oct. 4°.
Missing in 1839; see note at Wood 375(1), item 1720. Ed. not identified.
Wood 375(15). Wing C1685 (three) or C1685A (one). *Harv.*

5951. Somerset. *A true relation of the great and glorious victory . . . obtained by sir William Waller, sir Arthur Haslerig . . . against the marquesse Hartford.* [London]: f. E. Husbands, 1643, 14 July. 4°. Pp. 8.
Wood 377(24) (not in Bodl. CD cat.). Wing T2958A.

5952. Somerset. *A declaration of the gentry of Somerset-shire.* London: f. R. Royston, 1660. S.sh.
AW added to the year, 'Aprill'.
Wood 276a(220). Wing D678aA (3) ('O' not recorded in Wing).

5953. Somerset. *To the kings most excellent majesty. Most gracious soveraign, the glorious lord of heaven [signed by J. Paulet (earl of Winchester), et al., 9 June].* London: f. R. Royston, 1660. S.sh.
Wood 276a(207). Not in Wing (should be at T1497B). ESTCR 212415 (one) ('O' not recorded in ESTCR).

5954. Somerset, Henry. Worcester, marq. of. *A letter from the marquesse of Worcester to the committee of parliament . . . concerning his sons landing with Irish forces.* London: f. E. Husband, 1646, 9 June. 4°. Pp. 7.
Tp, '1ᵈ', prob. not by AW.
Wood 501(15). Wing W3536.

5955. Somner, William. *The antiquities of Canterbury*. London: J. L[egat] f. R. Thrale, 1640. 4°. Pp. [16], 516, [12].
Waste paper, upper, a few notes on the Seckworth family, not in AW's hand. Acquired 20 Nov. 1660, for an exchange of some books and 'giving 10^d to boot', LT 1.338 (see also 19 Oct. 1661, LT 1.416).
Wood 388. STC 22918.

5956. Somner, William. *Dictionarium Saxonico-Latino-Anglicum*. Oxonii: ex. G. Hall per authorem pro D. White Londinensi, 1659. 4°. Pp. [366], 80, [6].
Missing. Acquired 18 May 1661, 9^d, LT 1.400.
LT 1.400. Wing S4663. Madan 2458.

5957. Somner, William. *A treatise of gavelkind, . . . Shewing the true etymologie . . . of the one, the nature, antiquity*. London: R. a. W. Leyburn f. the authour, sold J. Crooke a. D. White, 1660. 4°. Pp. [14], 216. Pasteboard (blue) with parchment spine.
Flyleaf, upper, 1st and 2nd, printer's waste paper from *Mercurius publicus*. Flyleaf, lower, 1st and 2nd, printer's waste paper, from *Mercurius publicus*, numb. 14 [29 March-5 April 1660], pp. 217-220, 2E^2 (AW's copy, Wood 393).
Wood 585(1). Wing S4668.

5958. Somner, William, and White Kennett. Brome, James ed. *A treatise of the Roman ports and forts in Kent . . . to which is prefixt the life of mr. Somner*. Oxford: at the theatre, [sold G. West, J. Crosley, a. H. Clements] (cropped), 1693. 8°. Pp. [11], 118, [2], 117, [15].
A3^v, AW added '/92' to Febr. 18 '1693'. P. 118, AW added, '1692/3', below 'Feb 15. 1693'.
Wood 218(2). Wing S4669A.

5959. Sondes, George. Feversham, earl of. *Sir George Sondes his plaine narrative to the world, . . . upon the death of his two sonnes*. London: n.pub., 1655. Fol. Pp. [3], 38.
Tp, AW wrote, 'Sr George Sondes was bred in Cambridge under Dr Preston see p. 20', and '6^d'. Acquired 10 Jan. 1662, LT 1.428.
Wood 422(3a). Wing F832B ('O' not recorded in Wing).

5960. Sorbière, [Samuel de]. *Relation d'un voyage en Angleterre*. Paris: chez T. Iolly, 1664. 8°. Pp. [2], 8, [8], 232. Parchment.
Flyleaf, upper, 'Hen. Foulis. e Coll. Linc.' LT 2.179 (and 291; prob. not the purchase made 7 Apr. 1665, LT 2.33).
Wood 166. BN.

5961. South, Robert. *Musica incantans, sive poema exprimens musicae vires, juvenem in insaniam adigentis, et musici inde periculum*. Oxonii: typ. W. H[all], imp. G. West, 1667. 4°. [2nd. ed.] Pp. [2], 19.
Calf with 3 fillets, stamp decoration inside corners (2 leaves, sunflower sprouting a fleur-de-lis), and roll decoration at inner, spine edge (Ashm. binding); rebacked.
Flyleaf, upper, 1st, 'E Libris Musei Ashmoleani', and 'Will$^-$ Questions' (scribble?); 3rd, 'Miscellaneous Printed Paper[s]', cropped, not in AW's hand; ^{v}, list of 24 printed works in this vol., by an Ashm. librarian; and note at top, cropped, 'out 1655'. Tp, AW wrote, 'The 1st [cropped] edit. came out 1655' and '6^d'. AO 4.637.
Wood 483(1). Wing S4736. Madan 2786.

5962. Southaick, Cyprian. *Londons welcome to his most illustrious highness, William Henry, prince of Orange*. [London]: f. M. T., 1688. S.sh.
Wood 398(22). Wing S4751 (rare).

5963. Southampton. *To the right honorable the house of peers, . . . The humble petition of the county of Southampton*. London: f. J. Hunscott, 1641[2], 11 March. S.sh.
^{v}, AW lined out the former no., '25'.
Wood 373(34). Wing T1629.

5964. Southouse, Tho[mas]. *Monasticon Favershamiense in agro Cantiano: or a surveigh of the monastry of Faversham in . . . Kent*. London: f. T. Passenger, 1671. 8°. Pp. [18], 167 (2nd tp at p. 17).
Tp, AW wrote, '1^s.6^d', and 2nd tp, '1^s-3'. Flyleaf, lower^v, upside down, AW wrote, '1671. 1^s.3^d. stitcht' (the cost of a stitched vol.). The title is also on the portion of this leaf which extends beneath the marbled paper cover.
Wood 216(3). Wing S4772.

5965. Southworth, John. *The last speech and confession of mr. John Southworth a popish priest, at his execution at Tyburn June 28. 1654*. London: f. H. Brome, 1679. Fol. Pp. [2], 2.
Wood 422(2). Wing S4775.

5966. [Spagnuoli, Baptista]*, Mantuanus. *An answer to the Mantuan, . . . lately wrote against womankind*. London: n.pub., 1679. S.sh.
Wood 417(9). Wing A3424.

5967. Spagnuoli, Baptista, Mantuanus. *Mantuan English'd . . . or, the character of a bad woman*. [London?]: n.pub., [1680?]. Fol. Pp. 4.
Missing in 1841; see note by Kirtland at Wood 654a(1), item 4758. Traces of 2 leaves remain.
Wood 654a(30). Wing S4792. *O, Folg, Yale*.

5968. Spain. Archdeacon, Daniel, trans. *A true discourse of the armie which the king of Spaine . . . assembled in . . . Lisbon . . . against England*. London: J. Wolfe, 1588. 8°. Pp. 70 (without 'Distichon Coloniensium'). Pasteboard (blue) with parchment spine; traces of marbled paper, upper and lower flyleaves.
Flyleaf, upper, 1st, notes by F. Madan, 1917, on the mutilated state of item no. 9, and another note on the author of item no. 1; 2nd, AW wrote the titles of 17 printed works in this vol., within guidelines made with red ink. Flyleaf, upper, 'The Spanish forces for 88°.', not by AW.
Wood 511(1). STC 22999.

5969. Spain. P[hilip?], W., trans. *The edict and decree of Phillip king of Spaine:. . . touching the exchaungings and levyings of monyes . . . translated out of Spanish, and now out of French . . . by W. P. [20 Nov. 1596]*. London: [f.] J. Wolfe, 1597. 4°. A2-4,B⁴,C1-3.
Tp, top left hand corner, 'H1' (a shelf-mark?).
Wood 511(6). STC 22992.3 (two) (STC, Phillip, king and exchanging).

5970. Spain. *Clamor sanguinis martyrum, or the bloody inquisition of Spain*. London: A. M. f. F. Tyton, 1656. 12°. Pp. [52], 223. Pasteboard (brown) with calf spine. Traces of upper and lower flyleaves, marbled paper.
Flyleaf, upper, 1st, brief note by an Ashm. librarian, dated 1790; 2nd^v, AW wrote the titles of 2 printed works in this vol., within guidelines made with red ink. Tp, AW wrote '1^s:3^d:'. Bsm. (?), lined out.
Wood 219(1). Wing C4403.

5971. Spain. *The character of Spain: or, an epitome of their virtues and vices*. London: f. N. Brooke, 1660. 12°. Pp. [11], 93, [3] (3 pp. books sold by N. Brook).
Tp, bsm.
Wood 582(7). Wing C2024.

5972. [Spang, William]. Philalethes, Irenaeus, pseud. *Rerum nuper in regno Scotiae gestarum historia, . . . per Irinaeum Philalethen Eleutherium*. Dantisci [i.e., Amsterdam]: n.pub., 1641. 8°. Pp. [8], 576, [14]. Parchment.
Flyleaf, upper, a reference to the printed 'αυτοκατακρισις', 'Laudensium Authore Roberto Baily. pag. 502', not in AW's hand. Tp, bsm.
Wood 181. BL.

5973. Spanish Pilgrim. *The Spanish pilgrime: or, an admirable discovery of a Romish Catholicke*. London: B. A[lsop], sold T. Archer, 1625. 4°. Pp. [12], 136 (without dedic.).
Tp, 'Bought of M^r [John?] Huggins. P^{rt} xii^d', prob. not by AW (for Huggins, see LT 1.202). Bsm.
Wood 511(13). STC 19838.5.

5974. S[parke], M[ichael]. *The crums of comfort with godly prayers. [Followed by] Thankfull remembrances of Gods wonderfull deliverances of this land*. London: [T. Cotes] f. M. Spark, 1629 (1630). 24°in 12's. 10th ed. A-P¹². Parchment with rectangle fillets.
P. 12, scribbles, including 'Dorothe', may not be by AW.
Wood 760. STC 23017 (rare) (STC, imperf.).

5975. [Sparke, Michael]. *Scintilla, or a light broken into darke warehouses. With observations upon the monopolist of seaven several patents*. London: not for profit, no where to be sold, 1641. 4°. Pp. [2], 6. Calf with 3 fillets, stamp decoration (flower) inside corners; roll decoration at spine edge (Ashm. binding).
Flyleaf, upper, 2nd, the titles of 18 printed works (really 16) in this vol., by an Ashm. librarian (same hand in Wood 276a). This volume is made up of works on theology. The binders cropped a number of notes at

the margins. 1st item, tp, 'This (as Will: Turner the printer told me) was first sett on foot & published by Michael Sparks of St Dunstans London.', not by AW. P. 6, correction in same hand.
[MS.] Wood B. 36(1) (not in Bodl. CD cat.). Wing S4818B.

5976. [Sparke, Michael]. Scintilla, M., pseud. *The narrative history of king James, for the first fourteen years. . . . II. The proceedings touching the divorce betwixt the lady Frances Howard and Robert earl of Essex, . . . III. A declaration of his majesties revenue . . . IV. The commissions and warrants for the burning of two hereticks.* London: f. M. Sparke [and] R. Cotes, sold M. Sparke, 1651. 4°. Pp. [11], 192, [4], 72, [2], 18, [8] (3 tpp). Calf with 2 fillets and 2 vertical fillets.
Flyleaf, upper, AW wrote, 'Gresham a conjurer p. 43. 20'. Passim, vertical lines in margins, identifications (e.g., a2^v, at 'Scintilla', he wrote 'Spark'), underscoring, corrections, dates, and additional information, sometimes in ink over pencil (e.g., p. 54, a correction concerning Thomas Overbury: 'he was educated in Queens Coll in Oxon' over a pencilled note). Much from here is in AO 2.133-8.
Wood 347. Wing S4818.

5977. Sparrow, Henry. *Cupid's sports and pastimes.* [London]: I. M. f. W. Thackeray, [1684]. 8°. A^8,B^4.
Tp, AW wrote dates, '1677 & 1684'.
Wood 69(5). Wing S4835 (rare).

5978. Speculum. *Speculum politiae. Or Englands mirrour: being a looking-glasse for the body politick of this nation.* London: f. S. B., 1660. 12°. Pp. [6], 68, [2].
Each 12° leaf is pasted on an 8° template.
Wood 739(5). Wing S4852.

5979. Speech of a Warden. *The speech of a warden to the fellowes of his company: touching the great affaires of the kingdome. . . . by Antibrownistus Puritanomastix.* [London]: f. N. V., 1642. 4°. A^4.
Wood 614(55). Wing S4862.

5980. [Speed, John], graven by. *The kingdome of Great Britaine and Ireland.* London: solde by J. Sudbury a. G. Humble, 1610. S.sh. 432 x 564 mm (untrimmed).
^v, former no., '13'. Signature, 'Anthony Wood'. Reprinted in Speed, *Theatre*.
Wood 276b(14). See STC 23041ff..

5981. Speed, John. *The history of Great Britaine under the conquests of the Romans, Saxon, Danes, and Normans.* London: (W. Hall a. J. Beale,) solde J. Sudbury & G. Humble, 1611. Fol. Pp. [21], 1237, [87].
Missing. Acquired 16 Jan. 1666, 14^s, LT 2.70. Ed. not identified.
LT 2.70. STC 23045ff. (variant, 23048, *Hunt*).

5982. S[peed], J[ohn]. Goos, Abraham Amstelodamensis, sculpsit. *America with those known parts in that unknowne worlde both people and manner of buildings. Discribed and inlarged by J. S. Ano [sic]. 1626.* [London]: sold by G. Humble, 1626. S.sh. 426 x 546 mm (untrimmed).
Reprinted in Speed, *Prospect*, between pp. 9-10.
Wood 276b(9). See STC 23039g.7.

5983. S[peed], J[ohn]. Goos, Abrahamum, sculptum apud. *Asia with the islands adjoyning described, . . . newly augmented by J. S.* [London]: sold by G. Humble, 1626. S.sh. 408 x 532 mm (untrimmed).
Reprinted in Speed, *Prospect*, between pp. 3-4.
Wood 276b(3). See STC 23039g.7.

5984. Speed, Jo[hn]. Goos, Abrahamum, sculptum apud. *Europ, and the cheife cities conta^y ned [sic] therin.* [London]: soul[d by G. Humble], 1626. S.sh. (some mutilation). 395 x 512 mm. (untrimmed).
Reprinted in Speed, *Prospect*, between pp. 7-8.
Wood 276b(4). See STC 23039g.7.

5985. Speed, John. Ελλας *Greece revised by John Speed.* [London]: sold by G. Humble, 1626. S.sh. 429 x 560 mm (untrimmed).
Reprinted in Speed, *Prospect*, between pp. 11-12.
Wood 276b(10). See STC 23039g.7.

5986. Speed, J[ohn]. *Italia newly augmented by J: Speede.* [London]: sold by G. Humble, 1626. S.sh. 437 x 562 mm (untrimmed).
Reprinted in Speed, *Prospect*, between pp. 25-6.
Wood 276b(8). See STC 23039g.7.

5987. [Speed, John]. *A new and accurat map of the world drawne according to ye truest descriptions latest discoveries & best observations y^t have beene made by English or strangers.* [London]: sold by G. Humble, 1626. S.sh. 432 x 550 mm. (untrimmed).
Repaired with a portion of a parchment ms. Reprinted in Speed, *Prospect*, between pp. 1-2.
Wood 276b(2). R.W. Shirley, *The Mapping of the World* (1993), item 317.

5988. S[peed], J[ohn]. Goos, Abraham, sculpsit. *Africae, described, the manners of their habits, . . . newly done into English by J. S.* [London]: publ. at the charges of G. Humble Ano [sic] 1626, [1631]. S.sh. 427 x 542 mm. (untrimmed).
Repaired with portion of a parchment ms. Reprinted in Speed, *Prospect*, between pp. 5-6.
Wood 276b(5). See STC 23039g.7.

5989. [Speed, John]. *A new mape of ye XVII provinces of Low Germanie, mended a new in manie places. Anno 1626.* [London]: sould by G. Humble, [1631]. S.sh. 439 x 553 mm (untrimmed).
Reprinted in Speed, *Prospect*, between pp. 21-2; ^v, scribble, illegible.
Wood 276b(11). See STC 23039g.7.

5990. S[peed], R[obert]. *The counter scuffle. Whereunto is added the counter-ratt. . . . by R. S.* London: R. B., sold A. Crook, 1658. 4°. A-F^4,G1-3.
Tp, AW wrote, 'The counter-scuffle in Woodstreet Counter -'.
Wood 500(5). Wing S4892.

5991. Speede, William. *Epigrammata juvenilia.* Londini: J. Redmayne ap. G. Kettilby, 1669. 8°. Pp. [6], 64, [1].
Tp, AW wrote, 'in part 4'. Bsm.
Wood 113(3). Wing S4908.

5992. [Speke, Hugh]. *By his highness William Henry, prince of Orange. A third declaration.* [London]: n.pub., 1688. 4°. Pp. 8.
Tp, AW wrote, 'sold in Oxon in the beg. of Dec. [/] said to be written by Sam. Johnson author of Julian, without the knowledge of the P. of O' (see Johnson, Wood 835(7), item 3891, and also note at [MS.] Wood D. 29(1), item 2445). Pp. 5, line in margin at the printed no injury 'to the Person even of a Papist'; 6, identification in margin, 'K. Jam. 2. of Eng'. LT 3.292.
Wood 529(5). Wing S4914C.

5993. [Spelman, Clement?] (see below). *The mystery of the good old cause briefly unfolded in a catalogue of such members of the late long parliament.* London: n.pub., 1660. 8°. Pp. [6], 56, [1]. Pasteboard (brown) with calf spine. Upper flyleaf, 1st, marbled paper.
Flyleaf, 4th^v, AW wrote the titles of 3 printed works in this vol. (really 2; 2 entries for Wood 209(2)), within guidelines made with red ink. Also, 2 hands pointing to his 2 lengthy notes: 'Note that I have The Traytors Perspective glass &c. [Wood 369(9), item 6113]. In my vol. of pamphlets entit. Tryalls, & Executions of regicides &c as also a little book in 12° entit. The lives, actions & Execution of the prime actors of the horrid murder of K. Ch. 1. &c. by George Bate' [Wood 304(2), item 895] and 'Note that there is extant The Oglio of Traytors, including the illegal tryal of his Majestie with a Catalogue of his pretended judges &c. printed at Lond. in 8° [Wing W188] - but this I have not'. 1st item, tp, AW wrote, 'Of the author see at the end of the epistle to the Reader', all lined out, and 'July: 14: 1660 A. à Wood - 8^d –This book was cheifly composed from a pamphlet intit. A Narrative of the Late Parliament so called &c. printed 1657. Especially from the 2^d narrative (for there were two) printed 1658. I have them both. [Wood 620(14-5, items 2705, 6532].' P. [5] (end of epistle to the reader; AW, apparently, covered the following note with a slip which was later removed, mutilating the note): 'Clement Spellman (son of Sr Henry Spelman) now Cursitor Baron was author of this book. so Mr Dugd. 1676' (repeated in AO 4.8). In pencil, red ink, and dark ink, frequent marks in margins, hand-pointers, cross-references ('v[ide] infra' 'v. p. 19'), identifications, corrections, and comments, some sharp, e.g., p. 3, at 'Edward Bishe, Gartel [sic] Herald, . . . an honest man.', AW corrected and wrote: 'Garter. A knave to my knowledge'; p. 11, at 'Mr. Squib Clarenceux Hereld [sic]', AW wrote: 'A pityfull Herald god wot.'; at p. 27, at Edmund Prideaux, 'Fasti 1625' (AOF, 1.424); p. 28, at printed, 'Sir Benjamin Rudyard had given him [Francis Rous, provost of Eton] 5000 l.', AW wrote: 'He received 6000^li in recompence for the loss of the surveyourship of the Court of Wards'; p. 30, at a statement that Sir Walter Strickland refused 5000 pounds from John Selden, AW wrote: 'How doth that appeare[?]'; p. 50, at Thomas Kelsey, 'A Button maker, as I have heard' and 'Governour of Oxon.' LT 2.453.
Wood 209(1). Wing M3191 ('O' not recorded in Wing).

5994. Spelman, Henry. *De sepultura.* London: R. Young, sold M. Walbancke a. W. Coke, 1641. 4°. Pp. [2], 38.
P. 34-5, lines in margin, in pencil, may not be by AW. All 3 items in this vol. seem have been bound together when Wood acquired the 1st and 2nd in Jan. 1660, see LT 1.301 (prob. not 'Sepulchra veterum', acquired 23 Nov. 1663, 2ˢ, LT 1.503).
[MS.] Wood B. 32(3) (not in Bodl. CD cat.). Wing S4924.

5995. Spelman, Henry. *De non temerandis ecclesiis, churches not to be violated . . . with a new epistle.* Oxford: H. Hall, 1646. 4°. 3rd ed. Pp. [32], 40.
Flyleaf, upper, 2ndᵛ, AW wrote, 'This book, was published at Lond. the 2ᵈ time 1616. 8°·' (STC 23067.6), and tp, 'Ant: Woode: A: D: M:DC:Lix:'. LT 1.301.
[MS.] Wood B. 32(2). Wing S4921. Madan 1858.

5996. Spelman, Henry. Stephens, Jeremiah, ed. *Tithes too hot to be touched. Certain treatises, wherein is shewen that tithes are due. . . . Written by sʳ· Henry Spelman, . . . and others. [2nd pt. entitled] An apology of the treatise de non temerandis ecclesiis.* London: (J. L.) f. P. Stephens, (1646). 4°. Pp. [52], 189, [37], 27 (2 tpp) (t leaf of pt. 1 is mutilated). Parchment over pasteboard.
Pastedown, upper, AW wrote, 'Ant: Woode: Jan: 21: A: D: 1659[60]:'. Flyleaf, upper, 3rdᵛ, AW wrote the titles of 3 printed works in this vol., with the heading, 'Libri in hoc volumine compacti.', perhaps at the time he acquired the vol. After 1st item (in 3 parts), AW added, 'published againe with additions by Jer. Stephens B. D. Lond 1647' (Wing S4928; ESTCR 21992). Tp, AW added the year, '1647'. a1 (1st p. [17]), AW wrote, 'This epistle to the Reader was written by Jerem. Stephens S. T. bac. of Br[asenose] Coll. Oxon.' LT 1.301.
[MS.] Wood B. 32(1). Wing S4931.

5997. Spelman, Henry. *Villare Anglicum: or a view of the townes of England.* London: R. Hodgkinsonne, 1656. 4°. a⁴,A⁴-2A⁸,2B⁴ (a1, 2B4 blank). Pasteboard (blue) with parchment spine.
Flyleaf, upper, 'A witty & pleasant preface is prefaced by the printer', not in AW's hand. Tp, 'Ant: Woode: Merton Coll: Oxon: 1669 [over '1659']'. Passim, entries are marked in margins, in pencil; correction or cross-reference, G6ᵛ, M7, in ink.
Wood 385. Wing S4932.

5998. Spelman, Henry. *Of the law-terms: a discourse.* London: f. M. Gillyflower, 1684. 8°. Pp. [4], 88. Pasteboard (blue) with parchment spine.
Flyleaf, upperᵛ, AW wrote the titles of 2 printed works in this vol., within guidelines made with red chalk. P. [1], AW wrote '9ᵈ Jan. 10. 1683[4]'.
Wood 677(1). Wing S4929.

5999. [Spelman, John]. *[Ælfredi magni Anglorum regis . . . vita].* [Oxonii]: [e theatro Sheldoniano], 1678. Fol. Plates 1-3, 5-7, only.
LT 2.449. AO 3.62-3, 4.443-4.
Wood 423(6-11). Wing S4934. Madan 3197.

6000. Spencer, John. *The schism of the Church of England &c. demonstrated in four arguments . . . by two Catholic disputants [extr. from Scisme unmaskt, by J. Spencer].* Oxon: H. Cruttenden, 1688. 4°. Pp. [2], 10.
Tp, AW wrote, 'printed in the printing house belonging to Mʳ Obad. Walker in Univ. Coll. Ox [/] mihi dedit H Cruttenden May 12. an 1687.' LT 3.470.
[MS.] Wood D. 26(15). Wing S4957A.

6001. Spencer, Tho[mas]. *Englands warning-peece: or the history of the gun-powder treason.* London: T. N. f. T. Pierrepont, 1659. 8°. Pp. 80, [6].
Tp, AW wrote, 'Taken for the most part from Jo. Speeds chronicle. q[uaere]'.
Wood 453(3). Wing S4961.

6002. [Spenser, Edmund]. *The shepheardes calender, conteining twelve aeglogues [signed Immerit].* London: J. Wolfe [a.] (T. East) f. J. Harrison, 1586. 4°. Ff. [4], 52. Pasteboard (blue) with parchment spine.
1st upper and last lower flyleaves, marbled paper; 'E.E.W. Rebᵈ. 24-1.[19]44'.
Flyleaf, upper, 2ndᵛ, AW wrote the titles of 7 printed works in this vol., within guidelines made with orange chalk. Tp, AW wrote, 'Anthony Woode Mert Coll.' (early hand) and 'The first edit. of this was printed at Lond. 1579. 4°'; ᵛ, 'This book is set downe in Bodlies catalogue under the letters E. K, but Edm. Spen[s]er was the authour as tis generally knoune.' F. 12ᵛ, scribble.

[MS.] Wood C. 17(1) (in Bodl. CD cat., imprint date, 1568). STC 23091.

6003. [Spinoza, Benedict]. Blount, Charles, trans. *Miracles, no violations of the laws of nature [a tr. of chap. 6 of Spinoza's Tractatus theologica-politicus, with extr. from Hobbes and Burnet].* London: f. R. Sollers, 1683. 4°. Pp. [6], 31.
Tp, AW wrote, 'Written, as 'tis said by Cha. Blount'.
Wood 643(11). Wing B3310.

6004. Spittlehouse, John. *An answer to one part of the lord protector's speech: or, a vindication of the Fifth Monarchy-men.* London: f. L. Chapman, 1654. 4°. Pp. [4], 24.
Tp, bsm.
Wood 609(38). Wing S5003.

6005. Spragge, Edward. *A true and perfect relation of the happy successe . . . against the Turks of Argiers at Bugia, by his majesties fleet.* [London]: T. Newcomb, 1671. Fol. Pp. 8 (plus 1 sheet, copper cut of Bugia).
Wood 559(7). Wing S5027.

6006. Sprat, Thomas. Rochester, bp. of. *The history of the Royal-Society.* [London]: T. R. f. J. Martyn, a. J. Allestry, 1667. 4°. Pp. [16], 438, [1].
Missing. MS. Wood 2(70), p. 14, with a dozen p. references and notes. Also listed in MS. Wood F. 51, f. 44.
MS. Wood E. 2(70), p. 14. Wing S5032. *O.*

6007. Sprat, Thomas. Rochester, bp. of. *Observations on monsieur de Sorbier's voyage into England.* [London] in the Savoy: f. J. Martyn and J. Allestry, 1668. 12°. Pp. [2], 256. Calf with 2 fillets and stamp decoration, sunflower sprouting a fleur-de-lis, in corners (Ashm. binding); rebacked.
Tp, in pencil, 'v. p. 154', not by AW, and bsm. P. 154, passage, 'true Sovereign Power amongst us resides in the People . . . ', marked, prob. not by AW.
Wood 163. Wing S5036.

6008. [Sprat, Thomas]. Rochester, bp. of. *Copies of the informations and original papers relating to the proof of the horrid conspiracy against the late king [by J. Keeling, J. Romzey, et al.].* [London] in the Savoy: T. Newcomb, 1685. Fol. Pp. [2], 141.
LT 3.58.
Wood 428(33) (listed with Wood 428(32) in Bodl. CD cat.). Wing S5029A.

6009. [Sprat, Thomas]. Rochester, bp. of. *A true account and declaration of the horrid conspiracy against the late king.* [London] in the Savoy: T. Newcomb, sold S. Lowndes, 1685. Fol. Pp. [5], 167.
Tp, AW wrote the price, '7ˢ', the name of the author, 'By Tho. Sprat B. of Roff.' [sic, i.e., Rochester], and 'This was published about a fortnight before the D. of Monmouth with his Rebells landed at Lyme– He landed xi. June 1685'. LT 3.58.
Wood 428(32). Wing S5066.

6010. Sprat, Thomas. Rochester, bp. of. *A letter . . . to . . . the earl of Dorset and Middlesex . . . concerning his sitting in the late ecclesiastical commission.* [London], in the Savoy: E. Jones, 1688[9]. 4°. Pp. 20.
Tp, AW wrote 'Tho. Sprat.' P. 4, line in margin.
Wood 611(3). Wing S5033.

6011. Sprat, Thomas*. Rochester, bp. of. *An answer to the bishop of Rochester's first letter to the earl of Dorset . . . concerning the late ecclesiastical commission.* London: f. W. Haight in Bloomsberry, 1689. 4°. Pp. [4], 30.
Tpᵛ, 'said to be written by Mʳ. Charlton.' not in AW's hand. P. 11, at 'Curate of *Mark-Lane*, the Curate of *Timothy*', AW wrote 'Tim. Hall'. AO 4.730.
Wood 611(4). Wing A3388.

6012. Sprat, Thomas. Rochester, bp. of. *The bishop of Rochester's second letter to . . . the earl of Dorset and Middlesex.* [London], in the Savoy: E. Jones, 1689. 4°. Pp. [2], 64.
Tpᵛ, 'Imprimatur March. 27. 1689 Williā Cant: This was in other printed Copies.', not in AW's hand. P. 11, lines in margin, in pencil.
Wood 611(5). Wing S5049.

6013. Sprigge, Joshua. *Certain weighty considerations humbly tendered . . . to . . . the high court of*

justice for the tryal of the king. London: n.pub., 1648[9]. 4°. Pp. 13.
Tp, AW underscored the name of 'Josuah Sprigge', in red ink.
Wood 364(6). Wing S5071.

6014. [Sprigge, William]. *Philosophicall essayes with brief adviso's.* London: J. S. f. R. Blaggrave [sic] at Oxon, 1657. 12°. Pp. [10], 105.
Tp, AW wrote '6^d' and 'Will. Sprigge the authour'; ^{v}, 'Will. Sprigg M. A. Fellow of Lync. Coll. Oxon. was the author of this booke/'.
Wood 739(4). Wing S5080. Madan 2353.

6015. [Sprigge, William]. *A modest plea for an equal common-wealth against monarchy.* London: f. G. Calvert, 1659. 4°. Pp. [14], 102, [1].
Tp, AW wrote, 'first published in Aug. 1659', 'There came out another edition in 8° about X^{t}mas 1659', and below, pasted a slip over his own note, 'Liber Ant. Woode ex dono Guil. Sprigge Coll Lincol: Oxōn socii et authoris: Decemb: x: A° D. m DC lix'. On the visible side of the slip he wrote, 'Will Sprigge M.A. the Author'. P. 45-6, at an attack on universities, AW made a correction and, at a derogatory reference to domineering wives, 'Q. R. &c.', wrote in the margin, 'Queen Regent is the wife of a Head of a College'; 49 (i.e., 48), underscoring of 'Galli', explained in the printed text as 'priests of Mars who used to geld themselves'. LT 1.288, 295.
Wood 626(14). Wing S5078.

6016. Sprigge, William*. *A modest reply, in answer to the modest plea [of W. Sprigge], for an equal common-wealth: against monarchy. In three letters.* London: n.pub., 1659. 4°. Pp. [2], 22.
P. 7, on a repair slip, 5 words in pencil, illeg. Acquired 10 Dec. 1659, 4^d, LT 1.288, 295.
Wood 626(15). Wing M2371.

6017. [Sprigge, William]. *The royal and happy poverty: or, a meditation.* London: f. G. Calvert, 1660. 8°. Pp.[10], 96, [9] (7 pp. books sold by G. Calvert). Calf with 2 fillets, with 1 vertical line of 2 fillets.
Flyleaf, upper^v, 'Anth: Woode'. Tp, AW wrote 'Aug. 29. 1660. Donum Will: Sprigge Authoris et Socii Coll Lync. Oxon:' (LT 1.331).
Wood 122. Wing S5081 (two).

6018. Squire, Edward*. Bacon, Francis, by (?). *A letter written out of England to an English gentleman remaining at Padua, containing a true report of a . . . conspiracie, contrived betweene Edward Squire, . . . and Richard Wallpoole.* London: deputies of C. Barker, 1599. 4°. Pp. [2], 13.
Acquired 29 Ap. 1658 out of G. Langbaine's study, LT 1.247.
Wood 586(9). STC 10017.

6019. Stafford, Anthony*. *Staffords heavenly dogge: or the life, and death of Diogenes.* London: G. Purslowe f. J. Budge, 1615. 12°. Pp. [20], 112. Parchment.
Pastedown, upper and lower, notes on pasted down sides, illeg.; flyleaf, upper, AW wrote, 'Anthony Wood' and 'the heavenly dogge'; scribbles, not in AW's normal manner. Some pencil marks, not in AW's normal manner (e.g., p. 50-1). Flyleaf, lower, last^v, scribbles.
Wood 280. STC 23128.

6020. Stafford, Anthony*. *Honour and vertue, triumphing over the grave. Exemplified in a . . . life, . . . of Henry lord Stafford.* London: J. Okes, sold R. Lownds, 1640. 4°. Pp. [20], 92, [42].
Tp, 'A. woode. [sic] Aug: 16 A: 1660: 9^d'. Bsm. P. [3], signatures 'Ambrose Mountfort', 'Robertus Coke', and scribbles. Q4^v, emendation, W'alwyn'; T1, correction; V1^v, signature of George Prinne. LT 1.327.
Wood 535(7). STC 23126.

6021. Stafford, Robert. *A geographicall and anthologicall description of all the empires.* London: N. Okes, f. S. Waterson, 1634. 4°. Pp. [6], 55, [3]. Pasteboard (blue) with parchment spine.
Flyleaf, upper, 1st, 'Antonii A Wood'; 2nd^{r-v}, the titles of 20 printed works in this vol., within guidelines made with red ink. The numbers in this cat. follow the order of pamphlets in the vol. (AW missed item 3, and the Bodl. CD cat. numbers pamphlets in an irregular order and omits no. 17). Tp, AW wrote, 'This booke was for the most part made by Jo: Prideux Rector of Exon Coll. & since B. of Worcester but afterwards published by his scholler Rob. Stafford under his owne name', and 'printed at Lond. 1618. qu[aere]'. LT 1.425-6.
Wood 386(1). STC 23137.

6022. Stafford, William, ed. (?). Smith, Thomas, attrib. to. *A compendious or brief examination of certayne ordinary complaints, . . . By W. S.* London: T. Marsh, 1581. 4°. Ff. [4], 55.

Tp, AW wrote below W. S., 'The author Will. Stafford'.
Wood 618(6) (not in Bodl. CD cat.). STC 23134.

6023. Staley, William*. *A true relation of the execution of mr. William Staley. At Tyburn . . . for high treason [21 Nov.].* London: f. D. M., 1678. 4°. Pp. 8.
Wood 586(18). Wing T2949 ('O' not recorded in Wing).

6024. Stalham, John. *The summe of a conference at Terling . . . held betweene 3. ministers [J. Stalham et al.] . . . pleading for, and 2. catabaptists . . . denying infants baptisme.* London: I. L. f. C. Meredith, 1644. 4°. Pp. [8], 36.
Tp, '14' over former no., '15'. Bsm.
Wood 647(14). Wing S6166.

6025. Stanbridge, John. *Stanbrigii embryon relimatum, seu vocabularium metricum olim ā Iohanne Stanbrigio digestum, dein à Thoma Newtono aliquantulum repurgatum . . . industriā Joh: Brinslaei.* Londini: typ. T. Cotes, & venales prostant a T. Alchorne, 1636. 4°. A-H⁴.
Missing. MS. Wood E. 2(70), p. 16, 'Joh. Stanbridge Embryon relimatum - 1636. 4°'.
MS. Wood E. 2(70), p. 16. STC 23193.2. O, BL.

6026. Stanbridge, John, and Richard Whitington. *Accidentia ex Stanbrigiana editione nuper recognita & castigate lima Roberti Whitintoni.* ?: ?, 1515ff. Pp.?
Missing. MS. Wood E. 2(70), p. 74, 'Rob Whitington or Joh. Stanbridge { Grammar– with his picture before it'. Ed. not identified.
MS. Wood E. 2(70), p. 74. STC 23147.2ff..

6027. Standish, John. *A lytle treatyse composed . . . against the protestacion of R. Barnes.* London: (in aed. R. Redmani) or (ex aed. E. Pykerynge viduae R. Redmani), (1540, 3 non. oct.) or (1540, 13 cal. dec). 8°.
Missing. MS. Wood E. 2(70), p. 9. Ed. not identified.
MS. Wood E. 2(70), p. 9. STC 23209 and 23210.

6028. Stanley, James*. Derby, earl of. *Good newes out of Cheshire. Being a certaine relation of the late passages of that great malignant, James earle of Darby.* London: f. J. Davis, [1642]. 4°. Pp. 8.
Tp, AW wrote the year, '1642', and earlier, '1644 qu[aere]', in pencil. P. 3, at decease of the Earl of Derby's father, he wrote 'Will. [Stanley] his father died 29 Sept. 1642'; pp. 3-4, some underscoring.
Wood 375(23b). Wing G1074.

6029. Stanley, James. Derby, earl of. *The true speech of James earl of Derby upon the scaffold at Bolton in Lancashire . . . 15. day of October 1651.* N.p.: n.pub., [1651?]. 4°. Pp. 8.
P. 8, AW wrote, 'Given to me by Sʳ Will. Dugdale Garter K. of Arms at what time I was with him at Blith Hall' (AW first visited Blythe Hall, in Warwickshire, 12-17 March 1677, LT 2.371; again, 31 Aug. 1680, LT 2.494).
Wood 367(7). Not in Wing (should be at D1094A). Not in ESTCR.

6030. Stanyhurst, Richard. *De rebus in Hibernia gestis, libri quattuor, . . . Accessit . . . appendix, ex Silvestro Giraldo Cambrensi . . . collecta.* Antverpiae: ap. C. Plantinum, 1584. 4°. Pp. 264, [8].
Pp. 4 to 232, some notes, marks in margins, and underscoring, not in AW's hand.
Wood 534(6) (not in Bodl. CD cat.). BL.

6031. Stanyhurst, Richard. *Hebdomada Mariana, ex orthodoxis Catholicę Romanę ecclesiae patribus collecta.* Antverpiae: ap. J. Moretum, 1609. 8°. Pp. 208, [48]. Parchment.
Tp, 'pretium - 18ᵈ.' and Q8, 'Henrici Jacksoni Oxon. Collegi Christi. MDC.' Passim, underscoring and marks in margin by Jackson. Flyleaf, lower, brief homily by Jackson. LT 1.459-60 (and 1.331).
Wood 781. BL.

6032. Stanyhurst, Richard. *Brevis praemunitio pro futurā concertatione cum Jacobo Usserio . . . qui in suā historicā conatur probare, pontificem Romanum . . . esse antichristum.* Duaci: ex typog. B. Belleri, 1615. 8°. Pp. 38, [1]. Calf with 3 fillets and also 3 vertical fillets, stamp decoration (dragon) in corners (Ashm. binding).
Flyleaf, upper, 2nd, list of 5 printed works in this vol., by an Ashm. librarian. Passim, brief notes (some cropped), underscoring, and vertical lines in margins, not by AW.
Wood 183(1). BL.

6033. Staplehill, John. *Severall informations and examinations taken concerning lieutenant colonell John*

Lilburn, shewing his apostasy. London: H. Hills, f. G. Calvert a. T. Brewster, 1653. 4°. Pp. [2], 14.
Wood 368(13). Wing S5255 ('O' not recorded in Wing).

6034. S[tarling], S[amuel]. *An answer to the seditious and scandalous pamphlet, entituled, the tryal of W. Penn and W. Mead [written by the former]*. London: W. G., 1671. 4°. Pp. [2], 38.
Pp. 2, 10, 2 corrections made from errata, prob. not by AW. Responds to Wood 645(18), item 5166.
Wood 645(19). Wing S5296.

6035. State Martyrology. *The state martyrologie. Or, innocent blood speaking its mournful tragedy*.
London: T. Creake, sold E. Thomas, 1660. S.sh.
Missing in 1922. No. 18, by AW's count, or no. 19, by the 1st Ashm. count, was removed after 1840. The title 'State Martyrology–', appears on the flyleaf without a comment by Kirtland and in the Whiteside cat., but does not appear in the Milford hand-list.
Wood 367(19). Wing S5300 (one) (BL Thomason, 23 May).

6036. Stayley, William*. *An account of the digging up of the quarters of William Stayley, lately executed*.
London: f. R. Pawlet, 1678. S.sh.
AW wrote the price, '2ᵈ'.
Wood 424(2). Wing A276.

6037. Stayley, William*. *The tryal of William Stayley, goldsmith; for speaking treasonable words . . . and received sentence . . . November the 21ᵗʰ*. London: f. R. Pawlet, 1678. Fol. Pp. 10 (misnumbering, 1-8, 7-10).
Pasteboard (blue) with parchment spine; rebacked and repaired.
AW's table of contents for this vol. was prob. lost when the vol. was repaired., The Whiteside cat. gives a summary of the contents and '31. Pamphlets'. The Milford hand-list records that nos. 3, 15, and 16 were missing in 1922. There is no way to find out the names of the authors or the titles of the lost items. To form this vol., AW brought together items from different bundles, all concerning the Popish Plot (1678-80). This is indicated by former numbers on several items (these former nos. are not recorded in the individual entries for this vol.). Tp, AW wrote the price '1ˢ'.
Wood 424(1). Wing T2237.

6038. Stella, Cherubino di. *Poste per diverse parti del mondo. & il viaggio di s. Iacomo di Galitia*.
Lyon: par B. Rigaud, 1572. 16°. Ff. 94, [4]. Parchment wrapper.
Wood 151. *Bibl. Lyon*. 3.284.

6039. Stent, Peter. *Stipendium peccati mors hodie mihi cras tibi*. N.p.: printed and sould by P. Stent, sould by J. Hind, 1643-67. S.sh. (engr.).
Wood 276b(28). Not in Wing. Not in ESTCR.

6040. Stephens, Anthony, ed. *Miscellany poems and translations by Oxford hands*. London: f. A. Stephens, 1685. 8°. Pp. [8], 205, [2] (1 p. books sold by A. Stephens).
P. 196, pencil line at Seneca's *Agamemnon*.
Wood 112(5). Wing M2232.

6041. [Stephens, Edward]. *Observations upon a treatise intituled, Of humane reason [by M. Clifford]*.
London: f. J. Leigh, 1675. 12°. Pp. [2], 73.
Tp, AW wrote '6ᵈ', 'published Decemb. 1674.', and 'Written by Edw. Stephens of Cherrington in Glocestersh.' Wood 841(2-4) all respond to M. Clifford, Wood 841(1), item 1920.
Wood 841(2). Wing S5340.

6042. [Stephens, Edward]. *Reflections upon the occurrences of the last year [5 Nov. 1688 - 5 Nov. 1689]*.
London: n.pub., 1689. 4°. Pp. 36.
Tp, AW wrote, 'Edw. Stephens an Attorney in com. Glouc. (related to Sʳ Mathew Hale) was the author of this. So Ja. Harryngton of ch.ch. who gave it to me 15 Mar. 1689[90].' LT 3.328.
Wood 533(18). Wing S5437 (Wing, occurences).

6043. S[tephens], J[ohn]. *An historical discourse, briefly setting forth the nature of procurations*. London:
R. Hodgkinson, 1661. 4°. Pp. [11], 146, [1].
Tp, AW wrote after printed 'J. S.', 'Jo. Stephens'; and below, '1ˢ.3ᵈ.'
Wood 370(5). Wing S5448.

6044. [Stephens, Philemon]. *A true relation of the ceremonies at the creating of the knights . . . of the Bath, the 18, & 19. April 1661*. London: f. P. Stephens, [1661]. 4°. Pp. 12.
Wood 536(6). Wing S5453 (Wing, to the ceremonies).

6045. Stevenson, M[atthew]. *The twelve moneths, or, a pleasant . . . discourse of every action, . . . proper to each particular moneth.* London: M. S. f. T. Jenner, 1661. 4°. Pp. [4], 59.
Tp, AW wrote, 'One Jo. Lane wrot a poem called <u>The</u> twelve months.', in red ink, and '10ᵈ'. Bsm.
[MS.] Wood C. 17(4). Wing S5510.

6046. Stewart, Charles*. *The horrible and bloody conspiracy undertaken by many desperate persons . . . to cry up and introduce the interest of Charles Stewart.* London: f. T. Vere, a. W. Gilbertson, 1658.
8°. Pp. [2], 14.
Wood 367(14). Wing H2855 (two).

6047. Stewart, William, capt. *A full relation of the late victory obtained . . . by the forces under the command of generall Lesley, the lord Fairfax, and the earl of Manchester.* London: J. F. f. L. Blaiklock, 1644, 11 July. 4°. Pp. 16.
Dupl. at Wood 612(21).
Wood 377(19) (not in Bodl. CD cat.). Wing S5530.

6048. Stewart, William, capt. *A full relation of the late victory obtained . . . by the forces under the command of generall Lesley, the lord Fairfax, and the earl of Manchester.* London: J. F. f. L. Blaiklock, 1644, 11 July. 4°. Pp. 16.
Tp, AW wrote 'Du–', in pencil (cropped at side). Dupl. at Wood 377(19).
Wood 612(21). Wing S5530.

6049. Stillingfleet, Edward. Worcester, bp. of. *The grand question, concerning the bishops right to vote in parlament [sic] in cases capital.* London: f. M. P., sold R. Rumball, 1680. 8°. T leaf is a cancel. Pp. [4], 188.
Tp, Bodl. shelf-mark, 'and 8° F. 23. Jur.', not in AW's hand, lined out (a copy is no longer at this shelf-mark) and above, 'Tanner', in a later hand (a copy is at Tanner 913).
Wood 574(2). Wing S5594.

6050. Stirling, James. *Naphtali, or the wrestlings of the church of Scotland for the kingdom of Christ.* [Holland?]: n.pub., 1667. 8°. Pp. [80], 306. Calf with 2 fillets; rebacked.
Flyleaf, upper, 'Pret: 5ˢ-6ᵈ.' not by AW; ᵛ, AW wrote 'This book was printed in Lat. at Lond. 1672 in qu[arto] under this tit. Naphtali: seu colluctationes Theologicae - sub nomine Jac. Calvert.' (Wing C319). Introduction, AW numbered pp. 1-78.
Wood 783. Wing S5683.

6051. Stirrup, Thomas. *The artificers plain scale: or, the carpenters new-rule.* London: R. & W. Ley-bourne f. T. Pirrepont [sic], 1651. 8°. Pp. [15], 119.
Wood 704(9). Wing S5686.

6052. Stirrup, Thomas, and William Leybourn. *Horometria: or, the compleat diallist. . . . Whereunto is added an appendix, shewing how the parallels of declination; . . . may be easily inscribed.* London: R. & W. Leybourn, f. T. Pirrepont, 1659. 4°. 2nd ed. Pp. [7], 181, [3] (4 pp. books sold by Pirrepont).
Tp, AW wrote, '2ˢ. Feb: 4. 68[9]'. Bsm. LT 2.151.
Wood 481(3). Wing S5689.

6053. Stockwood, John. *Disputatiuncularum grammaticalium libellus.* Londini: T. Judson pro J. Harrison, 1598. Ff. [13], 114, [31]. A-V⁸. Parchment with 2 clasp holes.
Wood 30. STC 23278.

6054. Stoppa, Giovanni Battista, ed. *A collection or narative [sic] . . . concerning . . . massacres . . . on . . . protestants . . . in the vallies of Piedmont.* [London]: f. H. Robinson, 1655. 4°. Pp. [16], 43.
Dupl. at Wood 609(39).
Wood 365(13). Wing S5746B.

6055. Stoppa, Giovanni Battista, ed. *A collection or narative [sic] . . . concerning . . . massacres . . . on . . . protestants . . . in the vallies of Piedmont.* [London]: f. H. Robinson, 1655. 4°. Pp. [16], 43.
Below imprint, AW wrote 'Dup'. Dupl. at Wood 365(13).
Wood 609(39). Wing S5746B.

6056. Storer, Thomas. *The life and death of Thomas Wolsey cardinall.* London: [V. Simmes f.] T. Dawson, 1599. 4°. A-K⁴ (K4 blank).
Tp, signature of former owner, 'John Lee of Merton Colledge in Oxford' (LT 1.313). Tpᵛ, AW quotes: '–
Atque ō utinam &c quod Wolsaeo, aedificatori magnificentissimi collegii Christi, praestitum ab ingenioso

poëta est, &c, sic Dr Alber. Gentilis in Lib. cui tit. est. Laudes Academiae Perusinae et Oxoniensis, edit. Hanouiae 1605. p. 41' (AW could have used the Bodl. copy, 8° G 14(3) Jur.). Text, some marks in margin and corrections, e.g., A3-A3^v, K3^v. Note at G1, not in AW's hand. Possibly lent to John Beby, 4 Mar. 1663, LT 1.470.
Wood 345(12). STC 23294.

6057. Story, John*. *A copie of a letter lately sent by a gentleman, student in the lawes of the realme, to a frende of his concernyng. D. Story [4 June 1571].* [London]: [J. Day?], [1571]. 8°. A-B^4,C^2. Pasteboard (grey) with parchment spine; 1st upper and last lower flyleaves, marbled paper.
Flyleaf, upper, 2nd, AW wrote the titles of 22 printed works in this vol. (really 23, he omitted item no. 10b), within guidelines made with red ink. W. K[irtland] entered 'Deest' at item 20. Arabic nos. on tpp, after item 2, are in red ink. The 8 items, 3-10a, formed a group for the pp. were numbered by hand, 1-412. This was done prob. before AW acquired them. Apparently all 8 were from G. Langbaine's library. AW recorded in his diary the acquisition from Langbaine of 'Treasons of Campion, Throckmorton, Parry, Lopez, Squire and Wolpole, Essex, and Gowry', LT 1.247. 1st item, each 8° leaf is pasted on a 4° template. Tp, AW wrote, 'Of Dr Joh. Storie, see what I have said in Hist. et Antiq. Univ. Oxon. lib. 2. p. 40. a.' (*Hist. and Antiq.*, 2.856). Signature of a former owner, Phyllyp Meteyeard; top left, 'H1' (a shelf-mark?). ^{v}, drawing of a dog. Text, a few notes by a former owner, prob. Meteyeard. LT 1.247.
Wood 586(1). STC 23296.

6058. Stoughton, William. *An assertion for true and Christian church-policie.* [Middelburg]: [R. Schilders], [1604]. 8°. Pp. 16 (dedication only).
P. 1, signature of Hum: Dyson, lined out. P. 16, printed name of author, lined out.
Wood 774(3b). STC 23318.

6059. Stow, John. *The annales of England. Untill 1605.* London: f. G. Bishop a. T. Adams, [1605]. 4°. Pp. [26], 1-1439, 1311-1318.
Missing in 1837. 'Stows Chronicle – Lond. 1604' in Whiteside cat. (presumably the 1605 edition). Acquired from Davis on 23 Feb. 1670, 8^d, LT 2.187. (STC lists no ed. with imprint date of 1604).
Wood 132. STC 23337. *Folg, Hunt* (Oxford binding).

6060. Stow, John. [Munday, Anthony, ed.]. *The survay of London.* London: G. Purslowe, 1618. 4° in 8's. Pp. [12], 980, [4]. Calf with 3 fillets; spine, 4 bands and hatching.
Flyleaf, upper, 1st, 'Anthony: Woode 1661:', and '3^s'; 4th^v, 'Grey Fryers, p 588' (house and church in London), '1. Edit. Lond. 1603. 4°. 2. 1618. 3. 1633. fol. fol. [sic]', and, 'Anthony Munday Citizen & Draper of London, continued this Survey of Lond. from Jo. Stowes death an. 1605 to 1618. & thence againe to his owne death, 10. Aug. 1633. æt. 80. buried in S. Stevens Church Colemanstreet–'. P. 368, 'S. Michaels church.', in margin. At p. 672-3, AW pasted in a small slip with, 'one Godwinus with his wife Turgunda gave the Abby of Malmsbury (Warinus then Abbat) the church of St Nicholas in London AD. 1084 soe in the book of Malmsbury f°. 55.1. which I have [/] A. Woode. Oxōn [/] see Stow p. 672'. P. 690, at sepultus G. Lloyd, red line in margin.
Wood 472. STC 23344.

6061. Stow, John*. *A recital of Stow's collection concerning the rise, profitableness, and continuance of the court of requests.* [London]: n.pub., [1640?]. S.sh.
Torn down the middle and some text is missing. AW, prob., wrote in 3 missing words.
Wood 630(24). STC 23346.

6062. Stradling, John . *Epigrammatum libri quatuor.* Londini: [Eliot's Court Press] imp. G. Bishop & J. Norton, 1607. 8°. Pp. [2], 176, [5].
Tp, AW wrote 'AW Oxon' and '6^d.' 'R' in upper right corner. Acquired 8 Mar. 1662, LT 1.433; see also 2.152.
Wood 82(2). STC 23354.

6063. S[trange], R[ichard]. *The life and gests of s. Thomas Cantilupe, bishop of Hereford.* Gant: Robert Walker, 1674. 8°. Pp. [32], 333, [2]. Calf with 2 fillets; 2nd rectangle with 3 fillets and stamp decoration around rectangle and on spine.
Pastedown, upper, signature of – (?) Mertonensis, lined out. Flyleaf, upper, first: '7. Aug. 1681. Given to me by Will. Bernard M.A. fellow of Mert. coll. [/] Ant. à Bosco [/] Rich. Strange borne in the countie of Northumberland, who entred into the societie of Jesus at Watten neare S. Omers an. 1631. aet. 21. was the authour of this booke. [/] Anton. à Bosco.' LT 2.550.
Wood 67. Wing S5810.

6064. Strangwayes, George*. *The unhappy marksman. Or a . . . discovery of . . . murther committed by mr. George Strangwayes*. London: T. N. f. R. Clavell, 1659. 4°. Pp. 32.
Tp, AW wrote, '1658[9].' and, p. 27, corrected 'Warmsley' to 'Warmstrey'.
Wood 365(16). Wing U68.

6065. Straparola, Giovanni Francesco. Louveau, Jean, trans. *Les facecieuses nuictz . . . traduitte d'Italien en François*. Lyon: par G. Rouille, 1560. 8°. Pp. 367. Calf with 1 gold-stamped fillet and oval centrepiece; rebacked.
Acquired from his brother, Robert Wood. Tp, '1647', 'Monseiur Du Four', and scribbles by more than one owner. P. 4, 'de Lyon ce premier Jour de May 1647'; 112, 'Je confess de Domo [?] a monsieur Dufour Robert Wood'; 225, 'le vingt troisieme jour de Mars 1647'; 365, 'Arise frome sinne thou wicked mane' etc., not in AW's hand; 367, a note in French; 367ᵛ and pastedown, lower, sketches of heads, scribbles, including 'Wood', 'Halley', 'Du Four', 'Halleus me possidet', and 'Henricus Jacobius coll mert.' LT 1.52.
Wood 70. *Bibl. Lyon.* 9.271.

6066. S[treater], J[ohn]. *The continuation of this session of parliament, justified; and the action of the army . . . defended*. London: n.pub., 1659. 4°. Pp. 16.
Tp, above, AW wrote 'Bund. 1', in pencil; the author's name after initials 'Streater qu[aere]', in pencil; below, 'This was written upon the Army's inviting the members of the Long parliam. to resit in the H. of Commons, after they had been dissolved in Apr. 1653 – in May 1659'.
Wood 620(18). Wing S5946 ('O' not recorded in Wing).

6067. Streater, J[ohn]. *A shield against the Parthian dart, or, a word to the purpose, shot into Wallingford-house*. [London]: n.pub., 1659. 4°. Pp. 23.
Tp, AW wrote 'Bund 1', in pencil; bsm.
Wood 620(22). Wing S5950 ('O' not recorded in Wing).

6068. Strype, John. *A sermon [on 1 Sam. xii. 7] preached at the assizes at Hertford [8 July]*. London: f. R. Chiswell, 1689. 4°. Pp. [4], 32.
Tp, AW wrote, 'Nov. 6. an. 1690 dedit mihi Rich. Chiswell'. LT 3.206, 251.
Wood 633(13). Wing S6025.

6069. Stubbe, Henry. *Illustrissimo, summaeque spei juveni Henrico Vane . . . Henricus Stubbe*. [Oxford]: [L. Lichfield], [1656]. 8°. S.sh.
AO 3.1072; LT 1.303.
Wood 383(7). Wing S6048 (two). Madan 2313.

6070. Stubbe, Henry. *The Savilian professours case stated . . . by Henry Stubbe*. [London]: J. T. f. A. Crook [f. R. Davis in Oxon], [1658]. 4°. Pp. [4], 22 (imprint mutilated).
Tp, AW added beneath the line that was excised, '& are to be sold at Ric: Davis his shop in Oxōn. 1658' (AO 3.1073-6). Pp. 3, 21-2, lines in margins, in ink and pencil. Acquired 23 Apr. 1658, LT 1.242. Responds to Wallis, Wood 515(20), item 6424.
Wood 515(21). Wing S6065 (Wing, Stubbs). Madan 2371.

6071. S[tubbe], H[enry]. *The common-wealth of Israel, or a brief account of mr. Prynne's anatomy of the good old cause*. London: T. Brewster, 1659. 4°. Pp. [2], 6 (misnumbering).
Tp, AW wrote the no. in a former bundle, '14', in pencil, and the author's name after initials, H. Sᵗtubbe of xᵗ ch:' and 'AWood. donum Authoris'. LT 1.303.
Wood 613(19). Wing S6035.

6072. S[tubbe], H[enry]. *A letter to an officer of the army concerning a select senate mentioned by them in their proposals to the late parliament*. London: printed, sold by T. B., 1659. 4°. Pp. [2], 76 (i.e., 68, misnumbering).
Tp, no. '13', in pencil, in a former bundle. P. 61, correction to 'Deut. 23'.
Wood 626(6). Wing S6054aA.

6073. [Stubbe, Henry]. *A light shining out of darknes: or occasional queries submitted to the judgment*. London: n.pub., 1659. 4°. Pp. [8], 37.
Acquired 11 Nov. 1659, 18ᵈ, LT 1.287, 295; AO 3.1076f.
Wood 617(2). Wing S6056. Madan 2428.

6074. Stubbe, Henry. *The miraculous conformist: or an account of severall marvailous cures performed by the stroaking of the hands of mʳ Valentine Greatarick*. Oxford: H. Hall f. R. Davis, 1666. 4°. Pp. [6], 44.

Tp, AW wrote, 'Miracles'. Former no., '1'. Prob. acquired 9 March 1666, 6ᵈ, LT 2.73; AO 3.1077f.
Wood 643(8). Wing S6062. Madan 2758.

6075. Stubbe, Henry. *Campanella revived, or an enquiry into the history of the Royal Society, whether the virtuosi there do not pursue the projects of Campanella for the reducing England unto popery. . . . With a postscript concerning the quarrel depending betwixt H. S. and dr. [Chr.] Merrett*. London: f. the author, 1670. 4°. Pp. [6], 22.
Tp, AW wrote at year, 'June 14.' (taken from the text, p. 22). P. [5], lines in margin; p. 21, at C. Merrett and J. Goddard, lines in margin, in red ink. LT 1.354.
Wood 640(8). Wing S6030.

6076. Stubbe, Henry. *A censure upon certaine passages contained in the history of the Royal Society [of T. Sprat], as being destructive to the established religion*. Oxford: [W. Hall] f. R. Davis, 1670. 4°. Pp. [4], 64.
Tp, AW wrote, 'Feb' and 'Feb. 16 1669'. P. 8 the name 'Mr. Sprat' blocked out and 'our Author' in margin, not in AW's hand. LT 1.354.
Wood 640(2). Wing S6033. Madan 2866.

6077. Stubbe, Henry. *Legends no histories: or, a specimen of some animadversions upon the history of the Royal Society [of T. Sprat]. . . . Together with the plus ultra of mr. Joseph Glanvill reduced to a non-plus*. London: sold by the Book-sellers there, 1670. 4°. Pp. [28], 127 (p. [1] blank) (2 pts.). Pasteboard (grey) with parchment spine; traces of upper and lower flyleaves, marbled paper.
Flyleaf, upper, 2ndᵛ, AW wrote the titles of 7 (really 7; a modern corrector assumed 2 items for the single item, 5-6) printed works in this vol., within guidelines made with red ink. 1st item, p. [1], AW wrote 'Oct. 1669'. Tp, AW wrote, 'This came out in Oct. 1669.' (a modern writer, in a brief note, argues that it was written then but did not appear until after Stubbe's *The Plus Ultra Reduced*; in support, he cites Stubbe's words at b2r (but the publication details of the items 1, 5 and 6 in this vol. are complex in that they were issued separately and together; see ESTCR 21316, 204833, and 24632)). †2, vertical double line in margin; †3, line in margin and AW wrote the p. no., '13' and commented on the 'Bishop of Winchester': 'while he sate at Worcester-' (George Morley). LT 1.354.
Wood 640(1). Wing S6053.

6078. Stubbe, Henry. *The plus ultra reduced to a non plus: or, a specimen of some animadversions upon the plus ultra of mʳ. Glanvill*. London: f. the Author, 1670. 4°. Pp. [16], 179 (misnumbering; 2 sets of 115-6 and 178-9) (2 tpp.).
Flyleaf, upperᵛ, AW wrote, 'Mʳ Glanvills Plus Ultra in [sic, i.e., is] printed in 8°, which I have', i.e., Wood 681, item 3228, which he purchased in 1681. After the 2nd tp, pp. 2-3, the corrections entered from errata on p. [13]. P. 178, at a ref. to Dr. Lower, AW added vertical lines. LT 1.354, 2.30.
Wood 640(5-6). Wing S6063 [and S6067).

6079. Stubbe, Henry. *A reply unto the letter written [by J. Arderne] to mʳ. Henry Stubbe in defense of the history of the Royal Society. Whereunto is added a preface against Ecebolius Glanvill; and an answer to the letter of dʳ Henry More*. Oxford: [L. Lichfield] f. R. Davis, 1671. 4°. Pp. 79, [1] (2 tpp.) (also issued as pt. 2 of Wing S6034).
P.16, AW wrote in margin, 'Dʳ Mer. Casaubon', and at p. 31, 'Dʳ Th. Sprat', both in red ink. P. 32, 'a bishop' lined out, not by AW. Pp. 34-5, 43, 63: AW identified in margins, Ch M. as 'Christopher Merret', B. as 'Baxter', a virtuoso as 'v. Hobs', and a family as 'Lord Conway'. LT 1.354.
Wood 640(7). Wing S6063A. See Madan 2911 (2 pts.).

6080. [Stubbe, Henry]. *The Paris gazette. Paris, anno Dom. 1490. The emperour Maximilian having courted Anne sole daughter and heir to the duke of Britain*. [London?]: n.pub., [1673?]. S.sh. (r-v) (and a preliminary sheet).
On the preliminary sheet ʳ, AW wrote 'Matters relating to the Duke of York do follow-'; ᵛ, a portrait of Prince James, 4°, pasted on to the fol. p., under which AW wrote '1660'. ᵛ of the s.sh., lines in margin at a reference to an Oxford, 1600, discourse; below, AW wrote, 'written by Hen. Stubb M.A, when the Duke of York was about to marry the Princess of Modena-'.
Wood 660c(14). Wing P359B.

6081. Stubbes, Philip. *The anatomie of abuses. Containing a description of such notable vices and enormities . . . especiallie in this realme of England*. London: [J. Danter f.] R. Johnes, 1595. 4°. 4th ed. Pp. [8], 144. Pasteboard (blue) with parchment spine. 1st upper flyleaf, marbled paper; rebacked.
Flyleaf, upper, 3rdᵛ, AW wrote the titles of 7 printed works in this vol., within guidelines made with red

ink. Tp, AW wrote, 'The author of this book hath written another see p. 97'. P. 1, 2 signatures, Wredeth (?).
Wood 653(1). STC 23379.

6082. Stubbes, Philip. *A christal glasse for Christian women. Containing a most excellent discourse, of the godly life, and . . . death of . . . Katherine Stubbes*. London: [J. Haviland] f. J. Wright, 1626. 4°. A-C⁴.
Wood 532(12). STC 23390 (two).

6083. Stukeley, Thomas*. *The famous history of stout Stukley*. London: R. I. f. F. Grove, [1650 ca.]. 8°. A⁸,B⁴.
Wood 254(13). Wing F378A (rare).

6084. Sturtevant, Simon. *Metallica. Or the treatise of metallica*. London: G. Eld, 1612, May 22. 4°. Pp. [16], 112.
Fore-edge, name of author and title. Tp, AW wrote a former no., '10', lined out; and '8ᵈ'. P. 96, line in margin, in pencil.
Wood 316(4) (not in Bodl. CD cat.). STC 23411.

6085. Stuteville, Thomas*, and Phelim O'Neill*. *A true relation of every remarkable circumstance in relieving of Tredagh, by captaine Thomas Steutevile. Also the copy of sir Phelome Oneal's commission*. [London]: J. R. f. C. M., 1642. 4°. Pp. 8.
Tp, AW wrote, 'Jan. 24', in pencil.
Wood 507(29). Wing T2904 ('O' not recorded in Wing).

6086. [Styward, Thomas], and Luis Gutierrez de la Vega. Lichefild, Nicolas, trans. *The pathwaie to martiall discipline. [Followed by] A compendious treatise entituled, de re militari*. London: T.E[ast, J. Kingston, W. How, J. Charlewood] imp. M. Jenyngs (T. East), 1582, (1 Jan.). 4°. Pp. [4], 166; ff. [2], 20 and 3 foldouts (wanting the t leaf to the 1st work; tp and dedic. to 2nd work placed (dedic. leaf pinned) at beginning). Parchment.
[MS.] Wood C. 21 (2 items in Bodl. CD cat.). STC 23414 ('O' not recorded in STC).

6087. Suckling, John*, pseud. *A letter sent by sir John Suckling from France*. London: n.pub., 1641. 4°. Pp. [2], 6.
Tp, AW wrote, 'A feign'd ridiculous thing', and '26. Jun. 1641'.
Wood 373(3). Wing L1591.

6088. Suckling, John*. *Newes from sir John Sucklin [sic] being a relation of his conversion from a papist to a protestant*. [London]: f. M. Rookes, 1641. 4°. A⁴.
[MS.] Wood B. 40(13). Wing N1002 ('O' not recorded in Wing) (Wing, London).

6089. Surius, Laurentius. *Commentarius brevis rerum in orbe gestarum*. Coloniae: ap. haer. J. Quentel & G. Calentium, 1566. 8°. Pp. [14], 641, [22] (misnumbering). Parchment.
Tp, '2ˢ6ᵈ' and note against 'Surium', 'convitiatorem egregium' [an egregious railer] (Surius was a Carthusian), neither by AW. Bsm. Text, a few marks in margins and underscorings, not by AW.
Wood 177. NUC.

6090. Susenbrotus, Joannes. Συν δε θεοι μακαρες. *Epitome troporum ac schematum*. Londini: J. Kyngstonus, 1576. 8°. Pp. [2], 105, [5]. Parchment.
Cover, upper, inside, notes in early hands; lower, inside, 'Eyre – 3ˢ'. P. 82, 'Edward Wood his booke'.
Wood 55. STC 23439 (two).

6091. [Sutcliffe, Matthew]. *The subversion of Robert Parsons his . . . A treatise of three conversions of England*. London: [R. Field] f. J. Norton, 1606. 4°. Pp. [16], 144, [2]. Parchment.
Responds to R. Persons, Wood 223, item 5194.
Wood 322. STC 23469.

6092. Sutcliffe, Matt[hew]. *A threefold answer unto the third part of a . . . treatise . . . by Rob. Parsons*. London: [R. Field] f. J. Norton, 1606. 4° in 8's. Pp. [9], 316, [4].
Flyleaf, upperᵛ, 'n' (?). Pp. 103, brief note, and 175-185, long vertical lines in margins, in pencil, not in AW's usual manner. Responds to R. Persons, Wood 856 and 872, items 5197-8.
[MS.] Wood B. 33 (not in Bodl. CD cat.). STC 23470.

6093. Sutton, Edward. *The serpent anatomized. A morall discourse wherein that . . . vice of base flattery is . . . discovered*. London: [M. Flesher] f. J. Marriot, 1626. 4°. Pp. [2], 43.

Tp, scribbles, not in AW's hand.
Wood 499(6). STC 23497.

6094. S[wadlin], T[homas]. *Divinity no enemy to astrology*. London: J. G. f. N. Brooke, 1653. 4°. Pp. [4], 28.
Missing. MS. Wood E. 2(70), p. 39, 'Divinity no enemy to astrology – 1643' (1643 prob. refers to the year in which the sermon was delivered, AO 3.888).
MS. Wood E. 2(70), p. 39. Wing S6215. *O, Harv, Folg, Yale*.

6095. Swan, John. *Calumus mensurans. The measuring reed. Or, the standard of time . . . The second part*. London: f. J. Williams, 1653. 4°. Pp. [8], 77, [1].
Wood 473(3). Wing S6235 (Wing, mensurans: the).

6096. Swan, John. *The standard of time. Or the measuring-reed. Containing an exact chronological computation of the years of the world*. London: A. Rice, 1656. 4°. Pp. [8], 249, [6] (t leaf is a cancel (torn and later repaired); part 1 of Wood 473(3)).
Tp, AW wrote the price, '2ˢ'. Bsm. Acquired 27 Feb. 1662, LT 1.431.
Wood 473(2). Wing S6240B (rare).

6097. Swearing-master. *The swearing-master: or, a conference between two country-fellows*. (London): (f. N. T.), (1681). Fol. Pp. 4.
AW added to the date, 'Oct. or Nov'. Dupl. at Wood 417(77).
Wood 276a(568) (now placed after 576). Wing S6244.

6098. Swearing-master. *The swearing-master: or, a conference between two country-fellows*. (London): (f. N. T.), (1681). Fol. Pp. 4.
P. 4, AW wrote 'Oct. or Nov.' Dupl. at 276a(568).
Wood 417(77). Wing S6244.

6099. [Swedish Intelligencer]. *The continuation of the German history. The fifth part [of the Swedish intelligencer]*. London: [T. Harper] f. N. Butter, a. N. Bourne, 1633. 4°. Pp. [14], 163.
Wood 485(2). STC 23525.4.

6100. Swetnam, Joseph. *The arraignment of lewd, idle, froward, and unconstant women: or, the vanitie of them; chuse you whether*. London: A.M[athewes] f. T. Archer, 1628. 4°. Pp. [8], 64.
Tp, 'R:G. -' (prob. not in AW's hand; cropped at side). Diff. ed. at Wood 499(7) and Wood 654a(3).
Wood 499(5). STC 23539.

6101. Swetnam, Joseph. *The arraignment of lewd, idle, froward, and unconstant women: or, the vanity of them, chuse you whether*. London: T. C[otes] f. F. Gro[ve], 1637. 4°. Pp. [8], 63.
Flyleaf, upperᵛ, AW wrote, 'A pamphlet called Constantia Munda written against Joseph Swetnam – 4°. L. 78. Arts in bib. Bodl.' (still at this location; STC 18257); tp, 'Jos. Swetnam the Author.' and below, 'An edition of this booke came out in 1645 at Lond. but not so true as this' and 'Another edit. in 1621'. Diff. ed. at Wood 499(5) and Wood 499(7).
Wood 654a(3) (645a(3) in Bodl. CD cat.). STC 23542 (two).

6102. Swetnam, Joseph. *The arraignment of lewd, idle, froward, and unconstant women: or, the vanity of them, chuse you whether*. London: R. Cotes, 1645. 4°. Pp. [8], 63 (t leaf is mutilated).
Tp, 'Duplicate'. Diff. ed. at Wood 499(5) and Wood 654a(3).
Wood 499(7). Wing S6251 (two).

6103. Sykes, Thomas. *A sermon [on 1 Kings 8.18] preached at the consecration of Trinity-college chappel in Oxford April 12. 1694*. Oxford: at the theater, 1694. 4°. Pp. [7], 32.
See LT 3.449 and Wood 276a(11), item 1184.
[MS.] Wood D. 23(6). Wing S6324.

6104. Syms, Christopher. *The swords apology, and necessity in the act of reformation. . . . with a more lucide exposition of the first prophecy of mother Shipton*. London: f. T. Warren, 1644. 4°. Pp. [5], [18] (misnumbering after p. 11).
Wood 646(8). Wing S6364.

6105. Synesius of Cyrene. Fleming, Abraham, trans. *A paradoxe, proving by reason and example, that baldnesse is much better than bushie haire . . . Hereunto is annexed the pleasant tale of Hemetes the heremite, . . . Newly recognized*. [London]: H. Denham, 1579. 8°. A-D⁸ (imperf.). Calf with 2 fillets and a

vertical line. Most of the 10 items in this vol. were cropped. Prob. an Ashm. binding.
If there was a list of contents, it is now lost. Tp, 'Ant. Woode Mert Coll Oxōn: 1656', lined out.
Wood 736(1). STC 23603.

6106. [Synge, Edward]. Tuam, abp. of. *A gentleman's religion: with the grounds and reasons of it. . . . By a private gentleman [E. Synge. Pt. 1.].* London: f. A. a. J. Churchil, 1693. 12°. Pp. [2], 136, [5] (5 pp. books sold by Churchil).
Tp, AW wrote '9^d' and 'bought at Oxon 7. Jan. 1692[3]'.
Wood 773(2). Wing S6378.

6107. Szilágyi, Georgius. *Acrostichon hoc laudi & honori universitatis Oxoniensis . . . die Julii 5.* [London?]: n.pub., [1671]. S.sh.
Wood 276a(521). Wing S6391 (rare). Madan 2876.

6108. T., B. *Policy, no policy: or, the devil himself confuted. Being an answer to a clause of a letter [28 March].* [London]: n.pub., 1660. 4°. Pp. [2], 5.
Former no. in a bundle, '4'.
Wood 608(1b). Wing T1.

6109. T., D. *Hieragonisticon: or, Corah's doom, being an answer to two letters of enquiry [by J. Eachard] into the grounds . . . of the contempt of the clergy and religion.* London: T. Milbourn f. D. Newman, 1672. 8°. Pp. [2], 198, [1].
Tp, bsm., '1.2'. See note at Eachard, Wood 843(5), item 2390.
Wood 884(6). Wing T4.

6110. T., F. *The case is altered. How? Aske Dalio, and Millo.* London: J. Norton f. R. Bird, 1630. 4°. A-C^4.
Wood 614(11). STC 21616 (two).

6111. T., G. *The method of a synod.* London: printed, sold W. Larnar, 1642. 4°. Pp. 6 (unopened).
[MS.] Wood D. 31(38) (not in Bodl. CD cat.). Wing T9.

6112. T., G. *A list of abhorrors: or, the names of such persons as were lately under custody . . . for abhorring.* [London?]: 'I do appoint Mr. Benjamin Harris to Print this, that it may appear to all true English Protestants, that he once Printed Truth. G. T.' (Harris, a Whig, did not publish this for the Tory, G. T.), [1681]. S.sh.
After t, AW wrote, 'the petitioning for parliaments'; after entry of Henry Aulnet, 'or Alnot of Ibston com. Oxon', and, at 'G. T.', '1680' in red ink.
Wood 276a(98). Wing L2376.

6113. T., I. *The traytors perspective-glass. Or, sundry examples of Gods just judgments . . . upon . . . regicides, . . . Whereunto is added three perfect characters.* London: H. B. f. P. Stephens the younger, 1662. 4°. Pp. [3], 43, [1] (1 p. books printed by Stephens).
P. 33, AW wrote in margin, 'This is false'. See notes at items 869 and 5993.
Wood 369(9). Wing T15A.

6114. T., N. *Very sad newes from Ireland, two strong garrisons taken from [really by] the rebels: Mariborough fort, and the castle of Athlone. . . . A remonstrance of the protestant clergy [25 Oct. 1646].* London: f. N. S., 1646. 4°. Pp. [2], 6.
Tp, in t, 'by' above the printed 'from', may be by AW.
Wood 509(11). Wing T41 ('O' not recorded in Wing).

6115. T., N. *The passage of the treatie for the surrender of Oxford to sir Thomas Fairfax.* London: E. Purslow, 1646, 20 May. 4°. Pp. [2], 6.
Tp, '1^d', prob. not by AW.
Wood 501(12). Wing T36. Madan 1866.

6116. T., N. *The resolver continued, . . . about the putting of the late king to death.* London: J. Clowes, f. H. Allen, 1649. 4°. Pp. [2], 22.
Tp, AW wrote 'N. T.' Some scribbles, numbers, and a note lined out; a 2nd note, 'Thomas Wharton botanist anatomist Her[–?]', not in AW's hand (see AO 3.1000).
Wood 364(22). Wing T39 ('O' not recorded in Wing).

6117. T., R. *De templis, a treatise of temples: wherein is discovered the ancient manner of building,*

consecrating, and adorning of churches. London: R. Bishop f. T. Alchorn, 1638. 12°. Pp. [16], 237. Calf with 3 fillets.
Wood 766. STC 23625.

6118. T., R. *The opinion of witchcraft vindicated. In an answer to . . . The question of witchcraft debated.* London: E. O[kes] f. F. Haley, 1670. 8°. Pp. [2], 63.
Responds to J. Wagstaffe, Wood 705 and 708(1), items 6375f.
Wood 708(2). Wing T50.

6119. T., S. *An historical account of the heroick life . . . of . . . James duke of Monmouth.* London: f. T. Malthus, 1683. 8°. Pp. [6], 142.
Flyleaf, upper, heading, 'Duke of Monmouth', may not be by AW.
Wood 245(3). Wing T53.

6120. Table. *[A table] shewing the most profitable order and m[ethod for r]eading of history.* [London]: n.pub., [1620 ca.]. S.sh. (cropped at edges).
Wood 276a(46) (Wood 376a(46) in Bodl. CD cat.). STC 13528.5 (rare).

6121. Tabula Chronologica. *Tabula chronologica . . . ad annum 4000 [and] Tabula chronologica . . . ad annum MDCLXXXV . . . partim ex Dionysii Petavii Chronologià.* (Cantabrigiae): (J. Hayes, impen. G. Graves), (1685). Fol. Pp. IV.
Wood 276a(47-49). Wing T94 (two).

6122. Talbot, Richard*. Tyrconnel, earl of. *The popish champion: or, a compleat history . . . of Richard earl of Tyrconnel [and] the life . . . of father Petre, &c.* London: f. J. Dunton, 1689. 4°. Pp. [4], 58, [2] (2 pp. books printed f. J. Dunton).
Tp, AW wrote, 'Bought at Oxon. Nov. 1689' (LT 3.315). Tp[v], 'Rich. Talbot Earl of Tyrconnell died in Lymerick while it was besieged by the forces of K. Will. 3, on the 14 of Aug. 1691[.] the ill condition of the then Irish affaires having broke his heart. [/] He was buried in Lymerick on the 16 of the said month, at which time was a commission produced from K Jam. 2 which M[r] Plowden (formerly one of the commissioners of the revenew in Ireland) brought lately from France, appointing S[r] Alex Fitton, S[r] Rich Neagle & the said M[r] Plowden, Justices of Ireland –'. P. [60], line in margin at a book advertisement.
Wood 535(12). Wing P2944.

6123. Tale of the Tubs. *A tale of the tubbs or Romes master peice defeated.* [London]: f. the Loyal Protestant, 1679, 11 Nov. S.sh. Obl.
Missing in 1922. See note at item Wood 417(1), item 781.
Wood 417(14b). Wing T128. *O, Hunt, Harv.*

6124. Tangier. *A description of Tangier, . . . with an account of . . . Gayland, the present usurper of the kingdome of Fez.* London: f. S. Speed, 1664. 4°. Pp. [7], 84.
Acquired 15 Nov. 1664, LT 2.23.
Wood 386(9). Wing D1151.

6125. Tangier. *The present interest of Tangier.* [London]: n.pub., [1679]. Fol. Pp. 4.
Wood 559(16). Wing P3248.

6126. Tangier. *An exact journal of the siege of Tangier:. . . In three letters, written by three eye-witnesses [25 March - 19 May].* London: f. J. Hindmarsh, 1680. Fol. Pp. [2], 13 (A-D²).
Tp, the letter 'c̄'. The 2nd part, Wood 559(13), 'A letter from Tangier-Bay' (17 May), pp. 7-13, is separated from the 1st by a blank leaf.
Wood 559(12-13). Wing E3649.

6127. Tangier. *A particular narrative of a great engagement between the garison [sic] of Tangier, and the Moors.* [London]: T. Newcombe, 1680. Fol. Pp. 8.
Wood 559(14). Wing P593.

6128. Tanner, Tho[mas]. New College. *The entrance of Mazzarini. Or; some memorials of the state of France, between the death of . . . Richelieu and the beginning of the late regency.* Oxford: H. H[ill] f. T. Robinson, 1657. 12°. Pp. [10], 114 (unopened). Pasteboard (blue) with parchment spine.
Tp, AW wrote, 'by Tho. Tanner'; p. [7], underscored Tanner's reference to his age, 'five lustres', and wrote, 'The authour then 25 yeares of age'. AW traded a copy of this to Forrest in Oct. 1657, LT 1.230. AO 4.60.
Wood 565(1). Wing T140. Madan 2354.

6129. [**Tanner, Thomas**]. New College. *The entrance of Mazzarini, continued through the first years regency, of Anna Maria of Austria.* Oxford: A. Lichfield, 1658. 12°. Pp. [6], 141, [3] (unopened).
On authorship, see AO 4.60.
Wood 565(2). Wing T141. Madan 2415.

6130. Tanner, Thomas. New College. *Euphuia, or the acts, and characters of a good nature.* London: f. J. Crook, 1665. 8°. Pp. [6], 111.
Tp, AW underscored Tanner, in red ink, and wrote '8ᵈ'. Acquired 24 Dec. 1667, LT 2.122.
Wood 752(3). Wing T142 (two) (Wing, Euphuia: or,).

6131. Tanner, Thomas. St. Asaph, bp. of. *Notitia monastica or a short history of the religious houses.* Oxford: at the theatre, sold, A. a. J. Churchill, London, 1695. 8°. Pp. [94], 288, [40].
Missing in 1837. 'Tanner's Notitia Monastica – Oxon. 1695', in Whiteside cat. LT 3.452-3.
Wood 201. Wing T148B. *O, Hunt, Folg.*

6132. Tany, [Thomas]. *I proclaime from the lord of hosts the returne of the Jewes . . . Aprill 25. 1650.* London: C. Sumptner f. G. Calvart, 1650. S.sh.
Wood 276a(263). Wing T154 ('O' not recorded in Wing).

6133. Tasborough, John*, and Ann Price*. *The tryal and conviction of John Tasborough and Ann Price for subornation of perjury, in endeavouring to perswade mʳ. Stephen Dugdale to retract.* London: f. R. Pawlett, 1679/80. Fol. Pp. [3], 59, [1] (last p. books lately printed by Pawlett).
Wood 426(3). Wing T2161.

6134. Tatham, John. *Aqua triumphalis; being a true relation of the honourable the city of Londons entertaining their sacred majesties.* London: f. the author, by T. Childe a. L. Parry, 1662. Fol. Pp. [6], 12, [1].
Wood 398(20). Wing T218.

6135. Tatham, John. *Londons triumphs celebrated the 29th of October, 1664. In honour to . . . sir John Lawrence . . . lord maior of . . . London: and performed at the costs . . . of haberdashers.* London: W. G. f. H. Brome, 1664. 4°. Pp. [4], 16 (wanting sigs. D1-2; pp. 17-20).
Wood 537(19). Wing T227 (Wing, London's).

6136. Taunton, Siege. *A letter sent to the right honourable William Lenthall, . . . concerning the raising of the siege of Taunton.* London: E. Husbands, 1645, 10 July. 4°. Pp. 7.
Tp, AW overwrote a former no., '10'.
Wood 378(12). Wing L1625.

6137. Taylor, Jeremy. Down and Connor, bp. of. *The measures and offices of friendship: with rules of conducting it. To which are added, two letters.* London: J. G. f. R. Royston, 1657. 12°. 2nd ed. Pp. 203, [8] (5 pp. books advertised).
Wood 818(2). Wing T317.

6138. Taylor, Jeremy, and Christopher Hatton, eds. *The Psalter of David with titles and collects according to the matter of each psalme. [Followed by] Devotions for the helpe and assistance of all Christian people. [The collects and devotions by J. Taylor, the whole work compiled by lord Hatton.].* Oxford: L. Lichfield, 1644. 8°. Pp. [22], 392, 63. Calf with 2 gold-stamp fillets, and gold-stamp decoration inside the corners; gold fore-edges.
Backing, upper, scribbles and name, not signature, of lord Hatton. Flyleaf, upper, 1st, signatures, 'Mary Wood', 'Thomas Wood', and 'Anthony Wood'; 2nd, 'For my noble & much honored frend Sʳ John Culpeper [Colepeper] Kᵗ Master of the Roles [sic] from your affectionate & obliged servant Chr: Hatton [name of Hatton lined out]: 7° Maii 1644', and signature, 'Edward Wood', and below, AW wrote 'Sʳ Joh. Culpeper Kᵗ then lodging in my mothers house against Merton Coll. Christop. Lord Hatton then in Oxon sent him this book, which after Culpepers departure, came into the hands of my brother Edw. Wood'; ᵛ, AW wrote 'These Psalmes with the devotions at the end, were collected & published by Christopher Lord Hatton' and at a later time, 'But written by Dʳ Jer. Taylor of Alls. Coll.' Tp, 'by the Lord Hatton' not by AW. LT 1.69. Diff. ed. at Wood 848.
Wood 811. Wing B2402. Madan 1626.

6139. Taylor, Jeremy, and Christopher Hatton, eds. *The psalter of David: with titles and collects according to the matter of each psalme. [Followed by] Devotions.* London: J. F. f. R. Royston, 1655. 12°. 5th ed. Pp. [55], 283. Calf with 2 fillets; rebacked.

Flyleaf, upper, 2nd, AW wrote 'The 1. edit. of this book came out at Oxon. an. 1644. collected, written & published by Christopher Lord Hatton/', i.e., Wood 811.
Wood 848. Wing B2461. Madan 1626..

6140. Taylor, John. *Taylor on Thame Isis: or the description of the two famous rivers*. London: J. Haviland, 1632. 8°. A2-8,B^8 (B8 blank). Pasteboard with parchment spine. 'Travell & Rambles' written on spine (bound in or after 1691).
Flyleaf, upper, 3rd^v, list of 6 printed works in this vol., written within guidelines made with red ink. Tp, 'Musaeum Ashmoleanum'.
Wood 155(1). STC 23803 (3).

6141. Taylor, John. *The old, old, very old man: or, the age and long life of Thomas Par*. London: [A. Mathewes] f. H. Gosson, 1635. 4°. A2-4,B-D^4.
D3, D4, scribbles, not by AW.
[MS.] Wood B. 35(4). STC 23782.5.

6142. Taylor, John. *The carriers cosmographie. Or a briefe relation, of the innes, ordinaries, . . . in, and neere London*. London: A. G[riffin], 1637. 4°. A-C^4.
Wood 465(7). STC 23740.

6143. Taylor, John. *A sad and deplorable loving elegy consecrated to the living memory of . . . Richard Wyan [16 Aug. 1638]*. [London]: [J. Okes], [1638]. S.sh.
^{v}, AW wrote, 'Rich. Wyan 1638'.
Wood 429(3). STC 23790 (rare).

6144. Taylor, John. *Part of this summers travels, or news from Hell, Hull, and Hallifax*. [London]: J. O[kes], [1639]. 8°. Pp. [iv], 48.
Tp, AW wrote 'Water poet, 1639'. P. 42, note, in pencil, '3 qu-bus [?] and 500 queans'. P. 48, correction, 'Noster' for 'ncster'.
Wood 155(2). STC 23783.

6145. Taylor, John. *Englands comfort, and Londons joy: expressed in the . . . entertainment of . . . king Charles, at his . . . returne from Scotland*. London: f. F. Coules, 1641. 4°. Pp. 8.
Wood 537(15). Wing T456.

6146. [Taylor, John], attrib. to. *The Irish footman's poetry. Or George [Richardson] the runner, against Henry the Walker in defence of John the swimmer [John Taylor] . . . The author George Richardson*. [London]: n.pub., 1641. 4°. Pp. [2], 9.
Tp, AW wrote, 'Hen. Walker Ironmonger.'
Wood 483(11). Wing T471.

6147. Taylor, John. *New preachers, new. Greene the feltmaker, Spencer the horse-rubber, . . . Whereunto is added . . . the disorderly preachment of mr. Barebones the leather-seller [19 Dec.]*. [London]: f. G. T., 1641. 4°. A^4 (t leaf is cropped at bottom).
Tp, AW added the year, '1641'.
Wood 647(7). Wing T486 (Wing, for C. J.).

6148. Taylor, John. *A reply as true as steele*. [London]: n.pub., 1641. 4°. Pp. [2], 6 (misnumbering).
Missing in 1841. See flyleaf, upper 2nd^v and continuing to tp of item no. 1: 'deest W. K[irkland] 1841'. On the last leaf of (38), item 6398, blotting of Ashm. no. XXXIX written on the removed tp.
Wood 614(39). Wing T506. *Hunt, Harv, Yale*.

6149. Taylor, John. *The anatomy of the separatists, alias, Brownists, the factious brethren in these times*. London: n.pub., 1642. 4°. Pp. [2], 6.
Wood 647(12). Wing A3060B.

6150. Taylor, John. *The whole life and progresse of Henry Walker the ironmonger*. London: n.pub., 1642. 4°. A^4.
Missing since 1994.
Wood 531(2). Wing T530.

6151. Taylor, John. *An apology for private preaching. In which those formes are warranted . . . (Viz.) { preaching in a tub . . . Or . . . any place, according to inspiration*. [London]: f. R. Wood, T. Wilson, a. E. Christopher, [1642], 28 June. 4°. A^4.

Wood 647(9). Wing T429.

6152. [**Taylor, John**]. *A letter sent to London from a spie at Oxford, to his . . . friends m. Pym, m. Martin, &c. . . . which letter was intercepted . . . and committed to the presse by the aforesaid Thorny Ailo.* [Oxford]: [H. Hall], 1643. 4°. Pp. [2], 14.
Wood 632(11). Wing T474. Madan 1447.

6153. [**Taylor, John**]. *Mercurius aquaticus; or, the water-poets answer to all that hath or shall be writ by Mercurius Britanicus. [The text, with a parody, of] Pag. 121, and number 16. of Mercurius Britanicus.* [Oxford]: [L. Lichfield] Printed in the Waine of the Moone, 1643[4]. 4°. A-C⁴ (C4 blank) Pp. [4], '121-126', [12]. Pasteboard (grey) with parchment spine; rebacked. 1st and last flyleaves, marbled paper.
Board, upper, inside, AW wrote 'Writers of Mercuries & Almanacks'. Flyleaf, 3rd, AW wrote the titles of 25 printed works in this vol., within guidelines made with red ink. Nos. 2-3 are one work; no. 4 was 'torn out' before 1922; and no. 9 was removed to Hope adds. 1133 and restored in Jan. 1932. AW wrote Arabic nos. on tpp. P. 121, at marginalia of the satire, AW wrote 'see 4 leaves after', i.e., 2nd pp. [1]ff. (a parodic answer to the satire).
Wood 622(1). Wing T481. Madan 1510.

6154. **T[aylor], J[ohn]**. *A preter-pluperfect, spick and span new nocturnall, or Mercuries weekly night-newes; wherein . . . the banquet of Oxford mice described.* [Oxford]: [H. Hall] (for those that will reade, . . . to be bought where they are sold), [1643]. 4°. Pp. 20.
P. 10, at 'T. Gol. Iacke of all Trades', AW wrote 'Golledge' (? see note, LT 1.56-7).
Wood 613(10a). Wing T498. Madan 1434.

6155. **Taylor, John**. *Truth's triumph: or, old miracles newly revived in the . . . preservation of . . . the king.* [Oxford]: [H. Hall], 1643. 4°. Pp. [1], 8.
Wood 483(12). Wing T523 (rare). Madan 1580.

6156. **Taylor, John**. *No Mercurius aulicus; but some merry flashes of intelligence, with the pretended parliaments forces besiedging of Oxford.* [Oxford]: [L. Lichfield], 1644. 4°. Pp. 8.
Tp, AW wrote, 'This came forth about the beginning of June.'
Wood 622(5). Madan 1652. Wing T489.

6157. **Ta[ylor], Jo[hn]**. *Oxford besiedged, surprised, taken, . . . on Munday the second of June last.* [Oxford]: [L. Lichfield], 1645. 4°. Pp. [1], 7.
Tp, at 'Io -Ta.', AW wrote, 'Joh Taylor'. Dupl. at Wood 514(15a).
Wood 378(3). Wing T494 (rare, 2 at O). Madan 1786..

6158. **Ta[ylor], Jo[hn]**. *Oxford besiedged, surprised, taken, . . . on Munday the second of June last.* [Oxford]: [L. Lichfield], 1645. 4°. Pp. [1], 7.
Tp, below 'Io-Ta' in the t, AW wrote, 'John Taylor the water-poet'. P. 4, AW wrote '31. May 1644' in the margin. Dupl. at Wood 378(3).
Wood 514(15a). Wing T494 (rare, 2 at O). Madan 1786.

6159. **Taylor, John**. *Rebells anathematized, and anatomized: or, a satyricall salutation to the rabble of seditious, pestiferous pulpit-praters.* Oxford: [H. Hall], 1645. 4°. Pp. 8.
Waste paper, upper, upside down, a Latin disputation topic, not in AW's hand.
Wood 622(11). Wing T501. Madan 1778.

6160. **Taylor, John**. Iππ-αθρωπος *or, an ironicall expostulation with death and fate for the losse of the lord mayor of London [sir J. Warner] who on October 27. 1648. expired . . . Also a . . . discourse between col. Rainsborough and Charon.* [London]: n.pub., 1648. 4°. Pp. [2], 6.
Missing since 1994. In Whiteside cat.
Wood 531(11). Wing H2069.

6161. **Taylor, John**. *John Taylors wandering, to see the wonders of the west.* [London]: n.pub., 1649. 4°. Pp. [2], 21 (some pp. cropped at top).
Each small 4° leaf is pasted on a 4° template.
Wood 465(2). Wing T528.

6162. **T[aylor], J[ohn]**. *The number and names of all the kings of England & Scotland.* London: T. H. sold F. Coles, 1650. 8°. Pp. 16. Pasteboard (grey) with parchment spine. Traces of upper and lower flyleaves, marbled paper.
Flyleaf, upper, 2ndᵛ, AW wrote the titles of 5 printed works in this vol., within guidelines made with red

ink. Tp, AW entered the author's name after initials.
Wood 240(1). Wing T493.

6163. Taylor, John. *The names of all the dukes, marquesses, earls, viscounts, & barons*. London: n.pub., 1653. 8°. Pp. 23 (1-2 blank).
P. 1 (blank), the t, not in AW's hand.
Wood 445(4). Wing T485.

6164. Taylor, Silas. *The history of gavel-kind, with the etymology . . . To which is added a short history of William the conquerour*. London: f. J. Starkey (G. Wilson pro J. Starkey), 1663. 4°. Pp. [24], 211, [10] (2nd tp, p. 181) (2nd pp. [1-2] books printed and sold, J. Starkey).
Tp, AW wrote the price, '2ˢ 4ᵈ'. Acquired 11 Nov. 1663, LT 1.503.
Wood 585(2). Wing T553.

6165. [Teixeira, José]. M[unday], Anthony, trans. *The strangest adventure that ever happened:. . . containing a discourse . . . of the king of Portugall dom Sebastian, from the time of his voyage into Affricke [1578 to 6 Jan. 1601]*. London: [R. Field] f. F. Henson, 1601. 4°. Pp. 90.
Wood 511(7). STC 23864.

6166. Tell-Truth, Robert, pseud. *Advice to the nobility, gentry, & commonalty of this nation in the qualifications and election*. [London]: n.pub., [1679]. Fol. Pp. 4.
Wood 276a(273). Wing A660.

6167. Temple, John. *The copie of a letter from Dublin in Ireland, . . . relating the . . . taking the castle of Carrick-Maine [29 Mar.]*. London: f. L. B., 1642. 4°. Pp. [2], 5.
Wood 508(2). Wing T626.

6168. Temple, John. *The Irish rebellion: or, an history of the beginnings and first progresse of the generall rebellion raised within . . . Ireland . . . October, . . . 1641*. London: R. White f. S. Gellibrand, 1646. 4°. Pp. [16], 136; 55 (2 pts.). Pasteboard (grey) with parchment spine.
Board, upper, beneath pastedown, AW wrote, '6ᵈ for binding to . . . Chambers 8. Nov. 1692'. Flyleaf, upperᵛ, AW gave himself, within guidelines made with red ink, a specific reminder: 'Note that with this book of the Irish rebellion is bound another entituled – A collection of certaine horrid murthers in several counties in Ireland, an. 1641' (Wood 506(2), item 3796). Tp, price, 'Iˢ.6ᵈ.', may be in AW's hand; bsm. 1st p. 52, identification of 'Sʳ Joh. Temple'; 1st pp. 24-5, 44, 67, lines in margin, in pencil.
Wood 506(1). Wing T627.

6169. [Temple, William]. *Memoirs of what past in Christendom, from the war begun 1672. to the peace concluded 1679*. London: R. R. f. R. Chiswell, 1692. 8°. 2nd ed. Pp. [8], 392. Calf, speckled, with 2 fillets and stamp decoration in corners; spine, 4 bands and some blind stamp decoration at top and bottom.
Flyleaf, upper, frag., 'Edd Lhwd' (Edward Lhwyd, Keeper of the Ashm. Museum, 1690-1709); 2ndᵛ, 'Second Memoires – [by?] of Sʳ Will Temple – See Roger Cokes Detection 2nd part or vol. p 214', in pencil, prob. by AW.
Wood 171. Wing T643.

6170. Tennulius, Samuel. *Honori illustris viri, nobilissimi jurisconsulti, . . . Nicolai Witsenii, . . . libens meritoque posuit Samuel Tennulius*. N.p.: n.pub., [1679]. S.sh. (2 cols., 46 and 45 lines).
AW wrote, 'mihi dedit J[ohn] L[amphire] MD: 1679', in red ink. LT 3.262.
Wood 276a(535). Not in BL, NUC, BN.

6171. Terence. Bernard, Richard, trans. *Terence in English*. Londini: Ex off. J. Legatt, 1614. 4°. Pp. [6], 428. 4th ed. Calf, 4 fillets, inner rectangle of 4 fillets with stamp decoration inside inner corners; repaired and rebacked.
MS. Wood E. 2(70), p. 10. Probable copy found. Folger Library copy 3: pastedown, upper, book-plate of Thomas Jefferson McKee. Tp, 'AW', prob. by Anthony Wood, and 'James Crouch', thrice. Text, passim some underscoring; to p. 17 some annotation (+ and x marks), prob. not by AW.
Folger Library, copy 3. STC 23892. *Folg* (copy 3).

6172. Terence. Webbe, [Joseph, [sic in STC]], trans. *The first comedy of Pub. Terentius, called Andria, or the woman of Andros, English and Latine [or] The second comedie of Pub. Terentius called Eunuchus*. London: ?, 1629. 4°.
Missing. MS. Wood E. 2(70), p. 11, 'Dr George Webbe part of Terence Englished'. 'George' Webbe in AO 3.30. Ed. not identified.

MS. Wood E. 2(70), p. 11. STC 23896 and STC 23898 and STC 23898a. *Folg* and *Folg.*

6173. Terry, Edward. *A voyage to East-India*. London: T. W. f. J. Martin a. J. Allestrye, 1655. 8°. Pp. [24], 545, [2]. Pasteboard (grey) with parchment spine. 1st and last flyleaves, marbled paper.
Covers, outside, scribbles, 1-8, and 'Musaeum Ashmoleanum'. Spine, title, prob. in AW's hand. Flyleaf, upper, 2nd[v], 'With this book entit A Voyage . . . is bound America . . . ' (by N. N., Wood 154(2), item 4590), written within guidelines made with red ink. Tp, bsm. Board, lower, outside, scribble in Ashm. Museum. Acquired 10 Feb. 1664, LT 2.5.
Wood 154(1). Wing T782 (Wing, Allstrye).

6174. Thauler, John*. *The history of the life of . . . dr. Joh. Thauler*. London: S. Dover, f. L. Lloyd, 1660. 8°. Pp. [8], 158.
Tp, AW wrote, '10[d].' Bsm.
Wood 292(5). Wing H2168bA ('O' not recorded in Wing).

6175. Theatre of Compliments. *The theater of compliments*. London: ?, 1654. Pp.?
Missing in 1837. 'Theatre of Compliments – Lond. 1654' in Whiteside cat.
Wood 63(2). Not in Wing. See Wing T844A (1689). Not in ESTCR.

6176. Themut, James. *By his majesties permission. In the name of our saviour Jesus Christ. Know that there is come hither a High-Dutch physitian*. N.p.: n.pub., [1661]. S.sh. (r-v). 4°.
Inserted in Wood Diaries 5 after f. 5. [v], AW wrote, 'The vulgar apt to admire strangers - They flocked to this man & left the universitie phisitians', and 'ffeb: 1660[1]: within a mounth after this mans comming, he rann away & cozenned his patients of grat [sic] quantity of money: that he had taken of them before hand'; and a brief note in another hand. LT 1.377.
[MS.] Wood Diaries 5b (not in Bodl. CD cat.). Not in Wing. Not in ESTCR.

6177. Theyer, John. *Aerio-mastix, or, a vindication of the apostolicall . . . government of the church . . . against the schismaticall Aërians*. Oxford: [H. Hall] f. W. Webb, 1643. 4°. Pp. [14], 161, [5].
LT 2.268. AO 3.997.
[MS.] Wood D. 25(9). Wing T889. Madan 1416.

6178. Third Advice to a Painter. [Fragment]. Sig. B: *The third advice to a painter, on our last summers success, with French and Dutch. 1666. Written by the same hand as the former was*. N.p.: n.pub., [1667?]. 8°. Pp.'(17)' to '(33)'. B[8] (neither signatures nor p. nos. follow from Wood 84(6), item 3156).
Wood 84(7). Not identified (see Wing T898, London 1679).

6179. Thomas, William (died 1554). *The historie of Italie*. London: T. Marshe, (1561). 4°. Ff. [3], 216, [4], plus a table.
Missing. MS. Wood E. 2(70), p. 48, AW wrote 'Will. Thomas esq. Hist. of Italie – 1561. note of him before the booke'.
MS. Wood E. 2(70), p. 48. STC 24019. *Folg, Hunt.*

6180. Thomas, William, M. P. *Master William Thomas esquire his speech in parliament, June 1641. Concerning deanes, and their office*. London: T. Harper, 1641. 4°. A-B[4] (1st leaf blank).
Tp, Former no., '16'. Bsm.
[MS.] Wood D. 31(27). Wing T983.

6181. Thomas, William, capt. *Good newes from sea, being a true relations of the late sea-fight*. London: f. L. Blaiklock, 1643, 26 June. 4°. Pp. [2], 7 (really, 5).
Tp, AW altered the former no., '14'; and on p. 7[v], wrote the date, '20. Jun'.
Wood 376(15). Wing T993.

6182. [Thompson, Nathaniel]. *A letter written from Oxford by m[r] Stephen Colledge to his friends in London, . . . writen [sic] by himself*. (London): (N. T[hompson]), (1681). S.sh. (r-v).
In t, at 'himself', AW wrote, 'another'. For spurious author, see DNB, S. College.
Wood 427(29). Wing C5225.

6183. Thompson, Nathaniel*; William Pain*, and John Farwell*. *The tryal of Nathaniel Thompson, William Pain, and John Farwell. . . . To which is added by way of appendix, several other affidavits*. London: f. T. Simmons, 1682. Fol. Pp. [3], 53 (2nd tp at p. 37).
Tp, AW wrote the price, '1. 6'.
Wood 427(45-6). Wing T2207.

6184. Thompson, Richard*. *The visor pluckt off from Richard Thompson of Bristol.* [London]: n.pub, [1681]. Fol. Pp. 4.
In t, 'visor' underlined in red ink. P. 4, AW wrote, 'published in Januar. 1680'. AOF 2.297.
Wood 276a(186). Wing V661.

6185. Thompson, Robert. *Sponsa nondum uxor: or the marriage between the lady Katharine Fitz-Gerald and Edward Villiers esq; asserted . . . an answer to a treatise, . . . of Dudley Loftus.* London: f. B. Tooke, 1677. 4°. Pp. [6], 35.
Tp, AW underlined the names of authors in red ink. Bsm.
Wood 644(4). Wing T1007A.

6186. Thompson, William, Leveller. *Englands freedome, souldiers rights: vindicated against all arbitrary unjust invaders of them , . . . Or, the just declaration, . . . of William Thompson.* [London]: n.pub., [1647]. 4°. Pp. 10.
P. 10, after a list, AW wrote, 'All Levellers'.
Wood 632(58). Wing T1016.

6187. Thompson, William, Leveller. *Englands standard advanced. Or a declaration from m. Will. Thompson and the oppressed people of this nation, . . . in Oxfordshire [6 May].* [London]: n.pub., [1649]. 4°. Pp. 3.
Tp, AW wrote, 'A Levelling pamphlet'. AW pasted over the final p., 3ᵛ, which has the heading, 'FOR A New Parliament BY THE AGREEMENT OF THE PEOPLE' with a sheet of waste paper. He did this after 1684, for he had written on the pasted down side of the waste paper the date of a different item, 'Published about a fortnight after the King's death 5 [or 6?] Feb. 1684/5'. The printed heading on p. 3ᵛ refers to a tract by John Lilburne, *An agreement of the free people of England*, included in a diff. ed. of the Thompson pamphlet; see Wing T1018 and L2079.
Wood 503(2). Wing T1017.

6188. [Thornborough, John]. Bristol, bp. of. *The joiefull and blessed reuniting the two mighty & famous kingdomes, England & Scotland . . . By John Bristoll.* Oxford: J. Barnes, sold S. Waterson [London], [1605]. 4°. Pp. [6], 80.
Tp, AW wrote after Bristoll, 'John Thornborough Bishop of Bristoll.' AO 3.5. Diff. ed. at Wood 258(5).
Wood 594(3). STC 23036. Madan 274.

6189. Thornborough, John. Bristol, bp. of. *The great happinesse of England and Scotland [and 2nd t:] A discourse, shewing the great happinesse, . . . to . . . England and Scotland, by re-uniting them. By John Bristol.* London: R. Hearne (f. C. Duncomb), 1641. 12°. 2 pts. Pp. [44], 286 (pp. unopened).
Diff. ed. at Wood 594(3).
Wood 258(5) (not in Bodl. CD cat.). Wing T1042A ('O' not recorded in Wing).

6190. Thorowgood, Thomas. *Jewes in America, or, probabilities that the Americans are of that race.* London: W. J. f. T. Slater, 1650. 4°. Pp. [41], 136, [137-8] (i.e., T1, unnumbered) (wanting sig. T2). Pasteboard (grey) with parchment spine. 1st upper and last lower flyleaves, marbled paper.
Flyleaf, upper, 2nd, AW wrote, 'Tything table q[uaere]', in pencil (see Wood 370(4), item 1260); 3ᵛ, AW wrote the titles of 4 printed works (no. 4-5, by Prynne 'in two parts', were prob. issued together; here, 2 entries) in this vol., within guidelines made with red chalk. Tp, note by 'NT' (?), 'pret 1ˢ 8ᵈ' and 'NT June 10th 1650'.
Wood 637(1). Wing T1067.

6191. [Thou, Jacques Auguste de]. B[arksdale], C[lement], comp. *Doctorum virorum elogia Thuanea.* Londini: ap. S. Hickman, 1671. 8°. Pp. [15], 130, [6]. Stab marks indicate that this item was once bound in another bundle.
P. 34, scribble, not by AW.
Wood 299(2). Wing T1073.

6192. Three Merry Wives. *The three merry wives of Green Goose fair.* London: ?, 1686. Pp.?
Missing in 1837. 'The Three merry wives of Green Goose Fair – Lond. 1686' in Whiteside cat.
Wood 61(7). Not in Wing. See Wing T1104A (1694). Not in ESTCR.

6193. Throckmorton, Francis. *A discoverie of the treasons practised and attempted against the queenes majestie and the realme.* [London]: [C. Barker], 1584. 4°. ²,A-C⁴.
Flyleaf, upper, waste paper, Latin disputation topic(?), 'Intellectus 4'. Tp, scribble, illeg. Text, some underscoring, B4ᵛ-C1, prob. not by AW. Acquired 29 Ap. 1658 out of G. Langbaine's study, LT 1.247. Diff.

ed. at Wood 616(12).
Wood 586(6). STC 24051.

6194. Throckmorton, Francis. *A discoverie of the treasons practised and attempted against the queenes majestie and the realme.* [London]: [C. Barker], 1584. 4°. ²,A-C⁴.
Tp, AW wrote 'Ant Woode: 1658' (lined out); and 'dupl', twice in pencil. Diff. ed. at Wood 586(6). See LT 1.247, note 4.
Wood 616(12). STC 24050.5.

6195. Throgmorton, Robert*, et al. *The lives, apprehension, araignment & execution of Robert Throgmorton. William Porter. John Bishop.* London: [E. Allde] f. H. Gosson, 1608. 4°. A-C⁴ (C4 blank).
Wood 371(11). STC 24053.5 (rare).

6196. Thurman, Hen[ry]. *A defence of humane learning in the ministry.* Oxford: A. Lichfield f. R. Davis, 1660. 8°. Pp. [6], 50, [6] (6 pp. books sold by R. Davis).
Flyleaf, upperᵛ, AW wrote, 'Henr. Thurman of Ch. ch. in Oxon was the author of the following book. [/] An apologie of the use of the fathers & secular learning - By Ægeon Askew - 1605. See in the first vol. of Athenae et Fasti Oxon. p. 282' (AO 1.756). Tp, 'AWood'. 4 items marked at Davis's advertisement at the end. Acquired 2 Jan. 1664, 6ᵈ, LT 2.2.
Wood 130(2). Wing T1139. Madan 2531.

6197. Thwing, Thomas. *The last speech of Thomas Thwing priest; executed at York [23 Oct.].* N.p.: n.pub., [1680]. S.sh.
See ref. to 'nu 30' at Wood 426(1), item 4790.
Wood 426(30). Wing L505dA (rare).

6198. Tichborne, Robert*, and John Ireton*. *The apology of . . . a vindication of themselves and the good old cause.* London: for every body but . . . , [1660]. 4°. Pp. 8.
Tp, AW wrote, 'March: 1659'.
Wood 613(27). Wing A3557aA.

6199. Tichborne, Robert*, and John Ireton*. *Brethren in iniquity: or a beardless pair: held forth in a dialogue betwixt Titchburn and Ireton.* [London]: f. D. Webb, 1660. 4°. Pp. 8.
Tp, AW wrote 'Aprill:'.
Wood 610(57). Wing B4381A.

6200. Tillotson, J[ohn]. Canterbury, abp. of. *A letter written to my lord Russel in Newgate [20 July].* (London): (f. R. Baldwin), (1683). S.sh. Pp. 2.
Wood 428(10). Wing T1201.

6201. Tillotson, John*. Canterbury, abp. of. *Some select queries humbly offered to the consideration of the d- of C-t-b-y.* [London]: f. H. Jones, [1683]. S.sh.
AW wrote, 'Dʳ Tillotson Deane of Canterbury'; an emendation, 'vicar' over the printed 'D– of Bray'; and after the pub., '1683'.
Wood 631(13). Wing S4611A (one) ('O' not recorded in Wing).

6202. Tilnay, Edmund. *A briefe and pleasant discourse of duties in mariage, called the flower of friendship.* London: H. Denham, 1577. 8°. A-D⁸,E1-7 (wanting the final leaf).
Tp, 'Ant Woode Merton: Col .. Oxōn 1656', lined out.
Wood 736(3). STC 24077a.

6203. Tirrell, Henry. *A great and glorious victory obtained by the lord Inchequin . . . over the Irish rebels [6 Sept.].* [London]: f. V. V., 1647. 4°. Pp. [2], 6.
Tp, AW lined out a former no., '24'.
Wood 509(25). Wing G1653.

6204. [Titus, Silas]. *Killing, no murder: with some additions briefly discourst in three questions, . . . By William Allen [pseud.].* London: n.pub., 1659. 4°. Pp. 13.
Tp, AW wrote, 'written as tis said by one Capt. Silas Titus formerly of Ch. church Oxon.' (Christian name, 'Silas', added later by AW); and, at a later date, 'The 2ᵈ edition / the first came out in A° 1657.' MS. Wood E. 2(70), p. 32, 'answered by Mich. Hawk. of the Middle Temple' (i.e., Wood 631(15), item 3470).
Wood 631(14). Wing T1311.

6205. Tolmach, Thomas*. *An elegy in commemoration of the honourable lieutenant-general Talmash*

[12 June 1694]. London: J. Wilkins, 1694. S.sh.
AW wrote in the margin, 'Tho. Talmarsh'. LT 3.381, 455, 459.
Wood 429(51) (not in Bodl. CD cat.). Wing E349A (rare).

6206. Tom, Black*. *The unlucky citizen; or, a pleasant history of the life of black Tom.* London: J. M. f. J. Blare, 1686. 12°. A^8,B^4.
Wood 254(14). Wing U85 (two).

6207. Tom Thumb*. *Tom Thumb his life and death.* [London]: f. F. Coles. J. Wright. T. Vere. a. W. Gilbertson, [1655-58]. 12°. A^8,B^4.
Wood 259(5). Wing T1789A (rare).

6208. Tom Tram*. *Tom Tram of the west, son-in-law to mother Winter.* [London]: f. W. T[hackeray], sold J. Gilbertson, [1688-89]. 12°. A^8,B^4.
Flyleaf, upper, 'The most stupid stuff that ever was penned', in a later hand.
Wood 259(8). Wing T1790D (rare).

6209. [Tomkis, Thomas]. *Lingua: or, the combate of the tongue, and the five sences.* London: A. Mathewes, f. S. Waterson, 1632. 4°. A-K^4 (imperf., wanting quire L).
Wants the last leaves and in the following item, S. Harding, Wood 330(7), item 3402, the 1st leaves.
Wood 330(6). STC 24108.

6210. Tomlin, Richard, cursitor baron. *Baron Tomlinson's [sic] learned speech to the sheriffs of London and Middlesex.* London: n.pub., 1659. 4°. Pp. 8.
Tp, AW wrote, 'Ridiculous', in pencil. No. 55 in a former bundle.
Wood 610(18). Wing B900.

6211. Tompkins, Nathaniel. *The whole confession and speech of . . . made . . . at the time of his execution [5 July].* London: f. P. Cole, [1643]. 4°. Pp. 8.
Tp, '4', indicating its place in an earlier bundle or pile. Dupl. at Wood 612(2).
Wood 366(15). Wing T1865.

6212. Tompkins, Nathaniel. *The whole confession and speech of . . . made . . . at the time of his execution [5 July].* London: f. P. Cole, [1643]. 4°. Pp. 8.
Dupl. at Wood 366(15).
Wood 612(2). Wing T1865.

6213. Tonge, Ezerel. *The new design of the papists detected: or, an answer to the last speeches of the five Jesuites lately executed, viz. Tho. White [et al.].* London: f. R. Boulter, J. Hancock, R. Smith, a. B. Harris, 1679. Fol. Pp. [2], 6.
Tp, AW wrote the price, '1^d'. Purchased from Vade in July or August 1679, see his record of purchase in MS. Wood F. 50, f. 11. LT 2.506.
Wood 424(24) (Wood 428(24) in Bodl. CD cat.). Wing T1878.

6214. [Tonge, Ezerel]. *The popish damnable plot against our religion . . . letters and papers of intelligence.* London: f. R. Janeway, 1680. Fol. Pp. [2], 31.
Dupl. at Wood 426(18).
Wood 425(24). Wing T1879A.

6215. [Tonge, Ezerel]. *The popish damnable plot against our religion . . . letters and papers of intelligence.* London: f. R. Janeway, 1680. Fol. Pp. [2], 31.
1st blank, 'Dupl.', and a former no., '19'. Dupl. at Wood 425(24).
Wood 426(18). Wing T1879A.

6216. [Torrentinus, Hermannus]. *[Elucidarius poeticus continens historias, poeticas, fabulas].* [Viennae Allobrogum, cited in dedication, A2]: [Johannes Poyet? cited in dedication, A2], [1623? (not 1535)]. 16°. Pp. 2-182. A2-8,B-L^8,M2-3 (wanting A1,M1 and M4) (A2, line 1: NOBILIBUS ET). Calf, 4 blind-stamp fillets, and 1, gold stamp; blind-stamp 'R.P.' on boards; spine, hatching.
Pastedown, upper, 'Richard: Phillipps his booke' (twice).
Wood 27 (not in Bodl. CD cat.). Not identified.

6217. Torriano, Gio[vanni]. *Select Italian proverbs.* Cambridge: R. Daniel, 1642. 12°. Pp. [8], 100.
Tp, bsm.
Wood 60(2). Wing T1931.

6218. Torriano, Gio[vanni]. *New and easy directions for the attaining of the Thuscan Italian tongue.* Cambridge: R. Daniel, [1645?]. 4°. Pp. [8], 16 (from p. 1 on, unopened). Wood 310(2). Wing T1926.

6219. Tory, Timothy, pseud. *Sejanus: or the popular favourite, . . . Written for the consolation of e. S. [earl of Shaftesbury] the famous Bromigen protestant.* (London): (f. Smith, Curtiss, Janeway, Baldwin), [1681]. Fol. Pp. 4. P. 1, AW wrote the year, '1683', in pencil. Wood 417(120). Wing S2419.

6220. Tory, and Tantivy. *The phanatick in his colours: being a full and final character of a Whig; in a dialogue between Tory and Tantivy.* (London): (f. N. Thompson), (1681). Fol. Pp. 4. P. 4, AW wrote 'in Sept. or Octob.' Wood 417(70). Wing F394.

6221. Tory; Towzer, and Tantivee. *The time-servers: or, a touch of the times. Being a dialogue between Tory, Towzer, and Tantivee.* London: f. W. H., sold R. Janeway, 1681. S.sh. At Towzer, AW wrote, 'i.e. L'Estrange'. Wood 417(49). Wing T1278.

6222. [Touchet, George]. *Historical collections, out of several grave protestant historians.* London: n.pub., 1674. 8°. Pp. [6], 558, [2]. Calf with 2 fillets and stamp decoration in corners (flower, see similar binding at Wood 301, item 5711). Flyleaf, upper, 'Duplicat.' (a Sheldon duplicate), lined out; 2nd, Sheldon's price, '4^s-0^d', 'In Posterum' (Ralph Sheldon's motto, see LT 3.104-5) in dark heavy ink, in the hand of Sheldon. Wood 241. Wing T1954.

6223. Touchet, James. Castlehaven, earl of (1617-1684). *The memoires of James Lord Audley . . . in the wars of Ireland . . . With an appendix.* London: f. J. Brome, 1681. 8°. Pp. [8], 3-136, [7], 79. A1, torn out. Pasteboard (brown) with calf spine. 1st upper and last lower flyleaves, marbled paper. Flyleaf, upper, 2nd^v, AW wrote the titles of 3 printed works in this vol., within guidelines made with red ink. Tp, AW wrote, '1^s. 3^d' and 'This book came out in Sept. 1680 or rather in June or July-'. Wood 202(1). Wing C1235.

6224. Touchet, Mervin*. Castlehaven, earl of (1585-1631) (see also at Touchet, item 297). *The trial of the lord Audley, earl of Castlehaven, for inhumanely causing his own wife to be ravished and for buggery.* London: n.pub., 1679. Fol. Pp. [2], 13. Pasteboard (blue) with parchment spine; 1st and late flyleaves, marbled paper; some repairing. Flyleaf, 3rd^{r-v}, AW wrote the titles of 18 printed works in this vol., within guidelines made with red ink (really 20, he made 2 entries for item 6, and omitted 3b, 13b and 19). Tp, AW wrote the year, '1631' (date of Touchet's execution). Wood 422(1). Wing T2227 ('O' not recorded in Wing).

6225. Toulouse. *A relation of the two pretended apostles, that came invisibly into . . . Tholouse.* London: f. R. Janeway, 1680. S.sh. [MS.] Wood B. 35(31). Wing R883 (two).

6226. Townley, Zouch, and Degory Wheare, eds. *Oratio in memoriam clarissimi viri Guilielmi Camdeni . . . prolata per Zoucheum Townley [and] Parentatio historia . . . per Degoreum Whear.* [Oxoniae]: [J. Lichfield & J. Short], [1624]. 4°. ¶-2¶⁴,3¶² (wanting A-F⁴,G²). Wood 512(6-7). STC 19028. Madan 517.

6227. Treatise. *A notable treatyse wherin is shewed, that by the word of God we may at al times eat such meates as God hath created.* London: R. Stoughton, [1550?]. 8°. Pp. [18]. Wood 736(6). STC 24229 (two).

6228. Treby, George, ed. *A collection of letters and other writings, relating to the horrid popish plot.* London: f. S. Heyrick, T. Dring, a. J. Wickins, 1681. Fol. Pp. [5], 127, [1]. Wood 426(31). Wing T2102.

6229. Treby, George, ed. *The second part of the collection of letters . . . relating to the horrid popish plot.* London: f. S. Heyrick, T. Dring, a. J. Wickins, 1681. Fol. Pp. [3], 34. 1st blank, AW wrote the price, '1^s'. Wood 426(32). Wing T2104.

6230. Trenchfield, Caleb. *Christian chymistrie, extracting the honey of instruction from variety of objects*. London: M. S. f. H. Crips, 1662. 12°. Pp. [4], 203.
Tp, bsm. Pp. 10-198, some pp. have horizontal lines at anecdotes, prob. not by AW.
Wood 864(3). Wing T2121.

6231. Trent, Council of. Parker, Matthew (?), trans. [Flacius Illyricus, Matthias, by]. *A godly and necessarye admonition of the decrees and canons of the counsel of Trent*. London: J. Day, 1564. 4°. Pp. [12], 125.
Tp, a ref., cropped at top; signature of Wylliam Palmer. Some marks in margins, not in AW's manner.
[MS.] Wood B. 36(13). STC 24265.

6232. Trewman, John. *The Irish martyr. Or, a true relation of the lamentable sufferings of . . . who . . . was hang'd, drawn and quarter'd in Carickfargus*. London: f. F. C. & T. V., 1641. 4°. Pp. [2], 6.
Wood 507(3). Wing I1040 ('O' not recorded in Wing).

6233. Trial of Wit. *Tryal of wit*. London: ?, 1674. Pp.?
Missing in 1837. 'Tryal of Wit – Lond. 1674' in Whiteside cat.
Wood 64(8). Not in Wing. Not in ESTCR.

6234. Tritonius, Ruggerius. Titi, Roberto ed. *Vita Vincentii Laurei s. r. e. cardinalis Montis Regalis*. Bononiae: ap. haer. J. Rossii, 1599. 4°. Pp. [8], 86.
Tp, 'pretium. xviii^d.', not by AW. Passim, notes, not by AW. P. 86, Jackson lined out the errata and wrote, 'emendata.'; below, 'Liber Henr. Jacksoni Oxōn. Coll. Corp. X̄i.' LT 1.459 (and 1.331).
Wood 477(2). BL.

6235. [Tromp, Maarten Harpertszoon]. *Amsterdam, and her other Hollander sisters put out to sea, by Van Trump, Van Dunck, & Van Dumpe. Or, a true description of those so called Hoghens Mogens*. London: f. R. Harper, 1652. 4°. Pp. 11.
Wood 609(32). Wing A3029.

6236. [Tuke, Samuel]. *A character of Charles the second, written by an impartial hand*. London: f. G. Bedell, 1660. 4°. Pp. 8.
Tp, AW wrote, 'Aprill: said to be writt by Colonell Tuke///'.
Wood 533(16). Wing T3232.

6237. Tuke, Thomas. *A treatise against paintng [sic] and tincturing of men and women*. London: T. Creed a. B. Allsope f. E. Merchant, 1616. 4°. T leaf is a cancel. Pp. [14], 62.
Flyleaf, upper, 4 headings from the tp, not in AW's hand. Tp, bsm.
Wood 653(4). STC 24316.

6238. [Tully, Thomas], trans. *A briefe relation of the present troubles in England: written from London . . . to a minister of one of the Reformed churches in France [22 Jan. 1644]*. Oxford: H. Hall, 1645. 4°. Pp. [4], 60.
Tp, AW wrote, 'Relating to the Parliament'; and 'by Tho Tully', in pencil, prob. not by AW. MS. Wood E. 2(70), p. 69, after the entry of the t, 'I cannot find this pamphlet'. Diff. ed. at Wood 616(18).
Wood 519(4). Wing B4630. Madan 1813.

6239. [Tully, Thomas], trans. *A letter concerning the present troubles in England*. [Oxford]: [H. Hall], [1645]. 4°. Pp. [2], 60 (wanting the tp).
Diff. ed. at Wood 519(4).
Wood 616(18) (not in Bodl. CD cat.). Wing L1354. Madan 1812.

6240. T[ully], T[homas]. *A letter written to a friend [T. Gore] in Wilts, upon occasion of a . . . pamphlet, wherein was inserted a pretended prophecie of Thomas Becket's [signed T. T.]*. London: R. D., 1666. 4°. Pp. [2], 16.
Pp. 1, AW identified T. G. as 'Tho: Gore of Alderton in Wilts.'; 6, 8, 15, corrections; 16, after T. T., 'Thom: Tully'. AW owned a 2nd work on Becket's prophecy, see Wood 646(12), item 919, and AO 3.1056.
Wood 646(13). Wing T3246.

6241. T[ully], T[homas]; Jos Williamson, and C. Ellys. *Memoriae sacrum Lanceloti Dawes S: T: D: [March 1654]*. [Oxford?]: n.pub., [1654]. S.sh.
ᵛ, AW wrote, 'Lanc. Dawes 1654'.
Wood 429(8). Wing M1682B (rare) (Wing, Lancelot:). Not in Madan.

6242. Turberville, Edward. *The information of Edward Turbervill of Skerr . . . delivered at the bar of the house of commons [9 Nov.]*. London: by the assigns of J. Bill, T. Newcomb, and H. Hills, 1680. Fol. Pp. 12 (1st p. blank).
Wood 426(23). Wing T3252.

6243. Turberville, Edward. *The full narrative and further discovery of Edward Turbervill of Kerr . . . of the popish plott*. London: f. N. Nelson, 1681. Fol. Pp. [5], 14.
AW wrote the price, '6ᵈ'.
Wood 426(24). Wing T3251A ('O' not recorded in Wing).

6244. Turberville, George. *[Epitaphs, epigrams, songs and sonets]*. (London): (H. Denham), (1570). 8°. Ff. [14], 143 (wanting t leaf). Calf with 2 fillets, 2nd rectangle with 3 fillets and stamp decoration outside corners; stamped centrepiece; rebacked.
A few lines, e.g., f. 72ᵛ; 77ᵛ, AW wrote, at epitaph of Richard Edwardes, 'see f. 142.b' (i.e., cross-ref. to f. 142ᵛ, a 2nd epitaph for Edwards), and below, note in pencil, prob. not by AW; 143ᵛ, scribble, 'Georg'. On the cover, lower, a loose sheet, torn to octavo size, is now pasted; it has 14 lines of notes (J. Aubrey's?), crossed out and severely cropped: 'at Wakefield 1660 [cropped] Although the brother Edward the youn [cropped] d. of [cropped] of' and 'dated, March , aᵒ 5.' etc.
Wood 89. STC 24327.

6245. Turke, Great. *The strangling and death of the great Turke, and his two sons*. London: J. D[awson] f. N. Bourne a. T. Archer, 1622, 15 July. 4°. Pp. [4], 17.
Wood 345(8). STC 18507.62.

6246. Turler, Jerome. *[The traveiler of Jerome Turler, devided into two bookes]*. (London): (W. How, f. A. Veale), [1575]. 8°. Pp. [8], 192 (wanting tp). Pasteboard (brown) with calf spine. 1st and last flyleaves, marbled paper; rebound.
Flyleaf, upper, 3rdᵛ, AW wrote the titles of 3 printed works in this vol., within guidelines made with red ink.
Wood 167(1) (not in Bodl. CD cat.). STC 24336.

6247. Turner, Franc[is]. *Affectuum decidua, or due expressions in honour of . . . Charles Capell*. Oxford: [H. Hall], 1656. 4°. Pp. [2], 28.
Pp. 2, 4, 28, brief notes, lined out.
Wood 319(5). Wing T3273. Madan 2296.

6248. Turner, Francis. Ely, bp. of. *A letter to the clergy of the diœcess [sic] of Ely, . . . before, and preparatory to his visitation*. Cambridge: J. Hayes, 1686. 4°. Pp. [2], 24.
Flyleaf, upperʳ 'Lord Bp of Ely' and 'Byshop', may not be in AW's hand; ᵛ, scribbles, in pencil.
Wood 633(3). Wing T3277.

6249. Turner, James*. *The life and death of James, commonly called collonel Turner*. London: f. T. J., 1663. 4°. Pp. [4], 36.
Wood 372(7). Wing L1997.

6250. Turner, James. *The speech and deportment of col. James Turner at his execution*. London: W. Godbid f. N. Brook a. H. Marsh, 1663[4]. 4°. Pp. 14.
Wood 372(5). Wing T3293A ('O' not recorded in Wing).

6251. Turner, James*. *The triumph of truth: in an exact . . . relation of the life . . . of cᵒˡ· James Turner*. London: W. G[odbid] f. N. Brook, a. H. Marsh, 1663[4]. 4°. Pp. [2], 32.
Wood 372(6). Wing T2293.

6252. Turner, James*. *A true and impartial account of the arraignment, tryal, . . . of col. James Turner*. London: W. Godbid f. N. Brook a. H. Marsh, 1663[4]. 4°. Pp. 86.
P. 9, figures, addition, prob. not by AW.
Wood 372(4). Wing T2488.

6253. Turner, John. *The history of the Whiggish-plot: or, a brief historical account . . . of William lord Russel [et al.]*. London: T. B., sold R. Taylor, 1684. Fol. Pp. [4], 71.
P. [4], after author, AW wrote, 'of Christs Coll. in Cambridge'.
Wood 428(31) (not in Bodl. CD cat.). Wing H2190B.

6254. Turner, Robert. *Maria Stuarta, regina Scotiae, . . . martyr ecclesiae, innocens à caede Darleana:*

vindice Oberto Barnestapolio. Coloniae: sumpt. P. Henningii, 1627. 8°. Pp. 68, [1].
For more on the author, see AO 1.680ff.
Wood 890(3) (listed with R. Scotus, Wood 890(2), item 5820, in Bodl. CD cat.). BL.

6255. Turner, Thomas. *The case of the bankers and their creditors.* [London]: n.pub., 1675. 4°. 2nd time printed. Pp. [8], 56.
Wood 628(5) (not in Bodl. CD cat.). Wing T3337.

6256. Turner, William. *Avium praecipuarum, quarum apud Plinium et Aristotelem mentio est, brevis . . . historia.* Coloniae: excud. J. Gymnicus, 1544. 8°. A-K^8 (last leaf blank). Parchment; upper and lower flyleaves, printer's waste paper.
Flyleaf, upper^v, AW wrote 'In bib. Bod' (smudged; among Selden's books). Tp, former no. '9'; bsms. Pastedown and flyleaf, upper^r, Latin lines and 'minister Aedis Christi', not by AW. Text, passim, underscoring and marks in margin, not in AW's manner, and pages are numbered and a few notes, not by AW. K7^v-K8^{r-v}, index, not in AW's hand.
Wood 701. BL.

6257. Turner, W[illiam]. *Ad nobilem Britannium. Or an abstract for Englands royall peeres.* [London]: n.pub., 1641. 4°. Pp. [2], 5.
Tp, at author, AW wrote 'a bold impudent Atheist'.
Wood 616(21). Wing T3342.

6258. Turnor, Edward. *The several speeches of sr. Edward Turner . . . to the king's . . . majesty [10 May].* London: f. J. Williams, 1661. Fol. Pp. 12.
Wood 657(42). Wing T3349.

6259. Turnor, Edward. *The speech of s^r Edw. Turnor . . . to the kings . . . majesty at the adjournment of the parliament [30 July].* London: f. H. Twyford, 1661. Fol. Pp. [2], 8.
Wood 657(39). Wing T3352.

6260. Turvil, W. *Terrible and bloudy newes from the disloyall army in the north. Likewise, . . . the proceedings of the Levellers in Liecester-shire [sic]. Also, strange newes from the prince of Wales.* [London]: n.pub., 1648. 4°. Pp. [2], 6.
Tp, AW wrote, 'A most ridiculous pamphlet' and 'Sept. 7'.
Wood 502(66). Wing T3367.

6261. Tusser, Thomas. *Five hundred points of good husbandry.* London: [T. Purfoot] f. Co. of Stationers, 1630. 4° in 8's. Corrected. Pp. 161, [3].
Tp, AW wrote, ''Twas published at London 1614'. Text, some scribbles, e.g., p. 5, 41 (on taking tobacco), not by AW.
[MS.] Wood C. 17(2). STC 24391.

6262. [Tutchin, John]. *The bloody assizes: or, a compleat history of the life of George lord Jefferies.* London: f. J. Dunton, sold R. Janeway, 1689. 4°. Pp. 70, [1] (1 p. books on Jeffreys).
Tp, AW wrote, 'bought at Ox. 26 Feb 1688[9] 1^s', in pencil. LT 3.299.
Wood 368(24). Wing T3370A.

6263. [Tutchin, John]. *The dying speeches, letters, and prayers, &c. of those . . . who suffered . . . under . . . lord chief justice Jefferys.* London: sold by booksellers in London and Westminster, 1689. 4°. Pp. [4], 40.
Tp, AW wrote, 'published in Janu. 1688[9] - 6^d'. LT 3.294.
Wood 368(28). Wing T3372B.

6264. Twells, John. *Grammatica reformata, or a general examination of the art of grammar, as it hath been successively delivered . . . and methodiz'd by the Oxford Grammarian.* London: S. Roycroft, f. R. Clavell, 1683. 8°. Pp. [4], 26, 63 (traces of a cancelled leaf, 2nd 32-3, torn out).
Flyleaf, upper, AW wrote 'Joh. Twells'; ^{v}, cropped, cursive and prob. not by AW, '[See] which of these [is] wanting in y^e [Bodleian] Library –', and a smudged line. This was one of the four which went from AW to the Bodleian apparently before 1695; see the note at Wise, 8° A 153(1) Art., item 6648. Tp, 'Grammarian' in t is underlined and 'W[anting]' is cropped at side. 1st pp. 13-17, AW marked with short red lines in margins numerous lines, and on p. 13 in margin, wrote (cropped), 'All this y^t is comm–d [?] with red i[nk] is taken o[ut] of Th. Hay[ne] preface t[o] Grammar.' and two more words (cropped). See Hayne, at Wood 42(2), item 3480, which has similar red lines in margins at the passages borrowed by Twells.

8° A 153(3) Art. Wing T3394A.

6265. Twelve Seasonable Queries. *Twelve seasonable queries proposed to all true zealous protestants and English free-men*. [London]: n.pub., 1659. 4°. Pp. [2], 6.
Tp, AW wrote 'Written after the the [sic] relignes [?] of the Long . . . ' (i.e., Parliament, cropped at bottom), and, in pencil, the no. in a former bundle '2-' (cropped).
Wood 613(40). Wing T3403.

6266. Twenty-Seven Queries. *Twenty seven queries relating to the general good of the three nations*. London: n.pub., 1659. 4°. Pp. 8.
Tp, no. '40', in pencil, in a former bundle (cropped at bottom).
Wood 613(46). Wing T3416.

6267. Twisse, Thomas. *An elegy upon the unhappy losse of the noble earle of Essex*. London: J. Benson, 1646. 4°. Pp. 7.
Missing since 1994. In Whiteside cat.
Wood 531(9). Wing T3417.

6268. Twyne, Brian. *Antiquitatis academiae Oxoniensis apologia*. Oxoniae: J. Barnesius, 1608. 4°. Pp. [8], 384, [21], after which, [48], all interleaved with blanks (wanting the final leaf). Parchment.
Parchment, upper, inside, 'Anthony Woode: Merton Coll: Anno Domini M DC LX: July', and, possibly in AW's hand, a list of 3 books, e.g. 'Radulphus Agasus: his discriptio Oxon'. AW had this vol. bound on 22 May 1658, at the cost of 8^d (LT 1.249), with the insertion of blank leaves after sig. 3E3, and some of Langbaine's notes were cropped by the binder. The annotation on the blank leaves is all in AW's hand, much in his early hand. Flyleaf, upper, 3rd^v, AW wrote notes on 'Nomina Collegiorum eo ordine Collocati quo eorum praefecti Concionantur.' Tp, signature of Gerard Langbaine and a Greek phrase, and 'Anthony Woode: 1658: 5^s'; see Plate V. In addition to underscorings, there are numerous marks and notes in the margins; notes on 7 slips which AW pasted (pp. 47, 179, 200, blank before sig. 3K4) or pinned to pp. (46, 144 (now loose)); and notes on the interleaved pp. of the last section. For AW's early hand, besides his signature on the tp, see the interleaved blank after 3G2 (with his note of Twyne's omissions: 'There is another provost that Mr Twine hath omitted in his foregoing Catalouge [sic] . . . ') (Plate VI), and on the blank leaves after 3L3 in the index.
In general, AW is responsible for all the notes on the slips; for most but not all in the margins (see esp. the cross references to MS. Twyne XXI and XXIII described in LT 4.214, paragraph 236) on pp. 47, 90, 114, 154, 170, 182, 252, 265, 376-8, 3H3 (blank preceding); and for entries on all blank leaves including the final indices. Langbaine's annotations are present on pp. 184-5 (cropped), 201, 203, 206 (after 1st note), 210-1 (cropped), 217 (cropped), [240] (misnumbered as 340), sigs. 3G3 (cropped), 3G4^{r-v}, 3K4^v; see also T. Fuller, *History of Worthies* (1811), 1.239, who wrote that Langbaine was revising this book of Twyne's and see also AO 3.448). On the final flyleaf, AW wrote notes on John Caius, *de antiquitate Cantabrig.* (from his copy at Wood 480(1) (he owned another copy as well, Wood 179(1), items 1267, 1265) 'Note that Caii in his antiq: of Cant lib. 1. p. 152. saith from [Richardus] Crocus in his 2^d oration that Oxonia ē Colonia vestra [in source, Crocus wrote that: 'Oxonium Cantebrigiensium Coloniam esse'], & though the s^d Crocus was orator of that Univers. & accou[n]ted one that introduced the græc. tongue in Cambridge yet he was pupill to Grocius an Oxford man. & Croke confesses v histor. 1497. v. orat: eius p 44 v. histor 1134.' Below there are 2 busts drawn; a smaller above a more complete lower one which may be a self portrait, see Plate IV. Acquired 29 Ap. 1658 out of G. Langbaine's study, 6^s 6d (but see above, 5^s on tp), LT 1.247 and also 4.223. AW made a payment of 4^s to William Dewey 'for Twin's Antiq.' on 18 April 1662 (a 2nd copy or, less likely, a 2nd binding), LT 1.436. He lent a copy to E. Benlowes, 13 June 1668, LT 2.139. See also Madan 302.
Wood 602. STC 24405. Madan 302.

6269. Twyne, John. Twyne, Thomas, ed. *De rebus Albionicis, Britannicis atque Anglicis*. Londini: E. Bollifantus, pro R. Watkins, 1590. 8°. Pp. [6], 162. Parchment wrapper, a ms. deed, Latin.
Cover, upper, inside, 'AWoode 166j'. Pp. 6-9, marks in margin and a note, not in AW's hand.
Wood 182. STC 24407.

6270. Twyne, John*. *An exact narrative of the tryal and condemnation of John Twyn, . . . for printing, publishing*. London: T. Mabb f. H. Brome, 1664. 4°. Pp. [8], 78.
Acquired 13 Mar. 1664, 6^d, LT 2.7.
Wood 368(20). Wing E3668.

6271. Tyler, Tom. *Tom Tyler: or, the nurse*. [London]: n.pub., [1688]. S.sh.

AW wrote, 'published some few dayes before Christmas, 1688'. LT 3.294.
Wood 417(165). Wing T1791 (Wing, or the).

6272. Tyro, T., pseud. *The meane in spending.* London: V. Simmes, 1598. 4°. F2-4,G1-2 (pp. mutilated). Contains *meane*, only).
Traces of 2 leaves, neither belonging to this complete work, preceding F2. G2ᵛ, Latin disputation topic, not in AW's hand.
Wood 499(3). STC 24477 (olim 17760).

6273. U[dall], T[homas]. *A briefe viewe of the weake grounds of popery; as it was propounded to D. Norrice.* London: H. Lownes f. S. Macham a. M. Cooke, 1606. 8°. Pp. [24], 101, [8].
Former owner, John Speed. Acquired 24 Sept. 1661, see Wood 794(1), item 902, and LT 1.416.
Wood 794(3). STC 24508.5.

6274. [Udall, William]. *The historie of the life and death of Mary Stuart [dedic. signed, W. Stranguage].* London: J. Haviland f. W. Barret, 1624. Fol. T leaf is a cancel. Pp. [11], 250. Pasteboard (blue) with parchment spine, 1st upper and last lower flyleaves, marbled paper.
Pasteboard, upper, inside, an early Ashm. shelf-mark, W. 556, before 1717 when the Whiteside cat. established the permanent shelf-marks (Wood 551-558 are now vols. of Gazettes). A 2nd flyleaf, upper, is missing, the blotting of 'Maria Scotice Reg.' remains on the ᵛ of the 1st flyleaf. 2nd flyleafʳ, some additions; ᵛ, AW wrote the titles of 4 printed works, unnumbered here, in this vol., within guidelines made with red ink. After the 1st entry, AW wrote, 'This was also published in 8° by W. Udall, 1636' (his copy is at Wood 261, item 6275). Pp. [4], scribble; [9], at Mary's sadness upon the death of her husband, Francis, AW wrote, 'Notwithstanding all this mourning shee soon after took a 2ᵈ husband & after that a 3ᵈ'; 2, 73, 92-3, 96, 142, 148-9, 152, 154, 167-8, lines, underscoring, or brief notes in margin; 13, 'The Earl of Leycester (Rob. Dudley) his wife was murdered at Comnore [Cumnor] in Berks – in the place house [i.e., chief residence] there – But given out that she had been kill'd with a fall downe stayres –'.
Wood 660e(1). STC 24509.

6275. Udall, W[illiam]. *The historie of the life and death of Mary Stuart.* London: J. Haviland, sold W. Sheares, 1636. 12°. Pp. [20], 491 (last p. mutilated). Parchment.
Flyleaf, upper, 'Treaty of Edenburg to be inserted by . . . ', may be in AW's hand; ᵛ, AW wrote, 'One W. Udall published this book, being the very same that Nich. Stranguage published in fol. 1624' (for the latter, see Wood 660e(1), item 6274). Tp, 'AWood-', and 'W. Udall the author'. Bsm. Brief note or marks in margin, A3 and pp. 144-5.
Wood 261. STC 24510.

6276. Ufflet, John. *The kingdomes key, to lock out, or let in an enemy: or, certain parliamentary proceedings, concerning . . . Lovingland [Suffolk].* London: n.pub., 1646. 4°. Pp. [2], 14 (misnumbering).
Wood 612(40). Wing U19.

6277. Unfortunate Son. *The unfortunate son.* [London]: [J. M. f. J. Deacon & T. Passinger (or J. M. f. J. Deacon & C. Dennisson)], [1682-88]. 12°.
Missing in 1837. 'The unfortunate Son –' in Whiteside cat.
Wood 66(12). Wing U58B (rare) or U58C (rare). CM, and CM.

6278. Unhappy Marksman. *The unhappy marks-man: or, twenty three queries offered to the consideration of the people.* [London]: n.pub., 1659. 4°. Pp. 8.
Tp, no. '44', in pencil, in a former bundle.
Wood 613(49). Wing U69.

6279. Unicorn. *Unicorns horn [advertisement for a medicinal drink].* Fragment. N.p.: n.pub., [1675 ca.]. S.sh. 4° (wanting 1st words of t, cropped at top).
Wood 534(3e). Not identified.

6280. Unton, Henry*. [Wright, Robert, ed.]. *Funebria nobilissimi . . . Henrici Untoni.* Oxoniae: J. Barnesius, 1596. 4°. ¶⁴,A-H⁴ (H3-4 blank).
C2ᵛ, Sing. written out in full, 'Singleton'. C4ᵛ, at Richardus Pigotus, line in margin, and a correction; D2ᵛ, long line in margin; E4ᵛ, at Thomas Peacocke, line in margin; H1, at E. Scorie, 'AO. 2.90', by a later annotator (see AO 2.770); H1ᵛ, at Johannes Digby, line in margin. AO 1.647f.
Wood 460(4). STC 24520 (two). Madan 159.

6281. Urquhart, Thomas. *Epigrams, divine and morall. By sir Thomas Urchard.* London: f. W. Leake,

1646. 4°. Pp. [6], 60, [1].
Tp, signature of 'Ja: Hales'.
Wood 483(8). Wing U136.

6282. Ursin, Johann Heinrich. *Acerra philologica mille, variarum historiarum, physicarum . . . libri quinque, cum mantissa*. Francofurti: sump. C. Hermsdorffii, typ. B. C. Wustii, 1659. 12°. Pp. [2], 534, [64] (tp misbound after p. 22). Calf with 3 fillets; flyleaves, 1st and last, printer's waste paper.
Flyleaf, upper, 1st, '2 s' and 'Anth. Wood 1659'. Flyleaf, lower, 2nd^v, scribble, 'Sr Rolph'.
Wood 694. Not in BL.

6283. Ursinus, Joachimus, pseud. [Gentillet, Innocent, by]. *The Romane conclave. . . . Romane emperours, from Charles the great, to Rodulph now reigning*. London: [J. Windet] f. J. Jagger, 1609. 4°. Pp. [4], 243. Parchment with 2 clasp holes.
Pastedown, upper, 'k/y' (bsm.). Tp, AW wrote the date of acquisition, 'Sept. XIIII MDclx'.
Wood 353. STC 24526.

6284. Ussher, James. Armagh, abp. of. *A geographicall and historicall disquisition, touching . . . Lydian Asia*. Oxford: H. Hall, 1643. 4°. Pp. [4], 32, [3].
Wood 386(7). Wing U177. Madan 1583.

6285. Ussher, James*. Armagh, abp. of. *An elegie on the miraculously learned, . . . bishop of Armagh*. London: F. Leach, 1656. 4°. Pp. [1], 7.
Tp, 'Usher', prob. not by AW.
Wood 319(4). Wing E423 (one) ('O' not recorded in Wing).

6286. Ussher, James. Armagh, abp. of. *Strange and remarkable prophesies and predictions of . . . James Usher, . . . Giving an account of his foretelling I. The rebellion in Ireland*. London: f. R. G., 1678. 4°. Pp. 8.
Tp, AW wrote the year, '1678'.
Wood 646(14). Wing U225.

6287. Uxbridge, Treaty of. *Considerations touching the late treaty for a peace held at Uxbridge. With some reflexions upon the . . . frustration thereof*. Oxford: L. Lichfield, 1645. 4°. Pp. [2], 36.
Tp, no. 42 in a former bundle.
Wood 612(34). Wing C5920. Madan 1773.

6288. V., T. *A true relation of the late battell neere Newbery*. London: f. J. Wright, 1643, 26 Sept. 4°. Pp. [2], 6.
Tp, AW altered the former no., '36'; and, p. 6, wrote 'A Bishop kill'd at Newbury q[uaere]', and below, at a statement of the great losses of commanders at Oxford, AW made a vertical line and wrote, 'a lye'.
Wood 376(39). Wing T2977.

6289. Valcaren, Johann Peter von. *A relation or diary of the siege of Vienna. . . . drawn from the original*. London: f. W. Nott a. G. Wells, 1684. Fol. Pp. 112 (plus 2 sheets, maps of Vienna).
Tp, bsm.
Wood 559(21). Wing V21.

6290. Valla, Laurentius. [Gilles, Pierre, preface by]. *Historiarum Ferdinandi, regis Aragoniae: libri treis*. Pariis: ex aed. S. Colinaei, 1521 (septimo [i]des Augusti). 8°. Ff. [1], 70. Parchment with 2 clasp holes.
Flyleaf, upper^v, list of 6 printed works 'In hoc volumine', 'Binding.–x^d.', and 'Horum pretium VII – ' (lined out, illeg.), not by AW. Tp, 'pretium - 3^s.' and 'Liber Henrici Jacksoni Oxoniensis, Collegii Corpori Christi Sacri. MDC [altered to MDCX] Maii- xxi°.' Passim, underscoring, marginal marks, and notes, in more than 1 hand, none by AW. LT 1.459 (and 1.331).
Wood 477(1). BL.

6291. V[allans], W[illiam]. *The honourable prentice: or, this taylor is a man. Shewed in . . . sir John Hawkewood, . . . with the famons [sic] history of . . . Fitzwalter, lord of Woodham . . . also of . . . Dunmow, . . . [and] of Robert Hall*. London: [J. Beale] f. H.Gosson, 1616. 4°. Pp. [6], 34. Pasteboard (blue) with parchment spine. 1st upper and last lower flyleaves, marbled paper.
AW's list of titles (5) was removed, perhaps purposefully to hide the theft of item (4) (see item 4497). Item 1, tp, scribbles and 'Charles', not by AW; p. 34, signature of Charles Prichard and scribbles.
[MS.] Wood C. 32(1). STC 24589 (rare, 2 at O).

6292. Vane, Henry. S^r. *Henry Vane his speech in the house of commons, . . . for the bill against episcopall-*

government, m^r. Hide sitting in the chaire [11 June]. London: f. F. Constable, 1641. 4°. Pp. [2], 9.
Tp, AW underscored the name of the author, in red ink; 'Edw.' added before Hide, may be by AW.
[MS.] Wood D. 31(4). Wing V76.

6293. Vane, Henry*. *Sir Harry Vane's last sigh for the committee of safety, . . . in discourses . . . with . . . vice-admiral Lawson [17 Dec.]*. London: n.pub., 1659. 4°. Pp. 14.
Wood 610(15). Wing S3877A.

6294. Vane, Henry*. *The tryal of sir Henry Vane, k^t· at . . . Westminster [2, 6 June]*. [London?]: n.pub., 1662. 4°. Pp. 134 (pp. 1-2 blank).
Flyleaf, lower, 1st^v, scribble 'SL', in pencil (?). LT 1.443.
Wood 369(10). Wing T2216 ('O' not recorded in Wing).

6295. [Varillas, Antoine]. *Reflexions on dr. Gilbert Burnet's travels . . . written . . . in Latin . . . and now done into English*. London: printed, sold R. Tayler, 1688. 8°. Pp. [47], 164.
P. [1], former no. '3', in pencil, and AW wrote 'These reflexions answer the first impression of Dr Burnets Letters'. From p. 23 to the end, AW added p. nos. from his ed. of Burnet's *Travels* (Wood 724(1), item 1198); there were at least 10 other eds.) above printed p. nos. and some additional p. references, e.g., at p. 120, Cardinal Howard, he wrote '190' (he also marked these places with pencil in his ed. of Burnet).
Wood 724(2). Wing V114 ('O' not recorded in Wing).

6296. Vaughan, Hugh, and John Vaughan. *The case of Hugh Vaughan & John Vaughan, executors of Charles Vaughan*. N.p.: n.pub., [1676?]. S.sh.
A correction, not in AW's hand.
Wood 276b(80). Wing C919AC (rare) (Wing, 'and').

6297. Vaughan, Robert. *British antiquities revived: or a friendly contest touching the soveraignty of the three princes of Wales*. Oxford: H. Hall, f. T. Robinson, 1662. 4°. Pp. [4], 44.
Tp, AW wrote the price, '6^d'; and pp. 6, 24, 38, 42-4, made corrections from the errata list, which was printed in J. Price, Wood 478(2), item 5349. P. 40, AW identified an author as 'Percy Enderbie.' Acquired 6 June 1662, LT 1.441. AO 3.728-9.
Wood 478(3). Wing V139. Madan 2616.

6298. [Vaughan, Thomas]. *Anima magica abscondita: or a discourse of the universall spirit of nature, . . . by Eugenius Philalethes* (response at H. More, Wood 859(3), item 4548). London: T. W. f. H. B[lunden], 1650. 8°. Pp. [14], 56 (wanting the final leaf, E4).
Wood 859(2). Wing V142.

6299. [Vaughan, Thomas]. *Anthroposophia theomagica: or a discourse of the nature of man and his state after death; . . . by Eugenius Philalethes*. London: T. W. f. H. Blunden, 1650. 8°. Pp. [16], 70 (pp. 31-2 is mutilated (for cancellation?)). Pasteboard (blue) with parchment spine; remnants of upper and lower flyleaves of marbled paper.
Flyleaf, upper, 2nd^v, AW wrote the titles of 4 printed works in this vol., within guidelines made with red chalk. AO 3.723.
Wood 859(1). Wing V143.

6300. [Vaughan, Thomas]. *Magia Adamica: or the antiquitie of magic, . . . by Eugenius Philalethes*. London: T. W. f. H. Blunden, 1650. 8°. Pp. [26], 140.
Response at H. More, Wood 859(3), item 4548.
Wood 726(2). Wing V151.

6301. [Vaughan, Thomas]. *The man-mouse taken in a trap, and tortur'd to death for gnawing the margins of Eugenius Philalethes*. London: sold at the castle in Corn-hill, 1650. 8°. Pp. [14], 116 (contains 'errata' to Vaughan, Wood 726(2), item 6300). See note at item 345, and response at item 4548.
Wood 726(3). Wing V153A.

6302. [Vaughan, Thomas], ed. *The fame and confession of the fraternity . . . of the Rosie Cross. With a praeface . . . by Eugenius Philalethes*. London: J. M. f. G. Calvert, 1652. 8°. Pp. [70], 64.
Wood 726(4). Wing F350A ('O' not recorded in Wing).

6303. Vaughan, William. *The golden-grove, moralized in three books*. London: S. Stafford, 1600. 8°. A-2C^8 (wanting sig. H1). Parchment.
Pastedown, note by a librarian, 23/7/47. Flyleaf, upper, 'Henry: Foulis Booke D: 1 July: 1653 // P: 4^d.'
Text, E8^v-F1, 2C7^v, marks in margin, underscoring and scribbles, not by AW. Flyleaf, lower^r-v, an index

of over 150 topics, not by AW. LT 2.180.
Wood 743. STC 24610.

6304. V[aux], F[rancis]. *Detur pulchriori: or, a poem in the praise of the university of Oxford.* [Oxford]: [L. Lichfield], 1658. 4°. Pp. [4], 4.
Tp, AW wrote, 'written by one of Queens coll.'
Wood 515(18). Wing V164. Madan 2372.

6305. [Vaux, Francis]. *An elegy upon the death of . . . John Cleaveland.* [Oxford]: [L. Lichfield], [1658]. S.sh.
Name of author supplied, prob. by AW, 'Fra: Vaux. e Coll: Reg: Oxon.', followed by '1658', in AW's hand; ᵛ, AW wrote 2 similar notes, e.g., 'Joh. Cleaveland May 1658'. AOF 1.499. LT 1.250.
Wood 429(13). Wing V165 (rare). Madan 2418.

6306. Vaux, F[rancis]. *In the praise of typography.* [Oxford]: [L. Lichfield], [1658?]. S.sh. 4°.
AOF 1.499.
Wood 614(2). Wing V165A (rare). Madan 2373.

6307. Vegetius, Renatus Flavius. Sadler, John, trans. *[The foure bookes of Flavius Vegetius Renatus, briefelye contayninge a plaine forme . . . of martiall policye].* (London): (T. Marshe), [1572]. 4°. Ff. [8], 66, [8] (wanting the t leaf). Parchment, rough; ms. backing, Latin.
Cover, upperᵛ and passim, signature, 'Edward Sadleir o[wn]eth this booke witnesseth Thomas Holbage[,] Thomas Gilbarte and Richarde Walker[,] Martine Holbage' (elsewhere, also the 'witness' Thomas Witbe); and 'Thomas Locker'; passim, scribbles especially by Edward Sadler. F. 57, 'Theodore Sadler'. No annotation by AW. LT 1.426.
[MS.] Wood C. 18. STC 24631.

6308. Verax, Theophilus, pseud. *Serious sober state-considerations, relating to the government of England and the garrison of Dunkirk.* London: W. G., 1660. 4°. Pp. 8.
Tp, AW wrote 'Aprill:'.
Wood 608(6a) (not in Bodl. CD cat.). Wing S2618.

6309. [Vergil, Polydore]. [Langley, Thomas, ed.]. *[An abridgement of the notable works of Polidore Virgile].* (London): (J. Tisdale), [[1560 ca.]]. 8°. Ff. 152, [14] (wanting tp). Pasteboard (brown) with calf spine; rebacked.
Flyleaf, upper, 5thᵛ, note by librarian of a perfect copy at Ash. 697. Some notes and scribbles by earlier owners; at t8ᵛ and x7ᵛ, longer notes, now pasted over with blank leaves and illeg.; x6-x7, 'This is John Shelbourne[s] booke' and scribbles, by Shelbourne. Prob. acquired 9 Jan. 1663, 1ˢ4ᵈ, LT 1.467.
Wood 228. STC 24658.

6310. Vergil, Polydore. Lilius, G., ed. *Historia Anglica.* Duaci: n.pub., 1603. 8° (fragment). Pp. 817-942, 643-4.
Pp. 824-827, notes, prob. not by AW.
Wood 225(4). BL.

6311. Vergil, Polydore. *The works of the famous antiquary, Polydore Virgil.* London: f. S. Miller, 1663. 8°. Pp. [4], 311, [23]. Pasteboard (brown) with calf spine. 1st and last flyleaves, marbled paper.
Tp, AW wrote, '1ˢ-3ᵈ'.
Wood 178. Wing V596.

6312. Vernon, Christopher. *Considerations for regulating the exchequer.* [London]: T. Harper, sold M. Walbanke, L. Chapman, W. Cooke, a. R. Best, 1642. 8°. Pp. [8], 118, [1]. Pasteboard (blue) with parchment spine (rebound). 2nd upper and 2nd last lower flyleaves, marbled paper.
Flyleaf, upper, 4thʳ⁻ᵛ, AW wrote the titles of 25 printed works in this vol., within guidelines made with red ink. 1st item, each 8° leaf is pasted on a 4° template.
Wood 630(1). Wing V244.

6313. V[ernon], F[rancis]. *Oxonium poema. Authore F. V.* Oxon: typ. W. Hall, imp. R. Davis, 1667. 4°. Pp. [2], 26.
Tp, AW wrote the author's name above initials and 'Oxōn', and below, the date of acquisition, 'Sept. 22. an. 1667 4ᵈ'. LT 2.118. Pp. 8, 2 identifications of Latin place-names; 20-1, corrections; 21, at printed 'The Tower with Ivy' at Merton Col., AW wrote, 'Where is yt?'.
Wood 513(4). Wing V245. Madan 2761.

6314. [**Vernon, George**]. *A letter to a friend concerning some of dr. Owens principles and practices.* London: J. Redmayne f. S. Hickman, 1670. 4°. Pp. [6], 78.
Tp, 2 notes, cropped at side, one in Latin and the second in English, identifying the author, both cropped, neither in AW's hand. LT 2.212.
Wood 611(6) (Bodl. CD cat., 'girl friend'). Wing V247.

6315. Vernon, George. *The life of . . . dr. Peter Heylyn, chaplain to Charles I. and Charles II.* London: f. C. Harper, 1682. 8°. Pp. [26], 292 (2 pp. books sold by Harper). Calf, speckled, with 2 fillets; rebacked. Front-edge, marbled decoration.
Tp, date underlined in pencil.
Wood 295. Wing V248.

6316. [**Vernon, Samuel**]. *The trepan: being a true relation, . . . of the strange practices of Mehetabel . . . Jones, and Elizabeth . . . Pigeon.* [London]: T. M., 1656. 4°. Pp. [8], 34.
Tp, 'The Trepan', not in AW's hand, and p. 34, scribble.
Wood 654a(18). Wing V253B (one) ('O' not recorded in Wing).

6317. Veron, François. S[heldon], E[dward], trans. *The rule of Catholick faith.* Paris: J. Billain, 1660 [really 1672]. 8°. Pp. [24], 144. Calf with 2 gold-stamp fillets.
Flyleaf, upper, 3rd[v], 'Antony à Wood. Given to me by Ralph Sheldon of Weston in Warw. Esquire Nov. 3. 1672. The 1. impression an. 1660. the 2[d] surreptiously [sic] procured by the said Esquire Sheldon 1672, which is this, though the old date put to it: printed at London. Translated by his uncle Edw. Sheldon, Esquire.' LT 2.252 (see also 2.234-5; AW received 36 copies from Sheldon to be sold at 6[d], and he passed 12 on to the bookseller Richard Davis and six to the bookseller, West, LT 2.253). Tp, line at date of publication.
Wood 812. Wing V255.

6318. [**Vicars, John**]. *True information of the beginning and cause of all our troubles: how they have been hatched, and how prevented.* London: n.pub., 1648. 4°. Pp. [2], 42 (last 2 pp. unnumbered).
Flyleaf, upper[v], AW wrote, 'Note that this pamphlet following called <u>true information</u> &c which is <u>A brief review of the most material parliamentary proceedings</u> &c is the first edition of it: And because it hath more cuts [19 vs. 8] in it, than the second edition of it, which immediatly followes after it, therefore do I preserve, & put it here' (see Wood 519(6)). Tp[v], note, pasted over. LT 1.153.
Wood 519(5). Wing V331A.

6319. [**Vicars, John**]. *A brief review of the most material parliamentary proceedings . . . continued untill the act of oblivion, February 24, 1652 [and] The several speeches of Duke Hamilton [et al.].* London: M. S. f. T. Jenner, 1652. 4°. Pp. [2], 30, 36.
Tp[v], AW wrote, 'Not so many cuts in this as the other–' (only 8 vs. 19, all 8 appear in the earlier ed., *True information*, Wood 519(5)); also, '9' and 'H1' (a shelf-mark?). LT 1.153.
Wood 519(6). Wing V294A.

6320. Vicars, John. *Dagon demolished: or, twenty admirable examples of Gods severe justice . . . against the subscribers . . . against . . . Charls the second.* London: T. Mabb f. E. Thomas, 1660. 4°. Pp. 15.
Tp, AW underlined 'John Vicars' and wrote 'Aprill'. P. 12, at the sudden death in bed of Master [Col. John] Ven, line in margin, in red ink (retold in AO 3.278f.).
Wood 617(4). Wing V298.

6321. Vicars, Thomas. Χειραγωγια *manuductio ad artem rhetoricam.* London: typ. A. Matthaei, 1621. 8°.
Missing. MS. Wood E. 2(70), p. 16.
MS. Wood E. 2(70), p. 16. STC 24702 (two). O.

6322. Vidua, D. D. *Bishops defended from scripture, laws, and other undeniable authors, . . . An humble motion to the parliament.* [London]: n.pub., 1641. 8°. 2nd ed. Pp. 15.
[MS.] Wood D. 25(5). Wing V354.

6323. Vienna. *A true and exact relation of the raising of the siege of Vienna and the victory . . . over the Ottoman army [12 Sept.].* (London): (f. S. Crouch), (1683). Fol. Pp. 7.
Wood 559(20). Wing T2459.

6324. Vignier, Nicolas (elder). *Rerum Burgundionum chronicon.* Basileae: per T. Guarinum, 1575. 4°. Pp. [8], 184, [23]. Parchment with 2 clasp holes.

Pastedown, upper, 'a./h./B.' (?). Tp, name of a former owner, torn out, and the price, 'ii^s.vi^d'. A second owner wrote, 'Qui habet Christum habet omnia [/] Thomas Birdall:'.
Wood 461. BL.

6325. Villegas, Alfonso de. Kinsman, W., trans. out of F. Ribadeniera. *The lives of saints.* [St. Omer]: [C. Boscard f. J. Heigham], 1621. 4°. 2nd ed. Pp. [8], 1050, [1]. Parchment with 2 clasp holes.
Pastedown, upper, a price, '2^s 6.', and flyleaf, lower^v, another, '0 - 8 - 0'. Prob. acquired 24 Dec. 1656, 2^s, LT 1.210. See note at item 290.
Wood 351. STC 24731b (two). ARCR 2.480.

6326. Villiers, Francis*. *Elegie on the untimely death of . . . Francis, lord Villiers, brother to the duke of Buckingham [7 July 1648].* [London]: n.pub., [1648]. S.sh.
^{v}, AW wrote, 'Franc. Lord Villiers 1648.'
Wood 429(5). Wing E443.

6327. Villiers, George. Buckingham, duke of. *The declaration of . . . the duke of Buckingham, . . . and other lords . . . with three letters [6 June].* London: n.pub., 1648. 4°. Pp. [2], 5.
Wood 502(18) (not in Bodl. CD cat.). Wing B5310.

6328. Villiers, George. Buckingham, duke of. **Manuscript.** *Though Philis youer prevailings charmes . . . Made by the duke of Buckingham one the 20 of Julii 1665 / addrest to his mistris.* N.p.: n.pub., [1665]. S.sh.
AW wrote, 'This I found written in a spare leafe before a Romance called Eliana. Lond. 1661. fol' (Wing E499). The poem is not in the hand of AW (*pace* Bliss, AO 4.211). Bliss made an inaccurate transcription; Clark transcribed accurately, LT 2.42-3; a diplomatic transcription follows: 'Though Philiz youer preuailings [sic] Charmes [/] hath forct my Celias frome mine Armes [/] Thinke not youer Conquest to Mantaine [/] by rigor or unjust disdayne [/] In vaine fare Nimph in vaine you striue [/] for Love douth seldome hope suruiue [/] My hearte may Langish for a time [/] As all Beautyes in theire prime [/] Cane Justifie such Crueltye [/] by the same fate that Conquerd mee [/] When Age shall come att whose Command [/] Those troopes of beautye must disbande [/] A Tirants strenth once tooke away [/] what slaues soe dull as to obey [/] But if you will Learne a Nobler way [/] to keepe this Empire frome decay [/] And theire for euer fix youer Throne [/] bee kinde but kinde to mee alone [/] Made by the Duke of Buckinham [sic] one [sic] the 20th of Julij 1665/ Addrest to his Mistris'.
Wood 416(110).

6329. [Villiers, George]. Buckingham, duke of. *An epitaph upon Thomas late lord Fairfax. Written by a person of honour.* [London]: n.pub., [1679?]. S.sh. Pp. 2.
AW supplied the name of the author, 'viz. George Villiers Duke of Bucks, who had married his daughter, the Lady Mary-'; p. 2, AW wrote the year, '1671', in pencil.
Wood 429(31). Wing B5311.

6330. Villiers, George. Buckingham, duke of. *The duke of Buckingham his grace's letter, to the unknown author of a paper, entituled, a short answer . . . concerning religion, toleration.* (London): (J. L. f. L. Meredith), (1685). Fol. Pp. 4.
Tp, former no. '(3)' in pencil, may not be by AW.
Wood 657(19). Wing B5314.

6331. Villiers, George*. Buckingham, duke of. *A reply to . . . the duke of Buckingham's letter to the author of a paper, entituled, an answer . . . concerning religion, toleration.* (London): (W. D. f. T. Graves), (1685). Fol. Pp. 4.
Tp, former no. '(4)' in pencil, may not be by AW.
Wood 657(20). Wing R1060.

6332. Villiers, George*. Buckingham, duke of. *A short answer to . . . the d. of Buckingham's paper, concerning religion, toleration, and liberty of conscience.* London: f. S. G., sold R. Taylor, 1685. 4°. Pp. [4], 36.
Tp, no. '(2)', in pencil, may not be by AW.
Wood 611(8). Wing S3561.

6333. Villiers, George. Buckingham, duke of. *A short discourse upon the reasonableness of men's having a religion, or worship of God.* London: J. Leake f. L. Meredith, 1685. 4°. 3rd ed. Pp. [6], 21, [3] (2 pp. books printed, sold, by Meredith).
Tp, above, former no, in pencil, cropped; below, AW wrote, 'The i edit. came out in 1685' (cropped at

bottom). Responses at Wood 611(10) and 611(11), items 1398, 5173.
Wood 611(7). Wing B5330.

6334. Villiers, Robert. *A true state of the proofs offered at the bar of the house of lords, by Robert son . . . of Robert, and grandson of John late lord viscount Purbeck.* [London?]: n.pub., [1678]. Fol. Pp. [4].
Wood 276b(97) (old no., (75), in Bodl. CD cat.). Wing T3118A (two).

6335. Vilvain, Rob[ert]. *A compend of chronography: containing four thousand thirty yeers complet, from Adams creation to Christ's birth.* London: R. Hodgkinsonne (f. the author), 1654. 4°. Ff. [2], 17.
[MS.] Wood B. 36(7). Wing V394.

6336. Vilvain, Robert. *Enchiridium epigrammatum Latino-Anglicum. An epitome of essais.* London: R. Hodgkinsonne, 1654. 8°. Ff. [12], 191. Calf, speckled, with 2 fillets.
Flyleaf, upper, 2nd^v, 'Anth. à Wood. Received by the gift of Mr Rich Isack Chamberlayne of Exeter. / . 3. May 1680'. LT 2.485.
Wood 85. Wing V395.

6337. [Vilvain, Robert]. *A short survey of our Julian English yeare.* [London]: n.pub, [1656]. S.sh.
AW wrote the author's name, 'Rob. Vilvaine M. D.', in pencil; also, a note in a later hand. ^v, AW wrote 'The Julian Engl. yeare'.
Wood 276a(45). Wing V396 (rare).

6338. Vincent, Thomas. *Holy and profitable sayings of that reverend divine.* London: D. M., 1680. S.sh.
AW wrote, 'Tho. Vincent a grand phanatick'. LT 2.565.
Wood 532(8). Wing V446 (rare).

6339. Vindex Anglicus. *Vindex Anglicus; or, the perfections of the English language. Defended, and asserted.* [Oxford]: [H. Hall], 1644. 4°. Pp. [2], 6.
P. 3, vertical lines in margin. Dupl. at Wood 614(14).
Wood 310(9). Wing V461. Madan 1759.

6340. Vindex Anglicus. *Vindex Anglicus; or, the perfections of the English language. Defended, and asserted.* [Oxford]: [H. Hall], 1644. 4°. Pp. [2], 6.
Dupl. at Wood 310(9).
Wood 614(14). Wing V461. Madan 1759.

6341. Vindication of Certain Citizens. *A vindication of certaine citizens that lately went to the leaguer, then before Oxford, or, their answer unto . . . an epistle, lately published by William Dell.* London: E. Purslow f. T. Vere, 1646. 4°. Pp. [2], 14.
Wood 514(17). Wing V472. Madan 1895.

6342. Vindication of Learning. *A vindication of learning from unjust aspersions.* London: f. J. Hardesty, 1646. 4°. Pp. [2], 30. Pasteboard (grey) with parchment spine.
Flyleaf, upper, 2nd^v, AW wrote the titles of 10 printed works (really 8, AW lists parts of 2 items as separate items and omits no. (6)) in this vol., within guidelines made with red ink, and the heading, 'For, & against, humane Learning' (defined in [MS.] Wood B. 24(8), item 3679, as 'the knowledge of Arts and Sciences, divers Tongues, and much reading', p. 2). Tp, names, 'John' and 'Thomas Sprynevell [?]'. See LT 1.296, 367.
[MS.] Wood B. 24(1). Wing V480 ('O' not recorded in Wing).

6343. Vinegar. *Vinegar & mustard or wormwood lectures.* London: ?, 1656. Pp.?
Missing in 1837. 'Vinegar & Mustard or Wormwood Lectures – Lond.1656' in Whiteside cat.
Wood 61(6). Not in Wing. See Wing W175 (1673) and W175A (1686). Not in ESTCR.

6344. [Vineis, Raimundus de]. Senensis, Caterinus, trans.; Fenn, John, trans. *The life of the blessed virgin, sainct Catharine of Siena [from Vita miracolosa della . . . Catherina da Siena by L. Politi].* [Douai]: [P. Auroi f. J. Heigham], 1609. 8°. Pp. [6], 455, [9]. Parchment with 2 clasp holes.
Flyleaf, upper, '3^s.'
Wood 257. BL. ARCR 2.272.

6345. Vines, Richard. *The hearse of the renowned . . . Robert earle of Essex . . . as it was represented in a sermon [22 Oct.].* London: T. R. a. E. M. f. A Roper, 1646. 4° (wanting the frontisp.). Pp. [8], 38.
Missing since 1994. In Whiteside cat.
Wood 531(7). Wing V553.

6346. Virel, Mathieu. *Regulae generales et perpetuae, de rebus ad calendarium spectantibus*. Basileae: ex off. T. Guarini, 1579. 8°. Pp. [6], 40, [1]. Parchment ms., Latin, from a service book, with gold and coloured initials.
Tp, '3ᵈ'; pp. 7ᵛ, dates; 40, a correction (Tho. Monfeti to Muffeti), may be by AW.
Wood 17. BL.

6347. Viret, Peter. Brooke, John, trans. *A faithfull and familiar exposition upon the prayer of our Lord*. London: H. Middleton f. R. Sergier, 1579 [an error for 1582?]. 4°. Ff. [6], 5-196, [5].
Missing. MS. Wood E. 2(70), p. 4, 'Lond. 1579. 4°'. AO 1.536 has 1582. In the Bodl. copy examined, the year was scratched out.
MS. Wood E. 2(70), p. 4. STC 24780 (1582). *O, BL, Folg*.

6348. Viret, Peter. Stocker, Thomas, trans. *The cauteles, canon, and ceremonies, of the . . . popish masse*. London: T. Vautrollier f. A. Maunsell, 1584. 8°. Pp. [6], 156 (i.e., 256, misnumbering) (wanting the t leaf). Parchment.
Wood 855. STC 24775.

6349. Virgil. Stanyhurst, Richard, trans. *The first foure bookes of Virgils Aeneis*. London: H. Bynneman, 1583. 8°. Pp. [14], 106 (H3 removed; H4, mutilated). Parchment wrapper, ms., 12th-century Latin, English provenance, Vergil, Aen. VI, 116ff. (with a note by B. C. Barker-Benfield and a reference to C. Baswell, *Virgil in Medieval England* (Cambridge, 1995)).
Tp, p. 106, notes, not in AW's hand. Text, some underscoring and marks in margins, prob. not by AW.
Wood 106. STC 24807.

6350. Virgil. Phaer, Thos. a. Thos. Twyne, trans. *The thirteene bookes of Aeneidos*. London: B. Alsop, assignement of C. Knight, 1620. 4°. ⁴,A-U⁸,X⁴.
Missing. MS. Wood E. 2(70), p. 50. Acquired 1 Oct. 1664, LT 2.22.
MS. Wood E. 2(70), p. 50. STC 24805a. *O, Folg, Hunt*.

6351. Virgil. Vicars, John, trans. *The XII Aeneids*. [Cambridge]: [T. Buck] sold N. Alsop [London], 1632. 8°. Pp. [16], 418. Parchment.
Tp, bsm. or shelf-mark, 'd.3.3'.
Wood 102. STC 24809.

6352. [Virgil]. Farnaby, Thomas, ed. *[Opera cum notis Thomae Farnabii]*. [Amstelaedemi]: [typ. J. Blaeu], [1650]. 12°. Pp. 2-384 (wanting tp). Calf with 2 fillets; 2nd rectangle with 3 fillets and stamp decoration outside corners.
P. 3, at 'Bucolica', 'Belonging to a Shepheard or pastour the same with Pastoralii.', prob. by AW. P. 384, signature of 'Robt Powell me tenet'. Pastedown, lower, scribbling, quotations from the text, and initials 'W. S.'
Wood 52. NUC.

6353. Virgil. Waller, Edmund, trans.; Godolphin, Sidney, trans. *The passion of Dido for Aeneas*. London: f. Humphrey Moseley, 1658. 8°. A-E⁸,F⁴. Calf with 2 fillets.
Flyleaf, upper, 1stʳ, 'Mr [Richard] Reevs – 73', i.e., 1673. LT 2.280.
Wood 97. Wing V633.

6354. [Vischer, Nicholas]. *Africae nova discriptio*. Amstelodami: ap. C. Allard, 1679. S.sh.
ᵛ, 'Ex dono Gul. Rowlands Antonius a Wood', in the hand of Rowlands. Below title, 'per Nichol. Vischer', may be in AW's hand. LT 2.475. There were 576 items on the 1717 list written on the upper flyleaves. No. 577, *At a General Meeting of the Vice-Chancellor, . . . on Saturday Nov. 27. 1714*, was added to Wood 276a after 1717. That item is not included in this current catalogue.
Wood 276a(576). Bod. Map cat.

6355. Vizier, Grand. *A true representation of the grand visir's standard taken at Vienna*. [London]: n.pub., [1653/4]. S.sh. (with some Arabic) (engr.).
AW added the date, '1684', in pencil. LT 3.121.
Wood 276a(29). Wing T3095C (two) ('O' not recorded in Wing).

6356. Vocabulary. *Den ġrooten vocabulaer / Enghels ende Duyts:. . . The great vocabuler, in English and Dutch*. Rotterdam: de weduwe van M. Bastiaensz, [1639] (cropped). 8°. 4th impression. A-H⁸ (with blank sheets added at end) (tp mutilated). Parchment.
H8ᵛ, signature of Edward Creed. 2 blank leaves at end, a few lines of basic phrases in Dutch, not in AW's

hand. Possibly acquired 10 Dec. 1663, LT 1.507.
Wood 29 (not in Bodl. CD cat.). STC 24869.5 (rare).

6357. Vorst, Conrad. *Christiana & modesta responsio, ad articulos quosdam, nuper ex Angliā trans-missos, & typis hīc descriptos, passimque in vulgus latè dispersos.* Lugduni Batavorum: excud. T. Basson, 1611. 4°. Pp. [12], 36 [i.e., 35].
[MS.] Wood B. 36(17-18). Not in BL.

6358. W., C. *Perfecta narratio totius processus supremi tribunalis justitiae in examine rrgis [sic] [20, 22 Jan., by C. W. followed by] Regis Caroli oratio habita . . . immediatè ante executionem [30 Jan.].* Londini: in offic. G. Bentley, imp. G. Shears, 1649. 8°. Pp. [2], 22 (2 tpp).
Tp, price, '2ᵈ/'. Eng. versions at *Perfect Narrative*, items 4731-4.
Wood 670(3). Wing P1531 (1st ed.). ESTCR 215047 (one) ('O' not in ESTCR). FFMadan 103.

6359. W., C., and Richard Sandys. *A full relation of the desperate designe of the malignants, for the betraying of Monmouth [Nov. 4] . . . Likewise, a copy of col. Sandys letter.* London: f. T. Bates, 1645. 4°. Pp. [2], 6.
Tp, AW wrote the month, 'Nov', in pencil, and overwrote the former no., '36'.
Wood 378(39). Wing W7.

6360. W., D. *A perspicuous compendium of several irregularities and abuses in the present practice of the common laws of England.* London: T. Lock f. H. Flesher, 1656. 4°. Pp. [8], 18.
Wood 630(16). Wing W11.

6361. W., F., ed. *Warme beere, or a treatise wherein is declared by many reasons, that beere so qualified is farre more wholsome then that which is drunke cold.* Cambridge: R. D. f. H. Overton, 1641. 24°. Pp. [22], 143.
Each 24° leaf is pasted on an 8° template. P. [21], 4 emendations to a poem by W. B. on warm beer.
Wood 679(7). Wing W27 (Wing, beere.).

6362. W., J. *Happy newes from Sherborn and Sherborne castle: relating, the death of colonel [Thomas] Lunsford, the lord [John, earl of Winchester] Paulet.* London: F. Cowles, 1642, 13 Sept. 4°. Pp. 7.
Tp, AW overwrote the former no. '16' with '9', underscored 'death of . . . Paulet', and wrote 'qu[aere]'.
Wood 375(9). Wing W57.

6363. W., J. *A letter from New-England concerning their customs, manners, and religion. . . . about a quo warranto brought against that government.* London: f. R. Taylor, 1682. Fol. Pp. [2], 9.
Tp, 'ō' (?).
Wood 559(17). Wing W59.

6364. W., L. *Merry dialogue between Andrew and his sweet heart Joan.* London: A. M[ilbourn] f. J. Deacon a. C. Dennisson, [1682 or later]. 8°.
Missing in 1837. 'Merry dialogue between Andrew & his Sweet heart Joan – Lond.' in Whiteside cat.
Wood 66(10). Wing W79cA (one). CM.

6365. W., R. *A great fight at Chepstow castle . . . betwixt the forces under the command of lieutenant gen. Cromwell, and the cavaliers commanded by sir William Kelmish. Also . . . the late skirmish at White-hall.* London: f. R. Williamson, 1648. 4°. Pp. [8].
Wood 502(8). Wing W93.

6366. W., R. *The declaration of the Brittish in the north of Ireland. With some queres of colonel Monke.* [London]: n.pub., 1648[9] 'Printed . . . 1648'. 4°. Pp. [2], 6. Pasteboard (grey) with parchment spine.
On the spine, AW wrote, Ireland 1649 &c. Vol. 7. Flyleaves, upper, 1st-3rd, AW wrote the titles of 37 printed works in this vol., within guidelines made with red ink. The Whiteside cat. entry has '37 Pamphlets'. Item 38, printed in 1692, has annotation in AW's hand, and AW may have added it after he wrote the table of contents. Tp, AW wrote after the year, '9' and '9. Apr 16. May' (dates given in the text; this pamphlet was also printed in 1649). Dupl. at Wood 609(20a).
Wood 510(1). Wing W89A (two).

6367. W., R. *The declaration of the Brittish in the north of Ireland. With some queres of colonel Monke.* [London]: n.pub., 1648[9] 'Printed . . . 1648'. 4°. Pp. [2], 6.
Tp, AW wrote 'Dupl', in pencil. Year, blotted out and '1649' written in. Dupl. at Wood 510(1).
Wood 609(20a). Wing W89A (two).

6368. W., R. *A necessary family-book, both for the city & country, . . . for taking and killing all manner of vermin on land and in water*. London: f. J. Harris, 1688. 12°. Pp. [3], 80, [12] (12 pp. books sold by Harris).
A1, the title, pasted over with leaf, not in AW's hand.
Wood 727(3). Wing W100 (two).

6369. W., R. *An essay on grief. With the causes and remedies of it*. Oxford: L. Lichfield f. H. Clements a. J. Howell, 1695. 12°. Pp. [8], 220.
Wood 733(2). Wing W91 ('O' not recorded in Wing).

6370. W., T. *Strange and true newes of an ocean of flies dropping out of a cloud upon the towne of Bodnam [in verse]*. [London]: n.pub., 1647. S.sh.
Repaired by AW (his numbering is on the repair).
[MS.] Wood D. 28(9). Wing W131 (two).

6371. W., T. *Strange and wonderful news from Norwich*. [London]: n.pub., [1681]. S.sh. (r-v).
Wood 276a(157). Wing W132.

6372. Wadsworth, James. Bedell, William, ed. *The copies of certaine letters which have passed betweene Spaine and England in matter of religion*. London: W. Stansby f. W. Barret a. R. Milbourne, 1624. 4°. Pp. [12] ([1-2] blank), 162, [1].
All items in this vol. came from Francis Isaac, see Wood 587(1), item 3164.
Wood 587(2) (not in Bodl. CD cat.). STC 24925.

6373. Wadsworth, James. *The English Spanish pilgrime. Or, a new discovery of Spanish popery, and Jesuiticall stratagems*. London: T. Cotes, a. R.C[otes] f. M. Sparke, 1630. 4°. 2nd ed. Pp. [6], 100.
On the upper flyleaf, at his list of items, AW wrote after this entry, 'best edition'. Tp, bsm. AW annotated lightly: corrections, lines in margin (in ink and pencil), and identifications, pp. 9, 13, 20-1, 24, 27, 59, 73 (i.e., 72).
Wood 648(3). STC 24927.

6374. Wadsworth, James. *Further observations of the English Spanish pilgrime*. London: F. Kyngston f. R. Allot, 1630. 4°. Pp. [21], 35 (quire G (33f.) out of order).
AW made lines in margins, in pencil, pp. 18; 23; 26; and on 24, wrote in margin, 'M^r – Scot'.
Wood 648(4). STC 24928a.

6375. W[agstaffe], J[ohn], and Lucian. More, T., trans. *The question of witchcraft debated; or a discourse against their opinion that affirm witches. [Followed by]* Φιλοψύδεις *[sic]. Lovers of lies. A dialogue . . . by . . . Lucian*. London: n.pub, 1669. 8°. Pp. [6], 128. Pasteboard (blue) with parchment spine. 1st upper and last lower flyleaves, marbled paper.
Tp, AW wrote 'The authour Jo. Wagstaff, M.A. somtimes of Oriel Coll.' LT 2.4. Diff. ed. at Wood 705. Response at T., R., Wood 708(2), item 6118.
Wood 708(1) (Wood 705(1) in Bodl. CD cat.). Wing W198A.

6376. Wagstaffe, John, and Lucian. More, T., trans. *The question of witchcraft debated. Or a discourse against their opinion that affirm witches. [Followed by]* ΦΙΛΟΨΕΙΔΕΣ *[sic] lovers of lies: a dialogue . . . by . . . Lucian [trans. T. More]*. London: f. E. Millington, 1671. 8°. 2nd ed. Pp. [12], 198. Calf, speckled, with 2 fillets and a vertical lines.
Flyleaf, upper, 2nd^v, AW wrote '23 May 1675 Whitsunday [/] Given to me by the Author in his lodgings in Holborne Lond. over [over, added above] against the end of Chancery Lane.' LT 2.314. Diff. ed. at Wood 708(1).
Wood 705 (Wood 70 in Bodl. CD cat.). Wing W199.

6377. Wagstaffe, Thomas. *A vindication of king Charles the martyr*. London: f. J. Hindmarsh, 1693. 8°. Pp. 46.
Tp, AW wrote '6^d', and 'Tho. Wagstaff chanc. of Chichester [Chichester, lined out] Lichfield the author – Bought at Oxō 4. Jul. 1693' (LT 3.427). Pp. 30-1, AW explained the origin of a letter, 'written by way of Letter to Sr Will. Dugdale garter K[ing] of Armes', and made a correction. Last leaf, a tp of *The life and death of King Charles . . . by R. Per[r]inchief* (1693) (Wing P1595; FFMadan 67) on which AW wrote, 'I have this book printed in a larg oct. 1676, with this title The Royal Martyr or the Life &c', i.e., Wood 238(1), item 5191. See LT 2.270.
Wood 363(16). Wing W218. FFMadan 175.

6378. [**Wagstaffe, Thomas**]. *A letter out of Suffolk to a friend in London. Giving some account of the last sickness and death of dr. William Sancroft.* London: n.pub., 1694. 4°. Pp. 39 (pp. 1-2 blank).
Tp, AW wrote, 'published about the middle of March 1693[4]'. P. 7, underscoring of 1 word. LT 3.434.
[MS.] Wood D. 23(12). Wing W209.

6379. **Wake, Isaac**. *Oratio funebris habita in templo Beatae Mariae Oxon [on J. Rainolds].* Oxoniae: excud. Jos. Barnesius, 1608. 12°. A2-9.
Tp, AW wrote, 'This oration rendred into Engl[ish] by Mr Tho. Fuller in his Abel [redivi]vus, printed [1651] 4. at Lond. p. 492.' (cropped), i.e., Wood 352, item 3107.
Wood 196(4). STC 24936. Madan 317.

6380. **Wake, Isaac**. *A three fold help to political observations contained in three discourses.* London: f. A. Crook, 1655. 8°. Pp. [16] 119.
Tp, pencil note, illeg. and cropped at bottom; bsms.
Wood 666(5). Wing W228.

6381. **Wake, Isaac**. *Rex platonicus. Sive de potentissimi principis Jacobi . . . [2nd tp:] Oratio funebris . . . Joannis Rainoldi.* Oxoniae: typ. W. Hall, impen. G. West, 1663 (1662). 12°. 6th ed. Pp. [8], 239, [15]. A-L^12 (2nd tp at L5) (L12 blank).
P. 52, cross mark in margin at speech concerning 'Athenas Majestatis suae'. AW lent an ed. to W. Hall, 5 Aug. 1662, and may have received this new ed. in return, LT 1.452.
Wood 62(2) (and 62(3)). Wing W227. Madan 2628.

6382. [**Wake, William**]. *Canterbury, abp. of. A continuation of the present state of the controversy, between the Church of England, and the church of Rome.* London: f. R. Chiswell, 1688. 4°. Pp. [16], 76.
P.[1], 'By Mr Wake:', not in AW's hand.
[MS.] Wood B. 40(4). Wing W234.

6383. **Wakeman, George***, and **William Marshall***, et al. *The tryals of sir George Wakeman barronet. William Marshall, William Rumley, and James Corker, Benedictine monks. For high treason.* London: f. H. Hills, T. Parkhurst, J. Starkey, D. Newman, T. Cockeril, T. Simmons, 1679. Fol. Pp. 84.
Tp, AW wrote the price, '2-6^d.'; pp. 13-17, underscored an anwer of a witness for the prosecution, Mr. [Stephen] Dugdale, and added two notes, 'Dugdale shews himself to have no good memorie/', and 'Dugdale shewd himself so contradictory in his evidence, that the judge for feare he should make the matter worse dismissed him. v. p. 19.'; 55-6, notes on the testimony of the witness, Philip Lloyd: 'Sr Phil. Lloyd one of the clerks of the councill.', and 'In the beginning of Oct. 1679 Sr Phil. Lloyd was examined before the Kings councill about his evidence in Sr Georg Wakemans Triall, & was severely check'd by the Lord presid. Shaftesbury, who told him he should have taken the Councills advice about the buisness [sic] first, to which he aswered [sic] that he thought there was no need of that, being onlie sent for at the triall to speak the truth, of what he had heard, which no considerations in the world should ever make him smother = this answer was approved, & so he was dismissed; bus[iness] suspended [p. 56] suspended [sic] in the middle of Oct. for saying there was no plot – suspended from his place during the Kings pleasure'. P. 84, notes: at the verdict, 'Not Guilty', AW wrote 'At which there was a great shout made, either for joy or out of Custome'. At the end of the trial, 'Scroggs the judge did afterward take great paines to persuade the people that though these men were cleered, yet tis certaine there is a plot'; and at end of advertisements, 'July 19 an. 1679 Mr Will Plessington a Romish preist suffered death for being a preist onlie, at Chester. His speech at the gallowes is printed in half a sheet of paper' (Wood 425(10), item 5274); and 'Aug. 22 an. 1679 Mr Franc. Johnston, alias Dormore, alias Webbe alias Wall a Romish preist suffered death at Worcester, for being onlie a preist: His speech is printed in one sheet of paper, with simple animadversions theron by another pen of another persuasion (presbiterian I thinke.)' (Wood 425(15), item 3887). LT 2.456, 461, 465. Purchased from Vade in July or August 1679, see his record of purchase in MS. Wood F. 50, f. 11.
Wood 425(8). Wing T2259.

6384. **Waking Vision**. *The waking vision; or, reality in a fancy.* London: N. T., 1681. S.sh.
AW wrote below, 'Apr.'
Wood 417(54). Wing W282.

6385. **Walbancke, Matthew** (includes poems by Drayton, Michael, et al.) *Annalia Dubrensia. Upon the yeerely celebration of m^r. Robert Dovers Olimpick games upon Cotswold-hills.* London: R. Raworth, f. M. Walbancke, 1636. 4°. A^2,B-I^4,K^2 (K2 blank; wanting frontisp.).
B2^v, AW wrote, 'J. Trussell of Winchester, the same I suppose that continued Sam. Daniels History.' (STC 24297, Wing T3145f.). Other short notes, B4, D1^v, D3^r-v, E4, F4^v, etc. to end. F2^v, 'Tho. Cole fellow of

Oriel Coll. whose aunt Isabell Cole was first married to . . . . [blank] Sanford of Bristow, afterward to Rob. Dover'; F4, at William Basse, 'an old poet living at Moreton neare Thame, in Cō. Oxō somtimes a servant in the family of the Lord Waynm [cropped, i.e., Wenman] at Thame Parke'; at end, K1ᵛ, at Thomas Heywood, 'a Comedian of London', and at end, 'Sʳ Will. Davenant hath also a copie of verses on these games somewhere among his poetry'.
Wood 483(7). STC 24954.

6386. Walby, Anthony. *Good newes from the traine bands and auxiliars.* London: B. Alsop, 1643. 4°. Pp. [2], 5.
Tp, AW altered the former no. and wrote 'Sept 2', in pencil. P. 7, AW corrected 'Soulden in Oxfordshire' to 'Souldern'.
Wood 376(33). Wing W282B (rare).

6387. Walcot, Tho[mas]. *A true copy of a paper written by capt. Tho. Walcott in Newgate, . . . immediately before his execution.* (London): (f. T. Goodwin), (1683). S.sh. Pp. 2.
Wood 428(8). Wing W285.

6388. Walcot, Thomas*, et al. *The tryals of Thomas Walcot, William Hone, William lord Russell, John Rous & William Blagg.* London: f. R. Royston, B. Took, a. C. Mearn, 1683. Fol. Pp. [2], 81.
Tp, AW wrote the price, '1ˢ. 6ᵈ'; p. 55, identified 'Heneage Finch Esq. son of Heneage Earl of Notting:'.
Wood 428(4). Wing T2265.

6389. [Walker, Anthony]. *A true account of the author [J. Gauden] of . . .* Εικων Εασιλικη *[sic].* London: f. N. Ranew, 1692. 4°. Pp. 37.
Tp, AW wrote, 'Dr. Anth. Walker the Author of this book.', 'Bought at Oxon on May day 1692', and in pencil, 'May da[y] 1692'. A brief note, not in AW's hand, 'for Lycencing this Book . . . '. Tpᵛ, AW wrote, 'James Frazer a Presbyterian Scot, made one of the licensers of the press at London upon the comming in of the Prince of Aurange (in the place of Sʳ Roger Lestrange) was bound over to appeare at the sessions in the Old Baylee, for licensing this pestilent pamphlet, & afterwards deprived of his place.' (Frazer had licensed AO); p. 37, 'Dr. Anth. Walker was buried at (Fyfield) [brackets in red chalk] in Essex 18. Apr. 1692 - Josiah Woodward min[iste]r of Poplar [co. of London] preached his fun[eral] serm.' For more on Frazer, see LT 3.398.
Wood 363(6). Wing W310 ('O' not recorded in Wing). FFMadan 167.

6390. Walker, Cle[ment]. *An answer to col: Nathaniel Fiennes relation concerning . . . Bristol.* [London]: n.pub., 1643. 4°. Pp. [3], 13.
Tp, AW altered the former no. and wrote 'By Clem. Walker', also underscored in red ink.
Wood 376(28). Wing W320.

6391. [Walker, Clement]. *The mysterie of the two junto's, Presbyterian and Independent. Or, the serpent in the bosome, . . . By Theodorus Verax.* [London]: n.pub., 1647. 4°. Pp. [2], 20.
Wood 617(17). Wing W332.

6392. [Walker, Clement]. *The history of Independency, with the rise, growth, and practices of that . . . faction.* [London]: n.pub., 1648. 4°. Pp. [8], 72 (misnumbering).
Tp, initials 'L. G.', twice, and below, c (reversed) and c. Pp. 23-4, 17 (misnumbering), 2nd p. 24, marks in pencil, not in AW's usual style (though AW went through this book, see note at El., M., Wood 620(8), item 2412, and AO 3.294 and 4.7-8).
Wood 617(18). Wing W329A.

6393. [Walker, Clement]. *The triall, of lieut. collonell John Lilburne, . . . the 24, 25, 26. of Octob. 1649.* [London]: Publ. by Theodorus Varax. Printed by H. Hils in Southwark, [1649]. 4°. Pp. [4], 168.
Wood 368(11). Wing W338.

6394. [Walker, Clement]. *The high court of justice. Or Cromwells new slaughter house in England. Being the III. part of the history of Independency.* [London?]: n.pub., 1651 ('Printed Anno Dom. 1651'). 4°. Pp. 71.
Wood 619(4). Wing W326 (Wing, Anno Domini 1651).

6395. Walker, Clement, and William Prynne. *Articles of impeachment and accusation, exhibited in parliament, against colonell Nathaniel Fiennes.* London: n.pub., 1643. 4°. Pp. 16.
Tp, AW lined out a former no., '47' and underscored 3 names in t. AW owned several pamphlets concerning the surrender of Bristol by Fiennes and he recorded several of them in his 1681 ms. cat., MS. Wood E.

2(70), p. 37. He also referred to them in his [MS.] Wood D. 22(7) (item 1602), *An exact catalogue of all printed books . . . by William Prynne* (1660), p. 4, at the entry, *Doome of cowardize*, where he wrote 'cat. 3. 37.', i.e., MS. Wood E. 2(70), p. 37.
Wood 376(51) (not in Bodl. CD cat.). Wing A3856.

6396. [**Walker, Edward**]. *Iter Carolinum, being a succinct relation of the . . . marches, retreats.* London: W. Godbid, 1660. 4°. Pp. [4], 32.
Tp, 'R S' (Ralph Sheldon), LT 3.105. Pp. 11, 14-8, to 31, some notes, identifications, corrections, and marks in margins, most by AW. E.g., pp. 11, at printed 'Liskerd Mr. Jeane', 'Jos. Jane perhaps father to Dr Will. Jane of Oxōn the kings prof. of Div. for he was borne at Liscard.'; 14, at the king's retreat from Lestichiel [i.e. Lestwithiel, modern Lostwithiel], 'see p. 12 - Those men mention'd there, which were taken by the Kings forces & by the King pardoned, fought here in this battell more manfull than any parliamentiers. Base ingratitude!'.
Wood 364(17). Wing W339.

6397. Walker, George. *A true copie of the disputation held betweene master Walker and a Jesuite . . . concerning the ecclesiasticall function.* [London]: n.pub, 1641. 4°. A⁴.
Wood 647(6). Wing W391.

6398. [**Walker, Henry**]. *Taylors physicke has purged the divel. Or, the divell has got a squirt, and . . . Taylor . . . is now soundly cudgelled . . . By Voluntas Ambulatoria.* [London]: n.pub., 1641. 4°. A⁴,B².
See note at Wood 614(39), item 6148
Wood 614(38). Wing W388.

6399. Walker, Henry. *A collection of several passages concerning his late highnesse Oliver Cromwell, in the time of his sickness, . . . Written by one that was then groom of his bed-chamber.* London: R. Ibbitson, 1659. 4°. Pp. [2], 22.
Missing since 1994.
Wood 531(22). Wing W370 (Wing, has late).

6400. [**Walker, Obadiah**]. ΠΕΡΙΑΜΜΑ ΕΠΙΔΗΜΙΟΝ, *or vulgar errours in practice censured.* London: f. R. Royston, 1659. 8°. Pp. [14], 112.
Wood 68(2). Wing W408 (Wing, 'errour').

6401. [**Walker, Obadiah**]. *Some instructions concerning the art of oratory.* London: J. G. f. R. Royston, 1659. 8°. Pp. [6], 128. Calf with 3 fillets and stamp decoration (dragon) in corners (Ashm. binding).
Flyleaf, upper, 3rdᵛ, list of 5 printed works in this vol. (including sections of one work), by an Ashm. librarian.
Wood 68(1). Wing W410.

6402. [**Walker, Obadiah**]. *The description of Greenland.* [Oxon]: [at the theater], [1680]. Fol. (unfolded) Sig. A1-2.
2 proof sheets with corrections, not by AW. AO 4.442-3 gives some bibliog. details of the published result, 'This is in the first vol. of the *English Atlas*, printed at Oxon in that year.' Madan does not include this proof sheet, though he refers to Walker's part in the preparation of Pitt's *English Atlas* (Madan 3253).
Wood 658(772-3). Wing P2306 (part of).

6403. Walker, Obadiah. *Of education. Especially of young gentlemen.* Oxford: at the theater f. A. Curteyne, 1687. 12°. 5th ed. Pp. [12], 309. Pasteboard (grey) with parchment spine. 1st upper and last lower flyleaves, marbled paper.
Flyleaf, upper, 3rdᵛ, AW wrote the titles of 5 printed works in this vol., within guidelines made with red ink.
Wood 754(1). Wing W403. See Madan 3161.

6404. W[**alkley**], **T**[**homas**], collected by. *A catalogue of the nobility of England, Scotland, and Ireland.* London: [E. Allde] f. T. Walkley, 1630. 4°. Pp. [2], 14, [28].
Tp, AW wrote after initials, 'Walkley', in red ink. Text, a few lines in margin and brief notes, pp. 2-3, 5, 7, and final leaf, F3ᵛ (where the 1st note, only, on Sir Ralph Clare of Worc., is in AW's hand).
Wood 445(2). STC 24974.

6405. [**Walkley, Thomas**]. *A new catalogue of the names of the knights . . . for this parliament . . . 3 of Novem. 1640.* London: f. T. Walkley, 1644. 8°. 5th ed. A⁸.
Flyleaf, upperᵛ, AW distinguished between 2 Joh. Brownes, 2 Rich. Brownes, and Sam. Browne, 'Joh.

Browne parl. man for Cliften in Devon. [/] Joh. Browne Parl. man for Dorsetsh. [/] Rich. Browne Parl. man for Rumney [?] in Kent [/] Rich. Browne Governour of Abendon, commonly called Maj. Gen. Browne, was a Recruiter in the Long Parl. for Wycomb in Bucks. in Octob. 1645 [/] In a pamphlet called The Great Champions of England – tis said that Sam Browne was a parl. man for a borough in Devonsh. [in dark ink, and added in pencil:] or coming [?] of it.' (the folded s.sh., T. Fairfax (1646), Wood 620(3), item 2904, where AW underscored the name of Samuel Browne). Text, passim, some underscoring, marks in margins and additions, in pencil, red ink, and dark ink. A8ᵛ, and 6 blank leaves, inserted, with details from, apparently, the heading AW wrote on A8ᵛ, 'Parl. vol. 3. nu. 3'. 1st leaf begins, 'The names of such persons, who were elected as Recruiters in the Long parliament, in the places of such that left it & retired to the K[ing] at Oxon & sate there, or that died, between the yeare 1642 & 1646.'; 11 pp. of counties and names of representatives, in ms., follow.
Wood 358(6). Wing W463 ('O' not recorded in Wing).

6406. Walkley, Tho[mas], collected by. *A new catalogue of the dukes, marquesses, earls, viscounts, barons, of England . . . Collected by T. W.* London: f. T. Walkley, 1658. 8°. Pp. [6], 175.
Tp, AW wrote after initials, 'Tho. Walkley', in red ink. Text, a few lines in margins, underscorings, corrections, and brief notes, e.g., pp. 102, 106, 110, 112-4, 119, 120, 122, 126, 152-3, 155, 158-9, 162-8, 171, 174-5; and flyleaf, lower, 1st, 'Knights made by Richard [Cromwell] Protect– [/] 1658 - Oct 26 – Morgan General a very gallant person [/] 1658 Dec. 7 Capt. . . Beke'.
Wood 444(2). Wing W465.

6407. Waller, Edmund. *Upon the late storm, and of the death of his highnesse [O. Cromwell] ensuing the same.* London: f. H. H.?, [1658]. S.sh.
Missing since 1994.
Wood 531(25). Wing W532/3.

6408. [Waller, Edmund]. *To my Lady Morton on New-years-day, 1650. At the Louver [sic] in Paris.* London: f. H. Herringman, 1661. S.sh.
'By Edm: Waller Esq.', in Aubrey's hand, and, in a later hand, 'Aubray's note', in pencil.
Wood 416(9). Wing W527 (two).

6409. W[aller], E[dmund]. *To the queen, upon her majesties birth-day. By E. W.* [London]: H. Herringman, [1663]. S.sh.
After initials of author, 'Mʳ Waller', not in AW's hand, and, by AW, 'Edm. Waller' (sprinkled with some gold flakes).
Wood 276a(528). Wing W530A.

6410. Waller, Hardresse. *The declaration of sir Hardresse Waller . . . 28. of December.* London: J. Macock, 1659[60]. S.sh. Rpt. of Dublin: W. Bladen edition.
Wood 276a(229). Wing W536. Steele 2P 607.

6411. W[aller], H[ardresse]*. *The manner of the arraignment of those twenty eight persons [H. W. et al.].* London: f. J. S. a. E. Thomas, 1660. 4°. Pp. 8.
Wood 369(2). Wing M462 ('O' not recorded in Wing).

6412. Waller, William*. *A great over-throw: given to sir Ralph Hopton's whole army by sir William Waller neere Farnham.* London: f. J. Hammon, 1643. 4°. Pp. 8.
Tp, AW lined out the former no., '48'; below, 'Nov. 28'.
Wood 376(52). Wing G1741 (two) ('O' not recorded in Wing).

6413. Waller, William*. *The souldiers report concerning sir William wallers [sic] fight against Basing-house on Sunday last November the 12.* [London]: J. Hammond, 1643. 4°. A⁴.
Tp, AW lined our the former no., '46'.
Wood 376(50). Wing S4431 (3).

6414. Waller, William*. *A true relation of the late fight betweene sʳ William Wallers forces, and those sent from Oxford.* London: G. Dexter, f. R. Dunscum, 1643. 4°. Pp. [2], 5.
Tp, AW lined out the former no., '17'.
Wood 376(19). Wing T2981.

6415. Waller, William*. *A famous victorie obtained against the cavaliers in the county of Gloucester: by sir William Waller on Munday last.* London: f. R. Wood, 1643, 25 Feb. 4°. Pp. [2], 6.
Tp, AW wrote, twice, '1642'.

Wood 375(37). Wing F387.

6416. Waller, William. *A letter . . . from . . . to . . . Robert earl of Essex . . . of a . . . victory . . . obtained at Malmsbury [23 March]*. London: E. Husbands, 1643, 28 Mar. 4°. Pp. 8.
Missing in 1918, according to a librarian's note; for more, see Wood 375(1), item 1720.
Wood 375(47). Wing W542. *Folg.*

6417. Waller, William*. *A true relation of the great and glorious victory through Gods providence, obtained by sir William Waller, sir Arthur Haslerig.* [London]: f. E. Husbands, 1643, 14 July. 4°. Pp. 8.
Tp, AW lined out the former no., '18'.
Wood 376(20). Wing T2958A.

6418. Waller, William*. *A narration of the great victory, (through Gods providence) obtained by the parliaments forces under sir William Waller.* [London]: E. Husbands, [1643], 16 Dec. 4°. Pp. 8.
Tp, AW lined out former no., '49'.
Wood 376(53). Wing N159.

6419. Waller, William*. *A true discovery of the great and glorious victory of . . . William Waller.* London: F. Leach f. M. Walbancke, 1644. 4°. Pp. [2], 6.
Wood 377(4). Wing T2682.

6420. Waller, William*. *A full relation of the late proceedings, victory, and good success (through Gods providence) obtained by the parliaments forces under sir William Waller.* [London]: J. Field, 1644, 8 Jan. 4°. A⁴.
Tp, AW altered a former no. and entered the year, '1643'. A3, a line in the margin.
Wood 376(56). Wing F2364.

6421. Waller, William*. *A glorious victorie, obtained by sir William Waller, . . . neare Alsford.* [London]: f. T. Bates, 1644, 1 April. 4°. Pp. [1], 8.
Wood 377(3). Wing G871 ('O' not recorded in Wing).

6422. Waller, William* (died in 1699). *Dagon's fall: or the knight [William Waller] turn'd out of commission.* [London]: n.pub., [1680]. S.sh. (r-v).
Above, AW wrote 'Duke of Monmouth q[uaere]', in pencil, and at title, 'Sʳ Will. Waller in Ap. 1680'. LT 2.484.
Wood 417(21a). Wing D111.

6423. Wallis, John. *Grammatica linguae Anglicanae.* Oxoniae: L. Lichfield. Veneunt ap. T. Robinson, 1653. 8°. Pp. [24], 128. Calf with 3 fillets and stamp decoration (dragon) in corners (Ashm. binding).
Flyleaf, upper, 1st, 'Anthony a Wood', not in AW's hand. Also note, 'L'Amour & la Mort . . . ' not in AW's hand; 2ndᵛ, list of 6 printed works in this vol., by an Ashm. librarian. Tp, bsm. Acquired 15 Sept. 1662, 6ᵈ, LT 1.454.
Wood 42(1). Wing W584. Madan 2238.

6424. [Wallis, John]. *Reasons shewing the consistency of the place of custos archivorum with that of a Savilian professor.* [Oxford]: n.pub., [1658]. S.sh.
AW wrote, '1657. Febr:'; and at another time, 'published by Dʳ Joh. Wallis–', in red ink. LT 1.232. Response, Stubbe, Wood 515(21), item 6070.
Wood 515(20). Wing W601 (two). Madan 2325.

6425. Wallis, John. *Serenissimo regi Carolo, regni anno decimo quarto, cum celsissima principe Katharina, nuptias consummanti [from Domiduca Oxoniensis].* [Oxford]: n.pub., [1662]. S.sh.
'1662', in a later hand.
Wood 416(96). Wing W603A (rare). Madan 2578.

6426. Wallis, John. *A defence of the Royal Society, and the Philosophical transactions, particularly those of July, 1670. In answer to the cavils of dr. William Holder.* London: T. S. f. T. Moore, 1678. 4°. Pp. 33, [1].
LT 1.309-10.
Wood 534(2). Wing W573.

6427. Wallis, Ralph. *Room for the cobler of Gloucester . . . with several cartloads of . . . priests.* [London]: f. the author, 1668. 4°. Pp. 40.
Tp, AW wrote, 'written by a cabal of phanaticks & non-conformists.' Some identifications, underscoring,

and lines in margins, e.g., pp. 7 (correction), 9 (correction), 13 (identification of the Bishop of Worcester: 'Dr Skinner', and of Mr. Moore: 'Tho. de la More a madman'), 18, 20-2, 27, 30, 34, 36 (identification of the Vice-chancellor in the printed phrase, 'as very a Dunce as the Vice-Chancellor', as 'Dr Fell'), 38-9, in ink and pencil.
Wood 350(2). Wing W619.

6428. Wallis, Ralph. *The life and death of Ralph Wallis the cobler of Glocester: . . . with some inquiring into . . . conventicleism.* London: E. Okes, f. W. Whitwood, 1670. 4°. Pp. [4], 43.
Tp, AW wrote, '6^d. March 69/70'.
Wood 350(3). Wing L2008.

6429. Walper, Otto. *Grammatica Graeca, ex optimis quibusque autoribus, in usum academiae Marpurgensis, ceterarumque scholarum Hassiacarum.* Marpurgi: typ. P. Egenolphi, 1590. 8°. Pp. [8], 471, [1]. Calf, speckled, 18th century.
Tp, 'ABosco', and, not in AW's hand, 'Ad spes hortamur' and initials, 'P. K.' Bequeathed to Jesus College in 1712 by Jonathan Edwards, Principal.
Jesus College N. 1. 4. Bodl, VD.

6430. W[alsingham], E[dward]. *Brittanicae virtutis imago. Or, the effigies of true fortitude, expressed to the life, . . . of . . . major generall [John] Smith.* Oxford: H. Hall, 1644. 4°. Pp. [4], 28.
P. [3], after initials, AW wrote in his early hand, 'Edw. Walsyngham Secretary to S^r Jo. Smyth.', and later added 'q[uaere]'; 12, at 'Mr. Dugdale', mark in margin; 14, identification, 'Henry Parker was then secretary to Essexs Army'; 15, line in margin at a heroic military deed of Smith's.
Wood 535(9). Wing W649. Madan 1660.

6431. [Walsingham, Edward]. *Alter Britanniae heros: or the life of . . . sir Henry Gage . . . epitomiz'd.* Oxford: L. Lichfield, 1645. 4°. Pp. [2], 29.
Tp, AW wrote in his early hand 'Edw. Walsingham the author. qu[aere] p. 24.' (at p. 24 there is a poem signed by him); and, at a later time, 'written by Hen. Walsingham a Rom. Cath. & under-secretary to the Lord Georg Digby princ. secr. of State – so D^r Th. Barlow, but his name was Edw.' P. 21, at March, correction to 'Jan.' LT 1.113.
Wood 535(10). Wing W648. Madan 1814.

6432. Walther, Rudolph (elder). Οικετης, *sive servus ecclesiasticus: id est de officio ministrorum ecclesiae oratio.* Tiguri: ap. C. Froschoverum, [1548]. 4°. Ff. 10.
Ff. 1^v, several initials, 'G. S.'; 3, note, prob. not by AW. LT 1.459 (and 1.331).
Wood 477(6). BL.

6433. Walther, Rudolph* (elder and younger). *In d. Joannis Parkhursti episcopi Nordovicensis . . . obitum, epicedia Rodolphi Gualtheri . . . patris et filii.* [Zürich]: [n.pub.], [1576]. A-C^4 (C4 blank) (tp, mutilated).
See note at item 5134. Flyleaf, lower^{r-v}, 9 poems, in Latin, by G[eorge] S[adleir].
Wood 460(3). BL.

6434. Walton, Brian*. St. Martin Orgar, minister of. *The articles and charge proved in parliament against doctor Walton, . . . Wherein his subtile tricks, and popish innovations are discovered.* London: n.pub., 1641. 4°. Pp. [2], 14.
Tp, former no., '36'.
[MS.] Wood D. 31(37). Wing A3809.

6435. Walton, Izaak. *The compleat angler or the contemplative man's recreation . . . To which is added the laws of angling.* London: J. G. f. R. Marriot, 1661. 8°. 3rd ed. Pp. [16], 255, [17] (t leaf is mutilated; t from cat.). Pasteboard (blue) with parchment spine. Remnants of 1st upper and last lower flyleaves, marbled paper.
Flyleaf, upper, 2nd^v, AW wrote the titles of 3 printed works in this vol., within guidelines made with red ink. Some additions in a later hand. Tp, AW wrote '2^s in q[uarto]. 2. edit. 1655' (i.e., Wing W662, 12°). Lent to [Roger] Brent, 25 Nov. 1663, LT 1.507.
Wood 728(1). Wing W663.

6436. Walton, Izaak. *The life of Mr. Richard Hooker.* London: J. G., f. Rich. Marriott, 1665. 8°. Pp. 208.
Missing. Lent to P. Nicolls, 'Hooker's Life', 1665, LT 2.27. Acquired 9 Feb. 1665, 1^{s}4^d, LT 2.29. See also Wood 229(2), item 6437, and LT 2.197.

LT 2.29. Wing W670. *Hunt.*

6437. Walton, Izaak. *The lives of dr. John Donne, sir Henry Wotton, mr. Richard Hooker, mr. George Herbert.* London: T. Newcomb f. R. Marriott, 1670. 8°. Pp. [13], 88, [1], 79, 140, 104 (4 tpp).
See note at Nepos, Wood 229(1), item 4624, and LT 2.197. A1ᵛ, Walton wrote, 'ffor Mʳ Wode [crossed out and:] Wood. Iz: Wa:'. A number of lines in margins, corrections, and comments, passim, mainly in ink, and especially in the life of Hooker. Much annotation was cropped (fore-edges may have been cut when rebacked). Most notes and marks by AW, but some corrections were not. A4ᵛ (prob. by AW), pp. 2-3, 7, 17; in life of Wotton, pp. 17, 20, 29, 35, 38 ('Album is not so calld because the paper is white.'), 39; in life of Hooker, pp. 21 (Hooker 'Admitted M.A. 29 March an[no] 1577'), 23 (at Cambden's Testimonies, 'where, or in what booke.'), 26 (at Hebrew lecture, '[?]o by letters from AW of Oxon.'), 55-6, 92-3, 116 (on Hooker's last three volumes, destroyed by Mr. Charke, AW noted that Charke was 'A puritan', 'Tis strange that Seravia [Saravia, Hadrian] could not secure them'), 118; in the life of Herbert, pp. 14, 32-3 (corrections not by AW). See LT 2.429, for AW's note on Walton's life of bishop Sanderson.
Wood 229(2). Wing W671.

6438. Wandering Whore. *The fifth and last part of the wandring whore: a dialogue between Magdalena a crafty bawd, . . . With an additional list of . . . the crafty bawds, common whores.* N.p.: n.pub., 1661. 4°. Pp. 16.
Tp, AW wrote, 'I could never see any other parts but this –'.
Wood 654a(21). Wing F888. ESTCR 21972.

6439. Waram Bank. Manuscript. *The description and cituation of Waram Banck wᵗʰ the rivers, bridges.* N.p.: n.pub., n.d. S.sh. 440 x 577 mm (untrimmed; mutilated).
Prob. not in AW's hand.
Wood 276b(16)

6440. Ward, John*, and Danseker*. *Ward and Danseker, two notorious pyrates.* London: [E. Allde] f. N. Butter, 1609. 4°. A-D⁴. See also items 817f.
Wood 371(10). STC 25022.5 (two).

6441. [Ward, Nathaniel]. Guard, Theodore de la, pseud. *The simple cobler of Aggawam in America.* London: J. D[ever] a. R. I[bbetson] f. S. Bowtell, 1647. 4°. Pp. [4], 80. Pasteboard (grey) with parchment spine; traces of upper and lower marbled flyleaves.
Flyleaf, upper, 2ndᵛ, list of 3 printed works in this vol., written within guidelines made with red ink. Tp, '10', at bottom of page (prob. a former no. in a bundle).
Wood 350(1). Wing W787.

6442. Ward, Patience, and Robert Clayton. *The speech of . . . lord mayor elect, Sept. 29, . . . Together with the speech of . . . sir Robert Clayton.* (London): (f. T. Collins a. B. Aylmer), (1680). Fol. Pp. 4.
Wood 276a(152). Wing W794.

6443. Ward, S. *The animadversions and remarks upon collonel Sydney's paper answered.* (London): (f. the author S. Ward), (1684). S.sh. (r-v).
At the t, 'animadversions', AW wrote, 'qu[aere] where are those'.
Wood 428(22b). Wing W808A.

6444. [Ward, Seth]. Salisbury, bp. of. *Vindiciae academiarum containing, some briefe animadversions upon mʳ Websters book, stiled, the examination of academies. Together with an appendix concerning what m. Hobbes, and m. Dell have published on this argument. [Signed H. D. With a prefatory epistle by J. Wilkins].* Oxford: L. Lichfield f. T. Robinson, 1654. 4°. Pp. [2], 65.
Tp, AW wrote, 'By Seth Ward D.D & Astronomy professor in Oxōn:'. P. 7, at 'Mr Warners', AW wrote, 'The Mathematician' and under 'N. S.', 'JohN WalliS' and later, in a different ink, 'rather JohN WilkinS'. Short vertical lines in margin: pp. 15, at printed 'John Dee'; 19, at 'Herrigon', and 'Herrit or Heriot v p. 20'; 20, at Harriot; 29, at discussion of 'Musick'; 38, at 'Essex-Lyon'; and 62, at Dell. Pp. 50 and 65, at printed 'H. D.', 'SetH WarD'. LT 1.294-5; AO 4.249f.
[MS.] Wood B. 24(7). Wing W832. Madan 2251.

6445. Ware, James. *Archiepiscoporum Casseliensium & Tuamensium vitae. . . . Quibus adjicitur historia coenobiorum Cisterciensium Hiberniae.* Dublinii: ex off. Soc. Bibliop., 1626. 4°. Pp. [6], 81.
Pp. 5-6, brief note and mark prob. by an earlier owner, cropped.
Wood 343(2). STC 25064.

6446. Ware, James. *De praesulibus Lageniae, sive provinciae Dubliniensis.* Dublinii: ex off. Soc. Bibliop., 1628. 4°. Pp. [6], 104, [2]. Pasteboard (grey) with parchment spine. 1st and last flyleaves, marbled paper. Flyleaf, upper, 3rd^v, AW wrote the titles of 3 printed works in this vol., within guidelines made with red ink. Some glosses in pencil, not by AW. Tp, 'AWoode Sept 1 MDCLX: 1^s-2^d'. LT 2.94.
Wood 343(1). STC 25065.

6447. Ware, James. *De scriptoribus Hiberniae.* Dublinii: ex typog. Soc. Bibliop., 1639. 4°. Pp. [6], 143.
Tp, AW wrote, 'Anthony Woode: Merton Coll: Oxōn:' (his early hand). Bsm. Pp. 66, 84, 86, 121, 129, etc., notes prob. by AW (early hand). Pp. 6-7, 9, 13, 21, 44-7, 50-1, 61, 69, 72-3, 87, and 133, etc. marks or notes, prob. not by AW. Dupl. at Wood 343(3).
[MS.] Wood C. 26(14). STC 25066.

6448. Ware, James. *De scriptoribus Hiberniae.* Dublinii: ex typog. Soc. Bibliop., 1639. 4°. Pp. [6], 143.
Tp, bsm., and a number, cropped. Pp. 77-82, 135-8, at names of some authors, vertical lines in margins, a 'q[uaere]' letter, and one underscoring (p. 81, Thomas Browne), in ink and pencil. Dupl. at [MS.] Wood C. 26(14).
Wood 343(3). STC 25066.

6449. Ware, James. *De Hibernia & antiquitatibus ejus, disquisitiones. . . . Accesserunt rerum Hiberni- carum regnante Henrico VII, annales.* Londini: typ. E. Tyler, imp. J. Crook, 1658. 8°. 2nd ed. Pp. [15], 356, [3], 99 (2nd tp at 2A3). Calf with 3 fillets and stamp (dragon) decoration in corners; rebacked (Ashm. binding).
Acquired 10 Feb. 1664, LT 2.5.
Wood 206(1). Wing W844.

6450. Ware, James. *Rerum Hibernicarum annales, regnantibus Henrico VII. . . . Maria.* Dublinii: J. Crook, 1664. Fol. Pp. [6], 227.
Tp, bsm.
Wood 415(2). Wing W847aA.

6451. Ware, James. *De praesulibus Hiberniae, commentarius.* Dublinii: typis J. Crook, vaeneunt Londini & Dublinii ap. S. Dancer, 1665. Fol. Pp. [12], 283. Calf, with 3 fillets; 2nd rectangle with 3 fillets and stamp decoration on inside of fillets and floral decoration at 4 corners; rebacked (Ashm. binding).
Pasteboard, upper, note by a later librarian 'Vide et 343' (i.e., Wood 343, for more on Ireland by same author). Flyleaf (waste paper), upper, 1st, AW wrote '28. March 1668. for binding this book in pastborde 1^s. to M^r [Edmund] Thorne' (in his diary, AW referred to this as 'de Episcopis', LT 2.130; this vol. was rebound by the Ashm.), and 'AWoode'. 3rd-5th, 'Irish Bishops that I guess to have been Oxon men from 1501. to this present, which hereafter may be inserted in Athenae Oxōn, when I find good proofe for them', followed by dioceses, names of bishops, death dates and p. references of those who had Oxford connections, e.g. 'Ep. Armachani { Georg Cromer ob. 1542. – p. 23, 25 [/] Georg Doudall ob. 1558 – p. 23 [i.e., 25] . . . [/] Thom. Lancaster ob. 1584 – p. 27 [/] Joh. Garvey ob. 1594. – p. 28, 82' etc. to 'Alladenses { Eugene O'Conner – 1605-6' [p. 272], almost 100 entries in all. The 4th has 10 more entries plus a slip, pasted in, with the same names written on both sides, but with appointment dates. The 6th^v has an index of bishoprics, with slip, pasted in, 'The names in English of these Bishopricks see in my English Camden in Ireland. p. 74' (AW received a Camden, *Britain*, in English from Sheldon in July 1675, LT 2.319, but it is no longer in the Wood collection; see item 1370). Tp, '7' (bsm?). Text, mainly in dark ink, but also red ink and pencil, frequent underscoring, cross references, and notes. The notes are mainly biographical details, e.g., college membership and quotations from epitaphs, some cropped by a binder, and slips, some loose and some attached, on which AW recorded details from monuments and biographical or bibliographical information. Slips are after pp. 24, 38, 50 (2), 58 (2), 70, 72, 82 (2), 92, 94, 116, 119, 128, 130, 148, 150 (e.g., 'James Ware in his book de pr[a]esul. Lageniae [Wood 343(1)], which is but the first edition of this – saith that Jonas Wheeler was borne in Devon. – In this Edit. Oxoniensis – I have searchd matric. books for his name, & I can not find his name – nor any degree he took', AO 2.890-1), 170, 172, 198, 260, 272. AW went through this book carefully. A copy acquired from Davis, 16 Mar. 1666, 5^s, LT 2.73. Turned back for a replacement to Davis, 11 Apr. 1666, LT 2.76.
Wood 415(1). Wing W845A.

6452. Ware, Robert, ed. *Historical collections of the church in Ireland, during the reigns of k. Henry, VIII. Edward, VI. and q. Mary:. . . set forth in the life and death of George Browne.* London: sold R. Tayler, 1681. 4°. Pp. [2], 18.
Tp, AW wrote in margin, at names in t, 'Dr Cole' and 'G. Browne Archb.'
Wood 510(34). Wing W848.

6453. [Waring, Robert]. *A publike conference betwixt the six Presbyterian ministers, and some Indepen-dent commanders: held at Oxford [12 Nov.].* [London]: n.pub., 1646. 4°. Pp. [2], 14.
AO 3.453. Dupl. at Wood 514(22).
Wood 617(16). Wing W868. Madan 1906.

6454. [Waring, Robert]. *A publike conference betwixt the six Presbyterian ministers, and some Indepen-dent commanders: held at Oxford [12 Nov.].* [London]: n.pub., 1646 ('Printed in the Yeare, 1646'). 4°. Pp. [2], 14.
Tp, AW wrote the name of the author, 'Rob. Waryng', in red ink. AO 3.453. Dupl. at Wood 617(16).
Wood 514(22). Wing W868. Madan 1906.

6455. [Waring, Robert]. *An account of m^r Pryn's refutation of the university of Oxfords plea. . . . in a second letter from Oxford [signed Basilius Philomusus, 20 Jan.].* [London]: [f. R. Royston], 1648. 4°. Pp. [2], 12.
Tp, AW wrote 'Rob. Waring', and beneath a slip pasted over, 'written by the same author of the privileges of the Univers. of Oxon in point of visitation' followed by, in red ink, 'qu[aere]' (also lined out). AW initially accepted Waring's statement (p. 1) that he was the author of Fell's (et al.) *Privileges*, Wood 514(33), item 2968). Pp. 2, 10-1 line in margin. Dupl. at Wood 609(10).
Wood 514(35). Wing W859 (Wing, [Oxford]). Madan 1961.

6456. [Waring, Robert]. *An account of m^r Pryn's refutation of the university of Oxfords plea. . . . in a second letter from Oxford [signed Basilius Philomusus, 20 Jan.].* [London]: [f. R. Royston], 1648. 4°. Pp. [2], 12.
Dupl. at Wood 514(35).
Wood 609(10). Wing W859 (Wing, [Oxford]). Madan 1961.

6457. [Waring, Robert]. *Amoris effigies. Sive quid sit amor efflagitanti responsum.* Londini: excud. R. Daniel, [1657]. 12°. Pp. 138, [5]. Calf with 3 fillets, stamp decoration inside corners (dragons), and roll decoration on spine (Ashm. binding).
Flyleaf, upper, 2nd, the titles of 4 printed works in this vol., written by an Ashm. librarian.
Wood 733(1). Wing W860.

6458. Waring, Tho[mas]. *An answer to certain seditious and Jesuitical queres, heretofore purposely and maliciously cast out, to retard and hinder the English forces.* London: W. Du-GARD, 1651. 4°. Pp. [8], 56 (wanting the final sheet I^4).
Pp. [5], 'Henry' before Ireton, may be by AW; 11, correction; 29, 31-2, line(s) in margin.
Wood 510(18). Wing W872 (Wing, Du-gard).

6459. Warmestry, Thomas. *A convocation speech, by Thomas Warmstry, . . . against images, altars . . . &c.* London: [f. W. Cooke], 1641. 4°. Pp. [2], 22.
Wood 494(2). Wing W882.

6460. W[armstrey] T[homas]. *The oaths of supremacy & allegiance, . . . now taken by both houses of parliament.* London: f. W. Sheares, 1660. 4°. Pp. [6], 18.
Tp, AW wrote, 'July: 21: 1660:'.
Wood 608(22). Wing W124 (Wing, at W., T.).

6461. [Warner, John]. Rochester, bp. of. *The devilish conspiracy, hellish treason, . . . and damnable murder, committed, and executed by the Jewes.* London: n.pub., 1648[9]. 4°. Pp. [2], 45.
Tp, 'Prius de Christo, deinceps de Carolo', may be in AW's hand. P. 25, vertical line in margin, in pencil.
Wood 364(33). Wing W902.

6462. [Warner, John], Jesuit. *A vindication of the Inglish [sic] Catholiks from the pretended conspiracy against the life . . . of his sacred maiesty.* Antwerp: permissu superiorum, 1680. 4°. Pp. [2], 59 (unopened after p. 40).
Tp, AW wrote, 'see p. 38, where the author sayes he does s[c]arce reckon the Bishop of Linc. [T. Barlow] for a protestant Bishop.', and, 'This came out in Jul. or Aug. 1680'. AW wrote about this item at [MS.] Wood E. 27(2), item 1599 (see Plate VIII): '4to about 7. sheets of paper – Though said to be printed at Antwerp, yet the paper & letter shewes it to be printed at Lond – either in Jul. or Aug.'
Wood 426(11). Wing W912A.

6463. Warner, John*. *An account of a vindication [by J. Warner, Jesuit] of the English Catholicks from the pretended conspiracy.* London: f. J. Vade, 1681. 4°. Pp. 36.

Tp, AW wrote the price, '6^{d}', and 'came out in Octob. 1680'. Answer to Wood 426(11), item 6462. Dupl. at Wood 608(62).
Wood 426(12). Wing A194.

6464. Warner, John*. *An account of a vindication [by J. Warner, Jesuit] of the English Catholicks from the pretended conspiracy.* London: f. J. Vade, 1681. 4°. Pp. 36.
AW wrote 'Dupl', in pencil. Dupl. at Wood 426(12).
Wood 608(62). Wing A194.

6465. Warning for All. *A warning for all the counties of England to awake speedily . . . and apply themselves to all just meanes, for the recoverie . . . of their liberties.* [London]: n.pub., [1646]. 4°. Pp. 19, [1].
Wood 612(70). Wing W917 (one) ('O' not recorded in Wing).

6466. Warning Piece. *A warning piece to all his majesties subjects of England. Containing the motives by which some of them have been drawn into the rebellion.* London: f. C. King, 1660. 4°. Pp. 7.
Tp, AW altered the year to 16'59 March'.
Wood 610(12) (Bodl. CD cat. has diff. t). Wing W934.

6467. Warr, John. *The corruption and deficiency of the lawes of England soberly discovered.* London: f. G. Calvert, 1649. 4°. Pp. [2], 18.
Pp. 1-4, 6, 10-1, 12, 14, 16, marks in margin in pencil, mainly 'x' marks, prob. none by AW.
Wood 630(4). Wing W945.

6468. W[arre], J[ames]. *The merchants hand-maide: or, a booke containing . . . tables, for the speedie casting up, and true valuing of any commoditie.* London: W. Jones, 1622. 4°. Pp. [10], 28.
Tp, '3^{d}', not by AW.
[MS.] Wood C. 14(3). STC 24908.

6469. Warren, Albertus. *An apology for the discourse of humane reason, written by Ma. Clifford . . . With the author's epitaph.* London: f. W. Davis, 1680. 12°. Pp. [22], 144.
Tp, AW wrote '8^{d}'. Bsm. Wood 841(2-4) all respond to M. Clifford, Wood 841(1), item 1920.
Wood 841(4). Wing W950.

6470. Warren, William. *Strange, true, and lamentable newes from Exceter.* London: J. Hammond, 1643. 4°. A^{4}.
Tp, AW altered the former no.
Wood 376(35). Wing W981.

6471. Warwick, Petition. *Wee the knights, . . . of the county of Warwick.* London: f. R. L., 1660. S.sh.
AW altered the date to 16 '59: ffeb:'.
Wood 276a(211). Wing W1182.

6472. Warwick, Philip. *The case of sir Philip Warwick respondent, to the appeal of sir Oliver Boteler, bar^{t}. appellant.* N.p.: n.pub., [1694?]. S.sh.
Wood 276b(78). Wing C997A (rare).

6473. Wase, Christopher. *In mirabilem Caroli II. . . . . restitutionem carmen gratulatorium.* [London]: (impr. D. Maxwell, sumpt. C. Adams), (1660). Fol. Pp. [4].
Wood 416(81). Wing W1018.

6474. Wase, Christopher. *Considerations concerning free-schools, as settled in England.* Oxford: at the theatre. . . . And [sold] in London at S. Millers, 1678. 8°. Pp. [8], 112.
Flyleaf, upper^{v}, note by a later writer. Madan comments on Wase's cumbersome writing style; for Wood's view, AO 3.884.
Wood 131(3). Wing W1015. Madan 3198.

6475. Wase, Christoph[er]. *Stricturae Nonianae. Lucilius bis térve castigatus.* Oxonii: L. Lichfield, 1685. 4°. Pp. [6], 10.
Wood 483(23) (not in Bodl. CD cat.). Wing W1024.

6476. Waterhouse, Edward. *An humble apologie for learning and learned men.* London: T. M. for M.M.[,] G. Bedell, and T. Collins, 1653. 8°. Pp. [8], 263 (pp. 1-263 follow item (5) in this vol.).
Tp, bsm. Acquired 28 Nov. 1663, 1^{s}6^{d}, LT 1.503.

Wood 130(4). Wing W1048.

6477. Waterhouse, Edward. *A discourse and defence of arms and armory, shewing the nature and rises of arms and honour in England.* London: T. R., f. S. Mearne, 1660. 8°. Pp. [7], 232. Pasteboard (blue) with parchment spine.
Flyleaf, upper, 2nd, AW wrote 'E Libris Antonii à Wood E Coll Mert Artium Magistri.', and, later, 'Quarto Kalendas Julii Anno Do. 1675.' Tp, AW wrote the price, '1ˢ.6ᵈ.' Bsm.
Wood 447(1). Wing W1044.

6478. Waterhouse, Edward. *A short narrative of the late dreadful fire in London.* London: W. G. f. R. Thrale and J. Thrale, 1667. 8°. Pp. [2], 190. Calf with 3 fillets and stamp decorations (dragon) in corners (Ashm. binding).
P. 1, AW wrote, '2. Sept 1666. lasted to the 5. of the said mounth.' Acquired 11 Feb. 1667, 1ˢ2ᵈ, LT 2.98.
Wood 210(1). Wing W1050.

6479. [Watkins, Richard]. *Newes from the dead. Or a . . . narration of the . . . deliverance of Anne Greene, . . . executed at Oxford . . . afterwards revived [14 Dec. 1650].* Oxford: L. Lichfield [a. H. Hall] f. T. Robinson, 1651 ('. D. 1651'). 4°. 2nd impr. with additions. Pp. [1-2], 1-14, 5-22. A-D⁴,E² (E2 blank).
Tp, AW wrote, 'Anthony Woode Coll: Merton.' P. 1, 'This relation in prose was written by Mʳ Rich. Watkins somtimes student of Ch. ch. now Rector of Whichford in Warwick shire.' (AOF 2.103; LT 1.165-6, 169). Pp. 2-3, 13-14, brief notes or identifications. At pp. 21-2, D4ᵛ-E1, a printed 52-line poem by 'Ant. Wood, Schol. of Mert. Coll.', 1st 2 lines: 'I'le stretch my *Muse*, but that a verse [/] I'le *hang* upon thy *living hearse*.' The general view is that this poem is by AW's brother, Edward Wood of Merton; see LT 1.169-70, Hearne 6.237, and Madan 2160. Yet AW's name remained for three editions, and he owned copies of all three. In none of the three copies did AW make any annotation on the pp. which the poem appears. In the AO (3.397) AW gave credit to Edward Wood (died, 1655, aged 28) for his 4 sermons published in one vol., not for any poetry. Diff. ed. at Wood 484(10) and Wood 516(7).
Wood 515(12). Wing W1073 (two). Madan 2160 (tp, line 9, 'Physitians').

6480. [Watkins, Richard]. *Newes from the dead. Or a . . . narration of the . . . deliverance of Anne Greene, . . . executed at Oxford . . . afterwards revived [14 Dec. 1650].* Oxford: L. Lichfield [a. H. Hall] f. T. Robinson, 1651. 4°. 2nd impr. with additions. Pp. [1-2], 1-14, 5-22. A-D⁴,E² (E2 blank).
Tp, AW identified the author, but erred in the college (should be Ch. Ch.), 'Mʳ Watkins. C:C:C: Ox:'. Diff. ed. at Wood 515(12), q.v., and Wood 516(7).
Wood 516(7). Wing W1074. Madan 2161.

6481. [Watkins, Richard]. *Newes from the dead. Or a true . . . narration of the . . . deliverance of Anne Greene, . . . executed at Oxford . . . afterwards revived [14 Dec. 1650].* Oxford: L. Lichfield f. T. Robinson, 1651 ('. D. 1651'). 4°. 2nd impr., enlarged. Pp. [1-2], 1-14, 5-22. A-D⁴,E² (E2 blank).
Diff. ed. at Wood 515(12), q.v., and Wood 516(7).
Wood 484(10). Wing W1075 (two). Madan 2162.

6482. Watson, Lion. *A more exact relation of the late battell neer York.* London: M. Simmons f. H. Overton, 1644. 4°. Pp. 8.
Pp. 6, note, partially cropped, 'for Mʳ Robert Warner these deliver in [Warwick]', not in AW's hand.
Wood 377(18). Wing W1082.

6483. Watson, Ri[chard]. *Historicall collections of ecclesiastick affairs in Scotland.* London: G. D. f. J. Garfield, 1657. 8°. Pp. [14], 210, [2] (2 pp. books sold by Garfield).
Tp, bsm.
Wood 172(2). Wing W1091.

6484. Watson, Richard. *The panegyrike and the storme two poëtike libells by Ed. Waller . . . answered by more faythfull subjects.* [London]: n.pub., 1659. 4°. 2 pts. Pp. [6], 24, [26].
Tp, AW wrote, 'Ol Cromwell', in pencil.
Wood 383(2). Wing W1092.

6485. Watson, R[ichard]. *An answer to Elymas the sorcerer.* (London): (f. N. Woolfe), (1682). S.sh. (r-v).
Responds to T. Jones, Wood 427(47), item 3913.
Wood 427(50). Wing W1085.

6486. Watson, Rich[ard]. *A fuller answer to Elimas the sorcerer.* London: H. Brugis, f. N. Wolf, 1683.

Fol. Pp. [2], 29.
Responds to T. Jones, Wood 427(47), item 3913.
Wood 427(51) (50 in Bodl. CD cat.). Wing W1090 (Wing, f. N. Woolfe).

6487. Way. *The way to promotion. Or, the young man's guide to preferment.* London: f. H. Haley, 1682.
12°. Pp. [24], 144.
Tp, bsm.
Wood 754(4). Wing W1170.

6488. Webb, John. *A vindication of Stone-heng restored.* London: R. Davenport f. T. Bassett, 1665. Fol.
Pp. [7], 232.
Sig. 2X1, (p. 173), red ink line in margin. LT 1.461; 2.181, 258, and AO 4.753-4.
Wood 413(3). Wing W1203.

6489. Webster, Jo[hn]. *Academiarum examen, or the examination of academies.* London: f. G. Calvert,
1654. 4°. Pp. [16], 110.
LT 1.294.
[MS.] Wood B. 24(5). Wing W1209. Madan 2252.

6490. Webster, John. *The saints guide, or, Christ the rule, and ruler of saints.* London: f. G. Calvert,
1654. 4°. Pp. [10], 38.
[MS.] Wood B. 24(6). Wing W1213.

6491. Webster, William. *Websters tables.* London: M. Flesher f. N. Bourne, 1629. 8°. 2nd ed. A-G⁸ (G1
placed at end).
Bsm.
Wood 21(2). STC 25183.

6492. Weever, John. *Ancient funerall monuments within the united monarchie of Great Britaine.* London:
T. Harper, sold L. Sadler, 1631. 8°. Pp. [18], 871, [15]. Calf, with 3 fillets; 2nd rectangle with 3 fillets and
stamp decoration on inside of fillets and floral decoration at 4 corners; rebacked (Ashm. binding).
Flyleaf, upper, 1st, contents, in pencil, not in AW's hand; on a slip 14.6 cm. x 8 cm pasted to this flyleaf
AW wrote notes on both sides: ʳ, on Weever, 'Mʳ Charlet [/] Before Weevers monuments [/] Joh. Weever
borne in Lancashire 1577 of Queens Coll. – Camb. p. 500. 864. Travelled p. 568 144. 150 217 647 Especially
in Engl. & part of Scotland, epistl. p. 2 - p. 358. Rector of Le[o]snes p. 337. 778 - qu[aere] He dyed 1632.
aged about 56 burial at Clarkenwell – Stowe Survey p. 900 [for the epitaph on tomb] of low stature p. 528
[?]'; and ᵛ, random notes, lined out. Text, pp. 514-5, 521, 530, 660, a line in margin; 660, 672, corrections;
673, note, at Camden's monument in Westminster Abbey, 'Near to him lies buried Isaac Casaubon, who
died Kal. Jun. 1614 æt. 54', and at the verse to Camden, AW made some corrections; 734, he wrote a
reference to an ancient roll in the possession of Aug. Vincent, 'After his death that Rolle came to John
Vincent his son, & after Johns death to Ralph Sheldon of Beoly in com. Wygorn.' See LT 3.102 for other
references to the Vincents, their collection of mss., and the sale of these to Sheldon. AW went through
this book carefully. Bound, Dec. 1661, LT 1. 420 (but also a payment, belated, on 4 Jan. 1662 of 7ˢ, to E.
Forrest for this book, LT 1.427).
Wood 414(1). STC 25223.

6493. Welby, Henry*. Heywood, Thomas, attrib. to. *The phoenix of these late times: or the life of mr.
Henry Welby.* [London]: [N. Okes sold by R. Clotterbuck], [1637]. 4°. A-E⁴,F1-3 (t leaf mutilated; wanting
the imprint).
Tp, scribbles, 'London print by'. A3ᵛ, AW wrote, 'See the following copie, or the copie that should follow,
at the end' (the catchword, on A3ᵛ, 'Upon', is for A4, now at the end; titled 'Upon Mr. Henry Welby').
[MS.] Wood B. 35(3). STC 25226.5.

6494. W[eldon], A[nthony]. *The court and character of king James. . . . continued unto . . . these
unhappy times.* London: R. I, sold J. Collins, 1651. 8°. Pp. [6], 1-175, [2], 176-226, [6] (2nd tp at 2nd [2]).
Calf with 2 fillets.
Flyleaf, upper, note, 'Sir Ant. Weldon Knighted at Berwick, May 11. 1617', may not be by AW. 2ndᵛ, a
portrait of James 1 pasted, with 'Jacobus Primus' and 'Jacobus D. G. Ang. Fr. Scot & Hib Rex.', prob. by
AW. Pp. 206, 209, 217 line in margins, in pencil and ink.
Wood 271. Wing W1274.

6495. [Weldon, Anthony]. *A cat may look upon a king.* London: f. W. Roybould, 1652. 12°. [5], 105, [5]
(5 pp. books sold by Roybould).

Each 12° leaf is pasted on an 8° template. A1, 'Most of the bad things concerning the Kings are here published, but none that are good = Therfore a malitious peice. ABosco. 1681'. F6-F6ᵛ, in the Roybould list of books sold the name of author Dr. N. Homes is underlined at 3 different entries.
Wood 240(2). Wing W1271 ('O' not recorded in Wing).

6496. [**Weldon, Anthony**]. *A perfect description of the people and country of Scotland.* London: f. J. S., 1659. 12°. Pp. [2], 21.
Wood 582(2). Wing W1277AB.

6497. Weldon, Ralph, and Edmund Fortescue. *The articles of agreement, for the surrender of Charles Fort . . . agreed upon between . . . Ralph Weldon . . . and sir Edmund Fortescue.* London: E[lizabeth] P[urslowe], 1646, 4 June. 4°. Pp. [2], 6.
Wood 501(14). Wing A3834. Madan 1869.

6498. [**Wells, John**]. *Academy. By the kings priviledge [in English and French].* [London]: n.pub., [1675 ca.]. S.sh. (yellow paper).
Wood 276a(123). Wing W1294A (rare).

6499. [**Wellwood, James**]. *An answer to the late king James's declaration to all his pretended subjects in . . . England [8 May].* London: f. D. Newman, 1689. 4°. Pp. [4], 31, [1] (1 p. advertisement).
Wood 608(68). Wing W1298.

6500. [**Wellwood, James**], attrib. to. Defoe, Daniel, also attrib. to. *An answer to the late k. James's last declaration, dated at St. Germains, April 17.* London: f. R. Baldwin, 1693. 4°. Pp. [4], 40.
Wood 608(69). Wing D827C.

6501. Welsh Man. *The Welsh-mans inventory, her armory. Her poulty. Her cattle. Han infentory of the coods of William Morgan.* London: f. F. Coles, T. Vere, J. Wright, and J. Clarke, [1674-79?]. S.sh.
At written out date in text, AW wrote the same in numerals '1849' [sic] and scribbles; ᵛ, 'yong W–ot [Wilmot?] shewed me a copie dated 1685', in pencil. See Wing W1325aA (1641).
Wood 417(148) (in Bodl. CD cat., 1649). Not in Wing. Not in ESTCR.

6502. Welwood, William. *The sea-law of Scotland.* Edinburgh: R. Waldegrave, 1590. 8°. A1-4,B⁸,C⁶ (pp. [33]) (1st leaf blank).
Tp, signature of 'Daniel Dun – prec - vjᵈ.' LT 1.426.
[MS.] Wood C. 13(2). STC 25242.

6503. Welwood, William. *An abridgement of all the sea-lawes.* London: [T. Harper f.] assignes of J. Man a. B. Fisher, 1636. 8°. Pp. [14], 253. Parchment.
Tp, bsm, 'o'.
Wood 725. STC 25238.

6504. Welwood, William. *De dominio maris, juribusque ad dominium praecipuè spectantibus, assertio brevis ac methodica.* Hagae-Comitum: ex typog. A. Vlac, 1653. 4°. Pp. [4], 41 (pp. unopened).
[MS.] Wood C. 13(8). BL.

6505. Wentworth, Thomas*. Strafford, earl of. *Annotations upon the earle of Straffords conclusion [12 April].* [London]: n.pub., 1641. 4°. Pp. [2], 6. Pasteboard (grey) with parchment spine.
Flyleaf, upper, 1stᵛ, AW wrote, 'Here in this book p. 34. should be the cut of his execution' (there is no p. 34 in this item; this flyleaf formerly was attached to another 'book'). 3rdʳ⁻ᵛ, AW wrote the titles of 34 printed works in this vol., within guidelines made with red ink. Tp, 'The charge of the Scotch commissioners against the Earl of Strafford, see in this vol. num. 19' (i.e., Wood 366(19), item 5790). Pp. 2, 6, two similar references, e.g., 'See [B.] Whit[e]lock's Memorials p. 42.8.' (i.e., Wing W1986).
Wood 366(1). Wing A3245.

6506. Wentworth, Thomas*. Strafford, earl of. *A declaration shewing the necessity of the earle of Straffords suffering.* [London]: n.pub., 1641. 4°. A-B⁴ (A1, B4, blank).
Wood 366(7). Wing D795.

6507. Wentworth, Thomas*. Strafford, earl of. *A declaration shewing the necessity of the earle of Straffords suffering.* [London]: n.pub., 1641. 4°. A⁴ (sig. 'A2' is present).
Tp, bsm. A2, note, not in AW's hand.
Wood 614(34). Wing D795A (Wing, Earl and 4 leaves).

6508. Wentworth, Thomas*. Strafford, earl of. *A description of the passage of Thomas late earle of Strafford, over the river of Styx.* [London]: n.pub., 1641. 4°. A⁴.
Tp, AW wrote, 'Nothing but fooleries & rascallities'. Bsm.
Wood 366(11). Wing D1166.

6509. Wentworth, Thomas*. Strafford, earl of. *The downfall of greatnesse. . . . a short survay of Thomas lord Wentworth.* [London]: n.pub., 1641. 4°. Pp. 8.
Tp, bsm.
Wood 366(10). Wing D2086.

6510. Wentworth, Thomas. Strafford, earl of. *The earle of Straffords letter to his . . . majestie [4 May].* [London]: n.pub., 1641. 4°. Pp. [2], 4.
Wood 366(3). Wing S5789A.

6511. Wentworth, Thomas*. Strafford, earl of. *Great satisfaction concerning the death of the earle of Strafford.* [London]: n.pub., [1641?]. 4°. Pp. [1], 7.
Wood 366(6). Wing G1751 ('O' not recorded in Wing).

6512. Wentworth, Thomas*. Strafford, earl of. *Great Straffords farewell to the world.* [London]: n.pub., 1641. 4°. A⁴.
Tp, AW wrote, 'in verse'. Bsm.
Wood 366(8). Wing G1756 ('O' not recorded in Wing).

6513. Wentworth, Thomas*. Strafford, earl of. *In answer to the earle of Strafords conclusion [13 April].* [London]: n.pub., 1641. 4°. Pp. [2], 6.
Wood 366(2). Wing I109 ('O' not recorded in Wing) (Wing, answere).

6514. Wentworth, Thomas*. Strafford, earl of. *A short and true relation of the life and death of sir Thomas Wentworth.* [London]: n.pub., 1641. 4°. Pp. [2], 6.
Wood 366(9). Wing S3557A ('O' not recorded in Wing).

6515. Wentworth, Thomas*. Strafford, earl of. *The truest relation of the earle of Straffords speech on the scaffold [12 May].* [London]: n.pub., 1641. 4°. Pp. [2], 6.
Tp, bsm.
Wood 366(5). Wing S5798.

6516. Wentworth, Thomas. Strafford, earl of. *The two last speeches, of Thomas Wentworth late earle of Strafford.* N.p.: n.pub., 1641. 4°. A⁴.
Tp, a note, lined out, 'This is a spurious broth unworthy and unlike that – [?] the maker of it', not in AW's hand, and a second note, not in AW's hand, also denying, in vigorous terms, that the first speech is by Strafford. A3ᵛ, a note affirming that the 2nd speech is by Strafford, not in AW's hand.
Wood 366(4). Wing S5799.

6517. Wentworth, Thomas, and Francis Annesley. Strafford, earl of; and Valentia, visct. *A true copie of the sentence of warre pronounced [by T. Wentworth] against sir Francis Annesley, . . . Together with his lordships petition against Thomas earle of Strafford [7 Nov. 1640].* London: f. J. B., 1641. 4°. Pp. [2], 15. Pasteboard (blue) with parchment spine.
Flyleaves, upper, 2nd-4th, AW wrote the titles of 48 printed works in this vol. (item 49 was added later), within guidelines made with red ink. AW rearranged the order of the pamphlets in an earlier bundle, and many show these earlier nos. in addition to the nos. of his final arrangement. Several, e.g. 33, 35, 38, 39, 43-4, also show a 3rd set of nos. at the bottom, which show an even earlier order.
Wood 507(1). Wing T2665.

6518. Were, John. *The apologie of colonell John Were, in vindication of his proceedings since the beginning of this present parliament.* London: n.pub., 1644. 4°. Pp. 8 (misnumbering).
Wood 612(29). Wing W1364.

6519. West, Robert. *An answer to a late paper, intituled a true copy of a paper written by capt. Tho. Walcot.* (London): (printed a. sold, W. Davis), (1683). S.sh. (r-v).
Tp, AW wrote, '1ᵈ'.
Wood 428(9). Wing W1382.

6520. West, William. *The first part of simboleography . . . now newly augmented with divers presidents.* London: [A. Islip f.] T. Wight, 1603. 4°. *⁴,A-2Q⁸,2R⁶.

Missing. MS. Wood E. 2(70), p. 10, 'Will West 2ᵈ pt of presidents – 1603'.
MS. Wood E. 2(70), p. 10. STC 25270. *O, Folg, Hunt.*

6521. Western Wheel. *The western-wheele turnd round to the last spoke, being a discourse betwixt the mr. of the ceremonies & the state-juglers that have ruled.* London: Theodorus Microcosmus, 1660. S.sh.
AW altered 1660 to 16 '59 feb:'.
Wood 416(50). Wing W1414 (two) (Wing, turned).

6522. Westminster. *The sad, and bloody fight at Westminster between the souldiers of the parliaments guard and the club-men of Surrey. With a copy of their petition.* London: f. H. Becke, 1648. 4°. Pp. [2], 6.
Tp, AW wrote after the year, 'May 16'.
Wood 502(10). Wing S227.

6523. Westminster. *On the six new pinnacles upon Westminster hall, or a size of traytors heads.* London: T. Mabb, 1661. S.sh.
'To my very loving friend Mʳ Thomas', not in AW's hand; ᵛ, AW wrote, '1660/1' (mutilated at top). 'Mʳ J Sheldon' [sic] accounts' and 'Mʳ Joseph Sheldon's account', neither in AW's hand (a Joseph Sheldon was nephew of abp. Sheldon, LT 2.550).
Wood 416(90). Wing O326 (rare).

6524. [Weston, Richard]. Hartlib, Samuel ed. *A discourse of husbandrie used in Brabant and Flanders.* London: f. W. Du-Gard, 1652. 4°. 2nd ed. Pp. [8], 27, [3].
On tp, on a slip pasted in by R[eginald] H[ill], 14. 3. 23, 'See also no. 3 in this volume, a later ed. without author's name'. No. 3 has since been stolen. Tp, author's name entered by a later librarian.
Wood 618(8). Wing W1483.

6525. Weston, Richard. Reeve, Gabriel, ed. *Directions left by a gentleman to his sonns: for the improvement of . . . land.* London: E. T. a. R. H. f. R. Royston, 1670. 4°. Pp. [12], 34.
Missing in 1992. Stolen between 1923 and 1992 (see notes on upper flyleaf, Wood 618(1), item 6712, and slip at tp of Wood 618(8), item 6524).
Wood 618(3). Wing R671. *O, Hunt, Folg, Union.*

6526. Wetenhall, Edward. Kilmore and Ardagh, bp. of. *Miserere cleri. A sermon [26 July].* [London] in the Savoy: T. N. f. J. Collins, sold A. Brocas in Exon, 1668. 4°. Pp. [4], 25, [1] (1 p. books printed a. sold by J. Collins).
Tp, AW underscored 'Wetenhall', in red ink.
Wood 633(15). Wing W1505.

6527. Weymouth, Whale. *A great miracle at sea: or, a perfect relation of a mighty great whale, . . . having opened it's [sic] belly, found a Romish priest.* N.p.: n.pub., [1645]. 4°. Pp. [2], 6.
Tp, AW wrote, '1645'. Another ed. at [MS.] Wood B. 35(12).
[MS.] Wood B. 35(13). Wing G1712 (rare).

6528. Weymouth, Whale. *A true and wonderfull relation of a whale . . . certified by divers mariners of Weymouth, . . . there was found in the belly of it a Romish priest.* [London]: I. H., [1645]. 4°. Pp. 8.
Tp, AW wrote, 'Noe date or yeare to be found in this pamphlet'. Pp. 3, AW wrote at '19 of October', 'qu[aere] in what yeare.'; and 8, line in margin, in pencil, and 'ridiculous'. Another ed. at [MS.] Wood B. 35(13).
[MS.] Wood B. 35(12). Wing T2587 (two).

6529. Whalley, Edward. *A message and declaration sent . . . to . . . William Lenthal . . . concerning the kings majesties royall person, and engagement.* London: f. G. Whittington, 1647, 7 Dec. 4°. Pp. [2], 5.
Wood 612(56a). Wing W1529.

6530. Whalley, Edward. *The declaration and unanimous resolution of colonel Whaley, and . . . of his regiment [14 May 1649].* London: J. Clowes, 1648. 4°. Pp. 12. Calf, rough, with 3 fillets, stamp decoration inside corners (tulip with pin), and roll decoration at inner, spine edge (Ashm. binding); rebacked, R. H[arvey], 29.10.[19]53.
Flyleaf, upper, the titles of 48 printed works in this vol., by an Ashm. librarian (same hand in Wood 276a). Numbering on tpp of items in this vol. is in Roman numerals (by an Ashm. librarian).
Wood 609(1). Wing W1526.

6531. [Wharton, George]. *Englands Iliads in a nut-shell.* Oxford: n.pub., 1645. 8°. A², B-C⁸, D⁶. Pasteboard (grey) with parchment spine. 1st and last flyleaves, marbled paper.

Flyleaf, upper, 2nd[v], AW wrote the titles of 5 printed works in this vol., within guidelines made with red ink. Tp, AW wrote, 'Written by George Wharton'.
Wood 207(1). Wing W1544. Madan 1794.

6532. [**Wharton, George**]. *A second narrative of the late parliament (so called) . . . With some quaeries sadly proposed there upon, by a friend to the good old cause of justice, . . . To which is added a third narrative.* [London?]: n.pub., 1658. 4°. Pp. 55.
Flyleaf, upper, 1st[v], AW wrote, 'The Second Narrative &c. [/] This pamphlet seems to have been written by a fift monarchy man. [/] The 3[d] Narrative is at the end of this'. At the lists of vignettes, pp. 13-32, 34, AW wrote brief identifications (e.g., p. 14 at Henry Lawrence: 'A Recruiter in the Long Parliam.' and later wrote in pencil, 'Westmorland'), added Christian names or titles, added a p. no. (at p. [25]), and made ink and pencil lines in margin. Acquired 28 March 1659, LT 1.271. See also Wood 620(14), item 2705.
Wood 620(15-16). Wing W1556B ('O' not recorded in Wing).

6533. [**Wharton, Henry**]. Harmer, Anthony, pseud. *A specimen of some errors and defects in the history of the reformation of the Church of England; wrote by Gilbert Burnet, . . . By Anthony Harmer.* London: f. R. Taylor, 1693. 8°. Pp. [8], 199, [1].
Responds to Burnet, Wood 611(1), item 1207. See also item 6695.
Wood 206(4). Wing W1569.

6534. Wharton, Henry. *Historia de episcopis & decanis Londinensibus; necnon de . . . Assavensibus.* Londini: R. Chiswell, 1695. 8°. Pp. [32], 395, [5] (5 pp. books sold by Chiswell).
Wood 210(3). Wing W1565.

6535. Wharton, Philip, et al. *Eight speeches spoken in Guild-hall upon Thursday night, Octob. 27.* London: f. P. Cole, 1642. 4°. Pp. 22 (p. 1 or 2, wanting).
On p. preceding tp, AW wrote, 'The speeches following are chiefly to give the citizens of London an account of the battle at Edghill, on their behalf (full of Lyes) & to encourage them to go on in the work against the Malignants (Cavaliers) by giving more contributions'. Tp, AW wrote, 'two speeches' before Wharton and underscored names of the 5 authors. P. 7, at 'the plain truth my own', he wrote 'And afterwards the L. Wharton hid himself in a saw-pit/' (a detail which AW inserted into AO 3.177).
Wood 375(18). Wing E262.

6536. Whately, Cr[eswel]. *Upon the horrid, and most abominable gunpouder treason.* N.p.: n.pub., [1680 ca.]. S.sh.
AW's wrote, 'when printed I find not', in dark ink, and, after the author, 'a puritanicall Banburian', in red ink.
Wood 276a(542). Not in Wing. Not in ESTCR.

6537. Wheadle, Madam. *Mad[m] Wheadle.* London: ?, 1678. Pp.?
Missing in 1837. 'Mad[m] Wheadle – Lond. 1678' in Whiteside cat.
Wood 123. Not in Wing. Not in ESTCR.

6538. Wheare, Degory. *Pietas erga benefactores contines, parentationem historicam manibus Camdeni oblatam. . . . Necnon epistolarum eucharisticarum. [Followed by] Charisteria.* Oxon.: excud. G. Turner, 1628. 8°. Pp. [8], 48, 133, [1].
Tp, AW wrote '10[p]'. P. 35, 133, some minor corrections. AO 3.219.
Wood 710(2). STC 25327. Madan 602.

6539. Wheare, Degory, and Nicholas Horseman. Bohun, Edmund, trans. *The method and order of reading both civil and ecclesiastical histories.* London: M. Flesher f. C. Brome, 1685. 8°. Pp. [46], 362, [14]. Pasteboard (blue) with parchment spine.
Flyleaf, upper, 3rd[v], AW wrote the titles of 2 printed works in this vol., within guidelines made with red ink. Tp, price, '3[s]'. A2, at name of Whear[e], AW underscored 'examiner of the Lads'. P. 174, AW marked Sherbury in 'Lord Herbert of Sherbury'.
Wood 584(1). Wing W1592.

6540. Wheare, Degory, and N[icholas] H[orseman]. *Relectiones hyemales, de ratione & methodo legendi utrasque historias, civiles & ecclesiasticas. . . . Quibus jam appenditur mantissa . . . per N[icholas] H[orseman].* Oxoniae: excud. W. Hall. Imp. E. & J. Forrest, 1662. 8°. 4th ed. Pp. [32], 342, 16. Calf with 2 fillets and also 2 vertical fillets; rebacked.
Flyleaf, upper, 1st torn out, traces of a note on the price and author remain; 2nd, signature, 'Robertus Robinson Martii 25th 1670'. Tp, at 'Mantissa', AW wrote 'v. p. 151'. P. 151, at Mantissa, 'per Nich.

Horsman' (AO 3.217; 4.616-7).
Wood 189. Wing W1595. Madan 2619.

6541. Wheeler, John. *A treatise of commerce*. London: J. Harison, 1601. 4°. Pp. 126 (misnumbering) (cropped).
From tp to p. 17, p. nos. entered at top, 413-429, in a former collection, not by AW.
Wood 618(5). STC 25331.

6542. Whetcombe, Tristram. *The copy of a letter from . . . Tristram Whittecombe . . . to his brother Benjamin Whitecombe [21 Ap.]*. London: f. J. Hunscott, 1642. 4°. A⁴.
Tp, below, '47'.
Wood 508(13). Wing W1636 ('O' not recorded in Wing).

6543. W[hetcombe], T[ristram]. *The state of Dublin, as it stood the 27. of December, and of other parts of Ireland. Being the copy of a letter*. London: f. N. Butter, 1642. 4°. A⁴.
Tp, AW wrote after the t, '1641'.
Wood 507(20). Wing W1639 ('O' not recorded in Wing).

6544. Whetcombe, Tristram. *A most exact relation of a great victory, obtained by the poor protestants in Ireland . . . Also severall depositions taken before the maior of Kinsale*. London: f. J. Hunscott, 1642, 3 Oct. 4°. Pp. 16.
Tp, former no., overwritten by a new no.
Wood 508(33). Wing W1637.

6545. Whetstone, George. *A mirror of treue honnour and Christian nobilitie, . . . the life, death, . . . of . . . lorde Frauncis earle of Bedford*. London: R. Jones, 1585. 4°. A-D⁴. Pasteboard (blue) with parchment spine; rebacked.
Flyleaf, upper, 2nd^v, AW wrote the titles of 13 printed works in this vol., within guidelines made with red ink (he joined 2 items at entry no. (2) and made 2 entries for entry no. (12)). Tp, 2 corrections of 'June' to 'July', may not be in AW's hand; ^v, AW quoted, 'Francis [Russell] Earl of Bedford - a man so religious & of such a noble courteous nature, that I can never speak ought so highly in his commendation, but his vertue will farr surpass the same - Camden at the end of Bedfordshire, in Britannia.'
Wood 535(1). STC 25342.

6546. Whiston, Edward. *The life and death of mr. Henry Jessey, . . . With an elegy upon the death of mr. William Bridg*. [London]: n.pub., 1671. 8°. Pp. [6], 108, [109-110].
Pp. 6, 7, 40, 50-1, a few marks in margins and underscorings; p. 99, AW corrected to 'good', in margin, at 'God morrow, God night'. P. [109], AW first wrote the date of the elegy, '1664 q[uaere]', which he lined out and replaced with '1670-1'.
Wood 289(3). Wing W1679.

6547. Whitaker, Edward. *A letter from mr. Edward Whitaker to the protestant joyner [S. College] upon his bill being sent to Oxford*. (London): (f. N. T.), (1681). S.sh. Pp. 2.
Wood 427(27). Wing W1704.

6548. Whitaker, Tobias. Περι υδροποσιας: *or, a discourse of waters*. London: [A. Mathewes] f. J. Grismond, 1634. 12°. Pp. [16], 159, [1].
Missing. MS. Wood E. 2(70), p. 11.
MS. Wood E. 2(70), p. 11. STC 25355. *Folg*.

6549. White, Francis. *A true relation of the proceedings in the businesse of Burford*. London: R. Austin, 1649. 4°. Pp. [2], 16.
Wood 503(5). Wing W1766.

6550. White, John. Winchester, bp. of. *Diacosiomartyrion. id est ducentorum virorum testimonium, de veritate corporis, et sanguinis Christi . . . adversus Petrum Martyrem*. Londini: in aed. R. Cali, 1553. 4°. Ff. [6], 102, [2]. Pasteboard (grey) with parchment spine.
Pasteboard, upper^v (and on parchment spine), AW wrote 2 short titles of contents. Flyleaf, upper, 1st, is a thin pasteboard cover; the recto is painted red and blue, with initials 'E:H:'. 2nd^v, AW wrote one-word titles of the 2 printed works in this vol. Tp, signature of 'Joannes Goad', in ink, over 'Joannes Godd', in pencil, and '1632', in pencil. To f. 16, some notes and marks in margin, none in AW's hand; ff. 89ff. some f. numbers added; f. 90^v, AW underscored 'Hylsaeus', in red ink, and wrote 'Joh. Hylsey' in margin, in red ink.

Wood 334(1). STC 25388.

6551. White, John (1590-1645). *Mr. Whites speech in parliament [17 Jan.] . . . Concerning the triall of the XII. bishops.* London: f. F. Coules a. T. Bancks, [1642]. 4°. Pp. [2], 5.
Tp, AW wrote 'Joh. White', in red ink.
[MS.] Wood D. 31(16). Wing W1772.

6552. [White, John] (1590-1645). *The first century of scandalous, malignant priests, . . . or, . . . the causes for which the parliament hath ordered the sequestration of the benefices.* London: G. Miller, 1643. 4°. Pp. [8], 51.
Tp, 'pret: 2 - 6', not in AW's usual style. Bsm. ^v, AW wrote 'Few, or no Oxford scholars are mention'd in this most vile century –'. P. 2, AW underscored 'Charles Forbench' and wrote '[He] lived af[ter]wards [in] Sanford [ne]are Oxon [and] was mi[n]ister there.', cropped at side (the source of AW's note in MS. Wood E. 1, fol. 189, see LT 1.403, and 1.105). Pp. 4-14, 16-19, etc., to p. 41, frequent short horizontal lines in margins (especially at the oft-used accusation, and variants of, 'common Ale-house haunter'); and some vertical lines. Pp. 17, 36, year in margin (both cropped).
Wood 619(11) (not in Bodl. CD cat.). Wing W1771E.

6553. [White, John] (1586-1671). *Miscellanea variegata, anagramata, epigrammata, disticha.* [London]: impressa pro authore, 1663. 8°. Pp. [2], 80, [1].
Tp, 'Autore Joanne White teste Wood', prob. by AW. Errata page and flyleaf, lower, some 30 errata, transcribed from a printed insert contained in other copies, see, e.g., Ashm. 1559, prob. not in AW's hand. This, or the next item, or both, acquired from another member of Merton College, [Edmund] Dickinson, 4 Dec. 1663, LT 1.507.
Wood 105(3). Wing W1785D (two).

6554. White, John (1586-1671). *Miscellanea variegata, anagrammata.* Londini: pro authore, 1664. 8°. Pp. 55.
P. 55^v, list of 9 errata, prob. not by AW. For time of acquisition, see the preceding item, Wood 105(3).
Wood 105(4). Wing W1785E. ESTCR 188784.

6555. White, Thomas. *A discoverie of Brownisme: or, a briefe declaration of some of the errors and abhominations . . . among the English company.* London: W. A[llde] f. N. Fosbroke, 1605. 4°. Pp. [6], 26, [3].
Pasteboard (grey) (with a black, white, red, mottled paper pasted over) with parchment spine (repaired). 2nd upper and 2nd last lower flyleaves, marbled paper.
Flyleaf, upper, 3rd^{r-v}, AW wrote the titles of 25 printed works (3 at no. 17) in this vol., within guidelines made with red ink. 1st item, tp repaired, perhaps by AW. Bsm.
Wood 647(1). STC 25408.

6556. [White, Thomas] (1593-1676). *Chrysapis to Querela, a letter publish't by a friend of Chrysapis.* London: n.pub., 1660. 8°. A-C⁸. Pasteboard (brown) with calf spine; flyleaf, upper, blue colouring on recto and flyleaf, lower, on verso.
Flyleaf, upper, 2nd, AW wrote the titles of 4 printed works in this vol. (really 3 and 2 pts. of Wood 127(3)), within guidelines made with red chalk. Tp, AW wrote 'Tho. de Albiis author' and 'Antonii Wood. Ex dono Th. Blount interioris Templi &c. Maii 1670'. LT 2.191. A6^v-A7, corrections in text.
Wood 127(1). Wing W1813.

6557. White, Thomas (1593-1676). *Controversy-logicke. Or, the methode to come to truth in debates of religion.* Roan: n.pub., 1674. 12°. 2nd ed. Pp. [2], 250. Calf with 2 fillets; rebacked.
Flyleaf, upper, AW wrote '28 May 1675. Given to me by Thomas Blount of the Inner Temple Lond. Esq. at my departure from him there. [/] Thomas de Albijs commonly White Living in Drury Lane the Authour –', and later 'Tho. White the Author'. LT 2.314.
Wood 798. Wing W1817.

6558. White, Thomas*, William Harcourt*, et al. Jesuits. *Some account of the tryals of the five notorious Jesuits . . . Thomas White . . . William Harcourt, John Fenwick, John Gavern, and Anthony Turner.* London: n.pub., 1679. 'Printed in the year 1679'. 4°. Pp. 8.
Wood 586(21). Not in Wing (not S4469-70). Not in ESTCR.

6559. White, Thomas, William Harcourt, et al. Jesuits. *The last speeches of the five notorious traitors and Jesuits: viz. Thomas White . . . William Harcourt . . . John Gavan . . . . Anthony Turner. . . . John Fenwick, . . . June 20, 1679.* [London]: n.pub., [1679]. Fol. Pp. 8.
P. 8, AW wrote, 'These speeches were not spoken at the Gallowes, but are faigned & published to get

money: But it is false as I have since understood[.] The Jesuits gave the originalls in Newgate to their respective freinds before they went to execution. And when they all denied the fact for which they suffered, then the report went that the speeches were not spoken by them'. LT 2.453.
Wood 424(21). Wing L506.

6560. White, Thomas*, William Harcourt*, et al. Jesuits. *The manner of the execution of the five notorious Jesuits [Thomas White, William Harcourt, John Fenwick, John Gavern, Anthony Turner].* [London]: n.pub., [1679]. Fol. Pp. 4.
LT 2.453.
Wood 424(22). Wing M471.

6561. White, Thomas, William Harcourt, et al. Jesuits. *The true speeches of Thomas Whitebread, . . . William Harcourt, . . . John Fenwick, . . . John Gavan, and Anthony Turner, . . . before their execution . . . With animadversions thereupon.* London: f. H. Hills, T. Parkhurst, J. Starkey, D. Newman, T. Cockeril, a. T. Simmons, 1679. Fol. Pp. [2], 8, 24.
Tp, AW wrote the price, '1ˢ'. Purchased from Vade, see his record of purchase in MS. Wood F. 50, f. 11. LT 2.453.
Wood 424(25). Wing T3099.

6562. White, Thomas*, William Harcourt*, et al. Jesuits. *The tryals and condemnation of Thomas White, alias Whitebread, . . . William Harcourt, . . . John Fenwick, . . . John Gavan . . . Anthony Turner.* London: f. H. Hills, T. Parkhurst, J. Starkey, D. Newman, T. Cockeril, and T. Simmons, 1679. Fol. Pp. [2], 95.
P. 95, after a description of the execution of 6 (including Richard Langhorn), AW wrote, 'And their bodies being allowed buriall, were buried in S. Giles ch. yard in the feilds'. LT 2.435, 453.
Wood 424(20) (424(2) in Bodl. CD cat.). Wing T2247 (Wing, Whitbread).

6563. [White, William]. *Guilielmi Phalerii ad grammaticen ordinariam supplementa.* London: excud. R. White or R. W. pro R. Davis Oxoniensi, 1652. 8°.
Missing. MS. Wood E. 2(70), p. 16.
MS. Wood E. 2(70), p. 16. Wing W1855A (one) or 1856 (two). Madan 2209*. *BL.*

6564. Whitehall, J[ohn]. *Behemoth arraign'd: or, a vindication of property against a fanatical pamphlet.* London: f. T. Fox, 1680. 8°. Pp. [8], 92, [2] (2 pp. books sold by Fox).
Tp, bsms.
Wood 213(3). Wing W1865.

6565. W[hitehall], R[obert]. Τεχνη πολιμογαμια: *or, the marriage of armes and arts, July 12. . . . . Being an accompt of the act at Oxon.* London: J. G[rismond] f. R. Royston, 1651. 4°. A⁴.
Tp, AW outlined in red his earlier ms. entry, 'Dʳ Greenwood being then Vicecanc: who being a morose & strict man in his office, caused the souldiers who were then garrisoned in Oxon to awe the rude schollers all the act time in Sᵗ Maries church: &c:.', and later wrote below in red ink, 'Rob. Whitehall of Merton Coll. supposed to be the author –'. A3, 3 identifications, 'meaning Dʳ Dan: Greenwood then vicecanc:', 'Finmore of Xᵗchurch Coll:' and 'at Snow hill Lond.' A3ᵛ, note, 'Terrae Filii', and identifications of 2, Tho: Careless and Will: Levins, in dark ink, and later bracketed by AW in red ink. A4, correction of 'Nepotia' to 'Repotia'. LT 2.563-4; AO 4.177.
Wood 515(11). Wing W1876 (Wing, Greek, one word with [sic]). Madan 2163.

6566. Whitehall, R[obert]. *Illustrissimo domino dⁿᵒ Richardo Cromwel, in honoratissimum cancellarii Oxoniensis officium & dignitatem faeliciter electo . . . Carmen onomasticon gratulatorium.* [London]: n.pub., (1657). S.sh.
AO 4.177.
Wood 423(32). Wing W1873 (two). Madan 2326.

6567. Whitehall, Robert. *Viro, favore regio, et meritis suis honoratissimo, amplissimoque domino, Edvardo Hide.* [London]: n.pub., [1660]. S.sh.
AW underscored the name of the author, in red ink, and wrote the year, 'an[no] 1660'.
Wood 423(34). Wing W1879 (two). See Madan 2476, 2544.

6568. Whitehall, Ro[bert]. *The coronation. A poem.* London: f. J. Playford, 1661. 4°. Pp. [2], 6.
A copy acquired 27 Apr. 1661, LT 1.389. Dupl. at Wood 416(88).
Wood 319(13). Wing W1870.

6569. Whitehall, Ro[bert]. *The coronation. A poem.* London: f. J. Playford, 1661. 4°. Pp. [2], 6.
AW wrote, 'Dupl' in red ink, and former no., '90'. A copy acquired 27 Apr. 1661, LT 1.389. Dupl. at Wood 319(13).
Wood 416(88). Wing W1870.

6570. [Whitehall, Robert]. Manuscript. *The answeare [/] freind Edmund [Gayton]. [/] Since the world must know it [/] That water-ratt's turn'd water-poet.* N.p.: n.pub., 1666. Pp. 6.
Verse, not in AW's hand; in response to Gayton, Wood 416(114), item 3181. Apparently never published (see AO 3.757). At top, AW wrote, 'Edm. Gayton', and 'by Rob. Whitehall'. AO 3.757.
Wood 416(116).

6571. Whitehall, Ro[bert]. *Urania, or a description of the painting of the top of the theater at Oxon.* London: T. Ratcliffe a. T. Daniel, 1669. Fol. Pp. [2], 9.
AO 4.177-8; LT 2.164.
Wood 423(42). Wing W1878. Madan 2818.

6572. W[hitehall], R[obert]. *To the no less vertuous than ingenious m^{ris} Mary More; upon her sending sir Thomas More's picture . . . to . . . Oxon.* [Oxford]: [at the Sheldonian], 1674, 26 Decem. S.sh.
AW completed the last line, 'yours R. double U.' and the author's name after initials, W'hithall, E Coll. Merton', ^{v}, date and note, 'See Walpole's Anecdotes of Painting, vol. III. p. 148', not in AW's hand. LT 2.300; AO 4.178.
Wood 423(46). Wing W1877 (rare). Madan 3029.

6573. Whitelocke, Bulstrode. *The message from the house of commons to the lords . . . February 22.* London: E. Griffin, 1642. 4°. A^4.
AW underscored the surname of the author; below, no. '3'.
Wood 375(36). Wing W1987.

6574. Whitelocke, Bulstrode. *My lord Whitelocks reports on Machiavil; or his recollections for . . . students of modern policy.* London: f. T. Bateman, 1659[60]. 4°. Pp. [2], 8.
Tp, AW wrote after the year, 'Jan'. P. 3-4, lines in margin, in pencil.
Wood 613(14). Wing W1991 (Wing, report).

6575. Whitelocke, Bulstrode; Charles Fleetwood, and John Disbrowe. *Three speeches made to . . . the lord maior . . . of London, . . . at Guildhall [8 Nov.].* London: n.pub., 1659. 4°. Pp. [2], 6.
Tp, nos. 28 and 26 in former bundles.
Wood 610(22). Wing W1994.

6576. [Whitelocke, James]. B., J., ed. *A learned and necessary argument to prove that each subject hath a propriety in his goods. . . . Together with a remonstrance presented to the kings . . . majesty by the . . . commons, in . . . 1610. . . . By a late learned judge.* London: R. Bishop f. J. Burroughes, 1641. 4°. Pp. [4], 66.
Tp, AW underscored 'learned judge' in red ink, and wrote '[Henry] Yelverton, the presumed judge' in the margin.
Wood 527(2). Wing W1995.

6577. White-Paper Makers. *The case of the company of white-paper-makers.* [London]: n.pub., [1689]. Fol. Pp. 4.
P. 4, AW wrote, 'This paper was dispersed in the coffey houses in Oxon, in the latter end of Dec. 1689'.
Wood 276b(89). Wing C1052.

6578. [Whittel, John]. *An exact diary of the late expedition of . . . the prince of Orange . . . from . . . the Hague, to . . . Torbay; and from thence to . . . White-hall.* London: f. R. Baldwin, 1689. 4°. Pp. [8], 75.
Pp. 16, 23, AW wrote, 'an. 1688.'
Wood 530(2). Wing W2040A.

6579. Whorwood, Thomas. *Argumentum ad hominem; or an argument against protestants, who hold that papists, . . . may be saved.* London: f. N. Ranew, 1679. 4°. Pp. [16], 17, [1] (1 p. books sold by Ranew) (wanting 4 pp. at end).
Flyleaf, lower, 'Liber Anthoni Wood A: M: Ex dono Authoris anno 1679', not by AW, and, AW wrote, 'Author natus apud Hedington, Educatus in aul. S. M. Magd. sub Tutore Hen. Wilkinson Seniore.' AO 3.1228 (AW had a low opinion of the Puritan Whorwood and this book; LT 2.475 assumes, incorrectly, that both references are to the following pamphlet, (6), by C. Davenport, item 2176).

[MS.] Wood B. 40(5). Wing W2070 (Wing, hominem:).

6580. Widdrington, William. *A true and exact relation of the great victories obtained by the earl of Manchester, and the lord Fairfax; . . . Together with two letters . . . the one from . . . lo: Fairfax; the other from sir John Meldrum.* [London]: f. E. Husbands, 1643, 19 Oct. 4°. Pp. 8.
Tp, AW altered a former no., '40', underscored 'Fairfax', and wrote 'Ferdinando Lord Fairfax'.
Wood 376(44). Wing W2089.

6581. Widecombe-in-the-Moor. *A second and most exact relation of those sad and lamentable accidents, which happened in . . . Wydecombe neere the Dartmoores [21 Oct.].* London: G. M[iller] f. R. Harford, 1638. 4°. Pp. [5], 37.
Tp, 'George Miller', in pencil, in a modern hand; bsm.
[MS.] Wood D. 28(7). STC 25607.

6582. Widowes, Thomas. *The just devill of Woodstock. Or, a true narrative of the several apparitions, . . . inflicted upon the rumpish commissioners sent thither, to survey the mannors and houses belonging to his majestie.* London: n.pub., 1649 [i.e., 1660]. 4°. Pp. [4], 13.
Missing in 1839; see note by W. Kirtland at [MS.] Wood B. 18(1), item 1148. On a sheet preceding the missing item, AW wrote, 'Rob. Plot Ll.D. in his Natural History of Oxfordshire, printed 1677, cap. 8. paragr. 37. 38 39. 40 &c. hath an account of The just Devill of Wodstock, not from this printed copie which he never saw, as he himself hath told me, but from the relation of severall people, that then [1649] lived, & so consequently, as it does, differs much from this printed relation of Tho. Widdowes – [/] He sayes their first comming to the mannour house to sit, & take a survey of it, was on the 13 of Oct. 1649'. AW owned this in 1681, see Bod. MS. Wood E. 2(70), p. 24. See also AO 3.398. Found. The item is now in the Houghton Library, *EC65 W6333 660j, acquired or catalogued 6 June 1936 (from an unknown source). Tp, upper right corner, '90'; below title, AW wrote 'by Thom. Widowes, schoolmr of Woodstocke.' Below imprint, 'This came out in December A: 1660.' A1v, A3r, pp. 4, 10, 13, some identifications, mainly in ink; p. 1, underscoring; p. 4, 'q[uaere]' in pencil. LT 1.158.
[MS.] Wood B. 18(9). Wing W2091A (two).

6583. Wilbee, Amon. *Prima pars. De comparatis comparandis:. . . or of the justification of king Charles comparitively [sic] against the parliament.* Oxford [really London]: n.pub., 1647. 4°. Pp. [2], 40, [6].
2nd p. [1], AW wrote the p. no. '41' at the top; p. [6 (last p.], below, 'Mr Lilbourne', may be by AW (see LT 1.72, to a ref. to a trial of 'Lillburne' in 1642).
Wood 631(17). Wing W2113. Madan 1938.

6584. [Wilbee, Amon]. *Tertia pars de comparatis comparandis:. . . or of the justification of king Charles comparatively against the parliament.* Oxford [really London]: n.pub., 1648. 4°. Pp. [2], 58.
Wood 631(19). Wing W2115. Madan 1991.

6585. Wilbraham, Roger. *Three letters concerning the surrender of many Scotish lords to the high sheriffe of . . . Chester, . . . taken prisoners by the parliament forces.* London: f. J. Wright, 1648, 28 Aug. 4°. Pp. [2], 6.
Dupl. at Wood 632(20).
Wood 502(56). Wing W2116.

6586. Wilbraham, Roger. *Three letters concerning the surrender of many Scotish lords to the high sheriffe of . . . Chester, . . . taken prisoners by the parliament forces.* London: f. J. Wright, 1648, 28 Aug. 4°. Pp. [2], 6.
Tp, 2 former nos., '20' and '31'. Dupl. at Wood 502(56).
Wood 632(20). Wing W2116.

6587. W[ilcox], T[homas]. *The unfouldyng of sundry untruths . . . latelye propounded by one I. B[annester?] a greate favourer of the . . . libertines.* London: (T. Dawson) f. T. Man, 1581. 8°. A-K8.
Former owner, Henry Jackson. To B3, some lines and marks in margins and underscoring, not in AW's manner. LT 1.459-60 (see also 1.331).
Wood 776(2). STC 25631.

6588. [Wild, Robert]. *The tragedy of Christopher Love at Tower-hill. By the ingenious author of Iter boreale.* London: f. R. Crofts, 1660. 4°. Pp. 8.
Tp, AW wrote the surname of the author, 'Dr . . . . [Robert] Wild.'
Wood 367(5). Wing W2150.

6589. [Wild, Robert]. *Iter Boreale. Attempting somthing upon the . . . march of . . . George Monck, from Scotland, to London.* London: n.pub., 1660, 23 Apr. 4°. Pp. 20.
AW wrote, 'By Rob: Wilde minister of Ainhoe [Aynho] comm: N.Hamps:', and 'Aprill:'.
Wood 465(5). Wing W2133.

6590. Wild, Robert*. *An answer to Wild. Or, a poem, upon the imprisonment of Robert Wild.* [London]: n.pub., [1663?]. S.sh.
ᵛ, AW wrote '1662' twice in pencil.
Wood 416(101). Wing A3460 (Wing, Wild: or,).

6591. Wild, Robert. *A poem upon the imprisonment of mr. [Edmund] Calamy in Newgate.* [London]: n.pub., [1663]. S.sh.
AW wrote the year, '1662[3]'; and underscored 'Wild' in red ink. Acquired 3 Feb. 1663, LT 1.468.
Wood 416(98). Wing W2146 (Wing, [1662]).

6592. [Wild, Robert]*. *A rod for the fools back: or, an answer to a scurrilous libel, called the changeling.* [London]: n.pub., [1663]. S.sh.
ᵛ, AW wrote the year, '1663[4]'; this poem was prob. acquired 12 March 1664, 2ᵈ, LT 2.6, but see also the ballad Wood 416(99), item 827.
Wood 416(100). Wing R1769A.

6593. [Wild, Robert]. *The grateful non-conformist; or, a return of thanks to sir John Baber . . . who sent the author ten crowns.* London: n.pub., 1665. S.sh.
AW wrote, 'Dʳ Jo. Wild qu[aere]', in pencil; and figures, a long addition, in pencil, may not be by AW.
Diff. ed. at Wood 416(109).
Wood 276b(98). Wing W2127.

6594. [Wild, Robert]. *The grateful non-conformist; or, a return of thanks to sir John Baber.* [London]: n.pub., [1665]. S.sh.
AW wrote, above, 'q[uaere] an. 1665', in pencil; below, 'Temp Ol. Cr. protect.' lined out by pencil, 'Lond printed, an 1665' and 'by Dʳ Jo. Wild. qu[aere]'. 'Coyn' glossed in margin by 'wine'. Diff. ed. at Wood 276b(98).
Wood 416(109). Wing W2127A.

6595. [Wild, Robert]. *Upon the rebuilding the city, the right honourable the lord mayor [5 May].* [London]: n.pub., 1669. S.sh. Line 1 ends, 'have [/] (stole'.
Dupl. at Wood 416(118).
Wood 276a(527). Wing W2152. ESTCR 220366.

6596. [Wild, Robert]. *[Upon] the rebuilding the city, the right honourable the lord mayor [5 May].* [London]: n.pub., 1669. S.sh. (cropped at top).
Dupl. at 276a(527).
Wood 416(118). Wing W2152. ESTCR 220366.

6597. W[ild], R[obert]. *Olivers Cromwells ghost: or old Noll newly revived.* [London]: n.pub., [1679]. Fol. Pp. 4.
P. 1, AW wrote '(1680)', and p. 4, under initials R. W., 'Rob. Wilde/'.
Wood 417(40). Wing W2143.

6598. Wilde, George. Derry, bp. of. *A sermon preached upon Sunday the third of March in Sᵗ Maries Oxford [on Ps. 122.8, 9].* Oxford: L. Lichfield, 1643[4]. 4°. Pp. [4], 31. Parchment with gold-stamp fillet and centrepiece (leaf below, 3 stylized leaves, and cone above).
[MS.] Wood C. 47(1). Wing W2160. Madan 1548.

6599. W[ildgoos], A[nthony]. *The young-mans second warning-peece: or, a miracle of mercies. Being a true relation . . . wherwith Satan assaulted me.* London: f. A. Wildgoose, 1643. 4°. 2nd ed. Pp. [2], 6.
[MS.] Wood B. 35(11). Wing W2A (rare).

6600. [Wilkins, John]. Chester, bp. of. *The first book. The discovery of a new world. Or, a discourse tending to prove, that 'tis probable there may be another habitable world in the moone. [Followed by] A discourse concerning a new planet.* [London]: J. Norton [a.] (R. H[earne]) f. J. Maynard, 1640. 8°. 3rd impr. Pp. [16], 242, [14], 246, [2] (2 tpp.). Pasteboard (blue) with parchment spine.
Frontispieceᵛ, 2 titles of the single imprint in this vol., not by AW.
Wood 687. STC 25641.

6601. Wilkins, John. Chester, bp. of. *A discourse concerning the gift of prayer*. London: T. R. a. E. M. f. S. Gellibrand, 1653. 8°. 5th ed. Pp. [8], 232. Pasteboard (blue) with parchment spine. 1st upper and last lower flyleaves, traces of marbled paper; rebacked.
Flyleaf, upper, 1st^v, AW wrote the titles of 3 printed works in this vol., within guidelines made with red ink. Pasteboard, lower, inside, scribble, 'Kirtland', by William Kirtland, ca. 1837-41, other scribbling covered over in rebinding.
Wood 889(1). Wing W2180.

6602. Wilkins, John. Chester, bp. of. *Ecclesiastes, or, a discourse concerning the gift of preaching: as it falls under the rules of art*. London: T. R. a. E. M. f. S. Gellibrand, 1656. 8°. 5th ed. Pp. [6], 133, [4].
Pp. 80-2, vertical line, in margin at author of sermons 'Con.' Socinians, and 'Con' Anabaptists, and, 'Pro' and 'Con' Antinomians; 95, 97, 99-100, 2nd p. 101 (in pencil), 104 (i.e., 106). 2nd p. [4], some marks in margin at authors on religion, in ink and in pencil.
Wood 889(2). Wing W2192.

6603. Wilkinson, Henry. *The hope of glory or Christs indwelling in true believers . . . a sermon at Hasely . . . at the funerall of m^ris Margaret Corbet*. Oxford: A. Lichfield, 1657. 8°. Pp. [8], 87.
AO 4.285.
Wood 836(9). Wing W2237. Madan 2359.

6604. Wilkinson, Henry. *Conciones duae [on Eccles. 9.12 and 2 Cor. 5.14] apud academicos Oxonii nuper habitae*. Oxoniae: excud. H. Hall, impen. T. Robinson, 1659. 8°. Pp. [12], 59.
Tp, AW underscored the name of the author, in red ink and wrote 'A: W: [lined out and:] ex dono Authoris MDclix'. AO 4.285.
Wood 883(7). Wing W2231. Madan 2462.

6605. Wilkinson, Henry. *Concio de brevitate opportuni temporis*. Londini: ap. S. Gellibrand, 1660. 4°. Pp. [6], 23.
Tp, AW wrote, 'Lib Ant Wood; [lined out, and:] ex dono Authoris Aug: xxviij: MDCLXI'. LT 1.407 and 453.
Wood 634(14). Wing W2230.

6606. Wilkinson, Henry, captain. *The information of ca^pt. Hen. Wilkinson, of what hath passed betwixt him and some other persons . . . to swear high treason against the earl of Shaftsbury*. London: f. H. Wilkinson, 1681. Fol. Pp. [8], 11 (misnumbering).
Tp^v, 25 lines about Wilkinson's information, from the London *Gazette*, not in AW's hand. Pp. [6-7], 12 to 2nd p. 9, double lines in margin, not in AW's usual manner.
Wood 427(38). Wing W2218 (Wing, Wilksinson).

6607. Willes, Richard, and Christopher Johnson. *Poematum liber . . . [2nd tp] In suorum poemat. librum . . . scholia. His accesserunt C. Jonsoni . . . carmina*. Londini: ex bib. Tottellina, 1573. 8°. A-E^8,F^4 (pp. 68); (2nd pt.) A-D^8,E^4. Pasteboard (grey) with parchment spine to protect inner binding, parchment with gold stamped centrepiece and an inner and outer fillet; pastedowns of parchment, marbled paper.
Pasteboard, upper^v, AW wrote 'Poemata [/] Anagrammata'. Flyleaf, upper^v, AW wrote the titles of 4 printed works in this vol., within guidelines made with red ink. Tp, signature, 'Stephen Risselsden his book. pr^m. f.s.' (5 shillings?). 2nd C1, note, not in AW's hand: 'Inscius Actaeon vidit / sine veste Dianam, / Praeda suis canibus / non minus illi fuit.'
Wood 105(1). STC 25671 (with rpt. of 14656.7).

6608. William 3*. *The maner of quartering the p^r. of Orange his army both horsse and foote*. N.p.: n.pub., 1685 or after. S.sh. Engraving, 'Fig: 5. Par: 3. Cap: 2.'
Wood 276b(118) (not in Bodl. CD cat.). Not identified.

6609. William 3*. *An account of the reasons of the nobility and gentry's invitation of . . . the prince of Orange into England. Being a memorial from the English protestants concerning their grievances*. London: f N. Ranew a. J. Robinson, 1688. Fol. Pp. [3], 28.
Tp, AW wrote 'Bought at Oxon in the later end of Januar 1688[9] i^s-', LT 3.297-8.
Wood 660c(37). Wing A379.

6610. William 3*. *An answer to a paper, intitled, Reflections on the prince of Orange's declaration*. [London]: n.pub., [1688]. 4°. Pp. 8.
P. 8, AW wrote, 'commonly sold in Oxon. in the latter end of Nov. & beg. of Dec.' LT 3.286.
Wood 529(4). Wing A3331.

6611. William 3*. *A letter to the author of the Dutch design, anatomized. Written by a citizen of London [8 Nov.].* [London]: n.pub., [1688]. 4°. Pp. 4.
P. 1, AW wrote, 'The Dutch designe was an Answer to the P. of O his Declaration.', an identification of initials of a publisher, 'Hen. Hill', and an underscoring. LT 3.286.
Wood 529(6). Wing L1724 ('O' not recorded in Wing).

6612. William 3. *The prince of Orange his declaration: shewing the reasons why he invades England [10 Oct.].* London: R. Taylor, 1688. 4°. Pp. 32.
Tp, AW wrote, 'The additional or 2^d. Declaration is here, p. 16.' Bsm. Pp. 10, line in margin; 32, 'These remarks were commonly sold in Ox in the latter end of Nov. 1688'. LT 3.285.
Wood 529(2). Wing W2331.

6613. William 3*. *A review of the reflections on the prince of Orange's declaration.* [London]: (f. W. Churchil), 1688. Fol. Pp. 4.
P. 4, AW wrote, 'In the beginning of Dec - 88'. LT 3.286.
Wood 529(9). Wing R1199 ('O' not recorded in Wing).

6614. William 3*. *Seasonable and honest advice to the nobility, clergy, gentry, souldiery, and other the king's subjects, upon the invasion of . . . the prince of Orange.* (London): (printed and sold R. Taylor), (1688). 4°. Pp. 8.
P. 8, AW wrote, 'commonly sold in Oxon in the middle of Nov. 1688'. LT 3.286.
Wood 529(7). Wing S2214 ('O' not recorded in Wing).

6615. William 3*. *Some reflections upon . . . the prince of Oranges declaration [of 10 Oct. 1688].* (London): n.pub., (1688). 4°. Pp. 12.
P. 12, AW wrote, 'commonly sold at Oxon 17. Nov. 1688'. LT 3.286.
Wood 529(3). Wing S4589 ('O' not recorded in Wing).

6616. William 3 and Mary 2. Coronation. *A description of the ceremonial proceedings at the coronation of . . . king William III. and queen M[ary] [11 Apr.].* [London]: n.pub., [1689]. S.sh. (mutilated).
Wood 276a(105). Wing D1154A (two).

6617. William of Newburgh. Silvius, G. ed. *Rerum Anglicarum libri quinque.* Antverpiae: ed. G. Silvius, 1567. 8°. Pp. [16], 519, [20]. Calf with two sets of 3 fillets, some stamp decoration and clasp holes; spine, 4 bands.
A4-10, some notes, not in AW's hand.
Wood 220. BL.

6618. Williams, John. Chichester, bp. of. *The history of the gunpowder-treason, collected from approved authors.* London: f. R. Chiswel, 1679. 4°. 2nd impr. Pp. [4], 31, [1].
Tp, bsm.
Wood 608(49). Wing W2705.

6619. [Williams, John]. Chichester, bp. of. *An impartial consideration of those speeches, which pass under the name of the five Jesuits. Lately executed.* London: f. R. Chiswell, 1679. Fol. Pp. [2], 14.
Wood 424(27). Wing W2709.

6620. [Williams, Nathaniel]. *A Pindarique elegy on the most famous . . . physitian d^r· Willis.* [Oxford]: [L. Lichfield], [1675]. 8°. Pp. 4.
P. 4, AW wrote, 'Printed at Oxon. by L. Lichfeild 22. Nov. 1675'. AOF 2.353; LT 2.329; AO 1047ff.
Wood 429(34). Wing W2748. Madan 3082.

6621. Williams, William. *The speech of . . . to the . . . house of commons, upon the electing of him speaker in the parliament . . . with his speeches to his . . . majesty.* Oxford: L. Lichfield f. G. Kunholt, London, 1681. Fol. Pp. 17 (p. 1 blank).
P. 1, former no., 'q[uaere]', in pencil.
Wood 657(44). Wing W2782.

6622. [Wilmot, John]. Rochester, 2nd earl of. *A satyr against mankind.* [London]: n.pub., [1675?]. Fol. Pp. 4.
AW wrote the year, '1679', in pencil. Line 1, a correction. Response at Wood 417(8), item 5283
Wood 417(7). Wing R1759.

6623. Wilmot, John. Rochester, 2nd earl of. *Valentinian: a tragedy, as 'tis alter'd [from Valentinian by*

F. Beaumont and J. Fletcher]. London: f. T. Goodwin, 1685. 4° (cropped). Pp. [32], 82, [1].
Tp, AW wrote, 'Note that when this Trag. as altered by Joh. E. of Roch. was published at the latter end of his poems, printed 1691, the said preface was then omitted. Therefore keep this.' Pp. [4-9], AW made lines in margin, in pencil, at portions he later quoted in his AO 3.1231.
Wood 607(8). Wing F 1354.

6624. [Wilson, Arthur]. *The five yeares of king James, or, the condition of the state of England, . . . by s^r Foulk Grevill [or rather by A. Wilson.].* London: f. W. R., 1643. 4°. Pp. [2], 84.
Tp, under 'Grevill', 'v. Grey [?]', may not be in AW's hand. Bsm.
Wood 486(8). Wing W2887.

6625. Wilson, Arthur. *The history of Great Britain, being the life and reign of king James the first.*
London: f. R. Lownds, 1653. Fol. Pp. [13], 292, [8] (misnumbering at 153-160). Calf, mottled, with 2 gold-stamp fillets; spine, gold stamp decoration in 7 panels; rebacked.
Tp, bsm. P. [13], hand pointers in margin and underscoring of 'Presbyter' and 'Independent', may be by AW; 54, note, prob. not by AW; 67, 70, pencil lines in margin and 70, at Gresham, AW wrote 'Edward Gresham'; 72, at 'brought the news to Sir Thomas Overbury', AW wrote 'he was then dead', in pencil, and 'that could not be, because he was then dead', in ink; 120, pen line in margin; 152, hand pointer in margin; 158^v, he wrote, 'Dr Will. Rawley who hath excellently written the life of this great man L. Chanc. Bacon, hath none of these stories'; and 160^v, a correction, and, at printed 'his great spirit' (Bacon's), AW wrote, 'of a very poore spirit', and at his lack of funds, 'He had 2000^{li} per an. in Lands & offices when he died – so Dr Will. Rawley in the life of the Lord Bacon.' Also identifications, added information, corrections, and lines at pp. 172 (e.g., 'This seems to be false. See Howell, <u>Letters</u>, printed 1655. vol. 4. p. 79. 80. &c' (i.e., Wood 723a, item 3702)), 225-6, 229, 248, 257, 279, 286, and at 2 entries in the index.
Wood 407(1). Wing W2888.

6626. W[ilson], J[ohn]. *The English martyrologe conteyning a summary of the lives of . . . saintes . . . by a Catholicke priest.* [St. Omer]: [English College Press], 1608. 8°. Pp. [16], 356, [29]. Parchment with 2 clasp holes.
Tp,, 'ABosco, Bellositanus.' in red ink (LT 1.310). Passim, a few notes, dates, underscorings, in more than one hand. AW's hand is apparent on pp. 81 and 124, 2 cross-references; on p. 284 in the note at Ethelbrit [Etherbertus] and Ethelred: 'These 2 martyrs were buried at Wakering in <u>Kent</u> – ita liber Ramsey Cap[grave] 125', in red ink (See *Acta Sanctorum Octobris* (Bruxellis, 1853), 8.94); and on p. 56 the date '922'. The table and catalogue of martyrs has marks and some notes about the no. of martyred priests and laymen, prob. by AW. For response, see the following, Wood 586(14), item 6627.
Wood 296. STC 25771. ARCR 2.806.

6627. Wilson, John*. *The fierie tryall of Gods saints; . . . as a counter-poyze to J. W[ilson] priest his English martyrologe. And the detestable ends of popish traytors.* London: T. P[urfoot] f. A. Johnson, 1612. 4°. Pp. [4], 10, 40, [22].
Responds to the preceding, item 6626. Tp, signature, 'Tho Martial' [Marshall, AO 4.170], cropped at top. H4^v-I3 (pp. [16-21]), at a list of Catholic 'Traytors as were executed', AW wrote, in red ink, dates, identified martyrs or put in cities from which they came, and added 2 longer notes: H4^v, 'These addititions in red inke, were taken from Catal Martyrii pro releg. Cath. in Angl. occisorum ab an. 1570 ad an. 1612 – in oct[avo] prima edit. 1612. in oct[avo] – 2^a 1614. in oct[avo] [by T. Worthington, AO 2.407 and ARCR 2.846] quam mutuo accepi a Doctore Th. Martial – pret. 11^s - 6^d. e bib. Rich. Smith - (1682)' (AO 3.1034; AW owned 2 copies of the Smith sale cat., [MS.] Wood E. 16(3) and [MS.] Wood E. 23(6b), items 1616f.); and I3, 'There were two Th. Tichbournes, one a Laic, who was hanged at Lond. (Tyburne) 24 Aug. 1601[.] another a priest hanged 29. Ap. 1602. at Tyburne 29 Ap. 1602 [sic]'.
Wood 586(14). STC 24270.

6628. Wilson, John, musician. *Select musicall ayres and dialogues, in three bookes.* London: T. H. f. J. Playford, 1653. Fol. Pp. (2), 36, 33, (1). Calf with 3 fillets and 2 clasp holes; rebacked.
Flyleaf, upper, 2nd, score and words, 'Why soe pale and wan, fond lover', not in AW's hand. Tp, 'Ant: Wood; Jan: 26. 1664: pret: 2^s-8^d:' (LT 2.29); names of composers, J. Wilson, C. Colman, H. Lawes, W. Lawes, W. Webb, N. Lanneare, W. Smegergill, E. Colman, and J. Savile, underscored. Text, some marks, e.g., pp. 1, 3, 25, 33, 35; 8, 29. Final p., at index, 3 songs marked with X; below, at music books printed and sold by Playford, 5 are marked (see J. D. Shute, 'Anthony Wood and his MS D 19(4)' (Bodl. Diss. Films 817)).
Wood 397(1) (not in Bodl. CD cat.). Wing W2911.

6629. Wilson, Matthew. *A direction to be observed by N. N. if hee meane to proceede in answering the* *booke intituled Mercy and truth, or charity maintained by Catholiks. [W. Chillingworth's answer appeared as The religion of protestants].* [England]: [English Secret Press], 1636. 8°. Pp. 3-42. Each 12° leaf is pasted on an 8° template. Tp, 'Mr Chillingworths motives to forsake the Protestant Religion p. 37. Many notable things in this little book', not by AW, and below title, AW wrote 'Edw. Knott Jesuit, authour of this book' (Knott is an alias for Wilson). Text, pp. 7-13, etc. some marks in margins, not in AW's manner. Pp. 34, a correction; 37, at printed 'Motives', AW wrote 'under his owne hand p. 36.' Wood 869(2). STC 25777. ARCR 2.820.

6630. [Wilson, Samuel]. *An account of the province of Carolina in America.* London: G. Larkin f. F. Smith, 1682. 4°. Pp. 26 (misnumbering).
Wood 386(18). Wing W2932.

6631. Wilson, Thomas. *The arte of rhetorique.* London: (R. Graftonus), 1553, Jan. 4°. Ff. [8], 113, [3] or Ff. [6], 119, [5] check.
Missing. MS. Wood E. 2(70), p. 19, 'art of Rhetoricke – 1553 [/] art of Logick 1567'.
MS. Wood E. 2(70), p. 19. STC 25799. *O, Folg, Hunt.*

6632. Wilson, Thomas. *The rule of reason, conteinying the arte of logike.* London: J. Kingston, 1567, Feb. or 1567 [1584?]. 4°. Pp. [4], 89, [2] or Ff. [4], 88, [3].
Missing. MS. Wood E. 2(70), p. 19, 'art of Rhetoricke – 1553 [/] art of Logick 1567' Ed. not identified.
MS. Wood E. 2(70), p. 19. STC 25813 (ff. 89) and 25813.4. (ff. 88). *O, Folg, NYPL,* and *Hunt.*

6633. Wiltshire. *Wiltshires resolution, presented with the contributions . . . to his majesties commissioners at Oxford.* Oxford [London]: L. Leichfield [sic], 1642. 4°. Pp. 6, [1].
Tp, AW wrote the date, '20. Jan. 1641[2]'.
Wood 373(16). Wing W2961. Madan 1121.

6634. W[indsor], M[iles]. *Academiarum quae aliquando fuere et hodie sunt in Europa, catalogus & enumeratio brevis.* London: G. Bishop & R. Newberie, 1590. 4°. Pp. 60 (cropped at top). Calf with 3 fillets, stamp decoration (2 leaves and sunflower sprouting fleur-de-lis) inside corners, and roll decoration at inner, spine edge (Ashm. binding).
Flyleaf, upper, 1st, 'Museum Woodianum' (i.e., Wood Room at the Ashm. Museum) and 2nd, list of 15 printed works in this vol., by an Ashm. librarian (same hand in Wood 276a). Tp, AW wrote, 'Ant: Woode: 1657:'; 'Milo Windsore CC: Oxōn socius scripsit hunc lib:'; and a brief critique, 'Desunt hic Academiae Augustodunum [Freiburg i. Br.]; ubi fuit academia Maeni[a]na de qua Eumen[i]us [floruit A.D. 289-333] Rhetor vetus in panegyrico ad V. P. Galliae praesidem per scholis Erigendis: in bibliot: pub Oxōn cum aliis panegyricis:// Olympicorum Academia in Vincenza in Italia v: Antiquar: p. 349 [? or p. 319]:'. Name of a former owner and price, lined out. A3^v, a name, lined out. P. 42, an underscoring. See AO 2.358f.
Wood 498(1). STC 25841.

6635. Winerus, Christophorus. *Panegyris scholastica in memoriam anniversariam acerbissimae passionis, . . . Jesu Christi.* [Erfurt]: (typ. C. Stockheimii, impen. O. à Riswick), 1586. 8°. A-F⁸ (last leaf blank).
Tp, price '6^d.', not by AW; note rubbed out.
Wood 836(8). Not in BL. Not in Adams. Not in VD.

6636. Winstanley, William. *The loyall martyrology; . . . also dregs of treachery:. . . characters of those regicides.* London: T. Mabb, f. E. Thomas, 1665. 8°. Pp. [16], 173, [3].
Tp, after author's name AW wrote, 'a scribler for bread & a bare livelyhood.' Numerous men noted by marks in margin or underscoring, in pencil, red ink, or dark ink, e.g., p. 28, Doctor Levens; p. 30, Sir Henry Hide [sic], Brother to the Earle of Clarendon; p. 60, Earl of Carnarvan; p. 113, a note on Isaac Pennington; p. 116, at G. Millington the regicide, AW wrote, 'He was a drunken Fellow.' and below 'Gilb. Millington was a Nottinghamshire man borne, & after his Tryall for being one of the Kings Judges, was committed prisoner to the isle of Jersey, where he lived divers yeares, died & was buried – so Edward Millington a Bookseller of Lond. his Nephew told me'; p. 128, 'Will. Say of the Middle Temple counsellour, was 2^d son of Will. Say of Ilkenham in Middles. Esq – Dr Rob. Say provost of Oriel. Coll. Oxō was the 3rd son' and 'He & Val. Walton went into Switzerland' (after the Restoration). Also among the regicides, e.g., p. 138, William Cawley, 'A deformed fellow'; pp. 139-41, notes on Thomas Hammond, Vincent Potter, Aug. Garland, George Fleetwood and James Temple. Corrections, pp. 60, 94, 107, 139. Cross-references, pp. 107, 129 (to AO). Those executed are marked in margins by an outline of a scaffold (by AW?, see pp. 114, 121, 122, 124, 125, 12, 134, 137, 144, 145, 147, 156). Index, some names marked, corrections, and, at end, 'Where is Col. Franc. Hacker?'

Wood 209(2). Wing W3066.

6637. Winstanley, William. *The honour of merchant-taylors, wherein is set forth the noble acts . . . of merchant-taylors*. London: P. L. f. W. Whitwood, 1668. 4°. Pp. [6], 86.
Tp, after the author, AW wrote, 'an impertinent scribler'.
[MS.] Wood C. 32(5). Wing W3064.

6638. [Winstanley, William]. *Poor Robin's jests*. London: f. F. Kirkman, 1673. 8°. 3rd part. Pp. 94.
Missing in 1837. 'Poor Robin's Jests – Lond. 1673' in Whiteside cat. Diff ed. at Wood 66(6), item 6642.
Wood 57. Wing W3075E (rare). NLWales.

6639. [Winstanley, William]. *The delectable history of poor Robin the merry sadler of Walden*. [London]: f. J. Conyers, [1680?]. 12°. A⁸,B⁴ (1 p. of books sold by Conyers).
Tp, t altered to 'damnable history', not by AW; ᵛ, at Lawsintney, AW wrote, 'Winstanley', and below, 'Bought at Oxon 1688'.
Wood 259(7). Wing W3057C (two).

6640. [Winstanley, William]. *Poor Robins dream, or the visions of hell: with a dialogue between the two ghosts of dr. T. and capt. B*. London: M. S., 1681. Fol. Pp. [1], 6.
AW identified T. and B: T'onge' and B'edlow'.
Wood 417(62). Wing W3073A.

6641. Winstanley, William. *Histories and observations domestick and foreign*. London: f. W. Whitwood, 1683. 8°. Pp. [16], 304.
Tp, price, '1 . 9'.
Wood 584(2). Wing W3063.

6642. [Winstanley, William]. *Poor Robin's jests*. London: ?, 1685. Pp.?
Missing in 1837. 'Poor Robin's Jests – Lond. 1685' in Whiteside cat. Diff. ed. at Wood 57, item 6638
Wood 66(6). Not in Wing. See Wing W3075A-E. Not in ESTCR.

6643. Winstanley, William. *The lives of the most famous English poets*. London: H. Clark, f. Samuel Manship, 1687. 8°. Pp. [27], 221.
Flyleafᵛ, AW wrote, 'The book following entit. The lives . . . , was usually sold in Oxon, in Octob. an 1686. [/] Tho. Elderton the poet is mention'd in the epist. ded'. Plateᵛ, 'This picture resembles that of Dʳ Will. Harvey a noted physitian'. Tp, bsms. Text, passim, underscoring, lines, notes, additions, and corrections to numerous 'lives', e.g., pp. 18; 42-3; 49, at Surrey, 'This Frances was wife, & not mother of Hen. Howard.'; 55-6, etc. P. 193, at a reference to the death of Pagan Fisher, 'living. 1685', and at an unidentified source for the vignette of Edward Shirburn, the printed 'saith a learned Author', AW wrote, 'Edward Philipps in his Theat. poet'; 217, at the vignette of Edward Phillips 'why do you not mention his Theatrum poetarum [Wood 88, item 5230] from whence you have taken all your matter in this book'.
Wood 116(2). Wing W3065.

6644. Winstanley, William. *The lives of the most famous English poets*. London: H. Clarke f. S. Manship, 1687. 8°. Pp. [25], 221.
Missing in 1837.
Wood 887b(2). Wing W3065. *O, Hunt, Clark, Folg*.

6645. Winter, Salvator. *[Begin] Nothing without God. Who had more skil made alwayes lesser words [a hand bill put out by S. Winter and J. B. Quarenteni in commendation of their elixir or vegetable spirit]*. [London]: n.pub., [1664?]. S.sh.
AW wrote, 'At the X [Cross] inne in Oxōn June 11. 1664'. LT 2.14; 5.115.
Wood 498(7). Wing W3087A (rare) (Wing, 1669).

6646. [Winyard, Thomas]. *Midsummer-moone. Or lunacy-rampant. Being a character of master Cheynell, the arch visitor of Oxford*. [London]: n.pub., 1648. 4°. Pp. [2], 6.
Tp, AW wrote, 'Wynnyard', in red ink. Pp. 3, a correction; 6, AW wrote 2 identifications: 'Franc: Lownds' and 'Pidgeon the Chymney sweeper.'
Wood 514(47). Wing W3097. Madan 1998.

6647. [Winyard, Thomas]. *An owle at Athens: or, a true relation of the entrance of the earle of Pembroke into Oxford, April xi*. [London]: n.pub., 1648. 4°. A⁴.
Wood 514(48). Wing W3098. Madan 1987.

6648. [Wise, Thomas]. *Animadversions upon Lillies grammar, or Lilly scanned*. London: W. Stansby f. R. Hawkins, 1625. 8° (small). Pp. [4], 145, [3]. Pasteboard with marbled paper pasted over outer covers. Tp, 'Wanting', prob. not by AW. This note, also on 4 of the 5 tpp in the vol., indicates that the Bodleian possessed no such printed item at the time of accession. Nos. 2-5 in this vol. of books on grammar and rhetoric were owned by AW. 3 were in his possession in 1681 and are entered on p. 16 in MS. Wood E. 2(70) (items 1228, 3661, 4161; the 4th is item 6264). AW apparently sent the 4 together in a bundle to the Bodleian. No. 1 in the vol., by Wise, is a smaller 8° and may not have been AW's. In any case it was added to the bundle when sent to the binder. The binder cropped the margins and some annotation when the fore-edges were made even. The annotations in item 1, none by AW, include lined out portions in the errata (p. [4]) and notes and hand pointers in the margins of the text.
8° A 153(1) Art. STC 25867.

6649. Wiseman, Richard*. *Londons teares, upon the never too much to be lamented death of . . . s^r. Richard Wiseman [19 Jan.]*. London: f. J. Greensmith, 'P642' [1642]. S.sh.
Missing in 1922. The Harvard Houghton copy is mutilated and, on the ^v, is dated 'January 19 1642'.
Wood 429(4). Wing L2952 (4). *O, MH*.

6650. Wiseman, Ro[bert]. Palmer, R., sculp. *Le blazon or a short and easie way to attain to the art of heraldry*. Oxford: at the theatre, sold there a. by D. Major in London, [1678]. S.sh. (engr.).
Wood 276a(63). Wing W3111 (two). Madan 3200.

6651. [Wishart, George]. Edinburgh, bp. of. *The compleat history of the warrs in Scotland under the conduct of . . . Montrose*. [Holland]: n.pub., 1660. 8°. Pp. [8], 231, [1].
Flyleaf, upper, 2nd^v, AW wrote, 'Nota T. B. [Thomas Blount] de libro sequ.' on James Graham, Marquesse of Montrose, and A. S., the author: 'J[acobus] G[raemus] De rebus auspiciis sereniss. et potentiss. Caroli Dei grā[tiae?] mag. Britanniae, . . . Interprete A. S. – printed (at the Hague 1647. Oct.'; 5 lines on J. G.; and 'A[gricola] S[ophocardio] hanc Historiā composuit, Latioque <u>donavit</u> . . . Interpretis nomen erat (Wiseheart) et e literis illis (A. S.) nomen ejus indicantibus S. Sophocardium significat. [/] See the Fasti of the 2. vol. of <u>Ath.</u> Oxon. p. 819' (i.e., AOF 2.251). Acquired 26 Nov. 1659, 1^s3^d, LT 1.288.
Wood 172(3). Wing W3118.

6652. Wither, George. *The schollers purgatory, discovered in the stationers common-wealth, and discribed in a discourse apologeticall*. [London]: [G. Wood] f. the honest stationers, [1624]. 8°. Pp. [8], 131 (cropped).
Wood 699(3). STC 25919.

6653. [Wither, George]. *The great assises holden in Parnassus by Apollo and his assessours: at which sessions are arraigned Mercurius Britanicus, Mercurius aulicus [et al.]*. London: R. Cotes f. E. Husbands, 1645. 4°. Pp. [6], 44.
P. [3], AW corrected 'Thomas Cary' to Car'ew'.
Wood 622(12). Wing W3160.

6654. [Wither, George]. *Letters of advice touching the choice of knights and burgesses for the parliament:. . . Thereto are annexed certaine reasons for new elections*. London: n.pub., 1645. 4°. T leaf and pp. 17-22, only.
Tp, 'by G. Wither' in a modern hand; bsm.
Wood 620(2). Wing W3167.

6655. [Wither, George]. *Amygdala Britannica, almonds for parrets*. [London]: n.pub., 1647. Fol. Pp. [2], 10.
Missing in 1922.
Wood 615(26). Wing W3141. *O, Hunt, Folg, Harv* (two).

6656. Wither, George. *Carmen eucharisticon: a private thank-oblation, for . . . the routing of . . . Irish rebells before Dublin, by the sword of . . . Michael Jones [29 Aug.]*. London: R. Austin, 1649. 4°. Pp. [2], 6.
Wood 510(7). Wing W3148.

6657. Wither, George. *Salt upon salt: . . . upon the late storm and the death of his highness*. London: f. L. Chapman, 1659. 8°. Pp. [6], 65.
Wood 243(2). Wing W3188.

6658. Wither, George. *Fides-Anglicana. Or, a plea for the publick-faith of these nations, lately pawned, forfeited and violated by some of their former trustees*. London: n.pub., 1660. 8°. Pp. [2], 94. Calf with 2 fillets plus 2 horizontal fillets.

Board, upper, inside, 'Jo Aubrey R[egiae] S[ocietatis] S[ocius] p^r - 6.' over what seems to be his older signature, and a scribble, 'Elez [?] [/] Elenor'. Pp. 60, 68-71, 73, etc., pointers, not in AW's manner. Pp. 90-4, a list of Wither's 82 works, printed and unprinted, all marked by lines in margin by AW; at no. 11, *The Shepherds Pipe*, at the printed 'him and Mr. W. Brown', AW wrote, 'false' (see STC 3917-8). Flyleaf, lower, 2nd^v, a scribble, not in AW's hand. LT 2.117.
Wood 562. Wing W3157.

6659. Wither, George. *Mr George Withers revived: or, his prophesie of our present calamity, and (except we repent) future misery. Written . . . 1628.* [London?]: n.pub., [1680]. Fol. Pp. 4.
Wood 646(4). Wing W3172B (Wing, or his).

6660. W[ither], W[illiam]. *Proposals to the officers of the army, and to the city of London, for the taking off all excise, taxes, and custom.* London: f. R. Ibbitson, 1660. 4°. Pp. 8.
Tp, year of publ. altered to MDCLIX.
Wood 526(5). Wing W3212A.

6661. [Withers, Robert]. *A descripion [sic] of the grand signour's seraglio, or Turkish emperours court. By John Greaves.* London: f. J. Ridley, 1653. 8°. Pp. [8], 191. Pasteboard (brown) with calf spine. 1st and last flyleaves, marbled paper.
Flyleaf, upper, 2nd^v, 'Liber Musaei Ashmoleani Oxon', not in AW's hand; 3rd^v, AW wrote the titles of 5 printed works in this vol., within guidelines made with red ink. P. 1, scribble 'tv^v' (bsm?). Lent to J. Longford, 28 June 1664, LT 2.15.
Wood 156(1). Wing W3214.

6662. Witt, Richard, and Thomas Fisher. *Arithmeticall questions, touching the buying or exchange of annuities; . . . To which are added sundry sorts of breviats after the rate of 8 per cent [by T. Fisher].* London: T. Harper, sold J. Parker, 1634. 8°. Pp. [14], 222, [2]; A-C^8; [8], 52, [4]. 3 tpp. Calf with 2 fillets; rebacked.
Flyleaf, upper, 1st, scribbles, not by AW; 2nd, 'Joan Simons her book . . . 1670'. P. [224] and flyleaf, lower, scribbles and signatures of George Synge.
Wood 577. STC 25932.

6663. Wittewrong, John, and Tho[mas] Tyrrill. *The copy of a letter from Alisbury.* London: f. J. Wright, 1643, 19 May. 4°. A^4.
Tp, AW altered the former no., '11'.
Wood 376(12). Wing W3225 (Wing, Ailsbury).

6664. Witty Jester. *The witty jester.* London: ?, 1689. Pp.?
Missing in 1837. 'The Witty Jester – Lond. 1689' in Whiteside cat.
Wood 66(7). Not in Wing. Not in ESTCR.

6665. Wolleb, Johann. *Compendium theologiae Christianae.* Amsterdami: ap. G. Blaeu, 1638. 12°. Ed. nova. Pp. [6], a foldout, 273, [9]. Calf with 2 fillets.
Flyleaf, upper, 1st, signature of Anthony Woode, lined out; and initials, H B. Flyleaf, lower, 2nd^v, a brief Greek-Latin note, not by AW.
Wood 770. Not in BL.

6666. Wolleb, Johann. Ross, Alexander, trans. *The abridgment of Christian divinitie.* London: T. Mab a. A. Coles f. J. Saywell, 1650. 8°. Pp. [10], 340, [16]. Parchment.
Flyleaf, upper, scribbles. Frontispiece, former no. '24' over '23'.
Wood 840. Wing W3254.

6667. Wolley, Francis*. *The occasion and manner of mr. Francis Wolleys death, slaine by the earle of Chesterfield at Kensington, January 17. 1659.* [London]: n.pub., [1660]. Fol. Pp. 3.
P. 3, AW wrote, 'Jan: 1659'. Dupl. at Wood 657(17).
Wood 422(3b). Wing O123N ('O' not recorded in Wing).

6668. Wolley, Francis*. *The occasion and manner of mr. Francis Wolleys death, slaine by the earle of Chesterfield at Kensington, January 17. 1659.* [London]: n.pub., [1660]. Fol. Pp. 3.
Dupl. at Wood 422(3b).
Wood 657(17). Wing O123N ('O' not recorded in Wing).

6669. [Wolseley, Charles]. *The case of divorce and re-marriage thereupon discussed. By a . . . prelate*

of the Church of England and a private gentleman. London: f. N. Simmons, 1673. 12°. Pp. [10], 155.
Tp, bsm. (?).
Wood 795(8). Wing W3307.

6670. Wolsey, Thomas*, and William Laud*. *A true description, or rather a parallel betweene cardi-nall Wolsey, . . . and William Laud.* [London]: n.pub., 1641. 4°. Pp. 8.
Dupl. at Wood 366(20).
Wood 345(13). Wing T2679.

6671. Wolsey, Thomas*, and William Laud*. *A true description, or rather a parallel betweene cardi-nall Wolsey, . . . and William Laud.* [London]: n.pub., 1641. 4°. Pp. 8.
Flyleaf, lower, 'The Cardinall', not in AW's hand. Dupl. at Wood 345(13).
Wood 366(20). Wing T2679.

6672. Woman, Monstrous. *By his majesties authority. These are to give notice to all gentlemen and others, that here is come to this place, a monstrous young woman, born in Italy, about 10 yeares of age, . . . To be seen at [added in ms.: the Kings' head Oxon].* N.p.: n.pub., [1688]. S.sh.
Below, AW wrote the date, 'July 1688'. LT 3.273.
[MS.] Ballard 46, f. 173. Not in Wing. Not in ESTCR.

6673. Women. *To the supream authority of England the commons . . . The humble petition of . . . weomen, . . . Affectors and approvers of the petition of Sept. 11. 1648.* [London]: n.pub., [1649]. 4°. S.sh.
AW wrote, 'In behalfe of Joh Lilbourne & the Levellers'.
Wood 368(9). Wing T1724A (one) ('O' not recorded in Wing).

6674. Women. *Now or never: or, a new parliament of women assembled . . . neer the Popes-head in Moor-fields, . . . with their declaration, . . . to all London-prentices, young-men.* London: f. G. Horton, 1656. 4°. Pp. 8.
Wood 654a(17). Wing N1434 (two).

6675. Women. *The ladies remonstrance; or, a declaration of the waiting-gentlewomen, chamber-maids, and servant-maids.* London: f. Virgin Want, sold John Satisfie, [1659]. 4°. Pp. [2], 5, [1].
Tp, AW wrote, '1659[60] ffeb:'.
Wood 654a(19). Wing L160 (two).

6676. Women. *The character of a town misse.* London: f. W. L., 1675. 4°. Pp. 8.
Wood 654a(27). Wing C1994.

6677. Women. *The town-misses declaration and apology; or, an answer to the character of a town-misse.* London: f. J. T., 1675. 4°. Pp. 7.
Wood 654a(28). Wing T1977.

6678. Women. *The womens complaint against tobacco: or, an excellent help to multiplication.* London: n.pub., 1675. 4°. Pp. [2], 6.
P. 2, cross in margin, not in AW's manner.
[MS.] Wood D. 30(4). Wing W3328A (one) ('O' not recorded in Wing).

6679. Women. *Triumphs of female wit, in some Pindarick odes. Or, the emulation.* London: f. T. Malthus a. J. Waltho, 1683. 4°. Pp. [8], 20.
Wood 654a(33). Wing T2295.

6680. Women. *The parliament of women (or, a compleat history of the proceeding and debates of a particular juncto of ladies and gentlewomen, . . .).* London: ?, 1687. Pp.?
Missing in 1837. 'The Parliament of Women – Lond. 1687' in Whiteside cat. See Wing P506A (1684).
Wood 61(4). Not in Wing. Not in ESTCR.

6681. [Womock, Laurence]. St. Davids, bp. of. *Sober sadnes: or, historicall observations upon the pro-ceedings, pretences, and designes of a prevailing party in . . . parliament.* [Oxford]: f. W. Webb, 1643. 4°. Pp. [4], 47.
Wood 519(3b). Wing W3352 (Wing, [Oxford?]). Madan 1292.

6682. Wonder of Nature. *'There is to be seen in this Town, the Wonder of Nature, viz. A Girl almost eighteen years'.* N.p.: n.pub., [1679]. S.sh. 8° (12 lines).
Wood Diaries 23 (item 60), f. 22, above the advertisement, AW wrote, 'Shewed at Oxon. 5. 6. 7 &c. March

1678/9'. LT 2.445.
[MS.] Wood Diaries 23b (not in Bodl. CD cat.). Not in Wing. Not in ESTCR.

6683. Wonderful Blazing Star. *The wonderful blazing star: with the dreadful apparition of two armies in the air.* London: ?, 1681. S.sh.
Missing. Cut out after 1840. T given at [MS.] Wood D. 28(1). Not in the Bod. CD cat., hence stolen long ago. Ed. not identified.
[MS.] Wood D. 28(28). Wing W3362, 3362A, 3362B (1681).

6684. Wood, Anthony. [Fell, John, ed.; Peers, Richard, and Richard Reeves, trans.]. *Historia et antiquitates universitatis Oxoniensis.* Oxonii: e theatro Sheldoniano, 1674. Fol. 2 vols. in 1. Pp. [10], 414, [vol. 2] [2, i.e., a blank leaf], 447 [an unnumbered sheet, inserted after p. 444, Hobbes's one p. 'Epistola' to AW; n.b., this insert may be wanting in some copies, e.g., Merton 3.f.5], [5] (last 5 are: Quarundam literarum, Editor Lectori (Fell's rejoinder to Hobbes), blank, Contenta Libri I, and Collegium Universitatis). This copy does not contain Loggan's engravings (but contains 2 others, as is normal, the frontispiece, by 'AD Hennin inven:' and 'R: White sculpsit:', and at 1.364, 'Ichnographia Oxoniae'). Calf with 2 fillets, 2nd rectangle with 2 fillets and stamp decoration, floral, outside corners. 2 chain holes remain on upper cover. Wastepaper, upper, brief notes in margin, not in AW's hand. Flyleaf, upper, title, in pencil, not in AW's hand, ^{v}, 5 pressmarks, 4 lined out, and the current one, '3.f.4'. Half title p., 'Liber Collegii Mertonensis ex dono Egregii Authoris Sept^{ris}. 29. Anno D^{ni}. 1674', not in AW's hand. Tp^v, small engraving of the Merton College coat of arms, pasted in. AW corrected a number of errors that he had noted in his proof copy in as many printed copies as he could, and put a note on the engraving, 'Ichnographia Oxoniae', to be inserted at 1.364, see details given at Wood 430. After 2.444, on Hobbes's letter, 'add pag. 344, 345' were lined out and 'inter pag. 444 et 445. in Lib. 2.' were added (not by AW). The same person who wrote the *ex dono* note on the t added, 'Responsio Editoris Vid. ad Lib: Calcem'. There are also 5 corrections on the p, at lines 14, 16, 24, 36, and 54.
Merton College 3.f.4. Wing W3385. Madan 2996.

6685. Wood, Anthony. [Fell, John, ed.; Peers, Richard, and Richard Reeves, trans.]. *Historia et antiquitates universitatis Oxoniensis.* Oxonii: e theatro Sheldoniano, 1674. Fol. 2 vols. in 1. Pp. [10], 414; [vol. 2] [2, i.e., a blank leaf], 447 [an unnumbered sheet, inserted after p. 444, Hobbes's one p. 'Epistola' to AW], [3 (wanting Fell's rejoinder)]. Calf with 3 fillets, 2nd rectangle with stamp decoration at corners, and 2nd and 3rd rectangles with fillets and stamp decoration inside fillets; rebacked (Ashm. binding).
Pastedown, upper, collation by later librarian. Flyleaf, upper, note by W. H. Black, 1838, about 'The original plates used in this work are still in the possession of the Delegates of the University Press except that of the Frontispiece.' (the frontispiece: Charles 2 hands over a seal; AD Hennin inven., R. White sculpsit. The Loggan plates were not finished in time to be included in copies distributed in 1674). The 'Ichnographia Oxoniae' is present, inserted between pp. 363-3. This is a proof copy. AW discovered errors on different sheets at various stages in the printing process and recorded them, e.g., in vol. 1, p. 13, at the missing footnote designator for the last note on the p., he inserted a (g) and wrote, 'mended in all the copies'; 1.15a, line 33, 'Neotus', lined out; 1.16, last line, note k, at 'cap. 4', he corrected the chapter heading to '5' and wrote, 'mended in all copies'; 1.55a, 56b, at the headings which are missing, a 'C', he wrote, 'mended in all the copies' (see also 1.107b lines 16 and 20, 1.155b line 39 (see Merton Library copy, 3. f. 4, included in this catalogue, and a 2nd Merton copy, 3. 4. 5); 2.34a, insertion of 'vice': 'mended in all copies'. At 2.134a, 139b, he noted minor errors in Roman numerals at a later stage and commented, 'ldots / false in 200 sheets' (in these latter 2 cases neither Merton copy is corrected).
AW retained this proof copy, apparently in an unbound state, as his working copy. It was bound by the Ashm. after his death, and many of his notes in the outer margins are cropped, and notes in the inner margins are obscured by the tight binding. Three mss. were inserted before the binding: 1. between 1.232-3, AW's copy of the preface, 'Author Lectori' (4 leaves, 8 pp. of ms.; there are differences between this and the printed version); 2. between 2.288-9, his ms. plan, or ichnography, of Christ Church Cathedral, in ink, 'Christ Church Cath., Oxon, with the names of those (for the most part) that have been there buried from the year 1639 to [blank, J. Fell's burial site he added later, after 10 July 1686]' and dated 'AW 1671'; and 3. at end, 5 leaves, 10 pp. of ms., which AW titled 'Faults without comparing with the Engl. Either omitted in the transl. or in writing the orig.'; many of the comments in this appendix also appear at the relevant places in the text.
AW wrote well over 1000 annotations, some extensive; at 1.3, 1 of the 6 notes on this p. has 120 words, and the length of this note is not unusual. He made these annotations over a period of time, for notes on the same p. are often in different shades of brown ink and in his different handwriting styles. They range from simple emendations and corrections, new information, especially updated information on Oxford alumni,

to angry comments. What prompted most of the latter, and the preparation of the final ms. appendix, were the deletions, additions and changes made by Dr. John Fell, with whom he began his quarrel in a 34-word ms. response on the 1st p. of the text. Here Fell had inserted the phrase, 'excultas fuisse literas,' (p. 1a). AW made other comments on pp. 2-5, equally long, and wrote 'Dr. Fell', or forms thereof, 25 times in the margins on the first 13 pages. Fell's name or 'D^r F' reappears time and again, with lessening frequency, almost to the end, to 2.378b. AW's marginal comments concerning Fell, aside from his protests at deletions, are some times clearly correct (1.2a, 'parentes nostros armis à *Romanis* victos': 'Dr Fells putting in but tis improper for an Engl. man to say so of the Britannes'); some times perhaps correct (1.2b, Fell added a section in which he gave an etymology for 'Druid' as Celtic 'Deru', 'originem habuisse censeamus', in opposition to AW's explanation of a Greek source, Δρυς); and some times quibbling. Fell had also deleted material and caused equally vigorous responses from AW. E.g., at 1.15b, he wrote, 'Here is a great de[al] left out by the mea[nes] of Dr. Fell, because he said Oracles were ceased – See tran[s,] p. 32. 33' (some cropped at side); at 1.27b, 'See something scored out in the, trans. copie p. 64'.
Everywhere AW is a stickler for correct detail and correct quotation from sources. On 1.10a Fell receives the blame for putting a lengthy section from Gildas in italics. AW wrote in the margin, 'Dr. Fell put this in Ital. but it should not be so, because tis not verbatim out of the author here cited'. The most notorious example of Fell's editing occurs at AW's vignette of Thomas Hobbes, 2.376-7, which prompted a single sheet printed letter of rejoinder by Hobbes. Hobbes had learned of Fell's editing from John Aubrey, via Wood himself (see AW's diary, 'the author acquaints J[ohn] A[ubrey], Mr. Hobbes' correspondent, with all that had passed' (LT 2.292ff.)), and responded with vigour, first in a letter privately to AW, and then publically in a published letter. AW inserted a copy of the published letter in vol. 2 between pp. 444 and 445 and it must have been with the greatest pleasure (Fell apparently removed the pp. from some copies). AW's ms. comments in his copy, at 2.376-7, are: at 'cum ingenio acri & industrio', 'put so in the place of sobrio by Dr Fell'; at 'in omni genere Philosophae versatissimo', 'viroque optimo blotted out by Dr Fell'; and, at four additions by Fell which he underscored, 'rebus permiscendis natum', 'monstrosissimum', 'publico damno', and 'in re praesertim Mathematica, cui musis reclamantibus paralogismorum perpetuus artifex operam infelicissimam addixit', he put 'Dr Fell' in the margin. AW had shown the copy of the private letter to Fell, but when Fell learned that AW had later inserted Hobbes' published letter in the work, he took the opportunity to respond, for, in AW's words, 'the last sheet of paper being then in the presse, and one leafe thereof being left vacant, the deane supplied it with his answer'.
AW did not insert Fell's rebuttal, 'Editor Lectori', normally after p. [448], 'Quarundam literarum', into his proof copy. Clark gives a detailed account of the whole matter, LT 2.259-61, 290-94; see also notes at Wood 276a(18), item 3616, another copy of Hobbes' letter. AW quarrelled as well with the translator Richard Peers (e.g., 1.249b 'Peers his doings'; 2.58a 'All this is to be in Rom, but because I put it in, was therfore forsooth by the means of Mr Peers, to the deane of Ch. put in Ital.'; 2.247b '. . . but Mr Peers very impudently scratched it out & put in this without my consent or knowle[dge] – partiallity'; 2.275; and 2.343b 'Mr Peers put this in, because his son is of ch. ch. & of his drunken acquaintance'). The 2nd translator, Richard Reeves, is not mentioned by name, but the name of Obadiah Walker appears at 2.57b, 'much here on the Engl. omitted by the business of Mr. [Obadiah] Walker'; and Ralph Bathurst at 2.301, 'these words [were] put out by D- [Bath]urst because [I?] made it.' (cropped at side). Nor did the compositor, Mr. Gallot escape his wrath, for he had failed to follow his instructions, 'This to be in Ital. but Mr Gallot would not do it.' (1.104a). Time and again he noted wrong italic or roman fonts.
Wood's own initials, 'AW', occur frequently, especially near the beginning. This may refer to his authoritative statements or to his victories in pre-publication battles. In his proof copy of AO, Wood 431a, he used 'AW' to begin marginal rebuttals to accusations (see the document pasted in between the 'Preface' and 'To the Reader'). In sum, AW was very unhappy with the editing of Fell, the translation and translators, the interference of university leaders, and the typesetting. He immediately began to prepare an edition in English, and he used this proof copy as as a rough source book for his draft of a new history of the university. This would appear in print long after his death, edited by John Gutch, 1786-96; see LT 4.231. AW's ms. index to this is at MS. Wood F. 37, ff. 1-28.
Wood 430. Wing W3385. Madan 2996.

6686. [**Wood, Anthony**]. *Athenae Oxonienses. An exact history of all the writers and bishops who have had their education in the . . . university of Oxford from the fifteenth year of king Henry the seventh, Dom. 1500, to the end of the year 1690. . . . To which are added, the fasti or annals.* London: f. T. Bennet, 1691 and 1692. Fol. 2 vols. Vol. 1, pp. [8], cols. 904 (Fasti, 634-904), pp. [5] (advertisements of books printed for and sold by Tho. Bennet, 1 p., and index, 4 pp.); vol. 2, pp. [6], cols. 906 (Fasti, 687-905), pp. [7] (index only, wanting the list of subscribers). Calf, 2 fillets around edges, and inner rectangle with roll decoration and ornaments outside corners. Each vol. has different roll decoration and ornaments. Rebacked with new flyleaves inserted.

Probably the copy given to Jonathan Edwards for the Jesus College Library. LT 3.365. Evidence of Wood's presentation may have been removed with the original flyleaves.
Jesus College Q. 12. 7-8. Wing W3382 and 3383A.

6687. [Wood, Anthony]. *Athenae Oxonienses. An exact history of all the writers and bishops who have had their education in the . . . university of Oxford from the fifteenth year of king Henry the seventh, Dom. 1500, to the end of the year 1690. . . . To which are added, the fasti or annals.* London: f. T. Bennet, 1691 and 1692. Fol. 2 vols. in 1. Vol. 1, pp. [10], cols. 904 (Fasti, 635-904), pp. [5] (advertisements of books printed for and sold by Tho. Bennet, 1 p., and index, 4 pp.); vol. 2, pp. [6], cols. 906 (Fasti, 687-905), pp. [10] (an index, 7 pp., and list of 331 subscribers, 3 pp.). Calf, rough, with 3 fillets, and 2 inner rectangles, both with stamp decoration outside fillets or between fillets; rebacked.
In this volume, the proof copy, AW has made thousands of minor corrections in the text, virtually on every page, from the time of publication, 1691-2, until his death in 1695. He has also pasted in nearly as many slips, some with a few words, and some with several hundred, to indicate major changes or additions for a new edition. Open pp. showing 4 cols. have as many as 10 or more slips pasted in (e.g., 1.31-34, 1.581-584, 1.837-840, 2.219-222, 2.487-490, 2.709-712 (19 slips), 2.789-792, 2.833-836, 2.837-840, 2.853-6, 2.857-860). The slips range in size from 2-3 x 4-5 cm., to octavo and quarto size sheets. Many are waste paper from various sources, e.g., between the 'Preface' and 'To the Reader', AW inserted a sheet on which he had copied Thomas Barlow's critical letter concerning the *Historia*. This was shortly after printed in Barlow's posthumous *Genuine Remains* (1693). 1.28-9, has a slip torn from a sheet once intended as a list of contents for (currently) Wood 752 with portions of his entries of printed works 1, 2, 4, and 5 (he had to make a later list to incorporate a new item, no. 3). At 2.815-6, an anonymous writer wrote on 9 May 1692 of work by W. Holder now at the press. AW responded: 'I have the book & the title runs thus A Treatise of the natural Grounds & Principles of Harmony. Lond. 1694. oct. He hath also written Discourse concerning Time . . . 1694' (Wood 147; see items 3633f.). At 2.877, the slip is a torn piece from a tp of *Poemation Latinum* [and below t] 'Nec fonte labra prolui Caballino [/] Nec in bicipiti &c. Pers. Prol. [1.1]', 4°, by Francis Digby (prob. Queen's Coll., B.A. 1677; this work that does not seem to have survived in any other copy, see ESTCR 31191, with a publ. date of '1715?'; see F. Digby, Wood 431c, item 2260); it has AW's note, 'Tobacco wrapt up in this paper in the beginning of May 1693'. At 2.903 AW used a slip torn from a letter written by another person addressed to 'Henry Clement, bookseller in Oxford'. He ransacked earlier ms. bundles for slips, e.g., at 1.211, he pasted a note on Bagshaw, dated by himself, 'AWood 1663'. Practically all of the notes on slips are by AW, but see, e.g., 1.323, a note by an unknown person. At 1.332, there is a letter from W. Hopkins to A. Charlett in which Hopkins found in the new ed. of AO 'as few mistakes as can be expected in a work of that nature', pointed out 2 errors in AW's entry of Harmar (among others), wished AW had 'forborn some spitefull characters taken upon fame, or the credit of mens Adversaries', and concluded, 'It will be well, if he scapes with his life when the second volume comes out, in which he will be likely to abuse some persons whose relations have a more tender concern for them, than y^u [sic] have for y^r founders'). Charlett, whose intentions were not always positive, passed this letter on to Wood. At 2.627, there is a note on S. Ward and R. Bathurst in the hand of A. Charlett (the author is identified in a note added by a later writer); and at 1.901, 2.702, and finally, 2.711, there are portions of a long letter from E. Sherburne to AW, 2 and 3 Aug. 1694, with material to be included in a new edition. The proofs of the 1691 ed. of the *Athenae* were delivered to the London publisher, T. Bennet, in early Nov 1690; vol. 1 was published 18 June 1691, and vol. 2, 18 July 1692. See LT 2.290; 3.364f., 395; 4.232. Thomas Tanner whom AW chose in Nov. 1695 to prepare the 2nd ed. for publication, implied in a letter written 15 May 1713 to a Dr. Clark that he had himself pasted in all the slips in these 2 vols. (but see 'The Booksellers to the Reader', after the tp in the 2nd ed., vol. 1, 'some Thousands of Additions and Amendments are intermixed, which the Author had with his own Hand inserted in one of the Copies of the former Edition, now reposited in the *Musaeum Ashmoleanum*'. Tanner stated in another letter, 8 July 1713 to Jacob Tonson, the publisher of the 2nd edition, that some 'hard Characters which not being true, nor just' he would be unwilling to have published 'unless they be softned a little'. T. Hearne quotes a letter from Tanner to him which also indicates that Tanner did some editing: 'There were (I must own to you) several hard words & passages more in the Original, which I thought good manners & Christian Charity, and a regard to the old Gentleman's memory, obliged me to strike out.' Hearne did not approve of Tanner's actions or of the condescending way in which he wrote of Wood (Hearne, 22 Nov. 1621, 7.300-1). The material on the slips now present in the text, apparently pasted in by Tanner, were incorporated with few changes (but see also LT 4.232). Tanner must have borrowed the vol. from the Ashm. and later returned it, for the *Athenae* is listed in the Whiteside cat. at 431a (for more on Tanner's role, see M. J. Sommerlad, 'The Continuation of Anthony Wood's *Athenae*', *BLR* 7 (1966): 268ff.
Wood 431a. Wing W3382 and W3383A.

6688. Wood, Edward. 'Published since his death by his brother A[nthony] W[ood] M. A.' Γνωστον του Θεου, . . . or, that which may be known of God by the book of nature [five sermons]. Oxford: H. H[all] f. J. Godwin and E. Forrest, 1656. 8°. Pp. [12], 240 (91-110 omitted).
Missing. AW purchased a copy 1 July 1659, 10^d, LT 1.200, 279, 418; purchased 12 copies in sheets, 13 Aug. 1662, 6^d, LT 1.450; purchased again 12 copies 2 Nov. 1663, 6^s, for which he paid half, 3^s, to J. Godwyn on this date, LT 1.503, and a 2nd payment to Godwyn, 12 January 1664, 3^s, LT 2.1; and another 6 copies, 4 May, 1664, 3^s, LT 2.12. Presented by AW as gifts, LT 1.470. See also LT 1.477 (copies bound); 1.503, 2.36 (copy or copies lent); and AO 3.397. In MS. Wood F. 51, f. 44^{r-v}, 'M^r. Woods Duplicats', there are 2 entries noting the presence of 'four of the same' of this item and yet another 'in sheets'. AW prepared a dedication to Jonathan Goddard in both the 1656 and 1674 eds., signed it in 1656 (in print) 'Antonius Wood' and in 1674 (in print) 'Antonius à Wood'.
LT 1.200. Wing W3387. Madan 2319.

6689. Wood, Edw[ard] à. Γνωστον του Θεο, . . . or, that which may be known of God by the book of nature. Oxford: H. H[all] f. E. Forrest, 1674. 8°. 2nd ed. Pp. [4], 240 (91-110 omitted).
Missing in 1837. On the tp the printed 'à' is now added to the name of AW's brother, as is, below the name of the author, 'To which is added the Authors last Sermon' (this replaces 'Published since his death by his brother A. W. M. A.'. The 'last Sermon' is, however, present in the 1st ed., and this 2nd ed. is no more than a reissue of the 1st (see Madan 2319 and 3033). The dedication is signed (in print) 'Antonius à Wood'. Neither a copy 1st ed. (1656) nor of the 2nd ed. is now in his collection. See the note at the 1st ed. Wood 881(1). Wing W3388 (5). Madan 3033. *O.*

6690. Wood, John. *Progymnasmata quaedam, quibus in philosophici Tyrocinii jam praeterlapsi specimen decertabunt . . . Sub praesidio Joan. Sylvii.* Edinburgi: A. Anderson, 1670. 8°. Pp. [6], 14. Gold fore-edge.
Tp, 'Donum Autoris viz Joan. Wood philosophiae professoris in Acad. Edinburg. Oct. 3. 1670'. LT 2.202f.
Wood 113(5). Wing W3404.

6691. Wood, John. *The poor gift of John Wood, bell-man.* [London]: n.pub., [1675]. S.sh.
^{v}, AW wrote the year, '1675'; in another hand, '1675 Belmans' Verses of Southwarke'.
Wood 416(130). Wing W3403 (rare).

6692. [Wood, Thomas]. *A dialogue between mr. Prejudice, . . . and mr. Reason, a student . . . being a short vindication of the university from popery.* London: f. T. Sawbridge, 1682. 4°. Pp. [2], 24.
[MS.] Wood B. 40(7). Wing W3408.

6693. W[ood], T[homas]. *The dissenting casuist: or, the second art of a dialogue between prejudice, . . . and reason.* London: f. T. Sawbridge, 1682. 4°. Pp. [4], 35.
Flyleaf, upper, AW wrote, 'This came out in Easter terme.', and in pencil, 'Th. Wood of New Coll the authour'.
[MS.] Wood B. 40(8) (not in Bodl. CD cat.). Wing W3409.

6694. [Wood, Thomas]. *A Pindarick ode, upon the death of . . . king Charles the second.* Oxford: L. Lichfield, f. A. Stephens bookseller, 1685. Fol. Pp. [2], 6.
Wood 429(39). Wing W3410B.

6695. [Wood, Thomas]. *A vindication of the historiographer of the university of Oxford and his works, from the reproaches of the lord bishop of Salisbury [Gilbert Burnet], in his letter . . . concerning . . . A specimen of some errors and defects in the history of the reformation . . . by Anthony Hurmer [sic, see Wharton/Harmer, Wood 206(4), item 6533, and Burnet, Wood 611(1), item 1207]. Written by E. D. To which is added the historiographer's answer to certain animadversions . . . which treats of the divorce of queen Catherine.* London: printed, sold R. Taylor, 1693. 4°. Pp. 30.
Tp, AW underscored the error in 'Hurmer' (Harmer, i.e., Henry Wharton, AO 4.331) and wrote after author, E. D., '20 March 1692[3]'. Pp. 5, 8, 11, 13-18, 20-2, corrections. Pp. 22-5, 27-9, extensive notes, written in dark and red ink, most are cropped. E.g., 22, at the author's explanation of how 'many bold and undeniable Truths' of AO, vol. 2, caused 'several Persons (whose Relations had been Actors in, or submitters to the Men in the said unparallel'd Rebellion,) have endeavored to make them Abuses and Libels, thereby to bring the Author into trouble', AW wrote, 'And [as, lined out] yo[u] shall find some ill things put into the book by other hands (the Author being then in a remote place) & thereby indead [sic] he has been made a Tool to speak the sense of envious persons, for which he has in some degree sufferd', and added in red ink, 'put out of the [copie]' (cropped at bottom); 23, an added reference, in dark ink, severely cropped, followed by, in red ink, 'put out [of] the cop[ie] by the L[icen]ser'; and also on p. 23, below, a 2nd note concerning an omitted reference in the printed text, '(*) Works of the Learned &c. before mention'd,

p. 4.' (i.e., [MS.] Wood E. 24a, item 1537, which includes on p. 4 a publication notice of AO), and below added later in red ink, 'omitted by the printer'; 25, at printed, 'Had it not been for Mr. *Harmer's* reference to a passage in the Second Volume of the *Athenae Oxon* the Character of a *Scribler*, and other most terrible things of the <u>Historiographer</u> [AW lined out the last 8 printed words, 'and . . . <u>Historiographer</u>], would not have been mention'd', and, in the margin at lined out words, wrote, 'no such [thing?] in the orig[inal] copie.' (cropped at side); 27, note of about 10 words on Bishop Ward, badly cropped, and added later in red ink, 'put out [by] the Lic[enser]; 28, at a lengthy quotation from 'To the Reader' in the *Athenae* (AO 1.clvi) in which AW argued that the '*Herculean* Labour' of the AO would have been more proper for a 'Head, or Fellow of a College, or for a Publick Professor . . . a Virtuoso, and to know all Men, . . . Or for one who frequents much Society', he inserted a footnote marker after 'much Society' and wrote in the margin the phrase printed in the AO but omitted here 'in common rooms, at public fires, in coffey-houses, assignations, clubs, &c.' and later added in red ink, 'put out by the Licenser', P. 29, other longer notes, badly cropped, followed by 'put out' by the Licenser. This work, signed 'E. D.', is assumed to have been by his nephew Thomas Wood, who aided AW in the trial for libel brought against him by Henry Hyde, second earl of Clarendon, but AW certainly had a hand in the composition. He recorded in his diary, 28 March 1693, that the final copy went to the printer: 'my *Vindication* went to London in More's waggon'. A printed copy came to Oxford on 20 April. LT 3.419-20.
Wood 614(7). Wing W3412.

6696. Woodhouse, John. *A guide for strangers in the kingdome of Ireland.* London: f. J. Rothwell, 1647. 8°. A⁸ (wanting the map).
Tp, AW wrote, 'To be put betw. p. 24 & 25' (i.e., of Wood 510(21), item 6697). AW's binder inserted Gookin, Wood 510(22a), item 3260, in the wrong place, between the 2 items by Woodhouse.
Wood 510(22b). Wing W3464 (two).

6697. Woodhouse, John. *The map of Ireland, with the exact dimensions of the provinces . . . and . . . with the names . . . alphabetticly set downe. [Followed by] The returns of the surveys from Ireland [and by] A summary relation of the benefits . . . to all such as have adventured for lands in Ireland.* London: M. Simmons f. T. Jenner, 1653. 4°. Pp. 1-8, 1-4, 9-24, 25-31 [2nd segment should be at end; last segment misplaced in vol.], and a fol. map.
1st p. 3, 4 entries in margin, not by AW. LT 1.181.
Wood 510(21). Wing W3465.

6698. Woodstock. Manuscript. *Rosamonds bower at Woodstock Park.* N.p.: n.pub., n.d. S.sh.
Drawings, script, and professional analysis of the archeological site, not in AW's hand (see Sylvia Landsberg, *The Medieval Garden* (London, 1995): 21 and fig., and Simon Turley, *The Royal Palaces of Tudor England* (New Haven and London, 1993): 167, fig. 215).
Wood 276b(43).

6699. Woodstock Grammar School. Gregory, Francis, ed. *Votivum Carolo, or a welcome to . . . Charles the II.* [Oxford]: [H. Hall], 1660. 4°. Pp. [8], 20.
Tp, below, AW wrote, 'June: 1660'.
Wood 319(10). Wing W3475. Madan 2540.

6700. Woodward, Hezekiah. *Christ-mas day, the old heathens feasting day.* London: f. H. Cripps, 1656. 4°. Pp. [6], 3-28 (imperf., wanting pp. 1-2).
Tp, AW wrote a former no., 'numb. 6'; a scribble above, '6Agt' (?), not by AW.
[MS.] Wood C. 17(6). Wing W3482.

6701. Woolnough, Tho[mas]. Χους επιστρεφομενος: *or, the dust returning to the earth. Being a sermon preached at the interrment of . . . Tho. Lloyd.* [London] in the Savoy: T. N. f. J. Collins, sold J. Jordan in Glocester, 1669. 4°. Pp. [2], 20.
Tp, 'Woolnough' underscored.
Wood 634(4). Wing W3530A (two).

6702. Worcester. *A true relation of the late battaile before Worcester.* London: f. T. Underhill, 1642, 30 Sept. S.sh.
ᵛ, AW wrote, 'Sept'; 'The Battell before Worcester 5th of September 1642', not in AW's hand.
Wood 375(12). Wing T2976 (3).

6703. Worcester. *A copy of the articles for the surrender of the city of Worcester . . . to major gen. Rainsborow.* London: f. F. Coles, 1646. 4°. Pp. [2], 6.

Dupl. at Wood 612(37).
Wood 501(21). Wing C6203A.

6704. Worcester. *A copy of the articles for the surrender of the city of Worcester, . . . to major gen. Rainsborow.* London: f. F. Coles, 1646. 4°. Pp. [2], 6.
Tp, '1ᵈ', may not be in AW's hand. Dupl. at Wood 501(21).
Wood 612(37). Wing C6203A.

6705. Word in Due Season. *A word in due season to the ranting royallists, and rigid Presbyterians.* [London]: n.pub., 1660. 4° (wanting all after p. 8). Pp. 8.
Tp, AW wrote 'Apr:'.
Wood 608(6b). Wing W3542.

6706. Word to Purpose. *A word to purpose: or, a Parthian dart, shot back to 1642, and from thence . . . to 1659.* [London]: n.pub., 1659. 4°. Pp. 15.
Tp, AW wrote 'Bund. 1. [/] After 12 queries' (i.e., after England, Parliament Satire (1659), Wood 613(41), item 2797), in pencil. P. 12 at second point, '2'.
Wood 620(21). Wing W3566.

6707. World's Wonder. *The worlds wonder. This is to give notice . . . a living busiee . . . out of the great mogul's country.* N.p.: n.pub., [1687?]. S.sh.
AW wrote, 'To be seen at the Flower de Luce in Oxon. Apr. 1687'. LT 3.218-9.
[MS.] Wood B. 35(33) (not in Bodl. CD cat.). Not in Wing. Not in ESTCR.

6708. Worthy Panegyric. *A worthy panegyrick upon monarchy.* London: f. W. B., 1680. S.sh.
AW wrote, at the date of publ., 'reprinted', in pencil; ᵛ, '1658', in pencil, and '1680'.
Wood 416(10). Wing W3633.

6709. [Wortley, Francis]. *Britanicus [Marchamont Nedham] his blessing. [Followed by] Britanicus his welcome.* Cambridge: R. Daniel, 1646. 4°. Pp. 6.
P. 3, AW wrote, 'His pedigree p. 26' (it is not clear to which book AW is referring).
Wood 483(3). Wing B4821.

6710. Wortley, Francis. *Characters and elegies.* [London]: n.pub., 1646. 4°. Pp. [8], 68.
Tp, after author, AW wrote, 'of Yorksh.'; below, 'Liber Gulielmi Dugdale. Ex dono Authoris [/] Given to me Ant. à Wood by Sʳ Will. Dugdale Garter . . . [remainder, cropped at bottom]' (Dugdale was appointed Garter king of arms in 1677 and died in 1686). Pp. [6-7], pencil marks in margin, not in AW's usual manner; 32, 39, 45 (correction by AW), 34, 36, 49, 61, underscoring or line in margin, prob. by AW. LT 2.505.
Wood 483(2). Wing W3634.

6711. [Wortley, Francis]. *Mercurius Britanicus his welcome to hell: with the devills blessing to Britanicus.* [London]: n.pub., (1647). 4°. Pp. 8.
P. 1, AW wrote the name of the author, 'Sʳ Fr. Wortley' and below, some additions, '13ᵖ· 8ᵈ·' minus '4. 10.' equals '8. 10', plus '13. 8' equals 'long. 22. 6.', and 'alb: min. 11. 0' and 'max. 12.8'. P. 8, line in margin at the 'Epitaph', in pencil.
Wood 622(14). Wing W3641.

6712. Wotton, Henry. *The elements of architecture, collected by . . . from the best authors and examples.* London: J. Bill, 1624. 4°. Pp. [10], 123. Rough calf with 3 fillets, stamp decoration inside corners (Ashm. binding); rebacked.
Flyleaf, upper, 2nd, the titles of 9 printed works in this vol., by an Ashm. librarian. Item no. (3) (cat. item 6525) was 'found to be missing in April 1992' (it was present in 1923, see note on slip at no. (8), item 6524). Tp, bsms.
Wood 618(1). STC 26011.

6713. Wotton, Henry. *A parallel betweene Robert late earle of Essex, and George late duke of Buckingham.* London: n.pub., 1641. 4°. Pp. [2], 14.
Flyleaf, upper, waste paper, a Latin disputation topic, 'A Substantiu sit prior accidenta. 18.', not in AW's hand.
Wood 535(5). Wing W3647.

6714. Wotton, Henry. *A short view of the life and death of George Villers, [sic] duke of Buckingham.* London: f. W. Sheares, 1642. 4°. Pp. [2], 28.
Tp, bsm. P. 17, AW identified 'a travelled Doctor', 'Sam. Turner'.

Wood 535(6). Wing W3653.

6715. Wotton, Henry. *Reliquiae Wottonianae. Or a collection of lives, letters, poems.* London: T. Maxey f. R. Marriot, G. Bedel, a. T. Garthwait, 1654. 12°. Pp. [11], 515. Calf with 2 fillets and also 2 vertical fillets.
Flyleaf, upper, 1st, AW wrote, 'another edit. 1672 with add[.] another 1651'. Pp. 58, 467, 470, and 493, cross-references and note, not in AW's hand.
Wood 287. Wing W3649.

6716. Woulfe, Philip. *Carolo secundo Angliae, Scotiae, Franciae et Hiberniae regi, acrostichis.* [London]: n.pub., [1660]. S.sh.
ᵛ, AW wrote, '1660 May June'.
Wood 416(82). Wing W3661.

6717. Wouwerus, Joannes, and Janus Dousa. *Dies aestiva, sive de umbra paegnion. Unà cum Jani Dousae f. in eandem declamatione.* Oxonii: G. Turner, imp. G. Webb, 1636. 12°. Pp. [24], 156, [22]. Parchment.
Tp, 'pretium:- 10ᵈ.', and below, bsm(?), 'n.c' (or n. i).
Wood 53. STC 26013. Madan 838.

6718. W[right], J[ames]. *A compendious view of the late tumults.* London: E. Jones, f. S. Lownds, 1685. 8°. Pp. [16], 209, [15] (3 pp. of books printed for Lowndes [sic]).
Tp, AW wrote the name of author, and 'published about a fortnight after the Kings death, which hapned . . . Feb. 1684[5]'. Bsm. A few notes or marks in margins, e.g., p. 33, 'Titus Oates' and a correction; 105, AW underscored the printed reference to the engravings to accompany the 'History and Antiquities of the University', given as a gift to the Queen; 160, at name of an emperour of Fez and Morocco, 'False'; and P8ᵛ (last leaf), not by AW, 'Here followes the Relation of the King death.' (Wood 236(4), item 1827). LT 2.504, 549; 3.18.
Wood 236(3). Wing W3692.

6719. W[right], J[ames]. *On the death of the reverend dr. John Goad.* N.p.: n.pub., [1689?]. S.sh.
After initials, J.W., 'W'right M. Templi', prob. by AW. LT 1.151.
Wood 429(47). Wing W3696A (rare).

6720. Wurtzfeld, Johann. *Johannis Wurtzfeldi lachrymae justae ad busta juvenis clarissimi Hilgeri Bruelii.* Ultraiecti [Utrecht]: ex off. Abrahami ab Herwiick & H. Ribbii, 1634. S.sh.
ᵛ, AW wrote, 'Joh. Wertzfeld 1634. ad H. B.', and 'H. Bruell 1634'.
Wood 429(2). Not in BL. Not in NUC. Not in BN.

6721. Wyborne, Edward. *Serenissimae Eboracensium duci Mariae felici, faustos, fertilesq; annos.* Londini: excud. T. Newcomb, 1674. Fol. Pp. 12.
Tp, AW wrote, 'This poem of the queens being with child, was given to me by Will. Rogers of Lincolns Inne, in the presence of the author, they both being then, with others, at the Miter Inne in Oxōn. 23 Apr (Sᵗ Georges day) 1675. Anth. à Wood'. LT 3.312.
Wood 660c(15). Wing W3737A ('O' not recorded in Wing).

6722. Wyborne, Edward. *Epitaphium potentissimi et nobilissimi principis Guillelmi Howard.* Parisiis: ex typog. J.-B. Nego, 1683. Fol. '"Pp. [2], 8.
Frontispiece, AW wrote, 'This mon. & epitaph following are not over the grave of Visc. Stafford.' Tp, 'Edw. Wyburn of Sussex Esq. the authour. R. C.', and below, 'Edw Wyburn Esq authour', in pencil. LT 2.562.
Wood 427(9). Not in BL. Not in NUC. Not in BL.

6723. Wycliffe, John. James, Thomas, ed. *Two short treatises, against the orders of the begging friars.* Oxford: J. Barnes, 1608. 4°. Pp. [8], 62, [2].
Tp, former nos. in bundles, '3' and '9'. AO 2.468. All items in this vol. came from Francis Isaac, see Wood 587(1), item 3164.
Wood 587(4). STC 25589. Madan 318.

6724. Wynne, William. *Morall observations.* London: [by a.] f. E. Allde, 1616. 8°. A-B⁸,C⁴ (1st leaf blank).
Tp, bsm.
Wood 824(6). STC 26060 (two).

6725. Xenophon. Hervet, Gentian, trans. *Xenophons treatise of house holde.* (London): (J. Allde), 1573.

8°. Ff. 44 (i.e. 64, misnumbering).
Missing. MS. Wood E. 2(70), p. 25.
MS. Wood E. 2(70), p. 25. STC 26075. *O, BL, Hunt.*

6726. Y., M. *The Hartford-shire wonder. Or, strange news from Ware being an exact . . . relation of one Jane Stretton.* London: f. J. Clark, 1669. 8°. Pp. [4], 12.
Wood 707(9). Wing Y3 (two).

6727. Y[alden], J[ohn]. *Compendium politicum, or, the distempers of government.* London: f. R. Clavel, 1680. 8°. Pp. [22], 80.
Tp, AW entered after initials 'Joh. Yalden the author'.
Wood 240(3). Wing Y6.

6728. Yalden, Tho[mas]. *On the conquest of Namur. A pindarique ode.* London: f. J. Tonson, 1695. Fol. Pp. [2], 11.
Wood 657(5). Wing Y7.

6729. Yearwood, Randolph. *The penitent murderer. . . . Nathaniel Butler.* London: T. Newcomb f. J. Rothwell a. T. Matthews, 1657. 8°. Pp. [31], 80. Pasteboard (brown) with calf spine. 1st and last flyleaves, marbled paper.
Flyleaf, upper, 2nd[v], AW wrote the titles of 6 printed works in this vol., within guidelines made with red ink (bound after 14 May 1691). Possibly acquired 27 Sept. 1657, 6[d], LT 1.226.
Wood 173(1). Wing Y23.

6730. Y[eokney], W[alter]. *The entertainment of the lady Monk, at Fishers-folly. . . . with an addresse . . . by a member of the colledge of bedlam at her visiting those phanatiques.* [London]: n.pub., 1660. S.sh.
AW wrote the month, 'Aprill:'; and [v], the date, 'Ap. 60', and a former no., '63', in pencil.
Wood 398(10). Wing Y31.

6731. Yerworth, Samuel. *Introductio ad linguam Ebraeam, brevissima.* Oxoniae: H. Hall, venund. G. Webb, 1650. 8°. Pp. [4], 40, [1]. Calf with 3 fillets and a vertical line of 3 fillets.
Flyleaf, upper, 3rd[v], AW wrote the titles of 3 printed works in this vol., in dark ink with nos. in red ink.
Tp, AW wrote 'Ant– Woode: 1657', erased and lined out. AO 3.276f.
Wood 875(1). Wing Y36 (rare). Madan 2040.

6732. York. *The humble petition of the gentrie and commons of the countie of York, presented to his majestie . . . [22 April]. And his majesties message . . . concerning . . . Hull [24 April].* London: R. Barker, assigns of J. Bill, 1642. 4°. Pp. [2], 6.
Tp, AW wrote 'Dup', in pencil. There is a slightly diff. petition at Wood 373(50).
Wood 614(45). Wing H3503.

6733. York. *The humble petition of the gentry, ministers, . . . of the county of York . . . April 5.* London: f. C. Greene, 1642. 4°. Rpt. of York edition. A[4].
Tp, AW overwrote the former no. with '50'; below, a no., '34'.
Wood 373(50). Wing H3509.

6734. York. *Newes from York, and the North, June 7.* London: f. F. Coules, 1642. 4°. A[4].
Tp, AW lined out a former no., '63', altered '16' to '15'; wrote 'The contents of this is mostly in the pamphlet, nu. 64' (i.e., Wood 374(16), item 1728); and after date of publ. added 'Jun 3 Jun. 4'.
Wood 374(15). Wing N1027A (3) (Wing, York and).

6735. York. *Two petitions of the county of Yorke.* [London]: f. F. Coles, 1642. 4°. Pp. 8.
Tp, AW lined out former no., '62'.
Wood 374(14). Wing T3507A.

6736. York. *Horrible newes from Yorke, Hull, and Newcastle, concerning the kings majesties intent to take up armes.* London: f. T. Ryder, 1642, 24 May. 4°. A[4].
Tp, AW lined out 1 former no., '59', and let a 2nd stand, '67'; 'v. nu. 58' (former no. of preceding pamphlet, England, Parliament (1642), Wood 374(3), item 2647); and, at 'May 24', '– 20'.
Wood 374(4). Wing H2860A.

6737. York. *An abstract from Yorke . . . from the twenty-fourth of June to the first of July.* London: f. B. Allen, 1642, 5 July. 4°. Pp. 8.
Tp, AW lined out the former no., '6', and altered '75' to '25'; and p. 3, identified the Archb. of York, 'Jo.

Williams'.
Wood 374(25). Wing A115A.

6738. York. *Advertisements from Yorke and Beverly, July the 20*[th]. London: n.pub., 1642, 28 July. 4°. Pp. [2], 6.
Tp, AW lined out the former no., '73'.
Wood 374(29). Wing A627.

6739. York. *An extract of letters*. London: R. O. & G. D. f. B. Allen, 1642, 9 Aug. 4°. Pp. [2], 5.
Tp, AW lined out the former nos., '76', '9'.
Wood 374(32). Wing E3909.

6740. York. *Exact and certaine newes from the siege at Yorke*. London: M. Walbanke, 1644, 3 July. 4°. A⁴.
Wood 377(16). Wing E3592 ('O' not recorded in Wing).

6741. York. *The declaration of the lords knights and gentlemen of the county of York with a letter to . . . lord general Monk*. London: T. Leach, 1659[60]. S.sh.
AW added to the year, 'ffeb:'.
Wood 276a(243). Not in Wing. Not in ESTCR. Similar to Wing L1345 and Steele 3153, but this, a solicitous letter to Monck, 13 lines, followed by 'The Declaration', 12 lines, and 27 names, has a different title.

6742. York. *An extract of a letter from York, dated the 31. of Decemb. 1659. concerning the lord Fairfax's raising that county in arms against illegal taxes . . . in 1648*. London: n.pub., 1659[60]. S.sh.
Lines in margin at Fairfax and t, in ink and pencil.
Wood 276a(119). Wing E3906.

6743. York. *The proceedings at the assizes holden at York. The 24th. day of July, 1680. . . . against several prisoners then indicted for the . . . popish plot*. London: f. T. Simmons, 1681. Fol. Pp. [4], 32.
Tp, 'bought of Mr Rich Davis 15. Jan. 1680[1] – 1ˢ-0', and 'of Mr Davis Jan. 15. 80[1]'. Bsm. P. 5, line in margin, in pencil. LT 2.512.
Wood 426(29). Wing P3573B (3) ('O' not recorded in Wing).

6744. Younge, Richard. *Anti-Quakerism, or, a character of the Quakers spirit*. London: for the author, 1659[60]. S.sh.
Wood 416(71). Wing A3507 (two).

6745. Your Servant. *Your servant gentlemen, or what think you of a query or two more?*. London: n.pub., 1659[60]. 4°. Pp. 8.
Tp, no. '46', in pencil, in a former bundle.
Wood 613(51). Wing Y202.

6746. Youth's Treasury. *Youth's treasury; or, a store-house of wit and mirth*. London: f. I. Blare, 1688. 8°. Pp. [4], 20.
Missing in 1837. 'Youths Treasury – 1688' in Whiteside cat.
Wood 94(7). Wing Y212 (rare). *O* (Harding C3595; cropped at top, note rubbed out).

6747. Zacharias. *The song of Zacharias called benedictus*. [Oxford]: [L. Lichfield], [1693]. S.sh.
AW wrote, 'Impr. per Len. Lichfield Oxōn 22. Nov. 1693'. LT 3.435.
Wood 276a(515) (not in Bodl. CD cat.). Not in Wing. Not in ESTCR.

6748. Z[achary], T[homas]. *A word to the officers of the army*. (London): (f. G. Calvert), (1657). 4°. Pp. 8.
Tp, scribble in pencil (3?).
Wood 609(43). Wing Z4.

6749. Zampini, Matteo. *De origine, et atavis Hugonis Capeti*. Parisiis: ap. T. Brumennium, 1581. 8°. Ff. [8], 102 and fold out. Parchment with 2 clasp holes.
Tp, bsm. A7, 'Henrici Jackoni Oxon. Coll. Corp. Christi. MDC.' Passim, a few notes and underscoring, most prob. by Jackson (LT 1.442, 459), or, a 3rd person (A2ᵛ). Flyleaf, lower, last, names, rubbed out, and 'Smythe'.
Wood 239. BL.

6750. Zarate, Augustin de. Nicholas, Thomas, trans. *The strange and delectable history of the discoverie*

and conquest of the provinces of Peru. London: [J. Charlewood, W. How, a. J. Kingston f.] R. Jhones, 1581. 4°. Ff. [4], [1-12], 13-88, [4] (ff. 1-12 unnumbered at beginning) (wanting the added t leaf and the epistle to the reader).
[MS.] Wood B. 40(17). STC 26123.

6751. Zeale, John. *A narrative of the phanatical plot, setting forth the treasonable and wicked designs . . . the evil practices of John Rowse, . . . William Lewis . . . and others.* [London]: f. the author, sold by most booksellers in Westminster and London, 1683. Fol. Pp. [8], 36.
Tp, AW wrote, '1s'.
Wood 428(6). Wing Z10.

6752. Zouche, Richard. *Elementa jurisprudentiae, . . . Quibus accessit descriptio juris & judicii temporalis.* Oxoniae: excud. L. Lichfield, 1636. 4°. Pp. [12], 145, [7], 51, [7], 60, [1] (3 tpp).
Missing. MS. Wood E. 2(70), p. 46, 'Elementa jurispr. juris et judicii temporalis'.
MS. Wood E. 2(70), p. 46. STC 26132. Madan 839. *O, Folg, Hunt.*

6753. Zouche, Richard. *Cases and questions resolved in the civil law.* Oxoniae: exc. H. Hall per t. Robinson, 1657. 8°.
Missing. 19 Oct. 1657, 'I exchanged these following bookes in sheets with Mr. Forrest, for . . . [sic]: Zouch Questions, 8° . . . All amounting to a crowne', LT 1.230. Ed. not identified.
LT 1.230. Wing Z16Af. See Madan 2210.

6754. Zouche, Richard. *Eruditionis ingenuae specimina.* Oxoniae: excud. H. Hall, impen. T. Robinson, 1657. 12°.
Missing. MS. Wood E. 2(70), p. 46.
MS. Wood E. 2(70), p. 46. Wing Z19. Madan 2361. *O.*

6755. Zrõnyi, Miklũs. *The exact effigies of a monstrous Tartar taken in Hungary by . . . count Serini [engraving and verse].* London: f. W. Gilbertson a. H. Marsh, 1664. S.sh.
Dupl. at Wood 276a(3) missing.
[MS.] Wood B. 35(25). Wing E3644B (rare).

6756. Zrõnyi, Miklũs. *The exact effigies of a monstrous Tartar taken in Hungary.* London: f. W. Gilbertson a. H. Marsh, 1664. S.sh. (engr.).
Missing in 1939 (a delete sign before the entry in the 1717 list). Dupl. at [MS.] Wood B. 35(25), in a vol. which AW had bound with his table of contents before 1695.
Wood 276a(3). Wing E3644B (rare).

6757. Zutphen. *A particuler, of the yeelding uppe of the towne of Zutphen, and the beleagering of Deventer. With the . . . enterprise of sir Roger Williams.* London: J. Charlwood, solde W. Wright, 1591. 4°. Pp. 23 (1-2 blank).
Wood 615(11). STC 26134.

6758. Zwingli, Ulrich. Cottesforde, Thomas, trans. *The accompt rekenynge and confession of the faith of Huldrik Zwinglius.* [Emden] Geneva: [E. van der Erve], 1555. 8° (cropped at top). Pp. [32], 109.
P. 53, note, not by AW. Flyleaf, lower^v, scribbles.
Wood 736(8). STC 26140.

Addenda

See items 5423b and 5432b.

Appendix I
Cross Listings of Second Authors, Editors, Translators, Titles, and Peers

This appendix lists names of second authors, editors, and translators and alternative names (including titles of peers) with cross listings to main headings.

A., P., trans.: 1649
Abbott, George. See James 1 and George Abbott: 3829
Account of a vindication. See Warner, John: 6463
Account of marriage. See Marriage: 4378
Acolastus, translated. See Fullonius, G.: 3109
Adlington, W., trans.: 256
Advice from Parnassus. See News From: 4713
Aemilius, Georgius, trans.: 2148
Aggas, Edward, trans.: 3507, 3998
Agricola, Rodolphus. See Boethius, A. M. T. S.: 1027
Ailesbury, earl of. Robert Bruce: 1459
Ailmer, John, trans.: 972
Ailo, Thorny. See Taylor, John: 6152
Alanus de Insulis, ed.: 3185
Albemarle, duke of. See George Monck: 631ff., 4511ff.
Albemarle, 2nd duke of. Christopher Monck: 4510
Alfred, king. See Shepherd and the King: 752
Allen, Thomas. See Terne, Christopher, et al.: 1624
Allen, William, pseud. See Titus, Silas: 6204
Almansa y Mendoza, A. de, by: 1697
Anabaptists. See Levellers, et al.: 4138
Anabaptists. See Quakers, et al.: 5495
Anchoran, John, ed.: 3985
Andreas ab Habernfeld. See Prynne, William: 5426
Andrewes, Lancelot. See Du Moulin, P., et al.: 2331
Anglesey, earl of. Arthur Annesley: 246ff., 1439
Annesley, Francis, See Wentworth, T., et al.: 6517
Anonomus, Philanax. See Oxford, University: 4909
Another new-years-gift. See England, Law: 2572
Antibrownistus Puritanomastix. See Speech: 5979
Antidote against carnal love. See Marriage: 4377
Arch-confraternity of the holy rosary: 1642
Archdeacon, Daniel, trans.: 5968
Argoll, Richard, ed.: 4079f.
Argyle, earl of. Archibald Campbell: 1383f.

Argyle, marq. of. Archibald Campbell: 1379ff.
Armagh, abp. of. James Ussher: 6284ff.
Armagh, abp. of. Petrus Lombardus: 4213
Army. See England, Army: 2503
Arthur, king. See Knights of the Round Table: 3983
Articles of agreement. See Weldon, R., et al.: 6497
Articles of high treason. See Montagu, Edward: 4534
Arundel. See London: 4222
Arundell, Charles, attrib. to: 5193, 5199
Ashe, Simeon, by: 4664f., 4716f.
Ashley, Robert, trans.: 42
Ashmolean Museum Catalogue. See Oxford: 1523
Ashton, John. See Graham, Richard, et al.: 3277
Aston, Edward, trans.: 1026
Atkins, William. See Brommich, Andrew, et al.: 1142
Atterbury, Francis, trans.: 2316
Audland, John. See Butler, Samuel: 1247
Audley, Mervin. See also Touchet, Mervin: 297, 6624
Augustus, emperor. See Dio Cassius: 2274
Aylworth, Henry. See Becket, St. Thomas: 919
B., A. See H., J. and A. B.: 3358
B., A., i. e., Lassels, Richard, trans.: 881
B., D. See Plat, Hugh and D. B.: 5269
B., H., ed.: 3358
B., H. L., ed.: 3882
B., I., written by: 3971
B., J., ed.: 6576
B., S., trans.: 234
B., T. See Eachard, John: 2389
B., W., trans.: 4467
Bacon, Francis, by (?): 6018
Baildon, Joshua, trans.: 4464
Baker, Humfrey, trans.: 74
Bale, John, trans. or ed.: 3142, 4094
Balmerino, baron. John Elphinstone: 2433
Balsame, Robert. See H.,W. and R. Balsame: 3363
Banbury, earl of: 3984

Garter, Order of the. See George, Saint: 3187
Gataker, Thomas, See Outram, William, et al.: 1580
Gavan, John. See White, Thomas, et al.: 6559
General summons. See Hen Peckt Frigate: 532
General bill of mortality. See Griffith, Matthew: 3321
Geneva. See Litany from Geneva: 593
Gentilis, Robert, trans.: 5752
Gentillet, Innocent, author: 6283
Georgieviz, Bartholomeus. See Dordevic, Bart.: 2290
Gerbier, Balthazar, possibly by: 4270
Germany, Tears. See Lacrimae Germaniae: 4004
Gibbons, John. See Love, Christopher, et al.: 4295
Gibbs, James. See Ghibbesius, Jacobus A.: 3202
Gibson, Edmund, ed.: 244, 2310
Gilles, Pierre, preface by: 6290
Gillian. See Shepherd and the King: 752
Gilpin, George, trans.: 4375
Giraldus Cambrensis. See Ponticus, L. V., et al.: 5299
Gislenius, Augerius de Busbecq. See Busbequius: 1226
Glanvill, Joseph. See Crosse, Robert: 425
Glareanus, H. L. See Loritus Glareanus, H.: 4286
Glemham, Thomas, governor (Oxford): 4867
Gloucester, bp. of. Edward Fowler: 3076f.
Goad, Thomas. See G., T.: 3125
Goddard, Jonathon, sculp.: 3207
Godignus, Nicolaus. See Godinho, Nicolao: 3239
Godolphin, Sidney, trans.: 6353
Godwin, mr. See Godwin, Master: 3246
Golding, Arthur, trans.: 1101, 1166, 5839, 5846
Goodall, Charles. See Royal College of Phys.: 5635
Goode, William, by: 4664, 4716f.
Googe, Barnaby, trans.: 3526
Goos, Abraham, sculp.: 5773, 5982ff., 5988
Gouge, William, ed.: 5868
Gowrie, earl of. John Ruthven: 5675
Grahame, David. See Ker, George, et al.: 3958
Grand account. See England, Parliament: 2675
Grant, Edward, ed.: 271
Gray, Jane, lady. See Dudley, Jane: 2350
Greaves, John: 355, 6661
Grebner, Ezekiel. See Cowley, Abraham: 2044
Green, Thomas. See Preston, T., et al.: 5346f.
Greenwood, Daniel, vice-chancellor: 4953
Gregory, Francis, ed.: 6699
Gregory, John, ed.: 5578
Greville, Fulke. See Wilson, Arthur: 6624
Griffin, Roger, mayor: 4965, 4971
Grifoni, Giovanni Andrea: 5618
Grimald, Nicholas, trans.: 1893
Grimeston, Edward: 2760, 3272, 4072, 4418, 6684
Groans and pangues. See London, Tyburn: 4275
Grotius, Hugo, ed.: 5279
Grove, John. See Ireland, William, et al.: 3802
Gruber, Daniel. See Hentzner, Paulus, et al.: 3514
Gualdi, abbot. See Leti, Gregorio: 4131
Gualtperius, Otho. See Walper, Otto: 6429
Guard, Theodore de la, pseud.: 6441
Guevara, Antonio de. See Fenton, Geoffrey: 2980
Gulielmus Neubrigensis (William of Newburgh): 6617
Gutierrez de la Vega, Luis. See Styward, Tho.: 6086
Guydot, Thomas. See Guidott, Thomas: 3342
H., D. See C., D. and D. H.: 1253
H., D. See H., J. and D. H.: 3359
H., F., trans.: 5295

H., I., trans.: 1857
H., R., trans.: 2060
H., W., trans.: 2829f.
Habington, Thomas, trans.: 3220
Halifax, marq. of. George Savile: 5766ff.
Hall, John, ed. or trans.: 3495, 3582
Hall, Robert, pseud., i.e., Heylyn, Peter: 3544
Hamilton, R. See Scott, James: 5803
Hanmer, Meredith. See Campion, Edm., et al.: 1387
Happy return (ballad): 460f.
Harcourt, William. See White, Thomas, et al.: 6558ff.
Harmer, Anthony, pseud., i.e., Wharton, Henry: 6533
Harrington, James. See Charles 1, et al.: 1776
Harrison, Robert, trans.: 4058
Hartlib, Samuel, ed.: 2381, 6524
Hartwell, Abraham, trans.: 1148, 3366
Harward, S. See Lawson, William, et al.: 4067
Hasclock, John. See Haslock, John: 3463
Haselrigge, Arthur. See Haslerig, Arthur: 3454ff.
Hasolle, James, trans.: 2201
Hatcher, Thomas, ed.: 1414
Hatton, Christopher, ed.: 6138f.
Hawkins, Henry, trans.: 5479
Hawkins, Thomas, trans.: 1063, 3670
Hay, John, trans.: 1424
Hayward, John. See Cotton, Robert, et al.: 2032
Healey, John, trans.: 2838, 3382
Heigham, Edward, ed.: 2033
Hellowes, Edward, trans.: 3338
Hemetes the heremite. See Synesius of Cyrene: 6105
Hennin, AD, inven.(?): 6684-5
Henry 2. See Mansfield, Miller of: 621
Heraclides. See Aelian: 23
Herbert, Philip. See Hyde, Edward: 3741
Herbert, Philip. See Pinke, Robert, et al.: 5259
Hereford, bp. of. Francis Godwin: 3242ff.
Hereford, bp. of. Herbert Croft: 2062
Hervet, Gentian, trans.: 6725
Hesilrige, Arthur. See Haslerig, Arthur: 3454ff.
Hewetson, Michael. See Hewson, Michael: 3539
Hexham, H., by (?): 5814f.
Heylyn (Heylen), Peter, ed.: 3541ff., 4653f. 4750
Heylyn, Peter. See L'Estrange, Hamon: 4104
Heywood, Jasper, trans.: 5838
Heywood, Thomas, attributed to: 6493
Hickes, Francis, trans.: 4301
Hickes, Thomas, ed.: 4301
Hickman, Francis, trans.: 2316
Hickman, Spencer, trans.: 302
Hide, Henry. See Hyde, Henry: 3747
Higden, Ranulf. See England, *Chronicle*: 2509
Higgins, John. See Higgens, John: 3585
Higgins, Richard, See Emmerson, Chr., et al.: 465
High German artist. See Bartholomew Fair: 886
Hill, Lawrence. See Green, Robert, et al.: 3293f.
Himerius, sophist. See Polemon, Antonius, et al.: 5296
Hind?, I., ed.: 3298
Hobbes, Thomas. See Spinoza, Benedict: 6003
Hoeschelius, David, ed.: 290
Holdsworth, Richard. See Houldsworth, Richard: 1327
Holiday, Barten. See Holyday, Barten: 3657
Holland. See Netherlands: 4625f.
Holland, Philemon, trans.: 1370
Holyoke, Francis, ed.: 5576

Appendix II
Shelf-mark and Record Number Concordance

Each item in the shelf-list below is followed by the record number in the main part of the catalogue. If '(-CD)' follows the shelf-mark, it is not in the current Bodleian Library CD catalogue (the new version of the catalogue, on the Bodleian Library WEB site, will include these). If there are glaring errors in the shelf-marks given in the CD catalogue, a very brief reference to the erroneous volume number or item number in a volume is followed by a comma and 'CD'. More information can be had by consulting the particular record number in this Wood catalogue. The fourteen manuscript items in the Wood collection of printed books are entered below, followed by '(Ms.)' (see Index, 'Manuscript items').

Over 530 printed items once in the Wood collection are no longer present. These are entered in the concordance below and marked by (M), or they are listed at locations where they have been discovered. The missing items can be divided into two main categories: those which disappeared for one reason or another before librarians in the Ashmolean Museum made the first records of the collection; and those which disappeared after librarians in the Ashmolean Museum made these first records.

At least 211 printed items are in the first category. The evidence for Wood's ownership of these is found mainly in his shelf-list of 1681 (MS. Wood E. 2(70); see the Intro., pp. xxiif. and note 74). 128 items that Wood recorded on this shelf-list of 1681 are no longer present. Wood made 30 references in his diaries to books that he owned and that are no longer in his collection. He made 15 notes, mainly 'habeo', in his books, manuscripts and bibliographies to once-owned items. A different recorder, in 'Mr. Wood's Duplicates', noted 12 duplicates, bringing the total to 185. These include some multi-volume series such as three runs of newsbooks which he at one time owned: the *Loyal protestant*, *Mercurius civicus*, and *Philosophical transactions*. The last he sold to Robert Plot in 1686 when Plot was Keeper of the Ashmolean Museum, though they have since gone elsewhere (see item 4742). Finally, Wood sold, or donated, 26 items which are now in the Bodleian Library among Art. or Ashm. collections (see items 6648, 4508, and 6672) or in Jesus College library. All 211 items are listed at the end of the concordance below.

The second category is of made up of at least 323 items which left Wood's collection after 1717. These were assigned Wood shelf-marks and are listed in the Whiteside catalogus (1716- 7). Most of the missing items were noted by William Kirtland in his inventory of 1837-1841. He listed 52 volumes that were no longer present (five were later found, see Intro. note 80) as well as dozens that were removed from composite volumes (there are also vacancies, some later filled with non-Wood books, see Append. IV, note 11). In all Kirtland noted that 139 printed items were stolen. In most but not all cases the titles in the stolen volumes and the titles of individual items removed from the composite volumes are known, for they are either in the Whiteside catalogus or in Wood's own lists on the upper flyleaves of the volumes in which they at one time had been bound. There are no lists for five missing volumes: Wood 399, 400, 449, 692 and [MS.] Wood C. 50. No description of the contents of the last three exists, hence their contents are unknown. For the first two, however, Wood 399 and 400, the Whiteside catalogus recorded at each entry, 'Ballads'. Kirtland had no idea how many ballads were in these two volumes, but it has since been discovered that they contained about 107 ballads. They are now in two modern collections, the Roxburghe in the British Library and the Euing in Glasgow University Library (see notes at Wood 399 and 400, items 741-7 and 374; the ballads in Wood 399 are listed in this catalogue; for the ballads in Wood 400 see the Intro., pp. xxi, xlvii-xlviii and notes 28, 80 and 81).

The whole collection was transferred to the Bodleian Library in 1860 and in 1922 R. T. Milford prepared a hand-list of Wood 1-899. He noted the absence of an additional 26 items, and again the Whiteside catalogus and Wood's lists in the volumes give the titles of these lost items. Various inventories of the large single sheet volumes, Wood 276a and b, made between 1889 and 1939, revealed the loss of 23 more items. Fortunately Wood 276a contains a list of the contents made in 1717, and we know what has been lost (see notes at items 5241 and 3306).

In very recent times the collection has been more stable, but the absence of one volume, Wood 531 with 30 items, has piqued the curiosity of more than one scholar. I suspect that it is somewhere in the bowels of the Bodleian, but at the present time it remains hidden (see Intro., p. xlviii, note 82).

Wood 1 : 69 (M)
Wood 2(1) (-CD) : 76
Wood 2(2) (-CD) : 77
Wood 2(3) (-CD) : 3605
Wood 3(1) (-CD) : 78
Wood 3(2) (-CD) : 79
Wood 3(3) (-CD) : 3606
Wood 4 : 50
Wood 5 : 163
Wood 6 : 51
Wood 7 : 5531
Wood 8(1) : 98
Wood 8(2) (-CD) : 2976
Wood 9(1) (-CD) : 3274
Wood 9(2) (-CD) : 74
Wood 9(3) (-CD) : 75
Wood 9(4) (-CD) : 70
Wood 9(5) (-CD) : 186
Wood 10(1) : 197
Wood 10(2) : 198
Wood 10(3) (-CD) : 199
Wood 10(4) : 200
Wood 10(5) : 201
Wood 10(6) : 202
Wood 10(7) : 203
Wood 10(8) : 204
Wood 10(9) : 205
Wood 10(10) : 206
Wood 11 : 5703
Wood 12(1) (-CD) : 127
Wood 12(2) (-CD) : 128
Wood 12(3) (-CD) : 130
Wood 12(4) (-CD) : 129
Wood 12(5) (-CD) : 131
Wood 12(6) (-CD) : 132
Wood 12(7) (-CD) : 133
Wood 12(8) (-CD) : 134
Wood 12(9) (-CD) : 135
Wood 13(1) (-CD) : 136
Wood 13(2) (-CD) : 137
Wood 13(3) (-CD) : 138
Wood 13(4) (-CD) : 139
Wood 13(5) (-CD) : 140
Wood 13(6) (-CD) : 141
Wood 13(7) (-CD) : 142
Wood 13(8) (-CD) : 143
Wood 13(9) (-CD) : 144
Wood 13(10) (-CD) : 145
Wood 14(1) (-CD) : 146
Wood 14(2) (-CD) : 147
Wood 14(3) (-CD) : 148
Wood 14(4) (-CD) : 149
Wood 14(5) (-CD) : 150
Wood 14(6) (-CD) : 151
Wood 14(7) (-CD) : 152
Wood 14(8) (-CD) : 153
Wood 14(9) (-CD) : 154
Wood 14(10) (-CD) : 155
Wood 15(1) (-CD) : 173
Wood 15(3) (-CD) : 112
Wood 15(2) (-CD) : 174
Wood 15(4) (-CD) : 113
Wood 15(5) (-CD) : 114

Wood 15(6) (-CD) : 5232
Wood 15(7) (-CD) : 99
Wood 15(8) (-CD) : 180
Wood 15(9) (-CD) : 115
Wood 16 : 3666
Wood 17 : 6346
Wood 18(1) : 3667
Wood 18(2) : 5164
Wood 18(3) : 5533
Wood 19 : 1673
Wood 20 : 3732
Wood 21(1) : 3478
Wood 21(2) : 6491
Wood 21(3) : 184
Wood 21(4) : 5556
Wood 21(5) : 1907
Wood 21(6) : 4333
Wood 22 : 1436
Wood 23(1) : 3631
Wood 23(2) : 3632
Wood 24(1) : 5557
Wood 24(2) : 5548
Wood 25 : 5338
Wood 26 : 4018
Wood 27 (-CD) : 6216
Wood 28 : 4313
Wood 29 (-CD) : 6356
Wood 30 : 6053
Wood 31 : 1924
Wood 32 : 1375
Wood 33(1) : 5537
Wood 33(2) : 5536
Wood 34 : 1179
Wood 35(1) : 5722
Wood 35(2) : 3985
Wood 36(1) : 5103
Wood 36(2) : 3525
Wood 36(3) : 3051
Wood 37(1) : 3527
Wood 37(2) : 2004
Wood 37(3) : 5898
Wood 37(4) : 965
Wood 38 : 5539
Wood 39(1) : 2259
Wood 39(2) : 995
Wood 39(3) : 1218
Wood 40 : 3719
Wood 41 : 5143
Wood 42(1) : 6423
Wood 42(2) : 3480
Wood 42(3) : 4577
Wood 42(4) : 948
Wood 42(5) : 3253
Wood 42(6) : 5737
Wood 43 : 2950
Wood 44 : 220
Wood 45 : 3930
Wood 46 : 4160
Wood 47 : 3883
Wood 48 : 324
Wood 49 : 5512
Wood 50 : 1683 (M)
Wood 51 : 261 (M)

Wood 52 : 6352
Wood 53 : 6717
Wood 54 : 4447
Wood 55 : 6090
Wood 56 : 3577 (M)
Wood 57 : 6638 (M)
Wood 58 : 3828 (M)
Wood 59(1) : 243
Wood 59(2) : 3710
Wood 60(1) : 325
Wood 60(2) : 6217
Wood 60(3) : 5504
Wood 61(1) : 3116 (M)
Wood 61(2) : 3117 (M)
Wood 61(3) : 3673 (M)
Wood 61(4) : 6680 (M)
Wood 61(5) : 532 (M)
Wood 61(6) : 6343 (M)
Wood 61(7) : 6192 (M)
Wood 61(8) : 3254 (M)
Wood 62(1) : 3329
Wood 62(2) (and 62(3)) : 6381
Wood 62(4) : 3413
Wood 62(5) : 3407
Wood 62(6) : 3411
Wood 62(7) : 3415
Wood 63(1) : 13 (M)
Wood 63(2) : 6175 (M)
Wood 64(1) : 3179 (M)
Wood 64(2) : 1111 (M)
Wood 64(3) : 1113 (M)
Wood 64(4) : 3008 (M)
Wood 64(5) : 3007 (M)
Wood 64(6) : 5356 (M)
Wood 64(7) : 5355 (M)
Wood 64(8) : 6233 (M)
Wood 64(9) : 1391 (M)
Wood 64(10) : 1038 (M)
Wood 64(11) : 4327 (M)
Wood 64(12) : 4529 (M)
Wood 65 : 5257
Wood 66(1) : 1050 (M)
Wood 66(2) : 2415 (M)
Wood 66(3) : 4444 (M)
Wood 66(4) : 1839 (M)
Wood 66(5) : 5289 (M)
Wood 66(6) : 6642 (M)
Wood 66(7) : 6664 (M)
Wood 66(8) : 5676 (M)
Wood 66(9) : 3881 (M)
Wood 66(10). : 6364 (M)
Wood 66(11) : 5587 (M)
Wood 66(12) : 6277 (M)
Wood 66(13) : 4455 (M)
Wood 66(14) : 2107 (M)
Wood 66(15) : 5129 (M)
Wood 66(16) : 4570 (M)
Wood 67 : 6063
Wood 68(1) : 6401
Wood 68(2) : 6400
Wood 68(3) : 4607
Wood 68(4) : 3371
Wood 69(1) : 5648

Wood 69(2) : 265
Wood 69(3) : 5762
Wood 69(4) : 4350
Wood 69(5) : 5977
Wood 69(6) : 2058
Wood 69(7) : 332
Wood 69(8) : 1037
Wood 69(9) : 5352
Wood 69(10) : 2034
Wood 70 : 6065
Wood 71 : 1180
Wood 72 : 37
Wood 73 : 5728
Wood 74 : 4852 (M)
Wood 75 : 3380
Wood 76(1) : 4854 (M)
Wood 76(2) : 1161
Wood 76(3) : 3216
Wood 76(4) : 3334
Wood 77 : 5524 (M)
Wood 78 : 854
Wood 79(1) (Arch. G.f.2) : 5549
Wood 79(2) (Arch. G.f.2) : 932
Wood 79(3) (Arch. G.f.2) : 3379
Wood 79(4) (Arch. G.f.2) : 2123
Wood 79(5) (Arch. G.f.2) : 2215
Wood 79(6) (Arch. G.f.2) : 3145
Wood 79(7) (Arch. G.f.2) : 4386
Wood 79(8) (Arch. G.f.2) : 5140
Wood 79(9) (Arch. G.f.2) : 5860
Wood 80 : 5861
Wood 81 : 3671
Wood 82(1) : 3032
Wood 82(2) : 6062
Wood 82(3) : 4431
Wood 83 : 3714
Wood 84(1) : 337
Wood 84(2) : 3398
Wood 84(3) : 5610
Wood 84(4) : 1645
Wood 84(5) : 4304
Wood 84(6) : 3156
Wood 84(7) : 6178
Wood 84(8) : 3062
Wood 84(9) : 4443
Wood 84(10) : 3376
Wood 84(11) : 5621
Wood 84(12) : 1914
Wood 84(13) : 2108
Wood 84(14) : 344 (M)
Wood 84(15) : 4362
Wood 84(16) : 5128
Wood 85 : 6336
Wood 86 : 3657 (M)
Wood 87(1) : 4851
Wood 87(2) : 4850
Wood 87(3) : 2161
Wood 88 : 5230
Wood 89 : 6244
Wood 90(1) : 2948
Wood 90(2) : 3006
Wood 90(3) : 4436
Wood 90(4) : 4187
Wood 90(5) : 3873

Wood 90(6) : 1674
Wood 90(7) : 4423
Wood 90(8) : 40
Wood 91(1) : 1608
Wood 91(2) : 1621
Wood 91(3) : 1609
Wood 91(4) : 1634
Wood 91(5) : 1507
Wood 91(6) : 1456
Wood 92(1) : 4820
Wood 92(2) (-CD) : 2199
Wood 92(3) : 5252
Wood 93 : 3516
Wood 94(1) : 3158 (M)
Wood 94(2) (-CD) : 2220 (M)
Wood 94(3) (-CD) : 4326 (M)
Wood 94(4) : 3161 (M)
Wood 94(5) (-CD) : 3147 (M)
Wood 94(6) (-CD) : 3149 (M)
Wood 94(7) : 6746 (M)
Wood 94(8) (-CD) : 2825 (M)
Wood 94(9) : 3163 (M)
Wood 94(10) (-CD) : 3148 (M)
Wood 94(11) : 3144 (M)
Wood 94(12) (-CD) : 3162 (M)
Wood 94(13) : 3143 (M)
Wood 94(14) : 3146 (M)
Wood 94(15) (-CD) : 3151 (M)
Wood 94(16) (-CD) : 3150 (M)
Wood 94(17) : 3155 (M)
Wood 94(18) : 3157 (M)
Wood 94(19) (-CD) : 3153 (M)
Wood 94(20) : 3154 (M)
Wood 94(21) : 3152 (M)
Wood 94(22) (-CD) : 3159 (M)
Wood 94(23) (-CD) : 3160 (M)
Wood 95 : 357
Wood 96 : 4087
Wood 97 : 6353
Wood 98 : 25
Wood 99 : 1566
Wood 100 : 4806
Wood 101 : 4437
Wood 102 : 6351
Wood 103 : 1096
Wood 104 : 3202
Wood 105(1) : 6607
Wood 105(2) : 1847
Wood 105(3) : 6553
Wood 105(4) : 6554
Wood 106 : 6349
Wood 107 : 3332
Wood 108 : 3047
Wood 109 : 1892
Wood 110(1) : 3973
Wood 110(2) : 3972
Wood 110(3) : 1876
Wood 110(4) : 1877
Wood 110(5) : 1878
Wood 110(6) : 1879
Wood 110(7) (-CD) : 5354
Wood 110(8) : 2104
Wood 110b : 1880 (M)
Wood 111 : 1139

Wood 112(1) : 32
Wood 112(2) : 5480
Wood 112(3) : 3689
Wood 112(4) : 4269
Wood 112(5) : 6040
Wood 112(6) : 2205
Wood 112(7) : 234
Wood 112(8) : 1098
Wood 113(1) : 5876
Wood 113(2) : 4406
Wood 113(3) : 5991
Wood 113(4) : 3141
Wood 113(5) : 6690
Wood 113(6) : 3416
Wood 113(7) : 5939
Wood 114 : 3497
Wood 115 : 1158
Wood 116(1) (-CD) : 5902
Wood 116(2) : 6643
Wood 116(3) : 4027
Wood 117 : 5279
Wood 118 (-CD) : 4297
Wood 119 : 1865
Wood 120(1) : 5272 (M)
Wood 120(2) : 5719 (M)
Wood 120(3) : 4206 (M)
Wood 121 (-CD) : 5273
Wood 122 : 6017
Wood 123 : 6537 (M)
Wood 124 : 1145
Wood 125 : 5271
Wood 126 (-CD) : 3597
Wood 127(1) : 6556
Wood 127(2) : 3225
Wood 127(3) : 5133
Wood 128 : 3624
Wood 129 : 3031
Wood 130(1) : 5781
Wood 130(2) : 6196
Wood 130(3) : 860
Wood 130(4) : 6476
Wood 130(5) : 887
Wood 131(1) : 4567
Wood 131(2) : 4621
Wood 131(3) : 6474
Wood 132 : 6059 (M)
Wood 133 : 3172
Wood 134(1) : 4094
Wood 134(2) : 3942
Wood 134(3) : 22
Wood 135 : 4532
Wood 136 : 5532
Wood 137 : 2511
Wood 138 : 1480
Wood 139(1) : 1891
Wood 139(2) : 1160
Wood 140 : 2336
Wood 141 : 1403
Wood 142(1) : 4551
Wood 142(2) : 1925
Wood 142(3) : 3275
Wood 142(4) : 5619
Wood 143 : 4186
Wood 144 (-CD) : 3273

Wood 145 : 3490
Wood 146 : 222
Wood 147 : 3633
Wood 148 : 4071
Wood 149(1) : 4095
Wood 149(2) : 3262
Wood 150 : 6
Wood 151 : 6038
Wood 152(1) : 2299
Wood 152(2) : 3239
Wood 153(1) : 5541
Wood 153(2) : 3224
Wood 154(1) : 6173
Wood 154(2) : 4590
Wood 155(1) : 6140
Wood 155(2) : 6144
Wood 155(3) : 2064
Wood 155(4) : 5570
Wood 155(5) : 2284
Wood 155(6) : 2372
Wood 156(1) : 6661
Wood 156(2) : 2290
Wood 156(3) : 5118
Wood 156(4) : 3569
Wood 156(5) : 3817
Wood 157 : 3514
Wood 158(1) : 3196
Wood 158(2) : 2268
Wood 158(3) : 2111
Wood 158(4) : 5870
Wood 159 : 4043
Wood 160 : 5714
Wood 161 : 5299 (M)
Wood 162 : 3091
Wood 163 : 6007
Wood 164(1) : 3218
Wood 164(2) : 4201
Wood 165 : 4202
Wood 166 : 5960
Wood 167(1) (-CD) : 6246
Wood 167(2) : 3058
Wood 167(3) : 5312
Wood 168 : 3697
Wood 169 (-CD) : 1415
Wood 170 : 3720
Wood 171 : 6169
Wood 172(1) : 3896
Wood 172(2) : 6483
Wood 172(3) : 6651
Wood 173(1) : 6729
Wood 173(2) : 3903
Wood 173(3) : 43
Wood 173(4) : 1061
Wood 173(5) : 5830
Wood 173(6) : 5849
Wood 174 : 4469
Wood 175 : 5313
Wood 176 : 221
Wood 177 : 6089
Wood 178 : 6311
Wood 179(1) : 1265
Wood 179(2) : 1266
Wood 180 : 2128
Wood 181 : 5972

Wood 182 : 6269
Wood 183(1) : 6032
Wood 183(2) : 3042
Wood 183(3) : 3041
Wood 183(4) : 922
Wood 183(5) : 3220
Wood 184 : 3678
Wood 185(1) : 3065
Wood 185(2) : 3064
Wood 186 : 3544
Wood 187 : 5915
Wood 188 : 987
Wood 189 : 6540
Wood 190 : 1135
Wood 191 : 3066
Wood 192 : 5717 (M)
Wood 193 : 3201
Wood 194 : 5219
Wood 195 : 4424
Wood 196(1) : 961
Wood 196(2) : 5789
Wood 196(3) : 4762
Wood 196(4) : 6379
Wood 197 : 23
Wood 198 : 3608
Wood 199 : 1959
Wood 200(1) : 4200
Wood 200(2) : 4342
Wood 200(3) : 4344
Wood 201 : 6131 (M)
Wood 202(1) : 6223
Wood 202(2) : 248
Wood 202(3) : 1056
Wood 203 : 3810
Wood 204 : 3625
Wood 205 : 896
Wood 206(1) : 6449
Wood 206(2) : 5144
Wood 206(3) : 5884
Wood 206(4) : 6533
Wood 207(1) : 6531
Wood 207(2) : 5680
Wood 207(3) (-CD) : 888
Wood 207(4) (-CD) : 5679
Wood 207(5) : 3607
Wood 208 : 4339
Wood 209(1) : 5993
Wood 209(2) : 6636
Wood 210(1) : 6478
Wood 210(2) : 3938
Wood 210(3) : 6534
Wood 211(1) : 1124
Wood 211(2) : 4004
Wood 211(3) : 1958
Wood 211(4) : 2048
Wood 212 : 1373
Wood 213(1) : 894
Wood 213(2) : 3619
Wood 213(3) : 6564
Wood 214 : 1169
Wood 215 : 1055
Wood 216(1) : 3496
Wood 216(2) : 2186
Wood 216(3) : 5964

Wood 217 : 3500
Wood 218(1) : 3090
Wood 218(2) : 5958
Wood 218(3) : 3290
Wood 219(1) : 5970
Wood 219(2) : 4279
Wood 220 : 6617
Wood 221 : 5255
Wood 222 : 1151
Wood 223 : 5194
Wood 224 : 1597
Wood 225(1) : 5519
Wood 225(2) : 5606
Wood 225(3) : 1012
Wood 225(4) : 6310
Wood 226 : 4309
Wood 227 : 3923
Wood 228 : 6309
Wood 229(1) : 4624
Wood 229(2) : 6437
Wood 230 : 1416
Wood 231(1) : 1066
Wood 231(2) : 4149
Wood 232(1) : 4481
Wood 232(2) : 258
Wood 233(1) : 4465
Wood 233(2) : 5752
Wood 234(1) : 1971
Wood 234(2) : 1426
Wood 234(3) : 3686
Wood 234(4) : 3688
Wood 235(1) : 5647
Wood 235(2) : 1015
Wood 235(3) (-CD) : 1794
Wood 235(4) : 2858
Wood 235(5) : 2168
Wood 236(1) : 4190
Wood 236(2) : 5350
Wood 236(3) : 6718
Wood 236(4) : 1827
Wood 237 : 2411
Wood 238(1) (-CD) : 5191
Wood 238(2) (-CD) : 5192
Wood 239 : 6749
Wood 240(1) : 6162
Wood 240(2) : 6495
Wood 240(3) : 6727
Wood 240(4) : 3687
Wood 240(5) : 2032
Wood 241 : 6222
Wood 242(1) : 1264
Wood 242(2) : 3846
Wood 242(3) : 1831
Wood 242(4) : 1826
Wood 243(1) : 2189
Wood 243(2) : 6657
Wood 243(3) : 3059
Wood 243(4) : 3492
Wood 244(1) : 1770
Wood 244(2) : 1058
Wood 244(3) : 3555
Wood 244(4) : 3553
Wood 245(1) : 2169
Wood 245(2) : 4360

Wood 276a(127). Arch. 530 : 1746
Wood 276a(128) : 1748
Wood 276a(129) : 1804
Wood 276a(130) : 2734
Wood 276a(131) : 1717
Wood 276a(132) : 1721
Wood 276a(133) : 1791
Wood 276a(134) : 2613
Wood 276a(135) : 2690
Wood 276a(136-141) : 4724
Wood 276a(142) : 3086
Wood 276a(143) (-CD) : 2732
Wood 276a(144) (-CD) : 1817
Wood 276a(145) (112, CD) : 2144
Wood 276a(146) : 4473
Wood 276a(147) : 2547
Wood 276a(148) (-CD) : 2575
Wood 276a(149) : 1654
Wood 276a(150) : 2272
Wood 276a(151) : 5689
Wood 276a(152) : 6442
Wood 276a(153) : 3523
Wood 276a(154) : 1392
Wood 276a(155) : 3744
Wood 276a(156) : 3934
Wood 276a(157) : 6371
Wood 276a(158) : 4135
Wood 276a(159-160) : 4799
Wood 276a(161) : 1802
Wood 276a(162) : 4323
Wood 276a(163) (-CD) : 2434
Wood 276a(164) : 4081
Wood 276a(165) : 3401
Wood 276a(166) : 1041
Wood 276a(167) : 1044
Wood 276a(168-9) : 1821
Wood 276a(170) : 4596
Wood 276a(171) : 4244
Wood 276a(172) : 4723
Wood 276a(173) : 5609
Wood 276a(174) : 1133
Wood 276a(175) : 4260
Wood 276a(176) : 1393
Wood 276a(177) : 1102
Wood 276a(178-179) : 2417
Wood 276a(180-181) (-CD) : 2416
Wood 276a(182) : 3827
Wood 276a(183) : 4440
Wood 276a(184-185) : 1089
Wood 276a(186) : 6184
Wood 276a(187) (-CD) : 3924
Wood 276a(188) : 5090
Wood 276a(189) (274a, CD) : 5507
Wood 276a(190) : 3458
Wood 276a(191) : 4249
Wood 276a(192) : 2486
Wood 276a(193) : 3960
Wood 276a(194) : 2717
Wood 276a(195) : 5724
Wood 276a(196) : 3417
Wood 276a(197) : 850
Wood 276a(198) : 5912
Wood 276a(199) : 3459
Wood 276a(200) : 5460

Wood 276a(201) : 3054
Wood 276a(202) : 3894
Wood 276a(203) : 3723
Wood 276a(204) : 2294
Wood 276a(205) : 4258
Wood 276a(206) : 1852
Wood 276a(207) : 5953
Wood 276a(208) : 4167
Wood 276a(209) : 3955
Wood 276a(210) : 4231
Wood 276a(211) : 6471
Wood 276a(212) : 2926
Wood 276a(213) : 1077
Wood 276a(214) : 2721
Wood 276a(215) (-CD) : 4780
Wood 276a(216) : 1788
Wood 276a(217) : 2943
Wood 276a(218) : 3954
Wood 276a(219) : 2293
Wood 276a(220) : 5952
Wood 276a(221) : 5095
Wood 276a(222) : 5896
Wood 276a(223) : 2849
Wood 276a(224) : 4232
Wood 276a(225) : 1937
Wood 276a(226) : 2507
Wood 276a(227) : 5470
Wood 276a(228) : 5508
Wood 276a(229) : 6410
Wood 276a(230) : 230
Wood 276a(231) : 4109
Wood 276a(232) : 5452
Wood 276a(233) : 4247
Wood 276a(234) : 2792
Wood 276a(235) : 2689
Wood 276a(236) : 5094
Wood 276a(237) : 4238
Wood 276a(238) : 4116
Wood 276a(239) : 4118
Wood 276a(240) : 5695
Wood 276a(241) : 2736
Wood 276a(242) : 2384
Wood 276a(243) : 6741
Wood 276a(244) : 1174
Wood 276a(245) : 2727
Wood 276a(246) : 2728
Wood 276a(247) : 4772
Wood 276a(248) : 1256
Wood 276a(249) : 4110
Wood 276a(250) : 5254
Wood 276a(251) : 5602
Wood 276a(252) : 5253
Wood 276a(253) : 5793
Wood 276a(254) : 950
Wood 276a(255) : 2869
Wood 276a(256) : 2247
Wood 276a(257) : 5291
Wood 276a(258) : 5290
Wood 276a(259) : 1017
Wood 276a(260) : 2934
Wood 276a(261) : 2936
Wood 276a(262) : 5495
Wood 276a(263) : 6132
Wood 276a(264) : 4012

Wood 276a(265) : 4015
Wood 276a(266) : 4011
Wood 276a(267) : 4013
Wood 276a(268) : 2939
Wood 276a(269) : 3455
Wood 276a(270) : 2566
Wood 276a(271) : 253
Wood 276a(272) : 1417
Wood 276a(273) : 6166
Wood 276a(274) : 5945
Wood 276a(275) : 3748
Wood 276a(276) : 5828
Wood 276a(277) : 2571
Wood 276a(278) : 2532
Wood 276a(279) : 1966
Wood 276a(280) : 5238
Wood 276a(281) : 4789
Wood 276a(282) : 5822
Wood 276a(283) : 5311
Wood 276a(284) : 2287
Wood 276a(285) : 5132
Wood 276a(286) : 2281
Wood 276a(287) : 5706
Wood 276a(288) : 1960
Wood 276a(289) : 1961
Wood 276a(290) : 5547
Wood 276a(291) : 3432
Wood 276a(292) : 4180
Wood 276a(293) : 5639
Wood 276a(294) : 5640
Wood 276a(295) : 5642
Wood 276a(296) : 5643
Wood 276a(297) : 5644 (M)
Wood 276a(298) : 5638 (M)
Wood 276a(299) : 5645
Wood 276a(300) (-CD) : 5646
Wood 276a(301) : 5627
Wood 276a(302) : 5628
Wood 276a(303) : 5629
Wood 276a(304) : 3429
Wood 276a(305) : 2548
Wood 276a(306) : 1815
Wood 276a(307) : 4863
Wood 276a(308) : 4868
Wood 276a(309) : 4874
Wood 276a(310) : 4947
Wood 276a(311) : 2576
Wood 276a(312) : 2577
Wood 276a(313) : 4960
Wood 276a(314) : 4967
Wood 276a(315) : 4968
Wood 276a(316) : 4966
Wood 276a(317) : 4970
Wood 276a(318) : 4931
Wood 276a(319) : 4952
Wood 276a(320) : 4961
Wood 276a(321) : 1282
Wood 276a(322) : 4972
Wood 276a(323) : 4989 (M)
Wood 276a(324) : 4975
Wood 276a(325) : 4976
Wood 276a(326) : 4957
Wood 276a(327) : 4984
Wood 276a(328) : 4978

Wood 276a(329) (-CD) : 4964
Wood 276a(330) : 4990
Wood 276a(331) : 2397
Wood 276a(332-3) : 2378
Wood 276a(334) : 2502
Wood 276a(335) : 4513
Wood 276a(336) : 4066
Wood 276a(337) : 3053
Wood 276a(338) : 4515
Wood 276a(339) : 3990
Wood 276a(340) : 3278
Wood 276a(341) : 4869
Wood 276a(342) : 4867
Wood 276a(343) : 4898
Wood 276a(344) (-CD) : 4953
Wood 276a(345) : 4954
Wood 276a(346) : 4955
Wood 276a(347) : 4956
Wood 276a(348) : 4958
Wood 276a(349) : 4959
Wood 276a(350) : 4962
Wood 276a(351) : 5029
Wood 276a(352) : 4920
Wood 276a(353) : 5030
Wood 276a(354) : 4963
Wood 276a(355a) : 4922
Wood 276a(355b) : 4926
Wood 276a(356) : 5031
Wood 276a(357) : 5032
Wood 276a(358) : 4923
Wood 276a(359) : 4927
Wood 276a(360) : 4971
Wood 276a(361) : 5033
Wood 276a(362) : 4928
Wood 276a(363) (-CD) : 4925
Wood 276a(364) : 4965
Wood 276a(365) : 4924
Wood 276a(366) : 4921 (M)
Wood 276a(367) (-CD) : 4969
Wood 276a(368) (-CD) : 5034
Wood 276a(369) : 4930
Wood 276a(370) : 4929
Wood 276a(371) : 5035
Wood 276a(372) : 4973
Wood 276a(373) : 4982
Wood 276a(374) : 4974
Wood 276a(375) : 5036
Wood 276a(376) : 4977
Wood 276a(377) : 4979
Wood 276a(378) : 4983
Wood 276a(379) : 4985
Wood 276a(380) : 4986
Wood 276a(381) : 4988
Wood 276a(382) : 5041
Wood 276a(383) : 5047
Wood 276a(384) : 4914
Wood 276a(385) : 5001
Wood 276a(386) : 5002
Wood 276a(387) : 5003
Wood 276a(388) : 5004
Wood 276a(389) : 5005
Wood 276a(390) : 5006
Wood 276a(391) : 5007
Wood 276a(392) : 5008

Wood 276a(393) : 5009
Wood 276a(394) : 5013
Wood 276a(395) : 5014
Wood 276a(396) : 5015
Wood 276a(397) : 5019
Wood 276a(398) : 5022
Wood 276a(399) : 5023
Wood 276a(400) : 5024
Wood 276a(401) : 5025
Wood 276a(402) : 5026
Wood 276a(403) : 5027
Wood 276a(404a) : 5028
Wood 276a(405) : 5018
Wood 276a(406a) : 5017
Wood 276a(407) : 5611
Wood 276a(408) : 4981
Wood 276a(409) : 4987
Wood 276a(410) : 4946
Wood 276a(411a) : 9
Wood 276a(411b) : 10
Wood 276a(412) : 5063
Wood 276a(413) : 5064
Wood 276a(414) : 5065
Wood 276a(415) : 5066
Wood 276a(416) : 5067
Wood 276a(417) : 5068
Wood 276a(418) : 5070
Wood 276a(419) : 5069
Wood 276a(420) : 5071
Wood 276a(421) : 5072
Wood 276a(422) : 5075
Wood 276a(423) : 5073
Wood 276a(424) : 5074
Wood 276a(425) : 5076
Wood 276a(426) : 5077
Wood 276a(427) : 5078
Wood 276a(428) : 5079
Wood 276a(429) : 5080
Wood 276a(430) : 5081
Wood 276a(431) : 5082
Wood 276a(432) : 5083
Wood 276a(433) : 5084
Wood 276a(434) : 5085
Wood 276a(435) : 5086
Wood 276a(436) : 5087
Wood 276a(437) : 5088
Wood 276a(438a) : 1303
Wood 276a(438b) : 1304
Wood 276a(439a) : 1315
Wood 276a(439b) : 1363
Wood 276a(440) : 1327
Wood 276a(441) : 1350
Wood 276a(442a) : 1367
Wood 276a(442b) : 1343
Wood 276a(443) : 1365
Wood 276a(444) : 1340
Wood 276a(445) : 1293
Wood 276a(446) : 1339
Wood 276a(447) : 1358
Wood 276a(448) : 1351
Wood 276a(449) : 1307
Wood 276a(450) : 1311
Wood 276a(451) : 1309
Wood 276a(452) : 1308

Wood 276a(453) : 1301
Wood 276a(454) : 1366
Wood 276a(455) : 1314
Wood 276a(456) : 1359
Wood 276a(457) : 1316
Wood 276a(458) : 1322
Wood 276a(459) : 1331
Wood 276a(460) : 1357
Wood 276a(461) : 1356
Wood 276a(462) : 1329
Wood 276a(463) : 1330
Wood 276a(464) : 1352
Wood 276a(465) : 1353
Wood 276a(466) : 1312
Wood 276a(467) : 1320
Wood 276a(468) : 1354
Wood 276a(469) : 1318
Wood 276a(470) : 1355
Wood 276a(471) : 1319
Wood 276a(472) : 1313
Wood 276a(473) : 1321
Wood 276a(474) : 1296
Wood 276a(475) : 1326
Wood 276a(476) : 1347
Wood 276a(477) : 1336
Wood 276a(478) : 1345
Wood 276a(479) : 1298
Wood 276a(480) : 1290
Wood 276a(481) : 1337
Wood 276a(482) : 1346
Wood 276a(483) : 1299
Wood 276a(484) : 1291
Wood 276a(485a) : 1335
Wood 276a(485b) : 1342
Wood 276a(486) : 1310
Wood 276a(487) : 1305
Wood 276a(488) : 1328
Wood 276a(489) : 1349
Wood 276a(490) : 1302 (M)
Wood 276a(491) : 1289
Wood 276a(492) : 1295
Wood 276a(493) : 1292
Wood 276a(494) : 1332
Wood 276a(495) : 1338
Wood 276a(496) : 1333
Wood 276a(497) : 1323
Wood 276a(498) : 1297
Wood 276a(499) : 1306
Wood 276a(500) : 1360
Wood 276a(501) : 1294
Wood 276a(502) : 1362
Wood 276a(503) : 1325
Wood 276a(504) : 1317
Wood 276a(505) : 1364
Wood 276a(506) : 1334
Wood 276a(507) : 1348
Wood 276a(508) : 1344
Wood 276a(509) : 1300
Wood 276a(510) : 1324
Wood 276a(511) : 1341
Wood 276a(512) : 1361
Wood 276a(513) : 4885
Wood 276a(514) : 4888
Wood 276a(515) (-CD) : 6747

Wood 276a(516) (-CD) : 1288
Wood 276a(517) : 4082
Wood 276a(518-9) : 944
Wood 276a(520) : 369
Wood 276a(521) : 6107
Wood 276a(522) (384, CD) : 1118
Wood 276a(523) : 2814
Wood 276a(524) : 3946
Wood 276a(525) : 2810
Wood 276a(526) : 477
Wood 276a(527) : 6595
Wood 276a(528) : 6409
Wood 276a(529) : 3832
Wood 276a(530) : 456
Wood 276a(531) (-CD) : 385
Wood 276a(532) : 5701
Wood 276a(533) (-CD) : 436
Wood 276a(534) : 5011
Wood 276a(535) : 6170
Wood 276a(536) : 4857
Wood 276a(537) (-CD) : 3630 (Ms.)
Wood 276a(538) : 3213
Wood 276a(539-40) (276, CD) : 3927
Wood 276a(541) : 864
Wood 276a(542) : 6536
Wood 276a(543) : 616
Wood 276a(544) : 595
Wood 276a(545) : 415
Wood 276a(546) : 419
Wood 276a(547) : 641
Wood 276a(548) : 654
Wood 276a(549) : 460
Wood 276a(550) : 2212
Wood 276a(551-2) (276, CD) : 862
Wood 276a(553-4) : 530
Wood 276a(556) (-CD) : 555
Wood 276a(557) : 567
Wood 276a(558) : 4162 (M)
Wood 276a(559) : 608
Wood 276a(560) : 2317
Wood 276a(561) : 2318
Wood 276a(562) : 4835
Wood 276a(563-4) : 4836
Wood 276a(565) : 4676
Wood 276a(566) : 4796
Wood 276a(567) : 2816
Wood 276a(568) : 6097
Wood 276a(569) : 5381
Wood 276a(570) (-CD) : 5405
Wood 276a(571-2) : 5416
Wood 276a(573) : 1870 (M)
Wood 276a(574) : 5761
Wood 276a(575) : 2280
Wood 276a(576) : 6354
Wood 276b(1) (Maps) : 3306
Wood 276b(2) : 5987
Wood 276b(3) : 5983
Wood 276b(4) : 5984
Wood 276b(5) : 5988
Wood 276b(6) : 5773
Wood 276b(7) : 4823
Wood 276b(8) : 5986
Wood 276b(9) : 5982
Wood 276b(10) : 5985

Wood 276b(11) : 5989
Wood 276b(12) : 4824
Wood 276b(13) : 4891
Wood 276b(14) : 5980
Wood 276b(15) : 941
Wood 276b(16) : 6439 (Ms.)
Wood 276b(17) : 3892
Wood 276b(18) : 3893
Wood 276b(19) : 2400
Wood 276b(20-24) : 4500 (M)
Wood 276b(25) : 4415
Wood 276b(26) : 5754
Wood 276b(27) : 2964
Wood 276b(28) : 6039
Wood 276b(29) : 3207
Wood 276b(30) : 4866
Wood 276b(31) : 4211
Wood 276b(33) : 2300
Wood 276b(34) : 4768
Wood 276b(35) : 4769
Wood 276b(36) : 946
Wood 276b(39) : 5914
Wood 276b(40) : 5874
Wood 276b(41) : 5875
Wood 276b(42) : 5630
Wood 276b(43) : 6698 (Ms.)
Wood 276b(44) : 5038
Wood 276b(45) : 5040
Wood 276b(46) : 4088
Wood 276b(47) : 5039
Wood 276b(48) : 5042
Wood 276b(49) : 5043
Wood 276b(50) : 5044
Wood 276b(51) : 5045
Wood 276b(52) : 5037
Wood 276b(53) : 5046
Wood 276b(54) : 5048
Wood 276b(55) : 5049
Wood 276b(56) : 5050
Wood 276b(57) : 5051
Wood 276b(58) : 5052
Wood 276b(59) : 5053
Wood 276b(60) : 5054
Wood 276b(61) : 5055
Wood 276b(62) : 5056
Wood 276b(63) : 5057
Wood 276b(64) : 5058
Wood 276b(65) : 5059
Wood 276b(66) : 5060
Wood 276b(67) : 5061
Wood 276b(68) : 5062
Wood 276b(69) : 5624
Wood 276b(70) : 5182
Wood 276b(71) (-CD) : 4282
Wood 276b(72) : 1974
Wood 276b(73) : 2875
Wood 276b(74) : 3984
Wood 276b(75) ((52) in CD) : 3851
Wood 276b(76) : 3234
Wood 276b(77) (-CD) : 2874
Wood 276b(78) : 6472
Wood 276b(79) : 900
Wood 276b(80) : 6296
Wood 276b(81) (-CD) : 2873

Wood 276b(82) (60, CD) : 3684
Wood 276b(83) : 5885
Wood 276b(84) (62, CD) : 3685
Wood 276b(85) : 5181
Wood 276b(86) : 4336
Wood 276b(87) (65, CD) : 3682
Wood 276b(88) : 2187
Wood 276b(89) : 6577
Wood 276b(90) : 2256
Wood 276b(91) : 4781
Wood 276b(92) (-CD) : 1888
Wood 276b(93) (-CD) : 1889
Wood 276b(94) (-CD) : 1887
Wood 276b(95) : 5774
Wood 276b(96) (74, CD) : 3221
Wood 276b(97) (75, CD) : 6334
Wood 276b(98) : 6593
Wood 276b(99) : 3884
Wood 276b(100) : 509
Wood 276b(101) : 804
Wood 276b(102) (-CD) : 644
Wood 276b(103) (-CD) : 680
Wood 276b(104) : 658
Wood 276b(105) : 394
Wood 276b(106) : 479
Wood 276b(107) : 2803
Wood 276b(108) : 2740
Wood 276b(109) : 294
Wood 276b(110) : 5183
Wood 276b(111) : 5389
Wood 276b(112) : 3304 (Ms.)
Wood 276b(113) : 3190
Wood 276b(114-7) : 4862 (Ms.)
Wood 276b(118) (-CD) : 6608
Wood 276b(119) : 5099
Wood 276b(120) (98, CD) : 4792
Wood 276b(121) : 5370
Wood 276b(122) : 3128
Wood 276b(123-25) : 3080
Wood 277 (-CD) : 4203
Wood 278 (-CD) : 4205
Wood 279 (-CD) : 4204
Wood 280 : 6019
Wood 281 : 5558
Wood 282 : 3350 (M)
Wood 283 : 224
Wood 284(1) : 2832
Wood 284(2) : 5130
Wood 284(3) : 3465
Wood 284(4) : 3563
Wood 284(5) : 5764
Wood 284(6) : 5765
Wood 284(7) : 3396
Wood 284(8) : 3600
Wood 284(9) : 949
Wood 284(10) : 1263
Wood 285 : 5585
Wood 286 : 359
Wood 287 : 6715
Wood 288 (-CD) : 5528
Wood 289(1) : 4285
Wood 289(2) : 962
Wood 289(3) : 6546
Wood 289(4) : 3135

Wood 289(5) (-CD) : 5732
Wood 289(6) : 3628
Wood 289(7) : 4842
Wood 290 : 1166
Wood 291 : 300
Wood 292(1) : 2970
Wood 292(2-3) (-CD) : 5474
Wood 292(4) : 5846
Wood 292(5) : 6174
Wood 292(6) : 2379
Wood 292(7) (-CD) : 4648
Wood 292(8) : 3166
Wood 292(9) : 3113
Wood 293(1) : 856
Wood 293(2) : 857
Wood 293(3) : 858
Wood 293(4) : 859
Wood 293(5) : 861
Wood 294 : 4433
Wood 295 : 6315
Wood 296 : 6626
Wood 297 : 1657
Wood 298 : 4191 (M)
Wood 299(1) : 1374
Wood 299(2) : 6191
Wood 299(3) : 1176
Wood 300 : 5325
Wood 301 : 5711
Wood 302 : 3978
Wood 303 : 3603
Wood 304(1) : 5574
Wood 304(2) : 895
Wood 305 : 39
Wood 306 : 4178
Wood 307(1) : 5131
Wood 307(2) : 2367
Wood 307(3) : 908
Wood 307(4) : 3928
Wood 307(5) : 955
Wood 307(6) : 891
Wood 307(7) : 847
Wood 308 : 5576
Wood 309(1) : 272
Wood 309(2) : 4390
Wood 310(1) : 5747
Wood 310(2) : 6218
Wood 310(3) : 5748
Wood 310(4-5) : 5362
Wood 310(6) : 1114
Wood 310(7) : 3448
Wood 310(8) : 4270
Wood 310(9) : 6339
Wood 310(10) : 3530
Wood 311 : 2041
Wood 312 : 1125
Wood 313 : 1999
Wood 314 : 4438
Wood 315 : 3711
Wood 316(1) : 3764
Wood 316(2) : 3419
Wood 316(3) : 1003
Wood 316(4) (-CD) : 6084
Wood 317 : 3026
Wood 318(1) : 3914

Wood 318(2) : 5487
Wood 318(3) : 2310
Wood 318(4) : 5832
Wood 319(1) : 1690
Wood 319(2) : 5685
Wood 319(3) : 4940
Wood 319(4) : 6285
Wood 319(5) : 6247
Wood 319(6) : 2429
Wood 319(7) : 5117
Wood 319(8) : 2223
Wood 319(9) : 1136
Wood 319(10) : 6699
Wood 319(11) : 2883
Wood 319(12) : 5202
Wood 319(13) : 6568
Wood 319(14) : 2307
Wood 320(1) : 2320
Wood 320(2) : 2313
Wood 320(3) : 2321
Wood 320(4) : 1032
Wood 320(5) : 5872
Wood 320(6) : 2273
Wood 320(7) : 5862
Wood 320(8) : 916
Wood 320(9) : 4900
Wood 321(1) : 1109
Wood 321(2) : 3890
Wood 321(3) : 5622
Wood 321(4) : 969
Wood 321(5) : 3659
Wood 321(6) : 14
Wood 322 : 6091
Wood 323 : 4171
Wood 324 : 4039 (M)
Wood 325 : 3109
Wood 326(1) : 2807
Wood 326(2) : 4453
Wood 326(3) : 4454
Wood 326(4) : 4459
Wood 326(5) : 5185
Wood 326(6) : 5184
Wood 326(7) : 4044
Wood 327 : 1287
Wood 328 : 361
Wood 329(1) : 3169
Wood 329(2) : 3170
Wood 330(1) : 5497
Wood 330(2) : 2222
Wood 330(3) : 4374
Wood 330(4) : 5496
Wood 330(5) : 3915
Wood 330(6) : 6209
Wood 330(7) : 3402
Wood 330(8) : 915
Wood 330(9) : 4373
Wood 330(10) : 1420
Wood 331 : 1028
Wood 332 : 2258
Wood 333 : 1369
Wood 334(1) : 6550
Wood 334(2) : 5134
Wood 335 : 3559
Wood 336(1) : 2510

Wood 336(2) : 1049
Wood 336(3) : 3469
Wood 337(1) : 5913
Wood 337(2) : 4418
Wood 338 : 3305
Wood 339 : 1371
Wood 340 : 5847
Wood 341 : 1843
Wood 342 : 290
Wood 343(1) : 6446
Wood 343(2) : 6445
Wood 343(3) : 6448
Wood 344 : 3242
Wood 345(1) : 3618
Wood 345(2) (-CD) : 2311
Wood 345(3) : 1405
Wood 345(4) : 917
Wood 345(5-6) : 875
Wood 345(7) : 358
Wood 345(8) : 6245
Wood 345(9) : 1903
Wood 345(10) : 42
Wood 345(11) : 1653
Wood 345(12) : 6056
Wood 345(13) : 6670
Wood 345(14) : 2853
Wood 345(15-20) : 1964
Wood 345(21) : 4287
Wood 346 : 5122
Wood 347 : 5976
Wood 348 : 3565
Wood 349 : 5907
Wood 350(1) : 6441
Wood 350(2) : 6427
Wood 350(3) : 6428
Wood 351 : 6325
Wood 352 : 3107
Wood 353 : 6283
Wood 354 : 3134
Wood 355 : 4079
Wood 356 : 4080
Wood 357 : 1034
Wood 358(1) : 2760
Wood 358(2) : 2761
Wood 358(3) : 2763
Wood 358(4) : 2762
Wood 358(5) : 2764
Wood 358(6) : 6405
Wood 358(7) : 2769
Wood 358(8) : 2773
Wood 359 : 4072
Wood 360 : 269
Wood 361 : 285
Wood 362 : 5323
Wood 363(1) (-CD) : 4305
Wood 363(2) : 3937
Wood 363(3) : 3651
Wood 363(4) (-CD) : 4306
Wood 363(5) : 3653
Wood 363(6) : 6389
Wood 363(7) : 2438
Wood 363(8) : 3652
Wood 363(9) (-CD) : 4281
Wood 363(10) : 968

Wood 363(11) : 3650
Wood 363(12) : 2439
Wood 363(13) : 2440
Wood 363(14) : 4307
Wood 363(15) : 3654
Wood 363(16) : 6377
Wood 364(1) (-CD) : 5681
Wood 364(2) : 5438
Wood 364(3) : 3174
Wood 364(4) : 3388
Wood 364(5) : 4243
Wood 364(6) : 6013
Wood 364(7) : 1767
Wood 364(8) : 2688
Wood 364(9) : 2683
Wood 364(10) : 4730
Wood 364(11) : 1761
Wood 364(12) : 4731
Wood 364(13) : 1757
Wood 364(14) : 4733
Wood 364(15) : 1766
Wood 364(16) : 1773
Wood 364(17) : 6396
Wood 364(18) : 1973
Wood 364(19) : 1082
Wood 364(20) : 1764
Wood 364(21) : 1390
Wood 364(22) : 6116
Wood 364(23) : 329
Wood 364(24) (-CD) : 4288
Wood 364(25) : 3811
Wood 364(26) : 1768
Wood 364(27) : 1775
Wood 364(28) (-CD) : 1765
Wood 364(29) : 3970
Wood 364(30) : 3971
Wood 364(31) : 3353
Wood 364(32) : 5247
Wood 364(33) : 6461
Wood 364(34) : 4102
Wood 364(35) : 1153
Wood 364(36) : 5190
Wood 364(37) : 5112
Wood 365(1) : 2357
Wood 365(2) : 1070
Wood 365(3) : 5538
Wood 365(4) : 4581
Wood 365(5) : 4838
Wood 365(6) : 5336
Wood 365(7) : 2855
Wood 365(8) : 4218
Wood 365(9) : 229
Wood 365(10) : 2697
Wood 365(11) : 3583
Wood 365(12) : 5698
Wood 365(13) : 6054
Wood 365(14) : 1242
Wood 365(15) : 4471
Wood 365(16) : 6064
Wood 365(17) : 2003
Wood 365(18) : 1656
Wood 365(19) : 3986
Wood 365(20) : 2419
Wood 365(21) : 1250

Wood 365(22) : 3347
Wood 365(23) : 3099
Wood 365(24) : 4242
Wood 365(25) : 4843
Wood 365(26) (-CD) : 3573
Wood 365(27) : 4478
Wood 365(28) : 4276
Wood 365(29) : 3075
Wood 365(30) : 2385
Wood 365(31) : 5795
Wood 365(32) : 3364
Wood 365(33) : 3627
Wood 365(34) : 3256
Wood 365(35) : 3439
Wood 366(1) : 6505
Wood 366(2) : 6513
Wood 366(3) : 6510
Wood 366(4) : 6516
Wood 366(5) : 6515
Wood 366(6) : 6511
Wood 366(7) : 6506
Wood 366(8) : 6512
Wood 366(9) : 6514
Wood 366(10) : 6509
Wood 366(11) : 6508
Wood 366(12) : 3352
Wood 366(13) : 1130
Wood 366(14) : 1123
Wood 366(15) : 6211
Wood 366(16) : 1680
Wood 366(17) : 5265
Wood 366(18) : 2592
Wood 366(19) : 5790
Wood 366(20) : 6671
Wood 366(21) : 4046
Wood 366(22) : 4045
Wood 366(23) : 4049
Wood 366(24) : 3524
Wood 366(25) : 4051
Wood 366(26) : 4050
Wood 366(27) : 4054
Wood 366(28) : 1217
Wood 366(29) : 3550
Wood 366(30) : 4055
Wood 366(31) : 260
Wood 366(32) : 2554
Wood 366(33) : 5897
Wood 366(34) : 3386
Wood 367(1) : 4292
Wood 367(2) : 4293
Wood 367(3) : 4295
Wood 367(4) (-CD) : 3209
Wood 367(5) : 6588
Wood 367(6) : 3746
Wood 367(7) : 6029
Wood 367(8) : 3980
Wood 367(9) : 2093
Wood 367(10) : 3191
Wood 367(11) : 3193
Wood 367(12) : 5177
Wood 367(13) : 5751
Wood 367(14) : 6046
Wood 367(15) : 5917
Wood 367(16) : 3532

Wood 367(17) : 3533
Wood 367(18) : 5446
Wood 367(19) : 6035 (M)
Wood 367(20) : 3276
Wood 367(21) : 279
Wood 367(22) : 278
Wood 367(23) : 3077
Wood 368(1) : 4840
Wood 368(2) : 297
Wood 368(3) : 4349
Wood 368(4) : 4347
Wood 368(5) : 4569
Wood 368(6) : 2481
Wood 368(7) : 2882
Wood 368(8) : 4846
Wood 368(9) : 6673
Wood 368(10) : 4848
Wood 368(11) : 6393
Wood 368(12) : 4154
Wood 368(13) : 6033
Wood 368(14) : 867
Wood 368(15) : 3910
Wood 368(16) : 1380
Wood 368(17) : 1381
Wood 368(18) : 1382
Wood 368(19) : 3595
Wood 368(20) : 6270
Wood 368(21) : 1383
Wood 368(22) : 1384
Wood 368(23) : 4341
Wood 368(24) : 6262
Wood 368(25) : 3858
Wood 368(26) : 3857
Wood 368(27) : 3859
Wood 368(28) : 6263
Wood 368(29) : 2382
Wood 369(1) : 2722
Wood 369(2) : 6411
Wood 369(3) : 3014
Wood 369(4) : 5209
Wood 369(5) : 3443
Wood 369(6) : 3442
Wood 369(7) : 870
Wood 369(8) : 869
Wood 369(9) : 6113
Wood 369(10) : 6294
Wood 370(1) : 5883
Wood 370(2) : 238
Wood 370(3) : 2524
Wood 370(4) : 1260
Wood 370(5) : 6043
Wood 370(6) : 3753
Wood 370(7) : 5457
Wood 370(8) : 2713
Wood 370(9) : 4856
Wood 370(10) : 3073
Wood 371(1) : 2209
Wood 371(2) : 3296
Wood 371(3) : 2208
Wood 371(4) : 5575
Wood 371(5) : 3299
Wood 371(6) : 1906
Wood 371(7) : 3982
Wood 371(8) : 2244

Wood 371(9) : 1637
Wood 371(10) : 6440
Wood 371(11) : 6195
Wood 372(1) : 3599
Wood 372(2) : 2993
Wood 372(3) : 5682
Wood 372(4) : 6252
Wood 372(5) : 6250
Wood 372(6) : 6251
Wood 372(7) : 6249
Wood 372(8) : 2952
Wood 372(9) : 2352
Wood 372(10) : 5305
Wood 372(11) : 1246
Wood 372(12) : 3644
Wood 372(13) : 3485
Wood 372(14) : 2130
Wood 372(15) : 5707
Wood 372(16) : 2155
Wood 372(17) : 5854
Wood 372(18) : 5855
Wood 373(1) : 2598
Wood 373(2) : 3263
Wood 373(3) : 6087
Wood 373(4) : 5228
Wood 373(5) : 5229 (M)
Wood 373(6) : 5276
Wood 373(7) : 913
Wood 373(8) : 1704
Wood 373(9) : 2599
Wood 373(10) : 2615
Wood 373(11a) : 4534
Wood 373(11b) : 4670
Wood 373(12) : 3391 (M)
Wood 373(13) : 4215
Wood 373(14) : 3286
Wood 373(15) : 1173
Wood 373(16) : 6633
Wood 373(17) : 4666
Wood 373(18) : 4660
Wood 373(19) : 4673
Wood 373(20) : 4751
Wood 373(21) : 4669
Wood 373(22) : 4753
Wood 373(23) : 4661
Wood 373(24) : 4773
Wood 373(25) : 5089
Wood 373(26) : 5091
Wood 373(27) : 4725
Wood 373(28) : 2604
Wood 373(29) : 2608
Wood 373(30) : 4726
Wood 373(31) : 5109
Wood 373(32) : 2600
Wood 373(33) : 1702
Wood 373(34) : 5963
Wood 373(35) : 4752
Wood 373(36) : 4727
Wood 373(37) : 4662
Wood 373(38) : 2231
Wood 373(39) : 2616
Wood 373(40) : 2633
Wood 373(41) : 4663
Wood 373(42) : 2594

Wood 373(43) : 4728
Wood 373(44) : 4219
Wood 373(45) : 2636
Wood 373(46) : 2632
Wood 373(47) : 4779
Wood 373(48) : 4729
Wood 373(49) : 4574
Wood 373(50) : 6733
Wood 373(51) (-CD) : 2629
Wood 373(52) : 3935
Wood 373(53) : 2637
Wood 373(54) : 1707
Wood 373(55) : 3721
Wood 373(56) : 1722
Wood 373(57) : 2621
Wood 373(58) : 1726
Wood 373(59) : 2626
Wood 373(60) : 1714
Wood 373(61) : 1706
Wood 373(62) : 3949
Wood 373(63) : 2618
Wood 373(64) : 1725
Wood 373(65) : 1709
Wood 373(66) : 2635 (M)
Wood 373(67) : 1724
Wood 374(1) : 2624
Wood 374(2) : 2265
Wood 374(3) : 2647
Wood 374(4) : 6736
Wood 374(5) : 4745
Wood 374(6) : 4740
Wood 374(7) : 2639
Wood 374(8) : 1710
Wood 374(9) : 1730
Wood 374(10) : 1727
Wood 374(11) : 3676
Wood 374(12) : 4746
Wood 374(13) : 2627
Wood 374(14) : 6735
Wood 374(15) : 6734
Wood 374(16) : 1728
Wood 374(17) : 1065
Wood 374(18) : 4667
Wood 374(19) : 1711
Wood 374(20) : 1718
Wood 374(21) : 2628
Wood 374(22) : 3314
Wood 374(23) : 2640
Wood 374(24) : 5328
Wood 374(25) : 6737
Wood 374(26) : 2622
Wood 374(27) : 4747
Wood 374(28) : 4672
Wood 374(29) : 6738
Wood 374(30) : 2263
Wood 374(31) : 4748
Wood 374(32) : 6739
Wood 374(33) : 5308
Wood 374(34) : 845
Wood 374(35) : 2623
Wood 374(36) (-CD) : 1713
Wood 375(1) : 1720
Wood 375(2) : 1719
Wood 375(3) : 2648

Wood 375(4) : 1918
Wood 375(5) : 315
Wood 375(6) : 2257
Wood 375(7) : 5310
Wood 375(8) : 5309 (M)
Wood 375(9) : 6362
Wood 375(10) : 5668
Wood 375(11) : 2235
Wood 375(12) : 6702
Wood 375(13) : 5744
Wood 375(14) : 4358
Wood 375(15) : 5950 (M)
Wood 375(16) : 3966
Wood 375(17) : 2996
Wood 375(18) : 6535
Wood 375(19) : 2630
Wood 375(20) : 2767
Wood 375(21) : 4220
Wood 375(22) : 5566
Wood 375(23a) : 2582
Wood 375(23b) : 6028
Wood 375(24) : 2465
Wood 375(25) : 2649
Wood 375(26) : 4248
Wood 375(27) : 2978
Wood 375(28) : 5092
Wood 375(29) : 2237
Wood 375(30) : 4750
Wood 375(31) : 1723
Wood 375(32) : 2644
Wood 375(33) : 1896
Wood 375(34) : 1897
Wood 375(35) : 1898
Wood 375(36) : 6573
Wood 375(37) : 6415
Wood 375(38) : 2645
Wood 375(39) : 3313 (M)
Wood 375(40) : 3311
Wood 375(41) : 3312
Wood 375(42) : 3310
Wood 375(43) : 3505
Wood 375(44) : 3545
Wood 375(45) : 3668
Wood 375(46) : 3547
Wood 375(47) : 6416 (M)
Wood 376(1) : 3001
Wood 376(2) : 3677 (M)
Wood 376(3) : 5651
Wood 376(4) : 4166
Wood 376(5) : 2236
Wood 376(6) : 1071
Wood 376(7) : 3315
Wood 376(8) : 1883
Wood 376(9) : 1884
Wood 376(10) : 5280
Wood 376(11) : 3731
Wood 376(12) : 6663
Wood 376(13) : 2466
Wood 376(14) : 5650
Wood 376(15) : 6181
Wood 376(16) : 1872
Wood 376(17) : 3609
Wood 376(18) : 3722
Wood 376(19) : 6414

Wood 376(20) : 6417
Wood 376(21) : 5591
Wood 376(22) : 2464
Wood 376(23) : 2068 (M)
Wood 376(24) : 1128
Wood 376(25) : 2998
Wood 376(26) : 3000
Wood 376(27) : 1129
Wood 376(28) : 6390
Wood 376(29) : 2997
Wood 376(30) : 1737
Wood 376(31) : 5936
Wood 376(32) : 2242
Wood 376(33) : 6386
Wood 376(34) : 4421
Wood 376(35) : 6470
Wood 376(36) : 2292
Wood 376(37) : 3233
Wood 376(38) (-CD) : 2261
Wood 376(39) : 6288
Wood 376(40) : 3072
Wood 376(41) : 2332
Wood 376(42) : 5300
Wood 376(43) : 2884
Wood 376(44) : 6580
Wood 376(45) : 4535
Wood 376(46) : 5895
Wood 376(47) : 924
Wood 376(48) : 4771
Wood 376(49) : 2188
Wood 376(50) : 6413
Wood 376(51) (-CD) : 6395
Wood 376(52) : 6412
Wood 376(53) : 6418
Wood 376(54) : 5281
Wood 376(55) : 2013
Wood 376(56) : 6420
Wood 376(57) : 5180
Wood 376(58) : 1051
Wood 376(59) : 4222
Wood 376(60) : 3806
Wood 376(61) : 4598
Wood 376(62) : 3813
Wood 376(63) : 4582
Wood 376(64) : 5797
Wood 376(65) : 2124
Wood 376(66) : 2469 (M)
Wood 376(67) : 2467 (M)
Wood 376(68) : 3316
Wood 376(69) : 5652
Wood 376(70) : 4744
Wood 376(71) : 4647 (M)
Wood 376(72) : 3548
Wood 376(73) : 2654
Wood 377(1) : 1225
Wood 377(2) : 1
Wood 377(3) : 6421
Wood 377(4) : 6419
Wood 377(5) : 5615
Wood 377(6) : 2885
Wood 377(6a) : 2886
Wood 377(7) : 5282
Wood 377(8) : 4716
Wood 377(9) : 334

Wood 377(10) : 4388
Wood 377(11) : 4399
Wood 377(12) : 4315
Wood 377(13) : 5567
Wood 377(14) : 2966
Wood 377(15) : 2431
Wood 377(16) : 6740
Wood 377(17) : 2887
Wood 377(18) : 6482
Wood 377(19) (-CD) : 6047
Wood 377(20) : 4330
Wood 377(21) : 4100
Wood 377(22) : 4477
Wood 377(23) : 4664
Wood 377(24) (-CD) : 5951
Wood 377(25) : 4665
Wood 377(26) : 5653 (M)
Wood 377(27) : 327
Wood 377(28) : 2666
Wood 377(29) : 4223
Wood 377(30) : 4355
Wood 377(31) : 844
Wood 377(32) : 2468
Wood 377(33) : 5683
Wood 377(34) : 3724
Wood 377(35) : 890
Wood 377(36) : 1156
Wood 377(37) : 1103
Wood 377(38) : 2348
Wood 377(39) : 2470 (M)
Wood 377(40) : 2662
Wood 377(41) : 3005
Wood 377(42) : 1648
Wood 377(43) : 2374
Wood 378(1) : 2001
Wood 378(2) : 2069 (M)
Wood 378(3) : 6157
Wood 378(4) : 1411
Wood 378(5) : 5482
Wood 378(6) : 2892
Wood 378(7) : 2930
Wood 378(8) : 2901
Wood 378(9) : 2071
Wood 378(10) : 4651
Wood 378(11) : 4652
Wood 378(12) : 6136
Wood 378(13) : 4152
Wood 378(14) : 923
Wood 378(15) : 2902
Wood 378(16) : 1873
Wood 378(17) : 2891
Wood 378(18) : 5798
Wood 378(19) : 2903
Wood 378(20) : 4101
Wood 378(21) : 5825
Wood 378(22) : 3592
Wood 378(23) : 5654
Wood 378(24) : 5661
Wood 378(25) : 2072 (M)
Wood 378(26) : 3363
Wood 378(27) : 4775
Wood 378(28) : 2471
Wood 378(29) : 5330
Wood 378(30) : 5335

Wood 378(31) : 5205
Wood 378(32) : 2076
Wood 378(33) : 4036
Wood 378(34) : 5332
Wood 378(35) : 5334
Wood 378(36) : 2074
Wood 378(37) : 5662
Wood 378(38) : 1777
Wood 378(39) : 6359
Wood 378(40) : 2893
Wood 378(41) : 5657
Wood 378(42) : 5656
Wood 378(43) : 2894
Wood 378(44) : 4504
Wood 378(45) : 2475
Wood 378(46) : 2897
Wood 378(47) : 1104
Wood 378(48) : 2895
Wood 378(49) : 5658
Wood 378(50) : 2126
Wood 378(51) : 2896
Wood 378(52) : 2476
Wood 378(53) : 4038
Wood 378(54) : 2127
Wood 378(55) : 1105
Wood 378(56) : 2931
Wood 378(57) : 5660
Wood 378(58) : 2900
Wood 378(59) : 5663
Wood 378(60) : 2898
Wood 378(61) : 5659
Wood 378(62) : 2899
Wood 378(63) : 4331
Wood 378(64) : 5206
Wood 378(65) : 4564
Wood 378(66) : 1430
Wood 379 : 2850
Wood 380 : 5296
Wood 381 : 5745
Wood 382(1) : 5623
Wood 382(2) : 2170
Wood 382(3) : 432
Wood 382(4) : 5285
Wood 382(5) : 5286
Wood 382(6) : 4392
Wood 382(7) : 5287
Wood 382(8) : 5288
Wood 383(1) : 5592
Wood 383(2) : 6484
Wood 383(3) : 4547
Wood 383(4) : 3027
Wood 383(5) : 2226
Wood 383(6) : 4183
Wood 383(7) : 6069
Wood 384 : 244
Wood 385 : 5997
Wood 386(1) : 6021
Wood 386(2) : 3195
Wood 386(3) : 5162
Wood 386(4) : 3362
Wood 386(5) : 4324
Wood 386(6) : 4394
Wood 386(7) : 6284
Wood 386(8) : 4031

Wood 386(9) : 6124
Wood 386(10) : 3346
Wood 386(11) : 4634
Wood 386(12) : 4506
Wood 386(13) : 3976
Wood 386(14) : 5871
Wood 386(15) : 17
Wood 386(16) : 5607
Wood 386(17) (-CD) : 5414
Wood 386(18) : 6630
Wood 386(19) : 5329
Wood 386(20) : 4193
Wood 386(21) : 5523
Wood 387(1) : 2302
Wood 387(2) : 5933
Wood 387(3) : 984
Wood 387(4) : 5780
Wood 387(5) : 2040
Wood 387(6) (-CD) : 2371
Wood 387(7) : 2113
Wood 387(8) : 2159
Wood 387(9) : 5677
Wood 387(10) : 3992
Wood 387(11) : 3397
Wood 387(12) : 5220
Wood 387(13) : 2395
Wood 387(14) : 2396
Wood 387(15) : 2160
Wood 388 : 5955
Wood 389(1) : 4701
Wood 389(2) : 4738
Wood 390 : 4739
Wood 391 : 4679
Wood 392(1, 3) : 4680
Wood 392(2) : 4737
Wood 393 : 4705
Wood 394 : 4706
Wood 395 : 3063 (M)
Wood 396 : 4286
Wood 397(1) (-CD) : 6628
Wood 397(2) (-CD) : 4060
Wood 398(1) : 2540
Wood 398(2) : 500
Wood 398(3) : 3916
Wood 398(4) : 4523
Wood 398(5) : 3918
Wood 398(6) : 848
Wood 398(7) : 3919
Wood 398(8) : 3920
Wood 398(9) : 3921
Wood 398(10) : 6730
Wood 398(11) : 5542
Wood 398(12) : 1806
Wood 398(13-4) : 3756
Wood 398(15) : 3758
Wood 398(16) : 1813
Wood 398(17) : 2224
Wood 398(18) : 4808
Wood 398(19) : 1810
Wood 398(20) : 6134
Wood 398(21) : 4351
Wood 398(22) : 5962
Wood 399(1) : 741 (M)
Wood 399(2) : 747 (M)

Wood 399(3) : 742 (M)
Wood 399(4) : 746 (M)
Wood 399(5) : 745 (M)
Wood 399(6) : 743 (M)
Wood 399(7) : 744 (M)
Wood 400 : 374 (M)
Wood 401(1) : 752
Wood 401(2) : 526
Wood 401(3) : 621
Wood 401(4) : 439
Wood 401(5) : 547
Wood 401(6) : 542
Wood 401(7) : 552
Wood 401(8) : 548
Wood 401(9) : 540
Wood 401(10) : 727
Wood 401(11) : 753
Wood 401(12) : 725
Wood 401(13) : 549
Wood 401(14) : 553
Wood 401(15) : 726
Wood 401(16) : 550
Wood 401(17) : 546
Wood 401(18) : 539
Wood 401(19) : 551
Wood 401(20) : 710
Wood 401(21) : 543
Wood 401(22) : 464
Wood 401(23) : 756
Wood 401(24) : 406
Wood 401(25) : 673
Wood 401(26) : 688
Wood 401(27) : 495
Wood 401(28) : 377
Wood 401(29) : 442
Wood 401(30) : 686
Wood 401(31) : 536
Wood 401(32) : 523
Wood 401(33) : 538
Wood 401(34) : 389
Wood 401(35) : 380
Wood 401(36) : 755
Wood 401(37) : 769
Wood 401(38) : 779
Wood 401(39) : 444
Wood 401(40) : 375
Wood 401(41) : 818
Wood 401(42) : 819
Wood 401(43) : 435
Wood 401(44) : 557
Wood 401(45) : 764
Wood 401(46) : 637
Wood 401(47) : 636
Wood 401(48) : 716
Wood 401(49) : 598
Wood 401(50) : 428
Wood 401(51) : 518
Wood 401(52) : 513
Wood 401(53) : 646
Wood 401(54) : 569
Wood 401(55) : 407
Wood 401(56) : 661
Wood 401(57) : 841
Wood 401(58) : 586

Wood 401(59) : 508
Wood 401(60) : 730
Wood 401(61) : 443
Wood 401(62) : 679
Wood 401(63) : 572
Wood 401(64) : 571
Wood 401(65) : 674
Wood 401(66) : 754
Wood 401(67) : 675
Wood 401(68) : 677
Wood 401(69) : 702
Wood 401(70) : 703
Wood 401(71) : 676
Wood 401(72) : 678
Wood 401(73) : 734
Wood 401(74) : 400
Wood 401(75) : 648
Wood 401(76) : 709
Wood 401(77) : 731
Wood 401(78) : 649
Wood 401(79) : 524
Wood 401(80) : 839
Wood 401(81) : 483
Wood 401(82) : 465
Wood 401(83) : 670
Wood 401(84) : 706
Wood 401(85) : 590
Wood 401(86) : 635
Wood 401(87) : 579
Wood 401(88) : 402
Wood 401(89) : 485
Wood 401(90) : 623
Wood 401(91) : 582
Wood 401(92) : 775
Wood 401(93) : 698
Wood 401(94) : 398
Wood 401(95) : 404
Wood 401(96) : 628
Wood 401(97) : 529
Wood 401(98) : 629
Wood 401(99) : 527
Wood 401(100) : 751
Wood 401(101) : 489
Wood 401(102) (-CD) : 409
Wood 401(103) : 662
Wood 402(1) (-CD) : 786
Wood 402(2) : 525
Wood 402(3) : 544
Wood 402(4) : 545
Wood 402(5) : 541
Wood 402(6) : 512
Wood 402(7) : 440
Wood 402(8) : 405
Wood 402(9) : 778
Wood 402(10) : 376
Wood 402(11) : 817
Wood 402(12) : 522
Wood 402(13) : 672
Wood 402(14) : 537
Wood 402(15) : 624
Wood 402(16) : 427
Wood 402(17) : 715
Wood 402(18) : 660
Wood 402(19) : 587

Wood 402(20) : 708
Wood 402(21) (-CD) : 729
Wood 402(22) (-CD) : 556
Wood 402(23) : 750
Wood 402(24) : 459
Wood 402(25) (-CD) : 1965
Wood 403 : 2304
Wood 404 : 4849
Wood 405 : 3504
Wood 406 : 1387
Wood 407(1) : 6625
Wood 407(2) : 4104
Wood 408 : 2509
Wood 409 : 339
Wood 410 : 3115
Wood 411-2 : 3136
Wood 413(1) : 3904
Wood 413(2) : 1835
Wood 413(3) : 6488
Wood 414(1) : 6492
Wood 414(2) : 1219
Wood 415(1) : 6451
Wood 415(2) : 6450
Wood 416(1) : 4435
Wood 416(2) : 4434
Wood 416(3) : 2105
Wood 416(4) : 502
Wood 416(5) : 4409
Wood 416(6) : 2791
Wood 416(7) : 2788
Wood 416(8) : 1913
Wood 416(9) : 6408
Wood 416(10) : 6708
Wood 416(11) : 3943
Wood 416(12) : 2314
Wood 416(13) : 390
Wood 416(14) : 1084
Wood 416(15) : 1083
Wood 416(16) : 467
Wood 416(17) : 330
Wood 416(18) : 254
Wood 416(19) : 468
Wood 416(20) (-CD) : 469
Wood 416(21) : 473
Wood 416(22) : 671
Wood 416(23) : 4649
Wood 416(24) : 633
Wood 416(25) : 367
Wood 416(26) : 2798
Wood 416(27) : 584
Wood 416(28) : 3917
Wood 416(29) : 534
Wood 416(30) : 3537
Wood 416(31) : 640
Wood 416(32) : 796
Wood 416(33) : 2800
Wood 416(34) : 583
Wood 416(35) : 470
Wood 416(36) : 408
Wood 416(37) : 476
Wood 416(38) : 475
Wood 416(39) : 632
Wood 416(40) : 712
Wood 416(41) : 821

Wood 416(42) : 5104
Wood 416(43) : 510
Wood 416(44) : 4233
Wood 416(45) : 480
Wood 416(46) : 720
Wood 416(47) : 474
Wood 416(48) : 631
Wood 416(49) : 412
Wood 416(50) : 6521
Wood 416(51) : 478
Wood 416(52) (-CD) : 777
Wood 416(53) : 2804
Wood 416(54) : 511
Wood 416(55) : 1808
Wood 416(56) : 4460
Wood 416(57) : 472
Wood 416(58) : 2806
Wood 416(59) : 5503
Wood 416(60) : 471
Wood 416(61) : 401
Wood 416(62) : 2723
Wood 416(63) : 667
Wood 416(64) : 4105
Wood 416(65) : 2802
Wood 416(66) : 2173
Wood 416(67) : 4108
Wood 416(68) : 1086 (M)
Wood 416(69) : 1803
Wood 416(70) : 383
Wood 416(71) : 6744
Wood 416(72) : 331
Wood 416(73) : 1005
Wood 416(74) : 4303
Wood 416(75) : 1809
Wood 416(76) : 395
Wood 416(77) : 820
Wood 416(78) : 396
Wood 416(79) : 4812
Wood 416(80) : 1792
Wood 416(81) : 6473
Wood 416(82) : 6716
Wood 416(83) : 3048
Wood 416(84) : 1793
Wood 416(85) : 1938
Wood 416(86) (-CD) : 3757
Wood 416(87) (-CD) : 3759
Wood 416(88) : 6569
Wood 416(89) : 2286
Wood 416(90) : 6523
Wood 416(91) : 795
Wood 416(92) : 504
Wood 416(93) : 506
Wood 416(94) : 494
Wood 416(95) : 2288
Wood 416(96) : 6425
Wood 416(97) : 5702
Wood 416(98) : 6591
Wood 416(99) (-CD) : 827
Wood 416(100) : 6592
Wood 416(101) : 6590
Wood 416(102) : 1956 (M)
Wood 416(103) : 403
Wood 416(104) : 3849
Wood 416(105) : 1638

Wood 416(106) : 651
Wood 416(107) : 2309
Wood 416(108) : 3808
Wood 416(109) : 6594
Wood 416(110) : 6328 (Ms.)
Wood 416(111-2) : 384
Wood 416(113) : 386
Wood 416(114) : 3181
Wood 416(115) : 3180
Wood 416(116) : 6570 (Ms.)
Wood 416(117) : 655
Wood 416(118) : 6596
Wood 416(119) : 3197
Wood 416(120) : 1421
Wood 416(121) : 4809
Wood 416(122-3) : 1247
Wood 416(124) : 3015
Wood 416(125) : 393
Wood 416(126) : 692
Wood 416(127) : 693
Wood 416(128) : 690
Wood 416(129) : 713
Wood 416(130) : 6691
Wood 416(131) : 1882
Wood 416(132) : 5848
Wood 416(133) : 5227
Wood 417(1) : 781
Wood 417(2) : 4810
Wood 417(3) : 3238
Wood 417(4) : 411
Wood 417(5) : 388
Wood 417(6) : 5234
Wood 417(7) : 6622
Wood 417(8) : 5283
Wood 417(9) : 5966
Wood 417(10) : 1412
Wood 417(11) : 5770
Wood 417(12) : 531
Wood 417(13) : 5368
Wood 417(14a) : 5948
Wood 417(14b) : 6123 (M)
Wood 417(15) : 5126
Wood 417(16) : 4832
Wood 417(17) : 3766
Wood 417(18) : 3130
Wood 417(20) : 4127
Wood 417(21a) : 6422
Wood 417(21b) : 4636
Wood 417(22) : 1285
Wood 417(23) : 3765
Wood 417(24) : 562 (Ms.)
Wood 417(25) : 799
Wood 417(26) : 5124
Wood 417(27) : 2227
Wood 417(28) : 4811
Wood 417(29) : 5823
Wood 417(30) : 5821
Wood 417(31) : 4163
Wood 417(32) : 4713
Wood 417(33) : 4126
Wood 417(34) (349, CD) : 614
Wood 417(35) : 615
Wood 417(36) : 612
Wood 417(37) : 790

Wood 417(38) : 1967 (M)
Wood 417(39) : 800
Wood 417(40) : 6597
Wood 417(41) : 927
Wood 417(42) : 3833 (M)
Wood 417(43) : 1262
Wood 417(44) : 3947
Wood 417(45) : 413 (M)
Wood 417(46) : 2812
Wood 417(47) : 2815
Wood 417(48) : 481
Wood 417(49) : 6221
Wood 417(50) : 611
Wood 417(51) : 1871
Wood 417(52) : 4709
Wood 417(53) : 2811
Wood 417(54) : 6384
Wood 417(55) : 2213
Wood 417(56) : 373
Wood 417(57) : 568
Wood 417(58) : 528
Wood 417(59) : 701
Wood 417(60) : 642
Wood 417(61) (-CD) : 437
Wood 417(62) : 6640
Wood 417(63) : 785
Wood 417(64) : 617
Wood 417(65) : 733
Wood 417(66) : 1980
Wood 417(67) : 3696
Wood 417(68) : 4793
Wood 417(69) : 4795
Wood 417(70) : 6220
Wood 417(71) : 4794
Wood 417(72) : 4791
Wood 417(73) : 801
Wood 417(74) : 760
Wood 417(75) : 5520
Wood 417(76) : 282
Wood 417(77) : 6098
Wood 417(78) : 3725
Wood 417(79) : 610
Wood 417(80) : 558
Wood 417(81) : 5544
Wood 417(82) : 490
Wood 417(84) : 461
Wood 417(85) : 665
Wood 417(86) : 457
Wood 417(87) : 563
Wood 417(88) (-CD) : 663
Wood 417(89) : 593
Wood 417(90) : 488
Wood 417(91) : 418
Wood 417(92) : 4837
Wood 417(93) : 697
Wood 417(94) : 455
Wood 417(95) : 933
Wood 417(96) : 4272
Wood 417(97) : 1189
Wood 417(98) : 1194
Wood 417(99) : 1193
Wood 417(100) : 1191
Wood 417(101) : 1192
Wood 417(102) : 2319

Wood 417(103) : 3189
Wood 417(104) : 4510
Wood 417(105) : 4123
Wood 417(106) : 1988
Wood 417(107) : 1646
Wood 417(108) : 397
Wood 417(109) : 491
Wood 417(110) : 613
Wood 417(111) : 609
Wood 417(112) : 768
Wood 417(113) : 453
Wood 417(114) : 514
Wood 417(115) : 789
Wood 417(116) (517, CD) : 4918
Wood 417(117) : 391
Wood 417(118) : 826
Wood 417(119) : 5869
Wood 417(120) : 6219
Wood 417(121) : 417
Wood 417(122) : 1992
Wood 417(123) : 728
Wood 417(124) : 5671
Wood 417(125) : 5211
Wood 417(126) : 762 (M)
Wood 417(127) : 326
Wood 417(128) : 5284
Wood 417(129) : 520
Wood 417(130) : 5546
Wood 417(131) : 5306
Wood 417(132) : 4302
Wood 417(133) : 368
Wood 417(134) : 761
Wood 417(135) : 420
Wood 417(136) : 659
Wood 417(137) : 387
Wood 417(138-9) : 863
Wood 417(140) : 737
Wood 417(141) : 20 (Ms.)
Wood 417(142) : 1968
Wood 417(143) : 564
Wood 417(144) : 736
Wood 417(145) : 515
Wood 417(146) : 770
Wood 417(147) : 458
Wood 417(148) : 6501
Wood 417(149) : 650
Wood 417(150) : 865
Wood 417(151) : 782
Wood 417(152) : 430
Wood 417(153) : 767
Wood 417(154) : 507
Wood 417(155) : 4019
Wood 417(156) : 5186
Wood 417(157) : 5154
Wood 417(158) : 5156
Wood 417(159) : 740
Wood 417(160) : 739
Wood 417(161) : 399
Wood 417(162) : 832
Wood 417(163) : 798
Wood 417(164) : 492
Wood 417(165) : 6271
Wood 417(166) : 559
Wood 417(167) : 711

Wood 417(168) : 824
Wood 417(169) : 717
Wood 417(170) : 684
Wood 417(171) : 620
Wood 417(172) : 825
Wood 417(173) : 570
Wood 417(174) : 431
Wood 417(175) : 985
Wood 417(176) : 516
Wood 417(177) : 521
Wood 417(178) : 630
Wood 417(179) : 566
Wood 417(180) : 830
Wood 417(181) : 774
Wood 417(182) : 3926
Wood 417(183) : 696
Wood 417(184) : 664
Wood 418 (-CD) : 2363
Wood 419 (-CD) : 2365
Wood 420 (-CD) : 2362
Wood 421(1-2) : 4798
Wood 421(3) : 4797
Wood 421(4) : 5940
Wood 421(5) : 2010
Wood 421(6) : 3393
Wood 421(7) : 898
Wood 421(8) : 1047
Wood 421(9) : 1962
Wood 421(10) : 5733
Wood 421(11) : 1286
Wood 421(12) : 1048
Wood 421(13) : 3476
Wood 421(14-16) : 3277
Wood 421(17) : 5922
Wood 422(1) : 6224
Wood 422(2) : 5965
Wood 422(3a) : 5959
Wood 422(3b) : 6667
Wood 422(4) : 5863
Wood 422(5) : 5864
Wood 422(6-7) : 3574
Wood 422(8) : 1209
Wood 422(9) : 1093
Wood 422(10) : 4675
Wood 422(11) (-CD) : 5926
Wood 422(12) : 3087
Wood 422(13a) : 3888
Wood 422(13b) : 988
Wood 422(14) : 3440
Wood 422(15) : 5120
Wood 422(16) : 4786
Wood 422(17) : 4124
Wood 422(18) : 5730
Wood 422(19) : 3033
Wood 423(1) : 3640
Wood 423(2) : 3641
Wood 423(3) : 1274
Wood 423(4-5) : 4025
Wood 423(6-11) : 5999
Wood 423(12) : 4889
Wood 423(13) : 4892 (M)
Wood 423(14) : 4945
Wood 423(15) : 4948
Wood 423(16) : 4949

Wood 423(17) : 501
Wood 423(18) : 4903
Wood 423(19) : 4951
Wood 423(20) : 2574
Wood 423(21) : 1276
Wood 423(22) : 4875
Wood 423(23-6) : 4999
Wood 423(27) : 2684
Wood 423(28) : 370
Wood 423(29) : 4910
Wood 423(30) : 1278
Wood 423(31) : 2326
Wood 423(32) : 6566
Wood 423(33) : 4524
Wood 423(34) : 6567
Wood 423(35) : 11
Wood 423(36) : 4886
Wood 423(37) : 4884
Wood 423(38) : 503
Wood 423(39) : 505
Wood 423(40) : 5250
Wood 423(41) : 2308
Wood 423(42) : 6571
Wood 423(43) : 5096
Wood 423(44) : 943
Wood 423(45) : 945
Wood 423(46) : 6572
Wood 423(47) : 3617
Wood 423(48) : 5012
Wood 423(49) : 3252
Wood 423(50) : 4916
Wood 423(51) : 4941
Wood 423(52) : 5020
Wood 423(53) : 5016
Wood 423(54) : 4942
Wood 423(55) (-CD) : 4890
Wood 423(56) : 4943
Wood 423(57) : 4917
Wood 423(58) : 4980
Wood 423(59) (723, CD) : 5475
Wood 423(60) : 4919
Wood 423(61) : 5476
Wood 423(62) : 5477
Wood 423(63) : 3372
Wood 423(64) : 4463
Wood 423(65) : 4882
Wood 423(66) : 3434
Wood 423(67) : 5097
Wood 423(68) : 5098
Wood 424(1) : 6037
Wood 424(2) : 6036
Wood 424(4) : 1942
Wood 424(5) : 1943
Wood 424(6) : 3802
Wood 424(7) : 1819
Wood 424(8) : 3293
Wood 424(9) : 3591
Wood 424(10) : 3237
Wood 424(11) : 928
Wood 424(12) : 1224
Wood 424(13) : 4788
Wood 424(14) : 5543
Wood 424(17) : 2744
Wood 424(18) : 2865

Wood 424(19) : 5340
Wood 424(20) (2, CD) : 6562
Wood 424(21) : 6559
Wood 424(22) : 6560
Wood 424(23) : 1018
Wood 424(24) (428, CD) : 6213
Wood 424(25) : 6561
Wood 424(26) : 3509
Wood 424(27) : 6619
Wood 424(28) : 5204
Wood 424(29) : 2291
Wood 424(30) : 1429
Wood 424(31) : 2748
Wood 425(1) : 321
Wood 425(2) : 4035
Wood 425(3) : 4033
Wood 425(4) : 4034
Wood 425(5) : 4032
Wood 425(6) : 926
Wood 425(7) : 1856
Wood 425(8) : 6383
Wood 425(9a) : 5921
Wood 425(9b) : 4396
Wood 425(10) : 5274
Wood 425(11) : 3120
Wood 425(12) : 2857
Wood 425(13) : 322
Wood 425(14) : 4140
Wood 425(15) : 3887
Wood 425(16) : 1141
Wood 425(17) : 1142
Wood 425(18) : 3860
Wood 425(19) : 5339
Wood 425(20) : 4787
Wood 425(21) : 2368
Wood 425(22) (-CD) : 5924
Wood 425(23) : 4361
Wood 425(24) : 6214
Wood 425(25) : 2150
Wood 425(26) : 235
Wood 425(27) : 2153
Wood 425(28) : 4571
Wood 425(29) : 1033
Wood 425(30) : 1080
Wood 426(1) : 4790
Wood 426(2) : 3171
Wood 426(3) : 6133
Wood 426(4) : 4125
Wood 426(5) : 1667
Wood 426(6) : 1670
Wood 426(7) : 3061
Wood 426(8) : 2154
Wood 426(9) : 1668
Wood 426(10) : 5341
Wood 426(11) : 6462
Wood 426(12) : 6463
Wood 426(13) : 5235
Wood 426(14) (427, in CD) : 1669
Wood 426(15) : 2369
Wood 426(16) : 815
Wood 426(17) : 1672
Wood 426(18) : 6215
Wood 426(19) : 2151
Wood 426(20) : 2152

Wood 426(21) (-CD) : 2360
Wood 426(22) : 2944
Wood 426(23) : 6242
Wood 426(24) : 6243
Wood 426(25) : 3861
Wood 426(26) : 4141
Wood 426(27) : 2359
Wood 426(28) : 2945
Wood 426(29) : 6743
Wood 426(30) : 6197
Wood 426(31) : 6228
Wood 426(32) : 6229
Wood 426(33) : 3361
Wood 426(34) : 5824
Wood 426(35) : 2572
Wood 427(1) (-CD) : 3694
Wood 427(2) : 3016
Wood 427(3) : 3692
Wood 427(4) : 3695
Wood 427(5) : 3691
Wood 427(6) : 3693
Wood 427(7) : 5113
Wood 427(8) : 5925
Wood 427(9) : 6722
Wood 427(10) : 2749
Wood 427(11) : 2007
Wood 427(12) : 5121
Wood 427(13a) : 1401
Wood 427(13b) (-CD) : 1671
Wood 427(14) : 3038
Wood 427(15) : 5844
Wood 427(16) : 3034
Wood 427(17) : 3039
Wood 427(18) : 3035
Wood 427(19) : 3036
Wood 427(20-1) : 3040
Wood 427(22) : 3037
Wood 427(23) : 1227
Wood 427(24) (26, CD) : 1948
Wood 427(25) : 1949
Wood 427(26) : 1947
Wood 427(27) : 6547
Wood 427(28) : 1946
Wood 427(29) : 6182
Wood 427(30) : 1951
Wood 427(31) : 1950
Wood 427(32) : 1978
Wood 427(33) : 1987
Wood 427(34) : 1983
Wood 427(35) : 1979
Wood 427(36) : 1977
Wood 427(37) : 1982
Wood 427(38) : 6606
Wood 427(39) : 1984
Wood 427(40) : 1985
Wood 427(41) : 1989
Wood 427(42) : 1990
Wood 427(43) : 1991
Wood 427(44) : 1993
Wood 427(45-6) : 6183
Wood 427(47) : 3913
Wood 427(48) : 5212
Wood 427(49) : 1399
Wood 427(50) : 6485

Wood 427(51) : 6486
Wood 428(1) : 1394
Wood 428(2) : 1395
Wood 428(3) : 5670
Wood 428(4) : 6388
Wood 428(5) : 5614
Wood 428(6) : 6751
Wood 428(7) : 5669
Wood 428(8) : 6387
Wood 428(9) : 6519
Wood 428(10) : 6200
Wood 428(11) : 5672
Wood 428(12) : 5852
Wood 428(13) : 5851
Wood 428(14) : 5893
Wood 428(15) : 4128
Wood 428(16) : 5673
Wood 428(17) : 1824
Wood 428(18) : 1825
Wood 428(19) : 5901
Wood 428(20) : 5900
Wood 428(21) : 5853
Wood 428(22a) : 4597
Wood 428(22b) : 6443
Wood 428(23) : 1029
Wood 428(24) : 3392
Wood 428(25) : 1081
Wood 428(26) : 2984
Wood 428(27) : 957
Wood 428(28) : 3655
Wood 428(29) (-CD) : 263
Wood 428(30) : 262
Wood 428(31) (-CD) : 6253
Wood 428(32) : 6009
Wood 428(33) : 6008
Wood 429(1) : 3850
Wood 429(2) : 6720
Wood 429(3) : 6143
Wood 429(4) : 6649 (M)
Wood 429(5) : 6326
Wood 429(6) : 3965
Wood 429(7) : 5899
Wood 429(8) : 6241
Wood 429(9) : 3021
Wood 429(10) : 5859
Wood 429(11) : 5214
Wood 429(12) : 1917
Wood 429(13) : 6305
Wood 429(14) : 3022
Wood 429(15) : 3412
Wood 429(16) : 1854
Wood 429(17) : 3488
Wood 429(18) : 3360
Wood 429(19) : 3491
Wood 429(20) : 3933 (M)
Wood 429(21) : 2109
Wood 429(22) : 2990
Wood 429(23) : 3023
Wood 429(24) : 4586
Wood 429(25) : 4320
Wood 429(26) : 2225
Wood 429(27) : 2174
Wood 429(28) : 3024
Wood 429(29) (-CD) : 4526

Wood 429(30) : 4175
Wood 429(31) : 6329
Wood 429(32) : 4539
Wood 429(33) : 5481
Wood 429(34) : 6620
Wood 429(35) : 2110
Wood 429(36) : 3049
Wood 429(37) : 1115 (M)
Wood 429(38) : 5760
Wood 429(39) : 6694
Wood 429(40) : 1650
Wood 429(41) : 1116
Wood 429(42) : 1400
Wood 429(43) : 2972
Wood 429(44) : 878
Wood 429(45) : 1652
Wood 429(46) : 3029
Wood 429(47) : 6719
Wood 429(48) : 225
Wood 429(49) : 4561
Wood 429(50) : 1076
Wood 429(51) (-CD) : 6205
Wood 429(52) : 3342
Wood 429(53) : 266
Wood 430 : 6685
Wood 431a : 6687
Wood 431b : 3620
Wood 431c : 2260
Wood 432 : 881
Wood 433(1) : 5888
Wood 433(2) : 4595
Wood 433(3) : 1190
Wood 433(4) : 877
Wood 434 : 3626
Wood 435(1) : 4041
Wood 435(2) : 4042
Wood 435(3) : 301
Wood 435(4) : 343
Wood 436 : 3983
Wood 437 : 5125
Wood 438 : 4555
Wood 439 : 2876
Wood 440(1) : 5755 (M)
Wood 440(2) : 5636 (M)
Wood 440(3) : 4408 (M)
Wood 441 : 3939
Wood 442(1) : 990
Wood 442(2) : 5720
Wood 442(3) : 5943
Wood 443 : 3728
Wood 444(1) : 989
Wood 444(2) : 6406
Wood 445(1) : 3823
Wood 445(2) : 6404
Wood 445(3) : 2557
Wood 445(4) : 6163
Wood 445(5) : 2696
Wood 445(6) : 2306
Wood 445(7) : 3981
Wood 445(8) : 2534
Wood 445(9) : 1146
Wood 445(10) : 2508
Wood 445(11) : 2366
Wood 446 : 3206

Wood 447(1) : 6477
Wood 447(2) : 1419
Wood 448 : 5930
Wood 449 : 4501 (M)
Wood 450 : 5521
Wood 451 : 2343
Wood 452 : 5598
Wood 453(1) : 1916
Wood 453(2) : 3718
Wood 453(3) : 6001
Wood 454 : 2867
Wood 455 : 3057
Wood 456 : 5193
Wood 457(1) : 3369
Wood 457(2) : 5833
Wood 457(3) : 3646
Wood 458 : 4834
Wood 459 : 903
Wood 460(1) : 4935
Wood 460(2) : 4936
Wood 460(3) : 6433
Wood 460(4) : 6280
Wood 460(5) : 1404
Wood 460(6) : 3351
Wood 460(7) : 4932
Wood 460(8) : 4933
Wood 460(9) : 4142
Wood 461 : 6324
Wood 462 : 1101
Wood 463 : 4040
Wood 464 : 1397
Wood 465(1) : 4764
Wood 465(2) : 6161
Wood 465(3) : 4174
Wood 465(4) : 999
Wood 465(5) : 6589
Wood 465(6) : 4405
Wood 465(7) : 6142
Wood 466 : 3643
Wood 467(1) : 4766
Wood 467(2) : 1232
Wood 467(4) : 3613
Wood 467(5) : 1691
Wood 467(6) : 3907
Wood 467(7) : 3636
Wood 467(8) : 1699
Wood 468 : 2590
Wood 469 : 3543
Wood 470 : 1413
Wood 471 : 3961
Wood 472 : 6060
Wood 473(1) : 5363
Wood 473(2) : 6096
Wood 473(3) : 6095
Wood 474 : 4194
Wood 475 : 1955
Wood 476(1) : 3868
Wood 476(2) : 3869
Wood 476(3) : 3872
Wood 476(4) : 3865
Wood 476(5) : 3870
Wood 476(6) : 3867
Wood 476(7) : 3862
Wood 476(8) : 3864

Wood 476(9) : 3871
Wood 476(10) : 3318
Wood 476(11) : 3319
Wood 476(12) : 5704
Wood 476(13) : 4784
Wood 476(14) : 5705
Wood 476(15) : 4062
Wood 476(16) : 4061
Wood 476(17) : 4815
Wood 476(18) (-CD) : 4284
Wood 477(1) : 6290
Wood 477(2) : 6234
Wood 477(3) : 304
Wood 477(4) : 3739
Wood 477(5) : 1177
Wood 477(6) : 6432
Wood 478(1) : 2282
Wood 478(2) : 5349
Wood 478(3) : 6297
Wood 478(4) : 1230
Wood 478(5) : 5107
Wood 478(6) : 918
Wood 479(1) : 4090
Wood 479(2) : 4093
Wood 479(3) : 4092
Wood 479(4) : 4091
Wood 480(1) : 1267
Wood 480(2) (-CD) : 1268
Wood 480(3) : 1269
Wood 481(1) : 3604
Wood 481(2) : 5678
Wood 481(3) : 6052
Wood 481(4) : 2270
Wood 481(5) : 2234
Wood 481(6) : 2060
Wood 482(1) : 2156
Wood 482(2) : 1840
Wood 482(3) : 3672
Wood 482(4) : 3094
Wood 482(5) : 3093
Wood 482(6) : 2401
Wood 482(7) : 1886
Wood 483(1) : 5961
Wood 483(2) : 6710
Wood 483(3) : 6709
Wood 483(4) : 2019
Wood 483(5) : 1283
Wood 483(6) : 3847
Wood 483(7) : 6385
Wood 483(8) : 6281
Wood 483(9) : 3235
Wood 483(10) : 3474
Wood 483(11) : 6146
Wood 483(11a) : 4639
Wood 483(11b) : 4741
Wood 483(12) : 6155
Wood 483(13) (482, CD) : 4172
Wood 483(14) : 935
Wood 483(15) : 2042
Wood 483(16) : 1137
Wood 483(17) : 4650
Wood 483(18) : 1059
Wood 483(19) : 4845
Wood 483(20) : 4017

Wood 483(21) : 2316
Wood 483(22) : 3060
Wood 483(23) (-CD) : 6475
Wood 483(24) : 5213
Wood 484(1) : 4894
Wood 484(2) : 4934
Wood 484(3) : 4897
Wood 484(4) : 4911
Wood 484(5) : 1023
Wood 484(6) : 4938
Wood 484(7) : 4937
Wood 484(8) : 2033
Wood 484(9) : 4096
Wood 484(10) : 6481
Wood 484(11) : 3931
Wood 485(1) : 3483
Wood 485(2) : 6099
Wood 485(3) : 1257
Wood 486(1) : 5127
Wood 486(2) : 2025
Wood 486(3) : 2030
Wood 486(4) : 2031
Wood 486(5) : 2399
Wood 486(6) : 3482
Wood 486(7) : 4608
Wood 486(8) : 6624
Wood 486(9) : 3165
Wood 486(10) : 4452
Wood 486(11) : 3703
Wood 486(12) (-CD) : 4614
Wood 486(13) : 3551
Wood 486(14-16) : 5742
Wood 486(17) : 5210
Wood 486(18) : 1431
Wood 487(1) : 2181
Wood 487(2) : 5450
Wood 487(3) : 3589
Wood 487(4) : 2779
Wood 487(5) : 3698
Wood 487(6) : 2206
Wood 487(7) : 4605
Wood 487(8a) : 4069
Wood 487(8b) : 4068
Wood 487(9) : 4557
Wood 487(10) : 4558
Wood 488(1) : 4195
Wood 488(2) : 4196
Wood 489 : 26
Wood 490(1) : 5517 (M)
Wood 490(2) : 3009 (M)
Wood 490(3) : 1112 (M)
Wood 490(4) : 4316 (M)
Wood 490(5) : 5223 (M)
Wood 491 : 2021
Wood 492(1) : 1769
Wood 492(2) : 2409
Wood 492(3) : 4489
Wood 492(4) : 3856
Wood 493 : 2022
Wood 494(1) : 2603
Wood 494(2) : 6459
Wood 495 : 5635
Wood 496(1) : 5270
Wood 496(2) (-CD) : 4464

Wood 497 : 3137
Wood 498(1) : 6634
Wood 498(2) : 2020
Wood 498(3) : 2061
Wood 498(4) (Ashm., CD) : 2325
Wood 498(5) : 3289
Wood 498(6) : 2015
Wood 498(7) : 6645
Wood 498(8) : 5260
Wood 498(9) : 5626
Wood 498(10) : 3074
Wood 498(11) : 3288
Wood 498(12) : 18
Wood 498(13) : 3905
Wood 498(14) : 61
Wood 498(15) : 100
Wood 499(1) : 352
Wood 499(2) : 4439
Wood 499(3) : 6272
Wood 499(4) : 3295
Wood 499(5) : 6100
Wood 499(6) : 6093
Wood 499(7) : 6102
Wood 499(8) : 2981
Wood 499(9) : 1432
Wood 499(10) : 4509
Wood 500(1) : 4273
Wood 500(2) : 842
Wood 500(3) : 4274
Wood 500(4) : 2559
Wood 500(5) : 5990
Wood 500(6) : 3177
Wood 500(7) : 2567
Wood 500(8) : 4075
Wood 500(9) : 4632
Wood 500(10) : 1696
Wood 500(11) : 4264
Wood 500(12) : 1695
Wood 501(1) : 4099
Wood 501(2) : 4505
Wood 501(3) : 2868
Wood 501(4) : 2906
Wood 501(5) : 2907
Wood 501(6) : 1779
Wood 501(7) : 4644
Wood 501(8) : 1752
Wood 501(9) : 4643
Wood 501(10) : 5791
Wood 501(11) : 2908
Wood 501(12) : 6115
Wood 501(13) : 4876
Wood 501(14) : 6497
Wood 501(15) : 5954
Wood 501(16) : 4871
Wood 501(17) : 4877
Wood 501(18) : 4150
Wood 501(19) : 5799
Wood 501(20) : 5878
Wood 501(21) : 6703
Wood 501(22) : 2929
Wood 501(23) : 2927
Wood 501(24) : 2909
Wood 501(25) : 1259
Wood 501(26) : 5207

Wood 501(27) : 3462
Wood 501(28) : 3
Wood 501(29) : 2845
Wood 501(30) : 2916
Wood 501(31) : 1231
Wood 501(32) : 4468
Wood 501(33) : 2681
Wood 501(34) : 3203
Wood 501(35) : 2917
Wood 501(36) : 2910
Wood 501(37) : 2915
Wood 501(38) : 1006
Wood 501(39) : 3531
Wood 501(40) : 2920
Wood 501(41) : 1022
Wood 501(42) : 2675
Wood 501(43) : 5151
Wood 502(1) : 4718
Wood 502(2) : 5800
Wood 502(3) : 4029
Wood 502(4) : 2847
Wood 502(5) : 4037
Wood 502(6) : 4296
Wood 502(7) : 5327
Wood 502(8) : 6365
Wood 502(9) : 866
Wood 502(10) : 6522
Wood 502(11) : 1934
Wood 502(12) : 3952
Wood 502(13) : 3951
Wood 502(14) : 3953
Wood 502(15) : 2693
Wood 502(16) : 2921
Wood 502(17) : 3950
Wood 502(18) (-CD) : 6327
Wood 502(19) : 3957
Wood 502(20) (-CD) : 2918
Wood 502(21) : 3264
Wood 502(22) : 2080
Wood 502(23) : 3956
Wood 502(24) : 5666
Wood 502(25) : 3749
Wood 502(26) : 310
Wood 502(27) : 5664
Wood 502(28) : 5694
Wood 502(29) : 1782
Wood 502(30) : 2846
Wood 502(31) : 2919
Wood 502(32) : 3266
Wood 502(33) : 4719
Wood 502(34) : 3461
Wood 502(35) : 5163
Wood 502(36) : 5608
Wood 502(37) : 897
Wood 502(38) : 3265
Wood 502(39) : 1781
Wood 502(40) : 3385
Wood 502(41) : 3267
Wood 502(42) : 2480
Wood 502(43) : 3359
Wood 502(44) : 3374
Wood 502(46a) : 5777 (M)
Wood 502(46b) : 4720
Wood 502(47) : 2081

Wood 502(48) : 2101
Wood 502(49) : 3268
Wood 502(50) : 901
Wood 502(51) (-CD) : 2583
Wood 502(52) : 4594
Wood 502(53) : 2082 (M)
Wood 502(54) : 4721
Wood 502(55) : 2083
Wood 502(56) : 6585
Wood 502(57) : 4030
Wood 502(58) : 2077
Wood 502(59) : 1783
Wood 502(60) : 314
Wood 502(61) : 2694
Wood 502(62) : 5665
Wood 502(63) : 1935
Wood 502(64) : 1933
Wood 502(65) : 4700
Wood 502(66) : 6260
Wood 502(67) (-CD) : 1780
Wood 502(68) : 2086
Wood 502(69) : 2079 (M)
Wood 502(70) : 3988
Wood 502(71) : 2084
Wood 502(72) : 2085
Wood 502(73) : 4722
Wood 502(74) : 2848
Wood 502(75) (-CD) : 1677
Wood 503(1) : 1787
Wood 503(2) : 6187
Wood 503(3) : 1784
Wood 503(4) : 4136
Wood 503(5) : 6549
Wood 503(6) : 3760
Wood 503(7) : 1785
Wood 503(8) (-CD) : 2923
Wood 503(9) : 1254
Wood 503(10) : 2700
Wood 503(11) : 2484
Wood 503(12) : 2483
Wood 503(13) : 2485
Wood 503(14) : 2482 (M)
Wood 503(15) : 2088 (M)
Wood 503(16) : 2090
Wood 503(17) : 2584
Wood 503(18) : 2091 (M)
Wood 503(19) : 2585
Wood 503(20) : 2094
Wood 503(21) : 4528
Wood 503(22) : 5686
Wood 503(23) : 1042
Wood 503(24) : 1045
Wood 503(24a) : 1043
Wood 503(25) : 1046
Wood 503(26) : 4016
Wood 503(27) : 1851
Wood 503(28) : 4517
Wood 503(29) : 1241
Wood 503(30) : 5468
Wood 503(31) : 5894
Wood 503(32) : 4756
Wood 503(33) : 4757
Wood 503(34) : 5637
Wood 503(35) : 1010

Wood 503(36) : 2588
Wood 503(37) (-CD) : 2589
Wood 504(1) : 317
Wood 504(2) : 1658
Wood 504(3) : 2185
Wood 504(4) : 2386
Wood 505(1) : 5562
Wood 505(2) : 5563
Wood 505(3) : 5564
Wood 505(4) (504, CD): 4588
Wood 505(5) : 5267
Wood 506(1) : 6168
Wood 506(2) : 3796
Wood 507(1) : 6517
Wood 507(2) : 4457
Wood 507(3) : 6232
Wood 507(4) : 3771
Wood 507(5) : 3769
Wood 507(6) : 2053
Wood 507(7) : 2433
Wood 507(8) : 5718
Wood 507(9) : 298
Wood 507(10) : 2606
Wood 507(11) : 2593
Wood 507(12) : 1073
Wood 507(13) : 4671
Wood 507(14) : 4668
Wood 507(15) : 2341
Wood 507(16) : 2271
Wood 507(17) : 3770
Wood 507(18) : 4817
Wood 507(19) : 4334
Wood 507(20) : 6543
Wood 507(21) : 3774
Wood 507(22) : 2147
Wood 507(23) : 3773
Wood 507(24) : 2947
Wood 507(25) : 1233
Wood 507(26) : 1002
Wood 507(27) : 3898
Wood 507(28) : 1693
Wood 507(29) : 6085
Wood 507(30) : 1074
Wood 507(31) : 1001
Wood 507(32) : 3736
Wood 507(33) : 3772
Wood 507(34) : 3776
Wood 507(35) : 2995
Wood 507(36) : 3317
Wood 507(37) : 4659
Wood 507(38) : 4209
Wood 507(39) : 1895
Wood 507(40) : 2610
Wood 507(41) : 5904
Wood 507(42) : 3899
Wood 507(43) : 287
Wood 507(44) : 4585
Wood 507(45) : 1939
Wood 507(46) : 1701
Wood 507(47) : 953
Wood 507(48) : 954
Wood 507(49) : 4657
Wood 508(1) : 4542
Wood 508(2) : 6167

Wood 508(3) : 5712
Wood 508(4) : 3384
Wood 508(5) : 1715
Wood 508(6) : 4860
Wood 508(7) : 1940
Wood 508(8) : 3466
Wood 508(9) : 2766
Wood 508(10) : 4217
Wood 508(11) : 2641
Wood 508(12) : 5569
Wood 508(13) : 6542
Wood 508(14) : 3775
Wood 508(15) : 1075
Wood 508(16) : 4239
Wood 508(17) : 5906
Wood 508(18) : 4714
Wood 508(19) : 1020
Wood 508(20) : 2462
Wood 508(21) : 2115
Wood 508(22) : 4456
Wood 508(23) : 1235
Wood 508(24) : 3780
Wood 508(25) : 3781
Wood 508(26) : 3782
Wood 508(27) : 3399
Wood 508(28) : 1185
Wood 508(29) : 3783
Wood 508(30) : 3901
Wood 508(31) : 3246
Wood 508(32) : 1731
Wood 508(33) : 6544
Wood 508(34) : 276
Wood 508(35) : 341
Wood 508(36) : 3778
Wood 508(37) : 5690
Wood 508(38) : 3639
Wood 508(39) : 3777
Wood 508(40) : 2339
Wood 508(41) : 4533
Wood 508(42) : 2660
Wood 508(43) : 5188
Wood 508(44) : 2657
Wood 508(45) : 2659
Wood 508(46) : 1741
Wood 508(47) : 3784
Wood 508(48) : 2052
Wood 508(49) : 4566
Wood 508(50) : 3699
Wood 508(51) : 4800
Wood 508(52) : 3785
Wood 509(1) : 2361
Wood 509(2) : 2473
Wood 509(3) : 1749
Wood 509(4) : 3786
Wood 509(5) : 3787 (M)
Wood 509(6) : 1237
Wood 509(7) : 5692
Wood 509(8) : 1236
Wood 509(9) : 3789
Wood 509(10) : 2264
Wood 509(11) : 6114
Wood 509(12) : 3788
Wood 509(13) : 1750
Wood 509(14) : 2670

Wood 509(15) : 3790
Wood 509(16) : 2673
Wood 509(17) : 5473
Wood 509(18) : 1756
Wood 509(19) : 4544
Wood 509(20) : 4803
Wood 509(21) : 2340
Wood 509(22) : 5616
Wood 509(23) : 4802
Wood 509(24) : 4559
Wood 509(25) : 6203
Wood 509(26) : 4804 (M)
Wood 509(27) : 3908
Wood 509(28) : 4801
Wood 509(29) : 3791
Wood 509(30) : 4805
Wood 509(31) : 3750
Wood 509(32) : 1762
Wood 509(33) : 1240
Wood 509(34) : 3665
Wood 509(35) : 1239
Wood 510(1) : 6366
Wood 510(2) : 3018
Wood 510(3) : 1786
Wood 510(4) : 2698
Wood 510(5) : 3909
Wood 510(6) : 1995
Wood 510(7) : 6656
Wood 510(8) : 2100
Wood 510(9) : 2699
Wood 510(10) : 889
Wood 510(11) : 3792
Wood 510(12) : 2087
Wood 510(13) : 934
Wood 510(14) : 3794
Wood 510(15) : 2089
Wood 510(16) : 2383
Wood 510(17) : 3804
Wood 510(18) : 6458
Wood 510(19) : 2702
Wood 510(20) : 2145
Wood 510(21) : 6697
Wood 510(22a) : 3260
Wood 510(22b) : 6696
Wood 510(23) : 3271
Wood 510(24) : 2487
Wood 510(25) : 1121
Wood 510(26) : 3911
Wood 510(27) : 1998
Wood 510(28) : 1996
Wood 510(29) : 1997
Wood 510(30) : 1078
Wood 510(31) : 4208
Wood 510(32) : 1079
Wood 510(33) : 4
Wood 510(34) : 6452
Wood 510(35) : 1828
Wood 510(36) : 3539
Wood 510(37) : 3798
Wood 510(38) : 4164
Wood 511(1) : 5968
Wood 511(2-3) : 1664
Wood 511(4) : 5514
Wood 511(5a) : 5845

Wood 511(5b) : 2580
Wood 511(6) : 5969
Wood 511(7) : 6165
Wood 511(8) : 5811
Wood 511(9) : 5817
Wood 511(10) : 5814
Wood 511(11) : 5816
Wood 511(12) : 5554
Wood 511(13) : 5973
Wood 511(14) : 1659
Wood 511(15) : 5155
Wood 511(16) : 340
Wood 511(17) : 1377
Wood 512(1) : 4553
Wood 512(2) : 3729
Wood 512(3) : 3638
Wood 512(4) : 5769
Wood 512(5) : 3248
Wood 512(6-7) : 6226
Wood 512(8) : 4939
Wood 512(9) : 5361
Wood 512(10) : 1220
Wood 512(11) : 3816
Wood 512(12) : 3291
Wood 512(13) : 2324
Wood 512(14) : 4404
Wood 512(15) : 3410
Wood 512(16) (-CD) : 5010
Wood 513(1) : 4024
Wood 513(2) : 4023
Wood 513(3) : 3110
Wood 513(4) : 6313
Wood 513(5) : 1284
Wood 513(6) : 3114
Wood 513(7) : 1529
Wood 513(8) : 1509
Wood 514(1) : 4048
Wood 514(2) : 4901
Wood 514(3) : 4902
Wood 514(4) : 4899
Wood 514(5) : 4052
Wood 514(6) : 7
Wood 514(7) : 4864
Wood 514(8) : 2250
Wood 514(9) : 5259
Wood 514(10) : 1778
Wood 514(11) : 4098
Wood 514(12) : 4865
Wood 514(13) : 1868
Wood 514(14) : 2373
Wood 514(15a) : 6158
Wood 514(15b) : 4658
Wood 514(16) : 2667
Wood 514(17) : 6341
Wood 514(18) : 4873
Wood 514(19a) : 4870
Wood 514(19b) : 2905
Wood 514(20) : 4878
Wood 514(21) : 4904
Wood 514(22) : 6454
Wood 514(23) : 1863
Wood 514(24) : 2842
Wood 514(25) : 1860
Wood 514(26) : 1861

Wood 514(27) : 2678
Wood 514(28) : 4991
Wood 514(29) : 4993
Wood 514(30) : 5000
Wood 514(31) : 5738
Wood 514(32) : 4992
Wood 514(33) : 2968
Wood 514(34) : 5434
Wood 514(35) : 6455
Wood 514(36) : 351
Wood 514(37) : 2685
Wood 514(38) : 2692
Wood 514(39) : 2691
Wood 514(40) : 4906
Wood 514(41) : 4696
Wood 514(42) : 4997
Wood 514(43) : 4995
Wood 514(44) : 993
Wood 514(45) : 4710 (Ms.)
Wood 514(46) : 4994
Wood 514(47) : 6646
Wood 514(48) : 6647
Wood 514(49) : 872
Wood 514(50) : 5245
Wood 514(51) : 3437
Wood 514(52) : 4181
Wood 514(53) : 371
Wood 514(54) : 4909
Wood 515(1) : 4950
Wood 515(2) : 2327
Wood 515(3) (513, CD) : 5093
Wood 515(4) : 4879
Wood 515(5) : 4026
Wood 515(6) : 3761
Wood 515(7) : 4711 (Ms.)
Wood 515(8) : 2166
Wood 515(9) : 1279
Wood 515(10) : 3377
Wood 515(11) : 6565
Wood 515(12) : 6479
Wood 515(13) : 3799
Wood 515(14) : 5488
Wood 515(15) : 3712
Wood 515(16) : 4883
Wood 515(17) : 3300
Wood 515(18) : 6304
Wood 515(19) (-CD) : 5302
Wood 515(20) : 6424
Wood 515(21) : 6070
Wood 515(22) : 4912
Wood 515(23) : 996
Wood 515(24) : 4887
Wood 515(25) : 4525
Wood 515(26) : 3020
Wood 515(27) : 446
Wood 515(28a) : 3123
Wood 515(28b) : 447
Wood 515(29) : 3801
Wood 515(30) : 3800
Wood 515(31) : 4063
Wood 515(32) : 4881
Wood 515(33a) : 3441
Wood 515(33b) : 3373 (M)
Wood 515(34) : 4129

Wood 516(1) : 4896
Wood 516(2) : 2351
Wood 516(3) : 241
Wood 516(4) : 4944
Wood 516(5) : 2614
Wood 516(6a) : 1732
Wood 516(6b) : 1733
Wood 516(7) : 6480
Wood 516(8) : 3709
Wood 516(9) : 846
Wood 516(10a) : 5911
Wood 516(10b) : 356
Wood 517(1) : 2889
Wood 517(2) : 3895
Wood 517(3) : 2890
Wood 517(4) : 5918
Wood 517(5) : 5135
Wood 517(6) : 2157
Wood 518(1) : 5516
Wood 518(2) : 2942
Wood 518(3a) : 2609
Wood 518(3b) : 2027
Wood 518(4) : 2029
Wood 518(5) : 2686
Wood 518(6) : 5439
Wood 518(7) : 3704
Wood 518(8) : 5782
Wood 518(9) : 5471
Wood 519(1) : 2617
Wood 519(2) : 2591
Wood 519(3a) : 2602
Wood 519(3b) : 6681
Wood 519(4) : 6238
Wood 519(5) : 6318
Wood 519(6) : 6319
Wood 519(7) : 2771
Wood 519(8) : 2703
Wood 519(9) : 2701
Wood 519(10) : 2136
Wood 519(11) : 967
Wood 519(12) : 2718
Wood 520 : 4707
Wood 521(1) : 4708
Wood 521(2) : 4678
Wood 521(3) : 4712
Wood 522 : 4702
Wood 523 : 4703
Wood 524 : 4704
Wood 525 : 1837
Wood 526(1) : 2028
Wood 526(2) (-CD) : 2664
Wood 526(3) : 2665
Wood 526(4) : 4280
Wood 526(5) : 6660
Wood 526(6) : 3995
Wood 526(7) : 3468
Wood 526(8) : 4587
Wood 526(9) : 2045
Wood 526(10) : 5218
Wood 527(1) : 3368
Wood 527(2) : 6576
Wood 527(3) : 5710
Wood 527(4) : 5425
Wood 528(1) : 4389

Wood 528(2) : 1175
Wood 528(3) : 2345
Wood 529(1) : 4593
Wood 529(2) : 6612
Wood 529(3) : 6615
Wood 529(4) : 6610
Wood 529(5) : 5992
Wood 529(6) : 6611
Wood 529(7) : 6614
Wood 529(8) : 245
Wood 529(9) : 6613
Wood 529(10) : 3840
Wood 529(11) : 4755
Wood 529(12) : 4278
Wood 529(13) : 4262
Wood 529(14) : 3848
Wood 529(15) : 3819
Wood 529(16) : 3841
Wood 529(17) : 3845
Wood 529(18) : 1204
Wood 529(19) : 2985
Wood 529(20) : 3844
Wood 529(21) : 1202
Wood 529(22) : 3576
Wood 530(1) : 1200
Wood 530(2) : 6578
Wood 530(3) : 1031
Wood 531(1) : 5242 (M)
Wood 531(2) : 6150 (M)
Wood 531(3) : 5486 (M)
Wood 531(4) : 1926 (M)
Wood 531(5) : 2463 (M)
Wood 531(6) : 2238 (M)
Wood 531(7) : 6345 (M)
Wood 531(8) : 2240 (M)
Wood 531(9) : 6267 (M)
Wood 531(10) : 2856 (M)
Wood 531(11) : 6160 (M)
Wood 531(12) (-CD) : 4615 (M)
Wood 531(13) : 4613 (M)
Wood 531(14) : 3521 (M)
Wood 531(15) : 3700 (M)
Wood 531(16) : 3517 (M)
Wood 531(17) : 3519 (M)
Wood 531(18) : 3520 (M)
Wood 531(19) : 4813 (M)
Wood 531(20) : 3522 (M)
Wood 531(21) : 3518 (M)
Wood 531(22) : 6399 (M)
Wood 531(23) : 4074 (M)
Wood 531(24) (-CD) : 2095 (M)
Wood 531(25) : 6407 (M)
Wood 531(26) : 2096 (M)
Wood 531(27) : 2098 (M)
Wood 531(28) : 2097 (M)
Wood 531(29) : 4633 (M)
Wood 531(30) : 2103 (M)
Wood 532(1) : 4765
Wood 532(2) : 5147
Wood 532(3) : 1216
Wood 532(4) : 1025
Wood 532(5) : 4774
Wood 532(6) : 3127
Wood 532(7) : 3269

Wood 532(8) : 6338
Wood 532(9) : 4380
Wood 532(10) : 2328
Wood 532(11) : 2350
Wood 532(12) : 6082
Wood 532(13) : 1857
Wood 532(14) (-CD) : 1053
Wood 532(15) : 904
Wood 533(1) : 1057
Wood 533(2) : 2296
Wood 533(3) : 4185
Wood 533(4) : 4184
Wood 533(5) : 3270
Wood 533(6) : 5426
Wood 533(7) : 5428
Wood 533(8) : 1747
Wood 533(9) : 1758
Wood 533(10) : 998
Wood 533(11) : 5200
Wood 533(12) : 2133
Wood 533(13) : 2969
Wood 533(14) : 4617
Wood 533(15) : 5158
Wood 533(16) : 6236
Wood 533(17) : 4120
Wood 533(18) : 6042
Wood 533(19) : 5835
Wood 534(1) : 4743
Wood 534(2) : 6426
Wood 534(3a) : 2138
Wood 534(3b) : 2137
Wood 534(3c) : 2139
Wood 534(3d) : 1923
Wood 534(3e) : 6279
Wood 534(4) : 3471
Wood 534(5) : 5763
Wood 534(6) (-CD) : 6030
Wood 534(7) : 3028
Wood 535(1) : 6545
Wood 535(2a) : 5199
Wood 535(2b) : 5597
Wood 535(3) : 1904
Wood 535(4) : 1024
Wood 535(5) : 6713
Wood 535(6) : 6714
Wood 535(7) : 6020
Wood 535(8) : 5573
Wood 535(9) : 6430
Wood 535(10) : 6431
Wood 535(11) : 4519
Wood 535(12) : 6122
Wood 536(1) : 3542
Wood 536(2) : 3187
Wood 536(3) : 3186
Wood 536(4) : 4298
Wood 536(6) : 6044
Wood 537(1) : 2426
Wood 537(2) : 3167
Wood 537(3) : 4328
Wood 537(4) : 2356
Wood 537(5) : 3681
Wood 537(6) : 4198
Wood 537(7) : 2207
Wood 537(8) : 1388

Wood 537(9) : 3096
Wood 537(10) : 3095
Wood 537(11) : 1698
Wood 537(12) : 1697
Wood 537(13) : 1229
Wood 537(14a) : 3561
Wood 537(14b) : 5571
Wood 537(15) : 6145
Wood 537(16) : 1036
Wood 537(17) : 5938
Wood 537(18) : 4234
Wood 537(19) : 6135
Wood 537(20) : 3922
Wood 538 : 3730
Wood 539 : 1150
Wood 540 : 5430
Wood 541 : 4715
Wood 542 : 4681
Wood 543 : 4682
Wood 544 : 4683
Wood 545 : 4684
Wood 546 : 4685
Wood 547 : 4686
Wood 548 : 4687
Wood 549 : 4688
Wood 550 : 4689
Wood 551 : 4690
Wood 552 : 4691
Wood 553 : 4692
Wood 554(1) : 4693
Wood 554(2) : 4020
Wood 555 : 4694
Wood 559(1) (-CD) : 5167
Wood 559(2a) : 5176
Wood 559(2b) (-CD) : 5168
Wood 559(3) : 5169
Wood 559(4) : 5172
Wood 559(5) : 3068
Wood 559(6) : 5687 (M)
Wood 559(7) : 6005
Wood 559(8) : 4332
Wood 559(9) : 1932
Wood 559(10) : 5691
Wood 559(11) : 4638
Wood 559(12-13) : 6126
Wood 559(14) : 6127
Wood 559(15) : 4655
Wood 559(16) : 6125
Wood 559(17) : 6363
Wood 559(18) : 1099
Wood 559(19) : 4291
Wood 559(20) : 6323
Wood 559(21) : 6289
Wood 559(22) : 2158
Wood 559(23) : 5796
Wood 560(1) : 1829
Wood 560(2) : 4448
Wood 560(3) : 3575
Wood 561 : 3675
Wood 562 : 6658
Wood 563 : 4308
Wood 564(1) : 4616
Wood 564(2) (-CD) : 4635
Wood 565(1) : 6128

Wood 565(2) : 6129
Wood 566(1) : 1686
Wood 566(2) : 1687
Wood 567 : 267
Wood 568 (-CD) : 4573
Wood 569 : 1163
Wood 570 : 1062
Wood 571 : 353
Wood 572 : 951
Wood 573(1) : 71
Wood 573(2) : 2864
Wood 574(1) : 3648
Wood 574(2) : 6049
Wood 574(3) : 3734
Wood 575 : 956
Wood 576 : 5146
Wood 577 : 6662
Wood 578 : 5931
Wood 579 (-CD) : 966
Wood 580(1) : 2424
Wood 580(2) : 2422
Wood 580(3) : 2421
Wood 580(4) : 2425
Wood 581(1) : 1418
Wood 581(2) : 5239
Wood 582(1) : 2977
Wood 582(2) : 6496
Wood 582(3) : 2860
Wood 582(4) : 3084
Wood 582(6) : 3807
Wood 582(7) : 5971
Wood 583(1) : 4001
Wood 583(2-3) : 1095
Wood 583(4) : 3452
Wood 583(5) : 3529
Wood 583(6) : 5505
Wood 583(7) : 3534
Wood 584(1) : 6539
Wood 584(2) : 6641
Wood 585(1) : 5957
Wood 585(2) : 6164
Wood 586(1) : 6057
Wood 586(2) : 4579
Wood 586(3) : 1385
Wood 586(4) : 1663
Wood 586(5) : 1662
Wood 586(6) : 6193
Wood 586(7) : 5141
Wood 586(8) : 1665
Wood 586(9) : 6018
Wood 586(10a) : 336
Wood 586(10b) : 5818
Wood 586(11) : 5675
Wood 586(12) : 3958
Wood 586(13) : 3390
Wood 586(14) : 6627
Wood 586(15) : 1255
Wood 586(16) : 4410
Wood 586(17) : 2141
Wood 586(18) : 6023
Wood 586(19) : 3330
Wood 586(20) : 3294 (M)
Wood 586(21) : 6558
Wood 586(22) : 5502

Wood 587(1) : 3164
Wood 587(2) (-CD) : 6372
Wood 587(3) : 3852
Wood 587(4) : 6723
Wood 587(5) : 4143
Wood 588 : 3929
Wood 589 : 237
Wood 590(1) : 4214
Wood 590(2) : 1035
Wood 590(3) : 1272
Wood 590(4) : 938
Wood 590(5) : 2172
Wood 590(6) : 4425
Wood 590(7) : 4263
Wood 591 : 5115
Wood 592 : 3104
Wood 593 : 4213
Wood 594(1) : 4531
Wood 594(2) : 3261
Wood 594(3) : 6188
Wood 594(4) : 3481
Wood 594(5) : 3444
Wood 595 : 3506
Wood 596 : 5294
Wood 597 : 2275
Wood 598 : 5620
Wood 599 : 3499
Wood 600 : 3528
Wood 601 : 3705
Wood 602 : 6268
Wood 603 : 5422
Wood 604 : 3272
Wood 605(1) : 5150
Wood 605(2) : 1171
Wood 605(3) : 2852
Wood 605(4) (-CD) : 1666
Wood 606 (506, CD) : 1372
Wood 607(1) : 4057
Wood 607(2) : 5258
Wood 607(2a) : 1838
Wood 607(3) : 1434
Wood 607(4) : 5145
Wood 607(5) : 4403
Wood 607(6) : 2009
Wood 607(7) : 2312
Wood 607(8) : 6623
Wood 607(9) : 3194
Wood 608(1a) : 5161
Wood 608(1b) : 6108
Wood 608(2) : 3279
Wood 608(3) : 2861
Wood 608(4) : 291
Wood 608(5) : 2872
Wood 608(6a) (-CD) : 6308
Wood 608(6b) : 6705
Wood 608(7) : 4111
Wood 608(8) : 4549
Wood 608(9) : 1795
Wood 608(10) : 1261
Wood 608(11) : 1799
Wood 608(12) : 1800
Wood 608(13) : 4255
Wood 608(14) : 1796
Wood 608(15) : 2725

Wood 608(16) : 1994
Wood 608(17) : 2726
Wood 608(18) : 3324
Wood 608(19,20) : 4538
Wood 608(21) : 2974
Wood 608(22) : 6460
Wood 608(23) : 3713
Wood 608(24) : 2262
Wood 608(25) : 1798
Wood 608(26) : 3325
Wood 608(27) : 4107
Wood 608(28) : 4117
Wood 608(29) : 4256
Wood 608(30) : 4245
Wood 608(31) : 232
Wood 608(32) : 3502
Wood 608(33) : 4735
Wood 608(34) : 1090
Wood 608(35) : 3457
Wood 608(36) : 2935
Wood 608(37) : 2099
Wood 608(38) : 4785
Wood 608(39) : 4398
Wood 608(40) : 1811
Wood 608(41) : 3357
Wood 608(42) : 2835
Wood 608(43) : 1814
Wood 608(44) : 4121
Wood 608(45) : 5778
Wood 608(46) : 4179
Wood 608(47) : 2742
Wood 608(48) : 2274
Wood 608(49) : 6618
Wood 608(50) : 4391
Wood 608(51) : 4622
Wood 608(52) : 5360
Wood 608(53) : 3536
Wood 608(54) : 914
Wood 608(55) : 3139
Wood 608(56) : 5767
Wood 608(57) : 2829
Wood 608(58) : 1981
Wood 608(59) (-CD) : 5768
Wood 608(60) : 2983
Wood 608(61) : 5727
Wood 608(62) : 6464
Wood 608(63) : 308
Wood 608(64) : 3838
Wood 608(65) : 4130
Wood 608(66) : 316
Wood 608(67) : 3843 (Ms.)
Wood 608(68) : 6499
Wood 608(69) : 6500
Wood 608(70) : 5431
Wood 608(71) : 1684
Wood 608(72) : 2504
Wood 609(1) : 6530
Wood 609(2) : 4998
Wood 609(3) : 4385
Wood 609(4) : 3735
Wood 609(5) : 2078
Wood 609(5a) : 2687
Wood 609(6) : 4732
Wood 609(7) : 4734

Wood 609(8) : 1759
Wood 609(9) : 1972
Wood 609(10) : 6456
Wood 609(11) : 2210
Wood 609(12) (-CD) : 4275
Wood 609(13) : 5435
Wood 609(14) : 1936
Wood 609(15) : 4224
Wood 609(16) : 275
Wood 609(17) : 4612
Wood 609(18) : 4847
Wood 609(19) : 4880
Wood 609(20a) : 6367
Wood 609(20b) : 3762
Wood 609(20c) : 3763
Wood 609(21) : 3793
Wood 609(22) : 3701
Wood 609(23) : 1931
Wood 609(24) : 3747
Wood 609(25) : 4630
Wood 609(26) : 4491
Wood 609(27a) : 1144
Wood 609(27b) (-CD) : 960
Wood 609(28) : 1703
Wood 609(29) : 4337
Wood 609(30) : 4642
Wood 609(31) : 4401
Wood 609(32) : 6235
Wood 609(33) : 2960
Wood 609(34) (-CD) : 1252
Wood 609(35) (-CD) : 5699
Wood 609(36) : 3192
Wood 609(37) : 2092
Wood 609(38) : 6004
Wood 609(39) : 6055
Wood 609(40-41) : 2266
Wood 609(42) : 5443
Wood 609(43) : 6748
Wood 609(44) (-CD) : 5359
Wood 609(45) : 2245
Wood 609(46) : 5358
Wood 609(47) : 1862
Wood 609(48) (-CD) : 2961
Wood 610(1) : 2709
Wood 610(2) : 2500
Wood 610(3) : 2501
Wood 610(4a) : 1900
Wood 610(4b) : 4591
Wood 610(5) : 5890
Wood 610(6) : 333
Wood 610(7) : 2716
Wood 610(8) : 4322
Wood 610(9) : 4321
Wood 610(10) : 3108
Wood 610(11) : 4228
Wood 610(12) : 6466
Wood 610(13) : 1085
Wood 610(14) : 5786
Wood 610(15) : 6293
Wood 610(16) : 4097
Wood 610(17) : 2067 (M)
Wood 610(18) : 6210
Wood 610(19) : 1833
Wood 610(20) : 2733

Wood 610(21) : 4520
Wood 610(22) : 6575
Wood 610(23) : 991
Wood 610(24) : 5447
Wood 610(25) : 2490
Wood 610(26) : 2706
Wood 610(27) : 3456
Wood 610(28) : 3535
Wood 610(29) : 4010
Wood 610(30) : 3394
Wood 610(31) : 1245
Wood 610(32) : 2924
Wood 610(33) : 4512
Wood 610(34) : 2493
Wood 610(35). : 2795
Wood 610(36) : 2794
Wood 610(37) : 4511
Wood 610(38) : 2707
Wood 610(39) : 2134
Wood 610(40) : 2562
Wood 610(41) : 2489
Wood 610(42) : 1210
Wood 610(43) : 2496
Wood 610(44) : 911
Wood 610(45) : 4913
Wood 610(46) : 849
Wood 610(47) : 2494
Wood 610(48) : 4572
Wood 610(49) : 4259
Wood 610(50) (-CD) : 2495
Wood 610(51) : 2710
Wood 610(52) : 2695
Wood 610(53-4) : 2922
Wood 610(55) : 5449
Wood 610(56) : 5448
Wood 610(57) : 6199
Wood 610(58) : 2563
Wood 610(59) : 3250
Wood 610(60) (-CD) : 4366
Wood 610(61) : 2953
Wood 610(62) : 2730
Wood 610(63) : 4522
Wood 610(64) : 4115
Wood 611(1) : 1207
Wood 611(2) : 2038
Wood 611(3) : 6010
Wood 611(4) : 6011
Wood 611(5) : 6012
Wood 611(6) : 6314
Wood 611(7) : 6333
Wood 611(8) : 6332
Wood 611(9) : 5175
Wood 611(10) : 1398
Wood 611(11) : 5173
Wood 611(12) : 5174
Wood 611(13) : 4420
Wood 611(14) : 2149
Wood 611(15) : 1030
Wood 611(16-17) : 4583
Wood 611(18) : 3742
Wood 611(19) : 5364
Wood 612(1) : 1736
Wood 612(2) : 6212
Wood 612(3) : 2333

Wood 612(4) : 2661
Wood 612(5) : 1740
Wood 612(6-8) : 1735
Wood 612(9) : 1734
Wood 612(10a) : 2652
Wood 612(10b) : 2651
Wood 612(10c) : 1885
Wood 612(11) (-CD) : 2650
Wood 612(12) : 5545
Wood 612(13) : 2
Wood 612(14) : 1738
Wood 612(15) : 1745
Wood 612(16) : 1744
Wood 612(17) : 4717
Wood 612(18) : 4400
Wood 612(19) : 1743
Wood 612(20) : 2432
Wood 612(21) : 6048
Wood 612(22) : 2822
Wood 612(23) : 2823
Wood 612(24) : 2239
Wood 612(25) : 2125
Wood 612(26) : 4599
Wood 612(27) : 5429
Wood 612(28) : 2663
Wood 612(29) : 6518
Wood 612(30) : 2472
Wood 612(31) : 2073
Wood 612(32) : 5331
Wood 612(33) : 5333
Wood 612(34) : 6287
Wood 612(35) : 1238
Wood 612(36) : 2671
Wood 612(37) : 6704
Wood 612(38) : 1120
Wood 612(39) : 1751
Wood 612(40) : 6276
Wood 612(41) : 2928
Wood 612(42) : 3463
Wood 612(43) : 2241
Wood 612(44) : 4872
Wood 612(45) : 4536
Wood 612(46) : 1277
Wood 612(47) : 2677
Wood 612(48) : 2911
Wood 612(49) : 5617
Wood 612(50) : 2682
Wood 612(51) : 1755
Wood 612(52a) : 2679
Wood 612(52b) : 4153
Wood 612(52c) : 2680
Wood 612(53) : 1753
Wood 612(54) : 1754
Wood 612(55) : 2676
Wood 612(56a) : 6529
Wood 612(56b) : 5792
Wood 612(57) : 3866
Wood 612(58) : 3716
Wood 612(59a) : 2789
Wood 612(59b) : 3395
Wood 612(60) : 1681
Wood 612(61) : 2478
Wood 612(62) : 3355
Wood 612(63) : 2912

Wood 612(64) : 4138
Wood 612(65) (-CD) : 2913
Wood 612(66) : 1776
Wood 612(67) : 4156
Wood 612(68) : 3863
Wood 612(69) : 4905
Wood 612(70) : 6465
Wood 612(71) : 5947
Wood 612(72) : 5946
Wood 613(1) : 2719
Wood 613(2) : 280
Wood 613(3) : 1790
Wood 613(4) : 4289
Wood 613(5) : 5208
Wood 613(5a) : 223
Wood 613(6) : 2827
Wood 613(7) : 5455
Wood 613(8) : 2546
Wood 613(9) : 4137
Wood 613(10) : 868
Wood 613(10a) : 6154
Wood 613(11) : 2714
Wood 613(12) (-CD) : 3178
Wood 613(13) : 1258
Wood 613(14) : 6574
Wood 613(15) : 3055
Wood 613(16) : 247
Wood 613(17) : 5462
Wood 613(18) : 5594
Wood 613(19) : 6071
Wood 613(20) : 5453
Wood 613(21) : 5111
Wood 613(22) : 2793
Wood 613(23) : 2492
Wood 613(24) : 3717
Wood 613(25) : 2940
Wood 613(26) : 1846
Wood 613(27) : 6198
Wood 613(28) : 231
Wood 613(29) : 2801
Wood 613(30) : 5106
Wood 613(31) : 2737
Wood 613(32) : 2738
Wood 613(33) : 1243
Wood 613(34) : 1244
Wood 613(35) : 2799
Wood 613(36) : 5110
Wood 613(37) : 2809
Wood 613(38) : 2805
Wood 613(39) : 4106
Wood 613(40) : 6265
Wood 613(41) : 2797
Wood 613(42) : 4518
Wood 613(43) : 2711
Wood 613(44) : 2221
Wood 613(45) : 2408
Wood 613(46) : 6266
Wood 613(47) : 1281
Wood 613(48) : 4763
Wood 613(49) : 6278
Wood 613(50) : 2279
Wood 613(51) : 6745
Wood 613(52) : 2712
Wood 613(53) : 2102

Wood 613(54) : 2497
Wood 613(55) : 986
Wood 613(56) : 2564
Wood 613(57) : 2503
Wood 613(58) : 5458
Wood 613(59) (-CD) : 2826
Wood 613(60) (6, CD) : 3941
Wood 613(61) : 3886
Wood 613(62) : 2731
Wood 613(63) : 2808
Wood 614(1) : 3111
Wood 614(2) : 6306
Wood 614(3) : 4895
Wood 614(4) : 4907
Wood 614(5) : 992
Wood 614(6) : 4022
Wood 614(7) : 6695
Wood 614(8) (18, CD) : 5149
Wood 614(9) : 3298
Wood 614(10) : 3297
Wood 614(11) : 6110
Wood 614(12) : 3251
Wood 614(13) : 4603
Wood 614(14) : 6340
Wood 614(15) : 3743
Wood 614(16) : 2254
Wood 614(17a) : 3510
Wood 614(17b) : 4348
Wood 614(18) : 1280
Wood 614(19) : 5739
Wood 614(20) (-CD) : 5348
Wood 614(21-22) : 1849
Wood 614(23) : 4816
Wood 614(24) : 2418
Wood 614(25) : 2596
Wood 614(26) (-CD) : 5483
Wood 614(27-28) : 3400
Wood 614(29) : 2611
Wood 614(30) : 2601
Wood 614(31) : 5484
Wood 614(32) : 2595
Wood 614(33) : 5485
Wood 614(34) : 6507
Wood 614(35) : 1705
Wood 614(36) : 2597
Wood 614(37) : 2305
Wood 614(38) : 6398
Wood 614(39) : 6148 (M)
Wood 614(40-41) : 3467
Wood 614(42) : 2638
Wood 614(43) : 4625
Wood 614(44) : 1708
Wood 614(45) : 6732
Wood 614(46) : 1716
Wood 614(47) : 3902
Wood 614(48) : 2625
Wood 614(49) : 2646
Wood 614(50) : 1729
Wood 614(51) : 2406
Wood 614(52) : 3741
Wood 614(53) : 2634
Wood 614(54) : 2198 (M)
Wood 614(55) : 5979
Wood 614(56) : 2620

Wood 614(57) : 1712
Wood 614(58) : 328
Wood 614(59) : 2787
Wood 614(60) : 3493
Wood 614(61) : 3779
Wood 614(62) : 2619
Wood 615(1) : 3348
Wood 615(2) : 3507
Wood 615(3) : 3508
Wood 615(4) : 4290
Wood 615(5) : 5815
Wood 615(6) : 1832
Wood 615(7) (617, CD) : 4749
Wood 615(8) : 3656
Wood 615(9a) : 5813
Wood 615(9b) : 4417
Wood 615(10) : 2423
Wood 615(11) : 6757
Wood 615(12) : 5337
Wood 615(13) : 2407
Wood 615(14) : 4451
Wood 615(15) : 5261
Wood 615(16) : 3370
Wood 615(17) : 1688
Wood 615(18) : 5709
Wood 615(19) : 4819
Wood 615(20) : 1097
Wood 615(21) : 4182
Wood 615(22a) : 5879
Wood 615(22b) : 5880
Wood 615(23) : 2938
Wood 615(24) : 4640
Wood 615(25) : 2171
Wood 615(26) : 6655 (M)
Wood 616(1) : 2203
Wood 616(2) : 72
Wood 616(3) : 1660
Wood 616(4) : 4476
Wood 616(5) : 2204
Wood 616(6) : 3824
Wood 616(7) : 2491
Wood 616(8) : 2715
Wood 616(9) : 338
Wood 616(10) : 2820
Wood 616(11) : 4600
Wood 616(12) : 6194
Wood 616(13) : 5866
Wood 616(14) : 3805
Wood 616(15) : 1661
Wood 616(16) : 2387
Wood 616(17) : 1215
Wood 616(18) (-CD) : 6239
Wood 616(19) : 4047
Wood 616(20) : 4053
Wood 616(21) : 6257
Wood 616(22) : 3997
Wood 616(23) : 3900
Wood 616(24) : 4335
Wood 616(25) : 4560
Wood 617(1) : 3549
Wood 617(2) : 6073
Wood 617(3) : 255
Wood 617(4) : 6320
Wood 617(5) (-CD) : 2039

Wood 617(6) : 4427
Wood 617(7) : 3387
Wood 617(8) : 2443
Wood 617(9) : 2002
Wood 617(10) : 5317
Wood 617(11) : 2871
Wood 617(12) : 5910
Wood 617(13) : 3803
Wood 617(14) : 2987
Wood 617(15) : 3503 (M)
Wood 617(16) : 6453
Wood 617(17) : 6391
Wood 617(18) : 6392
Wood 617(19) : 5105
Wood 617(20) : 2830
Wood 617(21) : 5812
Wood 618(1) : 6712
Wood 618(2) : 5785
Wood 618(3) : 6525 (M)
Wood 618(4) : 2881
Wood 618(5) : 6541
Wood 618(6) (-CD) : 6022
Wood 618(7) : 3449
Wood 618(8) : 6524
Wood 618(9) : 5269
Wood 619(1) : 4353
Wood 619(2) : 2195
Wood 619(3) : 233
Wood 619(4) : 6394
Wood 619(5) (-CD) : 5779
Wood 619(6) : 5596
Wood 619(7) : 1858
Wood 619(8) : 2525
Wood 619(9) : 4199
Wood 619(10) : 2381
Wood 619(11) (-CD) : 6552
Wood 619(12) : 1855
Wood 619(13) : 3067
Wood 620(1) : 2765
Wood 620(2) : 6654
Wood 620(3) : 2904
Wood 620(4) : 2914
Wood 620(5) : 5432a
Wood 620(6) : 5433
Wood 620(7) : 4059
Wood 620(8) : 2412
Wood 620(9) : 2768
Wood 620(10) : 2413
Wood 620(11) : 5437
Wood 620(12) : 5436
Wood 620(13) : 2770
Wood 620(14) : 2705
Wood 620(15-16) : 6532
Wood 620(17) : 1975
Wood 620(18) : 6066
Wood 620(19) : 246
Wood 620(20) : 5461
Wood 620(21) : 6706
Wood 620(22) : 6067
Wood 620(23) : 2772
Wood 620(24) : 1869
Wood 620(25) : 2708
Wood 620(26) : 5463
Wood 620(27) : 5451

Wood 620(28) : 5456
Wood 620(29) (2a, CD) : 5454
Wood 620(30) : 5469
Wood 620(31) (623, CD) : 5464
Wood 620(32) : 5466
Wood 620(33) : 2774
Wood 620(34) : 2303
Wood 620(35) : 5467
Wood 620(36) : 4494
Wood 620(37) : 2724
Wood 620(38) : 2735
Wood 620(39) : 2776
Wood 620(40) : 2720
Wood 621(1) : 2747
Wood 621(2) : 2754
Wood 622(1) : 6153
Wood 622(2-3) (-CD) : 1040
Wood 622(4) : 1039 (M)
Wood 622(5) : 6156
Wood 622(6) : 1910
Wood 622(7) : 1911
Wood 622(8) : 1859
Wood 622(9) : 4697
Wood 622(10) : 4698
Wood 622(11) : 6159
Wood 622(12) : 6653
Wood 622(13) : 1912
Wood 622(14) : 6711
Wood 622(15) : 4155
Wood 622(16) : 5221
Wood 622(17) : 4445
Wood 622(18) : 1915
Wood 622(19) : 3962
Wood 622(20) : 3126
Wood 622(21) : 4618
Wood 622(22) : 4158
Wood 622(23) : 4157
Wood 622(24) : 4114
Wood 622(25) : 3129
Wood 623 : 4653
Wood 624 : 4654
Wood 625 : 4754
Wood 626(1) : 268
Wood 626(2) : 4826
Wood 626(3) : 3257
Wood 626(4) : 3422
Wood 626(5) : 3420
Wood 626(6) : 6072
Wood 626(7) : 4492
Wood 626(8) : 5160
Wood 626(9) : 3426
Wood 626(10) : 3424
Wood 626(11) : 3423
Wood 626(12) : 3427
Wood 626(13) : 3425
Wood 626(14) : 6015
Wood 626(15) : 6016
Wood 626(16) : 3421
Wood 626(17) : 4623
Wood 626(18) : 5445
Wood 626(19) : 2037
Wood 626(20) : 4112
Wood 627(1) : 5743
Wood 627(2) : 937

Wood 627(3) : 3375
Wood 628(1) : 3011
Wood 628(2) : 1253
Wood 628(3a) : 2121
Wood 628(3b) (-CD) : 2122
Wood 628(4) : 3768
Wood 628(5) (-CD) : 6255
Wood 628(6) : 4584
Wood 628(7) : 5369
Wood 629(1) : 2570
Wood 629(2) : 5424
Wood 629(3) : 3647
Wood 629(4) : 5759
Wood 629(5) : 2746
Wood 629(6) : 3475
Wood 629(7) : 3515
Wood 629(8) : 295
Wood 630(1) : 6312
Wood 630(2) : 5932
Wood 630(3) : 2553
Wood 630(4) : 6467
Wood 630(5) : 2932
Wood 630(6) : 2556
Wood 630(7) : 2558
Wood 630(8) : 360
Wood 630(9) : 2879
Wood 630(10) : 5589
Wood 630(11) : 5588
Wood 630(12) : 3885
Wood 630(13) : 2560
Wood 630(14) : 2561
Wood 630(15) : 1922
Wood 630(16) : 6360
Wood 630(17) : 4086
Wood 630(18) : 1941
Wood 630(19) : 2565
Wood 630(20) : 3199
Wood 630(21) : 5225
Wood 630(22) : 1138
Wood 630(23) : 5224
Wood 630(24) : 6061
Wood 630(25) : 5237
Wood 631(1) : 4908
Wood 631(2) : 3435
Wood 631(3) : 1221
Wood 631(4) : 5136
Wood 631(5) : 3428
Wood 631(6) : 1223
Wood 631(7) : 3431
Wood 631(8, 9) : 3430
Wood 631(10) : 1655
Wood 631(11) : 5465
Wood 631(12) : 3076
Wood 631(13) : 6201
Wood 631(14) : 6204
Wood 631(15) : 3470
Wood 631(16) : 1122
Wood 631(17) : 6583
Wood 631(18) : 2672
Wood 631(19) : 6584
Wood 631(20) : 909
Wood 632(1) : 3829
Wood 632(2) : 5506
Wood 632(3) (-CD) : 2999

Wood 632(4) : 2243
Wood 632(5) : 2655
Wood 632(6) : 2656
Wood 632(7) : 5676
Wood 632(8) : 3546
Wood 632(9) : 2653
Wood 632(10) : 4442
Wood 632(11) : 6152
Wood 632(12) : 5937
Wood 632(13) : 2888
Wood 632(14) : 2349
Wood 632(15) : 1379
Wood 632(16) : 2479
Wood 632(17) : 2477
Wood 632(18) : 4829
Wood 632(19) : 4830
Wood 632(20) : 6586
Wood 632(21) : 5246
Wood 632(22) : 4537
Wood 632(23) : 4996
Wood 632(24) : 274
Wood 632(25) : 2498
Wood 632(26) : 4527
Wood 632(27) : 3989
Wood 632(28) : 4168
Wood 632(29) : 2505
Wood 632(30) : 1131
Wood 632(31) : 2398
Wood 632(32) : 2859
Wood 632(33) : 2499
Wood 632(34) : 2488
Wood 632(35) : 2120
Wood 632(36) : 4514
Wood 632(37) : 2880
Wood 632(38) : 3454
Wood 632(39) : 4009
Wood 632(40) : 3991
Wood 632(41) (-CD) : 4395
Wood 632(42) : 4619
Wood 632(43) : 5684
Wood 632(44) : 4402
Wood 632(45) : 1801
Wood 632(46) : 4014
Wood 632(47) : 4134
Wood 632(48) : 4133
Wood 632(49) : 3996
Wood 632(50) : 5262
Wood 632(51) : 4119
Wood 632(52) : 4235
Wood 632(53) : 2569
Wood 632(54) : 3831
Wood 632(55) : 5758
Wood 632(56) : 3945
Wood 632(57) : 2070
Wood 632(58) : 6186
Wood 632(59) : 2075
Wood 632(60) : 273
Wood 632(61) : 4516
Wood 632(62) : 2925
Wood 632(63) : 4207
Wood 632(64) : 5303
Wood 632(65) : 3460
Wood 632(66) : 1921
Wood 632(67) : 2587

Wood 632(68) : 4254
Wood 632(69) : 3815
Wood 632(70) : 4257
Wood 632(71) : 5159
Wood 632(72) : 4568
Wood 632(73) : 4521
Wood 632(74) : 4132
Wood 632(75) : 4113
Wood 632(76) : 4419
Wood 632(77) : 5794
Wood 632(78) (-CD) : 2506
Wood 633(1) : 2512
Wood 633(2) : 3336
Wood 633(3) : 6248
Wood 633(4) : 1963
Wood 633(5) : 5249
Wood 633(6) : 5248
Wood 633(7) : 448
Wood 633(8) : 3124
Wood 633(9) : 2298
Wood 633(10) : 4428
Wood 633(11) : 2375
Wood 633(12) : 947
Wood 633(13) : 6068
Wood 633(14) : 5775
Wood 633(15) : 6526
Wood 633(16) : 5935
Wood 633(17) : 3570
Wood 633(18) : 3571
Wood 633(19) : 3572
Wood 634(1) : 1206
Wood 634(2) : 5581
Wood 634(3) : 905
Wood 634(4) : 6701
Wood 634(5) : 4006
Wood 634(6) : 3738
Wood 634(7) : 41
Wood 634(8) (-CD) : 15
Wood 634(9) : 2047
Wood 634(10) : 3629
Wood 634(11) (-CD) : 249
Wood 634(12) (-CD) : 910
Wood 634(13) : 2194
Wood 634(14) : 6605
Wood 634(15) : 4482
Wood 635(1) (-CD) : 2461
Wood 635(2) : 5944
Wood 635(3) : 5444
Wood 635(4) : 1970
Wood 635(5) : 5559
Wood 635(6) : 5561
Wood 635(7) : 3540
Wood 636 (1-2) : 3708
Wood 636(3) : 5510
Wood 636(4) : 5244
Wood 636(5) : 1181
Wood 637(1) : 6190
Wood 637(2) : 852
Wood 637(3) : 3875
Wood 637(4) : 5442
Wood 637(5) (-CD) : 5441
Wood 638 : 2255
Wood 639(1) : 4552
Wood 639(2) : 2839

Wood 640(1) : 6077
Wood 640(2) : 6076
Wood 640(3) : 257
Wood 640(4) : 5641
Wood 640(5-6) : 6078
Wood 640(7) : 6079
Wood 640(8) : 6075
Wood 641 : 980
Wood 642(1) : 1072
Wood 642(2) : 292
Wood 642(3) : 2821
Wood 642(4) : 1008
Wood 642(5) : 4122
Wood 642(6) : 3433
Wood 643(1) : 3236
Wood 643(2a) : 4240
Wood 643(2b) : 1214
Wood 643(3) : 3876
Wood 643(4) : 2834
Wood 643(5) : 4311
Wood 643(6) : 2837
Wood 643(7a) : 2836
Wood 643(7b) : 109
Wood 643(8) : 6074
Wood 643(9) : 4192
Wood 643(10) : 3287
Wood 643(11) : 6003
Wood 643(12) : 1159
Wood 644(1) : 31
Wood 644(2) : 259
Wood 644(3) : 5831
Wood 644(4) : 6185
Wood 644(5) : 293
Wood 644(6) : 3963
Wood 644(7) (-CD) : 3975
Wood 645(1) : 3078
Wood 645(2) : 3586
Wood 645(3) : 5489
Wood 645(4) : 5440
Wood 645(5) : 5490
Wood 645(6) : 4610
Wood 645(7) : 2197
Wood 645(8) : 2196
Wood 645(9) : 3322
Wood 645(10) : 5491
Wood 645(11) : 4397
Wood 645(12) : 3079
Wood 645(13-14) : 3002
Wood 645(15) : 5492
Wood 645(16) : 5472
Wood 645(17) : 5493
Wood 645(18) : 5166
Wood 645(19) : 6034
Wood 645(20) : 307
Wood 645(21) : 594
Wood 645(22) : 4354
Wood 645(23) : 5494
Wood 645(24) : 4575
Wood 645(25) : 5170
Wood 645(26) : 5171
Wood 646(1) : 2044
Wood 646(2) : 3993
Wood 646(3) : 5721
Wood 646(4) : 6659

Wood 646(5) : 5366
Wood 646(6) : 4446
Wood 646(7) : 3292
Wood 646(8) : 6104
Wood 646(9) : 4450
Wood 646(10) : 175
Wood 646(11) : 5367
Wood 646(12) : 919
Wood 646(13) : 6240
Wood 646(14) : 6286
Wood 646(15) : 1909
Wood 646(16) (656, CD) : 625
Wood 646(17) : 108
Wood 647(1) : 6555
Wood 647(2) : 5783
Wood 647(3) : 2933
Wood 647(4) : 5788
Wood 647(5) : 3436
Wood 647(6) : 6397
Wood 647(7) : 6147
Wood 647(8) : 5526
Wood 647(9) : 6151
Wood 647(10) : 227
Wood 647(11) : 228
Wood 647(12) : 6149
Wood 647(13) : 5236
Wood 647(14) : 6024
Wood 647(15) : 3501
Wood 647(16) : 4777
Wood 647(17a) : 2430
Wood 647(17b) : 5525
Wood 647(17c) (-CD) : 5527
Wood 647(18) : 4277
Wood 647(19) : 2000
Wood 647(20) : 3320
Wood 647(21) : 983
Wood 647(22) : 5605
Wood 647(23) : 2568
Wood 648(1) : 3182
Wood 648(2) : 3183
Wood 648(3) : 6373
Wood 648(4) : 6374
Wood 649 : 899
Wood 650 : 977
Wood 651(1) : 5347
Wood 651(2) : 5346
Wood 652 : 1689
Wood 653(1) : 6081
Wood 653(2) : 3119
Wood 653(3) : 1275
Wood 653(4) : 6237
Wood 653(5) : 5927
Wood 653(6) : 3383
Wood 653(7) : 3889
Wood 654a(1) : 4758
Wood 654a(2) : 3258
Wood 654a(3) (645a, CD) : 6101
Wood 654a(4) : 714
Wood 654a(5) : 4470
Wood 654a(6) : 3588
Wood 654a(7) : 4221
Wood 654a(8) : 4479
Wood 654a(9) : 4629
Wood 654a(10) : 4628

Wood 654a(11) : 4611
Wood 654a(12) : 1899
Wood 654a(13) : 2790
Wood 654a(14) : 4345
Wood 654a(15) : 4631
Wood 654a(16) (-CD) : 3809
Wood 654a(17) : 6674
Wood 654a(18) : 6316
Wood 654a(19) : 6675
Wood 654a(20) : 4227
Wood 654a(21) : 6438
Wood 654a(22) : 3101
Wood 654a(23) : 1408
Wood 654a(24) : 1409
Wood 654a(25) : 1407
Wood 654a(26) : 880
Wood 654a(27) : 6676
Wood 654a(28) : 6677
Wood 654a(29) : 311
Wood 654a(30) : 5967 (M)
Wood 654a(31) : 1901
Wood 654a(32) : 5771
Wood 654a(33) : 6679
Wood 654a(34) : 4377 (M)
Wood 654b : 5553
Wood 654c(1) : 1556
Wood 654c(2) : 1557
Wood 655(1) : 2402
Wood 655(2) : 3259
Wood 655(3) : 2403
Wood 655(4) : 2404
Wood 656 : 4085
Wood 657(1a) : 5908
Wood 657(1b) : 2377
Wood 657(1c) : 2376
Wood 657(2) : 4426
Wood 657(3) : 1774
Wood 657(4) : 2813
Wood 657(5) : 6728
Wood 657(6) : 3622
Wood 657(7) : 5427
Wood 657(8) (-CD) : 882
Wood 657(9) : 2023
Wood 657(10) : 3968
Wood 657(11) : 3969
Wood 657(12) : 5850
Wood 657(13) : 2322
Wood 657(14) : 5865
Wood 657(15-16) : 2182
Wood 657(17) : 6668
Wood 657(18) (659, CD) : 1100
Wood 657(19) : 6330
Wood 657(20) : 6331
Wood 657(21) : 2315
Wood 657(22) : 5766
Wood 657(23) : 1807
Wood 657(24) : 2729
Wood 657(25) : 1248
Wood 657(26) : 3208
Wood 657(27) (-CD) : 4645
Wood 657(28) : 3751
Wood 657(29) : 2140
Wood 657(30) : 236
Wood 657(31) : 1816

Wood 657(32) : 2739
Wood 657(33) : 2674
Wood 657(34) : 2817
Wood 657(35) : 4261
Wood 657(36) : 2759
Wood 657(37) : 1797
Wood 657(38) : 1812
Wood 657(39) : 6259
Wood 657(40) : 1830
Wood 657(41) : 1820
Wood 657(42) : 6258
Wood 657(43) : 1976
Wood 657(44) : 6621
Wood 657(45) : 5478
Wood 657(46) : 4230
Wood 657(47) : 4251
Wood 657(48) : 2756
Wood 657(49) (-CD) : 4474
Wood 657(50) : 2757
Wood 657(51) : 1222
Wood 657(52) (-CD) : 2753
Wood 657(53) : 3487
Wood 657(54) : 4818
Wood 657(55) : 5365
Wood 657(56) : 2051
Wood 657(57) : 2050
Wood 657(58) : 5216
Wood 657(59) : 4267
Wood 657(60) : 4268
Wood 657(61) : 2818
Wood 657(62) : 264
Wood 657(63) : 4674
Wood 657(64) : 2752
Wood 657(65-66) : 2751
Wood 657(67) : 2782
Wood 657(68) : 5634
Wood 657(69) : 5631
Wood 657(70) : 2758
Wood 657(71) : 5633
Wood 657(72) : 5632
Wood 657(73) : 5021
Wood 658(1-772) : 1562
Wood 658(772-3) : 6402
Wood 658(774) : 5393
Wood 658(775) : 1589
Wood 658(776) : 1822
Wood 658(777-8) (-CD) : 2542
Wood 658(779) : 5415
Wood 658(780) : 5371
Wood 658(781) : 5264
Wood 658(782) : 5413
Wood 658(783) : 3340
Wood 658(784) : 5406
Wood 658(784a) : 931
Wood 658(784b) : 5387
Wood 658(784c) : 929
Wood 658(784d) : 930
Wood 658(784e) : 5409
Wood 658(784f) : 5407
Wood 658(785) (-CD) : 5398
Wood 658(786a) (-CD) : 5391
Wood 658(786b) : 5396
Wood 658(786c) : 5417
Wood 658(787) : 5395

Wood 658(788) : 5383
Wood 658(789) : 5390
Wood 658(790) : 5397
Wood 658(791a) : 5404
Wood 658(791b) : 5402
Wood 658(791c) (-CD) : 5401
Wood 658(792) : 5399
Wood 658(793) : 5400
Wood 658(794) : 5385
Wood 658(795) : 5403
Wood 658(796) : 5411
Wood 658(797) : 1149
Wood 658(798) : 4915
Wood 658(799) : 5388
Wood 658(800) : 5394
Wood 658(801) : 5410
Wood 658(802) : 5384
Wood 658(803) : 5380
Wood 658(804) (-CD) : 5374
Wood 658(805) (-CD) : 1016
Wood 658(806) : 5378
Wood 658(807) : 5408
Wood 658(808) : 5386
Wood 658(809) (-CD) : 3341
Wood 658(810) : 5412
Wood 658(811a-b) (-CD) : 5373
Wood 658(812) : 5379
Wood 658(813) : 5392
Wood 658(814) : 5418
Wood 658(815a) : 5377
Wood 658(815b) : 5375
Wood 658(816) : 1583
Wood 658(817) : 1590
Wood 658(818, 819a) : 4656
Wood 658(819b) (-CD) : 1471
Wood 658(820) : 1472
Wood 659 : 1140
Wood 660a : 2854
Wood 660b(1) : 1477
Wood 660b(2) : 1563
Wood 660b(3, 5-6) : 1478
Wood 660b(4) : 1565
Wood 660b(7) : 1443
Wood 660b(8) : 1584
Wood 660b(9) : 1585
Wood 660b(10) (-CD) : 1588
Wood 660b(11) : 1591
Wood 660b(12) : 1473
Wood 660b(13) : 1587
Wood 660b(14) : 1564
Wood 660b(15) : 1445
Wood 660b(16a) : 1592
Wood 660b(16b-c) : 5372
Wood 660c(1) : 2982
Wood 660c(2) : 5804
Wood 660c(3) : 5805
Wood 660c(4a) : 5806
Wood 660c(4b) : 5808
Wood 660c(5) : 5809
Wood 660c(6) : 1823
Wood 660c(7) : 735
Wood 660c(8) : 5803
Wood 660c(9) : 5810
Wood 660c(10) : 5696

Wood 660c(11) : 3118
Wood 660c(12a) : 5697
Wood 660c(12b) : 3418 (Ms.)
Wood 660c(13) : 2248
Wood 660c(14) : 6080
Wood 660c(15) : 6721
Wood 660c(16) : 3204
Wood 660c(17) : 2992
Wood 660c(18) : 3205
Wood 660c(19) : 4449
Wood 660c(20) : 2750
Wood 660c(21) : 4393
Wood 660c(22) : 3464
Wood 660c(23) (-CD) : 3733
Wood 660c(24) : 2755
Wood 660c(25) : 1087
Wood 660c(26) : 5807
Wood 660c(27) : 3830
Wood 660c(28) : 3834
Wood 660c(29) : 3835
Wood 660c(30) : 5568
Wood 660c(31) : 3836
Wood 660c(32) : 3837
Wood 660c(33) : 2819
Wood 660c(34) : 323
Wood 660c(35) : 3839 (M)
Wood 660c(37) : 6609
Wood 660d(1) : 3365
Wood 660d(2) : 1172
Wood 660e(1) : 6274
Wood 660e(2) : 5741
Wood 660e(3) : 5513
Wood 660f(1) : 5753
Wood 660f(2) (600f, CD) : 2228
Wood 660f(3) : 2229
Wood 660f(4) : 2230
Wood 661 : 2435
Wood 662 : 5920
Wood 663 : 3552
Wood 664(1) : 3337
Wood 664(2) : 5501
Wood 664(3) : 3122
Wood 665 : 5837
Wood 666(1) (-CD) : 5582
Wood 666(2) : 4841
Wood 666(3) : 2016
Wood 666(4) : 4480
Wood 666(5) : 6380
Wood 667 : 3230
Wood 668 : 3232
Wood 669 : 4008
Wood 670(1) : 1186
Wood 670(2) : 1771
Wood 670(3) : 6358
Wood 670(4) : 5499
Wood 671 : 3071
Wood 672(1) : 3030
Wood 672(2) : 3222
Wood 672(3) : 4003
Wood 672(4) : 4002
Wood 672(5) : 3912
Wood 673(1) : 3821
Wood 673(2) : 4352
Wood 673(3) : 4147

Wood 673(4) : 4148
Wood 674 : 2346
Wood 675 : 1014
Wood 676 : 5578
Wood 677(1) : 5998
Wood 677(2) : 5530
Wood 678 : 3282
Wood 679(1) : 2866
Wood 679(2) : 2184
Wood 679(3) : 1954
Wood 679(4) : 5649
Wood 679(5) : 4462
Wood 679(6) : 4461
Wood 679(7) : 6361
Wood 679(8) : 5891
Wood 679(9) : 1927
Wood 679(10) : 1929
Wood 680(1-2) : 2201
Wood 680(3) : 5295
Wood 681 : 3228
Wood 682(1) : 3245
Wood 682(2) : 2132
Wood 683(1) : 4441
Wood 683(2) : 4357
Wood 683(3) : 4496
Wood 684 : 1437
Wood 685 : 3255
Wood 686(1) : 1867
Wood 686(2) : 3473
Wood 687 : 6600
Wood 688(1) : 34
Wood 688(2) : 33
Wood 689 : 5857
Wood 690 : 5307
Wood 691 : 1063
Wood 692 : 4502 (M)
Wood 693 : 4346
Wood 694 : 6282
Wood 695 : 893
Wood 696 : 5297
Wood 697(1) : 883
Wood 697(2) : 884
Wood 698 : 1134
Wood 699(1) : 3082
Wood 699(2) : 4145
Wood 699(3) : 6652
Wood 699(4) : 3056
Wood 699(5) : 1060
Wood 699(6) : 1054
Wood 700a : 1425
Wood 700b(1) : 4064
Wood 700b(2) : 3715
Wood 700b(3) : 1694
Wood 701 : 6256
Wood 702(1) : 5240
Wood 702(2) : 2338
Wood 703 : 24
Wood 704(1) : 3185
Wood 704(2) : 5351
Wood 704(3) : 5535
Wood 704(4) : 3814
Wood 704(5) : 3610
Wood 704(6) : 554
Wood 704(7) : 355

Wood 704(8) : 3637
Wood 704(9) : 6051
Wood 705 (70, CD) : 6376
Wood 706 : 4411
Wood 707(1) : 348
Wood 707(2) : 347
Wood 707(3) : 346
Wood 707(4) (-CD) : 2959
Wood 707(5) (-CD) : 2958
Wood 707(6) (-CD) : 5189
Wood 707(7) : 3494
Wood 707(8) : 5353
Wood 707(9) : 6726
Wood 707(10) : 5595
Wood 708(1) (705, CD) : 6375
Wood 708(2) : 6118
Wood 709 : 4493
Wood 710(1) : 1414
Wood 710(2) : 6538
Wood 711 : 5881
Wood 712 : 5217
Wood 713 : 1894
Wood 714 : 271
Wood 715 : 1226
Wood 716 : 4414
Wood 717 : 5674
Wood 718 : 2354
Wood 719 : 3556
Wood 720 : 4550
Wood 721 : 4601
Wood 722 : 2057
Wood 723a : 3702
Wood 724(1) : 1198
Wood 724(2) : 6295
Wood 724(3) : 1199
Wood 724(4) : 1201
Wood 725 : 6503
Wood 726(1) : 345
Wood 726(2) : 6300
Wood 726(3) : 6301
Wood 726(4) : 6302
Wood 727(1) : 5304
Wood 727(2) : 3594
Wood 727(3) : 6368
Wood 728(1) : 6435
Wood 728(2) : 853
Wood 728(3) : 5179
Wood 729(1) : 4367 (M)
Wood 729(2) : 5565 (M)
Wood 729(3) : 1944 (M)
Wood 729(4) : 2347 (M)
Wood 729(5) : 1945 (M)
Wood 730(1) : 5320
Wood 730(2) : 912
Wood 730(3) : 5324
Wood 730(4) : 2043
Wood 730(5) : 2863
Wood 730(6) : 5693
Wood 731(1) (-CD) : 1902
Wood 731(2) : 1212
Wood 731(3) : 3240
Wood 732 : 2017
Wood 733(1) : 6457
Wood 733(2) : 6369

Wood 733(3) : 3906
Wood 733(4) : 239
Wood 734 : 5723 (M)
Wood 735(1) : 2838
Wood 735(2) : 3378
Wood 735(3) : 3541
Wood 736(1) : 6105
Wood 736(2a) : 958
Wood 736(2b) : 2941
Wood 736(3) : 6202
Wood 736(4) : 73
Wood 736(5) : 4170
Wood 736(6) : 6227
Wood 736(7) : 2232
Wood 736(8) : 6758
Wood 737 : 3584
Wood 738 : 4814
Wood 739(1) : 2394
Wood 739(2) : 5819
Wood 739(3) : 3974
Wood 739(4) : 6014
Wood 739(5) : 5978
Wood 740 : 4839
Wood 741(1) : 2988
Wood 741(2) : 2063
Wood 741(3) : 3301
Wood 742 : 1893
Wood 743 : 6303
Wood 744 : 3582
Wood 745 : 3484
Wood 746 : 2841
Wood 747(1) : 2114
Wood 747(2) : 5868
Wood 747(3) : 2329
Wood 748a : 102 (M)
Wood 748b : 58 (M)
Wood 749 : 4379 (M)
Wood 750(1) : 3358
Wood 750(2) : 4378
Wood 750(3) : 2278
Wood 750(4) : 3004
Wood 750(5) : 4383
Wood 751 : 3382
Wood 752(1) : 2035
Wood 752(2) : 2335
Wood 752(3) : 6130
Wood 752(4) : 5522
Wood 752(5) : 4343
Wood 753 : 3486
Wood 754(1) : 6403
Wood 754(2) : 2211
Wood 754(3) : 313
Wood 754(4) : 6487
Wood 754(5) : 5178
Wood 755 : 1642 (M)
Wood 756 : 942
Wood 757(1) : 2515
Wood 757(2) : 978
Wood 758 : 1064 (M)
Wood 759 : 907
Wood 760 : 5974
Wood 761 : 3142
Wood 762 : 2513
Wood 763 : 1641

Wood 764 : 974
Wood 765 : 1525
Wood 766 : 6117
Wood 767 : 3498
Wood 768 : 226
Wood 769(1) : 335
Wood 769(2) : 2014
Wood 770 : 6665
Wood 771 : 5600
Wood 772 : 5784
Wood 773(1) : 5
Wood 773(2) : 6106
Wood 774(1) : 5625
Wood 774(2) : 5801
Wood 774(3a) : 1841
Wood 774(3b) : 6058
Wood 774(4) : 873
Wood 774(5) : 5802
Wood 774(6) : 4310
Wood 774(7) : 1165
Wood 775 : 2129
Wood 776(1) : 3217
Wood 776(2) : 6587
Wood 776(3) : 3214
Wood 777 : 3219
Wood 778 : 3339
Wood 779 : 362
Wood 780 : 4782
Wood 781 : 6031
Wood 782 : 2965
Wood 783 : 6050
Wood 784 : 5201
Wood 785 : 2844
Wood 786 : 892
Wood 787 : 2963
Wood 788(1) : 5572
Wood 788(2) : 5552
Wood 789(1) : 2049
Wood 789(2) : 363
Wood 789(3) : 5222
Wood 790 : 2370 (M)
Wood 791 : 4076 (M)
Wood 792(1) : 5827
Wood 792(2) : 3131
Wood 792(3) : 1866
Wood 792(4) : 8
Wood 792(5) : 4176
Wood 793 (-CD) : 4077
Wood 794(1) : 902
Wood 794(2) : 1842
Wood 794(3) : 6273
Wood 795(1) : 5231
Wood 795(2) : 5187
Wood 795(3) : 3854
Wood 795(4) : 5593
Wood 795(5) : 3580
Wood 795(6) : 5731
Wood 795(7) : 3097
Wood 795(8) : 6669
Wood 796 : 4084
Wood 797 : 4413
Wood 798 : 6557
Wood 799 : 4139
Wood 800(1) : 4833

Wood 800(2) : 3366
Wood 800(3) : 3092
Wood 800(4) : 3581
Wood 801 : 4540
Wood 802 : 2112 (M)
Wood 803 : 5750
Wood 804 : 3578
Wood 805 : 1396
Wood 806 : 982
Wood 807 : 4314
Wood 808 : 5580
Wood 809 : 4412
Wood 810 : 4546
Wood 811 : 6138
Wood 812 : 6317
Wood 813 : 5708
Wood 814 : 1919
Wood 815 : 906
Wood 816 : 2392
Wood 817(1) : 3409
Wood 817(2) : 3408
Wood 817(3) : 972
Wood 818(1) : 1834
Wood 818(2) : 6137
Wood 818(3) : 4364
Wood 819 (891, CD) : 1908
Wood 820 : 5667
Wood 821 : 4776
Wood 822 : 35
Wood 823 : 4381
Wood 824(1) : 3044
Wood 824(2) : 2036
Wood 824(3) : 3381
Wood 824(4) : 4236
Wood 824(5) : 3081
Wood 824(6) : 6724
Wood 825 : 4783
Wood 826 : 5142
Wood 827 : 3106 (M)
Wood 828 : 2055
Wood 829 : 5928
Wood 830 : 2008
Wood 831 : 5886
Wood 832 : 3964
Wood 833 : 306
Wood 834 : 1611
Wood 835(1) : 855
Wood 835(2) : 5256
Wood 835(3) : 2989
Wood 835(4) : 1639
Wood 835(5) : 963
Wood 835(6) : 964
Wood 835(7) : 3891
Wood 836(1) : 5326
Wood 836(2) : 2179
Wood 836(3) : 3098
Wood 836(4) : 3706
Wood 836(5) : 3102
Wood 836(6-7) : 4507
Wood 836(8) : 6635
Wood 836(9) : 6603
Wood 836(10-11) : 3879
Wood 836(12) : 1874
Wood 836(13) : 4458

Wood 837 : 3309
Wood 838 : 1152
Wood 839 : 920
Wood 840 : 6666
Wood 841(1) : 1920
Wood 841(2) : 6041
Wood 841(3) : 4318
Wood 841(4) : 6469
Wood 842 : 3231 (M)
Wood 843(1) : 57
Wood 843(2) : 309
Wood 843(3) : 2437
Wood 843(4) : 2436
Wood 843(5) : 2390
Wood 843(6) : 5152
Wood 843(7) : 3707
Wood 843(8) : 2353
Wood 844 : 2148
Wood 845 : 1068
Wood 846 : 364
Wood 847 : 5858
Wood 848 : 6139
Wood 849 : 5887
Wood 850 : 5735
Wood 851 : 45
Wood 852 : 3283
Wood 853 : 5579
Wood 854 : 3210
Wood 855 : 6348
Wood 856 : 5198
Wood 857 : 939
Wood 858 : 5716
Wood 859(1) : 6299
Wood 859(2) : 6298
Wood 859(3) : 4548
Wood 859(4) : 1007
Wood 860 : 5700
Wood 861 : 5584
Wood 862(1) (682, CD) : 2539
Wood 862(2) (-CD) : 5157
Wood 863(1) : 5196
Wood 863(2) : 5195
Wood 864(1) : 3406
Wood 864(2) : 3331
Wood 864(3) : 6230
Wood 865 : 3200
Wood 866 : 1178
Wood 867 : 3882
Wood 868(1) : 4325
Wood 868(2) : 4637
Wood 868(3) : 3405
Wood 868(4-5) : 4407
Wood 868(6) : 3052
Wood 868(7) : 5941
Wood 869(1) : 1402
Wood 869(2) : 6629
Wood 869(3) : 5843
Wood 869(4) : 2056
Wood 869(5) : 3959
Wood 869(6) : 1957
Wood 870(1) : 1157
Wood 870(2) : 2267
Wood 870(3) : 4340
Wood 870(4) (-CD) : 2337

Wood 871 : 4761
Wood 872 : 5197
Wood 873(1) : 971
Wood 873(2) : 979
Wood 874(1) : 36
Wood 874(2) : 2330
Wood 875(1) : 6731
Wood 875(2) : 2301
Wood 875(3) : 5114
Wood 876(1) : 4466
Wood 876(2) : 1410
Wood 876(3) : 5601
Wood 876(4) : 1188
Wood 876(5) : 250
Wood 876(6) (-CD) : 2180
Wood 876(7) (-CD) : 3877
Wood 877 : 1640
Wood 878 : 44
Wood 879(1) : 342
Wood 879(2) : 5757
Wood 879(3) : 5756
Wood 880 : 4177
Wood 881(1) : 6689 (M)
Wood 881(2) : 3737 (M)
Wood 882 : 4416
Wood 883(1) : 1864
Wood 883(2) : 5834
Wood 883(3) : 2544
Wood 883(4) : 2543
Wood 883(5) (-CD) : 3307
Wood 883(6) : 2177
Wood 883(7) : 6604
Wood 884(1) : 2388
Wood 884(2) : 1088
Wood 884(3) : 2389
Wood 884(4) : 2393
Wood 884(5) : 2391
Wood 884(6) : 6109
Wood 885(1) : 16
Wood 885(2) : 3649
Wood 886 : 5919
Wood 887a : 970 (M)
Wood 887b(1) : 5903 (M)
Wood 887b(2) : 6644 (M)
Wood 887b(3) : 4028 (M)
Wood 888(1) : 2460
Wood 888(2) : 2334
Wood 888(3) : 5138
Wood 888(4) : 1004
Wood 889(1) : 6601
Wood 889(2) : 6602
Wood 889(3) : 3999
Wood 890(1) : 5736
Wood 890(2) : 5820
Wood 890(3) : 6254
Wood 891 (-CD) : 1627
Wood 892 : 4821
Wood 893(1) (-CD) : 2555
Wood 893(2) : 1424
Wood 893(3) : 940
Wood 893(4) : 1675
Wood 893(5) : 1213
Wood 894 : 1182
Wood 895 : 5916

Wood 896(1) : 1524
Wood 896(2) : 1579
Wood 896(3) : 1512
Wood 896(4a) : 1619
Wood 896(4b) : 1618
Wood 896(5) : 1444
Wood 896(6) : 1481
Wood 896(7) : 1487
Wood 896(8) (-CD) : 1451
Wood 896(9) (-CD) : 5376
Wood 897 : 1488
Wood 898(1) : 1489
Wood 898(2) : 5500
Wood 898(3) : 3414
Wood 899(1) : 1531
Wood 899(2) : 1530
Wood 899(3) (-CD) : 1449
Wood 899(4) (-CD) : 382
Wood 899(5) (-CD) : 2796
Wood 899(6) (-CD) : 1454
Wood 899(7) (-CD) : 1453
Wood 899(8) (-CD) : 1474
Wood Alm. A(1) : 118
Wood Alm. A(2) : 119
Wood Alm. A(3) : 105
Wood Alm. A(4) : 189
Wood Alm. A(5) : 190
Wood Alm. A(6) : 191
Wood Alm. A(7) : 52
Wood Alm. A(8) : 53
Wood Alm. A(9) : 2459
Wood Alm. A(10) : 101
Wood Alm. A(11) : 55
Wood Alm. A(12-13) : 56
Wood Alm. A(14-15) : 177
Wood Alm. A(16) : 63
Wood Alm. A(17) : 176
Wood Alm. B(1) : 192
Wood Alm. B(2) : 193
Wood Alm. B(3) : 194
Wood Alm. B(4) : 195
Wood Alm. B(5) : 196
Wood Alm. B(6) : 97
Wood Alm. B(7) : 96
Wood Alm. C(1) : 207
Wood Alm. C(2) : 208
Wood Alm. C(3) : 209
Wood Alm. C(4) : 210
Wood Alm. C(5) : 211
Wood Alm. C(6) : 212
Wood Alm. D(1) : 81
Wood Alm. D(2) : 82
Wood Alm. D(3) : 83
Wood Alm. D(4) : 84
Wood Alm. D(5) : 91
Wood Alm. D(6) : 93
Wood Alm. D(7) : 94
Wood Alm. D(8) : 95
Wood Alm. E(1) : 181
Wood Alm. E(2) : 185
Wood Alm. E(3) : 116
Wood Alm. E(4) : 47
Wood Alm. E(5) : 217
Wood Alm. E(6) : 161

[MS.] Wood B. 37(12) : 2538
[MS.] Wood B. 37(13) : 2536
[MS.] Wood B. 38(1) : 1376
[MS.] Wood B. 38(2) : 2946
[MS.] Wood B. 39(1) : 1021
[MS.] Wood B. 39(2) : 4197
[MS.] Wood B. 39(3) : 5321
[MS.] Wood B. 39(4) : 5322
[MS.] Wood B. 39(5) : 2066
[MS.] Wood B. 39(6) : 2405
[MS.] Wood B. 39(7) : 289
[MS.] Wood B. 39(8) : 2474
[MS.] Wood B. 39(9) : 4807
[MS.] Wood B. 40(1) : 3855
[MS.] Wood B. 40(2) : 2251
[MS.] Wood B. 40(3a) : 2005
[MS.] Wood B. 40(3b) : 2006
[MS.] Wood B. 40(4) : 6382
[MS.] Wood B. 40(5) : 6579
[MS.] Wood B. 40(6) : 2176
[MS.] Wood B. 40(7) : 6692
[MS.] Wood B. 40(8) (-CD) : 6693
[MS.] Wood B. 40(9) : 4770
[MS.] Wood B. 40(10) : 1905
[MS.] Wood B. 40(11) : 5119
[MS.] Wood B. 40(12) : 5836
[MS.] Wood B. 40(13) : 6088
[MS.] Wood B. 40(14) : 5949
[MS.] Wood B. 40(15) : 12
[MS.] Wood B. 40(16) : 3438
[MS.] Wood B. 40(17) : 6750
[MS.] Wood B. 41 : 3526
[MS.] Wood C. 13(1) : 3140
[MS.] Wood C. 13(2) : 6502
[MS.] Wood C. 13(3) : 1067
[MS.] Wood C. 13(4) : 3562
[MS.] Wood C. 13(5) : 2283
[MS.] Wood C. 13(6) : 2586
[MS.] Wood C. 13(7) : 2295
[MS.] Wood C. 13(8) : 6504
[MS.] Wood C. 13(9) : 3281
[MS.] Wood C. 14(1) : 3936
[MS.] Wood C. 14(2) : 4578
[MS.] Wood C. 14(3) : 6468
[MS.] Wood C. 14(4) : 1155
[MS.] Wood C. 14(5) : 2824
[MS.] Wood C. 14(6) : 2605
[MS.] Wood C. 14(7) : 1154
[MS.] Wood C. 14(8) : 3874
[MS.] Wood C. 14(9) : 3752
[MS.] Wood C. 14(10) : 2843
[MS.] Wood C. 14(11) : 1952
[MS.] Wood C. 14(12) : 1836
[MS.] Wood C. 14(13) (3, CD) : 5165
[MS.] Wood C. 14(14) : 5318
[MS.] Wood C. 15 : 3998
[MS.] Wood C. 16 : 3593
[MS.] Wood C. 17(1) : 6002
[MS.] Wood C. 17(2) : 6261
[MS.] Wood C. 17(3) : 1110
[MS.] Wood C. 17(4) : 6045
[MS.] Wood C. 17(5) : 1127
[MS.] Wood C. 17(6) : 6700
[MS.] Wood C. 17(7) : 1423

[MS.] Wood C. 18 : 6307
[MS.] Wood C. 19(1) : 286
[MS.] Wood C. 19(2) : 2018
[MS.] Wood C. 20 : 4767
[MS.] Wood C. 21 : 6086
[MS.] Wood C. 22 : 2323
[MS.] Wood C. 23 : 5560
[MS.] Wood C. 24 : 2269
[MS.] Wood C. 25(1) : 4372
[MS.] Wood C. 25(2) : 4368
[MS.] Wood C. 25(3) : 4369
[MS.] Wood C. 25(4) : 4370
[MS.] Wood C. 25(5) : 4371
[MS.] Wood C. 25(6) : 4067
[MS.] Wood C. 26(1) : 1498
[MS.] Wood C. 26(2) : 1499
[MS.] Wood C. 26(3) : 1500
[MS.] Wood C. 26(4-5) : 1501
[MS.] Wood C. 26(6-7) : 1503
[MS.] Wood C. 26(8) : 1502
[MS.] Wood C. 26(9) : 1504
[MS.] Wood C. 26(10) : 1610
[MS.] Wood C. 26(11) : 1603
[MS.] Wood C. 26(12) : 1533
[MS.] Wood C. 26(13) : 1534
[MS.] Wood C. 26(14) : 6447
[MS.] Wood C. 26(15) : 303
[MS.] Wood C. 26(16) : 4606
[MS.] Wood C. 26(16a-b) : 1452
[MS.] Wood C. 26(17) : 981
[MS.] Wood C. 26(18) : 2937
[MS.] Wood C. 26(19) : 1535
[MS.] Wood C. 26(20) : 1539
[MS.] Wood C. 27 : 4301
[MS.] Wood C. 28 : 1528
[MS.] Wood C. 29 (-CD) : 1508
[MS.] Wood C. 30 : 1532
[MS.] Wood C. 31(1) : 2216
[MS.] Wood C. 31(2) : 3538
[MS.] Wood C. 31(3) : 4602
[MS.] Wood C. 31(4) : 4541
[MS.] Wood C. 31(5) : 2059
[MS.] Wood C. 32(1) : 6291
[MS.] Wood C. 32(2) : 2217
[MS.] Wood C. 32(3) : 2218
[MS.] Wood C. 32(4) : 4497 (M)
[MS.] Wood C. 32(5) : 6637
[MS.] Wood C. 33 : 5215
[MS.] Wood C. 34(1) : 3338
[MS.] Wood C. 34(2) : 2980
[MS.] Wood C. 35 : 3173
[MS.] Wood C. 36(1) : 270
[MS.] Wood C. 36(2) : 3333
[MS.] Wood C. 37 : 5243
[MS.] Wood C. 38 : 936
[MS.] Wood C. 39(1) : 1969
[MS.] Wood C. 39(2) : 3812
[MS.] Wood C. 39(3) (39c, CD) : 1649
[MS.] Wood C. 40(1) : 2192
[MS.] Wood C. 40(2) : 2193
[MS.] Wood C. 40(3) : 2190
[MS.] Wood C. 40(4) : 2191
[MS.] Wood C. 41 : 5251

[MS.] Wood C. 42 (-CD) : 5421
[MS.] Wood C. 43 : 1406
[MS.] Wood C. 44(1) : 5856
[MS.] Wood C. 44(2) : 1428
[MS.] Wood C. 44(3) : 366
[MS.] Wood C. 44(4) : 4580
[MS.] Wood C. 45 : 3557
[MS.] Wood C. 46 : 3446
[MS.] Wood C. 47(1) : 6598
[MS.] Wood C. 47(2) : 2967
[MS.] Wood C. 48 : 3842
[MS.] Wood C. 49 (-CD) : 2833
[MS.] Wood C. 50 : 4498 (M)
[MS.] Wood D. 21(1) : 3244
[MS.] Wood D. 21(2) : 3243
[MS.] Wood D. 22(1) : 1527
[MS.] Wood D. 22(2) : 1522
[MS.] Wood D. 22(3) : 1581
[MS.] Wood D. 22(4) (-CD) : 1490
[MS.] Wood D. 22(5) (-CD) : 1620
[MS.] Wood D. 22(6) : 1545
[MS.] Wood D. 22(7) (3, CD) : 1602
[MS.] Wood D. 22(8) : 1625
[MS.] Wood D. 22(9) : 4736
[MS.] Wood D. 22(10) : 1505
[MS.] Wood D. 22(11) : 1519
[MS.] Wood D. 22(12) : 1486
[MS.] Wood D. 22(13) : 1491
[MS.] Wood D. 22(14) : 1476
[MS.] Wood D. 22(15) : 1606
[MS.] Wood D. 22(16) : 1438
[MS.] Wood D. 22(17) : 2541
[MS.] Wood D. 22(18) : 1448
[MS.] Wood D. 23(1) : 921
[MS.] Wood D. 23(2) : 2441
[MS.] Wood D. 23(3) : 3940
[MS.] Wood D. 23(4) : 3948
[MS.] Wood D. 23(5) : 1208
[MS.] Wood D. 23(6) : 6103
[MS.] Wood D. 23(7) : 3585
[MS.] Wood D. 23(8) : 2135
[MS.] Wood D. 23(9) : 3579
[MS.] Wood D. 23(10) : 2442
[MS.] Wood D. 23(11) : 2444
[MS.] Wood D. 23(12) : 6378
[MS.] Wood D. 23(13) : 3303
[MS.] Wood D. 24(1) : 4073
[MS.] Wood D. 24(2) : 3853
[MS.] Wood D. 24(3) : 5590
[MS.] Wood D. 24(4) : 3125
[MS.] Wood D. 24(5) : 4858
[MS.] Wood D. 24(6) : 4859
[MS.] Wood D. 24(7) : 3302
[MS.] Wood D. 24(8) : 2026
[MS.] Wood D. 24(9) : 3133
[MS.] Wood D. 24(10) : 2062
[MS.] Wood D. 25(1) : 2514
[MS.] Wood D. 25(2) : 2530
[MS.] Wood D. 25(3) : 2517
[MS.] Wood D. 25(4) : 2518
[MS.] Wood D. 25(5) : 6322
[MS.] Wood D. 25(6) : 2520
[MS.] Wood D. 25(7) : 2521
[MS.] Wood D. 25(8) : 4021

[MS.] Wood D. 25(9) : 6177
[MS.] Wood D. 25(10) : 2986
[MS.] Wood D. 25(11) : 2331
[MS.] Wood D. 26(1) : 2668
[MS.] Wood D. 26(2) : 2669
[MS.] Wood D. 26(3) : 1805
[MS.] Wood D. 26(4) : 283
[MS.] Wood D. 26(5) : 994
[MS.] Wood D. 26(6) : 5342
[MS.] Wood D. 26(7) : 5787
[MS.] Wood D. 26(8) : 2831
[MS.] Wood D. 26(9) : 5233
[MS.] Wood D. 26(10) : 4620
[MS.] Wood D. 26(11) : 5344
[MS.] Wood D. 26(12) : 312
[MS.] Wood D. 26(13) : 5343
[MS.] Wood D. 26(14) : 3726
[MS.] Wood D. 26(15) : 6000
[MS.] Wood D. 26(16) : 4319
[MS.] Wood D. 27(1) : 1162
[MS.] Wood D. 27(2) : 959
[MS.] Wood D. 27(3) : 1143
[MS.] Wood D. 27(4) : 997
[MS.] Wood D. 27(5) : 2862
[MS.] Wood D. 27(6) : 3284
[MS.] Wood D. 27(7) : 1685
[MS.] Wood D. 27(8) : 2741
[MS.] Wood D. 27(9, 10) : 3367
[MS.] Wood D. 28(1) : 1692
[MS.] Wood D. 28(2) : 3453
[MS.] Wood D. 28(3) : 2550
[MS.] Wood D. 28(4) : 3596
[MS.] Wood D. 28(5) : 5203
[MS.] Wood D. 28(6) : 1270
[MS.] Wood D. 28(7) : 6581
[MS.] Wood D. 28(8) : 38
[MS.] Wood D. 28(9) : 6370
[MS.] Wood D. 28(10) : 3477
[MS.] Wood D. 28(11) : 1000
[MS.] Wood D. 28(12) : 5867
[MS.] Wood D. 28(13) : 4641
[MS.] Wood D. 28(14) : 2342
[MS.] Wood D. 28(15) : 3345
[MS.] Wood D. 28(16) : 3070
[MS.] Wood D. 28(17) : 3069
[MS.] Wood D. 28(18) : 3045
[MS.] Wood D. 28(19) : 3017
[MS.] Wood D. 28(20) : 3088
[MS.] Wood D. 28(21) : 4592
[MS.] Wood D. 28(22) : 3085
[MS.] Wood D. 28(23) : 4159
[MS.] Wood D. 28(24) : 5534
[MS.] Wood D. 28(25) : 4265
[MS.] Wood D. 28(26) : 4266
[MS.] Wood D. 28(27) : 3797
[MS.] Wood D. 28(28) : 6683 (M)
[MS.] Wood D. 28(29) : 5909
[MS.] Wood D. 28(30) : 1850
[MS.] Wood D. 28(31) : 3818
[MS.] Wood D. 29(1) : 2445
[MS.] Wood D. 29(2) : 2446
[MS.] Wood D. 29(3) : 2447
[MS.] Wood D. 29(4) : 2448
[MS.] Wood D. 29(5) : 2449

[MS.] Wood D. 29(6) : 2450
[MS.] Wood D. 29(7a) : 2452
[MS.] Wood D. 29(7b) : 2451
[MS.] Wood D. 29(8) : 2453
[MS.] Wood D. 29(9) : 2454
[MS.] Wood D. 29(10) : 2455
[MS.] Wood D. 29(11) : 2456
[MS.] Wood D. 29(12) : 2457
[MS.] Wood D. 29(13) : 4299
[MS.] Wood D. 29(14) : 1196
[MS.] Wood D. 29(15) : 1197
[MS.] Wood D. 29(16) : 1195
[MS.] Wood D. 29(17) (-CD) : 2458
[MS.] Wood D. 29(18) : 1203
[MS.] Wood D. 29(19) (-CD) : 1205
[MS.] Wood D. 30(1) : 3356
[MS.] Wood D. 30(2) : 4365
[MS.] Wood D. 30(3) : 3822
[MS.] Wood D. 30(4) : 6678
[MS.] Wood D. 30(5) : 1928
[MS.] Wood D. 30(6) : 3560
[MS.] Wood D. 30(7) : 5419
[MS.] Wood D. 30(8) : 5540
[MS.] Wood D. 30(9) (-CD) : 3566
[MS.] Wood D. 30(10) : 2743
[MS.] Wood D. 30(11) : 284
[MS.] Wood D. 31(1) : 5420
[MS.] Wood D. 31(2) : 5423a
[MS.] Wood D. 31(3) : 2253
[MS.] Wood D. 31(4) : 6292
[MS.] Wood D. 31(5) : 1427
[MS.] Wood D. 31(6) : 1678
[MS.] Wood D. 31(7) : 2522
[MS.] Wood D. 31(8) : 2526
[MS.] Wood D. 31(9) : 2612
[MS.] Wood D. 31(10) : 4778
[MS.] Wood D. 31(11) : 3349
[MS.] Wood D. 31(12) : 3590
[MS.] Wood D. 31(13) : 3326
[MS.] Wood D. 31(14) : 2643
[MS.] Wood D. 31(15) : 2631
[MS.] Wood D. 31(16) : 6551
[MS.] Wood D. 31(17) : 288
[MS.] Wood D. 31(18) : 4499 (M)
[MS.] Wood D. 31(19) (-CD) : 4056
[MS.] Wood D. 31(20) : 1763
[MS.] Wood D. 31(21) : 1760
[MS.] Wood D. 31(22) : 252
[MS.] Wood D. 31(23) : 3175
[MS.] Wood D. 31(24) : 5734
[MS.] Wood D. 31(25) : 2233
[MS.] Wood D. 31(26) : 5612
[MS.] Wood D. 31(27) : 6180
[MS.] Wood D. 31(28) : 5108
[MS.] Wood D. 31(29) : 3280
[MS.] Wood D. 31(30) : 4495
[MS.] Wood D. 31(31) : 2877
[MS.] Wood D. 31(32) : 2523
[MS.] Wood D. 31(33) : 2642
[MS.] Wood D. 31(34) : 3013
[MS.] Wood D. 31(35) : 3012
[MS.] Wood D. 31(36) : 3354
[MS.] Wood D. 31(37) : 6434
[MS.] Wood D. 31(38) (-CD) : 6111

[MS.] Wood D. 31(39) : 318
[MS.] Wood D. 31(40) : 1147
[MS.] Wood D. 31(41) : 4241
[MS.] Wood D. 31(42) : 4844
[MS.] Wood D. 31(43) : 1845 (M)
[MS.] Wood D. 31(44) : 1844 (M)
[MS.] Wood D. 31(45) : 2658
[MS.] Wood D. 31(46) : 281
[MS.] Wood D. 31(47) : 876
[MS.] Wood D. 31(48) : 3994
[MS.] Wood D. 31(49) : 2118
[MS.] Wood D. 31(50) : 2117
[MS.] Wood D. 31(51) : 2116
[MS.] Wood D. 31(52) : 2119
[MS.] Wood D. 31(53) : 4376
[MS.] Wood E. 3 (ff. 298-331) : 1513
[MS.] Wood E. 13(1) : 1614
[MS.] Wood E. 13(2) : 1536
[MS.] Wood E. 13(3) : 1552
[MS.] Wood E. 13(4) : 1635
[MS.] Wood E. 13(5) : 1515
[MS.] Wood E. 13(6) : 1510
[MS.] Wood E. 14(1) : 1628
[MS.] Wood E. 14(2) : 1567
[MS.] Wood E. 14(3) : 1496
[MS.] Wood E. 14(4) : 1497
[MS.] Wood E. 14(5) : 1463
[MS.] Wood E. 14(6) : 1465
[MS.] Wood E. 15(1) : 1623
[MS.] Wood E. 15(2) : 1541
[MS.] Wood E. 15(3) : 1544
[MS.] Wood E. 15(4) : 1520
[MS.] Wood E. 15(5) : 1462
[MS.] Wood E. 15(6) : 1580
[MS.] Wood E. 16(1) : 1593
[MS.] Wood E. 16(2) : 1594
[MS.] Wood E. 16(3) : 1617
[MS.] Wood E. 16(4) : 1605
[MS.] Wood E. 16(5) : 1521
[MS.] Wood E. 16(6) : 1440
[MS.] Wood E. 16(7) : 1633
[MS.] Wood E. 16(8) : 1630
[MS.] Wood E. 17(1) : 1607
[MS.] Wood E. 17(2) : 1479
[MS.] Wood E. 17(3) : 1543
[MS.] Wood E. 17(4) : 1517
[MS.] Wood E. 17(5) : 1475
[MS.] Wood E. 17(6) : 1582
[MS.] Wood E. 17(7) : 1568
[MS.] Wood E. 17(8) : 1569
[MS.] Wood E. 17(9) : 1578
[MS.] Wood E. 17(10) : 1546
[MS.] Wood E. 17(11) : 1458
[MS.] Wood E. 17(12) : 1631
[MS.] Wood E. 18(1) : 1518
[MS.] Wood E. 18(2) : 1542
[MS.] Wood E. 18(3) : 1441
[MS.] Wood E. 18(4) : 1596
[MS.] Wood E. 18(5) : 1571
[MS.] Wood E. 18(6) : 1572
[MS.] Wood E. 18(7) : 1622
[MS.] Wood E. 18(8) : 1573
[MS.] Wood E. 18(9) : 1624
[MS.] Wood E. 18(10) : 1493

[MS.] Wood E. 18(11) : 1457
[MS.] Wood E. 19(1) : 1464
[MS.] Wood E. 19(2a) : 1482
[MS.] Wood E. 19(2b) : 1492
[MS.] Wood E. 19(3) : 1439
[MS.] Wood E. 19(4) : 1455
[MS.] Wood E. 19(5) : 1483
[MS.] Wood E. 19(6) : 1547
[MS.] Wood E. 20(1) : 1485
[MS.] Wood E. 20(2) : 1559
[MS.] Wood E. 20(3) : 1636
[MS.] Wood E. 20(4) : 1574
[MS.] Wood E. 20(5) : 1447
[MS.] Wood E. 20(6) : 1560
[MS.] Wood E. 20(7) : 1526
[MS.] Wood E. 20(8) : 1459
[MS.] Wood E. 20(9) : 1615
[MS.] Wood E. 20(10a) (-CD) : 1446
[MS.] Wood E. 20(10b) : 1466
[MS.] Wood E. 20(11) : 1553
[MS.] Wood E. 20(12) : 1613
[MS.] Wood E. 21(1) : 1575
[MS.] Wood E. 21(2) : 1629
[MS.] Wood E. 21(3) : 1576
[MS.] Wood E. 21(4) : 1467
[MS.] Wood E. 21(5) : 1450
[MS.] Wood E. 21(6) : 1516
[MS.] Wood E. 21(7) : 1468
[MS.] Wood E. 21(8) : 1494
[MS.] Wood E. 22(1) : 1550
[MS.] Wood E. 22(2) : 1469
[MS.] Wood E. 22(3) : 1470
[MS.] Wood E. 22(4a) : 1555
[MS.] Wood E. 22(4b) : 1604
[MS.] Wood E. 22(5) : 1460
[MS.] Wood E. 22(6) : 1551
[MS.] Wood E. 22(7) : 1548
[MS.] Wood E. 22(8) : 1549
[MS.] Wood E. 22(9) : 1598
[MS.] Wood E. 22(10) : 1461
[MS.] Wood E. 22(11) : 1495
[MS.] Wood E. 22(12) : 1577
[MS.] Wood E. 23(1) : 1612
[MS.] Wood E. 23(2) : 1595
[MS.] Wood E. 23(3) : 1558
[MS.] Wood E. 23(4a) : 1586
[MS.] Wood E. 23(4b) : 1442
[MS.] Wood E. 23(5) : 1632
[MS.] Wood E. 23(6a) : 1570
[MS.] Wood E. 23(6b) : 1616
[MS.] Wood E. 24a : 1537
[MS.] Wood E. 24b : 1561
[MS.] Wood E. 25(1) : 451
[MS.] Wood E. 25(2) : 811
[MS.] Wood E. 25(3) : 682
[MS.] Wood E. 25(4) : 802
[MS.] Wood E. 25(5) : 808
[MS.] Wood E. 25(6) (-CD) : 691
[MS.] Wood E. 25(7) : 836
[MS.] Wood E. 25(8) : 433
[MS.] Wood E. 25(9) : 619
[MS.] Wood E. 25(10) : 379
[MS.] Wood E. 25(11) : 441
[MS.] Wood E. 25(12) : 606

[MS.] Wood E. 25(13) : 792
[MS.] Wood E. 25(14) : 578
[MS.] Wood E. 25(15) : 657
[MS.] Wood E. 25(16) : 787
[MS.] Wood E. 25(17) : 838
[MS.] Wood E. 25(18) : 422
[MS.] Wood E. 25(19) : 517
[MS.] Wood E. 25(20) : 462
[MS.] Wood E. 25(21) : 719
[MS.] Wood E. 25(22) : 766
[MS.] Wood E. 25(23) : 843
[MS.] Wood E. 25(24) : 694
[MS.] Wood E. 25(25) : 634
[MS.] Wood E. 25(26) : 577
[MS.] Wood E. 25(27) : 772
[MS.] Wood E. 25(28) : 592
[MS.] Wood E. 25(29) : 814
[MS.] Wood E. 25(30) : 645
[MS.] Wood E. 25(31) : 666
[MS.] Wood E. 25(32) : 588
[MS.] Wood E. 25(33) : 597
[MS.] Wood E. 25(34) : 573
[MS.] Wood E. 25(35) : 681
[MS.] Wood E. 25(36) : 627
[MS.] Wood E. 25(37) : 837
[MS.] Wood E. 25(38) : 561
[MS.] Wood E. 25(39) : 599
[MS.] Wood E. 25(40) : 497
[MS.] Wood E. 25(41) : 424
[MS.] Wood E. 25(42) : 788
[MS.] Wood E. 25(43) : 449
[MS.] Wood E. 25(44) : 757
[MS.] Wood E. 25(45) : 581
[MS.] Wood E. 25(46) : 416
[MS.] Wood E. 25(47) : 780
[MS.] Wood E. 25(48) : 704
[MS.] Wood E. 25(49) : 381
[MS.] Wood E. 25(50) : 580
[MS.] Wood E. 25(51) : 783
[MS.] Wood E. 25(52) : 596
[MS.] Wood E. 25(53) (-CD) : 438
[MS.] Wood E. 25(54) : 560
[MS.] Wood E. 25(55) : 486
[MS.] Wood E. 25(56) : 807
[MS.] Wood E. 25(57) : 803
[MS.] Wood E. 25(58) : 748
[MS.] Wood E. 25(59) : 689
[MS.] Wood E. 25(60) : 705
[MS.] Wood E. 25(61) : 601
[MS.] Wood E. 25(62) : 496
[MS.] Wood E. 25(63) : 700
[MS.] Wood E. 25(64) : 498
[MS.] Wood E. 25(65) : 835
[MS.] Wood E. 25(66) : 392
[MS.] Wood E. 25(67) : 749
[MS.] Wood E. 25(68) : 638
[MS.] Wood E. 25(69) : 759
[MS.] Wood E. 25(70) : 423
[MS.] Wood E. 25(71) : 452
[MS.] Wood E. 25(72) : 466
[MS.] Wood E. 25(73) : 813
[MS.] Wood E. 25(74) : 607
[MS.] Wood E. 25(75) : 493
[MS.] Wood E. 25(76) : 793

[MS.] Wood E. 25(77) : 575
[MS.] Wood E. 25(78) : 721
[MS.] Wood E. 25(79) : 604
[MS.] Wood E. 25(80) : 656
[MS.] Wood E. 25(81) : 687
[MS.] Wood E. 25(82) : 426
[MS.] Wood E. 25(83) : 771
[MS.] Wood E. 25(84) : 791
[MS.] Wood E. 25(85) : 707
[MS.] Wood E. 25(86) : 499
[MS.] Wood E. 25(87) : 603
[MS.] Wood E. 25(88) : 602
[MS.] Wood E. 25(89) : 647
[MS.] Wood E. 25(90) : 600
[MS.] Wood E. 25(91) : 685
[MS.] Wood E. 25(92) : 652
[MS.] Wood E. 25(93) : 378
[MS.] Wood E. 25(94) : 823
[MS.] Wood E. 25(95) : 585
[MS.] Wood E. 25(96) : 669
[MS.] Wood E. 25(97) : 758
[MS.] Wood E. 25(98) : 776
[MS.] Wood E. 25(99) : 784
[MS.] Wood E. 25(100) (-CD) : 653
[MS.] Wood E. 25(101) (-CD) : 519
[MS.] Wood E. 25(102) : 591
[MS.] Wood E. 25(103) : 533
[MS.] Wood E. 25(104) : 589
[MS.] Wood E. 25(105) : 410
[MS.] Wood E. 25(106) (-CD) : 639
[MS.] Wood E. 25(107) : 565
[MS.] Wood E. 25(108) : 723
[MS.] Wood E. 25(109) : 833
[MS.] Wood E. 25(110) (-CD) : 683
[MS.] Wood E. 25(111) : 482
[MS.] Wood E. 25(112) : 829
[MS.] Wood E. 25(113) : 718
[MS.] Wood E. 25(114) : 834
[MS.] Wood E. 25(115) : 831
[MS.] Wood E. 25(116 (-CD) : 738
[MS.] Wood E. 25(117) : 643
[MS.] Wood E. 25(118) : 828
[MS.] Wood E. 25(119) (-CD) : 805
[MS.] Wood E. 25(120) : 773
[MS.] Wood E. 25(121) : 429
[MS.] Wood E. 25(122) : 445
[MS.] Wood E. 25(123) : 722
[MS.] Wood E. 25(124) : 626
[MS.] Wood E. 25(125) (-CD) : 763
[MS.] Wood E. 25(126) : 816
[MS.] Wood E. 25(127) : 487
[MS.] Wood E. 25(128) : 484
[MS.] Wood E. 25(129) : 809
[MS.] Wood E. 25(130) : 822
[MS.] Wood E. 25(131) : 806
[MS.] Wood E. 25(132) : 668
[MS.] Wood E. 25(133) : 414
[MS.] Wood E. 25(134) : 454
[MS.] Wood E. 25(135) : 724
[MS.] Wood E. 25(136) : 372
[MS.] Wood E. 25(137) : 605
[MS.] Wood E. 25(138) (-CD) : 574
[MS.] Wood E. 25(139) : 618
[MS.] Wood E. 25(140) (29 in CD) :

450
[MS.] Wood E. 25(141) : 732
[MS.] Wood E. 25(142) : 463
[MS.] Wood E. 25(143) : 695
[MS.] Wood E. 25(144) : 699
[MS.] Wood E. 25(145) : 535
[MS.] Wood E. 25(146) : 812
[MS.] Wood E. 25(147) : 765
[MS.] Wood E. 25(148) : 622
[MS.] Wood E. 25(149) : 797
[MS.] Wood E. 25(150) : 810
[MS.] Wood E. 25(151) : 421
[MS.] Wood E. 25(152) : 434
[MS.] Wood E. 25(153) : 794
[MS.] Wood E. 26 : 1626
[MS.] Wood E. 27(1) : 1514
[MS.] Wood E. 27(2) : 1599
[MS.] Wood E. 27(3) : 1600
[MS.] Wood E. 27(4) : 1601
[MS.] Wood E. 27(5) : 1506
[MS.] Wood E. 28(1) : 1511
[MS.] Wood E. 28(2) : 1554
[MS.] Wood E. 28(3) : 1484
[MS.] Wood E. 28(4) : 1538
[MS.] Wood E. 28(5) : 1540
[MS.] Wood F. 27, ff. 233-6 : 2249
[MS.] Wood F. 50, f. 36 : 4237
[MS.] Wood F. 50, f. 37 : 5298
[MS.] Wood F. 50, f. 38 : 886
8° A 153(1) Art. : 6648
8° A 153(2) Art. : 4161
8° A 153(3) Art. : 6264
8° A 153(4) Art. : 1228
8° A 153(5) Art. : 3661
Libr. Records b. 466, 467 : 1523
[MS.] Ashm. 1820a, f. 221(-CD) :
4508
[MS.] Ashm. 1820a, f. 222 : 5277
[MS.] Ashm. 1820a, ff. 224-5 : 5278
[MS.] Ashm. 1820a, ff. 226-7 : 4338
[MS.] Ballard 46, f. 173 : 6672
Jesus C. 1. Arch. 2. 25(1) : 2200
Jesus C. 1. Arch. 2. 25(2) : 1187
Jesus C. 1. Arch. 2. 25(3) : 4893
Jesus C. 2. Arch. 2. 17(1) : 1875
Jesus C. 2. Arch. 2. 17(2) : 4565
Jesus C. E. 4. 7 : 2054
Jesus C. G. 1. 22 : 4375
Jesus C. H. 13. 23(1) : 2276
Jesus C. H. 13. 23(2) : 2870
Jesus C. L. 3. 2 : 1027
Jesus C. N. 1. 4 : 6429
Jesus C. N. 1. 8 : 2289
Jesus C. N. 3. 24 Gall.: 1881
Jesus C. Q. 12. 7-8 : 6686
Jesus C. R. 8. 16 : 3103
Merton C. 3.f.4 : 6684
Folger Library, copy 3 : 6171
Houghton Library : 6582
Huntington Library : 3313
BL : 1019(?)
BL : 1642(?)
BL : see 374 and 741-7
Univ. of Glasgow : see 374

MISSING BEFORE 1717
AND THE PREPARATION OF
THE WHITESIDE CATALOGUE
(185 PRINTED ITEMS)
MS. Wood E. 2(70), p. 1 : 5877
MS. Wood E. 2(70), p. 1 : 3660
MS. Wood E. 2(70), p. 1 : 5382
MS. Wood E. 2(70), p. 2 : 2979
MS. Wood E. 2(70), p. 2 : 5314
MS. Wood E. 2(70), p. 4 : 6347
MS. Wood E. 2(70), p. 4 : 4387
MS. Wood E. 2(70), p. 4 : 1386
MS. Wood E. 2(70), p. 5 : 4760
MS. Wood E. 2(70), p. 5 : 4078
MS. Wood E. 2(70), p. 5 : 3100
MS. Wood E. 2(70), p. 5 : 3513
MS. Wood E. 2(70), p. 5 : 4759
MS. Wood E. 2(70), p. 5 : 5479
MS. Wood E. 2(70), p. 6 : 4576
MS. Wood E. 2(70), p. 6 : 3987
MS. Wood E. 2(70), p. 6 : 5713
MS. Wood E. 2(70), p. 6 : 1126
MS. Wood E. 2(70), p. 6 : 3215
MS. Wood E. 2(70), p. 6 : 5148
MS. Wood E. 2(70), p. 8 : 3925
MS. Wood E. 2(70), p. 7 : 1092
MS. Wood E. 2(70), p. 7 : 3662
MS. Wood E. 2(70), p. 7 : 299
MS. Wood E. 2(70), p. 9 : 365
MS. Wood E. 2(70), p. 9 : 5577
MS. Wood E. 2(70), p. 9 : 3663
MS. Wood E. 2(70), p. 9 : 879
MS. Wood E. 2(70), p. 9 : 3249
MS. Wood E. 2(70), p. 9 : 3979
MS. Wood E. 2(70), p. 9 : 5729
MS. Wood E. 2(70), p. 9 : 6027
MS. Wood E. 2(70), p. 10 : 5841
MS. Wood E. 2(70), p. 10 : 6520
MS. Wood E. 2(70), p. 10 : 320
MS. Wood E. 2(70), p. 10 : 5345
MS. Wood E. 2(70), p. 11 : 1234
MS. Wood E. 2(70), p. 11 : 3932
MS. Wood E. 2(70), p. 11 : 6172
MS. Wood E. 2(70), p. 11 : 3658
MS. Wood E. 2(70), p. 11 : 5275
MS. Wood E. 2(70), p. 11 : 5929
MS. Wood E. 2(70), p. 11 : 3669
MS. Wood E. 2(70), p. 11 : 6548
MS. Wood E. 2(70), p. 14 : 6006
MS. Wood E. 2(70), p. 16 : 2951
MS. Wood E. 2(70), p. 16 : 2355
MS. Wood E. 2(70), p. 16 : 242
MS. Wood E. 2(70), p. 16 : 6025
MS. Wood E. 2(70), p. 16 : 4329
MS. Wood E. 2(70), p. 16 : 5618
MS. Wood E. 2(70), p. 16 : 3472
MS. Wood E. 2(70), p. 16 : 6321
MS. Wood E. 2(70), p. 16 : 6563
MS. Wood E. 2(70), p. 16 : 4165
MS. Wood E. 2(70), p. 16 : 1848
MS. Wood E. 2(70), p. 19 : 6632
MS. Wood E. 2(70), p. 19 : 1019
MS. Wood E. 2(70), p. 19 : 1435
MS. Wood E. 2(70), p. 19 : 6631

MS. Wood E. 2(70), p. 19 : 4000
MS. Wood E. 2(70), p. 19 : 3050
MS. Wood E. 2(70), p. 21 : 871
MS. Wood E. 2(70), p. 21 : 4169
MS. Wood E. 2(70), p. 22 : 3343
MS. Wood E. 2(70), p. 22 : 1117
MS. Wood E. 2(70), p. 22 : 354
MS. Wood E. 2(70), p. 23 : 5315
MS. Wood E. 2(70), p. 25 : 6725
MS. Wood E. 2(70), p. 25 : 2991
MS. Wood E. 2(70), p. 25 : 5293
MS. Wood E. 2(70), p. 26 : 64
MS. Wood E. 2(70), p. 31 : 3308
MS. Wood E. 2(70), p. 33 : 3645
MS. Wood E. 2(70), p. 35 : 3389
MS. Wood E. 2(70), p. 37 : 1211
MS. Wood E. 2(70), p. 38 : 3611
MS. Wood E. 2(70), p. 39 : 4283
MS. Wood E. 2(70), p. 39 : 5137
MS. Wood E. 2(70), p. 39 : 6094
MS. Wood E. 2(70), p. 39 : 4294
MS. Wood E. 2(70), p. 40 : 1433
MS. Wood E. 2(70), p. 40 : 3132
MS. Wood E. 2(70), p. 40 : 5518
MS. Wood E. 2(70), p. 41 : 3558
MS. Wood E. 2(70), p. 41 : 2414
MS. Wood E. 2(70), p. 41 : 2840
MS. Wood E. 2(70), p. 43 : 1013
MS. Wood E. 2(70), p. 45 : 5746
MS. Wood E. 2(70), p. 46 : 6752
MS. Wood E. 2(70), p. 46 : 5509
MS. Wood E. 2(70), p. 46 : 2949
MS. Wood E. 2(70), p. 46 : 6754
MS. Wood E. 2(70), p. 47 : 3247
MS. Wood E. 2(70), p. 48 : 4317
MS. Wood E. 2(70), p. 48 : 1107
MS. Wood E. 2(70), p. 48 : 6179
MS. Wood E. 2(70), p. 48 : 5613
MS. Wood E. 2(70), p. 49 : 1106
MS. Wood E. 2(70), p. 49 : 2046
MS. Wood E. 2(70), p. 49 : 5511
MS. Wood E. 2(70), p. 50 : 2285
MS. Wood E. 2(70), p. 50 : 6350
MS. Wood E. 2(70), p. 50 : 5905
MS. Wood E. 2(70), p. 51 : 5840
MS. Wood E. 2(70), p. 53 : 3670
MS. Wood E. 2(70), p. 53 : 5838
MS. Wood E. 2(70), p. 53 : 3323
MS. Wood E. 2(70), p. 54 : 3683
MS. Wood E. 2(70), p. 54 : 5139
MS. Wood E. 2(70), p. 55 : 4853
MS. Wood E. 2(70), p. 55 : 4300
MS. Wood E. 2(70), p. 56 : 3880
MS. Wood E. 2(70), p. 56 : 975
MS. Wood E. 2(70), p. 56 : 1422
MS. Wood E. 2(70), p. 56 : 1676
MS. Wood E. 2(70), p. 56 : 5123
MS. Wood E. 2(70), p. 59 : 49
MS. Wood E. 2(70), p. 60 : 240
MS. Wood E. 2(70), p. 60 : 5934
MS. Wood E. 2(70), p. 60 : 5842
MS. Wood E. 2(70), p. 61 : 5715
MS. Wood E. 2(70), p. 62 : 3112
MS. Wood E. 2(70), p. 63 : 425

MS. Wood E. 2(70), p. 69 : 3674
MS. Wood E. 2(70), p. 70 : 4503
MS. Wood E. 2(70), p. 74 : 6026
MS. Wood E. 2(70), p. 74 : 4089
[MS.] Wood E. 13(5) : 2380
MS. Wood F. 42, f. 79 : 5749
MS. Wood F. 51(3) : 5776
MS. Wood F. 51(7) : 3403
MS. Wood F. 51(9) : 3176
MS. Wood F. 51(12) : 2277
MS. Wood F. 51(13) : 3025
MS. Wood F. 51(15) : 2252
MS. Wood F. 51(16) : 5826
MS. Wood F. 51(35) : 3105
MS. Wood F. 51(40) : 4144
MS. Wood F. 51(47) : 2704
LT 1.182 : 3344
LT 1.200 : 6688 (numerous)
LT 1.210 : 2142
LT 1.230 : 305
LT 1.230 : 3944
LT 1.230 : 6753
LT 1.230 : 3598
LT 1.230 : 4855
LT 1.230 : 1108
LT 1.230 : 296
LT 1.238 : 5498
LT 1.247 : 5263
LT 1.287 : 3740
LT 1.307 : 4699
LT 1.400 : 5956
LT 1.444 : 2167
LT 1.458 : 3878
LT 2.5 : 4828
LT 2.15 : 3612
LT 2.29 : 6436
LT 2.70 : 5981
LT 2.192 : 2178
LT 2.203 : 1011
LT 2.248 : 277
LT 2.319 : 1370
LT 2.345 : 2364
LT 2.432 : 4831
LT 2.477 : 4359
LT 2.551 : 4695
LT 3.181 : 4742
Gore 302 : 2344
Gore 308 : 1368
Gore 313 : 2954
Gore 313 : 2956
Gore 313 : 2955
Gore 314 : 3285
Gore 315 : 3328
Gore 322 : 5116
Hearne 1 : 27
Habeo : 874
Habeo : 3634
Habeo : 5423b
Habeo : 5432b
Duplicate: 1742
Duplicate: 5726

Appendix III
PROVENANCES AND ITEMS WITH PUBLICATION DATES, 1691-5

There over 700 signatures of other persons in 577 different books, pamphlets or single sheets in the Wood collection. There are five different signers, mainly former owners, in items 362, 1955, 2839, 4552, 5576, 5539, 6138, and 6307, and four, in 4806, 4849, and 5919. Fortunately Wood did not obliterate these names. A few librarians in the Ashmolean Museum and later readers also signed books. For example, the Keeper Edward Lhwyd's signature is in 971 (probably Lhwyd's gift) and 6169; a young worker in the Ashmolean, Giliecholum McMulen, scribbled in 971, 979, and 3185; Browne Willis signed and donated a book which migrated to the Wood collection (4352), and W. Stott wrote his name in 5886.

Where there are consecutive numbers following a name, it generally means that the author gave Wood copies of his works, so after Christopher Davenport, items 2177, 2179, 2180, 2181, 2182, were given to Wood by Davenport. See also the entries of, for example, Payne Fisher, Increase (and Cotton) Mather, and William Sprigge. Booksellers often obtained books from estates of deceased scholars, and this explains the large number of signed items Wood acquired shortly after the deaths of Andrew Allam, Henry Foulis, Barton Holyday, and Gerard Langbaine. Friends or close acquaintances such as John Aubrey, Thomas Blount, Arthur Charlett, Henry Jackson (his distant cousin or uncle), and Ralph Sheldon gave Wood numerous books. Names of female signers are not common and the most prominent is his mother, Mary Wood, who owned sixteen books that went to her collector son (see Intro., p. xv). Other women's names that appear in printed items are Mary Applebee, Frances, Elizabeth and Susanna Ayliffe, Elizabeth Bland, Lady Digbie, Mary Foulis (via her brother Henry), Elizabeth Hales (3), Mary Haythe, Lucy Hesketh, Elizabeth Jobson, Mary Kembele, Dorothy Poole, Grisil Poyntz, Alice Rigby, Mary S—den, Marie Sheldon, Joan Simons, and Margaret Weddsmith (the last may not be a Wood book).

He apparently saved even his earliest acquisitions, mainly schoolbooks, and there are nineteen that he owned before 1650. Almost all have names of former owners or scribbles by friends (e.g., grammar books 4782 and 5576). Three of his early acquisitions have traces of his early bookplate (6, 1179, and 4160). The largest group came from family members. The signatures of his mother are in two and of his brothers Edward and Robert, in four. His brother Christopher signed his name in one (see also Intro., p. xv and note 15). The earliest printed items he may have acquired and saved were ballads by Lawrence Price and Martin Parker published in 1639 and 1640 (703 and 675). He owned Francis Meres's *Witts academy* in 1645 (4447). This item also has signatures of Robert Wood and an attestation from a class mate, 'Anthony Wood his booke Wittnesse John Cowdrey 1645'. A second book that he owned in 1645, *Riders dictionarie* (5576), passed through the hands of 'Robert Holman: amen. 1643', a class mate named Greenbarrow who signed his name in four places, and Edward Wood who signed his name in three different places. A third book which he acquired in the same year is by Alexander Nowell on Christian piety (4782). Wood obtained verification for his ownership from five others: 'Anthony Wood his Booke witness Walter Condery [?] and Adrian Barry [?] and Robert Holman and John Holman and Christopher Wod anen [sic]. 1648'. Edward Wood owned the book apparently before Anthony and signed his name in three different places. Other standard schoolbooks which he owned, most with signatures or names of other owners or readers, are William Lily's *Short Introduction of Grammar* (4160); Thomas Farnaby's book on Latin rhetoric and his edition of Virgil (2950 and 6352); John Bullokar's *English Expositor* in which the young Anthony scribbled his own ballad (1179); Edward Leigh's translation of Suetonius (4083), which apparently served as an aid for his Latin lessons; a calf volume with two printed items by Albertus Magnus formerly owned by Richard

Phillipps and acquired in 1649 (33 and 34); an edition of Gratian on canon law via a person named William Lowedall (3283); an English chronology of kings (2511); two on rhetoric (4329 and 5737); a memento mori (4540); and a sophisticated analysis of Greek tropes by J. Susenbrotus which came from his scholarly brother Edward (6090).

Further information about most of the other owners may be found in standard sources which follow the entries below (see Abbreviations and Conventions, p. 1): AO (including Bliss's edition of Wood's 'Life'), AOF, LT, DNB, F (with page and item numbers), and Venn (with volume and page numbers). Many of the identifications in F are based on circumstantial evidence, and the identifications in Venn are generally even less certain. Where the person may be difficult to identify, e.g., William Smith, the entry number in F may be followed by 'ff.' If the owner was a member of Wood's college, 'Merton' is added.

In general, booksellers are not included in this list. Wood acquired great numbers of books from a number of different booksellers and often included their names in his diaries. On occasion the names also appear in his books and these are recorded in notes to relevant items and are to be found in the general index. Booksellers' marks, idiosyncratic letters or combinations of letters and numbers, occur in 374 items. These are noted in entries by 'bsm' or 'bsms'.

–son, Aegid. : 3210
A., H. : 270
Aldewell, Robert : 5125
Aldridge, John (Venn 1.14?) : 1865
Aldridge, Samuel (related to preceding) : 1865
Alford, William (LT, F 14.38?) : 1150
Allam, Andrew (AO, LT, F 14.27) : 97, 163, 267, 357, 875, 896, 974, 982, 1265, 1266, 1518, 1542, 1578, 2345, 2839, 3071, 3232(?), 3489, 3552, 3648, 3649, 3708, 4346, 4493, 4552, 5142, 5191
Allam, Thomas (AO, LT 2.99, F 15.2) : 1894
Anderedon(?), John (see F 23.31 for John, father of James): 3272
Applebee, Mary : 1387
Argall, John (see Venn 1.38-9 for John, father of Charles and Samuel) : 3730
Ashmole, Elias (AO, LT, F 36.20) : 277, 5943
Astell, Thomas (Venn 1.50?) : 4782
Aubrey, John (AO, LT, DNB, F 44.22) : 91, 100, 371, 1145, 1476, 2347, 3111, 3341, 3620, 3625, 4182, 4767, 5329, 5370, 5374(?), 5400, 5700, 5735, 6408, 6658
Augustine, John : 2839, 4552
Ayliffe (Allyffe, Ayloffe), Frances : 5861
Ayliffe, Elizabeth : 5861
Ayliffe, Susanna : 5861
B., H. : 6665
Bale : 32
Banckes, Richard (F 67.14) : 2392
Banyster (Banister), E. (F 66.6?) : 4018
Barclay, John : 3329
Barcoll (Barcott?), Humphrey : 2063
Barker, Thomas (F 71.37ff.) : 4080
Barksdale, Clement (AO, LT, DNB, F 72.26): 854, 855
Barlow, Thomas (AO, LT, DNB, F 73.18): 362(?), 1149(?), 3024, 5681
Barrelli (Parrelli?) : 4431
Bate (?), Robert (F 87.27?) : 2021
Bathurst, Ralph (AO, LT, DNB, F 87.8) : 5406
Bayly (Baylie), Richard (AO, AOF, LT, F 91.16) : 5426
Bellone(?), Thomas : 1028
Bellott, Ananias : 1049(?)
Benlowes (Bendlowes), Edward (AO, LT, DNB, Venn 1.132) : 943, 945
Bernard, Edward (AO, LT, DNB, F 115.2, Venn 1.140) : 951, 5393, 5375(?)
Bernard, J. A.: 1288(?)
Bernard, William (F 115.19, Merton) : 6063
Bigby [Busby?], William (Busby, F 220.17f.) : 5531
Birdall, Thomas (F 128.7f.) : 6324

Bisse, James : 1288(?)
Bland, Elizabeth : 1387
Blayne, John (not Venn 1.165) : 2763
Blithe, Robert (not Venn 1.171) : 2850
Blount, Thomas (AO, LT): 250, 306, 987, 1014, 2175, 5667, 6556, 6557
Bodley, Thomas (AO, LT, DNB, F 143.37, Merton) : 3091
Boeing(?), Thomas : 4187
Bovett, Richard (F 157.26) : 3399
Bowerman [Bordman, Boreman], Andrew (F 159.42) : 1955
Bracey, Edward (LT) : 4546
Briscoe, William (LT, F 183.35, Merton) : 5530
Bristowe, James (LT?, F 183.40?) : 1893
Briten, John (LT?) : 4139
Brokett, John (LT, F 185.23) : 361
Browne : 1427
Busby, William (LT, F 220.17) : 5531
Cabotta, Sebastian, Venetus : 1049
Camden, William (AO, LT, DNB, F 232.23) : 3244
Campion, John (F 233.12?, Merton?) : 2839, 4552
Cartwright, Richard (London bookseller?) : 1150
Cary, Phillidelpha : 5215
Casaubon, Isaac (AO, AOF, LT, DNB, F 248.9) : 1673
Caverlay, — : 2851
Cawdrey, Robert : 1908
Chadley, William : 2162
Chamberlayne, Richard (LT, F 258.8ff.) : 1418
Chamden, Johannes : 2269
Charlett, Arthur (AO, LT, DNB, F 263.11) : 963, 1287, 1971, 2062, 3435, 3527, 4645, 5153, 5212, 5364, 5413, 5645, 5836
Charlton, Walter (AO, LT, DNB, F 263.32) : 1476
Charte, Richard : 259
Chau-, John : 1955
Chester, William (not Venn 1.330) : 3298
Chiswell, Richard (AO, LT, London bookseller, see items 1616-7) : 6068
Clark (Clarke), Godfrey (F 280.11) : 1369
Clark, Isaacke (Venn 1.342?) : 1125
Clark, John (LT?) : 5919
Cleyton, Thomas (F 288.1ff.) : 5146
Cliffe, Nicolas (F 290.39f.) : 44
Coffins, Francis : 3142
Coke (Cook), Robert (321.35) : 6020
Colby, William (LT, F 300.4, Merton) : 737
Cole, George (LT, F 301.1) : 3822
Cole, Thomas (F 302.1-3) : 4177
Colepeper, John (LT, DNB) : 6138
Collins, John (LT, DNB) : 1952
Collinson, Thomas (F 311.1) : 3678
Colson, mr. : 3757
Colson, Christopher (prob. not Venn 1.371) : 5907
Conant, Malachi (AOF, LT, F 315.25) : 1963
Cop-, John : 2511
Cotton, John (F 334.9?, Venn 1.403 several possibilities) : 4139
Coward, Christopher (AO, LT, F 338.6) : 5273
Cowbye, W. : 2148
Cowdrey, John (LT, F 338.19) : 4447
Crakanthorp, Richard (AO, LT, DNB, F 345.23) : 5244
Creech, Thomas (AO, LT, DNB, F 347.15) : 1483
Creed, Edward : 6356
Creed, William(?) (AO, LT, DNB, F 347.25) : 3719

Cressey, Serenus (Hugh) (AO, LT, DNB, F 348.22, Merton) : 5831
Crew, Nathaniel (AO, AOF, LT, DNB, F 349.13) : 5134
Crew, Thomas (son of preceding, DNB) : 5134
Croft (Crofts), John (LT?, F 351.14f.) : 5215
Cross, Nicholas(?) : 3822
Crouch, James (F 358.4?) : 6171
Crowther, Joseph (AOF, LT, F 359.1)) : 2573
Cruttenden, Henry (LT, F 360.6) : 1440, 1507, 1517, 1543, 1548, 1569, 1582, 1607, 1633, 6000
Cuffe (Guffe), Henry (LT, DNB, F 361.5, Merton) : 3930
Culme, Johannes (F 362.1?) : 4806
Culme, Nicolaus : 4806
Culpeper, John. See Colepeper, John
Cunningham, James (Venn 1.432?) : 2128
Daniell, Henry, 17 Decem. 1634 : 3732
Daudre, William (LT) : 4849
Davenport, Christopher (AO, LT, DNB, F 376.5, Merton) : 2177, 2179, 2180, 2181, 2182
Davis? : 1567
Day, John (AO, LT, DNB, F 387.31) : 29, 1267, 2190, 2191, 2192, 2193
Denton, William (AO, LT, DNB, F 396.25) : 2228, 2229, 2230, 5753
Dewey, William (AO, LT, F.400.18?) : 6268
Dickinson, Edmund (AO, LT, DNB, F 401.38, Merton) : 6553f.
Dier, Richard (LT 1.23, F 437.24f.) : 4851
Digbie, Lady (Anne, Venetia, Lettice? LT 3.90) : 5539
Dod, John (LT?, F 409.33ff.) : 1892
Dolliff, Francis (LT, F 412.27) : 1598
Doughty, John (AO, LT, F 417.5, Merton) : 2297
Dovaston, John : 2034
Dowland, John (AOF, DNB, F 418.27) : 3137
Drope, John (AOF, LT, DNB, F 426.7) : 2307
Dryden, John (AO, LT, DNB, Venn 2.69) : 2320
Dugard, William (AO, DNB, Venn 2.73): 5388
Dugdale, William (AO, AOF, LT, DNB, F 430.11) : 2362, 2363, 2364, 6029, 6710
Dun, Daniel (AO, LT, DNB, F 433.16) : 6502
Dyson, Humphrey (1582-1633, London book collector) : 873, 1165, 1841, 2276, 2870, 4310, 5625, 5801-2, 6058
Eainehill(?), Thomas : 1049(?)
Edwards, Jonathan (?) (AO, LT, DNB, F 449.9) : 6686
Ellis (Elys), Edmund (AO, LT, DNB, F 457.28) : 2441, 4550
Ellis, Thomas (AO, LT, DNB, F 459.7) : 1838
Erskin(?) : 4043
Evans, Thomas (All Souls, a later (1793) reader) : 5592
Everard, Thomas (possibly F 474.24) : 1134
Exton, Edward (LT, F 476.13) : 980
Eyre, William (AO, F 478.12) : 1152, 6090(?)
Fairfax, Thomas (3rd baron) (AO, LT, DNB, F 481.17) : 2905
Fayrfax : 23
Fearne, Peter : 1837
Fell, Philip (AOF, LT, F 490.35) : 3202
Ferrers, Edward (see AO 2.572, F 493.29) : 5115
Fichus, Thomas. See Vicars, Thomas
Fisher, Payne (AO, LT, F 501.1) : 3028, 3029, 3485
Forrest (Forest), Edward (father and son: LT, F 516.26-7) : 1403, 4437
Fortescue, Thomas (LT, F 518.37) : 3074
Foulis, Henry (AO, LT, DNB, F 522.1) : 25, 258, 655, 966, 1063, 1135, 1645, 2017, 3083, 3274, 3678, 4180, 4309, 4481, 5620, 5960, 6303
Foulis, Mary (related to preceding) : 4309
G., L.(?) : 6392
Garret, Anthony : 4540
Gerish, John(?) : 1684

Gibbon, John (LT, DNB, Venn 2.208) : 3206
Gilbert, Thomas (prob. not F 565.26f.) : 6307
Goad, John (AO, LT, DNB, F 574.20) : 6550
Godwin, Francis (AO, LT, DNB, F 584.12) : 3244
Godwin, Joseph (bookseller, AO, LT, F 585.4) : 1150, 2833
Goffe, Henry. See Cuffe, Henry
Gore, Thomas (AO, LT, DNB, F 587.35) : 1513, 1514
Gough, Roger : 1397
Greenbarrow : 5576
Gregory, John (AO, LT, DNB, F 603.11) : 1387
Griffin, Edward (steward to R. Sheldon, LT) : 5585
Grise (Gryse), Charles (Venn 2.265) : 3337
Guidott (Guydot), Thomas (AO, LT, DNB, F 618.3) : 3289, 3341
H., E. : 6550
Hales, Elizabeth (LT, married to George Sheldon, died 4 Oct. 1678) : 2841(?), 3468, 4120
Hales, James (LT) : 339, 4486, 6281
Hall, Henry (LT, F 632.2) : 1654
Hall, William (LT, F 635.14) : 6381
Halley : 6065
Halley, Edmund (AO, LT, DNB, F 635.39) : 100
Hallum, Thomas. See Allam, Thomas
Hamlett, William : 1955
Harford (Herford), John (F 650.29f.) : 5143
Harms, mr. : 4246
Harrington, James (AO, LT, DNB, F 653.35) : 4130, 5097, 6042
Harrison, John (F 661.6ff.) : 5323
Hatton, Christopher (AOF, LT, DNB, F 673.1) : 6138
Haythe, Mary : 5201
Haythe, Thomas : 5201
Herbert, Henry (AOF, DNB, F 695.17, Venn 2.356) : 1892
Herford, John. See Harford, John
Hesketh, Lucy : 4486
Hickmot, Charles (LT, F 704.14) : 2304
Higgs, Griffin (AO, LT, DNB, F 707.27) : 60, 105, 118
Ho., B. : 4314
Hoby, Edward (AO, DNB, F 721.19) : 2426
Hock, George (F 722.22) : 3730
Hodgkins, Thomas : 2301
Holbage, Martin (LT) : 6307
Holbage, Thomas (LT) : 6307
Holder, William (AOF, LT, DNB, F 728.35) : 3633
Holding, Maurice (F 729.3) : 1919
Holiday, Barton (AO, LT, DNB, F 732.29) : 1027, 1169, 1673
Holman, Robert (prob. not F 735.12) : 4782, 5576
Holme, Randolph. See 3702
Hoste, Matthaeus (LT) : 3675
Hoyeter, Jh– : 4189
Huband, John (LT, F 758.21) : 2132
Huggins, [John?] (LT, see F 760.11 and 760.15) : 5973
Hungerford, Robert (LT, F 770.2) : 39
Hurman, Stephen (LT, F 775.15) : 316
Hutton, Timothy (AO?) : 4199
I., W. (?) see W., I. : 176
Ingoldesby (see LT and F 787.6ff.) : 2950
Isaac, Francis (LT, F 790.19) : 3164, 3852, 4143, 6372, 6723
Isacke, Richard (AO, LT, DNB, F 792.17) : 6336
Itchener, William (F 791.14) : 1134
J., S. : 3083
J., T. : 2329

Jackson, Henry (AO, LT, F 794.21) : 193, 224, 304, 363, 1049, 1177, 1843, 2049, 2054, 3210, 3214, 3217, 3339, 3730, 3739, 4214, 5222, 6031, 6234, 6290, 6432, 6587, 6749
Jackson, Richard. See Keurden, Richard
Jackson, Robarte at Baldon : 5548, 5557
Jacob, Henry (AO, AOF, LT, F 797.13, Merton) : 6065
Jacson, Tho. (F 796.12ff.) : 25
James, Thomas (AO, LT, F 800.29) : 2336
Jobson, Elizabeth (see LT) : 362
Johnson, John (F 814.30ff.) : 1427
Johnston, Nathaniel (AO, Venn 2.480) : 3895
Jones, John (F 823.14ff.) : 2839, 3702, 4552, 5582
Jones, Richard : 1397
Joyner, Edward (AO, LT) 3926, 3928
K., P. : 6429
Kembele, Mary : 2022
Kennett, White (AO, LT, DNB, F 844.8) : 1592, 3948
Kettle, Thomas : 4601
Keurden, Richard (or Jackson, R.) (AOF, LT, F 795.33, Venn 2.457) : 5392
Killigrew, William (AO, LT, F 849.26) : 3964
King, Richard (F 853.22ff.) : 5539
Knight, John (F 861.25ff.) : 5839
Knight, Robert (F 862.24ff.) : 5737
L., J. : 3119
L., S. : 5196
L-on, Peter : 2988
Lambert, Thomas (F 871.31ff.) : 4849
Lambourne, William. See Painter, William
Lamphire, John (AOF, LT, F 872.28) : 1552, 4406, 5096, 5258, 6170
Lane, Richard (F 875.17ff.) : 5115
Langbaine, Gerard (AO, LT, F 876.18) : 22, 32, 336, 989, 1385, 1662, 1663, 1665, 2325, 2555, 3031, 3243, 3942, 4094, 4202, 5131, 5141, 5263, 5593, 5675, 5818, 6018, 6057 (see note), 6193, 6268
Laud, William (AO, LT, DNB, F 885.7) : 5426
Lee, John (LT, F 894.2) : 1532, 4308, 6056
Lee, Thomas (F 895.4?, Merton?) : 5115
Lee, William (F 895.13ff.) : 5539
Leigh, Henry (F 897.25ff.) : 2014
Leigh, Samuel (AO, LT, F 899.4, Merton) : 4087
LeOgle, E. J. (?) : 5620
Lewis, John (prob. not LT; F908.6ff.) : 1397
Ley (Leigh), John (AO, F 898.1) : 1522, 3745
Lhwyd, Edward (AO, LT, F 913.13) : 971, 6169, and see 1394
Littleton, Edward (AO, AOF, LT, F 919.19) : 4183, 4184, 4185
Lloyd, David (AOF, F 922.22) : 4554
Lloyd, Thomas (see note at entry; F 930.39ff.) : 4554
Locker, Thomas : 6307
Lockey, Thomas (AO, AOF, LT, F 933.14) : 3810
Lockstone, John : 4187
Loggan, David (AO, LT, DNB, F 935.2) : 4211
Looker, Thomas : 1955
Louis 14, King of France (not a Wood book) : 3642
Lowedall, William : 3283
Lower, Richard (AO, LT, F 943.26) : 5609
Leycestr., Comes : 5531
Lydall, John (AOF, LT, F 952.6) : 5735
M., Edward : 1182
M., H. : 920
Mainwaring, Thomas. See 3702
Mallett, F. G. : 942
Markham, Francis (LT, F 970.32-3?) : 5427

Rigby, Edward (F 1258.10-11) : 4486
Risselsden, Stephen (F 1259.18?) : 6607
Robert –and : 5187
Robins, Thomas (F 1266.13ff.) : 2022
Robinson, Leonard (F 1268.17f.) : 2839, 4552
Robinson, Robert (F 1268.31) : 6540
Robyns, Arthur : 5839
Rock, Josiah. See 3702
Rogers, John (LT, F 1274.17) : 2948
Rogers, William (LT, F 1277.9) : 2181, 2871, 6721
Rowlands, William (LT) : 6354
Royce, William : 366
S-ypp, Richard : 3201
S., G. (Smith, William?) : 6432
S., R. : 1035, 2590
Sadler [Sadleir], George (LT, prob. Venn 4.2) : 1404, 3351, 4142, 4932, 4933, 4935, 4936, 6280, 6433
Sadler, Edward (LT, prob. Venn 4.2) : 6307
Sadler, Theodore (Venn 4.3?) : 6307
St. George, Henry (AO, LT, and see F 1300.26) : 1133
Salmon, Edmund (prob. not Venn 4.8) : 4083
Salmon, Edward (F 1302.36) : 4083
Sandys, Edwin (AO, LT, F 1309.3) : 2258, 5745
Sandys, Henry (LT, F 1309.16) : 5745, 5763
Savile, Thomas (AO, F 1319.23, Merton) : 3930
Scaife, Robert (F 1322.19-20) : 4894
Scourfeild, Winifrid : 362
Selbie, Robert (possibly F 1332.23; prob. not Venn 4.41) : 5532
Selby, William (F 1332.27) : 4567
Serelus (if Serrell, John, then possibly F 1334.13) : 3366
Shelbourne, John : 6309
Sheldon, Frances (AO, LT) : 1068
Sheldon, George (LT) : 3490, 5521
Sheldon, Marie (LT) : 5711
Sheldon, Ralph (of Steeple Barton) (AO, LT, F 1343.10) : 321
Sheldon, Ralph (AO, LT, DNB) : 1226, 1370, 1429, 1529(?), 1614, 1618, 2005, 2006, 2007, 2008, 2057, 2365, 2741, 3242, 4043, 4079, 4843, 5346, 5347, 5600, 5708, 5831 (Cressey to Wood, via Sheldon), 6222, 6317, 6396
Shephy(?), Thomas : 5140
Sherburne, Edward (AOF, LT, F 1347.5) : 93, 4359
Sherlock, Richard (AO, LT, F 1348.19) : 5886, 5887
Shirley, B. (LT 3.407?) : 1494
Shirley, Thomas (AO, LT, M.D. in London) : 1681
Simons, Joan : 6662
Skeffington, John (see F 1360.25) : 1372
Sleddius, Johannes (F 1365.8 and Venn 4.89) : 3273
Smart(?), W. (F 1368.25?) : 4547
Smythe : 6749
Smith [Smithe], Jhon : 5728
Smith, Richard (AO, LT, F 1378.22, Merton) : 1177
Smith, Richard (LT, London bookseller, see items 1616-7) : 6627
Smith, Thomas (F 1382.2?) : 1410
Smith, William (may be 3 different persons) : 1908, 4849 (Oxford printer?), 6432(?)
Smith [Smyth], William (AO, LT, F 1384.7) : 4202
Snell, Nicholas : 2509
Snell, Oliver : 2509
Southcote, Edward (F 1392.26, Merton) : 1874, 4356
Speccott, Edmund (Venn 4.129) : 4806
Speed, John (AO, LT, F 1396.10) : 902, 1842, 6273
Sprigge, William (AO, AOF, LT, F 1401.13) : 6015, 6017

Spring, John: 2495
Sprynevell,Thomas : 6342
St–den(?), Mary : 5201
Stace, Christopher : 2950
Steamyn, Jacomyn : 300
Stobbert, John (?) : 335, 2014
Stott, W. (1766) : 5886
Stubbe, Henry (AO, LT, F 1439.5) : 6071
Styward, Ma. (LT 3.335?, Venn 4.161?) : 4058
Synge, George (AO, F 1452.28) : 6662
T., N. : 6190
Taylor, William (AO 3.519 and F 1464.9?) : 1893
Thomas, Evan (F 1471.13?) : 4301
Thomas, Lambert (see Venn 4.221) : 4849
Thomas, Mr. : 6523
Thomas, Wil.(?) (possibly AO 4.262, AOF 2.248, F 1474.37) : 2867
Thomas, William (Oxford citizen) : 5531
Tobing, Jerome (LT) : 3675
Tozer, Henry (AO, LT 1.444, F 1501.27) : 5745
Trelgon(?), Mynne : 1028
Tryme, George (F 1510.22) : 2905
Twyne, Brian (AO, LT, F 1525.25) : 2250, 2373, 3244
Tyron, Thomas (see Tyroe, F 1528.8 and Venn 4.285) : 2435
Tyrrell, James (AO, LT, F 1528.15) : 4754
Upton, John LT, F 1531.14ff.) : 3559
V., J. : 2590
Vaughan, John (AO, LT 1.209, F 1536.25) : 1892
Vicars [Fichus], Thomas (LT 2.549, stationer in Holywell) : 5230
Vincent, John (son of Augustine; AO 3.375, 503, LT 3.102, 4.297) : 259, 4079
Vincent, Robert (F 1546.23?) : 5115
W. i. (or I., W.) : 156, 176(?)
W., B. : 192
W., D. : 81
W., E. : 181
W., F. : 106
W., S. (?) : 1460
Wagstaffe, John (AO, LT, F 1552.4) : 6376
Walker, Richard (LT, F 1558.6ff.; if Camb., Venn 4.318) : 6307
Walmesley, Thomas (F 1563.8) : 3170
Waltham, Laurence : 1875
Walton, Izaak (AO, DNB; father of Isaac, F 1566.20) : 6437
Ward, I[saiah?] (LT, F 1569.18) : 3380
Warner, Robert (Venn 4.339?) : 2603, 4325, 5895, 6482
Watkins, Richard (AOF, LT, F 1581.16) : 3120
Weddsmith, Margaret : 1642
Wernon (Vernon?), Edmund : 36
West, G[eorge] (F 1600.12, bookseller). See Index
Wheare, John (prob. not F 1608.12) : 5919
Whetcombe, James (F 1609.34) : 4767
Whitby (Witbe), Thomas (Venn 4.385?, see also F 1612.23f.) : 6307
Whorwood, Thomas (AO, LT, F 1625.8) : 5338, 6579
Wickens, William (AO 4.61, LT, F 1625.19) : 1955
Widdowes, Thomas (AO, LT, F 1626.30) : 5539
Wilkinson, Henry (AO, LT, F 1634.2) : 6604, 6605
Williams, John (AO?, F 1640.9) : 1556
Williamson, Caesar (AOF, F 1647.21) : 1257
Willis, Browne (LT 2.188, F 1649.3) : 4352
Wilton, John (AO, LT, F 1658.10, Merton) : 920, 1267, 2194, 4090
Windser, Richard : 1049(?)

Wither, James (F 1664.12f.) : 3479
Withington, Edward (F 1665.27) : 3593
Wood, Christopher (AW's brother) : 4782
Wood, Edward (AW's brother and mentor, F 1670.15) : 6, 226, 4314, 4782, 5576, 6090, 6138
Wood, John (LT) : 6690
Wood, Mary (AW's mother) : 915, 1179, 1712, 2190, 2191, 2192, 2193, 2297, 2519, 2528, 2625, 2963, 3506, 4160, 5827, 6138
Wood, Robert (AW's brother, called 'monsieur' because he spent time in France) : 6, 4160, 4447, 5576, 6065
Wood, Thomas (AW's father) : 2190, 2191, 2192, 2193, 6138
Woolfe, Philip : 2941
Wortley, Francis (AO, LT, F 1682.16) : 6710
Wryght, Richard (F 1687.19ff.) : 1385
Wynn [Wynne], Ellis (see F 1694.10) : 4554
Wynn, Robert (F 1695.27) : 971
Young, Christopher (F 1703.29?) : 5919

PUBLICATION DATES, 1691-5

We know from the publication dates, 1691 to 1695, that Wood acquired 176 printed items during these last five years of his life. We can also be certain of dates of acquisition if they came from an estate sale, such as that of Barton Holiday, Henry Jackson, or Gerard Langbaine; or if he had entered a purchase of a specific item in his diaries, though frequently he entered only the price and not the specific item in his diaries. The dates he wrote in the items themselves do not always indicate when he acquired them. At times he entered the year, or the month, of the printing of an item, or of its arrival in Oxford. These dates must be distinguished from the dates of acquisition.

The following have publication dates of 1691 to 1695.

1691 (39): 89, 106, 156, 225, 278, 906, 983, 988, 1016, 1184, 1223, 1288, 1376, 1537, 1561, 2157, 2310, 2372, 2438, 2946, 3136, 3276, 3277, 3340, 3341, 3371, 3430, 3431, 3937, 4027, 4028, 4305, 4411, 4754, 5058, 5643, 5830, 6686, 6687.

1692 (47): 90, 91, 110, 157, 244, 284, 968, 1076, 1206, 1456, 1495, 1508, 1509, 1577, 2439, 2440, 2589, 3256, 3439, 3440, 3650, 3651, 3652, 3653, 3689, 3818, 3839, 3847, 3926, 3984, 4164, 4306, 4429, 4458, 4561, 4692, 4693, 5059, 5380, 5644, 5688, 5854, 5855, 6169, 6389, 6686, 6687.

1693 (37): 92, 93, 158, 219, 236, 696, 1207, 1438, 1448, 1535, 2441, 3432, 3433, 3654, 4020, 4246, 4281, 4307, 4888, 5009, 5028, 5060, 5088, 5370, 5371, 5372, 5373, 5378, 5756, 5757, 5958, 6106, 6377, 6500, 6533, 6695, 6747.

1694 (32): 19, 94, 107, 111, 159, 266, 1208, 1592, 1655, 2411, 2442, 2443, 3342, 3633, 3634, 3927, 4550, 4677, 4693, 4754, 5061, 5279, 5375, 5376, 5393, 5412, 5413, 5645, 6103, 6205, 6378, 6472.

1695 (21): 95, 160, 183, 1474, 1566, 2260, 2444, 2759, 3948, 4990, 5062, 5379, 5381, 5389, 5415, 5634, 5646, 6131, 6369, 6534, 6728.

Appendix IV
The Bindings in the Wood Collection

The bindings of the 996 volumes containing printed items in the Wood collection in the Bodleian Library are described briefly at the entry of the first item in each volume.[1] The bindings show whether or not 1. Anthony Wood had the volume bound; 2. the Ashmolean Museum had the volume bound; 3. Wood acquired a volume in a parchment cover; 4. Wood acquired a volume bound in calf; or 5. the binding is modern. They also reveal much about the collector himself. He could not afford to buy finely bound volumes and there are none in his collection. He acquired most of his printed items in sheets and during the last years of his life he had his books bound in relatively inexpensive bindings. Those that he did not have bound were sent in bundles to the Ashmolean Museum in 1695 and bound shortly after. Wood's bindings, while inexpensive, have stood up well over the centuries, and he took far better care of the contents of his volumes than did the binders for the Ashmolean Museum (see Intro., pp. xxiv-xxvii).

For volumes that Wood had bound, the parchment spine is noted as are the three types of boards: the plain uncovered pasteboard is described as 'grey'; the same with a brown paper covering is described as 'brown'; and the same with a blue paper covering is described as 'blue'.[2] So also the original flyleaves, mainly marbled paper, are noted if they survive. In practically all of these volumes, Wood's table of contents, usually a short title with the date and sometimes with the author's name, is on the upper flyleaves. Wood wrote Arabic numbers before items in the lists of contents and on the first flyleaves or title pages. In most cases his lists are accurate and still show what is in the volume today. He made very few errors, and if there is a discrepancy between a list and the contents, that is noted in the entry of the first item, (1), in a volume. In a few volumes Wood's brief instructions to his binders are still present. He had most binding done from about 1690 to his death. Earlier he had a few bound in parchment (see item 6268) or in calf (see items 4715 and 4681-4893 a large newsbook series with the first binding in January 1681; probably items 6, 4160, 4314, each with 'A W' stamped on the calf cover; and item 6492). He also had a few covered with

---

[1]For the count of volumes: 859 volumes in the series 1-899 (47 missing (see Intro. xlvif. and note 80 (48 including one non-Wood item) and more than one vol. at 110 (2), 276 (2), 700 (2), 748 (2), 887 (2), and 660 (6), and a gap at 556-8 (minus 3)); and 137 in the following series: Almanacs (6), Diaries (39), and [MS.] B. C. D. E. (92). See also Append. II.

[2]Those in brown paper over pasteboard with parchment spine are (26): 1168, 1608, 2169, 2259, 2411, 2427, 3032, 3329, 3527, 3973, 4095, 4200, 4465, 4551, 5541, 6309, 6556, 5781, 5876, 5970, 5993, 6223, 6311, 6661, 6729, 6246. Those in blue paper over pasteboard and parchment spine are (191): 5, 16, 268, 270, 300, 321, 342, 345, 856, 980, 990, 1072, 1109, 1140, 1148, 1157, 1162, 1186, 1198, 1200, 1225, 1394, 1414, 1418, 1464, 1477, 1485, 1511, 1514, 1518, 1524, 1527, 1537, 1550, 1562, 1575, 1593, 1607, 1614, 1623, 1626, 1640, 1686, 1690, 1692, 1720, 1787, 1834, 1867, 1902, 1920, 1969, 2001, 2028, 2044, 2114, 2162, 2209, 2216, 2255, 2282, 2302, 2320, 2357, 2388, 2394, 2426, 2445, 2460, 2514, 2540, 2570, 2590, 2598, 2617, 2624, 2668, 2722, 2747, 2760, 2765, 2807, 2838, 2866, 2889, 2977, 2982, 3001, 3010, 3011, 3078, 3182, 3236, 3245, 3305, 3356, 3358, 3365, 3368, 3369, 3406, 3542, 3599, 3640 (green, over blue) , 3648, 3694, 3820, 3823, 3850, 3868, 3904, 3936, 4024, 4048, 4058, 4064, 4073, 4099, 4273, 4292, 4305, 4384, 4389, 4441, 4467, 4542, 4593, 4653, 4654, 4701, 4703, 4705, 4706, 4707, 4708, 4718, 4739, 4754, 4758, 4764, 4765, 4766, 4790, 4798, 4840, 4849, 4950, 5150, 5167, 5240, 5304, 5320, 5363, 5420, 5516, 5562, 5572, 5578, 5592, 5623, 5736, 5743, 5747, 5753, 5827, 5883, 5902, 5957, 5968, 5997, 5998, 6002, 6021, 6037, 6081, 6128, 6224, 6274, 6291, 6299, 6312, 6375, 6435, 6477, 6517, 6539, 6545, 6600, 6601. Those with uncovered grey pasteboard and parchment spine are (78): 36, 127, 136, 146, 173, 272, 317, 325, 353, 364, 894, 989, 1124, 1161, 1374, 1402, 1498, 1770, 1916, 1971, 2035, 2189, 2201, 2361, 2402, 2539, 2851, 2988, 3140, 3196, 3210, 3274, 3337, 3478, 3496, 3667, 3764, 3896, 3914, 4041, 4188, 4190, 4214, 4325, 4466, 4531, 4553, 4567, 4616, 4624, 4833, 4896, 5103, 5131, 5270, 5574, 5604, 5647, 5681, 5913, 6057, 6077, 6140, 6168, 6190, 6153, 6162, 6173, 6342, 6366, 6403, 6441, 6446, 6505, 6531, 6550, 6555, 6607. A few have been rebound in modern times in pasteboard: 451, 1158, 1523, 5648, 6648 (the last has marbled paper pasted over the outer covers).

paper bindings, usually marbled paper. A number of these were later wrapped in parchment.[3]

Wood did not have time or money enough to bind all of the bundles in his library and a number of loose bundles of printed items went from Wood's library to the Ashmolean Museum. Wood had arranged most of the items in most of these bundles in his own order and 85 of these bundles were bound shortly after they arrived in 1695. The volumes are easy to identify by their calf bindings with fillets and small stamp decoration, mainly a dragon or floral design, inside the corners formed by the fillets.[4] The volumes are attractive, with the edges of the pages cut evenly, and the bindings have held up as well as those commissioned by Wood, though the contents were not at all as well protected. The binders in their zeal to present a handsome appearance shaped printed items to the bindings rather than the bindings to the printed items. The result is that the binders, by making the edges even, cut into and often destroyed Wood's annotation. At times they also mutilated printed notes in the margins of the pages. Either before or after the volumes were bound, an underkeeper made tables of contents on the upper flyleaves and on the title pages in the manner of Wood, though he numbered the items in Roman numerals, unlike Wood who used only Arabic numbers.

Most bindings described as 'parchment' predate Wood's ownership. For example, almost all of the twenty-three items he acquired from his cousin Henry Jackson were already bound in parchment.[5] These are inexpensive and undistinguished but they served their purpose in protecting the printed pages. Almost all described in the bibliography as 'calf' were purchased in these bindings. Wood was not wealthy enough to afford books bound mainly to show off their 'fine' bindings, but he acquired a number of calf volumes with blind-stamp centrepieces or gold-stamp decoration. A few were given to him by persons far wealthier than he, such as his benefactor Ralph Sheldon. Others in relatively expensive calf he bought from booksellers. A number of Gerard Langbaine's handsomely-bound books came into his possession after Langbaine's death in 1658.[6] Many volumes in calf have typical Oxford bindings. The earliest date from the late sixteenth century and the latest from shortly after 1650.[7] A number of early calf and parchment bindings have manuscript wrappers, manuscripts cut up to strengthen the backing, or manuscript waste used for pastedowns and flyleaves.[8] Other volumes bound in calf may have printer's waste paper, that is, printed sheets not used in printed books, proof sheets, or poorly printed sheets, serving as pastedowns or initial flyleaves.[9] Wood himself did not make use of manuscripts or printer's waste for any purpose, though there are two exceptions

[3]For paper bindings later wrapped in parchment, see 50, 51, 1145, 1642, 1508, 1919, 4203, 4204, 4205, 4381, 4413, 4550, 5273, 5708; or given modern covers (all 39 of his diaries). See Index, 'Wood, A. binding of books'.

[4]See Intro., p. xxvi and notes 37-8; and Index, 'Ashmolean Museum, binding'. Those bound by the Ashmolean Museum are (85 including 12 bound in rough (reversed) calf): 31, 32, 57, 337, 352, 855, 921, 961, 1027, 1057, 1206, 1207, 1376, 1531, 1736, 1769, 1829, 1864, 2021, 2156, 2181, 2203, 2362, 2363, 2365, 2461, 2512, 2555 (rough calf), 2709, 2719, 2948, 2970 (rough calf), 3030, 3044, 3082, 3090, 3111 (rough calf), 3115, 3136, 3185, 3338, 3348, 3483, 3549 (rough calf), 3604 (rough calf), 3618, 3708, 3821, 3829, 3855, 4001 (rough calf), 4057, 4285, 4353, 4743, 4827, 4894, 4908, 5127, 5161 (rough calf), 5231, 5301, 5326, 5519 (rough calf), 5549 (rough calf), 5582, 5888, 5908, 5961, 5975, 6007, 6032, 6105, 6401, 6423, 6449, 6451, 6457, 6458, 6478, 6492, 6530 (rough calf), 6634, 6685, 6712 (rough calf).

[5]All but one are in parchment volumes (see item numbers after Jackson in Appendix III). For more on early bindings, see Intro. p. xxiii and note 31.

[6]The following are more expensive bindings, with stamp centrepieces, or with marks of particular owners or pseudo-owners: 23, 57 (R. Sheldon), 845 (F. Sheldon), 920, 1169, 1226 (R. Sheldon), 1264 (R. Sheldon), 1265, 1267, 1387 (Charles, prince of Wales), 2008 (R. Sheldon), 2057 (R. Sheldon), 2128, 2513, 3031 (G. Langbaine), 3201, 3242 (R. Sheldon), 3243 (G. Langbaine), 3244 (B. Twyne?), 3282, 3283, 3675 (Bohemian and Saxon associations), 3930, 4043 (R. Sheldon), 4079 (R. Sheldon), 4094 (G. Langbaine), 4189, 4202 (G. Langbaine), 4433, 4776, 4782, 5146, 4189 (Charles rex), 5279, 5347 (R. Sheldon), 5557, 5711 (Sheldon), 5847, 5920 (G. M.), 6216 (R. P.), 6222 (R. Sheldon), 6244, 6317 (R. Sheldon). The following have some gold-stamp decoration: 1436, 1480, 2057, 2515, 3242, 3516, 3923, 4079, 4555, 5143, 5243, 5307, 5512, 5319, 5343, 5576, 5750, 6065, 6138, 6625, 6598, 6607 (the last, parchment).

[7]Oxford bindings are: 222, 1373, 1413, 1647, 2192, 2509, 3031, 3065, 3164, 3504, 3543, 3728, 4160, 4194, 4237, 4372, 4834, 5122, 5193 (green colouring on edges), 5313, 5430(?), 5497(?), 5856, 5858; and all volumes bound by the Ashmolean.

[8]Those with manuscript material are: 89, 171, 213, 339, 361, 899 (illum. ms.), 1265 (ms. backing), 2200, 2435, 3137, 3173, 3232, 3283, 3559, 3728, 3929, 3559, 4139, 4286, 4438, 4552, 4823, 5115, 5539, 5560, 5987, 6269, 6307, 6346, 6349.

[9]Printer's waste is found at: 30, 34, 226, 243, 286, 547, 893, 896, 907, 971, 1179, 1627, 1686, 1837, 1893, 2148, 2192, 2255, 2435, 2844, 3078, 3164, 3243, 3409, 3578, 3584, 3603, 3702, 3985, 4008, 4063, 4070 (Sidney's *Apologie*, 4085, 4143, 4308, 4313, 4314, 4372, 4416, 4540, 4702, 4703, 4704, 4707, 4708, 4776, 5307, 5430, 5532, 5539, 5625, 5735, 5857, 5957, 6256, 6282.

when he used blank excise forms for backing: at 547 and 769. Chain holes in calf volumes are frequent and indicate earlier binding. There is no indication that Wood ever used chains. Clasps or clasp holes that remain on any parchment or calf volumes are recorded in the notes.

At times Wood wished to bind items of smaller sizes into volumes in which the predominant size was large quarto or octavo. He then either made himself or had his binder make a template of the predominant size and pasted the item on to the template so that it would fit evenly in the volume. This appears in forty-six items.[10] On occasion he inserted a folio sheet into a quarto volume. Such a folio may be folded four or more times to fit into the quarto volume. On at least one occasion he resisted doing this and put the folio elsewhere (see Intro. p. xxvii and note 39).

Serious problems have resulted from the theft of both complete volumes and of particular printed items from bound volumes. Some volumes were removed before the preparation of the Whiteside catalogue in 1716-7. These caused gaps in the catalogue and there is no way to determine the contents of these volumes.[11] Thefts after the catalogue was made are easier to document. Almost all occurred while the Wood collection was still in the Ashmolean Museum. They were first noted in an inventory commissioned by the Keeper P. B. Duncan and carried out between 1837 and 1841 by the Underkeeper, William Kirtland. All missing items noted by Kirtland are recorded in both item (1) of the volume and at the location of the item within a volume. Appendix II lists all missing items. Some less serious problems were caused after 1860 when it was thought that particular items, certain newsbooks and works by Cotton and Increase Mather, should be removed to more specialized Hope and Mather collections (see items 2598, 2624, 4697, 6153, and 4411-14, and Plate I). These items have since been restored to their Wood locations.

It is fortunate that in more recent times the stewardship of the two institutions, the Ashmolean Museum and the Bodleian Library, has been exemplary. The first years were the most dangerous for the books, but since 1837 the collection has been stable. One volume, Wood 531, disappeared from the J-Floor stacks in 1994 (see Append. II, intro.). No volume can be declared 'lost' or 'stolen' for at least a decade since it may have been misplaced in the stacks themselves and not be restored to its correct location for an indeterminate time, sent to conservation and hidden in the labyrinthian piles of volumes that need repair (ten-year removals for restoration are not unknown), or removed for special research and for one reason or another not yet returned.

---

[10]Those pasted on to larger templates are: 114, 284, 348, 894, 895, 912, 938, 1110, 1157, 1161, 1175, 1212, 1264, 1410, 1690, 1835, 2044, 2056, 2132, 2161, 2168, 2170, 2189, 2329, 2345, 2460, 3011, 3257, 3358, 3368, 3383, 3647, 4214, 4567, 4826, 5487, 5623, 5649, 5843, 5978, 6057, 6161, 6312, 6361, 6495, 6629.

[11]See Appendix II, intro. Vacancies in 1716 were at Wood 276, 399, 400, 449, 692, [MS.] Wood C. 50. See notes at items 374, 741, 4430, 4498, 4501-2. Some of these vacancies were filled with Wood's own books; others were filled with non-Wood books and may have publication dates after 1695. Intrusions are at 1394, 1425, 1509(?), 2320(?), 3231(?), 3642, 3702 (Wood 723b; see also note at 4352). More obvious intrusions, and not entered in this current *Library* are at e.g., Wood 11a, 11b, and 11c (see note at 5703), 276a(404b-c) (see note at 5028), 276a(406b) (see note at 5017), 276a(577) (see note at 6354), 276c-e, 428b-428e, in the 660 series (g-s), 723b (623B in *LT*, 1.9.), and [MS.] Wood E. 34.

Appendix V
THE 'RARE' BOOKS
IN THE WOOD COLLECTION

There are well over 1000 publications that we would not have if Anthony Wood had not acquired, preserved, and bequeathed them to the Ashmolean Museum.[1] Most were printed in England and are either not in the current catalogues of books printed before 1700, the STC, Wing, N & S, or the ESTCR on-line catalog, or are listed in these catalogues as being present only in the Bodleian Library. These are designated in the entries of the Wood bibliography by '(rare)' after the STC, Wing, ESTCR, or N & S numbers.

Of these rare publications, 186 are not listed in the current editions the STC, Wing, or N & S.[2] 823 printed items are listed and, at the present time, are known to exist in one location, the Bodleian Library. Seventy-eight of these are in the STC and 742 are in Wing (and three in N & S).[3] In 117 cases, the Bodleian holds more than one copy, though this is generally not recorded in the catalogues. The second

---

[1] A 'rare' item is one that is known, according to editors of the standard catalogues, to exist in only one location. There are 1143 such in the Wood collection. A breakdown of the rare items is: 186 unrecorded in standard catalogues; 823 known to exist only in the Bodleian Library according to standard catalogues; fifty-eight ballads formerly at Wood 399 and 400 known to exist only at their present locations (Roxburghe and Euing collections); thirteen 'rare' garlands now lost and perhaps still in the Bodleian Library; and sixty-three continental books not known to exist in the standard catalogues. For details, see text below.

[2] Of these 186, sixteen items, mainly single sheet ballads and other ephemeral publications, have been added to the on-line ESTCR since the appearance of the latest printed editions of the standard catalogues. These are item numbers: 444, 539, 548, 560, 619, 637, 757, 769, 823, 1092, 1113, 1579, 1621, 2260, 2665, 5953. Of the remaining 170 items, thirty-five are among the missing books, all ephemera. The remaining 135 were not entered on the on-line catalogue before the end of A.D. 2000 but will be added in the near future. The 135 which have been submitted to the ESTCR editors are (the missing, not sent to the ESTCR, are noted by (M)): 19, 99, 127, 130, 346, 455, 499, 520, 521, 653, 654, 655, 657, 673, 726, 753, 817, 871 (M), 886, 931, 973, 1092 (M), 1111 (M), 1280, 1288, 1290, 1291, 1303, 1304, 1318, 1319, 1320, 1321, 1331, 1335, 1341, 1345, 1346, 1349, 1352, 1356, 1358, 1359, 1360, 1366, 1391 (M), 1446, 1451, 1453, 1454, 1490, 1491, 1505, 1581, 1606, 1619, 1620, 1768, 1822, 1850, 1852, 1956 (M), 2416, 2532, 2543, 2549, 2567, 2573, 2702, 2780, 2794, 2916, 2958, 2959, 3007 (M), 3008 (M), 3043, 3085, 3116 (M), 3117 (M), 3131, 3143 (M), 3144, (M) 3154 (M), 3157 (M), 3179 (M), 3241, 3254 (M), 3340, 3429, 3456, 3577 (M), 3673 (M), 3723, 3748, 3754, 3850, 3892, 3893, 4193, 4271, 4276, 4294 (M), 4327 (M), 4350, 4377 (M), 4410, 4415(?), 4452, 4455 (M), 4458, 4529 (M), 4530, 4575, 4627, 4881, 4890, 4950, 4965, 4970, 5006, 5031, 5032, 5033, 5034, 5035, 5036, 5098, 5100, 5129 (M), 5267, 5272 (M), 5289 (M), 5298, 5318, 5352, 5355 (M), 5356 (M), 5375, 5376, 5387, 5392, 5401, 5405, 5408, 5409, 5414, 5529, 5547, 5595, 6029, 6039, 6175 (M), 6176, 6192 (M), 6233 (M), 6343 (M), 6358, 6501, 6536, 6537 (M), 6558, 6642 (M), 6664 (M), 6672, 6680 (M), 6682, 6707, 6741, 6747.

[3] The 78 rare STC books are: 74, 184, 376, 513, 525, 572, 587, 624, 660, 672, 675, 676, 677, 678, 680, 702, 703, 754, 778, 786, 846, 873, 935, 958, 1095, 1109, 1293, 1315, 1327, 1340, 1343, 1350, 1363, 1365, 1367, 1527, 1645, 2203, 2215, 2351, 2510, 2515, 2870, 3081, 3222, 3274, 3296, 3563, 3690, 3884, 3889, 4287, 4325, 4384, 4434, 4891, 4898, 5063, 5064, 5065, 5066, 5068, 5069, 5070, 5071, 5231, 5266, 5361, 5505, 5561, 5827, 5860, 5974, 6120, 6143, 6195, 6291, 6356.

The 741 rare Wing books are: 8, 9, 10, 11, 14, 39, 45, 46, 51, 63, 96, 99, 107, 114, 116, 117, 127, 130, 164, 174, 185, 191, 265, 284, 294, 326, 332, 347, 356, 377, 379, 381, 385, 386, 389, 391, 392, 398, 399, 400, 402, 404, 410, 412, 415, 416, 418, 420, 422, 423, 424, 426, 427, 428, 431, 433, 434, 438, 439, 442, 443, 449, 450, 451, 452, 454, 455, 457, 463, 482, 483, 484, 485, 487, 489, 493, 497, 498, 500, 501, 502, 503, 504, 505, 506, 512, 514, 515, 516, 518, 519, 522, 523, 524, 526, 527, 529, 533, 535, 536, 537, 538, 541, 542, 543, 545, 546, 549, 552, 553, 556, 557, 559, 561, 569, 570, 571, 572, 573, 574, 575, 578, 580, 581, 582, 585, 586, 589, 590, 591, 592, 596, 597, 598, 599, 600, 601, 602, 603, 604, 605, 606, 607, 618, 621, 622, 623, 627, 628, 629, 630, 634, 635, 636, 638, 639, 644, 645, 647, 648, 649, 650, 652, 656, 661,

copy in the Bodleian may not be in the Wood collection, though Wood owned all six known copies of John Aubrey's prospectus, *Proposals for printing Monumenta Britannica* (5371ff.); all four of *The representation of colonell Inglesby's regiment in . . . Oxford* (3760ff.); and all three of the ballads *Epulae Oxonienses* (by Edmund Gayton, 504ff.) and *The goddesses glory* (514ff.).

Single sheet ballads form the largest group of the rare items, 233 of the 478 now in the Bodleian Library. Not included in this count are the fifty-eight rare ballads at one time in the volumes Wood 399 and Wood 400, both stolen before 1837.[4] Oxford items form the second largest group of rare items. He owned 550 publications concerning Oxford, mainly the university, and 186 are rare (most, 132, are found in the Oxford section 4862-5088; see Intro., p. xx and note 26). Other rare books are thirty-five pamphlets of riddles, proverbs, romances, jests, garlands, and pleasant histories (see Intro., p. xxi for these and for the lost thirteen garlands in Wood 94, a volume stolen before 1837); thirty-nine of the seventy-nine Cambridge act verses that he acquired at one time; twenty-nine prospectuses or specimen pages (including six of Aubrey's *Proposals*); eighteen catalogues (including six concerning books published at the Sheldonian Theatre), and sixteen almanacs.

While Wood's research and interests were focused on the domestic English scene and particularly on Oxford, he nevertheless formed a respectable collection of books printed on the continent, 300 in all. Sixty-three of these are not in the British Library catalogue or in any standard catalogue (NUC, BN, VD, or Adams).[5] Twenty-six others not in the British Library catalogue are found in one of the standard catalogues.

662, 666, 668, 670, 671, 679, 681, 686, 687, 688, 689, 690, 691, 697, 698, 700, 705, 706, 708, 709, 710, 715, 716, 717, 720, 722, 723, 724, 725, 730, 731, 732, 734, 749, 750, 751, 752, 755, 756, 758, 759, 761, 763, 764, 765, 767, 768, 770, 771, 773, 779, 780, 783, 784, 787, 788, 791, 793, 794, 797, 802, 803, 804, 805, 806, 807, 808, 809, 811, 812, 813, 814, 816, 819, 825, 832, 835, 838, 839, 843, 864, 865, 885, 900, 907, 930, 945, 949, 959, 960, 974, 985, 988, 997, 998, 1005, 1037, 1076, 1091, 1102, 1154, 1222, 1228, 1263, 1278, 1282, 1289, 1294, 1295, 1297, 1298, 1299, 1301, 1305, 1306, 1310, 1312, 1313, 1314, 1316, 1322, 1323, 1325, 1326, 1328, 1329, 1330, 1332, 1338, 1339, 1342, 1347, 1353, 1354, 1355, 1357, 1438, 1448, 1455, 1466, 1471, 1507, 1519, 1566, 1588, 1589, 1590, 1591, 1592, 1608, 1638, 1650, 1654, 1656, 1666, 1674, 1688, 1724, 1737, 1739, 1748, 1765, 1808, 1853, 1854, 1876, 1877, 1878, 1879, 1887, 1888, 1889, 1917, 1920, 1929, 1937, 1966, 1999, 2034, 2058, 2065, 2104, 2106, 2108, 2123, 2137, 2138, 2139, 2144, 2145, 2176, 2179, 2180, 2197, 2216, 2219, 2235, 2256, 2281, 2286, 2290, 2308, 2309, 2320, 2326, 2327, 2385, 2393, 2417, 2436, 2437, 2438, 2439, 2442, 2443, 2505, 2552, 2574, 2575, 2576, 2577, 2684, 2685, 2732, 2768, 2775, 2777, 2778, 2779, 2808, 2831, 2832, 2873, 2874, 2875, 2959, 2990, 2993, 3020, 3021, 3022, 3024, 3029, 3030, 3046, 3075, 3089, 3101, 3113, 3121, 3128, 3129, 3141, 3145, 3156, 3180, 3181, 3188, 3190, 3197, 3198, 3207, 3213, 3221, 3252, 3253, 3271, 3300, 3327, 3330, 3331, 3342, 3360, 3412, 3415, 3478, 3491, 3494, 3534, 3538, 3568, 3601, 3602, 3610, 3642, 3671, 3682, 3695, 3756, 3757, 3758, 3759, 3760, 3761, 3762, 3763, 3806, 3812, 3818, 3847, 3926, 3927, 3943, 3972, 3973, 3986, 4088, 4146, 4151, 4175, 4203, 4205, 4229, 4236, 4239, 4246, 4259, 4266, 4270, 4282, 4338, 4350, 4351, 4362, 4363, 4395, 4429, 4432, 4435, 4440, 4460, 4478, 4508, 4524, 4525, 4586, 4592, 4618, 4626, 4639, 4657, 4772, 4780, 4812, 4863, 4867, 4869, 4873, 4874, 4875, 4883, 4885, 4886, 4887, 4888, 4914, 4915, 4916, 4920, 4922, 4923, 4924, 4925, 4926, 4927, 4928, 4929, 4930, 4931, 4942, 4951, 4952, 4953, 4954, 4955, 4956, 4958, 4959, 4960, 4961, 4962, 4963, 4964, 4966, 4967, 4968, 4969, 4971, 4972, 4973, 4974, 4975, 4976, 4977, 4978, 4979, 4981, 4982, 4983, 4986, 4990, 4991, 4993, 4994, 4999, 5000, 5001, 5002, 5003, 5004, 5005, 5006, 5007, 5008, 5009, 5011, 5012, 5013, 5014, 5015, 5021, 5022, 5023, 5024, 5025, 5026, 5027, 5029, 5030, 5037, 5038, 5039, 5040, 5041, 5042, 5043, 5044, 5045, 5046, 5047, 5048, 5049, 5050, 5051, 5052, 5053, 5054, 5055, 5056, 5057, 5058, 5059, 5060, 5061, 5062, 5072, 5075, 5076, 5077, 5080, 5082, 5084, 5085, 5087, 5088, 5097, 5128, 5181, 5183, 5184, 5185, 5214, 5241, 5277, 5292, 5304, 5352, 5357, 5368, 5370, 5371, 5372, 5373, 5374, 5377, 5378, 5379, 5380, 5383, 5386, 5388, 5389, 5390, 5391, 5393, 5394, 5395, 5397, 5398, 5399, 5404, 5407, 5410, 5412, 5413, 5415, 5418, 5490, 5491, 5534, 5535, 5542, 5551, 5582, 5603, 5604, 5609, 5611, 5622, 5623, 5627, 5645, 5646, 5647, 5688, 5708, 5734, 5765, 5771, 5803, 5848, 5882, 5885, 5887, 5889, 5899, 5942, 5953, 5962, 5977, 6083, 6096, 6107, 6155, 6157, 6158, 6197, 6201, 6205, 6207, 6208, 6241, 6285, 6296, 6305, 6306, 6316, 6337, 6338, 6358, 6386, 6425, 6465, 6472, 6498, 6523, 6527, 6572, 6599, 6645, 6673, 6678, 6691, 6719, 6731, 6755. The three rare N & S items are: 1561, 1564, 4656.

[4]233 of the 478 ballads in the Bodleian Library are rare, and 58 of the 97 located in the Roxburghe and Euing collections are rare. The ratios of single recorded items in each location, in and out of the Bodleian, are consistent. For a discussion of these volumes and the list of contents, see also Intro., p. xxi, and note 28; Appendix II; and N. Kiessling, 'The Location of Two Lost Volumes of Ballads, Wood 399 and Wood 400', *BLR*, 15 (April 1996): 260-91. In the list of these stolen ballads on pp. 277ff., the rare ballads are noted by (1) after the STC or Wing references. 745 of his 1144 rare items are single sheets.

[5]Those not in the BL or standard catalogues are: 24, 31, 61, 69, 76, 77, 78, 79, 105, 221, 226, 259, 941, 1118, 1164, 1182, 1403, 1498, 1524, 1533, 1534, 1610, 1618, 1640, 1644, 1874, 1965, 2129, 2148, 3065, 3080, 3090, 3091, 3283, 3587, 3605, 3606, 3877, 4002, 4003, 4082, 4415(?), 4439, 4819, 4822, 4849, 5116, 5143, 5146, 5297, 5408, 5600, 5725, 5735, 5831, 5920, 6170, 6282, 6357, 6635, 6665, 6720, 6722.

In sum, Wood collected what few others were interested in. Without his collection we would have much less knowledge of especially the city and university of Oxford and of the ephemeral publications available for a general seventeenth-century audience. Major contemporary collectors who were interested in ephemera were uncommon; Pepys is the major exception. College or university keepers frowned upon these publications and made no effort to acquire them.

Appendix VI
THE PLACES OF PUBLICATION

Eighty per cent of Wood's printed items, 5354, were printed in London or were judged by editors of the STC, Wing or the ESTCR to have been printed in London. Ten per cent, 684, were printed in Oxford (a newsbook, item 4715, was printed in Oxford and London). 173 others were printed in Great Britain, Ireland, or the U.S., and 312 were printed on the continent.

There are also 200 items which have no city of publication and the majority of these were published in London (the 161 in English and many of the thirty-four in Latin were printed in England; four were printed in France, items 1874, 3080, 3877, and 4822; and one in Germany, item 1965). There are thirty-six which are lost and have a '?' at the place of publication.

Printed in Great Britain, Ireland, or the U.S. (except London).

Aberdeen: 9, 10, 2120, 2298.

Aqua Forti. See Bath.

Bath: 3342, Aqua Forti [i.e., Bath] 3892.

Boston in New-England: 4398, 4413.

Bristol: 3699.

Cambridge (122): 65, 66, 67, 68, 118, 119, 120, 121, 122, 123, 124, 125, 126, 178, 179, 213, 214, 1228, 1281, 1282, 1287, 1288, 1289, 1290, 1291, 1292, 1293, 1294, 1295, 1296, 1297, 1298, 1299, 1300, 1301, 1302, 1303, 1304, 1305, 1306, 1307, 1308, 1309, 1310, 1311, 1312, 1313, 1314, 1315, 1316, 1317, 1318, 1319, 1320, 1321, 1322, 1323, 1324, 1325, 1326, 1327, 1328, 1329, 1330, 1331, 1332, 1333, 1334, 1335, 1336, 1337, 1338, 1339, 1340, 1341, 1342, 1343, 1344, 1345, 1346, 1347, 1348, 1349, 1350, 1351, 1352, 1353, 1354, 1355, 1356, 1357, 1358, 1359, 1360, 1361, 1362, 1363, 1364, 1365, 1366, 1367, 1434, 2461, 3516, 3564, 3635, 4025, 4269, 4333, 4382, 4510, 4551, 5778, 5884, 6217, 6218, 6248, 6351, 6361, 6709, 6121, 3137.

[East Ham, not] Lovaine: 3581.

Edinburgh (21): 741, 742, 743, 744, 745, 746, 747, 970, 1152, 2488, 3820, 4340, 4512, 4531, 4532, 4538, 5395, 5801, 5804 [?], 6502, 6690.

Eleutheropoli: 3580.

England: 2526, 6629, and see Rouen.

Fawsley: 4376.

Ipswich: 5420.

Lovaine. See East Ham.

Oxford (684): 11, 58, 117, 190, 191, 234, 240, 241, 244, 249 [?], 255, 293, 303, 304, 305, 354, 355, 403, 473 [?], 500, 501, 502, 503, 504, 505, 506, 594, 846, 855, 857, 858, Mongomery, heretofore called Oxford [really London] 872, 883, 884, 890, 943, 944, 945, 947, 948, 951, 952, 965, 972, 976, Mongomery [i.e., Oxford but really London] 992, Mongomery [i.e., Oxford but really London] 993, 995, 999, 1012, 1023, 1024, London [i.e., Oxford] 1040, 1091, 1092, 1108, 1130, 1154, 1175, 1181, 1187, 1213, 1222, 1229, 1251, (Oxford, reprinted f. the U. of Cambridge) 1279, 1379, 1404, 1411, 1413, 1420, 1427, 1428, 1436, 1438 [?], 1455, 1490 [?], 1491, 1494, 1508, 1509, 1513, 1514, 1523, 1531, 1532, 1538, 1539, 1583, 1584, 1585, 1588, 1589, 1592, 1627, 1634, 1650, 1654, 1674, 1710, 1711, 1713, 1718, 1719, 1720, 1732, 1733, 1734, 1735, 1736, 1737, 1738, 1739, 1740, 1741, 1742, 1743, 1744, 1745, 1746, 1748, London [Oxford] 1755, 1815, 1820, 1840, 1849, 1883, 1890, 1896, 1898, 1910, 1927, 1929, Oxford [London] 1963, 2002, 2013, 2023, 2042, 2116, 2117, 2142, 2143, 2165, 2166, 2184, 2190, 2191, 2192, 2193, 2194, 2200, 2222, 2226, 2259, 2261, 2297, 2307 [?], 2308, 2309, 2310, 2316, 2324, 2325, 2326, 2327, 2329, 2345, 2348, 2349, 2351, 2353, 2354, 2361, 2366, 2373, 2374, [prob.] 2400, 2429, 2436 [?], 2437, 2466 [?], 2468, 2478, 2527, 2528, 2529, 2574, 2575, 2576, 2577, 2619, 2620, 2623, 2628, 2630, 2644, 2645, 2650, 2651, 2652, 2653, 2655, 2656, 2660, 2661, 2662, 2663, 2664, 2665, 2675, 2745, 2783, London [Oxford?] 2787, 2800, 2905, 2910, 2911, 2913, 2927, 2928, 2946, 2986, 2987, 2988, 3002, 3005, 3020 [?], 3032, 3050, 3085, 3110, 3111, 3115, 3131, 3136, 3180 [?], 3181 [?], 3196, 3247, 3248, 3252, 3253, 3262, 3288, 3291, 3302, 3351, 3355, 3402, 3410, 3411, 3415, 3416, 3428, 3434, 3435, 3437, 3441 [?], 3504, 3505, 3543, 3545, 3546, 3547, 3548, 3549, 3550, 3551, 3578, 3598, 3608, 3609, 3629, 3637, 3638, 3657, 3660, 3668, 3698, 3706, 3707, 3708, 3709, 3718, 3726, 3737, 3801, 3816, 3852, 3853, 3854 [?], 3912, 3926, 3927, 3943, 3944, 3948, 3966, 3975, 4021, 4022, 4026, 4027, 4028, 4052, 4053, 4055, 4063, 4083, 4089, 4098, 4160, 4166, 4181, 4182, 4187, 4210, 4211, 4248, 4283, 4297, 4301, 4329, 4338, 4381, 4389, 4404, 4405, 4406, 4408, 4409, 4426, 4435, 4442, 4524 [?], 4525 [?], 4553, 4561, 4577, 4586, 4624, 4653, 4654, 4657, 4658, 4697, 4698, 4710, Oxford and London 4715, 4724, 4750, Oxon [really London] 4785, 4826, 4855, 4863, 4867, 4868, 4869, 4870, 4871, 4872, 4873, 4874, 4875, 4881, 4884, 4885, 4886, 4887, 4888, 4893, 4894, 4895, 4896, 4897, 4898, 4900, 4901, 4903, 4905 [?], 4911, 4914, 4915, 4916, 4919, 4920, 4922, 4923, 4924, 4925, 4926, 4927, 4928, 4929, 4930, 4931, 4932, 4933, 4934, 4935, 4936, 4937, 4938, 4939, 4940, 4941, 4944, 4945, 4946, 4947, 4948, 4949, 4950, 4952, 4953, 4954, 4955, 4956, 4957, 4958, 4959, 4960, 4961, 4962, 4963, 4964, 4965, 4966, 4967, 4968, 4969, 4970, 4971, 4972, 4973, 4974, 4975, 4976, 4977, 4978, 4979, 4980, 4981, 4982, 4983, 4984, 4985, 4986, 4987, 4988, 4989, 4990, 4994, 5001, 5002, 5003, 5004, 5005, 5006, 5007, 5008, 5009, 5010, 5011, 5012, 5013, 5014, 5015, 5016, 5017, 5018, 5019, 5020, 5021, 5022, 5023, 5024, 5025, 5026, 5027, 5028, 5029, 5030, 5031, 5032, 5033, 5034, 5035, 5036, 5037, 5038, 5039, 5040, 5041, 5042, 5043, 5044, 5045, 5046, 5047, 5048, 5049, 5050, 5051, 5052, 5053, 5054, 5055, 5056, 5057, 5058, 5059, 5060, 5061, 5062, 5063, 5064, 5065, 5066, 5067, 5068, 5069, 5070, 5071, 5072, 5073, 5074, 5075, 5076, 5077, 5078, 5079, 5080, 5081, 5082, 5083, 5084, 5085, 5086, 5087, 5088, 5090, 5091, 5092, 5096 [?], 5098, 5100, 5105, 5117, 5123, 5132, 5133, 5138, 5151, 5157, 5162, 5189, 5237, 5249, 5258, 5275, 5277 [?], 5279, 5314, 5326, 5338, 5349, 5361, 5362, 5363, 5364, 5365, 5375, 5376, 5377, 5393, 5413, 5415, 5475, 5477, 5478, 5497, 5511, 5571, 5578, 5611, 5626, 5650, 5652, 5676, 5680, 5722, 5737, 5744, 5747, 5749, 5763, 5769, 5771, 5825, 5857, 5876, 5877, 5911, 5932, 5946, 5947, 5956, 5958, 5961, 5995, 5999, 6000, 6069, 6074, 6076, 6079, 6103, 6128, 6129, 6131, 6138, 6152, 6153, 6154, 6155, 6156, 6157, 6158, 6159, 6177, 6188, 6196, 6226, 6238, 6239, 6241 [?], 6247, 6268, 6280, 6284, 6287, 6297, 6304, 6305, 6306, 6313, 6339, 6340, 6369, 6379, 6381, 6402, 6403, 6423, 6424, 6425, 6430, 6431, 6444, 6474, 6475, 6479, 6480, 6481, 6531, 6538, 6540, 6572, Oxford [really London] 6583, Oxford [really London] 6584, 6598, 6603, 6604, 6620, 6621, Oxford [London] 6633, 6650, 6681, 6684, 6685, 6688, 6689, 6694, 6699, 6717, 6723, 6731, 6747, 6752, 6753, 6754.

Roan [i.e., England]: 306.

Rochester: 3841.

York: 192 [?], 1648, 1918.

Printed on the continent.

Amsterdam (30): 61, 69, 105, 226, 968, 1199, 1214, 1415, 1533, 1534, 2129, 2162, 2253, 2521, 2591, Lutetiae Parisiorum [really Amsterdam] 3329, 3497, 3914, 4305, 4306, 4391, 4412, 4819, 4854, 5550, 5916, [Dantisci, i.e., Amsterdam] 5972, 6354, 6352, 6665.

Antwerp (28): [Geneva, i.e., Antwerp] 362, 873, 921, 1424, 1791, 2255, 3092, 3172, 3218, 3719, 3720, 3930, 4071, 4169, 4177, 4387, 4439, 4783, 4824, 4833, 5119, 5548, 5620, 5728, 6030, 6031, 6462 (London?), 6617.

Arras: 5116.

Augsburg: 290.

Basil (12): 2839, 4552, 1848, 2289, 2854, 3044, 3728, 3739, 4286, 5539, 6324, 6346.

Bern: 1403, 4018.

Bologna: 6234.

Colloniae. See Paris.

Dantisci, see Amsterdam.

Delft: 3540.

Dordrecht: 5510.

Douai (12): 243, 942, 1150, 2177, 2178, 2181 [?], 2182, 3710, 4078, 6032, 6310, 6344.

Emden. See Geneva.

Erfurt: 6635.

Francfurt am Main (14): 220, 932, 961, 1169, 1437, 1498, 2199, 3031, 3185, 3500, 4820, 5252, 5678, 6282.

Francfurt an der Oder: 3675.

Franeker: 2311.

Freistadt: 1611.

Gent: 6063.

Geneva. See Antwerp.

Geneva: 37, 2054, 5920, 2850, 5296, [Emden, i.e., Geneva] 6758.

Haag (s'Gravenhage): 408, 2296, 2383, 3281, 4001, 4057, 4102, 4118, 6504.

Hanau: 1057, 4821.

Harlem: 1118.

Heidelberg: 3471, 3929.

Helicon [i.e. Holland]: 5813.

Herborn: 222, 1892, 5257.

Holland: 6050 [?], 6651.

Ingolstadt: 1066, 4149.

Köln (20): 259, 939, 1027, 1597, 1639, 2148, 2876, 3064, 3065, 3323, 4201, 4469, 4834, 5307, 5558, 5736, 5820, 6089, 6254, 6256.

La Rochelle: 1480.

Leipzig: 1160, 1891, 3328, 5557.

Leyden (21): 1072, 1182, 1373, 1610, 2258, 2299, 3498, 3587, 3604, 3882, 4082, 4346, 4509, 5297, 5592, 5703, 5735, 5789, 5858, 5930, 6357.

Liegnitz: 3332.

Louvain: 18, 237, 4103 [a. Liège], 4213.

Lovaine. See England, East Ham.

Lutetiae Parisiorum. See Amsterdam.

Liège [a. Louvain]: 4103.

Lyon (14): 23, 31, 33, 34, 1416, 1618, 3239, 4849, 5579, 5714, 5725, 5776, 6038, 6065.

Magdeburg: 4437.

Marburg: 6429.

Middelburg: 6058.

Mainz: 1843, 3740, 5256.

Neustadt an der Haardt: 2867.

Nürnberg: 3514, 3006, 3631, 3632.

Oberursel: 1062.

Padua [?]: 5779.

Paris (42): 24, 76, 77, 78, 79, [Colloniae, i.e., Paris] 881, 941, 966, 1226, 1402, 1640, 1641, 1673, 1689, 1959, 1789, 2055, 2061, 2336, 2344, 2954, 2955, 2956, 3283, 3605, 3606, 3883, 3983, 4043, 4178, 5146, 5263, 5264, [see St. Omer] 5479, 5480, 5667, 5960, 6317, 6722, 6749, 5193, 5731, 6290.

[Published abroad?]: 1165.

Roan. See Roan, i.e., England.

Rome (11): 1643, 1644, 1647, 3041, 3042, 3090, 3091, 3202, 5600, 5700, 5831.

Rotterdam: 5674, 6356.

Rouen: 44, 3201, 4761, 6557 [or England?].

St. Omer (10): 4770, 5194, 5195, 5196, 5197, 5198, Paris [i.e., St. Omer] 5479, 5585, 6325, 6626.

Strassburg: 1525, 2989, 3282, 4339, 5549, 5625.

Trier: 1386, 3210.

Tübingen: 4002, 4003, 3051.

Ulm: 1164.

Utrecht: 6720.

Ursellis. See Oberursel.

Venice: 917, 1524, 5313, 5610.

Vienne [? cited in dedication]: 6216.

Wesel: 2049 [?], 4310.

Wittemberg: 3200, 4433.

Zürich: 1177, 1178, 5131 [?], 5907, 6432, 6433.

Appendix VII
Subjects of Printed Items
in the Wood Library

The subjects listed below must be studied in conjunction with the seven major subjects already isolated in the body of the catalogue: Almanacs, Ballads, Cambridge Act Verses, Catalogues (book sales and auctions), Newsbooks, Oxford (city, colleges and university), and Prospectuses. In addition, items by or about major figures such as Charles I, Charles II, or Oliver Cromwell and his generals, may be found under their names in the catalogue. There is overlap between certain subjects below, e.g., Oxford and Parliament, or Ireland and Parliament, or Government and Parliament.

The subjects show Wood's professional and recreational interests. His professional interests led him to acquire massive collections of almanacs, catalogues, newsbooks and Oxfordiana. Printed items listed under the subjects of Army, Biography, Government, History, Ireland, Parliament and Theology supplied him with details of men and events which were vital to his own research and writing. Catholics and Sects are listed to show that he collected publications by and about them, though it must be emphasized that he was not interested in theological issues. These publications provided him with biographical and historical information. Quakers, for example, listed under 'Sects', were active in the city of Oxford and made an impact on both the city and the university. They were, therefore, important to Wood. He never marked theological discussions and debates in printed texts unless they provided some information relevant to his own work. Lists are included below even though they overlap with, for example, entries in the subjects of Army, Parliament, Theology and even Medicine. Lists of members of parliament, of the Royal College of Medicine, of Catholics, or of regicides and abhorrers, allowed him to track Oxford graduates or to distinguish between multiple persons with common names such as John Browne and Richard Browne (see note at item 6405). His collection of works on heraldry, while numbering only thirty, was still sizeable enough for him to have mastered the intricacies of this art. His manuscript notes are full of his drawings of heraldic devices but almost none of these found their way into his *Athenae Oxonienses*.

Less vital but for his entertainment were the ballads and grand collections of ephemera, almost a thousand different printed items. He apparently could not pass by a seller of riddles, romances, or ballads without buying. In general such publications were read and passed on until they were worn out, but Wood kept his.

The subject lists also indicate what Wood was not interested in. Abstruse practices such as alchemy or astrology were of little concern. His works on alchemy can be counted on one hand (1003, 2201, 5295) and those on astrology are very few (1000, 2858, 3105, 3126, 3132, 4157, 4158, 5232, 6094, 6683), though he held a number on astronomy. He owned only thirty-three items on economics and trade, seven having to do with usury. Rhetoric was a standard part of any education in the seventeenth century and Wood acquired most of his rhetoric books when he was young. He knew how he wanted to read and write and needed no theoretical exposition of rhetoric, so he got rid of a high proportion of these, thirty of the sixty-six, between 1681 and 1695. Twenty-nine of these thirty he had recorded in his manuscript catalogue (that is, MS. Wood E. 2(70)), but they did not go to the Ashmolean Museum in 1695 and were not recorded in the Whiteside catalogus of 1716-7. He gave, or sold, four of these thirty to the Bodleian Library (marked below in the list of books on 'Rhetoric'). The remainder of his books on rhetoric he may have traded for other books. His notes reveal that he traded some books for others (see, e.g., items 296, 305, and 6793, and LT

1.230), and others he may have given away. For more on subjects, see the Intro., pp. xxff.

America (35): 233, 280, 713, 1126, 1278, 2183, 2268, 3068, 3079, 4031, 4394, 4397, 4398, 4411, 4413, 4414, 4590, 4638, 4774, 4910, 5167, 5168, 5169, 5172, 5176, 5582, 5686, 5687, 5691, 5982, 6190, 6363, 6441, 6630, 6750.

Architecture and Surveying (15): 1067, 2270, 3090, 3091, 3194, 3290, 4180, 4509, 4767, 5678, 6038, 6051, 6052, 6117, 6712.

Army, including battles, civil war, sieges, and war (660): 1, 2, 3, 182, 223, 248, 273, 280, 310, 314, 315, 340, 341, 654, 844, 866, 888, 890, 894, 896, 897, 901, 923, 924, 953, 954, 1006, 1009, 1010, 1015, 1020, 1022, 1041, 1042, 1044, 1045, 1051, 1071, 1073, 1077, 1078, 1099, 1100, 1103, 1104, 1105, 1128, 1129, 1156, 1185, 1186, 1225, 1231, 1241, 1254, 1259, 1277, 1328, 1379, 1411, 1418, 1430, 1677, 1684, 1712, 1716, 1718, 1719, 1726, 1728, 1729, 1732, 1733, 1734, 1735, 1736, 1738, 1739, 1752, 1753, 1754, 1759, 1778, 1779, 1780, 1781, 1782, 1783, 1784, 1785, 1787, 1794, 1832, 1851, 1861, 1869, 1872, 1873, 1883, 1884, 1885, 1895, 1896, 1897, 1898, 1921, 1933, 1934, 1935, 1936, 1970, 1972, 1996, 1997, 1998, 2001, 2037, 2068, 2069, 2070, 2072, 2073, 2074, 2075, 2076, 2077, 2078, 2079, 2080, 2081, 2082, 2083, 2084, 2085, 2086, 2087, 2088, 2089, 2090, 2091, 2101, 2124, 2125, 2126, 2127, 2133, 2134, 2147, 2158, 2235, 2236, 2238, 2239, 2242, 2243, 2257, 2261, 2263, 2266, 2269, 2292, 2296, 2332, 2333, 2348, 2349, 2373, 2386, 2387, 2431, 2432, 2433, 2461-2507, 2582, 2583, 2584, 2585, 2589, 2607, 2628, 2641, 2651, 2652, 2656, 2659, 2662, 2663, 2666, 2673, 2677, 2681, 2693, 2694, 2695, 2702, 2708, 2712, 2715, 2718, 2719, 2765, 2797, 2801, 2845, 2846, 2847, 2848, 2859, 2868, 2880, 2885, 2886, 2887, 2888, 2891, 2892, 2893, 2894, 2895, 2896, 2897, 2898, 2899, 2900, 2901, 2902, 2903, 2905, 2906, 2907, 2908, 2909, 2910, 2911, 2912, 2913, 2914, 2915, 2916, 2917, 2918, 2919, 2920, 2921, 2922, 2923, 2924, 2927, 2928, 2929, 2930, 2931, 2953, 2966, 2989, 2996, 2997, 2998, 2999, 3000, 3001, 3018, 3030, 3053, 3055, 3062, 3072, 3085, 3173, 3176, 3194, 3203, 3233, 3246, 3249, 3257, 3264, 3265, 3266, 3267, 3268, 3278, 3311, 3313, 3314, 3315, 3316, 3359, 3363, 3374, 3385, 3394, 3404, 3423b, 3461, 3462, 3463, 3466, 3467, 3490, 3506, 3531, 3540, 3546, 3548, 3549, 3592, 3609, 3619, 3665, 3668, 3677, 3700, 3722, 3724, 3731, 3735, 3736, 3749, 3750, 3760, 3761, 3762, 3763, 3770, 3777, 3788, 3789, 3792, 3793, 3806, 3813, 3848, 3908, 3910, 3941, 3950, 3951, 3952, 3953, 3956, 3957, 3966, 3988, 3991, 4003, 4016, 4020, 4029, 4030, 4036, 4037, 4038, 4099, 4100, 4101, 4107, 4111, 4112, 4113, 4136, 4150, 4152, 4154, 4155, 4156, 4164, 4166, 4185, 4209, 4220, 4222, 4223, 4230, 4239, 4249, 4280, 4291, 4296, 4315, 4321, 4322, 4330, 4331, 4332, 4355, 4358, 4388, 4399, 4400, 4421, 4424, 4442, 4468, 4477, 4504, 4505, 4512, 4517, 4518, 4528, 4534, 4535, 4536, 4544, 4558, 4559, 4564, 4582, 4591, 4594, 4598, 4599, 4612, 4638, 4643, 4644, 4647, 4651, 4652, 4653, 4654, 4664, 4665, 4700, 4716, 4717, 4744, 4749, 4750, 4756, 4757, 4771, 4775, 4802, 4803, 4804, 4805, 4816, 4870, 4871, 4872, 4873, 4876, 4877, 4878, 5118, 5151, 5163, 5205, 5206, 5207, 5239, 5259, 5280, 5281, 5282, 5294, 5300, 5309, 5310, 5327, 5330, 5331, 5332, 5333, 5334, 5335, 5342, 5431, 5432, 5433, 5436, 5437, 5444, 5450, 5451, 5458, 5468, 5469, 5473, 5480, 5482, 5483, 5514, 5559, 5560, 5561, 5566, 5567, 5569, 5591, 5608, 5615, 5616, 5617, 5637, 5650, 5652, 5654, 5656, 5657, 5658, 5660, 5661, 5662, 5664, 5665, 5666, 5668, 5676, 5679, 5680, 5683, 5686, 5687, 5691, 5692, 5694, 5744, 5777, 5791, 5797, 5798, 5799, 5800, 5816, 5825, 5878, 5894, 5895, 5906, 5936, 5937, 5944, 5951, 5993, 6005, 6028, 6033, 6047, 6048, 6066, 6072, 6085, 6115, 6126, 6127, 6136, 6156, 6157, 6158, 6169, 6181, 6187, 6203, 6223, 6238, 6260, 6265, 6276, 6287, 6288, 6289, 6318, 6319, 6323, 6327, 6341, 6359, 6362, 6365, 6386, 6390, 6393, 6396, 6412, 6413, 6414, 6415, 6416, 6417, 6418, 6419, 6420, 6421, 6430, 6470, 6482, 6497, 6517, 6518, 6522, 6529, 6530, 6531, 6544, 6549, 6564, 6580, 6585, 6586, 6608, 6655, 6660, 6663, 6702, 6703, 6704, 6732, 6733, 6736, 6740, 6748, 6757.

Astronomy and Astrology (21): 355, 1000, 1091, 1145, 1673, 2858, 3105, 3126, 3132, 3452, 3529, 3534, 4157, 4158, 4359, 5232, 5703, 5857, 6094, 6600, 6683.

Biography, not including elegies, encomia, panegyrics (see Elegies, et al.) or funeral sermons (see Sermons) (211): 39, 40, 42, 271, 290, 342, 343, 346, 347, 348, 358, 359, 847, 856, 857, 858, 859, 861, 875, 877, 881, 882, 891, 895, 904, 908, 917, 955, 962, 1025, 1053, 1058, 1166, 1172, 1175, 1176, 1190, 1216, 1371, 1374, 1376, 1396, 1404, 1405, 1426, 1649, 1653, 1657, 1857, 1903, 1904, 1926, 2025, 2030, 2031, 2054, 2168, 2169, 2189, 2240, 2241, 2276, 2311, 2325, 2345, 2350, 2367, 2379, 2409, 2427, 2851, 2853, 2958, 2965, 2970, 2971, 3068, 3107, 3112, 3113, 3127, 3134, 3135, 3166, 3186, 3239, 3272, 3302, 3308, 3365, 3406, 3447, 3482, 3483, 3496, 3518, 3521, 3539, 3542, 3555, 3564, 3565, 3603, 3626, 3628, 3686, 3688, 3710, 3714, 3730, 3812, 3891, 3928, 4027, 4028, 4041, 4042, 4051, 4074, 4131, 4151, 4170, 4178, 4189, 4191, 4285, 4298, 4360, 4380, 4389, 4418, 4423, 4433, 4465, 4519, 4595, 4608, 4624, 4648, 4762, 4765, 4774, 4842, 5112, 5122, 5131, 5147, 5191, 5192, 5223, 5230, 5242, 5325, 5427, 5474, 5486, 5487, 5558, 5574, 5585, 5655, 5707, 5711, 5732, 5741, 5846, 5888, 5907, 5913, 6020, 6056, 6063, 6082, 6119, 6122, 6150, 6174, 6191, 6234, 6236, 6245, 6249, 6251, 6262, 6274, 6275, 6283, 6315, 6325, 6344, 6378, 6399, 6407, 6430, 6431, 6436, 6437, 6445, 6493, 6509,

6514, 6538, 6545, 6546, 6626, 6643, 6670, 6671, 6713, 6714, 6721.

Catholic and Anti-Catholic (413): 4, 12, 36, 44, 57, 161, 162, 218, 235, 250, 306, 320, 321, 322, 349, 365, 366, 492, 554, 562, 570, 597, 612, 620, 643, 683, 684, 690, 692, 693, 711, 718, 815, 831, 892, 902, 913, 914, 920, 925, 926, 927, 928, 936, 937, 939, 963, 964, 985, 1017, 1018, 1033, 1080, 1141, 1142, 1150, 1188, 1224, 1227, 1255, 1386, 1399, 1401, 1402, 1416, 1428, 1429, 1506, 1524, 1525, 1531, 1599, 1600, 1601, 1639, 1640, 1641, 1642, 1643, 1644, 1667, 1668, 1669, 1670, 1671, 1672, 1719, 1749, 1790, 1819, 1841, 1842, 1843, 1856, 1905, 1942, 1943, 1957, 1969, 2002, 2005, 2006, 2007, 2008, 2026, 2038, 2039, 2048, 2055, 2056, 2057, 2062, 2141, 2150, 2151, 2152, 2153, 2154, 2175, 2176, 2177, 2178, 2179, 2180, 2181, 2182, 2251, 2276, 2291, 2322, 2330, 2359, 2360, 2368, 2369, 2571, 2572, 2654, 2666, 2676, 2742, 2744, 2747, 2748, 2749, 2750, 2754, 2756, 2829, 2830, 2857, 2865, 2944, 2945, 2960, 2961, 2965, 2979, 3005, 3016, 3033, 3034, 3035, 3036, 3037, 3038, 3039, 3040, 3042, 3061, 3092, 3106, 3120, 3125, 3130, 3133, 3139, 3164, 3171, 3182, 3183, 3210, 3237, 3238, 3277, 3286, 3293, 3294, 3302, 3330, 3357, 3361, 3375, 3390, 3399, 3400, 3401, 3438, 3446, 3464, 3465, 3509, 3574, 3575, 3581, 3591, 3686, 3691, 3692, 3693, 3694, 3695, 3744, 3765, 3766, 3775, 3790, 3802, 3812, 3833, 3837, 3853, 3855, 3857, 3858, 3860, 3861, 3877, 3878, 3879, 3887, 3891, 3913, 3934, 3958, 3959, 3979, 4017, 4032, 4033, 4034, 4035, 4073, 4077, 4078, 4124, 4125, 4127, 4140, 4141, 4169, 4215, 4216, 4219, 4310, 4361, 4387, 4391, 4393, 4396, 4410, 4466, 4560, 4571, 4580, 4583, 4596, 4636, 4676, 4759, 4760, 4770, 4776, 4783, 4786, 4787, 4788, 4789, 4790, 4797, 4798, 4799, 4810, 4817, 4833, 4845, 4858, 4859, 4863, 4864, 5107, 5113, 5119, 5120, 5121, 5142, 5154, 5161, 5180, 5193, 5194, 5195, 5196, 5197, 5198, 5199, 5204, 5212, 5228, 5229, 5235, 5248, 5249, 5274, 5276, 5285, 5286, 5287, 5293, 5339, 5340, 5341, 5345, 5346, 5347, 5383, 5384, 5437, 5440, 5543, 5550, 5568, 5590, 5601, 5667, 5708, 5718, 5730, 5743, 5822, 5824, 5836, 5843, 5844, 5850, 5856, 5869, 5921, 5924, 5925, 5940, 5948, 5949, 5965, 5973, 6000, 6001, 6018, 6032, 6036, 6037, 6075, 6088, 6091, 6092, 6122, 6123, 6133, 6183, 6184, 6194, 6197, 6213, 6214, 6215, 6221, 6228, 6229, 6242, 6243, 6273, 6283, 6317, 6325, 6348, 6372, 6373, 6374, 6382, 6383, 6397, 6427, 6434, 6462, 6463, 6464, 6485, 6486, 6527, 6528, 6536, 6558, 6559, 6560, 6561, 6562, 6579, 6618, 6619, 6627, 6629, 6692, 6743.

Conduct (105): 13, 45, 265, 313, 332, 361, 856, 857, 858, 859, 861, 906, 907, 958, 1026, 1049, 1134, 1155, 1163, 1374, 1432, 1696, 1866, 2017, 2034, 2035, 2058, 2064, 2199, 2211, 2277, 2329, 2335, 2343, 2394, 2523, 2838, 2863, 2941, 2980, 2989, 3131, 3335, 3337, 3338, 3378, 3484, 3486, 3582, 3584, 3707, 4171, 4172, 4176, 4191, 4264, 4309, 4343, 4350, 4364, 4368, 4369, 4370, 4372, 4390, 4407, 4447, 4814, 4839, 4952, 4953, 4954, 4955, 4956, 4962, 4974, 4977, 4978, 4986, 4989, 5108, 5150, 5178, 5522, 5574, 5648, 5720, 5819, 5827, 5886, 5978, 5990, 6014, 6093, 6130, 6137, 6191, 6202, 6230, 6303, 63636403, 6487, 6545, 6724.

Crimes, Plots, Treason, Trials, not including Executions and Murders (357): 4, 223, 235, 295, 298, 308, 322, 334, 336, 400, 411, 417, 418, 419, 733, 785, 815, 898, 913, 914, 925, 926, 927, 957, 1005, 1006, 1017, 1018, 1033, 1047, 1048, 1051, 1080, 1081, 1082, 1123, 1224, 1227, 1249, 1250, 1253, 1255, 1380, 1381, 1383, 1384, 1390, 1394, 1395, 1399, 1401, 1407, 1408, 1409, 1417, 1599, 1600, 1601, 1637, 1662, 1667, 1668, 1669, 1670, 1671, 1672, 1692, 1756, 1757, 1761, 1764, 1767, 1795, 1819, 1824, 1825, 1942, 1943, 1946, 1947, 1948, 1949, 1962, 1973, 1977, 1978, 1979, 1980, 1982, 1983, 1984, 1985, 1987, 1989, 1993, 2007, 2010, 2050, 2051, 2052, 2093, 2141, 2150, 2151, 2152, 2154, 2155, 2244, 2245, 2359, 2360, 2368, 2369, 2406, 2430, 2434, 2554, 2571, 2572, 2592, 2595, 2596, 2598, 2631, 2654, 2666, 2674, 2683, 2688, 2740, 2744, 2747, 2748, 2749, 2750, 2754, 2865, 2944, 2945, 2978, 2984, 3005, 3014, 3016, 3033, 3034, 3035, 3036, 3038, 3039, 3061, 3101, 3120, 3130, 3171, 3175, 3191, 3192, 3235, 3263, 3276, 3277, 3286, 3357, 3361, 3390, 3391, 3392, 3393, 3395, 3401, 3493, 3515, 3517, 3536, 3644, 3686, 3691, 3722, 3785, 3857, 3858, 3859, 3860, 3861, 3865, 3866, 3867, 3868, 3869, 3870, 3871, 3872, 3910, 3913, 3941, 3958, 3982, 4033, 4035, 4108, 4117, 4124, 4125, 4128, 4138, 4141, 4153, 4215, 4219, 4222, 4223, 4242, 4265, 4277, 4296, 4349, 4361, 4396, 4534, 4545, 4569, 4571, 4579, 4596, 4614, 4615, 4670, 4671, 4674, 4675, 4730, 4731, 4732, 4733, 4734, 4777, 4784, 4786, 4787, 4788, 4789, 4790, 4797, 4798, 4799, 4816, 4818, 4829, 4830, 4831, 4836, 4840, 4844, 4863, 4864, 5120, 5121, 5166, 5180, 5209, 5212, 5216, 5222, 5229, 5235, 5276, 5277, 5278, 5300, 5305, 5311, 5328, 5340, 5341, 5405, 5422, 5438, 5473, 5485, 5525, 5527, 5543, 5599, 5670, 5673, 5675, 5704, 5705, 5730, 5733, 5790, 5809, 5818, 5821, 5822, 5823, 5824, 5844, 5851, 5852, 5854, 5855, 5869, 5893, 5901, 5921, 5922, 5924, 5940, 5948, 5959, 6001, 6008, 6009, 6013, 6018, 6033, 6034, 6037, 6046, 6133, 6182, 6183, 6193, 6194, 6200, 6214, 6215, 6224, 6228, 6229, 6242, 6243, 6253, 6316, 6383, 6388, 6393, 6395, 6411, 6440, 6462, 6463, 6464, 6485, 6486, 6505, 6510, 6513, 6536, 6547, 6558, 6606, 6618, 6743, 6751.

Economics and Commerce (47): 530, 1154, 1155, 1253, 1836, 1952, 2121, 2122, 2159, 2160, 2395, 2396, 2605, 2741, 2824, 2843, 2981, 3011, 3526, 3538, 3748, 3752, 3768, 3874, 3936, 4146, 4357, 4441, 4496, 4578, 4584, 4677, 5165, 5172, 5176, 5318, 5521, 5588, 5619, 5819, 6255, 6468, 6487, 6520, 6541, 6637, 6745.

Elegies and Encomia (86), and Panegyrics (19 panegyrics, or praises of the living, are marked by (P)): 225, 266, 864 (P): 878, 1023, 1076, 1287 (P), 1395, 1400, 1404, 1638 (P), 1650, 1652, 1690, 1765,

1917, 1990, 1991, 2033, 2109, 2110, 2174, 2225, 2314, 2429, 2972, 3021, 3024, 3029, 3048 (P), 3049, 3060 (P), 3213, 3310, 3329, 3342, 3351, 3353, 3360, 3411 (P), 3412, 3488, 3491, 3630 (P), 3638, 3729 (P), 3850, 3927, 3970, 3971, 4055, 4096, 4142, 4175, 4351 (P), 4510 (P), 4539, 4561, 4586, 4857, 4894 (P), 4897 (P), 4911 (P), 4932, 4933, 4934, 4935, 4936, 4937, 4938, 4939, 4940, 5117, 5214, 5227 (P), 5247, 5481, 5592 (P), 5653, 5685, 5760, 5804 (P), 5859, 5939 (P), 6107 (P), 6143, 6170 (P), 6205, 6241, 6247, 6267, 6280, 6285, 6305, 6326, 6329, 6379, 6381, 6433, 6546, 6620, 6649, 6694, 6710, 6719, 6720.

Entertainment (including various kinds of diversions from fishing to drinking, smoking, card playing, feasts, progresses and sideshows) (56): 270, 284, 853, 880, 885, 1037, 1229, 1388, 1654, 1698, 1928, 2207, 3095, 3333, 3356, 3560, 3566, 3681, 3754, 3756, 3757, 3758, 3759, 3822, 3922, 4075, 4198, 4234, 4272, 4328, 4365, 4368, 4408, 4409, 4530, 4632, 4633, 4808, 4820, 5099, 5100, 5179, 5419, 5529, 5540, 5571, 5636, 5755, 5762, 6135, 6145, 6385, 6435, 6678, 6682, 6730.

Exploration. See Travel and Exploration.

Executions and Murders (258): 20, 43, 229, 236, 262, 263, 264, 278, 279, 297, 321, 329, 363, 410, 524, 533, 535, 591, 597, 616, 723, 754, 776, 784, 869, 870, 895, 928, 988, 1029, 1061, 1070, 1093, 1130, 1141, 1142, 1153, 1168, 1186, 1209, 1242, 1263, 1382, 1396, 1429, 1663, 1680, 1766, 1771, 1775, 1828, 1856, 1901, 1933, 1950, 1951, 2003, 2008, 2099, 2130, 2153, 2246, 2291, 2352, 2357, 2382, 2385, 2419, 2568, 2697, 2855, 2857, 2878, 2882, 2952, 2993, 3037, 3040, 3075, 3077, 3080, 3087, 3099, 3164, 3193, 3209, 3237, 3238, 3256, 3293, 3294, 3314, 3330, 3347, 3352, 3364, 3386, 3396, 3439, 3440, 3442, 3443, 3465, 3470, 3476, 3485, 3509, 3532, 3550, 3551, 3563, 3573, 3574, 3575, 3583, 3591, 3595, 3599, 3600, 3610, 3627, 3648, 3654, 3655, 3692, 3693, 3694, 3695, 3734, 3746, 3747, 3796, 3802, 3819, 3837, 3887, 3888, 3903, 3977, 3980, 3986, 4032, 4034, 4046, 4054, 4102, 4140, 4218, 4276, 4293, 4295, 4347, 4348, 4397, 4460, 4471, 4478, 4560, 4581, 4597, 4810, 4819, 4838, 4843, 5113, 5141, 5177, 5204, 5210, 5265, 5274, 5336, 5337, 5339, 5359, 5360, 5430, 5446, 5499, 5502, 5538, 5614, 5669, 5672, 5682, 5698, 5699, 5707, 5751, 5764, 5765, 5810, 5820, 5830, 5849, 5853, 5863, 5864, 5865, 5897, 5900, 5917, 5925, 5926, 5949, 5965, 6023, 6029, 6035, 6036, 6049, 6057, 6064, 6113, 6116, 6195, 6197, 6204, 6211, 6212, 6213, 6232, 6245, 6249, 6250, 6251, 6252, 6254, 6262, 6263, 6294, 6358, 6387, 6443, 6461, 6479, 6480, 6481, 6506, 6507, 6508, 6509, 6511, 6512, 6514, 6515, 6516, 6519, 6559, 6560, 6561, 6562, 6588, 6619, 6627, 6667, 6668, 6729.

Gardening. See Horticulture or Husbandry.

Government, see also Parliament, below. Governmental and theological issues are often intertwined and the same items may appear under several subjects (556): 231, 232, 245, 246, 247, 253, 267, 268, 275, 283, 308, 330, 331, 338, 360, 388, 390, 395, 396, 397, 408, 413, 417, 418, 419, 437, 455, 457, 460, 461, 488, 490, 491, 510, 528, 534, 555, 558, 566, 567, 568, 583, 584, 593, 608, 609, 610, 614, 615, 640, 642, 663, 671, 697, 701, 711, 728, 733, 760, 781, 785, 789, 795, 796, 820, 821, 826, 827, 842, 868, 879, 903, 911, 919, 959, 960, 966, 986, 991, 994, 1005, 1017, 1021, 1031, 1062, 1090, 1122, 1135, 1146, 1182, 1191, 1192, 1193, 1194, 1198, 1199, 1200, 1201, 1202, 1203, 1205, 1212, 1245, 1262, 1415, 1417, 1646, 1658, 1659, 1681, 1685, 1705, 1747, 1758, 1790, 1795, 1799, 1805, 1807, 1814, 1818, 1829, 1846, 1849, 1862, 1881, 1900, 1905, 1908, 1921, 1931, 1980, 1986, 1988, 1992, 1994, 2001, 2008, 2016, 2027, 2028, 2029, 2045, 2067, 2095, 2096, 2097, 2102, 2103, 2132, 2141, 2198, 2210, 2212, 2213, 2221, 2229, 2254, 2279, 2295, 2297, 2306, 2358, 2378, 2381, 2397, 2408, 2434, 2435, 2445, 2446, 2447, 2448, 2449, 2450, 2451, 2453, 2454, 2455, 2456, 2457, 2458, 2490, 2492, 2493, 2497, 2500, 2504, 2506, 2512, 2546, 2562, 2563, 2564, 2566, 2569, 2578, 2587, 2818, 2819, 2820, 2822, 2823, 2826, 2827, 2829, 2830, 2843, 2859, 2861, 2863, 2871, 2872, 2935, 2939, 2940, 2961, 2969, 2985, 2991, 3003, 3009, 3015, 3057, 3058, 3071, 3098, 3108, 3139, 3142, 3178, 3191, 3192, 3257, 3261, 3270, 3278, 3279, 3284, 3331, 3355, 3357, 3367, 3368, 3382, 3388, 3391, 3394, 3395, 3401, 3420, 3421, 3422, 3423, 3424, 3425, 3426, 3427, 3455, 3468, 3470, 3481, 3493, 3502, 3535, 3536, 3537, 3538, 3541, 3546, 3576, 3656, 3696, 3701, 3702, 3713, 3716, 3717, 3725, 3733, 3742, 3743, 3751, 3803, 3805, 3815, 3819, 3830, 3832, 3833, 3834, 3835, 3836, 3838, 3839, 3840, 3841, 3842, 3843, 3844, 3845, 3848, 3862, 3863, 3875, 3886, 3917, 3990, 3991, 3998, 4002, 4010, 4011, 4012, 4013, 4015, 4019, 4031, 4066, 4093, 4107, 4110, 4111, 4112, 4113, 4115, 4116, 4117, 4118, 4119, 4120, 4126, 4132, 4135, 4137, 4138, 4168, 4184, 4195, 4197, 4224, 4228, 4243, 4245, 4254, 4257, 4262, 4272, 4273, 4278, 4289, 4308, 4337, 4341, 4366, 4376, 4392, 4393, 4395, 4401, 4410, 4419, 4483, 4491, 4492, 4493, 4511, 4512, 4514, 4515, 4538, 4541, 4552, 4554, 4555, 4573, 4583, 4587, 4593, 4596, 4616, 4617, 4620, 4622, 4623, 4630, 4631, 4635, 4639, 4754, 4763, 4789, 4792, 4793, 4796, 4799, 4826, 4830, 4831, 4832, 4834, 4847, 4905, 4944, 5104, 5106, 5111, 5126, 5155, 5156, 5158, 5159, 5161, 5169, 5199, 5200, 5208, 5211, 5217, 5218, 5223, 5224, 5225, 5237, 5238, 5253, 5254, 5262, 5290, 5291, 5303, 5311, 5317, 5320, 5345, 5348, 5358, 5364, 5421, 5422, 5425, 5428, 5429, 5443, 5445, 5449, 5453, 5455, 5462, 5503, 5517, 5518, 5521, 5544, 5546, 5568, 5594, 5597, 5598, 5602, 5671, 5695, 5742, 5758, 5759, 5779, 5787, 5796, 5807, 5812, 5813, 5814, 5815, 5820, 5822, 5835, 5845, 5870, 5890, 5910, 5916, 5931, 5947, 5973, 5978, 5992,

6004, 6010, 6011, 6012, 6015, 6016, 6019, 6022, 6042, 6061, 6071, 6108, 6112, 6152, 6177, 6178, 6179, 6186, 6188, 6194, 6198, 6199, 6204, 6219, 6239, 6254, 6257, 6265, 6266, 6278, 6286, 6293, 6295, 6308, 6312, 6320, 6330, 6331, 6363, 6380, 6394, 6422, 6465, 6466, 6499, 6500, 6504, 6521, 6536, 6574, 6575, 6578, 6590, 6591, 6592, 6593, 6594, 6609, 6610, 6611, 6612, 6613, 6614, 6615, 6618, 6624, 6658, 6705, 6727, 6745.

Heraldry (30): 1034, 1419, 1463, 1513, 1514, 2366, 2508, 2852, 2954, 3206, 3222, 3344, 3968, 3969, 3983, 4001, 4079, 4080, 4271, 4563, 5150, 5183, 5720, 5749, 5874, 5875, 5914, 6477, 6650.

History, not including Government or Parliament (421): 6, 22, 23, 34, 222, 227, 228, 248, 257, 258, 296, 302, 337, 339, 343, 344, 346, 348, 364, 387, 442, 717, 774, 825, 865, 892, 893, 899, 921, 922, 937, 939, 987, 1004, 1012, 1015, 1055, 1056, 1057, 1087, 1101, 1140, 1150, 1151, 1160, 1168, 1169, 1170, 1172, 1178, 1207, 1255, 1257, 1264, 1265, 1267, 1268, 1368, 1370, 1372, 1373, 1377, 1387, 1389, 1397, 1403, 1406, 1414, 1416, 1425, 1426, 1466, 1545, 1575, 1647, 1651, 1676, 1679, 1686, 1687, 1689, 1694, 1770, 1794, 1826, 1827, 1831, 1835, 1843, 1867, 1891, 1925, 1955, 1958, 1959, 2032, 2048, 2059, 2106, 2128, 2129, 2168, 2169, 2172, 2182, 2185, 2217, 2218, 2219, 2258, 2275, 2282, 2296, 2310, 2326, 2327, 2334, 2336, 2344, 2364, 2365, 2399, 2509, 2510, 2511, 2850, 2854, 2876, 2954, 2955, 2956, 2958, 2993, 3025, 3033, 3042, 3058, 3059, 3062, 3064, 3065, 3066, 3104, 3110, 3111, 3115, 3134, 3136, 3138, 3172, 3186, 3200, 3201, 3218, 3219, 3220, 3223, 3232, 3243, 3244, 3247, 3272, 3273, 3292, 3327, 3328, 3375, 3398, 3403, 3473, 3489, 3490, 3492, 3499, 3504, 3511, 3512, 3528, 3544, 3553, 3554, 3567, 3568, 3574, 3575, 3579, 3583, 3589, 3605, 3606, 3607, 3608, 3610, 3619, 3628, 3657, 3675, 3678, 3687, 3688, 3705, 3715, 3739, 3740, 3810, 3812, 3826, 3846, 3890, 3896, 3904, 3907, 3914, 3923, 3942, 3974, 3982, 4005, 4008, 4023, 4024, 4025, 4040, 4061, 4062, 4071, 4083, 4090, 4091, 4092, 4094, 4095, 4103, 4104, 4105, 4124, 4147, 4148, 4185, 4186, 4190, 4194, 4200, 4201, 4202, 4279, 4284, 4287, 4298, 4300, 4309, 4316, 4332, 4339, 4346, 4352, 4356, 4362, 4363, 4416, 4424, 4464, 4532, 4551, 4556, 4589, 4609, 4614, 4615, 4770, 4806, 4815, 4821, 4827, 5107, 5116, 5118, 5127, 5135, 5170, 5219, 5263, 5264, 5278, 5294, 5299, 5307, 5312, 5313, 5319, 5324, 5350, 5357, 5363, 5379, 5380, 5381, 5387, 5388, 5389, 5392, 5394, 5410, 5417, 5430, 5513, 5515, 5519, 5531, 5532, 5533, 5538, 5539, 5550, 5551, 5604, 5606, 5610, 5620, 5622, 5682, 5688, 5707, 5725, 5740, 5741, 5743, 5752, 5753, 5789, 5826, 5847, 5854, 5858, 5882, 5884, 5889, 5915, 5930, 5942, 5955, 5957, 5958, 5970, 5972, 5976, 5981, 5998, 6006, 6009, 6030, 6059, 6075, 6076, 6077, 6079, 6083, 6089, 6095, 6096, 6099, 6120, 6121, 6122, 6128, 6129, 6131, 6162, 6164, 6168, 6169, 6174, 6189, 6206, 6222, 6223, 6253, 6262, 6268, 6269, 6282, 6290, 6291, 6297, 6309, 6310, 6311, 6324, 6335, 6392, 6400, 6446, 6448, 6449, 6450, 6451, 6452, 6458, 6483, 6488, 6492, 6494, 6533, 6539, 6540, 6617, 6625, 6639, 6641, 6651, 6657, 6680, 6684, 6685, 6686, 6687, 6695, 6718, 6727, 6749, 6750.

Horticulture or Husbandry (20): 71, 305, 912, 1944, 1945, 2864, 2881, 3449, 3526, 3593, 4067, 4371, 4372, 4677, 5269, 5270, 5785, 6261, 6524, 6525.

Ireland (256): 4, 12, 248, 276, 287, 298, 317, 341, 825, 889, 934, 953, 954, 1001, 1002, 1020, 1022, 1055, 1056, 1073, 1074, 1075, 1077, 1078, 1079, 1121, 1126, 1185, 1203, 1233, 1235, 1236, 1237, 1238, 1239, 1240, 1255, 1370, 1373, 1387, 1658, 1693, 1700, 1701, 1715, 1731, 1741, 1749, 1750, 1756, 1762, 1786, 1828, 1895, 1939, 1940, 1995, 1996, 1997, 1998, 2044, 2048, 2052, 2053, 2087, 2089, 2100, 2115, 2144, 2145, 2147, 2185, 2264, 2271, 2339, 2340, 2341, 2361, 2383, 2386, 2387, 2433, 2462, 2473, 2487, 2504, 2506, 2593, 2606, 2610, 2611, 2637, 2638, 2641, 2657, 2660, 2670, 2673, 2681, 2698, 2699, 2702, 2766, 2947, 2995, 3018, 3033, 3246, 3260, 3271, 3317, 3361, 3384, 3399, 3400, 3449, 3466, 3467, 3539, 3639, 3665, 3699, 3736, 3750, 3769, 3770, 3771, 3772, 3773, 3774, 3775, 3776, 3777, 3778, 3779, 3780, 3781, 3782, 3783, 3784, 3785, 3786, 3787, 3788, 3789, 3790, 3791, 3792, 3793, 3794, 3795, 3796, 3797, 3798, 3804, 3898, 3899, 3900, 3901, 3902, 3908, 3909, 3911, 4164, 4200, 4208, 4209, 4213, 4217, 4239, 4334, 4335, 4347, 4348, 4349, 4456, 4457, 4508, 4513, 4533, 4542, 4543, 4544, 4559, 4566, 4585, 4588, 4659, 4668, 4671, 4701, 4714, 4738, 4739, 4800, 4801, 4802, 4803, 4804, 4805, 4817, 4860, 5188, 5217, 5218, 5267, 5328, 5395, 5460, 5473, 5562, 5563, 5569, 5616, 5617, 5690, 5692, 5712, 5718, 5730, 5790, 5904, 5906, 5954, 5980, 6030, 6032, 6085, 6114, 6122, 6167, 6168, 6203, 6223, 6232, 6286, 6366, 6367, 6404, 6410, 6445, 6446, 6447, 6448, 6449, 6450, 6451, 6452, 6458, 6517, 6542, 6543, 6544, 6656, 6696, 6697.

Law (159): 32, 295, 353, 360, 488, 590, 900, 956, 1011, 1014, 1016, 1137, 1138, 1183, 1307, 1308, 1311, 1341, 1343, 1350, 1443, 1444, 1445, 1573, 1594, 1640, 1887, 1888, 1889, 1902, 1922, 1941, 1974, 2022, 2029, 2041, 2066, 2187, 2244, 2245, 2256, 2346, 2405, 2552-2573, 2609, 2686, 2704, 2746, 2873, 2874, 2875, 2879, 2932, 3010, 3036, 3071, 3103, 3190, 3199, 3234, 3240, 3283, 3429, 3434, 3475, 3515, 3624, 3646, 3647, 3682, 3684, 3685, 3851, 3885, 3906, 3984, 4008, 4086, 4088, 4145, 4147, 4148, 4195, 4196, 4269, 4282, 4336, 4345, 4352, 4425, 4441, 4474, 4642, 4674, 4777, 4781, 4807, 4882, 4889, 4995, 4996, 5157, 5181, 5182, 5224, 5225, 5237, 5322, 5323, 5424, 5530, 5578, 5588, 5589, 5624, 5635, 5758, 5759, 5774, 5824, 5883, 5885, 5931, 5957, 5998, 6061, 6164, 6296, 6334, 6360, 6467, 6472, 6502, 6503, 6504, 6520, 6577, 6752, 6753.

Lists (e.g., of members of parliament, the Royal Society, abhorrers, prisoners, commanders,

prebendaries, Catholics, martyrs, etc.) (**91**): 46, 587, 1009, 1010, 1146, 1430, 1767, 1772, 1773, 1787, 1813, 1825, 1829, 2091, 2358, 2366, 2412, 2413, 2463, 2474, 2475, 2508, 2533, 2534, 2535, 2545, 2554, 2557, 2559, 2578, 2756, 2760, 2761, 2762, 2763, 2764, 2765, 2766, 2767, 2768, 2769, 2770, 2771, 2772, 2773, 2774, 2775, 2776, 2777, 2778, 2779, 2780, 2781, 2782, 2783, 2784, 2785, 2786, 2904, 3242, 3429, 3780, 3909, 3981, 4150, 4239, 4246, 4303, 4330, 4391, 4472, 4475, 5226, 5375, 5401, 5627, 5628, 5629, 5630, 5637, 5639, 5640, 5642, 5643, 5644, 5645, 5646, 5906, 6112, 6163, 6405, 6438.

Literature, including ephemera such as drama, garlands (marked by '(G)'; 21 of 24 are in Wood 94), jest books, prose fiction, and riddles, but not including ballads, elegies or marvels (417): 13, 14, 24, 25, 72, 234, 244, 256, 261, 271, 296, 324, 325, 335, 344, 346, 347, 348, 357, 361, 854, 915, 916, 933, 935, 958, 969, 995, 1032, 1038, 1050, 1068, 1092, 1096, 1097, 1098, 1109, 1111, 1112, 1113, 1139, 1157, 1158, 1161, 1171, 1246, 1275, 1391, 1412, 1420, 1421, 1645, 1674, 1676, 1679, 1683, 1834, 1837, 1839, 1840, 1880, 1886, 1906, 1914, 1956, 1965, 2009, 2014, 2019, 2059, 2065, 2104, 2106, 2107, 2108, 2123, 2161, 2170, 2171, 2199, 2203, 2204, 2205, 2206, 2208, 2209, 2215 (G), 2216, 2217, 2218, 2219, 2220 (G), 2222, 2226, 2252, 2260, 2273, 2285, 2312, 2313, 2314, 2316, 2317, 2318, 2319, 2320, 2321, 2401, 2832, 2840, 2841, 2850, 2938, 2957, 2958, 2959, 3007, 3008, 3032, 3047, 3089, 3093, 3094, 3109, 3116, 3117, 3119, 3141, 3143-3163 (G), 3169, 3170, 3179, 3180, 3181, 3185, 3188, 3202, 3216, 3254, 3295, 3296, 3297, 3298, 3299, 3323, 3327, 3334, 3350, 3376, 3378, 3379, 3380, 3381, 3402, 3405, 3450, 3451, 3469, 3472, 3498, 3500, 3511, 3512, 3516, 3559, 3567, 3568, 3577, 3610, 3631, 3632, 3658, 3659, 3669, 3670, 3671, 3672, 3673, 3683, 3689, 3698, 3808, 3814, 3828, 3849, 3881, 3890, 3915, 3926, 3931, 3932, 3943, 3963, 3972, 3973, 3975, 4005, 4027, 4028, 4039, 4044, 4068, 4069, 4087, 4183, 4187, 4188, 4236 (G), 4301, 4302, 4304, 4326, 4327, 4359, 4362, 4363, 4373, 4374, 4386, 4392, 4403, 4426, 4431, 4432, 4436, 4437, 4453, 4454, 4455, 4458, 4459, 4476, 4481, 4497, 4503, 4529, 4562, 4570, 4600, 4601, 4602, 4603, 4604, 4605, 4640, 4812, 4820, 4835, 4836, 4837, 4849, 4850, 4851, 4852, 4853, 4854, 5115, 5128, 5129, 5130, 5134, 5139, 5140, 5149, 5155, 5184, 5185, 5186, 5213, 5215, 5227, 5252, 5257, 5261, 5275, 5279, 5284, 5285, 5286, 5287, 5288, 5289, 5296, 5351, 5352, 5353, 5354, 5355, 5356, 5357, 5496, 5497, 5498, 5501, 5504, 5520, 5524, 5535, 5551, 5575, 5587, 5603, 5604, 5621, 5622, 5623, 5625, 5688, 5709, 5717, 5770, 5826, 5838, 5839, 5840, 5841, 5842, 5860, 5861, 5862, 5872, 5876, 5879, 5880, 5882, 5889, 5902, 5903, 5905, 5919, 5920, 5942, 5977, 6002, 6062, 6065, 6069, 6081, 6083, 6087, 6105, 6110, 6146, 6160, 6171, 6172, 6175, 6178, 6192, 6206, 6207, 6208, 6209, 6217, 6233, 6244, 6271, 6272, 6277, 6281, 6291, 6336, 6340, 6343, 6349, 6350, 6351, 6352, 6353, 6364, 6398, 6408, 6437, 6441, 6475, 6484, 6537, 6554, 6607, 6623, 6638, 6639, 6642, 6643, 6644, 6664, 6680, 6691, 6709, 6710, 6715, 6716, 6717, 6728, 6746.

Maps (33): 27, 1273, 2579, 2590, 2833, 3121, 3306, 3640, 3641, 3642, 3643, 4211, 4382, 4768, 4769, 4823, 4824, 4866, 5101, 5102, 5773, 5837, 5980, 5982, 5983, 5984, 5985, 5986, 5987, 5988, 5989, 6354, 6697.

Marvels, i.e., miracles, rarities, strange news, wonderful relations and wonders (102): 28, 38, 109, 251, 658, 659, 771, 885, 899, 1000, 1094, 1110, 1119, 1120, 1124, 1132, 1140, 1159, 1270, 1378, 1682, 1692, 1850, 1870, 1871, 2135, 2202, 2342, 2550, 2581, 2607, 2834, 2835, 2836, 2837, 2962, 2994, 3017, 3019, 3056, 3085, 3088, 3198, 3241, 3245, 3272, 3287, 3404, 3453, 3477, 3585, 3596, 3664, 3754, 3755, 3795, 3797, 3811, 3818, 4070, 4159, 4192, 4216, 4225, 4229, 4265, 4384, 4422, 4464, 4530, 4543, 4592, 4626, 4641, 4764, 4861, 5203, 5268, 5505, 5529, 5534, 5555, 5586, 5761, 5867, 5909, 6003, 6074, 6141, 6225, 6370, 6493, 6527, 6528, 6581, 6599, 6672, 6682, 6683, 6707, 6726, 6755.

Mathematics and Geometry (8): 1447, 2270, 3419, 4509, 5678, 6052, 6491, 6556.

Medicine, including advertisements, baths, cures (chocolate, coffee, tea, tobacco), plagues (18 marked with ('P')), the Royal College of Physicians (86): 18, 354, 883, 1054, 1060, 1117, 1157, 1158, 1159, 1447, 1481, 1482, 1593, 1688, 1815 ('P'), 1923 ('P'), 1927, 1928, 1929, 1944, 1954, 2015, 2105 ('P'), 2137, 2138, 2139, 2184, 2202 ('P'), 2203 ('P'), 2205 ('P'), 2267, 2575 ('P'), 2576 ('P'), 2577 ('P'), 2789 ('P', satire), 2866, 2867 ('P'), 2994, 3067, 3074, 3137, 3168, 3255, 3287, 3288 ('P'), 3289, 3343, 3356, 3370, 3471, 3601, 3602, 3674 ('P'), 3727, 3804 ('P'), 3808 ('P'), 3822, 3897, 3905, 4192, 4237, 4365, 4658, 4960 ('P'), 5240, 5260, 5261, 5266 ('P'), 5298, 5304, 5626 ('P'), 5627, 5628, 5629, 5630, 5631, 5632, 5633, 5634, 5635, 5649, 5735, 6074, 6176, 6279, 6548, 6645, 6678.

Murders. See Executions and Murders.

Music (79): 368, 399, 420, 430, 431, 458, 650, 736, 737, 739, 740, 761, 767, 770, 782, 824, 1118, 1147, 1229, 1361, 1388, 1436, 1557, 1598, 1865, 1876, 1877, 1878, 1879, 1882, 1919, 2060, 2170, 2234, 2376, 2377, 2825, 2948, 3006, 3080, 3597, 3632, 3756, 3757, 3758, 3759, 3975, 4018, 4044, 4060, 4203, 4204, 4205, 4206, 4286, 4297, 4438, 4459, 4969, 5011, 5012, 5184, 5185, 5271, 5272, 5273, 5285-8, 5338, 5548, 5557, 5719, 5745, 5908, 5961, 6628, 6747.

Oxford, see also Oxford city and university items from 4862 to 5088 (320): 7, 11, 27, 117, 241, 351, 356, 369, 370, 371, 446, 447, 448, 481, 500, 501, 502, 503, 504, 505, 506, 669, 750, 751, 772, 846, 863, 872, 914, 943, 945, 992, 993, 996, 1023, 1122, 1123, 1184, 1213, 1220, 1221, 1222, 1223, 1265, 1267, 1404, 1420, 1455, 1490, 1491, 1492, 1493, 1494, 1495, 1529, 1532, 1583, 1584, 1585, 1586, 1587, 1588, 1589, 1590, 1591, 1592, 1606, 1655, 1732, 1733, 1740, 1744, 1746, 1748, 1752, 1778, 1779, 1815, 1820, 1860, 1861, 1863, 1868, 1947, 1948, 1950, 1951, 2042, 2069, 2070, 2072, 2073, 2135, 2157, 2165, 2166, 2190, 2191, 2192, 2193, 2249, 2250, 2254, 2308, 2309, 2324, 2326, 2327, 2351, 2373, 2400, 2437, 2574, 2576, 2577, 2614, 2651, 2655, 2656, 2664, 2678, 2679, 2680, 2684, 2685, 2690, 2691, 2692, 2751, 2752, 2753, 2755, 2756, 2782, 2783, 2812, 2813, 2814, 2815, 2842, 2889, 2890, 2905, 2908, 2913, 2967, 2968, 2972, 3041, 3073, 3110, 3111, 3114, 3123, 3124, 3141, 3248, 3252, 3288, 3291, 3300, 3351, 3372, 3373, 3387, 3409, 3410, 3413, 3414, 3415, 3416, 3428, 3429, 3430, 3431, 3434, 3435, 3437, 3438, 3441, 3474, 3487, 3518, 3577, 3578, 3616, 3617, 3638, 3640, 3709, 3712, 3729, 3737, 3760, 3761, 3762, 3763, 3799, 3800, 3801, 3816, 3895, 3912, 3945, 3946, 3947, 3948, 4022, 4024, 4026, 4047, 4048, 4052, 4053, 4063, 4078, 4098, 4129, 4181, 4182, 4211, 4404, 4406, 4463, 4524, 4525, 4530, 4553, 4657, 4658, 4676, 4696, 4710, 4711, 4715, 5089, 5090, 5091, 5092, 5093, 5101, 5135, 5136, 5157, 5245, 5246, 5248, 5250, 5258, 5259, 5326, 5361, 5365, 5368, 5404, 5405, 5415, 5434, 5475, 5476, 5477, 5478, 5488, 5512, 5611, 5726, 5727, 5738, 5739, 5749, 5763, 5769, 5857, 5911, 6040, 6070, 6103, 6107, 6115, 6152, 6154, 6156, 6157, 6158, 6182, 6226, 6264, 6268, 6280, 6304, 6313, 6341, 6414, 6424, 6439, 6444, 6453, 6454, 6455, 6456, 6479, 6480, 6481, 6489, 6547, 6565, 6566, 6567, 6571, 6572, 6598, 6604, 6633, 6646, 6647, 6684, 6685, 6686, 6687, 6695.

Parliament, see also Government, above (666): 223, 288, 289, 291, 294, 333, 367, 382, 412, 467, 468, 469, 471, 472, 473, 474, 475, 476, 477, 478, 479, 480, 481, 482, 511, 631, 641, 669, 676, 849, 850, 913, 914, 950, 967, 997, 998, 1006, 1008, 1041, 1042, 1043, 1046, 1077, 1078, 1102, 1103, 1121, 1127, 1131, 1133, 1143, 1144, 1210, 1215, 1243, 1244, 1252, 1261, 1271, 1276, 1380, 1660, 1661, 1678, 1700, 1701, 1702, 1703, 1706, 1707, 1708, 1709, 1710, 1711, 1712, 1715, 1716, 1717, 1718, 1721, 1722, 1723, 1725, 1726, 1731, 1734, 1735, 1736, 1738, 1740, 1742, 1743, 1744, 1751, 1754, 1755, 1759, 1760, 1776, 1792, 1796, 1797, 1798, 1800, 1804, 1811, 1812, 1816, 1820, 1830, 1860, 1869, 1937, 1941, 1975, 1976, 1981, 1995, 1996, 1997, 1998, 2011, 2012, 2021, 2037, 2052, 2092, 2133, 2134, 2136, 2152, 2231, 2249, 2250, 2262, 2265, 2303, 2315, 2359, 2360, 2406, 2412, 2413, 2416, 2417, 2418, 2428, 2433, 2452, 2467, 2469, 2470, 2478, 2483, 2486, 2487, 2494, 2495, 2498, 2503, 2505, 2565, 2567, 2584, 2591-2816, 2904, 2905, 2914, 2916, 2917, 2922, 2925, 2926, 2942, 2944, 2960, 2974, 2983, 2995, 3013, 3054, 3055, 3079, 3081, 3221, 3234, 3263, 3314, 3324, 3325, 3352, 3354, 3369, 3371, 3377, 3429, 3434, 3435, 3454, 3456, 3457, 3458, 3459, 3460, 3487, 3510, 3517, 3519, 3523, 3547, 3645, 3646, 3647, 3648, 3676, 3704, 3734, 3735, 3741, 3748, 3774, 3798, 3831, 3851, 3864, 3865, 3866, 3894, 3899, 3900, 3911, 3945, 3946, 3947, 3955, 3989, 3996, 4009, 4037, 4059, 4098, 4099, 4106, 4108, 4109, 4130, 4134, 4141, 4153, 4167, 4179, 4230, 4268, 4275, 4292, 4322, 4385, 4391, 4448, 4449, 4451, 4457, 4474, 4494, 4495, 4513, 4516, 4518, 4520, 4521, 4522, 4537, 4549, 4560, 4572, 4574, 4611, 4612, 4627, 4628, 4629, 4640, 4646, 4655, 4660, 4661, 4662, 4663, 4666, 4667, 4668, 4669, 4670, 4671, 4673, 4718, 4719, 4720, 4721, 4722, 4723, 4724, 4725, 4726, 4727, 4728, 4729, 4740, 4751, 4752, 4753, 4773, 4778, 4780, 4800, 4801, 4813, 4818, 4846, 4865, 4876, 4879, 4880, 4882, 4899, 4901, 4902, 4903, 4991, 4993, 4999, 5000, 5089, 5090, 5091, 5093, 5109, 5110, 5180, 5228, 5292, 5431, 5432, 5433, 5435, 5436, 5437, 5438, 5439, 5447, 5450, 5451, 5452, 5454, 5456, 5460, 5461, 5463, 5464, 5465, 5466, 5467, 5469, 5470, 5471, 5483, 5484, 5492, 5494, 5508, 5516, 5582, 5609, 5612, 5635, 5663, 5676, 5681, 5710, 5726, 5727, 5766, 5767, 5768, 5782, 5791, 5792, 5793, 5794, 5802, 5817, 5828, 5833, 5904, 5932, 5945, 5946, 5954, 5963, 5993, 6001, 6049, 6066, 6067, 6072, 6154, 6166, 6180, 6221, 6242, 6258, 6259, 6276, 6292, 6318, 6319, 6322, 6395, 6405, 6434, 6460, 6471, 6518, 6529, 6532, 6551, 6552, 6573, 6576, 6583, 6584, 6585, 6586, 6621, 6654, 6660, 6673, 6674, 6680, 6681, 6706.

Philosophy, including alchemy, occult, and physics (44): 18, 30, 259, 884, 1003, 1027, 1028, 1060, 1187, 1293, 1303, 1304, 1315, 1339, 1340, 1348, 1363, 1434, 1435, 1838, 2043, 2201, 2329, 2337, 2975, 3225, 3611, 3620, 3625, 3634, 3882, 3883, 4000, 4057, 4340, 4550, 4893, 5133, 5145, 5258, 5295, 5512, 5528, 6690.

Plots. See Crimes, Plots, Treason, Trials.

Prophecies (27): 108, 175, 625, 919, 1110, 1909, 2044, 3185, 3292, 3565, 3590, 3993, 4046, 4287, 4416, 4446, 4450, 4610, 5366, 5367, 5368, 5721, 6104, 6225, 6240, 6286, 6659

Rhetoric, including logic and grammar (66; a high proportion, 30, are now 'missing' and marked by '(M)', or, if they went from Wood to the Bodleian before 1695, by '(M, Bodl.)'): 220, 948, 965, 1019 (M), 1108 (M), 1125, 1126 (M), 1228 (M, Bodl.), 1234 (M), 1251, 1375, 1433 (M), 1848 (M), 2004, 2131, 2143, 2289, 2335, 2355 (M), 2949 (M), 2950 (M), 2951 (M), 3050 (M), 3215 (M), 3253, 3480, 3525, 3527, 3530, 3624, 3661 (M, Bodl.), 4000 (M), 4089 (M), 4160, 4161 (M, Bodl.), 4165 (M), 4283 (M), 4577, 5103, 5148 (M), 5362, 5509 (M), 5537, 5618 (M), 5737, 5747, 5748, 5898, 5929 (M), 6025 (M), 6026

(M), 6053, 6090, 6218, 6264 (M, Bodl.), 6321 (M), 6401, 6423, 6429, 6557, 6563 (M), 6631 (M), 6632 (M), 6648 (M, Bodl., but not a Wood book), 6699, 6754 (M).

Royal Society (24): 257, 3228, 3230, 3614, 3615, 4742, 4743, 5385, 5638, 5639, 5640, 5641, 5642, 5643, 5644, 5645, 5646, 6006, 6075, 6076, 6077, 6078, 6079, 6426.

Sects, including items concerning non-Church of England Protestant groups such as Anabaptists, Brownists, the Family of Love, Fifth Monarchists, Independents, Levellers (14, marked with '(L)', Quakers (46, marked with '(Q)'), Presbyterians, Puritans, and Ranters; all of these fell under Wood's general general rubric of 'phanaticks'. These names sometimes have less to do with religious than with political affiliation (see Intro. p. xxi) (179): 103 (Q), 104 (Q), 227, 228, 229, 230, 231, 232, 233, 281, 283, 307 (Q), 312, 318, 333 (Q), 362, 369, 370, 371, 373, 383 (Q), 403, 494, 594 (Q), 617, 670, 706 (Q), 713 (Q), 994, 996 (Q), 1004 (Q), 1147, 1247 (Q), 1248 (Q), 1410, 1855, 1864, 1920, 2000, 2042, 2195 (Q), 2196 (Q), 2197 (Q), 2227, 2334, 2392, 2402, 2403, 2404, 2430, 2434, 2541, 2542, 2568, 2658, 2831, 2842, 2934-2940, 2964, 2974 (Q), 2986, 2987, 3002 (Q), 3078 (Q), 3079 (Q), 3102, 3122, 3197, 3214, 3229, 3259, 3279, 3300 (Q), 3322 (Q), 3342 (Q), 3395 (L), 3436, 3501, 3502, 3503, 3580, 3586 (Q), 3712 (Q), 3713 (Q), 3726, 3760 (L), 3761 (L), 3762 (L), 3763 (L), 3959, 3960, 4014, 4056, 4073, 4136 (L), 4137 (L), 4138 (L), 4241, 4277, 4318, 4319, 4353 (Q), 4354 (Q), 4395, 4397 (Q), 4412, 4428, 4575 (Q), 4610 (Q), 4620, 4711, 4777, 4844, 4848 (L), 4904, 5105, 5138, 5166 (Q), 5170 (Q), 5171 (Q), 5222, 5233, 5236, 5342, 5343, 5344, 5358, 5432b (L), 5440 (Q), 5472 (Q), 5488 (Q), 5489 (Q), 5490 (Q), 5491 (Q), 5492 (Q), 5493 (Q), 5494 (Q), 5495 (Q), 5525, 5526, 5527, 5552, 5572, 5593, 5596, 5605, 5783, 5787, 5788, 5812, 5894 (Q), 6034 (Q), 6041, 6147, 6149, 6151, 6177, 6186 (L), 6187 (L), 6220, 6260 (L), 6320, 6391, 6392, 6453, 6454, 6459 (L), 6549, 6555, 6587, 6602, 6693, 6705, 6744 (Q).

Sermons, including nineteen funeral sermons marked by '(F)' (see also Biography) (74): 15 (F), 41 (F), 229, 249, 891 (F), 905 (F), 910, 947, 1206 (F), 1208 (F), 1213, 1258, 1422, 1431 (F), 1627, 1657, 1963, 2047 (F), 2135, 2190, 2191, 2192, 2193, 2194, 2298, 2375, 2856 (F), 3300, 3336, 3570, 3571, 3572, 3598, 3629, 3660, 3674, 3737, 3738 (F), 3873, 3948, 4004, 4006 (F), 4054 (F), 4139, 4175 (F), 4311, 4377, 4427, 4428, 4482, 4546, 4785 (F, satire) 5137, 5231, 5248, 5249, 5581 (F), 5775, 5829, 5866 (F), 5935, 6068, 6094, 6103, 6345 (F), 6526, 6598, 6602, 6603 (F), 6604, 6605, 6688, 6689, 6701 (F).

Surveying. See Architecture and Surveying.

Theology, not including Catholics, Sects, or Sermons (578): 5, 8, 15, 16, 21, 22, 35, 41, 45, 73, 221, 224, 226, 239, 240, 243, 249, 252, 282, 284, 288, 293, 299, 300, 307, 309, 326, 333, 364, 393, 394, 593, 594, 798, 849, 852, 855, 868, 873, 874, 876, 882, 899, 905, 906, 907, 910, 921, 929, 930, 931, 932, 940, 942, 944, 947, 970, 971, 972, 973, 974, 975, 976, 977, 978, 979, 980, 982, 983, 1007, 1030, 1052, 1060, 1064, 1066, 1068, 1088, 1107, 1122, 1127, 1152, 1165, 1177, 1178, 1183, 1188, 1189, 1195, 1196, 1197, 1205, 1206, 1207, 1208, 1211, 1214, 1247, 1248, 1271, 1327, 1365, 1367, 1398, 1421, 1422, 1424, 1427, 1474, 1488, 1489, 1556, 1608, 1609, 1611, 1627, 1648, 1660, 1661, 1675, 1676, 1678, 1685, 1689, 1763, 1801, 1805, 1833, 1844, 1845, 1858, 1860, 1863, 1874, 1875, 1890, 1908, 1913, 1919, 1958, 1960, 1961, 1963, 1968, 2016, 2025, 2031, 2036, 2044, 2047, 2049, 2105, 2116, 2117, 2118, 2119, 2142, 2148, 2149, 2165, 2166, 2183, 2186, 2190, 2191, 2192, 2193, 2194, 2196, 2197, 2214, 2227, 2230, 2232, 2233, 2253, 2255, 2259, 2277, 2301, 2305, 2328, 2331, 2362, 2370, 2374, 2375, 2380, 2388, 2389, 2390, 2391, 2393, 2418, 2436, 2437, 2441, 2442, 2443, 2444, 2459, 2460, 2512, 2513, 2514, 2515, 2516, 2517, 2518, 2519, 2520, 2521, 2522, 2523, 2526, 2527, 2528, 2529, 2530, 2531, 2532, 2536, 2537, 2538, 2543, 2544, 2555, 2569, 2597, 2612, 2631, 2642, 2643, 2668, 2669, 2743, 2819, 2839, 2840, 2844, 2870, 2871, 2877, 2933, 2934, 2936, 2946, 2963, 2975, 2981, 2989, 3002, 3010, 3012, 3013, 3044, 3067, 3074, 3076, 3078, 3093, 3100, 3142, 3175, 3189, 3200, 3208, 3217, 3231, 3242, 3247, 3249, 3261, 3269, 3279, 3280, 3283, 3303, 3305, 3307, 3309, 3318, 3319, 3320, 3322, 3326, 3336, 3339, 3349, 3354, 3366, 3387, 3389, 3398, 3407, 3408, 3479, 3495, 3510, 3513, 3556, 3557, 3570, 3571, 3572, 3578, 3579, 3590, 3598, 3604, 3629, 3649, 3660, 3663, 3674, 3679, 3706, 3707, 3709, 3720, 3737, 3738, 3745, 3820, 3829, 3838, 3852, 3854, 3873, 3876, 3880, 3884, 3886, 3889, 3925, 3933, 3944, 3948, 3964, 3993, 3994, 3999, 4004, 4006, 4021, 4061, 4062, 4071, 4076, 4084, 4085, 4135, 4139, 4149, 4173, 4177, 4200, 4245, 4260, 4294, 4299, 4311, 4314, 4323, 4343, 4353, 4354, 4375, 4376, 4381, 4384, 4407, 4413, 4414, 4416, 4420, 4427, 4429, 4433, 4434, 4435, 4470, 4482, 4495, 4499, 4507, 4540, 4546, 4548, 4550, 4557, 4565, 4610, 4645, 4778, 4782, 4784, 4815, 4821, 4855, 5108, 5114, 5123, 5133, 5137, 5143, 5144, 5145, 5151, 5153, 5166, 5170, 5171, 5173, 5174, 5175, 5187, 5201, 5231, 5243, 5251, 5256, 5297, 5301, 5303, 5314, 5326, 5363, 5368, 5382, 5389, 5406, 5419, 5420, 5421, 5423, 5426, 5430, 5440, 5441, 5442, 5455, 5472, 5479, 5489, 5490, 5491, 5492, 5493, 5494, 5506, 5526, 5545, 5553, 5577, 5579, 5580, 5581, 5584, 5612, 5641, 5674, 5700, 5704, 5706, 5715, 5716, 5721, 5729, 5731, 5733, 5734, 5736, 5738, 5739, 5750, 5752, 5753, 5756, 5757, 5775, 5778, 5784, 5801, 5802, 5811, 5829, 5834, 5835, 5858, 5877, 5886, 5887, 5928, 5934, 5935, 5964, 5974, 5979, 5994, 5995, 5996, 6003, 6017, 6024,

6027, 6031, 6034, 6050, 6054, 6055, 6058, 6068, 6073, 6076, 6094, 6097, 6098, 6104, 6106, 6109, 6111, 6131, 6132, 6138, 6139, 6149, 6196, 6201, 6222, 6227, 6230, 6231, 6237, 6248, 6265, 6292, 6298, 6299, 6314, 6322, 6330, 6331, 6332, 6333, 6335, 6338, 6342, 6347, 6357, 6428, 6432, 6454, 6469, 6490, 6526, 6550, 6551, 6555, 6557, 6598, 6601, 6603, 6604, 6605, 6635, 6659, 6665, 6666, 6683, 6688, 6689, 6700, 6701, 6723, 6758.

Travel and Exploration (54): 984, 999, 1049, 1219, 1226, 1415, 2020, 2040, 2111, 2113, 2159, 2268, 2284, 2290, 2299, 2302, 2372, 2833, 2976, 3140, 3196, 3224, 3397, 3505, 3514, 3545, 3697, 3992, 4043, 4174, 4316, 4405, 4764, 4921, 5149, 5541, 5570, 5600, 5619, 5677, 5714, 5746, 5780, 5933, 5960, 6007, 6142, 6144, 6161, 6165, 6173, 6246, 6589, 6661.

Trials. See Crimes, Plots, Treason, Trials, not including Executions and Murders.

Witchcraft (42): 21, 30, 840, 956, 1069, 1148, 1249, 2024, 2146, 2162, 2163, 2164, 2246, 2552, 2878, 3010, 3211, 3212, 3226, 3227, 3445, 3494, 3635, 3820, 4007, 4058, 4411, 4467, 4545, 4646, 5189, 5315, 5316, 5351, 5353, 5583, 5595, 6118, 6375, 6376, 6582, 6726.

Women, including wives and marriage (139): 33, 107, 311, 378, 528, 531, 535, 569, 585, 591, 622, 638, 694, 695, 714, 748, 749, 752, 756, 782, 793, 806, 816, 838, 839, 841, 860, 880, 904, 988, 1095, 1167, 1181, 1252, 1300, 1407, 1408, 1409, 1834, 1899, 1901, 1949, 1969, 2146, 2274, 2278, 2307, 2353, 2354, 2414, 2790, 2982, 3004, 3095, 3096, 3101, 3254, 3258, 3358, 3494, 3588, 3708, 3809, 3943, 4067, 4103, 4214, 4221, 4227, 4237, 4336, 4345, 4350, 4364, 4369, 4377, 4378, 4379, 4383, 4452, 4467, 4470, 4479, 4485, 4486, 4487, 4565, 4611, 4628, 4629, 4630, 4631, 4758, 4814, 4839, 4900, 5132, 5138, 5152, 5230, 5244, 5510, 5529, 5535, 5583, 5771, 5781, 5927, 5966, 5967, 6082, 6100, 6101, 6102, 6137, 6172, 6185, 6192, 6202, 6224, 6237, 6274, 6316, 6400, 6425, 6438, 6487, 6565, 6669, 6672, 6673, 6674, 6675, 6676, 6677, 6678, 6679, 6680, 6682.

Appendix VIII
BOOK ADVERTISEMENTS
IN PRINTED ITEMS

140 books that Wood owned included lists of books for sale by the printer or publisher or at a specific book shop. A few have lists of books written by the same author (see 1207, 3175, 3625, 3702, 4200, 4281, and 5142). These are usually at the end of the main text on unnumbered pages. Wood marked some of the items in these lists, indicating that he looked at them with the same care that he reviewed his book sale and auction catalogues (items 1438-1636).

The item numbers of these are: 15, 16, 17, 81, 84, 102, 198, 199, 201, 202, 203, 204, 205, 206, 207, 208, 209, 210, 211, 233, 295, 302, 311, 345, 903, 906, 955, 962, 974, 1088, 1139, 1207, 1208, 1211, 1264, 1396, 1398, 1426, 1537, 1904, 1957, 1972, 2004, 2112, 2157, 2219, 2335, 2338, 2366, 2388, 2866, 2890, 3011, 3047, 3077, 3162, 3175, 3226, 3228, 3230, 3245, 3307, 3431, 3489, 3512, 3607, 3620, 3625, 3649, 3661, 3702, 3737, 3807, 3817, 3826, 3846, 3939, 3964, 4104, 4190, 4191, 4200, 4204, 4281, 4298, 4344, 4352, 4411, 4541(2), 4546, 4550, 4573, 4589, 4590, 4595, 4616, 4774, 5135, 5142, 5191, 5230, 5240, 5350, 5504, 5522, 5584, 5719, 5756, 5757, 5764, 5834, 5886, 5888, 5898, 5971, 6017, 6040, 6052, 6106, 6113, 6122, 6133, 6137, 6164, 6196, 6262, 6315, 6333, 6368, 6483, 6495, 6499, 6526, 6534, 6564, 6579, 6639, 6686, 6687, 6718.

PLATES

Plate I. Wood 373(1), item 2598. Wood listed on the upper flyleaves, within guidelines made with red ink, sixty-seven printed items concerning the rebellion that began in 1642. Items 1-30 are on this plate. The note at the top of the first flyleaf, 'Diurnals taken out' refers to fifteen items that were taken out to be placed among Hope adds. These fifteen were restored to this volume in 1932. William Kirtland checked the contents against this list in 1839 and at item 5 wrote, 'deest Octr 1839 W. K.'

Plate II. [MS.] Wood D. 21(1), item 3244. Francis Godwin, *De praesulibus Angliae commentarius* (1616). Five slips with notes by Wood are visible on this page.

Plate III. Wood 259(1), item 5604. *The lovers quarrel: or Cupids triumph* (1677). Wood wrote, within guidelines made with red ink, the short titles of the fifteen items in this volume which he had bound in pasteboard with a parchment spine. Eleven of the fifteen items of ephemera, that is, popular literature, are known to exist only in the Bodleian Library. The remaining four are known to exist today in the Bodleian and at one other location.

Plate IV. Wood 602, item 6268. Brian Twyne, *Antiquitatis academiae Oxoniensis apologia* (1608). On the lower flyleaf Wood wrote a six-line note and made a rough sketch, perhaps a self-portrait. For a full-length profile, see Wood 396, item 4286. See also Mrs. R. L. Poole, *Catalogue of Portraits* (Oxford, 1912): 69, 74, pl. 10, or Mrs. R. L. Poole, *Catalogue of Portraits Exhibited* (Oxford, 1920): 69f., 74.

Plate V. Wood 602, item 6268. Brian Twyne, *Antiquitatis academiae Oxoniensis apologia* (1608). On the title page are the signatures of Gerard Langbaine, with a Greek motto, and 'Anthony Woode'. Langbaine died on 10 February 1658 and at a sale of his library on 29 April Wood paid five shillings for this book. He had it bound in parchment on 22 May. Wood's early hand is on both this and the following plate. His later hand is shown on the preceding plate.

Plate VI. Wood 602, item 6268. Brian Twyne, *Antiquitatis academiae Oxoniensis apologia* (1608). All the annotation was written by Wood between 1658 and 1660.

Plate VII. [MS.] Wood E. 28(4), item 1538 (an earlier draft by Wood is at [MS.] Wood C. 26(20), item 1539). Gerard Langbaine, *An exact catalogue of all the comedies . . . that were ever yet printed* [Francis Kirkman may be the author; edited by Nicholas Cox] (1680). On the verso of the title page Wood drafted a letter to Kirkman and Cox in which he advised them to include the dates of editions they cite in their future revision. He may never have sent a final version of this letter. In any case, Kirkman and Cox did not include dates in the next edition (item 1540).

Plate VIII. [MS.] Wood E. 27(2), item 1599. *A compleat catalogue of all the stitch'd books and single sheets printed . . . of the popish plot* (1680). On pp. [1ᵛ] and [2], Wood listed thirteen additional works published in 1679 and 1680, though the last is not on the subject of the popish plot, *The claret drinkers song or the good fellowes design* by John Oldham (Wood 417(28), item 4811). He owned eight of those in his list. P. 1ᵛ, no. 1, Wood 276a(99), item 2781; no. 3, Wood 424(29), item 2291; no. 4, Wood 276a(274), item 5945 (a diff. edition); and no. 7, Wood 417(18), item 3130. P. 2, no. 1, Wood 426(11), item 6462; no. 2, [MS.] Wood B. 40(3a), item 2005; no. 5, [MS.] Wood D. 26(6), item 5342; and no. 6, Wood 417(28), item 4811.

Plate IX. Library Records d. 1071. Ff. 32ᵛ-33. This plate shows a typical page from the Whiteside Catalogus prepared by John Hausted. He recorded the presence of Wood 400, 'A Book of Ballads', which was missing in 1837, as William Kirtland noted on the opposite page. Items 401 and 402, also books of ballads, hold

103 and 24 ballads, respectively, though Hausted did not itemize them. Wood 416 and 417 contain large numbers of poems, song, ballads, and 'several things in Prose' (133 and 183 printed items, not itemized). Wood 421, contains fourteen items and the list of contents continues to the next page.

Plate X. MS. Wood D. 18, f. 135. An example of Wood's hand in 1660.

Plate XI. MS. Wood D. 18, f. 115. An example of Wood's hand in 1665.

Plate XII. MS. Wood D. 18, f. 216. An example of Wood's hand in 1676.

For plates of annotation in Wood 401, f. 87; in Wood 402, pp. [91] and 92; and in two Wood ballads now in the Euing Collection, Glasgow University Library, see *BLR* 15 (1996): 265, 267, 270, and 271.

For plates of Wood's catalogue of his printed items which he made in 1681, MS. Wood E. 2 (70), p. 1; and of the first Ashmolean Catalogue including manuscript entries of Wood and Ashmole printed items, Library Records b. 467, fol. 46, see *BLR* 16 (1999): 474 and 481.

For plates of Wood's hand in 1661, 1675, 1677, 1693, 1695, see LT, vol. 2, plates IV-X, after p. 560. For plates of the handwriting of Wood's contemporaries, see LT, vol. 4, plates I-IX, after p. 322.

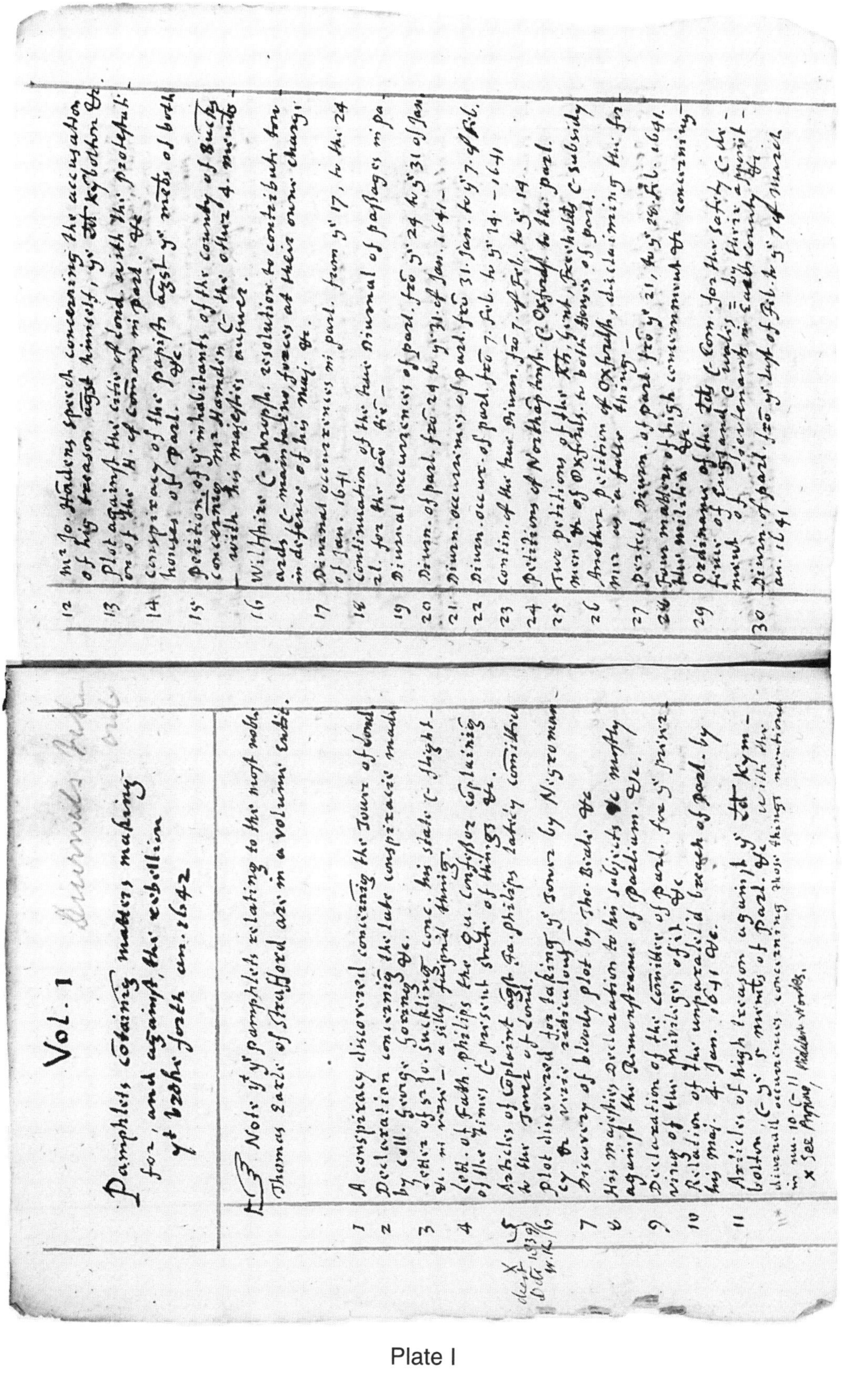

Vol. 1

Pamphlets conteining matters making
for, and against the rebellion
yt. broke forth an. 1642

☞ Note yt ys pamphlets relating to this next noble.
Thomas Earle of Strafford are in a volum. Entit.

1 A conspiracy discovered concerning the Tower of Lond.
2 Declaration concerning the late conspiracie made
  by coll. George Goring &c.
3 Letter of sr. Jo. Suckling concer. his state & flight -
  ni marg. - a silly designd thing.
4 Lett. of Fath. philips the Queens confessor explaining
  of the Kings & present state. of things &c.
5 Articles of Complaint agst Fa. philips latly committ.
  to the Tower of Lond.
6 Plot discovered for taking ye Tower by Nigromancy &c.
  vizt. ridiculous
7 Discovery of bloudy plot by Tho. Beale. &c.
8 His majestys Declaration to his subjects & mostly
  against the Remonstrance of Parlium. &c.
9 Declaration of the committee of parl. for ye prince
  vizt to the privileges of it &c.
10 Relation of the unparalel'd breugh of parl. by
  his maj. 4. Jan. 1641. &c.
11 Articles of high treason against ye 5 membs of parl. &c. with the lo. Kymbolton (- ys 5 membs of parl. &c. with the
  denial concerning those things mentioned
  in nu 10. (-11 Walden words.
  × SEE Appendix

12 mr Jo. Hotens speech concerning the accusation
  of his treason agst himself, & tt Kg Iohn &c.
13 Plot against this citie of Lond. with the protestat.
  on of the H. of commons ni parl. &c.
14 conspiracy of the papists agst ye mets of both
  houses of parl. &c.
15 Petition of ye inhabitants of the county of Bucks
  concerning mr Hamden (- the other 4. members
  with his majesties answer.
16 Wilt shire (- shrop &c. resolution to contribut toward
  maintaining forces at their own charge
  in defence of his maj. &c.
17 Diurnall occurrences ni parl. from ye 17 to the 24
  of Jan. 1641
18 Continuation of this true Diurnal of passages ni pa.
  rl. for the sam &c -
19 Diurnall occurrences of parl. feb ye 24 to ye 31 of Jan.
20 Diurn of parl. feb 24 to ye 31 of Jan. 1641 -
21 Diurn. occurrences of parl. feb 31. Jan. to ye 7 of feb.
22 Diurn. occur. of parl. feb 7. feb. to ye 14. - 1641
23 contin. of the true Diurn. Jan 7 of Feb. to ye 14
24 Petitions of Northamptonsh. (- Oxford to the parl.
25 Two petitions of the Kts Gent. Freeholds (- subsidy
  men &c of Oxfull. to both houses of parl.
26 Another petition of Oxfordsh, disclaiming the for
  mer on a false thing. -
27 A perfect Diurn. of parl. feb ye 21. Aug 1641.
28 Two matters of high commotion &c. the
  militia &c. concerning
29 Ordinance of the tts (- Com for the safety of the
  Kingdom (- Englend (- Wales & divers (- Leivtenants in severall count.
  ment of England (- parts -
30 Diurn. of parl. Jan ye 24 of Feb. to ye 7 of march
  an. 1641

Plate I

Godfridus Goodman fil Canon.
windsore 20 Dec. 1617
Theol Dr, Coll. Trinitatis
Cantabrig. alumnus
Sp Decano Roffensi Consecratus
Epis Glocest 1624 canonicatu
windsore una cum Rectoria
de Westhiblesley in Berks
post Comendat retinens

Epitaph of Giles Thompson
I have among may
Epitaphs of in
S. Georges chap.
at windr.

I would have the epitaph
of Godf. Goldes borowe
~corp Dean B. of Br.
at ye an 1579.

of magd. coll.
25. Jul. 1546.
recessit—it. an.
J 1546. et 97
electus iterū soc.
J febat. 26. July
1548
left magd.
coll. 1558. 59.
behr. magd. chap
1558. co magd.
chap 1559

of Archb. Heath see
in Dr Allens answer
to ye Libell of English
justice. p. 50.
I have it with a
black cover.

VR-
præter-
patus,
e per-
prop-
a nun-
s, Me-
adiunt
tquam
sburi-
ie Pe-
con-
is qui
ium illic anno
medio subla-
tuerit.
absolui
olendis
auerit,
tissent.
muta-
b pa-
Cœ-
reuerit extruere,
multum adiutus,
bus, quæ (vt as-
e conditæ. Hoc Cœ-
uit Diui Petri ; & Abbatem præfecit
dā (in Lichfeldensem Episcopum post-
operis aggrediendi author illi iampri-
m plus quam ducentis, in summa om-
la hoc Cœnobium efflorescens, à Da-
qui ædificijs euersis, à Wolphero tan-
tis

Qq

saxulfus. v. p. 364.

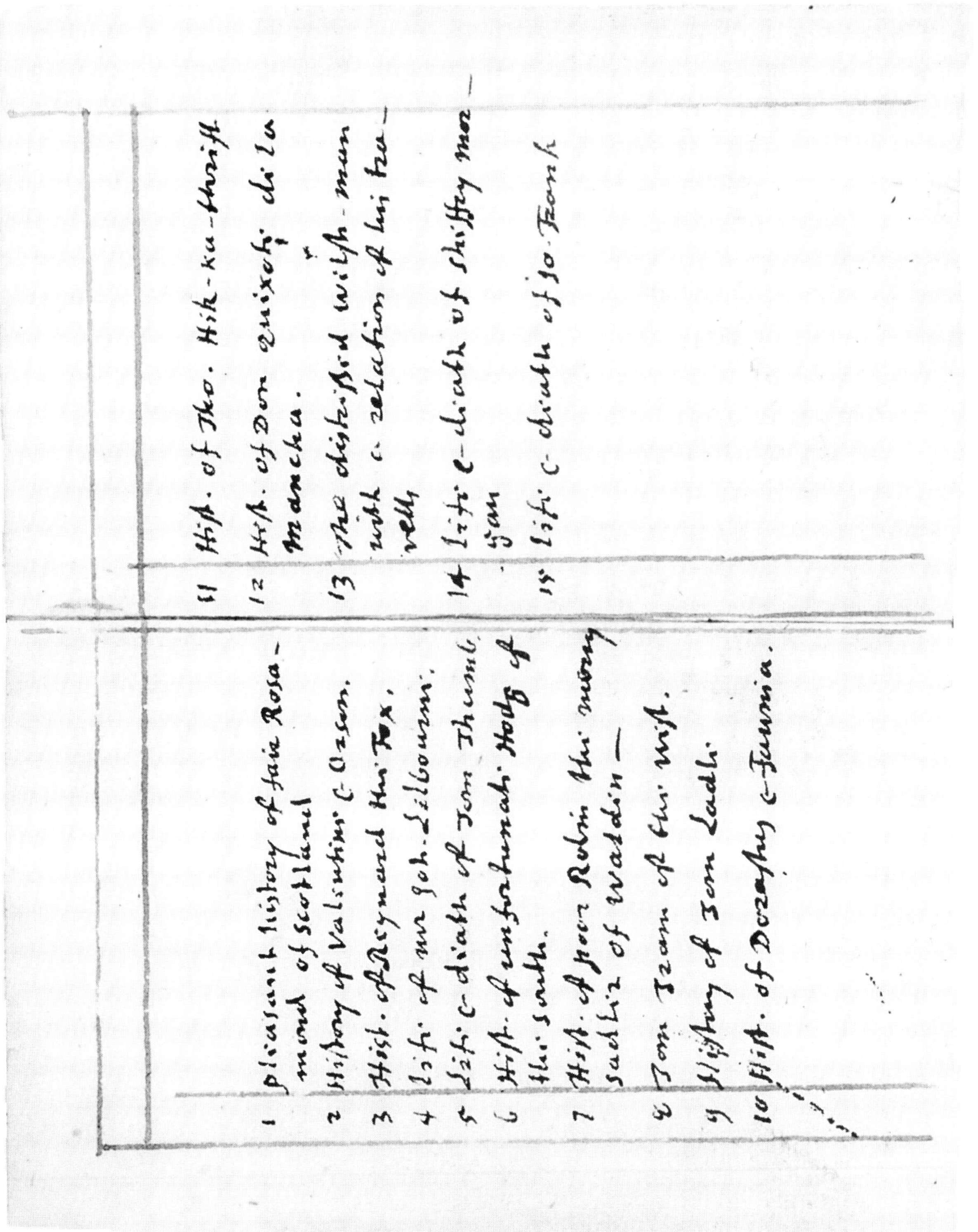

1. Pleasant history of fair Rosamond of Scotland
2. History of Valentine & Orson.
3. Hist. of Reynard the Fox.
4. Life of our Joh. Silbourn.
5. Life & death of Tom Thumb.
6. Hist. of unfortunate Hodg of
the south.
7. Hist. of poor Robin the merry
saddler of Walden —
8. Tom Jean of this wish.
9. History of Tom Ladle.
10. Hist. of Dorothy & Turvin.

11. Hist. of Tho. Hik-ka-thrift.
12. Hist. of Don Quixote de la
Mancha.
13. The distressed wife-man
with a relation of his travells.
14. Life & death of shifty man
Jan
15. Life & death of Jo. Frank

Plate III

Note yt Cay in his antiq: of Camb. lib.1. p. 152. saith from Crocus in his 2d oration of opaia e ceteria vesta, & though yt sd Crocus was doctor of yt vniuis. & accounted one of introducers yt grek. tongue in Cambridge yet he was proppe to Grocin an oxford man. & Crooke confesses v histor. 1497. v orat: eius p 44 v. histor 1134.

Plate IV

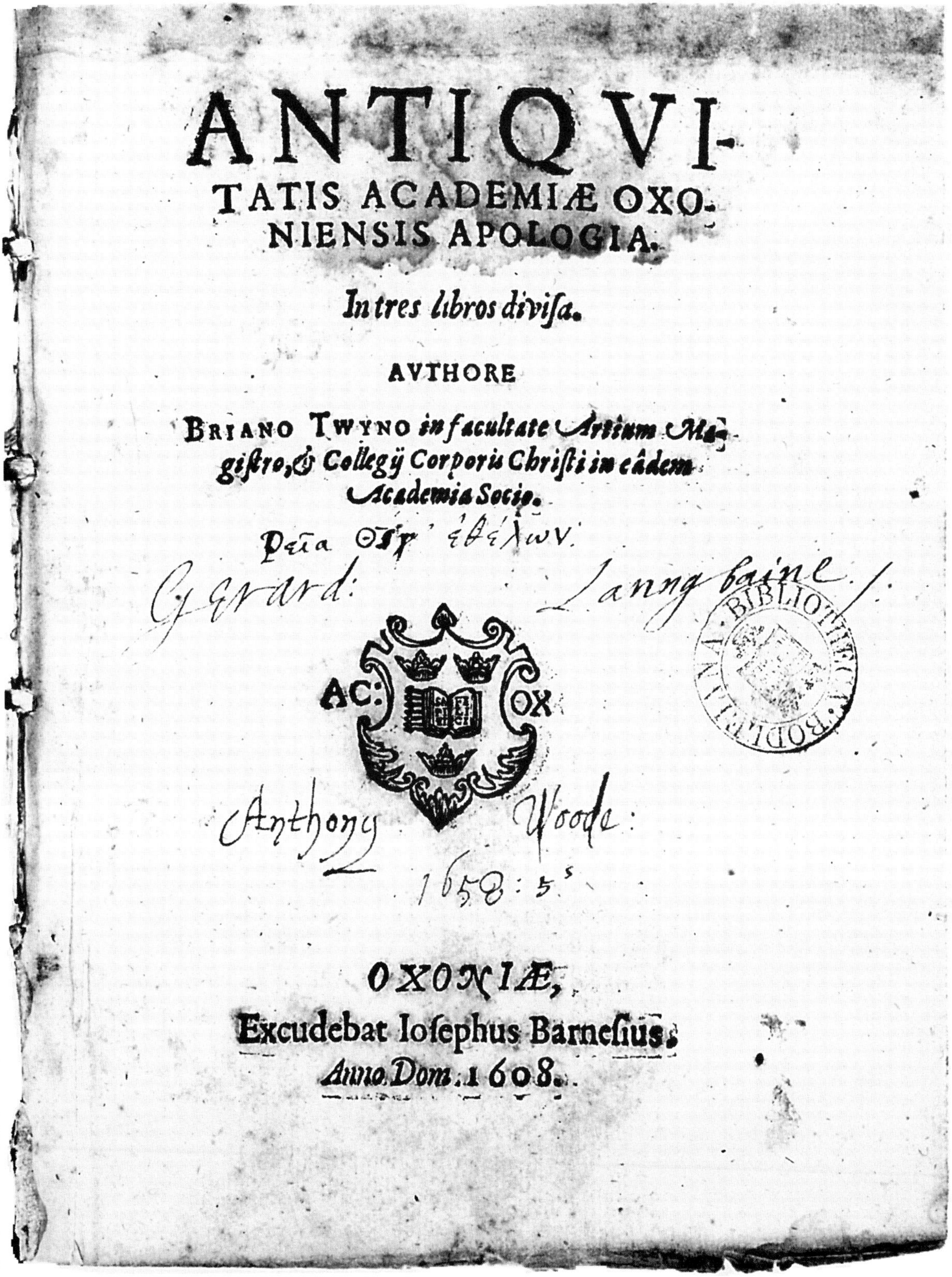

ANTIQVI-TATIS ACADEMIÆ OXO-NIENSIS APOLOGIA.

In tres libros divisa.

AVTHORE

BRIANO TWYNO *in facultate Artium Magistro, & Collegij Corporis Christi in eâdem Academia Socio.*

Ρεια θεῷ ἐθέλων.
Gerard: Langbaine
AC: OX
BIBLIOTHECA BODLEIANA
Anthony Woode:
1658: 5s

OXONIÆ,

Excudebat Iosephus Barnesius.

Anno Dom. 1608.

Plate V

Walter: Lyhert provost of Oriel coll: bish: of Norwich: Godwin calls him Hart: / omitted by fuller in his Church history:

I find in ye Register of Oriell 2 bishops omitted by ye said fuller: viz: Johan: Hale: Epus ~~Cestren:~~ & Tho: ~~Cornish~~ Epus: Tinens: / both provosts of ye said Coll: /

I find alsoe Jo: Carpenter yt was provost: to be a Learned writer, as is exprest in ye Register, whether his books are extant in ye Coll: Library, I cannot ~~[illegible]~~ tell: / quere:

There is alsoe another provost yt mr Twine hath omitted in his foregoing Catalouge, viz Joh: Maldon: as is exprest in ye said Regist: // and as he hath writt Edm: Mylford in his said Catal: I find in ye Register: to be Edm: Wilsford

Ao Dni 1564 obijt Dr Jo: Warner custos: a. An. legavit Balliot coll: 20li: ita ex regist: bal: c:

see in ye Lib. regr of ye visitors ye paps yt I collected there

Plate VI

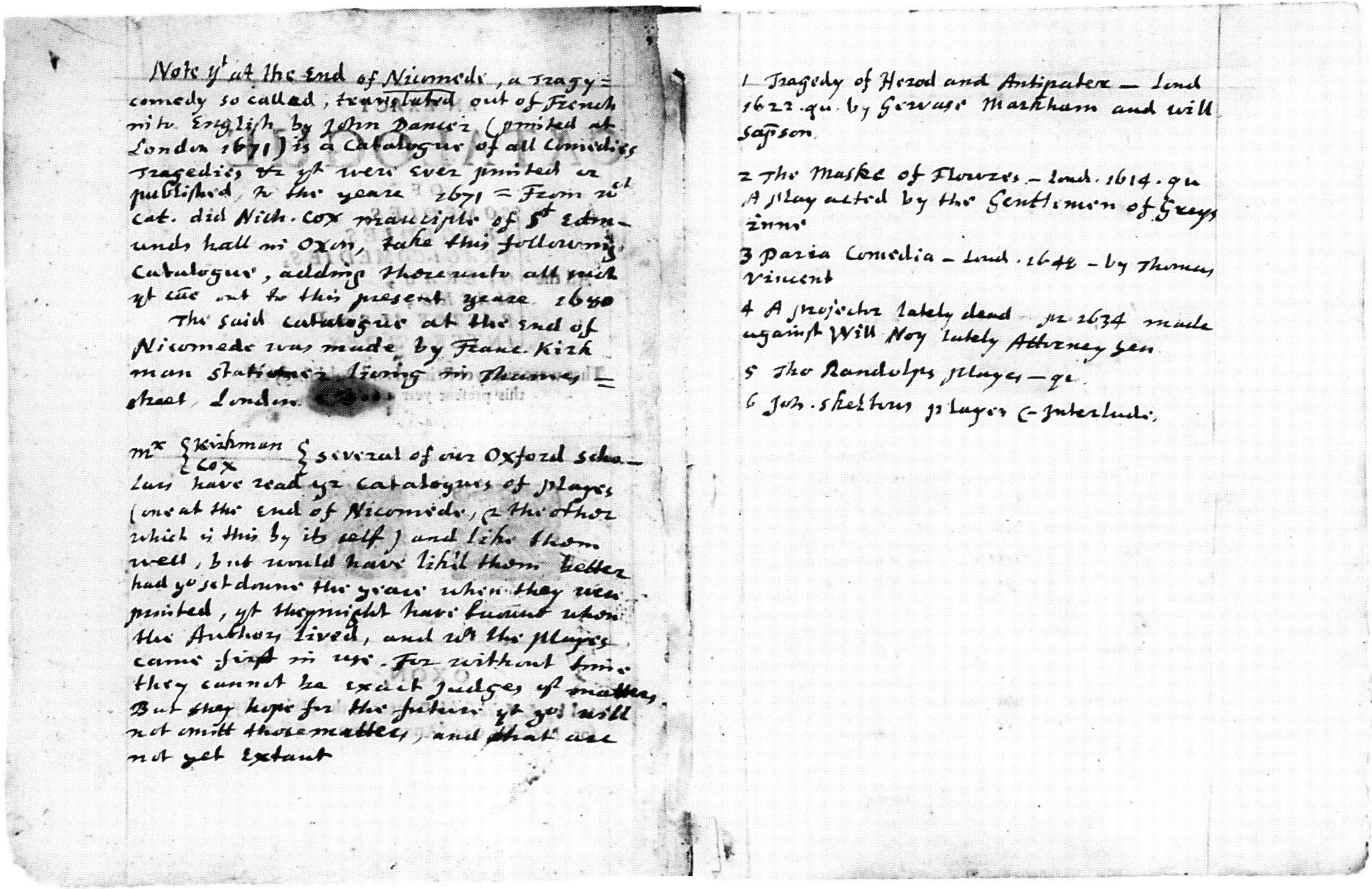

Note yt at the End of Nicomede, a Tragy-comedy so called, translated out of French wth English by John Dancer (printed at London 1671) is a Catalogue of all Comedies, Tragedies &c yt were ever printed & published to the year 1671 = From yt Cat. did Nich. Cox principally of St Edmund hall in Oxon take this following Catalogue, adding thereunto all such yt came out to this present year 1680 = The said Catalogue at the End of Nicomede was made by Franc Kirk men Stationer living in Thames way — street London.

mr Gwinman & several of our Oxford scho-lars have read ye Catalogues of Playes (mr Cox & several of our Oxford scho-lars have read ye Catalogues of Playes (mr at the End of Nicomede; & his others which is this by it self) and like them well, but wonld have wished them better had yo. ... this yiong who in they were praised, yt Huguenot have liv'd upon the Authors liv'd, and all the Playes they cannot be exact Judges of — Bul say hope for this fashion yt yo. woll not omit those matters, wm must cure are not yet Extant.

1 Tragedy of Herod and Antipater — Lond 1622 qu. by Gervase Markham and will Sampson.

2 The Masque of Flowers — Lond 1614. qu. A play acted by the Gentlemen of Grays Inne.

3 Paria Comedia — Lond. 1648 — by Thomas Vincent.

4 A proiecta lately dead — Ma 1634 made against Will Noy lately Attorney Gen.

5 The Randolphs players — q.

6 Jos. shelton 31 Lages (-shelton).

Plate VII

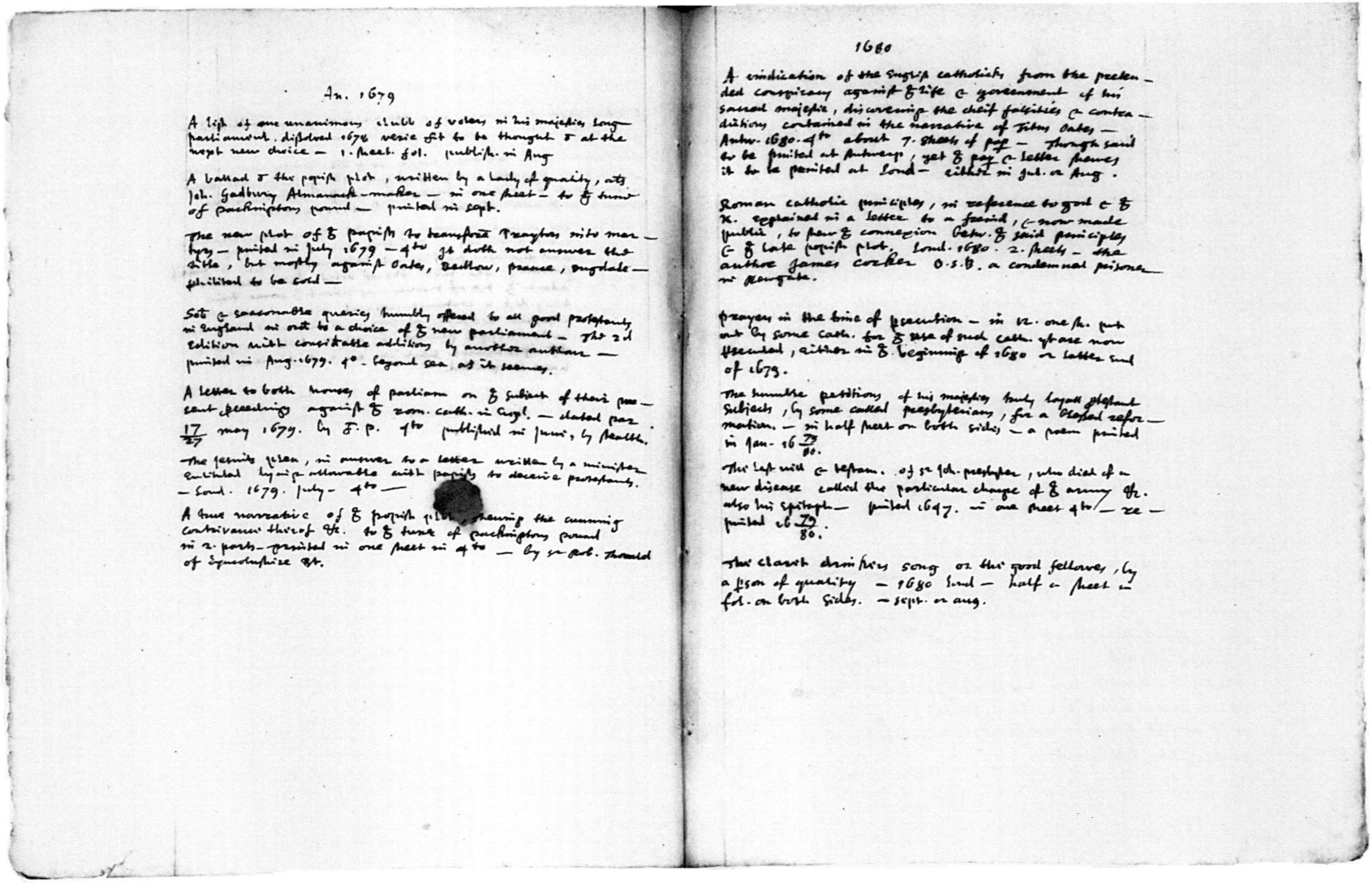

An. 1679

A list of one unanimous club of voters in his majesties long parliament, dissolved 1678 verie fit to be thought of at the next new choice — 1. sheet. fol. publish. in Aug

A ballad of the popish plot, written by a lady of quality, ats Joh. Gadbury Almanack-maker — in one sheet — to ye tune of packingtons pound — printed in Sept.

The new plot of ye papists to transform Traytors into martyrs — printed in July 1679 — 4to It doth not answer the title, but mostly against Oates, Bedlow, Prance, Dugdale — prohibited to be sold —

Sob & seasonable queries humbly offered to all good protestants in England in ord to a choice of ye new parliament — The 2d Edition with considerable additions by another author — printed in Aug. 1679. 4°. beyond sea as it seemes.

A letter to both houses of parliam on ye subject of their present proceedings against ye rom. cath. in Engl. — dated par 17/27 may 1679. by J. P. 4to published in June, by stealth.

The Jesuits plea, in answer to a letter written by a minister entituled lying allowable with papists to deceive protestants. — Lond. 1679. July — 4to —

A true narrative of ye popish p[illegible], shewing the cunning contrivance thereof &c. to ye tune of packingtons pound in 2. parts — printed in one sheet in 4to — by sr Rob. Thorold of Lincolnshire Bt.

1680

A vindication of the English catholicks from the pretended conspiracy against ye life & government of his sacred majestie, discovering the cheif falsities & contradictions contained in the narrative of Titus Oates — Antw. 1680. 4to about 7. sheets of pap — though said to be printed at Antwerp, yet ye pap & letter shewes it to be printed at Lond — either in Jul. or Aug.

Roman catholic principles, in reference to god & ye K. explained in a letter to a freind, & now made publick, to shew ye connexion betw. ye said principles & ye late popish plot. Lond. 1680. 2. sheets — the author James Corker O.S.B. a condemned prisoner in Newgate.

Prayers in the time of persecution — in 12. one sh. put out by some cath. for ye use of such cath. yt are now persecuted, either in ye beginning of 1680 or latter end of 1679.

The humble petitions of his majesties truly loyall protestant subjects, by some called presbyterians, for a blessed reformation. — in half sheet on both sides — a poem printed in Jan. 16 79/80.

The last will & testam. of sr Joh. presbyter, who died of a new disease called the particular charge of ye army &c. also his epitaph — printed 1647. in one sheet 4to — reprinted 16 79/80.

The clareth drinkers song or the good fellowes, by a person of quality — 1680 Lond — half a sheet in fol. on both sides. — sept. or aug.

Plate VIII

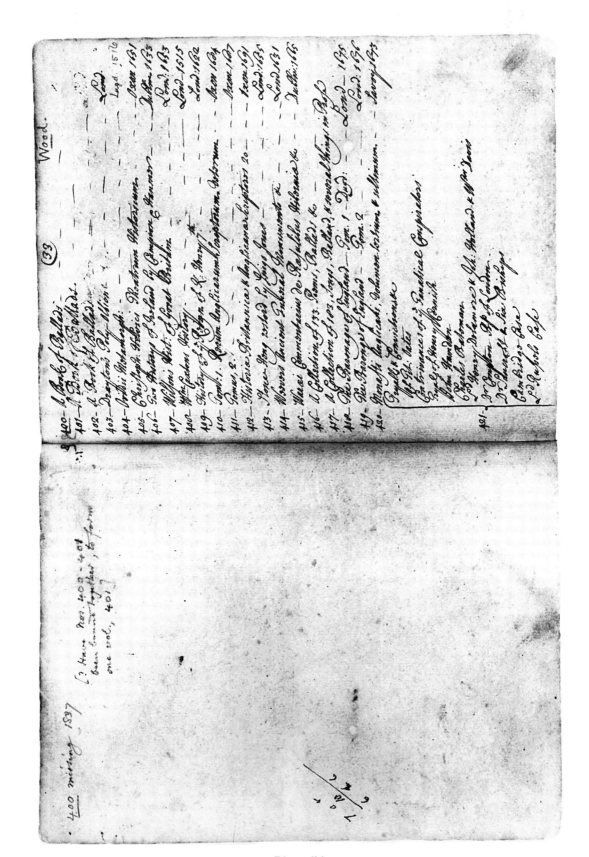

Plate IX

Octob: v. A.D. mDclx:

1

Ex Chronico Thomæ Wycke Canonici de osney iuxta oxon, quo-
-dã penes mẽu Tho: Allen ex aula Glocest: oxon nunc Biblioth:
v.C. Dni Tho: Cotton:

Initiũ Chronici. Aº ab incarnatione Dni MDcv obijt
Edw: Rex Anglorũ et successit Dux Haroldus:
Producit Chronicon suũ usqz ad An: Dni: MCClxxxxij:

Aº m.lxxi Lanfrancus Archieps Cantuar: et Thomas Eboracensis consecrantur. Eod Aº ædificatũ e castellũ Oxenford a Rotto de Oilly primo. viz Aº 5º post Conquestũ inquit Johes Rossus:

Aº m.lxxiiijº Editha Regina Regis Edwardi Uxor obijt: fundata e Ecca S Georgij in Castello oxenford a Rob de oilly primo, et Rogo de Ivery

Aº m.c.xxixº Eod Aº fundata e ecca S. mariæ in Insula quæ uocatur Osneya extra castrũ Oxenford posita a Rotto de Oilly 2º Constabulario Regis Hẽi primi; cui primus præfuit prior Ranulfus annis ix et mensibus v.

Aº m.c.xxxiijº mr Rottus pulein scripturas diuinas quæ in Anglia absoluerant apud oxon legere cœpit; qui postea cum ex doctrina eius Ecca tã anglicana quã Gallicana plurimũ profecissit a papa Lucio 2º uocatus et in Cancellariũ S Rom Eccæ promotus e:

Aº mcxxxviij obijt Radulphus primus prior eccæ nræ cui successit mr Wygodus qui ecca nra præfuit Annis 30 et mensibus 4: scilicet xv annis in 7 mensibus in priocatu, postea uero in Abbate promotus e:

A mcxxxix cepit Rex Stephanus Rogerũ epum saxum in castro Oxon et filiũ eius Rogeũ cognomento pauper Cancellariũ Regis, et Alexandrũ Lyncoln epum eosqz ad deditione castellorũ suorũ coegit. Nigellus 2dus Eliensis Eps et Adeling nepos Alexandri epi qui p idẽ tepus thesaurarius Regis fuit p fugã elapsi sunt:

Plate X

Ex libro vel nigro Hospitalis Jacobi et Johis de
Brackley com Nocthapton. ni Brehini
collegij magd: Oxon

Apr 20. 1665.

mr ffranc. Drope
Decanus eiusdē
collij.

continet. fol.
24. in 4to

fol. 5. 2. tis of first charter concerning lands belonging to
ye hospitall, after ye recitall of several popes Bulls. tis of
charter of R. Abbas eccle s. marie de prato de Legrecestre
vel Leycestre

fol. 10 carta qua margareta de Quincy Comitissa de
Winton dedit p salute sua et p salute aie Jozettæ
filie sue hospitali Beatorū Aplorum Jacobi et Johis
de Brackel molendinū cū ptinentijs ad tenementū
de Halzo cum secta et cum oīb ptinentijs, ita tñ
qd pdicti fres reddent annuatim moniatibj de Goldstow
unā marcā Argenti ni quietancia unius marcæ quā
Rob. Coes Leicestriæ contulit pdictis moniatibj de redditū
de Brackley

fo. 11. 2 Rog. de Quincy Comes Winton Constabularius
scotie. dedit hospitali scotē p saluto aīd suæ et aīd
Dñe Johanne de Ew Dñe de Criol Cōteisse Britan-
-nie. et. ocurrit ni alia carta dat. 1256

f. 20. ni a charter there of ye sd Rog. is mention made
of one Andrew Bonnalet. his nā also ocurres
as a witnesse to divs charters there

ib. ni a charter there dated 35. of H. 3. is mention made
is a witnesse one Theas. de Gnipwich

fo. 16 mention of ye house of Andr. Bonnalet ni Brackley
ni ye charter of Rog. de Quincy, to ye sd charter are
witnesses among other Wts Hen. de Batteolo f. 17. 1

21. 2. mention of Rog. foliot ni cart. Johes de Haya. cia
1271. et pet. foliot f. 35 among ye witnesses there ; there being
alia Rog. foliot also who follows pet. ni ye sd charter also ;
25. 2. a final concord made et Northapton aº H. 3. 11º corā
S. de Segrave will: fil Warini . will. de Wilton watt.
Basset justic. Itinerant. et.

note yf f. 8. 2. is ye first charter of ye font Rob 2. of Leye

f. 34. 2. nit: testes ad cartā willi de Henze milit de tris
ni Godmidon dat aº Ed. 1. 6. ocurrit quinta Maugerus
de Couel Clerie

S. Segrave

Plate XI

22. Aug. 1676. Mr Hen. Symons Secretary to
Barlow B^p of Lincoln. lent me a vol.
in fol. written by Dr Sandson Bishop
of Lincolne. Endors^d. Carta ✗.

The contents of wch follow.

ob. H. Symons
an 1679.
vel in initio
anni 1680.

Abstract from ye Engl. Leiger book containing all Evi-
-dences of Godstow nunnery by Oxford. p. 1. to p. 16.
Extracted out of ye originalls of m^r Randall Cathdrall
of Ottenton com. Oxon, an. 1616 p^r me Rob. Sandson.

Rand. Cath
rall was ori
ginally of
Horton in
chisn. for my
mss of any
of Oxfordsh.
Gentry.

Excerpta di cartis S. Mariæ de Thame in com. Oxon
p. 17. to 28. taken out of a book collected by the
said Randall Cathdrall —

Excerpta ex rotulo antiquo de Abendon, p. 29. 30. et de
Abbatibus tantu.

Chartæ miscellaneæ in custod. m^r R Cathdrall p. 31.

Excerpta ex libris procuratorū Univers. Oxon. p. 32. 33. to
41

Chartæ miscellan. ut habentur in libro quodam Jacobi
Chaloner. p. 42. ad p. 52.

Excerpta out of certaine Evidences in ye custodie if m^r
pet. Yate parson of Appleton in Berks, an. 1617. p. 52
53.

Excerpts out of a visitation book of Staffordsh. by Glover
an. 1583, written with m^r James Chaloners hand, but

Jam. chalon^r
visit p.

Plate XII

Oxford Bibliographical society. Errata list for *The Library of Anthony Wood*

ERRATA

p. xii, line 31: 'Keys' should be 'Key' (twice).

p. xii, 2nd line from bottom, and p. xiii, line 13: 'Kennet' should be 'Kennett'.

p. xvi, line 3: 'Charles Naudé' should be 'Gabriel Naudé'.

p. xx, note 24: 'Reynold's' should be 'Reynolds''.

p. xlviii, line 7: 'incompetents helpers' should be 'incompetent helpers'.

p. liii, line 22: 'Ashmolian' should be 'Ashmolean'.

p. 164, item 1726: at end, delete '(3)'.

p. 193, item 2061: at end, Wood 480(1) is item 1267.

p. 203, item 2168: 'Rene' should be 'René'.

p. 405, item 4375: 'Sant Aldegonde' should be 'Sint Aldegonde'.

p. 426, item 4618: '[Nedham, Marchamont]' should be '[Nedham, Marchamont]*'.

p. 483, item 5198, the cross-reference at the end to item 5193 should be to item 5196.

p. 690: Thomas, Evan is found at F (1715-1886) 1405.7.

p. 699: Basil, i.e., modern Basel.

p. 700: 'Francfurt' should be 'Frankfurt'.

INDEX

This index contains references to persons, places, or subjects in the introduction, ix-xlix (pages are cited in Roman numerals); in the annotations by Wood and others in the printed items 1-6760 (entries are cited in Arabic numbers); and in the appendices I-VIII (references begin with 'Append').

The index does not, in general, include information which can be found in the bibliographical entries or in the appendices I, III, and VII. For example, authors, headings or names mentioned in titles will not normally be in this index, nor will very minor annotations such as underscorings of the names of persons on the title pages (for this, see the entry in the bibliography or, for alternate names, Appendix I). Former owners of Wood books, with biographical references whenever possible, will be found in Appendix III. Subjects of the books (America, Architecture and Surveying, Army, Astronomy and Astrology, Biography, and thirty-two more) will be found in Appendix VII).

The index does not include the thousands of Wood's notes of the dates or months of publication (including his emendations from the new style to the old style, as 1 January to 25 March 1660 to 16'59'), of the dates of the arrival of items in Oxford, or of former item numbers in bundles or piles. There is some detail on these matters under the index entries 'Binding', 'Printing', and 'Oxford', and under Wood's name followed by specific topics.